2022 DIR National Minority and Women-Owned Busin
Fifty-Third Edition

HISTORY

Diversity Information Resources was founded in Minneapolis in 1968 by H. Peter Meyerhoff, a Honeywell aeronautics engineer, who sought to advance race relations by improving economic conditions for Blacks after the assassination of Dr. Martin Luther King, Jr. Meyerhoff and his wife were European Jews who managed to escape Hitler at the outset of World War II. Themselves victims of discrimination, they were motivated by Dr. King's death to launch the "Buy Black" directory - a 10 page directory of black-owned businesses.

In 2001 DIR partnered with an IT firm and developed an online Supplier Diversity Database Management Portal. The dynamic portal allows corporations online access to certified minority and women-owned businesses, veteran, service-disabled veteran, LGBT and HUBZone businesses, supplier registration, certification validation, and data cleansing. (Please contact Diversity Information Resources at (612) 781-6819 or www.diversityinforesources.com for more information). A Board of Directors, representative of major U.S. corporations set policy and direction for Diversity Information Resources (see back cover).

MISSION

To develop, maintain, and provide information resources that enhance supplier diversity initiatives and support the development and economic growth of diverse businesses.

INCLUSION CRITERIA AND LISTING PROCESS

In identifying minority-owned businesses, fifty-one percent of the business must be owned, operated and controlled by minority group members who are U.S. citizens, capable of national and/or regional sales and physically located in the United States or its trust territories. In identifying woman-owned businesses, at least fifty-one percent or more is owned by a woman (or women), who is a U.S. citizen, and who controls the firm by exercising the power to make policy decisions and operates the business by being actively involved in day-to-day management. It must be profit seeking and capable of national and/or regional sales.

CERTIFICATION

Information on certification(s) held is also validated and reported. Buyers are advised to contact firms directly if clarification on certification is needed. The following certifications are validated:

- State — State Agencies
- City — City Agencies
- WBENC — Women's Business Enterprise National Council
- NWBOC — National Women Business Owners Corporation
- NMSDC — National Minority Supplier Development Council
- CPUC — California Public Utilities Commission (M/WBE Clearinghouse)
- SDB — Small Business Administration's Small Disadvantaged Business
- 8(a) — SBA's 8(a) Business Development Program

OWNERSHIP CLASSIFICATION

The following code indicates ownership type:

- AA — African American
- Hisp — Hispanic American
- Nat Ame — Native American
- As-Pac — Asian Pacific American
- As-Ind — Asian Indian American

LIABILITY DISCLAIMER

Although the information listed herein has been compiled with the utmost care and is believed by the publisher to be reliable, its accuracy or completeness cannot be guaranteed. The publishers and sponsors assume no responsibility for transactions resulting from the use of information herein and do not guarantee the quality or reliability of products or services listed. The content of the advertising copy contained in this Directory is the sole responsibility of those firms, which submitted it. Diversity Information Resources assumes no responsibility for its accuracy.

USING THE DIRECTORY

Directory Format:

- The Table of Classifications on the next page gives the section numbers for each category and the range of numbers in that category. The Table of NAIC codes list the two-digit NAIC code for each category.
- Firms are listed by state, in alphabetical order, in each category.
- An alphabetical listing of companies (page ii-1) appears at the back of the directory.
- See codes to identify certification and ownership type on the back of the first printed page: "2022 DIR National Minority and Women-Owned Business Directory Fifty-Third Edition."

An Example:

If you are looking for a supplier to print a company brochure, first you look up "brochure" in the Keyword Index. You will see that the Keyword Index refers you to the "Printing and Engraving" category.

Turning to the "Printing and Engraving" section, you will find suppliers listed alphabetically, according to the state in which they reside. A typical entry might appear as follows:

7600   ABC Printing Company
1234 XYZ Avenue NE New York, NY 10001
(212) 555-1234   R. Smith, pres.
Fax: (212) 555 5678
Email: Rsmith@www.net
Web Site: www.print.com
4-5 color offset presses. In-house 4-color, bindery, die cutting,
mounting & finishing. (AA, est. 1965, empl 45, sales $4,000,000, cert: State, NMSDC, SDB)

OTHER PRODUCTS AND SERVICES PROVIDED BY DIVERSITY INFORMATION RESOURCES

"The Business of Supplier Diversity: A Handbook of Essential Contacts and Information for Navigating the Industry"

This eighth edition combines the best of DIR's previously published "Purchasing People in Major Corporations" and the "Supplier Diversity Information Resource Guide". This book provides a road map for diverse-owned suppliers and supplier diversity professionals by combining who-to-call with where-to-look. DIR, the leader in supplier diversity data management, combines a detailed contact list of over 1500 supplier diversity and procurement contacts from major corporations, government agencies, large nonprofit organizations, and educational institutions. It also details information on certification, legislation, regional and national networking opportunities, diverse business resources and much more.

Corporate Supplier Diversity Seminars

Now in their 36th year, these seminars teach methods to establish or enhance Supplier Diversity Programs. Diversity Information Resources offers "Building Strategic Phases of a Supplier Diversity Process" seminar and the "Best Practices in Supplier Diversity Strategies and Initiatives" seminar.

For further information on any of the above resources, please contact DIR at (612) 781-6819 or visit
www.diversityinforesources.com

TABLE OF CLASSIFICATIONS

TABLE OF NAICS

> **ADVERTISING**
> Advertising agencies which provide clients with full service from conception to completion. Other services listed in this category include graphic arts, direct mail & list maintenance, sign manufacturing and engraving. (See also PROFESSIONAL SERVICES: Public Relations/Marketing). NAICS Code 54

Arkansas

1000 The C3 Group
P.O. Box 157
Greenland, AR 72737
Contact: Bobby Cook President
Tel: 479-445-2657
Email: bcook@thec3group.net
Website: www.Thec3group.net
Advertising media buying, marketing consulting, promotional products, web development, interactive design, bilboards, banners. (Nat Ame, estab 2005, empl 5, sales $650,000, cert: State)

Arizona

1001 Creative Merchandise Displays Inc.
1839 W 1st Ave
Mesa, AZ 85202
Contact: Debra Mendoza COO
Tel: 480-668-7225
Email: deb@cmdracks.com
Website: www.cmdracks.com
Mfr point-of-purchase display racks, point-of-purchase display design, engineering, manufacturing, finishing, assembly & packaging. (Woman, estab 2008, empl 12, sales $686,921, cert: City, WBENC, SDB)

1002 Double T. Signs Inc.
1835 S Alvernon Ste 214
Tucson, AZ 85711
Contact: David Torres President
Tel: 520-750-0189
Email: dave@doubletsigns.com
Website: www.doubletsigns.com
Mfr & install signs: billboards, displays, electrical, neon, signboards, display lettering services, sign lettering, window dressing, ad displays, identification plates & tags. (Hisp, estab 1993, empl 6, sales $601,161, cert: State, City)

1003 Language Concepts Consulting LLC
8502 E Princess Dr, Ste 230
Scottsdale, AZ 85255
Contact: Katherine Paredes Managing Dir
Tel: 480-626-2926
Email: kathy.paredes@languageconceptsllc.com
Website: www.languageconceptsllc.com
Translation services: English, Spanish, Chinese, Portuguese, Korean, German & Vietnamese. Document Translation, Linguistic Validation, Linguist Testing and Bug Reporting (sites), Multilingual graphic design, Localization, Transcription. (Woman/Hisp, estab 2009, empl 1, sales $112,000, cert: NMSDC)

California

1004 1-Stop Translation
3700 Wilshire Blvd, Ste 630
Los Angeles, CA 90010
Contact: Diana Chi Mktg Mgr
Tel: 213-480-0011
Email: diana@1stoptr.com
Website: www.1stoptr.com
Translation and interpretation services with a specialty in Asian languages, including typesetting, desktop publishing, web localization, software testing, budding & subtitling services. (As-Pac, estab 2001, empl 8, sales , cert: CPUC)

1005 3V Signs & Graphics, LLC
434 Pacific Coast Hwy
Hermosa Beach, CA 90254
Contact: Pat Dacy Sec/Treas
Tel: 310-372-0888
Email: pat@3vsigns.com
Website: www.3Vsigns.com
Sign & graphic consultation & design, production, delivery & installation services: architectural signs, window, wall, ground or vehicle graphics, point-of-purchase posters or a building identification signs. (Woman/Hisp, estab 2010, empl 5, sales $186,000, cert: City)

1006 Artisan Creative Inc.
1830 Stoner Ave Ste 6
Los Angeles, CA 90025
Contact: Katty Douraghy President
Tel: 310-312-2062
Email: kattyd@artisancreative.com
Website: www.artisancreative.com
Design & development solutions: marketing, advertising, communications & production teams in the digital, broadcast, mobile & print space. (Woman, estab 1996, empl 15, sales $3,000,000, cert: WBENC)

1007 Canela Media
2715 Palomino Circle
La Jolla, CA 92037
Contact: Annette Salinas Director
Tel: 858-699-6640
Email: annette@canelamedia.com
Website: www.canelamedia.com
Create multimedia programs for brand and/or co-opt efforts. (Hisp, estab 2019, empl 12, sales $1,000,000, cert: NMSDC)

1008 Carmazzi of Florida, Inc.
8926 Beckington Dr
Elk Grove, CA 95624
Contact: Angela Carmazzi Presdient
Tel: 888-452-6543
Email: sales@carmazzi.com
Website: www.carmazzi.com/
Translations, interpretations & transcriptions. (Woman/Hisp, estab 1998, empl 8, sales $1,900,000, cert: CPUC)

1009   Coast sign inc
       1500 W Embassy St.
       Anaheim, CA 92802
       Contact: Charlie President
       Tel: 714-999-1900
       Email: charlie.alemi@coastsign.com
       Website: www.coastsign.com
Mfr electrical signage, ATM surrounds & kiosks, project
management, design, engineering, lighting, installation,
service & maintenance. (Woman, estab 1964, empl 220,
sales $80,535,032, cert: WBENC)

1010   Competitive Edge Media Management
       3261 S Higuera St Ste 110
       San Luis Obispo, CA 93401
       Contact: Suzy da Silva Presdient
       Tel: 805-788-0966
       Email: suzy@cemm.com
       Website: http://cemm.com
Media buying, brand promotion plans, product launch,
direct-to-consumer sales strategy, hybrid campaigns.
(Woman, estab 2007, empl 8, sales $6,874,176, cert:
WBENC)

1011   CR&A Custom, Inc.
       312 W Pico Blvd
       Los Angeles, CA 90015
       Contact: Carmen Rad Acct Exec
       Tel: 213-749-4440
       Email: carmen@cracustom.com
       Website: www.cracustom.com
Large format digital printing, embroidery, promotional
products, custom designs, carwraps, banners, billboards,
tents, POP displays. (Woman/Hisp, estab 1993, empl 31,
sales $5,900,000, cert: NMSDC, CPUC, 8a)

1012   Direct Results Radio, Inc.
       815 Hamton Dr, Ste 2
       Venice, CA 90291
       Contact: Sheri White Business Develop Dir
       Tel: 310-441-9100
       Email: sheriwhite@directresults.com
       Website: www.directresults.com
Advertising agency, audio & radio. (Woman, estab 2007,
empl 20, sales , cert: NWBOC)

1013   Everfield Consulting, LLC
       2075 W 235th Pl
       Torrance, CA 90501
       Contact: Delbara Dorsey Partner
       Tel: 310-251-7165
       Email: deldorsey@everfieldconsulting.com
       Website: www.everfieldconsulting.com
Marketing Consulting Services, Administrative & Manage-
ment, Display Advertising, Advertising, Public Relations,
Media Buying, Direct Mail Advertising, Advertising
Material Distribution Services. (Woman/AA, As-Pac, estab
2011, empl 2, sales , cert: State, City, CPUC)

1014   Exponential Interactive, Inc.
       5858 Horton St, Ste 300
       Emeryville, CA 94608
       Contact: Catherine Avenido Sr Mgr, Intl Ops
       Tel: 510-250-5500
       Email: mbe@exponential.com
       Website: http://exponential.com/
Advertising intelligence & digital media solutions. (As-Ind,
estab 2000, empl 690, sales $219,740,000, cert: NMSDC,
CPUC)

1015   Fraser/White, Inc.
       1631 Pontius Ave
       Los Angeles, CA 90025
       Contact: Renee Fraser CEO
       Tel: 310-319-3737
       Email: rfraser@frasercommunications.com
       Website: www.frasercommunications.com
Advertising, marketing, market research, display
advertising, media planning, media buying, qualitative
research, quantitative research, strategic planning,
outdoor advertising. (Woman, estab 1998, empl 25,
sales $40,000,000, cert: WBENC)

1016   Frisson, Inc.
       12 Geary St, Ste 607
       San Francisco, CA 94108
       Contact: Deboran N Loeb Presdient
       Tel: 415-922-1482
       Email: purchasing@brainchildcreative.com
       Website: www.brainchildcreative.com
Advertising agency; marketing-branding vonsulting
services; commercial production services. (Woman,
estab 2001, empl 7, sales $16,700,000, cert: CPUC,
WBENC)

1017   Global Language Solutions
       19800 MacArthur Blvd Ste 750
       Irvine, CA 92612
       Contact: Inna Kassatkina Presdient
       Tel: 949-798-1400
       Email: info@globallanguages.com
       Website: www.globallanguages.com
Translation svcs: document & web site translations,
conference interpretation, multimedia production &
graphic design services. (Woman, estab 1994, empl 50,
sales $16,300,000,000, cert: WBENC)

1018   Hawthorne Direct LLC
       1201 West 5th St., Ste T230
       Los Angeles, CA 90017
       Contact: Karla Crawford Kerr VP of Marketing
       Tel: 310-844-0606
       Email: diversity@hawthornedirect.com
       Website: www.hawthornedirect.com/
Advertising, strategic planning, creative development,
production, media planning, buying, analytics & campaign management. (Woman, estab 1986, empl 78, sales
$17,024,888, cert: WBENC)

1019   I. Studio, Inc.
       51 E Colorado Blvd
       Pasadena, CA 91105
       Contact: Gabriel Avalos Principal
       Tel: 626-683-3101
       Email: g.avalos@interiorstudioinc.com
       Website: www.interiorstudioinc.com
I, Studio, Inc, is a full service Interior Planning & Design
Firm. Our services included programming, schematic
design, design development, contract documents,
construction administration. (Hisp, estab 2006, empl 3,
sales , cert: State, NMSDC)

1020 IW Group, Inc.
      6300 Wilshire Blvd. Ste 2150
      Los Angeles, CA 90048
      Contact: Nita Song Presdient
      Tel: 310-289-5500
      Email: nita.song@iwgroupinc.com
      Website: www.iwgroupinc.com/
Advertising & PR, creative development, research, media
planning, media buying, production, events, cultural
training. (As-Pac, estab 1990, empl 50, sales $10,506,000,
cert: NMSDC, CPUC)

1021 Kramer Translation
      893 Massasso St
      Merced, CA 95341
      Contact: Keith Ensminger Principal
      Tel: 209-385-0425
      Email: keith@kramertranslations.com
      Website: www.kramertranslations.com
Translation svcs: personal, business & government documents. (Woman/As-Pac, estab 1995, empl 3, sales
$701,672, cert: State, NMSDC, CPUC)

1022 Limelight Media LLC, Inc.
      15619 Gaymont Dr
      La Mirada, CA 90638
      Contact: Christina Roach Presdient
      Tel: 818-501-4043
      Email: christina@limelightmedia.net
      Website: www.limelightmedia.net
Advertising and PR campaigns. (Woman, estab 2004, empl
, sales $2,000,000, cert: WBENC)

1023 Local Concept
      1510 Front St, Ste 200
      San Diego, CA 92101
      Contact: Localization Solutions Specialist
      Tel: 619-295-2682
      Email:
      Website: www.localconcept.com
Localization, translation, foreign language typesetting &
multimedia for all languages. (Hisp, estab 1985, empl 25,
sales $1,435,306, cert: NMSDC)

1024 Motivate, Inc.
      4141 Jutland Dr Ste 300
      San Diego, CA 92117
      Contact: SVP, Finance
      Tel: 866-664-4432
      Email:
      Website: www.MotivateROI.com
Media representation, consumer event marketing services.
(Woman, estab 1977, empl 25, sales $40,690,000, cert:
WBENC)

1025 Muse Communications, Inc.
      5358 Melrose Ave West Bldg, Ground Fl
      Hollywood, CA 90038
      Contact: Norma Keffer
      Tel: 323-960-4080
      Email: norma@museusa.com
      Website: www.musecordero.com
Advertising, marketing, promotions & public relations
programs. (AA, estab 1985, empl 35, sales $5,975,000,
cert: CPUC)

1026 Nonpareil Ventures LLC
      710 C St, Ste 206
      San Rafael, CA 94901
      Contact: Nicolas Campos Mgr
      Tel: 415-404-7409
      Email: drcampos2002@yahoo.com
      Website: www.instalogistics.biz
Advertising services, sign manufacturing, repair &
maintenance. (As-Ind, estab 2011, empl 5, sales
$250,000, cert: State)

1027 Paragon Language Services, Inc.
      5055 Wilshire Blvd Ste 835
      Los Angeles, CA 90036
      Contact: Marina Mintz Presdient
      Tel: 323-966-4655
      Email: marina@paragonls.com
      Website: www.paragonls.com
Foreign language translation, adaptation, interpreting,
typesetting/desktop publishing, internationalization,
globalization, localization, cultural and linguistic consulting, dialog/dialect coaching, captioning, subtitling,
narrations. (Woman, estab 1991, empl 10, sales
$2,600,000, cert: City, CPUC)

1028 Quigley-Simpson & Heppelwhite, Inc.
      11601 Wilshire Blvd 7th Fl
      Los Angeles, CA 90025
      Contact: Gerald Bagg Co-Chairman
      Tel: 310-996-5820
      Email: geraldb@quigleysimpson.com
      Website: www.quigleysimpson.com
Direct response advertising agency. (Woman, estab
2002, empl 180, sales , cert: WBENC)

1029 RBG Marketing, Inc, dba Crescendo
      5000 Executive Parkway Ste 350
      San Ramon, CA 94583
      Contact: A.K. AHUJA Managing Dir
      Tel: 925-939-1800
      Email: aka@crescendoagency.com
      Website: https://crescendoagency.com
Marketing & advertising, creative, media planning &
media buying in-house. (As-Ind, estab 2003, empl 30,
sales $9,000,000, cert: State, NMSDC, CPUC)

1030 RP & Associates, Inc.
      2205 Pacific Coast Hwy
      Hermosa Beach, CA 90254
      Contact: Lisa Pola CEO
      Tel: 310-372-9709
      Email: lpola@mac.com
      Website: www.rpandassociates.com
Marketing solutions, branded products & programs,
custom packaging, premiums & promotional items.
(Woman/Hisp, estab 1988, empl 34, sales
$2,306,595,900, cert: NMSDC)

1031 Sensis Inc.
      818 South Broadway, Ste 110
      Los Angeles, CA 90014
      Contact: Dreux Dougall
      Tel: 213-341-0171
      Email: ddougall@sensisagency.com
      Website: www.sensisagency.com
Advertising, digital marketing & communications
services, online media & marketing, web design &
development, online creative strategy, analytics &
planning. (Hisp, estab 1998, empl 90, sales $11,100,000,
cert: NMSDC)

1032　Simply Displays
　　　12200 Los Nietos Rd
　　　Santa Fe Springs, CA 90670
　　　Contact: Mila Thompson Presdient
　　　Tel:　888-767-0676
　　　Email: mthompson@simplydisplays.com
　　　Website: www.simplydisplays.com
Mfr Point of Purchase Displays & Store Fixtures, Sign Holders, Hospitality & Retail Signage (Woman, estab 2002, empl 16, sales $36,000,000, cert: WBENC)

1033　Think Ink
　　　927 Mariner St
　　　Brea, CA 92821
　　　Contact: Mary Sanchez Dir of Sales
　　　Tel:　714-672-0017
　　　Email: info@thinkinkinfo.com
　　　Website: www.thinkinkinfo.com
Creative marketing, graphic design, print & promotions. (As-Pac, Hisp, estab 2002, empl 5, sales $1,105,519, cert: NMSDC, CPUC)

1034　Tylie Jones & Associates, Inc.
　　　58 E Santa Anita Ave
　　　Burbank, CA 91502
　　　Contact: Sheri Lawrence Presdient
　　　Tel:　818-955-7600
　　　Email: slawrence@tylie.com
　　　Website: www.tylie.com
Broadcast advertising services: SD & HD audio & video spot duplication & digital distribution; post production, closed captioning, tagging, versioninig, encoding; production element vaulting/storage. (Woman, estab 1971, empl 35, sales , cert: WBENC)

1035　Unique Image, Inc.
　　　19365 Business Center Dr. Bldg. 1
　　　Northridge, CA 91324
　　　Contact: Wafa Kanan Presdient
　　　Tel:　818-727-7785
　　　Email: kelly@uniqueimageinc.com
　　　Website: www.uniqueimageinc.com
Printing & marketing svcs: strategic campaigns, print media, design & direct mail. (Woman, estab 1992, empl 10, sales $1,200,000, cert: CPUC, WBENC)

1036　Weldon Works, Inc.
　　　1650 Mabury Rd
　　　San Jose, CA 95133
　　　Contact: Jennifer Easom CEO
　　　Tel:　408-251-1161
　　　Email: jenn@weldonworks.com
　　　Website: www.weldonworks.com
Plastic Fabrication & Signage, Interior & Exterior Signs, ADA Signage, Lobby Signs, Window Graphics & Lettering, Menu Boards, Isle Signage, Banner, Stencils, Reflective Road Work/ Parking Signs, Full Color Digital Printing. (Woman, estab 1982, empl 3, sales $100,000, cert: State)

1037　Zeesman Communications, Inc.
　　　6255 Sunset Blvd. Ste 1040
　　　Los Angeles, CA 90028
　　　Contact: Bonnie Nijst President & CEO
　　　Tel:　323-658-8000
　　　Email: bonnie@zeesman.com
　　　Website: www.zeesman.com
Marketing, advertising & design: branding programs, logos, corporate identity, collateral, direct mail, print advertising & web design. (Woman/As-Pac, estab 1990, empl 4, sales $570,000, cert: NMSDC, CPUC, WBENC)

Colorado

1038　Altitude Technologies dba Chinook Medical Gear
　　　54 Girard St Ste A
　　　Durango, CO 81303
　　　Contact: Andrew Colbert
　　　Tel:　800-766-1365
　　　Email: andrew@chinookmed.com
　　　Website: www.chinookmed.com
Chinook offers the latest technology and competitive prices in medical supplies; specializing in custom medical solutions for the harshest environments on Earth! (Nat Ame, estab 1990, empl 23, sales , cert: State)

Connecticut

1039　Andrew Associates, Inc.
　　　6 Pearson Way
　　　Enfield, CT 6082
　　　Contact:　Dir Mktg & Business Devel
　　　Tel:　860-918-5041
　　　Email:
　　　Website: www.andrewdm.com
Data management, digital printing, bulk mailing services, labeling, inserting, stamping, sorting & literature fulfillment services. (Woman, estab 1985, empl 60, sales $7,600,000, cert: WBENC)

1040　Crew Design Inc.
　　　P.O. Box 400
　　　Kent, CT 6757
　　　Contact: Gil Aviles CEO
　　　Tel:　860-927-5001
　　　Email: gil@crewdesign.com
　　　Website: www.crewdesign.com
Custom in store display & merchandising equipment: signage, merchandising fixtures, point of purchase displays. (Hisp, estab 1998, empl 25, sales $11,000,000, cert: NMSDC)

1041　Desai Communication
　　　34 Oakwood Ave Ste 102
　　　Norwalk, CT 6850
　　　Contact: Amanda Desai Acct Exec
　　　Tel:　203-324-6000
　　　Email: amanda@desaicomm.com
　　　Website: www.desaicomm.com
Web design & hosting, promotions, premiums, fulfillment, graphic design, computer graphics, digital retouching, power point pesentations, pint avertising & promotional material, trade show displays, B/W & color printing. (Woman/Hisp, estab 1979, empl 11, sales $1,500,000, cert: State, NMSDC)

1042　Point View Displays, LLC
　　　200 Morgan Ave
　　　East Haven, CT 6512
　　　Contact: Cynthia Sedlmeyer Owner
　　　Tel:　203-468-0887
　　　Email: cindy@pointviewdisplays.com
　　　Website: www.pointviewdisplays.com
Press conference backdrops, displays, indoor/outdoor banner stands & graphics. (Woman, estab 2001, empl 4, sales $400,000, cert: WBENC)

1043 Tanen Directed Advertising
      12 South Main St
      South Norwalk, CT 6854
      Contact: Presdient
      Tel: 203-855-5855
      Email:
      Website: www.tanendirected.com
Advertising, direct marketing, integrated marketing, online marketing, direct mail, email, print ads, collateral, sales presentations, human resources communications, benefits communications materials, employee communications. (Woman, estab 1985, empl 10, sales $1,865,652, cert: WBENC)

District of Columbia

1044 APCO Worldwide LLC
      1299 Pennsylvania ave NW
      Washington, DC 20005
      Contact: Jim Moorhead
      Tel: 202-778-1000
      Email: jmoorhead@apcoworldwide.com
      Website: http://wwwapcoworldwide.com
Global communication consulting: advertising, antitrust & competition, branding, broadcast film, video & multimedia production, business diplomacy, coalition building, corporate restructuring communication. (Woman, estab 1984, empl 638, sales $240,000,000, cert: WBENC)

1045 SRB Communications, LLC
      1020 16th St, NW Ste 400
      Washington, DC 20036
      Contact: Sheila Brooks CEO
      Tel: 202-775-7721
      Email: sbrooks@srbcommunications.com
      Website: www.srbcommunications.com
Media & communications: video production, advertising, lay-out & design, copywriting services, media placement & webcasting. (Woman/AA, estab 1990, empl 7, sales , cert: State, City, NMSDC)

1046 The Language Doctors, Inc.
      412 H St NE Ste 302
      Washington, DC 20002
      Contact: Adam Bouc Dir of Sales and Marketing
      Tel: 202-544-2942
      Email: abou@tldinc.org
      Website: www.tldinc.org
Translation & intepretation svcs: advertising, banking, communications, computer svcs, legal, insurance, law enforcement. (AA, estab 1994, empl 4, sales $350,000, cert: State)

Delaware

1047 Keen Branding
      17601 Coastal Hwy., Ste. 11-416
      Nassau, DE 19969
      Contact: Alicia Stack Principal
      Tel: 302-644-6885
      Email: astack@keenbranding.com
      Website: www.keenbranding.com
Identity creation & design: logos, packaging, look & feel programs, identity mgmt. (Woman, estab 2000, empl 14, sales , cert: WBENC)

1048 Meetings by Design, Inc.
      312 Nonantum Dr

Newark, DE 19711
      Contact: Jan White Presdient
      Tel: 302-738-8318
      Email:
      Website: www.meetingsbydesign.net
Business meetings & special events production. (Woman, estab , empl , sales $200,000, cert: State, WBENC)

Florida

1049 Adventures in Advertising dba Resource Marketing
      2520 Illinois St
      Orlando, FL 32803
      Contact: Christyl Seymour President
      Tel: 407-228-0881
      Email: cseymour@advinadv.com
      Website: www.resourcemarketinginc.net
Graphic design/art services, product research support, custom design, online store solution, fulfillment svcs, direct import, promotional svcs, website searchable database, promotion design & implementation. (Woman, estab 2002, empl , sales $3,175,125, cert: WBENC)

1050 Avanza Advertising
      5465 NW 36 St Ste 100
      Miami Springs, FL 33166
      Contact: Alejandro Perez-Eguren CEO
      Tel: 786-565-7601
      Email: alejandro@avanzaad.com
      Website: www.avanzaad.com
Advertising, design, digital media & video. (Hisp, estab 2013, empl 6, sales $500,000, cert: NMSDC, CPUC, 8a)

1051 Baron Sign Manufacturing
      900 W 13th St
      Riviera Beach, FL 33404
      Contact: Jerry Foland CEO
      Tel: 800-531-9558
      Email: jerry@baronsign.com
      Website: www.baronsign.com
Interior & exterior signage, awards, plaques. (Woman, estab , empl , sales , cert: State, City)

1052 Black Dog Inc.
      4803 George Rd Ste 370
      Tampa, FL 33634
      Contact: Dorothy Johnson President
      Tel: 813-249-6398
      Email: djohnson@nextdaysignstampa.com
      Website: www.nextdaysignstampa.com
Vinyl signs, banners, digital printing, vehicle & boat graphics & lettering, directional signs, promotional signs, trade show & conventions, sandblasted, electrical, coroplast, point of purchase, magnets, screen printing, real estate, constrcution. (Woman, estab 2003, empl 3, sales $429,460, cert: State)

1053 BroadBased Communications, Inc.
      1301 Riverplace Blvd, Ste 1830
      Jacksonville, FL 32207
      Contact: Jan Hirabayashi CEO
      Tel: 904-398-7279
      Email: jan@bbased.com
      Website: www.bbased.com
Marketing plans, branding, direct mail, publication design, exhibit design, annual reports, web sites, fleet graphics, copywriting, art direction. (Woman, estab 1996, empl 7, sales $1,381,791, cert: WBENC)

1054   Catalyst Advertizing
       737 W Colonial Dr
       Orlando, FL 32804
       Contact: Edward Rees agent
       Tel: 407-425-5646
       Email: edrees@catalystholdingsco.com
       Website: www.catalystadvertizing.com
Advertising & marketing services, creative writing, art,
graphics, market analysis, planning, buying, media
relations, full design, production & coordination services.
(Hisp, estab 1989, empl 8, sales $750,000, cert: 8a)

1055   Celestar Corporation
       9501 East US Hwy 92
       Tampa, FL 33610
       Contact: Lori Larsen VP Business Devel
       Tel: 813-627-9069
       Email: llarsen@celestarcorp.com
       Website: www.celestarcorp.com
Media communications: marketing, training, branding,
mobile/portable distribution, broadcast media, internet,
entertainment. (AA, estab 2001, empl 58, sales
$5,615,000, cert: State)

1056   Certified Translations LLC
       11663 Vicolo Loop
       Windermere, FL 34786
       Contact: Mara Cawthorn Managing Dir
       Tel: 407-205-9494
       Email: certifiedtranslationsllc@gmail.com
       Website: http://certifiedtranslationsllc.com
Language Translation & Interpreting Services: Legal,
Technical, Mechanical, Medical, & Business / Finance.
Spanish, Portuguese, Creole, Mandarin, Cantonese,
French, Italian, German, etc. (Woman/Hisp, estab 2013,
empl 2, sales , cert: NMSDC)

1057   Eco Graphics Media
       7034 NW 50th St
       Miami, FL 33166
       Contact: Jose Contreras Project Mgr
       Tel: 305-640-9600
       Email: info@ecogm.com
       Website: www.ecogm.com/index.html
Corporate Image and Concept, Product and Trade Mark
Campaigns • Billboards • Trade shows and displays•
Banners - Posters • Gran Format prints • Signs and
Graphics • vehicle wraps • Trade Shows • Custom
Displays • Store Fixtures. (Hisp, estab 2005, empl 11,
sales $820,000, cert: NMSDC)

1058   KVJINC Consulting
       7016 San Ramon Pl Ste. 202
       Tampa, FL 33617
       Contact: Kimberly Jackson Owner
       Tel: 813-987-9083
       Email: kvjinc@yahoo.com
       Website: www.kvjincpr.com
Public, media relations, strategic, crisis communications,
press conferences, kits, event planning, image consulting,
sponsorship procurement & market research. (Woman/
AA, estab 1999, empl 3, sales $100,000, cert: State, City)

1059   LanguageSpeak, Inc.
       5975 Sunset Dr Ste 803
       Miami, FL 33143
       Contact: Annette Taddeo CEO
       Tel: 305-668-9797
       Email: acct@languagespeak.com
       Website: www.languagespeak.com
Language svcs: document translation, language instruction, conference interpretation, software localization,
website translation, cross cultural training. (Woman/
Hisp, estab 1995, empl 5, sales , cert: NMSDC, WBENC)

1060   Lombardi Enterprises, Inc.
       1145 N Tropical Trail
       Merritt Island, FL 32953
       Contact: Ann Lombardi Presdient
       Tel: 321-449-8857
       Email: ann@mihomeoffice.com
       Website:
Signs, labels & decals, asset control & printing software,
hardware, name badges & plates, promotional items &
marking products. (Woman, estab 2002, empl 4, sales ,
cert: City)

1061   MarkMaster, Inc.
       11111 N 46th St
       Tampa, FL 33617
       Contact: Deborah Jordan Sales Rep
       Tel: 813-988-6000
       Email: sales@markmasterinc.com
       Website: www.markmasterinc.com
Mfr rubber stamps, engraved & screened signage &
badges; industrial marking equip. (Hisp, estab 1933,
empl 65, sales $8,700,993, cert: NMSDC)

1062   Multi Image Group, Inc.
       1701 Clint Moore Rd
       Boca Raton, FL 33487
       Contact: Jim Ballentine Presdient
       Tel: 917-319-8127
       Email: ballentine@mig.cc
       Website: www.mig.cc
Meeting production & staging, video & audio production, graphic design, signage printing, set construction,
web & teleconferencing services, trade show exhibits,
lighting rentals. (Woman, estab 1979, empl 106, sales
$28,400,000, cert: NWBOC)

1063   Retail Solution Center
       475 N Cleary Road
       West Palm Beach, FL 33413
       Contact: Deborah Leo CEO
       Tel: 561-567-9000
       Email: debleo@rsc-ny.com
       Website: www.rsc-ny.com
Point of purchase displays, merchandising systems, mfr
& design. (Woman, estab 2003, empl 49, sales
$15,428,108, cert: WBENC)

1064 Sunlure, Inc.
       3700 NW 124 Ave Unit 140
       Coral Springs, FL 33065
       Contact: Craig Sage Mgr
       Tel: 754-484-7929
       Email: craig.sage@sunlure.com
       Website: www.sunlure.com
Promotional Products, Apparel Products, Custom imprinted apparel, Writing Products, etc. (Minority/Woman,
estab 2003, empl 7, sales $900,000, cert: State, NMSDC)

1065 T Wynne Art & Design Inc.
       1401 Manatee Ave W, Ste 1005
       Bradenton, FL 34205
       Contact: Tanya Wynne Williams President
       Tel: 941-906-7124
       Email: tanya@twynne.com
       Website: www.twynne.com
Package graphic design & and point of sale (POS) design.
(Woman, estab 1991, empl 8, sales $2,430,822, cert:
WBENC)

1066 The Language Corner, LLC
       2103 Coral Way Ste 700
       Miami, FL 33145
       Contact: Dir of Operations
       Tel: 888-422-9964
       Email:
       Website: http://thelanguagecorner.com
Translation services, document translation, website
localization, desktop publishing, editing & proofreading,
copywriting & technical writing, glossary development.
(Woman/Hisp, estab 2001, empl 2, sales $216,429, cert:
State)

1067 Thomas Sign and Awning Company, Inc.
       4590 118th Ave N
       Clearwater, FL 33762
       Contact: Aimee Pavlovich Marketing Mgr
       Tel: 727-573-7757
       Email: aimee.pavlovich@thomassign.com
       Website: www.thomassign.com
Design, mfr, install & service illuminated electrical signs.
LED, neon, vinyl graphics, permit acquisition, variance
applications, turnkey project mgmt. (Woman, estab 1969,
empl 156, sales $21,000,000, cert: WBENC)

Georgia

1068 AEE Productions
       1650 Westfork Dr, Ste 110
       Lithia Springs, GA 30122
       Contact: Yergan Jones Presdient
       Tel: 404-352-2201
       Email: yerganjones@aeeproductions.com
       Website: www.aeeproductions.com
Audio visual services. (AA, estab 1990, empl 6, sales
$975,000, cert: NMSDC)

1069 American Systems, Inc. dba Simon Sign Systems
       2158 Sylvan Rd
       Atlanta, GA 30344
       Contact: Simon Robinson President & CEO
       Tel: 404-766-5208
       Email: gen-info@simonsignsystems.com
       Website: www.simonsignsystems.com
Mfr signs: interior & exterior, banners, digital & screen
printing, posters, corporate apparel & promotional items.
(AA, estab 1989, empl 5, sales $300,670, cert: NMSDC)

1070 Basiqa, LLC
       1555 Oakbrook Dr Ste 135
       Norcross, GA 30093
       Contact: Winston Dzose VP Digital Marketing
       Tel: 678-824-6460
       Email: winston@basiqa.com
       Website: www.basiqa.com
Direct mail, advertising, material preparation services
for mailing or other direct distribution, digital printing.
(AA, estab 2009, empl 16, sales $3,000,000, cert:
NMSDC)

1071 CK&M Direct Mail Advertising, Inc.
       1250 Northmeadow Pkwy Ste 116
       Roswell, GA 30076
       Contact: Gary Kern GM
       Tel: 770-442-2166
       Email: gkern@ckmdirect.com
       Website: www.ckmdirectmail.com
Lettershop services, fulfillment, distribution, warehousing, list broker. (Hisp, estab 1992, empl 7, sales
$1,992,000, cert: NMSDC)

1072 Cloud Track, LLC
       36111 Indigo Creek Trail NW
       Kennesaw, GA 30144
       Contact: Samir Mullick CEO
       Tel: 404-934-7408
       Email: Samir.Mullick@cloudtrackusa.com
       Website: https://cloudtrackusa.com
Digital Branding, Lead Generation. (As-Ind, estab 2014,
empl 2, sales , cert: NMSDC)

1073 Display America
       195 Andrew Dr
       Stockbridge, GA 30281
       Contact: Carlos Quinones CEO
       Tel: 770-416-7047
       Email: carlos@displayamerica.com
       Website: www.displayamerica.com
Dist exhibit marketing products & turnkey services:
image & identity, rent exhibits, high impact graphics,
trade shows, conventions, expositions, hospitality &
retail environments. (Hisp, estab 2003, empl 15, sales
$1,400,000, cert: NMSDC)

1074 Dove Direct
       5601 Fulton Industrial Blvd SW
       Atlanta, GA 30336
       Contact: Travis L Benjamin Business Develop Exec
       Tel: 404-629-0122
       Email: tbenjamin@dovedirect.com
       Website: www.dovedirect.com
First class barcoding, third class mail, lettershop svcs,
personalization, list, data mgmt, fulfillment svcs, design
analysis, etc. (Woman/AA, estab 1987, empl 59, sales
$24,000,000, cert: NMSDC)

1075 Exhibits South
       1000 Satellite Blvd Ste 120
       Suwanee, GA 30024
       Contact: Nichole Holliday VP
       Tel: 678-225-5200
       Email: nholliday@exhibitssouth.com
       Website: www.exhibitssouth.com
Dist & rent portable, modular & custom displays, graphic
production & design department, tradeshow services,
logistics & exhibit storage. (Woman, estab 1983, empl
35, sales $10,750,000, cert: WBENC)

1076 Mail Centers Plus, LLC
17 Executive Park Dr Ste 230
Atlanta, GA 30329
Contact: John Smithson Business Devel Analyst
Tel: 404-321-1010
Email: jsmithson@mailcentersplus.com
Website: www.mailcentersplus.com
Document distribution & mail center solutions. (AA, estab 2000, empl 140, sales $5,500,000, cert: NMSDC)

1077 PM Publicidad
1776 Peachtree St
Atlanta, GA 30309
Contact: Philip Polk EVP, General Mgr
Tel: 404-844-5757
Email: info@pm3.agency
Website: http://pm3.agency
Multicultural advertising solutions in the Hispanic market segment, account services, broadcast production, media planning & buying, sports marketing, market research, strategic account planning, experiential & event marketing. (Hisp, estab 2004, empl 35, sales $23,307,370, cert: NMSDC)

1078 Profitmaster Displays Inc.
6190 Powers Ferry Rd Ste 510
Atlanta, GA 30339
Contact: Presdient
Tel: 800-633-5454
Email:
Website: www.profitmasterdisplays.com
Point of purchase displays & racks: wire, sheet metal, wood, plastic & corrugated paperboard. (Woman, estab 1984, empl 18, sales $20,000,000, cert: WBENC)

1079 Shared Vision LLC
225 Ottley Dr NE Ste 140
Atlanta, GA 30324
Contact: Doug Jackson Principal
Tel: 678-694-1965
Email: djackson@shared-vision.net
Website: www.shared-vision.net
Marketing & advertising, strategic & creative services. (Woman/AA, estab 2006, empl 20, sales $2,500,000, cert: NMSDC)

1080 TDEFERIAMEDIA, Inc.
9795 Talisman Dr
Johns Creek, GA 30022
Contact: Antenor Tony President
Tel: 404-630-0639
Email: contact@tdeferiamedia.com
Website: http://tdeferiamedia.com
Marketing, branding consulting & creative production, ethnic market study & plans, media buying, translation & interpretation in Spanish, digital & social media expertise. (Hisp, estab 2007, empl 1, sales $140,000, cert: NMSDC)

1081 The Symmetry Group, LLC
600 W Peachtree St Ste 510
Atlanta, GA 30308
Contact: Scott Robinson President
Tel: 404-237-2378
Email: scott@tsgatl.com
Website: www.tsgatl.com
Graphic design, radio/TV production, print/outdoor advertising production, event development, management & production, promotion development & execution. (AA, estab 2001, empl 6, sales $1,200,000, cert: NMSDC)

1082 Viswam Bala Enterprises
440 Barrett Pkwy, Ste 33
Kennesaw, GA 30144
Contact: Giridhar Iyer President
Tel: 770-421-8110
Email: giri.iyer@fastsigns.com
Website: www.fastsigns.com/201
Marketing strategy creation, brand /product identity creation, graphic design services, production/printing & installation services, static signs, banners, posters, decals, vehicle art/wraps, cutting-edge digital signs & visual magnetic solutions. (As-Ind, estab 1994, empl 6, sales $1,047,000, cert: City, NMSDC)

1083 Yellobee Studio
750 Hammond Dr Ste 350 Bldg 15
Atlanta, GA 30328
Contact: Alison Scheel Creative Director
Tel: 404-249-6407
Email: ascheel@yellobee.com
Website: www.yellobee.com
Bilingual design & marketing, promotional communications, brand identity & packaging, direct mail design, brochures, newsletters, web design, banner & poster art, tradeshow displays, court graphics, typography, illustration,photography. (Woman, estab 1998, empl 4, sales $850,000, cert: WBENC)

Illinois

1084 1st Metropolitan Translation Services, Inc.
875 North Michigan Ave Ste 3100
Chicago, IL 60611
Contact: Shannon Ewasiuk President
Tel: 312-621-1500
Email: firstmetro@sbcglobal.net
Website: www.1stmetropolitan.info
Foreign language interpreters & translations. (Woman, estab 2000, empl 1, sales $222,810, cert: State, WBENC)

1085 Angel Flight Marketing Services, Inc.
1006 S. Michigan Ave Ste 606
Chicago, IL 60605
Contact: Gabriel Mitchell President & CEO
Tel: 312-933-1878
Email: gmitchell@angelfly.com
Website: www.angelfly.com
Direct mail, graphic design, call center, market research. (AA, estab 1992, empl 10, sales $1,220,000, cert: City, NMSDC)

1086 commonground
600 W Fluton Fl 4
Chicago, IL 60661
Contact: Sherman Wright Managing Partner
Tel: 312-384-1906
Email: alicepollard@discovercg.com
Website: www.discovercg.com
Marketing, advertising, cultural consulting, brand strategy, promotions. (AA, estab 2003, empl 75, sales $24,367,000, cert: NMSDC)

1087   Cor Creative, Inc.
       1412 W Jarvis
       Chicago, IL 60626
       Contact: Linda Tuke-Larkin Presdient
       Tel: 773-381-3811
       Email: linda@corcreate.com
       Website: www.corcreate.com
Design, advertising, production, web site design & programming, strategy, branding, social media, marketing,
creative, media placement. (Woman, estab 2006, empl 1,
sales $100,000, cert: City)

1088   Jayne Agency, LLC
       1231 Eastwood Ave
       Highland Park, IL 60035
       Contact: Brooke Foley CEO
       Tel: 312-464-8100
       Email: brooke@jayneagency.com
       Website: http://jayneagency.com
Creative, Strategy, Media, Digital Strategy & Technology.
(Woman, estab 2009, empl 4, sales $484,000, cert:
WBENC)

1089   Linguanational Translations, Inc.
       401 N Michigan Ave Ste 1200 #12135
       Chicago, IL 60611
       Contact: Janie Markos Presdient
       Tel: 312-833-1399
       Email: jmarkos@linguanational.com
       Website: www.linguanational.com
Translation services: interpretation, typesetting, transcription & desktop publishing. (Woman, estab 2009, empl 3,
sales , cert: WBENC)

1090   Mail Everything, Inc.
       325 N Fourth St
       Libertyville, IL 60048
       Contact: Mary Trifunovich Presdient
       Tel: 847-573-9999
       Email: mary@maileverything.com
       Website: www.maileverything.com
Direct mail & fulfillment services: addressing, inserting,
tabbing, folding, mailing lists, printing, warehousing, dist
literature, product & promotional items, kitting & assembly. (Woman, estab 2002, empl 16, sales $3,000,000, cert:
WBENC)

1091   Media Link, Inc.
       1902 17th St
       Rock Island, IL 61201
       Contact: Marketing Consultant
       Tel: 309-786-5142
       Email:
       Website: http://medialinkinc.com
Media Buying, Advertising, Marketing, PR, Public Relations, Media Campaign, Marketing Research. (Woman,
estab 2001, empl 4, sales $1,046,821, cert: State, WBENC)

1092   Medius & Associates, Inc.
       13175 Cold Springs Dr
       Huntley, IL 60142
       Contact: Karen Holmes Presdient
       Tel: 847-609-8165
       Email: kholmes@mediusinc.com
       Website: www.mediusinc.com
Graphic design, illustration, photography & printing:
brochures, catalogs, ads, point of purchase, tradeshow
graphics & web design. (Woman, estab 1993, empl 2, sales
, cert: WBENC)

1093   NorthStar Strategies, Inc.
       448 Greenwood Ave
       Glencoe, IL 60022
       Contact: Dinny Cosyns Sr Partner
       Tel: 847-242-9107
       Email: dinny@northstarstrategies.biz
       Website: www.northstarstrategies.biz
Marketing & advertising agency. (Woman, estab 2004,
empl 3, sales $240,000, cert: State, WBENC)

1094   Suncraft Technologies, Inc.
       1301 Frontenac Road
       Naperville, IL 60563
       Contact: Holly Winters Diversity Lead
       Tel: 630-369-7900
       Email: hwinters@suncraft-tech.com
       Website: www.suncraft-tech.com
Inline and conventional direct mail with variable data.
digital storefront, signage, inventory management,
creative format design, graphic design, fulfillment, kitting
and mailing services. (Woman, estab 1993, empl 100,
sales $30,000,000, cert: WBENC)

Indiana

1095   L & D Mail Masters Inc.
       110 Security Pkwy
       New Albany, IN 47150
       Contact: Jill Peden Business Develop Mgr
       Tel: 812-981-7161
       Email: jpeden@ldmailmasters.com
       Website: www.ldmailmasters.com
Direct mail processing. (Woman, estab 1986, empl 110,
sales $25,000,000, cert: WBENC)

1096   RLR Associates, Inc.
       1302 N Illinois St
       Indianapolis, IN 46202
       Contact: Ryan Scott President
       Tel: 317-632-1300
       Email: ryan@rlr.biz
       Website: www.rlr.biz
Professional design services: corporate identity &
branding, signage, wayfinding programs, interiors &
interpretive spaces.
 (AA, estab 1994, empl 6, sales $710,000, cert: State,
City)

Kentucky

1097   Atomic Cowgirl, Inc.
       909 E Market St
       Louisville, KY 40206
       Contact: Maggie Harlow
       Tel: 502-585-4099
       Email: maggie@signaramadowntown.com
       Website:
Wood Based Sign Products. (Woman, estab 0, empl ,
sales , cert: WBENC)

1098   John F. Ruggles, Inc.
       93 Industry Dr
       Versailles, KY 40383
       Contact: Tim Cambron Presdient
       Tel: 859-879-1199
       Email: tim@rugglessign.com
       Website: www.rugglessign.com
Mfr & install signage. (Woman, estab 1946, empl 95,
sales $16,000,000, cert: WBENC)

1099 Life's Eyes Media, LLC
      1717 Dixie Hwy, Ste 150
      Fort Wright, KY 41011
      Contact: Kristan Getsy CEO
      Tel: 859-363-3916
      Email: kgetsy@lifeseyesmedia.com
      Website: www.lifeseyesmedia.com
Corporate Video, Commercial Video Production, Motion
Graphics, After Effects, DSLR Production, DSLR, Creative,
Creative Agency, Agency, Non-Profit Video, Scriptwriting,
Scripting, Web Video, Social Media Video. (Woman, estab
2005, empl 3, sales $263,704, cert: WBENC)

1100 New West LLC
      9630 Ormsby Station Rd
      Louisville, KY 40223
      Contact: Melvin Graham Managing Dir
      Tel: 888-867-7811
      Email: mgraham@newwestagency.com
      Website: www.newwestagency.com
Advertising, Public Relations, Brand Strategy, Website &
Mobile App Development, Social Media, Multicultural
Marketing, SEO/SEM/PPC, Event Planning & Video Produc-
tion. (AA, estab 2002, empl 28, sales $5,500,000, cert:
NMSDC)

1101 Vest Marketing Design, LLC
      3007 Sprowl Rd
      Louisville, KY 40299
      Contact: Keith Searles Healthcare Marketing Dir
      Tel: 502-267-5335
      Email: bizdev@urbangis.com
      Website: http://vestadvertising.com
Digital, video, print & comprehensive media strategy &
implementation. (Woman, estab 1991, empl 40, sales
$8,500,000, cert: WBENC)

Massachusetts

1102 Buyer Advertising & Talent Solutions
      189 Wells Ave Ste 201A
      Newton, MA 02459
      Contact: Charles Buyer Presdient
      Tel: 617-404-0860
      Email: cbuyer@buyerads.com
      Website: www.buyerads.com
Website Design & Development, Search Engine Optimiza-
tion (SEO), Search Engine Marketing, Mobile marketing,
Social Networking, Facebook Advertising, Facebook
Applications, Employer Brand Development, market
Research & Analysis. (Woman, estab 1966, empl 32, sales
$15,877,337, cert: State)

1103 Carroll Communications Group
      P.O. Box 401
      Milton, MA 02186
      Contact: Marc Carroll Principal
      Tel: 781-248-2125
      Email: mcarroll@carrollcommunications.net
      Website: www.carrollcommunications.net
Advertising agency: web design, graphic design, branding
strategies, social media strategies, on-line marketing,
media planning & media buying. (AA, estab 2008, empl 3,
sales $100,000, cert: State)

1104 Color Media Group, LLC
      4 Copley Pl, Ste 120
      Boston, MA 02116
      Contact: Josefina Bonilla President
      Tel: 617-266-6961
      Email: josefina@colorboston.com
      Website: www.colormagazineusa.com
Web advertising, signature events, event management,
strategic marketing initiatives, new markets, media
buying services, public relations. (Woman/Hisp, estab
2007, empl 3, sales $289,000, cert: State)

1105 Rapport International, LLC
      93 Moore Rd
      Sudbury, MA 01776
      Contact: Owner, Exec Director
      Tel: 978-443-2540
      Email:
      Website: www.rapporttranslations.com
Translation & interpretation services in over 100
languages. (Woman, estab 1987, empl 5, sales
$1,200,000, cert: WBENC)

1106 Sky Rise, LLC
      26 Howland St
      Plymouth, MA 02360
      Contact: Managing Dir
      Tel: 508-732-0455
      Email: nysbuilders@yahoo.com
      Website: www.skyrisellc.com
Marketing communications & advertising consulting,
corporate events, tradeshows, design exhibits, displays,
create logos, brochures, business cards, website design,
graphic design, & packaging. (AA, estab 2005, empl 3,
sales , cert: State)

1107 Spectrum Broadcasting Corporation
      114 Wrentham St
      Boston, MA 02124
      Contact: Tessil Collins CEO
      Tel: 617-287-8770
      Email: thewiz@spectrumbroadcasting.com
      Website: http://spectrumbroadcasting.com
Media streaming & production, advertising creative
services, training & management, internet, television,
radio, graphic & web design, product & artist management, training, facilitation & consultation services. (AA,
estab 1998, empl 5, sales , cert: State, City)

1108 TSM Design, Inc.
      293 Bridge St
      Springfield, MA 01103
      Contact: Nancy Urbschat Principal
      Tel: 413-731-7600
      Email: nancy@tsmdesign.com
      Website: www.tsmdesign.com
Integrated branding, multi-channel marketing &
standout graphic design services. (Woman, estab 2005,
empl 7, sales $900,000, cert: State)

Maryland

1109 21st Century Expo Group, Inc.
      3321 75th Ave, Ste P
      Landover, MD 20785
      Contact: Leslie McFarland Presdient
      Tel: 301-386-9771
      Email: lmcfarland@21stceg.com
      Website: www.21stceg.com
Exhibit mgmt, marketing, dist displays & decorating
svcs. (Woman/AA, estab 1991, empl 9, sales , cert:
NMSDC, WBENC)

1110 A. Bright Idea
      210 Archer St
      Bel Air, MD 21014
      Contact: CEO
      Tel: 410-836-7180
      Email:
      Website: www.abrightideaonline.com
Advertising, public relations & graphic design support.
(Woman, estab 1996, empl 35, sales $2,100,000, cert:
WBENC)

1111 American International Mailing, Inc.
      3916 Vero Rd Ste K
      Baltimore, MD 21227
      Contact: Tom Parry VP
      Tel: 410-247-4900
      Email: tomp@aimmailing.com
      Website: www.aimmailing.com
International mailing & distribution svcs: letter mail, direct
mail, catalogs, publications, parcels & freight. (Woman,
estab 2004, empl 25, sales $8,000,000, cert: WBENC)

1112 ArachnidWorks, Inc.
      5104 Pegasus Court Ste B
      Frederick, MD 21704
      Contact: Monica Kolbay CEO
      Tel: 240-285-9844
      Email: monica@arachnidworks.com
      Website: www.arachnidworks.com
Advertising, internet marketing, logo design, print media,
ad creation & copywriting, web design & development.
(Woman, estab 2008, empl 3, sales $158,335, cert: State)

1113 Barb Clapp Advertising and Marketing, LLC
      6115 Falls Rd Penthouse
      Baltimore, MD 21209
      Contact: Barb Clapp President
      Tel: 410-561-8886
      Email: lisa@barbclapp.com
      Website: www.clappcommunications.com
Advertising, marketing & public relations. (Woman, estab
2000, empl 6, sales $354,737, cert: State)

1114 Catalpha Advertising & Design
      6801 Loch Raven Blvd
      Towson, MD 21286
      Contact: Don Kelley VP
      Tel: 410-337-0066
      Email:
      Website: www.catalpha.com
Design & produce product & event promotional signs &
materials: banners, fact tags, headers, danglers, hang tags,
counter cards. (Woman, estab 1986, empl 6, sales
$720,000, cert: State)

1115 Harvey & Daughters, Inc.
      952 Ridgebrook Rd, Ste 1000
      Sparks, MD 21152
      Contact: Jade Reider Office Mgr
      Tel: 410-771-5566
      Email: jreider@harveyagency.com
      Website: www.harveyagency.com
Brand activation, purchasing strategy, package design, logo
development & graphic design. (Woman, estab 1986, empl
35, sales $6,000,000, cert: WBENC)

1116 Herrmann Advertising|Branding|Technology
      30 West St
      Annapolis, MD 21401
      Contact: Jane Farrell Sr. Acct. Exec.
      Tel: 410-267-6522
      Email: jane@herrmann.com
      Website: www.herrmann.com
Advertising agency: market research, creative design,
media management, print management, photography,
copy writing & technology. (Woman, estab 1979, empl
14, sales $3,663,968, cert: State, City, WBENC)

1117 Media Works, Ltd.
      1425 Clarkview Rd Ste 500
      Baltimore, MD 21209
      Contact: Michele Selby Presdient
      Tel: 443-470-4400
      Email: mselby@medialtd.com
      Website: http://medialtd.com
Advertising agency, research, plan & place media.
(Minority, Woman, estab 1989, empl 34, sales $887,604,
cert: City)

1118 Pure Advertising, LLC
      137 National Plaza Ste 300
      Oxon Hill, MD 20745
      Contact: Rick Tyner Managing Partner
      Tel: 301-646-4392
      Email: rick.tyner@prosum.com
      Website: www.pureadsww.com
Outdoor advertising & graphic design, taxi advertising,
transit, airport advertising & billboards. (AA, estab 2010,
empl 2, sales $200,000, cert: State, NMSDC)

Michigan

1119 Graphicolor Systems, Inc.
      12788 Currie Court
      Livonia, MI 48150
      Contact: Anita Mitzel Presdient
      Tel: 248-347-0271
      Email: anita@graphicolor.com
      Website: www.graphicolor.com
Design trade show displays & corporate signage.
(Woman, estab 1984, empl 8, sales $1,002,000, cert:
WBENC)

1120 Immersion Graphics Inc.
      1020 Metro Dr
      Commerce, MI 48390
      Contact: Pat Hernandez Presdient
      Tel: 248-624-6520
      Email: pat@immersion-graphics.com
      Website: www.immersion-graphics.com
Engineering & audio visual systems solutions. (Hisp,
estab 1998, empl 10, sales $3,439,000, cert: NMSDC)

1121 J & L Business Solutions
      1809 Haggerty Rd
      Commerce Township, MI 48390
      Contact: Natasha Vassallo Owner
      Tel: 248-960-7525
      Email: nata@signaramastore.com
      Website: www.signaramact.com
Design & install signs: interior & exterior architectural
signs, wayfinding signage, vehicle lettering, illuminated
signs, ADA, architectural signage, engraved tags &
plates. (Woman/AA, estab 2004, empl 3, sales $207,000,
cert: State)

1122   LA Exhibits, Inc.
1091 Centre Rd Ste 130
Auburn Hills, MI 48326
Contact: Della Dotson Presdient
Tel: 248-340-1144
Email: della@laexhibits.com
Website: www.laexhibits.com
Design, build & support tradeshow displays & events, portable, modular & custom displays, design & production, warehousing. (Woman, estab 1991, empl 6, sales , cert: WBENC)

1123   Languages International Inc.
4665 - 44th St SE Ste A1101
Grand Rapids, MI 49512
Contact: Beverly Wall Owner
Tel: 616-285-0005
Email: beverly@lang-int.com
Website: www.lang-int.com
Foreign language translation & interpreting services. (Woman, estab 1988, empl 7, sales $400,000, cert: WBENC)

1124   PALS International
900 Wilshire Dr, Ste 105
Troy, MI 48084
Contact: David Schroeder VP Business Dev
Tel: 248-362-2060
Email: dschroeder@palsintl.com
Website: www.palsintl.com
Translations & interpretations; language instruction; cross-cultural programs; accent reduction; global relocation; videovoice-overs. (Woman/Hisp, estab 1983, empl 80, sales $1,509,900, cert: NMSDC, WBENC)

1125   Pro-Motion Technology Group
29755 Beck Rd
Wixom, MI 48393
Contact: Brian Flewelling Acct Mgr
Tel: 248-668-3100
Email: hello@promotion.tech
Website: promotion.tech
Audiovisual technology solutions. (Woman, estab 2002, empl 45, sales $25,000,000, cert: WBENC)

1126   Stage 3 Productions
1532 N. Opdyke Rd Ste 700
Auburn Hills, MI 48326
Contact: Andre LaRoche Presdient
Tel: 248-955-1250
Email: andre@stage3.com
Website: www.stage3.com
Commercial, advertising photography, digital imaging, illustration, graphic design, stage rental. (AA, estab 1984, empl 8, sales , cert: NMSDC)

1127   The Ajamu Group, LLC.
29155 Northwestern Hwy, Ste 687
Southfield, MI 48034
Contact: Cheryl D Parks Ajamu CEO
Tel: 248-223-0904
Email: cheryl.ajamu@ajamugroup.com
Website: www.ajamugroup.com
The Ajamu Group, LLC. secures print, digital and mobile advertising for national media companies, and also provides Event Management services for local and national companies. (Woman/AA, estab 2004, empl 1, sales , cert: NMSDC, WBENC)

1128   Tiger Studio Co.
418 E 8th St
Holland, MI 49423
Contact: Luciano Hernandez Owner
Tel: 616-748-7532
Email: luciano@tigerstudiodesign.com
Website: http://tigerstudiodesign.com
Product, Interaction, Brand, and Strategy. (Hisp, estab 2000, empl 4, sales , cert: NMSDC)

1129   Trent Design LLC
114 E Second St
Rochester, MI 48307
Contact: Marilyn Trent Principal
Tel: 248-652-8307
Email: marilyn@trentcreative.com
Website: http://trentcreative.com
Graphic design, digital media, web design & development, advertising, social media marketing. (Woman, estab 1991, empl 5, sales $600,000, cert: WBENC)

1130   Wensco of Michigan Corporation
5760 Safety Dr NE
Belmont, MI 49306
Contact: Yolanda Cain Inside Sales Support
Tel: 800-253-1569
Email: ycain@wensco.com
Website: www.wensco.com
Dist signs: digital inkjet media & laminates, cut vinyls, banners, neon, l.e.d.'s, ballasts, plywood, metal & plastic substrates, aluminum, polycarbonate, acrylic, plexiglass, aluminum composite panels. (Woman, estab 1937, empl 50, sales , cert: WBENC)

Minnesota

1131   Bella Creative
16860 Judicial Rd
Lakeville, MN 55044
Contact: Stacy A Parizek Owner
Tel: 952-232-6411
Email: stacy@bella-creative.net
Website: www.bellaexhibts.com
Mfr trade show exhibits, off-the-shelf displays to custom booths. (Woman, estab 2008, empl 1, sales $200,000, cert: WBENC)

1132   Betmar Languages, Inc.
6260 Hwy 65 NE, Ste 308
Minneapolis, MN 55432
Contact: BETMAR LANGUAGES Presdient
Tel: 763-572-9711
Email:
Website: www.betmar.com
Translation svcs: on site interpreters; voice-over services for audio, video & interactive projects; typesetting; document translation; cultural diversity training. (Woman, estab 1985, empl 4, sales $949,266, cert: WBENC)

1133   cmnd+m LLC
867 Pierce Butler Route
St. Paul, MN 55104
Contact: Krista O'Malley
Tel: 612-867-6273
Email: accounting@cmndm.com
Website: http://cmndm.com
Design, production, engineering, retail, advertising, project management, construction, and training. (Woman/As-Pac, estab 2011, empl 11, sales $700,000, cert: NMSDC, WBENC)

1134 Deep Well, Inc.
      123 N 3rd St Ste 700
      Minneapolis, MN 55401
      Contact: Phil Nelson
      Tel: 612-338-7947
      Email: phil@crash-sues.com
      Website: www.crash-sues.com
Advertising, marketing, production, video editing, animation, 3D, traditional animation, stop motion, graphics, effects, color, media, web apps, strategy, creative, branding, brand development, ideation, web development, post-production. (Woman, estab 2008, empl 12, sales $1,600,000, cert: WBENC)

1135 Designer Sign Systems
      9975 Flanders Ct NE
      Blaine, MN 55449
      Contact: Karen Fisher CEO
      Tel: 763-784-5858
      Email: customerservice@designersign.com
      Website: www.designersign.com
Mfr & design architectural interior & exterior signage. (Woman, estab 1984, empl 30, sales $5,246,000, cert: WBENC)

1136 Dudak Production, Inc.
      582 Bavaria Lane
      Chaska, MN 55318
      Contact: Shirley Dudak President
      Tel: 952-443-0097
      Email: shirley.dudak@dudakproductioninc.com
      Website: www.dudakproductioninc.com
Advertising, Graphic Design Services, Marketing Consulting Services, Commercial Gravure Printing, Commercial Screen Printing, Packing & Crating, Print Advertising, Direct Marketing Fulfillment, Marketing & Distribution, Printing, Brand Marketing. (Woman, estab 1996, empl 3, sales $1,675,000, cert: WBENC)

1137 IN Food Mktg & Design, Inc.
      600 N Washington Ave Ste C101
      Minneapolis, MN 55401
      Contact: Anita M Nelson Presdient
      Tel: 612-353-3410
      Email: anita@infoodmktg.com
      Website: www.infoodmktg.com
Marketing & communications: brand building & product promotions. (Woman, estab 1995, empl 12, sales $1,215,000, cert: WBENC)

1138 Intercross Design, Inc.
      2238 Edgewood Ave S
      Minneapolis, MN 55426
      Contact: Lori Fuller VP
      Tel: 952-935-2080
      Email: lori.fuller@intercross.com
      Website: http://intercross.com
Advertising agency: branding, videos, websites, collateral & advertising. (Woman, estab 1997, empl 17, sales $3,100,000, cert: WBENC)

1139 JPG & Associates, Inc.
      8991 33rd St N
      Lake Elmo, MN 55042
      Contact: Jerry Grohovsky Presdient
      Tel: 651-779-1072
      Email: jerry@jpgassoc.com
      Website: www.jpgassoc.com
Technical publications, temporary staffing & off-site production, technical writing, instructional design, marketing writing, graphic design, desktop publishing, web site development, web-based help development. (Woman, estab 1993, empl 30, sales $2,000,000, cert: WBENC)

1140 KJ International Resources, LTD
      800 Washington Ave N, Ste 905
      Minneapolis, MN 55401
      Contact: Kristen Giovanis
      Tel: 612-288-9494
      Email: kgiovanis@kjinternational.com
      Website: www.kjinternational.com
Language translation & validation, desktop publishing, web translation & localization, voice-overs, etc. (Woman, estab 1994, empl 30, sales $6,400,000, cert: WBENC)

1141 KNOCK, inc.
      1307 Glenwood Ave
      Minneapolis, MN 55405
      Contact: Tom Newton VP Business Dev
      Tel: 612-333-6511
      Email: tom.newton@KNOCKinc.com
      Website: www.KNOCKinc.com
Graphic design, branding, marketing, advertising, packaging, illustration, photo art direction. (Woman/Hisp, estab 2001, empl 82, sales $22,323,878, cert: NMSDC, WBENC)

1142 Latitude Prime LLC
      80 S 8th St Ste 900
      Minneapolis, MN 55402
      Contact: Nat LeBrun
      Tel: 888-341-9080
      Email: email@latitudeprime.com
      Website: www.latitudeprime.com
Multilingual translation services, media & document translation, interpretation, localization, transcription, proofreading/editing & DTP services. (Woman/As-Ind, estab 2009, empl 15, sales , cert: State, City, NMSDC, WBENC, 8a)

1143 Northcott Banners, Inc.
      2645 - 26th Ave S, Ste 400
      Minneapolis, MN 55406
      Contact: Millie Northcott Owner
      Tel: 612-722-1733
      Email: millie@northcottbanner.com
      Website: www.northcottbanner.com
Mfr banners: fabric, vinyl, interior & exterior applications. (Woman, estab 1984, empl 9, sales $712,698, cert: WBENC)

1144 Oceandrum LLC dba Zydeco Design
      231 2nd St
      Excelsior, MN 55331
      Contact: Nathalie Wilson Presdient
      Tel: 612-202-7421
      Email: nathaliew@zydecodesign.com
      Website: www.zydecodesign.com
Brand & design, branding strategy, brand experience strategy, brand architecture, naming, identity, image system, packaging, annual reports, corporate social responsibility & sustainable development. (Woman, estab 2009, empl 2, sales $300,000, cert: State, WBENC)

1145 Peggy Lauritsen Design Group, Inc.
      125 Main St. SE Ste 125
      Minneapolis, MN 55414
      Contact: Linda Gosslin Chief Exec artist
      Tel: 612-623-4200
      Email: lgosslin@pldg.com
      Website: www.pldg.com
Corporate & brand identity, graphic & communications sesign, marketing communications, website design, event communications, print or electronic media. (Woman, estab 1979, empl 9, sales , cert: WBENC)

1146   Portage Marketing
2401 Sheridan Ave S
Minneapolis, MN 55405
Contact: Laureen Carlson Presdient
Tel: 612-381-0621
Email: lcarlson@portagemarketing.com
Website: http://portagemarketing.com
Advertising agency & media placement. (Woman, estab 2000, empl , sales $5,000,000, cert: WBENC)

1147   Tembua Inc (fka Precision Language Services)
17595 Kenwood Trail Ste 120
Lakeville, MN 55044
Contact: Paula Town Exec Admin Asst
Tel: 952-435-8178
Email: office@tembua.com
Website: www.tembua.com
Document translation: bilingual, bicultural translations. (Woman, estab 1993, empl 36, sales $700,000, cert: WBENC)

1148   Visual Commnications
475 Cleveland Ave N Ste 223
St. Paul, MN 55104
Contact: Principal
Tel: 651-644-4494
Email:
Website: www.visualcommunications.com
Experiential design, signage system design, graphic design, wayfinding, programming, ADA signage survey, Life Safety analysis, history walls, donor recognition & master plan development. (Woman, estab 1991, empl 4, sales $600,000, cert: State, WBENC)

1149   Wrap City Graphics
62 6th Ave S
Hopkins, MN 55343
Contact: Presdient
Tel: 952-920-4664
Email:
Website: http://WrapCityGraphics.com
Commercial signage & digitally printed wide-format adhesive backed vinyl graphics for vehicle graphics/wraps, window/wall graphics, dimensional letters/logos & architectural products. (Woman, estab 2005, empl 7, sales $745,000, cert: WBENC)

Missouri

1150   Brighton Agency, Inc.
7711 Bonhomme Ave Ste 100
Saint Louis, MO 63105
Contact: Tina VonderHaar CEO
Tel: 314-726-0700
Email: accounting@brightonagency.com
Website: www.brightonagency.com
Strategic planning, brand development, digital marketing & production, marketing consulting, public relations, advertising, promotions, media planning, audio & video production, event marketing, online, mobile & app development. (Woman, estab 1989, empl 71, sales $9,030,143, cert: State, WBENC)

1151   Harris Graphic Design
7309 Natural Bridge Rd
St. Louis, MO 63121
Contact: Lee Harris Designer
Tel: 314-389-2636
Email: harrisgd@anet-stl.com
Website:
Advertising svcs: annual reports, maps, posters, graphic design, A-V presentations, brochures, displays & exhibits, letterhead, newsletter, etc. (AA, estab 1978, empl 2, sales , cert: State)

1152   Language Solutions Inc.
230 South Bemiston Ave. Ste 610
St. Louis, MO 63105
Contact: Melissa Wurst Presdient
Tel: 314-725-3711
Email: melissa@langsolinc.com
Website: www.langsolinc.com
Written translation & multilingual typesetting: over 40 languages. (Woman, estab 1998, empl 2, sales $677,610, cert: WBENC)

1153   Schisla Design, LLC dba Enrich
12 N Sarah St
St. Louis, MO 63108
Contact: Suzanne Duvald'Adrian Marketing & Social Media
Tel: 314-553-9500
Email: suzanne@enrichcreative.com
Website: www.enrichcreative.com
Branding programs: audits & research, Strategy and Development, Naming, Logo Design, Strategic Messaging, Positioning, Brand Guides & Product, Service and Event Branding. (Woman, estab 2002, empl 4, sales $438,502, cert: WBENC)

North Carolina

1154   Crutchfield & Associates Inc.
515 College Rd, Ste 14
Greensboro, NC 27410
Contact: Bernadette Trinidad Presdient
Tel: 336-297-1222
Email: bernadette@ca-ideas.com
Website: http://ca-ideas.com
Advertising agency, integrated, strategic & innovative marketing & communications solutions. (Woman/Hisp, estab 1985, empl 3, sales $121,707, cert: NMSDC)

1155   Fly My Photo, LLC
560 Davidson Gateway Dr Ste 101
Davidson, NC 28036
Contact: Susan Boaz Presdient
Tel: 855-347-4922
Email: susan@flagology.com
Website: www.flagology.com
Mfr decorative flags, printed & appliqued, photo flags, monogram flags, signage, flag poles & brackets, door mats, monograms & personalized flags. (Woman, estab 2013, empl 1, sales , cert: WBENC)

1156   Jervay Agency, LLC
338 S Sharon Amity, Ste 302
Charlotte, NC 28211
Contact: Adria Jervay Media Acct Rep
Tel: 704-780-7004
Email: adria@thejervayagency.com
Website: www.TheJervayAgency.com
Advertising & marketing materials. (Woman/AA, estab 2012, empl 3, sales , cert: City)

1157   Language Resource Center Inc.
       P.O. Box 18066
       Charlotte, NC 28218
       Contact: Abdullahi Sheikh CEO
       Tel: 704-464-0016
       Email: abdullah.sheikh@languagerc.com
       Website: www.languagerc.com
Interpretation & translation service providers. (Woman/
AA, estab , empl , sales $1,428,268, cert: State, City)

1158   Main Street Mobile Billboards
       2610 Tuckaseegee Rd
       Charlotte, NC 28208
       Contact: Brendon Henderson CEO
       Tel: 888-788-7492
       Email: brendon@mainstreetmobilebillboards.com
       Website: www.mainstreetmobilebillboards.com
Mobile truck billboard & walking billboards advertising.
(AA, estab 2013, empl 2, sales , cert: State, City, NMSDC)

1159   Moving Ideas, Inc.
       7519 Royal Bliss Ct, Ste 205
       Denver, NC 28037
       Contact: Jennifer Moates Presdient
       Tel: 704-655-2870
       Email: jmoates@movingideasinc.com
       Website: www.movingideasinc.com
Advertising, Branding & Identity, Copywriting & Content,
Creative Campaigns, Direct Mail, Infographics, Email
Marketing, Graphic Design, Strategic Marketing Plans,
Naming, Social Media, Tradeshow, Video, Websites.
(Woman, estab 2005, empl 5, sales $500,000, cert:
WBENC)

New Hampshire

1160   Kelley Solution, Inc.
       210 West Rd Unit 3
       Portsmouth, NH 3801
       Contact: Lisa Finneral President
       Tel: 603-431-3881
       Email: lfinneral@kelleysolutions.com
       Website: www.kelleysolutions.com
E-business solutions & svcs: online fulfillment, graphic
design, strategic sourcing, warehousing, distribution,
integrated marketing campaigns & direct mail management. (Woman, estab 1972, empl 6, sales $2,200,000,
cert: WBENC)

1161   Polaris Direct
       300 Technology Dr
       Hooksett, NH 3106
       Contact: Judith Maloy CEO
       Tel: 603-626-5800
       Email: diversity@polarisdirect.net
       Website: www.polarisdirect.net
Direct mail, data processing, ink jet & laser personaliza-
tion, mailing services, bindery & print management.
(Woman, estab 2003, empl 66, sales $18,134,272, cert:
WBENC)

New Jersey

1162   Clark Media Corp.
       655 Jersey Ave
       Jersey City, NJ 07302
       Contact: Ken Clark COO
       Tel: 800-872-6752
       Email: kclark@resptrans.com
       Website: www.responsivetranslation.com
Translation & interpretation services: machine transla-
tion, translation memory, content management systems
& multi-platform publishing in 157 languages. (Woman/
As-Pac, estab 1990, empl 2, sales $1,628,455, cert:
WBENC)

1163   CQ fluency, Inc.
       2 University Plaza, STE 406
       Hackensack, NJ 07601
       Contact: Elisabete Miranda President & CEO
       Tel: 201-487-8007
       Email: info@cqfluency.com
       Website: www.cqfluency.com
Translation services: 180 languages, web localization,
cultural consulting, desktop publishing, phone interpretation, multimedia production, tape transcription.
(Woman/Hisp, estab 2000, empl 82, sales $3,844,722,
cert: State, NMSDC, WBENC)

1164   Digital Outdoor Advertising
       788 Shrewsbury Ave
       Tinton Falls, NJ 07724
       Contact: Christine Lanziano Presdient
       Tel: 732-491-8726
       Email: christine@digitaloutdooradvertising.com
       Website: www.digitaloutdooradvertising.com
Digital & static outdoor billboards, mall kiosks & bus
advertising. (Woman, estab 2012, empl 7, sales
$6,000,000, cert: WBENC)

1165   Eclipse Marketing Services Inc.
       490 Headquarters Plaza North Tower, 10th Fl
       Morristown, NJ 07960
       Contact: Margaret Boller Presdient
       Tel: 800-837-4648
       Email: mboller@eclipse2.com
       Website: www.eclipsemarketingservices.com
Advertising Services: campaigns; Hispanic Marketing
Consulting; Graphic Design; Website design; Marketing
programs; Promotional printing; Magazine advertising
and publishing; Coop Marketing & promotion; Digital &
social media. (Woman, estab 1992, empl 39, sales
$10,980,994, cert: WBENC)

1166   Encore Events, ltd. dba ENCORE DESIGN
       31 Industrial Ave., Ste 7
       Mahwah, NJ 07430
       Contact: Kathleen Orbe Principal & Creative
       Director
       Tel: 973-890-0088
       Email: encoredesign@mac.com
       Website: www.encoredesign.com
Design services: strategic identity & branding. (Woman,
estab 1994, empl 5, sales $425,000, cert: WBENC)

1167   Expect Advertising, Inc.
       1033 Route 46
       Clifton, NJ 07013
       Contact: Ravi Sachdev Presdient
       Tel: 973-777-8886
       Email: ravi.sachdev@expectad.com
       Website: www.expectad.com
Medical marketing & communications: advertising,
promotion, branding, web design, web marketing, sales
incentive programs, premiums, trade shows, public
relations, media planning, market research. (As-Ind,
estab 1996, empl 16, sales $2,000,000, cert: NMSDC)

1168   Graphic Matter, Inc.
       601 Route 206, Ste 26-405
       Hillsborough, NJ 08844
       Contact: Beverly Thomas Presdient
       Tel: 908-359-8760
       Email: wbe@graphicmatter.com
       Website: www.graphicmatter.com
Creative services: print & web. (Woman, estab 2002,
empl 6, sales $297,570, cert: State, WBENC)

1169   Iris Communications LLC
       11 Belaire Dr
       Roseland, NJ 07068
       Contact: Barbara Bochese Managing Dir
       Tel: 973-902-7027
       Email: bbochese@iriscommunications.org
       Website: www.iriscommunications.org
Marketing services, corporate communications &
branding, presentations-internal/corporate, brand
deliverables, educational/training, video production &
animation, website design & development, media
planning & buying. (Woman, estab 2011, empl 12, sales ,
cert: State, NWBOC)

1170   Jouard Wozniak LLC dba JWDesign
       165 Passaic Ave Ste 410
       Fairfield, NJ 07004
       Contact: Faith Wozniak Presdient
       Tel: 973-244-9191
       Email: faith@jwadv.com
       Website: www.jwadv.com
Advertising & design, creative, design & marketing
services, web & print, trade show graphics, promotional
events, video & audio production, photography &
retouching. (Woman, estab 1989, empl 4, sales
$178,000, cert: WBENC)

1171   Newtype, Inc.
       447 Route 10 East
       Randolph, NJ 07869
       Contact: Jo Ann Porto CEO
       Tel: 973-361-6000
       Email: accounting@newtypeinc.com
       Website: www.newtypeinc.com
Translations & desktop publishing svcs in over 130
languages. (Woman, estab 1966, empl 12, sales , cert:
WBENC)

1172   Para-Plus Translations, Inc.
       2 Coleman Ave
       Cherry Hill, NJ 08034
       Contact: Carlos Santiago VP
       Tel: 856-547-3695
       Email: csantiago@para-plus.com
       Website: www.para-plus.com
Translation & interpretation svcs: technical reports,
medical reports, legal documents, oral & written
depositions, audio tapes, video tapes, patents, manuscripts, manuals, product literature, web sites. (Woman/
Hisp, estab 1980, empl 15, sales $3,028,000, cert: State)

1173   Personal Mail International, Inc.
       5 Cold Hill Rd S, Ste 28
       Mendham, NJ 07945
       Contact: Debra Seyler Presdient
       Tel: 973-543-6001
       Email: dseyler@pmipmi.com
       Website: www.pmipmi.com
International & domestic mail & package forwarding
services. (Woman, estab 1987, empl 11, sales $950,000,
cert: WBENC)

1174   Seliger-Braun Inc. dba Keylingo Translations
       116 Village Blvd, Ste 200
       Princeton, NJ 08540
       Contact: Managing Dir
       Tel: 609-423-1077
       Email:
       Website: http://keylingo.com/
Translations services: localization, transcreation,
interpretation & tele-interpretation. (Woman, estab
2011, empl 2, sales $106,775, cert: State, WBENC)

1175   Sign Up Inc.
       255 Route 3 E
       Secaucus, NJ 07094
       Contact: President
       Tel: 201-902-8640
       Email:
       Website: www.fastsigns.com/153
Signs: vinyl, wood, windows, walls or vehicles, channel
letters, window graphics, trade show booths, exhibits
and displays, flags and banners, cut-outs, dimensional
letters, banner stands, vehicle graphics, vinyl lettering,
posters, murals. (Woman, estab 1992, empl 8, sales
$87,542,162, cert: State)

1176   Sunset Printing and Engraving Corp
       10 Kice Ave
       Wharton, NJ 07885
       Contact: Deron Wainer
       Tel: 732-335-2165
       Email: dwainer@sunsetcorpid.com
       Website: www.sunsetcorpid.com
Corporate identity campaigns: printing, engraving,
embossing & foil stamping. (Hisp, estab 1945, empl 28,
sales $3,820,000, cert: NMSDC)

1177 The S3 Agency
      716 Main St
      Boonton, NJ 07005
      Contact: Denise Blasevick CEO
      Tel: 973-257-5533
      Email: dblasevick@thes3agency.com
      Website: www.theS3agency.com
Advertising & marketing: print, tv, radio, outdoor, online,
public relations, collateral, direct mail & direct marketing,
e-marketing, websites, product launches, POP, business-to-
business & consumer marketing, internal communications.
(Woman, estab 2001, empl 25, sales $3,800,000, cert:
WBENC)

1178 TriStar Fulfillment Services, Inc.
      520 Pedricktown Rd
      Bridgeport, NJ 08014
      Contact: Susan Harker Owner
      Tel: 972-355-6256
      Email: sharker@tristarfulfillment.com
      Website: www.tristarfulfillment.com
Rebates, gift cards, merchandise, sweepstake offers, online order entry, reporting, tracking, billing, data entry,
data processing, telemarketing, ondemand printing,
sampling, direct mail, warehousing & distribution.
(Woman, estab 1976, empl 135, sales $30,000,000, cert:
WBENC)

New Mexico

1179 Greetings etc! inc.
      2505 Commercial NE
      Albuquerque, NM 87102
      Contact: Martin Candelaria CEO
      Tel: 505-242-7232
      Email: greetingsetc2@qwestoffice.net
      Website: www.greetingsetcprintandmail.com
Printing, direct mail, graphic design, fullfillment, bindery.
(Woman/Hisp, estab 1999, empl 7, sales $794,950, cert:
State)

Nevada

1180 AirGo USA LLC
      10161 Park Run Ste 150
      Las Vegas, NV 89145
      Contact: Norvel McDonald VP Marketing
      Tel: 702-835-6851
      Email: norvelm@airgousa.com
      Website: www.airgousa.com
Facilities maintenance and management, HVAC, electrical,
mechanical, grounds maintenance, custodial, security,
equipment installation and maintenance, fire & smoke
alarm installation & maintenance, security alarm installation (AA, estab 2002, empl 100, sales $7,000,000, cert:
State)

1181 El Mundo, Ltd.
      760 N Eastern Ave, Ste 110
      Las Vegas, NV 89101
      Contact: Hilda Escobedo CEO
      Tel: 702-649-8553
      Email: hescobedo@elmundo.net
      Website: www.elmundo.net
Advertising, display advertising, graphic design, Spanish
publication, Spanish readers, advertising in Spanish,
display ads in Spanish, Spanish, newspaper, (Woman/Hisp,
estab 1980, empl 9, sales $1,347,788, cert: State)

New York

1182 ADDO, LLC
      155 W 118th St, Ste 1
      New York, NY 10026
      Contact: S Courtney Booker, CEO
      Tel: 212-933-0670
      Email: courtney@theaddo.com
      Website: www.theaddo.com
Brand marketing. (AA, estab 2006, empl 1, sales , cert:
City, NMSDC)

1183 Adventium Marketing & Design
      320 E 35th St, Ste 5B
      New York, NY 10016
      Contact: Penny Chuang Presdient
      Tel: 212-481-9576
      Email: penny@adventium.net
      Website: www.adventium.net
Marketing collateral, graphic design, brochures, advertising, direct mail, corporate communications, newsletters,
catalogs, videos, invitations, logo design, media kits,
posters, signage, trade show exhibits, web design &
architecture, web banners. (Woman/As-Pac, estab 1992,
empl 3, sales $370,000, cert: State, City)

1184 Baseline Design, Inc
      236 W. 30th St 5th Fl
      New York, NY 10001
      Contact: Founder and Chief Brand Strategist
      Tel: 212-925-1656
      Email:
      Website: www.baselinegroupny.com
Design solutions, printing, logo design & corporate
identity programs, fund rollouts, conference support
materials, brochures, catalogs, newsletters, direct mail
pieces, advertising
& annual reports. (Woman, estab 1997, empl 8, sales ,
cert: State, WBENC)

1185 Brand Cool Marketing, Inc.
      2300 East Ave
      Rochester, NY 14610
      Contact: Sue Kochan CEO
      Tel: 585-381-3350
      Email: doorsopen@brandcoolmarketing.com
      Website: www.brandcool.com
Advertising services. (Woman, estab 1997, empl 20,
sales $4,360,000, cert: WBENC)

1186 Create Group NYC LLC
      180 Varick St Ste 212
      New York, NY 10014
      Contact: Presdient
      Tel: 646-682-7791
      Email:
      Website: www.createnyc.com
Pharmaceutical advertising services. (Minority/Woman,
estab , empl , sales $14,908,530, cert: WBENC)

1187 Crown Sign Systems
      7 Odell Plaza
      Yonkers, NY 10701
      Contact: Michelle Strum President
      Tel: 914-375-2118
      Email: mstrum@crownsigns.com
      Website: www.crownsigns.com
Mfr interior & exterior architectural signage. (Woman,
estab 1994, empl 14, sales $22,000,000, cert: State)

1188   Darby/Darby Creative
       2376 Adam Clayton Powell Jr Blvd
       New York, NY 10030
       Contact: Keith Darby President
       Tel: 646-489-1256
       Email: keithdarby01@netscape.net
       Website:
Advertising, marketing, advertising design services.
(Woman/AA, estab 2003, empl 2, sales , cert: State)

1189   DePirro/GarroneLLC
       25 W 13th St Ste 6NN
       New York, NY 10011
       Contact: Lisa Garrone CEO
       Tel: 212-206-6967
       Email: lgarrone@depirrogarrone.com
       Website: http://depirrogarrone.com
Creative advertising, size or media channel, traditional or
digital, online or offline. Flexible & scalable. (Woman,
estab 2008, empl 8, sales $1,000,000, cert: City, WBENC)

1190   Eriksen Translations Inc.
       360 Court St, #37
       Brooklyn, NY 11231
       Contact: Vigdis Eriksen President & CEO
       Tel: 718-802-9010
       Email: vigdis.eriksen@eriksen.com
       Website: www.eriksen.com
Multilingual services, translation, interpreting, typesetting,
project management, web localization & cultural consulting in over 75 languages. (Woman, estab 1986, empl 31,
sales $5,245,000, cert: State, City, WBENC)

1191   Fusia Communications, Inc.
       45 Main St, Ste 212
       Brooklyn, NY 11201
       Contact: Elizabeth Kay Presdient
       Tel: 718-643-0311
       Email: ekay@fusia.net
       Website: www.fusia.net
Marketing, strategic consulting, media planning & buying,
media tracking, design/production, copywriting, translations. (Woman/As-Pac, estab 2002, empl 4, sales $514,627,
cert: City, WBENC)

1192   Harquin Graphics, Inc.
       80 Surrey Dr
       New Rochelle, NY 10804
       Contact: Sherry Bruck Presdient
       Tel: 914-738-9620
       Email: sbruck@harquin.com
       Website: www.harquin.com
Graphic design, printing & web design. (Woman, estab
1992, empl 9, sales $450,000, cert: State, City)

1193   Keeper of the Brand
       894 Otsego Rd
       West Hempstead, NY 11552
       Contact: Donyshia Boston-Hill CEO
       Tel: 917-697-1699
       Email: db@keeperofthebrand.com
       Website: www.keeperofthebrand.com/
Marketing Plans & Strategies, Media Buying, TV, Radio,
Print & Digital Solutions, Broadcast Media Distribution,
Brand Development, Consumer Insight, Copyright, Trans-
actional Engagement, Programming & Campaign Mgmt,
Graphic Design, Creative Services. (Woman/AA, estab
2013, empl 6, sales $125,000, cert: State, NMSDC, WBENC)

1194   MAD Studio LLC
       1123 Broadway, Ste 707
       New York, NY 10010
       Contact: Principal
       Tel: 212-982-4613
       Email: smatiz@mad-nyc.com
       Website:
Brand marketing & design: positioning, logo development, stationery, brochures, email campaigns, websites,
exhibits, packaging, promotional items, advertising.
(Woman, estab 2011, empl 3, sales , cert: City, WBENC)

1195   Millennium Signs & Display, Inc.
       90 W Graham Ave
       Hempstead, NY 11550
       Contact: Saj Khalfan Presdient
       Tel: 516-292-8000
       Email: saj@msdny.com
       Website: www.msdny.com
Signage & Displays. (As-Ind, estab 2008, empl 28, sales
$5,255,000, cert: City, NMSDC)

1196   Mix On Digital, LLC
       1867 Amsterdam Ave Ste 3F
       New York, NY 10034
       Contact: Christina Mixon Managing Dir
       Tel: 917-383-8121
       Email: christina@mixondigital.com
       Website: www.mixondigital.com
Digital media design & consulting, social, mobile &
digital platforms. (Woman/AA, As-Pac, estab 2012, empl
2, sales $385,000, cert: City)

1197   Signs & Decal Corp.
       410 Morgan Ave
       Brooklyn, NY 11211
       Contact: Hasnain Khalfan VP Sales/Mktg
       Tel: 718-486-6400
       Email: salesadmin@signsanddecal.com
       Website: www.signsanddecal.com
Mfr & install signage, signs. (As-Ind, As-Pac, estab 1972,
empl 30, sales $7,204,781, cert: City)

1198   SpikeDDB, LLC
       437 Madison Ave 20 FL
       New York, NY 11201
       Contact: Sterling Green
       Tel: 718-596-5400
       Email: joel@spikeddb.com
       Website: www.spikeddb.com
Advertising agency. (AA, estab 1997, empl 30, sales
$6,000,000, cert: NMSDC)

1199   Squeaky
       55 Broadway 3th Fl
       New York, NY 10006
       Contact: Mailet Lopez Managing Dir
       Tel: 212-994-5270
       Email: mailet@squeaky.com
       Website: www.squeaky.com
Design interface, web design, flash animation, e-
commerce, database. (Hisp, estab 2001, empl 30, sales
$1,754,683, cert: State, NMSDC)

1200   The Language Shop
       114-26 146th St
       Jamaica, NY 11436
       Contact: Deborah Lockhart Dir of Operations
       Tel: 646-245-4129
       Email: deborah.lockhart@thelanguageshop.org
       Website: www.thelanguageshop.org
Translation & interpreting legal, medical, financial, corporate, commercial, marketing, online games, website translation & localization. (Woman/Nat Ame, estab 2007, empl 1, sales $122,000, cert: City)

1201   TITANIUM Worldwide LLC
       350 7th Ave Ste 1403
       New York, NY 10001
       Contact: Chief Financial Operations Officer
       Tel: 646-952-8440
       Email:
       Website: www.titaniumww.com
Media, marketing, communications & consulting: Branding/Creative/Strategy, Content/Messaging, Digital/Social/Mobile, Film/Video Production, Event Marketing, Business Intelligence, Data Warehousing, Development/Deployment. (Woman, estab 2014, empl 4, sales , cert: State, WBENC)

1202   Visual Citi Inc.
       110-30 Dunkirk St
       St. Albans, NY 11412
       Contact: Mirza Kermani Acct Exec
       Tel: 718-479-5500
       Email: mirza@visualciti.com
       Website: http://visualciti.com
Digitally Printed Signs & Graphics, Banners, POP Displays, Window Signs & Graphics, Cutout logos & letters, Silk Screen printing, ADA Signs, Etched Signs & Custom Fabrication. (As-Ind, estab 2004, empl 25, sales $200,000, cert: City, NMSDC)

1203   Womenkind, LLC
       114 E 25th St, Ste 710
       New York, NY 10010
       Contact: Sandy Sabean Partner / Chief Creative Officer
       Tel: 212-660-0400
       Email: sandy@womenkind.net
       Website: www.womenkind.net
Advertising & marketing communications. (Woman, estab 2007, empl 2, sales $1,800,000, cert: WBENC)

Ohio

1204   ASI Signage Innovations
       5201 W Erie Ave, Ste 99
       Lorain, OH 44053
       Contact: Eric Kremer Sales Consultant
       Tel: 216-831-1345
       Email: eric.kremer@asisignage.com
       Website: www.asisignage.com
Design, Manufacturing and Installation of interior and exterior signage. (Woman, estab 1989, empl 25, sales $4,335,802, cert: State)

1205   Baker Creative Ltd.
       386 Main St
       Groveport, OH 43125
       Contact: Michele Cuthbert Principal
       Tel: 614-836-3845
       Email: mbaker@baker-creative.com
       Website: www.baker-creative.com
Graphic Design, Marketing Consulting, Advertising, Public Relations, Display Advertising. (Woman/Hisp, estab 2003, empl 10, sales $150,000, cert: State, WBENC, SDB)

1206   Bernard R. Doyle, Inc.
       2102 St. Claire Ave NE
       Cleveland, OH 44114
       Contact: Kay Doyle President
       Tel: 216-523-2288
       Email: 333@fastsigns.com
       Website:
Create effective, high impact sign designs. (Woman, estab 1999, empl 10, sales $1,100,000, cert: City, WBENC)

1207   Brigadier Construction Services LLC
       3100 E 45th St Ste 526
       Cleveland, OH 44127
       Contact: Jason Schenk
       Tel: 216-857-4777
       Email: jschenk@brigadierconst.com
       Website: www.brigadierconstruction.com
Advertising services. (Woman/AA, estab 2004, empl 17, sales $13,362,998, cert: State)

1208   Bright Future Partners, Inc. dba RED212
       5509 Fair Lane
       Cincinnati, OH 45227
       Contact: Donna Zaring Dir Business Devel
       Tel: 513-772-1020
       Email: donnazaring@red212.com
       Website: www.red212.com
Marketing communications, production & post production services. (Woman, estab 2001, empl 18, sales $3,971,726, cert: WBENC)

1209   Commercial Cutting & Graphics, LLC
       208 Central Ave
       Mansfield, OH 44905
       Contact: Natl Sales Exec
       Tel: 714-493-4714
       Email:
       Website: www.commercialcutting.com
Design & mfr temporary point of purchase displays. (Woman, estab 1986, empl 42, sales $6,800,001, cert: WBENC)

1210   Dayton Mailing Services, Inc.
       888 Dayton St
       Yellow Springs, OH 45387
       Contact: Barbara Deer Sales Exec
       Tel: 937-222-5056
       Email: barbara.deer@dmsink.us
       Website: www.daytonmailing.com
Digital printing, variable printing, direct mail, inserting, inkjetting, product fulfillment, collation, labeling, tipping, folding/glue. (Woman/As-Pac, estab , empl , sales $8,625,000, cert: State, WBENC)

1211 INNERSOURCE Inc.
      755 Wick Ave
      Youngstown, OH 44505
      Contact: Gloria Byce Principal
      Tel: 330-799-7619
      Email: gbyce@innersourceinc.com
      Website: www.innersourceinc.com
Interior Signage, Exterior Signage, ADA Signage, Room
Identification Signage, Way Finding, Directories, Tempo-
rary Signage, Modular Systems, Custom Signage, Donor
Plaques, Dimensional Letters, Corporate Identity, Digital
Printing, Banners. (Woman, estab 1996, empl 7, sales ,
cert: WBENC)

1212 MRA Advertising/Production Support Services, Inc.
      3979 Erie Ave
      Cincinnati, OH 45208
      Contact: Stacey St. John Dir Business Devel
      Tel: 513-561-5610
      Email: diversity@mraservices.com
      Website: www.mraservices.com
Advertising production management & cost control.
(Woman/As-Pac, estab 1980, empl 25, sales $4,900,000,
cert: WBENC)

1213 Skyline Exhibits of Central Ohio, LLC
      2801 Charter St
      Columbus, OH 43228
      Contact: Mark Armbrust Presdient
      Tel: 614-684-2050
      Email: mark@skylineohio.com
      Website: www.skylineohio.com
Exhibits, displays, kiosks, graphics, accessories & services
for trade shows & events, pop ups, banner stands, portable displays, custom modular exhibits, hanging signs &
structures. (Woman, estab 2001, empl 12, sales
$3,108,655, cert: WBENC)

1214 Swath Design, LLC
      30 Garfield Place Ste 1020
      Cincinnati, OH 45202
      Contact: CEO
      Tel: 513-421-1773
      Email:
      Website: www.swathdesign.com
Environmental graphic design, wayfinding, signage,
interior design, architectural design, branding, marketing
& print communications & interactive media. (Woman,
estab 1991, empl 6, sales , cert: State, WBENC, SDB)

1215 Vocalink, Inc.
      405 W First St
      Dayton, OH 45402
      Contact: Jill A. Mead Compliance Counsel
      Tel: 877-492-7754
      Email: rfp@vocalinkglobal.com
      Website: https://vocalinkglobal.com/
Translation & web localization services: documentation &
online content, multimedia
Linguistic asset mgmt, terminology mgmt, web content &
e-commerce sites, server side scripting. (Woman/Hisp,
estab 1995, empl 450, sales $4,985,940, cert: State,
NMSDC, WBENC)

1216 Xela Group, LLC dba Grupo Xela
      1775 Mentor Ave, Ste 404
      Cincinnati, OH 45212
      Contact: Jose D. Cuesta Managing Partner
      Tel: 513-351-2200
      Email: info@grupoxela.com
      Website: www.grupoxela.com
Hispanic marketing research: questionnaire dev, focus
groups, bilingual moderators, surveys, data collection &
tabulation, interpreting, corporate identity, collateral
design, media buying, web dev, translation svcs. (Hisp,
estab 2002, empl 10, sales , cert: State)

Oregon

1217 Hanlon Brown Design
      2130 NW 29th Ave
      Portland, OR 97210
      Contact: Sr Acct Exec
      Tel: 503-944-1005
      Email:
      Website: www.hbdesign.com
Design services: print, web, interactive & catalog,
graphic design, programming, software engineering,
quality assurance & project management. (Woman,
estab 1978, empl 25, sales $5,500,000, cert: State,
WBENC)

Pennsylvania

1218 Anderson Advertising dba The Anderson Group
      879 Fritztown Rd
      Sinking Spring, PA 19608
      Contact: Julie LaSalle
      Tel: 610-678-1506
      Email: jlasalle@theandersongrp.com
      Website: www.theandersongrp.com
Brand development & continuity programs: strategic
planning, corporate identity, advertising & creative
services, interactive services, media placement & public
relations. (Woman, estab 1987, empl 18, sales
$2,961,323, cert: State, WBENC)

1219 Communications Media, Inc.
      2200 Renaissance Blvd Ste 160
      King of Prussia, PA 19406
      Contact: Theresa Heintz Exec. Dir., Operations
      Tel: 484-322-0880
      Email: theintz@cmicompas.com
      Website: www.cmimedia.com
Media planning specializing in Healthcare media.
(Minority, estab 1989, empl 40, sales $6,000,000, cert:
NMSDC)

1220 ConnectedSign, LLC
      120A W Airport Rd
      Lititz, PA 17543
      Contact: Loren Bucklin Presdient
      Tel: 866-833-2723
      Email: lbucklin@connectedsign.com
      Website: www.connectedsign.com
Digital Signage Software, Navori Tycoon Software, Digital
Signage Hardware, Digital Signage Content, Website
Development and Content, Kiosks Software, Kiosks
Hardware, Kiosks Content. (Woman, estab 2003, empl
12, sales $1,000,000, cert: WBENC)

1221   Domus Inc.
       Two Bala Plaza, Ste 300
       Bala Cynwyd, PA 19004
       Contact: Lisa Samara President & CEO
       Tel: 215-772-2800
       Email: lsamara@domusinc.com
       Website: www.domusinc.com/
Traditional advertising, public relations, soical media,
online advertising, internal/corporate communications.
(Woman, estab 1993, empl 13, sales $6,659,848, cert:
WBENC)

1222   Harmelin Media
       525 Righters Ferry Rd
       Bala Cynwyd, PA 19004
       Contact: Mary Meder Presdient
       Tel: 610-668-7900
       Email: mmeder@harmelin.com
       Website: www.harmelin.com
Media planning & buying company. (Woman, estab 1982,
empl 204, sales $25,000,000, cert: WBENC)

1223   Hoffmann Murtaugh Advertising, Inc.
       355 Chestnut St
       Sewickley, PA 15143
       Contact: Presdient
       Tel: 412-741-8618
       Email:
       Website: www.hoffmannmurtaugh.com
Media Immersion & Discovery, Discovery Worksheets,
Custom Exercises, Data Mining, Competitive/Challenge
Identification, Goal Setting, Brainstorming/ideation, Media
Research & Insights, 1st Party Data Analysis, Nielsen
Ratings, MRI. (Woman, estab 2004, empl 17, sales
$2,145,000, cert: WBENC)

1224   Ideamart Inc.
       232 Conestoga Rd
       Wayne, PA 19087
       Contact: Tom King Owner
       Tel: 610-971-2000
       Email: tom@23k.com
       Website: www.23k.com
Advertising, direct marketing, interactive, social media,
branding/identity, packaging & retail POS. (As-Pac, estab
1991, empl 15, sales $2,185,947, cert: NMSDC)

1225   Language Services Associates
       455 Business Center Dr, Ste 100
       Horsham, PA 19044
       Contact: Jerry Lotierzo Natl Sales Mgr
       Tel: 215-259-7000
       Email: jlotierzo@lsaweb.com
       Website: www.lsaweb.com
Foreign language translation & interpretation: 175
languages, sign language. (Woman/Hisp, estab 1991, empl
200, sales $45,000,000, cert: NMSDC, WBENC)

1226   Media Advantage, Inc.
       78 Second St Pike
       Southampton, PA 18966
       Contact: Adraiane Thomson President
       Tel: 800-985-5596
       Email: athomson@mediaadvantage.com
       Website: www.mediaadvantage.com
Sign and graphic design. (Woman, estab 2009, empl 8,
sales $675,000, cert: State)

1227   Mendoza Group Inc.
       9 W Front St
       Media, PA 19063
       Contact: Mia Mendoza CEO
       Tel: 610-627-1000
       Email: mmendoza@mendozagroup.com
       Website: www.mendozagroup.com
Translation, marketing & advertising agency. (Woman/
Hisp, estab 1995, empl 7, sales $1,984,611, cert: State,
NMSDC, WBENC)

1228   MTM LinguaSoft
       705 S 50th St, 2nd Fl
       Philadelphia, PA 19143
       Contact: Myriam Siftar Presdient
       Tel: 215-729-6765
       Email: siftar@mtmlinguasoft.com
       Website: www.mtmlinguasoft.com
Translation & localization services: websites, software &
online applications, e-learning modules, document
translation & multilingual desktop publishing services.
(Woman, estab 2003, empl 5, sales $496,685, cert:
WBENC)

1229   Munroe Creative Partners
       121 S. Broad St. Ste 1900
       Philadelphia, PA 19107
       Contact:
       Tel: 215-563-8080
       Email:
       Website: www.munroe.com
Corporate identity launches, brochures, print and online
advertising, direct mail campaigns, and web site creation. (Woman, estab 1989, empl 20, sales $2,019,757,
cert: State, WBENC)

1230   NetPlus Marketing, Inc.
       625 Ridge Pike, Blg E, Ste 300
       Conshohocken, PA 19428
       Contact: Robin Neifield CEO
       Tel: 610-897-2380
       Email: rn@netplusmarketing.com
       Website: www.netplusmarketing.com
Online advertising: branding & direct response objectives, sponsorships, email marketing & search engine
marketing. (Woman, estab 1996, empl 18, sales , cert:
WBENC)

1231   SSKJ Enterprises Inc. dba Vital Signs
       2812 Idlewood Rd
       Carnegie, PA 15106
       Contact: Sandy Burkett President
       Tel: 412-494-3308
       Email: sandy@vitalsignspgh.com
       Website: www.vitalsignspgh.com
Mfr interior & exterior signage, large digital format
printing, promotional items, ADA signage, architectural,
banners, bar code labels, business graphics, buttons,
channel letters, commercial awnings, corporate identification, custom displays. (Woman/Nat Ame, estab 2005,
empl 4, sales $342,350, cert: NMSDC)

Puerto Rico

1232   Arteaga & Arteaga Advertising
       P.O. Box 70336
       San Juan, PR 00918
       Contact: Juan Arteaga VP - Strategy & New Business
       Tel: 787-620-1600
       Email: jat@arteaga.com
       Website: www.arteaga.com
Advertising, marketing, public relations, media, creative, interactive, packaging design, event planning, strategic planning, youth marketing. (Hisp, estab 1984, empl 40, sales $21,000,000, cert: NMSDC)

South Carolina

1233   Harland Enterprises Inc.
       7364 Two Notch Rd
       Columbia, SC 29229
       Contact: Owner
       Tel: 803-462-0433
       Email:
       Website: http://signsbytomorrow.com/columbiane/
ADA & and digital graphics, Advertising specialties, Digital Signage. (AA, estab 2012, empl 5, sales $504,000, cert: State)

Tennessee

1234   FlagCenter.com, LLC
       4550 Summer Ave
       Memphis, TN 38122
       Contact: Maureen Criscuolo Owner
       Tel: 901-762-0044
       Email: maureen@flagcenter.com
       Website: www.flagcenter.com
Mfr custom nylon & vinyl signs, street banners, banners, flags, table covers & banners. (Woman, estab 2006, empl 6, sales $550,000, cert: State, City)

1235   Three Point Graphics, Inc.
       750 Eaton St
       Memphis, TN 38120
       Contact: Owner
       Tel: 901-537-0537
       Email:
       Website: www.3ptgraphics.com
Mission critical & complex graphic & signage products. (Woman, estab 2004, empl , sales $100,000,000, cert: State, City)

Texas

1236   Asher Media, Inc.
       15303 Dallas Pkwy Ste 1300
       Addison, TX 75001
       Contact: Kalyn Asher Presdient
       Tel: 972-732-6464
       Email: kalyn@ashermedia.com
       Website: www.ashermedia.com
Strategic planning & buying solutions. (Woman, estab 1999, empl 27, sales , cert: State, WBENC)

1237   B2B Enterprises Inc. dba Prism Sign Group
       3645 Dallas Pkwy, Ste 535
       Plano, TX 75093
       Contact: Bill Brooks CEO
       Tel: 972-403-7770
       Email: bbrooks@prismsigngroup.com
       Website: www.prismsigngroup.com
Mfr signs: banners, vehicle wraps, advertising specialties, business cards, awards/recognition. (AA, estab 2007, empl 4, sales , cert: State, NMSDC)

1238   Blue Sun LLC
       4650 Lockheed Lane, Unit 104
       Denton, TX 76207
       Contact: Gulnara Balic Owner
       Tel: 800-238-6064
       Email: gulnara@dallasdigitalsigns.com
       Website: www.dallasdigitalsigns.com
Mfr, install & repair Interior & exterior electrical signs, graphic design. (Woman/As-Pac, estab 2012, empl 6, sales $360,000, cert: State)

1239   Brown Graphics Inc.
       11404 Chairman Dr
       Dallas, TX 75243
       Contact: Melanie Brown President
       Tel: 214-553-9988
       Email: melanie@browngraphics.com
       Website: www.browngraphics.com
Designs & mfr architectural signs: monuments, wayfinding, suite signs, cubicle, reception area, garage, directories, crown & building signage. (Woman, estab 1989, empl 8, sales $765,816, cert: State)

1240   Cartel Creativo, Inc.
       5835 Callaghan Rd Ste 600
       San Antonio, TX 78228
       Contact: Sean Salas CEO
       Tel: 210-602-8880
       Email: ssalas@thecartel.com
       Website: www.thecartel.com
Advertising agency: research & planning, creative development, production & in-house audio. (Hisp, estab 1994, empl 10, sales $4,400,000, cert: NMSDC)

1241   Castle Business Solutions, LLC
       2777 North Stemmons Frwy Ste 1242
       Dallas, TX 75207
       Contact: Sharon King CEO
       Tel: 214-599-2880
       Email: sharon@castlebusinesssolutions.net
       Website: http://castlebusinesssolutions.com/
Directory & mailing list publishing, direct mail advertising, packaging & labeling services, warehousing & storage, custom computer programming services, data processing, hosting & related services. (Woman/AA, estab 2010, empl 3, sales $615,880, cert: State, NMSDC)

1242   Desert Star Enterprises, Inc
       8409 Sterling St Ste B
       Irving, TX 75063
       Contact: Myra Brown Presdient
       Tel: 972-915-6970
       Email: myra@highvaluesigns.com
       Website: www.highvaluesigns.com
Create & install signs: wayfinding signs, banners, car wraps & monument signs. (Woman, estab 2014, empl 3, sales $300,000, cert: State, WBENC)

1243 Digital Thrive, LLC
1910 Anita Dr
Austin, TX 78704
Contact: Co-Founder, CMO
Tel: 512-900-7699
Email: kevin@digthrive.com
Website: http://digthrive.com
Graphic design & media: website design, mobile application design & development, animation & video production, print collateral & promotional materials. (Woman, estab 2010, empl 10, sales , cert: State, WBENC)

1244 DMN3
2190 North Loop W, Ste 200
Houston, TX 77018
Contact: Pamela Lockard Presdient
Tel: 713-868-3000
Email: accounting@dmn3.com
Website: www.dmn3.com
Direct mail & print advertising, e-marketing, multicultural marketing, event promotions, internal communication, radio & TV placement, data processing & mgt, interactive & promotional mktg, outdoor media, sponsorships, print colateral. (Woman, estab 1985, empl 9, sales $4,267,600, cert: State, City, WBENC)

1245 Enigma, LLC
100 Crescent Ct. Ste 700
Dallas, TX 75201
Contact: Sherilyn K Smith-Rudolph Presdient
Tel: 214-459-8208
Email: sherilyn@enigmallc.com
Website: www.enigmallc.com
Advertising & marketing agency. (Woman/AA, estab 2003, empl 4, sales , cert: NMSDC, 8a)

1246 Excalibur Exhibits
7120 Brittmoore Rd, Ste 430
Houston, TX 77041
Contact: Peggy Swords Presdient
Tel: 713-856-8853
Email: pswords@excaliburexhibits.com
Website: www.excaliburexhibits.com
Design & build custom, portable, modular & system solutions. (Woman, estab 1997, empl 26, sales $5,628,500, cert: WBENC)

1247 Gilbreath Communications, Inc.
15995 N Barkers Landing, Ste 100 Ste 100
Houston, TX 77079
Contact: Debra Johnson VP
Tel: 281-649-9595
Email: debra@gilbcomm.com
Website: www.gilbcomm.com
Advertising: ad campaigns, promotional materials, media relations, public relations, press relations, community relations, employee communications, press conferences, press releases, press kits, speeches & scripts, graphic design, etc. (Woman/AA, estab 1990, empl 11, sales , cert: State, City, WBENC)

1248 JODesign
440 S Main St
Fort Worth, TX 76104
Contact: Business Dev Mgr
Tel: 817-335-0100
Email:
Website: www.jodesign.com
Full service marketing, public relations and advertising: branding, public relations, graphic design, market research, marketing campaigns, digital marketing, etc. (Woman, estab 1998, empl 10, sales $950,825, cert: WBENC)

1249 Latin Works Marketing LLC
2500 Bee Cave Rd Bldg 2
Austin, TX 78746
Contact: Alejandro Ruelas CMO
Tel: 512-479-4580
Email: a.ruelas@latinworks.com
Website: www.latinworks.com
Cultural Branding, Account Management, Strategic Planning & Research, Integrated Creative Development & Production, Digital & Social Media, Media Buying & Planning, Grassroots & Event Activations. (Hisp, estab 1998, empl 85, sales , cert: NMSDC)

1250 Latinworks
410 Baylor St
Austin, TX 78703
Contact: Marly Ramstad CEO
Tel: 512-479-6200
Email: m.ramstad@latinworks.com
Website: www.latinworks.com
Advertising agency. (Hisp, estab 1998, empl 174, sales , cert: State, NMSDC)

1251 Limb Design LLC
1702 Houston Ave
Houston, TX 77007
Contact: Partner
Tel: 713-529-1117
Email:
Website: www.limbdesign.com
Marketing, graphic design & web site design. (Woman, estab 1983, empl 14, sales $1,600,000, cert: WBENC)

1252 Lopez Marketing Group, Inc.
11169 La Quinta Pl
El Paso, TX 79936
Contact: Jose Luis Lopez Presdient
Tel: 915-772-8018
Email: jllopez1@lopezgroup.com
Website: www.lopezgroup.com
Advertising, Hispanic marketing, public relations. (Hisp, estab 1989, empl 16, sales $4,500,000, cert: State, NMSDC)

1253 MasterWord Services, Inc.
303 Stafford St
Houston, TX 77079
Contact: Ludmila Golovine Presdient
Tel: 281-589-0810
Email: hr@masterword.com
Website: www.masterword.com
Translation, interpretation, language training & assessments, cultural intelligence training & language compliance consulting. (Woman, estab 1993, empl 96, sales $14,620,522, cert: WBENC)

1254 Mentler & Company
4819 Broadway St
Addison, TX 75001
Contact: controller
Tel: 972-233-1414
Email:
Website: www.mentlerandcompany.com
Advertising & marketing, branding, design. (Woman, estab 1982, empl 21, sales $1,722,013, cert: State, WBENC)

1255 One Pytchblack, LLC DBA PytchBlack
      1612 Summit Ave Ste 415
      Fort Worth, TX 76102
      Contact: Andre Yanez Owner
      Tel: 817-570-0915
      Email: aryanez@pytchblack.com
      Website: www.pytchblack.com
Advertising agency, website design, trademark and identity design, product design, media buying & graphic design. (Hisp, estab 2013, empl 2, sales $115,000, cert: State, NMSDC)

1256 Preferred Translations, Inc.
      P.O. Box 42065
      Houston, TX 77242
      Contact: Gina Guerrero Managing Dir
      Tel: 281-882-3080
      Email: projects@preferredtranslationsinc.com
      Website: www.preferredTranslationsInc.com
Language Translation, Interpretation, Multilingual Desktop Publishing, Transcription, Voiceover, and subtitling. (Woman/Hisp, estab 2012, empl 1, sales , cert: State)

1257 Reach Media Inc.
      13760 Noel Rd Ste 750
      Dallas, TX 75240
      Contact: Reggie Denson VP Sales
      Tel: 972-789-1058
      Email: reggie.denson@reachmediainc.com
      Website: www.reachmediainc.com
African-American advertising for the Tom Joyner Morning Show. (AA, estab 2001, empl 92, sales $53,000,000, cert: State, NMSDC)

1258 St. Julien Communications Group, LLC
      P.O. Box 3724
      Houston, TX 77253
      Contact: Jaa St. Julien CEO
      Tel: 713-965-7084
      Email: jaa@stjuliencg.com
      Website: www.stjuliencg.com
Advertising, public relations, marketing, media placement, strategy development, graphic & web design, web development, mobile app development, photography, videography consulting, community outreach. (AA, Nat Ame, Hisp, estab 2007, empl 1, sales $196,000, cert: State, NMSDC)

1259 SuperLatina Inc.
      4200 South Frwy Ste 2370
      Fort Worth, TX 76115
      Contact: Andres Suarez CEO
      Tel: 214-431-5783
      Email: andres@aganarmedia.com
      Website: www.aganarmedia.com
Multicultural marketing services, video & interactive campaigns for television & digital (Woman/Hisp, estab 2007, empl 8, sales $787,000, cert: NMSDC)

1260 Techstyle Group LLC
      P.O. Box 692347
      Houston, TX 77269
      Contact: Laurel Prokop CEO
      Tel: 281-251-2436
      Email: lp.info@techstyle.com
      Website: www.techstylegroup.com
Document, presentation & written-content production. (Woman, estab 1986, empl 5, sales , cert: City)

1261 Universe Technical Translation, Inc.
      9225 Katy Frwy Ste 400
      Houston, TX 77024
      Contact: Andreas Nordquist BD Mgr
      Tel: 713-827-8800
      Email: marion@universe.us
      Website: www.universetranslation.com
Technical & legal written translation. (Woman, estab 1981, empl 40, sales $9,618,844, cert: State, WBENC)

1262 Web-Hed Technologies, Inc. dba Webhead
      1710 N Main Ave
      San Antonio, TX 78212
      Contact: Juanita I . Gonzalez CEO
      Tel: 210-354-1661
      Email: contracts@webheadtech.com
      Website: www.webheadtech.com
Hispanic interactive marketing svcs: media & animated graphics, online & interactive games & sweepstakes. (Woman/Hisp, estab 1995, empl 15, sales , cert: State)

1263 What's the Big Idea?
      5603 Kingston Court
      Richardson, TX 75082
      Contact: Tracy Cink President
      Tel: 972-509-0081
      Email: tracy_cink@wtbi.com
      Website: www.wtbi.com
Advertising & graphic design. (Woman, estab 0, empl , sales , cert: WBENC)

Utah

1264 Infinite Scale Design Group
      16 Exchange Place
      Salt Lake City, UT 84111
      Contact: Molly Mazzolini Managing Member
      Tel: 801-363-1881
      Email: molly@infinitescale.com
      Website: www.infinitescale.com
Brand strategy, logo design, creative briefs, identity systems, collateral, website design, environmental graphics, master plan, interpretive design, wayfinding signage, recognition & donor, signage, uniform systems, vehicle graphics. (Woman, estab , empl , sales , cert: State)

1265 U.S. Translation Company
      320 W 200 S
      Salt Lake City, UT 84101
      Contact: Kathy Sprouse Dir of Operations
      Tel: 801-393-5300
      Email: kathy@ustranslation.com
      Website: www.ustranslation.com
Language services, document formatting, interpreting services. (Hisp, estab 1995, empl 15, sales $2,987,864, cert: NMSDC)

Virginia

1266 AB Design, Inc.
      10005 Stonemill Rd
      Richmond, VA 23233
      Contact: Gladys Brenner President
      Tel: 804-346-4771
      Email: gbrenner@abdesignonline.com
      Website: www.abdesignonline.com
Environmental graphic design: interior & exterior signage, dev wayfinding systems & architectural graphics, site analysis/evaluation, master planning & comprehensive wayfinding systems. (Woman/Hisp, estab 1991, empl 3, sales $182,000, cert: State)

1267   Advanta Pacific International
       9336 Braymore Circle
       Fairfax Station, VA 22039
       Contact: Adam Tran Managing Dir
       Tel: 703-226-9605
       Email: contact@vernacularlanguage.com
       Website: http://vernacularlanguage.com
Translation & interpretation services in over 200 languages
and dialects, including sign language. (Woman/As-Pac,
estab 2009, empl 4, sales $150,000, cert: State)

1268   Capital Exhibits
       8245-B Backlick Rd
       Lorton, VA 22079
       Contact: Jennifer Warren Sales
       Tel: 540-219-9372
       Email: jennifer@capitalexhibits.com
       Website: www.capitalexhibits.com
Indoor & outdoor signage, tradeshow displays, banners &
banner stands, channel lettering, wayfinding & directional
signage, temporary signage, hard or thick signage, custom
flirting titles, fabric & vinyl signs. (As-Ind, estab 1994, empl
6, sales , cert: State)

1269   Eighth Day Design
       7653 Leesburg Pike
       Falls Church, VA 22043
       Contact: Dir of IWMS
       Tel: 703-562-3636
       Email:
       Website: www.eighthday.com
Productivity & image solutions, architecture & design,
programming, space planning, design dev, sustainable
design, exhibit design, construction documents, construction administration, move coordination & facilities maintenance support. (Woman, estab 1989, empl 25, sales
$3,800,000, cert: WBENC)

1270   Hybrid Studios LLC
       1940 Duke St Ste 200
       Alexandria, VA 22314
       Contact: Susan Yates Mgr
       Tel: 703-671-6975
       Email: susan@hybrid-studios.com
       Website: www.hybriddc.com
Communications solutions: print, interactive development,
advertising, corporate identity, direct marketing & social
media marketing services. (Woman, estab 2002, empl 2,
sales $532,000, cert: State)

1271   Mail Call Direct LLC
       5616 Eastport Blvd
       Henrico, VA 23231
       Contact: Lisa Jacoby Co-Owner
       Tel: 804-222-0608
       Email: lisa@mailcalldirect.com
       Website: www.MailCallDirect.com
Direct mail services, digital lasering, inkjet & insert, data
processing, mailing lists, barcode printing, variable data,
stamping, metering, permits, hand fulfillment, parcel
fulfillment, folding bindery services, glue dotting, poly
bagging. (Woman, estab 2014, empl 8, sales , cert: State)

1272   Nvision Media Group, LLC
       114 W Hicks St
       Lawrenceville, VA 23868
       Contact: David Fant Owner
       Tel: 866-848-8822
       Email: david.fant@nvisn.net
       Website: www.nvisn.net
Indoor advertising. (Woman/AA, estab 2006, empl 6,
sales $100,000, cert: State)

1273   Tandem By Design LLC
       306 N 26th St, Ste 227
       Richmond, VA 23223
       Contact: Bev Gray President
       Tel: 804-239-2539
       Email: bev@tandembydesign.com
       Website: http://tandembydesign.com
Marketing & advertising solutions,one-to-one marketing, B2B sales collateral, B2C POP/POS, packaging
design, corporate communications, corporate & brand
videos, grassroots campaigns, social media. (Woman,
estab 2012, empl 1, sales , cert: State)

Washington

1274   TDW+Co
       600 Stewart St, Ste 800
       Seattle, WA 98101
       Contact: Tim Wang Principal and Founder
       Tel: 206-623-6888
       Email: biz@tdwandco.com
       Website: www.tdwandco.com
Marketing communications & advertising agency. (As-
Pac, estab 2004, empl 25, sales $10,015,295, cert: State,
NMSDC, CPUC)

1275   Thinking Cap Communications & Design
       9 S Washington Ste 201
       Spokane, WA 99201
       Contact: Marvin Reguindin President
       Tel: 509-747-4930
       Email: marvo@tcapdesign.com
       Website: www.tcapdesign.com
Advertising & graphic design, creative & account
services, websites, radio & TV/video spots. (As-Pac,
estab 1995, empl 3, sales $124,753, cert: State, NMSDC)

1276   Translation Solutions Corp.
       1201 Pacific Ave Corp Ste 600
       Tacoma, WA 98402
       Contact: Rosa Capdevielle Project Mgr
       Tel: 808-404-1270
       Email: rosa@translationsolutions.org
       Website: www.translationsolutions.org
Translations & interpretation services. (Woman/Hisp,
estab 1994, empl 5, sales , cert: State, NMSDC)

1277   Trio Northwest Business Solutions, Inc.
       239 SW 41st St
       Renton, WA 98057
       Contact: Jeffrey Quint EVP Sales & Mktg
       Tel: 206-728-8181
       Email: info@triogroupnw.com
       Website: www.triogroupnw.com/
Brand management, advertising, marketing, strategy,
campaign development, project management, marcom
strategy, web development, mobile app development,
media buying, social media strategy & deployment. (Nat
Ame, estab 2000, empl 6, sales $1,300,000, cert:
NMSDC)

1278 Triple Threat Editorial
      18574 NE 57th St
      Redmond, WA 98052
      Contact: Jody Allard Owner
      Tel: 425-867-3224
      Email: allardjr@yahoo.com
      Website:
Writing & editing, marketing copy, web content, technical
writing, proofreading, basic web design & operate internal
web sites. (Woman, estab 2004, empl 1, sales , cert: State)

1279 Worktank Enterprises, LLC
      400 E Pine St, Ste 301
      Seattle, WA 98122
      Contact: Leslie Rugaber CEO
      Tel: 206-658-2555
      Email: leslie@worktankseattle.com
      Website: www.worktankseattle.com
Media strategy & production: integrated media & marketing campaigns, video & film production, CD, DVD & web
content production, software & product demos, webcast
management & production staffing services. (Woman,
estab 2001, empl 10, sales , cert: WBENC)

Wisconsin

1280 Everbrite, LLC
      4949 S 110th St
      Greenfield, WI 53228
      Contact: Nicki LaFrance Sales Admin
      Tel: 414-529-3500
      Email: supplierdiversity@everbrite.com
      Website: www.everbrite.com
Outdoor illuminated identification signage. (Woman, estab
1927, empl 850, sales , cert: WBENC)

1281 Revelation, LLC
      222 N Midvale Blvd Ste 18
      Madison, WI 53705
      Contact: Brian Lee Presdient
      Tel: 608-622-7767
      Email: brian@experiencerevelation.com
      Website: www.experiencerevelation.com
Public relations, media buying, ad buying, advertising,
social media consulting, internet marketing, web marketing & speaking engagements. (As-Pac, estab 2010, empl 3,
sales $170,000, cert: NMSDC)

1282 The Geo Group
      6 Odana Court
      Madison, WI 53719
      Contact: Georgia Roeming Presdient
      Tel: 608-230-1000
      Email: georgia.roeming@thegeogroup.com
      Website: www.thegeogroup.com
Translation of radio, TV, website & print advertising.
(Woman, estab 1991, empl 20, sales , cert: WBENC)

ADVERTISING SPECIALTIES
Supply advertising specialties, premium and promotional products, or travel incentives. Includes frims which do silkscreening and embroidery on various products. NAICS Code 42

Alabama

1283 Concepts & Associates
105 19th St S
Birmingham, AL 35210
Contact: Tim Hennessy President
Tel: 205-870-1111
Email: tim@conceptsusa.com
Website: www.conceptsusa.com
Corporate gifts & promotional products, embroidery & fulfillment center. (Woman, estab 1983, empl 15, sales , cert: State, WBENC)

1284 LogoBranders Inc.
1161 Lagoon Business Loop
Montgomery, AL 36117
Contact: Dean Flynn branding specialist
Tel: 334-277-1144
Email: dean@logobranders.com
Website: http://logobranders.biz/
Promotional items, executive gifts, embroidery, screen print, hardline, health and safety, computer and electronic products, wearables, bags, writing instruments, drinkwear, desk/office business accessories, calenders, person products, etc. (Woman, estab 1993, empl 34, sales $6,000,000, cert: WBENC)

Arizone

1285 Sunset Trading Company, LLC
15619 N 50th St
Scottsdale, AZ 85254
Contact: Owner
Tel: 602-494-6419
Email:
Website: www.sunsettradingco.com
Customer & employee reward, recognition & incentive programs, premiums & promotional advertising products. (Woman, estab 1999, empl , sales $935,000, cert: WBENC)

California

1286 Apropos Promotions
1401 N Broadway Ste 280
Walnut Creek, CA 94596
Contact: Ann Auelmann President
Tel: 925-274-5700
Email: ann@apropospromotions.com
Website: www.apropospromotions.com
Promotional merchandise: tradeshow giveaways, staff appreciation, gifts, special events, etc. (Woman, estab 2002, empl 4, sales , cert: WBENC)

1287 Avid Promotions
499 Nibus St Unit C
Brea, CA 92821
Contact: Dena Gibbs CEO
Tel: 949-387-9890
Email: dena@avidpromotions.com
Website: www.AvidPromotions.com
Promotional products, marketing materials, and apparel/corporate uniforms. (Hisp, estab 2009, empl 4, sales $540,000, cert: NMSDC, CPUC)

1288 Beyond Zebra Inc.
1443 E Washington Blvd, Ste 641
Pasadena, CA 91104
Contact: CFO
Tel: 818-435-8202
Email:
Website: www.beyondzebra.net
Promotional products: bags, desk accessories, apparel, hats, memo pads, housewares, sales incentive & corporate gift programs. (Woman/As-Pac, estab 2000, empl 4, sales $1,043,151, cert: WBENC)

1289 Elementi Designs
1655 22nd Ave
San Francisco, CA 94122
Contact: Ken Lou President
Tel: 415-887-3889
Email: elementidesigns@gmail.com
Website: www.elementidesigns.com
Corporate promotional items, apparel & printing, fashion jewelry & accessories, wedding party supplies, gift items, home decor products & car assortments. (Woman/As-Pac, estab 2004, empl 5, sales $194,902, cert: CPUC)

1290 Ellen's Silkscreening, Inc.
1500 Mission St
South Pasadena, CA 91030
Contact: Owner
Tel: 626-441-4415
Email:
Website: www.ellenssilkscreening.com
Screen printed & embroidered goods & promotional products. (Woman, estab 1978, empl 15, sales $2,087,125, cert: WBENC)

1291 Gorilla Marketing
4100 Flat Rock Dr, Ste A
Riverside, CA 92505
Contact: VP Operations
Tel: 951-353-8133
Email:
Website: www.gorillamarketing.net
Imprinted promotional products, advertising specialties. (Hisp, estab 1985, empl 10, sales $1,700,000, cert: NMSDC)

1292 Infocus Specialties, Inc.
1655 Hauser Circle
Thousand Oaks, CA 91362
Contact: Steve Leo Co-Owner
Tel: 805-379-9192
Email: steve@infocusspecialties.com
Website: www.infocusspecialties.com
Promotional and advertising impressions. (Woman, estab 2013, empl 2, sales $720,000, cert: WBENC)

1293   Intention Advertising
2995 Bonnie Lane
Pleasant Hill, CA 94523
Contact: Mara Villa Owner
Tel: 925-274-1774
Email: mara@intentionadvertising.com
Website: http://intentionadvertising.com
Promotional products, t-shirts to pens, etc. (Woman, estab 2011, empl 1, sales $400,000, cert: State)

1294   Janco & Winnex Inc
3018 Durfee Ave, Ste E
El Monte, CA 91732
Contact: Jennifer Renshaw President
Tel: 626-454-4882
Email: jenniferjan@yahoo.com
Website: www.jancoline.com
Dist folding chairs, promotional stationery & bags. (Woman/As-Pac, estab 1996, empl 9, sales , cert: State, 8a)

1295   JLT Promotions Inc.
24238 Hawthorne Blvd
Torrance, CA 90505
Contact: John Tulchin CFO
Tel: 310-791-7006
Email: jtulchin@thepromotionsdept.com
Website: www.instadiumpromotions.com
Sports & team promotional items & stadium giveaways. (Minority, Woman, estab 1990, empl 10, sales $5,700,000, cert: State, CPUC)

1296   Keystone Gifts
3182 Campus Dr, Ste 424
San Mateo, CA 94403
Contact: Elizabeth Tsuji Presdient
Tel: 650-401-6066
Email: liz@keystonegifts.com
Website: www.keystonegifts.com
Promotional branded merchandise: pins, pennants, rally towels, seat cushions, water bottles, cups, mugs, cooler bags, lunch bags, duffel bags, fanny packs, backpacks, caps, tee shirts, sweatshirts, jackets, jewelry, etc. (Woman/As-Pac, estab 1992, empl 2, sales $614,600, cert: State, NMSDC, CPUC)

1297   KV & Associates, LLC
5694 Mission Center Rd, Ste 357
San Diego, CA 92108
Contact: Kathy Valadez Presdient
Tel: 858-277-7036
Email: info@kvapromotions.com
Website: www.KVAPromotions.com
Promotional & merchandise, graphic design, corporate apparel, women, men, infant, jackets, polo's, long sleeve, short sleeve, caps, visors, T-shirts, embroidery, silk screen, writing pens, pencils, markers, cups. (Woman/Hisp, estab 2000, empl , sales $640,500, cert: NMSDC, WBENC, SDB)

1298   Laughing Willow, Inc.
1110 Quintana Rd
Morro Bay, CA 93442
Contact: Elizabeth Espy CEO
Tel: 805-772-4770
Email: liz@doghousepromotions.com
Website: www.doghousepromotions.com
Advertising specialty, apparel, awards, bags, banners, brand names, conventions, corporate gifts, custom merchandise, drink ware, eco-friendly, embroidery, gift baskets, headwear, hospitality, incentive programs. (Woman, estab 1998, empl 4, sales $2,029,491, cert: WBENC)

1299   Macro Industries, Inc
5595 Daniels St Ste F
Chino, CA 91710
Contact: Cynthia Phillips Marketing Mgr
Tel: 909-364-8100
Email: sales106@goldensundirect.com
Website: www.3cfactory.com
Dist safety vests, safety t-shirts, safety jackets, ANSI/ISEA 107-2004 Class 2, Class 3, gloves, caps, hats, uniforms, bags, backpacks, tote bags, custom-made orders, imprint, embroidery. (As-Pac, estab 2001, empl 7, sales $1,020,000, cert: CPUC)

1300   Matel Manufacturing Inc.
13205 Estrella Ave Unit A
Gardena, CA 90248
Contact: Nagendra Bolla Presdient
Tel: 310-217-9111
Email: bobbolla@matelinc.com
Website: www.matelinc.com
Leather & Metal desk accessories, letter trays, form holders, business cards, desk pads, pen sets, bill holders, book ends, memo boxes, coasters & conference pads. (As-Ind, estab 1985, empl 7, sales $720,000, cert: CPUC)

1301   Modernmart, Inc.
6120 Wilderness Ave.
Riverside, CA 92504
Contact: Alison Hsu
Tel: 909-573-0050
Email: alison@modernmart.com
Website: www.modernmart.com
Promotional products, pens, coffee mugs, caps, T-shirts with logos imprint & embroidery. (Woman/As-Pac, estab 2001, empl 12, sales $709,000, cert: 8a)

1302   O2 Marketing & Design, Inc.
367 Civic Dr Ste 15
Pleasant Hill, CA 94523
Contact: Sabina Rica Treasurer
Tel: 510-553-0202
Email: sabina@o2marketing.com
Website: www.O2MARKETING.COM
Promotional products: tradeshow giveaways, corporate branding, employee incentive programs, awards. (Woman/As-Ind, estab 2000, empl 8, sales $200,000, cert: CPUC, WBENC)

1303   PMP Products Inc.
        1210 W Jon St, Ste B
        Torrance, CA 90502
        Contact: Peter Newhouse Presdient
        Tel: 310-547-8064
        Email: petern@american-casuals.com
        Website: www.american-casuals.com
Promotional products, apparel (soft goods) headwear,
hard goods. (Woman/As-Pac, estab 2003, empl 10, sales ,
cert: NMSDC, WBENC)

1304   Red Cloud LLC
        1600 Sawtelle Blvd, Ste 108
        Los Angeles, CA 90025
        Contact: Denise Lyons Controller
        Tel: 310-444-5583
        Email: denise@redcloudllc.com
        Website: http://redcloudpromotions.com
Promotional products, advertising specialties. (Woman,
estab 2005, empl 10, sales , cert: WBENC)

1305   Resources Unlimited, Inc.
        317 Bay Shore Ave, Ste A
        Long Beach, CA 90803
        Contact: Tina Valdez Acct Mgr
        Tel: 310-717-0261
        Email: tina@resourcesunlimitedinc.com
        Website: www.resourcesunlimitedinc.com
Custom promotional materials, decorated apparel, screen
printed tees & embroidered hats & polos, logoed gifts.
(Minority, estab 1994, empl 3, sales $1,000,000, cert:
CPUC)

1306   Seba International
        1210 W Jon St
        Torrance, CA 90502
        Contact: Mariah M. Qian CEO
        Tel: 310-549-5122
        Email: seba@globalxlr.com
        Website: www.sebaintl.com
Promotional items: sports Jerseys, shirts, jackets,
sweatshirts, caps & hats. (Woman/As-Pac, estab 2013,
empl 8, sales $5,171,671, cert: NMSDC)

1307   Sun Coast Merchandise Corporation
        6315 Bandini Blvd
        Los Angeles, CA 90040
        Contact: Dilip Bhavnani Presdient
        Tel: 800-432-4274
        Email: dilip@sunscopeusa.com
        Website: www.sunscopeusa.com
Promotional products. (As-Pac, estab 1943, empl 48, sales
$108,000,000, cert: NMSDC)

1308   The Corporate Gift Service, Inc.
        4120 W Burbank Blvd
        Burbank, CA 91505
        Contact: Lydia Eltringham Accounting Dept
        Tel: 818-845-9500
        Email: accounting@corpgiftservice.com
        Website: www.thecorporategiftservice.com
Handmade Custom Gift Baskets, Embroidered Corporate
Apparel, High End Corporate Gifts, Branded Promotional
Products & Advertising Specialties. (Woman, estab 1990,
empl 7, sales $1,600,000, cert: WBENC)

1309   Together We Plan
        5104 Odin Ct
        Rocklin, CA 95765
        Contact: Carol Ann Whiteman Owner
        Tel: 916-435-4304
        Email: carolann@togetherweplan.com
        Website: www.togetherweplan.com
Advertising specialties, awards, custom labels, stationery
& business cards. (Woman/Hisp, estab 2002, empl 7,
sales , cert: State)

1310   TSG Direct LLC
        20992 Avenida Amapola
        Lake Forest, CA 92630
        Contact: Gregg Moschides Dir of Sales
        Tel: 650-224-9146
        Email: gmoschides@tsgdirectllc.com
        Website: www.tsgdirectllc.com
Print, direct mail & fulfillment services, promotional
products, branded apparel, uniforms & office supplies.
(Woman, estab 2014, empl 5, sales , cert: State, CPUC)

1311   Wearable Imaging, Inc.
        26741 Portola Pkwy Ste 1E
        Foothill Ranch, CA 92610
        Contact: Robin Richter Presdient
        Tel: 949-888-7837
        Email: robin@wearableimaging.com
        Website: www.wearableimaging.com
Screenprinting & embroidered apparel: t-shirts, polo's,
hats & caps, pens, travel mugs, etc. (Woman/Nat Ame,
estab 1992, empl 5, sales $941,828, cert: CPUC, WBENC)

Colorado

1312   AC Flag & Banner, Inc.
        10184 W Belleview Ave
        Littleton, CO 80127
        Contact: Wendy Willson President
        Tel: 303-948-9774
        Email: wendy@acflag.com
        Website: www.acflagandbanner.com
Custom logo flags & banners. (Woman, estab 2004, empl
4, sales $225,000, cert: WBENC)

1313   Artistic Promotions
        2168 S Birch St
        Denver, CO 80222
        Contact: Radhika Hess Sales Assoc
        Tel: 303-759-5559
        Email: sharon@artisticpromo.com
        Website: www.artisticpromo.com
Advertising specialties: marketing programs, special
events, promotional products, logo apparel, incentive &
safety programs, events items, trade shows, convention
gifts, corporate awards, etc. (Woman, estab 1991, empl
4, sales , cert: WBENC)

Connecticut

1314   Church Hill Classics
        594 Pepper St
        Monroe, CT 06468
        Contact: Sales/Mktg Mgr
        Tel: 800-477-9005
        Email:
        Website: www.diplomaframe.com
Corporate frames & gifts: custom designed insignias
awards, recognition certificates & events. (Woman,
estab 1991, empl 73, sales , cert: WBENC)

1315　GBG The Corporate Gift Source, Inc.
204 Spring Hill Rd
Trumbull, CT 06611
Contact: Charlotte O'Banion Presdient
Tel:　203-459-4424
Email: charlotte@gbginc.com
Website: www.gbginc.com
Promotional products, logoed apparel, warehousing & catalog programs, fulfillment services, employee award redemption programs, premiums & sales incentives. (Woman/As-Pac, estab 1987, empl 6, sales $3,700,000, cert: NMSDC)

1316　John Michael Associates, Inc.
94 Holmes Rd
Newington, CT 06111
Contact: Paul Sposito Exec VP
Tel:　860-666-1414
Email: paul@jmalogos.com
Website: www.jmalogos.com
Logo apparel & merchandise, corporate online stores, awards, recognition & loyalty programs, fulfillment, event, incentive & sales marketing, importing, trade shows & fundraisers, kitting, collating & custom packaging, creative services. (Woman, estab 1980, empl 27, sales $12,000,000, cert: State, WBENC)

1317　Preferred Promotions, LLC
1801 Berlin Turnpike
Berlin, CT 06037
Contact: Dottie Nelson Owner
Tel:　860-829-1317
Email: dnelson@preferredpromo.com
Website: www.preferredpromos.com
Promotional products: imprinted wearables, engraved awards.. (Woman/Nat Ame, estab 2003, empl 5, sales $725,000, cert: State)

District of Columbia

1318　The Hamilton Group
4406 Gault Place NE
Washington, DC 20019
Contact: Kaari Hamilton Presdient
Tel:　202-689-4304
Email: kayhhpbp@verizon.net
Website: www.thehamiltongroupllc.net
Dist office supplies, advertisement & promotional products, office equipment & clothing wearables. (Woman/AA, estab 2007, empl , sales $731,000, cert: City, NMSDC, WBENC)

Delaware

1319　Promo Victory, Inc.
4142 Ogletown-Stanton Rd, Ste 238
Newark, DE 19713
Contact: Vicki Lam Presdient
Tel:　800-385-7573
Email: vlam@promovictory.com
Website: www.promovictory.com
Promotional products. (Woman/As-Pac, estab 2008, empl 1, sales , cert: State, WBENC)

Florida

1320　Ad Specs of FL, LLC dba Proforma Global Sourcing
2415 N Albany Ave
Tampa, FL 33607
Contact: Michele Adams Presdient
Tel:　813-397-1655
Email: michele.adams@proforma.com
Website: www.proformaglobalsourcing.com
Print & promotional products. (Woman, estab 2005, empl 5, sales $1,230,000, cert: WBENC)

1321　American Traders Enterprises, Inc.
2900 Glades Circle, Ste 1250
Weston, FL 33327
Contact: Josie Musch Presdient
Tel:　954-888-9206
Email: josie@americantraders.com
Website: www.americantraders.com
Promotional products. (Woman/Hisp, estab 1996, empl 6, sales , cert: NMSDC)

1322　American Trading International Co, LLC
13866 SW 256 Terr
Homestead, FL 33032
Contact: Juan Penso Owner
Tel:　813-810-1610
Email: sales@atipromotions.com
Website: www.atipromotions.com
Promotional products, gifts, awards, souvenirs, business cards, advertising specialties. (Hisp, estab 2007, empl 1, sales , cert: State, NMSDC)

1323　Bilmor with Advertising Specialties Inc.
16155 SW 117th Ave, Unit B-19
Miami, FL 33177
Contact: Andrew Headley Director
Tel:　305-232-3323
Email: support@bilmoradv.com
Website: www.bilmoradv.com
Dist promotional items: custom embroidery, heat transfers, pad printing, hot stamping, awards & recognition gifts. (AA, estab 1985, empl 4, sales $614,000, cert: State)

1324　Design & Promotions Corp.
12333 SW 132nd Ct
Miami, FL 33186
Contact: Vicente Buraglia Presdient
Tel:　305-232-8119
Email: service@design-promotions.com
Website: www.design-promotions.com
Custom promotional products, custom packaging, custom displays, P.O.P. material, graphic design. (Hisp, estab 1990, empl 4, sales , cert: NMSDC)

1325　Entertainment Retail Enterprises, LLC
2437 E Landstreet Rd
Orlando, FL 32824
Contact: Melinda Wenderlein Dir of Finance
Tel:　407-649-6552
Email: melinda@ere-sri.com
Website: www.ere-sri.com
CAT workwear, menswear, thermos, lunch bags, mugs (Woman, estab 2008, empl 102, sales $45,000,000, cert: WBENC)

1326   I Love Promos, Inc.
       6627 NW 25th Way Ste 100
       Boca Raton, FL 33496
       Contact: Mary Turel SVP
       Tel: 866-546-7001
       Email: mary@ilovepromos.com
       Website: https://ilovepromos.com
Promotional products, apparel, writing instruments, eco-friendly items. (Woman/Hisp, estab 2013, empl 2, sales $3,200,000, cert: WBENC)

1327   JT Promotions
       4378 LB Mcleod Rd
       Orlando, FL 32811
       Contact: James Stillwell Owner
       Tel: 407-730-7990
       Email: info@aclipsemarketing.net
       Website: www.aclipsemarketing.net
Embroidery, silk screening, promotional & novelty items, event planning & execution. (AA, estab 2003, empl 4, sales $250,000, cert: NMSDC)

1328   LEGitimate Productions, Inc. dba Legwerks
       6822 22nd Ave N Ste 430
       Saint Petersburg, FL 33710
       Contact: Lisa René LeClair CEO
       Tel: 727-344-3082
       Email: lisa@legwerks.com
       Website: www.legwerks.com
Branding solutions, promotional products & gifts, employee recognition & customer acquision programs. (Woman, estab 2001, empl 1, sales $368,233, cert: State)

1329   Levy Recognition
       2415 N Albany Ave, Unit 1
       Tampa, FL 33607
       Contact: Michele Adams President
       Tel: 813-868-3923
       Email: michele.adams@levyrecognition.com
       Website: www.levyrecognition.com
Mfr medals, medallions & emblematic jewelry, custom design awards, promotional products, branded apparell & business gifts. (Woman, estab 1960, empl 38, sales $4,000,000, cert: WBENC)

1330   Merchandise Partners
       11111 N 46th St
       Tampa, FL 33617
       Contact: Wendy Knapp
       Tel: 404-460-7190
       Email: wendy@merchandisepartners.com
       Website: www.merchandisepartners.com
Corporate promotions, merchandising solutions, retail programs, sponsorship promotions, sales promotions, dealer networks, web stores. (Hisp, estab 2006, empl 6, sales $35,000,000, cert: NMSDC)

1331   MH Specialties LLC
       9896 White Sands Place
       Bonita Springs, FL 34135
       Contact: Tondalaya (Mike) Herbert CEO
       Tel: 313-268-5907
       Email: mike@mhspecialties.com
       Website: www.mhspecialties.com
Rewards & Recognition, wall/desk custom designed plaques, recognition jewelry, awards rings & promotional jewelry, premium incentives gifts for Safety Programs & Training, employees recognition awards, corporate awards/gifts. (Woman, estab 2002, empl 1, sales $300,000, cert: WBENC)

1332   SpringboardPC
       4517 W. Dale Ave
       Tampa, FL 33609
       Contact: Wendy Pepe Presdient
       Tel: 813-918-0371
       Email: wendy@springboardpc.com
       Website: www.springboardpc.com
Advertising specialty, promotional products. (Woman, estab 1992, empl 5, sales $2,400,000, cert: State, City, WBENC)

1333   Tampa T-Shirts
       5112 N 22nd St
       Tampa, FL 33610
       Contact: Juan Davis Mgr
       Tel: 813-879-3298
       Email: juan@fastlaneclothing.com
       Website: www.fastlaneclothing.com
Apparel, logo shirts, lab coats, promotional items. (Woman/Hisp, estab 1985, empl 19, sales $1,480,000, cert: State, City)

1334   Think Tank Studio
       626 Lakeview Rd, Ste A
       Clearwater, FL 33756
       Contact: Marlies Schoenau Presdient
       Tel: 727-441-4488
       Email: mus@thinktankstudio.com
       Website: http://thinktankstudio.com
Promotional marketing services, logo apparel, hats, drink ware, office items, pens, bags, awards, signage, trade-show hand-outs. (Woman, estab 1998, empl 7, sales $1,487,596, cert: WBENC)

1335   Underground Graphics Inc.
       13355 Belcher Rd S Unit H
       Largo, FL 33773
       Contact: Grace Newcomer President
       Tel: 727-535-9582
       Email: grace@undergroundgraphics.us
       Website: www.undergroundgraphics.us
Promotional products: pens, mugs, keychains etc. (Woman, estab 1993, empl 4, sales $165,000, cert: State)

1336   Wendt Productions Inc.
       17301 Solie Rd
       Odessa, FL 33556
       Contact: Susan Wendt Presdient
       Tel: 813-920-5000
       Email: swendt@wendtpro.com
       Website: www.wendtpro.com
Advertising, marketing & promotional products. (Minority, Woman, estab 1986, empl 9, sales $1,450,000, cert: State, City)

1337 Y-Not Design & Mfg. Inc.
1041 E 24th St Hialeah, FL 33013.
Hialeah, FL 33013
Contact: Angelina Garcia
Tel: 855-843-1422
Email: contactus@y-not.com
Website: https://y-not.com/
Promotional & gifts products. (Woman/Hisp, estab 2005,
empl 61, sales $39,000,000, cert: NMSDC, WBENC)

1338 Zoya, Inc.
641 SW 3rd Ave
Fort Lauderdale, FL 33315
Contact: Presdient
Tel: 954-523-6531
Email:
Website: www.zoyainc.com
Promotional items. (Woman, estab 2001, empl 4, sales ,
cert: WBENC)

Georgia

1339 Atlanta Brand Central LLC
880 Glenwood Ave se unit 1317
Atlanta, GA 30316
Contact: Darryl Armstrong Owner
Tel: 404-312-8777
Email: darryl@abcatl.com
Website: www.abcatl.com
Promotional products & sourcing. (AA, estab 2008, empl 4,
sales $170,000, cert: NMSDC)

1340 Atlanta Promotional Products
911 High Green Court
Marietta, GA 30068
Contact: Glynis Holihan Managing Partner
Tel: 770-310-9860
Email: glynis@atlpromo.com
Website: http://atlpromo.com
Advertising specialty, logoed merchandise, corporate gifts
& apparel. (Woman, estab 2004, empl 3, sales $1,196,294,
cert: CPUC)

1341 Barazzo, LLC
2221 Peachtree Rd NE Ste D357
Atlanta, GA 30309
Contact: Quiana Lloyd Member
Tel: 888-716-5785
Email: quiana@barazzo.com
Website: www.barazzo.com
Custom gift & accessory solutions, corporate brand
identity & marketing solutions. (Woman/AA, estab 2009,
empl 0, sales , cert: State, NMSDC, SDB)

1342 Blue Rose Promotions, LLC
2660 Holcomb Bridge Road Ste 200
Alpharetta, GA 30022
Contact: Jennifer Pines VP Sales
Tel: 770-695-7673
Email: jennifer@bluerosepromotions.com
Website: www.bluerosepromotions.com
Promotional marketing with access to over 700,000
products. (Woman, estab 2013, empl 4, sales $4,165,561,
cert: WBENC)

1343 Brand Spirit Inc.
245 N Highland Ave NE Ste 230-272
Atlanta, GA 30307
Contact: Jenna Banks Presdient
Tel: 877-804-7906
Email: jenna@gobrandspirit.com
Website: http://gobrandspirit.com
Branded gifts, promotional items, printed materials,
business forms, logo apparel, badges & credentials,
awards, uniforms, lanyards, brochures & business cards.
(Woman, estab 2012, empl , sales $430,400, cert:
NWBOC)

1344 Capital Ideas, Inc.
990 Hammond Dr Ste 620
Atlanta, GA 30328
Contact: Gina Sealey Acct Mgr/ VP
Tel: 678-320-1630
Email: gsealey@capitalideas.net
Website: www.capitalideas.net
Promotional products. (Woman, estab 1987, empl 8,
sales $4,162,000, cert: WBENC)

1345 Choice Premiums
560 Arlington Pl
Macon, GA 31201
Contact: Presdient
Tel: 478-741-8888
Email:
Website: www.choicepremiums.com
Promotional products & marketing. (Woman, estab
1996, empl 4, sales $402,067, cert: WBENC)

1346 Creative Corporate Ideas Inc
1010 Huntcliff Ste.1350
Atlanta, GA 30350
Contact: Creative Corporate Ideas Inc Owner
Tel: 404-252-2588
Email: cwalina@bellsouth.net
Website: www.creativecorporateideas.com
Promotional items, logo merchandise & wearables.
(Woman, estab 1993, empl 2, sales $500,000, cert:
WBENC)

1347 Creative Innovators, Inc.
1797 Spring Rd, Ste 6
Smyrna, GA 30080
Contact: Omar Horton Mgr
Tel: 770-435-7552
Email: sales@creativeinnovators.net
Website: www.creativeinnovators.net
Embroidery, screen printing, signs, banners, advertising
specialty & promotional items. (AA, estab 1999, empl 3,
sales $150,000, cert: State, City)

1348 FireSign Inc. Promotional Products & Print
4480-H S Cobb Dr, Ste 540
Smyrna, GA 30080
Contact: Jen Lyles Lead Ignitor
Tel: 678-574-2461
Email: jlyles@firesigninc.com
Website: www.firesigninc.com
Promotional product & print services, (Woman/AA,
estab 2003, empl 5, sales $1,295,000, cert: NMSDC)

1349   Henry-Aaron Inc.
       754 Woodson St
       Atlanta, GA 30315
       Contact: Aaron Turpeau President
       Tel: 404-622-4308
       Email: info@aarongroup.us
       Website: http://henry-aaroninc.logomall.com/
Premium & promotional items. (AA, estab 1991, empl 3,
sales $2,189,931, cert: State, NMSDC)

1350   Jansen Advertising
       5565 Glenrich Court
       Atlanta, GA 30338
       Contact: Paige Jansen-Nichols VP Sales
       Tel: 770-452-0252
       Email: paige@jansenadvertising.com
       Website: www.jansenadvertising.com
Custom promotional, incentive & recognition merchandise. (Woman, estab 1993, empl 9, sales , cert: WBENC)

1351   NorthStar Print, LLC
       6050 Peachtree Pkwy Ste 240359
       Norcross, GA 30092
       Contact: Jacki Suckow Presdient
       Tel: 770-490-6251
       Email: jacki@northstarprint.net
       Website: www.northstarprint.net
Print & promotional products, marketing materials,
traditional business forms, POP items, promotional items
& just-in-time digital printing, distribution & kitting
services. (Woman, estab 1991, empl 8, sales $3,000,000,
cert: NWBOC)

1352   Successful Images
       114 Oakview Club Dr
       Macon, GA 31216
       Contact: Anthony Steedley, CEO
       Tel: 478-923-9231
       Email: ssteedleya@aol.com
       Website: www.successfulimages.biz
Screen printing, embroidery, advertising specialties &
promotional products. (AA, estab 1993, empl 5, sales
$300,000, cert: State)

1353   Universal Graphics, Inc.
       2931 Lewis St, Ste 301
       Kennesaw, GA 30144
       Contact: Celia Reed Sales
       Tel: 678-581-1221
       Email: ccmem@aol.com
       Website: www.ugiinc.biz
Silk screening, embroidery, promotional items, corporate
apparel, printing. (AA, estab , empl , sales , cert: NMSDC)

Iowa

1354   World of Colors - Break The Cycle LLC
       1624 7th Ave SE, Ste 7000
       Cedar Rapids, IA 52403
       Contact: Rick Rodriguez Owner
       Tel: 319-447-7282
       Email: rrodri7855@aol.com
       Website: www.worldofcolors.us
Design, print & dist screen printed bags, shirts, hats &
specialty items. (Hisp, estab 2012, empl 5, sales , cert:
NMSDC)

Illinois

1355   Action Bag Company
       1001 Entry Dr.
       Bensenville, IL 60640
       Contact: Martha Quintero
       Tel: 866-349-8853
       Email: mquintero@actionbag.com
       Website: www.actionhealth.com
Printed bags, bags, retail packaging products, printed
promotional products, promotional items, packaging
supplies, labels, tissue paper, gift cards, specialty
packaging, custom bags, custom printed items, rush
orders, in-stock products. (Woman, estab , empl , sales
, cert: City, WBENC)

1356   B. Gunther & Company, Inc.
       4742 Main St
       Lisle, IL 60532
       Contact: Jeanne Brommer President
       Tel: 630-969-5595
       Email: jeanne@bgunther.com
       Website: www.bgunther.com
Promotional products, business gifts, imprinted pens
to the leather portfolio or high end wearables.
(Woman, estab 1985, empl 9, sales $1,220,000, cert:
WBENC)

1357   Corporate Identity, Inc.
       223 W Main St
       Barrington, IL 60010
       Contact: Debbie Story Sales Mgr
       Tel: 847-304-8550
       Email: msparks@Corpid.com
       Website: www.corpid.com
Promotional products, awards, logo apparel, trade
show giveaways, corporate gifts, notepads, golf balls,
banners, table throws, business forms, labels, folders,
nameplates, tags. (Woman, estab 1976, empl 9, sales ,
cert: WBENC)

1358   eLead Resources, Inc. DBA eLead Promo
       125 S Clark St 17th Fl
       Chicago, IL 60603
       Contact: Michael Wheeler VP
       Tel: 888-420-1788
       Email: mike@eleadresources.com
       Website: www.eleadresources.com
Promotional marketing products & brand consulting.
(AA, estab , empl , sales $4,328,835, cert: NMSDC)

1359   Essential Creations Chicago, Inc.
       2112 W 95th St
       Chicago, IL 60643
       Contact: Sandtricia Andrews-Strickland'
       Presdient
       Tel: 773-238-1700
       Email: sandtricia@ecreations2000.com
       Website: www.ecreations2000.com
Custom Embroidery, Patches, Screen Printing and
Sublimation. We also do promotional Products.
(Woman/AA, estab 2000, empl 3, sales $222,000, cert:
State, WBENC)

1360 Excel Screen Printing & Embroidery, Inc.
10507 Delta Pkwy
Schiller Park, IL 60176
Contact: Leon Johnson Presdient
Tel: 847-801-5200
Email: leon@excelscreenprinting.com
Website: www.excelscreenprinting.com
Screen printed & embroidered apparal, imprinted glass-ware, premiums, etc. (AA, estab 2005, empl 63, sales $4,500,000, cert: State)

1361 Global Sourcing Connection, Ltd.
2610 Lake Cook Road Ste 190
Riverwoods, IL 60015
Contact: Jennifer Arenson CEO
Tel: 847-317-9000
Email: jarenson@gloso.com
Website: www.gloso.com
Mfr & import headwear, apparel & promotional items. (Woman, estab 2001, empl 24, sales $9,200,000, cert: WBENC)

1362 Konik and Company, Inc.
7535 North Lincoln Ave
Skokie, IL 60076
Contact: Amy Lederer Owner
Tel: 847-933-1805
Email: amy@konik.com
Website: www.konik.com
Premium & promotional products: apparel, drinkware, dental sampling bags, bag, plush toys, technology items, brand name products, desk accessories, conference items, awards/recognition gifts, etc. (Woman, estab 1991, empl 18, sales $11,000,000, cert: WBENC)

1363 L and N Promotions, Inc.
99 Oak Leaf Lane #203
Vernon Hills, IL 60061
Contact: Kristi Marquardt Presdient
Tel: 847-612-9215
Email: lnpromotionsinc@aol.com
Website: www.companycasuals.com/lnpromotions
Promotional, incentive & specialty premium items. (Woman, estab 1996, empl 2, sales $585,000, cert: WBENC)

1364 LinJen Promotions, Inc.
15519 Harbor Town Dr
Orland Park, IL 60462
Contact: Linda Heyse-Highland Presdient
Tel: 708-478-8222
Email: sales@linjen.com
Website: www.linjen.com
Promotional solutions ideas & products. (Woman, estab 2000, empl 6, sales $1,250,000, cert: WBENC)

1365 M.R. Nyren Company
600 Academy Dr Ste 110
Northbrook, IL 60062
Contact: Kim Nyren Acct Exec
Tel: 800-323-8066
Email: kim@nyren-tms.com
Website: www.companycasuals.com/nyrencompany
Textile & promotional products: apparel, bags, hats, towels, blanets, golf accessories, etc. (Woman, estab 1963, empl 7, sales $4,880,454, cert: WBENC)

1366 Premium Surge Promotions, L.L.C.
640 N. LaSalle Ste 540
Chicago, IL 60654
Contact: Pam Crain EVP Marketing/Client Service
Tel: 312-951-2303
Email: pcrain@surge-innovations.com
Website: http://surge-creates.com/
Marketing, creative & promotional product design and manufacturing. (Nat Ame, Hisp, estab 2001, empl 15, sales $33,000,000, cert: NMSDC)

1367 Pro Biz Products LLC
350 N Orleans St Ste 9000N
Chicago, IL 60654
Contact: Richard Smith Presdient
Tel: 312-961-4513
Email: r.smith@probizproducts.com
Website: www.probizproducts.com
Screen printing or embroidery, office supplies, furniture, janitorial products & promotional items. (AA, estab 2014, empl 6, sales $15,000,000, cert: State, NMSDC)

1368 Stitch Me
329 W 18th St, Unit 308
Chicago, IL 60616
Contact: Brenda Nelson Owner
Tel: 312-933-2608
Email: brenda@stitchmeapparel.com
Website: www.stitchmeapparel.com
Embroidered Sportswear, Hats, Caps, Jackets, T-Shirts, Fleece, Sweaters, Tote Bags, Cut Goods, Finished Goods, Polo Shirts, Women's Wear, Promotional Products Screen Printed Apparel - T-shirts, Jackets, Hats, Team Uniforms, Sports (Woman/AA, estab 2011, empl 3, sales , cert: City, NMSDC, 8a)

1369 TBK Promotions, Inc.
3055 W 111th St 2 South
Chicago, IL 60655
Contact: Kevin Flynn Dir of Sales
Tel: 773-239-2222
Email: k@tbkpromotions.com
Website: www.tbkpromotions.com
Promotional products, advertising specialties & branded wearable items. (Woman, estab 1990, empl 5, sales $502,500, cert: State, WBENC)

1370 The Certif-a-gift Company Inc.
1625 E Alqonqion Rd
Arlington Heights, IL 60005
Contact: Trish Duh President
Tel: 847-718-0300
Email: tduh@certif-a-gift.com
Website: www.certif-a-gift.com
Incentive programs. (Woman, estab 1954, empl 50, sales $15,600,000, cert: WBENC)

1371 Windy City Silkscreening, Inc.
      2715 S Archer
      Chicago, IL 60608
      Contact: Jessica Trojanowski Cstmr Service
      Tel: 312-842-0030
      Email: jessicat@wcstshirts.com
      Website: http://wcsshirts.com
Custom screen printed apparel: t-shirts, sweats, hats,
jackets, towels, hot-market printing, rally towels, promotional products. (Woman, estab 1978, empl 36, sales
$1,380,000, cert: WBENC)

1372 World Of Promotions
      1310 Louis Ave
      Elk Grove Village, IL 60007
      Contact: Layla Rosenfeld President
      Tel: 847-439-7930
      Email: rosenfeldlayla@yahoo.com
      Website: www.aworldofpromotions.com
Promotional products: pens, mugs, hats, clothing, bags.
(Woman, estab 2003, empl 8, sales $1,120,000, cert: State)

Indiana

1373 Awards Unlimited, Inc.
      3031 Union St
      Lafayette, IN 47904
      Contact: Stacey Shirar President
      Tel: 765-447-9413
      Email: sjs@awardsunlimitedinc.net
      Website: http://awardsunlimitedinc.net
Advertising specialties. (Woman, estab 1978, empl 12,
sales $500,000, cert: WBENC)

1374 Bardach Awards, Inc.
      4222 W 86th St
      Indianapolis, IN 46268
      Contact: Diane Bardach Beck CEO
      Tel: 317-872-7444
      Email: dbardach@bardachawards.com
      Website: www.bardachawards.com
Custom corporate awards: plaques, trophies, crystal,
acrylic, plates, marble, glass, leather items such as portfolios, name badges, medals, ribbons, bronze castings, donor
recognition, signage, jewelry, executive gifts. (Woman,
estab 1969, empl 36, sales $2,960,000, cert: State)

1375 Karm Corporation
      2017 N Bedford Ave
      Evansville, IN 47711
      Contact: Kena Campbell President
      Tel: 812-426-1323
      Email: kcampbell@promarkin.com
      Website: http://promarkin.com
Screen printing, embroidery, labels, stickers, decals,
promotional products, t-shirts, uniforms. (Woman, estab
1976, empl 24, sales $2,900,000, cert: State, WBENC)

1376 Linz and Company
      8231 Hohman Ave Ste 200
      Munster, IN 46321
      Contact: Heather Koetteritz Sales/Import Mgr
      Tel: 708-757-7800
      Email: heather@linzco.com
      Website: www.linzco.com
Promotional products: apparel, housewares, novelties,
personal care items, etc. (Woman, estab 2000, empl 4,
sales $3,007,000, cert: WBENC)

1377 M. Nelson and Associates
      4011 Vincennes Rd
      Indianapolis, IN 46268
      Contact: Carolina Pimental-Nelson Presdient
      Tel: 317-228-1422
      Email: carolina@mnelson.com
      Website: www.mnelson.com
Promotional products, printing services, graphic design
& screen-print/embroidery of apparel. (Woman/Hisp,
estab 1991, empl 4, sales , cert: State, 8a)

1378 Metro Printed Products, Inc.
      1001 Commerce Pkwy South Dr Ste H
      Greenwood, IN 46143
      Contact: Gloria James Marketing
      Tel: 317-885-0077
      Email: gloria.james@proforma.com
      Website: www.metroprintedproducts.com
Advertising specialties and promotional products.
(Woman, estab 1989, empl 6, sales $2,361,600, cert:
WBENC)

1379 OmniSource Marketing Group, Inc.
      8945 N Meridian St Ste 150
      Indianapolis, IN 46260
      Contact: Janet Calderon Goldberg Presdient
      Tel: 317-575-3318
      Email: jgoldberg@omnisourcemarketing.com
      Website: www.omnisourcemarketing.com
Custom promotional products & packaging, embroidery,
fulfillment, graphic services & design, screen printing.
(Woman, estab 1988, empl 30, sales $10,400,000, cert:
WBENC)

1380 PlaqueMakerPlus, Inc.
      5713 Park Plaza Ct
      Indianapolis, IN 46220
      Contact: Edson Pereira President
      Tel: 317-594-5556
      Email: edson@plaquemakerplus.com
      Website: www.plaquemakerplus.com
Mfr awards, plaques, name badges, name plates & signs.
(Minority, Woman, estab 1995, empl 6, sales $640,000,
cert: State)

1381 Pro-Am Team Sports
      1650 US Highway 41 Ste E
      Schererville, IN 46375
      Contact: Mary Dolan Owner
      Tel: 219-515-6900
      Email: mary@pro-amteamsports.com
      Website: http://pro-amteamsports.com
Branded, customized name-brand apparel & equipment.
(Woman, estab 2014, empl 60, sales $4,200,000, cert:
WBENC)

1382 Smiling Cross Inc.
      700 S College Ave, Ste A
      Bloomington, IN 47403
      Contact: Rula Hanania Presdient
      Tel: 812-323-9290
      Email: rhanania@smilepromotions.com
      Website: www.smilepromotions.com
Promotional products. (Woman/Hisp, estab 2003, empl
10, sales $2,400,000, cert: State, NMSDC)

1383 Table Thyme Designs
217 W 10th St Ste 125
Indianapolis, IN 46202
Contact: Laurie Rice Owner
Tel: 317-634-0281
Email: coloredthreads@sbcglobal.net
Website: www.colored-threads.com
Promotional products & embroidered apparel & accessories, screen printing. (Woman, estab 2002, empl 2, sales , cert: State, City)

1384 Thomas E. Slade, Inc.
6220 Vogel Road
Evansville, IN 47715
Contact: Lisa Slade Presdient
Tel: 812-437-5233
Email: tom@sladeprint.com
Website: www.sladeprint.com
Printing, graphic design, website design, wide format posters & banners, mailing, promotional products, letterhead, envelopes, business cards, labels, tags, inserts, marketing services, augmented reality, QR codes for tracking, signs. (Woman, estab 1993, empl 17, sales $2,500,000, cert: State)

1385 Wolf Run Marketing
6020 N Emerson Ave
Indianapolis, IN 46220
Contact: Susan Fryer Owner
Tel: 317-445-5180
Email: susan@wolfrunmarketing.com
Website: www.wolfrunmarketing.com
Promotional products, logoed apparel, service & safety awards, employee & customer recognition awards, tradeshow handouts, conference materials, incentives, safety apparel, graphic design, logo devel. (Woman, estab 2009, empl 2, sales $200,000, cert: City)

Kansas

1386 Grapevine Designs, LLC
8406 Melrose Dr
Lenexa, KS 66214
Contact: Bob Offord VP Business Dev
Tel: 913-307-0225
Email: bob.offord@abrandcompany.com
Website: http://grapevinedesigns.com/
Promotional marketing, promotional products, creative design, corporate giveaways, tradeshow giveaways, corporate branding, branded merchandise. (Woman, estab 2000, empl 72, sales $8,000,000, cert: WBENC)

1387 Promo Depot Inc.
2266 N Ridge Rd
Wichita, KS 67205
Contact: Rick McKay Presdient
Tel: 316-722-2500
Email: rick@4mypromo.com
Website: www.4mypromo.com
Promotional products: logo wearables & printed ad specialty products, embroidery & screeen printing, wards & recognition products. (Hisp, estab 1997, empl 15, sales $2,600,000, cert: NMSDC, NWBOC)

Kentucky

1388 Ad-Venture Promotions
2625 Regency Rd
Lexington, KY 40503
Contact: Cathy Stafford Owner
Tel: 859-263-4299
Email: cathy@ad-venturepromotions.com
Website: www.ad-venturepromotions.com
Advertising specialties & promotional products. (Woman, estab 2004, empl 6, sales , cert: WBENC)

1389 Presence Inc.
2311 Mohican Hill Ct
Louisville, KY 40207
Contact: Gail Iwaniak President
Tel: 502-365-4616
Email: gail@stuffology.com
Website: www.stuffology.com
Promotional marketing & products. (Woman, estab 1989, empl 2, sales $350,000, cert: City)

1390 The Logo Warehouse
1963 Meadowcreek Dr
Louisville, KY 40218
Contact: Leah Scott Owner
Tel: 502-451-5421
Email: lscott@thelogowarehouse.com
Website: www.thelogowarehouse.com
Promotional products & apparel. (Woman/AA, estab 2008, empl 1, sales , cert: City, WBENC)

1391 Walker Flags, Inc.
8134 New LaGrange Rd, Ste 200
Louisville, KY 40222
Contact: Donna Walker Mancini Owner
Tel: 502-394-1474
Email: customercare@walkerflags.com
Website: www.walkerflags.com
Flags, Banners, Flagpoles, Flag & Flagpole Accessories. (Minority, Woman, estab 1960, empl 3, sales , cert: State)

Louisiana

1392 Augie Leopold Advertising Specialties, Inc.
3214 Roman St
Metairie, LA 70001
Contact: Leeanne Leopold CEO
Tel: 504-836-0525
Email: leeanne@augieleopold.com
Website: www.augieleopold.com
Advertising specialties, promotional items, premium gifts, casino monthly giveaways, safety programs. (Woman, estab 0, empl , sales , cert: WBENC)

1393 Executive Promotions, LLC
P.O. Box 81916
Lafayette, LA 70598
Contact: Rebecca Bell Owner
Tel: 337-261-9025
Email: epart@bellsouth.net
Website: www.executivepromotionsla.com
Promotional products, t-shirts, caps, drink ware, safety awards, uniforms, etc. (Woman, estab 2004, empl 3, sales $230,591, cert: State)

1394 Impress Marketing Studios, LLC
      P.O. Box 38845
      Shreveport, LA 71133
      Contact: Janelle Marks Owner
      Tel: 888-773-0183
      Email: jmarks@impressmarketingstudios.com
      Website: www.ImpressMarketingStudios.com
Marketing & promotional, premiums, advertising specialties, apparel & signage. (Woman/AA, estab 2014, empl 2,
sales $127,000, cert: NMSDC)

1395 The Creative Touch, Inc.
      7725 Jefferson Hwy
      Baton Rouge, LA 70809
      Contact: Maureen Kahl President
      Tel: 225-925-0022
      Email: maureen@creativetouchembroidery.com
      Website: www.creativetouchembroidery.com
Embroidery, silk screening, promotional products,
(Woman, estab 1982, empl 7, sales $489,000, cert:
WBENC)

1396 Wilkin Enterprises, Inc.
      2323 Bainbridge St, Bldg B, Ste 13
      Kenner, LA 70062
      Contact: Kathleen Wilkin Presdient
      Tel: 504-464-2520
      Email: kwilkin@gosafeguard.com
      Website: www.safeguardprints.com
Full color printing, promotional items & embroidered
apparel. (Woman, estab 1993, empl 7, sales $1,458,066,
cert: WBENC)

Massachusetts

1397 Ellco Promotions, Inc.
      113 Smoke Hill Ridge Road
      Marshfield, MA 02050
      Contact: Max Cohen VP
      Tel: 508-641-6274
      Email: max@ellcopromotions.com
      Website: www.ellcopromotions.com
Promotional/premium product & apparel agency.
(Woman, estab 2010, empl 2, sales $150,000, cert: State)

1398 GAP Promotions LLC
      1 Washington St
      Gloucester, MA 01930
      Contact: Gayle Piraino President
      Tel: 978-281-0083
      Email: gayle.piraino@gappromo.com
      Website: www.gappromo.com/
Promotional programs and products. (Woman, estab 2006,
empl 10, sales $5,602,133, cert: WBENC)

1399 Infinart, Inc.
      44 Mechanic St
      Newton, MA 02464
      Contact: Felicity Green President
      Tel: 617-964-3279
      Email: felicityinfinart@gmail.com
      Website: www.infinart.com
Custom branding, logo embroidery, silk screening, imprinted promotional products, awards, corporate gifts
incentives, signage, banners. (Woman, estab 1980, empl 5,
sales $105,000, cert: State)

1400 Jazzy Sportswear Promotional Co.
      90 Munroe
      Lynn, MA 01903
      Contact: Vincent Williams Presdient
      Tel: 781-593-7197
      Email: jazzypc@jazzysportswear.com
      Website: www.jazzysportswear.com
Screen printing, embroidery, and a wide array of
promotional items, banners, awards. (AA, estab 1997,
empl 1, sales $189,000, cert: State, NMSDC)

Maryland

1401 APISource, Inc.
      7850 Walker Dr Ste 400
      Greenbelt, MD 20770
      Contact: Cindy Brown President & CEO
      Tel: 301-731-6100
      Email: cindy.brown@apisource.com
      Website: www.apisource.com
Promotional products: t-shirts, collared shirts, polo
shirts, hats, jackets, bags, computer accessories, pens,
note pads, mugs, novelties, giveaways, awards, premiums, incentives, fulfillment services. (Woman, estab
1965, empl 140, sales $36,000,000, cert: WBENC)

1402 Debbie Lynn, Inc.
      952 Ridgebrook Rd Ste 1100
      Sparks, MD 21152
      Contact: Stephanie Bloom Operations Mgr
      Tel: 443-595-8178
      Email: stephanie@debbielynn.net
      Website: www.debbielynn.net
Writing instruments, office accessories, Back to School &
novelty products. (Woman, estab 1998, empl 5, sales
$10,200,000, cert: WBENC)

1403 Products 2 Brand, LLC
      8217 Cloverleaf Dr
      Millersville, MD 21108
      Contact: Macgill Antor Presdient
      Tel: 301-787-0077
      Email: macgill@products2brand.com
      Website: http://products2brand.com
Promotional product brand merchandise, tradeshow
registration bags, totes, briefcases, luggage, lanyards,
name badges. (Woman, estab 2007, empl 22, sales ,
cert: City)

1404 projectWorks, LLC
      6900 English Muffin Way, Ste E
      Frederick, MD 21703
      Contact: Michelle Stephens CEO
      Tel: 301-682-4800
      Email: michelle@projectworks.com
      Website: www.projectworks.com
Fulfillment & marketing support svcs: warehouse &
distribution, assembly & order fulfillment, printing &
direct mail, eCommerce & inventory mgmt, advertising
specialties & premiums. (Hisp, estab 1998, empl 7, sales
$808,117, cert: State)

1405 Williams Solutions Group, LLC
      20140 Scholar Dr, Ste 315
      Hagerstown, MD 21742
      Contact: Peter E. Perini, Sr. VP
      Tel: 301-739-7532
      Email: peter.perini@williamssolutionsgroup.com
      Website: www.WilliamsSolutionsGroup.com
Promotional items, marketing items, tchotchkies, give-away items, logo branded items. (AA, estab 2009, empl 2, sales $100,000, cert: State)

Michigan

1406 Alfie Logo Gear
      2425 Switch Dr
      Traverse City, MI 49684
      Contact: Bonnie Alfonso Presdient
      Tel: 231-935-1488
      Email: bonnie@goalfie.com
      Website: www.GoAlfie.com
Logowear, embroidery, screen printing & promotional products, uniforms, rewards & incentives, trade show giveaways. (Woman, estab 1990, empl 18, sales $2,863,520, cert: WBENC)

1407 Antina Promotions, LLC
      84 Leslie Lane
      Waterford, MI 48328
      Contact: Christina Concord Managing Partner
      Tel: 248-254-3845
      Email: christina@antinapromo.com
      Website: www.antinapromo.com
Promotional Products, Exhibit Displays, Corporate Gifts, Awards, Signage, Branded Apparel, Company Stores, Custom Packaging, Marketing Materials. (Woman, estab 2010, empl 2, sales , cert: WBENC, SDB)

1408 Graphix 2 Go
      7200 Tower Rd
      Battle Creek, MI 49014
      Contact: Amy Howard Sales Mgr
      Tel: 269-969-7321
      Email: amy@graphix2goinc.com
      Website: www.graphix2goinc.com
Promotional products. (Woman, estab 1997, empl 8, sales $2,500,000, cert: WBENC)

1409 Krystal Marketing, Inc.
      1120 E Long Lake Rd, Ste 200
      Troy, MI 48085
      Contact: Carolyn Boccia Mktg Mgr
      Tel: 248-619-9000
      Email: carolyn@krystalmarketing.com
      Website: www.krystalmarketing.com
Promotional products, awards & incentives. (Woman, estab 1987, empl 10, sales , cert: WBENC)

1410 Mendoza Enterprises LLC
      1847 N Main St
      Royal Oak, MI 48073
      Contact: Sue Johnson Presdient
      Tel: 248-588-0335
      Email: sue@mendozaenterprises.us
      Website: www.mendozaenterprises.us
Printing and promotional products. (Hisp, estab 0, empl , sales , cert: NMSDC)

1411 Mercury P&F
      35610 Mound Rd
      Sterling Heights, MI 48310
      Contact: Betsy Canova Business Dev Mgr
      Tel: 586-825-9300
      Email: canovab@mercuryfs.com
      Website: www.mercuryfs.com
Branded merchandise & premiums. (Woman/AA, estab 1996, empl 70, sales $25,000,000, cert: NMSDC, WBENC)

1412 Mixed Promotions, LLC
      3759 S Baldwin Rd, Ste 222
      Lake Orion, MI 48359
      Contact: Lona Carson CEO
      Tel: 248-783-4099
      Email: lcarson@mixedpromotions.com
      Website: www.mixedpromotions.com
Promotional products. (Woman/As-Pac, estab 2000, empl , sales $462,000, cert: NMSDC, WBENC)

1413 Premier Sales & Marketing, Inc.
      2328 Livernois Ste 1050
      Troy, MI 48083
      Contact: Janine Brown President
      Tel: 248-526-9792
      Email: qualimotive2@wwnet.net
      Website:
Promotional products. (Woman, estab 1992, empl 3, sales $177,000, cert: WBENC)

1414 Promotion Concepts Inc.
      414 S Burdick St
      Kalamazoo, MI 49007
      Contact: Lauren A. Powers President
      Tel: 269-488-2987
      Email: laurene.powers@promotionconcepts.com
      Website: www.promotionconcepts.com
Incentive marketing svcs, sales promotion, promotional products, premium incentives programs, awards, recognition, brand-building. (Woman, estab 1982, empl 18, sales , cert: WBENC)

1415 Promotional Solutions LLC
      48530 Van Dyke Ave
      Shelby Township, MI 48317
      Contact: Kathy Ferguson Member
      Tel: 586-739-1132
      Email: promotionalsolutions@onemain.com
      Website: http://promotionalsolutionsonline.com
Advertising specialty goods & services. Logowear embroidered or screen print,
wwards & trophys, special event gifts, employee appreciation items. (Woman, estab 2001, empl 8, sales $622,000, cert: WBENC)

1416 The Bradley Company, Inc.
      26777 Central Park Blvd Ste 180
      Southfield, MI 48076
      Contact: Marci Taran CEO
      Tel: 248-538-1909
      Email: marcit@thebradco.com
      Website: www.thebradco.com
Advertising specialties, Assembly, Awards, Branded merchandise, Branding, Commemorative items, Corporate apparel, Corporate gifts, Corporate identity, Corporate webstores, Custom packaging, etc. (Woman, estab 2004, empl 11, sales $5,000,000, cert: WBENC)

1417 Tier One Marketing
      3160 Belle Terre
      Commerce Township, MI 48382
      Contact: Jeanne Snyder Presdient
      Tel: 313-274-1179
      Email: jeannesnyder@sbcglobal.net
      Website: www.tierone.biz
Ad specialties: coffee cups, pens, portfolios, golf items,
technology driven give-a-ways, coolers, tote bags, flash-
lights, key chains, awards, custom pieces, collectables.
(Woman, estab 2003, empl 2, sales $250,000, cert:
WBENC)

1418 Unique Expressions, LLC
      22050 Woodward Ave
      Ferndale, MI 48220
      Contact: Beverly Bantom CEO
      Tel: 248-547-9300
      Email: info@uniquex.net
      Website: www.UniqueX.net
Dist promotional products. (AA, estab 1999, empl 6, sales
$1,000,000, cert: NMSDC)

Minnesota

1419 2020 Brand Solutions
      135 Grand Ave East
      South St. Paul, MN 55075
      Contact: Dan Livengood VP Sales/Mktg
      Tel: 651-451-3850
      Email: dan.livengood@2020brands.com
      Website: www.2020collection.com
Corporate Apparel & Uniform Programs, Branded Mer-
chandise, Incentives & Recognition, Print Management &
Specialty Fulfillment. (Nat Ame, estab 2014, empl 62, sales
$20,000,000, cert: NMSDC)

1420 Corporate Advertising & Incentives
      6289 Niagara Lane N
      Maple Grove, MN 55311
      Contact: Loni Spence Promotional Consultant
      Tel: 763-559-8388
      Email: lspence@corpadvertising.net
      Website: www.corpadvertising.net
Promotional products. (Woman, estab 2003, empl 3, sales
$150,000, cert: WBENC)

1421 Creality Promo+Retail, inc.
      3201 West County Rd. 42 Ste 105
      Burnsville, MN 55306
      Contact: Tony Pesante Presdient
      Tel: 952-854-9202
      Email: tonyp@crealitypromo.com
      Website: www.crealitypromo.com
Promotional products, logo merchandise, custom apparel,
gift store merchandise, give-away items, premiums,
awards. (Woman/Hisp, estab 1999, empl 19, sales
$6,850,000, cert: NMSDC)

1422 Creative Resources Agency
      1208 5th St South
      Minneapolis, MN 55343
      Contact: Caren Schweitzer CEO
      Tel: 952-988-9407
      Email: caren@acreativeresource.com
      Website: www.acreativeresource.com
Promotional products, direct mail, trade show give-aways,
corporate holiday gifts, lead generators & client thank-you
gifts. (Woman, estab 1995, empl 24, sales $5,700,000,
cert: WBENC, 8a)

1423 Ithaca Promotions
      P.O. Box 220
      Wahkon, MN 56386
      Contact: Katrina Chang President
      Tel: 612-669-7833
      Email: katrina@ithacapromotions.com
      Website: www.ithacapromotions.com
Promotional, incentive, corporate gifts, gift certificates,
gift checks, American Express Gift Cheques, banners,
etc. (Woman/As-Pac, estab 1991, empl , sales $631,227,
cert: State, NMSDC)

1424 J Michael Industries
      1086 W 7th St
      St Paul, MN 55102
      Contact: Jamie Flynn Owner
      Tel: 651-698-3333
      Email: jamiemm@extendedexposure.com
      Website: www.extendedexposure.com
Design, create & source give-away mementos, memorable keepsakes & corporate gifts. (Woman, estab 1999,
empl 7, sales $1,200,000, cert: WBENC)

1425 M Plus Embroidery & Promotions
      5 Viking Dr W
      Little Canada, MN 55117
      Contact: Beth Mulcahy Owner
      Tel: 651-777-3624
      Email: beth@mplus-embroidery.com
      Website: www.mplus-embroidery.com
Embroidery, silk screening, direct to garment, polo's, t-
shirts, sweatshirts/pants, caps, hats, bags, etc. (Woman,
estab 1984, empl 7, sales $324,800, cert: WBENC)

1426 Rutabaga Rags, Inc.
      8700 West 36th St Ste 3E
      St. Louis Park, MN 55426
      Contact: Julie Miller Owner
      Tel: 952-938-4841
      Email: julie@rutabagarags.com
      Website: www.rutabagaragsshop.com
Promotional products & stadium giveaways: baseball
caps, jerseys, bats, gloves, toys, banks, bracelets, lip
balm, magnets, pens, schedules, memo pads, padfolios,
portfolios, duffles, bags, backpacks, cinch sacks, mugs,
coffee tumblers, stuffed animals. (Woman, estab 1993,
empl 3, sales $600,000, cert: WBENC)

1427 Spartan Promotional Group, Inc.
      711 Hale Ave N
      Oakdale, MN 55128
      Contact: Dan Perdue Sales Assoc
      Tel: 309-827-2215
      Email: phyllisohenwald@spartanpromo.com
      Website: www.spartanpromo.com/index.html
Advertising specialties: keychains, magnets, pens,
distribution services, promotional marketing programs.
(Woman, estab 1966, empl 80, sales , cert: WBENC)

Missouri

1428   Accent Group Solutions
     1154 Reco Ave
     St. Louis, MO 63126
     Contact: Erica Hughes CEO
     Tel: 314-965-5388
     Email: ehughes@accentgroupsolutions.com
     Website: www.AccentGroupSolutions.com
Custom Fulfillment, Publisher Services, Logo Apparel & Promotional Products, Printing, Converting Printed Materials, Literature Fulfillment, Container Management. (Woman, estab 2003, empl 26, sales $6,621,042, cert: WBENC)

1429   Blue Sky Apparel & Promotions, LLC
     12732 Pennridge Dr
     Bridgeton, MO 63044
     Contact: Kathy Gralike Owner
     Tel: 314-739-4531
     Email: kgralike@aol.com
     Website: www.blueskypromotion.com/
Promotional products: pens, coffee mugs, apparel & caps. (Woman, estab 2002, empl 5, sales $1,369,654, cert: State)

Mississippi

1430   Zebra Marketing Corporation
     289 Commerce Park Dr, Ste E
     Ridgeland, MS 39157
     Contact: Sharon Thompson Sales Exec
     Tel: 251-438-2422
     Email: sharon.thompson@zebrapromos.com
     Website: www.zebrapromos.com
Advertising specialties, service awards, clothing-jackets, t-shirts, sport shirts, trade show give aways. (Woman, estab 2000, empl 14, sales $7,000,000, cert: WBENC)

North Carolina

1431   Adsource Media, Inc.
     8313-101 Six Forks Rd
     Raleigh, NC 27615
     Contact: brand acct Exec
     Tel: 919-871-9990
     Email:
     Website: www.am3adsource.com
Branded merchandise, decorated apparel, medical educational material, dimensional packaging, imported product, trade show supplies, direct mailing, signage, training board games. (Woman, estab 1999, empl 4, sales $675,000, cert: WBENC)

1432   Austin Business Forms Inc.
     P.O. Box 1905
     Matthews, NC 28016
     Contact: Acct Exec
     Tel: 704-821-6165
     Email:
     Website: www.printwithaustin.com
Printing, graphic design, screen printing & embriodery, promotional products. (Woman, estab 1991, empl 6, sales $1,514,990, cert: WBENC)

1433   Blue Dove Promotions
     3529 Old Greensboro Road
     Winston-Salem, NC 27101
     Contact: Joyce Williams Owner
     Tel: 336-624-5223
     Email: jwilliams@bluedovepromotions.com
     Website: www.bluedovepromotions.com
Promotional products. (Woman/AA, Nat Ame, estab 2012, empl 1, sales , cert: State, NMSDC)

1434   Bob Williams Specialty Co.
     5539 Monroe Rd
     Charlotte, NC 28212
     Contact: VP Sales
     Tel: 704-568-3411
     Email:
     Website: www.bobwilliamsspecialty.com
Imprinted promotional products. (Woman, estab 1961, empl 5, sales $800,000, cert: City)

1435   BrandRPM, LLC
     4910 Starcrest Dr
     Monroe, NC 28110
     Contact: Keith Brent VP Strategic Sales
     Tel: 704-225-1800
     Email: keithb@brandrpm.com
     Website: www.brandrpm.com
Corporate apparel & branded merchandise. (Woman/As-Pac, estab 2008, empl , sales $5,000,000, cert: State, NMSDC)

1436   Crown Trophy Winston-Salem
     2869 Reynolda Rd
     Winston-Salem, NC 27106
     Contact: Michael Robinson Presdient
     Tel: 336-723-7400
     Email: crowntrophy419@bellsouth.net
     Website: www.crowntrophy.com
Awards & recogniton: badges, signage, corporate awards, plaques, trophies, ribbons, medallians, promotional items, cast bronze, etc. (Woman/AA, estab , empl , sales , cert: State, City)

1437   Daybreak Marketing Services, LLC
     14460 Falls of Neuse Rd Ste 149-326
     Raleigh, NC 27614
     Contact: Dawn Nakash COO
     Tel: 919-926-1452
     Email: dawn@daybreakmarketing.com
     Website: http://DaybreakMarketing.com
Promotional Products, Advertising Specialties, Silk Screening, Embroidery, Debossing, Embossing Imprinted, Pens, mugs, t-shirts, magnets, pins, buttons, uniforms, awards, bags, desk and auto accessories, flash drives, power banks. (Woman, estab 1998, empl 1, sales $150,000, cert: State)

1438   G. ALAN Inc.
     5317 Highgate Dr Ste 212
     Durham, NC 27713
     Contact: Gregory Harris
     Tel: 919-544-0055
     Email: gregory@imwithg.com
     Website: www.imwithg.com
Embroidery, screenprinting & promotional products. (AA, estab 1994, empl 2, sales $422,500, cert: State, NMSDC)

1439 PIA International LLC
      P.O. Box 481232
      Charlotte, NC 28269
      Contact: Donna Daniels Owner
      Tel: 704-593-1256
      Email: donna@piapromo.com
      Website: http://piapromo.com
Promotional products, ad specialties, t-shirts, sports
uniforms & equipment, safety wear, etc. (Woman/AA,
estab 2003, empl 1, sales , cert: State, NMSDC)

1440 PROMOQUEST Inc.
      1308 Ballyclare Ct
      Raleigh, NC 27614
      Contact: Pam Williams Presdient
      Tel: 919-845-3448
      Email: pam@promoquest.com
      Website: www.promoquest.com
Imprinted promotional products: screenprinting, embroidery, lithography, digital printing, emboss, deboss, laser, t-
shirts, jackets, fleece, athletic apparel, pants, bumper
stickers, signs, buttons, pens note pads. (Woman/AA, estab
1994, empl 1, sales , cert: State)

New Jersey

1441 3D Promoplastic, Inc.
      31 Summer Rd
      Flemington, NJ 08822
      Contact: Sibel Toy Owner
      Tel: 469-955-6282
      Email: mail@3dpromoplastic.com
      Website: www.3d-promo.com
Promotional products, plastic promotional products,
custom mold clip pens, promotional give aways, ballpoint
pens, pen holders & eco friendly products. (Woman, estab
2002, empl 50, sales $500,000, cert: State)

1442 Aberson Narotzky & White
      945 Lincoln Ave E
      Cranford, NJ 07016
      Contact: Shelly Aberson Presdient
      Tel: 908-789-2700
      Email: shelly@anwinc.com
      Website: www.anwinc.com
Advertising specialties, promotional products. (Woman,
estab 1989, empl 7, sales $3,100,000, cert: WBENC)

1443 Action Calendar & Specialty Co., Inc.
      5 Underwood Ct
      Delran, NJ 08075
      Contact: Lora Dunnigan President
      Tel: 856-764-4000
      Email: lora.dunnigan@renpromo.com
      Website: www.wellnesseducationkits.com
Dist promotional products, on-site distribution center,
graphic arts, web dev, customer care call center, on-line
company stores. (Woman, estab 1975, empl 10, sales
$6,121,000, cert: WBENC)

1444 Artcraft Promotional Concepts
      1270 Glen Ave.
      Moorestown, NJ 08057
      Contact: Sarah Bowling
      Tel: 856-727-5200
      Email: sbowling@artcraftpromos.com
      Website: http://artcraftpromos.com
Advertising specialties. (Woman, estab 1946, empl 175,
sales $52,000,000, cert: WBENC)

1445 Balady Promotions, Inc.
      1719 Route 10 Ste 103
      Parsippany, NJ 07054
      Contact: CEO
      Tel: 973-682-8440
      Email:
      Website: www.balady.com
Promotional product & decorated apparel programs,
trade show exhibits, signage & giveaways, business gifts/
premiums & award programs for employee achievement, sales rewards & years of service. (Woman, estab
1989, empl 7, sales $2,951,425, cert: WBENC)

1446 Blank2Branded powered by Axis
      160 Main Rd
      Montville, NJ 07045
      Contact: Marcia Tarnoff Presdient
      Tel: 973-917-3100
      Email: marcia@blank2branded.com
      Website: www.blank2branded.com
Promotional solutions. (Woman, estab 2013, empl 5,
sales $1,900,000, cert: WBENC)

1447 Compas, Inc.
      4300 Haddonfield Rd Ste 200
      Pennsauken, NJ 08109
      Contact: Robert Kadar SVP
      Tel: 856-667-8577
      Email: rkadar@cmicompas.com
      Website: www.compasonline.com
Media & promotional svcs. (AA, estab , empl , sales
$250,000,000, cert: NMSDC)

1448 Daystar Promotions, Inc.
      83 Bergerville Rd
      Freehold, NJ 07728
      Contact: President
      Tel: 732-409-0531
      Email:
      Website: www.daystarpromotions.com
Promotional products & branded merchandise. (Woman,
estab 1989, empl 3, sales , cert: WBENC)

1449 East West Connection
      389 Pittstown Rd
      Pittstown, NJ 08867
      Contact: Presdient
      Tel: 908-797-0917
      Email:
      Website: www.eastwestconnection.com
Premium & promotional merchandise, custom design,
graphic & web design services, promotional writing, gift
wrapping, custom design projects, warehouse & fulfillment services. (AA, estab 1990, empl 75, sales
$12,200,000, cert: NMSDC)

1450 Glazer Design, LLC
      330 Franklin Turnpike
      Mahwah, NJ 07430
      Contact: Trish Glazer Office Mgr
      Tel: 201-684-1132
      Email: trish@glazerpromos.com
      Website: www.glazerpromos.com
Promotional products. (Woman, estab 2002, empl 7,
sales $669,828, cert: City, WBENC)

1451 Graphics Solutions
     473 Chapel Heights Rd
     Sewell, NJ 08080
     Contact: Steven Riggs Owner
     Tel: 877-931-1636
     Email: support@graphics-solution.com
     Website: www.graphics-solution.com
Marketing communications products, print products, promotional products, customized apparel, signage, graphic design, web design, marketing consulting, audio/ video production. (AA, estab 2008, empl 5, sales $423,000, cert: NMSDC)

1452 Ideas to Impress, LLC
     35 Longman St
     Toms River, NJ 08753
     Contact: Debbie Dennerlein Presdient
     Tel: 201-750-0222
     Email: debbie@ideastoimpress.com
     Website: www.ideastoimpress.com
Dist promotional products, company brand / logo, customized printed, embroidered & laser etched products: t-shirts, polo shirts, sweatshirts & uniforms, pens, desk accessories, to signs, and table covers, executive gift & give-aways. (Woman, estab 2006, empl 1, sales $103,211, cert: WBENC)

1453 Imprint Source LLC
     15 Charles St
     Westwood, NJ 07675
     Contact: Karen Adler Acct Exec
     Tel: 201-358-1010
     Email: karen@theimprintsource.com
     Website: www.TheImprintSource.com
Imprinted promotional products. (Woman, estab 1994, empl 6, sales $2,733,386, cert: WBENC)

1454 Progressive Promotions Inc.
     145 Cedar Lane
     Englewood, NJ 07631
     Contact: Julie Levi President & CEO
     Tel: 201-945-0500
     Email: julie@progressivepromotions.com
     Website: www.progressivepromotions.com
Promotional products: corporate apparel, gifts, awards, uniforms, web stores, fulfillment, packaging & assembly. (Woman, estab 1987, empl 30, sales , cert: WBENC)

1455 Sabella Gabino Inc. dba Bella Marketing Inc.
     5 Deer Path
     Holmdel, NJ 07733
     Contact: Isabella Petruzzelli CEO
     Tel: 917-951-3025
     Email: isabella@bellamarketinginc.com
     Website: www.bellamarketinginc.com
Custom designed, promotional branded products specializing in the medical & pharmaceutical industry. (Woman/ Hisp, estab 2001, empl 1, sales , cert: NMSDC, WBENC)

1456 Stackable Sensations
     2200 Route 10 W Ste 206
     Parsippany, NJ 07054
     Contact: Shari Verrone Presdient
     Tel: 973-442-2831
     Email: shariv@stackablesensations.com
     Website: www.stackablesensations.com/
Promotional products, logoed apparel, advertising specialties. (Woman, estab 2003, empl 10, sales $1,750,000, cert: WBENC)

1457 Thomas Direct Sales, Inc.
     30 Plymouth St
     Fairfield, NJ 07004
     Contact: Guy DAndrea COO
     Tel: 973-614-2307
     Email: mmarinzulich@thomasdirect.com
     Website: www.thomasdirect.com
Promotional products, premium & incentive programs, importing, on-site design & illustration, graphic arts, technology & website development. (Woman, estab 1986, empl 12, sales $1,000,000, cert: WBENC)

Nevada

1458 Eagle Promotions
     4575 W Post Rd Ste 100
     Las Vegas, NV 89118
     Contact: Mario Stadtlander Presdient
     Tel: 702-388-7100
     Email: mario@eaglepromotions.com
     Website: www.eaglepromotions.com
Advertising specialties: apparel, awards, catalog, company store fulfillment programs. (As-Pac, estab 2001, empl 203, sales $36,400,000, cert: NMSDC)

New York

1459 AIA New Dimensions in Marketing, Inc.
     124 S Central Ave
     Elmsford, NY 10523
     Contact: Maria Perex Presdient
     Tel: 914-348-4872
     Email: perez@effectivepromos.com
     Website: www.effectivepromos.com
Promotional & specialty advertising items. (Woman/ Hisp, estab 1999, empl 3, sales $355,000, cert: State, WBENC)

1460 Crown Awards
     9 Skyline Dr
     Hawthorne, NY 10532
     Contact: Jeannette Weigelt Corporate Sales
     Tel: 914-347-7700
     Email: jweigelt@crownawards.com
     Website: www.crownawards.com
Mfr awards. (Woman, estab 1978, empl 500, sales $75,000,000, cert: WBENC)

1461 Dakota Print and Premiums LLC
     150 Barton Road
     White Plains, NY 10605
     Contact: Stuart Standard President
     Tel: 914-831-9101
     Email: stuart@fuseprinting.com
     Website: www.fuseprinting.com
Promotional products, commercial printing, wide format & transit advertising, vehicle wraps, directories, transit & marketing tools provider, screen printing, banners, posters, postcards, journals, award items, etc. (Woman/ AA, estab 2004, empl 3, sales $606,000, cert: State, City, NMSDC)

1462   DRSolutions, Inc.
       41 Ridgefield Dr
       Shoreham, NY 11786
       Contact: Trisha Stolfi CEO
       Tel: 631-209-1086
       Email: trisha.stolfi@proforma.com
       Website: www.proforma.com/drsolutions
Dist printed material: forms, labels, posters & displays,
promotional items, work aprons, etc. (Woman, estab 2002,
empl 2, sales , cert: State)

1463   Fulcrum Group
       135 W 41st St
       New York, NY 10036
       Contact: Partner
       Tel: 203-909-6362
       Email:
       Website: www.fulcrumgrp.com
Incentive Programs, Apparel, Promotional Merchandise,
Printing & Creative Services, Large Format & Signage,
Event Production, E-commerce& Fulfillment, Print Media.
(Woman, estab 2010, empl 7, sales $1,200,000, cert:
WBENC)

1464   Innovative Premiums Inc.
       3571 Hargale Rd
       Oceanside, NY 11572
       Contact: VP
       Tel: 516-766-3800
       Email:
       Website: www.innovativepremiums.com
Custom & standard promotional merchandise. (Woman,
estab 1980, empl 14, sales $9,000,000, cert: WBENC)

1465   inQueue Designs LLC
       25 Central Park W
       New York, NY 10023
       Contact: Alison Schneiderman Co-Owner
       Tel: 917-699-8259
       Email: alison@inqueuedesigns.com
       Website: www.inQueuedesigns.com
Custom branded, designed products, stationery goods,
seasonal promotions, corporate gifts, journal books, log
books, die-cut folders & boxes, ipad book case, (Woman,
estab 2010, empl 2, sales , cert: WBENC)

1466   KarSun Enterprises, Inc.
       1133 Broadway, Ste 1311
       New York, NY 10010
       Contact: Sung Park Presdient
       Tel: 212-420-6688
       Email: sung@customdirectpromo.com
       Website: www.karsunenterprises.com
Promotional & merchandise bags, backpacks & duffels.
(Woman/As-Pac, estab 1996, empl 10, sales $3,500,000,
cert: NMSDC)

1467   Multi Media Promotions
       33 Southwick Court S
       Plainview, NY 11803
       Contact: Managing Partner
       Tel: 516-935-0553
       Email: beth@mmpromos.com
       Website: www.mmpromos.com
Promotional advertising & premium incentives, logos,
graphic design, printing, imprinting, embroidery, embossing & engraving. (Woman, estab 2004, empl 3, sales
$1,200,000, cert: State, City, WBENC)

1468   National Gifts Ltd.
       6 Poole St
       Oceanside, NY 11572
       Contact: Elaine Goodman CEO
       Tel: 516-763-9000
       Email: elaine@nationalgifts.com
       Website: www.nationalgifts.com
Advertising specialities, premiums, gifts, awards,
trophies, wearables, promotional items, etc. (Woman,
estab 1983, empl 6, sales $12,250,000, cert: WBENC)

1469   Print & Mail Partners, Inc.
       2152 Ralph Ave Ste 317
       Brooklyn, NY 11234
       Contact: Rose Mazzone President
       Tel: 646-771-4245
       Email: rose.mazzone@theperfectpromo.com
       Website: www.theperfectpromo.com
Custom imprinted T-shirts, advertising specialties,
promotional items, buttons, badges, premiums, corporate merchandise & giveaways. (Woman, estab 1997,
empl 3, sales , cert: State, City)

1470   Sauerbach Associates
       1745 Merrick Ave Ste 27
       Merrick, NY 11566
       Contact: Janet Silver President
       Tel: 516-868-9650
       Email: customerservice@sauerbach.com
       Website: www.sauerbach.com
Sales incentive programs, promotional products pro-
grams, company stores, trade show marketing, new
product launches, road shows, sales training meetings.
(Woman, estab 1954, empl 6, sales $1,600,000, cert:
WBENC)

1471   Sentec Promotions, Inc
       4367 Harlem Rd
       Amherst, NY 14226
       Contact: Susan Cataudella Presdient
       Tel: 716-839-2294
       Email: susiespec@aol.com
       Website: www.susiespecialties.com
Promotional products.
 (Woman, estab 1994, empl 3, sales $1,090,404, cert:
WBENC)

1472   United Print Group, Inc.
       36-36 33rd St
       Long Island City, NY 11106
       Contact: Bob Sanchez Presdient
       Tel: 718-392-4242
       Email: rsanchez@unitedpg.com
       Website: www.unitedpg.com
Promotional products, commerical printing, signage &
table skirts. (Hisp, estab , empl , sales $6,000,000, cert:
NMSDC)

1473   Von Pok & Chang
       60 E 42 St, Ste 666
       New York, NY 10165
       Contact: Peter Sebastian Sales
       Tel: 212-599-0556
       Email: peter.sebastian@vonpok.com
       Website: www.vonpok.com
Contract mfr & import promotional products. (As-Pac,
estab 1981, empl 8, sales , cert: NMSDC)

Ohio

1474   889 Global Solutions
     1943 W 5th Ave.
     Columbus, OH 43212
     Contact: Govt Sales Project Mgr
     Tel: 614-235-8889
     Email: info@889GLOBALSOLUTIONS.COM
     Website: www.889globalsolutions.com
Promotional products.
 (Woman/As-Pac, estab 2000, empl 20, sales , cert: State, NMSDC)

1475   Airmate Company
     16280 County Rd D
     Bryan, OH 43506
     Contact: Carol Czech Presdient
     Tel: 419-636-3184
     Email: carol@airmatecompany.com
     Website: www.airmatecompany.com
Safety signs, promotional products, custom fabrication, custom printing. (Woman, estab 1946, empl 35, sales $4,200,000, cert: WBENC)

1476   Arrasmith Promotions LLC
     6115 Wiehe Rd
     Cincinnati, OH 45237
     Contact: Jerry Arrasmith Jr. Presdient
     Tel: 513-681-9400
     Email: sales@arrasmithpromotions.com
     Website: www.arrasmithpromotions.com
Advertising specialties & promotional items. (Woman, estab 2003, empl 6, sales $2,100,000, cert: WBENC)

1477   Bouzounis LLC dba Artina Promotional Products
     50 S Liberty St Ste 250
     Powell, OH 43065
     Contact: Lesley Jennings Sr Acct Exec
     Tel: 614-635-8865
     Email: ljennings@artina.com
     Website: www.artina.com
Promotional products. (Woman, estab 1967, empl 22, sales $4,353,500, cert: WBENC)

1478   City Apparel, Inc.
     120 Bentley Court
     Findlay, OH 45840
     Contact: Hilary Orians Acct Solutions Mastermind
     Tel: 419-434-1157
     Email: hilary@cityapparel.net
     Website: www.cityapparel.net
Uniform programs, corporate casual apparel, promotional products, employee incentive programs & integrated e-commerce solutions. (Woman, estab 2001, empl 9, sales $2,300,000, cert: WBENC)

1479   Eat It Read It Placemats
     45 W Main St
     McConnelsville, OH 43756
     Contact: Heather Hill CEO
     Tel: 740-962-6899
     Email: hbhill@ergraphics.com
     Website: www.ergraphics.com
Advertising specialties, apparel, uniforms, signs, website design, printing. (Woman/AA, estab 2001, empl 3, sales $175,000, cert: State)

1480   EB ART EB ADS LLC
     9045 Spooky Ridge Ln
     Cincinnati, OH 45242
     Contact: Eileen Bloustein CEO
     Tel: 513-405-6469
     Email: sales@ebartebads.com
     Website: www.ebartebads.com
Dist promotional products: corporate awards, portraits, limited editions giclee, digital art & sculpture. (Woman, estab 1999, empl 1, sales , cert: WBENC)

1481   Global Promotions & Incentives, LLC
     3375 Gilchrist Rd
     Mogadore, OH 44260
     Contact: Jonathan Thornton Regional Dir Key Accts Exec
     Tel: 330-798-5175
     Email: jdthornton@aswglobal.com
     Website: http://shopglobalpai.com/
Promotional & incentive products, programs & event planning. (AA, estab 2002, empl 31, sales $5,500,000, cert: NMSDC)

1482   Ketterer Company
     12110 Ellington Ct
     Cincinnati, OH 45249
     Contact: Kimberly W. Ketterer CEO
     Tel: 513-247-0100
     Email: kim_ketterer@kettererco.com
     Website: www.getLOGOstuff.com
Promotional advertising: logo design, graphic art, warehousing, distribution & fulfillment services, company stores & online rewards programs. (Woman, estab 1955, empl 6, sales $3,609,077, cert: WBENC)

1483   Leader Promotions, Inc.
     790 E Johnstown Rd
     Columbus, OH 43230
     Contact: Stephanie Leader CEO
     Tel: 614-416-6565
     Email: supplierdiversity@leaderpromos.com
     Website: www.leaderpromos.com
Fulfillment programs, corporate apparel, promotional products & uniforms. (Woman, estab 1995, empl 105, sales $50,000,000, cert: WBENC)

1484   LIZard Apparel & Promotions
     775 Congress Park Dr
     Dayton, OH 45459
     Contact: Kelly Davis VP Sales
     Tel: 937-848-7100
     Email: kelly@lizardap.com
     Website: www.lizardap.com
Promotional, recognition & rewards programs, uniform fittings, Shoe programs, Uniform accessories, name badges, stethoscopes, scissors, arm sleeves. (Woman, estab 2013, empl 10, sales $1,231,824, cert: WBENC)

1485   Outreach Promotional Solutions
     111 Liberty St Ste 101
     Columbus, OH 43215
     Contact: Nevin Bansal President & CEO
     Tel: 216-452-5319
     Email: bansal@outreachpromos.com
     Website: www.outreachpromos.com
Provides creative promotional product solutions. (As-Ind, estab 2012, empl 12, sales $1,000,000, cert: State)

1486 Palmer Promotions
5245 Indian Run
Cincinnati, OH 45243
Contact: Steven Palmer Owner
Tel: 800-697-0053
Email: steve@palmerpromotions.com
Website: www.palmerpromotions.com
Promotional products, awards, business gifts & decorated apparel. (As-Pac, estab 1983, empl 2, sales $578,066, cert: NMSDC)

1487 Park Place Services
8800 E Pleasant Valley Rd
Cleveland, OH 44131
Contact: Bill Byrne Presdient
Tel:
Email: bbyrne@proforma.com
Website: http://proforma.com/parkplace
Printing, Promotional products, Corporate Apparel, Marketing literature, Packaging, Trade Show Supplies & giveaways, Business Forms, labels, envelopes. (Woman, estab 1996, empl 700, sales $500,000,000, cert: NWBOC)

1488 Proforma Albrecht & Co.
1040 Technecenter Dr
Milford, OH 45150
Contact: Suzette Albrecht
Tel: 202-237-2828
Email: suzette@albrechtco.com
Website: www.albrechtco.com
Promotional products, tees & clothing, custom logos & designs, decorated corporate gifts. (Woman, estab 1999, empl 150, sales $2,200,000, cert: WBENC)

1489 Proforma Joe Thomas Group
13500 Pearl Rd, Ste 139-107
Cleveland, OH 44136
Contact: Joe Thomas Presdient
Tel: 440-268-0881
Email: joe@proformajoethomasgroup.com
Website: www.proformajoethomasgroup.com
Advertising specialties. (As-Ind, estab 1999, empl 2, sales $1,123,000, cert: NMSDC)

1490 PromoHits! Ltd.
141B N Main St
Bluffton, OH 45817
Contact: Melinda Bowden Owner
Tel: 419-358-0700
Email: mbowden@wcoil.com
Website: www.promohitsltd.com
Promotional items: gift & specialty baskets, jackets, shirts, sweatshirts, pants, hats, windshirts, mousepads, pencil holders, pens, paperclips, USB drives, flash drives/ memory drives. (Woman, estab 2000, empl 4, sales $382,780, cert: WBENC)

1491 Promotions Etc., LLC
5000 Acme Dr. Unit A
Fairfield, OH 45014
Contact: Julie Holderbach CEO
Tel: 513-795-7021
Email: julie@mypromotionsetc.com
Website: www.mypromotionsetc.com
Promotional products: apparel & uniforms, corporate gifts, give-a-ways, awards, engraved items, decals, labels, trade show give-a-ways, booth display & signage. (Minority, Woman, estab 2012, empl 2, sales $125,000, cert: State)

1492 Race Ahead
7100 Euclid Ave Ste 175
Cleveland, OH 44103
Contact: Beth Eaton Presdient
Tel: 440-554-7018
Email: beth@raceaheadcle.com
Website: http://raceaheadcle.com
Customized apparel & branded accessories. (Woman, estab 2016, empl 1, sales $260,000, cert: City)

1493 RJ Manray - Promotional Products
9500 Springfield Rd, Unit 5
Poland, OH 44514
Contact: Rowena Henderson CEO
Tel: 234-201-0160
Email: rrlimos18@gmail.com
Website: www.rjmanray.com/
Dist personalized and custom logo tote bags. (Woman, estab 1986, empl 11, sales $640,000, cert: WBENC)

1494 Schaffer Partners, Inc.
6545 Carnegie Ave
Cleveland, OH 44103
Contact: Susan Mayrant VP Business Dev
Tel: 863-299-6392
Email: susan.mayrant@spihq.com
Website: www.pfi-awards.com
Incentive merchandise fulfillment & program administration resources, design & manage online & paper based solutions, brand name merchandise awards, travel rewards & event tickets. (Woman, estab 1968, empl 40, sales $10,017,858, cert: WBENC)

1495 Ten 10 Design LLC
119 Main St
Chardon, OH 44024
Contact: Joe Zulandt VP New Business Development
Tel: 440-286-4367
Email: joe@ten10design.com
Website: www.ten10design.com
Printing (offset and digital), promotional items, ad specialties, mailing services, labels & decals, graphic design, web design. (Woman/AA, estab 2009, empl 6, sales $3,093,663, cert: State, NMSDC, WBENC)

1496   The AG Group, Inc. dba AG PrintPromo Solutions
      960 Graham Rd, Ste 1
      Cuyahoga Falls, OH 44221
      Contact: Anup Gupta Presdient
      Tel: 330-315-9600
      Email: agupta@theaggroup.com
      Website: www.theaggroup.com
Dist promotional products, gifts, corporate apparel, embroidered & screen printed. (Woman/As-Ind, As-Pac, estab 1996, empl 5, sales $3,300,000, cert: State)

1497   The Callard Company
      811 Green Crest Dr Ste 300
      Westerville, OH 43081
      Contact: Robin Welch Acct Exec
      Tel: 614-933-0303
      Email: rwelch@callard.com
      Website: www.callard.com
Promotional products & creative marketing: awards, trade show giveaways, team rewards, client gifts, recruitment incentives & golf outing supplies. (Woman, estab 1987, empl 24, sales , cert: WBENC)

1498   The John K. Howe Company, Inc.
      7188 Main St
      Cincinnati, OH 45244
      Contact: CEO
      Tel: 513-651-1888
      Email:
      Website: www.ehowe.com
Branded apparel, promotional products & business recognition. (Woman, estab 1972, empl 10, sales $2,232,110, cert: WBENC)

1499   Vorce & Associates
      1335 Dublin Rd Ste 216C
      Columbus, OH 43215
      Contact: Donna Vorce Owner
      Tel: 614-488-5450
      Email: donna@firstimpressionsohio.com
      Website: www.firstimpressionsohio.com
Promotional & imprinted apparel. (Woman, estab 1983, empl 2, sales $810,000, cert: State)

Oregon

1500   Enthusias Media Group
      1631 NE Broadway, Ste 614
      Portland, OR 97232
      Contact: Marcy Hall Reg Acct Mgr
      Tel: 503-376-6839
      Email: info@enthusiastmediagroup.com
      Website: www.enthusiastmediagroup.com
Promotional & print items. (Woman, estab 2005, empl 7, sales $2,000,000, cert: State)

Pennsylvania

1501   As You Wish Promotions
      3801 Germantown Pike Ste 202
      Collegeville, PA 19426
      Contact: Alyssa Heininger Client Relationship Coord
      Tel: 484-973-6565
      Email: aheininger@wishpromo.com
      Website: www.wishpromo.com
Promotional products, graphic arts capabilities, marketing, service, client support & customer relations, trade show give-aways, corporate gifts, promotional apparel & employee awards. (Woman, estab 1992, empl 5, sales $1,913,640, cert: WBENC)

1502   BDJ Ventures, LLC
      3024 Bainbridge Dr
      Lansdale, PA 19446
      Contact: Bernard Wright Principal
      Tel: 215-266-2062
      Email: bwright@bdjventuresllc.com
      Website: www.bdjventuresllc.com
Premiums & promotional products. (AA, estab 2009, empl 3, sales , cert: State, NMSDC)

1503   Bry-Lex Promotional LLC
      19 Nelson Dr
      Southampton, PA 18966
      Contact: Bev Kaytes CEO
      Tel: 800-251-9101
      Email: bev@brylex.com
      Website: www.bry-lex.com
Promotional items, imprinted logos, blank logos, embroidery/silkscreen. (Woman, estab 1996, empl 11, sales $550,000, cert: State, WBENC)

1504   Carol Philp Inc
      336 1st St
      Pittsburgh, PA 15215
      Contact: Carol Philp President & CEO
      Tel: 412-782-2675
      Email: info@cpicreative.com
      Website: www.cpicreative.com
Design & fulfil custom programs: service awards, safety, sales incentives, fundraising, trade shows, education, product introduction, ad specialties & innovative products. (Woman, estab 1994, empl 5, sales $3,370,160, cert: WBENC)

1505   Signature Promotions
      715 Twining Road Ste 107
      Dresher, PA 19025
      Contact: Maureen Coffey Owner
      Tel: 215-641-1168
      Email: sigpro@comcast.net
      Website: www.sigpromo.com
Promotional advertising products, grahic design, product development & fulfillment capabilities. (Woman, estab 1992, empl 1, sales , cert: WBENC)

Rhode Island

1506   Ahlers Designs, Inc.
       999 Main St, Unit 707
       Pawtucket, RI 02860
       Contact: Gail Ahlers Artistic Director / CEO
       Tel: 401-365-1010
       Email: operations@ahlersdesigns.com
       Website: www.ahlersdesigns.com
Designs & mfr custom corporate gifts & awards, engraving,
custom cards or packaging. (Woman, estab 1989, empl 3,
sales $132,751, cert: State, WBENC)

South Carolina

1507   2 Oceans Promotions
       6175 Caravelle Court
       Awendaw, SC 29429
       Contact: Michele Johnson Owner
       Tel: 843-971-8499
       Email: michele@2oceanspromotions.com
       Website: www.2oceanspromotions.com
Promotional marketing & products. (Woman, estab 2001,
empl 6, sales $2,100,000, cert: WBENC)

1508   Promotions Unlimited, LLC
       327 Miller Rd, Ste E
       Mauldin, SC 29662
       Contact: Dir of Sales
       Tel: 864-527-1193
       Email:
       Website: www.promoultd.com
Promotional Items, Uniform Programs (Woman, estab
2005, empl 9, sales $2,254,086, cert: State, WBENC)

1509   Red Iron Brand Solutions, LLC
       104 Saluda Run Dr
       Piedmont, SC 29673
       Contact: Vishnu Jampala Owner
       Tel: 800-325-3824
       Email: vishnujam@rwts.net
       Website: www.redironbrand.com
Mfr & import event display items: Tablecovers & runners
in stretch fabric, polyester, polyvalue, plastic (cut table
covers and imprinted banquet rolls), and 400 denier.
(Woman, estab 2016, empl 10, sales $250,000, cert: State,
WBENC)

Tennessee

1510   Imagination Specialties, Inc.
       623 Old Hickory Blvd.
       Old Hickory, TN 37138
       Contact: Lori Armes Controller
       Tel: 615-255-5688
       Email: loria@imaginationbranding.com
       Website: www.imaginationbranding.com
Ad specialty & promotional products, corporate gifts,
baskets, event planning, event room drops, custom
printing, invitations, mail outs, online company stores,
warehousing, distribution & fulfillment services. (Woman,
estab 1989, empl 39, sales $11,275,000, cert: WBENC)

1511   Signet, Inc.
       1801 N Shelby Oaks Dr, Ste 12
       Memphis, TN 38134
       Contact: Elizabeth Tate CEO
       Tel: 901-387-5555
       Email: etate@gosignet.com
       Website: www.gosignet.com
Promotional products, branding, kitting, warehousing,
event management. (Woman, estab 0, empl , sales
$11,000,000, cert: WBENC)

1512   The Barr Group, Inc.
       230 Great Circle Road, Ste 234
       Nashville, TN 37228
       Contact: Jim Barr Dir of Sales
       Tel: 615-612-0444
       Email: jim@barrgroupinc.com
       Website: www.barrgroupinc.com
Promotional products, printing, indoor & outdoor
signage, corrugated packagin, MRO items, transportation brokerage & hauling. (Woman/Hisp, estab 1999,
empl 6, sales $2,505,000, cert: WBENC)

Texas

1513   Ad-Image Creative Promotions Co.
       851 Lakeview Dr
       Coppell, TX 75019
       Contact: Terri Finazzo President
       Tel: 972-462-0919
       Email: adimagedallas@aol.com
       Website: www.adimagedallas.com
Advertising specialties & promotional products.
(Woman, estab 1999, empl 2, sales , cert: State,
WBENC)

1514   Austin Ad Group
       5960 W Parker Rd, Ste 278 PMB 272
       Plano, TX 75093
       Contact: Rhonda Aicklen Presdient
       Tel: 972-307-7100
       Email: orders@austinadgroup.com
       Website: www.AustinAdGroup.com
Promotional logo/branded items: apparel, pens, bags,
hats, cups, trinkets, coolers, armbands, badges, balloons, bandana, buttons, flashlights, floor mats, jewelry,
tattoos, stuffed animals, awards, grills, etc. (Woman,
estab 1993, empl 7, sales , cert: State)

1515   Aztec Promotional Group, LP
       2815 Manor Rd
       Austin, TX 78722
       Contact: Patti Winstanley President
       Tel: 512-744-0195
       Email: patti@aztecworld.com
       Website: www.aztecworld.com
Sscreen printed & embroidered textiles, advertising
specialty items & design. (Woman/AA, estab 1995,
empl 25, sales $1,350,000, cert: State, WBENC)

1516   Beehive Specialty Co.
       8701 Wall St, Ste 900
       Austin, TX 78754
       Contact: Kelli Dillon Mgr/new business dept
       Tel: 512-912-7940
       Email: kelli@specialbee.com
       Website: www.beehivespecialty.com
Promotional products, custom product fabrication, on-line programs, high impact mail, packaging, fulfillment & integrated project management. (Woman, estab 1998, empl 12, sales $8,000,000, cert: WBENC)

1517   Cadena Specialty Advertising
       P.O. Box 150655
       Arlington, TX 76015
       Contact: Olga Quiroz Owner
       Tel: 817-459-4474
       Email: olga_cadenaspecialty@yahoo.com
       Website: www.cadenausa.com
Dist promotional marketing products: pens, cups, key tags, calendards, silkscreened & embroidered caps & apparel, employee recognition & safety awards & gifts. (Woman/Hisp, estab 1993, empl 1, sales $155,000, cert: State, City)

1518   CFJ Manufacturing
       701 Eight Twenty Blvd. Ste 145
       Fort Worth, TX 76106
       Contact: Sharon Evans CEO
       Tel: 817-625-9559
       Email: marketing@cfjmfg.com
       Website: www.cfjmfg.com
Promotional marketing & employee recognition solutions. (Woman, estab 1983, empl 201, sales $50,000,000, cert: State, WBENC)

1519   Creative Menus & Folders, LLC dba Texas Covers
       409 Old Hwy 80
       Olden, TX 76466
       Contact: Renee Forguson Asst Production Mgr
       Tel: 254-653-2775
       Email: reneeforguson@texascovers.com
       Website: http://texascovers.com
Presentation/Executive Binders, folders, business cards, printing (screen, digital, offset, foil stamp, deboss, specialty color cast printing, plastic ID badge holders, ID badges, name tags, souvenir printing, banners, signage, laminating, caps. (As-Pac, estab 2015, empl , sales $135,353, cert: NMSDC)

1520   Davis & Stanton, Inc.
       4002 W Miller Rd, Ste 140
       Garland, TX 75041
       Contact: Charlee Castillo Owner
       Tel: 214-340-1321
       Email: charlee@davstan.com
       Website: http://davstan.com
Advertising specialties, promotional products, plaques & awards & police commendation bars. (Woman/Hisp, estab 1949, empl 26, sales $5,000,000, cert: State, WBENC)

1521   DBS Marketing & Promotions LLC
       24466 Pipestem Dr
       Magnolia, TX 77355
       Contact: Sue Becknell Presdient
       Tel: 281-356-2386
       Email: sue@dbspromo.com
       Website: www.dbspromo.com
Logo branded promotional products, corporate apparel, awards, pens, notepads, shirts, caps, jackets, screen printing, laser engraving, embroidery, pad folios, backpacks, duffel bags, tote bags, tee shirts, golf items, flyers, etc. (Woman, estab 2005, empl 3, sales $1,230,000, cert: WBENC)

1522   Distinctive Marketing Ideas
       3415 Custer Rd, Ste 133
       Plano, TX 75023
       Contact: Bonnie Shackelford Owner
       Tel: 972-612-0050
       Email: bonnie.shack@dmipromotions.com
       Website: www.dmipromotions.com
Promotional products/premiums, warehouse & fulfillment. (Woman, estab 1992, empl 4, sales $1,750,000, cert: State, WBENC)

1523   Henya Direct LLC
       5555 W University Blvd
       Dallas, TX 75209
       Contact: Terence Johnson Natl Sales Mgr
       Tel: 214-701-0671
       Email: tjohnson@henyadirect.com
       Website: www.henyadirect.com
Promotional merchandise: uniforms, hats, cups, stress balls, pens, bags, watches, etc. (Woman, estab 2007, empl 3, sales $1,500,000, cert: WBENC)

1524   Holden Custom Products
       7920 Beltline Rd Ste 960
       Dallas, TX 75254
       Contact: MARNIE HOLDEN Dir Major Accts
       Tel: 214-543-1133
       Email: holdenll@flash.net
       Website: www.holdenbrand.com
Corporate packaging, promotional products, imports & wearables. (Woman, estab 1978, empl 16, sales $9,500,000, cert: State)

1525   I Chispa, LLC
       129 Thunderbird
       El Paso, TX 79912
       Contact: Horacio Arras VP Sales/Mktg
       Tel: 915-239-7430
       Email: horacio@ichispa.us
       Website: www.ichispa.us
Promotional & sports items. (Woman/Hisp, estab 2010, empl 5, sales , cert: State, NMSDC)

1526 IncentiveAmerica, Inc.
18208 Preston Rd Ste D924
Dallas, TX 75252
Contact: Elizabeth Montgomery Presdient
Tel: 972-380-9990
Email: elizabethm@incentiveamerica.com
Website: www.incentiveamerica.com
Pre-paid MasterCard gift cards & dining gift cards, personalized, premium note card & gold-embossed greeting card. (Woman/AA, estab , empl , sales $968,290, cert: State, NMSDC, 8a)

1527 Insignia Marketing
32731 Egypt Lane Ste 301
Magnolia, TX 77354
Contact: Christine McAtee Presdient
Tel: 281-465-0040
Email: orders@visicare.com
Website: www.VisiCare.com
Promotional advertising: corporate brand identity, creativity, pens, coffee mugs, t-shirts & awards. (Woman, estab 2002, empl 3, sales $2,000,000, cert: State, WBENC)

1528 Malkoff Promotions
4904 Stony Ford Dr
Dallas, TX 75287
Contact: Lynne Malkoff President
Tel: 972-248-4354
Email: lynne@lmpspecialties.com
Website: www.lmpspecialties.com
Marketing & promotional solutions. (Woman, estab 1989, empl 5, sales , cert: State, WBENC)

1529 Network Embroidery Inc.
10600 Shadow Wood Dr Ste 201
Houston, TX 77043
Contact: Lily Clark Presdient
Tel: 713-865-8032
Email: micael.shea@networkinterstateco.com
Website: www.networkinterstateco.com
Mfr & dist promotional products, catalog programs, awards, trophies, graphics, warehousing & fulfillment. (Woman, estab 0, empl , sales , cert: WBENC)

1530 Potenza Promotions, LLC
810 Genoa
Argyle, TX 76226
Contact: Laura Hulke President
Tel: 940-595-9555
Email: lhulke@potenzapromotions.com
Website: www.potenzapromotions.com
Promotional products: mugs, pens, stress balls, awards, office items, USB pens, etc. (Woman, estab 2006, empl 6, sales $147,000, cert: State)

1531 Power Of Two Productions, LLC
9901 Brodie Ln, Ste 160-279
Austin, TX 78748
Contact: LeeAnn Wick CEO
Tel: 512-872-5000
Email: leeann@ptwopromo.com
Website: www.PTwoPromo.com
Promotional products, business gifts, trade show giveaways, wellness programs, incentives, awards, safety, screen printing, embroidery, apparel, employee retention, sustainable, eco friendly, tote bags, promotions. (Woman/Hisp, estab 2007, empl 3, sales $419,000, cert: State, NMSDC, WBENC)

1532 RedMan I Am Promotions
1516 Wimberly Ct
Bedford, TX 76021
Contact: Robert Whistler Owner
Tel: 817-229-6271
Email: redmaniam@msn.com
Website:
Custom imprinted logo merchandise: awards, aprons, badges, balls, balloons, banners, bottle openers,calculators, calendars, candy, caps, clocks, cups, desk sets, food gifts, first aid kits, flashlights, etc. (Nat Ame, estab 2011, empl 1, sales , cert: State)

1533 RG Apparel Co.
2912 N MacArthur, Ste 103
Irving, TX 75062
Contact: Joe Temple COO
Tel: 972-793-0583
Email: jt@rgapparel.com
Website: www.rgapparel.com
Mfr textiles: uniforms, work shirts, polos, tees, woven button up shirts & headwear, promotional marketing items & gifts. (AA, estab 2006, empl 6, sales $3,200,000, cert: State, NMSDC)

1534 The Donna Bender Company
6860 North Dallas Parkway Ste 200
Plano, TX 75024
Contact: Donna Bender President
Tel: 214-520-8577
Email: donna@donnaco.com
Website: www.donnaco.com
Promotional products; specialty advertising; business gifts; service, achievement & recognition awards; incentive & awareness programs. (Woman, estab 2007, empl 3, sales , cert: State, WBENC)

1535 TLC Adcentives LLC
21101 Kingsland Blvd. Ste. 1113
Katy, TX 77450
Contact: Terri Hornsby President
Tel: 281-828-2270
Email: terri@tlcadcentives.com
Website: www.tlcadcentives.com
Advertising promotional incentives, awards & trophies, cups & mugs, apparel & headgear, desk accessories, writing instruments, portfolios, briefcases. (Woman/AA, estab 1995, empl 4, sales $175,000, cert: State, NMSDC, WBENC)

1536 Trademarks Promotional Products
11333 Todd St
Houston, TX 77055
Contact: Kelli Cochran Acct Mgr
Tel: 713-680-3000
Email: tpp@tmarks.com
Website: www.trademarkspromos.com
Promotional products, screenprinting, embroidery, direct digital garment printing, graphic design, award engraving, ad specialty items. (Woman, estab 1979, empl 60, sales $7,100,001, cert: State, WBENC)

1537 Trinity Enterprise Group LLC
400 S Zang Blvd, Ste 240
Dallas, TX 75208
Contact: Casey Gonzales COO
Tel: 214-785-6741
Email: casey@tegroup.biz
Website: www.tegroup.biz
Advertising items, Apparel, Uniforms, Hats, Gifts, Trophies, Awards, Nameplates, PPE, Sports Bags, Pens, Business Supplies, Technology items, Signage, and Custom ordered goods. (Hisp, estab 2020, empl 4, sales , cert: NMSDC)

1538 W. M. Martin Advertising
P.O. Box 795818
Dallas, TX 75379
Contact: Wendy Fahle Owner
Tel: 972-732-8040
Email: cs@wmmadv.com
Website: www.wmmadv.com
Advertising specialties: pens, shirts, caps, calendars, golf items. (Woman, estab 1983, empl 4, sales $850,000, cert: State, WBENC)

Virginia

1539 E&R Sales Inc.
4800 Market Square Lane
Midlothian, VA 23112
Contact: Elissa Mast Presdient
Tel: 804-744-8000
Email: headcoach@ersales.com
Website: www.ersales.com
Balloons, pens and novelty trend items. (Minority/Woman, estab , empl , sales , cert: WBENC)

1540 Fishnet, LLC
P.O. Box 7311
Charlottesville, VA 22906
Contact: David Goloversic Sr Acct Exec
Tel: 434-409-6177
Email: contactus@fishnetllc.com
Website: www.fishnetllc.com
Printing & promotional products: writing instruments, office accessories, food and drink ware, doormats, banners, flags, tents, table covers, displays, retractors, bags, health and safety items, coloring books, business cards. (Woman/Hisp, estab 2006, empl 2, sales , cert: State)

1541 Global Partner's of Virginia, LLC
3005 E Boundary Terr, Ste G
Midlothian, VA 23112
Contact: Norm Falkner VP
Tel: 804-744-8112
Email: logos@globalpromosonline.com
Website: www.globalpromosonline.com
Logo wear, embroidery, silk screen, screen printing, direct to garment ink jet printing, heat transfer. Corporate apparel, mens, ladies, kids, uniforms. Promotional Products, pens, magnets, calendars, Bags, towels, luggage, sportwear, team uniforms. (Woman, estab 2001, empl 4, sales $350,000, cert: State)

1542 It's A Breeze Specialties, LLC
8221 Little Florida Rd
Mechanicsville, VA 23111
Contact: Shirley Husz President
Tel: 804-779-0183
Email: shirley@itsabreez.com
Website: www.itsabreez.com
Promotional products, corporate apparel, screen printed & embroidered, awards, incentives & award programs. (Woman, estab 2002, empl 2, sales $140,000, cert: State)

1543 Rivanna Natural Designs, Inc.
3009 Lincoln Ave
Richmond, VA 23228
Contact: Crystal Mario President
Tel: 434-244-3447
Email: cmario@rivannadesigns.com
Website: www.rivannadesigns.com
Environmentally responsible gifts, plaques & awards. (Minority, Woman, estab 0, empl , sales , cert: State)

1544 The Advertising Specialist, L.C.
P.O. Box 5325
Midlothian, VA 23112
Contact: Jeanette Mayo Presdient
Tel: 804-744-0044
Email: advertisingspecialist@verizon.net
Website: www.advertisingspecialist.com
Promotional products, banners, sport uniforms, T-Shirts, Website Design, Screen Printing & Embroidery. (Woman/AA, estab 1997, empl 3, sales , cert: State)

Washington

1545 Bravo! Promotional Products
569 Occidental Ave S
Seattle, WA 98104
Contact: Peggie Dickens President
Tel: 206-682-3953
Email: peggie@bravobranding.com
Website: www.bravobranding.com
Offshore sourcing, fulfillment services, creative art services, event fulfillment. (Woman, estab 1995, empl 12, sales $5,969,545, cert: WBENC)

1546 Unique Experience Custom Embroidery & Screen-Print
234 First St
Bremerton, WA 98337
Contact: Ronald Flemister Mgr
Tel: 360-373-2076
Email: un234@silverlink.net
Website: www.companycasuals.com/uniqueexperience

Custom embroidery, screen printing & promotional products. (Woman/AA, estab 1990, empl 3, sales $250,000, cert: State)

Wisconsin

1547 A Branovan Company, LLC.
6505 W Calumet Rd
Milwaukee, WI 53223
Contact: Marie Branovan CEO
Tel: 414-352-5000
Email: marie@abcgifts.com
Website: www.abcgifts.com

Advertising specilties: custom embroidery & screen printing apparel. (Woman, estab 1996, empl 12, sales $3,712,200, cert: WBENC)

1548 Actualink Designs LLC
N65W12525 Sycamore Ln
Menomonee Falls, WI 53051
Contact: Anthony Martin Owner
Tel: 414-349-4367
Email: info@actualinkdesigns.com
Website: www.actualinkdesigns.com

Embroidery, screen printing & digital printing, polo shirts, caps, graphic design studio. (AA, estab 2012, empl 3, sales , cert: NMSDC)

1549 on3 Promotional Partners, LLC
1543 Sheridan Rd
Kenosha, WI 53140
Contact: Lora Lehmann Owner
Tel: 262-551-8715
Email: llehmann@on3promopartners.com
Website: www.on3promopartners.com

Promotional products, incentive & loyalty programs, fulfillment, packaging & collateral print needs. (Woman, estab 2005, empl 6, sales $1,850,000, cert: State, WBENC)

1550 Quali T Inc.
513 Center St
Luxemburg, WI 54217
Contact: Susan Heim Presdient
Tel: 920-845-1010
Email: sales@qualitinc.com
Website: www.QualiTInc.com

Embroidery, screen printing, promotional products, custom apparel, advertising specialties, uniforms, safety apparel, USA made apparel, work wear, Jackets, headwear, outerwear, dress shirts, polos, sport shirts, etc. (Woman, estab 1990, empl 25, sales $1,500,000, cert: State)

1551 Royal Recognition, Inc.
S83 W19105 Saturn Dr
Muskego, WI 53150
Contact: Joseph Cull VP
Tel: 262-679-6050
Email: jcull@royalrec.com
Website: www.royalrec.com

Employee service awads, corporate apparel, recognition/sales awards & promotional items. (Woman, estab 1983, empl 52, sales , cert: State)

ALARM SYSTEMS
Manufacturers or wholesalers of fire, security, intercom, CCTV, or other alarm components or systems. NAICS Code 33

Alabama

1552   Firelake Construction Inc.
85 Trico Dr
Guntersville, AL 35976
Contact: William D. Slavin CEO
Tel: 256-302-2355
Email: bslavin@firelakeconstruction.com
Website: www.firelakeconstruction.com
Security alarm solutions: integrated systems design & installation, access control systems, closed circuit television (CCTV) systems, perimeter protection & integrated biometric technologies. (Nat Ame, estab 2010, empl 8, sales $1,900,000, cert: State)

Arizona

1553   American Fire Equipment
3107 W Virginia Ave
Phoenix, AZ 85009
Contact: Rose Koppy Admin
Tel: 602-433-2484
Email: info@americanfire.com
Website: www.americanfire.com
Sells, designs, installs, services & repairs all types of fire protection systems, special hazards fire protection, building fire alarm, mass notification, fire sprinkler, kitchen fire suppression. (Woman, estab 1992, empl 125, sales $12,331,853, cert: WBENC)

1554   Mountain Power Electrical Contractor, Inc.
4301 S Country Club
Tucson, AZ 85714
Contact: Josette Washington Business Dev Mgr
Tel: 520-294-1131
Email: josette@mtnpower.com
Website: www.mtnpower.com
Commercial lighting & power, industrial wiring, hospitals, fire alarms, sound systems, communications, substations, power line installation, traffic signals & underground power. (Woman/Hisp, estab 1985, empl 80, sales $6,229,000, cert: State)

California

1555   Aponi Products and Services
3805 Florin Rd Ste 1228
Sacramento, CA 95823
Contact: Lisa M Davis lacy Owner
Tel: 916-392-6571
Email: lisad@aponitelecommunication.com
Website: http://aponitelecom.com
Telecommunication Equipment, Installation, Voice, Data, Cabling, Maintenance, Repair, Security System, DVR, Security Cameras. (Nat Ame, estab 2007, empl 7, sales $360,000, cert: State, 8a)

Colorado

1556   FAS Systems Group, LLC
4800 W 60th Ave
Arvada, CO 80003
Contact: Business Dev Mgr
Tel: 303-298-7900
Email:
Website: www.fassystemsgroup.net
Fire alarm detection & security system solutions for new construction & end-users. (Woman, estab 2005, empl 37, sales $5,800,000, cert: WBENC)

District of Columbia

1557   MJS Communications LLC
1343 First St NW
Washington, DC 20001
Contact: Marlon Boykin Presdient
Tel: 888-829-1658
Email: mboykin@mjscommunications.biz
Website: www.mjscommunications.biz
Information technology, telecommunications services, structure cabling system, voice/data cabling, CCTV cabling, POS & wireless, CCTV, digital video recorders, Interior/exterior cameras, monitors, perimeter security. (AA, estab 2009, empl 2, sales $110,000, cert: State, City)

Florida

1558   Aegis Fire and Integrated Services, LLC
156 Industrial Loop S
Orange Park, FL 32073
Contact: Shelli Schmid Reg Sales
Tel: 904-215-9669
Email: sschmid@afps.com
Website: www.aegisfis.com
Fire sprinkler, extinguishers & alarm systems. (As-Pac, estab 2004, empl 42, sales , cert: State, NMSDC)

1559   Audio Video Systems, Inc.
1860 Old Okeechobee Rd, Ste 104
West Palm Beach, FL 33409
Contact: Angela Barnard Presdient
Tel: 561-686-4473
Email: angela@cctvrepair.com
Website: www.cctvrepair.com
Commercial audio, video & electronic security projects, sales, service, installation & integration: burglar alarm, access control, CCTV/video surveillance, commercial audio, commercial video, business class projectors & displays. (Woman, estab 1981, empl 6, sales $800,000, cert: State, City)

1560   Carter Brothers Security Services LLC
1 Portofino Dr
Pensacola Beach, FL 32561
Contact: John F. Carter CEO
Tel: 770-954-7010
Email: cbregistrations@carterbrothers.com
Website: www.carterbrothers.com
Project & program management, fire safety & security systems. (AA, estab 2019, empl 4, sales $350,000, cert: State, NMSDC)

1561 HDJ Security, Inc.
      4105 LaFayette St
      Marianna, FL 32446
      Contact: Harvey Daniels, Jr. President
      Tel: 850-482-8660
      Email: harvey@hdjsecurity.com
      Website: www.hdjsecurity.com
Dist & install electronic security, CCTV, access control,
intrusion detection, fire alarms, mass notification. (AA,
estab 2003, empl 9, sales $890,000, cert: 8a)

1562 Mainstream IP Solutions, Inc.
      6905 El Dorado Dr
      Tampa, FL 33615
      Contact: Arnie Solomon Acct Mgr
      Tel: 813-549-7768
      Email: asolomon@mcsoftampa.com
      Website: www.mainstreamipsolutions.com
Electrical, structured cabling, audio-visual, security & fire
alarm systems. (AA, estab 2010, empl 5, sales $250,000,
cert: State, NMSDC, 8a, SDB)

Georgia

1563 AAA Fire Protection Resources, Inc.
      P.O. Box 1122
      Lawrenceville, GA 30046
      Contact: Presdient
      Tel: 770-963-0887
      Email:
      Website: http://aaafirepro.com
Fire Extinguisher Sales & Service, Recharging & Inspections, Emergency Exit Lighting. (Woman, estab 1982, empl
4, sales $977,756, cert: WBENC)

1564 Alliance Fire Protection Services, Inc.
      P.O. Box 1798
      Loganville, GA 30052
      Contact: Angie Jordan Office Mgr
      Tel: 770-554-5004
      Email: acjordan@alliancefire.com
      Website: www.alliancefire.com
Life Safety Inspections & Service, Fire Alarm, Fire Sprinkler,
Extinguishers, Hydrants, Backflows & Fire Pumps. (Woman,
estab 1999, empl 75, sales $7,768,000, cert: City, WBENC)

1565 DH Security Solutions
      303 Perimeter Center N Ste 300
      Atlanta, GA 30346
      Contact: Tina Dungy Presdient
      Tel: 678-341-9451
      Email: tdungy@dhsecuritysolutions.com
      Website: www.dhsecuritysolutions.com
Locksmith, access control, card readers, door hardware,
door closers, electronic gates, safes, vaults, CCTV, door
repair, high security solutions. (Woman/AA, estab 2011,
empl 12, sales $510,000, cert: NWBOC)

1566 Strickland Security & Safety Solutions
      541 Tenth St NW, Ste 135
      Atlanta, GA 30318
      Contact: Robert Strickland Owner
      Tel: 800-422-9075
      Email: rob@stricklandsecurity.com
      Website: www.stricklandsecurity.com
Service & equipment replacement: CCTV & alarm systems
components. (AA, estab 2007, empl 12, sales $2,150,000,
cert: NMSDC)

1567 UMC Inc. dba Unity ITS
      3420 Oakcliff Rd Ste 105
      Doraville, GA 30340
      Contact: David Park CEO
      Tel: 770-234-0221
      Email: dpark@unityits.com
      Website: www.unityits.com
PC based camera security & surveillance system.
(Woman/As-Pac, estab 2001, empl 3, sales $221,681,
cert: State)

Illinois

1568 Applied Controls & Contracting Services, Inc.
      537 W Taft Dr
      South Holland, IL 60473
      Contact: George Kinnison Presdient
      Tel: 708-596-7400
      Email: gkinnison@accshome.com
      Website: www.accshome.com
Engineering design, project management & estimations,
technical analysis, emergency dispatch services installation, design security ad alarm systems, fire detection
systems, closed circuit tv system & card access. (AA,
estab 1990, empl 11, sales $1,090,522, cert: State,
NMSDC)

Indiana

1569 Geyer Fire Protection, LLC
      700 N High School Rd
      Indianapolis, IN 46214
      Contact: Rosemily Geyer
      Tel: 317-490-9357
      Email: rosemily@geyerfire.com
      Website: www.geyerfire.com
Design, install, serve & maintain fire sprinkler systems,
fire extinguishers & alarms. (Woman/Hisp, estab 2011,
empl 12, sales $686,733, cert: State, City, NMSDC)

Louisiana

1570 Fire Boss of Louisiana, Inc.
      7905 Hwy 90 W
      New Iberia, LA 70560
      Contact: Debra Denais Romero Presdient
      Tel: 337-365-6729
      Email: debbie@fireboss.com
      Website: www.fireboss.com
Fire & safety protection services, DBI/SALA authorized
distributor/repair center, fire & gas detection/suppres-
sion system design, engineering & installation, commercial inspection of portable fire extinguishing systems,
foam & water systems. (Woman, estab 1975, empl ,
sales , cert: WBENC)

1571 Fire Tech Systems, Inc.
      721 N Ashley Ridge Loop
      Shreveport, LA 71106
      Contact: Linda Biernacki Presdient
      Tel: 318-688-8800
      Email: lbiernacki@firetechsystems.com
      Website: www.firetechsystems.com
Design, install & service fire sprinkler systems, fire
suppression systems, fire extinguishers. (Woman, estab
1990, empl 85, sales , cert: WBENC)

Massachusetts

1572   Big East Security Integrations LLC
30 Melanie Ln
Wrentham, MA 02093
Contact: Marcus Vaughn CEO
Tel: 774-307-3435
Email: bigeastsillc4@gmail.com
Website:
Security Consulting and Sale of Integrated Solutions
Covering Access Control, CCTV Video Surveillance, Intrusion Detection, Visitor Management and Intercom systems. (AA, estab 2017, empl 4, sales , cert: State)

Maryland

1573   Digital Video Solutions, Inc.
7526 Connelley Dr Ste A
Hanover, MD 21076
Contact: John Webster President
Tel: 240-547-0143
Email: jwebster@remoteeyes.com
Website: http://digitalvideosolutions.biz
Designs & integrate physical security systems: CCTV, access control, alarm, public address & intercom systems. (AA, estab 2008, empl 3, sales $302,000, cert: State, NMSDC)

1574   G TECH Contracting, LLC
8008 Dorado Terr
Brandywine, MD 20613
Contact: CEO
Tel: 240-793-8908
Email:
Website: www.gtechcontracting.com
Integrated security, voice/data communications, residential & small commercial A/V systems. (Hisp, estab 2013, empl 5, sales $1,200,000, cert: 8a)

1575   Truth Technology, Inc.
5201 Maries Retreat Dr
Bowie, MD 20720
Contact: April Brown President & CEO
Tel: 240-472-9833
Email: atb@trutechi.com
Website: www.trutechi.com
CCTV, Key Card Access System, and Biometric devices, network & computer equipment, software. (Woman/AA, estab 2006, empl 2, sales $475,000, cert: 8a)

Michigan

1576   Edgewood Electrical, LLC
3633 Michigan Ave Ste 100
Detroit, MI 48216
Contact: Robert Bell Sr Project Mgr
Tel: 313-263-0440
Email: robertb@edgewoodelectric.com
Website: www.edgewoodelectric.com
Electrical Installations, Design/Build, Design/Assist, Fire Alarm & Low Voltage Systems. (AA, estab 2008, empl 45, sales $12,000,000, cert: NMSDC)

Minnesota

1577   Castle Cop Inc.
17003 E Lake Netta Dr
Ham Lake, MN 55304
Contact: Barb Underdahl CEO
Tel: 763-438-2761
Email: castlecopinc@earthlink.net
Website: www.castlecop.com
Dist stainless steel doorjamb reinforcing device.
(Woman, estab 2003, empl 1, sales , cert: State)

1578   Lloyd Security Incorporated
5051 Highway 7 Ste 270
Minneapolis, MN 55416
Contact: Me'Lea Connelly GM
Tel: 612-874-9295
Email: info@lloydsecurity.com
Website: www.lloydsecurity.com
Installation, repair, service & monitoring of security systems, access control, surveillance and video, perimeter detection, safe rooms, CCTV & ballistic solutions. (Woman, estab 2001, empl 14, sales , cert: State, City)

Mississippi

1579   HC Services Fire Protection
1455 West Dr
Laurel, MS 39440
Contact: Sue Bridges President
Tel: 601-399-4800
Email: sue@hcservicesinc.com
Website: www.hcservicesinc.com
Dist, service & install fire protection products: extinguishers, fire systems, detection, fire alarms, access control, sprinklers, Fm-200, inergen, halon & speciality hazards. (Woman, estab 1991, empl 13, sales $13,000,000, cert: State, City, WBENC)

North Carolina

1580   Video & Security Specialists
2313 Wedgewood Dr
Matthews, NC 28104
Contact: Erika Gordon Partner
Tel: 704-821-9396
Email: egordon@carolina.rr.com
Website: www.videoandsecurityspecialists.com
Dist electrical & security products: alarm/security systems, fire alarm systems, structured wiring, access control, security cameras, networking, phone system, intercom & gates. (Woman, estab 1975, empl 7, sales $220,866, cert: State)

New York

1581   ASM Security Inc.
8003 Myrtle Ave
Glendale, NY 11385
Contact: Simon Ruderman Presdient
Tel: 718-839-6000
Email: sruderman@asmintegrators.com
Website: https://asmintegrators.com
Design, engineering, filing & expediting fire alarm & security systems. (Woman/Hisp, estab 2006, empl 28, sales $2,000,000, cert: State, City)

1582 Care Security Systems
      9 Hemion Road
      Montebello, NY 10952
      Contact: Eli Ribowsky Acct Mgr
      Tel: 845-282-1245
      Email: eribowsky@care-inc.com
      Website: www.caresecuritysystems.com
Design, assembly, testing, installation, maintenance, and
management of high-level integrated security systems.
(Woman, estab 1987, empl 30, sales , cert: City, WBENC)

Ohio

1583 Advance Federated Protection
      2000 lee road #202
      Cleveland Heights, OH 44118
      Contact: Alan Lewis Managing Dir
      Tel: 216-321-1369
      Email: afp044@aol.com
      Website: http://afpsecurity.net
Low Votage Technolgy Burglar Alarm system, Surveillance
Cameras-CCTV Fire System, Access Control Medal Detectors (Walk Thru), Guards/ Consulting. (AA, estab 1984,
empl 9, sales $184,622, cert: State, City)

1584 Alarm Core, LLC
      4555 Renaissance Pkwy, Ste 103
      Warrenville Heights, OH 44128
      Contact: Kenneth Liddell President
      Tel: 216-831-2871
      Email: alarmcoreohio@aol.com
      Website:
Install commercial & residential fire & burgular alarms,
CCTV, remote surveillence systems, satellite systems. (AA,
estab 1999, empl 8, sales , cert: State)

1585 Gene Ptacek & Son Fire Equipment Co, Inc.
      7310 Associate Ave
      Brooklyn, OH 44144
      Contact: Gene Ptacek VP
      Tel: 216-651-8300
      Email: gene@gpsfire.com
      Website: www.gpsfire.com
Fire extinguishers, fire suppression systems, Fire alarm &
fire sprinkler systems, Inspections, fire extinguisher
training, dist fire hose, brass adapters & nozzles. (Woman,
estab 1975, empl 52, sales , cert: City)

1586 Rika Group Corporation
      13701 Enterprise Ave
      Cleveland, OH 44135
      Contact: Ryan Temple Dir of Operations
      Tel: 216-325-1006
      Email: ryan@pcsurveillance.net
      Website: www.pcsurveillance.net
Design, dist & install surveillance equipment & systems.
(Woman, estab 2001, empl 20, sales $1,600,000, cert: City)

1587 TaiParker Consulting LLC
      4020 Sara Dr
      Uniontown, OH 44685
      Contact: Tai Parker Owner
      Tel: 330-472-2115
      Email: tai@taiparkerconsulting.com
      Website: www.taiparkerconsulting.com
Video Systems Installation / Monitoring / Service, Real
Time Remote Video Monitoring, Remote Video Storage,
Cellular Only Video Camera Solutions, WiFi / IP Video
Camera Solutions, Alarm Systems Installation / Monitor-
ing / Service. (AA, estab 2010, empl 1, sales , cert: State,
NMSDC)

1588 Veterans Electrical Group LLC
      3700 Northfield Rd, Ste 353
      Highland Hills, OH 44122
      Contact: London Burnett Presdient
      Tel: 216-600-5808
      Email: london@vetelectrical.com
      Website:
High & low voltage electric services & computer cabling
& security alarms, CCTV Cabling. (AA, estab 2014, empl
12, sales , cert: City)

Pennsylvania

1589 Arora Systems Group, LLC
      61 Wilmington-West Chester Pike Ste 100
      Chadds Ford, PA 19317
      Contact: Adam Oliver GM
      Tel: 610-500-0714
      Email: aoliver@arorasystemsgroup.com
      Website: www.arorasystemsgroup.com
Facility Maintenance, testing, management, and code
consulting, Fire Alarm testing, maintenance & repair,
Fire Suppression, sprinkler system testing maintenance
& repair, Hydrant, Standpipe & Fire extinguisher testing.
(As-Ind, estab 2004, empl 17, sales $2,885,827, cert:
City, NMSDC)

1590 Fire Fighter Sales & Service Company
      791 Commonwealth Dr
      Warrendale, PA 15086
      Contact: Richard Malady VP
      Tel: 724-720-6000
      Email: rmalady@all-lines-tech.com
      Website: www.firefighter-pgh.com
Alarms, sprinkler systems & fire protection. (Woman,
estab 1946, empl 125, sales $12,500,000, cert: WBENC)

Puerto Rico

1591 EAS Systems, Inc.
      P.O. Box 482
      Mercedita, PR 00715
      Contact: Pedro Bonnin Presdient
      Tel: 787-284-4007
      Email: pbonnin@eas-pr.com
      Website: www.eas-pr.com
Install & Service Security: CCTV, Security Analog Cam-
eras, Security IP cameras, Access Control Systems,
Intrusion Detection Systems, Intercom Systems, Perim-
eter protection Systems, Barriers, Turnstiles, Wireless.
(Hisp, estab 1995, empl 14, sales $1,280,879, cert: 8a)

1592 Guardmax Corporation
      N 20, Ste B, Fagot Ave
      Ponce, PR 716
      Contact: Manuel Santana CEO
      Tel: 787-806-5525
      Email: manuelsantana@guardmaxpr.com
      Website: www.guardmaxpr.com
Security services, security technology integration, service
& maintenance, access control, asset conservation,
automatic door repair & service, burglar alarms, CCTV,
analog & Matrix Systems, IP Systems, Wireless IP. (Hisp,
estab 2014, empl 16, sales , cert: NMSDC)

1593 One Corps, Inc
      P.O. Box 79767
      Carolina, PR 984
      Contact: Sonia Fuentes
      Tel: 787-776-0062
      Email: sfuentes@one-corps.com
      Website: www.one-corps.com
Armed & Unarmed Security Guards, IP Monitoring Station
with Patrol Response Service, Sales, Installation & Maintenance of Cameras, Access Control, Fire Watch. (Hisp, estab
2007, empl 134, sales $2,641,716, cert: NMSDC)

1594 Puerto Rico Alarm Systems, Inc.
      P.O. Box 488
      Dorado, PR 646
      Contact: Jose Sanchez Presdient
      Tel: 787-883-4587
      Email: jsanchez@pralarms.com
      Website: www.pralarms.com
Dist, install & service commercial fire, access control,
burglar, page, close circuit tv, nurse call, interlock & infant
protection systems, security alarm monitoring service &
conduits. (Hisp, estab 1997, empl 20, sales $1,823,161,
cert: NMSDC)

1595 The Security Group Corp.
      Urb. Villa Blanca 42 Aquamarina
      Caguas, PR 725
      Contact: Luis Benet Presdient
      Tel: 787-743-3299
      Email: info@securitygroupcorp.com
      Website: www.securitygroupcorp.com
Electronic security & automation: design, sale, installation,
programming, service & maintenance of electronic
security & automation systems. (Hisp, estab 1988, empl
18, sales $901,822, cert: NMSDC)

South Carolina

1596 Quintech Security Consultants, Inc.
      102 Sangaree Park Court Ste 4
      Summerville, SC 29483
      Contact: Harold Gillens President
      Tel: 843-695-0170
      Email: hgillens@quintechengineering.com
      Website: www.quintechengineering.com
Security risk assessments, emergency response planning,
security site surveys, surveillance system design, alarm
system design, access control systems, AV/intercom
systems. (AA, estab 1997, empl 11, sales $5,227,488, cert:
NMSDC)

Texas

1597 Action Fire Alarm and Action Automatic Sprinkler
      200 Sharron Dr
      Woodway, TX 76712
      Contact: Patricia Green Sales Coord
      Tel: 254-235-8300
      Email: pbreen@actionfirepros.com
      Website: www.actionfirepros.com
Inspect, service & install fire extinguishers, fire alarms,
fire sprinkler & backflows. (Woman, estab 1993, empl
72, sales $9,005,218, cert: State, WBENC)

1598 Asez Inc.
      1716 S San Marcos, Ste 120
      San Antonio, TX 78207
      Contact: Robert Lozano CEO
      Tel: 210-736-6200
      Email: corporate@asezinc.com
      Website: www.asezinc.com
Armed & unarmed security officers, security systems
services, security alarm systems, fire alarm systems,
access control, closed circuit television, alarm monitoring, intergraded system. (Hisp, estab 2000, empl 75,
sales $2,575,000, cert: State, 8a)

1599 Champion Life Safety Solutions
      2701 W. Plano Parkway Ste 500
      Plano, TX 75075
      Contact: Chuck Henderson Presdient
      Tel: 972-663-5000
      Email:
      charles.henderson@championfiresecurity.com
      Website: www.championfiresecurity.com
Design, install, inspect & monitor fire sprinkler & other
suppression systems, fire alarm systems & security
systems for new construction, retrofit to existing
facilities. (AA, estab 2001, empl 112, sales $14,200,000,
cert: State, NMSDC)

1600 CLS Technology, Inc.
      5206 E 3rd St
      Katy, TX 77493
      Contact: Amber Wolfe Accountant Clerk
      Tel: 281-347-7973
      Email: monitoring@clstechnology.net
      Website: www.clstechnology.net
Fire alarm and sound systems, annual inspections,
installations, sound, shooter detection, temperature
taking devices, access control systems and install.
(Woman, estab 2006, empl 50, sales $8,000,000, cert:
WBENC)

1601 Laredo Technical Services, Inc.
      22011 Roan Bluff
      San Antonio, TX 78259
      Contact: Joseph Lukowski Presdient
      Tel: 210-705-2904
      Email: joseph@laredotechnical.com
      Website: www.laredotechnical.com/
Dist SpiderTech Security perimeter detection systems.
(Hisp, estab 2007, empl 23, sales $6,210,000, cert: State,
NMSDC, 8a)

1602   Nationwide Investigations & Security, Inc.
       2425 West Loop South, Ste 200
       Houston, TX 77027
       Contact: Allen G Hollimon CEO
       Tel: 713-297-8830
       Email: ahollimon@ntwinvestigations.com
       Website: www.ntwinvestigations.com
Security guard services, investigations, dignitary protection, communications cabling, CCTV/CATV, alarms, automated controls, networking, home theaters. (AA, estab
1999, empl 123, sales $398,000, cert: State, NMSDC)

1603   TotalCom Management Inc
       P.O. Box 460230
       San Antonio, TX 78246
       Contact: Moe Oroian President
       Tel: 210-366-1116
       Email: moe@totalcom-inc.com
       Website: http://totalcom-inc.com
Dist, install & service voice & data cabling, fire systems,
security systems, access control systems, CCTV/CATV,
cameras & DVR recording systems, alarm monitoring,
telephone systems, blown fiber. (As-Ind, estab 1994, empl
19, sales $1,755,237, cert: State)

Virginia

1604   Quality CCTV Systems, Inc.
       3513 Gregory Pond Rd
       Richmond, VA 23236
       Contact: Dianne Rust President
       Tel: 804-276-7300
       Email: dianne@qualitycctv.net
       Website: www.qualitycctv.net
Install & maintain security systems to include: video
surveillance, CCTV, access control systems, burglar & fire
systems, etc. (Woman, estab 1989, empl 14, sales
$1,240,000, cert: State)

APPAREL
Manufacturers or wholesalers of men's and women's clothing, accessories and notions. Many firms listed are contract sewing houses. NAICS Code 54

California

1605 Abell Marketing Group, Inc.
15057 Avenida De Las Flores
Chino Hills, CA 91709
Contact: James Lohan Project Mgr
Tel: 909-456-8905
Email: james@abellmarketinggroup.com
Website: www.abellmarketinggroup.com
Protective clothing & medical/industrial nitrile, vinyl & latex gloves. (Woman, estab 1998, empl 2, sales $375,000, cert: WBENC)

1606 Blubandoo Inc.
27128-B Paseo Espada Ste 602
San Juan Capistrano, CA 92675
Contact: Cindy Benedict President
Tel: 949-240-2617
Email: cindy@blubandoo.com
Website: www.blubandoo.com
Cooling headwear: caps/hats, fashionable visors, neckbands, cool ties, headbands & doorags. (Woman, estab 1993, empl 2, sales $5,500,000, cert: CPUC)

1607 Clipper Corporation
21124 Figueroa St
Carson, CA 90745
Contact: Deena Conner VP, Business Units
Tel: 310-533-8585
Email: deena.conner@clippercorp.com
Website: www.clippercorp.com
Mfr & dist uniforms & smallwares. (Woman/As-Pac, Hisp, estab , empl 45, sales $30,000,000, cert: WBENC)

1608 College Express West, LLC
1392 E Palomar St Ste 403
Chula Vista, CA 91913
Contact: Mgr
Tel: 866-448-7865
Email:
Website: www.expressluggageworldwide.com
Dist luggage, briefcases, notebook/computer cases & accessories. (AA, estab 2005, empl 3, sales , cert: State)

1609 ECO Trend Cases, LLC
14242 Ventura Blvd Ste 203
Sherman Oaks, CA 91423
Contact: Sandy Rouse CEO
Tel: 310-770-6422
Email: srouse@ecostylecases.com
Website: www.ecostylecases.com
Mfr laptop, netbook & iPad cases: topload shoulder case, backpack, messenger case, rolling case & sleeves. (Woman, estab 2009, empl 4, sales $150,000, cert: WBENC)

1610 Kool Breeze Solar Hats, Inc.
827 E Princeton
Fresno, CA 93704
Contact: Tommie Nellon Owner
Tel: 559-456-8510
Email: tnellon@koolbreezesolarhat.com
Website: www.koolbreezesolarhat.com
Mfr solar cooling hats, Kool Breeze Solar Hats. (Woman/AA, estab 2012, empl 11, sales $205,000, cert: City)

1611 The Green Garmento, LLC
20109 Nordhoff St
Chatsworth, CA 91311
Contact: Jennie Nigrosh CEO
Tel: 323-512-2600
Email: jennie@thegreengarmento.com
Website: www.thegreengarmeno.com
A reusable dry-cleaning bag, eco-friendly all-in-one laundry, reusable hanging garment bag, carrying & duffel bag, hanger hamper, "green" drycleaning bag. (Woman, estab 2008, empl 6, sales , cert: WBENC)

Connecticut

1612 PrintabiliTees, LLC
180 Turn Of River Rd Ste 13D
Stamford, CT 06905
Contact: Jere Eaton President
Tel: 203-322-3390
Email: jere@printabilitees.com
Website: www.printabilitees.com
Custom apparel: screen printing, embroidery, document printing & promotional products. (Woman/AA, estab 2004, empl 1, sales $180,000, cert: State, NMSDC)

Florida

1613 Supreme Discount Uniforms, LLC
7410 SW 15th St
Plantation, FL 33317
Contact: Victor Albo Dir Sales/Marketing
Tel: 877-535-2540
Email: victor@supremediscountuniforms.com
Website: http://discountuniformsonline.com
Uniforms, embroidered lab coats, maintenance uniforms, housekeeping uniforms & embroidered polo t-shirts. (Hisp, estab 2009, empl 2, sales $168,000, cert: State)

1614 Tampa T-Shirts
5112 N 22nd St
Tampa, FL 33610
Contact: Juan Davis Mgr
Tel: 813-879-3298
Email: juan@fastlaneclothing.com
Website: www.fastlaneclothing.com
Apparel, logo shirts, lab coats, promotional items. (Woman/Hisp, estab 1985, empl 19, sales $1,480,000, cert: State, City)

1615 Tavarez Sporting Goods
1840 22nd St
Miami, FL 33145
Contact: Manuel Tavarez Managing Partner
Tel: 347-441-9690
Email: tavarezsports@gmail.com
Website: www.tavarezsports.com
Sporting goods & fitness apparel, baseballs, softballs, baseball bats, gloves, batting gloves, catcher's equipment, helmets, volleyballs, soccer balls, basketballs, boxing equipment, martial arts equipment, sports bags to sports apparel. (Hisp, estab 2014, empl 5, sales , cert: NMSDC)

1616 The Beach Collection, Inc.
4855 Pembroke Rd
Hollywood, FL 33021
Contact: Oscar Guzman Presdient
Tel: 954-393-4029
Email: animalprints@bellsouth.net
Website:
Embroidery scrubs, uniforms, t-shirts, sweatshirts, beach towels. (Hisp, estab 1981, empl 3, sales $500,000, cert: NMSDC)

1617   Uniform Advantage Corporate Solutions
       101 NE 3rd Ave Ste 2000
       Fort Lauderdale, FL 33301
       Contact: Dir of Strategic Business Dev
       Tel: 844-694-8358
       Email:
       Website: http://uacorporate.com/
Develops, manufactures, and distributes uniforms for the
healthcare, culinary, and hospitality industries. (Woman,
estab 2002, empl 432, sales , cert: WBENC)

Georgia

1618   ERB Industries, Inc.
       1 Safety Way
       Woodstock, GA 30188
       Contact: Jackie Barker EVP
       Tel: 770-926-7944
       Email: jbarker@e-erb.com
       Website: www.e-erb.com
Mfr & dist personal protective equipment & uniform
apparel: head, eye, face, body & hand protection, hard
hats, safety glasses, high visibility apparel, aprons, smocks,
lab coats. (Woman, estab 1956, empl 100, sales , cert:
WBENC)

1619   J.W. Outfitters
       3012 Oakcliff Industrial St
       Atlanta, GA 30340
       Contact: Michael Brautigan Controller
       Tel: 800-554-7662
       Email: michael.brautigan@jwoutfitters.com
       Website: www.jwoutfitters.com
Uniform programs, logo apparel & corporate apparel.
(Woman, estab 1975, empl 48, sales $7,500,000, cert:
WBENC)

1620   O.G.I.H. Enterprises, Inc.
       201 17th St NW, Ste 30303
       Atlanta, GA 30363
       Contact: Benny Nesbitt, Jr. CEO
       Tel: 404-478-7852
       Email: b.nesbitt@ogih-enterprises.com
       Website: www.invisibleigloves.com
Dist work safety gloves, protective clothing. (AA, estab
2012, empl 4, sales , cert: State)

1621   Staffwear 2
       155 Westridge Pkwy, Ste 307
       McDonough, GA 30253
       Contact: Towanda Scott Presdient
       Tel: 800-727-9289
       Email: t.scott@staffwear2.com
       Website: www.staffwear2.com
Corporate branded apparel & national uniform programs.
(Woman/AA, estab 2008, empl 10, sales $502,438, cert:
NMSDC)

Hawaii

1622   Coradorables,LLC
       1707 Mahani Loop
       Honolulu, HI 96819
       Contact: Cora Spearman CEO
       Tel: 808-782-4267
       Email: coraspearman@hotmail.com
       Website: http://coradorables.com
Men , women, children's hats and clothing, specializing in
men's button down s/s shirts, boys button down s/s shirts,
girls dresses. (Woman/AA, Nat Ame, estab 2010, empl 20,
sales , cert: WBENC)

Illinois

1623   JERO Medical Equipment & Supplies, Inc.
       4108 W Division St
       Chicago, IL 60651
       Contact: President
       Tel: 312-829-5376
       Email:
       Website: http://jeromedical.com
Mfr disposbable wearing apparels, kit assembler, 1st aid,
disaster, admission. (AA, estab 1987, empl 24, sales
$4,000,000, cert: City)

1624   McKlein Company, LLC
       4447 W. Cortland St
       Chicago, IL 60639
       Contact: Parinda Saetia CEO
       Tel: 773-235-0600
       Email: psaetia@mckleincompany.com
       Website: www.mckleincompany.com
Mfr briefcases, computer cases, luggage, travel bags.
(Woman/As-Pac, estab 1997, empl 12, sales $7,507,695,
cert: WBENC)

Indiana

1625   RiverCity Workwear LLC
       4020 Earnings Way
       New Albany, IN 47150
       Contact: Tina Dotson
       Tel: 812-948-9020
       Email: tina@rivercityworkwear.com
       Website: www.rivercityworkwear.com
Dist safety glasses, hard hats, safety vest, shirts,
rainwear, steel & non steel toe boots, tshirts, polos,
jackets. (Woman, estab 2004, empl 3, sales , cert: State)

Louisiana

1626   Abform, Inc.
       167 Industrial Pkwy
       Lafayette, LA 70508
       Contact: Kim Leblanc Comptroller
       Tel: 337-837-9675
       Email: kim@abform.com
       Website: www.abform.com
Dist uniforms & work wear. (Woman, estab 1981, empl
20, sales , cert: WBENC)

1627   Cayenne Marketing
       2224 Shumark Trail
       Bossier City, LA 71111
       Contact: Jennifer LaPierre Owner
       Tel: 318-828-4684
       Email: jennifer@cayennemarketing.com
       Website: www.cayennemarketing.com
Advertising specialties, promotional items, custom
apparel to gifts. (Woman, estab 2004, empl 2, sales
$600,000, cert: WBENC)

1628   Denison Consulting Group LLC
       6221 S Claiborne Ave Ste 450
       New Orleans, LA 70125
       Contact: Dianne Denison CEO
       Tel: 504-982-6110
       Email: sales@denisonconsultinggroup.com
       Website: www.denisonconsultinggroup.com/
Dist corporate work wear, uniforms, apparel, protective
work wear, industrial clothing, flame retardant (FR)
clothing, FR shirts, FR pants, FR coveralls, FR coats, FR
jackets, FR jeans, rainwear, raingear. (Woman, estab
2015, empl 6, sales , cert: WBENC)

Maryland

1629   janlitlfeather
       3813 Terka Circle
       Randallstown, MD 21133
       Contact: Stephanie Gladden CEO
       Tel: 410-830-9244
       Email: janlitlfeather@aol.com
       Website: http://janlitlfeather.com
Signature feathered ponytail holder, key chains, car mirror
hangs, bow ties, earrings, neck ties, hat clips & hair
accessories. (Woman/AA, estab 2010, empl 1, sales , cert:
NMSDC)

1630   Unitec Distribution Systems
       289 E Green St
       Westminster, MD 21157
       Contact: Elise Elfman CEO
       Tel: 410-876-6227
       Email: eelfman@unitec-corp.com
       Website: www.unitec-corp.com
Provide uniforms & Total Uniform Management Solution
(TUMS). (Woman, estab 1927, empl 22, sales $5,000,000,
cert: State, WBENC)

Michigan

1631   BluCase
       6026 Kalamazoo Ave. Ste. 237
       Grand Rapids, MI 49508
       Contact: Bill McCurdy CEO
       Tel: 708-263-9522
       Email: bmccurdy@blucase.com
       Website: http://blucase.com
Mfr innovative cellphone accessory products. (AA, estab
2014, empl 5, sales $12,000,000, cert: NMSDC)

1632   Stars Clothing Manufacturing Company
       300 River Place, Ste 5350
       Detroit, MI 48226
       Contact: Darrell Washington Presdient
       Tel: 734-476-6709
       Email: dw@starsactivewear.com
       Website: http://starsactivewear.com
Mfr men and women apparel. (AA, estab 2017, empl 3,
sales , cert: NMSDC)

1633   StarSource Management Services, Inc.
       39080 Webb Dr
       Westland, MI 48185
       Contact: Melvin Brown CEO
       Tel: 734-721-8540
       Email: sales@starsourceinc.com
       Website: www.starsourceinc.com
Dist uniforms, protective clothing, cutting tools, fasteners,
janitorial chemical supplies, cleaning equipment, paper
towels, plastic liners, welding supplies, automotive
cleaning supplies, cooling tower chemicals, laundry
services. (AA, estab , empl , sales $6,000,000, cert:
NMSDC)

Missouri

1634   Cherry
       1712 Main St, Ste 232
       Kansas City, MO 64108
       Contact: Thalia Cherry Presdient
       Tel: 816-377-1832
       Email: info@cherrysportsgear.com
       Website: www.cherrysportsgear.com
Sporting goods, corporate apparel, tee shirts, athletic
equipment & uniforms. (AA, estab 2011, empl 3, sales ,
cert: NMSDC)

North Carolina

1635   Century Hosiery, Inc.
       P.O. Box 1410
       Denton, NC 27239
       Contact: Presdient
       Tel: 336-859-3806
       Email:
       Website: www.centuryhosiery.com
Mfr hosiery products. (Woman, estab 1989, empl 120,
sales $6,000,000, cert: State, WBENC)

1636   Gems Manufacturing Systems division of Indogem
       Inc.
       706 Statesville Road
       North Wilkesboro, NC 28659
       Contact: Presdient
       Tel: 610-481-0132
       Email:
       Website: www.gemsmfg.com
Mfr special purpose gloves for the military. (As-Ind, As-
Pac, estab 1993, empl 20, sales $1,600,000, cert: State,
City)

New Jersey

1637   Design Alternatives NY LLC
       169 Boyd Ave
       Jersey City, NJ 07304
       Contact: Cenia Peredes Presdient
       Tel: 973-583-9553
       Email: cenia@ceniany.com
       Website: https://goo.gl/3f8E3Q
Women's Apparel (Minority, estab , empl 2, sales , cert:
NMSDC)

1638   Shani International Corporation
       8 Conifer Dr
       Warren, NJ 07059
       Contact: Arti Mohin VP
       Tel: 908-484-7070
       Email: arti@shaniintl.com
       Website: www.shaniintl.com
Mfr & import uniforms (knit & woven tops & bottoms),
lab & chef coats, aprons, non-woven bags & basic
fashion items. (Woman/As-Ind, estab 2005, empl 4, sales
, cert: NMSDC)

1639   Tronex International Inc
       300 International Dr
       Mount Olive, NJ 07828
       Contact: Edmund Tai VP, Healthcare Division
       Tel: 973-355-2888
       Email: etai@tronexcompany.com
       Website: www.tronexcompany.com
Dist disposable gloves & apparel products. (As-Pac, estab
, empl , sales , cert: NMSDC)

Nevada

1640   Dellrone Services LLC
       8550 W Charleston Blvd, Ste 228
       Las Vegas, NV 89117
       Contact: Willie Endsley President
       Tel: 702-457-7855
       Email: admin@dellroneservices.com
       Website: www.dellroneservices.com
Dist safety clothing & equipment: fire safety jacket &
pants, helmets, construction safety clothing: helmets,
jackets, parkas, rain coats, safety vest, goggles & shoes.
(Woman/AA, estab 2010, empl 4, sales , cert: NMSDC)

New York

1641 Hamburger Woolen Company
23 Denton Ave
New Hyde Park, NY 11040
Contact: Ilene Rosen President
Tel: 516-352-7400
Email: irosen@hwcny.com
Website: www.hwcny.com
Dist uniform fabrics, law enforcement & public safety equipment: duty belts, flashlights, raincoats, reflective vests, protective eyewear & earwear. (Woman, estab 1940, empl 12, sales $6,105,831, cert: State, City)

1642 PKP Industries, Inc.
1407 Broadway Ste 3412
New York, NY 10018
Contact: Puneet Pasricha
Tel: 646-586-3044
Email: puneet@pkpindustries.com
Website: www.pkpindustries.com
Wholesale apparel, clothing, women's tops, bottoms, skirts, dresses, pants. (Woman/As-Ind, estab 2014, empl 1, sales , cert: NMSDC)

1643 S & H Uniform Corp.
1 Aqueduct Rd
White Plains, NY 10606
Contact: RRosa Greco VP
Tel: 914-937-6800
Email: info@sandhuniforms.com
Website: www.sandhuniforms.com
Workwear & footwear, outerwear/jackets, coveralls, hats, shirts, polos, t-shirts, pants, shorts, vests, flame resistant wear, Hi visibility, boots & shoes, medical uniforms, aprons, chef's apparel. (Woman, estab 1969, empl 40, sales $8,500,000, cert: City)

1644 Salsa-The Designer Solution LLC.
1441 Broadway 3 Fl, Ste 3021
New York, NY 10018
Contact: Gigi De Jesus-Frerichs Presdient
Tel: 212-575-6565
Email: gigi@gicleeapparel.com
Website: www.SalsaProfessionalApparel.com
Mfr uniforms, sports apparel, collegiate apparel, varsity-wear, tees, tanks, polo shirts, sweatshirts, shorts, pants, lounge-wear & pajamas. (Woman/Hisp, estab 2000, empl 6, sales $10,000,000, cert: State, City, NMSDC, WBENC)

Ohio

1645 Alma Mater Designs LLC
117 W Church St
Oxford, OH 45056
Contact: Owner
Tel: 513-368-9839
Email:
Website: www.AlmaMaterDesigns.com
Custom woven, logo-branded fabric elements. (Woman, estab 2011, empl 2, sales , cert: NWBOC)

1646 Liniform Service
1050 Northview Ave
Barberton, OH 44203
Contact: Jennifer Peroli VP
Tel: 330-825-6911
Email: jenniferperoli@liniform.com
Website: http://liniform.com
Uniforms: lab coats, scrubs, jackets, warm-up jackets, maintenance uniforms, chef coats & cook apparel. Linens: patient gowns, mammo capes, sheets, pillow-cases, blankets, towels & washcloths, tablecloths, skirting, napkins. (Woman, estab 1924, empl 60, sales $4,700,000, cert: WBENC)

1647 MASCOT Workwear
320 Springfield Dr, Ste 150
Fairlawn, OH 44333
Contact: Michael Allio Sales
Tel: 330-618-3997
Email: michael@maworkwear.com
Website: www.mascotworkwear.com
Dist MASCOT Workwear in North America. (Woman, estab 2013, empl 7, sales $1,000,000, cert: WBENC)

1648 RJ Manray - Promotional Products
9500 Springfield Rd, Unit 5
Poland, OH 44514
Contact: Rowena Henderson CEO
Tel: 234-201-0160
Email: rrlimos18@gmail.com
Website: www.rjmanray.com/
Dist personalized and custom logo tote bags. (Woman, estab 1986, empl 11, sales $640,000, cert: WBENC)

1649 VDP Safety & Uniforms Ltd.
11811 Shaker Blvd Ste 416
Cleveland, OH 44120
Contact: Phoebe Lee Presdient
Tel: 216-352-1026
Email: info@vdpsafety.com
Website: www.vdpsafety.com
Uniform apparel & safety supplies/equipment: high visibility shirts, safety vests, hard hats, traffic cones, jackets, hospital uniforms. (Woman/AA, estab 2013, empl 1, sales , cert: State)

Texas

1650 Career Uniforms
3800 Juniper
Houston, TX 77087
Contact: Presdient
Tel: 713-645-3600
Email:
Website: www.careeruniforms.com
Mfr uniforms: medical, governmental & restaurant. (As-Ind, estab 1980, empl 25, sales , cert: NMSDC)

1651 Fresh Comfort, Inc.
3200 Rifle Gap Rd, Ste 1470
Frisco, TX 75034
Contact: Maria E. Valencia President & CEO
Tel: 214-705-0408
Email: maria.valencia@freshcomfortinc.com
Website: http://freshcomfortinc.com
Adaptive intimate apparel (bras, panties, boxers), front Velcro & zipper closure bras for easy dressing & undressing, seamless bra & underwear. (Woman/Hisp, estab 2012, empl 1, sales , cert: State)

1652   RG Apparel Co.
       2912 N MacArthur, Ste 103
       Irving, TX 75062
       Contact: Joe Temple COO
       Tel: 972-793-0583
       Email: jt@rgapparel.com
       Website: www.rgapparel.com
Mfr textiles: uniforms, work shirts, polos, tees, woven button up shirts & headwear, promotional marketing items & gifts. (AA, estab 2006, empl 6, sales $3,200,000, cert: State, NMSDC)

1653   Santex
       4211 W Illinois, Ste 100
       Dallas, TX 75211
       Contact: Jose Lopez Owner
       Tel: 214-256-2169
       Email: karla.leal@santexallsports.com
       Website: www.santexallsports.com
Manufacturing business uniforms. (Hisp, estab 2013, empl 4, sales $160,000, cert: State)

1654   Wholesale T-shirts Depot, Inc.
       11311 Harry Hines Blvd, Ste 201
       Dallas, TX 75229
       Contact: Joe Turner Exec VP
       Tel: 972-243-4785
       Email: info@wtdapparel.com
       Website: www.wtdapparel.com
Licensed military branded apparel & accessories. (As-Pac, estab 2006, empl 18, sales $2,500,000, cert: NMSDC)

Virginia

1655   First Due Gear
       2111 Apperson Dr
       Salem, VA 24153
       Contact: Sarah Fuhrman Owner
       Tel: 540-725-8850
       Email: firstduegear@yahoo.com
       Website: www.firstduegear.com
Dist Fire, EMS, swiftwater & technical rescue gear, apparel & equipment. (Woman, estab 2006, empl 1, sales , cert: State)

1656   Global Partner's of Virginia, LLC
       3005 E Boundary Terr, Ste G
       Midlothian, VA 23112
       Contact: Norm Falkner VP
       Tel: 804-744-8112
       Email: logos@globalpromosonline.com
       Website: www.globalpromosonline.com
Logo wear, embroidery, silk screen, screen printing, direct to garment ink jet printing, heat transfer. Corporate apparel, mens, ladies, kids, uniforms. Promotional Products, pens, magnets, calendars, Bags, towels, luggage, sportwear, team uniforms. (Woman, estab 2001, empl 4, sales $350,000, cert: State)

1657   Sayre Enterprises Inc.
       45 Natural Bridge School Rd
       Natural Bridge Station, VA 24579
       Contact: Danielle Ayres Commericial Rep
       Tel: 800-552-6064
       Email: dayres@sayreinc.com
       Website: www.sayreinc.com
Reflective products: vests, belts, headbands, wrist & arm bands. (Woman, estab 1987, empl 104, sales $9,092,000, cert: State)

1658   The Todd Venture Group
       11625 Busy St
       Richmond, VA 23236
       Contact: Andy Todd VP Sales
       Tel: 804-379-4269
       Email: andy@hitechribbongroup.com
       Website: www.snapsupplies.com
Dist disposable gloves. (Woman, estab 1983, empl 6, sales $1,600,000, cert: State)

1659   The Uniform Store, LLC
       10 Weems Lane
       Winchester, VA 22601
       Contact: President & CEO
       Tel: 540-678-8711
       Email:
       Website: www.uniformstoreonline.com
Dist ChefWorks, Edwards Garments & Uncommon Threads for men & women in chef coats (executive chef & basic), kitchen shirts, pants, aprons, headwear, neckwear, front of the house (shirts, blouses, pants, vests, ties). (Woman, estab 2009, empl 5, sales $455,781, cert: State, WBENC)

Washington

1660   Bootie Shoe Cover Inc
       5616 NE 55 Circle
       Vancouver, WA 98661
       Contact: Marla Gillette Presdient
       Tel: 360-903-0992
       Email: info@bootieshoecover.com
       Website: www.bootieshoecover.com
Dist reusable shoe covers. (Woman, estab 2009, empl 3, sales , cert: WBENC)

ARCHITECTS
Most firms have agreements with other state architects permitting them to work anywhere in the nation. Nearly all are members of the American Institute of Architects (AIA). (See ENGINEERING & SURVEYING SERVICES for civil, structural, electrical and mechanical engineers).   NAICS Code 54

Arizona

1661 Fore Dimensions LLC
      3337 E. Sells Dr
      Phoenix, AZ 85018
      Contact: Lisa Foreman Principal
      Tel: 602-748-4664
      Email: lisa@foredimensions.com
      Website: www.foredimensions.com
Architectural consulting, remodel, tenant improvements & new construction for transportation facilities, wet & dry labs, clean rooms, testing buildings, office & training centers. (Woman, estab 2001, empl 2, sales $500,000, cert: State, City, WBENC)

California

1662 Aetypic, Inc.
      7 Freelon St
      San Francisco, CA 94107
      Contact: Dennis Wong
      Tel: 415-762-8388
      Email: dennis.wong@aetypic.com
      Website: http://aetypic.com
Architecture & engineering services: structural engineering, civil engineering, construction engineering & inspection, technology integration, & sustainable design. (As-Pac, estab 2011, empl 25, sales , cert: State, NMSDC)

1663 Blackbird Associates, Inc.
      2320 J St
      Sacramento, CA 95816
      Contact: Franc Blackbird Presdient
      Tel: 916-446-6227
      Email: franc@blackbirdassoc.com
      Website: www.blackbirdassoc.com
Architecture and Project Management. (Woman/Nat Ame, estab 1994, empl 7, sales $1,311,000, cert: NMSDC, WBENC)

1664 H. Hendy Associates
      4770 Campus Dr Ste 100
      Newport Beach, CA 92660
      Contact: Heidi Hendy Principal
      Tel: 949-851-3080
      Email: hhendy@hhendy.com
      Website: www.hhendy.com
Interior architecture firm. (Woman, estab 1979, empl 30, sales $4,800,000, cert: CPUC, WBENC)

1665 Line2Line Architectural Design Group, LLP
      2413 Webb Ave Ste D
      Alameda, CA 94501
      Contact: Angelus Cheng Principal
      Tel: 510-995-8278
      Email: info@line2lineadg.com
      Website: www.line2lineadg.com
Architectural & design, Feasibility Studies, ADA Consultation, Sustainability, Programming, Urban/Site Planning, Entitlement, Due Diligence, Project Mgmt, Site & Building Evaluations, Interior Design, Design presentations. (Woman/As-Pac, estab 2012, empl 4, sales $354,156, cert: NMSDC)

1666 M+M Design Construction Project Management
      1503 Bainum Dr
      Topanga, CA 90290
      Contact: Mohan Joshi Presdient
      Tel: 310-455-0064
      Email: mjoshi@mpji.net
      Website: www.mpji.net
Architecture, interior design, planning & advisory services. (As-Ind, estab 2002, empl 1, sales , cert: NMSDC, 8a)

1667 Source West
      1631 Aspen Grove Lane
      Diamond Bar, CA 91765
      Contact: Roberto Manzini Dir Business Dev
      Tel: 909-872-0010
      Email: r.manzini@greencubicles.com
      Website: www.greencubicles.com
Commercial architecture & interior design. (Woman, estab 1988, empl 25, sales $2,500,000, cert: State)

1668 Torres Architects, Inc.
      400 Crenshaw Blvd Ste 200
      Torrance, CA 90503
      Contact: Denise Torres Managing Principal
      Tel: 310-320-6285
      Email: denise@tarci.com
      Website: www.tarci.com
Architect, Interior Design, Computer Aided Drafting, Design, Mechanical Engineering, Electrical Engineering, Plumbing Engineering. (Hisp, estab 1991, empl 5, sales $1,127,237, cert: NMSDC)

1669 TSAO Design Group
      160 Pine St, Ste 650
      San Francisco, CA 94111
      Contact: Jonathan Tsao Principal
      Tel: 415-398-5500
      Email: jtsao@tsaodesign.com
      Website: www.tsaodesign.com
Architectural & interior design. (As-Pac, estab 1981, empl 12, sales $1,750,000, cert: CPUC)

Colorado

1670 Coover-Clark & Associates, Inc.
      1936 Market St
      Denver, CO 80202
      Contact: Carol Coover-Clark Presdient
      Tel: 303-783-0040
      Email: marketing@cooverclark.com
      Website: www.cooverclark.com
Architectural planning & design services, commercial & military aviation facilities. (Woman, estab 1987, empl 22, sales $2,800,000, cert: WBENC)

Connecticut

1671 Bavier Design, LLC
      277 Rowayton Ave
      Rowayton, CT 06853
      Contact: Anne Bavier Principal
      Tel: 203-388-1818
      Email: abavier@bavierdesign.com
      Website: www.bavierdesign.com
Architectural & interior design. (Woman, estab 2004, empl 8, sales $1,255,000, cert: WBENC)

District of Columbia

1672   Systems Design, Inc.
       1420 9th St NW
       Washington, DC 20001
       Contact: Darlene Mathis CEO
       Tel: 202-232-5631
       Email: meka_mathis@msn.com
       Website: www.systemsdesignbuild.com
Interior design, space planning, architectural design svcs,
also dist lamps, tables, tile, window treatments & systems
furniture. (Woman/AA, estab 2002, empl 6, sales
$700,000, cert: 8a)

Florida

1673   Architechnical, Inc.
       2908 Clubhouse Dr
       Plant City, FL 33566
       Contact: Erick Gulke Presdient
       Tel: 813-312-2455
       Email: egulke@architechnical.biz
       Website: www.architechnical.biz
Architectural design solutions & environments. (Hisp,
estab 2008, empl 3, sales , cert: City)

1674   Architectural Design Collaborative
       235 Alcazar Ave
       Coral Gables, FL 33134
       Contact: Raymundo Feito Presdient
       Tel: 305-442-1188
       Email: rfeito@adcinternational.net
       Website: www.adcinternational.net
Architectural, planning & interior design. (Hisp, estab
1984, empl 25, sales $7,600,000, cert: NMSDC)

1675   MGE Architects, Inc.
       3081 Salzedo St, 3rd Fl
       Coral Gables, FL 33134
       Contact: Jose Estevez Presdient
       Tel: 305-444-0413
       Email: jestevez@mgearchitects.com
       Website: www.mgearchitects.com
Architectural services: private health systems, major
government hospitals, teaching facilities & small community hospitals. (Hisp, estab 1982, empl 23, sales
$7,937,182, cert: State)

1676   Rhodes+Brito Architects
       605 E Robinson St, Ste 750
       Orlando, FL 32801
       Contact: Office Mgr
       Tel: 407-648-7288
       Email:
       Website: www.rbarchitects.com
Architectural Services. (AA, estab 1996, empl 19, sales
$3,024,653, cert: State, City, 8a)

Georgia

1677   GSB Architects & Interiors, Inc.
       3091 E Shadowlawn Ave NE
       Atlanta, GA 30305
       Contact: Jennifer Mercier Interior Designer
       Tel: 770-633-5952
       Email: jennifer@gsbarchitects.com
       Website: www.gsbarchitects.com
Architectural and interior design. (Woman/Hisp, estab
1998, empl 9, sales $2,900,000, cert: NMSDC, WBENC)

Illinois

1678   Bailey Edward Design, Inc.
       35 E Wacker Dr Ste 2800
       Chicago, IL 60601
       Contact: Ellen B. Dickson President
       Tel: 312-440-2300
       Email: edickson@baileyedward.com
       Website: www.baileyedward.com
Architectural services, Interior design services, Drafting
services, Building inspection services
Engineering Services, Historical Preservation, Cost
Estimating (Woman, estab 1991, empl 39, sales
$2,973,760, cert: State, City, WBENC, SDB)

1679   Bauer Latoza Studio, Ltd.
       2241 S Wabash
       Chicago, IL 60616
       Contact: Edward Torrez Presdient
       Tel: 312-567-1000
       Email: etorrez@bauerlatozastudio.com
       Website: www.bauerlatozastudio.com
Architectural design, evaluation & renovation services.
(Hisp, estab 1990, empl 12, sales $2,195,986, cert: State)

1680   Brook Architecture
       2325 S Michigan Ave Ste 300
       Chicago, IL 60616
       Contact: Jeanne Franks Dir of Marketing
       Tel: 312-528-0890
       Email: jfranks@brookarchitecture.com
       Website: http://brookarchitecture.com
Design, urban planning, consulting, project management
& services, new construction & renovation of institutional, residential, office & retail spaces. (Woman/AA,
estab 1995, empl 6, sales $1,495,915, cert: State, City,
NMSDC, 8a)

1681   EC Purdy & Associates
       53 W Jackson Blvd Ste 1631
       Chicago, IL 60604
       Contact: Elizabeth Purdy architect
       Tel: 312-408-1631
       Email: ecpurdy@ecpurdy.com
       Website: www.ecpurdy.com
Architectural, interior design planning services.
(Woman/As-Pac, estab 1994, empl , sales $563,878, cert:
State)

1682   Muller & Muller Ltd.
       700 N Sangamon
       Chicago, IL 60642
       Contact: Mark Stromberg Principal
       Tel: 312-432-4180
       Email: mstromberg@muller2.com
       Website: www.muller2.com
Architectural services: Feasibility Studies; Building
Analysis; Schematic Design; Design Development;
Construction Documents; LEED; ADA Review; Presenta-
tions; Renderings; 3D Animations; Specifications; Cost
Estimating. (Woman, estab 1984, empl 20, sales
$2,000,000, cert: State, City)

1683 Studio AH LLC dba HPZS
      213 West Institute Place Ste 502
      Chicago, IL 60610
      Contact: April Hughes Owner
      Tel: 312-944-9600
      Email: ahughes@hpzs.com
      Website: www.hpzs.com
Architectural design, Interior Design, Historic Preservation,
Facade Maintenance & Sustainable Design, green renova-
tion & design services. (Woman, estab 2015, empl 4, sales
$133,310, cert: State, WBENC)

1684 Tigerman McCurry Architects
      444 N Wells St Ste 206
      Chicago, IL 60654
      Contact: Margaret McCurry Presdient
      Tel: 312-644-5880
      Email: tma@tigerman-mccurry.com
      Website: http://Tigerman-McCurry.com
Architectural & interior design services. (Woman, estab
1967, empl 10, sales $1,200,000, cert: City)

Indiana

1685 Brenner Design Incorporated
      620 N Delaware St
      Indianapolis, IN 46204
      Contact: Diana Brenner Presdient
      Tel: 317-262-1220
      Email: dbrenner@brennerdesign.com
      Website: www.brennerdesign.com
Architecture; Interior Architecture; Historic Preservation;
Interior Design; Furniture Management Services; Owner's
Representative Services; Space Planning; Project Manage-
ment. (Woman, estab 1992, empl 10, sales , cert: State,
City, WBENC)

1686 Jung Design, Inc.
      8910 Purdue Rd Ste 680
      Indianapolis, IN 46268
      Contact: Connie Jung President
      Tel: 317-471-1221
      Email: cjung@jungdes.com
      Website: www.jungdes.com
Architectural & interior design services, master planning,
signage, programming, space planning. (Woman, estab
2004, empl 3, sales $200,000, cert: State)

1687 Rowland Design, Inc.
      702 N Capitol Ave
      Indianapolis, IN 46204
      Contact: Sarah Schwartzkopf CEO
      Tel: 317-636-3980
      Email: smschwartzkopf@rowlanddesign.com
      Website: http://rowlanddesign.com
Architecture, interior design & graphic design. (Woman,
estab 1968, empl 32, sales $4,050,000, cert: State)

1688 Studio 3 Design, Inc.
      8604 Allisonville Rd Ste 330
      Indianapolis, IN 46250
      Contact: Heather Leslie President
      Tel: 317-595-1000
      Email: hleslie@studio3design.net
      Website: www.studio3design.net
Architectural & interior design services. (Woman, estab
2002, empl 7, sales , cert: State)

1689 WDi Architecture, Inc.
      15 W 28th St
      Indianapolis, IN 46208
      Contact: Williams-Dotson Daryl CEO
      Tel: 317-251-6172
      Email: daryl_wd@wdiarchitecture.com
      Website: www.wdiarchitecture.com
Architectural design, space planning & programming,
feasibility studies, facilities evaluation, project
managment & existing conditions documentation.
(Woman/AA, estab 1995, empl 5, sales $400,000, cert:
State, City, WBENC)

Kentucky

1690 First World Architects Studio, PSC
      15 E 9th St
      Covington, KY 41011
      Contact: B. Charles Alexander Presdient
      Tel: 859-431-1999
      Email: alexcama@fuse.net
      Website: www.1stworldarchitectsstudio.com
Architectural & engineering services: master planning &
project mgmt, construction mgmt, design/build, facility
assessments. (AA, estab 1982, empl 6, sales $415,000,
cert: State, 8a)

Louisiana

1691 Marrero Couvillon & Associates, LLC
      4354 S Sherwood Forest Blvd, Ste D200
      Baton Rouge, LA 70816
      Contact: Stacey Vincent Procurement Mgr
      Tel: 225-408-8249
      Email: svincent@mca-llc.com
      Website: http://mca-llc.com
Architectural Services and Construction Management
(Hisp, estab 1968, empl 17, sales $2,800,000, cert: State,
NMSDC, 8a, SDB)

Maryland

1692 K. Dixon Architecture, PLLC
      137 National Plaza, Ste 300
      National Harbor, MD 20745
      Contact: Principal
      Tel: 301-364-5053
      Email:
      Website: www.kdixonarchitecture.com
Architectural design & planning services: commercial,
education, government, residential, and institutional.
(Woman/AA, estab 2003, empl 1, sales $100,000, cert:
State, City, WBENC)

1693 Mimar Architects & Engineers, Inc.
      7004 Security Blvd Ste 210
      Baltimore, MD 21244
      Contact: Maria Khalid Marketing Coord
      Tel: 410-944-4900
      Email: mkhalid@mimarch.net
      Website: http://mimarch.net
Architectural-engineering, architectural/planning,
interior/graphic design, engineering & construction
management services. (As-Ind, estab 1995, empl 25,
sales $3,991,379, cert: State)

1694 NFD, Inc.
124 Lakefront Dr
Hunt Valley, MD 21030
Contact: Laura Schlicht Business Develop Dir
Tel: 410-785-7795
Email: lschlicht@nfd.com
Website: www.nfd.com
Commercial interior design & planning: programming & budgeting; schematic design; furniture/equipment inventorying; space planning; 3D modeling; furniture & finish specs; project coordination. (Woman, estab 1978, empl 9, sales $973,000, cert: State, City, WBENC)

1695 Sugar Associates, LLC
2909 Old Court Rd
Baltimore, MD 21208
Contact: Karen Sugar Presdient
Tel: 410-602-2909
Email: karen@sugarassociates.com
Website: www.sugarassociates.com
Interior design & planning, space programming, 24-hour-turn-around space planning & facility planning services. (Minority, Woman, estab , empl , sales $212,000, cert: State, City)

Michigan

1696 Gala & Associates Inc.
31455 Southfield Rd
Beverly Hills, MI 48025
Contact: Chuni Gala Presdient
Tel: 248-642-8610
Email: cgala@galaandassociates.com
Website: www.galaandassociates.com
Electrical, mechanical, structural, civil & architectural engineering svcs, CAD services. (Nat Ame, As-Ind, Hisp, estab 1987, empl 50, sales $6,000,000, cert: NMSDC)

Minnesota

1697 Studio Hive Inc.
901 N Third St, Ste 228
Minneapolis, MN 55401
Contact: Shari Bjork Principal
Tel: 612-279-0430
Email: sbjork@studiohive.com
Website: www.studiohive.com
Architectural & interior design. (Woman, estab 2003, empl 8, sales $1,098,036, cert: State)

1698 Welsh Architecture LLC
4350 Baker Rd Ste 400
Minnetonka, MN 55343
Contact: Linda Solberg Dir Corporate Services
Tel: 952-897-7854
Email: lsolberg@welshco.com
Website: www.welshco.com
Providing comprehensive architectural, design & project management services. (Woman, estab 1995, empl 11, sales $2,300,000, cert: WBENC)

Missouri

1699 Arcturis, Inc.
720 Olive St Ste 200
St. Louis, MO 63101
Contact: Julie Keil Principal
Tel: 314-206-7100
Email: jkeil@arcturis.com
Website: www.arcturis.com
Architecture, interior design, landscape architecture, urban planning, graphic design, workplace optimization, master planning, site planning & building evaluation services. (Woman, estab 1977, empl 50, sales $8,500,000, cert: State, WBENC)

1700 Bozoian Group Architects, LLC
2201 S Brentwood Blvd Ste 105
St. Louis, MO 63144
Contact: Katherine Bozoian President
Tel: 314-962-4100
Email: information@bozoiangroup.com
Website: www.bozoiangroup.com
Architectural svcs: master planning, facility & needs assessment, new building design, renovation, interior design, adaptive re-use, re-purpose, sustainable design, owners representation, construction administration. (Woman, estab 1996, empl 6, sales $958,000, cert: State, WBENC)

1701 CORE10 Architecture
4501 Lindell Blvd Ste 1a
St. Louis, MO 63108
Contact: Michael Byrd
Tel: 314-726-4858
Email: mbyrd@core10architecture.com
Website: http://core10architecture.com
Architecture, Interior Design, Master Planning, Sustainable Design, LEED, Residential, Mixed Use, Multi-Family, Commercial, Office, Industrial. (AA, As-Pac, Hisp, estab 2007, empl 6, sales $881,934, cert: State, City)

1702 Gray Design Group, Inc.
Nine Sunnen Dr, Ste 110
Saint Louis, MO 63143
Contact: Lorrie Kramer
Tel: 314-646-0400
Email: lkramer@graydesigngroup.com
Website: www.graydesigngroup.com
Commercial architecture & interior design. (Woman, estab , empl , sales $2,397,779, cert: State, City)

1703 Kennedy Associates/Architects, Inc.
2060 Craigshire Rd
St. Louis, MO 63146
Contact: Michael B. Kennedy, Jr. Presdient
Tel: 314-241-8188
Email: kaibuild@kai-db.com
Website: www.kai-db.com
Architecture, planning & interior design, mechanical engineering, electrical, plumbing. (AA, estab 1980, empl 110, sales $26,000,000, cert: State, City, NMSDC)

1704 Oculus Inc.
      1 S Memorial Dr, Ste 1500
      St. Louis, MO 63102
      Contact: Shevaun McNaughton Marketing Dir
      Tel: 314-367-6100
      Email: shevaunm@oculusinc.com
      Website: www.oculusinc.com
Architecture, strategic planning, interior design & move
management. (Woman, estab 1994, empl 42, sales
$6,338,825, cert: State, WBENC)

North Carolina

1705 Arcons Design Studio Professional Corporation
      10550 Independence Point Pkwy Ste 300
      Matthews, NC 28105
      Contact: Rajeev Bhave Presdient
      Tel: 704-542-5252
      Email: rbhave@arconsds.com
      Website: www.arconsds.com
Architectural services, retail, commercial, institutional and
mixed use projects. (As-Ind, Hisp, estab 2004, empl 7, sales
$1,400,000, cert: State)

1706 CSBO Architecture P.C.
      1589 Skeet Club Rd Ste 102-172
      High Point, NC 27265
      Contact: Carlos Sanchez Presdient
      Tel: 336-617-3079
      Email: carlos.sanchez@csboinc.com
      Website: www.csboinc.com
Architectural design services. (Hisp, estab 2002, empl 2,
sales , cert: State)

1707 Espinosa Architecture + Consulting, PC
      937 Bryansplace Rd
      Winston-Salem, NC 27104
      Contact: Carlos V Espinosa Presdient
      Tel: 336-407-8419
      Email: arlos@espinosaarchitecture.com
      Website: www.espinosaarchitecture.com
Architecture services, architectural design, space planning,
needs evaluation & programming, evaluation of existing
structures, cost analysis, interior design. (Hisp, estab 2014,
empl 3, sales , cert: State)

1708 Neighboring Concepts, PLLC
      1230 W Morehead St Ste 204
      Charlotte, NC 28208
      Contact: Robin Holloway Dir of Mktg
      Tel: 704-374-0916
      Email: robin@neighboringconcepts.com
      Website: www.neighboringconcepts.com
Architectural design: concept, construction, post-construction services, urban planning, development & revitaliza-
tion. (Woman/AA, As-Pac, Hisp, estab 1996, empl 17, sales
$1,903,763, cert: State)

New Jersey

1709 Gramieri Design Services
      353 Georges Rd, Ste C
      Dayton, NJ 08810
      Contact: Frank Gramieri Presdient
      Tel: 732-274-9540
      Email: fgramieri@gdsinc.net
      Website: www.gdsinc.net
Interior architectural & engineering services: site
analysis, design development, project budgeting &
programming, space planning, schematics design, 3D
rendering & modeling, architectural & engineering
contract documents. (As-Ind, Hisp, estab 1992, empl 7,
sales $638,903, cert: City, NMSDC)

1710 Kamlesh Shah Designs Inc.
      18 Lovell Dr
      Plainsboro, NJ 08536
      Contact: Kamlesh Shah Principal
      Tel: 609-655-9908
      Email: kshah@ksdarchitects.com
      Website: www.ksdarchitects.com
Architectural, Interior Space Planning, Programing, Lab
Design, Process Manufacuring Design, Mechanical,
Electrical, Plumbing, Engineering Services. (As-Pac, estab
1998, empl 6, sales $2,115,234, cert: State)

1711 O&S Associates, Inc.
      145 Main St
      Hackensack, NJ 07601
      Contact: Kelly O'Leary Dir Business Devel
      Tel: 201-488-7144
      Email: kaoleary@oandsassociates.com
      Website: www.oandsassociates.com
Planning, Design and Restoration of full building envelope, inclusive of roof, windows, facade. Specializing in
parking planning, design & restoration. Engineers and
Architects. (As-Pac, Hisp, estab 1996, empl 40, sales
$6,500,000, cert: NMSDC)

Nevada

1712 KME Architects LLC
      231 W Charleston Blvd
      Las Vegas, NV 89102
      Contact: Melvin Green Principal
      Tel: 702-888-2088
      Email: melvin@kmearchitects.com
      Website: www.kmearchitects.com/
Architectural services, interior design, landscape design,
sustainable design, Historic preservation, tenant
improvements, fire code violations, master planning,
laser scanning. (AA, Hisp, estab 2009, empl 9, sales ,
cert: NMSDC)

New York

1713 Avinash K. Malhotra Architects (AKM)
      148 W 24th St
      New York, NY 10706
      Contact: Richard Saunderson associate
      Tel: 212-808-0000
      Email: rsaunderson@akmarch.com
      Website: www.akmarch.com
Architectural solutions: high-rise buildings, large scale
conversions, historical preservation & landmarks re-use,
renovations & architectural interiors. (As-Ind, estab
1982, empl 10, sales $1,900,000, cert: State, City,
NMSDC)

1714 AWA Lighting Designers Inc.
      61 Greenpoint Ave
      Brooklyn, NY 11222
      Contact: Abhay Wadhwa CEO
      Tel: 212-473-9797
      Email: abhay@awalightingdesigners.com
      Website: www.awalightingdesigners.com
Architectural lighting design, design & implement lighting solutions for commercial, civic, cultural & residential projects. (As-Ind, estab 2011, empl 27, sales $259,715, cert: State)

1715 Foit-Albert Associates, Architecture, Engineering and Surveying, P.C.
      215 W 94th St, Ste 517
      New York, NY 10025
      Contact: Gregory Carballada Presdient
      Tel: 716-856-3933
      Email: cstoebe@foit-albert.com
      Website: www.foit-albert.com
Architecture, Engineering, Environmental & Land Surveying Consulting. (Hisp, estab 1977, empl 70, sales $10,000,000, cert: State, City)

1716 JJ Falk Design LLC
      315 Fifth Ave, 11 Fl
      New York, NY 10016
      Contact: Managing Principal
      Tel: 212-685-1913
      Email:
      Website: www.jjfalk.com
Architecture services: interior design. (Woman/AA, As-Pac, estab 1998, empl 16, sales $1,700,000, cert: State, WBENC)

1717 Kahn Architecture & Design, PC
      2 West 45th St Ste 501
      New York, NY 10036
      Contact: Heidi Kahn Presdient
      Tel: 646-253-9864
      Email: hwiley@kahnarchitecture.com
      Website: www.kahnarchitecture.com
Architecture, interior design & planning solution services to commercial and retail clients. (Woman, estab 2005, empl 17, sales $2,200,000, cert: State, City, WBENC)

1718 Kenne Shepherd Interior Design Architecture PLLC
      54 W 21st St, Ste 1208
      New York, NY 10010
      Contact: Kenne Shepherd Principal
      Tel: 212-206-6336
      Email: kshepherd@kenneshepherd.com
      Website: www.kenneshepherd.com
Multi-disciplinary interior architectural, workspace, retail store or residence, strategic planning, site evaluation, code/zoning analysis, lease/workletter review, architectural design, sustainable design, construction documents, construction observation (Woman, estab 1993, empl 3, sales , cert: WBENC)

1719 Lewandowska Architect PLLC
      14 Wall St, 20th Floor
      New York, NY 10005
      Contact: Barbara Lewandowska Principal
      Tel: 212-787-4558
      Email: barbara@lewandowskaarchitect.com
      Website: www.LewandowskaArchitect.com
Architectural, interior design & space planning services. (Woman, estab 2002, empl 3, sales $200,000, cert: State, City)

1720 SWITZER Architecture, P.C.
      255 W 36th St Ste 1101
      New York, NY 10018
      Contact: Gregory T Switzer Principal
      Tel: 212-391-1519
      Email: gswitzer@switzerarchitecture.com
      Website: www.switzerpc.com
Architectural design & holistic management. (AA, estab 2003, empl 6, sales $750,000, cert: NMSDC)

1721 ZELJKA ONE Management LLC dba: Green Way Pavement
      P.O. Box 2927
      Binghamton, NY 13902
      Contact: Robert V Gerard Co-Owner
      Tel: 607-724-2438
      Email: robertgerard@me.com
      Website: www.greenwaypavements.com
LEED architects & construction services. (Minority, Woman, estab 2011, empl , sales $11,000,000, cert: State)

Ohio

1722 Brockman Designs LLC
      27600 Chagrin Blvd Ste 260
      Cleveland, OH 44122
      Contact: Sharon Brockman Principal
      Tel: 216-504-4040
      Email: sbrockman@brockmandesigns.com
      Website: www.brockmandesigns.com
Interior design, healthcare spaces & facilities, higher education & corporate offices, interior space planning, interior finish selections & specifications, furniture planning & specifications, project coordination. (Woman, estab 2001, empl 2, sales , cert: State, City)

1723 Calvin Singleton & Associates
      13426 Cedar Rd
      Cleveland Heights, OH 44118
      Contact: Calvin M Singleton Jr. President
      Tel: 216-321-9953
      Email: csa101@att.net
      Website:
Architecture & planning services: commercial office, retail, educational, medical, transportation, institutional, restaurant, recreational, residential, new & renovated design work & interior design & planning services. (AA, estab 1984, empl 1, sales , cert: State)

1724 DNK Architects, Inc.
      2616 Central Pkwy
      Cincinnati, OH 45214
      Contact: Guinette Kirk VP
      Tel: 513-948-4146
      Email: gkirk@dnkarchitects.com
      Website: www.dnkarchitects.com
Interior design & space planning services, Cadd drafting. (AA, estab 1986, empl 20, sales $2,000,000, cert: State, NMSDC)

1725 MD Interior Environments dba Design Details
      700 W Pete Rose Way
      Cincinnati, OH 45203
      Contact: President
      Tel: 513-793-0404
      Email:
      Website: www.designstls.com
Interior design services. (Woman, estab 1994, empl 1, sales , cert: WBENC)

1726 Moody Nolan, Inc.
      300 Spruce St Ste 300
      Columbus, OH 43215
      Contact: Jonathan Moody President & CEO
      Tel: 614-461-4664
      Email: kzook@moodynolan.com
      Website: www.moodynolan.com
Architecture, engineering & interior design. (AA, estab ,
empl 240, sales $49,053,240, cert: State)

1727 Quinn Engineering & Employment Network LLC
      125 W Market St, Ste 221
      Warren, OH 44481
      Contact: Candys Mayo Owner
      Tel: 330-423-1923
      Email: info@queen-ohio.com
      Website: www.queen-ohio.com
Computer Aided Drafting and Engineering/Architecture
support, Naval Architecture and Aerospace. (AA, estab
2015, empl 2, sales , cert: State)

1728 Robert P Madison International, Inc
      1215 Superior Ave E Ste 110
      Cleveland, OH 44114
      Contact: R. Kevin Madison, AIA Presdient
      Tel: 216-861-8195
      Email: rklann@rpmadison.com
      Website: www.rpmadison.com
Architectural svcs; civil, structural, electrical & mechanical
engineering. (Woman/AA, estab 1954, empl 13, sales
$1,692,000, cert: State, City)

1729 Ubiquitous Design, Ltd.
      3443 Lee Rd
      Shaker Heights, OH 44120
      Contact: W. Daniel Bickerstaff, II Founder and
      Principal Architect
      Tel: 216-752-4444
      Email: arcatek@udltd.com
      Website: http://udltd.com
Architectural design services, conceptual design/feasibility
analysis, construction administration. (AA, estab 2001,
empl 2, sales $200,000, cert: City)

1730 Van Auken Akins Architects LLC
      1422 Euclid Ave Ste 1010
      Cleveland, OH 44115
      Contact: Jill Van Auken AIA Principal
      Tel: 216-241-2220
      Email: jvanauken@vaakins.com
      Website: www.vaakins.com
Architectural services. (Woman, estab 1992, empl 25, sales
, cert: State, City)

1731 WA, Inc. (dba WA Architects, Inc.)
      807 Broadway St 2nd Fl
      Cincinnati, OH 45202
      Contact: Wade Price Principal
      Tel: 513-641-0111
      Email: wprice@wa-inc.biz
      Website: www.wa-architectsinc.com
Healthcare Design & Planning. (AA, estab 1971, empl 16,
sales $1,750,000, cert: State, NMSDC)

1732 Wanix Architects, LLC
      4208 Prospect Ave
      Cleveland, OH 44103
      Contact: Xin Wan Owner
      Tel: 440-570-9829
      Email: xinwan@wanixarchitects.com
      Website: www.wanixarchitects.com
Architectural design, site planning, interior space
planning & 3D. (Woman/As-Pac, estab 2008, empl 2,
sales , cert: City)

Pennsylvania

1733 Alexander Perry Inc.
      2929 Arch St, Ste 1700
      Philadelphia, PA 19104
      Contact: Patricia Sanford CEO
      Tel: 215-948-8148
      Email: psanford@alexanderperryinc.com
      Website: www.alexanderperryinc.com
Interior design, project management, construction
management, flooring & window treatments, furniture,
signage. (Woman/AA, estab 1992, empl 13, sales , cert:
State, City, NMSDC, WBENC)

1734 DJDC Inc.
      12300 Perry Hwy, Ste 204
      Wexford, PA 15090
      Contact: Marcia Guth Principal
      Tel: 412-996-6771
      Email: mguth@djdc.com
      Website: www.djdc.com
Interior architecture design, space planning & facilities
planning svcs. (Woman, estab 1972, empl 6, sales
$243,000, cert: WBENC)

1735 Genesis Architects Inc.
      1850 N Gravers Rd
      Plymouth Meeting, PA 19462
      Contact: Meryl Towarnicki Presdient
      Tel: 610-592-0280
      Email: mtowarnicki@geiarc.com
      Website: www.geiarc.com
Architecture, Engineering, Commissioning & Construction Management. (Woman, estab 2017, empl 50, sales
$60,480,129, cert: WBENC)

1736 MKSD. LLC
      1209 Hausman Rd, Ste A
      Allentown, PA 18104
      Contact: Presdient
      Tel: 610-366-2081
      Email:
      Website: www.mksdarchitects.com
Architecture, planning, design & construction for new
buildings, additions & renovations. (Woman, estab 2005,
empl 16, sales $3,103,884, cert: State, WBENC)

1737 SMC Consulting, LLC d/b/a/ Studio SMC
      379 Insurance St
      Beaver, PA 15009
      Contact: Sam McWilliams Managing Partner
      Tel: 724-728-8625
      Email: sam@studio-smc.com
      Website: www.studio-smc.com
Interior Design, Space Planning, Furniture Planning,
Furniture Specification, Move Management, Project
Management, Construction Administration. (Minority,
Woman, estab 1999, empl 5, sales $213,544, cert: State)

1738 Styer & Associates, Inc.
      412 Dekalb St
      Norristown, PA 19401
      Contact: Amy Styer Tahtabrounian Principal
      Tel: 610-275-6000
      Email: amy@styergroup.com
      Website: www.styergroup.com
Architecture, engineering, interior design, construction,
project management, purchase management. (Woman,
estab 1985, empl 9, sales $190,000,000, cert: WBENC)

Puerto Rico

1739 Arco Caribe Architects, PSC
      Cond. San Alberto, Ste 607 605 Condado St
      San Juan, PR 00907
      Contact: Alberto Arroyo
      Tel: 787-504-7104
      Email: aarroyo@arcocaribe.com
      Website: www.arcocaribe.com
Architectural & engineering design services. (Hisp, estab
1999, empl 2, sales $385,000, cert: 8a)

1740 CMA Architects & Engineers LLC
      1509 Ave FD Roosevelt
      Guaynabo, PR 00968
      Contact: Jorge A. Tirado, PE Managing Member
      Tel: 787-792-1509
      Email: jtirado@cmapr.com
      Website: www.cmapr.com
Architectural design services, preparation of construction
documents, field & construction management, environmental & permitting, electrical, mechanical, structural,
transportation & infrastructure engineering. (Hisp, estab
1959, empl 90, sales $8,300,000, cert: NMSDC, SDB)

1741 UNIPRO Architects Engineers LLP
      P.O. Box 10914
      San Juan, PR 00922
      Contact: Jose R. Gonzalez Dir planning/projects
      Tel: 787-793-3950
      Email: jgonzalez@uniproaep.net
      Website: www.uniproaep.com
Architecture, civil engineering, structural engineering,
mechanical engineering, electrical engineering, environmental engineering, construction management. (Hisp,
estab 1980, empl 30, sales $3,200,000, cert: NMSDC)

South Carolina

1742 Waldon Studio Architects PC
      1100 Queensborough Blvd Ste 202
      Mt Pleasant, SC 29464
      Contact: Michael Janaskie, AIA, NCARB Managing
      Principal
      Tel: 843-518-3900
      Email: mjanaskie@waldonstudio.com
      Website: http://waldonstudio.com
Architecture & interior design, building, project adminis-
tration, additions, modernizations & interiors experience.
(As-Pac, estab 2003, empl 26, sales $6,897,425, cert: State)

Texas

1743 Architect for Life - A Professional Corporation
      2450 Louisiana St, Ste 400-233
      Houston, TX 77006
      Contact: Lolalisa King
      Tel: 888-986-7771
      Email: lking@architectforlife.com
      Website: www.architectforlife.com
Green consulting professional services, develop &
manage energy efficient strategies, programs, &
projects, retrofit strategies, benchmarking building
energy performance, long-term energy management &
water saving goals assessment. (Woman/AA, estab
1995, empl , sales $108,000, cert: City)

1744 BSA Design Group Inc.
      8750 N Central Expressway, Ste 1725
      Dallas, TX 75231
      Contact: Vanessa Witliff Presdient
      Tel: 214-818-0563
      Email: vwittliff@bsa-designgroup.com
      Website: http://bsa-designgroup.com
Architectural, interior design, design build, project
management, programming and scheduling, studies and
analyses, specifications, furnishing procurement.
(Woman, estab 1989, empl 13, sales $5,000,000, cert:
WBENC)

1745 Interprise/Southwest Interior & Space Planning
      5080 Spectrum Dr Ste 115E
      Addison, TX 75001
      Contact: Lesley Leahy VP Business Dev
      Tel: 972-385-3991
      Email: lleahy@interprisedesign.com
      Website: www.interprisedesign.com
Commerical interior design & space planning. (Woman,
estab 1981, empl 36, sales $4,500,000, cert: WBENC)

1746 R & T Architects, Inc.
      3300 S Gessner, Ste 119
      Houston, TX 77063
      Contact: Spencer Tsui Principal
      Tel: 713-974-2008
      Email: rtarch@swbell.net
      Website: www.rtarch.net
Architectural services: design & built. (As-Pac, estab
1982, empl 4, sales $110,000, cert: State, City)

1747 STOA International Architects, Inc.
      6001 Savoy Dr, Ste 100
      Houston, TX 77036
      Contact: Alice Hu
      Tel: 713-995-8784
      Email: stoaintl@globalxlr.com
      Website: www.stoaintl.com
Architectural design, interior design, planning, construction management, architectural rendering. (As-Pac,
estab 1995, empl 10, sales $750,000, cert: State, City,
NMSDC)

1748 The idGroup, LLC
2641 Irving Blvd
Dallas, TX 75207
Contact: Principal
Tel: 214-638-6800
Email:
Website: www.idgroupdallas.com
Interior space planning, retail design & rollout, architectural services. (Woman, estab 2001, empl 28, sales $4,845,619, cert: WBENC)

1749 VAI Architects Inc.
16000 N Dallas Pkwy, Ste 200
Dallas, TX 75248
Contact: William Vidaud Principal
Tel: 972-934-8888
Email: wvidaud@vaiarchitects.com
Website: www.vaiarchitects.com
Architecture, master planning, feasibility analysis, interior planning & design, building condition assessments, CADD, renovation, alteration & expansion, demolition specifications, roofing assessments/corrective design. (Hisp, estab 1985, empl 28, sales $4,945,000, cert: State)

Virginia

1750 nbj Architecture
11537-B Nuckols Rd
Glen Allen, VA 23059
Contact: Neil Bhatt President
Tel: 804-273-9811
Email: nbhatt@nbjarch.com
Website: www.nbjarch.com
Architectural, space planning, interior design, construction administration, feasibility studies & value engineering. (As-Ind, estab 2000, empl 12, sales $2,000,000, cert: State)

1751 SandHurst-AEC
1069 W Broad St, Ste 777
Falls church, VA 22046
Contact: Kwafo Djan Principal
Tel: 703-533-1413
Email: kdjan@sandhurstaec.com
Website: www.sandhurstaec.com
Architecture & Urban Planning, Program Management, Site Analysis, Feasibility Studies, Architectural Design, Construction, Documentation, Interior Design Services, Space Planning, Project Management. (AA, estab 2013, empl 3, sales , cert: State, 8a)

Washington

1752 Ato Apiafi Architects PLLC
10940 NE 33rd Place Ste 208
Bellevue, WA 98004
Contact: Jeff Thompson
Tel: 425-202-7760
Email: jeff.t@atoapiafi.com
Website: www.atoapiafi.com
Full service architectural firm. (AA, estab 2004, empl 2, sales , cert: State, NMSDC)

Wisconsin

1753 Continuum Architects + Planners, S.C.
228 S First
Milwaukee, WI 53204
Contact: Ursula Twombly Principal
Tel: 414-220-9649
Email: ursula.twombly@continuumarchitects.com
Website: www.continuumarchitects.com
Master planning site selection site planning, pre-design studies. (Woman, estab 1996, empl 13, sales $1,700,000, cert: City)

AUTOMOBILES
New and used car dealerships. Distributors of single cars, trucks and fleet sales. Provide rental and leasing services. NAICS Code 44

California

1754　Premiere Solutions, LLC
　　　11501 Dublin Blvd Ste 200
　　　Dublin, CA 94568
　　　Contact: Holly Michael
　　　Tel:　925-467-1000
　　　Email: holly@premieresolutionsllc.com
　　　Website: www.premieresolutionsllc.com
Fleet management services: vehicle acquisition (lease, purchase or rental), vehicle disposal, fuel card, preventative maintenance, accident management, roadside assistance, transportation, licensing & registration. (AA, estab 2005, empl 7, sales $15,807,000, cert: NMSDC, CPUC)

1755　Rotolo Chevrolet, Inc.
　　　16666 S Highland Ave
　　　Fontana, CA 92336
　　　Contact: Jamie Harshman Dir fleet sales
　　　Tel:　909-822-1111
　　　Email: jamie@rotolo.com
　　　Website: www.rotolochevy.com
Sell & service Chevrolet light duty cars & trucks. (Woman, estab 1971, empl 104, sales $81,651,283, cert: CPUC)

Colorado

1756　Burt Fleet Services, Inc.
　　　5210 S Broadway
　　　Englewood, CO 80113
　　　Contact: Lloyd Chavez CEO
　　　Tel:　303-789-6701
　　　Email: lgchavezjr@burt.com
　　　Website: www.burt.com
National fleet vehicle sales & leasing. (Woman/Hisp, estab 2009, empl 6, sales $600,001, cert: NMSDC)

Florida

1757　NM1, LLC
　　　16725 NW 57th Ave
　　　Miami Gardens, FL 33055
　　　Contact: Rogelio (Roger) Tovar President & CEO
　　　Tel:　888-423-7756
　　　Email: rogeliotovar@gmail.com
　　　Website: http://palmetto57nissan.com
Sell new & used cars, parts & service. (Hisp, estab 2012, empl 110, sales $74,101,851, cert: NMSDC)

1758　Sun State International Trucks, LLC
　　　6020 Adamo Dr
　　　Tampa, FL 33619
　　　Contact: Dave Metcalf VP,Dir of Sales
　　　Tel:　813-769-2541
　　　Email: dave.metcalf@sunstateintl.com
　　　Website: www.sunstateintl.com
Medium & heavy duty commercial truck dealership. (AA, estab 1982, empl 163, sales $115,000,000, cert: NMSDC)

Illinois

1759　Advantage Chevrolet
　　　9510 W. Joliet Rd
　　　Hodgkins, IL 60525
　　　Contact: Rick Zureick GM
　　　Tel:　847-561-5281
　　　Email: rzureick@advantagechev.com
　　　Website: www.advantagechev.com
Automotive & commercial truck sales. (AA, estab 2000, empl 122, sales $91,265,959, cert: NMSDC)

1760　Sutton Ford, Inc.
　　　21315 Central
　　　Matteson, IL 60443
　　　Contact: Michael Miller Fleet Mgr
　　　Tel:　708-720-8034
　　　Email: mmiller@suttonford.com
　　　Website: www.suttonford.com
Ford cars, trucks, sales, service & parts. (AA, estab 1989, empl 80, sales , cert: State, NMSDC, CPUC)

Indiana

1761　Truck City of Gary, Inc.
　　　P.O. Box 64800
　　　Gary, IN 46401
　　　Contact: Gerri Davis-Parker CEO
　　　Tel:　219-949-8595
　　　Email: wbe@mytruckcity.com
　　　Website: www.mytruckcity.com
Heavy Duty Trucks: Agricultural, Landscaping, Bucket, Vacuum, Fuel, Aerial, Welding, Digger Derrick, Pole, Straight, Box, Flat-bed, Bucket, Service, Platform, Dump, Runway Snow Plow, Railway, Refuse, Logging, Mounted Cranes, etc. (Woman, estab 1946, empl 58, sales $45,799,499, cert: State, WBENC)

Maryland

1762　K. Neal International Trucks, Inc.
　　　5000 Tuxedo Rd
　　　Hyattsville, MD 20781
　　　Contact: Sharon Calomese CEO
　　　Tel:　301-772-5100
　　　Email: scalomese@knealinternational.com
　　　Website: www.knealinternational.com
Commercial truck dealership: International, Hino, Mitsubishi Fuso trucks & IC Bus. Sales, service, parts & body shop services, leasing & rental services. (AA, estab 1982, empl 90, sales $110,000,000, cert: State, City, NMSDC)

Michigan

1763　Hall Whitener Investments, Inc.
　　　13475 Portage Rd
　　　Vicksburg, MI 49097
　　　Contact: Laura Awe Customer Relations Dir
　　　Tel:　269-649-2000
　　　Email: laura.awe@vicksburgchrysler.com
　　　Website:
　　　www.vicksburgchryslerdodgejeepram.com
Sale & service Chrysler, Dodge, Jeep , Ram vehicles. (AA, estab 2013, empl 32, sales , cert: NMSDC)

1764   Vicksburg Chrysler Dodge Jeep
       13475 Portage Rd
       Vicksburg, MI 49097
       Contact: Monti Long Presdient
       Tel: 269-649-2000
       Email: mlong007@comcast.net
       Website: http://VicksburgChryslerDodge.com
New & used cars, Chrysler, Dodge, Jeep retail, lease & fleet
services. (AA, estab 1989, empl 46, sales $22,521,322,
cert: NMSDC)

Minnesota

1765   Holt Motors, Inc
       245 Cokato St W
       Cokato, MN 55321
       Contact: Presdient
       Tel: 320-286-2176
       Email:
       Website: www.holtmotors.com
Ford Vehicles, Commercial Ford Fleet Program. (Woman,
estab 1951, empl 48, sales , cert: WBENC)

Nevada

1766   SVI. Inc.
       440 Mark Leany Dr
       Henderson, NV 89011
       Contact: Nancy Munoz Sales Mgr
       Tel: 702-567-5256
       Email: nancy.munoz@specialtyvehicles.com
       Website: www.specialtyvehicles.com
Sales & distributer of people mover products, ie Buses,
Trams, Trolleys, Golf Carts, Ground Maintence Vehicles and
vehicle parts. (Woman/Hisp, estab 2003, empl 13, sales
$14,036,900, cert: State, WBENC)

Ohio

1767   Bob Ross Auto Group
       85 Loop Rd
       Centerville, OH 45459
       Contact: Fleet FSP Mgr
       Tel: 937-433-0990
       Email: fleet@bobrossauto.com
       Website: www.bobrossauto.com
New Vehicle Dealer, automobiles & light/medium duty
trucks: Buick, GMC Light Duty Trucks, Vans and SUVs; Fiat
Automobiles; Alfa Romeo Automobiles & Specialized
Equipped Fleet & Commercial Vehicles. (Woman/AA, estab
1974, empl 92, sales $66,226,386, cert: State, WBENC)

Pennsylvania

1768   Buick GMC of Moosic Inc.
       4230 Birney Ave
       Moosic, PA 18507
       Contact: Lori Guitson Presdient
       Tel: 570-414-1000
       Email: lori@sunbpg.com
       Website: www.sunbuickgmc.com
New Buick GMC's, economical cars to vehicles for executives. (Woman, estab 2004, empl 18, sales $14,000,000,
cert: WBENC)

Texas

1769   Ancira
       10807 W IH 10
       San Antonio, TX 78230
       Contact: Betty Ferguson Mgr
       Tel: 210-558-1500
       Email: ljust@ancira.com
       Website: www.ancira.com
Automobile dealership. (Hisp, estab 1985, empl 25, sales
, cert: State)

1770   Kahlig Enterprises, Inc
       351 IH 35 South
       New Braunfels, TX 78130
       Contact: Larry Brown Exec Director Fleet Sales
       Tel: 210-426-3295
       Email: lbrown@kahligauto.com
       Website: www.npbbfleet.com
New Ford, Lincoln & Jeep automobiles, light trucks &
SUVs. (Hisp, estab 1984, empl 212, sales $343,000,000,
cert: NMSDC)

1771   North Park Lincoln Mercury
       P.O. Box 790467
       San Antonio, TX 78279
       Contact: Larry Brown ED Fleet Sales
       Tel: 210-426-3295
       Email: lbrown@kahligauto.com
       Website: http://npbbfleet.com
Automotive service, mechanical & body shop services.
(Hisp, estab 1982, empl 254, sales $266,000,000, cert:
State, NMSDC)

1772   Rio Motor
       4350 E Hwy 83
       Rio Grande City, TX 78582
       Contact: O.C. Canales President
       Tel: 956-487-2596
       Email: riomotorco@aol.com
       Website: www.riomotors.com
Sell Chevrolet cars, trucks, van parts & servicing. (Hisp,
estab 1953, empl 29, sales , cert: State)

DIR
DIVERSITY INFORMATION RESOURCES

Driving Supplier Diversity Success since 1968.

1960's

1968 The "Buy Black Campaign" is founded by Peter and Rose Meyerhoff as a not-for-profit organization and prints its first directory of black-owned businesses in Minneapolis.

1968 The first Board of Directors is established and an office space is secured on Plymouth Ave. N. in Minneapolis.

1969 DIR publishes the "Buy Black" directory nationally.

1970's

1972 The "Buy Black" directory changes to "TRY US" and includes Black-, Hispanic-, Asian- and Native American-owned businesses.

1975 First edition of "Purchasing People in Major Corporations" directory is published.

1977 DIR's Board of Directors expands to include national corporations.

1980's

1986 DIR holds its first Supplier Diversity Seminars.

1992 First edition of the "Supplier Diversity Information Resources Guide" is published.

1990's

1995 DIR holds its first "Best Practices in Supplier Diversity Strategies and Initiatives"

1998 DIR creates an online, searchable database for its "Purchasing People in Major Corporations" directory.

2000 TRY US becomes Diversity Information Resources, Inc., to reflect the ongoing and ever-changing diverse-supplier categories.

2000's

2001 DIR hires SupplierGATEWAY as a technology partner.

2001 The "Buy Black" directory is now "National Minority and Women-Owned Business Directory" and includes certified women-owned businesses.

2006 DIR's verification and validation expertise expands to include Veteran-, Service-Disabled Veteran, and GLBT-owned businesses.

2011 DIR greatly expands online presence and redesigns identity to better reflect the open horizon for Supplier Diversity development.

2010's

2013 DIR celebrates its 45th Anniversary and looks forward to a thriving future!

2015 DIR responds to corporate and diverse-suppliers request for consolidated information and publishes a new directory and handbook: "The Business of Supplier Diversity".

AUTOMOTIVE PARTS & ACCESSORIES

Manufacturers of batteries, cables, recapping of tires, remanufacturing of auto parts, etc. Also lists wholesale distributors of automotive supplies & equipment. NAICS Code 42

California

1773 Concours Direct, Inc.
3212 El Camino Real
Atascadero, CA 93422
Contact: William M Vega
Tel: 805-466-4040
Email: wvega@concoursdirect.com
Website: www.concoursdirect.com
Dist Automotive & Truck Performance Parts, Ford Performance Racing Parts, Edelbrock, MSD, Airaid, Readylift, MBRP, Moroso, Diablosport, Bullydog, Performance Automatic, Centerforce, Tremec, Powermaster, Holly, etc. (Hisp, estab 2005, empl 2, sales $2,412,993, cert: NMSDC, CPUC)

1774 VIAIR Corporation
15 Edelman
Irvine, CA 92618
Contact: Alan Basham Dir of Operations
Tel: 949-585-0011
Email: alanb@viaircorp.com
Website: www.viaircorp.com
Dist Air Compressor, Air Tank, LED Light, Air accessories for automotive industry. (As-Pac, estab 1998, empl 32, sales $22,000,000, cert: NMSDC)

Florida

1775 Astra/CFX Holdings, LLC
11971 NW37th St
Coral Springs, FL 33065
Contact: Sharon McTurk Presdient
Tel: 954-494-3948
Email: smcturk@astraservices.com
Website: www.astraservices.com
3PL Tire and Wheel Assembly, heavy Sub Assembly for all major vehicle modules. (Woman/Hisp, estab 1989, empl 217, sales $8,950,000, cert: NMSDC, WBENC)

1776 Indus Solutions LLC
4260 NW 1st Ave
Boca Raton, FL 33433
Contact: Sandeep Vijay
Tel: 248-875-8010
Email: sv@indus-sol.com
Website: www.indus-sol.com
Mfr automotive parts & components, sub assemblies & assemblies of door, hood & tailgate systems, exhaust, steering & suspension, gaskets, rubber mounts, engine, electrical & electronics parts, wire harness & integrated products & prototyping. (As-Ind, estab 2015, empl 15, sales , cert: NMSDC)

1777 NM1, LLC
16725 NW 57th Ave
Miami Gardens, FL 33055
Contact: Rogelio (Roger) Tovar President & CEO
Tel: 888-423-7756
Email: rogeliotovar@gmail.com
Website: http://palmetto57nissan.com
Sell new & used cars, parts & service. (Hisp, estab 2012, empl 110, sales $74,101,851, cert: NMSDC)

1778 Vehicle Maintenance Program, Inc.
3595 N Dixie Hwy, Bay 7
Boca Raton, FL 33431
Contact: Presdient
Tel: 561-362-6080
Email:
Website: www.vmpparts.com
Dist vehicle repair parts: filters, wiper blades, lenses, lamps, bulbs, mirrors, batteries, seals, bearings, brake drums. (Woman, estab 1988, empl 15, sales $20,140,327, cert: State, WBENC)

Georgia

1779 Battle and Battle Distributors, Inc
2410 Park Central Blvd.
Decatur, GA 30035
Contact: Sylvia Battle VP
Tel: 770-987-8147
Email: sylvia@battleandbattle.net
Website: www.battleandbattle.net
Dist industrial batteries, automotive, batteries & battery equip. (AA, estab , empl , sales , cert: NMSDC)

Illinois

1780 Bearings & Industrial Supply
431 Imen Ave
Addison, IL 60101
Contact: Sejal Khandwala Acct Exec
Tel: 630-628-1966
Email: Sejal@BearingsNow.Com
Website: www.bearingsnow.com
Dist bearings & power transmission products; pump & pump repair parts, HVAC & electrical parts. (As-Pac, estab , empl , sales , cert: NMSDC)

1781 Chicago Parts & Sound, LLC
1150 Lively Blvd
Elk Grove Village, IL 60007
Contact: Dennis Hoffberg Sales Mgr
Tel: 630-350-1500
Email: sales@clickoncps.com
Website: http://clickoncps.com/
Dist automotive parts, commodity lines such as Anco wiper blades. (Woman/Hisp, estab 1978, empl 80, sales , cert: City)

1782 Reliance Distributing
3609 Pebble Beach Rd
Northbrook, IL 60062
Contact: Anne Chessick CEO
Tel: 847-372-6125
Email: annieparts@aol.com
Website: http://reliancedistributing.com
Automotive & truck lighting, flashers, wiper blades, fuses, hose clamps, halogen headlight sockets, permatex products (Woman, estab 2012, empl 1, sales , cert: WBENC)

Kentucky

1783 HJI Supply Chain Solutions
13200 Complete Court
Louisville, KY 40223
Contact: Lynn Moore VP Finance & Admin
Tel: 502-638-8064
Email: lmoore@hjisolutions.com
Website: www.hjisolutions.com
Automotive parts: door panel/trim, switch bezels, running boards, driveshafts, shocks, corner pillars, floor mats & hub caps. (Minority, Woman, estab 0, empl , sales , cert: NMSDC)

1784 LB Manufacturing
360 Industry Dr
Springfield, KY 40069
Contact: Keith Hamilton CEO
Tel: 859-336-0090
Email: hamiltonk@leanbmfg.com
Website: http://leanbmfg.com
Automotive stamping, welding & mfg assemblies, mig & resistance, robotic, window glass & exhaust system assemblies. (AA, estab 1998, empl 40, sales $17,000,000, cert: NMSDC)

Michigan

1785 Advanced Assembly Products, Inc.
1300 East Nine Mile Road
Hazel Park, MI 48030
Contact: Ron Waring IT Systems Mgr
Tel: 248-543-2427
Email: rwaring@aapincorp.com
Website: www.aapincorp.com
Body hardware, door hinges, door checks, strikers, hood hinges, deck lid hinges, stampings, welded assemblies, mechanical assemblies. (As-Ind, estab 1993, empl 140, sales $18,000,000, cert: NMSDC)

1786 CAMACO, LLC
40000 Grand River Ste 110
Novi, MI 48375
Contact: Pamela Cooper Admin coord
Tel: 248-442-6800
Email: pcooper@camacollc.com
Website: www.camacollc.com
Mfr auto components & assemblies. (As-Ind, estab 1987, empl 68, sales , cert: NMSDC)

1787 Capsonic Automotive & Aersopace
3121 University Dr, Ste 120
Auburn Hills, MI 48326
Contact: George E. Albrecht CQA
Tel: 248-754-1100
Email: georgea@capsonic.com
Website: www.capsonic.com
Automotive assemblies. (AA, estab 1996, empl 449, sales $37,000,000, cert: NMSDC)

1788 Concept Industries, Inc.
4950 Kraft Ave SE
Grand Rapids, MI 49512
Contact: David Foote, Troy Caswell CFO
Tel: 616-554-9000
Email: dfoote@conceptind.com
Website: www.conceptind.com
Thermoforming, interior acoustical applications, engine side noise absorbers, dash insulators, package trays, load floors, undercarpet absorbers, headliners, trunk liners, needle punch, laminating, plastic vacuum forming, die cut. (Woman/As-Ind, As-Pac, estab 1984, empl 150, sales $20,000,000, cert: NMSDC)

1789 Dawson Mfg Co. - Benton Harbor Division
1042 N Crystal Ave
Benton Harbor, MI 49022
Contact: Neil Trivedi VP
Tel: 269-925-0100
Email: neil.trivedi@vibracoustic.com.com
Website: http://dawsonmfg.com
Mfr body mounts, engine mounts, strut mounts, link assemblies & bushings, dist anti-vibration components, rubber injection molding. (As-Pac, estab 1988, empl 90, sales $36,000,000, cert: NMSDC)

1790 Detroit Chassis LLC
6501 Lynch Rd
Detroit, MI 48234
Contact: Darin Burns VP Business Dev
Tel: 313-571-2100
Email: dburns@detroitchassis.com
Website: www.detroitchassis.com
Niche vehicle, motor home chassis & commercial truck assembly; complex sub-assemblies & sub-assemblies. (AA, estab 1998, empl 150, sales $7,615,052, cert: NMSDC)

1791 Diversitech, Inc.
16620 Industrial St
Roseville, MI 48066
Contact: Roger Olle President
Tel: 586-445-7600
Email: rho@div-techusa.com
Website: www.div-techusa.com
Design & build automation assembly machines, leak test, special machines for powertrain & body & assembly, parts feeding & handling systems. (As-Ind, estab 2009, empl 4, sales $1,500,000, cert: NMSDC)

1792 Global Enterprises
26909 Woodward Ave
Huntington Woods, MI 48070
Contact: Pat Vizcarra Business Dev Mgr
Tel: 248-542-2000
Email: pvizcarra@globalent.org
Website: www.globalent.org
Extrusion, die-cutting, compression molding, laminating & glueing interior trim components & assemblies. (Minority/Woman, estab 1998, empl 280, sales , cert: WBENC)

1793 H.R. Technologies, Inc.
      32500 N. Avis Dr
      Madison Heights, MI 48071
      Contact: Tushar Patel Presdient
      Tel: 248-284-1170
      Email: tpatel@hrtechinc.com
      Website: www.hrtechinc.com
Laminate fabrics & vinyl, carpet, die cutting, headliner
glass fiber reinforcements, headliner glass polypropylene
substrate materials. (As-Ind, estab 1996, empl 48, sales
$11,000,000, cert: NMSDC)

1794 Integrated Manufacturing and Assembly, LLC
      5200 Auto Club Dr
      Dearborn, MI 48126
      Contact: Leslie Thumm Financial Anyalyst
      Tel: 313-593-9246
      Email: lthumm@lear.com
      Website: www.comerholdings.com/about.htm
Interior Systems; seat assemblies, foam & trim assemblies
& injection molded & painted interior components -
Exterior Systems; Exterior mirror assemblies, inection
molded & painted interiors. (AA, estab 1996, empl 700,
sales , cert: NMSDC)

1795 Intex Technologies LLC
      3133 Highland Blvd
      Hudsonville, MI 49426
      Contact: Randi Sniegowski Sales
      Tel: 616-662-0276
      Email: randi.sniegowski@intextech.net
      Website: www.intextech.net
Mfr integral skin flexible foam automotive interior parts:
arm rests, center console, console door, sun visor, steering
wheel, soft-touch points on door handles, cup holders,
seals, jounce bumpers & insulation components. (Hisp,
estab 2008, empl 50, sales $14,800,000, cert: NMSDC)

1796 La Solucion Corp.
      19930 Conner
      Detroit, MI 48234
      Contact: Patricia Leon CEO
      Tel: 313-893-9760
      Email: patleon@la-solucion.com
      Website: www.la-solucion.com
Mfr & dist liquid & air filtration systems. (Woman/Hisp,
estab 1999, empl 4, sales , cert: NMSDC, WBENC)

1797 Marimba Auto, LLC
      41133 Van Born Rd Ste 200
      Belleville, MI 48111
      Contact: Venkat Chigulla VP Admin
      Tel: 734-398-9000
      Email: vchigulla@marimbaauto.com
      Website: www.marimbaauto.com
Import tubing, tube processing, global supply mgmt, in-
house engineering, warehousing. (As-Pac, estab 2003,
empl 35, sales $17,000,000, cert: NMSDC)

1798 McKechnie Vehicle Components
      27087 Gratiot Ave, 2 Fl
      Roseville, MI 48066
      Contact: Linda Torakis Presdient
      Tel: 586-491-2622
      Email: ltorakis@mvcusa.com
      Website: www.mvcusa.com
Mfr decorative trim products: nickel chrome plating on
plastic and stainless surfaces, plastic injection molding,
metal stamping, base and clear coat painting and assembly. (Woman, estab 0, empl , sales , cert: WBENC)

1799 Modular Automotive Systems, LLC
      26195 Bunert Rd
      Warren, MI 48089
      Contact: RJ La Pointe Presdient
      Tel: 586-779-2602
      Email: info@hollingsworthllc.com
      Website:
Dist Automotive Supplies & Parts. (Nat Ame, estab 2000,
empl 130, sales , cert: NMSDC)

1800 Need a Part Now, LLC
      1157 Manufacturers Dr
      Westland, MI 48186
      Contact: Erin Brazill VP
      Tel: 888-201-9061
      Email: erina@needapartnow.com
      Website: www.needapartnow.com
Mfr parts from AutoCad, blueprints, drawings, sketches,
or reverse engineer. (Woman, estab 2006, empl 20, sales
$363,281, cert: WBENC)

1801 NYX Inc.
      30111 Schoolcraft Rd
      Livonia, MI 48150
      Contact: Dan DePalma VP Sales
      Tel: 734-462-2385
      Email: sales@nyxinc.com
      Website: www.nyxinc.com
Automotive interior solutions: Door Panels, Center
Consoles, Overhead Consoles, Glove Box Systems, Knee
Bolster Assemblies, Interior Garnish, Seating Compo-
nents, Rear Shelf package Trays, Design and Engineering.
(As-Pac, estab 1985, empl 2100, sales , cert: NMSDC)

1802 Piston Automotive
      12723 Telegraph Rd
      Redford, MI 48239
      Contact: James Edwards Sales Mgr
      Tel: 313-541-8674
      Email: jedwards@pistongroup.com
      Website: www.pistongroup.com
Manufacturing, module assembly & sequencing, &
logistics management. (AA, As-Pac, Hisp, estab 1995,
empl 750, sales , cert: NMSDC)

1803 Sigma International
      36800 Plymouth Rd
      Livonia, MI 48150
      Contact: Alessandra Konopczyk Operations Mgr
      Tel: 248-230-9681
      Email: akonopczyk@sigmaintl.com
      Website: www.sigmaintl.com
Mfr labels, decals, badges, chrome abs parts, wheel
center caps, dimensional graphics, stone chip protection
film. (AA, estab 2003, empl 10, sales , cert: NMSDC)

1804 Sino Brite (USA), Inc.
      30600 Telegraph Rd, Ste 1131
      Bingham Farms, MI 48025
      Contact: Julinda Kong Presdient
      Tel: 659-819-7871
      Email: sales@sinobrite-sg.com
      Website: www.sinobrite-sg.com
Motor Vehicle Supplies & New Parts Merchant Wholesalers. (As-Pac, estab 2003, empl 5, sales , cert: NMSDC)

1805   Ventura Manufacturing
      471 E Roosevelt
      Zeeland, MI 49464
      Contact: Ana Figueroa Finance
      Tel: 616-772-7405
      Email: ana.figueroa@venturamfg.com
      Website: www.venturamfg.com
Mfr automotive dimming rearview mirror components, wire processing components, overhead grabhandles. (Woman/Hisp, estab 1997, empl 140, sales $26,000,000, cert: NMSDC)

Minnesota

1806   DV Roland Enterprises, Inc.
      15171 Freeland Ave N
      Hugo, MN 55038
      Contact: Kenny Scamp GM
      Tel: 651-429-9012
      Email: ken@jtservicesinc.com
      Website: www.jtservicesinc.com
Dist & service industrial diesel engines & diesel engine parts. Supporting diesel engines for aerial lifts, air compressors, backhoes, dozers, excavators, forklifts, generators, light towers, rollers, skid steer loaders, tractors, welders. (AA, estab 2004, empl 6, sales $1,433,333, cert: City, NMSDC)

Missouri

1807   JCM Machine, Inc.
      5655 Old Hwy 21
      House Springs, MO 63051
      Contact: Laura Borrini Owner
      Tel: 636-942-4567
      Email: lborrini@jcmmachineandcoatings.com
      Website: www.jcmmachineandcoatings.com
Automotive machine shop, cylinder head & engine rebuilding, certified ceramic coatings applicators & dry film lubricants. (Woman, estab 1976, empl 4, sales $223,000, cert: State)

New Jersey

1808   Wexco Industries
      3 Barnet Rd
      Pine Brook, NJ 07058
      Contact: Paula Lombard President & CEO
      Tel: 973-244-5777
      Email: plombard@wexcoind.com
      Website: www.wexcoind.com
Dist complete windshield wiper systems. (Woman, estab 1991, empl 30, sales $18,367,600, cert: WBENC)

Ohio

1809   Auld Technologies, LLC
      2030 Dividend Dr
      Columbus, OH 43228
      Contact: Project Coord
      Tel: 614-755-2853
      Email:
      Website: www.auldtech.com
Dist decorative emblems, trim, labels, overlays & coating solutions. (Woman, estab 2009, empl 26, sales $3,500,000, cert: WBENC)

Pennsylvania

1810   American Cable Company
      1200 E Erie Ave
      Philadelphia, PA 19124
      Contact: Brian Thomas Direct of Operations - Contract Div.
      Tel: 215-456-0700
      Email: bthomas@americancableco.com
      Website: www.americancableco.com
Mfr motor vehicular equipment components, battery cables, wiring harness, grounding straps, panel assemblies & related components. (Hisp, estab 2009, empl 5, sales , cert: NMSDC, SDB)

Tennessee

1811   Wingard Quality Supply, LLC
      5901 Shallowford Rd Ste 20
      Chattanooga, TN 37421
      Contact: James Wingard Presdient
      Tel: 423-521-4600
      Email: james@wingard.biz
      Website: www.wingardll.com
Automotive assembly: tire & wheel. (AA, estab 2002, empl 25, sales $60,000,000, cert: NMSDC)

CHEMICALS

Manufacturers and distributors of organic and inorganic chemicals, fertilizers, blasting materials, radioactive, cosmetic & industrial chemicals, paints, glues, drilling mud, oil derivatives, pharmaceutical preservatives, blowing agents, coatings, lubricants and solvents. Also chemical and custom packaging. NAICS Code 42

Alabama

1812   Stutton Corporation
          1256 McCaig Rd
          Lincoln, AL 35096
          Contact: Lorraine Studin Presdient
          Tel: 205-763-2000
          Email: info@stuttoncorp.com
          Website: www.stuttoncorp.com
Mfr & dist chemicals: lubricants, greases, degreasers, cleaners, sealers, epoxy strippers, paint strippers, citrus solvents, deodorizers, corrosion barriers, rust penetrants, spray insulation, sealers, adhesives. (Woman, estab 1977, empl 12, sales $1,900,000, cert: State)

Arkansas

1813   Chemical Distribution Solutions, LLC
          1125 Oak St Ste 303
          Conway, AR 72032
          Contact: Anthony Wilmington President
          Tel: 501-978-1111
          Email: admin@chemicalds.com
          Website: www.chemicalds.com
Custom Blending, Valued Products, Chemical Distribution (AA, estab 2011, empl 4, sales $7,198,033, cert: NMSDC)

California

1814   Anahau Energy, LLC
          2041 Rosecrans Ave, Ste 322
          El Segundo, CA 90245
          Contact: Suyen Pell CEO
          Tel: 310-414-2300
          Email: proposals@anahauenergy.com
          Website: www.anahauenergy.com
Electric power, natural gas, and renewable products. (As-Pac, estab 2005, empl 10, sales , cert: NMSDC)

1815   Apac Chemical Corp.
          150 N. Santa Anita Ave, Ste 850
          Arcadia, CA 91006
          Contact: Tom Kusaka
          Tel: 626-203-0066
          Email: sales@apacchemical.com
          Website: www.apacchemical.com
Mfr Sorbic acid & Potassium sorbate. (As-Pac, estab 1999, empl 7, sales $19,000,000, cert: NMSDC)

1816   Ensunet Consulting Corporation
          10679 Westview Pkwy, 2nd Fl
          San Diego, CA 92126
          Contact: Paul Robinson Presdient
          Tel: 858-348-4690
          Email: paul.robinson@ensucorp.com
          Website: www.ensunet.com
Dist lubricants, fuel additives & safety fluids. (AA, estab 2008, empl 8, sales $165,000, cert: NMSDC)

1817   Ferco Color
          2315 Baker Ave
          Ontario, CA 91761
          Contact: Jennifer Thaw Presdient
          Tel: 909-930-0773
          Email: info@fercocolor.com
          Website: www.fercocolor.com/
Mfr color & additives for plastics, bottles, closures. (Woman, estab 1994, empl 48, sales $16,000,000, cert: WBENC)

1818   Genard, inc. dba Lennova
          1717 Boyd St
          Santa Ana, CA 92705
          Contact: Tony Genova VP Sales/Mktg
          Tel: 562-860-3213
          Email: tony@lennova.net
          Website: www.lennova.net
Install epoxy & urethane protective floor & wall coatings. (Hisp, estab 2000, empl 15, sales $2,387,000, cert: CPUC)

1819   Impact Absorbents, Inc.
          5255 Traffic Way
          Atascadero, CA 93422
          Contact: Tammy Rayner Dir of Corporate Sales
          Tel: 800-339-7672
          Email: trayner@spillhero.com
          Website: spillhero.com
Mfr & dist granular absorbents, sorbent pads, sorbents socks, spill clean up programs and products, non-hazardous, earth friendly, cost effective. XSORB, FiberDuck, FiberLink, Spill Station, Spill Caddy, Spill Rack, Biohazard Kit. (Woman, estab 1992, empl 30, sales $5,300,000, cert: State)

1820   LMC Enterprises, dba Chemco Products Company
          6401 Alondra Blvd
          Paramount, CA 90723
          Contact: Erica Utz Wochna VP of Human Resources
          Tel: 866-243-6261
          Email: erica@chemcoprod.com
          Website: www.chemcoprod.com
Chemical commodities: sodium hydroxide, potassium hydroxide, sulfuric acid, phosphoric acid, citric acid, sodium hypochlorite. (Woman, estab 1976, empl 125, sales $43,324,790, cert: WBENC)

1821   Pinnacle Petroleum, Inc.
          16651 Gemini Lane
          Huntington Beach, CA 92647
          Contact: Liz McKinley Presdient
          Tel: 714-841-8877
          Email: lmckinley@pinnaclepetroleum.com
          Website: www.pinnaclepetroleum.com
Dist petroleum & lubricants, fuel management services. (Woman, estab 1995, empl 25, sales $176,000,000, cert: WBENC)

1822 Pynergy, LLC
      4495 S Santa Fe Dr
      Englewood, CA 80110
      Contact: Darrell Jackson Presdient
      Tel: 303-292-5005
      Email: djackson@pynergy.com
      Website: www.pynergy.com
Dist Diesel, On-Site Refueling, Gasoline, Wet Hose Refuel-
ing, High Octane Fuels, Diesel Generator Fuel Delivery,
Ethanol, Diesel Fuel Treatment Program, Biodiesel Kero-
sene, Lubricant/Fuel Management, Aviation Fuel &
Lubricants. (Woman/AA, estab 1999, empl 44, sales
$31,103,590, cert: City)

1823 Ramos Oil Company, Inc.
      1515 S River Rd
      West Sacramento, CA 95691
      Contact: Sarah Russell
      Tel: 916-371-2570
      Email: sarahr@ramosoil.com
      Website: www.ramosoil.com
Dist fuel & oils. (Hisp, estab 1951, empl 185, sales , cert:
CPUC)

1824 STARDUST Spill Products, LLC
      640 N Tustin Ave, Ste 100
      Santa Ana, CA 92705
      Contact: Timothy B. McDuffie Product & Business
      Devel Consultant
      Tel: 714-550-4999
      Email: tim@stardustspillproducts.com
      Website: www.stardustabsorbent.com
Mfr STARDUST Super Absorbent™: absorbs animal,
vegetable, mineral, petroleum & chemical liquids. (AA,
Hisp, estab 2018, empl 4, sales $1,000,000, cert: NMSDC)

1825 Sungro Products
      810 E 18th St
      Los Angeles, CA 90021
      Contact: Teke Negus President
      Tel: 213-747-4125
      Email: tnegus@sungroproducts.com
      Website: www.sungroproducts.com
Dist chemicals, water treatment, Institutional insecticides,
herbicides, rodenticides, detergents, hand soaps, air
fresheners, metal polishes, degreasers, deodorants, glass
cleaners. (AA, estab 1967, empl 10, sales $1,500,000, cert:
8a)

1826 Western States Distributing
      1790 S 10 St
      San Jose, CA 95112
      Contact: Louis Burford Admin
      Tel: 482-292-1041
      Email: slopes@lubeoil.com
      Website: www.lubeoil.com
Dist petroleum. (Hisp, estab 1956, empl 44, sales , cert:
CPUC)

Colorado

1827 Birko Corporation
      9152 Yosemite St
      Henderson, CO 80640
      Contact: Kelly Green President
      Tel: 303-289-1090
      Email: kgreen@birkocorp.com
      Website: www.birkocorp.com
Mfr & dist chemicals, industrial hygiene, hand soaps &
sanitizers, surface sanitizers & cleaners, specialty white-
oil based lubricants, chemical dispensing equipment,
chemical allocation tracking equipment, steam/water
temperature control valves. (Woman, estab 1952, empl
59, sales , cert: WBENC)

Connecticut

1828 Hartford Technologies, Inc.
      1022 Elm St, Ste 201
      Rocky Hill, CT 06067
      Contact: Vickie Brown Dir Natl Sales
      Tel: - -
      Email: vbrown@htco.com
      Website: www.htco.com
Dist adhesives & coatings. (Woman, estab 1930, empl
129, sales , cert: WBENC)

1829 Prochimie International, Inc.
      2 Waterside Crossing
      Windsor, CT 06095
      Contact: Anna Malz VP
      Tel: 860-683-8500
      Email: amalz@prochimieinternational.com
      Website: www.prochimieinternational.com
Chemical products: Automotive/Tire, Agrochemical, Oil
field, Water Treatment, Pharmaceutical, Photographic
and Specialty chemicals. (Woman, estab 1975, empl 10,
sales $6,000,000, cert: WBENC)

1830 U.S. Chemicals, LLC
      22 Thorndal Circle
      Darien, CT 06820
      Contact: Carol Piccaro Presdient
      Tel: 203-202-2808
      Email: cpiccaro@uschemicals-wob.com
      Website: www.uschemicals-wob.com
Dist chemicals. (Woman, estab 0, empl 15, sales
$90,000,000, cert: WBENC)

Florida

1831 Algon Corporation
      12000 SW 132 Court
      Miami, FL 33186
      Contact: Eduardo Suarez-Troconis Director
      Tel: 305-253-6901
      Email: edal@algon.com
      Website: www.algon.com
Chemical raw materials, laboratory supplies & machine
parts. (Woman/Hisp, estab 1989, empl 24, sales
$20,570,883, cert: NMSDC)

1832 Bell Performance
1340 Bennett Dr
Longwood, FL 32750
Contact: Deb Moon Dir of Sales
Tel: 407-831-5021
Email: dmoon@bellperformance.net
Website: www.bellperformance.net
Mfr commercial grade treatments for diesel, ethanol, gasoline, fuel oil & power plant fuels. (Woman, estab 1909, empl 16, sales $1,543,035, cert: WBENC)

1833 Burck Oil Co., Inc.
1401 53rd St
West Palm Beach, FL 33407
Contact: Jefffrey Burck President
Tel: 561-842-3600
Email: jeffburck@burckoil.com
Website: www.burckoil.com
Dist oil, grease & lubricants; food grade lubricants. (Woman, estab 1996, empl 4, sales $3,600,000, cert: State)

1834 Chemical Systems
P.O. Box 810
Zellwood, FL 32798
Contact: Corky Thein President
Tel: 407-886-2329
Email: corky.thein@chemicalsystems.com
Website: www.chemicalsystems.com
Mfr sanitation & specialty chemicals. (Hisp, estab 1979, empl 23, sales $20,000,000, cert: State, NMSDC)

1835 Graham Trading Company, LLC
3001 N. Rocky Point Dr. East, Ste 200
Tampa, FL 33607
Contact: Darrell Graham CEO
Tel: 855-256-8237
Email: info@gratraco.com
Website: www.gratraco.com
Dist diesel, gasoline, jet fuel & lubricants. (AA, estab 2014, empl 2, sales $250,000, cert: State, NMSDC)

Georgia

1836 DES Wholesale, LLC
601 West Crossville Road
Roswell, GA 30075
Contact: Sales Exec
Tel: 404-671-9593
Email:
Website: https://diversifiedenergysupply.com/
Dist natural gas, electric power & fleet fuel. (Woman, estab 2011, empl 20, sales $149,224,828, cert: CPUC, WBENC)

1837 DJG Chemical, Inc.
4761 Hugh Howell Rd D
Tucker, GA 30084
Contact: Carla Doleman CEO
Tel: 404-244-4606
Email: cdoleman@djgchem.com
Website: www.djgchemical.com
Mfr & dist chemical products: adhesives, janitorial, lubricants, raw materials, water treatment chemicals, foam soaps, herbicides, cosmetic chemicals, etc. (AA, estab 2003, empl 8, sales , cert: NMSDC)

1838 PS Energy Group, Inc.
4480 North Shallowford Rd Ste 100
Dunwoody, GA 30338
Contact: Allison Laudano Sales & Marketing Asst
Tel: 800-334-7548
Email: allison.laudano@psenergy.com
Website: www.psenergy.com
Dist natural gas, vehicle fleet fuel mgmt, diesel fuel, gasoline, jet fuel, propane, etc. (Woman/Hisp, estab , empl , sales $165,000,000, cert: NMSDC, WBENC)

1839 Simcol Group, LLC
3455 Peachtree Rd NE, 5th Fl
Atlanta, GA 30326
Contact: Simon Guobadia CEO
Tel: 404-995-7037
Email: simon@simcolgroup.com
Website: www.simcolgroup.com
Fuel, gasoline, jet fuel, aviation fuel, diesel fuel, lubricants, wax. (AA, estab 2009, empl 10, sales , cert: NMSDC)

1840 Supreme Resources, Inc.
285 E Smoketree Terr
Alpharetta, GA 30005
Contact: Victor Tan Business Dev Mgr
Tel: 770-475-4638
Email: victortan@supremeresources.com
Website: www.supremeresources.com
Dist chemicals, resins, adhesives & raw materials. (As-Pac, estab 1988, empl 10, sales , cert: NMSDC)

1841 TDMC Enterprises Inc.
370 Great Southwest Pkwy
Atlanta, GA 30336
Contact: Chuck Smith President
Tel: 404-699-5404
Email: cesmith@chemstationatlanta.com
Website: www.chemstation.com
Mfr industrial chemicals: cleaners, degreasers, vehicle & airplane cleaners, food processing, odor control, parts washing, scrubber soaps, asphalt release products, strippers, etc. (AA, estab 1991, empl 14, sales $870,000, cert: NMSDC)

Iowa

1842 Searle Petroleum Co.
P.O. Box A
Council Bluffs, IA 51502
Contact: David Bills VP
Tel: 712-323-2441
Email: davidb@redgiantoil.com
Website:
Dist engine oils, hydraulic, compressor, journal, grease. (Woman, estab 1910, empl 88, sales $53,500,000, cert: WBENC)

Illinois

1843 Blackdog Corporation
2305 Enterprise Dr
Westchester, IL 60154
Contact: Marc Whitaker Chief Marketing Officer
Tel: 877-617-4104
Email: marc@blackdogcorp.com
Website: www.blackdogcorp.com
Dist fuel, oil & lubricants. (As-Pac, estab 2006, empl 46, sales $23,500,000, cert: City, NMSDC)

1844 Budnick Converting Inc.
200 Admiral Weinel Blvd
Columbia, IL 62236
Contact: Lori Baltz Acct Mgr
Tel: 800-282-0090
Email: samwi@budnickconverting.com
Website: http://budnickconverting.com
Convert & dist adhesive tapes & foams, cutting, slitting, laminating, printing & spooling. (Woman, estab 1952, empl 85, sales $20,000,000, cert: WBENC)

1845 Cedar Concepts Corporation
4342 S Wolcott Ave
Chicago, IL 60609
Contact: Roxanne Hubbard Marketing Mgr
Tel: 773-890-5790
Email: roxanne@cedarconcepts.net
Website: www.cedarconcepts.net
Mfr surfactants & chemical intermediates. (Woman/AA, estab 1991, empl 41, sales $15,000,000, cert: WBENC)

1846 Celta Chemical, Inc.
1301 W First St, Ste 1A
Granite City, IL 62040
Contact: Patrick Riordan VP
Tel: 314-440-6194
Email: pat@celtachem.com
Website: www.celtachem.com
Chemical & food ingredient toll manufacturer and supplier. (Woman, estab 2014, empl 8, sales $15,000,000, cert: WBENC)

1847 Essential Water Technologies LLC
6625 N. Avondale Ave
Chicago, IL 60631
Contact: Presdient
Tel: 630-344-6770
Email:
Website: http://essentialwatertech.com
Water treatment chemicals & services. (Woman, estab 2011, empl 8, sales $902,221, cert: WBENC)

1848 Natural Enrichment Industries
1002 S Park St
Sesser, IL 62884
Contact: Richard Degler Inside Sales
Tel: 618-625-2112
Email: irichardd@neitcp.com
Website: www.neitcp.com
Mfr tricalcium phosphate. (Woman, estab 2000, empl 26, sales $7,000,000, cert: State)

1849 Quimex, Inc.
14702 S Hamlin
Midlothian, IL 60445
Contact: Felipe Estrada Acct Mgr
Tel: 708-597-6201
Email: quimex@quimexinc.com
Website: www.quimexinc.com
Dist industrial chemicals, oils, lubricants, solvents & coatings. (Hisp, estab 1975, empl 14, sales $6,309,695, cert: City)

1850 West Fuels Inc.
82 S La Grange Road Ste 201
La Grange, IL 60525
Contact: Deborah Stange Presdient
Tel: 708-588-1900
Email: dstange@westfuels.com
Website: www.westfuels.com
Dist petroleum products. (Woman, estab 1991, empl 9, sales $10,600,000, cert: State, City, WBENC)

Indiana

1851 Advance Energy LLC
3580 N Hobart Rd, Ste C
Hobart, IN 46342
Contact: Vance Kenney Managing Partner
Tel: 219-794-1277
Email: vance.kenney@advanceegy.com
Website: www.advanceegy.com
Petroleum related products & services: gas, diesel & oil related products. (AA, estab 2012, empl 10, sales , cert: NMSDC)

1852 Harris and Ford, LLC
9307 E 56th St
Indianapolis, IN 46216
Contact: Tim Harris II Business Dev Mgr
Tel: 317-591-0000
Email: tth@harrisandford.com
Website: www.harrisandford.com
Dist chemicals & ingredients. (AA, estab 1994, empl 50, sales $220,000,000, cert: NMSDC)

1853 J2 Systems and Supply, LLC
803 E 38th St
Indianapolis, IN 46205
Contact: James Leonard Owner
Tel: 317-602-3940
Email: jleonard@j2ssllc.com
Website: www.j2systemsandsupply.com
Dist chemicals: water treatment, waste-water treatment, metal surface cleaning & coating, food ingredients & additives, industrial floor & general purpose cleaners. (AA, estab 2007, empl 5, sales $245,949, cert: State, NMSDC)

1854 Lemak, LLC dba Lemak Lubricants
P.O. Box 1381
Noblesville, IN 46061
Contact: Elizabeth Reynolds Presdient
Tel: 260-906-6433
Email: beth@lemakllc.com
Website: www.lemakllc.com/
Dist petroleum & chemicals: Industrial & Automotive Lubricants, Propane, Fuels, Coolants and Cutting Fluids, Antifreeze, Specialty & Commodity Chemicals. (Woman, estab 2008, empl 2, sales $3,289,096, cert: State, WBENC)

1855 Mays Chemical Company
5611 E 71st St
Indianapolis, IN 46220
Contact: Julie Brown Inventory Planning Admin
Tel: 317-558-2045
Email: julieb@mayschem.com
Website: www.mayschem.com
Dist process chemicals: bags, drums & totes, technical, reagent & USP/FCC grades. Electronic grade chemicals, antifreeze, caustic soda, etc. (Woman/AA, estab 1980, empl 70, sales $95,000,000, cert: NMSDC)

1856 Supreme Oil Company
      1319 Vincennes St
      New Albany, IN 47150
      Contact: Matt Sexton VP
      Tel: 812-945-5266
      Email: msexton@heritageoil.com
      Website: www.supremelubricants.com
Mobil & Chevron oils, lubricants & greases, hydraulic oil,
motor oil, gear oil, synthetic oil, biodegradeable oil,
antifreeze, coolants & cleaners. (Woman, estab 1937, empl
7, sales $15,359,000, cert: NWBOC)

1857 VTI Contracting, Inc.
      831 Elston Dr
      Shelbyville, IN 46176
      Contact: Judy Montgomery President
      Tel: 317-398-7911
      Email: jm@vtitotalsolutions.com
      Website: http://vtitotalsolutions.com
Concrete coatings, sealants, epoxy and resinous coatings,
polishing, repair, staining, traffic coatings, striping,
caulking, expansion joints, joint filler, fire proof caulking,
air barriers, waterproofing. (Woman, estab 1985, empl 30,
sales $3,000,010,000, cert: State, City)

1858 WLS Enterprises, Inc.
      8108 Woodland Dr
      Indianapolis, IN 46278
      Contact: Andre Warren VP
      Tel: 317-337-1020
      Email: andre@wls-enterprises.com
      Website: www.wls-enterprises.com
Dist chemicals, custom packaging, lab analysis.
 (Woman/AA, estab 2000, empl 12, sales $15,000,000,
cert: State)

Kentucky

1859 Big Meadow Oil Company
      4564 Big Meadow Rd
      Knob Lick, KY 42154
      Contact: Betty Gentry Presdient
      Tel: 270-432-7081
      Email: bigmoil@scrtc.com
      Website:
Dist fuel: gasoline, kerosene, diesel, lubricants, etc.
(Woman, estab 1981, empl 10, sales $3,000,000, cert:
WBENC)

1860 Hexagon Technologies, Inc.
      P.O. Box 23163
      Louisville, KY 40223
      Contact: Mr. Kiran Shah Presdient
      Tel: 502-429-8990
      Email: hexafloc@bellsouth.net
      Website: www.hexagontech.net
Water & wastewater treatment chemicals & services. (As-
Ind, estab 1982, empl 6, sales , cert: NMSDC)

1861 Mid American Chemical Supply Co, Inc.
      115 MacArthur Ct
      Nicholasville, KY 40356
      Contact: Leon Higgins Acct Exec
      Tel: 859-885-6400
      Email: leonhiggins@hotmail.com
      Website: www.midamericanchemical.com
Dist industrial & personal supplies, chemicals, non-durable
goods, industrial machinery & equipment. (AA, estab
1978, empl 54, sales , cert: State)

Louisiana

1862 Golden Leaf Energy, Inc.
      P.O. Box 3605
      Harvey, LA 70059
      Contact: Troy Clark CEO
      Tel: 504-252-4838
      Email: troyclark@goldenleafenergy.com
      Website: http://goldenleafenergy.com
Mfr biodiesel for use as a solvent as well as bio-based
lubricants & other products. (AA, estab 2011, empl 9,
sales , cert: State)

Massachusetts

1863 Grimes Oil Co., Inc.
      P.O. Box 276
      West Tisbury, MA 02575
      Contact: Calvin Grimes, Jr. Presdient
      Tel: 617-825-1200
      Email: sales@grimesoil.com
      Website: www.grimesoil.com
Dist distillate & risidual heating oils, diesel fuels &
gasoline. (AA, estab 1940, empl 4, sales $3,925,000,
cert: State, City, NMSDC)

Maryland

1864 HIC Energy, LLC
      5937 Belair Rd
      Baltimore, MD 21206
      Contact: Troy Holland Mgr
      Tel: 410-914-7161
      Email: th@hicenergy.com
      Website: http://hicenergy.com
Dist natural gas. (AA, estab 2015, empl 5, sales , cert:
NMSDC)

Michigan

1865 2V Industries, Inc.
      48553 West Rd
      Wixom, MI 48393
      Contact: Sharron Craig
      Tel: 248-624-7943
      Email: scraig@2vindustries.com
      Website: www.2vindustries.com
Dist metalworking compounds, coolants, RPS, cleaners,
etc. (As-Ind, estab 1968, empl 20, sales , cert: NMSDC)

1866 Adhesive Systems, Inc.
      14410 Woodrow Wilson
      Detroit, MI 48238
      Contact: Randall Jaymes Tech. Sales Acct Mgr
      Tel: 313-530-6654
      Email: randallj@dchem.com
      Website: www.dchem.com
Mfr hot melt, water base & pressure sensitive adhesives.
(AA, estab 1985, empl 28, sales $60,000,000, cert:
NMSDC)

1867 Adhezion, Inc.
      7730 Childsdale Ave
      Rockford, MI 49341
      Contact: Chris Telman Regional Acct Mgr
      Tel: 616-726-1775
      Email: ctelman@adhezioninc.com
      Website:
Adhesives & coatings. (Woman, estab 2010, empl 7,
sales , cert: WBENC)

1868 C.J. Chemicals, LLC
      47635 Old US 23
      Brighton, MI 48114
      Contact: Eric Earl Regional Mgr
      Tel: 269-788-2317
      Email: eric@cjchemicals.net
      Website: www.cjchemicals.net
Dist Chemicals, Solvents & Oils used for water & wastewater treatment, cleaning, painting, metal finishing & other industrial & commercial applications. (Woman, estab 2011, empl 10, sales , cert: WBENC)

1869 ChemicoMays, LLC
      25200 Telegraph Rd
      Southfield, MI 48034
      Contact: Dave Macleod VP, Bus Dev
      Tel: 248-723-3263
      Email: dmacleod@chemicomays.com
      Website: www.chemicomays.com
Chemical management, purchasing, distribution & logistics. (AA, estab 2005, empl 250, sales $86,000,000, cert: NMSDC)

1870 Chrysan Industries, Inc.
      14707 Keel St
      Plymouth, MI 48170
      Contact: Suk-Kyu Koh CEO
      Tel: 734-451-5411
      Email: skoh@chrysanindustries.com
      Website: www.chrysanindustries.com
Mfr industrial lubricants, cleaners, rust-preventatives, cutting fluids, stamping compounds, specialty chemicals, chemical mgmt. (As-Pac, estab 1977, empl 21, sales $10,300,000, cert: NMSDC)

1871 Diversified Chemical Technologies, Inc.
      15477 Woodrow Wilson
      Detroit, MI 48238
      Contact: Michael Joseff Dir of Sales
      Tel: 313-530-6630
      Email: mjoseff@dchem.com
      Website: www.dchem.com
Dist chemicals. (AA, Hisp, estab 1971, empl 185, sales $80,000,000, cert: NMSDC)

1872 Infiniti Energy & Environmental, Inc.
      24755 W Five Mile Rd Ste 100
      Redford, MI 48239
      Contact: Sherman Larkins Presdient
      Tel: 313-538-0172
      Email: sl@infinitigroup.us
      Website: www.infinitigroup.us
Dist natural gas, oil, lubricant & petroleum products, waste recycling, consulting & industrial cleaning, waste hauling. (AA, estab 1997, empl 5, sales $2,300,000, cert: NMSDC)

1873 Infiniti Energy & Environmental, Inc. dba Infiniti
      15930 19 Mile Rd, Ste 150
      Clinton Township, MI 48038
      Contact: Mark Coaster Marketing Mgr
      Tel: 616-583-9292
      Email: coaster@lakeshoreenergy.com
      Website: www.lakeshoreenergy.com
Natural gas brokering & supply management. (AA, estab 1997, empl 8, sales $3,000,000, cert: NMSDC)

1874 IPAX Atlantic LLC
      8301 Lyndon Ave
      Detroit, MI 48238
      Contact: Olti Tile Business Develop Mgr
      Tel: 313-933-4211
      Email: akatz@ipax.com
      Website: www.ipax.com
Mfr cleaning compounds. (Woman, estab 0, empl , sales , cert: WBENC)

1875 LCF - Farmer Group
      4581 S. Lapeer Road Ste G
      Lake Orion, MI 48359
      Contact: Forest Farmer Presdient
      Tel: 248-322-7079
      Email: rfarmer@mti-farmergrp.com
      Website: www.thefarmergroup.com
Paints, cleaners, wipes, rags, paint-booth related products, cleaning supplies, oil, lubricants, janitorial and floor care. (AA, estab 1994, empl 7, sales $2,822,500, cert: NMSDC)

1876 MCEM LLC
      31153 Plymouth Rd
      Livonia, MI 48150
      Contact: BK Masti Presdient
      Tel: 517-881-1226
      Email: bkm@mcem.com
      Website: www.mcem.com
Lubricants, valves, conduit fittings. (As-Pac, estab 2011, empl 5, sales , cert: NMSDC)

1877 Parson Adhesives Inc.
      3345 Auburn Rd, Ste 107
      Rochester Hills, MI 48309
      Contact: Hammie Dogan Natl Acct Mgr
      Tel: 248-299-5585
      Email: hammie@parsonadhesives.com
      Website: www.parsonadhesives.com
Industrial adhesives in small and large packing sizes, (As-Pac, estab 2002, empl 45, sales , cert: NMSDC)

1878 RKA Petroleum Company, Inc.
      28340 Wick Rd
      Romulus, MI 48174
      Contact: Timothy Dluzynski Natl Acct Exec
      Tel: 734-946-2202
      Email: tdluzynski@rkapetroleum.com
      Website: www.rkapetroleum.com
Dist refined & renewable fuel products and fuel management solutions. (Woman, estab 1969, empl 49, sales $675,365,826, cert: WBENC)

1879 Roy Smith Company
      14650 Dequindre
      Detroit, MI 48212
      Contact: Peter Wong Owner
      Tel: 313-883-6969
      Email: angela.summers@rscmain.com
      Website: www.rscmain.com
Industrial gases & welding, dist industrial bulk gas systems, packaged & cylinder specialty gases, welding equipment & consumables. (As-Pac, estab 1924, empl 20, sales $24,000,000, cert: NMSDC)

1880   Vik-Jay Industries, Inc.
       P.O. Box 3347
       Farmington, MI 48333
       Contact: Vik Bedi GM
       Tel: 248-661-6228
       Email: vbedi@vikjay.com
       Website: www.vikjay.com
Dist metalworking lubricants, fluids & cleaners. (As-Ind,
estab 1983, empl 36, sales $1,200,000, cert: NMSDC)

Minnesota

1881   LKT Laboratories, Inc.
       545 Phalen Blvd
       Saint Paul, MN 55130
       Contact: Luke Lam Presdient
       Tel: 651-644-8424
       Email: llam@lktlabs.com
       Website: www.lktlabs.com/
Mfr biochemicals for life science research, inhibitors,
activators, modulators, and many other high purity small
molecules, phytochemical isolation and analysis. (As-Pac,
estab 1990, empl 11, sales $1,300,000, cert: NMSDC)

Missouri

1882   Mind Safety Management, LLC/ M-Cubed Info
       1509 Washington Ave, Ste 650
       St. Louis, MO 63103
       Contact: Ralph Thompson COO
       Tel: 314-436-3233
       Email: ralphthompson@mcubedinfo.com
       Website: www.mindsafety.com
Dist adhesive products. (AA, estab 2001, empl 5, sales ,
cert: State)

1883   The Kiesel Company
       4801 Fyler Ave
       St. Louis, MO 63166
       Contact: Larry Gooden VP
       Tel: 314-351-5500
       Email: larry.gooden@kieselco.com
       Website: www.thekieselcompany.com
Dist fuels & lubricants, emergency response services to
chemical & petroleum product releases, railroad tank car
cleaning, barge cleaning, non-hazardous & hazardous
waste disposal, demolition & petroleum-contaminated
waste water treatment & disposal. (Woman, estab , empl
48, sales $75,010,000, cert: City)

1884   Wallis Oil Company
       106 E Washington St
       Cuba, MO 65453
       Contact: Dave Anthes Managing Dir
       Tel: 573-885-2277
       Email: dave.anthes@wallisco.com
       Website: www.wallisco.com
Dist petroleum. (Woman, estab 1968, empl 550, sales
$266,169,874, cert: State)

North Carolina

1885   Continental Chemicals, LLC
       4525 Park Rd Ste B-202
       Charlotte, NC 28209
       Contact: Brandon Lowery Natl Acct Exec
       Tel: 704-535-1215
       Email: blowery@continentalchemicals.com
       Website: www.continentalchemicals.com
Dist chemicals & raw materials. (Nat Ame, estab 1975,
empl 5, sales $30,100,000, cert: NMSDC)

1886   NDR Energy Group, LLC
       4822 Albemarle Rd Ste 209
       Charlotte, NC 28205
       Contact: Solomon RC Ali CEO
       Tel: 888-756-0555
       Email: solomon.ali@ndrenergy.us
       Website: www.ndrenergy.us
Dist natural gas, propane, refined products, fuels &
energy efficient lighting, asset management services.
(AA, estab 2005, empl 7, sales $65,000,000, cert:
NMSDC)

1887   Newbold Corporation
       8015 W Kenton Cir Ste 115
       Huntersville, NC 28078
       Contact: Amoura Carter Acct Rep
       Tel: 704-659-7800
       Email: amoura.carter@newboldonline.com
       Website: www.newboldonline.com
Dist MRO & chemical products & services, strategic
sourcing & reporting, outsourced procurement services.
(AA, estab 2000, empl 10, sales $14,000,000, cert:
NMSDC)

1888   PHT International Inc.
       8133 Ardrey Kell Road Ste 204
       Charlotte, NC 28277
       Contact: Ansley Proctor Cockerham Acct Rep
       Tel: 704-246-3480
       Email: acockerham@phtchemical.com
       Website: www.phtchemical.com
Mfr & source fine chemicals, organic intermediates &
API's. (Woman/As-Pac, estab 1993, empl 112, sales
$88,900,000, cert: NMSDC, WBENC)

1889   PolySi Technologies, Inc.
       5108 Rex McLeod Dr
       Sanford, NC 27330
       Contact: LYNN RICHARDSON Operations Mgr
       Tel: 919-775-4989
       Email: lynn@polysi.com
       Website: www.polysi.com
Mfr silicone, synthetic greases & silicone fluids, industrial packaging, retail packaging, contract filling &
custom packaging. (Woman, estab 1995, empl 25, sales
$7,000,000, cert: WBENC)

1890   Red Star Oil Company
       802 Purser Dr
       Raleigh, NC 27603
       Contact: Paula Milliron Acct Mgr
       Tel: 919-772-1944
       Email: paula@redstaroil.com
       Website: www.redstaroil.com
Deliver gasolines, diesel, non highway fuel, bio
fuel,kerosene. Sell motor oils, provide fuel polishing.
(Minority, estab 1969, empl 30, sales $38,489,046, cert:
State)

New Jersey

1891   Ash Ingredients, Inc.
     65 Harristown Rd, Ste 307
     Glen Rock, NJ 07452
     Contact: Phetmany Falconi Acct Mgr
     Tel:
     Email: phet@ashingredients.com
     Website: www.ashingredients.com
Mfr over 81 complex Intermediates for customers with CDA's in place. (Woman/As-Pac, estab 1999, empl 4, sales , cert: State, City)

1892   Assaycell Technologies LLC
     36 Chestnut St
     Avenel, NJ 07001
     Contact: Director
     Tel: 732-429-0199
     Email:
     Website: www.assaycell.com
Dist biochemical reagents, bacterial & mammalian cell culture media, reagents, assaykits, molecular biology reagents, plastic ware glassware, laboratory supplies, technical consultation. (Woman/As-Ind, estab 2017, empl 2, sales $120,000, cert: State, SDB)

1893   Bel-Ray Co.
     P.O. Box 526
     Wall, NJ 07719
     Contact: Bob Shrewsbury Acct Mgr
     Tel: 270-585-9005
     Email: rshrewsbury@belray.com
     Website: www.belray.com
Mfr & dist high performance lubricants made for the Mining, Industrial & Powersports markets world wide. (Woman, estab 1946, empl 150, sales , cert: State)

1894   BKM Resources, Inc. Global Chemicals
     P.O. Box 327
     Eatontown, NJ 07724
     Contact: Nancy Engkilterra President
     Tel: 732-264-2300
     Email: nengkilterra@bkmresources.com
     Website: www.bkmresources.com
Dist commodity & specialty chemicals. (Woman/AA, estab 1986, empl 10, sales $7,000,000, cert: NMSDC)

1895   Elan Chemical Co., Inc.
     268 Doremus Ave
     Newark, NJ 07105
     Contact: Isabel Couto VP
     Tel: 973-344-8014
     Email: icouto@elan-chemical.com
     Website: www.elan-chemical.com
Natural benzaldehyde, flavors, natural ingredients, synthetic ingredients, vanilla, extracts, acetaldehyde, ethyl benzoate, iso amyl alcohol, aldehydes, natural esters, ethyl caproate, acetic acid, natural aromatic chemicals, ethyl-2-methyl. (Woman, estab 1985, empl 50, sales , cert: State, WBENC)

1896   Foodtopia, Inc.
     11 Harrisotwn Rd, Ste 101
     Glen Rock, NJ 07452
     Contact: Tae Kim GM
     Tel: 201-444-8810
     Email: tkim@foodtopiausa.com
     Website: www.foodtopiausa.com
Food Additives, Nutritional Raw Materials, Amino Acids, Sweeteners, Food Chemicals (As-Pac, estab 1997, empl 7, sales $4,000,000, cert: State)

1897   GJ Chemical
     40 Veronica Ave
     Somerset, NJ 08873
     Contact: Fiore Masci Sr Acct Mgr
     Tel: 973-589-4176
     Email: customerservice@gjchemical.com
     Website: www.gjchemical.com
Mfr & dist raw chemical. (Woman, estab 1974, empl 75, sales $30,000,000, cert: WBENC)

1898   Global Essence Inc.
     8 Marlen Dr
     Hamilton, NJ 08691
     Contact: Jeanna Johnson VP Sales
     Tel: 732-677-1100
     Email: jjohnson@globalessence.com
     Website: www.globalessence.com
Dist flavor & fragrance raw materials: essential oils, organic essential oils, oleoresins, concretes, absolutes an& d synthetic aroma chemicals. (Woman, estab 1993, empl 34, sales $54,700,000, cert: State, WBENC)

1899   INDOFINE Chemical Company
     121 Stryker Ln Bldg 30, Ste 1
     Hillsborough, NJ 08844
     Contact: Sujata Moton VP
     Tel: 908-359-6778
     Email: indofine@indofinechemical.com
     Website: www.indofinechemical.com
Provide custom synthesis, contract research & process development. (Woman/As-Ind, estab 1981, empl 8, sales $1,000,000, cert: NMSDC, WBENC)

1900   Kingchem
     5 Pearl Ct
     Allendale, NJ 07401
     Contact: Daniel Kukovski Diversity Supplier Mgr
     Tel: 201-825-9988
     Email: d.kukovski@kingchem.com
     Website: www.kingchem.com
Mfr fluoro-organic compounds. (As-Pac, estab 1994, empl 13, sales $69,780,000, cert: NMSDC)

1901   Su International Group, Inc.
     1430 Rte 206, Ste 210
     Bedminster, NJ 07921
     Contact: Dan Downs Project Mgr
     Tel: 908-901-0102
     Email: ddowns@suintl.com
     Website: www.suintl.com
Mfr chemicals: synthetic vitamins, food chemical, & artificial sweeteners. (Woman/As-Ind, As-Pac, estab 1996, empl 6, sales $18,946,253, cert: NMSDC, NWBOC)

New York

1902   Ampak Co., Inc.
     1890 Palmer Ave, Ste 203
     Larchmont, NY 10538
     Contact: Cindy Sturm Business Develop Mgr
     Tel: 914-833-7070
     Email: csturm@ampakcompany.com
     Website: www.ampakcompany.com
Dist amino acids, antioxidants, preservatives, cellulosics, hight intensity sweetners, humectants, hydrocolloids, phosphates, colors, vitamins & minerals. (As-Ind, estab 1978, empl 19, sales $80,544,821, cert: NMSDC)

1903   Crescent Chemical Co., Inc.
       2 Oval Dr
       Islandia, NY 11749
       Contact: President
       Tel: 631-348-0333
       Email: creschem@aol.com
       Website: www.crescentchemical.com
Dist pesticides & herbicides. (Woman, estab 1947, empl 8, sales $3,000,000, cert: City, WBENC)

1904   Infinite Energy Corp d/b/a Definite Energy Group
       410 Park Ave, 15th Fl
       New York, NY 10022
       Contact: Deborah Pinto Presdient
       Tel: 212-759-7426
       Email: dpinto@definiteenergy.com
       Website: www.definiteenergy.com
Dist petroleum products. (Woman, estab 1994, empl , sales $16,814,844, cert: State, City, WBENC)

1905   Miles Petroleum Corp., Inc.
       66 Marine St
       Farmingdale, NY 11735
       Contact: Angela Stern Presdient
       Tel: 631-694-4488
       Email: astern@milesoil.com
       Website: www.milesoil.com
Dist lubricating oils & greases. (Woman, estab 1937, empl 14, sales $4,300,000, cert: State)

1906   Tra-Lin Corp.
       248 Buell Road
       Rochester, NY 14624
       Contact: Linda Fedele President
       Tel: 585-254-6010
       Email: lindafedele@rochester.rr.com
       Website: www.samsonfuel.com/
Dist fuel & additives. (Woman, estab 1984, empl 10, sales $663,110, cert: State)

Ohio

1907   Accurate Lubricants & Metalworking Fluids Inc.
       P.O. Box 3807
       Dayton, OH 45401
       Contact: Marilyn Kinne Presdient
       Tel: 937-461-9906
       Email: mgkinne@acculube.com
       Website: www.acculube.com
Sales & technical support of industrial lubricants, metalworking fluids, water treatment chemicals & ancillary sales & services. (Woman, estab 0, empl , sales , cert: WBENC)

1908   Calvary Industries, Inc.
       9233 Seward Rd
       Fairfield, OH 45014
       Contact: Austin Morelock New Business Devel
       Tel: 513-874-1113
       Email: acmorelock@calvaryindustries.com
       Website: www.calvaryindustries.com
Mfr industrial & inorganic chemicals. (Nat Ame, estab 1983, empl 120, sales $78,000,000, cert: NMSDC)

1909   Coolant Control, Inc.
       5353 Spring Grove Ave
       Cincinnati, OH 45217
       Contact: Jorge Costa Owner
       Tel: 513-471-8770
       Email: jcosta@coolantcontrol.com
       Website: www.coolantcontrol.com
Site chemical management services, mfr emulsifiers, corrosion inhibitors, cleaners, washers, coolants, coolant additives & odor control. (Hisp, estab 1975, empl , sales $100,000, cert: NMSDC)

1910   Global Environmental Products
       4624 Interstate Dr
       Cincinnati, OH 45406
       Contact: Mike Mamaligas Presdient
       Tel: 513-984-5444
       Email: info@gepltd.com
       Website: www.gepltd.com
Dist absorbents, oil & chemical spill cleanup products. (AA, estab 2002, empl 5, sales $1,200,000, cert: NMSDC)

1911   Hightowers Petroleum Company
       3577 Commerce Dr
       Middletown, OH 45005
       Contact: David Konopka Sr Director
       Tel: 513-423-4272
       Email: david@hightowerspetroleum.com
       Website: www.hightowerspetroleum.com
Dist & transport fuel & petroleum products: gasoline, diesel fuel, lubricants, oils, greases, speciality chemicals. (AA, estab 1985, empl 37, sales $219,922,573, cert: NMSDC)

1912   Lianda Corporation
       8285 Darrow Rd Ste 200
       Twinsburg, OH 44087
       Contact: Lifang Mao Presdient
       Tel: 330-653-8341
       Email: lmao@liandacorp.com
       Website: www.liandacorp.com
Import & dist synthetic rubber & related chemicals. (Woman/As-Pac, estab 1995, empl 11, sales , cert: NMSDC)

1913   Next Generation Fuel, LLC
       3589 Commerce Dr
       Middletown, OH 45005
       Contact: Dawn Lindsey CEO
       Tel: 513-435-4337
       Email: dawn@nxtgenfuel.com
       Website: www.nxtgenfuel.com
Dist unleaded gasoline, high & low sulfur diesel fuels, bio-diesel, ethanol & fuel additives. (Woman/AA, estab 2014, empl , sales $10,519,712, cert: NMSDC, WBENC)

1914   Orchem Corporation
       4927 Beech St
       Cincinnati, OH 45212
       Contact: Denise Ramey COO
       Tel: 513-874-9700
       Email: denise.ramey@orchemcorp.com
       Website: www.orchemcorp.com
Mfr cleaning & sanitation chemicals. (Woman/AA, estab 1996, empl 28, sales $4,200,000, cert: NMSDC)

1915 Phymet
75 N Pioneer Blvd
Springboro, OH 45066
Contact: Amy Minck Presdient
Tel: 937-743-8061
Email: alachman@micropoly.com
Website: www.micropoly.com
Mfr MicroPoly, a solid lubricant system made of plastics &
oil used in bearing lubrication and conveyor chain lubrica-
tion. (Woman, estab 1986, empl 18, sales $3,000,000, cert:
WBENC)

1916 Stevenson Oil & Chemical Corp.
30130 Lakeland Blvd
Wickliffe, OH 44092
Contact: Suzanne Harkey
Tel: 440-943-3337
Email: info@stevensonoil.com
Website: www.stevensonoil.com
Dist industrial lubricants: engine oil, hydraulic oil, gear oil,
cutting oil, metalworking fluid, turbine oil, general
purpose lubricants, transmission oil, quenching oil, bio-
friendly lubricants, grease & solvents. (Woman, estab
1969, empl 3, sales $1,904,092, cert: WBENC)

1917 Tedia Company, Inc.
1000 Tedia Way
Fairfield, OH 45014
Contact: Jennifer Herber Key Accts Mgr
Tel: 513-889-6468
Email: jherber@tedia.com
Website: www.tedia.com
Mfr & dist high purity solvents & reagents: research,
industrial & analytical applications. (Woman/As-Pac, estab
1975, empl 120, sales , cert: NMSDC)

1918 The Blackfoot Company
6061 Telegraph Rd, Ste P
Toledo, OH 43612
Contact: Leroy Pepion CEO
Tel: 419-478-8650
Email: tblkftco@aol.com
Website: www.theblackfootcompany.com
Dist industrial chemicals, winter maintenance products,
facility & janitorial supplies, water treatment, parking lot
maintenance. (Nat Ame, estab 1994, empl 5, sales
$650,000, cert: State)

1919 Westwood Finishing Company
5881 Wolf Creek Pike
Trotwood, OH 45426
Contact: Owner
Tel: 937-854-6608
Email:
Website: http://westfinish.com
Apply all types of paint material: wet coating, epoxy,
urethane, enamels and copper coatings (EMI and RFI
shielding. (Woman, estab 1995, empl 11, sales $530,864,
cert: WBENC)

Oklahoma

1920 Advance Research Chemicals
1110 W Keystone Ave
Tulsa, OK 74015
Contact: Mat Cleveland Sales Mgr
Tel: 918-266-6789
Email: mathercleveland@fluoridearc.com
Website: www.fluoridearc.com
Inorganic fluorides (As-Ind, estab 1987, empl 125, sales
$50,000,000, cert: NMSDC)

1921 Sage Energy Trading, LLC
8023 E 63rd Pl, Ste 350
Tulsa, OK 74133
Contact: Cindy Hughes President
Tel: 918-362-2310
Email: chughes@sageenergytrading.com
Website:
Dist natural gas. (Woman, estab 2004, empl , sales
$9,359,750, cert: WBENC)

1922 Tiger Natural Gas, Inc.
1422 E 71st St, Ste J
Tulsa, OK 74136
Contact: Johnathan Burris VP Marketing
Tel: 918-491-6998
Email: diversity@tigernaturalgas.com
Website: www.tigernaturalgas.com
Dist natural gas. (Woman/Nat Ame, estab 1991, empl
46, sales , cert: NMSDC, WBENC)

Oregon

1923 YOLO Colorhouse LLC
519 NE Hancock St, Ste B
Portland, OR 97212
Contact: Rick Barnard VP Operations
Tel: 503-493-8275
Email: rick@colorhousepaint.com
Website: www.colorhousepaint.com
Premium paints: no-VOC, low-odor & earth friendly.
(Woman, estab 2006, empl 11, sales $780,000, cert:
WBENC)

Pennsylvania

1924 American Energy Supply Corporation
1704 Chichester Ave
Upper Chichester, PA 19061
Contact: Kristen Baiocco Presdient
Tel: 610-494-4874
Email: kb@fueloilnow.com
Website: http://fueloilnow.com
Diesel Fuel Delivery and Fuel Tanks for rent or sale.
(Woman, estab 2009, empl 9, sales $2,454,000, cert:
WBENC)

1925 Biopeptek Pharmaceuticals LLC
5 Great Valley Pkwy Ste 100
Malvern, PA 19355
Contact: John Zhang CEO
Tel: 610-643-4881
Email: johnzhang@biopeptek.com
Website: www.biopeptek.com
Mfr custom peptides services. (As-Pac, estab , empl ,
sales $5,000,000, cert: NMSDC)

1926 Crystal Inc. PMC
      601 W Eighth St
      Lansdale, PA 19446
      Contact: Karen Roorda Exec Asst
      Tel: 215-368-1661
      Email: kroorda@pmc-group.com
      Website: www.crystalinc-pmc.com
Specialty & performance chemicals, sodium & potassium stearates, wax emulsions, specialty antifoams, rubber & plastics additives, process chemicals & cable filling jellies. (As-Pac, estab 1929, empl 80, sales , cert: NMSDC)

1927 Crystal, Inc.
      601 W 8th St
      Lansdale, PA 19446
      Contact: Lynne Currie Exec/mktg Asst
      Tel: 215-368-1661
      Email: epalincrystal@pmc-group.com
      Website: www.pmc-group.com
Dist specialty & performance chemicals, sodium & potassium stearates, wax emulsions, specialty antifoams, rubber & plastics additives, process chemicals & cable filling jellies. (Minority, estab 1929, empl 80, sales , cert: NMSDC)

1928 EMSCO Scientific Enterprises, Inc.
      5070 Parkside Ave
      Philadelphia, PA 19131
      Contact: Roderick Clifford Asst VP
      Tel: 215-477-5601
      Email: rpclifford2@emscoscientific.com
      Website: http://emscoscientific.com
Dist production & laboratory chemicals. (AA, estab 1980, empl 9, sales $19,800,000, cert: City, NMSDC)

1929 GRP Services
      P.O. Box 41
      Pittsburgh, PA 15221
      Contact: Ernest Groover President
      Tel: 412-271-5231
      Email: egroover@grpservices.net
      Website: www.grpservices.net
Natural gas brokerage, utility cost recovery, telecommunications svcs. (AA, estab 2002, empl 3, sales $100,000, cert: NMSDC)

1930 Muscle Products Corp.
      752 Kilgore Rd
      Jackson Center, PA 16133
      Contact: Sharon Murphy-Dittrich Presdient
      Tel: 814-786-0166
      Email: sharon@mpclubricants.com
      Website: www.mpclubricants.com
Manufacture Lubricants & Greases, for General Industry & Automotive Use. (Woman, estab 1986, empl , sales , cert: WBENC)

1931 Naughton Energy Corp.
      Rte 940
      Pocono Pines, PA 18350
      Contact: Sean Naughton VP
      Tel: 570-646-0422
      Email: sean@naughtonenergy.com
      Website: www.naughtonenergy.com
Energy products, energy services & lubricants: gasoline, heating oil, diesel, marine, kerosene,jet, residual & re-refined oil, Anthracite, Bituminous & Synfuel, natural gas. (Woman/As-Pac, estab 1976, empl 8, sales $14,000,000, cert: State, City, NMSDC)

1932 Randall Industries LLC
      1401 Forbes Ave
      Pittsburgh, PA 15219
      Contact: Gregory Spencer CEO
      Tel: 412-281-6903
      Email: g.spencer11@verizon.net
      Website: www.randall-industries.net
Mfr chemicals. (AA, estab 2006, empl 10, sales $800,000, cert: State)

Puerto Rico

1933 Lanco Manufacturing Corp.
      Urb. Aponte 5
      San Lorenzo, PR 00954
      Contact: Nelson Soto Category Mgr
      Tel: 787-736-4221
      Email: nsoto@lancopaints.com
      Website: http://lancopaints.com
Paints (Water and Oil Based), Enamels, Caulking, Spackling, Wood Stains, Wood Fillers, Adhesive, Roof Sealers, Concrete Bonding Agents and Solvents(Paint removers, Lacquer Thinners, Mineral Spirits). (Hisp, estab 1978, empl 250, sales $69,320,794, cert: NMSDC)

1934 Mays Ochoa
      NO 515 Calle 2
      Catano, PR 00962
      Contact: Rafael Marti VP/GM
      Tel: 787-788-8000
      Email: gloria.rosado@maysochoa.com
      Website: www.mayschem.com
Chemicals. (Hisp, estab 1984, empl 50, sales , cert: NMSDC)

1935 Sachs Chemical Inc.
      P.O. Box 191670 KM 0 02 LOT, 18 RR 175
      San Juan, PR 00725
      Contact: Laura Conde Accountant
      Tel: 787-745-2520
      Email: laura@sachschem.com
      Website: www.sachschem.com
Dist chemicals. (Hisp, estab 1986, empl 33, sales $32,000,000, cert: NMSDC)

Rhode Island

1936 Blue Sky Natural Gas & Petroleum, Inc.
      99 Charlotte Dr
      East Greenwich, RI 02818
      Contact: Leslie Mathews President
      Tel: 401-465-1111
      Email: blueskynaturalgas@gmail.com
      Website:
Dist petroleum products, natural gas & electricity, low sulfur heating oil, low sulfur diesel fuel, bio-diesel, propane, #4 & #6 residual fuels, gasoline, kerosene etc. (Woman, estab 1992, empl 10, sales , cert: State)

South Carolina

1937 AmberTech Technologies LLC
2037 Summerton Hwy
Summerton, SC 29148
Contact: Tom Massey Director
Tel: 803-696-1152
Email: tmassey001@sc.rr.com
Website: http://ambertech-global.com
A USDA certified 99% bio-based metal conditioner used in all lubrication applications to reduce friction and heat. (Woman, estab 2011, empl 7, sales $1,600,000, cert: NWBOC)

Tennessee

1938 K-Chemicals, Inc
301 Industrial Dr
Bean Station, TN 37708
Contact: Jeffery Kyle President
Tel: 865-767-2342
Email: jeffkyle@k-chemicals.com
Website: www.k-chemical.com
Mfr specialty chemicals: car wash, janitorial & industrial chemicals, package & distribute production chemicals, solvents, caustics, acids, powdered products. (AA, Nat Ame, As-Pac, estab 1989, empl 10, sales $3,000,000, cert: NMSDC)

1939 Quality Adhesives LLC
3791 Air Park
Memphis, TN 38118
Contact: curtis hunt Presdient
Tel: 901-375-3991
Email: curtish@qualityadhesivesinc.com
Website: www.qualityadhesivesinc.com
Mfr & dist hot melt & liquid adhesives. (AA, estab 1999, empl 8, sales $8,000,000, cert: NMSDC)

Texas

1940 American Chemie, Inc.
13706 Research Blvd Summit Executive Ctr, Ste 302
Austin, TX 78750
Contact: Mike Kamdar Presdient
Tel: 512-219-7400
Email: mike@americanchemie.com
Website: http://americanchemie.com
Dist Emulsifiers, Emollients, Esters, Fatty alcohols, Eco-Cert Natural Refined Shea Butter and other body Butters, Preservatives & Surfactants. (Woman/As-Ind, estab 1991, empl 9, sales $10,086,762, cert: State, NMSDC, WBENC)

1941 AmPac Chemical Company Inc.
P.O. Box 272848
Houston, TX 77277
Contact: Sonia Fujimoto Presdient
Tel: 713-660-9383
Email: sonia@ampacchemical.com
Website: www.ampacchemical.com
Dist chemicals. (Woman/As-Pac, estab 1996, empl , sales $2,217,678, cert: State, City, NMSDC)

1942 Atlantic Petroleum & Mineral Resources Inc.
723 Main St, Ste 207
Houston, TX 77002
Contact: Donald Sheffield
Tel: 713-223-2767
Email: drsheffield@atlantic-petro.com
Website: www.atlantic-petro.com
Dist branded & unbranded petroleum products. (AA, estab 2005, empl 8, sales $476,200, cert: State, City, NMSDC)

1943 Avalon Chemicals, Inc.
10101 Southwest Frwy Ste 400
Houston, TX 77074
Contact: Vinay Deshmane Presdient
Tel: 713-219-1457
Email: info@avalonchemicals.com
Website: www.avalonchemicals.com
Phenolic antioxidants (BHT, TBHQ, BHA), antioxidants (DODPA). (As-Ind, estab 2002, empl 2, sales $1,260,000, cert: State, NMSDC)

1944 Champion Fuel Solutions
P.O. Box 210191
Bedford, TX 76095
Contact: Patti Russell President
Tel: 877-909-9191
Email: prussell@championfs.com
Website: www.championfs.com
Dist gasoline & diesel fuel, biodiesel, kerosene, oils & lubricants. (Woman, estab 2010, empl 2, sales , cert: State, WBENC)

1945 Cole Chemical & Distributing, Inc.
1500 S Dairy Ashford Ste 450
Houston, TX 77077
Contact: Rebecca Cooper CEO
Tel: 713-465-2653
Email: weborders@colechem.com
Website: www.colechem.com
Mfr & dist thermoformed products. (Woman/As-Pac, estab 0, empl 0, sales $47,000,000, cert: State, City, NMSDC, WBENC)

1946 Dien, Inc.
3510 Pipestone Rd
Dallas, TX 75212
Contact: Dian Davis Presdient
Tel: 214-905-1528
Email: dian@dieninc.com
Website: www.dieninc.com
Dist chemicals: industrial, food, solvents, greases & lubricants, pharmaceutical & personal care. (Woman/Nat Ame, estab , empl , sales $46,627,700, cert: State, NMSDC)

1947 Diversified Chemical and Supply, Inc.
P.O. Box 1297
Humble, TX 77347
Contact: Donna Rosenstein President
Tel: 713-461-9610
Email: dcsupply@sbcglobal.net
Website: www.diversifiedchem.com
Dist janitorial & industrial chemicals & supplies. (Woman, estab 1990, empl 3, sales $2,508,119, cert: State, WBENC)

1948 Elevation Energy Group LLC
      P.O. Box 6036
      Austin, TX 78762
      Contact: Gwen Kyle Presdient
      Tel: 317-333-7281
      Email: tri@elevationeg.com
      Website: http://elevationeg.com
Natural gas supply and associated services. (As-Pac, estab 2014, empl 15, sales , cert: NMSDC)

1949 Energy Utility Group, LLC
      1402 Clearview Loop
      Round Rock, TX 78664
      Contact: Melinda Zito O'Brien CEO
      Tel: 512-805-8321
      Email: melinda@energyutilitygroup.com
      Website: www.energyutilitygroup.com
Energy consulting & electricity & natural gas brokering company. (Woman, estab , empl , sales , cert: State, City, CPUC, WBENC)

1950 FSTI Inc.
      6300 Bridge Point Pkwy, Ste 1-200
      Austin, TX 78730
      Contact: Coulter Gibson Dir of Packaged Products
      Tel: 512-278-8800
      Email: cgibson@fstichem.com
      Website: www.fstichem.com
Dist chemicals. (Woman, estab 1998, empl 50, sales $19,100,000, cert: State, WBENC)

1951 Gasochem International LLC
      9509 Pemberton Crescent Dr
      Houston, TX 77025
      Contact: Charu Jain President
      Tel: 713-837-6116
      Email: charu@gasochem.com
      Website: www.gasochem.com
Dist chemicals: oilfield, water treatment, industrial, agricultural & pharmaceutical. (Woman/As-Pac, estab 2012, empl 2, sales $167,000, cert: State, WBENC)

1952 Genoa International
      2245 Texas Dr, Ste 300
      Sugar Land, TX 77479
      Contact: Pamela Kahn Principal
      Tel: 281-313-0120
      Email: pkahn@genoaint.com
      Website: www.genoaint.com
Specialty chemicals, surfactants, drilling fluids, solvents, lubricants & commodities. (Woman, estab 0, empl , sales $4,000,000, cert: State, WBENC)

1953 Global Amchem Inc.
      407 E Methvin, Ste 200
      Longview, TX 75606
      Contact: Debbie Scott Office Admin
      Tel: 903-236-0138
      Email: debbie@amcheminc.com
      Website: www.amcheminc.com
Dist solvents & chemicals. (Hisp, estab 1993, empl 6, sales $430,505, cert: State, NMSDC)

1954 GND Consulting & Supply LLC
      1836 Snake River Rd, Ste A
      Katy, TX 77449
      Contact: Jose Camacho Sales Mgr
      Tel: 832-415-4100
      Email: camachojo@gndsc.com
      Website: http://gndsc.com
Dist non-toxic, environmentally-safe cleaners, degreasers, solvents, lubricants & specialty chemical products. (Woman/Hisp, estab 2011, empl 8, sales $603,242, cert: State, NMSDC, WBENC)

1955 Gold Star Petroleum, Inc.
      P.O. Box 11151
      Spring, TX 77391
      Contact: JJ Rodriguez President
      Tel: 281-379-5928
      Email: goldstarpetro@comcast.net
      Website:
Dist gasolines & diesel fuels. (Hisp, estab 1981, empl 6, sales $34,100,000, cert: State, NMSDC)

1956 KAP TechnoChem USA, Inc.
      4934 Cotter Lake Dr
      Missouri City, TX 77459
      Contact: PRAVIN kapadia
      Tel: 281-403-0242
      Email: hpkaps@kaptechno.com
      Website: www.kaptechno.com
Dist organic solvents, hydrocarbons, alcohol, ketones, fatty acids, glycols, inorganic chemicals, oil & lubs carnauba wax, castor wax activated carbons etc. (As-Ind, estab 2005, empl 2, sales , cert: 8a)

1957 New K-Stone Management, Inc.
      10718 Sentinel St
      San Antonio, TX 78217
      Contact: Dana Stone Presdient
      Tel: 210-494-0507
      Email: dstone@kstoneinc.com
      Website: www.kstonesupply.com
Industrial chemicals for automotive, animal shelters, food processing plants, physical plant supplies & chemicals for lab animal research. (Woman, estab 1997, empl 15, sales $1,147,125, cert: State)

1958 One Nation Energy Solutions, LLC
      4404 Blossom St
      Houston, TX 77007
      Contact: Terry Pierce President
      Tel: 713-861-0600
      Email: tpierce@onenationenergy.com
      Website: www.onenationenergy.com
Dist & market gas & power. (Woman, estab 2003, empl , sales $68,601,802, cert: City, CPUC)

1959 Oxyde Chemicals, Inc.
      225 Pennbright Dr Ste 101
      Houston, TX 77090
      Contact: Elva Rojas Sales Agent
      Tel: 281-874-9100
      Email: rojase@oxydeusa.com
      Website: www.oxydeusa.com
Dist petrochemicals & plastics. (Hisp, estab 1950, empl 60, sales $650,000,000, cert: State, NMSDC)

1960 Premier Polymers LLC
16800 Imperial Valley, Ste 200
Houston, TX 77060
Contact: Melwani Kwan Supply Chain Mgr
Tel: 281-902-0909
Email: mkwan@premierpolymers.com
Website: www.premierpolymers.com
Dist Plastic Resin. (As-Pac, estab 2009, empl 22, sales ,
cert: State, NMSDC)

1961 Ricochet Fuel Distributors, Inc.
1201 Royal Pkwy
Euless, TX 76040
Contact: Jason Cox Mktg Coord
Tel: 800-284-2540
Email: sales@ricochetfuel.com
Website: www.ricochetfuel.com
Dist diesel, gasoline, oil, antifreeze & kerosene, fuel mgmt
& monitoring programs. (Woman, estab 1988, empl 27,
sales $63,847,000, cert: WBENC)

1962 SolvChem, Inc.
1904 Mykawa
Pearland, TX 77546
Contact: Stacey Barrett Acct Mgr
Tel: 832-300-4067
Email: stacey_barrett@solvchem.com
Website: www.solvchem.com
Dist aircraft chemicals, chemicals blends, calibrating fluids,
purging fluids. (Hisp, estab 1980, empl 40, sales
$2,707,198, cert: State, NMSDC)

1963 Texican Natural Gas Company
500 Dallas St ONE ALLEN CENTER STE 1150
Houston, TX 77002
Contact: Rob Sellers Dir of Finance
Tel: 713-650-6579
Email: rsellers@texican.com
Website: http://Texican.com
Dist Natural gas, fuel oil, propane, Natural gas consulting.
(Hisp, estab 1985, empl 38, sales $500,000,000, cert:
NMSDC)

1964 The Green Chemical Store, Inc.
11837 Judd Ct, Ste 104
Dallas, TX 75243
Contact: The Green Chemical Store Presdient
Tel: 972-429-1719
Email: operations@thegreenchemicalstore.com
Website: www.thegreenchemicalstore.com
Dist chemicals for building maintenance trades. (Woman,
estab 2009, empl 5, sales $150,000, cert: WBENC)

1965 Tri-Chem Specialty Chemicals, LLC
P.O. Box 2056
Cresson, TX 76035
Contact: CEO
Tel: 972-745-6875
Email:
Website: www.tri-chem.net
Custom liquid & dry chemical blending, chemical &
additive distribution. (Woman/Hisp, estab 1989, empl 14,
sales $4,777,000, cert: WBENC)

1966 XD Ventures, LLC
2555 South Shore Blvd. Ste C
League City, TX 77573
Contact: Xan Difede Presdient
Tel: 832-557-6622
Email: xan@fidelityfuels.com
Website: www.fidelityfuels.com
Dist aliphatic solvents, mineral spirits & mineral seal oils.
(Woman, estab 2014, empl 1, sales , cert: State, WBENC)

Utah

1967 CP Industries, LLC
560 North 500 West
Salt Lake City, UT 84116
Contact: Erica Sellers Presdient
Tel: 801-521-0313
Email: accounting311@cpindustries.net
Website: www.cpindustries.net
Mfr ice melting compounds, customer chemical blend-
ing, liquid & powder detergents. (Woman, estab 1949,
empl 19, sales $5,510,415, cert: WBENC)

1968 FYVE STAR, Inc.
1972 E Dan Dr
Layton, UT 84040
Contact: Celeste Gleave CEO
Tel: 801-552-9100
Email: celeste@fyvestar.com
Website: www.fyvestar.com
Mfr & dist deicers. Calcium Chloride, Blends, Solar Salt,
Water Conditioning Salts, primary supplier to the US
Military on Liquid Runway & Aircraft Deicers. (Woman,
estab 1993, empl 2, sales $400,000, cert: State)

1969 The Horrocks Company LLC dba Volu-Sol
5095 West 2100 South
Salt Lake City, UT 84120
Contact: Celeste Horrocks Owner
Tel: 801-974-9474
Email: celeste.horrocks@volusol.com
Website: www.volusol.com
Mfr chemicals, alcohols, reagents, diagnostic stains &
counterstains. (Woman, estab 2013, empl 10, sales
$470,000, cert: WBENC)

Virginia

1970 Coyanosa Gas Services Corporation
1765 Greensboro Station Place Ste 900
McLean, VA 22102
Contact: Jerry Curry Presdient
Tel: 703-938-7984
Email: jerry@coyanosagasservices.com
Website: www.coyanosagasservices.com
Dist natural gas & energy utilization consulting. (AA,
estab 1995, empl , sales $20,000,000, cert: NMSDC,
CPUC, SDB)

1971 Creative Maintenance Solutions, LLC
1171 Polk Rd
Edinburg, VA 22824
Contact: Nancy Barnett
Tel: 540-984-8172
Email: nancy@cmsolutionsus.com
Website: www.cmsolutionsus.com
Dist polymer/epoxy & coatings. (Woman, estab , empl ,
sales , cert: State)

1972   Enspire Energy, LLC
       134 N Battlefield Blvd
       Chesapeake, VA 23320
       Contact: julie hashagen Dir of Operations
       Tel: 757-963-9123
       Email: jhashagen@enspireenergy.com
       Website: www.enspireenergy.com
Natural gas marketing & transportation. (Woman, estab 2005, empl 3, sales $979,376, cert: WBENC)

1973   James River Solutions
       10487 Lakeridge Parkway
       Ashland, VA 23005
       Contact: Elizabeth Austin Commercial Project Mgr
       Tel: 804-358-9000
       Email: eaustin@jrpetro.com
       Website: http://JamesRiverPetroleum.com
Bulk Deliveries, Gasoline, Diesel, Dyed Diesel, Heating Oil, DEF, Mobile Fueling, Fleet Fueling Cards. (Woman, estab 2005, empl 61, sales $251,000,000, cert: State)

Washington

1974   Allied Fuel LLC
       2400 Harbor Ave SW, Ste 100
       Seattle, WA 98126
       Contact: James E Hasty Presdient
       Tel: 206-582-2020
       Email: james@alliedfuel.net
       Website: http://alliedfuel.net
Dist fuel. (AA, estab 2009, empl 5, sales $51,350,000, cert: NMSDC)

1975   Dunkin & Bush, Inc.
       P.O. Box 97080
       Kirkland, WA 98083
       Contact: Deidre Dunkin President
       Tel: 425-885-7064
       Email: ddunkin@dunkinandbush.com
       Website: www.dunkinandbush.com
Industrial painting, scaffolding, insulation, rigging, containment, lead abatement, shop coating aplication, concrete restoration, plural applied tank linings, abrasive blasting, specialty blasting, water jetting, high heat coating applications. (Woman, estab 2008, empl 300, sales , cert: WBENC)

Wisconsin

1976   ChemCeed LLC
       1720 Prosperity Court
       Chippewa Falls, WI 54729
       Contact: Myra Detienne Sales Rep
       Tel: 715-726-2300
       Email: customerservice@chemceed.com
       Website: www.chemceed.com
Dist chemicals in bulk tankwagons, drums, totes, or custom packaging, ethanols, alcohols, reagents, & other solvents. (Woman/As-Pac, estab 2009, empl 10, sales , cert: NMSDC, WBENC)

1977   Power Lube Industrial LLC
       4930 S 2nd St, Ste 300
       Milwaukee, WI 53207
       Contact: Sarah Herr Exec VP of Sales
       Tel: 800-635-8170
       Email: sarah@powerlubeind.com
       Website: http://powerlubind.com
Automatic lubrication equipment and supplies, Memolub, Greaseomatic, and ATS Electrolub single point and multi- point product lines. (Woman, estab 1998, empl 10, sales $2,200,000, cert: WBENC)

CLEANING PRODUCTS, SUPPLIES & SERVICES
Manufacturers and distributors of maintenance supplies: all purpose cleaners, deodorizers, floor waxes, wax removers, oven cleaners, dishwashing & laundry detergents, soaps, hand cleaners, furniture & metal polishes, rug & upholstery shampoos, ammonia, janitorial services, etc. Janitorial services. NAICS Code 32

Arizona

1978   The Riley Kraus Group, LLC
2325 W. Cypress St.
Phoenix, AZ 85009
Contact: Al Kraus CFO
Tel: 602-252-9402
Email: info@maintenancemart.com
Website: www.maintenancemart.com
Dist commercial janitorial supplies, tools, motorized equipment, paper, trash liners, walk-off mats, indoor & outdoor receptacles & ash urns. (Woman/Hisp, estab 2001, empl 18, sales $4,510,000, cert: City)

California

1979   Ahtna Government Services Corporation
3100 Beacon Blvd.
West Sacramento, CA 95691
Contact: Craig O'Rourke Presdient
Tel: 916-372-2000
Email: info@ahtnagov.com
Website: www.ahtnagov.com
Ahtna provides high quality services worldwide and is CPUC-certified. Ahtna is one of the fastest growing small business firms in the United States. (Nat Ame, estab 1999, empl 120, sales $60,100,000, cert: CPUC)

1980   Avery Group Inc.
400 W Redondo Beach Blvd, Unit C
Gardena, CA 90248
Contact: Leatora Morse Presdient
Tel: 310-217-1070
Email: leatora@averygroup-inc.com
Website: www.averygroup-inc.com
Mfr restroom hygiene products. (Woman/AA, estab 2003, empl 167, sales $7,348,953, cert: State)

1981   Ayota, LLC
122 15th St, Ste 681
San Diego, CA 92014
Contact: Toya McWilliams Acct Mgr
Tel: 914-548-6193
Email: tm@ayotainternational.com
Website: http://ayotainternational.com
Dist janitorial supplies. (Woman/AA, estab 2012, empl 3, sales , cert: State)

1982   BriteWorks, Inc.
620 Commerical Ave.
Covina, CA 91723
Contact: Anita Ron Presdient
Tel: 626-337-0099
Email: anitaron@briteworks.com
Website: www.briteworks.com
Commercial & industrial janitorial services. General cleaning, construction cleaning, floor care & carpet care, window cleaning. (Woman/Hisp, estab 1997, empl 130, sales $6,866,357, cert: NMSDC, CPUC, WBENC)

1983   Continental Building Maintenance
13316 Mapledale St
Norwalk, CA 90650
Contact: Sanggwon Kim Presdient
Tel: 562-926-7474
Email: sgkim@continentalbm.com
Website: www.continentalbm.com
Janitorial Services & Supplies. (As-Pac, estab 2003, empl 120, sales $2,950,000, cert: CPUC)

1984   Corporate Image Maintenance
2700 S Main St, Ste D
Santa Ana, CA 92707
Contact: Gil Gamboa President
Tel: 714-966-5325
Email: corpimage@sbcglobal.net
Website: www.cimservices.com
Janitorial services: office, industrial & warehouse, carpet cleaning, pressure washing & window cleaning. (Hisp, estab 1995, empl 70, sales $1,176,190, cert: State)

1985   Eurow & O'Reilly Corp.
51 Moreland Rd
Simi Valley, CA 93065
Contact: Martin Mair Dir Inside Sales
Tel: 805-421-4310
Email: mmair@eurow.com
Website: www.eurow.com
Dist janitorial cleaning products. (Woman, estab 1983, empl 26, sales $40,000,000, cert: WBENC)

1986   Kim Gardner, Inc.
1727 E 28th St
Signal Hill, CA 90755
Contact: Dori Bailey Dir Business Dev
Tel: 562-988-7901
Email: dori@mjmservices.com
Website: http://mjmservices.com
Facility Support Services, Custodial, Waste Management, Pest Control/Grounds, Maintenance Landscaping, Air Duct Cleaning, - General Office Cleaning, Construction Clean Up, Pressure Washing, Carpet & Upholstery. (AA, estab 1986, empl 35, sales $605,000, cert: 8a)

1987   Los Angeles Chemical Co., Inc.
845 Sandhill Ave
Carson, CA 90746
Contact: Office Mgr
Tel: 310-323-7111
Email:
Website: www.lacco.com
Dist industrial chemicals, raw materials, janitorial cleaning supplies & equipment, food service supplies, personal care, safety supplies & institutional packaging. (Woman/As-Ind, estab 2015, empl 6, sales , cert: WBENC)

1988   Mar-Len Supply Inc.
23159 Kidder St
Hayward, CA 94545
Contact: Shirley Winter Owner
Tel: 510-782-3555
Email: marlensupply@aol.com
Website: www.marlensupply.com
Dist & service industrial cleaning equipment & cleaning agents. (Woman, estab 1956, empl 4, sales $1,000,000, cert: CPUC)

1989 NMS Management Inc.
155 W 35th St Ste A
National City, CA 91950
Contact: Dir Business Devel
Tel: 619-425-0440
Email:
Website: www.nms-management.com
Custodial services for military establishments, healthcare
facilities, institutions of higher education, public housing
agencies, public transportation authorities & federal, state
& municipal agencies. (Hisp, estab 1985, empl 168, sales
$3,822,801, cert: CPUC)

1990 Right Tek Enterprises
1775 N Lee St
Simi Valley, CA 93065
Contact: Sandy Cohen Owner
Tel: 877-208-3717
Email: righttek@pacbell.net
Website: www.righttekenterprises
Dist preventative maintenance cleaning products:
magentic card readers, bill validators, thermal printers,
point of sale (pos) machines and key lock systems.
(Woman, estab 2001, empl 1, sales $272,000, cert:
WBENC)

1991 SDI Systems Division, Inc.
21 Morgan
Irvine, CA 92618
Contact: Jon Korbonski Presdient
Tel: 949-583-1001
Email: sdi@sdinetwork.com
Website: www.sdinetwork.com
Manufacture and distribute cleaning equipment &
supplies. (Hisp, estab 2008, empl 20, sales $3,700,000,
cert: NMSDC)

1992 SeaYu Enterprises Inc.
236 West Portal PBM 399
San Francisco, CA 94127
Contact: Quincy Yu CEO
Tel: 415-566-9677
Email: qyu@sea-yu.com
Website: www.becleanandgreen.com
Natural cleaners, stain removers and odor eliminators that
are effective, easy to use, biodegradable and safe for
people, pets and the planet. (Woman/As-Pac, estab 2001,
empl 2, sales , cert: NMSDC)

1993 Ultimate Maintenance Services, Inc.
4237 Redondo Beach Blvd
Lawndale, CA 90260
Contact: Sherly Cstmr Service
Tel: 310-542-1474
Email: sherly@umscorporation.com
Website: www.umscorporation.com
Janitorial services & construction clean up services.
(Woman/Hisp, estab 1990, empl 50, sales $350,000, cert:
State)

1994 UNISERVE Facilities Services
2363 S Atlantic Blvd
Commerce, CA 90040
Contact: Eugene Hwang Dir of Mktg
Tel: 213-533-1000
Email: ehwang@uniservecorp.com
Website: www.uniservecorp.com
Janitorial services. (As-Pac, estab 1966, empl 750, sales
$25,000,000, cert: NMSDC)

1995 US Metro Group, Inc.
135 S State College Blvd, Ste 200
Brea, CA 92821
Contact: Phil Gregg Contracts Compliance
Tel: 213-382-6435
Email: phil.g@usmetrogroup.com
Website: http://usmetrogroup.com/
Janitorial maintenance services. (As-Pac, estab 1975,
empl 1000, sales $15,908,576, cert: NMSDC, CPUC)

1996 V.S. Supply Company
910 81st Ave, Unit 11
Oakland, CA 94621
Contact: Vincent Stephenson CEO
Tel: 510-834-9560
Email: vstephenson@vssupply.com
Website: www.vssupply.com
Professional cleaning, dist cleaning supplies. (AA, estab
1990, empl 10, sales $375,901, cert: State)

Colorado

1997 AFL Maintenance Group, Inc.
1075 S. Yukon St, Ste 300
Lakewood, CO 80226
Contact: Bonnie Nash Business Development
Tel: 303-984-7400
Email: b.nash@afsg-us.com
Website: www.afsg-us.com
Facility maintenance, management & real estate
services. (Woman/Hisp, estab 1989, empl 500, sales
$19,500,000, cert: State, NMSDC)

1998 SDV Supplies & Services LLP
P.O. Box 13403
Denver, CO 80201
Contact: George Autobee CEO
Tel: 303-256-4736
Email: gautobee@sdv1.com
Website: www.sdv1.com
Office Supplies and Office Suites, Janitorial Supplies.
Also include IT and computer/wirless systems (Hisp,
estab 2006, empl 3, sales , cert: State)

Connecticut

1999 C & C Janitorial Supplies, Inc.
665 New Britain Ave
Newington, CT 06111
Contact: Grace Cafe President
Tel: 860-594-4200
Email: gracec@ccsupplies.com
Website: www.ccsupplies.com
Dist janitorial products, paper products & equip.
(Woman/As-Pac, estab , empl , sales $ 0, cert: NMSDC,
WBENC)

2000 Horizon Services Company
250 Governor St
East Hartford, CT 06108
Contact: Thomas Baerlein Sr Acct Exec
Tel: 860-291-9111
Email: tbaerlein@horizonsvcs.com
Website: www.horizonsvcs.com
Custodial services, supply & management, window
cleaning, clean room environmental svcs, hazardous
material site labor, exterior cleaning & landscaping, post
construction cleaning. (As-Pac, estab 1991, empl 412,
sales $7,400,000, cert: State, NMSDC)

2001 KEECLEAN Management Inc.
2 Corporate Dr, Ste 242
Shelton, CT 06484
Contact: Keith Jang Presdient
Tel: 203-397-2532
Email: keithjang@keeclean.com
Website: www.keeclean.com
Commercial cleaning, custodial & janitorial services: floor care service, carpet cleaning, window washing services. (As-Pac, estab 2007, empl 200, sales $3,444,178, cert: State, City, NMSDC)

Delaware

2002 Star Building Services, Inc.
106 Quigley Blvd
New Castle, DE 19720
Contact: Ernie Martin VP Sales/Mktg
Tel: 302-983-0275
Email: emartin@sbsclean.com
Website: http://sbsclean.com
Janitorial Services, Medical Device Cleaning Services. (Woman, estab 1953, empl 300, sales , cert: WBENC)

Florida

2003 ABCO Products, Inc.
6800 NW 36th Ave
Miami, FL 33147
Contact: Luis Janania Sales Mgr
Tel: 786-223-0944
Email: luisj@abcoproducts.com
Website: www.abcoproducts.com
Dist cleaning supplies. (Hisp, estab 1979, empl 54, sales $ 0, cert: State, NMSDC)

2004 All Pro Janitorial Service Inc.
3843 N Tanner Rd
Orlando, FL 32826
Contact: Glenda Lee Presdient
Tel: 407-649-8878
Email: glenda@allprojan.com
Website: www.procarpetcleanerorlando.com
Commercial janitorial cleaning, carpet cleaning, rug cleaning, upholstery cleaning, ceramic tile & grout cleaning, floor stripping, waxing, buffing & water restoration. (Woman/AA, estab 2000, empl , sales $166,000, cert: State, City, NMSDC)

2005 Clean Clean, Inc.
3580 NW 56th St, Ste 106C
Fort Lauderdale, FL 33309
Contact: Gary Plancher Sales Mgr
Tel: 954-777-9555
Email: gplancher@cleancleaninc.com
Website: www.cleancleaninc.com
Mfr personal wipes. (Woman/AA, estab 2004, empl 6, sales , cert: NMSDC)

2006 CRJ Management Services, Inc.
12 Miracle Strip Pkwy, Ste 203B
Fort Walton Beach, FL 32548
Contact: Lee Jones President
Tel: 850-936-5060
Email: crjmanagementservices@mchsi.com
Website:
Janitorial services: general office cleaning, floor care, stripping /waxing. (AA, estab 2003, empl 8, sales , cert: State)

2007 Cube Care Company
6043 NW 167th St Ste A-23
Miami Lakes, FL 33015
Contact: Susana Robledo CEO
Tel: 305-556-8700
Email: susana@cubecare.com
Website: www.cubecare.com
Janiorial Supplies, Window Treatments & Curtains, (Woman/Hisp, estab 1999, empl 70, sales $6,685,526, cert: NMSDC, WBENC)

2008 D&A Building Services, Inc.
321 Georgia Ave
Longwood, FL 32750
Contact: Albert Sarabasa CEO
Tel: 407-831-5388
Email: al@dabuildingservices.com
Website: www.dabuildingservices.com
Janitorial, window washing, pressure cleaning, caulking, carpet, cleaning, construction cleaning, seal buildings, light painting. (Hisp, estab 1985, empl 550, sales $8,200,000, cert: State, City)

2009 GEM Janitorial LLC
9031 Pembroke Rd
Pembroke Pines, FL 33025
Contact: Richard Addison Presdient
Tel: 954-682-3594
Email: homeownersservicesfla@gmail.com
Website: www.gemjanitorialcorp.com
Cleaning, Commercial Remodeling and Repair, Painting, Pressure Cleaning, Carpentry, Doors & Windows Installation, Drywall Repairs and Installation, Flooring Installation. (Woman/AA, estab 2006, empl 6, sales $320,000, cert: NMSDC)

2010 Grosvenor Building Services Iinc.
3398 Parkway Center Ct
Orlando, FL 32808
Contact: Lee McDaniel Business Develop Mgr
Tel: 407-292-3383
Email: lmcdaniel@grosvenorservices.com
Website: http://grosvenorservicescom
Janitorial Services. (Woman, estab 1984, empl 400, sales $6,000,000, cert: WBENC)

2011 Harvard Services Group, Inc.
201 S Biscayne Blvd FL 24
Miami, FL 33131
Contact: Nathalie Doobin CEO
Tel: 305-351-7300
Email: ndoobin@harvardservices.com
Website: www.harvardsg.com
Janitorial services & maintenance services. (Woman, estab 1986, empl 1500, sales $ 0, cert: WBENC)

2012 Jimco Maintenance Inc.
710 Commerce Dr, Ste 107
Venice, FL 34292
Contact: Lynn Moseley Presdient
Tel: 800-392-8678
Email: lynn@jimcos.com
Website: www.jimcos.com
Janitorial services. (Woman, estab 1983, empl 90, sales $12,180,000, cert: WBENC)

2013 Merton Partners LLC
692 Solana Court
Marco Island, FL 34145
Contact: Nanette Rivera President
Tel: 609-773-0145
Email: wordehoff@mertonpartners.com
Website: www.mertonpartners.com
Operations Management Consultants: SPC; facilities; maintenance; engineering; construction; validation; manufacturing; yield; optimization (Woman/Hisp, estab 2007, empl 50, sales $1,200,000, cert: NMSDC)

2014 RagsWarehouse & Cleaning Supplies
7221 NW 35th Ave
Miami, FL 33147
Contact: Luther Pierre Sales Mgr
Tel: 202-531-9225
Email: luther.pierre@ragswarehouse.com
Website:
Dist wiping materials ideal for painters or cleaners. (Woman/AA, estab 2015, empl 2, sales , cert: State)

2015 Siboney Contracting Co.
1000 Southern Blvd, Ste 300
West Palm Beach, FL 33405
Contact: Dante Sevi VP
Tel: 561-832-3110
Email: dsevi@siboneycc.com
Website: www.siboneycc.com
Hauling fill and aggregates, hauling hurricane debris (Hisp, estab 1972, empl 8, sales $23,789,190, cert: City)

2016 The American Cleaning Services Inc
8270 Woodland Center Blvd.
Tampa, FL 33614
Contact: Marty Hales GM
Tel: 813-961-6970
Email: callus1st@americancleaningservice.com
Website: http://americancleaningservice.com
Complete janitorial services, commercial & construction. (Woman/Hisp, estab 1989, empl 1, sales $367,000, cert: State)

2017 The Green Glider Company LLC
830 Harbor Cir
Palm Harbor, FL 34683
Contact: Presdient
Tel: 727-504-9441
Email:
Website: www.gogreenglider.com
Green Glider Mop Pad, Reusable, Washable, Durable & Adjustable mop pad that fits onto virtually all of the Swiffer style/type mopping systems. (Woman, estab 2010, empl 1, sales $225,000, cert: WBENC)

Georgia

2018 5 Star Enterprise, Inc.
4705-G Bakers Ferry Rd SW
Atlanta, GA 30336
Contact: Tracey Felder Presdient
Tel: 404-924-4290
Email: tfelder@5starchemicals.com
Website: www.5starchemicals.com
Mfr Green cleaning, soaps & detergent products, green certified chemicals. (Woman/AA, estab 2006, empl 10, sales $2,450,000, cert: WBENC)

2019 Frederick Hart Co. Inc.
4963 S Royal Atlanta Dr
Tucker, GA 30084
Contact: Dean-Paul Hart Presdient
Tel: 404-373-4030
Email: deanpaul@compacind.com
Website: www.compacind.com/
Mfr cleaning products: garbage disposal cleaner & deodorizer, scented sink strainer, bathroom, kitchen, auto, cleaners, closet & air fresheners, kitchen gadgets. (AA, estab 1979, empl 15, sales $3,500,000, cert: NMSDC)

2020 General Building Maintenance, Inc.
3835 Presidential Pkwy Ste 200
Atlanta, GA 30340
Contact: Joe Woodson Sr VP
Tel: 770-457-5678
Email: marketing@gbmweb.com
Website: www.gbmweb.com
Janitorial svcs: carpet shampooing, stripping & waxing floors, marble & stone care, clean room cleaning & recycling. (As-Pac, estab 1983, empl 271, sales $ 0, cert: NMSDC)

2021 GMI Group, Inc.
130 Stone Mountain St
Lawrenceville, GA 30046
Contact: Kayla Dang CEO
Tel: 678-482-5288
Email: kayla.dang@gmigroupinc.com
Website: www.thegmigroup.com
Commercial janitorial cleaning, marble maintenance & restoration, ReKRETE waterless concrete cleaning, pressure washing, graffiti removal, construction clean up. (Woman/As-Pac, estab 2005, empl 72, sales $4,867,904, cert: NMSDC, WBENC)

2022 ShockTheory Interactive, Inc.
12705 Century Dr Ste C
Alpharetta, GA 30004
Contact: Sonja Williams VP
Tel: 877-747-4625
Email: sonja.williams@shocktheory.com
Website: www.shocktheory.com
Web design and development, Interactive marketing, User Interface design, and social networking, collaboration and integration, ROI measurement and SEO strategies. (Woman/AA, estab 2003, empl , sales $120,000, cert: NMSDC)

2023 The Burks Companies, Inc.
2780 Bert Adams Road Ste 225
Atlanta, GA 30339
Contact: James Weisbrodt President & CEO
Tel: 678-686-3203
Email: jweis@theburkscompanies.com
Website: www.theburkscompanies.com
Janitorial services. (AA, estab 1991, empl 181, sales $7,980,000, cert: NMSDC)

2024 Unique Cleaning Service, Inc.
3330 Cumberland Blvd. Ste 175
Atlanta, GA 30339
Contact: Willie Sellers Presdient
Tel: 770-420-7660
Email: toney@uniqueclean.com
Website: www.uniqueclean.com
Commercial janitorial services, grounds maintenance services. (AA, estab 1996, empl 80, sales $ 0, cert: State)

Hawaii

2025   Building Maintenance Services, LLC
1541 S Beretania St, Ste 204
Honolulu, HI 96826
Contact: Barbara Beckmeier Owner
Tel: 808-983-1269
Email: barbara@bmsnationwide.com
Website: www.bmsnationwide.com
Janitorial services. (Woman, estab 2000, empl 45, sales ,
cert: WBENC)

Illinois

2026   A&R Janitorial Service, Inc.
10127 w. Roosevelt Rd.
Westchester, IL 60154
Contact: Deborah Pintor Sr Exec VP
Tel: 708-656-8300
Email: dpintor@arjanitorial.com
Website: www.arjanitorial.com
Janitorial services, commercial cleaning, carpet care, floor
care, power washing, snow removal, after construction
cleanup & emergency response cleaning. (Woman/Hisp,
estab 1967, empl 383, sales $19,752,715, cert: State, City,
NMSDC, WBENC)

2027   B & B Maintenance, Inc.
537 Capital Dr
Lake Zurich, IL 60047
Contact: Pamela Seiser VP, Sales
Tel: 847-550-6060
Email: pseiser@bandbmaint.com
Website: www.bandbmaint.com
Building maintenance: janitorial, window cleaning, &
painting, carpet care, power washing, hard surfaced floor
care, tile restoration, fire safety programs, porter service &
support personnel. (Woman/Hisp, estab 1979, empl 550,
sales $1,800,000, cert: City, NMSDC, WBENC)

2028   Clean Impressions Corp.
127 N Northwest Hwy
Palatine, IL 60067
Contact: Teresa Garvin President
Tel: 847-776-0706
Email: cic@cleanimpressionscorp.com
Website: www.cleanimpressionscorp.com
Janitorial service, building maintenance, floor care,
stripping & refinishing floor tile, carpet cleaning, stone
care, crystalizing & acoustical tile cleaning. (Woman, estab
1998, empl 40, sales $665,000, cert: WBENC)

2029   ELB Enterprises, Inc.
4709 Bond Ave
Alorton, IL 62207
Contact: Rhonda Jones
Tel: 618-394-1912
Email: rjones@elb1inc.com
Website: www.elbenterprisesinc.com
Dist janitorial supplies. (AA, estab 1993, empl 12, sales $
0, cert: State, NMSDC)

2030   Emeric Facility Services
918 S Green Bay Rd
Waukegan, IL 60085
Contact: Michael Ramirez Acct Exec
Tel: 847-623-6912
Email: mramirez@emericservices.com
Website: www.emericservices.com
Janitorial services & carpet cleaning services. (Woman/
Hisp, estab 2011, empl 46, sales $932,000, cert: City,
WBENC)

2031   IDSC, Inc.
P.O. Box 1055
Woodstock, IL 60098
Contact: Milissa Dooley Presdient
Tel: 815-337-8066
Email: milissa_ids@att.net
Website: www.idscinc.com
Dist sanitation supplies & equipment, PPE, paper goods,
maintenance supplies & equipment, hoses. (Woman,
estab 1990, empl 7, sales $480,000, cert: WBENC)

2032   Jelmar LLC
5550 W Touhy Ste 200
Skokie, IL 60007
Contact: Glenn Poticha VP Sales
Tel: 800-323-5497
Email: glenn@jelmar.com
Website: http://jelmar.com
Dist cleaning products. (Woman, estab , empl , sales
$36,745,934, cert: WBENC)

2033   LACOSTA Facility Support Services, Inc.
440 W Bonner Rd
Wauconda, IL 60084
Contact: Jeffrey Johnson Natl Dir Business
Development
Tel: 847-487-3103
Email: sales@cms4.com
Website: www.lacostaservices.com
Janitorial services, painting services, facility
maintanance services. (Woman/Hisp, estab 1988, empl
1700, sales $64,000,000, cert: NMSDC)

2034   United Building Maintenance, Inc.
165 Easy St
Carol Stream, IL 60188
Contact: Amy Cabrera-Goddard Dir of Sales &
Marketing
Tel: 630-653-4848
Email: agoddard@ubm-usa.com
Website: www.ubm-usa.com
Janitorial, painting, pressure washing, snow removal,
parking lot maintenance & landscape design. (Hisp,
estab 1979, empl 1500, sales $63,800,000, cert: NMSDC)

2035   White Glove Janitorial Services & Supply, Inc.
356 E Irving Park Rd
Wood Dale, IL 60191
Contact: Joyce Dickens Owner
Tel: 630-766-7466
Email: whtglove@msn.com
Website: http://whiteglovejanitorialservices.com
Janitorial services: carpet cleaning, landscaping, power
washing, food plant sanitation, floor scrubbing &
supplies. (Woman, estab 1975, empl 105, sales
$2,476,000, cert: City)

Indiana

2036   Suzy Q Cleaning Services
2401 N Tibbs Ave
Indianapolis, IN 46222
Contact: Suzett Moffitt Owner
Tel: 317-755-7664
Email: suzettsuzett@gmail.com
Website: www.suzyqcleaning.net
Janitorial, Ground and Building Maintenance, Commer-
cial, Home-Maker Services, Renovation, Construction,
Bridge, Road, Side Walk Repair. (Woman/AA, estab 2009,
empl 10, sales , cert: State, City)

Kentucky

2037 Facility Maintenance & Services Group
147 E Loudon Ave
Lexington, KY 40505
Contact: Frank HAll CEO
Tel: 859-554-6584
Email: info@facilitymsg.com
Website: http://facilitymsg.com
Janitorial, Facility Maintenance, Painting, Lawn Care,
Pressure washing, High Dusting. (AA, estab 2015, empl 42,
sales $1,000,019, cert: NMSDC)

2038 Superior Maintenance Co.
141 Howell Dr
Elizabethtown, KY 42701
Contact: Sid Shurn VP
Tel: 270-769-2553
Email: sid@smc.cc
Website: www.smc.cc
Janitorial & grounds maintenance, window cleaning, pest
control, facility maintenance, HVAC, plumbing, chemicals,
janitorial supplies & equip. (AA, estab 1988, empl 1200,
sales $ 0, cert: NMSDC)

Louisiana

2039 Economical Janitorial & Paper Supplies
1420F Sams Ave, Ste F
Harahan, LA 70123
Contact: Suzie Migliore President
Tel: 504-464-7166
Email: suzie@economicaljanitorial.com
Website: www.econoomicaljanitorial.com
Dist janitorial supplies, paper supplies, janitorial equip-
ment, food service supplies. (Woman, estab 1983, empl
85, sales $31,015,000, cert: WBENC)

Massachusetts

2040 Citron Hygiene US CORP
13 Linnell Circle
Billerica, MA 01821
Contact: Lisa Miller Sales Support Mgr
Tel: 978-495-5650
Email: lmiller@citronhygiene.com
Website: www.citronhygiene.com
Sanitary Disposal Service, Air Freshener Service, Ladies
Hygiene Vending Machine Service, Inline Sanitizer/Auto
Flush, Eco Urinal Screen Service, Urinal Mat Service, Auto
Soap, Auto Hand Sanitizer, Sharps Collection Service, Auto
Faucets. (Minority, Woman, estab , empl , sales
$6,000,000,000, cert: State)

2041 Dependable Facility Cleaning Services, LLC
1074 Hyde Park Ave, Ste 4
Hyde Park, MA 02136
Contact: Chuck Ojoko Managing Dir
Tel: 857-261-4582
Email: charles@dependablefacilitycleaning.com
Website: www.dependablefacilitycleaning.com
Commercial cleaning & janitorial services. (AA, estab 2015,
empl 6, sales , cert: NMSDC)

2042 Milhench Supply Company
121 Duchaine Blvd
New Bedford, MA 02745
Contact: Angie Prevost Inside Sales
Tel: 508-995-8331
Email: angie@milhench.com
Website: www.milhench.com
Dist janitorial, paper, packaging & facility maintenance
supplies. (Woman, estab 1932, empl 32, sales
$16,315,760, cert: State, City)

2043 Moura's Cleaning Service, Inc.
349 Lunenburg St
Fitchburg, MA 01420
Contact: Andre Thibodeau Sales Mgr
Tel: 978-562-1839
Email: andre@mourascleaningservice.com
Website: www.mourascleaningservice.com
Janitorial services: office cleaning, floor strip & wax,
restroom service, odor control service, concrete clean-
ing, maintenance & sealing, carpet steam cleaning,
upholstery steam cleaning, window cleaning, power
washing of buildings. (Hisp, estab 1988, empl 150, sales
$2,100,000, cert: State)

2044 Savin Products Co., Inc.
214 High St
Randolph, MA 02368
Contact: Dona D'Ambrosia Presdient
Tel: 781-961-2743
Email: donamarie@savinproducts.com
Website: www.savinproducts.com
Mfr cleaning products. (Woman, estab 1968, empl 10,
sales , cert: State)

2045 Unic Pro Inc.
415 Boston Tpk Ste 211B
Shrewsbury, MA 01545
Contact: Presdient
Tel: 877-881-8642
Email:
Website: www.unicpro.com
Commercial Business Cleaning Services, Commercial
Carpet Cleaning, Floor Washing & Waxing, Green
Cleaning Commercial Services, Industrial Cleaning
Services, Nightly Office Cleaning, Post-Construction
Cleaning. (Woman/Hisp, estab 2007, empl 54, sales
$2,450,000, cert: State, WBENC)

Maryland

2046 Associated Building Maintenance Co., Inc.
2140 Priest Bridge Court Ste 3
Crofton, MD 21114
Contact: Kurt Bender VP Sales
Tel: 410-721-1818
Email: kbender@abmcoinc.com
Website: www.abmcoinc.com/
Commercial general contract cleaning, window cleaning,
carpet cleaning, snow removal, floor stripping & other
building related services. (Woman, estab 1987, empl
1000, sales $25,599,000, cert: State)

2047   C.J. Maintenance, Inc.
9254 Bendix Rd
Columbia, MD 21045
Contact: Tyler Yoon Acct Exec
Tel: 410-720-5157
Email: cjmaintenance@hotmail.com
Website: www.cjmaint.com
Janitorial, custodial & housekeeping svcs: carpet cleaning, hard wood floors, marble floor restoration. (As-Pac, estab 1985, empl 700, sales $14,499,999, cert: State, NMSDC)

2048   Viking Chemicals, Inc.
2325 Banger St
Baltimore, MD 21230
Contact: Shannon Hodges VP
Tel: 410-525-2100
Email: shodges@vikingchem.com
Website: http://vikingjanitorsupplies.com
Dist janatorial supplies: paper, floor care equipement, sweepers, vacuums, matting, brooms, brushes, trash cans & trash can liners. (Woman, estab 1974, empl 6, sales $2,206,148, cert: State, City)

Michigan

2049   Caravan Facilities Management, LLC
1400 Weiss St
Saginaw, MI 48602
Contact: Victor Gomez Business Develop Mgr
Tel: 989-798-0977
Email: vg10@caravanfm.com
Website: www.caravanfm.com
Facilities mgmt: janintorial, landscaping, snow removal, HVAC, fleet mgmt & building services. (Hisp, estab 1997, empl 2344, sales $139,000,000, cert: NMSDC)

2050   Caravan Technologies, Inc.
3033 Bourke
Detroit, MI 48238
Contact: Robert Charleston CEO
Tel: 313-341-2551
Email: cti3033@aol.com
Website: www.caravantech.com
Mfr industrial & commercial cleaning solutions, disinfecting agents & parts washer detergents. (AA, estab 1979, empl 10, sales $495,961, cert: NMSDC)

2051   Choctaw-Kaul Distribution Company
3540 Vinewood
Detroit, MI 48208
Contact: Caitlin Johnson Customer Development Mgr
Tel: 313-895-3165
Email: cjohnson@choctawkaul.com
Website: www.choctawkaul.com
Mfr gloves & safety products, mgmt svcs, janitorial svcs, industrial specialty cleaning, paint booth cleaning, chemical mgmt, recycling, filter maintenance, truck repair, construction mgmt, parking lot maintenance, temp manpower, etc. (Nat Ame, As-Ind, As-Pac, estab 1998, empl 350, sales $107,000,000, cert: NMSDC)

2052   CMS Sourcing Solutions
29700 Harper Ave, Ste 2
St. Clair Shores, MI 48082
Contact: Cheryl King Exec VP of Sales
Tel: 586-879-0669
Email: cheryl.king@cmsgroup.us
Website: http://cmsgroup.us
Janitorial services, management, labor, supplies, equipment & systems. (Minority, Woman, estab 2009, empl 150, sales $5,500,110, cert: NMSDC)

2053   DFM Solutions (Devon Facility Management LLC)
777 Woodward Ave Ste 500A
Detroit, MI 48226
Contact: Chad Starnes Dir Business Devel
Tel: 313-221-1510
Email: cstarnes@dfm.solutions
Website: www.dfm.solutions
Facility management, janitorial & building maintenance & industrial cleaning services. (Woman, estab 2007, empl 298, sales $45,000,000, cert: WBENC)

2054   Ipax Cleanogel, Inc.
8301 Lyndon
Detroit, MI 48238
Contact: Veronika Maltsev CEO
Tel: 313-933-4211
Email: vmaltsev@ipax.com
Website: www.ipax.com
Mfr & dist quality cleaning & maintenance products. (Woman, estab 1988, empl 12, sales $1,680,000, cert: WBENC)

2055   LCF - Farmer Group
4581 S. Lapeer Road Ste G
Lake Orion, MI 48359
Contact: Forest Farmer Presdient
Tel: 248-322-7079
Email: rfarmer@mti-farmergrp.com
Website: www.thefarmergroup.com
Paints, cleaners, wipes, rags, paint-booth related products, cleaning supplies, oil, lubricants, janitorial and floor care. (AA, estab 1994, empl 7, sales $2,822,500, cert: NMSDC)

2056   Macomb Wholesale Supply Corp.
17730 E 14 Mile Rd
Fraser, MI 48026
Contact: Catherine David Presdient
Tel:
Email: online@macombwholesale.com
Website: www.macombwholesale.com
Dist Packaging, Safety, Janitorial & Facility Maintenance Supplies, corrugated, poly bags, tape, paper, chemical, packaging, gloves, safety & facility cleaning supplies. (Woman, estab 1988, empl 10, sales $2,500,000, cert: WBENC)

2057   Midwest Maintenance Services, Inc.
3704 Trade Center Dr
Ann Arbor, MI 48108
Contact: Linda Johnson President
Tel: 734-222-5902
Email: linda@midwestms.com
Website: www.midwestms.com
Janitorial services & building maintenance. (Woman, estab 1989, empl 35, sales $603,672, cert: WBENC)

2058   Perfection Commercial Services, Inc.
905 N Church St
Tekonsha, MI 49092
Contact: Lori Smith Controller
Tel: 888-933-3103
Email: lori@pcsmichigan.com
Website:
www.perfectioncommercialservicesinc.com
Perfection Commercial Services provides janitorial services and supplies, which includes window and floor care. (Woman, estab 1991, empl 212, sales $5,785,000, cert: WBENC, NWBOC)

2059 Polstar Commercial Cleaning Services
5124 Pontiac Trail
Ann Arbor, MI 48105
Contact: Kamil Krainski Sales Mgr
Tel: 800-557-9120
Email: kamil@polstar.us
Website: www.polstar.us
Contract janitorial & commercial cleaning services, floor stripping & waxing, disinfection service, antimicrobial coatings, carpet cleaning. (Woman, estab 2000, empl 25, sales $903,146, cert: WBENC)

2060 PrimeSource Group, LLC
4407 Center St
Saginaw, MI 48604
Contact: Brandon Bordeaux
Tel: 989-752-6443
Email: brandon@bandwmgmt.com
Website:
Dist janitorial supplies & equipment, equipment leasing & facilities management. (Hisp, estab 2003, empl 20, sales $ 0, cert: NMSDC)

2061 Sparkle Janitorial Service
4100 Woodward Ave, Ste 9
Detroit, MI 48201
Contact: Loretta Watson Presdient
Tel: 313-831-1535
Email: watsonlorettam@sparklejani.com
Website: www.saniglaze535.com
Complete janitorial service, window cleaning, carpet cleaning, construction clean-up, tile & grout restoration. (AA, estab 1989, empl 25, sales $330,604, cert: NMSDC)

2062 StarSource Management Services, Inc.
39080 Webb Dr
Westland, MI 48185
Contact: Melvin Brown CEO
Tel: 734-721-8540
Email: sales@starsourceinc.com
Website: www.starsourceinc.com
Dist uniforms, protective clothing, cutting tools, fasteners, janitorial chemical supplies, cleaning equipment, paper towels, plastic liners, welding supplies, automotive cleaning supplies, cooling tower chemicals, laundry services. (AA, estab , empl , sales $6,000,000, cert: NMSDC)

2063 Tri County Cleaning Supply, Inc.
7109 Dan McGuire Dr
Brighton, MI 48116
Contact: Geri Gee President
Tel: 810-229-6500
Email: g.gee@tcclean.com
Website: www.tcclean.com
Dist cleaning supplies. (Woman, estab 0, empl , sales $ 0, cert: WBENC)

Minnesota

2064 Allied National Services
6066 Shingle Creek Parkway #1105
Minneapolis, MN 55430
Contact: Presdient
Tel: 763-503-0707
Email:
Website: www.alliedns.com
Contract cleaning services. Floor care Restroom sanitation. (AA, estab 2002, empl 541, sales $17,610,000, cert: City, NMSDC, 8a)

2065 Diverse Maintenance Solutions Inc.
1523 94th Lane NE
Blaine, MN 55449
Contact: Rita Dumra Presdient
Tel: 763-230-7488
Email: rita.dumra@dmsimn.com
Website: www.dmsimn.com
Dist maintenance supplies, janitorial supplies, rubbermaid products, paper products, equipment, office supplies & tools. (Woman/As-Ind, estab 1988, empl 7, sales $966,055, cert: NMSDC, WBENC)

2066 Innovative Chemical Corporation
7769 95th St South
Cottage Grove, MN 55016
Contact: Shelly Meyers Sales Mgr
Tel: 651-649-1762
Email: smeyers@iccmn.com
Website: www.iccmn.com
Mfr eco friendly cleaning & maintenance products, green cleaning products. (As-Ind, estab 1994, empl 13, sales $2,000,000, cert: NMSDC)

Missouri

2067 Centaur Building Services, Inc.
4401 Ridgewood Ave
St. Louis, MO 63116
Contact: Business Development
Tel: 314-201-6805
Email:
Website: www.centaurservices.com
Janitorial services. (Woman/AA, Nat Ame, As-Pac, Hisp, estab 1985, empl 1300, sales $32,625,937, cert: WBENC)

2068 Eagle Environmental Products, Inc.
417 N High St
Jackson, MO 63755
Contact: Kenneth Waldron President
Tel: 573-243-8111
Email: kwaldron@eaglesystem.biz
Website: www.eaglesystem.biz
Dist hot steam vapor cleaners; automatic floor scrubbers; yellow grease handling & grease trap equipment; janitorial supplies; chemicals; solvents; gloves & safety products. (Nat Ame, estab 1991, empl 4, sales $147,000, cert: State)

2069 HI-Gene
1836 Linn St
North Kansas City, MO 64116
Contact: Barrie Evans Acct Mgr
Tel: 816-472-4118
Email: barrie@higenesjanitorial.com
Website: http://higenesjanitorial.com
Janitorial services. (Woman, estab 1969, empl 275, sales $6,151,289, cert: NWBOC)

2070 J&B Franchise Venture, Inc.
11684 Lilburn Park Rd
St Louis, MO 63146
Contact: Janet Mann President
Tel: 314-989-9997
Email: janet.mann@jan-prousa.com
Website: http://stlouis.jan-pro.com
Janitorial services, commercial cleaning, carpet cleaning, floor cleaning services. (Woman, estab 2004, empl 8, sales $2,000,000, cert: State)

2071   Peistrup Paper Products, Inc.
       1185 Research Blvd
       St. Louis, MO 63132
       Contact: Dennis Burjoski Acct Exec
       Tel: 314-993-0970
       Email: dburjoski@peistruppaper.com
       Website: www.peistrup.com
Dist janitorial, paper & safety supplies. (Woman, estab
1960, empl 9, sales $200,000, cert: State, WBENC)

2072   Rockwell Labs Ltd.
       1257 Bedford Rd
       North Kansas City, MO 64116
       Contact: Cisse Spragins CEO
       Tel: 816-283-3167
       Email: cspragins@rockwelllabs.com
       Website: www.rockwelllabs.com
Mfr & dist pest management & biological cleaning products: baits for roaches, ants bed bugs & other crawling
insects. (Woman, estab 1998, empl 11, sales $ 0, cert:
NWBOC)

2073   Tier One Property Services
       8601 E 63rd St
       Kansas City, MO 64133
       Contact: Joel Sanders Business Development
       Tel: 816-285-7439
       Email: jsanders@tier1usa.com
       Website: www.tier1usa.com
Janitorial services. (AA, estab 2011, empl 750, sales
$27,200,000, cert: NMSDC)

2074   Wexford Labs, Inc.
       325 Leffingwell Ave
       Kirkwood, MO 63122
       Contact: Mary Anne Auer CEO
       Tel: 800-506-1146
       Email: maryanne.auer@wexfordlabs.com
       Website: www.wexfordlabs.com
Mfr hard surface, EPA registered disinfectants, floor care
products, general purpose cleaners, hand soaps, alcohol
hand sanitizers. (Woman, estab , empl , sales $2,966,970,
cert: State)

Mississippi

2075   Jefferson Cleaning Services, LLC
       06 Ray C. Nicks Rd
       Jayess, MS 39641
       Contact: Presdient
       Tel: 601-803-1601
       Email:
       Website: jeffersoncleaningservices.weebly.com
Commercial janitorial services, corporate buildings, post
construction clean up, office space, hospitals, schools,
daycares, retail centers, etc. (Woman/AA, estab 2014, empl
1, sales , cert: City, WBENC)

North Carolina

2076   Century Products LLC
       404 Edwardia Dr
       Greensboro, NC 27409
       Contact: Evette Darden AVP of sales/gov accounts
       Tel: 336-292-8090
       Email: edb@centuryproductsllc.com
       Website: www.centuryproductsllc.com
Dist janitorial cleaning tools: mops, brooms, brushes for
institutions & food industry. (AA, estab 1987, empl 21,
sales , cert: NMSDC)

2077   Coverall Health Based Cleaning System
       2401 Whitehall Park
       Charlotte, NC 28273
       Contact: Shannon Krieser Sr Lead Generation
       Sales Associate
       Tel: 704-209-7113
       Email: shannon.krieser@coverall.com
       Website: www.coverall.com
Janitorial services. (Minority, estab 1985, empl 300, sales
$600,000, cert: NMSDC)

2078   Green's Commercial Cleaning
       4421 Stuart Andrew Blvd Ste 604
       Charlotte, NC 28217
       Contact: Kimberly Grace Dir of Sales
       Tel: 704-201-6209
       Email: kimberly@greenscommercialcleaning.com
       Website: www.greenscommercialcleaning.com
Janitorial services, medical curtain cleaning, floor &
carpet care, pressure washing & building maintenance.
(AA, estab 2003, empl 165, sales $2,300,000, cert: City,
8a)

2079   JAC Janitorial Services
       1101 Tyvola Rd, Ste 205
       Charlotte, NC 28217
       Contact: Jose Jaramillo Sales Mgr
       Tel: 980-201-9099
       Email: jjaramillo@jacjanitorialservice.com
       Website: www.jacjanitorialservice.com
Cleaning services, hospitals, schools, business parks,
government buildings, and more. (Hisp, estab 2006,
empl 15, sales , cert: State, City)

2080   Yu Ken Cut It Inc.
       3121 Sweeten Creek Rd
       Asheville, NC 28803
       Contact: Jonathan Bae Marketing Mgr
       Tel: 828-651-9770
       Email: jonathanbae@yukencutit.com
       Website: www.yukencutit.com
Janitorial services. (Woman/As-Pac, estab 1995, empl
300, sales $5,365,000, cert: NMSDC)

Nebraska

2081   Meylan Enterprises, Inc.
       6225 S. 60th St
       Omaha, NE 68117
       Contact: Tori Peitz Presdient
       Tel: 402-339-4880
       Email: tpeitz@meylan.net
       Website: http://meylan.net
Industrial cleaning services to include; 10,000-40,000 psi
high pressure waterblasting, vacuum services, blast
wave services (explosives) and specialty projects.
(Woman, estab , empl 160, sales $ 0, cert: WBENC)

New Jersey

2082   BRAVO! Building Services, Inc.
       29 King George Road
       Green Brook, NJ 08812
       Contact: Frank S. Wardzinski COO
       Tel: 732-465-0707
       Email: fwardzinski@bravobuildingservices.com
       Website: www.bravogroupservices.com
Janitorial svcs, day porters & matrons, HVAC, mail room
services. (Woman/Hisp, estab 1997, empl 3700, sales
$95,000,000, cert: NMSDC)

2083   Capstone Facilities Group LLC
       609 Park Ave
       Brielle, NJ 08730
       Contact: Jrhosaboy President
       Tel: 877-765-2242
       Email: jrhosaboyj@gmail.com
       Website: www.capstonefacilities.com
Dist foodservice, healthcare & janitorial disposables &
equipment: paper towels, toilet paper, handsoap, cleaning
chemicals, flatware, napkins. (AA, estab 2012, empl 3,
sales , cert: NMSDC)

2084   CSS Building Services Inc
       846 Livingston Ave
       North Brunswick, NJ 08902
       Contact: Liz Coury VP of Internal Operations
       Tel: 609-655-5000
       Email: lcoury@cssbuildingservices.com
       Website: www.cssbuildingservices.com
Janitorial, builiding maintenance, professional services.
(Woman, estab 1976, empl 450, sales $40,000,000, cert:
WBENC)

2085   Janel Inc.
       7 Mountain Ave
       Bound Brook, NJ 08805
       Contact: Colleen McAteer Presdient
       Tel: 732-271-4700
       Email: colleenm@janelinc.com
       Website: www.janelonline.com
Dist cleaning products, assemble, test & repair electronic
equipment. (Woman, estab 1960, empl 8, sales
$2,897,219, cert: State, WBENC)

2086   Shore Manufacturing LLC
       1709 Highway 34 Unit 5
       Wall, NJ 07727
       Contact: William Vogel Presdient
       Tel: 732-894-9810
       Email: williamjvogel@aol.com
       Website: www.shoremfgllc.com
Mfr non woven disposable food service wipers. (Woman,
estab 2013, empl 8, sales , cert: State, WBENC)

2087   TUCS Cleaning Service, Inc.
       166 Central Ave
       Orange, NJ 07050
       Contact: Ingrid Schaefer VP of accounts
       Tel: 973-673-0700
       Email: ischaefer@tucscleaning.com
       Website: www.tucscleaning.com
Janitorial svcs: window cleaning, general office & warehouse cleaning, strip & wax hard floors,carpet shampoo,
upholstery shampoo, cleaning above/below raised
computer floors, power washing & construction. (Hisp,
estab 1983, empl 600, sales $ 0, cert: City, NMSDC)

New Mexico

2088   Specialized Services, LLC
       3150 Carlisle NE Ste, 6
       Albuquerque, NM 87110
       Contact: Faith St. Clair
       Tel: 505-881-5237
       Email: faith.specializedservices@gmail.com
       Website: www.specializedservicesnm.com
Commercial maintenance, floor maintenance, strip &
waxing, cleaning & disinfecting tile & grout. (Hisp, estab
2009, empl 26, sales $125,165,468, cert: NMSDC)

Nevada

2089   Kamco Industries LLC
       6969 Speedway Blvd, Ste 107
       Las Vegas, NV 89115
       Contact: Delicia Liu Presdient
       Tel: 702-518-1253
       Email: delicia@kamco-online.com
       Website: www.kamco-online.com
Mfr & distribute nontoxic, plant-based industrial
cleaner, EPA-registered disinfectant and foaming hand
sanitizer. We also offer professional consultation for
janitorial issues for hotels, (Woman/As-Pac, estab 2010,
empl 1, sales $130,000, cert: State, NWBOC)

2090   Smalls Senibaldi Services LLC
       4127 Falcons Flight Ave
       North Las Vegas, NV 89084
       Contact: IRIS SENIBALDI CEO
       Tel: 702-636-1316
       Email: iris@smaseni.com
       Website: www.smaseni.com
Commercial & residential cleaning, janitorial services.
(Woman/AA, estab 2013, empl 20, sales , cert: NMSDC)

2091   Smart Cleaning Solutions LLC
       57 Spectrum Blvd
       Las Vegas, NV 89101
       Contact: Salvador Canales Mgr
       Tel: 702-685-7055
       Email: scanales@mysmartcleaningsolutions.com
       Website: www.smartcleaningsolutionsllc.vom
Escalator Step Cleaning, Escalator Step Refurbishment,
Powder Coating, Demarcations Lines, Commercial
Cleaning, Industrial Cleaning, Final Cleaning, Power
Wash, Custodial Services, Janitorial Services. (Woman/
Hisp, estab 2011, empl 38, sales $950,000, cert: State)

New York

2092   A&A Maintenance Enterprise, Inc.
       965 Midland Ave
       Yonkers, NY 10704
       Contact: Armando Rodriguez Jr. CEO
       Tel: 914-969-0009
       Email: arodriguez@aamaintenance.com
       Website: www.aamaintenance.com
Janitorial services. (Hisp, estab 1983, empl 2600, sales
$23,000,000, cert: City, NMSDC)

2093   Alliance Supply, Inc.
       1743-48 St
       Brooklyn, NY 11204
       Contact: President
       Tel: 347-564-0022
       Email: sylviasadv@yahoo.com
       Website: www.alliancesupply.net
Dist janitorial supplies & food service disposables.
(Woman, estab 2005, empl 4, sales $850,000, cert: City)

2094   American Maintenance Janitorial Services &
Supplies Co. Corp.
1074 Home St
Bronx, NY 10459
Contact: Jessica Ortiz-Gonzalez Acct Mgr
Tel: 718-409-0021
Email: americanmaintenance3jss@gmail.com
Website: www.americanmaint1807.com
Commercial janitorial services; custodial services
floor & carpet care; construction cleanup; window
cleaning; building maintenance. (Hisp, estab 2004, empl
25, sales $800,000, cert: State, City, NMSDC)

2095   Anthony's Janitorial/Maintenance Service Ltd.
24-20 Jackson Ave
Long Island City, NY 11101
Contact: Anthony Fisher Presdient
Tel: 718-737-5806
Email: anthonyjanitorialmaintenance@gmail.com
Website: http://
anthonysjanitorialmaintenance.com
Janitorial Supplies & Services. (AA, estab 2010, empl , sales
$450,000, cert: City)

2096   Gilbert International Inc.
1001 Ave of the Americas
New York, NY 10018
Contact: Kevin Gilbert Presdient
Tel: 212-628-5305
Email: kevin@gilbertinternational.com
Website: www.gilbertinternational.com
Integrated facilities services, janitorial & facilities support.
(Woman/Hisp, estab 1992, empl 266, sales $22,760,946,
cert: State, City, NMSDC, WBENC)

2097   Global Traders, Inc.
496 Powell St
Brooklyn, NY 11212
Contact: Charles Ossa President
Tel: 347-240-9900
Email: cossa@globaltradersusa.us
Website: www.globaltradersusa.us
Cavicide surface disinfectant & decontaminant cleaner.
(Woman/AA, estab 1999, empl 4, sales $400,000, cert:
State, City)

2098   H. Weiss LLC
12 Labriola Court
Armonk, NY 10504
Contact: Elizabeth Weiss Managing Member
Tel: 914-273-4400
Email: eweiss@hweiss.net
Website: http://hweiss.net
Dist disposables, janitorial, small wares & supply items for
the kitchen. (Woman/Nat Ame, estab 2003, empl 46, sales
$958,779,300, cert: WBENC)

2099   Premier Supplies
460 W 34th St
New York, NY 10001
Contact: Brad Singer Dir Jan/San Div
Tel: 732-240-6900
Email: bsinger@premiersupplies.com
Website: www.premiersupplies.com
Dist cleaning products & equipment. (Woman, estab 1962,
empl 7, sales $1,250,000, cert: State)

2100   Quality Building Services
801 Second Ave 8th Fl
New York, NY 10017
Contact: ANDREA BARRAGAN Research and
Development
Tel: 212-883-0009
Email: andrea.b@qbs.co
Website: www.qualitybuildingservices.com
Janitorial services: offices, conference rooms, kitchens,
bathrooms, lobbies and other common spaces. (Woman,
estab 2000, empl 600, sales $50,050,000, cert: City,
WBENC)

2101   Snappy Solutions
106 Sycamore Dr
East Hampton, NY 11937
Contact: President
Tel: 212-748-9030
Email:
Website: www.snappysolutions.com
Dist janitorial, material maintenance products & safety
products. (Woman, estab 2003, empl 2, sales $430,000,
cert: WBENC)

Ohio

2102   Ecoprocleaningsolutions Inc.
9001 Portage Pointe Dr, Ste R103
Streetsboro, OH 44241
Contact: Kevin White Presdient
Tel: 330-689-8196
Email: kwhite@ecoprocleaningsolutions.com
Website: www.ecoprocleaningsolutions.com
Full service janitorial service, carpet cleaning; floor
stripping; sanding; waxing; burnishing & window
cleaning. (Minority, estab 2012, empl 1, sales $ 0, cert:
NMSDC)

2103   J.T. Dillard, LLC dba ZayMat Distributors
25906 Emery Rd
Cleveland, OH 44128
Contact: Terrell Dillard Presdient
Tel: 440-605-9000
Email: terrell.dillard@zaymat.com
Website: www.zaymat.com
Full-service commercial cleaning services. (AA, estab
2003, empl 6, sales $2,600,000, cert: State, NMSDC)

2104   Janitorial Services Inc.
5795 Canal Rd
Valley View, OH 44125
Contact: Ronald Martinez Jr. VP
Tel: 216-341-8601
Email: rmartinez@jsijanitorial.com
Website: www.jsijanitorial.com
Commercial Cleaning Services, Construction Cleaning,
Window Washing, Wall Washing, Carpet Cleaning, Hard
Surface Floor Care. (Hisp, estab 1972, empl 400, sales $
0, cert: NMSDC)

2105   Poly Services Inc.
16606 S Waterloo Rd
Cleveland, OH 44110
Contact: Rhonda Bolden Office Mgr
Tel: 216-531-5681
Email: polyservices@sbcglobal.net
Website:
Dist janitorial & packaging products, gloves, paper
products, maintenance items. (AA, estab 1989, empl 5,
sales $952,323, cert: State, NMSDC)

2106 Ramos Cleaning LLC
      3660 Washington Park Blvd
      Newburgh Heights, OH 44105
      Contact: Marylin Ramos Owner
      Tel: 216-262-7655
      Email: ramoscleaningllc@sbcglobal.net
      Website:
Commercial Cleaning, Carpet Cleaning, Office Cleaning,
Post Construction Cleaning. (Woman/Hisp, estab 2008,
empl 1, sales $ 0, cert: City)

Pennsylvania

2107 Homeland Industrial Supp
      3045 McCann Farm Dr, Unit 102
      Garnet Valley, PA 19060
      Contact: COO
      Tel: 844-350-1550
      Email:
      Website: www.homelandindustrialsupply.com
Dist specialty maintenance products & janitorial supplies.
(Woman, estab 2014, empl 11, sales $1,500,000, cert:
State, City)

2108 T. Frank McCall's, Inc.
      601 Madison St
      Chester, PA 19013
      Contact: Lisa Witomski Presdient
      Tel: 610-876-9245
      Email: lisa@tfrankmccalls.com
      Website: www.tfrankmccalls.com
Janitorial, maintenance & dist paper. (Woman, estab ,
empl 23, sales $ 0, cert: WBENC)

2109 Watts Window Cleaning & Janitorial Company
      5025 Wayne Ave
      Philadelphia, PA 19144
      Contact: Sales
      Tel: 215-842-4900
      Email:
      Website:
Janitorial, window cleaning, ground care. (Minority, estab
1960, empl 5, sales $ 0, cert: NMSDC)

Rhode Island

2110 Universal Cleaning Concept LLC
      77 Burgess Ave
      East Providence, RI 02914
      Contact: Evanisio Oliveira Owner
      Tel: 401-952-2844
      Email: universalcc14@gmail.com
      Website: www.universalcleaning.org
Commercial office cleaning services. (AA, estab 2007, empl
, sales $145,000, cert: State, 8a, SDB)

South Carolina

2111 Clean Advantage, Inc.
      5 N Watson Rd
      Taylors, SC 29687
      Contact: Linda Black Presdient
      Tel: 800-322-6641
      Email: linda@cleanadvantage.com
      Website: www.cleanadvantage.com
Mfr & package specialty cleaning products, private label
packaging. (Woman, estab 1993, empl 25, sales $ 0, cert:
WBENC)

2112 Quality Touch Janitorial Service, Inc.
      7252 Investment Dr
      North Charleston, SC 29418
      Contact: John Brown Presdient
      Tel: 843-552-7303
      Email: jbrown@qualitytouchjanitorial.com
      Website: http://wwwqualitytouchjanitorial.com
Janitorial services, general cleaning, construction
cleanup & floor maintenance. (Woman/AA, estab , empl
, sales $1,650,000, cert: State, City, SDB)

Tennessee

2113 Action Chemical, Inc.
      275 Cumberland St
      Memphis, TN 38112
      Contact: Charles E. Barnes Presdient
      Tel: 901-522-8783
      Email: charles@actionjps.com
      Website: www.actionchemical.com
Dist janitorial supplies & equipment, maintenance
supplies & equipment, industrial supplies, paper
products, safety products, cleaning chemicals, odor
control products, skin care, personal hygiene products,
mops, brooms, brushes. (AA, estab 1994, empl 16, sales
$5,481,460, cert: State, City, NMSDC)

2114 Ezie's Cleaning Supply
      2524 Hospitality Dr
      Columbia, TN 38401
      Contact: Errol Murphy Owner
      Tel: 931-487-9933
      Email: eziesclean@cpws.net
      Website:
Dist janitorial & paper products supplies. (AA, estab
2004, empl 2, sales , cert: State, NMSDC)

2115 Fayette Janitorial Service LLC
      P.O. Box 866
      Sommerville, TN 38068
      Contact: Michael Kellon general sales Mgr
      Tel: 901-465-1529
      Email: mburns@fayettejanitorialservice.com
      Website: www.fayettejanitorialservice.com
Janitorial services. (Woman, estab 1995, empl 15, sales
$24,481,341, cert: CPUC, WBENC)

2116 Ladd Safety, LLC
      3901 Lighthouse Lane
      Lakeland, TN 38002
      Contact: Owner
      Tel: 901-268-2098
      Email:
      Website: www.laddsafety.com
Dist Safety PPE & Janitorial supplies. (Woman, estab
2016, empl 3, sales , cert: WBENC)

2117 Mason's Professional Cleaning Service, LLC
      1422 Menager Rd
      Memphis, TN 38106
      Contact: Dorothy Mason Presdient
      Tel: 901-775-7778
      Email: dotm20032003@yahoo.com
      Website:
      www.masonprofessionalcleaningservicellc.com
Commercial janitorial cleaning services, carpet cleaning,
hard surface flooring cleaning, pressure washing,
groundskeeping/landscaping service. (Woman/AA, estab
2000, empl 21, sales $550,000, cert: State, City, NMSDC)

2118 Premiere Building Maintenance Corporation
1416 McCalla Ave
Knoxville, TN 37915
Contact: Tom Poovey Dir of Business Devel
Tel: 865-773-9524
Email: tpoovey@premierebuilding.com
Website: www.premierebuilding.com
Full Janitorial Service, Maintenance & Facility Management (AA, estab 1996, empl 500, sales $13,900,000, cert: State, NMSDC)

2119 Strategic Cleaning Services
7320 Patsy Circle N
Memphis, TN 38125
Contact: Vincent Dandridge CEO
Tel: 901-755-4484
Email: vincentdanbridge@bellsouth.net
Website: www.strategiccleaningtn.com
Commercial cleaning services, carpet cleaning, stripping & waxing floors, window cleaning & pressure washing. (AA, estab 2007, empl 25, sales $300,000, cert: State)

2120 Universal Sanitizers and Supplies, Inc.
P.O. Box 50305
Knoxville, TN 37853
Contact: Emilia Rico-Munoz CEO
Tel: 865-573-7296
Email: emirico@msn.com
Website: www.universalsanitizers.com
Sanitation cleaners & sanitizers, conveyor lubricants, janitorial products, sanitation consulting, training & audits, contract cleaning, fogging, sanitation equipment, water treatment, environmental testing. (Woman/Hisp, estab 1994, empl 15, sales $3,000,000, cert: WBENC)

Texas

2121 AHI Facility Services, Inc.
625 Yuma Ct
Dallas, TX 75208
Contact: Bethany Lorentzen Marketing Coord
Tel: 800-472-5749
Email: bethanylorentzen@ahifs.com
Website: www.ahifs.com
Janitorial svcs, carpet & floor care, minor & general maintenance, landscaping, groundskeeping, parking lot sweeping & striping, garage maintenance, window washing, power washing, document shredding, recycle programs. (Woman, estab 1968, empl 1500, sales $39,000,000, cert: WBENC)

2122 Aztec Facility Management, LP
11000 S Wilcrest, Ste 125
Houston, TX 77099
Contact: Andrea Bradshaw Proposal & Marketing Mgr
Tel: 281-668-9000
Email: andrea@aztec1.com
Website: www.aztecfacility.com
Facility management & support services: janitorial, grounds & preventive maintenance, pest control, parking lot maintenance, construction clean-up, property warehousing, environmental services. (Woman/AA, estab 1981, empl 900, sales $23,500,000, cert: State, NMSDC)

2123 CalGar Enterprises, LLC
3712 Arapaho Rd
Addison, TX 75001
Contact: Rick Calabrese
Tel: 972-437-6555
Email: rbraucht@calgar-ent.com
Website: www.calgar-ent.com
Maintenance & Detailed Cleaning of Cleanrooms, Data Center, Sub-Flooring Cleaning, Terminal Cleaning, Construction Clean Services, Site Preparation Contractors, Janitorial, Custodial, Green Cleaning, LEED. (Hisp, estab 2005, empl 30, sales $1,200,000, cert: State)

2124 Competitive Choice, Inc.
P.O. Box 35743
Houston, TX 77235
Contact: Aundrea Williams Presdient
Tel: 832-724-5300
Email: aundrea@competitivechoice.net
Website: http://competitivechoice.net
Dist industrial maintenance & cleaning chemicals: lubricants, solvents, degreasers, hand cleaners & wipes, disinfectants, deodorizers, greases & oils, coil cleaners & pan tabs, drain & sewer maintainers, insecticdes & safety supplies. (Woman/AA, estab , empl , sales $700,000, cert: WBENC)

2125 Contractors Corner, LLC
9515 Maverick Point
San Antonio, TX 78240
Contact: Eduardo Garcia Owner
Tel: 210-462-3110
Email: agarcia@concorusa.com
Website: www.concorusa.com
Commercial janitorial services, floor care, strip & wax, buffing, polishing concrete floors & building maintenance services. (Hisp, estab 2009, empl 72, sales $1,000,000, cert: State)

2126 Entrust One Facility Services, Inc.
11142 Shady Trail
Dallas, TX 75229
Contact: Lupe Fernandez Marketing Coord
Tel: 972-669-8485
Email: lupe@entrust1.com
Website: www.entrust1.com
Janitorial Services, hard floor maintenance, carpet cleaning, marble restoration,powerwashing, window cleaning. (Woman/Hisp, estab 1983, empl 600, sales , cert: State, NMSDC)

2127 Evelyn's Professional Janitorial Services, Inc.
1617 N Central Exprwy
Dallas, TX 75075
Contact: Tammy Pearce business devel dir
Tel: 972-516-9550
Email: customerservice@alljanitorial.net
Website: www.alljanitorial.net
Janitorial service; window cleaning; power washing; floor maintenance; janitorial supplies; window cleaning equipment; window cleaning supplies; floor scrubbers; floor buffers; cleaning chemicals; floor sweepers; carpet vacuum. (Woman/Hisp, estab 1992, empl 110, sales $1,258,040, cert: State, NMSDC, WBENC)

2128 Industrial Solution Company
2514 Oak Hill Dr
Arlington, TX 76006
Contact: Barbara Oldums Owner
Tel: 214-200-6535
Email: industrialsolutions513@yahoo.com
Website: www.indsolbo.com
Mfr Disposable Towel TUF Towels, Dist Cloth Towels, Gloves, Safety Supplies, Packaging Supplies & Janitorial Supplies. (Woman/AA, estab 2011, empl 2, sales , cert: State, City)

2129 La Med Facility Maintenance
10815 Gulfdale
San Antonio, TX 78216
Contact: Eduardo Tijerina CEO
Tel: 210-464-0107
Email: edwardtij@hotmail.com
Website: www.lamedfm.com
Facility maintenance, commercial cleaning, transportation. (Woman/Hisp, estab 2011, empl 32, sales $1,250,987, cert: State)

2130 Lim Service Industries Inc.
5829 W Sam Houston Pkwy N, Ste 907
Houston, TX 77041
Contact: Frank Gortot Jr. VP Business Dev
Tel: 954-899-2257
Email: f.gortot.exit@gmail.com
Website: www.limsii.com
Janitorial nation wide. (As-Pac, estab 2013, empl 32, sales $6,000,000, cert: City, 8a)

2131 M.A.N.S. Distributors, Inc.
6719 Levelland Dr Ste 200
Dallas, TX 75252
Contact: Project Mgr
Tel: 972-380-2062
Email:
Website: www.mans.us
Dist industrial janitorial & maintenance supplies. (Woman/As-Pac, estab 1980, empl 5, sales $3,500,000, cert: State)

2132 MarFran Cleaning, LLC
15502 Old Galveston Rd, Ste 718
Webster, TX 77598
Contact: Naomi Scales Managing Member
Tel: 832-885-6692
Email: naomi@marfrancleaning.com
Website: www.marfrancleaning.com
Custodial/Janitorial Services, Landscaping Services, Carpet & Upholstery Cleaning, Facilities Maintenance Support, Painting & Flooring, Minor Construction, Remodeling & Renovations. (Woman/AA, estab 2006, empl 15, sales $543,650, cert: State, City, 8a)

2133 Prestige Maintenance USA Ltd.
1808 10th St, Ste 300
Plano, TX 75074
Contact: Rachel Sanchez CEO
Tel: 972-578-9801
Email: rsanchez@prestigeusa.net
Website: www.prestigeusa.net
Contract cleaning: retail, office, industrial & warehouse facilities. (Woman, estab 1976, empl 2900, sales $74,851,169, cert: WBENC)

2134 Redlee/SCS, Inc.
10425 Olympic Dr, Ste A
Dallas, TX 75220
Contact: John Gendreau CEO
Tel: 214-357-4753
Email: jgendreau@redleescs.com
Website: www.redleescs.com
Commerical janitorial services, carpet cleaning, & hard surface flooring maintenance & restoration. (Nat Ame, estab 1982, empl 225, sales $30,353,905, cert: State, NMSDC)

2135 SOYAC Industrial
12514 Willow Breeze Dr
Tomball, TX 77377
Contact: Roberto Schnakofsky President
Tel: 877-243-0445
Email: roberto@soyacindustrial.com
Website: http://soyacindustrial.com
Environmentally & Regulatory Friendly Solvents, Degreasers, Cleaners, Penetrating Lubricants. (Hisp, estab 2004, empl 3, sales $273,532, cert: State, City)

2136 Supply Sanitation Systems
1450 Preston Forest Sq, Ste 209
Dallas, TX 75230
Contact: Sally Seegers Sales
Tel: 972-458-2555
Email: sallys@supplysystemsusa.com
Website: www.supplysystemsusa.com
Mfr & dist cleaning chemicals. (Woman, estab 1992, empl 6, sales $ 0, cert: State)

2137 Texas Microfiber Incorporated
2515 Tarpley Rd, Ste 118
Carrollton, TX 75006
Contact: President & CEO
Tel: 800-742-2913
Email:
Website: www.texasmicrofiber.com
Mfr microfiber mop pads, microfiber mops, microfiber cloths, microfiber towels, telescopic microfiber high dusters & duster socks, aluminum mop handles & heads, cotton hand towels, cotton bar towels, logo cotton towels, logo microfiber towels. (Woman, estab 2010, empl 4, sales $725,000, cert: State, WBENC)

2138 TFOM Corpoation
1106 Clayton Ln, Ste 208E
Austin, TX 78723
Contact: Terry Christopher Presdient
Tel: 512-374-9167
Email: terrylc@jddainc.com
Website: www.jddainc.com
Facility maintenance & janitorial services. (AA, estab 2005, empl 13, sales $352,000, cert: 8a)

2139 The Entermedia Group, LLC
900 RR620 S Ste C101-153
Austin, TX 78734
Contact: Lorraine Jordan CEO
Tel: 512-553-8341
Email: lorraine.jordan@tegteam.com
Website: www.tegteam.com
We provide support with: (1) the tracking, monitoring and reporting of subcontracting initiatives, (2) program assessment/analysis, (3) procurement opportunities to minority, women, veteran and disabled veteran-owned business (Woman/AA, estab 2010, empl 10, sales , cert: State, NMSDC, WBENC)

2140 XD Ventures, LLC
2555 South Shore Blvd. Ste C
League City, TX 77573
Contact: Xan Difede Presdient
Tel: 832-557-6622
Email: xan@fidelityfuels.com
Website: www.fidelityfuels.com
Dist aliphatic solvents, mineral spirits & mineral seal oils.
(Woman, estab 2014, empl 1, sales , cert: State, WBENC)

Virginia

2141 A&L Service Industries, Inc
10366A Democracy Lane
Fairfax, VA 22030
Contact: Andrea Sax Presdient
Tel: 703-359-0555
Email: diversity@alsi.us.com
Website: www.alsi.us.com
Janitorial services, commercial & residential buildings, new
construction cleanup, parking lot/garage cleaning, day
porter service, carpet cleaning, window cleaning, floor
restoration. (Woman, estab 1978, empl 62, sales
$3,244,673, cert: State)

2142 D&R Williams, LLC
12220 Chattanooga Plaza, Ste 284
Midlothian, VA 23112
Contact: Rodney Williams Presdient
Tel: 804-350-6973
Email: rodney.w@dandrwilliamsllc.com
Website: http://dandrwilliamsllc.com
Janitorial services. (AA, estab 2010, empl 40, sales
$1,060,000, cert: 8a)

2143 Hutchins & Hutchins, Inc.
39 Hutchwood Lane
Waynesboro, VA 22980
Contact: Kristyn H Marketing Mgr
Tel: 540-949-6663
Email: marketing@yourcleanroomsupplier.com
Website: www.yourcleanroomsupplier.com
Dist clean room supplies & safety apparel. (Woman, estab
1984, empl 17, sales $4,503,300, cert: State)

2144 ROCK SOLID Janitorial, Inc.
2705 W Mercury Ave
Hampton, VA 23666
Contact: Arvella Gardner Presdient
Tel: 757-766-7223
Email: calltherock@aol.com
Website: www.rocksolidjanitorial.com
Certified green janitorial services: Complete Floor Care
Services (hard surface and carpet), Day & Evening Custo-
dial Support, Construction Cleanup. (AA, estab 1997, empl
226, sales $4,025,000, cert: State)

Washington

2145 AMEX Investments, LLC
730 West A St
Pasco, WA 99301
Contact: Deborah Bermudez Owner
Tel: 509-545-3903
Email: deb@acompletejanitorial.com
Website: www.acompletejanitorial.com
Cleaning supplies, chemicals, equipment & parts.
(Woman/As-Pac, estab 2012, empl 6, sales $500,000, cert:
State)

2146 Nexo Services LLC
12819 SE 38th St
Bellevue, WA 98006
Contact: Fatima Sotelo Principal
Tel: 206-518-3235
Email: patty@nexoservices.net
Website: www.nexoservices.net
Janitorial, Maintenance, Office, Industrial, Foodservice
Supplies. (Woman/Hisp, estab 2014, empl 1, sales , cert:
State)

Wisconsin

2147 Lavelle Industries, Inc.
665 McHenry St
Burlington, WI 53105
Contact: Megan Schmidt Natl Acct Mgr
Tel: 262-757-2213
Email: mschmidt@lavelle.com
Website: www.lavelle.com
Mfr Korky brand toilet repair products: toilet flappers,
toilet fill valves & flush valves. (Woman, estab 1912,
empl 450, sales , cert: WBENC)

2148 Performance Clean LLC
One Brewers Way
Milwaukee, WI 53214
Contact: Steven O'Connell GM
Tel: 414-902-4439
Email: info@performanceclean.com
Website: www.performanceclean.com
Janitorial & building maintenance. (AA, estab 2001,
empl 350, sales $4,381,330, cert: NMSDC)

2149 Rebel Green LLC
1009 Glen Oaks Lane
Mequon, WI 53092
Contact: Ali Florsheim Owner
Tel: 262-240-9992
Email: ali@rebelgreen.com
Website: www.rebelgreen.com
Mfr & dist eco-friendly cleaning products that do not
contain harsh chemicals. (Woman, estab 2009, empl 8,
sales $7,000,000, cert: WBENC)

> **CONSTRUCTION: General Contractors**
> Companies listed are bonded general contractors who perform or will perform on a regional or national basis. NAICS Code 23

Alaska

2150 Teya Technologies, LLC
101 E 9th Ave, Ste 9B
Anchorage, AK 99501
Contact: Ronald Perry CEO
Tel: 907-339-4901
Email: ron.perry@teyatech.com
Website: www.teyatech.com
Construction, demolition, project management, custodial and janitorial services, administrative services, product manufacturing, housing maintenance, and conference and event planning/management. (Nat Ame, estab 2005, empl 46, sales $14,422,189, cert: NMSDC)

Alabama

2151 Dine Modular Construction, LLC
2515 11th Avenue
Haleyville, AL 35565
Contact: Pam Morton Sr Project Mgr
Tel: 205-485-1267
Email: pparrish@dineconstruction.com
Website: www.dineconstruction.com
General construction: design/build construction, pre-engineered steel & modular buildings. (Woman/Nat Ame, estab 2003, empl 6, sales $1,000,002, cert: WBENC)

Arizona

2152 DAP Construction Management, LLC
516 W Vermont Ave
Phoenix, AZ 85013
Contact: Alicia Hernandez
Tel: 602-541-0229
Email: ahernandez@dapconstructionmgt.com
Website: www.dapconstructionmgt.com
General construction: self performing, rough framing, landscaping, roofing, painting, flooring & material supplies. (Woman/Hisp, estab 2009, empl 2, sales $102,000, cert: State, City, WBENC)

2153 Eagle EGC dba Miura Contracting
4001 S Contractors Way, Ste 121
Tucson, AZ 85716
Contact: Liz Joye Office Mgr
Tel: 520-292-3939
Email: ljoye@miuracontracting.com
Website: www.miuracontracting.com/
General Contracting, horizontal construction projects (highway, road, utilities, and site development) & vertical construction projects (commercial building and building improvements). (Hisp, estab 2008, empl 13, sales $1,400,000, cert: City, 8a, SBD)

2154 JOATMON Construction LLC
1308 N Stockton Hill Rd, Ste A305
Kingman, AZ 86401
Contact: J R Avila Managing Member
Tel: 928-718-2000
Email: jr@joatmonllc.com
Website: www.jclaz.com
General Contractor, Structural Steel Fabrication & Erection, Commercial & Industrial Construction & Maintenance, Communication Towers & Maintenance , Cell Tower Erection, Modification & Fabrication, Network Upgrades, Concrete Structures. (Hisp, estab 2000, empl 10, sales $1,000,000, cert: 8a)

2155 Pacificspan LLC
6908 W Southgate Ave
Phoenix, AZ 85043
Contact: John Lee President
Tel: 480-882-8015
Email: john@pacificspan.com
Website: www.pacificspan.com
Project feasibility planning, design development, & construction, remodeling of restaurants and bars, medical and research facilities, computer and chemical laboratories, salons and spas, apartment complexes, churches and offices, etc. (As-Pac, estab 2005, empl 8, sales $988,180, cert: 8a)

2156 Sentinel Fence and Contracting LLC
6908 East Thomas Road
Scottsdale, AZ 85251
Contact: Sharon Hamilton Presdient
Tel: 602-828-4866
Email: sharonh@sentinelfence.com
Website: www.sentinelfence.com
General contracting, commercial renovations, high security fencing, gates, bollards, barriers & barricades. (Woman/Hisp, estab 2002, empl 15, sales $3,219,351, cert: City, WBENC)

2157 Troon Inc.
16441 N 90th St
Scottsdale, AZ 85260
Contact: Ray Garcia President
Tel: 480-626-4300
Email: ray@trooninc.com
Website: www.trooninc.com
General contracting. (Hisp, estab 2002, empl 11, sales $11,000,000, cert: State)

California

2158 Anderson Burton Construction
121 Nevada St
Arroyo Grande, CA 93420
Contact: Joni Anderson Presdient
Tel: 805-481-5096
Email: joni@andersonburton.com
Website: www.andersonburton.com/
General Engineering, Procurement, General Contracting, Energy (Woman/Hisp, estab 1999, empl 155, sales $30,198,963, cert: CPUC)

2159   Aqual Corp.
       7951 North Ave
       Lemon Grove, CA 91945
       Contact: Lanette McAfee Business Operations
       Tel: 619-741-9028
       Email: lanette@aqualcorp.com
       Website: www.aqualcorp.com
Construction Management Cost Plus, GMP Design Build &
Lump Sum, Multi Family Commercial & Industrial Tenant
Improvements, Concrete, horizontal/vertical, drywall &
taping, painting, framing, carpentry, tile, doors, plumbing.
(AA, As-Pac, estab 2008, empl 4, sales $1,049,692, cert:
NMSDC)

2160   ATW Construction, Inc.
       1305 W Main St
       Barstow, CA 92311
       Contact: Michael Wilhoit Presdient
       Tel: 760-256-6451
       Email: desertsigns@verizon.net
       Website:
Engineering design, construction, environmental engineering and remediation. (Nat Ame, estab 2015, empl 3, sales
$5,606,340, cert: 8a)

2161   Bjork Construction Co. Inc.
       4420 Enterprise Place
       Fremont, CA 94538
       Contact: Jean Bjork Presdient
       Tel: 510-656-4688
       Email: jbjork@bjorkconstruction.com
       Website: www.bjorkconstruction.com
General contracting: self preforms, construction management, carpentry rough & finish, metal stud framing,
sheetrock systems & painting. (Woman, estab 1988, empl
115, sales $22,000,000, cert: CPUC, WBENC)

2162   Cabral Roofing & Waterproofing Corp.
       675 W. Terrace Dr
       San Dimas, CA 91773
       Contact: Desi Cabral PR/sales
       Tel: 323-832-9100
       Email: desi@cabralroofing.com
       Website: www.cabralroofing.com
General contracting: roofing & waterproofing (Hisp, estab
1997, empl 70, sales $ 0, cert: CPUC)

2163   Casco Contractors, Inc.
       9850 Irvine Center Dr.
       Irvine, CA 92618
       Contact: Cheryl Osborn Presdient
       Tel: 949-679-6880
       Email: cheryl@cascocontractors.com
       Website: www.cascocontractors.com
General contracting, TI construction, construction management. (Woman, estab 2001, empl 44, sales $32,000,000,
cert: CPUC, WBENC)

2164   Commercial Site Improvements, Inc.
       192 Poker Flat Rd
       Copperopolis, CA 95228
       Contact: Kim Batch Owner
       Tel: 209-785-1920
       Email: mainoffice@comimprovementsinc.com
       Website: www.comsiteimprovementsinc.com
Construction maintenance & remodeling. (Woman, estab
2012, empl 50, sales $130,000,000, cert: CPUC)

2165   Cornejo Construction Co.
       P.O. Box 22302
       Santa Barbara, CA 93121
       Contact: Jesse Cornejo Owner
       Tel: 805-448-2201
       Email: jcornejo@cornejoco.com
       Website: www.cornejoco.com
Remodeling assembly lines, replacing air ducts, replacing
equipment, moving walls, crane placement, building
hangars, epoxy flooring, etc. (Hisp, estab 1989, empl 7,
sales $250,000, cert: 8a)

2166   Fasone Construction inc
       9124 Norwalk Blvd
       Santa Fe Springs, CA 90670
       Contact: Andrea N Garrido
       Tel: 562-322-0828
       Email: andrea@fasonegbc.com
       Website: http://fasonegbc.com
Design & general construction contracting. (Woman/
Hisp, estab 1995, empl 21, sales $3,800,500, cert: City,
CPUC, 8a)

2167   FS3, Inc.
       1201 Puerta del Sol, #314
       San Clemente, CA 92673
       Contact: Garrett Terlaak Principal
       Tel: 949-445-3734
       Email: garrett@fs3h.com
       Website: www.fs3h.com
Project Management, Construction Management, CPM
Scheduling, Cost Estimating, Inspection, Constructibility
Analysis, Risk Management (Hisp, estab 2011, empl 10,
sales $1,200,000, cert: State)

2168   Gaff Group, Inc.
       2698 Junipero Ave, Ste 110
       Signal Hill, CA 90755
       Contact: Angela Foster Project Admin
       Tel: 562-989-3820
       Email: angelafoster@gaffgroup.com
       Website: www.gaffgroup.com
Demolition, concrete, steel stud framing & drywall,
acoustic ceilings/walls, pinting cabinetry, rough & finish
carpentry, plumbing, ceramic tile. (AA, estab 1972, empl
24, sales $5,500,000, cert: State)

2169   Health Education Services
       1000 Varian St, Ste A
       San Carlos, CA 94070
       Contact: Jenny Fernando
       Tel: 650-321-6500
       Email: jfernando@healtheducationservices.net
       Website: www.healtheducationservices.net
Health Education Services provides turnkey AED pro-
gram implementation and management - sales, compli-
ance, maintenance, database tracking, training.
(Woman, estab 1979, empl 18, sales $900,000, cert:
CPUC, WBENC)

2170   Herca Telecomm Services Inc
       18610 Beck St
       Perris, CA 92570
       Contact: Hector Castellon CEO
       Tel: 951-940-5941
       Email: hector.castellon@hercatelecomm.com
       Website: www.hercatelecomm.com
Tower erection, lines & antennas, microwave, general
construction, excavation, trenching, electrical, concrete,
demolition. (Hisp, estab 2005, empl 29, sales
$4,035,556, cert: State)

2171 Hollister Construction Company
4065 E La Palma Ave Ste C
Anaheim, CA 92807
Contact: Holli Evelyn Carpenter Presdient
Tel: 714-632-1800
Email: holli@hollico.net
Website: www.hollico.net
General contracting, turn-key design & constuction services. (Woman, estab 1992, empl 12, sales $2,150,000, cert: CPUC, WBENC)

2172 Interior Plus, Inc.
8620 Sorenson Ave, Ste 2
Santa Fe Springs, CA 90670
Contact: Presdient
Tel: 562-464-6950
Email:
Website: www.interiorplusinc.us
General contracting, commercial & industrial interior construction & improvements, tenant improvements. (Hisp, estab 1992, empl 11, sales $2,261,918, cert: CPUC, 8a)

2173 KW Construction
841 F St
West Sacramento, CA 95605
Contact: Kevin Wong President
Tel: 916-372-8600
Email: kwong@mgci.com
Website:
General contracting: electric, plumbing, HVAC, painting, grading & paving, finish & rough carpentry. (As-Pac, estab 1989, empl 15, sales $4,072,182, cert: State)

2174 Larco Development Inc.
540 S. Andreasen Dr. Ste E
Escondido, CA 92029
Contact: Paul Larez Presdient
Tel: 951-201-5126
Email: paul@larco-inc.com
Website: www.larco-inc.com
General contracting, in-house trades: Electrical, HVAC, Plumbing, Flooring, Concrete/Asphalt, Carpentry/Framing, Painting, Drywall, Interior Finishes, Underground Utilities, Communications
Landscape, Irrigation, Demolition. (Hisp, estab 1993, empl 46, sales $7,269,480, cert: 8a)

2175 Menco Pacific, Inc.
15110 Keswick St.
Van Nuys, CA 91405
Contact: Jenna Lockstedt Procurement Mgr
Tel: 760-747-4405
Email: jlockstedt@menco-pacific.com
Website: www.menco-pacific.com
Construction services. (Hisp, estab 2007, empl 100, sales $20,500,000, cert: State, CPUC)

2176 MSH Construction Co., Inc.
15301 Connector Lane
Huntington Beach, CA 92649
Contact: Lisa Moss Presdient
Tel: 714-899-9509
Email: lmoss@mshconstruction.com
Website: www.mshconstruction.com
General contractoring: tenant improvement & civil construction, concrete, demolition, grading & general maintanence labor. (Woman, estab 2003, empl 12, sales $6,679,909, cert: CPUC, WBENC)

2177 MZN Construction, Inc.
701 N Harbor Blvd
La Habra, CA 90631
Contact: Presdient
Tel: 562-694-5441
Email:
Website: www.mznconstruction.com
General Contracting, Facilities Management & Engineering Construction Management. (Hisp, estab 1984, empl 20, sales $5,400,000, cert: State)

2178 OST Trucks and Cranes, Inc.
2951 N Ventura Ave
Ventura, CA 93002
Contact: L. Dennis Zermeno Presdient
Tel: 805-643-9963
Email: ostcranes@aol.com
Website: www.ostcranes.com
General & hazardous substance removal & remedial action, hydraulic cranes 5 to 140. (Hisp, estab 1947, empl 69, sales $ 0, cert: City, NMSDC, CPUC)

2179 ProWest Engineering, Inc.
1442 E Lincoln St Ste 360
Orange, CA 92865
Contact: Sherri Barrera Sales/Marketing Dir
Tel: 866-278-0572
Email: sherri@prowest-engineering.com
Website: www.prowest-engineering.com
General contracting, asphalt paving removal or maintainance, concrete repairs, seal/slurry coat, stenciling & re-striping & ADA compliant (Woman/Hisp, estab 2005, empl 8, sales $1,500,000, cert: CPUC)

2180 Pub Construction, Inc.
23441 Golden Springs Dr, Ste 104
Diamond Bar, CA 91765
Contact: Chris Yi President
Tel: 909-455-0187
Email: pubconstruction@yahoo.com
Website: www.pubconstruction.com
General contracting services, building, carpet, flooring, tile, painting. (As-Pac, estab 2000, empl 13, sales $15,000,000, cert: NMSDC)

2181 Shames Construction Company, Ltd
5826 Brisa St, Ste E
Livermore, CA 94550
Contact: Carolyn Shames President & CEO
Tel: 925-606-3000
Email: cshames@shames.com
Website: www.shames.com
Commercial construction. (Woman, estab 1987, empl 48, sales $70,847,336, cert: CPUC)

2182 South City Construction Inc.
1111 Rancho Conejo Blvd Ste 205
Newbury Park, CA 91320
Contact: Andrew Solimine Presdient
Tel: 805-376-2000
Email: a.solimine@southcityconstruction.com
Website: www.southcityconstruction.com
General contracting, construction management, program management, value engineering, scheduling, cost estimating. (Woman, estab 2011, empl 8, sales $100,000, cert: CPUC)

2183   The G Crew
225 E Broadway Ste 202
Glendale, CA 91205
Contact: Ella Daya VP
Tel: 818-240-4157
Email: info@thegcrew.com
Website: www.thegcrew.com
Inspection, Construction Management, & Project Support services (Woman/As-Pac, estab 2001, empl 9, sales $ 0, cert: CPUC)

2184   True Champions
5234 Cushman Pl, Ste 200
San Diego, CA 92110
Contact: Kristi Vega Admin Mgr
Tel: 619-276-6999
Email: kristi@truechampions.net
Website: www.truechampions.net
General contracting, design build, concrete restoration/ protective coatings, waterproofing & commercial flooring. (Hisp, estab 1995, empl 23, sales $ 0, cert: State, CPUC)

2185   Vanir Construction Management, Inc.
4540 Duckhorn Dr, Ste 300
Sacramento, CA 95834
Contact: Dorene Dominguez Business Develop Dir
Tel: 916-575-8888
Email: melinda.guzman@vanir.com
Website: www.vanir.com
Construction management services. (Woman/Hisp, estab 1980, empl 334, sales $129,308,942, cert: NMSDC, CPUC)

2186   WMB Financial Solutions
1999 Harrison St Ste 1800
Oakland, CA 94612
Contact: Franck Waota Presdient
Tel: 510-210-8052
Email: fwaota@wmbgc.com
Website: http://wwww.wmbgc.com
General construction, tenant improvement & remodeling, design build, operation & maintenance of real estate properties (Residential & commercial). (Woman/AA, estab 2004, empl 25, sales $3,700,000, cert: State, 8a)

Colorado

2187   Alvarado Construction, Inc.
924 W Colfax Ave Ste 301
Denver, CO 80204
Contact: Jennifer Coons VP
Tel: 303-629-0783
Email: jcoons@alvaradoconstruction.com
Website: https://alvaradoconstruction.com
Commercial General Contracting, Construction Manager, Development, Design/Build & Property Management. (Woman/Hisp, estab 1976, empl 50, sales , cert: NMSDC, WBENC)

2188   B&M Construction, Inc.
3134 Beacon St
Colorado Springs, CO 80907
Contact: Barbara Myrick
Tel: 719-577-4550
Email: bmyrick@bmc-i.com
Website: www.bmc-i.com
Project Management, Design-Build Services, Furniture Acquisition & Procurement, Electrical Design & Installation, Construction/Infrastructure, Tenant Finish/Renovation Services, Satellite Communications Repair & Overhaul. (Woman/AA, estab 2005, empl 33, sales $13,000,000, cert: State, NMSDC, WBENC)

2189   Rhinotrax Construction, Inc.
1035 Coffman St
Longmont, CO 80501
Contact: Michele Noel President
Tel: 303-682-9906
Email: michelenoel@rhinotrax.com
Website: www.rhinotraxconstruction.com
General contracting: demolition, rough concrete, masonry, drywall & framing, doors & hardware, etc. (Woman, estab 2004, empl 12, sales $4,500,000, cert: City)

2190   Tah Yas JV 1
12655 W 54th Dr
Arvada, CO 80002
Contact: Douglas Wells Dir Business Dev
Tel: 719-352-6409
Email: dougwells@tahyas.com
Website: http://tahyas.com
Pre-construction & construction management services. (Nat Ame, estab 2002, empl 125, sales , cert: 8a)

2191   Torix General Contractors a Tepa Company
5045 List Dr
Colorado Springs, CO 80919
Contact: Marvin Maples GM
Tel: 719-596-8114
Email: marvin.maples@tepa.com
Website: www.tepa.com
New construction & rennovations: design-build, general contracting & construction management. (Nat Ame, estab 1988, empl 180, sales $105,000,000, cert: NMSDC)

Connecticut

2192   Diggs Construction, LLC
1010 Wethersfield Ave Ste 201
Hartford, CT 06114
Contact: Derrick Diggs VP
Tel: 860-296-1664
Email: ddiggs@diggsconstruction.com
Website: www.diggsconstruction.com
Program Management, Construction Management, Contract Administration & General Contracting solutions. (AA, estab 1999, empl 35, sales $11,000,000, cert: State, NMSDC)

2193   TRI-CON Construction Managers, LLC
59 Amity Rd, Ste 11
New Haven, CT 06515
Contact: Larry Stewart Exec Project Mgr
Tel: 203-772-4229
Email: lmstewart@tri-con.org
Website: www.tri-con.org
Construction management, general contracting, project management, value engineering, contract administration, estimating,owners representation services. (AA, estab 2002, empl 11, sales , cert: State, NMSDC)

2194   West Reach Construction Company, Inc.
P.O. Box 1328
Manchester, CT 06045
Contact: Kerry Hainsey Presdient
Tel: 860-649-7607
Email: westreachcon@comcast.net
Website: www.westreachconstruction.com
General contracting, commercial, industrial construction. (Woman, estab 1987, empl 18, sales $10,000,000, cert: WBENC)

District of Columbia

2195 Columbia Enterprises
1018 7th St SE
Washington, DC 20003
Contact: Presdient
Tel: 202-547-7979
Email:
Website: www.columbiadb.com
Construction management & general contracting services.
(AA, estab 1993, empl 15, sales $3,600,000, cert: State)

2196 Drake Incorporated
4315 Sheriff Rd NE
Washington, DC 20019
Contact: Stephanie Y Drake CEO
Tel: 202-291-3174
Email: sdrake@drake-inc.com
Website: www.drake-inc.com
Construction, design / build & project management.
(Woman/AA, estab 2002, empl 24, sales $7,088,479, cert:
State)

2197 The ELOCEN Group
1341 H St, NE Ste 301
Washington, DC 20002
Contact: Taryn Lewis Dir of Operations
Tel: 202-644-8500
Email: tarynl@elocengroup.com
Website: www.elocengroup.com
Program & Project Management, Construction Manage-
ment, Interior Design, Information Technology, Facilities/
Logistics, and Healthcare Facilities/Logistics/Management.
(Woman/AA, estab 2007, empl 62, sales $20,089,894, cert:
State, City, WBENC, 8a)

Florida

2198 Albu & Associates, Inc.
2711 W Fairbanks Ave
Winter Park, FL 32789
Contact: Jason Albu Presdient
Tel: 407-788-1450
Email: jasonalbu@albu.biz
Website: www.albu.biz
General contracting, design build, construction
management & consulting. (Hisp, estab 1994, empl 20,
sales $20,000,000, cert: City, NMSDC)

2199 Arkren Inc.
6278 N Federal Hwy Ste 430
Fort Lauderdale, FL 33308
Contact: Mark Barati Sr VP
Tel: 954-210-8886
Email: mark@arkren.com
Website: www.arkren.com
Telecommunications, general construction(commercial
and residential), design, Procurement, logistics, warehous-
ing, transportation, temporary housing/life support,
professional/craft labor, O&G/LNG. (Woman, estab 2013,
empl 15, sales $960,000, cert: WBENC)

2200 Cortes Construction Services, LLC
720 Anclote Rd
Tarpon Road, FL 34689
Contact: Michael Corral VP
Tel: 727-937-4700
Email: mcorral@cortesconstruction.com
Website: www.cortesconstruction.com
Commercial construction company specializing in hotel
renovations. (Hisp, estab 2004, empl 30, sales
$5,178,771, cert: State)

2201 Curtoom Companies, Inc.
1228 E 7th Ave
Tampa, FL 33675
Contact: Paul Curtis CEO
Tel: 813-405-8082
Email: support@curtoom.com
Website: www.curtoom.com
Construction cost consulting. (AA, estab 1989, empl 30,
sales $3,600,000, cert: State)

2202 Dominion Builders, LLC
4942 S LeJeune Rd Ste 203
Coral Gables, FL 33146
Contact: Mark Gemignani Presdient
Tel: 305-661-2700
Email: mgemignani@dominionbuild.com
Website: www.dominionbuild.com
General contracting services. (Nat Ame, estab 2008,
empl 7, sales $5,000,000, cert: State, 8a)

2203 Fine Line Construction contractors, Inc.
6500 Georgia Ave
Florida, FL 33405
Contact: Bob Waskiwicz VP
Tel: 561-582-7880
Email: bobw@finelinecontractors.com
Website: www.finelinecontractors.com
General contracting, commercial construction,
commecial buildout, commercial renovations, interior
remodel, building expansion, full buildout, interior
improvements, warehouse expansion, warehouse
renovations. (Woman, estab 2010, empl 15, sales
$5,867,874, cert: WBENC)

2204 Hatcher Construction & Development, Inc.
3300 S Congress Ave Ste 15
Boynton Beach, FL 33426
Contact: William Hatcher
Tel: 561-752-4100
Email: hatchergc@bellsouth.net
Website: www.hatcher-construction.com
Commercial Institutional Bldg, General Contractor,
Asphalt roofing, Asphalt Coating & Sealing, Concrete,
Painting, spraying, or coating, Facilities Support Mgmt,
Electrical, Residential Construction, multifamily, Land-
scaping. (AA, estab 1999, empl 7, sales $1,350,000, cert:
State, 8a)

2205 LEE Construction Group, Inc.
9485 NW 12 St
Miami, FL 33172
Contact: Felecia Batson Presdient
Tel: 305-216-7558
Email: fbatson@leecgi.com
Website: www.leecgi.com/
LEE Construction is also equipped and knowledgeable in
providing marine construction services such as dredging,
piling, seawalls, dock construction, and barge related
work. (Hisp, estab 2009, empl 40, sales $21,000,000,
cert: 8a)

2206 Nakitare Builders LLC
      11806 Foxglove Dr
      Clermont, FL 34711
      Contact: Robert Mack GM
      Tel: 352-857-0000
      Email: buld2006@aol.com
      Website: www.sustainable-roofs.com
Construction services, inspections. (AA, estab 2006, empl
5, sales $390,000, cert: NMSDC)

2207 R L Burns Inc.
      1203 W Gore St
      Orlando, FL 32805
      Contact: Elizabeth Duncan
      Tel: 407-839-1131
      Email: eduncan@rlburnsinc.com
      Website: www.rlburnsinc.com
Construction management svcs: project management,
consulting, cost estimating, pre-construction planning &
design, schedule / CPM management, general construction, design/build, new construction, renovation. (AA,
estab 1994, empl 9, sales $3,000,000, cert: City)

2208 Stoner Construction, Inc.
      100 SW 101st Terr
      Plantation, FL 33324
      Contact: Lynn Stoner President
      Tel: 954-474-8460
      Email: lynnstoner@aol.com
      Website:
General contracting: residential renovations, additions &
commercial tenant improvements. (Woman, estab 2004,
empl 9, sales , cert: City)

2209 T&G Corporation
      8623 Commodity Circle
      Orlando, FL 32819
      Contact: Mark Knott Dir Business Devel
      Tel: 407-352-4443
      Email: officedepot@t-and-g.com
      Website: www.t-and-g.com
General contracting: facility operation/maintenance
support services, commercial building, construction
management & design-build services. (Hisp, estab 1987,
empl 85, sales $23,214,524, cert: State, NMSDC)

2210 Thomco Enterprises Inc.
      745 Hollywood Blvd NW
      Fort Walton Beach, FL 32548
      Contact: Darryl Embrey President
      Tel: 850-244-0811
      Email: darryle@thomcoent.com
      Website: www.thomcoent.com
Construction, construction management, facility maintenance, renovations, upgrades, vertical construction, bank
facility construction, commercial & government construction, development, project management. (AA, estab 1993,
empl 35, sales $11,245,342, cert: State)

2211 Thornton Construction Company, Inc.
      13290 NW 42nd Ave
      Miami, FL 33054
      Contact: Nataly Guevara Business Dev Mgr
      Tel: 305-649-1995
      Email: nguevara@thornton-inc.com
      Website: www.thornton-inc.com
Contracting and construction management firm. (Hisp,
estab 1998, empl 55, sales $55,978,278, cert: State)

2212 Validus Construction Services LLC
      7130 S Orange Blossom Trail Ste 111
      Orlando, FL 32809
      Contact: Nicole Wickens Owner
      Tel: 407-413-5022
      Email: validuscs@gmail.com
      Website: http://validuscs.net
New construction, remodel, remediation, design-build,
renovation, office renovations, warehouse renovations,
landscaping, parking lot, sidewalks, windows, doors,
flooring, interiors, exteriors, HVAC, plumbing, electrical.
(Woman, estab 2012, empl 9, sales $5,337,114, cert:
WBENC)

2213 Veatic dba of Proxy Management Group
      2450 Smith St, Ste P
      Kissimmee, FL 34744
      Contact: Jon Andreasson Project Dev
      Tel: 888-474-2999
      Email: jandreasson@veatic.com
      Website: www.veatic.com
General Contractor, Site Development, Excavation,
Retention, Disaster Response, Grading, Foundations,
Underground Utilities, Demolition, Site Restoration, New
Building Construction. (Hisp, estab 2008, empl 32, sales
$3,801,885, cert: State, City, NMSDC)

Georgia

2214 Bryson Constructors, Inc.
      2847 Main St, Ste 200
      East Point, GA 30344
      Contact: Steve Barnes CEO
      Tel: 404-762-1000
      Email: sbarnes@brysonconstructors.com
      Website: www.brysonconstructors.com
Design/build commercial construction. (AA, estab , empl
, sales $7,351,431, cert: NMSDC)

2215 Colliers Facility Solutions, LLC
      1230 Peachtree St Ste 800
      Atlanta, GA 30309
      Contact: Hughes Holly CEO
      Tel: 404-574-1014
      Email: holly.hughes@colliers.com
      Website: www.colliers.com/atlanta
Facility management, project management, construction
management, interior, exterior & maintenance, energy
efficiency, systems optimization, risk mitigation & cost
savings. (Woman, estab 2014, empl 160, sales
$19,500,000, cert: WBENC)

2216 Pinnacle Services Group, Inc.
      10270 Oxford Mill Circle
      Alpharetta, GA 30022
      Contact: Jerry Peljovich Presdient
      Tel: 770-355-7156
      Email: jerryp@psginc-ga.com
      Website: www.PSGinc-ga.com
General contracting. (Hisp, estab 2004, empl 5, sales
$3,207,000, cert: State, City, NMSDC)

2217 Pioneer Construction, Inc.
      31 Park of Commerce Way Ste 100
      Savannah, GA 31405
      Contact: Whitney Butler Dir mktg/brand
      Tel: 912-650-1850
      Email: wbutler@pioneersavannah.com
      Website: www.pioneersavannah.com
General Contractors specializing in commercial construction. (Woman/As-Pac, estab 1994, empl 20, sales
$10,000,000, cert: State)

2218 Quantum Installation Group
889 Franklin Gateway, Ste 100
Marietta, GA 30067
Contact: Bob Turner VP Business Dev
Tel: 706-506-2262
Email: bob.turner@quantuminstall.com
Website: http://quantuminstall.com
General construction contractor, millwork, fixture & decor installation contractor. (Woman/As-Pac, estab 2012, empl 150, sales , cert: NMSDC, WBENC)

2219 Synergy Development Partners, LLC
83 Walton St, NW Ste 400
Atlanta, GA 30303
Contact: Brittany Montgomery Operations Mgr
Tel: 404-254-4755
Email: bmontgomery@synergydp.com
Website: www.synergydp.com
General contracting, construction management, drywall, framing, renovation, restoration, roof repair, carpentry, flooring, paint, trim, tentant build-out & new construction. (Woman/AA, estab 2003, empl 15, sales $3,568,712, cert: City, NMSDC)

2220 The Chester Group, Inc.
231 Peters St SW
Atlanta, GA 30313
Contact: Wallace Chester President
Tel: 786-586-3941
Email: wchester@thechestergroup.com
Website: www.thechestergroup.com
General contracting & construction mgmt: renovation; design/build; maintenance; roofing; concrete placement; debris removal; fencing; asphalt resurfacing; masonry; interior build-out; windows; doors; painting; flooring; electrical. (AA, estab 2002, empl 1, sales $100,000, cert: State)

2221 Time Out Systems, Inc.
308 Indian Creek Circle
Adel, GA 31620
Contact: Tim LeBlanc CFO
Tel: 229-896-6190
Email: admin@timeoutsystems.com
Website: www.timeoutsystems.com
General Construction, Remolding, Roofing, Painting, Security, Surround Sound, Televisions, Home Automation, Yard Maintenance, Door and Window Replacement, Blind Installation, Deck Construction, Bathroom Remolding. (Woman, estab 1991, empl 150, sales $6,000,000, cert: WBENC)

Iowa

2222 Gethmann Construction Company, Inc.
P.O. Box 160
Marshalltown, IA 50158
Contact: Jill Craft President
Tel: 641-753-3555
Email: jill@gethmann.com
Website: www.gethmannconstruction.com
Concrete work, excavation, backfill, foundations, slabs, pads, elevated slabs, concrete demo, structural steel fab, crane rental & operators. (Woman, estab 1937, empl 67, sales $22,000,000, cert: WBENC)

2223 Knight Eagle Contracting Group, Inc.
P.O. Box 5305
Coralville, IA 52241
Contact: Steve Marshall Business Develop Mgr
Tel: 319-338-7360
Email: smarshall@knighteagle.net
Website: www.knighteagle.net
Construction Services, General Contractor, Construction Management, Commercial Roofing, Professional Services, Staff Augmentation, Administration, Engineering, Safety. (Woman/Nat Ame, Hisp, estab 2010, empl 3, sales , cert: 8a)

Illinois

2224 CREA Construction
161 N Clark, Ste 4700
Chicago, IL 60601
Contact: Rea Johnson President
Tel: 312-371-3827
Email: rea1_23@yahoo.com
Website: www.creagc.com
Construction management, general contracting, estimating & engineering services. (Woman/AA, estab 2007, empl 10, sales $1,000,000, cert: State, NMSDC)

2225 Integrated Construction Technology Corp.
126 S Villa Ave
Villa Park, IL 60181
Contact: Les Shy President
Tel: 630-993-1800
Email: lshy@integratedusa.com
Website:
Design & build construction, general contracting, property managment, supplies & services. (AA, As-Pac, estab 1994, empl 30, sales $18,000,000, cert: City)

2226 Otis Construction Company
111 W Jackson Blvd Ste 1105
Chicago, IL 60604
Contact: Glenn Otis, Jr. President
Tel: 312-786-9877
Email: gotis@otiscc.com
Website: www.otiscc.com
Construction svcs: interior building alterations, commercial & industrial facilities, green construction & maintenance, specialty projects, facilities maintenance, emergency repairs. (AA, estab 1999, empl 4, sales $1,500,000, cert: NMSDC)

2227 The Landmark Group Companies LLC
6735 Vistagreen Way Ste 100
Rockford, IL 61107
Contact: Bob Sanches CEO
Tel: 815-639-0034
Email: bsanches@lmcos.com
Website: www.lmcos.com
Construction management of new & existing facilities. (Hisp, estab 2006, empl 8, sales $30,000,000, cert: NMSDC)

2228 Trinidad Construction, LLC
18505 West Creek Dr Ste 1B
Tinley Park, IL 60477
Contact: Brian Ortiz Presdient
Tel: 773-429-4600
Email: bortiz@trinidadllc.com
Website: http://trinidadllc.com
General contracting, construction management. (Hisp, estab 2010, empl 75, sales $25,000,000, cert: NMSDC)

2229   Vistara Construction Services, Inc.
     728 W Jackson Blvd, Ste 402
     Chicago, IL 60661
     Contact: Bina Nair President
     Tel: 312-986-8660
     Email: info@vistara.com
     Website: www.vistara.com
General construction. (Woman/As-Ind, estab 1994, empl 10, sales $ 0, cert: City)

Indiana

2230   Custom Mechanical Systems, Corp.
     691 Industrial Blvd
     Bargersville, IN 46106
     Contact: William Beach VP Business Dev
     Tel: 617-803-0714
     Email: wbeach@cms-corporation.com
     Website: www.cms-corporation.com
New construction, renovations, energy & sustainability, building operations maintenance & repairs. (Hisp, estab 1996, empl 110, sales $42,753,323, cert: State, NMSDC)

2231   Finch Constructors, Inc.
     5528 W 84th St
     Indianapolis, IN 46268
     Contact: Tammy Brooks Operations Mgr
     Tel: 317-916-6770
     Email: tbrooks@finchconstructors.com
     Website: www.finchconstructors.com
Industrial, commercial & municipal construction & management services: mechanical piping, equipment erection, HVAC & electrical services. (AA, estab 2004, empl 42, sales $20,000,000, cert: NMSDC)

2232   Harmon Construction, Inc.
     621 S State St
     North Vernon, IN 47265
     Contact: Ardell Mitchell Sr. Project Mgr/Estimator
     Tel: 812-346-2048
     Email: ardell.mitchell@harmonconstruction.com
     Website: www.harmonconstruction.com
Contracting, design-build capabilities. (AA, estab 1955, empl 81, sales $8,478,000, cert: State, NMSDC)

2233   K&S Construction Group, Inc.
     9148 Louisiana St, Unit F
     Merrillville, IN 46410
     Contact: Vance R. Kenney CEO
     Tel: 219-794-9550
     Email: vkenney@k-sconstruction.com
     Website: www.k-sconstruction.com
Heavy construction, construction mgmt, demolition, design build, excavation, reinforced concrete, concrete forming, sidewalk, curb, crushed granite, levees, revetments, carpentry, railroad construction, fencing, environmental. (AA, estab 1992, empl 25, sales $3,200,000, cert: State, NMSDC)

2234   Powers & Sons Construction Co, Inc.
     2636 W 15th Ave
     Gary, IN 46404
     Contact: Kelly Powers Baria Dir Business Dev
     Tel: 219-949-3100
     Email: kbaria@powersandsons.com
     Website: www.powersandsons.com
Construction svcs. (AA, estab 1967, empl 50, sales $30,390,330, cert: State, NMSDC)

2235   Shawnee Construction and Engineering
     7701 Opportunity Dr
     Fort Wayne, IN 46825
     Contact: Matt Schenkel Presdient
     Tel: 260-489-1234
     Email: matt@shawneeconstruction.com
     Website: http://ShawneeConstruction.com
General contracting, new construction & remodeling, commercial & industrial. (Hisp, estab 1968, empl 42, sales $17,300,000, cert: State, City)

2236   Taylor Bros. Construction Co, Inc.
     4555 Middle Rd
     Columbus, IN 47203
     Contact: Jeffrey Chandler VP
     Tel: 812-379-9547
     Email: jchandler@tbcci.com
     Website: www.tbcci.com
General contracting & construction mgmt svcs. (AA, estab 1933, empl 100, sales $24,000,000, cert: State)

Kansas

2237   NCRI-National Catastrophe Restoration, Inc.
     8447 E 35th St N
     Wichita, KS 67226
     Contact: Reuben Kerbs VP of Natl Accts
     Tel: 800-598-6274
     Email: r.kerbs@ncricat.com
     Website: www.ncricat.com
Emergency restoration svcs: fire, water, smoke, wind, mold, emergency dry out, structure repair, document & record restoration, mold remediation, dry ice blasting, airduct cleaning, drying equipment rental. (Woman, estab 1971, empl 90, sales $12,500,000, cert: WBENC)

Louisiana

2238   Lafayette Steel Erector
     313 Westgate Rd
     Lafayette, LA 70506
     Contact: John Prudhomme Presdient
     Tel: 337-234-9435
     Email: janice@l-s-e.com
     Website: www.LSEcrane.com
Crane, steel erection, precast erectors, equipment installation. (Nat Ame, estab 1957, empl 115, sales , cert: NMSDC)

2239   Tillage Construction LLC
     1824 N Acadian Thruway W
     Baton Rouge, LA 70802
     Contact: Etonya Senigaur
     Tel: 225-356-1700
     Email: esenigaur@tillageconstruction.com
     Website: www.tillageconstruction.com
Commercial building construction, commercial renovations, project manaagement, cabinets & millwork. (AA, estab 2001, empl 8, sales $ 0, cert: State)

2240   Triple L Management Corp.
     1181 Hawn Ave
     Shreveport, LA 71107
     Contact: O. J. Romero Dirmktg
     Tel: 318-424-8037
     Email: ojr@lllconstruction.com
     Website: www.lllconstruction.com
Construction services: concrete, dirt, pipe laying, building construction & renovation, industrial plant renovations & shoutdown project, etc. (AA, estab 1979, empl 72, sales $7,200,000, cert: State)

Massachusetts

2241 Essex Newbury North Contracting Corporation
65 Parker St, Unit 5
Newburyport, MA 01950
Contact: Delano Brooks Presdient
Tel: 978-463-5414
Email: delano_br@yahoo.com
Website: www.essexnewburynorth.com
General Contracting, construction management, commercial & industrial construction, lead abatement & asbestos remediation, finish carpentry, commercial & institutional bldg construction, painting & wall coverings, site preparation. (AA, estab 1997, empl 400, sales $31,000,000, cert: State, City, NMSDC)

2242 J&J Contractors, Inc.
101 Billerica Ave Bldg 5 Ste 2
North Billerica, MA 01862
Contact: Kamlesh Patel CEO
Tel: 978-452-9898
Email: kamp@jjcontractor.com
Website: www.jjcontractor.com
Construction management, general contracting & design/ build. (As-Ind, estab 1997, empl 50, sales $ 0, cert: State)

Maryland

2243 Buch Construction Inc.
11292 Buch Way
Laurel, MD 20723
Contact: Denise Buch Controller
Tel: 301-369-3500
Email: dbuch@buch.us.com
Website: www.buchconstruction.com
General contracting, interior construction, carpentry, drywall, electric, painting, new construction, doors & hardware, structural steel. (Woman, estab 1984, empl 65, sales $6,210,000, cert: WBENC)

2244 Capital Brand Group, LLC
12501 Prosperity Dr, Ste 400
Silver Spring, MD 20904
Contact: Max Brand Presdient
Tel: 301-358-1377
Email: mbrand@capitalbrandgroup.com
Website: www.capitalbrandgroup.com
Construction, Construction Management, A/E Services, Facility Management, Janitorial, Energy and Sustainability, landscaping, HVAC and Construction Services. (Hisp, estab 2013, empl 30, sales $3,512,178, cert: State, 8a)

2245 Estime Enterprises, Inc.
4640 Forbes Blvd Ste 100
Lanham, MD 20706
Contact: Lunique Estime Presdient
Tel: 301-731-8316
Email: lestime@estimeinc.com
Website: www.estimeinc.com
Construction management, renovation, environmental consulting services, green sustainable solutions (wind power generation, solar harvesting, triban antimicrobial systems, and photovoltaic roofing solutions). (AA, estab 1996, empl 35, sales $4,296,512, cert: State, NMSDC)

Michigan

2246 Blaze Contracting, Inc.
5640 St. Jean
Detroit, MI 48213
Contact: Gayl Turk Dir Business Dev
Tel: 313-361-1000
Email: gturk@blazecontracting.net
Website: www.blazecontracting.com
Site Preparation Contractor; Excavation, Grading, Storm Sewer, Sanitary Sewer, Watermain, Water Detention Systems; (AA, estab 2000, empl 120, sales $19,000,000, cert: NMSDC)

2247 Commercial Construction Inc.
7428 Kensington Rd
Brighton, MI 48116
Contact: ROBERT L. GARCIA Presdient
Tel: 248-685-3263
Email: pgarcia@cci-rigging.com
Website: www.cci-rigging.com
Millwright & migging contractor, install machinery, conveyors, robots, automation for automotive industry, industrial process. (Hisp, estab 1991, empl 40, sales $3,100,000, cert: NMSDC)

2248 Construction Logistic LLC
1360 Oakman Blvd
Detroit, MI 48238
Contact: Eric Means
Tel: 313-494-5527
Email: emeans@meansgroup.com
Website:
Construction management, General Contracting, Design/ Build, Program Management, Owner Representation, Development & Property Management. (AA, estab 2009, empl 3, sales $3,476,219, cert: NMSDC)

2249 Hale Contracting, Inc.
18407 Weaver St
Detroit, MI 48228
Contact: Lawrence Hale Presdient
Tel: 313-272-9400
Email: lawrence.hale@halecontracting.com
Website: www.Halecontracting.com
General contracting. (AA, estab 0, empl , sales $ 0, cert: NMSDC)

2250 Hamilton Contracting
30375 Northwestern Hwy Ste 102
Farmington Hills, MI 48334
Contact: Melissa Grundy Business Develop Exec
Tel: 734-895-3547
Email: mgrundy@hamilton-contracting.com
Website: www.hamilton-contracting.com
General contracting: demolition, machinery installation & relocation, conveyor installation, structural installation, platform installation, automation installation, preventative maintenance & machine precision alignments. (Woman, estab 2011, empl 45, sales $5,400,000, cert: WBENC)

2251 Harris Design & Construction Services
        2512 W Grand Blvd, Ste 100
        Detroit, MI 48208
        Contact: Karl Harris CEO
        Tel: 313-444-3307
        Email: kharris@harrisdesignconstruction.com
        Website: www.harrisdesignconstruction.com
Architectural design and construction services. (AA, estab 2014, empl 1, sales $100,000, cert: NMSDC)

2252 Ideal Contracting, LLC
        2525 Clark St
        Detroit, MI 48209
        Contact: Kevin Foucher VP
        Tel: 313-843-8000
        Email: kfoucher@idealcontracting.com
        Website: http://idealcontracting.com
General contracting, construction management & design/build services. (Hisp, estab 1998, empl 325, sales $191,613,602, cert: NMSDC)

2253 Jenkins Construction, Inc.
        985 E Jefferson, Ste 300
        Detroit, MI 48207
        Contact: Darwyn Parks Project Exec
        Tel: 313-625-7200
        Email: dparks@jenkinsconstruction.com
        Website: www.jenkinsconstruction.com
Design/build, construction management, general contractor & excavation. (AA, estab 1989, empl 50, sales $65,000,000, cert: NMSDC)

2254 McKissack & McKissack Midwest, Inc.
        1300 Broadway St 5th Fl
        Detroit, MI 48225
        Contact: Deryl McKissack President & CEO
        Tel: 313-962-6900
        Email: solicitationsmw@mckinc.com
        Website: www.mckinc.com
Architectural, engineering, and construction services. (Woman/AA, estab 2002, empl 35, sales $7,741,000, cert: NMSDC, WBENC)

2255 Optimum Contracting Solutions
        2211 Devonshire Rd
        Bloomfield Hills, MI 48302
        Contact: Anamaria Tet Owner
        Tel: 248-346-3069
        Email: anamaria.optimum@att.net
        Website: www.optimum1.net
General Contracting, Project Management, Residential Building & Remodeling Services , Commercial Remodeling Services, Roofing, Siding, Additions, Drywall, Rough and Finish Carpentry ,Painting, Electrical, HVAC, Doors & window installation. (Woman, estab 2010, empl 10, sales $400,000, cert: WBENC)

2256 PAT USA, Inc.
        2927 Waterview Dr
        Rochester Hills, MI 48309
        Contact: Fenar Mayes Sr Project Mgr
        Tel: 248-299-2410
        Email: fenar@pat-engineering.com
        Website: http://pat-engineering.com
General contracting services, engineering & construction services. (Woman, estab 2011, empl 10, sales , cert: WBENC)

2257 Payne Landscaping, Inc.
        5385 Rohns
        Detroit, MI 48213
        Contact: James Parker Sr VP of operations
        Tel: 313-995-2767
        Email: communicate2000@earthlink.net
        Website:
Landscape construction, grounds maintenance, janitorial, facilities management, tree services, lawn care, snow removal. (AA, estab 1989, empl 25, sales $500,000, cert: NMSDC)

2258 R.B. Construction Company
        6489 Metro Pkwy
        Sterling Heights, MI 48312
        Contact: Russell Beaver Presdient
        Tel: 586-264-9478
        Email: rbeaver@rb-construction.com
        Website: www.rb-construction.com
Construction, renovation, building, pre-engineered building, remodel. (Nat Ame, estab 1984, empl 7, sales $3,318,000, cert: NMSDC, 8a)

2259 Rickman Enterprise Group, LLC
        15533 Woodrow Wilson
        Detroit, MI 48238
        Contact: Lawrence Bost CEO
        Tel: 313-454-4000
        Email: lawrence@rickmanenterprise.com
        Website: www.RickmanEnterprise.com
Industrial Painting/Environmental, Flooring, Demo. (AA, estab 2007, empl 131, sales $10,000,000, cert: NMSDC)

2260 Sieler Construction
        11119 E US 223
        Blissfield, MI 49228
        Contact: Jeff Sieler VP
        Tel: 517-486-3050
        Email: lue@sielerconstruction.com
        Website: www.sielerconstruction.com
General Contracting, excavation, concrete, steel trades, steel fabrication, holding tanks, shut-down / machinery relocation, water & fire main repairs, water lines. (Woman, estab 2000, empl 12, sales , cert: WBENC)

2261 Stenco Construction Company, LLC
        12741 Farmington Rd
        Livonia, MI 48150
        Contact: Rick Kolozsi Presdient
        Tel: 734-427-8843
        Email: rkolozsi@stencoconstruction.com
        Website: www.stencoconstruction.com
General contruction: interior finish, earthwork, concrete, steel & rigging projects. (As-Pac, estab 1998, empl 20, sales $33,650,000, cert: NMSDC)

2262 The FOG Group, Inc.
        217 Fisher Building 3011 W Grand Blvd.
        Detroit, MI 48202
        Contact: Sherwood Merrill Chairman
        Tel: 313-309-2020
        Email: smerrill@powerlinkonline.com
        Website: http://powerlinkonline.com
Facilities management, maintenance services, & construction. (AA, estab 2002, empl 350, sales $15,900,000, cert: NMSDC)

2263 The Ideal Group
2525 Clark St
Detroit, MI 48209
Contact: Linzie Venegas Sales
Tel: 313-842-7290
Email: linzie@idealshield.com
Website: www.weareideal.com
Architectural & engineering svcs; general contracting &
construction mgmt, rigging. Mfr, dist, fabricate & erect
structural & misc steel. Patent for "Ideal Shield" Protective
Guard Rail System. (Hisp, estab 1979, empl 120, sales $ 0,
cert: NMSDC)

2264 Tooles Contracting Group LLC
500 Griswold St, Ste 1620
Detroit, MI 48226
Contact: Laura Ottman Mgr business dev
Tel: 313-221-8500
Email: laura.ottman@toolesgroup.com
Website: www.toolesgroup.com
Commercial & industrial construction, general contracting,
construction & pogram management, equipment installa-
tion, self perform services & design build. (AA, estab 2002,
empl 38, sales $119,996,211, cert: NMSDC)

2265 W-3 Construction Company
7601 Second Ave
Detroit, MI 48202
Contact: Walter E. Watson, Jr. CEO
Tel: 313-875-8000
Email: w3@w3group.net
Website: www.w3group.net
General contracting, project managers, self perform
concrete, drywall & accoustical. (AA, estab 1987, empl 49,
sales $19,901,023, cert: NMSDC)

2266 Zebing Solutions LLC
15617 Marksman Rd
Lanse, MI 49946
Contact: Arlan Friisvall Presdient
Tel: 877-585-8171
Email: info@zebingsolutions.com
Website: www.zebingsolutions.com
Construction, electrical, mechanical & engineering ser-
vices. (Nat Ame, estab 2011, empl 20, sales $500,000, cert:
NMSDC)

Minnesota

2267 Loeffler Construction and Consulting, LLC
20520 Keokuk Ave, Ste 100
Lakeville, MN 55044
Contact: Doug Loeffler Presdient
Tel: 952-955-9119
Email: dloeffler@loefflerconstruction.com
Website: www.loefflerconstruction.com
Construction and consulting services, new construction &
remodeling projects. (Woman/Nat Ame, estab 2010, empl
6, sales $21,922,187, cert: NMSDC)

2268 Moltron Builders Inc.
2900 North 2nd St
Minneapolis, MN 55411
Contact: Patrick Buckner President
Tel: 612-354-2730
Email: patrick.buckner@moltronbuilders.com
Website: www.moltronbuilders.com
General Construction, Construction Management & Design
Build. (AA, estab 2007, empl 5, sales , cert: State, City)

2269 Shaw-Lundquist Associates, Inc.
2757 W Service Rd
St. Paul, MN 55121
Contact: Hoyt Hsiao CEO
Tel: 651-454-0670
Email: hhsiao@shawlundquist.com
Website: www.shawlundquist.com
General construction & mgmt: commercial, industrial &
institutional, multi-unit residential, tenant improve-
ments, contract service work, etc. (As-Pac, estab 1974,
empl 98, sales $185,879,100, cert: NMSDC)

2270 Tarraf Construction, Inc.
7454 Washington Ave S
Eden Prairie, MN 55344
Contact: Salah Tarraf President & CEO
Tel: 612-623-4800
Email:
Website: www.tarrafconstruction.com
General construction, site development earthwork, site
utilities, demolition, carpentry, environment, specialty
maintenance, disposal system, supplies. (Hisp, estab ,
empl , sales $ 0, cert: State, City, NMSDC)

2271 Total Construction and Equipment, Inc.
10195 Inver Grove Trail
Inver Grove Heights, MN 55076
Contact: William Krech VP
Tel: 651-451-1384
Email: info@total-const.com
Website: www.total-const.com
General and electrical contracting, large facility mainte-
nance. (Woman, estab 1972, empl 350, sales
$53,000,000, cert: WBENC)

2272 Welsh Construction, LLC
4350 Baker Rd Ste 400
Minnetonka, MN 55343
Contact: Linda Solberg Corporate Services
Director
Tel: 952-897-7854
Email: lsolberg@welshco.com
Website: www.welshconstruct.com
General contracting, commercial new construction,
office & industrial, expansions & renovations of existing
office & industrial space. (Woman, estab 1977, empl 43,
sales $73,308,502, cert: WBENC)

Missouri

2273 Amodu Engineering Solutions, LLC
1201 Garden Village Dr
Florissant, MO 63031
Contact: Anthony Osuma President
Tel: 314-249-8623
Email: aosuma@amodu-engineering.com
Website: www.amodu-engineering.com
Mechanical design & consulting services, electrical
plumbing & fire protection systems, construction admin
services. (AA, estab 2007, empl 5, sales $100,000, cert:
State, City, NMSDC)

2274 Legacy Building Group
3242 S. Kingshighway
Saint Louis, MO 63139
Contact: Todd Weaver President
Tel: 314-361-3535
Email: weavert@legacybg.com
Website: www.legacybg.com
Doors & frames installation & concrete footings &
foundations. (AA, estab 2003, empl 20, sales
$7,123,000, cert: State, City, NMSDC)

2275 Tarlton Corporation
        5500 W Park Ave
        St. Louis, MO 63110
        Contact: Ted Guhr Dir Business Devel
        Tel: 314-633-3354
        Email: taguhr@tarltoncorp.com
        Website: www.tarltoncorp.com
General contracting & construction management.
(Woman, estab 1945, empl 350, sales $207,000,000, cert:
State, WBENC)

2276 Tehama, LLC
        1600 Genessee Ste 318
        Kansas City, MO 64102
        Contact: David Brewer GM
        Tel: 816-678-7510
        Email: david.brewer@tehamallc.com
        Website: www.tehamallc.com
Engineering/Architectural design, Environmental Consulting Services & Construction Support Services. (Nat Ame,
estab 2009, empl 2, sales , cert: 8a)

North Carolina

2277 Crescent Construction Services, LLC
        303 S Main GQ St
        Salisbury, NC 28146
        Contact: Presdient
        Tel: 704-633-9697
        Email:
        Website: www.crescentconstructionservices.com
Commissioning & engineering surveys, project management. (Woman, estab 2004, empl 15, sales $1,310,000,
cert: WBENC)

2278 Golden Sands General Contractors
        10924 Granite St, Ste 700
        Charlotte, NC 28273
        Contact: Jody Pinkston Project Coord
        Tel: 704-727-6000
        Email: jody.pinkston@goldensandsgc.com
        Website: www.goldensandsgc.com
Design/Build, New Construction, Tenant Improvements,
Major & Minor Renovations, Dedicated Facilities Maintenance Department, Dedicated Disaster Recovery Department. (Woman, estab 1988, empl 167, sales $62,000,000,
cert: WBENC)

2279 Holt Brothers Construction LLC
        421 Fayetteville St Stes 1300
        Raleigh, NC 27601
        Contact: Terrence Holt Presdient
        Tel: 919-787-1981
        Email: terrence@holtbrothersinc.com
        Website: www.holtbrothersconstruction.com
Construction management, design-build & general
contracting services. (AA, estab 2007, empl 22, sales
$32,500,000, cert: State)

2280 Marand Builders, Inc.
        4534 Old Pineville Rd Ste A
        Charlotte, NC 28217
        Contact: Francisco Alvarado CEO
        Tel: 704-525-1824
        Email: falvarado@marandbuilders.com
        Website: www.marandbuilders.com
Commercial & industrial general contracting: demolition,
new construction & renovations. (Hisp, estab 1999, empl
15, sales $75,822,000, cert: NMSDC)

2281 Metcon Inc.
        763 Comtech Dr
        Pembroke, NC 28372
        Contact: Aaron Thomas CEO
        Tel: 910-521-8013
        Email: athomas@metconus.com
        Website: www.metconus.com
General contracting, panelized metal studs & truss. (Nat
Ame, estab 1999, empl 75, sales $24,180,330, cert:
NMSDC)

2282 Miles McClellan Construction Co., Inc.
        2201-E Crownpoint Executive Dr
        Charlotte, NC 28227
        Contact: Melia Mauldin Sales & Marketing Coord
        Tel: 704-900-1170
        Email: melia.mauldin@mmbuildings.com
        Website: www.mmbuildings.com
Design & build, construction mgmt, general contracting,
masonry. (AA, estab 1978, empl 75, sales $50,889,458,
cert: State, NMSDC)

2283 Modern Construction Services, LLC
        5900 Harris Technology Ste D
        Charlotte, NC 28031
        Contact: Tracy Snowdy Presdient
        Tel: 704-765-9937
        Email: tsnowdy@modernconstructionsvc.com
        Website: http://modernconstructionsvc.com
General Contractor & Facility Repairs, Interior demolition & up-fits, exterior refreshes, parking lot repairs/
resurfacing, doors, windows, drywall, painting, rough &
finish carpentry, ADA upgrades. (Woman, estab , empl
20, sales $5,300,000, cert: State, City, WBENC)

2284 R.J. Leeper Construction, LLC
        601 MORRIS ST
        Charlotte, NC 28202
        Contact: Ken Holt CFO
        Tel: 704-334-3223
        Email: ken@leeperconstruction.com
        Website: www.leeperconstruction.com
Construction management & general contracting. (AA,
estab 1993, empl 18, sales $8,025,788, cert: State)

2285 Red Rooster Contractors, LLC
        5101 Summer Gate Dr
        Charlotte, NC 28226
        Contact: Milagritos Aguilar CEO
        Tel: 704-634-4622
        Email: mily.aguilar19@gmail.com
        Website:
Commercial & residential: roofing, windows, doors,
painting, gutters, flooring, carpentry interior & exterior
renovations. (Woman/Hisp, estab 2009, empl 1, sales
$250,000, cert: City)

2286 Sutton Industrial Maintenance & Piping, Inc.
        P.O. Box146
        Castalia, NC 27816
        Contact: Kim Sutton Presdient
        Tel: 919-853-6901
        Email: suttonkim@embarqmail.com
        Website:
General contract services, sheet metal fabrication, boiler
room, welding, pipefitting, general labor, mechanical
work. (Woman, estab 2001, empl 12, sales $1,047,068,
cert: WBENC)

New Jersey

2287   BTII Institute
414 Eagle Rock Ave Ste 100 D
West Orange, NJ 07052
Contact: Sharon Bussey Managing Partner
Tel: 973-325-9001
Email: Sharon.Bussey.SD@BTIIInstitute.com
Website: www.btiiinstitute.com/w/
BTII Institute is a consulting and training company specializing in Project Management, Professional Development and Microsoft. BTII's Portfolio/Program/Project Management services better enable organizations to achieve strategic objectives and a sustaina (Woman/AA, estab 2009, empl 5, sales $504,000, cert: NMSDC)

2288   Ferreira Construction Co Inc.
31 Tannery Rd
Branchburg, NJ 08876
Contact: Megan Carton Dir of Mktg
Tel: 908-534-8655
Email: mcarton@ferreiraconstruction.com
Website: www.ferreiraconstruction.com
Utility Construction: Gas, Transmission and Distribution, Foundations, Water, Sewer, Fiber Optic. Heavy Civil Construction: Bridges, Highways, Airports, Excavation, Sitework
Marine Construction: Dredging, Seawalls, Docks/Piers (Hisp, estab 1988, empl 1000, sales $410,000,000, cert: State, City, NMSDC, CPUC)

2289   HC Constructors, Inc.
P.O. Box 855
Whitehouse Station, NJ 08889
Contact: Lisa Chowansky Presdient
Tel: 908-534-3833
Email: lchowansky@hcconstructors.com
Website: www.hcconstructors.com
General contracting: Underground Excavation for Electrical & Telecommunication, Masonry, Bridgework, Sound Walls, Concrete - Wall, foundations & floors. (Woman, estab 1989, empl 15, sales $15,000,000, cert: WBENC)

2290   Hydro-Marine Construction Company, Inc.
1345 Route 38 West Tynddol Bldg
Hainesport, NJ 08036
Contact: President
Tel: 609-261-6353
Email:
Website: www.wjcastlegroup.com
Marine structures construction services: repair, replacement & maintenance of bulkhead & pier construction & rehabilitation, cable inspection & location, bridge undermining repairs, pile repair, underwater concreting, steel sheeting cofferdams. (Woman, estab 1997, empl 13, sales $2,000,000, cert: WBENC)

2291   Maysonet LLC
4 Orchard Terrace
Clark, NJ 07066
Contact: Mark Maysonet Managing Member
Tel: 732-396-0873
Email: info@maysonetllc.com
Website: www.maysonetllc.com
Commercial & residential construction: carpentry, drywall, framing, general contracting. (Hisp, estab 2005, empl 18, sales $751,588, cert: State)

2292   NC & Sons The Nicholson Corporation
201 Chambersbrook Rd
Branchburg, NJ 08876
Contact: Brandon Nicholson Presdient
Tel: 908-575-0055
Email: accounting@nicholsoncorp.com
Website: www.nicholsoncorp.com
General contracting &construction management. (Woman/Hisp, estab 1997, empl 225, sales $70,336,810, cert: State, NMSDC, WBENC)

2293   Wu & Associates, Inc.
100 Gaither Dr, Ste C
Mount Laurel, NJ 08054
Contact: Kirby Wu Presdient
Tel: 856-857-1639
Email: info@wuassociates.com
Website: www.wuassociates.com
General contracting: govt, commercial, institutional & industrial, renovations, new construction, environ cleanups. (As-Pac, estab 1990, empl 25, sales $14,474,000, cert: State, NMSDC)

New Mexico

2294   Zohnnie Construction Industries, Inc.
P.O. Box 745
Farmington, NM 87499
Contact: Harrietta Zohnnie President
Tel:
Email: zohninc@aol.com
Website: www.zohnnieconstruction.com
Construction administration & project management, residential construction, commercial & industrial Construction. (Woman/Nat Ame, estab 2004, empl 5, sales $600,000, cert: 8a)

Nevada

2295   Advanced Pro Remediation, a LLC
5961 McLeod Dr
Las Vegas, NV 89120
Contact: Racquel Toyozaki Owner
Tel: 702-252-0880
Email: info@calladvancedpro.com
Website: www.advancedprorestoration.com/
Construction/rebuild, water extraction, flood recovery, structural drying, remediation, mold removal & abatement, drywall, texture, mud, paint, cabinetry & finished carpentry. (Woman/As-Pac, estab 2003, empl 25, sales , cert: State)

2296   KMG Solutions, Inc.
7800 Via Costada St
Las Vegas, NV 89123
Contact: CFO
Tel: 503-754-7592
Email:
Website: www.KMGSolutionsInc.com
General Contracting & Construction Management, Carpentry, Painting & Flooring. (Woman, estab 2002, empl 5, sales $ 0, cert: WBENC)

New York

2297 ACC Construction Corporation
519 Eighth Ave 7th Floor
New York, NY 10018
Contact: Michele Medaglia President & CEO
Tel:
Email: mmedaglia@acc-construction.com
Website: www.acc-construction.com
General contracting & construction mgmt, phased, interior renovations. (Woman, estab 1984, empl 55, sales $28,748,041, cert: State, City, WBENC)

2298 Al-Pros Construction Inc.
109-20 121 St
South Ozone Park, NY 11420
Contact: Imran Ali Office Mgr
Tel: 718-848-3666
Email: iali@alprosconstruction.com
Website: www.alprosconstruction.com
General contracting & maintenance services. (As-Pac, estab 1995, empl 30, sales $500,000, cert: City)

2299 BLM Construction Company, Inc.
P.O. Box 316
Kendall, NY 14476
Contact: Presdient
Tel: 585-659-2784
Email:
Website: www.blmconstruction.com
General contracting: commercial & multi-family projects. (Woman, estab 2001, empl 14, sales $ 0, cert: WBENC)

2300 C.W. Brown Inc.
1 Labriola Court
Armonk, NY 10504
Contact: Erin Griffin Business Develop Mgr
Tel: 914-219-8323
Email: info@cwbrown.com
Website: www.cwbrown.com
General contracting/construction management. (Woman, estab 1984, empl 72, sales $48,000,000, cert: City, WBENC)

2301 Con Rac Construction Group LLC
1895 Walt Whitman Rd Ste 2
Melville, NY 11747
Contact: John Coleman EVP
Tel: 631-756-0101
Email: jcoleman@conracgroup.com
Website: www.conracgroup.com
General contracting & construction management. (Woman, estab 2010, empl 4, sales $13,009,136, cert: State, City)

2302 Construction and Service Solutions Corp.
216 Main Rd
Akron, NY 14001
Contact: Suzanne Witnauer President
Tel: 716-570-1352
Email: suzanne@csscbuilds.com
Website: www.csscbuilds.com
General contractor: drywall, doors & hardware, acoustic ceilings, siding, windows, cabinetry, countertops, framing, trim & finish carpentry installations. (Woman, estab 2002, empl 15, sales $340,860, cert: State, City, WBENC)

2303 Genesus One Enterprise, Inc.
43-24 54th Rd Ste 203
Maspeth, NY 11378
Contact: David Turner CEO
Tel: 718-361-7516
Email: office@genesusconstruction.com
Website: www.genesusconstruction.com
General contracting, construction management, interiors construction, site work, pavement, concrete, masonry, metal work & other trades. (AA, estab 1999, empl 16, sales $3,500,000, cert: State)

2304 Henegan Construction Co., Inc.
250 W 30th St
New York, NY 10001
Contact: MAUREEN HENEGAN CEO
Tel: 212-947-6441
Email: mahenegan@henegan.com
Website: www.henegan.com
Construction management & general contracting: interior building alterations, renovations & infrastructure upgrades. (Woman, estab 1959, empl 150, sales $238,724,000, cert: City, WBENC)

2305 Hybrid Building Solutions LLC
850 Main St
Corfu, NY 14036
Contact: Mari-Louise Merkwa Managing Partner
Tel: 716-741-7416
Email: ml@hybridbuildingsolutions.com
Website: https://hybridbuildingsolutions.com
General contractor specializing in steel & fabric building construction, salt storage buildings, cold storage, pre-engineered steel & fabric buildings. (Woman, estab 2010, empl 12, sales $4,201,259, cert: State, City)

2306 K-Pak Consulting, Inc.
29 Elves Ln
Levittown, NY 11756
Contact: Khurram Bajwa Presdient
Tel: 718-813-7755
Email: bajwa@kpakconsulting.com
Website: www.kpakconsulting.com
General contracting: remodeling, renovations, carpentry, drywall, cement, flooring, masonry, demolition, painting, doors & windows. (As-Ind, estab 2012, empl 4, sales $169,960, cert: State)

2307 Mamais Contracting Corp.
256 West 124th St
New York, NY 10027
Contact: Presdient
Tel: 212-865-1666
Email:
Website: www.mamais.com
General contracting, high-end alterations & renovations, rapid repair services. (Woman, estab 1968, empl 142, sales $17,367,537, cert: City, WBENC)

2308 Theodore Williams Construction Company, LLC
641 Lexington Ave
New York, NY 10022
Contact: Shelby Johnson Presdient
Tel: 212-593-9700
Email: sjohnson@twcc-llc.com
Website: www.twcc-llc.com
General contracting & construction management: interior buildouts, alterations, restorations & base building construction. (Woman, estab 1972, empl 24, sales $21,727,000, cert: WBENC)

Ohio

2309 Bambeck & Vest Associates, Inc.
49 E Fourth St, Ste 1020 Dixie Terminal Bldg
Cincinnati, OH 45202
Contact: Ed Roark Presdient
Tel: 513-621-5654
Email: ed@bambeckandvest.com
Website: www.bambeckandvest.com
General contracting, office renovations, new buildings, general repair work. (Woman, estab 1964, empl 35, sales $10,000,000, cert: WBENC)

2310 Better Built Construction Services, Inc.
P.O. Box 467
Middletown, OH 45042
Contact: Karen S. Tipton Presdient
Tel: 513-727-8637
Email: ksh@betterbuiltcs.com
Website: www.betterbuiltcs.com
Pre-engineered steel building, steel erection. (Woman/Nat Ame, estab 1995, empl 5, sales $1,245,340, cert: State)

2311 C&B Construction Company Ltd.
3713 Lee Rd
Cleveland, OH 44120
Contact: Barbara Coker President
Tel: 216-905-2617
Email: candbcont@sbcglobal.net
Website: www.candbconstoh.com
General construction, rehab, new construction, residential & commercial properties. (Woman/AA, estab 2007, empl 4, sales $990,000, cert: State)

2312 Construction Support Solutions, LLC
P.O. Box 48
Avon Lake, OH 44012
Contact: Anna Klee President
Tel: 440-541-6642
Email:
anna.klee@constructionsupportsolutions.com
Website: www.constructionsupportsolutions.com
Construction management: scheduling, estimating, constructability review, contract administration, project controls, on site inspections & close out services. (Woman, estab 2008, empl 3, sales $250,000, cert: State, WBENC)

2313 Cook Paving & Construction Co., Inc.
4545 Spring Road
Brooklyn Heights, OH 44131
Contact: Linda Fletcher President & CEO
Tel: 216-267-7705
Email: linda.fletcher@cookpaving.com
Website:
Construction management, underground utilities installation & maintenance telecommunication & electrical ductbank systems, directional boring, site development, commercial & heavy hwy hotmix asphalt & concrete paving, excavation & trenching. (AA, estab 1950, empl 100, sales $ 0, cert: State, City, NMSDC)

2314 D.A.G. Construction Company, Inc.
4924 Winton Rd
Cincinnati, OH 45232
Contact: Lindsay Wilhelm Mktg Dir
Tel: 513-542-8597
Email: lwilhelm@dag-cons.com
Website: www.dag-cons.com
General construction, construction management, design/build & renovations. (AA, As-Pac, estab 1990, empl 35, sales $21,000,000, cert: NMSDC)

2315 Dawn Incorporated
106 E Market St Ste 505
Warren, OH 44481
Contact: Dawn Ochman Presdient
Tel: 330-652-7711
Email: dawn@dawnincorporated.com
Website: www.dawnincorporated.com
General contracting, pre-construction planning, quality control & customer service. (Woman, estab 1993, empl 15, sales $1,014,000, cert: State)

2316 Dynamix Engineering Ltd.
855 Grandview Ave, 3rd Fl
Columbus, OH 43215
Contact: Eugene Griffin Presdient
Tel: 614-443-1178
Email: ggriffin@dynamix-ltd.com
Website: www.dynamix-ltd.com
Electrical, mechanical, plumbing, technology systems design; assessments & standard operating & maintenance procedures. (AA, estab 1997, empl 40, sales $11,700,000, cert: State, NMSDC)

2317 G. Stephens, Inc
133 N Summit St
Akron, OH 44304
Contact: Glen Stephens Presdient
Tel: 330-762-1386
Email: compliance@gstephensinc.com
Website: www.gstephensinc.com
Project & construction management, engineering services, real estate procurement, general contracting, managing consulting, contract compliance, specializing government, public, private sectors. (AA, estab 1992, empl 62, sales $ 0, cert: State, City)

2318 Hammond Corporation
1285 E 49th St
Cleveland, OH 44114
Contact: Janice Hopkins VP
Tel: 216-431-7861
Email: hammondco@aol.com
Website:
General construction, mechanical, HVAC, process piping, etc. (Woman/AA, estab 1985, empl 3, sales $6,397,841, cert: State, City)

2319 JWT&A LLC
3615 Superior Ave, Bldg 31-1J
Cleveland, OH 44114
Contact: John Todd President
Tel: 216-426-1580
Email: jwtassoc@sbcglobal.net
Website: www.jwta-construction.com
Construction management, general contractor, acoustical ceilings, drywall, drywall insulation, framing, gypsum board, metal studs & taping. (AA, estab 2005, empl 7, sales $969,473, cert: City)

2320   Kerricook Construction, Inc.
20355 Vermont St
Litchfield, OH 44253
Contact: Ann Smith Owner
Tel: 440-647-4200
Email: ann@kerricook.com
Website: www.kerricook.com
Ground-up construction, design build construction, tenant build-out construction, open store remodels, facilities maintenance. (Woman, estab 2003, empl 20, sales $5,393,450, cert: WBENC)

2321   MBJ Consultants, Inc.
30 W 3rd St, Ste 4M
Cincinnati, OH 45202
Contact: Monroe Barnes Presdient
Tel: 513-631-9600
Email: mbarnes@mbjconsultants.com
Website: www.mbjconsultnats.com
General contracting & construction management. (AA, estab 1992, empl 30, sales $1,300,000, cert: NMSDC)

2322   Mel Lanzer Co.
2266 N Scott St
Napoleon, OH 43545
Contact: Lyndsey Lucas Presdient
Tel: 419-592-2801
Email: llucas@mellanzer.com
Website: www.mellanzer.com
General contracting: renovations, additions, or new construction. (Woman, estab 1950, empl 30, sales $17,000,000, cert: WBENC)

2323   Ozanne Construction Co., Inc.
1625 E 25th St
Cleveland, OH 44114
Contact: Dominic L. Ozanne CEO
Tel: 216-696-2876
Email: dozanne1@ozanne.com
Website: www.ozanne.com
Multi-Diciplenary Construction Management; Construction Management Agency, Construction Management at Risk, Design-Build, Design-Bid-Build/General Contracting, Owner's Representative, Program Management, Task Order Contracting. (AA, estab 1956, empl 37, sales $50,000,000, cert: State, City, NMSDC)

2324   PPW Builders Inc.
11875 Bellaire Rd
Cleveland, OH 44135
Contact: Sandy Speck President
Tel: 216-862-1677
Email: sandy@ppwbuilders.com
Website: www.ppwbuilders.com
General contracting, high performance coatings, architectural finishes & carpentry, project management services, engineering, & design/build capable. (Woman, estab 2000, empl 5, sales $750,000, cert: 8a)

2325   Precision Engineering & Contracting, Inc.
31340 Solon Rd, Stes 25 & 26
Solon, OH 44139
Contact: Sekhar Narendrula Presdient
Tel: 440-349-1204
Email: kmoomaw@precisioneng.us
Website: www.precisioneng.us
Site work, demolition & construction. (As-Ind, estab 2001, empl 37, sales , cert: State)

2326   ProjDel Corporation
One North Commerce Park Dr, Level G
Cincinnati, OH 45215
Contact: Eric Browne Principal
Tel: 513-931-0900
Email: brownee@projdel.com
Website: www.projdel.com
Construction management, project management & construction technologies. (AA, estab 1995, empl 13, sales $1,500,000, cert: NMSDC)

2327   R L Hill Management, Inc.
31875 Aurora Road
Solon, OH 44139
Contact: Ralphael Hill Presdient
Tel: 440-439-0490
Email: pam@rlhillmgmt.com
Website: www.rlhillmgmt.com
General contracting, construction management, architectural millwork, drywall, etc. (AA, estab 1998, empl 12, sales $1,744,631, cert: State, City)

2328   R.J. Runge Company, Inc.
3539 NE Catawba Rd
Port Clinton, OH 43452
Contact: Amy Runge President
Tel: 419-740-5781
Email: arunge@rjrunge.com
Website: www.rjrunge.com
Construction Management, CM at Risk, General Contracting, Scheduling, Cost Management, Pre Construction Services, Electrical Contractor, Carpentry, Concrete, Site Work, Rough Carpentry, Interior Finishes. (Woman, estab 2004, empl 30, sales $5,571,511, cert: State, City)

2329   Regency Construction Services Inc.
14600 Detroit Ave, Ste 1495
Lakewood, OH 44107
Contact: Tari Rivera Presdient
Tel: 216-529-1188
Email: riverat@regencycsi.com
Website: www.regencycsi.com
General contracting & construction. (Woman, estab 1994, empl 70, sales $10,302,000, cert: City, WBENC)

2330   The Coniglio Co.
4400 Commerce Ave.
Cleveland, OH 44103
Contact: Gwenay Reaze-Coniglio President
Tel: 216-391-1800
Email: coniglioco@aol.com
Website: www.theconigliocompany.com
General contracting services, general trades, carpentry, custom cabinetry, pre-fabricated office structures. (Woman/AA, estab 1994, empl 20, sales $1,091,271, cert: City, NMSDC)

2331   The Mark Madison Company Inc.
7861 Hamilton Ave
Cincinnati, OH 45231
Contact: Mark Madison President
Tel: 513-522-7676
Email: mmadisoncompany@aol.com
Website:
Commercial contractin: demo & construction, metal framing, drywall, acoustical ceiling, insulation, sound attenuation, painting, doors, locks & hardware. (AA, estab 1990, empl 20, sales $ 0, cert: NMSDC)

2332 Welling Inc.
7781 Cooper Rd
Cincinnati, OH 45242
Contact: Amy Smith Acct Mgr
Tel: 513-793-6900
Email: amy@wellinginc.com
Website: www.wellinginc.com
Commercial Construction; install trash & linen chutes, security screens, interior window shading systems. (Woman, estab 1987, empl 6, sales $900,000, cert: WBENC)

2333 Wise Construction Management, Inc.
1705 Guenther Rd
Dayton, OH 45427
Contact: David Abney President
Tel: 937-854-0281
Email: dfa@wiseconstructionco.com
Website: www.wiseconstructionco.com
Construction management, design/build. (AA, estab 2001, empl 7, sales $804,000, cert: NMSDC)

Oklahoma

2334 DBG Construction, LLC
P.O. Box 674
Oklahoma City, OK 73101
Contact: Deemah Ramadan Managing Partner
Tel: 405-601-2700
Email: info@dbgconstruction.com
Website: www.dbgconstruction.com
Commercial Construction, Pre-Construction, Design/Build, General Contracting & Construction Management. (Woman, estab 2007, empl 15, sales $7,000,000, cert: WBENC)

2335 The Ross Group Construction Corporation
510 E 2nd St
Tulsa, OK 74120
Contact: Tammy Pameticky Mgr, Contracts Admin
Tel: 918-234-7675
Email: tammy.pameticky@withrossgroup.com
Website: www.withrossgroup.com
General contracting, construction management & facilities maintenance services. (Nat Ame, estab 1979, empl 125, sales $88,398,046, cert: NMSDC)

Oregon

2336 Art Cortez Construction, Inc.
15783 NW Dairy Creek Rd
North Plains, OR 97133
Contact: Art Cortez President
Tel: 503-841-5732
Email: art@artcortezconstruction.com
Website: http://artcortezconstruction.com
Commercial construction, general contracting, steel frame construction & interior systems, MEP services. (Hisp, estab 2007, empl 25, sales $3,185,945, cert: State)

2337 Cooper Zietz Engineers, Inc.
421 SW Sixth Ave, Ste 1210
Portland, OR 97204
Contact: Fred Cooper President
Tel: 503-253-5429
Email: fredc@coopercm.com
Website: www.coopercm.com
Construction management services. (Nat Ame, estab 1990, empl 35, sales $4,600,000, cert: State)

Pennsylvania

2338 AHJ Construction, LLC
1208 Main St
Darby, PA 19023
Contact: Henry Robinson President
Tel: 215-900-3508
Email: hrobinson@ahjconstructionco.com
Website: www.ahjconstructionco.com
Commercial & industrial construction projects. (AA, estab 2010, empl 8, sales $360,235, cert: State)

2339 CD & Associates, Inc.
725 Skippack Pike, Ste 140
Blue Bell, PA 19422
Contact: Lisa Casiello Presdient
Tel: 215-793-9069
Email: LCasiello@CDandAssociatesInc.com
Website: www.CDandAssociatesInc.com
Design & construction. (Woman, estab 1989, empl 24, sales $67,671,317, cert: WBENC)

2340 Chatham Properties, LLC
101 Lindenwood Dr Ste 225
Malvern, PA 19335
Contact: Jeff Berlin Mgr
Tel: 484-875-3073
Email: jeff.berlin@chathamprops.com
Website: http://chathamprops.com
Construction & property management, commercial & residential construction service, excavation, site preparation, refurbishments, repairs, refits or complete new build outs. (Nat Ame, estab 1999, empl 6, sales $706,880, cert: 8a)

2341 Crawford Consulting Services, Inc.
239 Highland Ave
East Pittsburgh, PA 15112
Contact:
Tel: 412-823-0400
Email:
Website: www.crawfordconsultingservices.com
Construction consulting services: cost estimating, value engineering, inspections, project (CPM) scheduling, project mgmt, construction mgmt, owner's representation & general construction. (Woman, estab 1993, empl 23, sales $1,050,000, cert: State, WBENC)

2342 DK Cleaning Contractors, LLC
6418 Woodland Ave Ste 1FF
Philadelphia, PA 19142
Contact: Chidozie Dike Presdient
Tel: 610-883-3133
Email: cdike@dkconstructionservicesllc.com
Website: www.dkconstructionservicesllc.com
Project & Construction Management, Repair & Renovation, Drywall & Insulation, Painting & Wall Covering, Framing, Masonry, & Siding Contractors, Plumbing, HVAC, Electrical, Mechanical, Carpentry, Demolition, Site work. (AA, estab 2010, empl 5, sales $300,000, cert: City, 8a)

2343 ecoservices, LLC
407 W Lincoln Hwy, Ste 500
Exton, PA 19341
Contact: President
Tel: 484-872-8884
Email:
Website: www.eco-pa.com
Construction management / project management,
industrial site rehabilitation, demolition, asbestos abate-
ment, roof removal, lead & mold abatement &
remediation. (Woman, estab 2009, empl 30, sales
$5,293,485, cert: State, City)

2344 Northeast Construction Contractors, Inc.
4827 Wingate St
Philadelphia, PA 19136
Contact: April Slobodrian President
Tel: 215-624-3667
Email: info@northeastconstructioninc.com
Website: www.northeastconstructioninc.com
General construction management, construction related
property maintenance, snow removal & general carpentry
work, walls, wall coverings, FRP, ACT, ceilings, doors,
windows, hardware, accessories, drywall, painting,
electrical, interior. (Woman, estab 2004, empl 12, sales
$1,520,000, cert: State)

2345 Perryman Building and Construction Services, Inc.
4548 Market St
Philadelphia, PA 19139
Contact: Angelo Perryman Presdient
Tel: 215-243-4109
Email: admin@perrymanbc.com
Website: www.perrymanbc.com
Genenral construction: commercial interiors, building &
project management services. (AA, estab 1998, empl 26,
sales $ 0, cert: NMSDC, 8a)

2346 Robert Ganter Contractors, Inc.
595 E Pumping Station Rd
Quakertown, PA 18951
Contact: Donna Ganter Presdient
Tel: 215-538-3540
Email: dganter@gantercontractors.com
Website: www.gantercontractors.com
Architectural roofing & sheet metal servicing, commercial,
industrial builders & architects. (Woman, estab 2000, empl
25, sales $37,735,416, cert: WBENC)

2347 Tracy Becker Construction, Inc.
7280 Dragonfly Lane
Macungie, PA 18062
Contact: Tracy Becker Presdient
Tel: 610-421-8590
Email: tb@tbcinstalls.com
Website: www.tbcinstalls.com
General contracting & construction. (Woman, estab 1997,
empl 15, sales $3,748,957, cert: WBENC)

2348 U.S Construction Group Inc.
6100 Henry Ave Ste 2N
Philadelphia, PA 19128
Contact: Yaw Danso Presdient
Tel: 215-756-1364
Email: ydanso@usconstructgroup.com
Website: www.usconstructgroup.com
General Construction, Sitework, Utilities, Demolition,
waste disposal, Hazardous waste disposal, Paving. (AA,
estab 2008, empl 5, sales $517,000, cert: State, City,
NMSDC)

2349 U.S. Facilities, Inc. PRWT Services Company
30 N 41st St Ste 400
Philadelphia, PA 19104
Contact: David Groomes Sr VP
Tel: 215-564-1448
Email: david.groomes@usfacilities.com
Website: www.usfacilities.com
Facilities support svcs, building operations & mainte-
nance, subcontract mgmt svcs, project mgmt. (AA, estab
2000, empl 462, sales $111,179, cert: City, NMSDC)

Puerto Rico

2350 BNS Engineering Inc.
Rafael Cordero, Ste 140 HC 02 Box 14212
Gurabo, PR 00778
Contact: Bienvenido Negron
Tel: 787-745-4848
Email: b.negron@bns-eng.com
Website: www.bns-eng.com
Construction design/build, project management,
equipment, maintenance, turnarounds, program/project
management, procurement & safety. (Hisp, estab 2001,
empl 25, sales $1,599,871, cert: NMSDC)

2351 CIC Construction Group, SE
P.O. Box 29726
San Juan, PR 00929
Contact: Gustavo Hermida Presdient
Tel: 787-287-3540
Email: ghermida@cic-pr.com
Website: www.cicconstuction.com
General Contracting, pre-construction, design & build,
and self-perform trade work that includes: Concrete ,
Architectural, demolition, metal framing, drywall,
flooring installation, and painting. (Hisp, estab 1983,
empl 850, sales $104,732,021, cert: NMSDC)

2352 CPM PR, LLC
44 Road 20 Ste 201
Guaynabo, PR 00966
Contact: Francisco (Paco) Martínez Business Dev
Mgr
Tel: 787-999-4000
Email: fmartinez@cpmintl.com
Website: www.cpmintl.com
Program, project & construction management &
consulting services. (Hisp, estab 1991, empl 125, sales
$9,849,191, cert: NMSDC)

2353 CSCG Inc.
P.O. Box 991
Aguada, PR 00602
Contact: Victor Jose Garcia Ruiz VP
Tel:
Email: vgarciaruiz@cscginc.com
Website: www.cscginc.com
Pre construction: Conceptual Estimating, Budget
Development, Project Phasing, General Contractor, Cost
Monitoring & Control, Subcontractor Management,
Safety Assurance, Quality Control, Civil and Structural
Works. (Hisp, estab 2000, empl 60, sales $13,107,533,
cert: NMSDC)

2354 Damiani Contractors, Inc.
HC 05 Box 23646
Lajas, PR 00667
Contact: Jabes Damiani Ramos Presdient
Tel: 787-899-5763
Email: damianicontractors@gmail.com
Website:
General construction in industrial installations & facilities for the pharmaceutical areas: interiors, electrical systems, plumbing, HVAC, sprinklers systems, steel structures & site utilities. (Hisp, estab 2009, empl 10, sales , cert: NMSDC)

2355 Ideal Engineering Solutions, PSC
RR 3 Box 7266
Cidra, PR 00739
Contact: Ismael Robles Presdient
Tel: 787-378-2948
Email: irobles.ies@gmail.com
Website: http://idealengineeringsolutions.com
General Construction, Electrical and Mechanical Installations, Instrumentation and Control Systems, Gypsum Board works. (Hisp, estab 2007, empl 5, sales $300,000, cert: NMSDC, 8a)

2356 JCD Engineering, Inc.
P.O. Box 192372
San Juan, PR 919
Contact: Juan C. del Pino President
Tel: 787-787-7211
Email: jcdelpino@jcdengineering.com
Website: www.jcdengineering.com
Civil, electrical & mechanical engineering: concrete & steel small buildings, interiors work, hung ceilings, floors, gypsum board, electrical power & controls, fiber optics, local area networks (LAN), process and AHU control systems. (Hisp, estab 1996, empl 11, sales $1,327,000, cert: NMSDC)

South Carolina

2357 ALS Services, Inc.
2395 Peach Orchard Rd
Sumter, SC 29154
Contact: Alfonza McCutchen President
Tel: 803-499-5045
Email: amccutchen@alsservices.net
Website: www.alsservices.net
Contracting svcs, new construction, renovation, landscaping, rehabilitation, repairs & additions, lead & asbestos, structures, roads, drainage systems, mechanical, electrical, communications & utility system requirements. (AA, estab 1998, empl 10, sales , cert: 8a)

2358 Built Right Construction, LLC
1524 Ashley River Rd
Charleston, SC 29407
Contact: Chris Pelletier Owner
Tel: 843-882-7632
Email: chris@brcsc.com
Website: www.brcsc.com
Construction management, equipment rental, development, HVAC & plumbing & facility operations & maintenance. (Nat Ame, estab 2007, empl 10, sales $1,000,000, cert: State, City)

2359 CCCS International, LLC
2414 Clements Ferry Rd
Charleston, SC 29492
Contact: Calvin Whitfield CEO
Tel: 843-856-4874
Email: cwhitfield@cccsinternational.com
Website: www.cccsinternational.com
On-site construction management, project operations, site security, site clearing, site utilities, deep foundations, waterproofing & sealants, pre-treatment for mold & termites, concrete slab on grade, miscellaneous concrete, masonry. (Woman/AA, estab , empl , sales $2,500,000, cert: State, City, NMSDC, SDB)

2360 Greenwood, Inc.
160 Milestone Way
Greenville, SC 29615
Contact: Sherry Harris Dir Sales/Marketing
Tel: 540-298-2628
Email: sharris@gwood.com
Website: www.GreenWoodInc.com
Construction, maintenance & workforce solutions. (Woman, estab 1990, empl 680, sales $60,000,000, cert: WBENC)

2361 Lipscomb Plant Services, Inc.
160 Milestone Way Ste B
Greenville, SC 29376
Contact: Eric Burnette Business Development
Tel: 864-244-9669
Email: eburnette@gwood.com
Website: www.Lipscombinc.com
Industrial maintenance, construction, construction management & workforce solutions. (Woman, estab 2009, empl 4, sales $2,635,406, cert: WBENC)

Tennessee

2362 MC Builders, LLC
2115 Chapman Rd Ste 131
Chattanooga, TN 37421
Contact: Linda Stooksbury Dir of Sales
Tel: 423-355-8118
Email: linda@mc-buildersllc.com
Website: www.mcbuildersllc.construction
Retail, Restaurant, Multi-Family Housing, Property Management, Hospitals, Universities, Commercial and Industrial Building maintenance. (Woman, estab 2012, empl 36, sales $4,000,000, cert: WBENC)

2363 SRS, Inc.
131 Saundersville Rd, Ste 210
Hendersonville, TN 37075
Contact: CEO
Tel: 615-230-2966
Email:
Website: www.srsincorp.com
Construction Management and Disaster Recovery Services (AA, estab 2001, empl 55, sales $16,974,636, cert: NMSDC)

Texas

2364 3i Construction, LLC
400 N Saint Paul St Ste 700
Dallas, TX 75201
Contact: Micheal Williams VP Business Dev
Tel: 214-231-0675
Email: mwilliams@3iconstruction.com
Website: www.3iconstruction.com
General commercial construction. (AA, estab 2001, empl 27, sales $22,146,587, cert: State, NMSDC)

2365 American Renewable Energy
3890 North Frwy, Unit F
Houston, TX 77022
Contact: JC Avila Mgr
Tel: 713-690-1116
Email: jca@arebuildingco.com
Website: http://arebuildingco.com
General contracting & design construction. (Woman/Hisp, estab 2010, empl 20, sales $5,000,000, cert: WBENC, 8a)

2366 Argent Associates, Inc.
2800 E Plano Pkwy Ste 400
Plano, TX 75074
Contact: Betty Manetta VP Supply Chain
Tel: 732-512-9009
Email: bmanetta@argentassociates.com
Website: www.argentassociates.com
Inventory mgmt, warehousing, dist, logistics, packaging, installation & commercial construction. (Woman/Hisp, estab 1998, empl 65, sales $181,676,013, cert: NMSDC, WBENC)

2367 Beach Construction, Inc.
1271 Record Crossing
Dallas, TX 75235
Contact: Denice VanBuren
Tel: 214-920-9100
Email: denice@beachconstructiontx.com
Website: www.beachconstructiontx.com
Commerical general contracting. (Woman/Hisp, estab 2002, empl 10, sales $2,740,000, cert: State)

2368 Davitz Group
6220 Pine Ridge Blvd
McKinney, TX 75070
Contact: Earl Davis President
Tel: 972-746-6045
Email: tarad@davitzgroup.com
Website: www.davitzgroup.com
Construction, design / build, LEED project design & construction, building information modeling (BIM), large projects & small task orders, procurement services. (AA, estab 2006, empl 3, sales $2,000,000, cert: State, 8a)

2369 Diversity Resources Group
101 E Park Blvd Ste 600
Plano, TX 75074
Contact: Wayne Lawrence Presdient
Tel: 214-352-2284
Email: wlawrence@diversityroofing.com
Website: www.diversityroofing.com/
Construction management, commercial roofing services. (AA, Hisp, estab 2015, empl 80, sales , cert: State, NMSDC)

2370 DMG Commercial Construction Services, Inc.
3939 Beltline Rd Ste 540
Addison, TX 75001
Contact: Stephanie Hilburn President
Tel: 972-630-6900
Email: stephanie@dmginc.net
Website: www.dmginc.net
General contracting: renovations, finish out, additions & new build construction. (Woman, estab 2006, empl 17, sales $3,600,000, cert: State, WBENC)

2371 Falkenberg Construction Company, Inc.
2435 109th St
Grand Prairie, TX 75050
Contact: Trish Gomez Business Develop Mgr
Tel: 214-324-4779
Email: pag@falkenbertconstruction.com
Website: http://falkenbergconstruction.com
Commercial general contracting. (Hisp, estab , empl , sales $6,000,000, cert: State)

2372 High Plains Contactors & Management Group, Inc.
414 S. Dumas Ave.
Dumas, TX 79029
Contact: Michael Ramirez Presdient
Tel: 806-935-5858
Email:
michael.ramirez@highplainsmanagement.com
Website: www.highplainsmanagement.com
General construction, project management, plumbing, dry ice blasting & powder coating services. (Hisp, estab 2009, empl 12, sales $8,500,000, cert: State, 8a)

2373 HJD Capital Electric, Inc.
5424 W Hwy 90
San Antonio, TX 78227
Contact: Heather Washburn Proposal Admin
Tel: 210-681-0954
Email: marketing@hjdcapital.com
Website: www.hjdcapital.com
Design Build, General construction, electrical, Plumbing, Sitework, SWPPP, Erosion control, Underground electrical, Overhead electrical, Datacomm, Telecommunications, Pole lighting bases, Electrical meters, Gas meters, Outside plant copper fiber. (Hisp, estab 1994, empl 150, sales $17,354,379, cert: State, City)

2374 Icon Construction, Inc.
9893 W University Dr Ste 119
McKinney, TX 75071
Contact: Joe Green Dir of Mktg
Tel: 214-504-9098
Email: jgreen@icon-construction.com
Website: www.icon-construction.com
General contracting, design/build permanent & relocatable modular buildings. (Nat Ame, estab 1998, empl 52, sales $3,540,844, cert: State)

2375 Largin Construction Services LLC
1959 Saratoga Blvd, Bldg. 10
Corpus Christi, TX 78417
Contact: Billy Largin VP
Tel: 361-723-1573
Email: billy@larginconstruction.com
Website: http://larginconstruction.com
General contracting: construction, new buildings, remodel & maintenance, new custom housing, remodel & repair, site work, concrete, masonry, metals, carpentry, environmental, doors & windows, finishes, specialties, equipment. (Woman, estab 2006, empl 25, sales $3,500,000, cert: State)

2376   Marvin Groves Electric Company, Inc.
        P.O. Box 2305
        Wichita Falls, TX 76307
        Contact: Marvin Groves President
        Tel: 940-767-2711
        Email: m.groves@marvingroveselectric.com
        Website: www.marvingroveselectric.com
Install electrical wiring for new and exist bldg. (Nat Ame,
estab 1972, empl 13, sales $ 0, cert: State)

2377   Midwest Steel Company, Inc.
        9825 Moers Rd
        Houston, TX 77075
        Contact: Christopher Given VP
        Tel: 713-991-7843
        Email: chrisgiven@midwest-steel.com
        Website: www.midwest-steel.com
Dismantling & demolition contracting. (Woman, estab
1968, empl 89, sales $10,755,892, cert: State, WBENC)

2378   North American Commercial Construction, LP
        11577 Goodnight Lane
        Dallas, TX 75229
        Contact: Lynn Dunlap Managing Partner
        Tel: 972-620-9975
        Email: lynn@naccolp.com
        Website: http://naccolp.com
General Contractor. (Woman, estab 2004, empl 10, sales
$12,000,000, cert: WBENC)

2379   Office Design Concepts, LLC
        6750 Brittmoore Rd
        Houston, TX 77041
        Contact: Joseph Sylvan President
        Tel: 713-849-3611
        Email: admin@odc-llc.com
        Website: www.odc-llc.com
Office furniture, carpet & flooring, moving services,
furniture installation, and painting (AA, estab 1999, empl
5, sales , cert: State, NMSDC)

2380   Pecos Construction
        8111 LBJ Freeway Ste 625
        Dallas, TX 75251
        Contact: Mitzi Green Business Develop Mgr
        Tel: 214-299-4900
        Email: mdgreen@pecosconstruction.com
        Website: www.pecosconstruction.com
Pre-construction, construction management, general
contracting, design-build, small projects, large projects &
self-perform services. (AA, estab 2003, empl 20, sales
$16,616,224, cert: State)

2381   Prim Construction LLC
        252 Roberts Cut Off Rd
        Fort Worth, TX 76114
        Contact: Trent Prim COO
        Tel: 817-885-7851
        Email: tprim@primconstruction.com
        Website: www.primconstruction.com
Commercial general contracting, end user/tenant improve-
ment/retail, mission critical, corporate campuses, health
care & institutional service providers. (Woman, estab
2007, empl 10, sales $10,000,000, cert: State, WBENC)

2382   Samaripa Oilfield Services, LLC
        2855 N Mechanic St
        El Campo, TX 77437
        Contact: Amy Samaripa Presdient
        Tel: 979-257-9385
        Email: amy@samaripaofs.com
        Website: www.samaripaofs.com
Pressure washing services, oil & chemical spill clean up,
disaster cleanup & disposal, construction site clean up &
reclamation, general construction, general labor hands
& transport of equipment and supplies. (Woman/Nat
Ame, Hisp, estab 2011, empl 15, sales $850,000, cert:
NMSDC, WBENC)

2383   Sun Builders Co.
        15012 FM 529 Rd
        Houston, TX 77095
        Contact: Mary Miller Sec/Treas
        Tel: 281-815-1020
        Email: mmiller@sunbuildersco.com
        Website: www.sunbuildersco.com
General Contractor. (Woman, estab 1979, empl 25, sales
$16,919,787, cert: WBENC)

2384   Synergy Project Consultants, Inc.
        1801 Wyoming, Ste 204
        El Paso, TX 79902
        Contact: Mark Young COO
        Tel: 915-613-1442
        Email: mcyoung@spc-pm.com
        Website: www.spc-pm.com
General contracting, construction renovation & repairs,
design-build construction, architectural, engineering
design management, construction project management,
commissioning. (Hisp, estab 2007, empl 29, sales
$2,100,000, cert: State)

2385   Tejas Premier Building Contractor, Inc.
        9200 Broadway, Ste 120
        San Antonio, TX 78217
        Contact: Julissa Carielo Presdient
        Tel: 210-821-5858
        Email: julissa@tejaspremierbc.com
        Website: www.tejaspremierbc.com
Commercial general contracting. (Woman/Hisp, estab
2006, empl 15, sales $2,280,000, cert: WBENC)

2386   The Trevino Group, Inc.
        11410 Brittmoore Park
        Houston, TX 77041
        Contact: Erin Trevino Sec/Treas
        Tel: 713-863-8333
        Email: etrevino@trevinogroup.com
        Website: www.trevinogroup.com
General contracting, construction management, design/
build. (Hisp, estab 1976, empl 65, sales $32,000,000,
cert: State, NMSDC)

2387   UCS Group LLC
        5910 N. Central Expy Ste 900
        Dallas, TX 75206
        Contact: Henry Rodriguez Dir of Marketing
        Business Development
        Tel: 214-349-1600
        Email: henryr@universaltx.com
        Website: www.universaltx.com
General contracting, tenant improvements, renovations,
design & build, construction management, ground up,
office space remodeling, restaurant build out. (Hisp,
estab , empl , sales $5,000,000, cert: State, NMSDC)

Virginia

2388 Alkat Electrical Contractors, Inc.
P.O. Box 6903
Richmond, VA 23230
Contact: Katherine Mickens
Tel: 804-354-0944
Email: katherinemickens@alkatelectric.com
Website:
Integrated building systems, conduit, raceways, fittings.
(AA, estab 1983, empl 45, sales $4,780,000, cert: State,
NMSDC)

2389 BFE Construction, Inc.
7620 Whitepine Rd
Richmond, VA 23237
Contact: Travis Bowers Presdient
Tel: 804-714-2540
Email: tbowers@bfe-llc.com
Website: www.bfe-llc.com
General contracting: bonded, commercial. (AA, estab
1998, empl 19, sales $ 0, cert: State, NMSDC)

2390 Diamonds Management Group, Inc.
10117 Residency Rd
Manassas, VA 20110
Contact: Glenn Bertrand President
Tel: 703-257-0017
Email: dmgincservices@outlook.com
Website: http://diamondsmanagement.com/
General contracting. (AA, estab 1994, empl 4, sales
$300,000, cert: State)

2391 J. L. Bennett Construction Inc.
P.O. Box 340
Hopewell, VA 23860
Contact: Joseph Bennett Presdient
Tel: 804-452-4209
Email: jlbennettconst@aol.com
Website:
Commercial & industrial construction svcs: masonry,
concrete, interior & exterior carpentry, floor covering,
drywall, painting & renovations. (AA, estab 1994, empl 6,
sales $250,000, cert: State)

2392 J. R. Caskey, Inc.
P.O. Box 305
Oilville, VA 23129
Contact: Ginger Caskey Presdient
Tel: 804-784-8001
Email: gec@jrcaskey.com
Website: www.jrcaskey.com
Engineering, Layout & Surveying, Clearing & Demolition,
Earthwork, Grading & Excavation, Erosion & Sediment
Control, Traditional Stormwater Management Systems,
Low-Impact Development Systems, Underground Water &
Sanitary Sewer Utilities. (Woman, estab 1985, empl 42,
sales $6,630,000, cert: State)

2393 Prestige Construction Group, Inc.
219 Turner Rd
Richmond, VA 23225
Contact: John Scott Presdient
Tel: 804-745-0000
Email: johns@prestigeconstruction.com
Website: www.prestigeconstruction.com
General contracting, construction management. (AA, estab
1991, empl 25, sales $10,919,532, cert: State)

2394 ProTech Restoration, LLC
3730 Glenmore Rd
Scottsville, VA 24590
Contact: Frank Trimble Presdient
Tel: 434-960-4456
Email: protechrestorationva@gmail.com
Website: www.protechva.com
Disaster restoration & construction services. (Minority,
Woman, estab 2015, empl 1, sales , cert: State)

2395 RMT Construction & Development Group, Inc.
571 Southlake Blvd
Richmond, VA 23236
Contact: Warren Thomas VP of Construction
Tel: 804-464-2673
Email: wthomas@rmt-construction.com
Website: www.rmt-construction.com
Commercial & industrial construction. (Woman/AA,
estab 2007, empl 10, sales $2,000,000, cert: State)

2396 Robra Construction, Inc.
522 Freeman Mill road
Suffolk, VA 234
Contact: Aubrey Wilson President
Tel: 757-438-9532
Email: wilson@robraconstruction.com
Website:
General construction. (AA, estab 1997, empl 9, sales
$4,100,000, cert: State)

2397 T. K. Davis Construction, Inc.
711 Dawn St
Richmond, VA 23222
Contact: Thomas Davis
Tel: 804-321-7822
Email: smosby@tkdavis.com
Website: www.tkdavis.com
General contracting: commercial, light industrial, retail,
medical, office, storage facilities, athletic facilities, multi-
family, design build, construction mgmt. (AA, estab 2001,
empl 9, sales $21,819,325, cert: State, NMSDC)

2398 United Unlimited Construction, Inc.
213 East Clay St, Ste A
Richmond, VA 23219
Contact: Merlin Hargrove Presdient
Tel: 804-343-7266
Email: mharuuc@cavtel.net
Website: www.uucirichmond.com
General contracting: painting, concrete, demolition,
renovations & retrofit, masonry, carpentry, miscella-
neous & structural steel. (AA, estab 1983, empl 32, sales
$1,946,879, cert: State)

2399 Wunna Contracting Corporation
43695 John Mosby Hwy
Chantilly, VA 20152
Contact: Darnell Ingram business devel dir
Tel: 703-957-4266
Email: dingram@wunnacontracting.com
Website: www.wunnacontracting.com
Concrete installation, rehabilitation & repair, building
entrances; foundations, driveways; walkways; stairs;
colums, walls, patios; landscape; retaining walls. (As-Ind,
estab 2007, empl 30, sales $3,000,000, cert: State)

Washington

2400 A&D Quality Construction Company, LLC
220 SW Sunset Blvd Ste E202
Renton, WA 98057
Contact: Annette Demps Owner
Tel: 425-271-7751
Email: annette@adqualityco.com
Website: http://In-Work
General contractoring: commercial & residential construction, demolition, excavation, site clearing, grading, dirt removal, utilities, footing, foundation & concrete. (Woman/AA, estab 1991, empl 2, sales $270,000, cert: State)

2401 Jimale Technical Services, LLC
1825 S Jackson St, Ste 102
Seattle, WA 98144
Contact:
Tel: 206-861-8000
Email:
Website: www.jtsmanageservices.com
Project controls & development: construction mgmt, project cost control, CPM scheduling, document control planning, reporting, construction inspection, construction admin. (Woman/AA, estab 1993, empl 5, sales $ 0, cert: State, WBENC)

2402 JTS Manage Services
526 Yale Ave North, Ste A
Seattle, WA 98109
Contact: Douglas Hamilton Marketing Coord
Tel: 206-861-8000
Email: douglas@jtsmanageservices.com
Website: www.jts-seattle.com/
Construction management & project controls. (Woman/AA, estab 1993, empl 10, sales $650,000, cert: State)

2403 MACNAK Construction LLC
2624 112th St S, Ste A1
Lakewood, WA 98499
Contact: Santiago Mateo Project Mgr
Tel: 253-212-2378
Email: smateo@macnak.com
Website: www.macnak.com
General Construction Design-Build & Design-Bid-Build projects, site work, concrete, rough carpentry, finish carpentry, plumbing, mechanical, electrical, painting & roofing, fire alarm system & access control systems. (Nat Ame, As-Pac, estab 2007, empl 35, sales $84,000,000, cert: State)

2404 RHD Enterprises, Inc.
817 78th Ave SW
Tumwater, WA 98501
Contact: Rozanne Garman President
Tel: 360-705-9459
Email: rozanne@rhdenterprises.com
Website: www.rhdenterprises.com
General contracting: marine/subsea construction, remodels, design/build services, new construcion, pre-engineered metal buildings, modular facilities, laboratory modernizations. (Woman/As-Pac, estab 2005, empl 25, sales $13,199,569, cert: NMSDC, WBENC, 8a)

Wisconsin

2405 Arteaga Construction, Inc.
4000 S Pine Ave
Milwaukee, WI 53207
Contact: Anthony Arteaga President
Tel: 414-744-7944
Email: anthony@arteagaconstruction.com
Website:
General contracting: masonry, carpentry, concrete, demolition & HVAC. (Hisp, estab 1986, empl 75, sales $25,000,000, cert: State, NMSDC)

2406 Sirrah Construction & Co, LLC
3430 N 53rd St
Milwaukee, WI 53216
Contact: James Harris Managing Member
Tel: 414-442-7477
Email: james@sirrahconstruction.net
Website:
General contracting: flatwork concrete & asphalt paving, demolition services. (AA, estab 2005, empl 6, sales $1,250,000, cert: State, City)

COSMETICS

Formulate, manufacture & distribute face and eye products, hair care products, perfumes, hand and body lotions, wig cleaners and sprays, and cosmetics for men. NAICS Code 32

California

2407   Garcoa, Inc.
26135 Mureau Rd Ste 100
Calabasas, CA 91302
Contact: Deborah Reidy
Tel: 818-225-0375
Email: debbie@garcoa.com
Website: http://Garcoa.com
Mfr branded, private label, control label & branded external liquid fill health & beauty products. (Woman, estab 1983, empl 48, sales $126,000,000, cert: WBENC)

2408   Plantlife Natural Body Care
961 Calle Negocio
San Clemente, CA 92673
Contact: Nancy Baldini Sales Mgr
Tel: 888-708-7873
Email: nbaldini@plantlife.net
Website: www.plantlife.net
Mfr All Natural Organic Aromatherapy products: Soaps, Lotions, Essential Oils, Body/Massage Oils, Bath Salts, Natural Homeopathic Pain Relief, Natural Pest repellent. (Woman, estab 1994, empl 20, sales $3,000,000, cert: WBENC)

Colorado

2409   Crossing Cultures LLC
1821 Lefthand Cir, Ste D
Longmont, CO 80501
Contact: Dennis O'Toole Natl Sales Mgr
Tel: 303-651-3678
Email: dennis@goddessgarden.com
Website: www.goddessgarden.com
Organic skincare products. (Woman, estab 2009, empl 12, sales $1,429,113, cert: WBENC)

2410   The Black Travel Box LLC
2100 Welton St, Unit 1111
Denver, CO 80205
Contact: Orion Brown CEO
Tel: 720-664-3586
Email: orion@theblacktravelbox.com
Website: www.blacktravelbox.com
We make travel ready hair and skin care products (AA, estab 2017, empl 1, sales , cert: State)

District of Columbia

2411   Shea Yeleen Health and Beauty, LLC
417 H St NE Ste 2
Washington, DC 20002
Contact: Rahama Wright CEO
Tel: 202-285-3435
Email: rwright@sheayeleen.com
Website: www.sheayeleen.com
Premium natural & organic shea butter bodycare products. (Woman/AA, estab 2012, empl 1, sales , cert: NMSDC)

Florida

2412   High End Beauty Inc.
1120 Holland Dr, Ste 2
Boca Raton, FL 33487
Contact: CEO
Tel: 561-665-1968
Email:
Website: www.highendbeauty.com
Dist hair, skin, cosmetics & nail products. (Woman, estab 2011, empl 6, sales , cert: WBENC)

2413   NAIWBE Natural As I Wanna Be
421 W Church St #601
Jacksonville, FL 32202
Contact: Presdient
Tel: 904-634-7607
Email:
Website: www.naiwbellc.net
Organic Skin Care Products. (Woman/AA, estab 2011, empl 3, sales $100,000, cert: State, City)

Indiana

2414   Elwood Staffing Services, Inc.
4111 Central Ave
Columbus, IN 47202
Contact: Kimberly Randall Dir Business Devel
Tel: 812-372-6200
Email: hope.lane@elwoodstaffing.com
Website: www.elwoodstaffing.com
Organic skincare products. (AA, estab 1980, empl 260, sales $95,010,000, cert: NMSDC)

Michigan

2415   Universal Products
854 Edgemont Park
Grosse Pointe Park, MI 48230
Contact: Jose Reyes CEO
Tel: 313-804-0042
Email: jose.reyes@universalproductsmarketing.com
Website: www.universalproductsmarketing.com
Health & beauty care, hair growth treatments and vitamin supplements. (Hisp, estab 1988, empl 6, sales $4,000,000, cert: NMSDC)

New Jersey

2416   Custom Essence
53 Veronica Ave
Somerset, NJ 08873
Contact: Colin O'Such Presdient
Tel: 732-249-6405
Email: cosuch@customessence.com
Website: www.CustomEssence.com
Manufacture Fragrance & Cosmetic Products. (As-Ind, estab 1985, empl 43, sales , cert: NMSDC)

2417   Health and Natural Beauty Corp LLC (SprinJene is a
       trade name)
       140 Ethel Rd, Ste W
       Piscataway, NJ 08854
       Contact: Alexandra DePierro Sales/Mktg Mgr
       Tel: 732-640-1832
       Email: a.depierro@sprinjene.com
       Website: http://sprinjene.com
Mfr oral care products. SprinJene is our line of superior
toothpastes combining the power of black seed oil, zinc,
and xylitol. (AA, estab 2012, empl 11, sales $250,000, cert:
State)

2418   US Organic Group Corp.
       90 Dayton Ave. STte132 Bldg 18, Unit 1P
       Passaic, NJ 07055
       Contact: Leonard Moon Presdient
       Tel: 201-252-4269
       Email: mij3461@us-organic.com
       Website: www.us-organic.com
Mfr USDA certified organic topical & personal care
products. (As-Pac, estab 2011, empl 7, sales $590,303,
cert: NMSDC)

2419   Xenna Corporation
       33 Witherspoon St Ste 200
       Princeton, NJ 8542
       Contact: Carol Buck CEO
       Tel: 609-921-1101
       Email: cbuck@xenna.com
       Website: www.xenna.com
Dist personal care products for foot care & hair care.
(Woman, estab 1996, empl 5, sales $3,355,705, cert:
WBENC)

Ohio

2420   Shema Global, LLC
       825 N Houk Rd
       Delaware, OH 43015
       Contact: mark butler Managing Dir
       Tel: 740-953-0292
       Email: contact@shemaglobal.com
       Website: www.shemaglobal.com
Mfr & dist all natural hair & body care products. (Woman/
AA, estab 2009, empl 2, sales , cert: State)

Tennessee

2421   Keystone Laboratories, Inc.
       1103 Kansas St
       Memphis, TN 38106
       Contact: Melinda Menke Owner
       Tel: 901-774-8860
       Email: mmburns@earthlink.net
       Website: www.keystone-labs.com
Personal care products, ethnic hair care, skin care, toiletries. (Woman, estab 1934, empl 21, sales $3,793,002, cert:
WBENC)

Texas

2422   826 & Co. LLC
       4301 Greatview Dr
       Round Rock, TX 78665
       Contact: Jaime Masters CEO
       Tel: 913-284-5536
       Email: jaime@826andco.com
       Website: www.826andCo.com
A full service botanical-based aromatherapy, skin and
hair care company. (AA, estab 2010, empl 1, sales , cert:
State)

2423   Clavél
       4150 E Overland Trail
       Abilene, TX 79601
       Contact: Dason Williams EVP Sales & Marketing
       Tel: 325-676-9655
       Email: dason@clavel.com
       Website: www.clavel.com
Private label, over the counter skin creams, pain creams,
and scar creams. (Woman, estab 1988, empl 11, sales
$2,854,152, cert: WBENC)

2424   NTE Legacy, LLC
       2919 Commerce St, Ste 480
       Dallas, TX 75226
       Contact: Nathan Townsie CEO
       Tel: 469-708-7546
       Email: ntownsie@naturelovesyouskincare.com
       Website: www.naturelovesyouskincare.com
Hand & Surface Sanitizer (Vegan), Citrus, Lavender, Rose,
Japanese Blossom, Lemongrass, Cucumber Melon, 4-in-1
Shave Oil (Organic), Moisturizing Rejuvenation Serum
(Organic). (AA, estab 2016, empl 1, sales , cert: NMSDC)

2425   Synergy Bodycare LLC.
       5653 Winding Woods Trail
       Dallas, TX 75227
       Contact: Rosie Hill CEO
       Tel: 214-460-1500
       Email: rosielh@synergibody.com
       Website: www.synergibody.com
Performance Skin & Hair Care for women & men of all
skin types, tones & hair. (Woman/AA, estab 2009, empl
1, sales , cert: State, NMSDC)

Virginia

2426   Tree Naturals Inc.
       4204 Riding Place Rd
       Richmond, VA 23223
       Contact: LaTresha Sayles CEO
       Tel: 804-514-4423
       Email: customerservice@treenaturals.com
       Website: www.treenaturals.com
Natural hair and body line created to add moisturize to
dry hair & skin. (Woman/AA, estab 2011, empl 1, sales ,
cert: State)

DETECTIVE & SECURITY AGENCIES
Provide civil, criminal and private investigations; security consulting services and security guard services. NAICS Code 54

Alaska

2427 NMS Security Services, LLC
800 E Domind Blvd, Ste 3-450
Anchorage, AK 99515
Contact: Mari Gallion Proposal Mgr
Tel: 907-273-2400
Email: registration@nmsusa.com
Website: http://nmsusa.com
Security and investigative services. (Nat Ame, estab 2007, empl 72, sales $4,910,108, cert: NMSDC)

Alabama

2428 Discreet Claim Assessment Investigations (DCA&I)
P.O. Box 94672
Birmingham, AL 35220
Contact: Rafael Portis Owner
Tel: 205-305-1782
Email: admin@dcainvestigations.com
Website: www.dcainvestigations.com
Video & photo surveillance, activity checks, background records investigations, recorded statements, elderly/disability interviews, hospital/pharmacy canvass & depo/trail testimony.
Workers Compensation Claims Investigations/Surveillance (AA, estab 2004, empl 1, sales , cert: State)

2429 Dothan Security Inc. dba DSI Security Services
600 W Adams St
Dothan, AL 36303
Contact: Boyd Clark Dir Sales/Marketing
Tel: 334-793-5720
Email: bclark@dsisecurity.com
Website: www.dsisecurity.com
Uniformed security officers. (Woman, estab 1969, empl 4000, sales $52,000,000, cert: WBENC)

2430 Employment Screening Services
2500 Southlake Park
Birmingham, AL 35244
Contact: Jared Balint Enterprise Sales Mgr
Tel: 314-282-0154
Email: jbalint@es2.com
Website: www.es2.com
Criminal checks, credit checks, drug testing, motor vehicle checks, electronic fingerprinting, education, employment & reference verifications. (Woman, estab 1994, empl 85, sales $12,500,000, cert: WBENC)

2431 Workable Solutions Investigative & Protective Services, LLC
5925 Carmichael Rd Ste D
Montgomery, AL 36117
Contact: CEO
Tel: 334-262-0432
Email:
Website: www.workable-solutions.org/
Security Guards & Patrol Services, Investigation Services, Special Events Security, Background Investigations, CCTV Monitoring, Loss Prevention, Home Watch, Protection/Bodyguard Services, Security Training. (AA, estab 2009, empl 25, sales , cert: State)

Arizona

2432 Hope Capital LLC
P.O. Box 74554
Phoenix, AZ 85087
Contact: Sarah Hope CEO
Tel: 602-899-1606
Email: sarah@verticalidentity.com
Website: www.verticalidentity.com
Develop, implement & provide screening programs, background investigations, Employment Verification, Criminal Background Checks, Motor Vehicle Record Check, Government Watch Lists, Fingerprinting. (Woman/Hisp, estab 2014, empl 6, sales , cert: WBENC)

2433 Law Enforcement Specialists, Inc.
P.O. Box 11656
Glendale, AZ 85318
Contact: Bonnie Lucas CEO
Tel: 623-825-6700
Email: bonnie@lesaz.com
Website: www.offdutypoliceofficers.com
Law Enforcement Officers off-duty armed, uniformed & plain clothes. (Woman, estab 1994, empl 8, sales $5,610,458, cert: WBENC)

California

2434 Accurate Background
7515 Irvine Center Dr
Irvine, CA 92618
Contact: Matthew Schneider Enterprise Acct Exec
Tel: 949-609-2277
Email: mschneider@accuratebackground.com
Website: www.accurate.com
Background screening: criminal background checks, drug screening, fingerprinting, verifications, & compliance services. (Hisp, estab 1997, empl 1700, sales $350,000,000, cert: NMSDC)

2435 AccuSource, Inc.
30650 Rancho California Road Ste D406-215
Temecula, CA 92591
Contact: Cynthia Woods VP Sales/Mktg
Tel: 888-649-6272
Email: diversity@accusource-online.com
Website: www.accusource-online.com
Screening services: criminal backgrounds checks, social security traces, DMV records, drug testing, international criminal & reference, employment verfications, domestic employment verification, license verification, I-9 compliance. (Woman, estab 1999, empl 30, sales $4,603,876, cert: WBENC)

2436 A-Check Global
1501 Research Park Dr
Riverside, CA 92507
Contact: Mike Primbsch Dir of Marketing
Tel: 951-750-1501
Email: diversity@acheckglobal.com
Website: www.acheckglobal.com
Screening services: background & drug-screening. (Woman/AA, estab 1998, empl 209, sales $24,200,000, cert: NMSDC, CPUC, WBENC)

2437 American Custom Private Security, Inc.
1110 W Kettleman Lane
Lodi, CA 95240
Contact: Rajesh Patti President
Tel: 209-369-1200
Email: rpatti@customofficers.com
Website: www.customofficers.com
Security solutions, unarmed/armed guards to local, state, federal governments & commercial customers. (As-Ind, estab 2008, empl 25, sales $419,000, cert: 8a)

2438 American Eagle Protective Services Inc.
425 West Kelso St
Inglewood, CA 90301
Contact: Maria Moreno business devel dept
Tel: 213-427-0715
Email: officeadmi@aeprotectiveservices.com
Website: www.aeprotectiveservices.com
Security guard services & patrol services. (Woman/AA, estab 2012, empl 102, sales , cert: NMSDC, CPUC)

2439 Apex Investigative Services Inc.
11171 Sun Center Dr Ste 120
Rancho Cordova, CA 95670
Contact: JR Robles CEO
Tel: 916-858-2999
Email: jr@apexpi.com
Website: www.apexpi.com
Investigation svcs: surveillance, workers compensation fraud, liability, disability mgmt, sexual harassment, due diligence, SIU fraud, employee terminations, background investigation, discrimination, witness interviews, etc. (Hisp, estab 1997, empl 55, sales $1,555,730, cert: NMSDC)

2440 Covenant Security & Patrol
P.O. Box 292
Etiwanda, CA 91739
Contact: Charles Christian Owner
Tel: 866-869-5653
Email: covenantsecurity@charter.net
Website:
Security guard services. (AA, estab 2006, empl 5, sales , cert: CPUC)

2441 Global Unit 1
15603 Firmona Ave
Lawndale, CA 90260
Contact: Ferdinand Ndedi COO
Tel: 310-760-1957
Email: ferdinandd@globalunit1.com
Website: http://globalunit1.com
Security guards, patrol services, access control, perimeter patrol, vehicle & bike patrol, special events & parties, control room surveillance, gate house & reception services. (Woman/AA, estab 2010, empl 500, sales , cert: State, City)

2442 Immediate Guard Services Inc.
P.O. Box 2008
Norwalk, CA 90651
Contact: Presdient
Tel: 866-415-0933
Email:
Website: www.immediateguardservices.com/campaign0415
Retail security guards, construction site security, commercial security guards, mobile security patrols, fire watch services, school security guards, event security. (Hisp, estab 2012, empl 90, sales , cert: State, CPUC)

2443 Infortal Associates, Inc. dba Infortal Worldwide
1590 The Alameda Ste 100
San Jose, CA 95126
Contact: Candice Tal CEO
Tel: 408-298-9700
Email: ctal@infortal.com
Website: www.infortal.com
Global security & risk mitigation, risk management & investigation services, business due diligence, reputation due diligence, M&A, board advisory, international executive travel, competitive intelligence, FCPA due diligence. (Woman, estab 1985, empl 12, sales $1,159,505, cert: WBENC)

2444 JLR Invesitgations
9375 Archibald Ave, Ste 103
Rancho Cucamonga, CA 91730
Contact: Ruth Riddle CEO
Tel: 909-888-8880
Email: ruth@jlrinvestigations.com
Website: https://jlrinvestigations.com
Investigative services, Surveillance & Sub Rosa, Background Investigations, AOE/COE Statements & Field Interviews, Activity Checks, Database Searches, Mortgage fraud Investigations. (Woman/AA, estab 2004, empl 34, sales $186,000, cert: NMSDC)

2445 Locked on Referrals Protection Inc.
4202 Atlantic Ave, Ste 212
Long Beach, CA 90807
Contact: Kris Potter CEO
Tel: 562-552-7972
Email: lorprotection@gmail.com
Website: www.lorprotection.com
Security guard services. (Woman/AA, estab 2013, empl 30, sales $247,000, cert: NMSDC, CPUC)

2446 National Eagle Security, Inc.
3200 Wilshire Blvd, Ste 1208
Los Angeles, CA 90010
Contact: Maria Castillo Business Dev Mgr
Tel: 213-637-0200
Email: nesbestone@yahoo.com
Website: http://nationaleaglesecurity.com
Security Officers, Public Relations Officers, Vehicle Patrol. (AA, estab 2014, empl 45, sales $768,194, cert: NMSDC, CPUC)

2447 Pacific Protection Services, Inc.
22144 Clarendon St, Ste 110
Woodland Hills, CA 91367
Contact: Bob Pina CEO
Tel: 818-313-9369
Email: bob.pina@pacific-protection.com
Website: http://pacific-protection.com
Uniform unarmed, armed security guard services & Law Enforcement Experience Agents (ODO). (AA, estab 1984, empl 400, sales $5,123,267, cert: NMSDC, CPUC)

2448 Private Eyes, Inc
2700 Ygnacio Valley Rd, Ste 100
Walnut Creek, CA 94598
Contact: Sandra James CEO
Tel: 925-927-3333
Email: sandra@pebackgroundchecks.com
Website: www.privateeyesbackgroundchecks.com
Pre-employment screening, employment background investigations. (Woman, estab 1999, empl 45, sales $6,500,000, cert: WBENC)

2449 RCI Associates
5030 Business Center Dr Ste 280
Fairfield, CA 94534
Contact: Mitchell Brooks
Tel: 866-668-4732
Email: mbrooks@rciassociatesinc.com
Website: www.rciassociatesinc.com
Corporate & Insurance Investigations, Security Consulting, Global Threat Management, Special Events & Specialized Unarmed & Armed Uniform Services. (Nat Ame, estab 2012, empl 5, sales $1,495,000, cert: NMSDC, 8a)

2450   Rene Garza and Associates, Inc.
2660 W. Shaw Lane, Ste 110
Fresno, CA 93711
Contact: Audra da Rosa Presdient
Tel: 559-399-3113
Email: audra@rga-pi.com
Website: www.rga-pi.com
Investigative Services: Workers Compensation, Criminal Defense, Pre-Employment Background & Reference Checks. (Hisp, estab 2009, empl 5, sales $284,000, cert: NMSDC)

2451   RMI International
8125 Somerset Blvd
Paramount, CA 90723
Contact: Roxanne Rodriguez President
Tel: 562-806-9098
Email: roxanner@rmiintl.com
Website: www.rodbat.com
Security svcs: armed & unarmed security, off-duty law enforcement protection, background screening, investigations, security system design & engineering, training, worldwide executive protection & consulting services. (Woman/Hisp, estab 1996, empl 60, sales , cert: NMSDC)

2452   Servexo Protective Services
1515 W 190th St, Ste 170
Gardena, CA 90248
Contact: Nick Chaires Dir of Corporate Accts
Tel: 323-527-9994
Email: nchaires@servexousa.com
Website: www.servexo.com
Security Services, Security solutions. (AA, estab 2013, empl 300, sales $5,000,000, cert: State)

2453   Spearhead Protection Inc.
P.O. Box 605
Antioch, CA 94509
Contact: Cherokee Martin Admin Asst
Tel: 925-308-7778
Email: cherokee.spearheadpro@hotmail.com
Website: www.spearheadpros.com
Security services. (AA, estab 2006, empl 22, sales $400,000, cert: State)

Colorado

2454   IBC
P.O. Box 1052
Arvada, CO 80001
Contact: Bob Linderman Dir Business Dev
Tel: 303-403-0807
Email: blinderman@industrialbuyers.com
Website: www.intelligentbackground.com
Employment background screening, workers comp credit identity, investigations. (Hisp, estab 1991, empl 35, sales , cert: NMSDC)

Florida

2455   Darwin Securities, LLC
16350 Bruce B Downs, Ste 47178
Tampa, FL 33646
Contact: Michael Dastolfo Owner
Tel: 813-468-3504
Email: michael@darwinsecurities.com
Website: www.darwinsecurities.com
Private Investigation, Executive Protection & Process Service Agency. (As-Pac, estab 2005, empl 2, sales , cert: State)

2456   Drakonx, Inc.
127 Grand Ave
Coral Gables, FL 33133
Contact: Fernando Alvarez Presdient
Tel: 866-224-1245
Email: info@drakonx.com
Website: www.drakonx.com
Private Investigations, Surveillance, Background Checks, Due Diligence, Skip Tracing, Executive Protection, Risk Assessments, Insurance Fraud, Employee Misconduct Investigations. (Hisp, estab 2003, empl 2, sales , cert: NMSDC)

2457   First Choice Background Screening
4611 S. University Dr Box 314
Davie, FL 33328
Contact: Nicole Morales
Tel: 888-222-9688
Email: sales@firstchoicebackground.com
Website: www.firstchoicebackground.com
Pre-employment background screening & drug testing, criminal history, motor vehicle records, social security verification, credit report. (Woman/Hisp, estab 1996, empl 48, sales $4,600,000, cert: NMSDC, WBENC)

2458   High Risk Security Services
5012 Strada Dr
Winter Haven, FL 33880
Contact: Juan Garcia Owner
Tel: 863-398-8881
Email: highrisk@att.net
Website: www.atrisksecurity.com
Executive, travel, anti-terrorism and personal security training. (Hisp, estab 2005, empl 1, sales , cert: State)

2459   P. Eagle Protection, LLC (Miami Branch)
777 Brickell Ave Ste 500, Rm 81
Miami, FL 33131
Contact: Daniel Peterson CEO
Tel: 305-721-2819
Email: dpeterson@miamipep.com
Website: www.MiamiPEP.com
Security services, camera installation, property patrols, crowd control, personal protection (body guards), personal escorts (private drivers), etc. (AA, estab 2016, empl 22, sales , cert: State)

2460   Westmoreland Protection Agency, Inc.
10194 NW 47th St
Sunrise, FL 33351
Contact: Paul Spence Presdient
Tel: 954-318-0532
Email: pspence@wpafla.com
Website: www.wpafla.com
Security svcs: armed & unarmed security officers. (AA, As-Ind, estab 2002, empl 101, sales $2,901,382, cert: NMSDC)

Georgia

2461   ALL(n)1 Security Services, Inc.
3915 Cascade Rd, Ste 340
Atlanta, GA 30331
Contact: Mary Parker CEO
Tel: 404-691-4915
Email: rrobinson@alln1security.com
Website: www.allnsecurity.com
Security officers, off-duty police, background checks, motor vehicle reports, drug screening, security surveys, risk assessment analysis, consulting, seminars & workshops & security system designs, CCTV monitors. (Woman/AA, estab , empl , sales $20,000,000, cert: State, NMSDC, WBENC)

2462 Confidential Security Agency, Inc.
P.O. Box 55188
Atlanta, GA 30308
Contact: Patrice Adams VP
Tel: 404-888-0801
Email: padams@confidentialsecurityagency.net
Website: www.confidentialsecurityagency.net
Security guard protective services. (AA, estab 1972, empl 267, sales $6,000,000, cert: State, NMSDC)

2463 ESA Investigations & Security, LLC
70 Whitaker Way
Midway, GA 31320
Contact: Gerard Easley Presdient
Tel: 912-312-9510
Email: gerard.easley@gmail.com
Website: www.esainvestigations.com
Investigative and security solutions. (AA, estab 2020, empl 15, sales , cert: NMSDC)

2464 Global Bureau of Security & Investigations
240 Auburn Ave
Atlanta, GA 30303
Contact: Robert Conley President & CEO
Tel: 404-876-7273
Email: chez@gbsillc.com
Website: www.gbsillc.com
Full service private investigation & security firm. (AA, estab 2012, empl 8, sales , cert: NMSDC)

2465 Global Investigations Inc.
P.O. Box 473
Fayetteville, GA 30214
Contact: Tracey Brown
Tel: 770-477-9879
Email: tbrown@globalpi.us
Website: www.globalpi.us
Surveillance, background checks & liability cliams. (Woman/AA, estab 2003, empl 10, sales $327,000, cert: NMSDC)

2466 Hawque Protection Services, LLC.
3017 Bolling Way
Atlanta, GA 30305
Contact: Chris Rich Presdient
Tel: 502-767-7479
Email: chris@hawque.com
Website: www.hpg.global
Veteran Security Personnel – Military and LEO, GPS tracked movement – monitored and recorded, Licensed, Armed and Trained in multiple weapons platforms (Pistol, Shotgun and Patrol Rifle) based on threat and client needs. (AA, estab 2019, empl 25, sales $400,000, cert: NMSDC)

2467 InfoMart
1582 Terrell Mill Rd
Marietta, GA 30067
Contact: Michelle Summers Supplier Diversity Admin
Tel: 770-984-2727
Email: infomartwbe@backgroundscreening.com
Website: www.backgroundscreening.com
Background checks, criminal history searches, reference checks, education verification, professional license certification, drug screening, business reports, credit/driving history. (Woman, estab 1989, empl 135, sales $17,404,193, cert: WBENC, NWBOC)

2468 IPROVEIT.COM
6340 Sugarloaf Parkway Ste 200
Duluth, GA 30097
Contact: Vaughn Harvey President
Tel: 770-239-1707
Email: vharvey@iproveit.com
Website: www.iproveit.com
Background screening, investigations, fingerprint services, fingerprint equipment. (AA, estab 2005, empl 3, sales $315,000, cert: NMSDC)

2469 Nu Image Protection Agency LLC
201 17th St NW, Ste 300
Atlanta, GA 30363
Contact: CEO
Tel: 678-860-4634
Email:
Website:
Armed & Unarmed Security Guard Svcs, Access Control; Executive Protection; Event Security; Escort Service; Rover Patrol, Law Enforcement Training Pre-employment background screening & Criminal record searches. (AA, estab 2012, empl 27, sales $844,000, cert: State, 8a)

2470 Safeguard Security Solutions LLC
1781 Hwy 42 N
McDonough, GA 30253
Contact: Rahul Anand CEO
Tel: 404-545-3023
Email: mrandall@safeguardsecurityllc.com
Website: www.safeguardsecurityllc.com
Security guards, staffing & janitorial services. (AA, estab 2010, empl 5, sales $348,000, cert: NMSDC, 8a)

2471 The Cedalius Group LLC
2900 Delk Rd, Ste 700
Marietta, GA 30067
Contact: Melissa Foiles CEO
Tel: 404-963-9772
Email: mfoiles@thecedaliusgroup.com
Website: www.thecedaliusgroup.com
Background screening, criminal, credit reports an& d drug screening, talent selection research support, vendor/franchisee vetting & international searches. (Hisp, estab 2012, empl 5, sales , cert: NMSDC)

2472 The Guardian Protective Services, LLC
2839 Church St
Atlanta, GA 30344
Contact: Jennifer Rocke VP accounting/business dev
Tel: 404-766-2611
Email: jenniferr@theguardiansecurity.com
Website: www.theguardiansecurity.com
Security guard service, armed & unarmed, security consultation & analysis, loss prevention, security concierge services, patrol services. (Woman/AA, estab 1998, empl 200, sales $1,900,000, cert: State)

Iowa

2473 3rd Degree Screening Inc.
100 E. Broadway Ste 201
Council Bluffs, IA 51503
Contact: Jeanie Waters Presdient
Tel: 712-256-1701
Email: jeanie.waters@3rddegreescreening.com
Website: www.3rddegreescreening.com
International comprehensive background screening, verifications services & drug testing services. (Woman, estab 2012, empl 8, sales $646,000, cert: WBENC)

Illinois

2474   AGB Investigative Services, Inc.
2033 W 95th St
Chicago, IL 60643
Contact: John Griffin Jr. President
Tel: 773-445-4300
Email: john.griffin@agbinvestigative.com
Website: http://AGBinvestigativeservices.com
Asset protection, risk mitigation, computer forensics & network security, fraud management, assurance services, private security services. (AA, estab 1999, empl 100, sales $2,600,000, cert: State, City, 8a)

2475   Allpoints Security & Detective, Inc.
2112 E 71st St
Chicago, IL 60649
Contact: Rhone Llevelyn CCO
Tel: 773-955-6700
Email: lrhone@allpointssecurityinc.com
Website: www.allpointssecurityinc.com
Armed/unarmed security guard & mobile patrol services. (Woman/AA, estab 2000, empl 210, sales $4,940,000, cert: State, City)

2476   Fact Finders Group, Inc.
4747 Lincoln Mall Dr, Ste 300
Matteson, IL 60443
Contact: Kenneth Webb Sr. CEO
Tel: 708-283-4200
Email: kenwebb@factfindersgroup.com
Website: www.factfindersgroup.com
Investigative & security consulting agency. (AA, As-Ind, estab 1996, empl 16, sales $1,000,000, cert: State, City, NMSDC, 8a)

2477   HLSA Inc. Security & Investigations
7561 W Myrtle
Chicago, IL 60631
Contact: Security Consultant
Tel: 773-315-1848
Email:
Website: http://HLSAINC.com
Uniformed Security Officers, Armed & Unarmed Security Guards, Executive protection, Armed Escort, High Value Freight, Private Investigators, Pre-Employment Screenings, Shopping Services, Integrity Checks, Mobile Patrol Vehicles. (Minority, estab 2012, empl 25, sales $125,000, cert: City)

2478   Page Security Inc.
9453 S Ashland Ave
Chicago, IL 60620
Contact: Henry Page COO
Tel: 773-239-5256
Email: pagesecurity@msn.com
Website: http://pagesecurityagency.net
Armed & unarmed security guards, live scan fingerprinting & background. (AA, estab 2001, empl 100, sales $1,500,000, cert: State)

2479   Securatex Ltd.
651 W Washington Blvd Ste 105
Chicago, IL 60661
Contact: Patricia J. DuCanto
Tel: 708-536-3771
Email: pducanto@securatex.com
Website: www.securatex.com
Armed & unarmed physical security/guards, patrol services, background investigations, pre-employment screenings. (Woman, estab 1986, empl 838, sales $12,518,000, cert: State, City)

2480   Security Professionals of Illinois, Inc.
7120 Windsor Lake Pkwy Ste 102
Loves Park, IL 61111
Contact: Angela Larson Dir of Development
Tel: 815-637-6950
Email: alarson@getspi.com
Website: www.getspi.com
Security risk management services & solutions. (Hisp, estab 2003, empl 50, sales $542,000, cert: State, City, 8a)

Louisiana

2481   Crescent Guardian
4640 S Carrollton Ave
New Orleans, LA 70119
Contact: Marian Pierre CEO
Tel: 504-483-7811
Email: guard504@aol.com
Website: www.crescentguardianinc.com
Professional armed & unarmed guard services. (Woman/AA, estab 1993, empl 300, sales , cert: State)

2482   L&R Security Services, Inc.
3930 Old Gentilly Rd
New Orleans, LA 70126
Contact: Edward Robinson Presdient
Tel: 504-943-3191
Email: ejrobinson@lrsecurity.com
Website: www.lrsecurity.com
Security guard & special events services. (AA, estab 1979, empl 250, sales , cert: NMSDC)

2483   Pinnacle Security & Investigation Inc.
332 N Jefferson Davis Pkwy
New Orleans, LA 70119
Contact: VP Dir of Business Dev
Tel: 504-934-1411
Email:
Website: www.securitybypinnacle.com
Security Guard Services, armed security, unarmed security, security patrols, CCTV monitoring, and security consulting. (Hisp, estab 2011, empl 175, sales $3,200,000, cert: NMSDC)

2484   Southern Guard Service, Inc.
P.O. Box 1030
Larose, LA 70373
Contact: VP
Tel: 985-693-4316
Email:
Website: www.southernguard.com
Armed & unarmed security guards. (Woman, estab 1972, empl 120, sales $2,400,000, cert: WBENC)

2485   Tracepoint, LLC
P.O. Box 24059
New Orleans, LA 70184
Contact: Kristi Barranco Owner
Tel: 504-284-2285
Email: kristi@tracepointllc.com
Website: http://tracepointllc.com
Background & drug screening. (Woman, estab 2012, empl 3, sales , cert: WBENC)

Maryland

2486 AU & Associates Inc.
3100 Ritchie Rd, Ste F
District Heights, MD 20747
Contact: Ade Uiyoshioria Presdient
Tel: 301-909-0076
Email: adeu@auanda.com
Website: www.auanda.com
Personality Fitting & Proficiency Testing, In-Depth Background Research, Drug Screening & Urinalysis Testing, Prior Work History Inspections, Information Technology Solutions. (Woman/AA, estab 2003, empl 5, sales $1,094,799, cert: State)

2487 Bradley Technologies Inc.
8701 Georgia Ave Ste 804
Silver Spring, MD 20910
Contact: President
Tel: 301-562-9201
Email:
Website: www.btisecurity.com
Unarmed & armed guard security guard services, access control & monitoring services. (Woman/AA, estab 2000, empl 157, sales $9,116,610, cert: State, NMSDC, WBENC, 8a)

2488 PChange LLC
4400 Stamp Rd Ste 302
Temple Hills, MD 20748
Contact: Rosa Griffin
Tel: 240-619-3507
Email: r.griffin@pchangellc.com
Website: www.pchangellc.com
Guard services & patrol. (Woman/AA, Hisp, estab 2003, empl 165, sales $5,388,000, cert: State, City)

2489 Security 1 Solutions LLC
845 Quince Orchard Blvd Ste Q
Gaithersburg, MD 20878
Contact: Bruce Alexander Presdient
Tel: 301-926-4957
Email: balexander@security1solutions.com
Website: www.security1solutions.com
Manned-guarding & related security solutions, Security staffing, Emergency response services, Special event security, Safety auditing & awareness, Security training, Conceptual security systems design. (AA, estab 2012, empl 80, sales $2,400,000, cert: State)

2490 Strategic Protective Services, Inc.
4300 Forbes Blvd Ste 220
Lanham, MD 20706
Contact: Brian Lassiter VP/COO
Tel: 301-322-9585
Email: blassiter@spsinc-usa.com
Website: www.spsinc-usa.com
Uniformed security guard & patrol services (AA, estab 2008, empl 65, sales $375,000, cert: 8a)

Michigan

2491 Del Ray Security
34215 Jefferson
Harrison Township, MI 48045
Contact: Rudy Garcia Presdient
Tel: 586-415-4518
Email: delraypd@aol.com
Website: www.delraysecurity.com
Armed/unarmed security guard services. (Hisp, estab 1998, empl 25, sales $400,000, cert: NMSDC)

2492 Lagarda Security
2123 S Center Rd
Burton, MI 48519
Contact: Elena Rathburn Accounting Specialist
Tel: 877-944-8400
Email: elenarathburn@lagardasecurity.com
Website: www.lagardasecurity.com
Security officers. (Woman, estab , empl , sales , cert: WBENC)

2493 Pyratech Security Systems, Inc.
20150 Livernois
Detroit, MI 48221
Contact: Larry Teamer Sales
Tel: 313-345-2000
Email: larry@pyratechsecurity.com
Website: www.pyratechsecurity.com
Security service: homeland security, alarm system design, uniformed security guards, private investigations, security & fire detection systems. (AA, estab 1993, empl 45, sales , cert: NMSDC)

2494 Tricon Security Group, LLC
3011 W Grand Blvd, Ste 407
Detroit, MI 48202
Contact: Michael Whittaker CEO
Tel: 877-641-2600
Email: mwhittaker@rsigsecurity.com
Website: www.triconsecurity.com
Uniformed security officers, loss prevention education, personal protection training, executive protective, event security. (AA, As-Pac, estab 2004, empl 1100, sales $10,000,000, cert: NMSDC)

Minnesota

2495 M & M Consultants, Inc.
7250 River Shore Ln
Champlin, MN 55316
Contact: Nancy McLaughlin CEO
Tel: 763-422-9299
Email: macnj9299@cs.com
Website:
Collection svcs: commercial receivables, consumer & commercial bad checks. (Woman, estab , empl 24, sales , cert: State)

2496 Twin City Security, Inc.
519 Coon Rapids Blvd
Coon Rapids, MN 55433
Contact: Jeff Flattum Reg Accts/ Sales Mgr
Tel: 763-784-4160
Email: j.flattum@twincitysecurity.com
Website: www.twincitysecurity.com
Armed & unarmed security guard services. (Woman, estab 1974, empl 650, sales , cert: State)

Missouri

2497 Discreet Check, LLC
655 NE Swann Circle
Lees Summit, MO 64086
Contact: Owner
Tel: 816-600-6200
Email:
Website: www.discreetcheck.com
Global Criminal Background Checks, National Criminal Background Checks, National Background Screenings, National Drug Testing. (Woman, estab 2012, empl 1, sales , cert: CPUC, WBENC)

Mississippi

2498   Sanjo Security Services, Inc.
       1615 S Gallatin St
       Jackson, MS 39201
       Contact: Kolean Sanders President
       Tel: 601-969-7205
       Email: koleanwsanders@aol.com
       Website: www.sanjosecurity.com
Electronic surveillance & physical security: management,
supervision, manpower, training, equipment, armed &
unarmed security guard services. (Woman/AA, estab 2000,
empl 54, sales $2,525,000, cert: State)

North Carolina

2499   J.P. Investigative Group, Inc.
       9716-B Rea Rd, Ste 211
       Charlotte, NC 28277
       Contact: Joe Paonessa Co-Owner
       Tel: 704-243-1137
       Email: info@jpinvestigations.com
       Website: http://jpinvestigations.com
Video surveillance & special investigations for potentially
fraudulent workers' compensation, property/casualty &
general liability claims. (Woman, estab 2000, empl 15,
sales $499,636, cert: State, WBENC)

2500   Professional Police Services Inc
       9731 Southern Pine Blvd Ste A
       Charlotte, NC 28273
       Contact: Candace Ratliff COO
       Tel: 704-442-9499
       Email: clratliff@pssprotection.com
       Website: www.pssprotection.com
Security guard and patrol services, law enforcements
services, alarm response, crowd control, surveillance,
escorts, personal protection. (Woman/AA, estab 2000,
empl 95, sales , cert: State)

2501   Safe & Secure Worldwide Protection Group
       4925 W Market St Ste 1142
       Greensboro, NC 27409
       Contact: Lance Jones President
       Tel: 888-476-6388
       Email: chiefjones@safesecureworldwide.com
       Website: www.safesecureworldwide.com
Security guards, armed guards, loss prevention agents,
executive protection agents. (Woman/AA, estab 2009,
empl 157, sales , cert: NMSDC)

2502   TriMetro Security Services LLC
       224 E Holding Ave, Unit 935
       Wake Forest, NC 27588
       Contact: Terry Walser CEO
       Tel: 919-623-4354
       Email: terrywalser@trimetrosecurity.com
       Website: www.TriMetroSecurity.com
Guard staffing & patrol services. (AA, estab 2009, empl 9,
sales $200,000, cert: State)

New Hampshire

2503   STANDA, Inc.
       41 Micah Terr
       Milton, NH 03851
       Contact: David G Duchesneau GM
       Tel: 603-652-7225
       Email: info@standa.com
       Website: www.standa.com
Security & Investigations consultant. (Woman, estab 1991,
empl 8, sales $150,000, cert: State)

New Jersey

2504   Data Access Inc.
       999 McBride Ave Ste C205
       Woodland Park, NJ 07424
       Contact: Karen Jacobsen Presdient
       Tel: 973-774-0030
       Email: karen@datascreening.com
       Website: www.datascreening.com
Background screening for pre-employment & tenant
screening. (Woman, estab 1996, empl 5, sales $300,000,
cert: State, City, WBENC)

2505   M.E.R.I.T. Investigative Services, Inc.
       1 Bloomfield Ave
       Newark, NJ 07104
       Contact: Jose Rodriguez President
       Tel: 973-483-9699
       Email: meritsecurity@verizon.net
       Website: www.merit-security.com
CCTV system design & installation, security assessments,
risk analysis, security guard services, investigations,
training. (Hisp, estab 2000, empl 6, sales $100,000, cert:
State)

2506   We See You limited liability
       116 N 2nd St Ste 208
       Camden, NJ 08102
       Contact: Raymond Jones President
       Tel: 609-914-5775
       Email: weseeyoullc@gmail.com
       Website: www.we-see-you.net
Unarmed security & safety, uniformed & plain clothes,
foot & vehicle patrols. (AA, estab 2010, empl 75, sales
$761,000, cert: NMSDC, 8a, SDB)

New York

2507   A.C. Roman & Associates, Inc.
       1350 RXR Plaza West Tower
       Uniondale, NY 11556
       Contact: Kamil Podlinski VP of Operations
       Tel: 516-596-3300
       Email: info@romansearch.com
       Website: www.romansearch.com
Insurance, corporate, fraud, surveillance & criminal
investigation services. (Hisp, estab 1998, empl 70, sales
$4,000,000, cert: City)

2508   AWICS Security & Investigations, Inc.
       962 East 31 St
       Brooklyn, NY 11210
       Contact: Barrington Pinto President & CEO
       Tel: 718-338-0882
       Email: awicslisa@gmail.com
       Website: www.iawics.com
Security, training, investigative & emergency management operations, armed & unarmed Peace Enforcement
Officers, private investigators. (AA, estab 2000, empl 12,
sales , cert: State)

2509   Bay Ridge Security Service, Inc.
       110 Bay Ridge Ave
       Brooklyn, NY 11220
       Contact: Anthony La Bella
       Tel: 718-238-2974
       Email: alabella@bayridgesecurity.com
       Website: www.bayridgesecurity.com
Uniformed & plainclothes security guard services,
armed & unarmed, executive protection, vehicle patrol
& armed transportation. (Woman, estab 1973, empl 175,
sales $3,159,632, cert: State, City)

2510 Care Security Systems
9 Hemion Road
Montebello, NY 10952
Contact: Eli Ribowsky Acct Mgr
Tel: 845-282-1245
Email: eribowsky@care-inc.com
Website: www.caresecuritysystems.com
Design, assembly, testing, installation, maintenance, and management of high-level integrated security systems. (Woman, estab 1987, empl 30, sales , cert: City, WBENC)

2511 Commercial Investigations LLC
622 Loudon Road Ste 201
Latham, NY 12110
Contact: Michelle Pyan Presdient
Tel: 800-284-0906
Email: info@commercialinvestigationsllc.com
Website: www.commercialinvestigationsllc.com
Employment background investigations, volunteer screening solutions, drug testing, pre-employment physicals, tenant background investigations, cyber investigations, executive due diligence reports. (Woman, estab 2004, empl 16, sales , cert: State, City, WBENC)

2512 ISS Action, Inc.
158-12 Rockaway Blvd
Queens, NY 11434
Contact: Pamela Newman CEO
Tel: 718-978-3000
Email: cdcohen@issaction.com
Website: www.issaction.com
Armed & unarmed uniformed security guard services. Aviation security, ramp security, mobile security. Security planning FCL Clearance Federal security contractor. (Woman, estab 1991, empl 200, sales $11,340,577, cert: State, City, 8a)

2513 Johnson Security Bureau, Inc.
609 Walton Ave
Bronx, NY 10451
Contact: Jessica A. Johnson Presdient
Tel: 718-402-3600
Email: info@johnsonsecuritybureau.com
Website: www.johnsonsecuritybureau.com
Watch, guard & patrol agency: armed & unarmed guard services. (Woman/AA, estab 1962, empl 120, sales $5,635,000, cert: City, NMSDC, WBENC)

2514 Lemire LLC
44 Wall St, Fl 12
New York, NY 10005
Contact: Christine O'Sullivan Analyst
Tel: 212-461-2158
Email: cosullivan@lemirellc.com
Website: www.lemirellc.com
Investigative due diligence, complex investigations, monitorships, background screening, sexual misconduct investigations, construction integrity monitoring & cyber forensics. (Woman, estab 2013, empl 10, sales , cert: State, City, WBENC)

2515 Miracle Security Inc.
193-49 Williamson Ave, Ste B Springfield Gardens
Queens, NY 11413
Contact: James Obayagbona President
Tel: 718-525-8030
Email: jambona193@aol.com
Website: www.miracle4security.com
Security guard services. (AA, estab 2005, empl 150, sales $200,000,000, cert: State)

2516 Outsource Consultants, Inc.
237 W 35th St, Fl 12A
New York, NY 10001
Contact: Diego Caballero President
Tel: 212-732-6933
Email: dcaballero@outsourceconsultants.com
Website: www.outsourceconsultants.com
building code and zoning consultation, offering a broad scope of services that includes approvals, permit expediting, and sign offs. (As-Ind, Hisp, estab 1993, empl 50, sales $5,500,000, cert: NMSDC)

Ohio

2517 Amerisearch Background Alliance
2529 S Ridge Rd E
Ashtabula, OH 44004
Contact: Kelley Groff Sales & Marketing
Tel: 800-569-6133
Email: kelleygroff@hotmail.com
Website: www.amerisearchbga.com
Background screening, electronic I-9s solutions, drug screening, behavioral assessments & information services. (Woman, estab 2006, empl 11, sales $750,000, cert: WBENC)

2518 National Alliance Security Agency, Inc.
7918 N Main St
Dayton, OH 45415
Contact: Presdient
Tel: 937-387-6517
Email:
Website: www.nationalalliancesecurity.com
Uniformed armed & unarmed security guard services. (Woman, estab 2005, empl 92, sales $1,091,995, cert: State, WBENC)

2519 Safe Choice LLC
11811 Shaker Blvd, Ste 415
Cleveland, OH 44120
Contact: Anthony Spencer VP
Tel: 216-231-7233
Email: safechoice1@att.net
Website: Safechoicellc.com
Armed & Unarmed Security Guards & Police Officers, Security for Public & Private Events, Traffic Control, Employee Investigations, Theft, Drug & Alcohol Testing, Professional & Secure, employee Removal Assistance, Body Guard Services. (Woman/AA, estab 2010, empl 382, sales $3,115,948, cert: State, SDB)

Oklahoma

2520 Superior Security
4419 N. Bryan Ave.
Shawnee, OK 74804
Contact: Louis Maltos CEO
Tel: 405-275-9072
Email: lmaltos@superiorsecurityusa.com
Website: www.superiorsecurityusa.com
Security svcs: physical security, executive & personal protection, access control, CCTV cameras, life safety, on call emergency response, pre-employment screening, terrorism watch list searches, security guard analysis, crisis mgmt. (Hisp, estab 1994, empl 140, sales $8,000,000, cert: NMSDC)

Pennsylvania

2521 Century Security Services, Inc.
6 Rose Lane
Wilkes Barre, PA 18702
Contact: Presdient
Tel: 800-927-0524
Email:
Website: www.centurysecurityservices.com
Armed & unarmed security officers, ambulance stand-by,
medical transports. risk assessment, general security
consultation, private investigation, alarm & surveillance
equipment. (Woman, estab 1984, empl 70, sales , cert:
State)

2522 Gentile and Associates, Inc.
3645 Brodhead Rd
Monaca, PA 15061
Contact: Christine Selden Principal
Tel: 724-775-3511
Email: cselden@gentilesecurity.com
Website: http://gentilesecurity.com
Pre-employment background screening, risk management,
workplace investigations, vulnerability analysis, executive
protection, surveillance, security guards. (Woman, estab
2009, empl 314, sales $15,000,000, cert: WBENC)

2523 Peak Security Inc.
103 Yost Blvd, Ste 100
Pittsburgh, PA 15221
Contact: Sales Consultant
Tel: 412-349-0850
Email:
Website: www.peaksecurityinc.com
Armed & unarmed guard services, emergency operations
planning & design, ID badging, security system services.
(Woman, estab 1997, empl 150, sales $678,000, cert:
State)

2524 Tactical Response Security Consulting Inc.
3565 Sepviva St
Philadelphia, PA 19134
Contact: Luis Torres Presdient
Tel: 888-755-9111
Email: tacresp@msn.com
Website: http://tacticalresponsesecurity.com
Security & detective services, armed & unarmed security &
investigative services. (Hisp, estab 2008, empl 50, sales
$1,800,000, cert: NMSDC)

Puerto Rico

2525 One Corps, Inc
P.O. Box 79767
Carolina, PR 00984
Contact: Sonia Fuentes
Tel: 787-776-0062
Email: sfuentes@one-corps.com
Website: www.one-corps.com
Armed & Unarmed Security Guards, IP Monitoring Station
with Patrol Response Service, Sales, Installation & Mainte-
nance of Cameras, Access Control, Fire Watch. (Hisp, estab
2007, empl 134, sales $2,641,716, cert: NMSDC)

2526 Vigilantes, Inc.
623 Ponce De Leon Ave, Ste 204
Hato Rey, PR 00917
Contact: Edgar Pedrosa President
Tel: 787-763-2080
Email: epvigilantes@gmail.com
Website:
Security & safety officers, special investigations & consult-
ing, electronic security systems. (Hisp, estab 1972, empl 1,
sales , cert: NMSDC)

South Carolina

2527 G&I Security Company, LLC.
9444 Two Notch Rd Ste B-1
Columbia, SC 29223
Contact: Melvin Dewitt CEO
Tel: 803-661-9221
Email: info@gisecuritycompany.com
Website: www.gisecuritycompany.com
Security services. (AA, estab 2011, empl 30, sales
$270,000, cert: State)

Tennessee

2528 Metropolitan Security Inc. dba Walden Security
100 E Tenth St Ste 400
Chattanooga, TN 37402
Contact: Lauren Tudor EVP of Marketing and Sales
Tel: 423-702-8200
Email: marketinginfo@waldensecurity.com
Website: www.waldensecurity.com
Security services. (Woman, estab 1990, empl 4550, sales
$232,247,039, cert: WBENC)

2529 Phelps Security Inc.
4932 Park Ave
Memphis, TN 38117
Contact: Andrew Phelps Business Mgr
Tel: 901-365-9728
Email: andy@phelpssecurity.com
Website: www.phelpssecurity.com
Armed/unarmed security officers, commercial/residen-
tial patrols, commercial alarm/emergency response,
investigations. (Woman, estab 1953, empl 375, sales
$8,000,000, cert: WBENC)

2530 Security Walls LLC
130 N Martinwood Rd
Knoxville, TN 37923
Contact: Juanita Walls Chief Mgr
Tel: 865-546-2597
Email: jwalls@securitywalls.net
Website: http://securitywalls.net
Security & Protective Services: security guard services,
armed & unarmed, visitor/access control, SCIF security,
international visitor escort/control, post & roving
patrols, electronic security monitoring, CCTV systems,
emergency plans & procedures. (Woman/AA, estab
2003, empl 376, sales $15,000,000, cert: State, City)

Texas

2531 Ameritex Guard Services
100 N Central Expwy, Ste 350
Richardson, TX 75080
Contact: Christopher ONeal Sr Acct Exec
Tel: 972-231-6395
Email: isf972@earthlink.net
Website: www.ameritexguardsaervices.com
Uniformed security guards. (Woman/Hisp, estab 1994,
empl 256, sales $7,400,000, cert: State, NMSDC)

2532 Asez Inc.
1716 S San Marcos, Ste 120
San Antonio, TX 78207
Contact: Robert Lozano CEO
Tel: 210-736-6200
Email: corporate@asezinc.com
Website: www.asezinc.com
Armed & unarmed security officers, security systems
services, security alarm systems, fire alarm systems,
access control, closed circuit television, alarm monitor-
ing, intergraded system. (Hisp, estab 2000, empl 75,
sales $2,575,000, cert: State, 8a)

2533 Boutchantharaj Corporation
5705 Airport Freeway
Fort Worth, TX 76117
Contact: Kit Boutchantharaj Presdient
Tel: 817-831-2000
Email: kit@dfwsecurityprotectiveforce.com
Website: http://dfwsecurityprotectiveforce.com
Provide unarmed & armed on-site security guard services.
(As-Pac, estab 2000, empl 250, sales $7,000,000, cert:
State, 8a)

2534 Nationwide Investigations & Security, Inc.
2425 West Loop South, Ste 200
Houston, TX 77027
Contact: Allen G Hollimon CEO
Tel: 713-297-8830
Email: ahollimon@ntwinvestigations.com
Website: www.ntwinvestigations.com
Security guard services, investigations, dignitary protec-
tion, communications cabling, CCTV/CATV, alarms, auto-
mated controls, networking, home theaters. (AA, estab
1999, empl 123, sales $398,000, cert: State, NMSDC)

2535 Night Eyes Protective Services Inc.
2407 E Yandell, Ste C
El Paso, TX 79903
Contact: Barbara Rodriguez VP
Tel: 915-549-0501
Email: nebarb01@night-eyes.com
Website: www.night-eyes.com
Security officers/guards, patrol officers & armored courier
services. (Hisp, estab 1999, empl 200, sales $3,400,000,
cert: State, NMSDC)

2536 Ruiz Protective Service, Inc.
2646 Andjon Dr
Dallas, TX 75220
Contact: Sales Mgr
Tel: 214-357-0820
Email:
Website: www.ruizservices.com/
Security guard & patrol services: armed & unarmed guard
services. (Hisp, estab 1998, empl 550, sales $6,000,000,
cert: State)

2537 Z-MAS International
2626 South Loop West, Ste 250
Houston, TX 77054
Contact: Janie Pinkney Managing Dir
Tel: 832-489-0960
Email: securitieszmas@outlook.com
Website: http://zmassecurity.wixsite.com/
zmassecurity
Certified, licensed, insured & bonded security officers,
armed guards, unarmed guards, investigations. (AA, estab
2017, empl 5, sales , cert: State)

Utah

2538 Toyakoi Ventures, LLC
95 Bridger Cir
Woodland Hills, UT 84653
Contact: Elliot Collins Presdient
Tel: 801-634-4194
Email: ecollins@toyakoi.com
Website: www.toyakoi.com
SAP consulting & full-service background checks. (Nat
Ame, estab 2010, empl 12, sales $664,000, cert: 8a)

Virginia

2539 AIVI Global Inc.
6412 Brandon Ave, Ste 712
Springfield, VA 22150
Contact: Raphaela O'Brien Presdient
Tel: 703-851-4521
Email: ella.obrien@aiviglobal.com
Website: www.aiviglobal.com
Security integration and engineering consulting, Physical
Access Control installation and management, Video
installation and management, IP infrastructure and
Security Investigations. (AA, Nat Ame, Hisp, estab 2019,
empl 4, sales , cert: State)

2540 Top Guard, Inc.
P.O. Box 55030
Norfolk, VA 23505
Contact: Chris Stuart VP
Tel: 757-722-3961
Email: cstuart@topguardinc.com
Website: www.topguardinc.com
Guard services, uniformed private security officers.
(Woman, estab 1996, empl 575, sales $15,250,000, cert:
State)

Washington

2541 Goldbelt Specialty Services LLC
200 W Thomas, Ste 420
Seattle, WA 98119
Contact: Gino DCafango Business Dev Mgr
Tel: 206-234-8759
Email: g.dcafango@gbss.us
Website: www.gbss.us
Security services: armored transpot, vehicle, foot patrol
& stationary security officers. (Nat Ame, estab 2005,
empl 18, sales $996,994, cert: NMSDC)

Wisconsin

2542 Nexus Pest Solutions, Inc.
3900 W Brown Deer Rd PMB 281
Brown Deer, WI 53223
Contact: Will White President
Tel: 414-355-3732
Email: wwhite@nexuspestsolutions.com
Website: www.nexuspestsolutions.com
We Provide pest control services for
commercial,industrial,institutional,manufacturing, and
hospitality facilities. (AA, estab 2007, empl 4, sales
$126,000, cert: State, City, NMSDC)

EDUCATIONAL MATERIALS
Manufacturers and wholesale distributors of text books, films, tapes, posters, magazines and teaching guides. NAICS Code 42

California

2543 El Mundo Communications
7444 E Chapman Ave Ste B
Orange, CA 92869
Contact: Martha Montoya Publisher
Tel: 714-366-3225
Email: martha@elmundous.com
Website: www.elmundous.com
Spanish language newspaper. (Hisp, estab 1988, empl 7, sales $700,000, cert: NMSDC)

Indiana

2544 Briljent, LLC
7999 Knue Road, Ste. 200
Indianapolis, IN 46250
Contact: Jennifer Duszynski Mgr, Client Services
Tel: 317-220-1563
Email: jduszynski@briljent.com
Website: www.briljent.com
Develop customized technical writing, education manuals, systems documentation, training & adult learner educational programs. (Woman, estab 1998, empl 120, sales $35,250,000, cert: State)

2545 HPC International, Inc.
5261 Fountain Dr, Ste A
Crown Point, IN 46307
Contact: Lynn Bell CEO
Tel: 219-922-4868
Email: lbell@hpcinterantionalinc.com
Website: www.hpcinternationalinc.com
Trade publishing: books, pamphlets, brochures, booklets, journals, newsletters, to comic books, e-zines, interactive DVD's, e-learning & web-based content. (AA, estab 1996, empl 20, sales , cert: NMSDC)

2546 MPM Marketing, Inc
8918 Squire Ct
Indianapolis, IN 46250
Contact: Mary Pat McKee Presdient
Tel: 317-440-9376
Email: marypat@mpmmarketinginc.com
Website: http://indyboomer.com
Publish an annual visitor guides for several hospitals in Indiana, sell advertising & work with large marketing departments. (Woman, estab 2005, empl 1, sales , cert: State)

New Jersey

2547 American Overseas Book Company, Inc.
550 Walnut St
Norwood, NJ 07648
Contact: Peter Lieb Dir of Operations
Tel: 201-767-7600
Email: plieb@aobc.com
Website: www.aobc.com
Dist books, CDs, DVDs & journal subscriptions. (Woman, estab 1969, empl 7, sales $4,500,000, cert: State)

Texas

2548 Complete Book & Media Supply, LLC
1200 Toro Grande Dr, Ste 200
Cedar Park, TX 78613
Contact: Cameron Bird Sales Dir
Tel: 800-986-1775
Email: cam@completebook.com
Website: www.completebook.com
Dist books. (As-Ind, estab 1996, empl 24, sales $19,259,500, cert: NMSDC, 8a)

2549 Minority Business News
13111 N Central Expressway, Ste 400
Dallas, TX 75044
Contact: Mia Smith Project Mgr
Tel: 214-369-3200
Email: mbnusa@globalxlr.com
Website: www.mbnusa.biz
Magazine/internet supplier diversity publishing. (AA, estab 1988, empl 10, sales $1,300,000, cert: NMSDC)

2550 Minority Opportunity News, Inc.
P.O. Box 763866
Dallas, TX 75376
Contact: Thurman Jones publisher
Tel: 972-516-4191
Email: businessoffice@northdallasgazette.com
Website: www.northdallasgazette.com
Newspaper: advertising & media, paper & internet. (AA, estab 1991, empl 5, sales , cert: State)

2551 Minority Print Media, LLC
2646 South Loop West Ste 600
Houston, TX 77054
Contact: Barry Simmons Advertising Dir
Tel: 713-748-6300
Email: advertising@stylemagazine.com
Website: www.stylemagazine.com
educated Urban view inside the worlds of celebrity, business, fashion, beauty, health, travel, transportation, culinary, real estate, arts, cultural and entertainment. (AA, estab 1989, empl 15, sales $539,868, cert: State, City, NMSDC)

2552   Southern Chinese Daily News LLC
      11122 Bellaire Blvd
      Houston, TX 77072
      Contact: Mia Smith Project Mgr
      Tel: 281-498-4310
      Email: scdn@globalxlr.com
      Website: www.scdaily.com/
Publishing, advertising. (As-Pac, estab 1978, empl 19, sales $2,327,224, cert: City, NMSDC)

Wisconsin

2553   Best Ed, LLC
      10936 N Port Washington Rd, Ste 269 Ste 269
      Mequon, WI 53092
      Contact: June Perry-Stevens Co-Owner
      Tel: 414-313-9762
      Email: contact@bestedbusiness.com
      Website: www.bestedbusiness.com
Dist school supplies, games, materials. (Woman/AA, estab 2004, empl 2, sales $525,000, cert: State, City, NMSDC)

ELECTRONIC ASSEMBLY

Electro-mechanical job shops. Manufacturers of electro-mechanical devices: PC boards, wire harnesses, cables, circuit components, housing, power supplies, etc. (See also ELECTRONIC & ELECTRICAL DIST. and ELECTRONIC & ELECTRICAL MFG.) NAICS Code 33

Alabama

2554 Mtronics.com, Inc.
325 Electronics Blvd SW Ste C
Huntsville, AL 35824
Contact: Mary Fields Mgr, quality Admin
Tel: 256-461-8883
Email: mary@mtronics.com
Website: www.mtronics.com
Mfr automotive electronic assemblies. (As-Ind, estab 1987, empl 61, sales $53,431,545, cert: NMSDC)

Arizona

2555 EDS Manufacturing Inc.
765 N Target Range Rd
Nogales, AZ 85621
Contact: Tony Milo VP of Sales & Marketing
Tel: 520-287-9711
Email: tmilo@edsmanufacturing.com
Website: www.edsmanufacturing.com
Molding, wire harness assembly, automatic cut, strip & crimp. (Hisp, estab 1990, empl 1800, sales $45,687,820, cert: NMSDC)

2556 Tooh Dineh Industries, Inc.
HC 61, Box E
Winslow, AZ 86047
Contact: Casey Dooley GM
Tel: 928-686-6477
Email: cdooley@toohdineh.com
Website: www.toohdineh.com
Electronic mfg services: surface mount technology, thru-hole technology, cables, harnesses. (Nat Ame, estab 1982, empl 63, sales $11,000,000, cert: State)

California

2557 Aeroflite Enterprises
261 Gemini
Brea, CA 92821
Contact: Pamela DePape Sales Mgr
Tel: 714-773-4251
Email: pdepape@aeroflite.com
Website: www.aeroflite.com
Dist aerospace electronics, custom cable assemblies & electrical connectors assemblies. (Woman, estab 1977, empl 65, sales $20,000,000, cert: NWBOC)

2558 Black Diamond Manufacturing Company
755 Bliss Ave
Pittsburg, CA 94565
Contact: Barbara Williams Supplier Diversity Administrator
Tel: 925-439-9160
Email: bwilliams@bwc.com
Website: www.blackdiamondmfg.com
Mechanical sub-assemblies, manufacture specialty parts, in-house manufacturing experiences & capabilities, single source solution for custom sub-assemblies. (Woman, estab 2008, empl 3, sales , cert: WBENC)

2559 Cal-Am Switch & Relay Co., Inc.
8837 Lankershim Blvd
Sun Valley, CA 91352
Contact: Max Beno COO
Tel: 818-252-0507
Email: lg@welcoelectronics.com
Website: http://welcoelectronics.com
Avionic components, batteries, bearings, bushings, cables assemblies, cable ties, capacitors, connectors, expando sleeve, fuses, circuit breakers, lacing cords, relays, resistors, semiconductors, switches, wire, cable, tubing. (Woman/Hisp, estab 1971, empl 7, sales $1,250,000, cert: NMSDC)

2560 Calpak USA, Inc.
13750 Prairie Ave
Hawthorne, CA 90250
Contact: Danish Qureshi VP
Tel: 310-937-7335
Email: danish@calpak-usa.com
Website: www.calpak-usa.com
Electronic Design, Electronics Engineering, Contract Manufacturing Services (CMS), Electronic Manufacturing Services (EMS), PCB Layout, PCB Design, PCB Assembly. (As-Pac, estab 1978, empl 15, sales $2,400,000, cert: State, NMSDC, SDB)

2561 LeeMAH Electronics Inc.
1088 Sansome St
San Francisco, CA 94111
Contact: Brent Liebel Business Development
Tel: 972-570-7170
Email: bliebel@leemah.com
Website: www.leemah.com
Cable harness, printed circuit board stuffing; SMT assembly. Machine-programmed auto. printed circuit board testing, coil winding, transformer production, radio frequency cables. Mfr for special communications systems. Custom injection molding. (As-Ind, estab 1971, empl 650, sales $46,000,000, cert: NMSDC)

2562 Micro Analog Inc.
1861 Puddingstone Dr
La Verne, CA 91750
Contact: Kim Bickmeier Dir of Sales
Tel: 909-392-8277
Email: kimbickmeier@micro-analog.com
Website: www.micro-analog.com
Mfr electronics: printed circuit board assembly PCBA, custom cable & wire harness assembly, box/system build. (Woman/As-Pac, estab 1991, empl 155, sales $15,698,000, cert: NMSDC)

2563 Sierra Proto Express, Inc.
1108 W Evelyn Ave
Sunnyvale, CA 94086
Contact: Greg Lawson Acct Rep
Tel: 408-735-7137
Email: gregl@protoexpress.com
Website: www.protoexpress.com
Mfr & assemble Printed Circuit Boards manufacturer, quick turn PCBs & medium production. (Woman/As-Ind, As-Pac, estab 1986, empl 353, sales , cert: NMSDC)

2564 Transline Technology, Inc.
      1106 S Technology Circle
      Anaheim, CA 92805
      Contact: Judy Warner President
      Tel: 714-533-8300
      Email: judy@translinetech.com
      Website: www.translinetech.com
Mfr printed circuit boards, PCB, PWB, hybrid, exotic, RF &
microwave, FR4 PCB. (As-Ind, estab 1996, empl 24, sales
$1,600,000, cert: 8a)

Colorado

2565 Premier Manufactuirng and Supply Chain Services
      7755 Miller Dr
      Frederick, CO 80504
      Contact: Edmond Johnson President
      Tel: 303-776-4145
      Email: ejohnson@pmscs.com
      Website: www.pmscs.com
Contract mfr of printed circuit board assemblies for
prototypes, production, sub assemblies, cable harness &
test. (AA, estab 2000, empl 55, sales $12,000,000, cert:
NMSDC)

Connecticut

2566 Accutron Inc.
      149 Addison Rd
      Windsor, CT 06095
      Contact: Jim Foss Outside Sales Mgr
      Tel: 860-683-8300
      Email: jfoss@accutroninc.com
      Website:
Printed circuit board assembly, surface mount assembly,
thru-hole assembly, box build assembly, ICT, functioanl
testing, flying probe testing. (As-Pac, estab 1989, empl
130, sales $25,000,000, cert: NMSDC)

2567 I C D I INC
      407 Brookside Rd
      Waterbury, CT 6708
      Contact: Steve Villodas President
      Tel: 203-753-8551
      Email: svillodas@icdi-inc.com
      Website: www.icdi-inc.com
Contract mfr electronic high tech equip & systems, turnkey
program mgmt, eng design, microprocessor systems, PC
layout, PC board & automated surface-mount assembly,
wave soldering, vapor degreasing, custom cables, ATE
testing. (Hisp, estab 1975, empl 22, sales $3,019,307, cert:
NMSDC)

Florida

2568 Aero Electronics Systems, Inc.
      411 S Park Ave
      Titusville, FL 32796
      Contact: Sales Mgr
      Tel: 321-269-0478
      Email:
      Website: http://aeroelectronics.net
Mfr custom cable assemblies, RF cables, Molded Cables,
Molded Ribbon Assemblies, Wiring Harnesses, Box Build.
(Woman, estab 2003, empl 80, sales $10,000,000, cert:
State)

2569 Hyper IC Florida Inc.
      5015 49th Ave N
      Saint Petersburg, FL 33703
      Contact: Nathalie Ouellet Presdient
      Tel: 727-822-7129
      Email: nathalie@hypericflorida.com
      Website: www.hypericflorida.com
Integrated Circuit. (Woman, estab 2008, empl 3, sales $
0, cert: WBENC)

2570 Mashack & Associates, Inc.
      503 Tuscanny St
      Brandon, FL 33511
      Contact: Brenda Rhym Presdient
      Tel: 813-662-7353
      Email: bdrhym@verizon.net
      Website:
CNC machining & printed circuit board assembly.
(Woman/AA, estab 1998, empl 2, sales $105,000, cert:
8a)

Georgia

2571 i-Tech e-Services, LLC
      4020 Steve Reynolds Blvd
      Norcross, GA 30093
      Contact: Racheal Hotran Presdient
      Tel: 770-455-8449
      Email: rhotran@itecheservices.com
      Website: www.itecheservices.com
PCB assembly, POS repair & refurbishment, deployment,
wiring sub systems & custom cable harnesses. (Woman/
As-Pac, estab 2004, empl 95, sales $5,000,000, cert:
WBENC, SDB)

2572 Lows Enterprise Inc.
      3966 Shirley Dr.
      Atlanta, GA 30336
      Contact: Barbara Whitlow President
      Tel: 404-699-0582
      Email: low1dl96@aol.com
      Website: www.lowsenterprise.com
Electronic mfg: printed wiring boards assemblies, cable
assemblies, wiring harnesses, power supplies. (Woman/
AA, estab 1984, empl 9, sales $ 0, cert: State)

2573 Nijsha Enterprise Inc
      9048 Jimmy Lee Circle
      Jonesboro, GA 30238
      Contact: Jerrell Johnson Presdient
      Tel: 770-210-1302
      Email: nijsha@att.net
      Website: www.nijshaenterprise.com
Custom cables & harness assemblies, coaxial cables, RF
cables & semi rigid, electronic components, electro
mechanical assemblies, PCB assemblies, surface mount
& through hole
assembly, box builds. (AA, estab 2006, empl 2, sales
$300,000, cert: State)

2574 Roytec Industries LLC
      306 Bell Park Dr
      Woodstock, GA 30188
      Contact: Amanda Chapman CEO
      Tel: 770-926-5470
      Email: mchapman@roytecind.com
      Website: www.roytecind.com
Mfr electrical wire harnesses & electrical wire assemblies. (Woman, estab 1984, empl 500, sales $36,734,238,
cert: WBENC)

Illinois

2575   Alpha Circuit Corporation
       730 N Oaklawn Ave
       Elmhurst, IL 60126
       Contact: Steven Ryan Business Dev Mgr
       Tel: 630-617-5555
       Email: stever@alphacircuit.com
       Website: www.alphacircuit.com
Mfr single sided, double sided & multilayer printed circuit
boards. (As-Ind, estab 1981, empl 42, sales $3,200,000,
cert: NMSDC)

2576   American Standard Circuits
       475 Industrial Dr
       West Chicago, IL 60185
       Contact: Anaya Vardya CEO
       Tel: 630-639-5444
       Email: anaya@asc-i.com
       Website: www.asc-i.com
Mfr quality rigid, metal-backed, flex & rigid-flex printed
circuit boards, RF/microwave printed circuit boards. (As-
Ind, estab 1988, empl 135, sales $31,000,000, cert:
NMSDC)

2577   CAMtek, Inc.
       2402 E Empire St
       Bloomington, IL 61704
       Contact: Presdient
       Tel: 309-661-0348
       Email:
       Website: www.camtek-mfg.com
Printed circuit board assembly, surface mount & through-
hole placement, fine pitch & ball grid array placements,
stencil, reflow, automated optical inspection, wave, wash,
wire stripping, cable assembly, potting, conformal coating.
(Woman, estab 1999, empl 86, sales $3,000,000, cert:
WBENC)

2578   Casco Manufacturing, Inc
       600 Territorial Dr Unit C
       Bolingbrook, IL 60440
       Contact: David Cohen Sales Rep
       Tel: 630-771-9555
       Email: dc@cascomanufacturing.com
       Website: www.cascomanufacturing.com
Mfr custom cable assemblies, wiring harnesses, fiber-optic
cables, patch cords, capabilities to solder, tin, and/or crimp
our terminals. (Woman, estab 1997, empl 25, sales
$3,100,000, cert: State)

2579   Circuitronics LLC
       201 N Gables Blvd
       Wheaton, IL 60510
       Contact: Shelley Lara VP Sales
       Tel: 630-668-5407
       Email: shelleylara@yahoo.com
       Website: www.circuitronicsllc.com
Mfr high tech printed circuit boards, exotic materials and
alternate finishes (As-Ind, estab 1993, empl 55, sales
$18,000,000, cert: NMSDC)

2580   General Circuit Corporation
       1370 Lively Blvd
       Elk Grove Village, IL 60007
       Contact: JANICE ROSARIO Sales/Marketing Mgr
       Tel: 847-758-8000
       Email: janice@deltapcb.com
       Website: www.Deltapcb.com
Mfr printed circuit boards: single, double & multi-layers
in small, medium & high volumes. (As-Ind, estab 1996,
empl 25, sales $4,600,000, cert: NMSDC)

2581   KLI Inc.
       304 Roma Jean Pkwy
       Streamwood, IL 60107
       Contact: Lisa Carso President
       Tel: 630-213-1283
       Email: support@kli-inc.com
       Website: www.kli-inc.com
Mfr electronic components; electronic assembly; main
harness & cable to mil specs. (Woman/As-Pac, estab
1987, empl 15, sales $ 0, cert: State, NMSDC)

2582   Midwest Molding, Inc.
       1560 Hecht Dr
       Bartlett, IL 60103
       Contact: Sanjay Patel Dir of purchasing
       Tel: 224-208-1110
       Email: sanjay.patel@mwmolding.com
       Website: www.mwmolding.com
Injection molding, insert molding, two shot molding,
IMD molding, wire harness assembly & multi-compo-
nent assembly. (As-Pac, estab 1996, empl 70, sales $ 0,
cert: NMSDC)

Indiana

2583   Precision Wire Assemblies, Inc.
       551 E Main St
       Hagerstown, IN 47346
       Contact: Penny Wickes President
       Tel: 765-489-6302
       Email: penny@pwawire.com
       Website: www.pwawire.com
Mfr wire harnesses & assemblies, cable assemblies.
(Woman, estab 1987, empl 75, sales $6,130,594, cert:
State)

Kansas

2584   S and Y Industries, Inc.
       606 Industrial Rd
       Winfield, KS 67156
       Contact: Dir Sales/Marketing
       Tel: 620-221-4001
       Email:
       Website: www.sandyindustries.com
Printed circuit boards, wire harnesses, cable assemblies,
connectors, surface mount. (Woman, estab 1984, empl
80, sales $7,660,639, cert: WBENC)

Massachusetts

2585 Cable Harness Resources, Inc.
One Robert Bonazzoli Ave
Hudson, MA 01749
Contact: Kim Nguyen
Tel: 978-562-4352
Email: knguyen@cableharnessresources.com
Website: www.cableharnessresources.com
Electrical wire harness& cable asembly, Mil-Spec source, cut, strip, tin, twist, splice, crimp, solder, coil, end-prep, connector/component installation. (Woman/As-Pac, estab 2008, empl 10, sales $800,000, cert: NMSDC)

Michigan

2586 Advanced-Cable, LLC
1179 Chicago Rd
Troy, MI 48083
Contact: Deanna Zwiesele Owner
Tel: 248-268-3167
Email: deanna@advanced-cable.com
Website: http://advanced-cable.com
Mfr custom cable assemblies (molded and non molded) & wire harnesses, dist bulk wire, cable & various electronic components. (Woman, estab 2012, empl 15, sales $2,000,000, cert: WBENC)

2587 American Hydrostatics Distribution Co.
6626 Sims Dr
Sterling Heights, MI 48313
Contact: Drew Parikh Business Dev Mgr
Tel: 248-649-2587
Email: dp@americanhydrostatics.com
Website: www.americanhydrostatics.com
Build small automation & assembly equipment, rebuild machines & general assembly services. (As-Pac, estab 1982, empl 25, sales $42,000,000, cert: NMSDC)

2588 GM&T Engineering, Inc.
775 Davis St Ste 4
Plymouth, MI 48170
Contact: Carlos Gutierrez Presdient
Tel: 734-679-8340
Email: cgutierrez@gmt-engineering.com
Website: www.gmt-engineering.com
Testing of Electrical Distribution Systems (Wire Harnesses, batteries), Engineering of EDS, Process and Product quality audits, Staffing and recruiting, Small Wire Harnesses and prototypes
Testing tooling and equipment. (Hisp, estab 2005, empl 16, sales , cert: NMSDC)

2589 Newtech 3, Inc.
28373 Beck Rd Ste H7
Wixom, MI 48393
Contact: Gail Gyenese Dir of Sales
Tel: 248-912-1062
Email: ggyenese@newtech3inc.com
Website: www.newtech3.com
Mfr lower to mid volume wire harness & circuit board assemblies. (AA, estab 2009, empl 32, sales $3,965,000, cert: NMSDC)

2590 Orri Corporation
5385 Perry Dr
Waterford, MI 48329
Contact: Angelo Doa Sales
Tel: 248-618-1104
Email: Sales@orricorp.com
Website: www.orricorp.com
Wire harnesses, cable assemblies, electrical test fixtures, robotic vision guidance software. (Woman, estab 2001, empl 12, sales $ 0, cert: WBENC)

2591 Saturn Electronics Corporation
28450 Northline Rd
Romulus, MI 48174
Contact: Parthiv Trivedi Dir Business Dev
Tel: 734-941-8100
Email: parthiv@saturnelectronics.com
Website: www.saturnelectronics.com
Printed circuit boards: prototype & production; 1 to 20 layers. (As-Ind, estab 1985, empl 190, sales $40,025,000, cert: NMSDC)

2592 Wolverine Assemblies, LLC
30260 Oak Creek Dr
Wixom, MI 48393
Contact: Adam Claytor Sr Lead Analyst
Tel: 248-822-8056
Email: aclaytor@taghold.com
Website: http://wolverine-llc.com/
Modular assembly, warehousing, sequencing, import & export, fabrication, machining, kitting, supply chain management, pre delivery inspection, repack and test, containment & sorting. (AA, estab 2010, empl 6, sales $12,000,000, cert: NMSDC)

Minnesota

2593 Aero Assemblies, Inc.
12012 - 12th Ave S
Burnsville, MN 55337
Contact: Anthony Winick Presdient
Tel: 952-894-5552
Email: tonyw@aeroassemblies.com
Website: www.aeroassemblies.com
Contract manufacturing, wire rope assembly, electronic cable assembly, print finishing, bindery, eyeletting (As-Pac, estab 1972, empl 16, sales $3,000,000, cert: NMSDC)

2594 Quantronic Corporation
8300 89th Ave N
Brooklyn Park, MN 55445
Contact: Gabriela Faouen Acct Mgr
Tel: 763-425-2602
Email: gfaouen@quantronic.net
Website: www.quantronic.net
Surface Mount & Thru Hole Assemblies, Incircuit & Functional testing, Prototype & Product development, Circuit Board Rework & modifications, Complete Product & and sub assemblies, Packaging Solutions, Conformal Coating. (As-Pac, Hisp, estab 1995, empl 65, sales $15,000,000, cert: NMSDC)

New Hampshire

2595   Custom Manufacturing Services
       235 Main Durnstable Rd
       Nashua, NH 3062
       Contact: Ray Durand VP Sales
       Tel: 603-883-1355
       Email: ray.durand@cms-nh.com
       Website: www.cms-nh.com
Contract assembly services, printed circuit board assembly, prototypes & production runs, ECO changes & PWB repairs, wave soldering, mechanical assembly, electro-mechanical assembly, chassis assembly & testing, cable & harness assembly. (Woman, estab 1976, empl 20, sales $ 0, cert: SDB)

New Jersey

2596   Delaire USA, Inc.
       1913 Atlantic Ave
       Manasquan, NJ 08736
       Contact: Presdient
       Tel: 732-528-4520
       Email:
       Website: www.delaireusa.com
Mfr custom RF & fiber optic cables & assemblies, box level assemblies, precision soldering & testing. (Woman, estab 1994, empl 19, sales $ 0, cert: State, WBENC)

2597   Precision Graphics, Inc.
       21 County Line Rd
       Somerville, NJ 08876
       Contact: Alec Weissman VP
       Tel: 908-707-8880
       Email: aweissman@precisiongraphics.us
       Website: www.precisiongraphics.us
Mfr printed circuit board assemblies, surface mount, through hole, or RoHs processing. (Woman, estab 1971, empl 55, sales $13,000,000, cert: NWBOC)

Nevada

2598   Power Assemblies LLC
       7061 W Arby Rd Ste 120
       Las Vegas, NV 89113
       Contact: Patricia Knowles Owner
       Tel: 541-610-6494
       Email: gknowles@powerassemblies.com
       Website: www.powerassemblies.com
Assemble portable power & industrial products, flexible power cable assemblies, connectors, generator docking stations, enclosed variable speed drives & cam lock panels, custom portable power products ranging from 20A to 4000A. (Woman, estab 2006, empl 9, sales $350,000, cert: State, WBENC)

New York

2599   Eltrex Industries, Inc.
       65 Sullivan St
       Rochester, NY 14605
       Contact: Avis Williams Business Dev Mgr
       Tel: 585-454-6100
       Email: avis.williams@eltrex.com
       Website: www.eltrex.com
Mechanical & electromechanical assemblies, remanufacturing, kitting & logistics services: material purchasing & consignment, packaging & distribution, warehousing. (AA, estab 1968, empl 200, sales $18,000,000, cert: State)

2600   Hazlow Electronics
       49 St. Bridgets Dr
       Rochester, NY 14605
       Contact: CEO
       Tel: 585-263-7852
       Email:
       Website: www.hazlow.com
Wire harnesses, printed circuit boards, cable assemblies, sub assembly. (Woman/Nat Ame, Hisp, estab 1971, empl 40, sales $3,500,000, cert: State, WBENC)

2601   Tony Baird Electronics, Inc.
       461 East Brighton Ave
       Syracuse, NY 13210
       Contact: Dan Strumlok VP
       Tel: 315-422-4430
       Email: dan@tonybairdelectronics.com
       Website: www.tonybairdelectronics.com
Mfr electronic components, printed circuit assembly, electronic assembly, fiber optic cable. (AA, estab 2005, empl 10, sales $4,894,647, cert: SDB)

Pennsylvania

2602   Contine Corporation
       1820 Nagle Rd
       Erie, PA 16510
       Contact: Constance Ellrich Presdient
       Tel: 814-899-0006
       Email: cellrich@continedbe.com
       Website: www.continedbe.com
Assembly & test mechanical & electro-mechanical devices, machining, sheet metal fabrication & plastic injection molding, switches, latches, rack assemblies, display units, control panels, wire harnesses etc. (Woman, estab 1981, empl 43, sales $9,175,996, cert: CPUC, WBENC)

2603   John A. Romeo & Associates, Inc.
       890 Pittsburgh Rd, Ste 7
       Butler, PA 16002
       Contact: CEO
       Tel: 724-586-6961
       Email:
       Website: www.jara-mfg.com
Mfr Custom Cables, Wiring Harnesses & Electromechanical Assemblies. (Woman, estab 1990, empl 15, sales $1,506,698, cert: WBENC)

South Carolina

2604   North American Assemblies, LLC
       2222 Cale Yarborough Hwy
       Timmonsville, SC 29161
       Contact: William Rucker
       Tel: 248-342-6500
       Email: warucker@naa-llc.com
       Website: www.naa-llc.com
Mfg & assembly services. (AA, estab 2004, empl 17, sales $3,000,000, cert: NMSDC)

Texas

2605   Accurate Connections Inc.
       13801 Hutton Dr, Ste 100
       Farmers Branch, TX 75234
       Contact: Presdient
       Tel: 972-484-8500
       Email:
       Website: www.accurateconnections.com
Cable assemblies, fiber optic & copper. (Woman, estab
2003, empl 26, sales $3,246,807, cert: State, WBENC)

2606   Arise Solutions Inc.
       5862 Cromo Ste 149
       El Paso, TX 79912
       Contact: Daniel Laing President
       Tel: 915-345-9134
       Email: sales@arisesolutions.biz
       Website: www.arisesolutions.biz
Custom designed wire harness, cable assembly, bulk wire,
signal cable, specialty bolts, screws, Nut Rivets, Inserts,
Fasteners, Spacers, Connectors & Fittings for automotive
industry. (As-Pac, estab 2012, empl 5, sales $1,000,000,
cert: State, NMSDC)

2607   Electro Plate Circuitry, Inc.
       1430 Century Dr
       Carrollton, TX 75006
       Contact: Nicolas Garcia President
       Tel: 972-466-0818
       Email: nickg@eplate.com
       Website: www.eplate.com
Mfr printed circuit boards: GF,GI, RF, insulators, heatsinks,
blind buried vias, controlled impedance. (Hisp, estab 1981,
empl 80, sales $9,000,000, cert: NMSDC)

2608   Electronic Assembly Services, Inc.
       4501 S Pinemont, Ste 108
       Houston, TX 77041
       Contact: Evelyn Fletcher CEO
       Tel: 713-686-4390
       Email: efletcher@easinchou.com
       Website: http://eashouston.com/
Custom electric & electronic assemblies & sub-assemblies:
control panels, cable wire harnesses, electro-mechanical
assemblies, printed circuit board assemblies, rack-mount
assemblies. (Woman/Hisp, estab 1987, empl 13, sales
$1,500,000, cert: State, NMSDC)

2609   Galaxy Electronics Company
       201 E Arapaho Rd
       Richardson, TX 75081
       Contact: Will Moore Sales Mgr
       Tel: 972-234-0065
       Email: wmoore@galaxyee.com
       Website: www.galaxyee.com
Fiber optic & copper cable assembly. (As-Pac, estab 1988,
empl 31, sales $ 0, cert: State, NMSDC)

2610   JG Haney & Associates LLC
       9711 Haven Crossing Court
       Houston, TX 77065
       Contact: Joyce Haney CEO
       Tel: 281-653-2441
       Email: haney@jghaneyassociates.com
       Website: www.jghaneyassociates.com
Telecommunications Services, IT products & services,
data acquisition systems, telemetry products, circuit
card assemblies, shipping containers, test set cases,
special nonmetallic, preformed packing material &
acquisition program management. (Woman/AA, estab
2011, empl 2, sales $300,000, cert: 8a)

2611   JVB Electronics dba Multilayer Technology
       3835 Conflans Rd
       Irving, TX 75061
       Contact: Johnnie Feathers Dir of Sales
       Tel: 972-790-0062
       Email: johnnie@multilayer.com
       Website: www.multilayer.com
Mfr printed circuit boards. (As-Ind, estab 1986, empl 45,
sales $720,000, cert: State, NMSDC)

2612   Optical Interconnect
       2621 Summit Ave Ste 100
       Plano, TX 75074
       Contact: Steve Wade Acct Exec
       Tel: 214-239-3988
       Email: swade@opticalinterconnect.com
       Website: www.opticalinterconnect.com
Dist fiber optic cable assemblies, copper cable assemblies, rack/wall mount metal enclosures. (Woman, estab
2004, empl , sales $100,000, cert: State, WBENC)

2613   THT Electronics Company, Inc.
       17000 Dallas Pkwy Ste 200
       Dallas, TX 75248
       Contact: Scott Sewell CEO
       Tel: 972-979-3204
       Email: scott.sewell@thtelec.com
       Website: www.thtelec.com
Electronic components, cable assemblies. (Nat Ame,
estab 1996, empl 6, sales $126,000, cert: State, NMSDC)

2614   Trendsetter Electronics
       2500 NE Inner Loop Bldg 1 Ste 105
       Georgetown, TX 78626
       Contact: Carol Williams Presdient
       Tel: 512-310-8858
       Email: stacyb@trendsetter.com
       Website: www.trendsetter.com
Stocking programs & stocking replinishment, kitting,
cable & harness assemblies, lead forming & modifying,
part sleeving & custom transformers. (Woman, estab
1995, empl 12, sales $5,536,114, cert: WBENC)

2615   Trilogy Circuits, Inc.
       1717 Firman Dr Ste 200
       Richardson, TX 75081
       Contact: Mark T McCrocklin
       Tel: 972-907-2727
       Email: mark@trilogycircuits.com
       Website: www.trilogycircuits.com
Printed circuit board design/layout. (As-Pac, estab 2001,
empl 27, sales $5,000,000, cert: State, NMSDC)

Wisconsin

2616 A1 Cable Solutions, Inc.
      665 Commercial Ave
      Waterloo, WI 53594
      Contact: Laurie Hoffmann Presdient
      Tel: 608-444-3072
      Email: ljhoffmann@usa1cable.com
      Website: www.usa1cable.com
Battery Cables, Ground Straps, Wire Harnesses, Electromechanical Assemblies, Panel Assembly & Wiring, Prototypes,
Testing & Reporting. (Woman, estab 2001, empl 2, sales ,
cert: WBENC)

ELECTRONICS & ELECTRICAL DIST.
Distribute a wide range of electrical or electronic products: battery chargers, communications equipment, video equipment, radios, measuring instruments, etc. (See also ELECTRONIC ASSEMBLY and ELECTRONICS & ELECTRICAL MFG.) NAICS Code 42

Alabama

2617 Mayer Electric Supply Company
3405 4th Ave S
Birmingham, AL 35222
Contact: James Lawrence Supplier Diversity Mgr
Tel: 205-583-3337
Email: jlawrence@mayerelectric.com
Website: www.mayerelectric.com
Dist electrical & lighting supplies. (Woman, estab 1930, empl 1035, sales $750,000,000, cert: State, WBENC)

2618 Scott Lighting Supply Co., Inc.
2301 Washington Cir NW
Huntsville, AL 35811
Contact: Joan Trew VP
Tel: 256-536-6776
Email:
Website: www.scottlighting.com
Dist lighting supplies, lamps, batteries, ballasts, emergency lighting, lighting fixtures & lamp parts. (Woman, estab 1992, empl 9, sales $1,863,518, cert: WBENC)

Arizona

2619 Aegis Electronic Group, Inc.
1465 North Fiesta Blvd. Ste 101
Gilbert, AZ 85233
Contact: Michelle Witt Technical Sales Rep
Tel: 480-635-8400
Email: michelle@aegiselect.com
Website: www.aegis-elec.com/
Dist industrial imaging equipment: cameras, lenses, monitors, cables, connectors, power supplies, frame grabbers, software, etc. (Woman, estab 1989, empl 17, sales $9,000,000, cert: WBENC)

2620 Infinite Supply LLC
15230 N 75th St, Ste 1001
Scottsdale, AZ 85260
Contact: Lucas White Reg VP
Tel: 623-242-1595
Email: lucas@infinite-supply.com
Website: www.infinite-supply.com
Mfg military hardware, electrical components, connects, back-shells & aircraft parts. (Woman, estab 2004, empl 10, sales $350,000, cert: State)

2621 Spirit Distribution and Logistics, Inc.
23910 N 19th Ave Ste 26
Phoenix, AZ 85085
Contact: Vickie Wessel Presdient
Tel: 480-998-1533
Email: v.wessel@spiritelectronics.com
Website: www.spiritelectronics.com
Dist passive components, memory products, obsolete & hard-to-find semiconductors & electromechanical devices. (Woman/Nat Ame, estab 1979, empl 15, sales $29,307,000, cert: NMSDC, WBENC)

2622 Tooh Dineh Industries, Inc.
HC 61, Box E
Winslow, AZ 86047
Contact: Casey Dooley GM
Tel: 928-686-6477
Email: cdooley@toohdineh.com
Website: www.toohdineh.com
Electronic mfg services: surface mount technology, thru-hole technology, cables, harnesses. (Nat Ame, estab 1982, empl 63, sales $11,000,000, cert: State)

California

2623 AAA Electrical Supply, Inc.
1014 S Montebello Blvd
Montebello, CA 90640
Contact: Alfred J. Alvarez Presdient
Tel: 323-721-2700
Email: zirma@aaaelectricalsupply.com
Website: www.aaaelectricalsupply.com
Dist electrical supplies: conduit fittings, wire, cable, steelboxes, weatherproof boxes, lighting, ballasts, hand tools, circuit breakers, panelboards, switchgear, transformers, wiring devices, lamps, incandescent, fluorescent, HID & LED lighting. (Hisp, estab 1988, empl 7, sales $3,426,300, cert: State, City, CPUC)

2624 Aeroflite Enterprises
261 Gemini
Brea, CA 92821
Contact: Pamela DePape Sales Mgr
Tel: 714-773-4251
Email: pdepape@aeroflite.com
Website: www.aeroflite.com
Dist aerospace electronics, custom cable assemblies & electrical connectors assemblies. (Woman, estab 1977, empl 65, sales $20,000,000, cert: NWBOC)

2625 American Industrial Control, Inc.
170 N Maple St Ste 104
Corona, CA 92880
Contact: Monica Pratt President & CEO
Tel: 951-520-0613
Email: monica@aicesupply.com
Website: www.aicesupply.com
Dist electrical supplies, mfr industrial control panels. (Woman/Hisp, estab 2000, empl 4, sales $1,010,254, cert: NMSDC, CPUC, WBENC)

2626 AREA51-ESG
51 POST
Irvine, CA 92618
Contact: Khanh Hoang OEM Sales
Tel:
Email: khanh.hoang@area51esg.com
Website: www.area51esg.com
Dist electronic components, cables, hardware, mil spec hardware, rotables, expandables, etc. (As-Pac, estab 2000, empl 53, sales $24,900,000, cert: NMSDC)

2627 AutoCell Electronics
7311 Greenhaven Dr
Sacramento, CA 95831
Contact: Mark Hardwick Acct Mgr
Tel: 888-393-6668
Email: mark@autocell.net
Website: www.autocell.net
CFLs (compact fluorescent lights), linear fluorescent lights, LED (Light Emitting Diode) lights, indoor & outdoor hardwired light fixtures (luminaires), LED Desk Lamps. (As-Pac, estab 2000, empl 5, sales $2,000,000, cert: CPUC)

2628 Bright Light LED Inc.
7751 Alabama Ave, Warehouse 7-8
Canoga Park, CA 91304
Contact: Rami Vardi CEO
Tel: 310-987-6670
Email: rvardi@brightlightled.net
Website: www.brightlightled.net
Residential & commercial LED bulbs & fixtures. (Minority, Woman, estab 2008, empl 200, sales $2,050,000, cert: NMSDC)

2629 C Plus Electronics, Inc.
17842 Irvine Blvd. Ste B144
Tustin, CA 92780
Contact: Carrie Fill Purchaser
Tel: 714-783-7141
Email: carrie.fill@cpluselectronics.com
Website: www.cpluselectronics.com
Dist electronic components: ICs, passives; interconnect products, memory modules & other computer related products. (Woman/Hisp, estab 2003, empl 15, sales $5,000,000, cert: NMSDC, SDB)

2630 Callor Sales, Inc
3850 Cedar Ave
Long Beach, CA 90807
Contact: Lori Nelson Owner
Tel: 562-426-6209
Email: lori.nelson@callorsales.com
Website: www.callorsales.com
Dist electrical, electronic & telecommunications materials & equipment. (Woman, estab 2005, empl 1, sales , cert: State)

2631 CE Supply
1111 W Victoria St
Compton, CA 90220
Contact: MobileVision Sales/Mktg
Tel: 310-735-2078
Email:
Website: www.mobilevisionus.com/
Dist wireless & electronics accessories. (Woman/As-Pac, estab 1990, empl 3, sales $2,879,544, cert: CPUC, WBENC)

2632 Cordelia Lighting, Inc.
20101 S Santa Fe Ave
Rancho Dominguez, CA 90221
Contact: Terence Yeh Presdient
Tel: 310-886-3490
Email: tyeh@cordelia.com
Website: www.cordelia.com
Fixtures/Lighting. (Woman/As-Pac, estab 1982, empl 140, sales $75,000,000, cert: State)

2633 DWY Inc.
911 S Primrose Ave, Ste I
Monrovia, CA 91016
Contact: Daniel Yohannes
Tel: 626-357-0500
Email: honeylyn@ecads-na.com
Website: www.ecads-na.com
Dist LED & solar products, energy saving LED bulbs & solar panels. (AA, estab 2001, empl 4, sales , cert: NMSDC)

2634 Electronic Distribution Services
5445 Peck Rd
Arcadia, CA 91006
Contact: Dr. G. Martin CEO
Tel: 626-258-0400
Email: drg.martin@eds-sales.com
Website: www.eds-sales.com
Dist electronics. (AA, estab 1995, empl 10, sales $ 0, cert: State)

2635 Forza Electronics
1110 S El Camino Real Ste C
San Clemente, CA 92672
Contact: James Cassano Presdient
Tel: 949-276-8686
Email: james@forzaelectronics.com
Website: www.forzaelectronics.com
Dist electronics components, semiconductors, capacitors, resistors, switches, relays, connectors, diodes, computer peripherals, computer hardware & electromechanical devices. (Woman, estab 2006, empl 5, sales $794,000, cert: WBENC)

2636 FTS Lighting Services, Inc.
160 S. Cypress St
Orange, CA 92866
Contact: Michele Davidson Presdient
Tel: 714-289-1957
Email: michele@ftslighting.com
Website: http://ftslighting.com
Energy Saving Lights & Analysis, LEDs, Induction, tubes, ballast, fixtures, aircraft, xenon, HID, Metal halide. (Woman/Hisp, estab 2010, empl 1, sales $350,000, cert: State, CPUC, WBENC)

2637 Integra Electronics, Inc.
1363 Lewis St
Anaheim, CA 92805
Contact: Victor Montez Presdient
Tel: 714-282-4990
Email: vicm@integrasmp.com
Website: www.integrasmp.com
Dist electronic components: Lampholders, Panel Mount indicator lights, incandescent & neon indicator lights, LED Panel lenses & Cable assemblies, Electro-Mechanial products. (Hisp, estab 1997, empl 11, sales $3,960,000, cert: State, NMSDC)

2638 MCV Technologies Inc.
6640 Lusk Blvd, Ste A102
San Diego, CA 92121
Contact: Edward Liang VP
Tel: 858-450-0468
Email: eliang@mcv-microwave.com
Website: www.mcv-microwave.com
MCV Microwave designs, manufactures and markets RF/ Microwave Filter, Antenna, Dielectric Resonator and Microelectronic Circuit. Bandpass Filter, Notch Filter, Lowpass Filter, Highpass Filter, Duplexer, Triplexer, Multiplexer. (Woman/As-Pac, estab 1995, empl 25, sales $2,000,000, cert: CPUC)

2639 Meritke Electronics Corp.
5160 Rivergrade Rd.
Baldwin Park, CA 91706
Contact: Oliver Su Presdient
Tel: 626-373-1728
Email: sales@meritekusa.com
Website: http://meritekusa.com
Dist electronics. (As-Pac, estab 1983, empl 36, sales $20,000,000, cert: NMSDC)

2640 Onesource Distributors, Inc.
3951 Oceanic Dr
Oceanside, CA 92056
Contact: Jeremy Schmidt Dir diversity & natl
Tel: 760-966-4500
Email: jschmidt@1sourcesupplysolutions.com
Website: www.1sourcedist.com
Dist electrical related materials. (Hisp, estab 1983, empl 310, sales $250,000,000, cert: NMSDC)

2641   Perfect Parts Corporation
7545 Irvine Center Dr, Ste 200
Irvine, CA 92618
Contact: Lulu Jaff Owner
Tel: 949-209-1655
Email: lulu@perfectelectronicparts.com
Website: www.perfectelectronicparts.com
Dist electronic components. (Woman, estab 2013, empl 5, sales , cert: WBENC)

2642   RAK Technologies LLC
23122 Mountain Pine
Mission Viejo, CA 92692
Contact: Mark Meeks President
Tel: 949-633-9845
Email: mark@rak-techca.com
Website: www.raktechca.com
Dist electronic components: semiconductors, connectors, power, sensors, relays etc. (Nat Ame, estab 2007, empl 4, sales , cert: NMSDC)

2643   SilenX Corporation
10606 Shoemaker Ave Ste A
Santa Fe Springs, CA 90670
Contact: PK Karunphan Sales Mgr
Tel: 562-941-4200
Email: pkarun@silenx.com
Website: www.silenx.com
Replace & install energy-efficient LED light tubes. (As-Pac, estab 2004, empl 6, sales $2,077,409, cert: NMSDC)

2644   Steven Engineering, Inc.
230 Ryan Way
South San Francisco, CA 94080
Contact: Bonnie A. Walter VP Marketing
Tel: 800-258-9200
Email: bonnie_walter@steveneng.com
Website: www.stevenengineering.com
Dist electronic pneumatic products, electronic components, electrical parts, industrial automation & controls. (Woman, estab 1975, empl 123, sales $46,500,000, cert: CPUC, WBENC)

2645   telCade.Com
2914-24th Ave
San Francisco, CA 94132
Contact: Jerry Chan VP Sales
Tel: 408-955-9268
Email: jerry@telcade.com
Website: http://catalog.telcade.com/
Custom cable & wire harness, coaxial connector & cables, xDSL/ VDSL filter/splitter, connectors, optical cables & connectors, power cord, power supply adapter/chargers. (Woman/As-Ind, estab 1993, empl 168, sales $6,100,000, cert: CPUC)

2646   THISAI LLC
1834 Blazewood St
Simi Valley, CA 93063
Contact: Ramalingam Subramaniam Owner
Tel: 747-206-3886
Email: ram@thisaillc.com
Website: www.thisaillc.com
Electrical products, cables, switches, wire, lighting fixtures, metal products, aluminum, sheet metal, laser cut, bent & fabricated. (As-Ind, As-Pac, estab 2015, empl 2, sales , cert: State)

2647   Unical Aviation Inc.
4775 Irwindale Ave
Irwindale, CA 91706
Contact: Ray Daljeet Mgr
Tel: 626-813-1901
Email: rdaljeet@unical.com
Website: www.unical.com
Kitts, connector, wire, hardware, flight component, Avionic, engine component, MROs. (As-Pac, estab 1990, empl 160, sales $2,000,000, cert: NMSDC)

2648   Waisun Corporation
13321 Alondra Blvd, Ste D
Santa Fe Springs, CA 90670
Contact: Albert Hui President
Tel: 562-394-6922
Email: optolight@msn.com
Website: www.optolight.com
Dist LED products, LED light bulbs, recess downlight, etc. (As-Pac, estab 1988, empl 8, sales , cert: CPUC)

Colorado

2649   Innov8 Solutions USA,LLC
1500 W 47th Ave
Denver, CO 80211
Contact: Dan Montoya Dir of sales operations
Tel: 303-328-8888
Email: dmontoya@innov8supplies.com
Website: www.innov8solutions.com
Dist electrical & telecommunications supplies, warehouse services of cable stubbing, custom cutting, order fulfillment & kitting operations. (Hisp, estab 2001, empl 20, sales , cert: NMSDC)

District of Columbia

2650   Ideal Electrical Supply Corporation
3515 V St NE
Washington, DC 20018
Contact: Cora Williams Presdient
Tel: 202-526-7500
Email: cwilliams@idealelectric.com
Website: www.idealelectric.com
Dist electrical, industrial, data & telecommunications, networking products, lighting tools & safety equipment. (Woman/AA, estab 1991, empl 17, sales $59,000,000, cert: NMSDC, WBENC)

Florida

2651   Aero Supply USA
21941 US Hwy 19 N
Clearwater, FL 33765
Contact: Robert Ramirez Business Develop Mgr
Tel: 727-754-4915
Email: rramirez@aerosupplyusa.com
Website: www.aerosupplyusa.com
Dist aerospace parts & electronic components. (Woman/Hisp, estab 2012, empl 12, sales $ 0, cert: NMSDC, SDB)

2652   Chase Components LLC
647 Arnau Dr
New Smyrna Beach, FL 32168
Contact: Cristal Dongilli CEO
Tel: 386-426-1367
Email: cristal@chasecomponents.com
Website: www.chasecomponents.com
Dist board level electronic components. (Woman, estab 2003, empl 10, sales $2,907,439, cert: WBENC)

2653 Efficient Lighting Technologies
      12555 Orange Dr Ste 4002
      Fort Lauderdale, FL 33330
      Contact: Jose Trevino Dir of Operations
      Tel: 954-623-7102
      Email: jtrevino@elt-us.com
      Website: www.elt-us.com
Dist LED light bulbs & linear fluorescent lamps. (Hisp, estab
2005, empl 22, sales $10,123,250, cert: NMSDC)

2654 LedZed International Inc.
      2240 Palm Beach Lakes Blvd
      West Palm Beach, FL 33409
      Contact: Helena Lahtinen CEO
      Tel: 954-629-0768
      Email: helena@ledzed.com
      Website: www.ledzed.com
Mfr & dist energy efficiency led lights. (Woman, estab
2011, empl 1, sales , cert: City)

2655 The Bernd Group Inc.
      1251 Pinehurst Rd
      Dunedin, FL 34698
      Contact: Pilar Bernd Presdient
      Tel: 727-733-0122
      Email: businessdevelopment@berndgroup.com
      Website: www.berndgroup.com
Material handling equip, safety products, hand & power
tools, pumps & compressors, motors, generators, electrical
hardware, batteries, lighting fixtures, lockers, bins,
shelving, lab equip. (Woman/Hisp, estab 1992, empl 66,
sales $ 0, cert: NMSDC)

Georgia

2656 AC & DC Power Technologies
      125 Cavalier Ct
      Fayetteville, GA 30215
      Contact: Charles McCartha Office Mgr
      Tel: 404-361-3788
      Email: charles@acdcpowertechnologies.com
      Website: www.acdcpowertechnologies.com
Integrate, dist & engineer electrical systems: transformers,
switchgear, batteries, generators, capacitor banks, resistors, ground fault protection, etc. (Woman/Hisp, estab
1997, empl 14, sales $3,800,000, cert: State, NMSDC,
WBENC)

2657 B & S Electric Supply Co., Inc
      4505 Mills Place
      S.W. Atlanta, GA 30336
      Contact: Clarence Robie
      Tel: 404-696-8284
      Email: c.robie@b-s-electric.com
      Website: www.bandselect.com
Dist electrical supplies. (AA, estab , empl , sales $ 0, cert:
NMSDC)

2658 GC Electrical Solutions, LLC
      120 Cecil Court
      Fayetteville, GA 30214
      Contact: George Lottier Presdient
      Tel: 770-716-5400
      Email: glottier@gcelectrical.com
      Website: www.gc-es.com
Dist electrical components: lamps, wire, conduit, panel
boards, transformers, fixtures, wiring devices. (AA, estab
2003, empl 5, sales , cert: NMSDC)

2659 NAECO, LLC
      100 NAECO Way
      Peachtree City, GA 30269
      Contact: Steven Jones Dir Sales & Marketing
      Tel: 770-487-6006
      Email: stevej@naeco.net
      Website: www.naeco.net
Dist Electrical Contacts, Contact Assemblies, Tungsten
based Heavy Metal Products & Machined Parts. (AA, As-
Pac, Hisp, estab 1999, empl 25, sales $11,111,301, cert:
NMSDC)

2660 Quality Standby Services, LLC
      1649 Sands Place SE Ste C
      Marietta, GA 30067
      Contact: Paul Whitaker GM
      Tel: 770-916-1747
      Email: paul@qualitystandbyservices.com
      Website: www.qualitystandbyservices.com
Dist, install, maintain & test standby power systems:
batteries, battery racks, chargers & spill containment.
(Woman, estab 2006, empl 19, sales $8,558,834, cert:
WBENC)

Illinois

2661 Bearings & Industrial Supply
      431 Imen Ave
      Addison, IL 60101
      Contact: Sejal Khandwala Acct Exec
      Tel: 630-628-1966
      Email: Sejal@BearingsNow.Com
      Website: www.bearingsnow.com
Dist bearings & power transmission products; pump &
pump repair parts, HVAC & electrical parts. (As-Pac,
estab , empl , sales $ 0, cert: NMSDC)

2662 Electric Motor Corporation
      3865 N Milwaukee Ave
      Chicago, IL 60641
      Contact: Isabell Siegel President
      Tel: 773-725-1050
      Email: isabell@electricmotorcorp.us
      Website: http://electricmotorcorp.us
Electric motor repair. (Woman, estab 1960, empl 25,
sales $2,488,000, cert: WBENC)

2663 Electro-Kinetics Inc.
      859 N Sivert Dr
      Wood Dale, IL 60191
      Contact: Aileen Sonderman President & CEO
      Tel: 630-595-6700
      Email: aileens@e-kinetics.com
      Website: www.e-kinetics.com
Dist electric & electronic components: sensors, relays,
contactors, controls, fuses, fuse blocks, circuit breakers,
solenoids, timers, transducers, boots/seals, cable
cordsets, cable ties, connectors, cord grips, current
operated switches. (Woman/As-Pac, estab 1957, empl 8,
sales $2,400,000, cert: NMSDC, WBENC)

2664 Electro-Wire Inc.
      933 E Remington
      Schaumburg, IL 60173
      Contact: Mike Schmidt VP
      Tel: 847-944-1500
      Email: mschmidt@electrowire.com
      Website: www.electrowire.com
Dist wire & cable, cable assemblies, mechanical cable,
harness assemblies & electromechanical sub-assemblies.
(As-Pac, estab 1978, empl 100, sales $80,000,000, cert:
NMSDC)

2665 Evergreen Supply Company
      312 N May St Ste B
      Chicago, IL 60607
      Contact: Colleen Kramer Owner
      Tel: 773-908-1021
      Email: info@evergreensupply.com
      Website: www.evergreensupply.com
Dist electronic supplies & materials. (Woman, estab 0,
empl , sales $ 0, cert: State, WBENC)

2666 Go Green LED-Alternatives, LLC
      6621 State Route 71
      Yorkville, IL 60560
      Contact: Sandra Goeken CEO
      Tel: 630-802-4213
      Email: s.miles@gogreenled.com
      Website: www.gogreenled.com
LED, light, lighting, security, value added reseller, control
systems, street lighti (Woman, estab 2008, empl 2, sales
$2,937,513, cert: CPUC, WBENC)

2667 Gordon Electric Supply Co.
      1290 N Hobbie
      Kankakee, IL 60901
      Contact: Randy Molthan CFO
      Tel: 800-892-1866
      Email: rmolthan@gordonelec.com
      Website: www.gordonelectricsupply.com
Dist elelctrical supplies. (Woman, estab 0, empl 20, sales
$8,500,000, cert: State, WBENC)

2668 Halogen Lighting Products Corp.
      P.O. Box 229
      Kaneville, IL 60144
      Contact: Gloria Stewart President
      Tel: 800-621-0001
      Email: info@halogen-lighting.com
      Website: www.halogen-lighting.com
LED & fluorescent industrial machine lights with with a
wide range of wattages, lumens capable of operating in
environments of 90 - 260 volts & some are compatible
with 24VDC. (Woman, estab 1993, empl 5, sales , cert: City,
NWBOC)

2669 Hinsdale Lighting
      777 N York Rd Ste 19
      Hinsdale, IL 60521
      Contact: David Laughter Warehouse Mgr
      Tel: 630-734-0662
      Email: hlighting@hinsdalelighting.com
      Website: www.hinsdalelighting.com
Lighting design, light fixture & light bulb distributor.
(Woman, estab 2008, empl 6, sales $1,100,000, cert:
WBENC)

2670 JP Simons & Co.
      1426 Brook Dr
      Downers Grove, IL 60641
      Contact: Jean Bradfield Presdient
      Tel: 630-693-0300
      Email: roger@jpsimons.net
      Website: www.jpsimons.com
Dist wiring devices & switches, electrical tapes, fittings,
wire, cable & cords, transformers, electrical boxes, tools &
testers, terminals & lugs, circuit breakers, fuses & terminal
strips, cables ties, etc. (Woman, estab 1919, empl 7, sales
$10,000,000, cert: State)

2671 Midco Electric Supply
      7237 W 90th Pl
      Bridgeview, IL 60455
      Contact: Tony Niedospial Sales
      Tel: 888-446-4326
      Email: tony@midcoelectric.com
      Website: www.midcoelectric.com
Dist motor controls, fuses, wire & wiring devices, circuit
breakers, switches, transformers, tie wraps, conduit &
accessories, liquid tight & fittings, signal towers, PLC's,
HMI's, relays, enclosures, timers, light fixtures, ballasts,
batteries, tape, etc (Woman, estab 1979, empl 11, sales
$13,500,000, cert: State, City, WBENC)

2672 Ottsie, LLC
      1412 Sioux Dr
      Ottawa, IL 61350
      Contact: Sally Rutledge Ott Presdient
      Tel: 815-378-7841
      Email: ottsiesupply@gmail.com
      Website: www.ottsiesupply.com
Dist electrical & plumbing supplies, generators. (Woman,
estab 2014, empl , sales $437,000, cert: State)

2673 Diesel Electrical Equipment, Inc.
      139 N Griffith Blvd
      Griffith, IN 46319
      Contact: Susan Pappas Presdient
      Tel: 219-922-1848
      Email: susan@dieselelectricalequipment.com
      Website: www.dieselelectricalequipment.com
Dist & service diesel electric locomotive components.
(Woman, estab 0, empl , sales, cert: WBENC)

2674 UV Solutions, LLC
      9118 Pinecreek Court
      Indianapolis, IN 46256
      Contact: Calvin Stewart CEO
      Tel: 317-345-9899
      Email: calvin@uvsolutions-indy.com
      Website: http://uvsolutions-indy.com
UV germicidal equipment & LED lighting. (AA, estab
2007, empl 3, sales $350,000, cert: State)

Kansas

2675 AJ Smith Enterprise Inc
      9320 Johnson Dr
      Merriam, KS 66203
      Contact: Leon Delmez
      Tel: 913-677-3008
      Email: leon.delmez@wattsuplighting.com
      Website: www.wattsuplighting.com
Dist lighting supplies: light bulbs, ballasts, sockets,
fixtures, capacitors, starters, lenses, emergency batteries
& emergency ballasts, lighting fixtures, LED bulbs & LED
tape. (Hisp, estab 1985, empl 7, sales $3,000,000, cert:
NMSDC)

Kentucky

2676 Asia-Link, Inc.
      12540 Westport Rd
      Louisville, KY 40245
      Contact: Andrew Lorenz Admin Mgr
      Tel: 502-394-3900
      Email: andrew.lorenz@asialnk.com
      Website: www.asialnk.com
Data & communication, coaxial cables & connectors,
communication connectors & kits, data/LAN cables,
telephone cords, voice & data connectors, wire terminals, insulation displacement connectors, shrink tubing.
(Woman, estab 1986, empl 18, sales $16,000,000, cert:
WBENC)

2677 BFW Inc.
      445 Baxter Ave, Ste 175
      Louisville, KY 40204
      Contact: Lynn Cooper Presdient
      Tel: 502-899-1808
      Email: lynn@bfwinc.com
      Website: www.bfwinc.com
High intensity LED portable and tethered headlights and
light sources. (Woman, estab 1994, empl 5, sales
$4,200,000, cert: WBENC)

Massachusetts

2678 C & D Electronics
      28 Appleton St
      Holyoke, MA 01040
      Contact: Shelly Kubereit Acct Mgr
      Tel: 413-493-1217
      Email: skubereit@cdindustries.com
      Website: www.cdindustries.com
Dist electronic parts & equipment. (Woman/AA, estab
1982, empl 18, sales $11,000,000, cert: NMSDC)

2679 Eastern States Components, LLC dba ES Components
      108 Pratts Junction Rd
      Sterling, MA 01564
      Contact: Michelle Aubrey Presdient
      Tel: 978-422-7641
      Email: maubrey@escomponents.com
      Website: www.escomponents.com
Dist electronic components. (Woman, estab 1981, empl
20, sales , cert: WBENC)

2680 Integrated Control Solutions Inc.
      28 Bridge Ave
      Scituate, MA 02066
      Contact: Tara Miller Presdient
      Tel: 781-545-5100
      Email: icstara@comcast.net
      Website: www.icsonline.net
Japanese, Korean, and Chinese MRO parts.
Omron, Fuji Electric, Mitsubishi, Idec Relays, motors, gear
reducer, sensors, solenoids, breakers, switches,
timers,counters (Woman, estab 1990, empl 3, sales
$1,400,000, cert: WBENC)

Maryland

2681 GreenerVolts
      801 N East St Ste 9A
      Frederick, MD 21701
      Contact: Business Dev Mgr
      Tel: 888-495-3629
      Email:
      Website: http://greenervolts.com
LED lighting, lighting controls, warehousing & fulfillment.
(Hisp, estab 2010, empl 5, sales $1,800,000, cert: NMSDC)

2682 IVS Solutions, LLC
      1040 West St
      Laurel, MD 20707
      Contact: Brian Smith President
      Tel: 240-487-0295
      Email: brian.smith@ivssolutions.net
      Website: www.ivssolutions.net
IVS Solutions is a supplier diversity data management
company that provides customized information technology
solutions to manage and enrich supplier diversity data for
corporations. Formed in 2011 to address industry needs
of (AA, estab 2011, empl 2, sales , cert: NMSDC)

2683 MX4 Electronics, Inc.
      2203 Greenspring Dr
      Timonium, MD 21093
      Contact: Susan Grill Owner
      Tel: 410-252-1192
      Email: susan@mx4elect.com
      Website: www.mx4elect.com
Dist electronic components & accessories. (Woman,
estab 1976, empl 3, sales $2,821,076, cert: State)

Michigan

2684 Arrow Motor & Pump Inc.
      692 Central Ave
      Wyandotte, MI 48192
      Contact: Gloria Marquess Inside Sales
      Tel: 734-285-5700
      Email: sales@arrowmotor.net
      Website: www.arrowmotor.net
Sales & repair electric motors, pumps & power transmission products, reducers, gearmotors, etc. (Woman, estab
1988, empl 14, sales $2,128,352, cert: WBENC)

2685 Bluecolt Lighting LLC
      4403 Concourse Dr STE B
      Ann Arbor, MI 48108
      Contact: Jaspreet Sawhney
      Tel: 734-864-5533
      Email: service@falconinnovations.com
      Website: www.bluecoltlighting.com
L.E.D. (Light Emitting Diode) lighting. (As-Ind, estab
2003, empl 9, sales $3,000,000, cert: NMSDC)

2686 Ebinger Manufacturing Company
      7869 Kensington Ct
      Brighton, MI 48116
      Contact: Janny Lu Presdient
      Tel: 248-486-8880
      Email: emc@ebinger-mfg.com
      Website: www.ebinger-mfg.com
Dist electrical, plumbing, work gloves, HVAC & safety
products. (Woman/As-Pac, estab 1974, empl 1, sales $
0, cert: NMSDC)

2687 Empire Electric
      3575 Vinewood
      Detroit, MI 48208
      Contact: Bob Pauline VP
      Tel: 313-895-1920
      Email: bob@empireec.com
      Website: www.empirewc.com
Dist electrical, industrial & networking products &
supplies. Also mfr wire harnesses & cable assemblies.
(AA, estab 2003, empl 10, sales $1,005,000,000, cert:
NMSDC)

2688 Industrial Control Service, Inc.
      9267 Riley St
      Zeeland, MI 49464
      Contact: Dale Venema VP
      Tel: 800-087-8672
      Email: dale@industrialcontrol.com
      Website: www.industrialcontrol.com
Dist controls: Cognex, DVT, Banner, Turck, Sunx, X-Rite,
Spectrum Illumination,Nerlite, RFID, Microscan, Eaton
Cutler-Hammer, Parker, Danaher, IAI, Panasonic, Hyde
Park, Giddings & Lewis, Nachi, Encoder Products, GE
Industrial. (Nat Ame, estab 1975, empl 10, sales
$5,157,803, cert: NMSDC)

2689   Manufacturing & Automation Cost Solutions, LLC
     28795 Goddard Rd, Bldg 6, Ste 201
     Romulus, MI 48174
     Contact: Kenneth M Presdient
     Tel: 248-321-2433
     Email: kgutierrez@macostsolutions.com
     Website: www.macostsolutions.com
Dist non-production maintenance spare parts in the
Electrical and Mechanical sector to support machines,
robots, automation and clean rooms. (Hisp, estab 2016,
empl 2, sales $500,000, cert: NMSDC)

2690   Opus Auto Systems, Inc.,
     4790 Mariners Point
     Harbor Springs, MI 49740
     Contact: Shige Baker President
     Tel: 248-613-3344
     Email: opusb@earthlink.net
     Website:
Dist electrical cables & wire harneses, Dc motors, step
motors & plastic resins. (Woman/As-Pac, estab 1999, empl
3, sales $510,000, cert: NMSDC)

2691   Sawyer Services Inc.
     46405 Continental Dr
     Chesterfield, MI 48047
     Contact: Kim Sawyer Office Mgr
     Tel: 586-646-5181
     Email: kim@sawyerservices.net
     Website: http://sawyer-services.com
Design, installation, management & maintenance of
facility lighting, electrical & sign systems to achieve
significant energy cost savings and more efficient facility
operations. (Woman/Hisp, estab 2009, empl 20, sales
$3,000,000, cert: NMSDC, WBENC)

2692   Strike Group LLC
     18800 Fairway Dr, Ste 10
     Detroit, MI 48221
     Contact: Lane coleman Presdient
     Tel: 313-586-0003
     Email: lanec@strikegroup.org
     Website: www.strikegroup.org
Dist electrical products. (AA, estab 1998, empl 3, sales
$3,200,000, cert: NMSDC)

2693   Vega Electric Supply, LLC
     11715 Hunters Creek Dr
     Plymouth, MI 48170
     Contact: Michael Vega Presdient
     Tel: 734-455-7360
     Email: mvega@juno.com
     Website:
Dist electrical supplies. (Hisp, estab 2006, empl 1, sales $
0, cert: NMSDC)

2694   York Electric Motors, Inc.
     611 Andre St
     Bay City, MI 48706
     Contact: Thomas Hunter Acct Mgr
     Tel: 989-684-7460
     Email: tomh@yorkelectric.com
     Website: www.yorkelectric.com
Dist & svc electric motors, generators, transformers,
inverters, pumps, etc. (Nat Ame, estab 1971, empl 37,
sales $ 0, cert: NMSDC)

Minnesota

2695   Carlo Lachmansingh Sales, Inc.
     4801 4th Ave S
     Minneapolis, MN 55419
     Contact: Carl Lachmansingh VP
     Tel: 612-827-2211
     Email: carlo@carloelectrical.com
     Website: www.carloelectrical.com
Dist electrical supplies. (As-Ind, estab 1990, empl 2, sales
$2,800,000, cert: State, 8a)

2696   JCB Enterprises, Inc. dba Reluminate
     1408 Northland Dr, Ste 105
     Mendota Heights, MN 55120
     Contact: Brigid Brady CEO
     Tel: 612-378-1677
     Email: brigid@reluminate.com
     Website: www.reluminate.com
Commercial lighting service, interior & exterior lighting.
(Woman, estab 2014, empl 10, sales $1,450,000, cert:
WBENC)

2697   Recycle Technologies, Inc.
     4000 Winnetka Ave North, Ste 210
     Minneapolis, MN 55427
     Contact: Lynn Petros CEO
     Tel: 763-559-5130
     Email: lynn@recycletechnologies.com
     Website: www.recycletechnologies.com
Recycle fluorescent bulbs, ballasts, batteries, electronics,
computers, mercury containing devices, & special
industrial waste. (Woman, estab 1993, empl 18, sales
$2,010,000, cert: WBENC)

Missouri

2698   Communications & Electrical Supplies, Inc.
     13288 Newt Dr
     Neosho, MO 64850
     Contact: Amanda Murphy Accounting Mgr
     Tel: 417-451-1789
     Email: amanda@ceslive.com
     Website: www.ceslive.com
Dist tools & electrical equipment. (Woman, estab 1990,
empl 8, sales $3,000,000, cert: WBENC)

2699   Cooling Components Inc.
     69 N Gore Ave
     Saint Louis, MO 63119
     Contact: morgan brewster Dir of sales
     Tel: 314-772-8311
     Email: morgan@coolingcomponents.com
     Website: www.ccicoolingtowerparts.com
Dist, service, repair & erect cooling towers & related
equipment. (Woman, estab 2000, empl 10, sales $ 0,
cert: State, WBENC)

2700   Electronic Supply Co, Inc.
     4100 Main St
     Kansas City, MO 64111
     Contact: Bob Niekamp Mgr
     Tel: 816-931-0250
     Email: bobn@eskc.com
     Website: www.eskc.com
Dist electronic parts, wire/cable, tools, test equipment,
security cameras & systems, access control systems,
computer networking equipment. (Woman, estab 1952,
empl 33, sales $17,300,000, cert: City)

2701 US Electronics Inc.
1590 Page Industrial Blvd
Saint Louis, MO 63132
Contact: Anil Arekapudi President
Tel: 314-423-7550
Email: anil@us-electronics.com
Website: www.us-electronics.com
Dist electrical & electronic components. Mfr electrical bulbs, Halogen, energy saving & LED bulbs. (As-Ind, estab 1995, empl 15, sales $2,200,000, cert: NMSDC)

North Carolina

2702 Tiger Controls Inc.
7615 Business Park Dr
Greensboro, NC 27409
Contact: Neeta Singh President
Tel: 336-889-6265
Email: neeta@tigercontrols.com
Website: www.tigercontrols.com
Dist electronic, electrical & industrial supplies. (Woman/As-Pac, estab , empl , sales $9,005,000, cert: NMSDC)

2703 Video & Security Specialists
2313 Wedgewood Dr
Matthews, NC 28104
Contact: Erika Gordon Partner
Tel: 704-821-9396
Email: egordon@carolina.rr.com
Website: www.videoandsecurityspecialists.com
Dist electrical & security products: alarm/security systems, fire alarm systems, structured wiring, access control, security cameras, networking, phone system, intercom & gates. (Woman, estab 1975, empl 7, sales $220,866, cert: State)

New Jersey

2704 Samson Electrical Supply Co Inc
1764 New Durham Road
South Plainfield, NJ 07080
Contact: Joan Cohen Presdient
Tel: 732-393-7070
Email: yourdiversesupplier@samsonelectrical.com
Website: www.samsonelectrical.com
Dist electrical supplies. (Woman, estab 1949, empl 51, sales $40,200,000, cert: State, City, WBENC)

2705 Weissco Power Limited Liability Company
516 Route 513
Califon, NJ 07830
Contact: Stacy Weiss Presdient
Tel: 908-832-2173
Email: sweiss@weisscopower.com
Website: www.weisscopower.com
DIst uninterruptible power supply products & services, preventative maintenance, emergency services, load testing, battery installation & removal, equipment removal & battery maintenance. (Minority, Woman, estab 1999, empl 10, sales $2,700,000, cert: State)

Nevada

2706 Codale Energy Services & Supply, LLC
3920 W Sunset Rd, Ste A
Las Vegas, NV 89118
Contact: Oscar Aliaga Presdient
Tel: 702-384-8500
Email: oscara@codaleess.com
Website: www.codaleess.com
Dist electrical supplies: commercial construction, hospitality MRO, solar, comm data, Outside plant, & Utility. (Hisp, estab 2010, empl 21, sales $21,500,000, cert: NMSDC)

New York

2707 Aurora Electric Inc.
141 Federal Circle
Jamaica, NY 11430
Contact: Veronica Rose President
Tel: 718-371-0385
Email: vrose@auroraelectric.org
Website: www.auroraelectric.org
Data communication & electrical installation & maintenance. (Woman, estab 1993, empl 17, sales $795,628, cert: State, City)

2708 Deep Roof Lighting
27 Hall St
Brooklyn, NY 11205
Contact: Jay Chen Exec
Tel: 718-243-9388
Email: deeproof@aol.com
Website: www.deeprooflighting.com
Software controlled patent daylight harvest dimming control system. Dimmanble LED, Dimmable and Non-dim Fluorescent, HID, Halogen Recess housings, Track lighting, Pendant lights, Flush mount ceiling. (As-Pac, estab 1997, empl 7, sales $2,000,000, cert: City)

2709 East Coast Metallic Tubing & Hardware Supply Corp
1951 Ocean Ave, Unit 4
Ronkonkoma, NY 11779
Contact: CEO
Tel: 631-676-5570
Email:
Website: www.eastcoastmetallic.com
Dist metallic & conduit hardware. (Woman, estab 2001, empl 2, sales , cert: State)

2710 Edge Electronics Inc.
75 Orville Dr.
Bohemia, NY 11716
Contact: Mitchel Auerbach VP Operations
Tel: 631-471-3343
Email: mauerbach@edgeelectronics.com
Website: www.edgeelectronics.com
Dist electronics. (Minority, Woman, estab 1990, empl 34, sales $33,009,000, cert: City, NMSDC, WBENC)

2711 Linrose Electronics Inc.
29 Cain Dr
Plainview, NY 11803
Contact: Debra Freedman Presdient
Tel: 516-293-2520
Email: debra@linrose.com
Website: www.linrose.com
Dist CML - Led indicators. (Woman, estab 1964, empl 5, sales $510,000, cert: WBENC)

2712   North Shore Components Inc.
       9 Sawgrass Dr
       Bellport, NY 11713
       Contact: David Hochhauser Acct Mgr
       Tel: 631-504-6038
       Email: davidh@nscomponents.com
       Website: www.nscomponents.com
Dist IC's, semiconductors, capacitors, connectors, resistors, diodes, etc. (Woman, estab 2001, empl 22, sales $ 0, cert: WBENC)

2713   Serendipity Electronics, Inc.
       152 E Main St
       Huntington, NY 11743
       Contact: Yovanna Camargo Acct Mgr
       Tel: 631-424-2244
       Email: yovannac@serendipityelectronics.com
       Website: www.serendipityelectronics.com
Dist electronic components; capacitors, resistors, diodes, computer peripherals, active & passive components. (Woman, estab 1992, empl 9, sales $19,000,000, cert: WBENC)

2714   Sheraden Lighting & Electrical Products Corp.
       15 Storer Ave, Unit B Unit B
       Staten Island, NY 10309
       Contact: Joseph Carlucci VP Sales
       Tel: 718-259-6480
       Email: Joe@sheraden.com
       Website: www.sheraden.com
Dist electrical supplies, pipe, wire, cable, breakers, smoke alarms, connectors, couplings, THHN, Lamps, Bulbs, tools, drill bits, anchors, intercoms, LED, fixtures, romex, BX, snakes, screws, threaded rod, fittings, plates. (Woman, estab 1981, empl 9, sales $3,000,000, cert: State, WBENC)

2715   Southtown Electronics Inc.
       75 Lake St
       Hamburg, NY 14075
       Contact: Heather Sidorowicz Owner
       Tel: 716-648-6565
       Email: heather@southtownav.com
       Website: www.southtownav.com
Dist & install commercial Audio Video Technology Solutions: Audio Video Systems, Digital Signage, Electronics Sales (TVs, Speakers, Racking Equipment), Music Systems, interactive Rooms & Conference rooms. (Woman, estab 1984, empl 6, sales , cert: State)

2716   Venus Power-Com Supply, LLC
       54-07 46th St
       Maspeth, NY 11378
       Contact: Presdient
       Tel: 646-248-7050
       Email:
       Website: www.venussupply.com
Dist electrical, data & power products. (Woman, estab 2014, empl 5, sales , cert: City, WBENC)

Ohio

2717   CEC Electronics Corporation
       1739 Akron Peninsula Rd
       Akron, OH 44313
       Contact: Valerie George Acct Rep
       Tel: 330-916-8100
       Email: vgeorge@cecelectronics.com
       Website: www.cecelectronics.com
Dist electronic components. (Hisp, estab 1981, empl 9, sales $ 0, cert: State)

2718   Daycoa, Incorporated
       50 Walnut Rd
       Medway, OH 45341
       Contact: Tamela Chenault Sales Consultant
       Tel: 937-849-1315
       Email: tami@daycoa.com
       Website: www.daycoa.com
Dist lighting products. (Woman, estab 1957, empl 14, sales $33,866,096, cert: WBENC)

2719   E-Z Electric Motor Service, Inc.
       8510 Bessemer Ave
       Cleveland, OH 44127
       Contact: Demetrius Ledgyard VP Sales
       Tel: 216-581-8820
       Email: demetrius@ezelectricmotor.com
       Website: http://www.ezelectricmotor.com
Dist & repair electric motors: complete rewinds, rebuild, machine shop services, repair pumps, & gearboxs, dynamic balancing. (AA, estab 1965, empl 16, sales $196,687, cert: State, NMSDC)

2720   Mirg Corporation
       6270 Este Ave
       Cincinnati, OH 45232
       Contact: Michael Griffie President
       Tel: 513-679-2020
       Email: mgriffie@mirgcorp.com
       Website: www.mirgcorp.com
Dist electrical supplies, electrical contracting. (AA, estab 1989, empl 9, sales $ 0, cert: State, NMSDC)

2721   Peak Electric, Inc.
       320 N Byrne Rd
       Toledo, OH 43607
       Contact: Milton McIntyre Presdient
       Tel: 419-726-4848
       Email: mmcintyre@peakelectrictoledo.com
       Website: www.peakelectrictoledo.com
Dist lighting, LED indoor & outdoor, fixtures, lamps, ballast & components, switchgear, transformers, panelboards & disconnects, fuses, wire, conduits, fittings & boxes, telecommunication equip, high voltage equip. (Woman/AA, estab 2000, empl 3, sales $7,000,000, cert: State, City, NMSDC)

2722   US Communications and Electric
       4933 Neo Pkwy
       Garfield Heights, OH 44128
       Contact: Jim Connole COO
       Tel: 216-478-0810
       Email: jconnole@uscande.com
       Website: www.uscande.com
Technology-based communications cabling systems, design & install outdoor copper systems, horizontal copper cabling solutions. (Woman, estab , empl , sales $17,000,000, cert: State, City, WBENC)

2723   Wheatley Electric Service Co.
       2046 Ross Ave
       Cincinnati, OH 45212
       Contact: Dorothy Elsbrock Presdient
       Tel: 513-531-4951
       Email: motor@fuse.net
       Website: www.wheatleyelectric.com
Dist & repair electric motors & pumps, recondition, rebuild & re-design motors. (Woman, estab 1934, empl 9, sales $ 0, cert: WBENC)

Oregon

2724 Super Stores Service
11170 SW 5th St
Beaverton, OR 97005
Contact: Mary Kroger Acct Mgr
Tel: 800-462-2370
Email: maryk@superstoresservice.com
Website: http://superstoresservice.com
Dist replacement parts for manual & electric pallet jacks used to handle palletized goods. (Woman, estab 1986, empl 20, sales $4,200,000, cert: WBENC)

Pennsylvania

2725 Decision Distribution America, Inc.
4548 Market St, Ste 215
Philadelphia, PA 19139
Contact: Bernie Hopewell Presdient
Tel: 215-493-4400
Email: bernie@ddistribution.com
Website: www.ddistribution.com
Dist electrical, hvac, mechanical, plumbing, supplies & equipment. (AA, As-Pac, estab 2004, empl 7, sales $14,000,000, cert: State, NMSDC)

2726 DEW Electric, Inc.
189 Enterprise Ln
Connellsville, PA 15425
Contact: Wendy Wiltrout CEO
Tel: 724-628-9711
Email: wendy@dewelectric.com
Website: www.dewelectric.com
Dust & repair motors, electronic drives, gearboxes, generators, control panel fabrication. (Woman, estab 1993, empl 4, sales $935,000, cert: WBENC)

2727 Electrical Systems & Construction Supplies
5131-37 N 2nd St, Bldg 12
Philadelphia, PA 19120
Contact: Bernard Hopewell CEO
Tel: 215-324-3291
Email: bhopewell@escsinc.net
Website: www.escsinc.net
Dist electrical equipment, construction supplies, wire & cable & lighting. (AA, estab 2003, empl 3, sales $1,440,000, cert: State, City)

2728 Lights for Less, LLC
500 N Walnut Rd
Kennett Square, PA 19348
Contact:
Tel: 610-925-5740
Email:
Website: http://l4less.com
Dist lamps, fixtures & ballasts. (Woman, estab 1998, empl 3, sales $1,330,000, cert: State, WBENC)

2729 R. Scheinert & Sons, Inc.
10092 Sandmeyer Ln
Philadelphia, PA 19116
Contact: Sheree Miller Presdient
Tel: 215-673-9800
Email: sheree@scheinert.com
Website: http://scheinert.com
Repair, rewind & dist AC & DC electric motors, pump repair & refurbish, new cooling tower technology, eliminating gearboxes, warranty center. (Woman, estab , empl 24, sales $6,000,000, cert: City, WBENC)

2730 Unity Electric Discount, LLC
5040 Overbrook Ave
Philadelphia, PA 19131
Contact: Clyde Mason CEO
Tel: 267-701-5856
Email: cmason215@verizon.net
Website:
Dist electric generation supplies. (AA, estab 2011, empl 4, sales , cert: City, NMSDC)

2731 Valenko Incorporated
4124 Clendenning Rd
Gibsonia, PA 15044
Contact: Jim Perko VP
Tel: 888-908-6322
Email: info@valenko.com
Website: http://valenko.com
Dist electrical products: custom transformers, panels, wire, cable, power distribution equipment, hand tools, conduit, couplings, cable assemblies, cable management, UPS, data center. (Woman, estab 2007, empl 5, sales $4,013,000, cert: State)

Puerto Rico

2732 Wholesale Electric Caribe Inc.
P.O. Box 2057
Barceloneta, PR 00617
Contact: Miguel Barrios Presdient
Tel: 787-846-5755
Email: sales@wecipr.com
Website: www.wecipr.com
Dist electronic products: automation & control products. (Hisp, estab 1999, empl 43, sales $7,331,560, cert: NMSDC)

South Carolina

2733 Carolina Product Solutions, LLC
P.O. Box 12901
Florence, SC 29504
Contact: Sean Tanner Presdient
Tel: 843-409-6922
Email: stanner@cpsled.com
Website: www.cpsled.com
LED Lighting. (Nat Ame, estab 2008, empl 4, sales $2,800,000, cert: NMSDC)

2734 Electritex
321 Alliance Parkway
Williamston, SC 29697
Contact: Tracie Craft President
Tel: 864-226-4438
Email: andersonoffice@electritex.com
Website: www.electritex.com
Dist & service electric motors. (Woman, estab 1980, empl 20, sales , cert: WBENC)

Tennessee

2735 Brighter Days & Nites, Inc.
2165 Troyer Aven
Memphis, TN 38114
Contact: Dorothy Sinclair CEO
Tel: 901-775-1902
Email: csallie@bdnincorp.com
Website: www.bdnincorp.com
Dist electrical materials. (Woman/AA, estab 2003, empl 5, sales $13,000,000, cert: NMSDC, WBENC)

2736   Diversified Supply, Inc.
     210 N Highland Park Ave
     Chattanooga, TN 37404
     Contact: Janice Brown Sales Mgr
     Tel: 423-544-8964
     Email: jbrown@diversifiedsupply.com
     Website: www.diversifiedsupply.com
DIst electrical & instrument materials. (AA, estab 1987, empl 58, sales $ 0, cert: NMSDC)

2737   Edwards Supply Company
     315 Oak Ridge Turnpike
     Oak Ridge, TN 37830
     Contact: Tracie Miller CEO
     Tel: 865-483-1766
     Email: tracie@edwardssupply.com
     Website: www.edwardssupply.com
Dist electrical supplies: ballast, batteries, conduit, electric, electrical, janitorial, lamps, lighting, motors, tools, wire. (Woman/Nat Ame, estab 1993, empl 23, sales $24,472,449, cert: NMSDC, WBENC)

2738   Industrial Sales Company of Memphis Inc.
     7520 Bartlett Corporate Dr
     Bartlett, TN 38133
     Contact: Judy May Owner
     Tel: 901-380-5460
     Email: judymay1@bellsouth.net
     Website:
Dist electrical components. (Woman/AA, estab 1965, empl 10, sales $4,800,000, cert: City, WBENC)

Texas

2739   Advanced Equipment Co. dba Prime Distributing
     P.O. Box 946
     Allen, TX 75013
     Contact: Carole Booth Inside Sales
     Tel: 972-562-0170
     Email: caroleb@primedistributing.com
     Website: http://primedistributing.com
Dist electronic components. (Woman, estab 1972, empl 8, sales $1,135,426, cert: WBENC)

2740   Crawford and Wilson Enterprises
     1251 Industrial Blvd, Ste A
     Plano, TX 75074
     Contact: Lena Wilson Owner
     Tel: 972-422-2280
     Email: cwelectric@att.net
     Website:
Electrical materials, GE lighting, indoor fixtures, outdoor fixtures, hazardous location, control systems, signage, non-led lamps, refit solutions, led lamps and modules, transportation, ballast and drivers, refrigerated display, wire, lamps. (Woman, estab 1978, empl 5, sales , cert: State)

2741   Demand Lighting USA Inc
     1321 Rutherford Lane Ste 150,
     Austin, TX 78753
     Contact: Gary Morrissey COO
     Tel: 512-822-1100
     Email: garymorrissey@demandlighting.com
     Website: www.demandlighting.com
Dist DLC, Energy Star LED lighting solutions. (Woman, estab 2013, empl 15, sales $1,000,000, cert: State, WBENC, SDB)

2742   IDM Products
     10500 Metric Dr, Ste 119
     Dallas, TX 75243
     Contact: Gerald Grimes Presdient
     Tel: 888-908-4580
     Email: gerald@idmproducts.com
     Website: www.idmproducts.com
Dist LED Lighting, Building Maintenance & Office Products, Industrial Products, Food Service Disposables and Healthcare Products. (AA, estab 2018, empl 4, sales $1,000,000, cert: NMSDC)

2743   Mavich LLC
     525 Commerce St.
     Southlake, TX 76092
     Contact: Vincent Manfredini Operations
     Tel: 682-503-4484
     Email: vincent.manfredini@mavich.com
     Website: www.mavich.com
Dist MRO & industrial supplies: electronic components, connectors, passives, resistors, etc. (Woman/Hisp, estab 2010, empl 10, sales $3,000,000, cert: State)

2744   NOVA Electronic Materials LLC
     1189 Porter Rd
     Flower Mound, TX 75022
     Contact: Presdient
     Tel: 972-478-7002
     Email:
     Website: www.novawafers.com
Dist silicon wafers & cleanroom consumables. (Woman, estab 1989, empl 5, sales $4,216,523, cert: State)

2745   Portable Power Systems Inc.
     2890 Market Loop
     Southlake, TX 76092
     Contact: Jordan Hamill VP Sales
     Tel: 303-460-8261
     Email: sales@portablepower.com
     Website: www.portablepower.com
Dist OEM battery and power products. (Woman/AA, Hisp, estab 1992, empl 13, sales $4,000,000, cert: State)

2746   Specialty Optical Systems, Inc.
     10210 Forest Ln
     Dallas, TX 75243
     Contact: Terry Nelson
     Tel: 214-340-8574
     Email: sales@sossupply.com
     Website: www.soslightbulbs.com
Dist lightbulbs: lamps & bulbs, ballasts & fixtures. (Woman, estab 1981, empl 14, sales $5,015,000, cert: WBENC)

2747   Supa Tech Inc.
     17304 Preston Rd Ste 800
     Dallas, TX 75252
     Contact: Sue Glover Presdient
     Tel: 972-238-8958
     Email: sglover@supatech.net
     Website: www.supatech.net
Information technology products & printed circuit boards. (Woman/Nat Ame, estab 1980, empl 3, sales $285,000, cert: State)

2748 Telecom Electric Supply Company
      1304 Capital Ave
      Plano, TX 75074
      Contact: Christy Moses Sales Exec
      Tel: 972-422-0012
      Email: cmoses@tes85.com
      Website: www.tes85.com
Dist electric, utility, construction & telecommunication
supplies. (AA, estab , empl , sales $33,858,031, cert: State,
NMSDC)

2749 Villarreal & Sons Enterprises, Inc.
      P.O. Box 2258
      Anthony, TX 79821
      Contact: Rick Villarreal President
      Tel: 915-351-2444
      Email: linda@electric-1.com
      Website: www.Electric-1.com
Electrical construction, voice, data & video network
cabling, power analysis, control systems repair & installation, custom lighting design. (Hisp, estab 1986, empl 10,
sales $ 0, cert: State)

2750 Wholesale Electric Supply of Houston
      4040 Gulf Fwy
      Houston, TX 77004
      Contact: Pam McKellop President
      Tel: 713-749-8461
      Email: khighland@wholesaleelectric.com
      Website: www.wholesaleelectric.com
Dist electrical & data communications material. (Woman,
estab 1949, empl 284, sales $ 0, cert: WBENC)

Virginia

2751 Bright Regards LLC
      5837 Governors Hill Dr
      Alexandria, VA 22310
      Contact: Yvonne Herrera Presdient
      Tel: 703-349-1709
      Email: yvonne@brightregards.com
      Website: www.brightregards.com
Commercial LED, induction & solar lighting solutions.
(Woman/As-Pac, estab 2014, empl 1, sales , cert: State)

2752 Delta Automation, Inc.
      2704 Charles City Rd
      Richmond, VA 23231
      Contact: Margarete Culley CEO
      Tel: 804-236-2800
      Email: plc@deltaautomation.com
      Website: www.deltaautomation.com
Industrial electronic control equipment, PLCs & drives.
(Woman, estab 1996, empl 19, sales $ 0, cert: State)

2753 Jo Kell, Inc.
      1716 Lambert Ct
      Chesapeake, VA 23320
      Contact: Patricia Galiney Sales
      Tel: 904-260-8420
      Email: customerservice@jokell.com
      Website: www.jokell.com
Dist electrical apparatus & equipment, wiring supplies &
related equipment. (Woman, estab 1977, empl 50, sales
$30,383,075, cert: WBENC)

2754 Reynolds Lighting Supply Co.
      606 Research Rd
      Richmond, VA 23236
      Contact: Valerie Reynolds President
      Tel: 804-897-2300
      Email: valarie@reynoldslighting.com
      Website:
Dist replacement light bulbs, ballasts, fixtures, electrical
& electronic items. (Woman, estab 1987, empl 7, sales
$2,250,000, cert: State)

Vermont

2755 Granite City Electric Supply
      14 Morse Rd
      Bennington, VT 05201
      Contact: Phyllis Papani Godwin Chairman of the
      Board
      Tel: 617-472-6500
      Email: phyllisg@granitecityelectric.com
      Website: www.granitecityelectric.com
Dist electrical products. (Woman, estab 1923, empl 70,
sales $90,000,000, cert: State)

Washington

2756 1 Industrial Source
      17627 E Lake Desire Dr SE
      Renton, WA 98058
      Contact: Tammie Cook Owner
      Tel: 206-354-4295
      Email: tammiecook@1industrialsource.com
      Website: www.1industrialsource.com
Dist LED lighting, hand dryers and other products used
in electrical upgrades. (Woman, estab 2009, empl 1,
sales , cert: State)

2757 Mobile Electrical Distributors, Inc.
      14050 Lake City Way NE
      Seattle, WA 98125
      Contact: Sales
      Tel: 206-363-2400
      Email:
      Website: www.mobileelec.com
Dist electrical supplies: ballasts, boxes, conduit &
fittings, lighting, service gear, tools, testers, wire, wiring
devices, motor controls, fuses, etc. (Woman, estab
1956, empl 11, sales $925,000, cert: State, WBENC)

2758 First American Engineered Solutions, LLC
      136 Jackson St, Ste C
      Oshkosh, WI 54901
      Contact: Gerald Morris President
      Tel: 920-231-8501
      Email: gmorris@firstamericanllc.com
      Website: www.firstamericanllc.com
Dist electronics, electrical equipment, industrial equipment & supplies, office equipment & supplies & ordnance. (Nat Ame, estab 1997, empl 12, sales
$4,500,000, cert: NMSDC, 8a)

ELECTRONICS & ELECTRICAL MFG.
Firms design, develop and make (turnkey) electro-mechanical devices on contract or market their own products such as power supplies, test equipment, guidance systems, robotics, radar, CMOS-IC, connectors, modems, military trainers, motors, etc. NAICS Code 33

Alabama

2759 Amphenol Tecvox, LLC.
4900 Bradford Dr Ste 1
Huntsville, AL 35805
Contact: Ryan Brown Financial Analyst
Tel: 256-417-4338
Email: ryan.brown@tecvox.com
Website: www.tecvox.com
Mfr finish electronic components, single, dual & multi channel headphones & remote contols, plastic & rubber products, metal stamping & cable assemblies. (Minority, estab 2002, empl 50, sales $3,300,000, cert: NMSDC)

2760 Global Manufacturing, Inc.
248 N Main St
Arab, AL 35016
Contact: Kathy Bennefield Mgr
Tel: 256-789-0948
Email: kathy@globalmanufacturing.us
Website: www.globalmanufacturing.us
Custom fabricated wire harnesses & cables, Data cables, MIL-SPEC, Coaxial, Power assemblies. (Hisp, estab 2014, empl 17, sales $1,824,260, cert: NMSDC)

California

2761 Abbott Technologies
8203 Vineland Ave
Sun Valley, CA 91352
Contact: Kerima Batte President & CEO
Tel: 818-504-0644
Email: kmbatte@abbott-tech.com
Website: www.abbott-tech.com
Power Management Solutions, Military Transformers & Rectifiers, Custom Power Supplies & Magnetic Components, Wide Range of AC to DC Standard. (Woman/Hisp, estab 1961, empl 43, sales $5,110,790, cert: State)

2762 American Industrial Control, Inc.
170 N Maple St Ste 104
Corona, CA 92880
Contact: Monica Pratt President & CEO
Tel: 951-520-0613
Email: monica@aicesupply.com
Website: www.aicesupply.com
Dist electrical supplies, mfr industrial control panels. (Woman/Hisp, estab 2000, empl 4, sales $1,010,254, cert: NMSDC, CPUC, WBENC)

2763 Berkeley Integration Group dba Fiber.com
2200 Powell St, Ste 1200
Emeryville, CA 94608
Contact: Sophia Mendoza-Hirano Acct/Sales Mgr
Tel: 510-227-5583
Email: sophia@fiber.com
Website: www.fiber.com
Fiber optic cables, connectors and accessories, fiber jumpers, patch cords, pigtails, multi-strand, armored, aerial, indoor/outdoor, plenum, LSZH. (As-Pac, estab 1989, empl 4, sales , cert: NMSDC)

2764 Bishop-Wisecarver Corporation
2104 Martin Way
Pittsburg, CA 94565
Contact: Barbara Williams Supplier Diversity Administrator
Tel: 888-580-8272
Email: bwilliams@bwc.com
Website: www.bwc.com
Mfr linear & rotary motion components, custom engineering services, bearings, vee guide wheels, linear guides, linear actuator, custom machine shop, XYZ systems, gantry, rotary tables, custom assembly, linear slides, linear bearing, dualvee. (Woman, estab 1950, empl 64, sales $21,000,000, cert: WBENC)

2765 Calpak USA, Inc.
13750 Prairie Ave
Hawthorne, CA 90250
Contact: Danish Qureshi VP
Tel: 310-937-7335
Email: danish@calpak-usa.com
Website: www.calpak-usa.com
Electronic Design, Electronics Engineering, Contract Manufacturing Services (CMS), Electronic Manufacturing Services (EMS), PCB Layout, PCB Design, PCB Assembly. (As-Pac, estab 1978, empl 15, sales $2,400,000, cert: State, NMSDC, SDB)

2766 Century Wire & Cable
7400 E Slauson Ave
Commerce, CA 90040
Contact: Bob Arthur Acct Exec
Tel: 800-999-5566
Email: arthur@centurywire.com
Website: www.centurywire.com
Mfr electrical wire & cable products. (Hisp, estab 1965, empl 110, sales $40,000,000, cert: City)

2767 Doc Stephens Scientific
5851 S Garth Ave
Los Angeles, CA 90056
Contact: David Stephens CEO
Tel: 310-568-9082
Email: david.stephens@dsscientific.com
Website: www.dsscientific.com
Equipment & electronic manufacturing services related to infrared, visual cameras & imaging systems, RF & high speed fiber optic telecommunication circuits, sensor designs, silicon III-V semiconductor processing. (AA, estab 2014, empl 2, sales , cert: NMSDC)

2768 Interlog Corporation
1295 N Knollwood Circle
Anaheim, CA 92801
Contact: Justin Kwon President
Tel: 714-529-7808
Email: jkwon@interlogcorp.com
Website: www.interlogcorp.com
Mfr lighting & signal products for commercial, construc-
tion & automotive market. (As-Pac, estab 1993, empl 26,
sales $9,000,000, cert: State)

2769 Johnson-Peltier Electric
12021 S Shoemaker Ave
Santa Fe Springs, CA 90670
Contact: Greg Kelley Business Development
Tel: 562-944-3408
Email: gkelley@johnson-peltier.com
Website: www.johnson-peltier.com
Industrial electrical contracting, including power distribu-
tion, medium & high voltage line work, control systems,
instrumentation, and communication integration. (Nat
Ame, estab 1957, empl 85, sales , cert: NMSDC, CPUC)

2770 KR Wolfe, Inc.
10015 Maine Ave
Lakeside, CA 92040
Contact: Kasey Pitchford Dir of Client Relations
Tel: 619-368-1544
Email: kasey.pitchford@krwolfe.com
Website: http://krwolfe.com
Low voltage systems installation & integration, design,
layout & installation/integration of A/V & control systems.
(Woman, estab 2007, empl 34, sales $5,500,000, cert:
WBENC)

2771 Ledtronics, Inc.
23105 Kashiwa Court
Torrance, CA 90505
Contact: Janelle Mika-Palmer Manufacturer Rep
Tel: 630-243-0412
Email: janemika@mikasales.com
Website: www.ledtronics.com
Design & mfr light emitting diodes (LEDs). (As-Ind, As-Pac,
estab 1983, empl 125, sales $12,470,700, cert: NMSDC,
CPUC)

2772 Magnuson Products LLC
1990 Knoll Dr Bldg A
Ventura, CA 93003
Contact: Nader Rayes Brand Mgr
Tel: 805-765-5562
Email: nader.rayes@magnusonproducts.com
Website: www.magnusonsuperchargers.com
Design, fabrication & mfr superchargers. (Woman, estab
2010, empl 60, sales $14,649,000, cert: WBENC)

2773 Micro Analog Inc.
1861 Puddingstone Dr
La Verne, CA 91750
Contact: Kim Bickmeier Dir of Sales
Tel: 909-392-8277
Email: kimbickmeier@micro-analog.com
Website: www.micro-analog.com
Mfr electronics: printed circuit board assembly PCBA,
custom cable & wire harness assembly, box/system build.
(Woman/As-Pac, estab 1991, empl 155, sales $15,698,000,
cert: NMSDC)

2774 Myers Power Products, Inc.
2950 E Philadelphia St
Ontario, CA 91761
Contact: Diana Grootonk CEO
Tel: 909-923-1800
Email: diana.grootonk@myerspower.com
Website: www.myerspower.com
Mfr low voltage & med voltage electrical distribution
equipment, 5,15,27 & 38kv switchgear, LV switchgear,
switchboards, panel boards, inverters, converters &
electrical products & circuit breakers. (Woman, estab
2001, empl 500, sales $263,101,084, cert: CPUC,
WBENC)

2775 NexEco Energy Conservation, Inc.
9370 Studio Court, Ste 168
Elk Grove, CA 95758
Contact: Nick Potter Acct Mgr
Tel: 855-711-6868
Email: nick@nexeco.net
Website: http://nexeco.net
Mfr energy efficient LED lighting products, LED Bulbs,
LED Fixtures, LED Hardwired Interior Ceiling Fixture, LED
Hardwired Exterior Porch lanterns, LED Hardwired Vanity
Fixture. (Woman/As-Pac, estab 2016, empl 5, sales
$800,000, cert: State)

2776 One-E-Way, Inc.
3016 E Colorado Blvd Ste 70848
Pasadena, CA 91107
Contact: Cedric Woolfork CFO/VP
Tel: 310-743-4081
Email: cedric@one-e-way.com
Website: http://wayvz.com/
Design & mgr electronic products. (AA, estab 2004, empl
5, sales , cert: NMSDC)

2777 Philatron Wire and Cable
15315 Cornet Ave
Santa Fe Springs, CA 90670
Contact: Phillip Ramos III GM
Tel: 562-802-2570
Email: p3@philatron.com
Website: www.philatron.com
Design & mfr electrical, electronic, instrumentation,
control & communication wire & cable. (Hisp, estab
1974, empl 85, sales $24,000,000, cert: NMSDC)

2778 Precise Panel Engraving CO, Inc.
12881 Western Ave, Unit B
Garden Grove, CA 92841
Contact: Joan VonKarvaly Presdient
Tel: 714-898-6510
Email: precisepanel@verizon.net
Website: www.government-vendor.us/
precisepanel
Industrial engraving: signs, labels, nameplates, control
panels; sheet metal fab; metal & plastic panel machin-
ing; mylar & metal marking. (Woman, estab 1978, empl
7, sales $255,000, cert: State)

2779 Pro-Lite
3505 Cadillac Ave, Bldg D
Costa Mesa, CA 92626
Contact: Andy Kaoh Presdient
Tel: 714-668-9988
Email: ak@pro-lite.com
Website: www.pro-lite.com
Mfr LED signs & LED displays. (As-Pac, estab 1981, empl
400, sales , cert: CPUC)

2780   Solartech Power, Inc.
     901 E Cedar St
     Ontario, CA 91761
     Contact: Sherry Fu Owner
     Tel: 714-630-8880
     Email: sherry.fu@solartechpower.com
     Website: www.solartechpower.com
Mfr solar photovoltaic panels & equipment. (Woman/As-Ind, estab 2001, empl 10, sales $3,000,000, cert: CPUC)

2781   Steren Electronics International, LLC
     6260 Sequence Dr Ste 110
     San Diego, CA 92121
     Contact: E'Lisa Jones Corp Dirof business devel
     Tel: 800-266-3333
     Email: elisa@steren.com
     Website: www.sterenusa.com
Mfr voice, video & data connectivity solutions. (Hisp, estab 1978, empl 100, sales $56,000,000, cert: CPUC)

2782   Transline Technology, Inc.
     1106 S Technology Circle
     Anaheim, CA 92805
     Contact: Judy Warner President
     Tel: 714-533-8300
     Email: judy@translinetech.com
     Website: www.translinetech.com
Mfr printed circuit boards, PCB, PWB, hybrid, exotic, RF & microwave, FR4 PCB. (As-Ind, estab 1996, empl 24, sales $1,600,000, cert: 8a)

2783   Unicorp, Inc.
     5780 Smithway St
     Commerce, CA 90040
     Contact: VP Business Dev
     Tel: 323-890-9246
     Email:
     Website: www.uninex.com
LED lighting technology, Indoor & Outdoor Electric Lighting Fixtures, Residential Electrical Lighting Fixture, Commercial, Industrial, Institutional Electrical Lighting Fixture, Other Lighting Equipment. (As-Pac, estab 1989, empl 14, sales , cert: State, CPUC)

Colorado

2784   Premier Manufactuirng and Supply Chain Services
     7755 Miller Dr
     Frederick, CO 80504
     Contact: Edmond Johnson President
     Tel: 303-776-4145
     Email: ejohnson@pmscs.com
     Website: www.pmscs.com
Contract mfr of printed circuit board assemblies for prototypes, production, sub assemblies, cable harness & test. (AA, estab 2000, empl 55, sales $12,000,000, cert: NMSDC)

2785   Quality Concepts Manufacturing Inc.
     1635 S Murray Blvd
     Colorado Springs, CO 80911
     Contact: Robert Millemon Program Mgr
     Tel: 719-574-1013
     Email: robert@qcmi.com
     Website: www.qcmi.com
Electronic Manufacturing Services, Quick-turn prototyping, pre-production & full production support services, mechanical assembly. (Woman, estab 1988, empl 30, sales , cert: City)

Connecticut

2786   I C D I Inc.
     407 Brookside Rd
     Waterbury, CT 06708
     Contact: Steve Villodas President
     Tel: 203-753-8551
     Email: svillodas@icdi-inc.com
     Website: www.icdi-inc.com
Contract mfr electronic high tech equip & systems, turnkey program mgmt, eng design, microprocessor systems, PC layout, PC board & automated surface-mount assembly, wave soldering, vapor degreasing, custom cables, ATE testing. (Hisp, estab 1975, empl 22, sales $3,019,307, cert: NMSDC)

Florida

2787   Avionics Support Group Inc.
     13155 SW 132nd Ave
     Miami, FL 33186
     Contact: Hugo L Fortes VP
     Tel: 305-378-9786
     Email: hfortes@asginc.net
     Website: www.asginc.net
Avionics engineering, mfg & installations. (Hisp, estab 1996, empl 25, sales , cert: State)

2788   CableNetwork Associates Inc.
     4800 N Federal Hwy, Ste E300
     Boca Raton, FL 33431
     Contact: Marcela Gutierrez
     Tel: 954-312-1200
     Email: mgutierrez@cablenetwork.net
     Website: www.cablenetwork.net
Mfr coax cable, drop & trunk cable. (Hisp, estab 1997, empl 300, sales $2,284,358,226, cert: NMSDC)

2789   Curtoom Companies, Inc.
     1228 E 7th Ave
     Tampa, FL 33675
     Contact: Paul Curtis CEO
     Tel: 813-405-8082
     Email: support@curtoom.com
     Website: www.curtoom.com
Provide construction cost consulting in both the Southeast United States and throughout the Atlantic seaboard areas. We have built a business and reputation supplying accurate and timely budgets, cost estimates, value engineering (AA, estab 1989, empl 30, sales $3,600,000, cert: State)

2790   LedZed International Inc.
     2240 Palm Beach Lakes Blvd
     West Palm Beach, FL 33409
     Contact: Helena Lahtinen CEO
     Tel: 954-629-0768
     Email: helena@ledzed.com
     Website: www.ledzed.com
Mfr & dist energy efficiency led lights. (Woman, estab 2011, empl 1, sales , cert: City)

2791 Mainstream IP Solutions, Inc.
6905 El Dorado Dr
Tampa, FL 33615
Contact: Arnie Solomon Acct Mgr
Tel: 813-549-7768
Email: asolomon@mcsoftampa.com
Website: www.mainstreamipsolutions.com
Electrical, structured cabling, audio-visual, security & fire
alarm systems. (AA, estab 2010, empl 5, sales $250,000,
cert: State, NMSDC, 8a, SDB)

2792 Paradym Engineering, LLC
8338 Windsor Bluff Dr
Tampa, FL 33647
Contact: Tim Keeley CEO
Tel: 888-667-5459
Email: tk@paradymengineering.com
Website: www.paradymengineering.com
Electrical & mechanical equipment & engineering services.
(AA, estab 2001, empl 6, sales $800,000, cert: State)

2793 PowerLogics, Inc.
1115 Marbella Plaza Dr
Tampa, FL 33619
Contact: Barbara Smith Sales Assoc
Tel: 813-645-2971
Email: barbarasmith@powerlogics.com
Website: www.powerlogics.com
Transient voltage surge suppression, uninterruptible
power systems, power conditioning equip, battery replace-
ments, generators, automatic transfer switches, AC & DC
invertors. (Woman, estab 1981, empl 6, sales $4,000,000,
cert: State)

Georgia

2794 Georgia Green Energy Services
335 Wilma Ct SW
Atlanta, GA 30331
Contact: Gavin Ireland CEO
Tel: 404-334-3323
Email: gireland@gagreenenergysvc.com
Website: www.gagreenenergysvc.com
Light retrofitting, LED lighting, occupancy sensors, solar
power systems, alternative & renewable energy systems,
Energy audting, energy reduction reports, energy audits.
(AA, estab 2007, empl , sales $1,099,000, cert: NMSDC, 8a)

2795 Roytec Industries LLC
306 Bell Park Dr
Woodstock, GA 30188
Contact: Amanda Chapman CEO
Tel: 770-926-5470
Email: mchapman@roytecind.com
Website: www.roytecind.com
Mfr electrical wire harnesses & electrical wire assemblies.
(Woman, estab 1984, empl 500, sales $36,734,238, cert:
WBENC)

2796 Southern States, LLC
30 Georgia Ave
Hampton, GA 30228
Contact: Amit Modi Sr reg Mgr
Tel: 770-946-4562
Email: a.modi@southernstatesllc.com
Website: www.southernstatesllc.com
Mfr high voltage electrical airbreak switchgear, power
fuses, circuit switchers & capacitor bank switching devices.
(As-Ind, estab 1916, empl 300, sales , cert: NMSDC)

Illinois

2797 AC Gentrol, Inc.
100 S Fourth St
Chillicothe, IL 61523
Contact: Allan Capati Presdient
Tel: 309-274-5486
Email: acapati@acgentrol.com
Website: www.acgentrol.com
Mfr specialized electrical controls systems. (Woman/As-
Pac, estab , empl , sales $1,100,000, cert: State)

2798 Capsonic Group, LLC
460 S Second St Slot B-8
Elgin, IL 60123
Contact: George Albrecht Reg Sales Mgr
Tel: 847-888-7242
Email: georgea@capsonic.com
Website: www.capsonicgroup.com
Insert & composite molding: product design, prototype,
automation. (AA, estab 1968, empl 225, sales , cert:
NMSDC)

2799 CEC Industries Ltd.
599 Bond St
Lincolnshire, IL 60069
Contact: Michelle Draper
Tel: 847-599-6132
Email: michelle@cecindustries.com
Website: www.ceclighting.com
Mfr miniature halogen lamps, LED lamps, electronic turn
signal flashers. (As-Ind, estab 1979, empl 66, sales , cert:
NMSDC)

2800 Ensign Corporation
P.O. Box 383
Addison, IL 52031
Contact: Ajay Sharma VP Sales/Mktg
Tel: 563-872-3900
Email: susan.h@ensigncorp.com
Website: www.ensigncorp.com
Build & dist power transformers, off-the-shelf & custom.
(As-Pac, estab 1939, empl 39, sales $3,000,000, cert:
NMSDC)

2801 KLI Inc.
304 Roma Jean Pkwy
Streamwood, IL 60107
Contact: Lisa Carso President
Tel: 630-213-1283
Email: support@kli-inc.com
Website: www.kli-inc.com
Mfr electronic components; electronic assembly; main
harness & cable to mil specs. (Woman/As-Pac, estab
1987, empl 15, sales , cert: State, NMSDC)

2802 PowerVolt Inc. (DBA Ensign Corporation)
300 W Factory Rd
Addison, IL 60101
Contact: Ajay Sharma VP Sales/Mktg
Tel: 630-628-9999
Email: ajays@powervolt.com
Website: www.ensigncorp.com
Mfr power transformers & DC power supplies. (As-Ind,
estab 1986, empl 39, sales $3,330,000, cert: NMSDC)

2803 S & M Group, Inc.
      2503 Pan Am Blvd
      Elk Grove Village, IL 60007
      Contact: Jay Vora
      Tel: 630-766-1000
      Email: jay@flextronassembly.com
      Website: www.flextronassembly.com
Electronics contract mfr: printed circuit boards & assemblies, proto through production, consignment or turnkey, leaded & lead-free, large boards, cable assemblies, wire harness, box & mechanical assemblies. (As-Pac, estab 2002, empl 25, sales $2,825,000, cert: State)

2804 Tempco Electric Heater Corp.
      607 N Central Ave
      Wood Dale, IL 60191
      Contact: William Kilberry CFO
      Tel: 630-350-2252
      Email: williamkilberry@tempco.com
      Website: www.tempco.com
Mfr thermal component products: electric heating elements, temperature controls, temperature sensors & turnkey process heating systems. (Hisp, estab 1972, empl 330, sales $28,500,000, cert: NMSDC)

2805 WarmlyYours.com Inc.
      590 Telser Rd, Ste B
      Lake Zurich, IL 60047
      Contact: Julia BIllen Presdient
      Tel: 800-875-5285
      Email: jbillen@warmlyyours.com
      Website: www.WarmlyYours.com
Manufacturer Electric Radiant Floor Heating Systems. (Woman, estab 1999, empl 28, sales $14,441,282, cert: WBENC)

Indiana

2806 ATEC Electrical Contractors
      419 Ransdell Rd
      Lebanon, IN 46052
      Contact: C. Shane Conner Presdient
      Tel: 765-482-8926
      Email: s.conner@atec-electric.com
      Website: www.atec-electric.com
Electrical and telecommunications sales, service and support, engineering, project management and sustainable energy consulting and installation. (Hisp, estab 2005, empl 25, sales $5,547,137, cert: NMSDC)

2807 Carson Manufacturing Company, Inc.
      5451 N Rural St
      Indianapolis, IN 46220
      Contact: Barbara Ferguson Presdient
      Tel: 317-257-3191
      Email: receptionist@carson-mfg.com
      Website: www.carson-mfg.com
Contract mfg electromechanical assemblies & equipment, mfr emergency vehicle sirens, rotary switches & voting machines. Prototyping, testing, quick turns, stocking programs & turn-key capabilities. (Woman, estab 1946, empl 20, sales $2,500,000, cert: State, City)

2808 Continental Manufacturing, LLC
      1524 Jackson St
      Anderson, IN 46016
      Contact: Chris Petty Natl Sales Mgr
      Tel: 765-298-8030
      Email: cpetty@solasray.com
      Website: http://solasray.com
Mfr, design, engineer & test LED technology lighting solutions for commercial, industrial & educational applications. (Woman, estab 2007, empl 10, sales $900,000, cert: State, WBENC)

2809 Electric Motors and Specialties, Inc.
      701 W King St
      Garrett, IN 46738
      Contact: Rick Moore President
      Tel: 847-559-6132
      Email: rmoore@emsmotors.com
      Website: www.emsmotors.com
Design, mfg & application of shaded pole, PSC & electronically commutated unit bearing motors. (Woman, estab 1946, empl 200, sales , cert: WBENC)

Kentucky

2810 Dollar Aisle, LLC
      165 Woods Dr
      Brandenburg, KY 40108
      Contact: rahul anand Presdient
      Tel: 502-303-4518
      Email: dollaraisle@gmail.com
      Website: www.wenlighting.com
Mfr led tube lights, wall packs, hig bays, led light bulbs etc. (As-Pac, estab 2011, empl 3, sales $650,000, cert: NMSDC)

Massachusetts

2811 Adcotron EMS
      12 Channel St
      Boston, MA 02210
      Contact: Don MacNeil Business Develop Mgr
      Tel: 617-598-3000
      Email: donimac@comcast.net
      Website: www.adcotron.com
Electronic mfg service, printed circuit board assembly, system integration, system assembly. (Woman/As-Pac, estab 1977, empl 100, sales $30,200,000, cert: State)

2812 International Coil, Inc.
      15 Jonathan Dr Unit 1
      Brockton, MA 02301
      Contact: George Machadinho Presdient
      Tel: 508-580-8515
      Email: gmachadinho@internationalcoil.com
      Website: www.internationalcoil.com
Mfr Transformers (wire wound products) & Power Supplies. (AA, estab 1995, empl 12, sales $1,000,000, cert: State)

Maryland

2813   Armacost Lighting LLC
       140 Baltic Ave
       Baltimore, MD 21225
       Contact: Terry Armacost Presdient
       Tel: 410-354-6000
       Email: tarmacost@armacostlighting.com
       Website: www.armacostlighting.com
Architectural quality LED lighting fixtures, LED tape lighting
is ultra-thin, flexible, fully dimmable, can be cut to size or
multiple strips. (Woman, estab 2011, empl 8, sales
$3,700,000, cert: WBENC)

2814   JEM Engineering, LLC
       8683 Cherry Ln
       Laurel, MD 20707
       Contact: Nancy Lilly CEO
       Tel: 301-317-1070
       Email: nlilly@jemengineering.com
       Website: www.jemengineering.com
Design & prototype military & commercial antennas: HF to
millimeter-wave, microstrip patch antennas & arrays, wire,
aperture, broadband, active & low-observable antennas.
(Woman/Hisp, estab 2001, empl 30, sales , cert: State)

Michigan

2815   AG Manufacturing Inc.
       319 Industrial Pkwy
       Harbor Beach, MI 48441
       Contact: Marlo Klaus Cstmr Service
       Tel: 989-479-9590
       Email: mklaus@agmanufacturing.com
       Website: www.agmanufacturing.com
Mfr wire harnesses. (AA, estab 2004, empl 101, sales ,
cert: NMSDC)

2816   Amtech Electrocircuits, Inc.
       701 Minnesota Dr
       Troy, MI 48083
       Contact: Jay Patel Presdient
       Tel: 248-583-1801
       Email: jrp@amelectro.com
       Website: www.amelectro.com
Electronic manufacturing services, contract manufacturer,
printed circuit boards, wire harnesses & electronic assemblies. (As-Ind, estab 1997, empl 10, sales $800,000, cert:
NMSDC)

2817   Eisen Electric Corporation
       3340 Pinetree Rd
       Lansing, MI 48911
       Contact: Lokesh Kumar GM
       Tel: 517-393-5850
       Email: lkumar@eisennet.com
       Website: www.eisennet.com
Mfr terminal screws, electrical fasteners & springs. (As-Ind,
estab 1994, empl 72, sales $4,200,000, cert: NMSDC)

2818   Empire Electric
       3575 Vinewood
       Detroit, MI 48208
       Contact: Bob Pauline VP
       Tel: 313-895-1920
       Email: bob@empireec.com
       Website: www.empirewc.com
Dist electrical, industrial & networking products & supplies. Also mfr wire harnesses & cable assemblies. (AA,
estab 2003, empl 10, sales $1,005,000,000, cert: NMSDC)

2819   Excel Electrocircuit Inc.
       50 Northpointe Dr
       Orion, MI 48359
       Contact: Nipur Shah President
       Tel: 248-373-0700
       Email: sales@excelcircuits.com
       Website: www.excelelectro.com
Mfr printed circuit boards. (As-Ind, estab 1970, empl 25,
sales , cert: NMSDC)

2820   Hart Precision Products, Inc.
       12700 Marion
       Redford, MI 48239
       Contact: Darlene Hart Presdient
       Tel: 313-537-0490
       Email: d.hart@hart-precision.com
       Website: http://Hart-Precision.com
Mfr precision components & assemblies for the Transportation Industry. (Woman, estab 1953, empl 48, sales
$5,100,000, cert: WBENC)

2821   Hybrid Design Services
       2479 Elliott Dr
       Troy, MI 48083
       Contact: James Pinon Presdient
       Tel: 248-298-3400
       Email: jpinon@hybriddesignservices.com
       Website: www.hybriddesignservices.com
Engineering, design, prototyping, testing services
specializing in hybrid vehicles & systems, electric
vehicles & systems, HEV systems, EV systems, hybrid and
electric vehicle R&D, high voltage systems, energy
storage. (Hisp, estab 2007, empl 20, sales $2,000,000,
cert: NMSDC)

2822   Industrial Control Repair - ICR Services
       28601 Lorna Ave
       Warren, MI 48092
       Contact: Marlies Davis Business Development
       Tel:
       Email: mdavis@icrservices.com
       Website: www.icrservices.com
Dist & repair industrial electronics: robots, PLCs drives,
welders, encoders, temperature controls, displays,
monitors, power sources, etc. (Hisp, estab 1992, empl
155, sales $80,000,000, cert: NMSDC)

2823   JA Quality Assurance Group, LLC
       537 Bradford
       Pontiac, MI 48341
       Contact: Julio Rodriguez CEO
       Tel: 248-506-3316
       Email: jrodriguez@jaqualityassurance.com
       Website: www.jaqualityassurance.com
Mfr prototype harnesses. (Hisp, estab 2000, empl 104,
sales $3,935,000, cert: NMSDC)

2824   JMC Electrical Contractor, LLC dba JMC Technolo-
       gies
       33651 Giftos
       Clinton Township, MI 48035
       Contact: Bob Locklear VP Technologies
       Tel: 586-773-8026
       Email: blocklear@jmcelectricllc.com
       Website: www.jmcelectricllc.com
Electrical service, installation, Structured Cable, Fiber
Optic Cable, Voice, Data, Security, CCTV, Intrusion
Detection, Access Control, Audio/Visual, CATV, Wireless,
Wi-Fi, DAS & Building Automation Systems installation.
(Woman, estab 2010, empl 45, sales $6,000,000, cert:
WBENC)

2825 Johnico LLC
     400 Monroe St Ste 480
     Detroit, MI 48226
     Contact: john economy Managing Partner
     Tel: 248-895-7820
     Email: johneconomy@yahoo.com
     Website: www.americasgreenline.com
Commercial & industrial LED manufacturer. (Woman, estab 2011, empl 10, sales $3,500,000, cert: WBENC)

2826 Myron Zucker, Inc.
     36825 Metro Ct
     Sterling Heights, MI 48312
     Contact: Mary Anderson Buyer
     Tel: 586-979-9955
     Email: dzobel@myronzucker.com
     Website: www.myronzucker.com
Engineer & mfr low-voltage power products: power factor correction capacitors, harmonic filters & surge suppressors. (Woman, estab 1967, empl 10, sales $1,050,000, cert: WBENC)

2827 Newtech 3, Inc.
     28373 Beck Rd Ste H7
     Wixom, MI 48393
     Contact: Gail Gyenese Dir of Sales
     Tel: 248-912-1062
     Email: ggyenese@newtech3inc.com
     Website: www.newtech3.com
Mfr lower to mid volume wire harness & circuit board assemblies. (AA, estab 2009, empl 32, sales $3,965,000, cert: NMSDC)

2828 Orri Corporation
     5385 Perry Dr
     Waterford, MI 48329
     Contact: Angelo Doa Sales
     Tel: 248-618-1104
     Email: Sales@orricorp.com
     Website: www.orricorp.com
Wire harnesses, cable assemblies, electrical test fixtures, robotic vision guidance software. (Woman, estab 2001, empl 12, sales , cert: WBENC)

Minnesota

2829 Electro Mechanical Industries (EMI)
     13300 6th Ave N
     Plymouth, MN 23606
     Contact: Holly Hicks Sales/Marketing Mgr
     Tel: 763-546-5998
     Email: hhicks@e-m-i.com
     Website: www.e-m-i.com
Low voltage switchgear, metal clad & metal enclosed medium voltage switchgear, paralleling switchgear, control panels, special wire ways, wall & floor ducts, pull boxes & sound-attenuated generator enclosures. (Woman, estab 1981, empl 36, sales $8,522,000, cert: WBENC)

2830 Telamco, Inc.
     636 Industrial Dr SE
     Lonsdale, MN 55046
     Contact: Tracy Humann Presdient
     Tel: 507-744-5504
     Email: tracy@telamcoinc.com
     Website: www.telamcoinc.com
Mfr custom heat sealed membrane switches & quality assemblies. (Woman, estab 1968, empl 11, sales $1,500,000, cert: NWBOC)

North Carolina

2831 TEC Electric, LLC
     6612G East WT Harris Blvd
     Charlotte, NC 28215
     Contact: Donald James Presdient
     Tel: 704-394-5097
     Email: donald.james@harriselec.com
     Website: www.harriselec.com
Electical contracting, engineering, controls & conveyor installation. (AA, estab 2006, empl 15, sales $1,900,000, cert: NMSDC)

2832 Thermal Control Products
     6324 Performance Dr
     Concord, NC 28027
     Contact: Geoff Nilsen Commercial Sales Exec
     Tel: 704-454-7605
     Email: gnilsen@thermalcontrolproducts.com
     Website: www.thermalcontrolproducts.com
Mfr thermal & protective components, Protective shielding / robotics, Weld splatter shielding, Weld head covers, Gun Bags, Computer monitor protectors, Weld screens, Transport bags. (Woman, estab 1993, empl 40, sales , cert: State)

Nevada

2833 VaOpto, LLC
     5178 W Patrick Lane
     Las Vegas, NV 89118
     Contact: Charles Li Acct Mgr
     Tel: 702-517-5789
     Email: charles.li@vaopto.com
     Website: www.vaopto.com
Mfr LED lightings & LED fixtures. (As-Pac, estab 2010, empl 5, sales $6,000,000, cert: NMSDC)

New York

2834 AmpliTech Inc.
     1373 Lincoln Ave
     Holbrook, NY 11741
     Contact: Walter Rojas President
     Tel: 631-521-7831
     Email: sales@amplitechinc.com
     Website: www.amplitechinc.com
Design, develop & mfr custom & standard RF components, microwave amplifiers & components. (Minority, estab 2002, empl 12, sales $2,000,000, cert: State)

2835 Integrated Control Corporation
     748 Park Ave
     Huntington, NY 11743
     Contact: CEO
     Tel: 631-673-5100
     Email:
     Website: www.goicc.com
Mfr electronic control & communication devices, system integrated design. (Woman, estab 1986, empl 21, sales $6,100,000, cert: WBENC, NWBOC)

2836 Tony Baird Electronics, Inc.
461 East Brighton Ave
Syracuse, NY 13210
Contact: Dan Strumlok VP
Tel: 315-422-4430
Email: dan@tonybairdelectronics.com
Website: www.tonybairdelectronics.com
Mfr electronic components, printed circuit assembly, electronic assembly, fiber optic cable. (AA, estab 2005, empl 10, sales $4,894,647, cert: SDB)

Ohio

2837 S & V Industries, Inc.
3535 S Smith Rd
Fairlawn, OH 44333
Contact: Denise Uher Acct Exec
Tel: 330-408-3078
Email: denise.uher@svindustries.com
Website: www.svindustries.com
Mfr gears, spur, helical, double helical, worm straight bevel, spiral bevel, herringbone, gear boxes, worm gear boxes, helical gear boxes, bevel helical gear boxes, custom or special gear boxes, geared motors. (As-Pac, estab 1993, empl 30, sales $40,000,000, cert: NMSDC)

Oregon

2838 Powin Energy Corporation
20550 SW 115th Ave
Tualatin, OR 97062
Contact: Victor Liu Sales
Tel: 503-598-6659
Email: victorl@powinenergy.com
Website: http://powinenergy.com
Design & develop advanced battery management technology & manufactures battery energy storage solutions. (As-Pac, estab 2011, empl 43, sales $183,187, cert: NMSDC)

Pennsylvania

2839 American Cable Co., Inc.
231 E Luzerne St
Philadelphia, PA 19124
Contact: Rolando Sanchez Business Development
Tel: 215-456-0700
Email: rsanchez@americancableco.com
Website: www.americancableco.com
Mfr battery cable assemblies, wire harnesses, and ground straps. (Hisp, estab 1976, empl 150, sales $15,000,000, cert: NMSDC)

2840 Contine Corporation
1820 Nagle Rd
Erie, PA 16510
Contact: Constance Ellrich Presdient
Tel: 814-899-0006
Email: cellrich@continedbe.com
Website: www.continedbe.com
Assembly & test mechanical & electro-mechanical devices, machining, sheet metal fabrication & plastic injection molding, switches, latches, rack assemblies, display units, control panels, wire harnesses etc. (Woman, estab 1981, empl 43, sales $9,175,996, cert: CPUC, WBENC)

2841 John A. Romeo & Associates, Inc.
890 Pittsburgh Rd, Ste 7
Butler, PA 16002
Contact: CEO
Tel: 724-586-6961
Email:
Website: www.jara-mfg.com
Mfr Custom Cables, Wiring Harnesses & Electromechanical Assemblies. (Woman, estab 1990, empl 15, sales $1,506,698, cert: WBENC)

2842 TJM Electronic Associates
2924 New Rogers Rd
Bristol, PA 19007
Contact: Donna McCarthy Dir New Business Devel
Tel: 215-788-2278
Email:
Website: www.tjmeast.com
Electronic contract mfr, electronic design, packaging & manufacturing, circuit board assembly, engineering, design,systems integration & test & turnkey production. (Woman, estab 1990, empl 60, sales $10,000,000, cert: NWBOC)

Puerto Rico

2843 Advanced Control Services, Inc.
425 Rd. 693, PMB 205, Ste 1
Dorado, PR 00646
Contact: Victor M. Taveras Operations Mgr
Tel: 787-502-8752
Email: victor@advcontrolservices.com
Website: www.advcontrolservices.com
Engineering & validation services, systems integration services, control panels, VFDs, electrical services, SCADA, HMI, instrumentation
services. (Hisp, estab 1999, empl 7, sales $621,123, cert: NMSDC)

2844 AG Group Inc.
Centro Industrial Minellas, Carr. 174TH KM 3.0
Bayamon, PR 00959
Contact: Elliott Gonzalez Sales Mgr
Tel: 787-707-0022
Email: info@aggpr.com
Website: www.aggroupinc.com
Engineering, System Integration, Installations, Calibrations, Validations. (Hisp, estab 1997, empl 105, sales $7,892,343, cert: State, NMSDC)

2845 Hi-Tech Products Inc.
P.O. Box 4956
Carolina, PR 00984
Contact: Daisy Maldonado Admin Officer
Tel: 787-257-1707
Email: admin@hi-techproducts.com
Website: www.hi-techproducts.com
Mfr reps for industrial control products, electronics, electrical & pneumatics. (Hisp, estab 1991, empl 30, sales , cert: NMSDC)

2846　Invision Engineering Corp.
　　　P.O. Box 6567
　　　Mayaguez, PR 00681
　　　Contact: Jose Vazquez Presdient
　　　Tel:　787-831-0070
　　　Email: jvazquez@invisioneng.com
　　　Website: www.invisioneng.com
Automation, Control System Design, System Integrations, Instrumentation, Calibrations and Installations, Electrical Installations, Computer System Validations, Software Validations, Software design. (Hisp, estab 2002, empl 35, sales $3,137,957, cert: NMSDC)

South Carolina

2847　Amec, LLC
　　　4601 E White Horse Rd
　　　Greenville, SC 29611
　　　Contact: Kevin Lindsey Project Mgr
　　　Tel:　864-269-0222
　　　Email: kevin@amecllc.net
　　　Website: www.amecsc.net
Industrial & commercial electrical applications, industrial electrical maintenance, thermal imaging, de-energized maintenance, studies for lighting improvements, breaker testing, power analysis, installation of service entrance equipment. (Woman, estab 2009, empl 11, sales $838,385, cert: State)

2848　Arva, LLC
　　　3705 Centre Circle
　　　Fort Mill, SC 29715
　　　Contact: Shahil Amin Director
　　　Tel:　803-336-2235
　　　Email: shahilamin@arva.us
　　　Website: www.hyliteledlighting.com/
Mfr energy-efficient, indoor & outdoor LED & Induction Lighting & Retrofit Kits. (Woman/As-Ind, estab 2010, empl 7, sales $1,200,000, cert: NMSDC)

Texas

2849　Blackhawk Management
　　　1322 Space Park Dr Ste A220
　　　Houston, TX 77058
　　　Contact: Gabrielle Busby Administrator
　　　Tel:　832-536-3703
　　　Email: busbyg@blackhawkmgmt.com
　　　Website: www.blackhawkmgmt.com
Electrical & mechanical engineering design services, prototyping, short production runs, printed circuit board design, 3D machining, digital, analog design, power electronics. (Woman/Nat Ame, estab 1992, empl 24, sales $10,000,000, cert: WBENC, SDB)

2850　Electro Plate Circuitry -Dragon Circuits
　　　1430 Century Dr
　　　Carrollton, TX 75006
　　　Contact: Gunny Babaria VP
　　　Tel:　972-466-0818
　　　Email: gunnyb@eplate.com
　　　Website: www.eplate.com
Mfr printed circuit boards: 40 layers, blind & buried vias, impedance control, heatsink bonding, small hole drilling & quick turn around. (Woman/As-Ind, estab 1985, empl 50, sales $8,000,000, cert: NMSDC)

2851　Electro Plate Circuitry, Inc.
　　　1430 Century Dr
　　　Carrollton, TX 75006
　　　Contact: Nicolas Garcia President
　　　Tel:　972-466-0818
　　　Email: nickg@eplate.com
　　　Website: www.eplate.com
Mfr printed circuit boards: GF,GI, RF, insulators, heatsinks, blind buried vias, controlled impedance. (Hisp, estab 1981, empl 80, sales $9,000,000, cert: NMSDC)

2852　FASIC Design LLC
　　　4105 Front Range Lane
　　　Austin, TX 78732
　　　Contact: Scott Buchanan Managing Member
　　　Tel:　214-298-7810
　　　Email: scott.buchanan@fasicdesigns.com
　　　Website: www.fasicdesigns.com
Design large to small semiconductor designs at low to large process nodes(350 nm to 4nm).
. (AA, estab 2008, empl 1, sales $151,366, cert: NMSDC)

2853　GCI Technologies
　　　1301 Precision Dr
　　　Plano, TX 75074
　　　Contact: Hinkki Chen CEO
　　　Tel:　972-423-8411
　　　Email: mike.beauchamp@gcitechnologies.com
　　　Website: www.gcitechnologies.com
Mfr magnetics: engineering, telecom, audio, power transformers, external power supplies, chokes, ferrite beads, cores. (As-Ind, As-Pac, Hisp, estab 1982, empl 420, sales $25,000,000, cert: NMSDC)

2854　MHC Semiconductor Processing Inc.
　　　13581 Pond Springs Rd
　　　Austin, TX 78729
　　　Contact: Marc Yeates Sales Dir
　　　Tel:　512-331-6632
　　　Email: myeates@mhcsemi.com
　　　Website: www.mhcsemi.com
Hybrid & chip die processing: wire application. (Woman, estab 1996, empl 8, sales , cert: State)

2855　PanAmerica Supply, Inc.
　　　21414 Provincial Blvd
　　　Katy, TX 77450
　　　Contact: Shaun Choi Presdient
　　　Tel:　281-646-8472
　　　Email: sychoi@pasihouston.com
　　　Website: www.pasihouston.com
Mfr power cables (HV, Med XLPE), transformer (up to 230kV). (As-Pac, estab 2005, empl 3, sales $8,000,000, cert: City)

2856　Roman Industries, Inc.
　　　10945 Estate Ln, Ste E115
　　　Dallas, TX 75238
　　　Contact: Shawn Quiroga Owner
　　　Tel:　214-503-3100
　　　Email: shawn@romanindustriesinc.com
　　　Website: www.romanindustriesinc.com
Mfr custom cable, dist power lugs & RF connectors. (Woman, estab 2008, empl 3, sales , cert: State)

2857 Telco Intercontinental Corporation
9812 Whithorn Dr
Houston, TX 77095
Contact: Paolo Longo Dir of Sales
Tel: 281-855-2218
Email: plongo@telcointercon.com
Website: www.telcointercon.com
Mfr electric motors, Permanent Magnet DC motor, PMDC, coreless, core-less DC, gearmotor, high speed, high torque, miniature, stepper, Brushless DC motor, BLDC, green energy efficient ECM motor, fan, blower. (As-Pac, estab 1985, empl 22, sales $19,000,000, cert: NMSDC)

2858 Texas Mgt Associates, Inc
7001 Fairgrounds Parkway
San Antonio, TX 78238
Contact: Dora Mendoza Business Development
Tel: 210-673-8422
Email: dmendoza@t-m-a.com
Website: www.t-m-a.com
Electrical engineering & mfg: cable harnesses, electrical components, test station fixtures, circuit boards, restraint test stations, electrical housings, both complex & simple. (Hisp, estab 1991, empl 20, sales $4,368,852, cert: State, NMSDC)

Virginia

2859 Atomized Products Group of Chesapeake, Inc.
808 Curtis Saunders Ct
Chesapeake, VA 23321
Contact: Lee Puckett Exec VP/Chief Operating Officer
Tel: 757-793-2922
Email: lee.puckett@atomizedproductsgroup.com
Website: www.atomizedproductsgroup.com
Mfr & dist negative plate expander for lead-acid battery applications. (Woman, estab 2013, empl 13, sales , cert: WBENC)

Washington

2860 CETS LLC
1441 N Northlake Way, Ste 211
Seattle, WA 98103
Contact: Tim Tracey Purchasing
Tel: 206-588-1239
Email: info@cetsinc.com
Website: www.cetsinc.com
Develop & build new electrical systems; constructing additions, alterations & repairs, UL508 LISTED Open & Closed Industrial Panel, marine electrical construction services, electrical power distribution design & repair. (AA, estab 2013, empl 12, sales $1,500,000, cert: City, NMSDC)

2861 Charter Controls, Inc.
1705 NE 64th Ave Ste B
Vancouver, WA 98661
Contact: Randy Ayala VP Industrial Sales
Tel: 360-695-2161
Email: randy@chartercontrols.us
Website: www.chartercontrols.us
Design, engineer & mfr industrial control systems. (Woman, estab 2004, empl 15, sales $3,000,000, cert: State)

2862 Cherry City Electric
8100 NE St. Johns Rd
Vancouver, WA 98665
Contact: Ray Ellis Presdient
Tel: 503-566-5600
Email: rellis@cherrycityelectric.com
Website: www.cherrycityelectric.com
Provide electrical construction, electrical remodels and electrical repair. Provide voice/data installations. (Woman, estab 1968, empl 275, sales $49,800,000, cert: WBENC)

2863 Eworld Solutions, Inc.
19550 7th Ave NE
Shoreline, WA 98155
Contact: Nasir Junejo CEO
Tel: 206-659-1988
Email: nasir@eworldsolutions.com
Website: www.eworldsolutions.com
Contractor placement for design and verification. Specializing in SystemVerilog, UVM and Mixed Signal verification. Consulting Service to audit verification and design environments, Consulting Service to create re-usable template (As-Ind, estab 2010, empl 3, sales , cert: NMSDC)

2864 Reliable Investments LLC
801 2nd Ave Ste 800
Seattle, WA 98104
Contact: Anthony Obiako Presdient
Tel: 800-918-4380
Email: anthony@reliableinvestmentsllc.com
Website: www.reliableinvestmentsllc.com
Procurement & supply chain management, field engineering, installation, repair, calibration and rental services. (AA, estab 2010, empl 3, sales $2,000,000, cert: State)

2865 Sybis LLC
9925 NE 134th Ct Ste 100
Kirkland, WA 98034
Contact: Jonathan Djajadi Partner
Tel: 206-686-8463
Email: jon@sybissolution.com
Website: http://sybissolution.com
Electronic lock system, electronic lock cylinders, programmable keys. (As-Pac, estab 2012, empl 3, sales $198,621, cert: State, NMSDC)

Wisconsin

2866 Arnev Products, Inc.
N1530 Spring Glen Rd
Keshena, WI 54135
Contact: Patricia Evensen Presdient
Tel: 715-799-5944
Email: arnev@frontiernet.net
Website: www.arnev.com
Mfr decorative electrical hardware. (Woman, estab 1990, empl 2, sales $550,000, cert: State)

2867   Convenience Electronics, Inc.
     4405 Triangle St
     McFarland, WI 53558
     Contact: J. Harry Lum President
     Tel: 608-838-4300
     Email: hlum@convenienceelectronics.com
     Website: www.convenienceelectronics.com
Mfr custom computer cables & harnesses, fiber optic
cables, molded cables, etc. (As-Pac, estab 1989, empl 45,
sales $4,000,000, cert: NMSDC)

2868   Dairyland Electric Co, Inc.
     12770 W. Custer Ave
     Butler, WI 53007
     Contact: Chris Martinez Presdient
     Tel: 262-783-1550
     Email: cmartinez@dairylandelectric.com
     Website: www.dairylandenergy.com/
Electrical construction, data & communication, cabling,
testing & certifying, electrical, telecom, fiber, alarms &
video installation. (Hisp, estab 1998, empl 11, sales , cert:
State, NMSDC)

2869   Electrical Testing Solutions
     2909 Green Hill Ct, Ste I
     Oshkosh, WI 54904
     Contact: Scott Banaski Business Develop Mgr
     Tel: 920-420-2986
     Email: sbanaski@electricaltestingsolutions.com
     Website: www.electricaltestingsolutions.com
Power system components for low, medium voltage &
parallel switchgear troubleshooting,
commissioning, design, analysis, repair & testing. (Hisp,
estab 2005, empl 25, sales $4,300,000, cert: State,
NMSDC)

2870   Professional Power Engineering Company, LLC
     W266 N7220 Kettle Ridge Ct
     Sussex, WI 53089
     Contact: Glenn Wilder Presdient
     Tel: 262-372-4220
     Email: gwilder@ppecompany.com
     Website: www.ppecompany.com
Uninterruptible power supply systems, generator sets,
automatic transfer switches, batteries, battery racks &
cabinets & preventive maintenance services. (AA, estab
2006, empl 3, sales $105,000, cert: NMSDC)

DIR
DIVERSITY INFORMATION RESOURCES

2022 Supplier Diversity Seminar

Sponsored by DIR: Driving Supplier Diversity Success since 1968

"Building Strategic Phases of a Supplier Diversity Process"

Date and Location TBD

AGENDA

Day One
[:]00 a.m. - 5:00 p.m. Seminar
[:]30 p.m. - 7:00 p.m. Reception

Day 2
[:]00 a.m. - 5:00 p.m. Seminar

[Lu]nch and continental breakfast
[se]rved both days.

"[Ex]cellent seminar conducted by a supplier [div]ersity expert. Covered a wide range [of i]nformation useful in educating peers [an]d formalizing a supplier diversity [pro]gram.
— 2019 Attendee

WHO ATTENDS?
Supplier Diversity Professionals
Purchasing Managers & Buyers
VP's of Materials and Purchasing
Procurement Managers
Small Business Liaison Officers
(SBLOs)

ACCOMMODATIONS
[Ho]tel reservation information is sent [wi]th your seminar registration [co]nfirmation. A limited number of [ro]oms will be available for seminar [at]tendees under DIR's special rate.

CEU (Continuing Education Units)
[Th]e Institute for Supply Management [(IS]M) awards 14.5 CEUs for this DIR [tr]aining.

REGISTRATION FEE: $TBD
[In]cludes breakfast and lunch both days, [ne]tworking reception and workbook [m]aterials.

REGISTER ONLINE
[Vi]sit www.DiversityInfoResources.com
[or] contact us: 612-781-6819,
[inf]o@DiversityInfoResources.com

KNOWLEDGE, NETWORKING, IMPLEMENTATION
This seminar is specifically designed to enable the creation of and/or improvement to an effective supplier diversity process. The proven tactics, information and ideas presented will enable you to return to work with actions that can be immediately implemented.

This seminar will provide participants with the knowledge and assistance in developing their skills in: building and maintaining an effective supplier diversity program, engaging leadership, customers and process owners of various supply chain operations necessary for an effective program, understanding the various aspects of supplier diversity including multiple tier engagement and accountability, technical tactical and strategic aspects of program reporting and effective processes in supplier engagement and development

"A great, well developed training for supplier diversity professionals; classroom interaction is fantastic."

RELEVANT TOPICS
- Supplier Diversity Program Overview
- Company Overview and Supply Chain Strategy
- Roles and Responsibilities of Supplier Diversity Professionals
- Program Governance (policies and regulations)
- Program Administration and Execution
- Creating a Supplier Diversity Strategic Plan and Small Business Subcontracting Plan
- How to Engage all of the Players that Impact Supplier Diversity Performance
- Awards and Recognition
- Data Management Solutions: An Overview of Tracking and Reporting Spend

```
┌─────────────────────────────────────────┐
│            ENGINEERING SERVICES          │
│   Most of these firms are engaged in     │
│   civil, structural                      │
│   and sanitation engineering services.   │
│   May also do                            │
│   land surveying, environmental impact   │
│   studies, test-                         │
│   ing and sampling, R&D, systems         │
│   engineering, manu-                     │
│   facturing, etc. Included are plant     │
│   noise studies, digi-                   │
│   tal design, radio active waste         │
│   disposal, nuclear                      │
│   power. (See also ENVIRONMENTAL         │
│   SERVICES).                             │
│   NAICS Code 54                          │
└─────────────────────────────────────────┘
```

Alabama

2871   Katmai Support Services, LLC
        701 E Tudor Rd, Ste 215
        Anchorage, AK 99503
        Contact: Katherine Tweidt Business Dev Mgr
        Tel: 907-333-7000
        Email: eric@anc8a.com
        Website:
Mfr, overhaul, repair & modification of advanced composites & bonded honeycomb structures for numerous space & airframe applications in new generations of aircraft and space vehicles. (Nat Ame, estab 2003, empl , sales $521,411, cert: State)

2872   Building & Earth Sciences, Inc.
        5545 Derby Dr
        Birmingham, AL 35210
        Contact: Matt Adams Dir of Corp Client Development - Principal
        Tel: 205-836-6300
        Email: madams@buildingandearth.com
        Website: www.buildingandearth.com
Consulting Engineering, geotechnical, environmental & construction materials testing & special inspection services. (Woman/As-Ind, estab 1998, empl 185, sales $19,000,000, cert: City, WBENC)

2873   GASmith Enterprises, Inc.
        464 Cahaba Park Cir
        Birmingham, AL 35242
        Contact: George A. Smith President
        Tel: 205-981-5391
        Email: info@signarama-bham.com
        Website: www.signarama-bham.com
SIGN-A-RAMA is your full service sign center. We use the latest technology and highest quality products to produce custom signs for your business. We can make the perfect signs to advertise your products or to inform your (AA, estab 2010, empl 6, sales $3,000,000, cert: State, NMSDC)

2874   Mesa Associates Inc.
        480 Production Ave
        Madison, AL 35758
        Contact: Darrell Christman Exec VP
        Tel: 865-671-5401
        Email: dchristman@mesainc.com
        Website: www.mesainc.com
Civil, electrical, mechanical, structural engineering services: integration, surveying, transmission, substation, controls, panel build, telecommunication, fiber optic engineering, robotic vehicle payloads & devices. (Woman/As-Pac, estab 1988, empl 356, sales $36,000,000, cert: NMSDC, WBENC)

Arizona

2875   Engineering Science Analysis, Corp.
        6105 S Ash Ave, Ste A-4
        Tempe, AZ 85283
        Contact: Martin Martinez Presdient
        Tel: 602-625-6259
        Email: martin.a.martinez@esacorp.com
        Website: www.esacorp.com
Product development, research & development, engineering design, advanced simulation analysis, manufacturing, test & advanced software tools for CAD/CAE applications. (Hisp, estab 1991, empl 8, sales $750,000, cert: State)

2876   G.D. Barri & Associates, Inc.
        6860 W Peoria Ave
        Peoria, AZ 85345
        Contact: CEO
        Tel: 623-773-0410
        Email:
        Website: www.gdbarri.com
Engineering, management & technical support: environmental assessment, analysis, design, systems, baseline engineering, training, procedure development, quality assurance & quality control. (Woman/AA, estab 1989, empl 331, sales $54,435,707, cert: CPUC, WBENC)

California

2877   Aetypic, Inc.
        7 Freelon St
        San Francisco, CA 94107
        Contact: Dennis Wong
        Tel: 415-762-8388
        Email: dennis.wong@aetypic.com
        Website: http://aetypic.com
Architecture & engineering services: structural engineering, civil engineering, construction engineering & inspection, technology integration, & sustainable design. (As-Pac, estab 2011, empl 25, sales , cert: State, NMSDC)

2878   Blair, Church & Flynn
        451 Clovis Ave, Ste 200
        Clovis, CA 93612
        Contact: David Mowry Principal
        Tel: 559-326-1400
        Email: dmowry@bcf-engr.com
        Website: www.bcf-engr.com
Engineering, land surveying, planning, civil engineering, landscape architecture & construction management. (Nat Ame, estab 1958, empl 49, sales $5,200,000, cert: CPUC)

2879   Calvada Surveying, Inc.
        411 Jenks Cir Ste 205
        Corona, CA 92880
        Contact: Armando Dupont President
        Tel: 951-280-9960
        Email: armando@calvada.com
        Website: www.calvada.com
Environmental site surveying & mapping, design topographic surveying & mapping, boundary surveys, construction staking, encumbrance mapping. (Hisp, estab 1989, empl 35, sales $4,200,000, cert: NMSDC, CPUC)

2880   Cynergy Professional Systems LLC
       23187 La Cadena, Ste 102
       Laguna Hills, CA 92653
       Contact: CFO
       Tel: 800-776-7978
       Email:
       Website: www.cynergy.pro
Engineering: communications systems, land mobile radio, microwave, aviation communications, marine radio, radio towers, computers, networking, data, all other communications systems engineering. APCO P25, Microwave, Satellite / SATCOM. (Hisp, estab 2009, empl 12, sales $25,000,000, cert: 8a)

2881   Eagle Engineering Construction Inc.
       1175 Palomar Dr, Ste 100
       Redwood City, CA 94062
       Contact: Curtis Brooks President
       Tel: 650-367-8000
       Email: clbrooks@sbcglobal.net
       Website:
General engineering & electrical contracting, civil, electrical, mechanical & construction management. (AA, estab 1993, empl 36, sales $3,000,000, cert: State, CPUC)

2882   Engineering/Remediation Resources Group, Inc.
       4585 Pacheco Blvd Ste 200
       Martinez, CA 94553
       Contact: Tyson Appel Sr Project Mgr
       Tel: 925-969-0750
       Email: tyson.appel@errg.com
       Website: www.errg.com
Engineering & remediation services, environmental, civil & geotechnical engineers, geologists, soil physicists, scientists, construction managers, construction superintendents, equipment operators, certified hazardous waste technicians. (Woman/As-Pac, estab 1997, empl 175, sales $81,494,792, cert: CPUC)

2883   Fakouri Electrical Engineering, Inc.
       30001 Comcercio
       Rancho Santa Margarita, CA 92688
       Contact: Ms. Findlay Corp facil
       Tel: 800-669-8852
       Email: lfindlay@fee-ups.com
       Website: www.fee-ups.com
Engineer, install & maintain UPS systems: batteries, power systems, etc. (Woman, estab 1979, empl 50, sales $14,000,000, cert: WBENC)

2884   GDSTA, LLC
       2000 Wyatt Dr, Ste 10
       Santa Clara, CA 95054
       Contact: Daphne Liu President
       Tel: 408-980-8399
       Email: daphneliu@gdsta.net
       Website: www.gdsta.net
Light emitting diode (LED) lighting & smart lighting devices, reduce carbon dioxide emission, energy usage, energy cost, lighting pollution, waste & return on investment (ROI). (Woman/As-Pac, estab 2009, empl 8, sales , cert: NMSDC)

2885   KDJA Services LLC
       223 Cynthia Ave
       Vallejo, CA 94589
       Contact: Karen Adams Owner
       Tel: 888-551-0227
       Email: karenadams2289@att.net
       Website:
Statistical report writing, qualitative & quantitative research, data collection & data analysis of laws & policies, demographic & geographic impact, strategic planning & recommendations. (Woman/AA, estab 2012, empl 1, sales , cert: State)

2886   Luster National, Inc.
       1701 Westwind Dr, Ste 117
       Bakersfield, CA 93301
       Contact: Stephanie Ochoa CEO
       Tel: 661-869-0157
       Email: sochoa@luster.com
       Website: www.luster.com
Construction & program mgmt svcs: transportation, building & water supply/wastewater treatment; planning, scheduling, estimating, cost control, quality assurance. (AA, estab 1990, empl 99, sales $9,000,000, cert: State)

2887   Mercado Associates
       25583 Ave Stanford
       Valencia, CA 91355
       Contact: Lizandro Mercado Principal
       Tel: 661-753-9295
       Email: monicaf@mercadoassociates.com
       Website: www.mercadoassociates.com
Structural consulting engineering services. (Hisp, estab 1998, empl 5, sales $480,000, cert: State, NMSDC)

2888   National Relocation Services, Inc. dba NRS, Inc.
       2671 Pomona Blvd
       Pomona, CA 91768
       Contact: Irene Ito CEO
       Tel: 909-869-5748
       Email: icito@nrsca.com
       Website: www.nrsca.com
Asset mgmt, online inventory, project & move mgmt, space planning, warehousing, inventory & bar coding, furniture installation, workstation, cubicle reconfiguration, furniture planning, CAD & CAFM. (Woman/As-Pac, estab 1994, empl 48, sales $4,373,000, cert: State, CPUC)

2889   Pari & Gershon Inc.
       2053 Lincoln Ave Ste A
       San Jose, CA 95125
       Contact: Romena Jonas Presdient
       Tel: 408-966-7184
       Email: rjonas@pgiinc.net
       Website: www.pgicompany.com
Environmental Consulting, Engineering Design & Construction. (Woman, estab 2009, empl 5, sales $100,000, cert: State, WBENC)

2890   Pivox Corporation
3240 El Camino Real Ste 230
Irvine, CA 92602
Contact: Sean Shahin VP
Tel: 949-727-1400
Email: sean@pivox.com
Website:
Remediation of soil & groundwater, demolition, project &
construction management, permitting, design, feasibility
study, treatment system installation (civil, mechanical,
electril, and instrumentation). (Woman, estab 2004, empl
20, sales $8,000,000, cert: CPUC)

2891   Quality Assurance and Risk Management
Services,Inc
22 Highridge Dr
American Canyon, CA 94503
Contact: Robert Navarro CEO
Tel: 707-557-1942
Email: rnavarro@qaandrm.com
Website: www.QAandRM.com
Safety & mission assurance (SMA) support for NASA
missions & payloads, safety, reliability & quality engineer-
ing/assurance & continuous risk management. (Hisp, estab
2005, empl 6, sales $667,971, cert: State)

2892   Quest Project Controls, Inc.
114 W Colorado Blvd
Monrovia, CA 91016
Contact: Robyn Coates CEO
Tel: 626-639-2613
Email: robyn@thecmsolution.com
Website: www.thecmsolution.com
Project controls services & staff augmentation, project
scheduling & planning, cost engineering, estimating &
management of change. (Woman, estab 2002, empl 23,
sales $1,959,183, cert: State, City, CPUC, WBENC)

2893   R.J. Roberts, Inc.
145 John Glenn Dr
Concord, CA 94520
Contact: Terri Van De Veire Acct Mgr
Tel: 925-689-8080
Email: van_t@robertscompanies.net
Website: www.robertscompanies.net
Consulting engineering services: civil, structural, electrical
& mechanical. (Woman, estab 1978, empl 80, sales
$9,712,761, cert: WBENC)

2894   RFE Engineering, Inc.
8680 Greenback Ln, Ste 107
Orangevale, CA 95662
Contact: Bob Eynck President
Tel: 916-989-3285
Email: reynck@rfeengineering.com
Website: http://RFEengineering.com
Surveying, boundary & topographic surveys, aerial control,
ALTA/ACSM, parcel/subdivision maps, construction staking
planning, military facility master planning, development
feasibility analysis, zoning & use permits, master planning.
(Hisp, estab 2003, empl 8, sales $640,000, cert: State,
CPUC, 8a)

2895   Solartech Power, Inc.
901 E Cedar St
Ontario, CA 91761
Contact: Sherry Fu Owner
Tel: 714-630-8880
Email: sherry.fu@solartechpower.com
Website: www.solartechpower.com
Mfr solar photovoltaic panels & equipment. (Woman/
As-Ind, estab 2001, empl 10, sales $3,000,000, cert:
CPUC)

2896   TEC, Inc.
510 S. La Brea Ave.
Inglewood, CA 90301
Contact: Steven Youschak Sales
Tel: 949-450-8200
Email: syouschak@teccm.com
Website: www.teccm.com
Engineering & construction mgmt svcs: CPM scheduling,
cost control, constructability review, claims analysis,
design mgmt & contract administration. (AA, estab 1988,
empl 32, sales , cert: NMSDC, CPUC)

2897   The CAD-Scan Connection
1111 Riveside Ave Ste 405
Paso Robles, CA 93446
Contact: Linda Martini Posner CEO
Tel: 805-237-9347
Email: lindap@cadscanconnection.com
Website: www.cadscanconnection.com
Engineering/architectural technical support services,
Conversion to CAD architectural, engineering drawings
to AutoCAD. Revit, Map 3D, ArcView,GIS, Large format
Description scanning. (Woman, estab 1998, empl 3, sales
, cert: CPUC)

2898   The R.E.M. Engineering Co., Inc.
1575 N Lake Ave, Ste 204
Pasadena, CA 91104
Contact: Robert Milton, Jr. GM
Tel: 626-296-7200
Email: remeng@remengr.com
Website: www.remengr.com
Engineering services: civil, structural, electrical &
mechanical, design & design-build, scheduling, project
status reporting, construction management. (AA, estab
1979, empl 7, sales $265,826, cert: State, CPUC)

2899   TTG Engineers
300 N Lake Ave 14th Fl
Pasadena, CA 91101
Contact: Marketing Mgr
Tel: 626-463-2800
Email:
Website: www.ttgcorp.com
Engineering services: mechanical, electrical, plumbing,
fire protection, structural & civil systems, cogeneration,
thermal energy storage, LEED project certification, solar
energy & commissioning. (As-Pac, estab 1955, empl 400,
sales $51,991,145, cert: NMSDC)

2900 Vistam, Inc.
2375 Walnut Ave
Signal Hill, CA 90755
Contact: Arley Tamayo Sales
Tel: 562-912-7779
Email: art.tamayo@vistam.com
Website: http://vistam.com
Electrical engineering & testing services, substation
maintenance & commissioning projects, scheduled
maintenance programs. (As-Pac, estab 1992, empl 18,
sales $1,752,000, cert: State)

2901 WRW Engineering
2104 Martin Way
Pittsburg, CA 94565
Contact: Barbara Williams Supplier Diversity
Administrator
Tel: 925-439-8272
Email: bwilliams@wrweng.com
Website: www.wrweng.com
Mechanical, electrical & software engineering, automated
flexible testing stations, smart products & autonomous
machines. (Woman, estab 2012, empl 2, sales , cert:
WBENC)

2902 Zelos Consulting, LLC
2400 Wyandotte St Ste A
Mountain View, CA 94043
Contact: Sabrina Sirwet Business Develop Mgr
Tel: 650-462-1696
Email: sabrina.sirwet@zelos.com
Website: www.zelos.com
Turnkey & customized engineering: staffing services,
payroll services, engineering project design services.
(Woman/As-Pac, estab 1996, empl 40, sales $3,000,000,
cert: CPUC, WBENC)

Colorado

2903 F&D International, LLC
5723 Arapahoe Ave Ste 1B
Boulder, CO 80303
Contact: Teri Ficken Presdient
Tel: 303-652-3200
Email: teri@fdi-one.com
Website: www.fdi-one.com
F&Engineering, architecture & construction management,
engineering consulting (civil & structural), facility condi-
tion assessments, site plans, construction consulting,
architectural design & CAD drawings. (Woman, estab 2001,
empl 10, sales $1,400,000, cert: WBENC)

2904 High Energy Inc.
625 Hudson St
Denver, CO 80220
Contact:
Tel: 303-399-1098
Email:
Website: www.highenergyinc.com
Engineering, design, drafting, project & construction
mgmt, EPC for transmission lines, substations, distribution
systems, operation & maintenance programs, feasibility,
system planning, grounding, insulation coord, protective
relaying. (Woman, estab 1998, empl 10, sales $392,600,
cert: WBENC)

2905 Special Aerospace Services LLC
3005 30th St
Boulder, CO 80301
Contact: Heather Bulk CEO
Tel: 303-625-1010
Email: hbulk@specialaerospaceservices.com
Website: www.specialaerospaceservices.com
Tactical engineering services: safety, mission assurance,
integration, design & concept development. (Woman,
estab 2007, empl 40, sales $3,000,000, cert: 8a)

Connecticut

2906 Access Consulting
31 Island Heights Circle
Stamford, CT 06902
Contact: Arun Sinha President
Tel: 203-975-2950
Email: contact@accessc.com
Website: www.accessc.com/
Corporate communications, marketing communications
& technical writing services. (As-Ind, estab 2003, empl 2,
sales , cert: NMSDC)

Delaware

2907 Bethrant Industries LLC
7 Midfield Rd
New Castle, DE 19720
Contact: Ashly Bethrant Presdient
Tel: 302-322-0521
Email: ashly17@comcast.net
Website: www.bethrantdesign.com
Design, engineering, CAD, graphics, illustration, render-
ing, prototype models & fixture fabrication, point of
purchase displays, shelving design, exhibit booth &
bathom furniture design. (Woman/AA, Hisp, estab 2016,
empl 4, sales , cert: NMSDC)

2908 Mechanical Design Solutions, Inc.
5577 S DuPont Pkwy
Smyrna, DE 19977
Contact: Dianne Bingham President
Tel: 302-659-0233
Email: dbingham@mds13.com
Website: www.mds13.com
Mechanical, electrical & instrument system design &
engineering, P&ID walkdown, verification, fabrication
orthography, isometrics, bill of material & scopes of
work, stress analysis (Rebis and AutoPIPE), PSV survey &
modeling, Installation. (Woman/Nat Ame, estab 1998,
empl 6, sales $875,000, cert: State)

2909 Mountain Consulting, Inc.
103 S Bradford St
Dover, DE 19904
Contact: Kim Adams Presdient
Tel: 302-744-9875
Email: kadams@mountainconsultinginc.com
Website: www.mountainconsultinginc.net
Engineering, land survey & technical services: Military
Housing Privatization, Resident Construction Manage-
ment, Contract Program Management, Title II Services,
and Project Oversight. (Woman/AA, estab 2003, empl 5,
sales , cert: State, NWBOC, 8a)

Florida

2910   Diversified Design & Drafting Services, Inc.
2374 Capital Circle NE
Tallahassee, FL 32308
Contact: Presdient
Tel: 850-385-1133
Email:
Website: www.dddsinc.com
Land surveying, boundary surveys, topographic surveys, LiDAR surveys, aerial surveys. (Woman, estab 1991, empl 15, sales $987,000, cert: State, City)

2911   Diversified Technology Consultants
650 Central Ave Unit 3
Sarasota, FL 34236
Contact: ROBERT HAMMERSLEY Program Mgr
Tel: 203-239-4200
Email: robert.hammersley@teamdtc.com
Website: www.teamdtc.com
Civil, environmental, transportation, structures, water pollution control, solid/hazardous waste mgmt, survey, electrical, mechanical, construction inspection & admin, CADD svcs, landscape architecture. (As-Pac, estab 1979, empl 55, sales $6,724,276, cert: State)

2912   EAC Consulting, Inc.
815 NW 57th Ave, Ste 402
Miami, FL 33126
Contact: Enrique Crooks President
Tel: 305-264-2557
Email: eac@eacconsult.com
Website: www.eacconsult.com
Civil structural, bridge & highway design, construction engineering & inspection svcs. (AA, estab 1994, empl 34, sales , cert: State)

2913   EDF Company
8390 Currency Dr, Ste 4
Riviera Beach, FL 33404
Contact: Karla Watkins Director
Tel: 561-863-6770
Email: karla@edfinc.com
Website: www.edfinc.com
Complex design & engineering support services to the Aerospace industry. Test Facilities & Test Equipment Design/Build for multiple Engine Test Programs, F100/F14, F119/F22, Joint Strike Fighter (JSF). (Woman, estab 1978, empl 25, sales $3,355,920, cert: WBENC)

2914   Engineered Design Services LLC
410 S Ware Blvd Ste 405
Tampa, FL 33619
Contact: Craig McKenzie Presdient
Tel: 813-816-0301
Email: craigmckenzie@edsengineers.com
Website:
Mechanical & Electrical Engineering, Process Design, Pumping Systems, 3D Modeling, Food Grade Piping Design, Structural/Concrete
Vessel Design, Dry Material Handling, Material Conveying & Dust Collection. (AA, estab 2013, empl 4, sales $119,829, cert: State)

2915   Frazier Engineering, Inc.
6767 N. Wickham Road, Ste 304
Melbourne, FL 32940
Contact: Michelle Shoultz Presdient
Tel: 321-253-8131
Email: mshoultz@fraziereng.com
Website: www.fraziereng.com
Civil, structural, environmental engineering & surveying: design, permitting & construction administration of site plans, utility improvements, water, sewer, reuse, drainage, roadway improvements, bridges. (Woman/As-Pac, estab 1992, empl 20, sales $17,700,000, cert: State, NMSDC)

2916   Holland Engineering Inspection Services dba HEIS
3900 Hollywood Blvd Ste 303
Hollywood, FL 33021
Contact: Catherine MacAskill CEO
Tel: 954-626-0550
Email: catherine@heisflorida.com
Website: www.heisflorida.com/
Civil engineering inspections & certifications, 5-Year Surface Water Management Renewals, Stormwater Certifications, Stormwater Drainage Cleaning & Repairs, SSES. (Minority, Woman, estab 2016, empl 2, sales $400,000, cert: State)

2917   ITG Global, LLC
11235 St. Johns Industrial Pkwy N Ste 2A
Jacksonville, FL 32246
Contact: Joseph Lukowski CEO
Tel: 904-425-4760
Email: almaferrante@itgtec.com
Website: www.itgtec.com
Automation Design, PLC Programming, Software Development, Technologies Consulting, Motion Design, Robot programming, MES, OEE, Data Analytics, Condition Monitoring, Control System Design, UL 508A Panel Shop, Control Panel. (Woman/Hisp, estab 2003, empl 27, sales $3,000,000, cert: NMSDC)

2918   JIRACOR
3275 Progress Dr Ste A
Orlando, FL 32825
Contact: Richard Coronado Presdient
Tel: 407-910-1146
Email: r.coronado@jiracor.com
Website: www.jiracor.com
Engineering services: aerospace, aviation, commercial & defense. (Woman/Hisp, estab 2011, empl 12, sales $1,000,000, cert: 8a)

2919   RLJ Enterprises Inc. dba Genesis VII, Inc.
1605 White Dr
Titusville, FL 32780
Contact: Robert Jordan CEO
Tel: 321-383-4813
Email: robert.jordan@genesisvii.com
Website: www.genesisvii.com
Engineering, Logistics & Constructions Services, Design Engineering, 3D CAD, Reverse Engineering, Procurement (Wholesale Procurement), Facilities Management, Construction Management. (AA, estab 1989, empl 9, sales $3,900,000, cert: NMSDC, SDB)

2920   Southern Energy Solution Group, LLC
       2336 S East Ocean Blvd, Ste 204
       Stuart, FL 34996
       Contact: Oswald Hoffler Managing Member
       Tel: 772-919-2844
       Email: ohoffler@soenergy-grp.com
       Website: www.soenergy-grp.com
Renewable Energy Generation and RECs (AA, estab 2010, empl 5, sales $250,000, cert: CPUC)

2921   The Med Writers LLC
       9314 Forest Hill Blvd, Ste 6
       Wellington, FL 33411
       Contact: Karen Vieira Presdient
       Tel: 561-247-2190
       Email: karen@themedwriters.com
       Website: http://themedwriters.com
Medical & scientific writing, offsite writing services. (Woman/AA, estab 2007, empl 8, sales $174,704, cert: CPUC)

Georgia

2922   A-Z Sophisticated Solutions
       12850 Hwy 9 N, Ste 600-205
       Alpharetta, GA 30004
       Contact: Ana Maria Marin Managing Dir
       Tel: 404-996-1358
       Email: ap@a-zssolutions.com
       Website: www.a-zssolutions.com
Engineering, Technical Writing, Technical Instruction & written Translation services. Technical Writing: brochures, user manuals, creation, proofread & editorial. Technical Instruction: plastics seminars & CAE plastics. (Woman/Hisp, estab 2010, empl 1, sales , cert: WBENC)

2923   BREED Enterprises, Inc.
       4501 Circle 75 Pkwy Ste A-1160
       Atlanta, GA 30339
       Contact: Bobby Reed CEO
       Tel: 678-324-0105
       Email: breed@breedenterprisesinc.com
       Website: www.breedenterprisesinc.com
LEED programs, LED lighting products. (AA, estab 2005, empl 45, sales $2,500,000, cert: State, NMSDC)

2924   Continental Technical Services
       260 Peachtree St, Ste 2200
       Atlanta, GA 30303
       Contact: Willie Dunlap CEO
       Tel: 404-527-6297
       Email: henri@ctsnationally.com
       Website: www.ctsnationally.com
Staff augmentation, temporary personnel, technical publications, integrated logistics support, validations & verifications, ECPs, technical writing, quality assurance & control, quality inspection. (AA, estab 1992, empl 54, sales $7,400,000, cert: NMSDC)

2925   Eubio, LLC
       P.O. Box 16555
       Atlanta, GA 30321
       Contact: Alita Anderson Principal
       Tel: 404-632-2435
       Email: alita@eubiomed.com
       Website: www.eubiomed.com
Medical communications, medical writing. (Woman/AA, estab 2012, empl 2, sales $885,503, cert: City, NMSDC, WBENC)

2926   Greenspeed Energy Solutions, LLC
       2148 Hills Ave NW Ste H
       Atlanta, GA 30318
       Contact: Thomas McNeill Business Develop Mgr
       Tel: 404-924-7400
       Email: tmcneill@greenspeedenergy.com
       Website: www.greenspeedenergy.com
Design/build energy services, audit & design, implementation (installation) of energy efficiency measures. (Minority, estab 2006, empl 20, sales $4,000,000, cert: State, NMSDC)

2927   Present Energi LLC
       411 S Greenwood St Ste B
       LaGrange, GA 30240
       Contact: Renee Warrick Managing Partner
       Tel: 706-883-7336
       Email: renee@presentenergi.com
       Website: www.presentenergi.com
Solar Photovoltaic & Solar Thermal systems for residential, commercial, industrial & utility scale customers; engineering, project management & construction for large scale systems. (Woman, estab 2009, empl 2, sales , cert: WBENC)

2928   R2T, Inc.
       580 W Crossville Road Stes 101-102
       Roswell, GA 30075
       Contact: Presdient
       Tel: 770-569-7038
       Email:
       Website: www.r2tinc.com
Civil & environmental engineering & construction services: watershed/stormwater mgmt, conceptual planning, water & wastewater system design, design/build construction. (Woman/AA, estab 2005, empl 57, sales $6,810,190, cert: City, NMSDC, WBENC)

2929   Research Analysis Group
       303 Perimeter Center N Ste 300
       Atlanta, GA 30346
       Contact: Tara Dixon Dir Business Devel
       Tel: 770-558-6302
       Email: info@evaluation-group.com
       Website: www.evaluation-group.com
Consulting, evaluation, scientific writing, technical assistance, strategic planning, metric development program design & data analysis & management services. (Woman/AA, Hisp, estab 2009, empl 7, sales $125,000, cert: 8a)

2930   The Black Book, Inc.
       3500 Lenox Ste 1500
       Atlanta, GA 30326
       Contact: Rochelle Brown Owner
       Tel: 888-808-9542
       Email: rochelle@theblackbookvip.com
       Website: www.theblackbookvip.com
The BLACK BOOK is a premiere luxury concierge service and lifestyle management agency. We serve a plethora of individuals from athletes and sports organizations , entertainers and production companies to high-net-individuals (Woman/AA, estab 2013, empl 5, sales $120,000, cert: NMSDC)

Illinois

2931 Advanced Cad/Cam Service dba EngineeringPeople
      801 W Main St
      Peoria, IL 61606
      Contact: Jim Montelongo CEO
      Tel: 309-621-5792
      Email: jim@engineeringpeople.com
      Website: www.engineeringpeople.com
Engineering service support, mechanical, electrical,
hydraulic, structural, engineering staffing. (Hisp, estab
1991, empl 60, sales $5,700,000, cert: NMSDC)

2932 CSMI-KAE Consultants, Inc.
      1750 E Golf Rd Ste 490
      Schaumburg, IL 60173
      Contact: Karen Eng Presdient
      Tel: 847-605-0080
      Email: keng@csmius.com
      Website: www.csmius.com
Engineering & design services: project management,
electrical, mechanical, packaging, automation engineering
& CAD services. (Woman/As-Pac, estab 1983, empl 24,
sales $3,900,000, cert: State, WBENC)

2933 Nest Builders
      303 W Erie St Ste 510
      Chicago, IL 60654
      Contact: Victor Avila Principal
      Tel: 312-915-0557
      Email: vavila@dbhms.com
      Website: http://dbhms.com
Engineering services: mechanical, electrical, plumbing &
fire protection design. (Hisp, estab 2002, empl 60, sales
$700,000, cert: City)

2934 PMA Consultants of Illinois LLC
      333 W Wacker Dr, Ste 880
      Chicago, IL 60606
      Contact: Gui Ponce de Leon Managing Principal
      Tel: 312-920-0404
      Email: kflood@pmaconsultants.com
      Website: www.pmaconsultants.com
Engineering consulting services: CPM scheduling, claims
mitigation, change order management, contract document
review, cost estimating, value engineering, training &
expert analysis and testimony. (Hisp, estab 1971, empl
190, sales , cert: State, NMSDC)

2935 Prairie Engineers
      107 N Main St, Ste 3C
      Columbia, IL 62236
      Contact: Michelle Chambliss Business Development
      Tel: 217-605-0403
      Email: mchambliss@prairieengineers.com
      Website: www.prairieengineers.com
Engineering services: planning, project management, civil
engineering, water resources engineering, land surveying,
land acquisition, environmental science & natural resources management & construction management.
(Woman, estab 2010, empl 20, sales $2,000,000, cert: City,
WBENC, 8a)

2936 Primera Engineers
      100 S Wacker Dr Ste 700
      Chicago, IL 60606
      Contact: Al Perla
      Tel: 312-606-0910
      Email: aperla@primeraeng.com
      Website: www.primeraeng.com
Engineering design: mechanical, electrical, plumbing,
fire protection, architecture, commissioning, structural,
civil, telecommunications, utility distribution & substation engineering. (Hisp, estab 1987, empl 170, sales
$21,910,784, cert: State, City, NMSDC)

2937 Solved Engineering
      55 E Monroe, Ste 3800
      Chicago, IL 60603
      Contact: Edward William Principal Engineer
      Tel: 800-975-9723
      Email: ewilliam@solvedeng.com
      Website: www.solvedeng,com
Electrical Engineer & and Consulting, Engineering
Design, Subject Matter Testimony & Engineering
Calculation / Studies Service. (AA, estab 2015, empl 5,
sales , cert: City, NMSDC, CPUC)

2938 Sterling Engineering, Inc.
      Two Westbrook Corporate Center Ste 300
      Westchester, IL 60154
      Contact: Rama Kavaliauskas Presdient
      Tel: 630-993-3433
      Email: rama@sterling-engineering.com
      Website: www.sterling-engineering.com
Engineering & technical staff augmentation solutions.
(Woman, estab 1969, empl 75, sales $2,691,294, cert:
WBENC)

2939 Structure Designs, Inc.
      309 W Washington St Ste 325
      Chicago, IL 60606
      Contact: Olufemi Oladeinde Presdient
      Tel: 312-551-9780
      Email: oao@structuredesignsinc.com
      Website: www.sdiengr.com
Civil Engineering, Structural Engineering, Architectural
Engineering, Land Surveying, Construction management.
(AA, estab 1994, empl 30, sales $12,500,000, cert:
NMSDC, 8a)

2940 Valdes Engineering Company
      100 West 22nd St
      Lombard, IL 60148
      Contact: Robert Valdes Mgr of External Affairs
      Tel: 630-792-1886
      Email: bmvaldes@valdeseng.com
      Website: www.valdeseng.com/
Engineering svcs to process facilities, chemical, food,
pharmaceutical, power & steel mfg plants in piping
design, mechanical, civil & structural engineering,
architecture & process engineering. (Hisp, estab 1992,
empl 200, sales , cert: NMSDC)

Indiana

2941 Americas Engineers, Inc.
1449 Kimber Ln, Ste 101
Evansville, IN 47715
Contact: KC Jain Presdient
Tel: 812-473-1905
Email: kcjain@americasengineers.com
Website: www.americasengineers.com
Civil engineering: surveying, site plans, drainage systems, grading & approach roads, access roads & storm water management. (As-Ind, estab 2004, empl 7, sales $1,200,000, cert: NMSDC)

2942 Consulting Management Inspection Design, Inc.
1402 N Capitol Ave Ste 250
Indianapolis, IN 46202
Contact: Stacey L. Harrell Exec Admin Asst
Tel: 317-917-4244
Email: sharrell@cmidinc.com
Website: www.cmidinc.com
Architectural, structural, mechanical, electrical, environmental, civil, commissioning & construction management & inspection services. (AA, estab 1996, empl 24, sales $3,500,000, cert: State, City)

2943 Durkin & Villalta Partners Engineering
8440 Woodfield Crossing Blvd, Ste 175
Indianapolis, IN 46240
Contact: Alvaro Villalta CEO
Tel: 317-472-3883
Email: avillalta@dvpe.net
Website: http://dvpe.net
Mechanical, electrical, plumbing & fire protection design firm. (Hisp, estab 2007, empl 22, sales $3,000,000, cert: 8a)

2944 K & S Engineers, Inc.
9715 Kennedy Ave
Highland, IN 46322
Contact: Debbie Pilawski Presdient
Tel: 219-924-5231
Email: dpilawski@kandsengineers.com
Website: www.kandsengineers.com
Geotechnical engineering & consulting, drilling soil borings & caissons, rock coring, lab & field testing of soil, concrete, asphalt & steel, environmental consulting & forensic investigation of construction materials. (As-Ind, estab 1984, empl 36, sales $4,515,115, cert: State, NMSDC)

Kansas

2945 Choson Resource LLC
1999 N Amidon, Ste 100B
Wichita, KS 67203
Contact: Kim Silcott President
Tel: 316-729-0312
Email: kim@chosonresource.com
Website: www.Chosonresource.com
Aerospace engineering & staffing services for the air, defense & space industries. (Woman/As-Pac, estab 2010, empl 4, sales $4,254,100, cert: NMSDC)

Kentucky

2946 LECGI Inc.
13113 Eastpoint Park Blvd Ste D
Louisville, KY 40223
Contact: Don Liu Presdient
Tel: 502-425-1647
Email: dliu@lecgi.us
Website: www.lecgi.us
Engineering design & structural steel detailing, structural steel connection design & structural analysis of steel structures, handrails, and stairs for steel fabricators. (As-Pac, estab 2004, empl 10, sales $633,000, cert: State, 8a)

2947 Pioneer Logistics Group, Inc.
2208 Sieger Villa Ct
Louisville, KY 40218
Contact: Phillip Shoulders President
Tel: 502-479-3546
Email: pioneergroupse@msn.com
Website: www.pioneergroupse.com
Logistics, inventory control management, warehouse services, facilities management, (AA, estab 2010, empl 25, sales $2,000,000, cert: NMSDC)

Louisiana

2948 Gulf South Engineering & Testing, Inc.
2201 Aberdeen St Ste B
Kenner, LA 70062
Contact: Chad Poche VP
Tel: 504-305-4401
Email: cpoche@gulfsoutheng.com
Website: www.gulfsoutheng.com
Geotechnical engineering, foundation engineering, soil borings, facility permitting, laboratory testing, construction materials testing & inspection, concrete testing, pile testing & inspection. (AA, estab 2010, empl 8, sales $550,000, cert: City)

2949 Smith Research Group
4811 Hooper Rd
Baton Rouge, LA 70811
Contact: James Smith, Jr. CEO
Tel: 225-356-9344
Email: jim@src1.net
Website: www.src1.net
Research, mgmt; facility planning, architectural design, engineering; mechanical, electrical, civil & structural; program mgmt, project mgmt, scheduling, construction mgmt, environ eng, technical support & computer processing. (AA, estab 1994, empl 10, sales , cert: State)

Massachusetts

2950 Corporate Environmental Advisors, Inc.
127 Hartwell St
West Boylston, MA 01583
Contact: Scott Soucy Health, Safety & Compliance
Tel: 800-358-7960
Email: contactus@cea-inc.com
Website: http://cea-inc.com/
Environmental engineering, consulting & contracting firm. (Woman, estab 1985, empl 20, sales $3,878,000, cert: State)

2951 RRMAE Engineering LLC
      46 Loring Ave
      Boxborough, MA 01719
      Contact: Anton Edmund Owner
      Tel: 508-517-4913
      Email: anton.edmund@rrmaeengineering.com
      Website: www.rrmaeengineering.com
Process Design, Process Improvement, Risk assessment,
Process Validation, Validation, Commissioning & Qualification, Quality Engineering, Data analysis, Lean management, Process Automation. (As-Ind, estab 2013, empl 2,
sales $267,000, cert: State)

Maryland

2952 Robotic Research, LLC
      555 Quince Orchard Road, Ste 300
      Gaithersburg, MD 20878
      Contact: Alberto Lacaze President
      Tel: 240-631-0008
      Email: lacaze@roboticresearch.com
      Website: www.roboticresearch.com
Robotics, intelligent control, sensor processing & specialized computer programming. (Hisp, estab 2002, empl 15,
sales $3,000,000, cert: State)

2953 Site Resources, Inc.
      14315 Jarrettsville Pike
      Phoenix, MD 21131
      Contact: Sharon Elliott Marketing Mgr
      Tel: 410-683-3388
      Email: selliott@siteresourcesinc.com
      Website: www.siteresourcesinc.com
Civil engineering, landscape architecture & land planning
services. (Woman, estab 1994, empl 28, sales $4,126,649,
cert: State, City)

2954 Strategic Technology Institute, Inc. (STi)
      6000 Executive Blvd Ste 205
      Rockville, MD 20852
      Contact: Rakesh Chopra Presdient
      Tel: 301-770-7077
      Email: rchopra@sti-inc.com
      Website: www.sti-inc.com
System effectiveness, design assurance, SRM&QA, main-
tainability, quality assurance, reliability, FMECA, SCA, EMI/
EMC, EMP, radiation effects, aging effects, engineering
svcs, FRACAS, hazard analysis, OSHA, system safety. (As-
Ind, estab 1986, empl 20, sales $1,500,000, cert: State)

2955 The Perara Group Inc.
      1610 Professional Blvd Stes E & F
      Crofton, MD 21114
      Contact: Yancey Brown telecomm dir
      Tel: 410-451-4141
      Email: ybrown@peraragroup.com
      Website: www.peraragroup.com
DNA research support, genetic models, bio-analytical
chemistry models, metabolism & pharmacokinetics,
oncology models, toxicology
lab diagnostics, vaccine & vector safety, bio-safety testing.
(Woman/AA, estab 2001, empl 7, sales $1,700,000, cert:
State)

2956 Titus LLC
      23219 Stringtown Rd Ste 155
      Clarksburg, MD 20871
      Contact: Otis Miller VP
      Tel: 240-252-1341
      Email: olmiller@titusllc.com
      Website: www.titusllc.com
Design, implement & maintain mechanical, electrical,
life safety, security & communication systems. critical
power solutions for data centers, communications
environments & data monitoring centers. (Woman/AA,
estab 2002, empl 9, sales $2,800,000, cert: State)

Michigan

2957 4D Systems
      4130 Market Place
      Flint Twp, MI 48507
      Contact: Jean-Pierre Rasaiah Presdient
      Tel: 248-535-0758
      Email: jp.rasaiah@4dsysco.com
      Website: www.4dsysco.com
Robotic Systems Build (Specializing in glass handling),
Robot Programming (All applications), Robotic Simula-
tion, Siemens software reseller, NX Design, Robcad
Simulation, Process Simulate Simulation, Controls
Design, Panel build. (As-Pac, estab 2010, empl 65, sales
$8,000,000, cert: NMSDC)

2958 ABE Associates, Inc.
      440 Burroughs St, Ste. 605
      Detroit, MI 48221
      Contact: Andre Brooks Presdient
      Tel: 313-961-5170
      Email: andreb@abe-engineers.com
      Website: www.abe-engineers.com
Architectural design, civil, environmental, fire protection, mechanical & structural engineering, project
management, program management, drafting, surveying, construction inspection, land acquisition services.
(AA, estab 1997, empl 3, sales $250,000, cert: State,
NMSDC)

2959 AMBE Engineering, LLC
      15424 Prestwick Circle
      Northville, MI 48168
      Contact: Rashmi Zaveri VP
      Tel: 734-667-3167
      Email: rashmis@ambeeng.com
      Website: www.ambeeng.com
Engineering: corrective actions implementations, design
optimization, CAD/CAE design support, quality containment support. (Woman/As-Pac, estab 2001, empl 120,
sales $8,000,000, cert: NMSDC, WBENC)

2960 Bigelow Family Holdings LLC
      3223 15 Mile Rd
      Sterling Heights, MI 48310
      Contact: Presdient
      Tel: 586-306-8962
      Email:
      Website: www.mettleops.com
Program management, engineering, and business
development. (Woman, estab 2013, empl 10, sales ,
cert: WBENC, 8a)

2961 Byce & Associates, Inc.
      487 Portage St
      Kalamazoo, MI 49007
      Contact: Brenda Longman VP
      Tel: 269-381-6170
      Email: Accounting@byce.com
      Website: www.byce.com
Structural, mechanical & electrical engineering design
services. (Hisp, estab 1959, empl 34, sales , cert: NMSDC)

2962 CAD Engineering Resources, Inc.
      6100 Auburn Rd
      Shelby Township, MI 48317
      Contact: Samantha Rutherford Mgr
      Tel: 586-884-6977
      Email: dmurphy@cergroupna.com
      Website: www.cergroupna.com
Dimmensional support, CMM inpsection, 3rd party quality
containment & rework, quality residency engineering,
assembly and warehouseing. (Nat Ame, estab 1996, empl
500, sales , cert: NMSDC)

2963 Capitol Reproductions, Inc.
      215 E 12 Mile Rd
      Madison Heights, MI 48071
      Contact: Laura Muresan GM
      Tel: 313-564-4820
      Email: lauram@capitolgroup.net
      Website: www.capitolgroup.net
Engineering, CAD design & technical Illustration services.
(Woman, estab 1946, empl 48, sales $6,750,000, cert:
WBENC)

2964 Crystal Engineering Solutions
      645 Executive Dr
      Troy, MI 48083
      Contact: Chris Kizy VP
      Tel: 248-588-1390
      Email: ckizy@crystaleng.com
      Website: www.crystaleng.com
Engineering Services, Controls Engineering (Hisp, estab
1999, empl 18, sales $10,000,000, cert: State)

2965 CTI and Associates, Inc.
      28001 Cabot Dr Ste 250
      Novi, MI 48377
      Contact: Jenny Armstrong Admin
      Tel: 248-486-5100
      Email: jarmstrong@cticompanies.com
      Website: www.cticompanies.com
Engineering consulting & construction management. (As-
Ind, estab 1976, empl 135, sales $21,000,000, cert:
NMSDC)

2966 Detroit Engineered Products (DEP).
      850 E Long Lake Rd
      Troy, MI 48085
      Contact: John Gelmisi Dir Business Devel
      Tel: 248-219-9838
      Email: john_gelmisi@depusa.com
      Website: www.depusa.com
Reverse Engineering, Benchmarking, Scanning,
Prototyping, Project Outsourcing, Offshore/Domestic
Design support, and Technical Services. (As-Ind, estab
1998, empl 380, sales $18,000,000, cert: NMSDC)

2967 Doshi Associates, Inc.
      5755 New King St Ste 210
      Troy, MI 48098
      Contact: Shailesh Doshi CEO
      Tel: 248-247-3030
      Email: shailesh.doshi@doshigroup.net
      Website: www.doshigroup.net
Architecturel, civil, structural, mechanical & electrical
engineering. (As-Pac, estab 1991, empl 30, sales
$2,550,000, cert: NMSDC)

2968 Engineering Design Solutions PLC
      5220 Lovers Lane, Ste LL-120
      Portage, MI 49002
      Contact: Irfan Ahmed, MSCE, PE President
      Tel: 269-903-2652
      Email: irfan.ahmed@enggdesigns.com
      Website: www.enggdesigns.com
Manufacturing & industrial building design & CAD
designing automobile facilities. (As-Ind, estab 2004,
empl 8, sales $600,000, cert: NMSDC)

2969 ETCS Inc.
      275 Executive Dr
      Troy, MI 48083
      Contact: Ravi Kapur Dir of Sales
      Tel: 248-763-9467
      Email: ravi@etcsinc.com
      Website: www.etcsinc.com
Engineering, reverse engineering, tool design, staffing,
offshore component sourcing. (As-Ind, As-Pac, estab
2003, empl 52, sales $4,826,000, cert: NMSDC)

2970 Feamold, Inc.
      1441 W Long Lake Rd, Ste 240
      Troy, MI 48098
      Contact: Shrikant Oak Presdient
      Tel: 248-680-4628
      Email: oak@feamold.com
      Website: www.feamold.com
Engineering Consulting. (Minority, estab 1994, empl 5,
sales , cert: NMSDC)

2971 Future Technologies, Inc.
      2490 E Midland Rd
      Bay City, MI 48706
      Contact: Brent Waldie Applications Engineer
      Tel: 989-686-6200
      Email: brentw@futuretechnologies.com
      Website: www.futuretechnologies.com
Custom leak testing systems, function testing equipment, welding & assembly automation & calibrated
standard leaks. (Hisp, estab 1989, empl 33, sales , cert:
NMSDC)

2972 Gala & Associates Inc.
      31455 Southfield Rd
      Beverly Hills, MI 48025
      Contact: Chuni Gala Presdient
      Tel: 248-642-8610
      Email: cgala@galaandassociates.com
      Website: www.galaandassociates.com
Electrical, mechanical, structural, civil & architectural
engineering svcs, CAD services. (Nat Ame, As-Ind, Hisp,
estab 1987, empl 50, sales $6,000,000, cert: NMSDC)

2973   Generalety, LLC
      5820 N Canton Center Rd Ste 140
      Canton, MI 48187
      Contact: Sheng-Dong Liu CEO
      Tel: 734-522-1488
      Email: sliu@generalety.com
      Website: www.generalety.com
Computer aided design (CAD) & computer aided engineering (CAE) services in the automotive industry. (As-Pac, estab 2003, empl 60, sales $1,250,000, cert: NMSDC)

2974   Global Supply Innovative Engineering LLC
      200 E Big Beaver
      Troy, MI 48083
      Contact: Dayle Farrimond VP
      Tel: 248-457-4592
      Email: dfarrimond@gsiengineering.com
      Website: www.gsiengineering.com
Injection Mold Building, Program Management, Engineering
Sample Facility, Production Manufacturing Facility. (Woman, estab 2005, empl 7, sales $2,800,000, cert: WBENC)

2975   Gonzalez Aerospace
      29401 Stephenson Hwy
      Madison Heights, MI 48071
      Contact: Pablo Calzada NBD Dir
      Tel: 248-867-8212
      Email: pcalzada@gonzalezaerospace.com
      Website: www.gonzalezaerospace.com
Production Systems; Manufacturing Engineering, Program Management, Automated Assembly System Integration, Contingent Workforce Services. (Hisp, estab 1975, empl 130, sales $64,000,000, cert: NMSDC)

2976   Good Fortune Trading Co. dba GFT Services
      3959 Nash Dr
      Troy, MI 48083
      Contact: Janice Girling Presdient
      Tel: 248-884-4635
      Email: janice.girling@gftservices.com
      Website: www.gftservices.com
Procurement services, project planning, technical writing. (Woman, estab 2016, empl 1, sales , cert: WBENC)

2977   Hybrid Design Services
      2479 Elliott Dr
      Troy, MI 48083
      Contact: James Pinon Presdient
      Tel: 248-298-3400
      Email: jpinon@hybriddesignservices.com
      Website: www.hybriddesignservices.com
Engineering, design, prototyping, testing services specializing in hybrid vehicles & systems, electric vehicles & systems, HEV systems, EV systems, hybrid and electric vehicle R&D, high voltage systems, energy storage. (Hisp, estab 2007, empl 20, sales $2,000,000, cert: NMSDC)

2978   I*LOGIC, Inc.
      999 Tech Row
      Madison Heights, MI 48071
      Contact: Sharon Weatherspoon Presdient
      Tel: 248-616-4506
      Email: sweatherspoon@goilogic.com
      Website: www.goilogic.com
Program management, containerization management, industrial engineering, material flow engineering, procurement services, design services & IT services. (Woman/As-Pac, estab 1995, empl 32, sales , cert: NMSDC, WBENC)

2979   Magnys Innovative Solutions LLC
      42500 W Eleven Mile Rd Ste B
      Novi, MI 48375
      Contact: Mary Willy Office Mgr
      Tel: 248-449-2600
      Email: mwilly@magnys.com
      Website: www.magnys.com
Design, oversee process, project engineering services, manufacturing engineering, 3-D simulation & PLC emulation software modeling. (AA, estab 1999, empl 210, sales $25,000,000, cert: NMSDC)

2980   MPS Group, Inc.
      38755 Hills Tech Dr
      Farmington Hills, MI 48331
      Contact: Bryon Lawrence Dir of Sales & Marketing
      Tel: 313-841-7588
      Email: blawrence@mpsgrp.com
      Website: www.mpsgrp.com
Environmental Consulting & Engineering. (AA, estab 1995, empl 495, sales $46,200,000, cert: NMSDC)

2981   Optimal Computer Aided Engineering, Inc.
      47802 W Anchor Court
      Plymouth, MI 48170
      Contact: Song Young CEO
      Tel: 734-414-7933
      Email: ksrinivas@optimalinc.com
      Website: www.optimalinc.com
CAD/CAM/CAE/PDM services, contract engineering services & metrology product sales & support. (As-Pac, estab 1986, empl 100, sales $10,000,000, cert: NMSDC)

2982   PAT USA, Inc.
      2927 Waterview Dr
      Rochester Hills, MI 48309
      Contact: Fenar Mayes Sr Project Mgr
      Tel: 248-299-2410
      Email: fenar@pat-engineering.com
      Website: http://pat-engineering.com
General contracting services, engineering & construction services. (Woman, estab 2011, empl 10, sales , cert: WBENC)

2983   Process Control & Engineering Inc.
      1091 Centre Rd, Ste 290
      Auburn Hills, MI 48326
      Contact: Theresa Dies Treasurer
      Tel: 248-340-1888
      Email: tdies@pcemonarch.com
      Website: www.pcemonarch.com
Monitoring & Control System for process air & fluid parameters, VOC emissions, air and fluid handling equipment. Monitoring and Control system for: Process parameters: air velocities, humidity, temperature, fluid flows, viscosity, chemical parameters. (As-Ind, As-Pac, estab 1994, empl 15, sales $9,000,000, cert: NMSDC)

2984   Renaissance S & S Inc.
      26637 Golfview
      Dearborn Heights, MI 48127
      Contact: Smith Sylvester CEO
      Tel: 313-561-3897
      Email: rssgroup@sbcglobal.net
      Website: www.renaissancessgroup.com
Engineering consulting services. (AA, estab 1996, empl 4, sales , cert: NMSDC)

2985 Sigma Associates, Inc.
1900 St. Antoine St
Detroit, MI 48226
Contact: Kathy Cotton Admin Asst
Tel: 313-963-9700
Email: kcotton@sigmaassociates.com
Website: www.sigmaassociates.com
Multi-disciplinary engineering, architectural, program management, construction contract admin, construction management, design-build capabilities & information technology services. (Woman, estab 1978, empl 51, sales , cert: State, WBENC, SDB)

2986 Universal Tool Equipment & Controls, Inc.
6525 Center Dr
Sterling Heights, MI 48312
Contact: Bill Bartolotta VP
Tel: 586-268-4380
Email: bbartolotta@universaltecinc.com
Website: www.universaltecinc.com
Automation & welding systems, robotics, weld guns, vision systems, sealant systems, drawn arc welders, projection welders, material handling end effectors & welding fixtures. (Woman/AA, estab 2009, empl 29, sales $10,000,000, cert: WBENC)

2987 WFQ, Inc.
5751 S. Sheldon Rd
Canton, MI 48188
Contact: Jennifer McGuire Sales Acct Mgr
Tel: 734-512-6284
Email: jmcguire@wfqinc.com
Website: http://wfqinc.com
GP12/Launch support, Resident Liaison / Customer representation Quality Engineering services (placement or hire) Containment, Inspection & Re-work Solutions Sequence / Kitting solutions Warehouse capabilities Proprietary Web-based Reporting System. (Woman, estab 2013, empl 150, sales $5,780,000, cert: WBENC)

2988 Willie Horton Inc.
7784 Ronda Dr
Canton, MI 48187
Contact: Deryl Horton Presdient
Tel: 248-855-2215
Email: dhorton@horton-inc.com
Website: www.horton-inc.com
Heat-treating, hardening, surface engineering, tool steel, mechcanical & electrical engineering. (AA, estab 2003, empl 20, sales $300,000, cert: NMSDC)

Minnesota

2989 EVS, Inc.
10025 Valley View Rd Ste 140
Eden Prairie, MN 55344
Contact: Andy Kim Presdient
Tel: 952-646-0236
Email: akim@evs-eng.com
Website: www.evs-eng.com
Civil engineering, site development, surveying & environmental, permits, assessments & NEPA documentation. (As-Pac, estab 1979, empl 61, sales $7,432,378, cert: NMSDC)

2990 Fourth Factor Engineering, LLC
10636 Maryland Ave S
Bloomington, MN 55438
Contact: Elizabeth Becker Presdient
Tel: 612-708-2562
Email: liz.becker@fourth-factor-engineering.com
Website: www.fourth-factor-engineering.com
Engineering analysis: system safety, software safety, human factors, reliability, maintainability, testability & logistics analysis. (Woman, estab 2010, empl 6, sales $1,049,233, cert: State, WBENC)

2991 Hansen Thorp Pellinen Olson, Inc.
7510 Market Place Dr
Eden Prairie, MN 55344
Contact: Tim Johnson Business Devel Dir
Tel: 952-829-0700
Email: tjohnson@htpo.com
Website: www.htpo.com
Engineering svcs: land surveying, civil engineering, landscape architecture design & construction. (Woman, estab 1980, empl 23, sales $2,876,105, cert: City)

2992 Questions & Solutions Engineering
1079 Falls Curve
Chaska, MN 55318
Contact: Rebecca Ellis
Tel: 612-309-0503
Email: rebecca.ellis@qseng.com
Website: www.QSEng.com
Commissioning program development, training & project execution, existing building troubleshooting, retro-commissioning, re-commissioning, HVAC system planning & implementing capital projects. (Woman, estab 2005, empl 4, sales $181,000, cert: City, WBENC)

2993 Sambatek
14800 28th Ave N, Ste 140
Plymouth, MN 55447
Contact: Erik Miller Sales
Tel: 763-476-6010
Email: emiller@sambatek.com
Website: www.sambatek.com
Civil engineering, land planning & surveying, water & waste water treatment process engineering, enviornmental assesments. (As-Pac, estab 1966, empl 46, sales $5,269,743, cert: State)

2994 Shepherd Data Services, Inc.
527 Marquette Ave
Minneapolis, MN 55402
Contact: Dennis Waldrop VP
Tel: 612-659-1234
Email: cchalstrom@shepherddata.com
Website: www.shepherddata.com
Data collection for litigation. (Woman, estab 2002, empl 12, sales $2,283,392, cert: WBENC)

2995 SM Engineering Co.
9 Ninth Ave N
Hopkins, MN 55343
Contact: Wayne Peterson COO
Tel: 952-938-7407
Email: wayne@smeng.com
Website: www.smeng.com
Utility management: electricity, natural gas, water & sewer. (As-Ind, estab 1982, empl 13, sales $2,921,000, cert: NMSDC)

Missouri

2996   Civil Design Inc.
5220 Oakland Ave
St. Louis, MO 63110
Contact: Lori Daiber Business Dev Mgr
Tel:
Email: ldaiber@civildesigninc.com
Website: www.civildesigninc.com
Civil & Site Engineering, Land Surveying, Transportation, Water Resources, Infrastructure & Analytics. (Woman, estab 1996, empl 52, sales $5,800,000, cert: State, WBENC, NWBOC)

2997   EFK Moen, LLC
13523 Barrett Parkway Dr Ste 250
St. Louis, MO 63021
Contact: Darrell Eilers VP
Tel: 314-729-4104
Email: dleilers@efkmoen.com
Website: www.EFKMoen.com
Civil engineering & land surveying, roadway/highway engineering, bridge/structural design, site/development engineering, water/wastewater, traffic/transportation engineering. (Woman, estab 1998, empl 35, sales $2,700,000, cert: State)

2998   Peoria Contract Services, LLC
6428 Lipizzaner Dr
Imperial, MO 63052
Contact: Kyle Pogue CEO
Tel: 314-761-5470
Email: kyle@peoriacontractservices.com
Website: www.peoriacontractservices.com
Engineering, Electrical, Mechanical, Chemical, Process, Civil, Structural, Patented Modular Extrusion Process; ASME/API Storage Vessels; Bulk Material Handling/Storage; Automation; Piping Design & Pipe Supply; Hydraulic & Pneumatic. (Nat Ame, estab 2012, empl 5, sales , cert: State, NMSDC)

2999   Webb Engineering Services, Inc.
4670 Lansdowne Ave, Ste 111
St. Louis, MO 63116
Contact: Stanley Webb President
Tel: 314-351-0440
Email: webbs@webb-engineering.com
Website: www.webb-engineering.com
Mechanical, electrical, fire protection, plumbing, & civil design services. (AA, estab 1999, empl 8, sales $1,000,000, cert: City, 8a)

North Carolina

3000   Crescent Construction Services, LLC
303 S Main GQ St
Salisbury, NC 28146
Contact: Presdient
Tel: 704-633-9697
Email:
Website: www.crescentconstructionservices.com
Commissioning & engineering surveys, project management. (Woman, estab 2004, empl 15, sales $1,310,000, cert: WBENC)

3001   ENPULSE Energy Conservation, Inc.
100 N Elm St, Ste 138
Greensboro, NC 27401
Contact: Derrick Giles President
Tel: 336-370-1088
Email: info@enpulse.com
Website: www.enpulse.com
Engineering services, energy management, utility bill audits, engineering studies, measurement & verification, building commissioning (AA, estab 2002, empl 3, sales , cert: State, City)

3002   Hurley Write Inc
19701 BETHEL CHURCH RD Ste 103-144
Cornelius, NC 28031
Contact: pamela hurley Presdient
Tel: 910-233-7670
Email: info@hurleywrite.com
Website: www.hurleywrite.com
Develop and teach customized onsite technical, business, and scientific writing courses, online writing courses, webinars and series. (Woman, estab 2000, empl 1, sales $388,000, cert: WBENC)

3003   ImmunoReagents Inc.
6003 Chapel Hill RdSte. 153
Raleigh, NC 27607
Contact: Ann Black CEO
Tel: 919-831-2240
Email: sales@immunoreagents.com
Website: www.immunoreagents.com
Mfr highly purified polyclonal antibodies used in the life sciences & immunodiagnostic industries. (Woman, estab 2005, empl 14, sales $1,636,402, cert: WBENC)

3004   John Davenport Engineering, Inc.
305 W Fourth St Ste 2A
Winston Salem, NC 27101
Contact: Shari Mauk Chief Admin officer
Tel: 336-744-1636
Email: smauk@davenportworld.com
Website: www.davenportworld.com
Roadway design, traffic signal design, transportation engineering, civil engineering, transportation planning, construction support, construction engineering & inspection, traffic data collection, turning movement counts. (AA, estab 2002, empl 21, sales $1,629,947, cert: State, City, 8a)

3005   Sud Associates PA
1813 Chapel Hill Rd
Durham, NC 27707
Contact: Ish Sud Presdient
Tel: 919-493-5277
Email: sudmain@sudassociates.com
Website: www.sudassociates.com
Energy svcs & studies: recycling process produced heat, energy conserving HVAC, electrical, plumbing. (As-Ind, As-Pac, estab 1980, empl 23, sales $2,000,000, cert: State, City)

3006 Whitsell Innovations Inc.
18 Kendall Dr
Chapel Hill, NC 27517
Contact: Robin Whitsell Presdient
Tel: 919-321-9017
Email: robin.whitsell@whitsellinnovations.com
Website: www.whitsellinnovations.com
Medical, scientific & technical writing, GCP, GMP & GLP, clinical regulatory writing, clinical study reports, protocols, investigator brochures, narratives & full submissions of investigational new drug, applications & new drug applications. (Woman, estab 2006, empl 32, sales $5,262,000, cert: WBENC)

New Jersey

3007 3A Engineering & Validation LLC
122 Lexington Ave
Maplewood, NJ 07040
Contact: Adebayo Boboye Principal Engineer
Tel: 973-715-0541
Email: adebayo.boboye@3a-engineering.com
Website: www.3a-engineering.com
Engineering services, qualification, commissioning & validation of manufacturing processes & products. (AA, estab 2007, empl 1, sales $120,000, cert: NMSDC)

3008 Industrial Fiberglass Services
145 Millbrook Rd
Washington, NJ 07882
Contact: Rita (Joanie) George CEO
Tel: 908-689-3417
Email: sales@industrialfiberglassservices.com
Website: www.industrialfiberglassservices.com
Civil, Mechanical, FRP Repair & Installation. (Woman, estab 2000, empl 7, sales $3,000,000, cert: WBENC)

3009 inRange Solutions II, LLC
695 Route 46 W, Ste 103
Fairfield, NJ 07004
Contact: Edwin Gomez Presdient
Tel: 845-548-2934
Email: ss@inrange-llc.com
Website: www.inrangesolutions.com
DAS, Wireless and Telecom Design and Engineering, Site Acquisition, Real Estate Negotiation, Zoning and Permitting, Project Management, Architectural Engineering and Design, Electrical Engineering and Design, Mechanical Engineering and Design. (As-Pac, estab 2011, empl 24, sales $6,000,000, cert: State, City, NMSDC)

3010 KS Engineers, P.C.
2 Riverfront Plaza 3rd Fl
Newark, NJ 07102
Contact: KAamal Shahid Presdient
Tel: 973-623-2999
Email: info@kseng.com
Website: www.kseng.com
Engineering, surveying & construction management. (As-Ind, estab 1991, empl 275, sales $25,000,000, cert: State, City, NMSDC)

3011 Matrix New World Engineering, Land Surveying and Landscape Architectur
26 Columbia Turnpike 2nd Fl
Florham Park, NJ 07932
Contact: Jayne Warne, PE Presdient
Tel: 973-240-1800
Email: jwarne@mnwe.com
Website: www.matrixneworld.com
Environmental, geotechnical, civil engineering, survey & building facility consulting & engineering firm. (Woman, estab 1990, empl 200, sales $28,899,396, cert: State, City, WBENC)

3012 MFS Consulting Engineers & Surveyor, DPC
2780 Hamilton Blvd
South Plainfield, NJ 07080
Contact: Jeffrey Clark Sr Project Administrator
Tel: 908-922-4622
Email: jac@mfsengineers.com
Website: www.MFSengineers.com
Site/civil, structural, geotechnical & foundation, environmental engineering, construction layout, sustainable design & construction management services. (As-Pac, Hisp, estab 2009, empl 32, sales $4,403,207, cert: State, City, 8a)

3013 Sovereign
111 A North Gold Dr
Robbinsville, NJ 08691
Contact: Michael Hanlon Mgr
Tel: 609-259-8200
Email: mhanlon@sovcon.com
Website: www.sovcon.com
Environmental consulting & remediation services, environmental, civil & geotechnical engineering; remediation system evaluation, optimization, design & construction/installation; environmental, land use & natural resources permitting. (As-Pac, estab 1999, empl 165, sales $35,466,433, cert: NMSDC)

New York

3014 Associated Renewable
1370 Broadway 5th Fl
New York, NY 10018
Contact: Manoj Patel CEO
Tel: 212-444-8214
Email: mbe@associatedrenewable.com
Website: www.associatedrenewable.com/
Energy management, cut energy costs, reduce energy wastage, meet regulatory requirements, building energy audits, install new energy-efficient equipment, supply electricity, natural gas & renewable energy. (As-Pac, estab 2010, empl 8, sales $420,000, cert: NMSDC)

3015 Dose Engineering, PLLC
817 Broadway, 4th Fl
New York, NY 10003
Contact: Anostere Jean Principal
Tel: 646-715-2096
Email: ajean@dose-engineering.com
Website: www.dose-engineering.com
Engineering design, engineering design drawings, due diligence reports Mechanical: HVAC Electrical: Lighting and Power Plumbing Fire Alarm Fire Protection LEED: Leadership in Energy and Environmental (AA, estab 2009, empl 5, sales $300,000, cert: City)

3016   Environmental Design & Research, DPC
217 Montgomery St Ste 1000
Syracuse, NY 13202
Contact: Joanne Stewart Associate
Tel: 315-471-0688
Email: jstewart@edrdpc.com
Website: www.edrdpc.com

Landscape architecture, civil engineering, community planning, visualization, environmental regulatory, ecological, geographic information systems mapping & analysis, historic preservation, cultural resources, archeology. (Woman, estab 1979, empl 38, sales $4,500,000, cert: State)

3017   Foit-Albert Associates, Architecture, Engineering and Surveying, P.C.
215 W 94th St, Ste 517
New York, NY 10025
Contact: Gregory Carballada Presdient
Tel: 716-856-3933
Email: cstoebe@foit-albert.com
Website: www.foit-albert.com

Architecture, Engineering, Environmental & Land Surveying Consulting. (Hisp, estab 1977, empl 70, sales $10,000,000, cert: State, City)

3018   Sabir, Richardson & Weisberg Engineers PLLC
37 W 39th St, Ste 1005
New York, NY 10018
Contact: Yvette Richardson Principal
Tel: 646-863-6160
Email: info@srw-eng.com
Website: www.srw-eng.com

Engineering svcs: architectural, mechanical, electrical, fire protection & plumbing consulting. (Woman/AA, Hisp, estab 2004, empl , sales $2,018,954, cert: State, City)

3019   SoundSense, LLC
46 Newtown Lane Ste 1
East Hampton, NY 11937
Contact: Maryann Buquicchio Sr Admin Asst
Tel: 631-324-2266
Email: maryann@soundsense.com
Website: www.soundsense.com

Acoustic consulting & design services, efficacy & compliance testing, site inspection services & innovative acoustical products. (Woman, estab 1981, empl 9, sales $2,623,444, cert: City, WBENC)

3020   W. Allen Engineering PLLC
400 Strawtown Rd
West Nyack, NY 10994
Contact: Wayne Allen Principal
Tel: 646-398-7870
Email: info@wallenengineering.com
Website: www.wallenengineering.com

Civil & mechanical engineering, construction inspection/management services, contract admin, owner representation, cost estimating, lead based paint abatement, drafting, HVAC design. (AA, estab 1997, empl 12, sales $1,200,000, cert: State, City)

3021   Watts Engineering & Architecture, P.C.
95 Perry St Ste 300
Buffalo, NY 14203
Contact: Edward Watts President
Tel: 716-836-1540
Email: ewatts@wattsengineers.com
Website: www.wattsengineers.com

Civil, environmental, mechanical & electrical engineering & architecture consulting. (AA, estab 1986, empl 73, sales $6,800,000, cert: City, NMSDC)

3022   WM Group Services, LLC
Two Penn Plaza Ste 552
New York, NY 10121
Contact: Hemant Mehta Controller
Tel: 646-827-6400
Email: hmehta@wmgroupeng.com
Website: www.wmgroupeng.com

Study, Design, optimization of Central Utilities Systems: cooling, heating & power. (As-Pac, estab , empl , sales $2,697,396, cert: NMSDC)

Ohio

3023   Airecon Manufacturing Corporation
5271 Brotherton Court
Cincinnati, OH 45227
Contact: Josh Jacobs President
Tel: 513-561-5522
Email: josh@airecon.com
Website: www.airecon.com

Design, fabricate & install industrial dust, mist & fume control equipment & systems, fume exhaust pneumatic conveying, supply & exhasut ventilation, clean air rooms & other industrial air handling systems. (Hisp, estab 1979, empl 40, sales $9,000,000, cert: NMSDC)

3024   AMG, Inc.
1497 Shoup Mill Rd
Dayton, OH 45414
Contact: LeAnn Thompson VP of Engineering
Tel: 937-274-0736
Email: jbaddour@amg-eng.com
Website: www.amg-eng.com

Feasibility studies, conceptual design, capital cost esimtates, detailed design engineering, project management through construction management, commissioning. (Hisp, estab 1980, empl 40, sales $16,921,031, cert: NMSDC)

3025   Atmos360, Inc
64 Circle Freeway Dr
Cincinnati, OH 45246
Contact: Icy Williams President & CEO
Tel: 513-330-6688
Email: iwilliams@atmos360.com
Website: www.atmos360.com

Engineering & design of air system & custom/specialty fabricated products, Dust/Aerosol Control, Process Air, Central Vacuum Cleaning, HVAC and Heated air Make-up Systems. (Woman/AA, estab 1989, empl 40, sales $17,000,000, cert: State, NMSDC, WBENC)

3026 Balance Product Development, Inc.
3615 Superior Ave. Ste 4402B
Cleveland, OH 44114
Contact: Rene Polin Presdient
Tel: 440-247-4711
Email: rene@balanceinc.com
Website: www.balanceinc.com
Industrial Design, product design, CAD development, prototype development, concept ideation, packaging design, graphic design, innovation, engineering, product research, ergonomic research, user interface design. (Hisp, estab 2004, empl 10, sales , cert: NMSDC)

3027 CAD Concepts, Inc.
2323 West 5th Ave Ste 120
Columbus, OH 43204
Contact: Joyce K Johnson
Tel: 614-485-0670
Email: certifications@ccitechs.com
Website: www.ccitechs.com
Engineering support services: CAD, GIS, field work & administrative services. (Woman, estab 1984, empl 26, sales , cert: State, WBENC)

3028 Crawford & Associates Services, LLC
100 E Campus View Blvd Ste 250
Columbus, OH 43235
Contact: Troy Crawford Principal
Tel: 614-557-1498
Email: tcrawford@cas-associates.com
Website: www.cas-associates.com
Commercial & Industrial Commissioning of Mechanical/Electrical/Plumbing Systems, including Heating, Ventilating and Air Conditioning Systems and Building Automatic Temperature Control Systems. (AA, estab 2007, empl 5, sales $293,055, cert: 8a)

3029 CTL Engineering, Inc.
2860 Fisher Rd
Columbus, OH 43204
Contact: C.K. Satyapriya President
Tel: 614-276-8123
Email: ctl@ctleng.com
Website: www.ctleng.com
Geotechnical, construction inspection, environmental, mining engineering, analytical chemistry, forensic science, metallurgy, product testing, research & development, roof engineering, existing structure evaluation, asbestos inspection. (Minority, estab 1928, empl 187, sales , cert: NMSDC)

3030 DHDC Engineering Consulting Services, Inc.
2390 Advanced Business Center Dr
Columbus, OH 43228
Contact: Savvas Sophocleous President
Tel: 614-527-7656
Email: sophocleous@dhdcinc.com
Website: www.dhdcinc.com
Laboratory testing services, geotechnical (engineering, drilling, and laboratory) & subsurface utility engineering (SUE). (As-Pac, estab 2012, empl 15, sales $500,000, cert: State)

3031 DLZ Industrial, LLC
6121 Huntley Rd
Columbus, OH 43229
Contact: Kurt Schmiegel CEO
Tel: 614-888-0040
Email: mbe@dlz.com
Website: www.dlz.com
Industrial surveying, close tolerance machinery surveying, setting & realignment, construction, topographical, hydrographic & property surveying. (As-Ind, As-Pac, estab 1989, empl 568, sales , cert: NMSDC)

3032 Moody Engineering, LLC
300 Spruce St Ste 200
Columbus, OH 43215
Contact: President & CEO
Tel: 614-280-8999
Email:
Website: http://moody-eng.com
Stormwater management, Site design, Sediment and erosion control, Roadway, Permits - NPDES, PTI, zoning, Vehicular access, Grading, Pedestrian traffic, Drainage, Parking lots, Wet and dry ponds, Utility design, Domestic water, Underground infrastructure. (AA, estab 2015, empl 10, sales $1,924,000, cert: State, City)

3033 On Line Design, Inc.
12059 Sheraton Ln
Cincinnati, OH 45246
Contact: Kimberly Persiani Client Advisor
Tel: 513-476-3113
Email: Persiani.K@o-l-design.com
Website: www.o-l-design.com
Engineering & technical personnel: plant & capital projects, design/build equipment. (Woman, estab 1989, empl 50, sales $2,200,000, cert: WBENC)

3034 R Engineering Team, LLC
3100 E 45th St, Ste 306
Cleveland, OH 44127
Contact: Tom Roberts President
Tel: 216-361-2500
Email: rengineeringteam@gmail.com
Website: www.rengineeringteam.com
Consulting engineering in the disciplines of electrical engineering, mechanical engineering, construction administration, and computer CAD drafting. (AA, estab 2008, empl 7, sales $687,194, cert: State, City, NMSDC)

3035 THORS, LLC
5054 Paramount Blvd.
Medina, OH 44256
Contact: Senthil Kumar Founder
Tel: 330-576-4448
Email: sales@thors.com
Website: www.thors.com
Mfg process training for procurement, design engineers & quality teams in commodities such as - castings, machining, gears, steel manufacturing, forgings, polymers with a tools center that includes a supplier manager, tooling manager & parts manager. (Woman/As-Pac, estab 2010, empl 11, sales , cert: NMSDC)

3036 Williams Engineering LLC
1836 Dana Ave
Cincinnati, OH 45207
Contact: Kennard Williams Presdient
Tel: 513-731-6400
Email: keino.williams@williamsenginedesign.com
Website: www.williamsenginedesign.com
Engineering & mfg services, 3D CAD modeling & product development of machine tools, aerospace, medical and automotive aftermarket parts. (AA, estab 2005, empl 1, sales , cert: State)

Oklahoma

3037 Aero Tech Service Associates, Inc.
909 S Meridian Ave, Ste 200
Oklahoma City, OK 73108
Contact: John Howard CEO
Tel: 405-946-2872
Email: atsa@atsainc.com
Website: www.atsainc.com
Aviation systems requirements, systems engineering & operations, information technology, communications, technical training, technical & administrative svcs & support. (AA, estab 1991, empl 180, sales , cert: State)

3038 Cherokee CRC
916 W 23rd St
Tulsa, OK 74107
Contact: John Sparkman Program Mgr
Tel: 918-582-9110
Email: jsparkman@cherokee-crc.com
Website: www.cherokee-crc.com
Research & development, administrative support services, construction management, environmental services & aviation consulting services. (Nat Ame, estab 2005, empl 40, sales $14,671,425, cert: State)

3039 Excellence Engineering, LLC
8670 S Peoria Ave
Tulsa, OK 74132
Contact: Deyona Hays CEO
Tel: 918-298-5500
Email: dee.hays@eeinco.com
Website: www.eeinco.com
Engineering, civil, structural, process, piping, mechanical, electrical, instrument, controls, startup & commissioning. (Woman, estab 2001, empl 40, sales , cert: WBENC)

3040 Greenwood Aviation, Inc.
2117 N Waverly
Ponca City, OK 74601
Contact: Chuck Greenwood President
Tel: 580-762-2580
Email: airport@cableone.net
Website: www.greenwoodaviation.com
Special mission aircraft: low level advanced atmospheric research, airborne surveillance & logistical operations at remote sites. (Nat Ame, estab 1982, empl 9, sales $650,000, cert: State)

Oregon

3041 Elcon Associates, Inc.
12670 NW Barnes Rd
Portland, OR 97229
Contact: Donna Freeman Marketing Mgr
Tel: 503-644-2490
Email: dfreeman@elcon.com
Website: www.elcon.com
Electrical energy: high voltage, project management, studies, cost estimating, and construction management, utility power systems, power distribution, PLC based control systems, energy management/SCADA. (As-Ind, estab 1975, empl 47, sales $5,600,000, cert: NMSDC)

Pennsylvania

3042 Advantus Engineers
300 Bilmar Dr Ste 150
Pittsburgh, PA 15205
Contact: Alicia Avick President
Tel: 412-489-9090
Email: aavick@advantusengineers.com
Website: www.advantusengineers.com
Facilities design engineering, commissioning, project management & construction management services for the commercial, institutional & light industrial markets. (Woman/Hisp, estab 2004, empl 10, sales $550,000, cert: State, WBENC)

3043 Aquatech International Corporation
1 Four Coins Dr
Canonsburg, PA 15317
Contact: Francis D'sa Reg Sales Mgr
Tel: 724-746-5300
Email: aic@aquatech.com
Website: www.aquatech.com
Mfr water & waste water treatment equip & systems. ASME tank & piping fabricators. (Woman/As-Ind, As-Pac, estab 1981, empl 450, sales $80,000,000, cert: NMSDC)

3044 Biopharm Project Solutions
119 Jaffrey Rd
Malvern, PA 19355
Contact: Surjit Sengha Presdient
Tel: 484-614-0869
Email: surjs@biopharmprojects.com
Website: www.biopharmprojects.com
Process engineering, equipment, utilities & equipment cleaning/sterilization systems, automation engineering, project management & engineering staffing, equipment design engineering, factory testing, start-up. (As-Ind, estab 1987, empl 10, sales $2,500,000, cert: NMSDC)

3045 Chester Engineers, Inc.
1555 Coraopolis Heights Rd
Moon Township, PA 15108
Contact: Elaine Talak Exec Asst
Tel: 412-809-6576
Email: etalak@chesterengineers.com
Website: www.chesterengineers.com
Engineering consulting services, construct. mgmt., water resource mgmt., scientific research & environmental mgmt. (AA, estab 1987, empl 200, sales $14,500,000, cert: NMSDC)

3046 Dawood Engineering, Inc.
2020 Good Hope Rd
Enola, PA 17025
Contact: Kristal Martinez
Tel: 717-732-8576
Email: kmartinez@dawood.cc
Website: www.dawood.cc
Civil Site Design, Survey & Mapping, Environmental Consulting, Mechanical & Electrical Engineering, Geotechnical Engineering Structural Engineering. (As-Ind, estab 1992, empl 161, sales $20,100,000, cert: NMSDC)

3047 Diversified Global Systems, LLC.
721 Arbor Way Ste 100
Blue Bell, PA 19422
Contact: Dale Hobbie Managing Dir
Tel: 703-963-4942
Email: dale.hobbie@diversifiedglobalsystems.com
Website: www.diversifiedglobalsystems.com
Finance, Site Development, Design, Engineering, Procurement Management, Construction Management (Pre-Construction and Construction), Project Management, Program Management & Operations & Maintenance services. (Nat Ame, estab 2016, empl 5, sales $265,000, cert: NMSDC)

3048 First Capital Engineering
48 S Richland Ave
York, PA 17404
Contact: Ann Luciani CEO
Tel: 717-845-3227
Email: annl@fcap.com
Website: www.fcap.com
Civil engineering, land surveying, landscape architecture, environmental & construction inspection services. (Woman, estab 1995, empl 17, sales $1,949,255, cert: State, WBENC)

3049 GAI Construction Monitoring Services, Inc. dba CMT Services Group
24 Portland Rd
Conshohocken, PA 19428
Contact: Valerie Moody Presdient
Tel: 610-731-0430
Email: v.moody@cmtservicesgroup.com
Website: www.cmtservicesgroup.com
Geotechnical engineering, environmental consulting, construction materials testing, special inspections, engineering materials forensic investigations. (Woman, estab 1986, empl 23, sales $2,200,000, cert: WBENC)

3050 IES Engineers
1720 Walton Rd
Blue Bell, PA 19422
Contact: Lisa Wallis Mgr, Accting & Admin Services
Tel: 610-828-3078
Email: lwallis@iesengineers.com
Website: www.iesengineers.com
Engineering & environmental, health & safety consulting, regulatory compliance. (As-Ind, estab 1991, empl 30, sales $8,223,000, cert: NMSDC)

3051 KB COMM LLC
985 State Rd
West Grove, PA 19390
Contact: Kathy Breuninger Owner
Tel: 610-357-8625
Email: kathy@kbcommllc.com
Website: www.kbcommllc.com
Scientific & technical writing services, business & marketing communications; instructions & procedures; installation, operation & maintenance manuals; computer documentation; training materials & document templates. (Woman, estab 2006, empl 8, sales $610,154, cert: WBENC)

3052 RNDT, Inc.
228 Maple Ave
Johnstown, PA 15901
Contact: VP Technical Dir
Tel: 814-535-5448
Email:
Website: www.rndt.net
Nondestructive testing services, radiographic, magnetic particle, liquid penetrant, ultrasonic and visual testing services. Also offer Positive Material Identification (PMI), remote video, certified welding inspector services (CWI). (Woman, estab 2002, empl 35, sales $5,800,000, cert: WBENC)

3053 Rodriguez Consulting LLC
1301 N 2nd St
Philadelphia, PA 19122
Contact: Yarelis Franco Marketing Coord
Tel: 215-839-8087
Email: yfranco@rodriguezconsulting.biz
Website: www.rodriguezconsulting.biz
Civil engineering, site design, environmental engineering, land surveying, traffic data collection and engineering, construction inspection & geographic information systems (GIS) services. (Hisp, estab 2007, empl 22, sales $909,000, cert: City, 8a)

3054 TesTex, Inc.
535 Old Frankstown Rd, Ste A
Pittsburgh, PA 15239
Contact: Robert Gormley Presdient
Tel: 412-798-8990
Email: r.gormley@testex-ndt.com
Website: www.testex-ndt.com
Electromagnetic NDT systems & services: inspect ferrous & non-ferrous components. (As-Ind, As-Pac, estab 1987, empl 50, sales $14,700,000, cert: NMSDC)

3055 TREC Group, Inc.
900 Old Marple Rd.
Springfield, PA 19064
Contact: Dir Business Devel
Tel: 610-328-6465
Email:
Website: www.trecgroup.com
Mechanical, electrical & civil engineering, project management, construction management, drafting & AUTOCAD capabilities. (Woman, estab 2001, empl 11, sales , cert: State, WBENC)

Puerto Rico

3056   CRB Caribe, LLP
BBVA Center Mail Box #21, 1738 Amarillo St Ste 314
San Juan, PR 00926
Contact: Tom Forester GM
Tel: 787-622-2720
Email: shirley.nieves@crbusa.com
Website: www.crbusa.com
Engineering & Architectural Consulting & Design Services, Construction and Use Permitting, Inspections and Construction Support (Hisp, estab 2004, empl 60, sales $8,729,275, cert: NMSDC)

3057   Intelligent Software Solutions Corporation
P.O. Box 363601
San Juan, PR 00936
Contact: Presdient
Tel: 787-625-1500
Email:
Website: www.isspr.com
Construction mgmt, inspection, project mgmt, autocad & microstation drafting, tagging, P&ID, drawing update, scheduling, validation, qualification, regulatory compliance, quality, risk mgmt, commissioning. (Hisp, estab 1990, empl 33, sales $14,960,000, cert: NMSDC)

3058   JCD Engineering, Inc.
P.O. Box 192372
San Juan, PR 00919
Contact: Juan C. del Pino President
Tel: 787-787-7211
Email: jcdelpino@jcdengineering.com
Website: www.jcdengineering.com
Civil, electrical & mechanical engineering: concrete & steel small buildings, interiors work, hung ceilings, floors, gypsum board, electrical power & controls, fiber optics, local area networks (LAN), process and AHU control systems. (Hisp, estab 1996, empl 11, sales $1,327,000, cert: NMSDC)

3059   LabChemS
P.O. Box 1022
Boqueron, PR 00622
Contact: Efrain Rivera Torres CEO
Tel: 787-920-4657
Email: efrain.rivera@labchemspr.com
Website: www.labchemscorp.com/
Engineering Consulting, Manufacturing & Packaging Equipments, Facilities & Manufacturing Process Validation, Quality Engineering & Six Sigma tools. (Hisp, estab 2009, empl 10, sales $1,200,000, cert: NMSDC)

3060   NOVO Consulting Group LLC
PMB 9 6400
Cayey, PR 00737
Contact: Claritza Millan Presdient
Tel: 787-413-7379
Email: cmillan@novo-pr.com
Website: www.novo-pr.com
Design Qualification, Engineering Studies, Installation Qualification, Operational Qualification, Performance Qualification, Process Verification/Validation, Project Management, Process Improvement/Optimization, Quality Assurance, CAPA, NCRs. (Woman/Hisp, estab 2015, empl 2, sales , cert: NMSDC)

3061   SQS, Inc. (Successful Quality Systems)
Palmas Industrial Park Road 869 KM. 2.0 Street 4
Catano, PR 00962
Contact: Wilda Aguirre President
Tel: 787-275-2424
Email: wildaaguirre@sqswarehouse.com
Website: www.sqswarehouse.com
Specialized Storage and Inventory Management Services of materials and products for the pharmaceutical, medical devices, biotech and consumer industries as well as to the safe-guarding of documents (Woman/Hisp, estab 2003, empl 8, sales $2,500,000, cert: NMSDC)

3062   UNIPRO Architects Engineers LLP
P.O. Box 10914
San Juan, PR 00922
Contact: Jose R. Gonzalez Dir planning/projects
Tel: 787-793-3950
Email: jgonzalez@uniproaep.net
Website: www.uniproaep.com
Architecture, civil engineering, structural engineering, mechanical engineering, electrical engineering, environmental engineering, construction management. (Hisp, estab 1980, empl 30, sales $3,200,000, cert: NMSDC)

3063   Visional Technology LLC
400 Calle Calaf, Ste 49
San Juan, PR 00918
Contact: Joyce Rotger Presdient
Tel: 787-717-0881
Email: joycemar@visionaltechnology.com
Website: www.visionaltechnology.com
Engineering services, dimensional metrology solutions, vision systems, coordinate measurement machines (CMM), laser measurements, 3D scanning, reverse engineering & computer aided inspections. (Woman/Hisp, estab 2013, empl 5, sales , cert: NMSDC)

South Carolina

3064   Amee Bay LLC
915 Commerce Cir
Hanahan, SC 29410
Contact: William Messing Sr Program Mgr
Tel: 843-725-6800
Email: bmessing@ameebay.com
Website: www.ameebay.com
General/mechanical contracting, power & pressure process piping installation, repair mechanical systems on commercial and industrial pressure vessels, conveyors & auxiliary systems. (Nat Ame, estab 2006, empl 184, sales $26,000,000, cert: State)

3065   AQuate II, LLC
508 Hampton St, Ste 204
Columbia, SC 29201
Contact: Deveda Hunter GM
Tel: 256-837-1774
Email: dhunter@aquate2.com
Website: www.aquate2.com
IT, engineering, base operations support, logistics, administrative, and technical support services. (Nat Ame, estab 2013, empl 80, sales , cert: 8a)

3066 Atlantic South Consulting Services
3030 Ashley Town Center Dr Ste 101A
Charleston, SC 29414
Contact: Adrian Williams
Tel: 843-266-3998
Email: awilliams@atlanticsouthconsulting.com
Website: www.atlanticsouthconsulting.com
Engineering, surveying, and right-of-way acquisition
services, transportation & utility designs, site development
& land planning, construction inspection & management
services, easement. (AA, estab 2004, empl 6, sales
$668,000, cert: State)

3067 Diverse Industries, Inc.
260 Morley Court, Ste A
Duncan, SC 29334
Contact: Laura Charles Office Mgr
Tel: 864-400-9741
Email: laurac@diverseii.com
Website: www.diverseii.com
Contract Robot Programming, Panel View & Thin Client
HMI's, Training, Robot & PLC, Vision, Robot Guidance,
Inspection & Code Reading. (Woman, estab 2007, empl 40,
sales $5,114,985, cert: State)

Tennessee

3068 GQSI
3777 Winchester Rd Ste 1
Memphis, TN 38118
Contact: Williette Graham Presdient
Tel: 901-365-9566
Email: willgraham@gqsi.net
Website: http://gqsi.net
Engineering & technical services, medical devices, process
& special processes equipment & validation, laser marking,
CMM inspection services, product inspection, engineering
support, supplier support services. (Woman/AA, estab
2005, empl 6, sales $160,000, cert: State)

Texas

3069 A. Miller Consulting Services, Inc.
4425 Plano Parkway, Ste 803
Carrollton, TX 75010
Contact: Carie Joyce Team Lead
Tel: 972-580-0812
Email: cjoyce@mcs.biz
Website: www.mcs.biz
Technical documentation: technical writing, project mgmt,
technical illustration & graphics creation, web design, web-
based training dev, manual dev & consolidation, proposal
writing & consulting, process dev & documentation,
engineering guides. (Woman, estab 2000, empl 13, sales
$2,449,127, cert: WBENC)

3070 Aerolution Inc.
10803 Gulfdale, Ste 208
San Antonio, TX 78216
Contact: Kyle kim President
Tel: 210-524-9831
Email: kkim@aerolutioninc.com
Website: www.aerolution.com
Structural/mechanical design & analysis, aircraft system
design & analysis, CAD capabilities, stress analysis & finite
element modeling, aircraft repair & modernization,
enhanced data management systems. (As-Pac, estab 2007,
empl 12, sales $1,900,000, cert: 8a)

3071 Aguirre Roden Inc.
10670 N Central Expressway 6th Fl
Dallas, TX 75231
Contact: Peter Aguirre, CFM SVP program devel
Tel: 972-789-2662
Email: paaguirre@aguirre.com
Website: www.aguirreroden.com
Architecture, mechanical, electrical & structural engi-
neering, general contracting. (Hisp, estab 1960, empl 65,
sales , cert: State, NMSDC)

3072 ALTECOR Engineering
3617 Flamingo Ave
McAllen, TX 78504
Contact: T. G. Altecor Sr staff engineer
Tel: 956-687-7389
Email: info@altecoreng.com
Website: www.altecoreng.com
Structural dynamics & control systems engineering,
equipment-machinery installations, optimizations,
maintenance, reliability. (Woman, estab 2007, empl 7,
sales $100,000, cert: State)

3073 Arias & Associates, Inc.
142 Chula Vista
San Antonio, TX 78232
Contact: Jeremy Arias VP
Tel: 210-308-5884
Email: purchaseorders@ariasinc.com
Website: www.ariasinc.com
Geotechnical engineering svcs, construction materials
testing & observation, environmental svcs. (Hisp, estab
1996, empl 96, sales , cert: State, City, SDB)

3074 Basal Solutions LLC
1301 Texas Ave Ste 122
Houston, TX 77002
Contact: Branden Morris
Tel: 713-393-8767
Email: branden@basalsolutionsllc.com
Website: http://basalsolutionsllc.com
Engineering & business management consulting, project
management, develop, test & integrate 0-D/1-D dynamic
mathematical models, create FMEA & DFMEA for
various vehicle platforms, test script design & implemen-
tation. (AA, estab 2014, empl 10, sales , cert: State,
NMSDC)

3075 Bastion Technologies, Inc.
17625 El Camino Real
Houston, TX 77058
Contact: Jorge Hernandez Presdient
Tel: 281-283-9330
Email: jhernandez@bastiontechnologies.com
Website: www.bastiontechnologies.com
Engineering design, analysis, systems engineering,
information technology applications, engineering
research, mechanical engineering, structural engineer-
ing, safety & reliability engineering, systems safety,
hazard analysis. (Hisp, estab 1998, empl 400, sales
$42,711,000, cert: State, NMSDC)

3076 BEPC, Inc.
3240 Executive Dr
San Angelo, TX 76904
Contact: Liza Dennis Dir of New Business
Tel: 325-944-0169
Email: liza.dennis@bepcinc.com
Website: www.bepcinc.com
Engineering services: validations of equipment, processes, audit & qualification of external suppliers, quality systems & validations, R&D product design & testing. (Hisp, estab 2005, empl 460, sales $20,038,327, cert: State, NMSDC)

3077 Charles Gojer & Associates, Inc.
11615 Forest Central Dr, Ste 303
Dallas, TX 75243
Contact: Charles Gojer President
Tel: 214-340-1199
Email: cgojer@cgojer.com
Website: www.cgojer.com
Civil & structural engineering. (Hisp, estab 1973, empl 10, sales , cert: State, NMSDC)

3078 Elements of Architecture, Inc.
1201 6th Ave Ste 100
Fort Worth, TX 76104
Contact: President
Tel: 817-333-2880
Email:
Website: www.elementsofarc.com
Architectural & engineering svcs: environmental, structure & facility, electrical, mechanical, fire protection, alarming. (Woman, estab 1996, empl 7, sales , cert: State, WBENC)

3079 Elevan LLC dba Elevate Systems
1919 NW Loop 410, Ste 200
San Antonio, TX 78213
Contact: Scott Gray CEO
Tel: 210-807-9981
Email: scott.gray@elevatesystems.com
Website: www.elevatesystems.com
Engineering and logistics services for Department of Defense Aging Weapon Systems, Subsystems, Components, Parts and Pieces. (Woman/Hisp, estab 2012, empl 4, sales $1,100,000, cert: State, SDB)

3080 First Assured Quality Systems, LLC
P.O. Box 535812
GRAND PRAIRIE, TX 75053
Contact: Brittany Stovall Presdient
Tel: 817-538-9240
Email: bstovall@assuredqualitysystems.com
Website: www.assuredqualitysystems.com
Quality Control Services- Containment, Sorting, Rework, Inspection, Liaison Support, Engineering Support & Launch Support. (Woman/AA, Hisp, estab 2013, empl 35, sales $2,872,632, cert: NMSDC, WBENC)

3081 Gap Engineering
21703 Kingsland Blvd, Ste 103
Katy, TX 77450
Contact: Mike Homma
Tel: 281-578-0500
Email: mhomma@gap-eng.com
Website: www.gap-eng.com
Engineering, design & drafting services, develop instrument Specs, Detail Design, Distributive Control Systems (DCS), Fieldbus, Programmable Logic Controllers (PLC), Safety Instrumented Systems (SIS), Fiber Optic Comm Networks. (As-Pac, estab 2004, empl 25, sales $2,800,000, cert: NMSDC, 8a)

3082 GMR Protection Resources, Inc.
1629 Smirl Dr, Ste 200
Heath, TX 75032
Contact: Scott Crawford Sr Dir of Business Development
Tel: 469-267-9144
Email: smcrawford@gmr1.com
Website: www.gmr1.com
ADA compliance inspections and risk/security assessments, security incident response assessments, security compliance reviews & crime report data development. (Woman, estab 1991, empl 100, sales $12,996,355, cert: WBENC)

3083 JAT Energy Services LLC
111 Soledad St, Ste 1900
San Antonio, TX 78205
Contact: Keith Allen Presdient
Tel: 916-429-9096
Email: keith@jatenergies.com
Website: http://JATEnergies.com
Energy solutions, engineering & management firm, custom engineered solutions to reduce energy consumption in commercial & industrial spaces. (AA, estab 2012, empl 8, sales $500,000, cert: State, NMSDC)

3084 Johnson & Pace Inc.
1201 NW Loop 281, Ste 100
Longview, TX 75604
Contact: Linda Bennett Presdient
Tel: 903-753-0663
Email: LindaB@johnsonpace.com
Website: www.johnsonpace.com
Engineering services: civil, mechanical, electrical, structural, architectural services, land surveying. (Woman, estab 1995, empl 45, sales $7,930,735, cert: State, WBENC)

3085 JQ Infrastructure, LLC
100 Glass St Ste 201
Dallas, TX 75207
Contact: Stephen Lucy Principal
Tel: 972-392-7340
Email: slucy@jqeng.com
Website: www.jqieng.com/
Surveying services, building, structures & components consulting, engineering consulting, civil engineering, concrete engineering, drainage engineering, foundation engineering, inspection, general/engineering. (As-Pac, estab 2003, empl 105, sales $6,471,893, cert: State, NMSDC)

3086 M.E.P. Consulting Engineers, Inc.
2928 Story Rd W
Irving, TX 75038
Contact: Camilla Beavers Admin Asst
Tel: 972-870-9060
Email: mail@mepce.com
Website: www.mepce.com
Mechanical, electrical, plumbing, fire protection & information technology design engineering & commissioning for aviation facilities, municipalities, educational facilities, government, health care & commercial facilities. (Woman, estab 1998, empl 14, sales $4,000,000, cert: State, WBENC)

3087 Maslowski Controls, LLC
1751 Hurd Dr, Ste 111
Irving, TX 75038
Contact: Jacqueline Sikorski Presdient
Tel: 817-999-1662
Email: jsikorski@maslowskicontrols.com
Website: www.maslowskicontrols.com
Control System Engineering, PLC Programming, Historian, SCADA, HMI
Control Systems signal/instrumentation, troubleshooting, testing, simulation, staff training. (Woman, estab 2017, empl 3, sales , cert: WBENC)

3088 MULTATECH
2821 W 7th St Ste 400
Fort Worth, TX 76107
Contact: Hong P. Chen Presdient
Tel: 817-877-5571
Email: hchen@multatech.com
Website: www.multatech.com
mechanical, electrical, plumbing & civil consulting engineering services, architectural design services. (Hisp, estab 1986, empl 74, sales $11,048,061, cert: State, NMSDC)

3089 QA Consulting Inc.
7500 Rialto Blvd Bldg 1, Ste 225
Austin, TX 78735
Contact: Amber Hilfiger Dir of Operations
Tel: 512-328-9404
Email: info@qaconsultinginc.com
Website: http://qaconsultinginc.com
Quality, Microbiology, Regulatory & Auditing consulting services, QMS development, design, risk management, biocompatibility, verification and validation. (Woman, estab 2000, empl 6, sales $1,294,768, cert: State, WBENC)

3090 SeaMax Corporation
3720 W Alabama St Ste 3108
Houston, TX 77027
Contact: Brendan Isidienu Structural Engineer
Tel: 713-584-3643
Email: ibrendan@seamax.org
Website: www.seamax.org
Engineering consulting, structural engineering & and design of offshore & onshore soil & gas structures. (AA, estab 2015, empl 10, sales , cert: NMSDC)

3091 Standard Industrial Products Company
12610 Galveston Rd
Webster, TX 77059
Contact: Walter Gomez Dir Operation & Mktg
Tel: 281-480-8711
Email: wgomez@sipco-mls.com
Website: www.sipco-mls.com
Engineering, Electro - Mechanical Design, Validation & System Integration, CNC Milling, CNC Turning, Sawing, Mechanical System assembly & integration, Gearing - Design, Sourcing, Assembly & System Integration. (Hisp, estab 1984, empl 15, sales $2,099,000, cert: NMSDC)

3092 STS Systems Integration, LLC
1077 Central Pkwy S Bldg A, Ste 150
San Antonio, TX 78232
Contact: Dan Beard Sr Program Mgr
Tel: 210-888-2631
Email: daniel.beard@ssi-anc.com
Website: www.ssi-anc.com
System engineering, performance, mission readiness & sustainment for weapon systems, propulsion systems & information systems. (Nat Ame, estab 2011, empl 143, sales $13,000,000, cert: 8a)

3093 Sunland Group
10400 Westoffice Dr, Ste 116
Houston, TX 77042
Contact: Sales/Marketing
Tel: 713-467-8484
Email: info@sunlandgrp.com
Website: www.sunlandgrp.com
Design build: civil, structural, environmental engineering, architecture, design & construction surveying, value engineering. (Hisp, estab 1985, empl 85, sales $8,200,000, cert: State)

3094 Systems Integration, Inc.
7316 Business Pl
Arlington, TX 76001
Contact: Rhonda Smith Acct Mgr
Tel: 817-468-1494
Email: rsmith@sitexas.com
Website: www.sitexas.com
Engineering & Design, Reverse Engineering, Fabrication, Installation, Structural & Civil, Manufacturing, Machinery, Mechanical, CNC Machining, Electrical & Controls, Test Structures, Tooling. (Hisp, estab 1992, empl 20, sales $4,000,000, cert: State)

3095 TECHNIKOS Information Development, LLC
P.O. Box 2693
Stafford, TX 77497
Contact: Ora Gibson CEO
Tel: 281-568-7955
Email: ora@technicallyclear.com
Website: www.technicallyclear.com
Technical writing, editing, formatting, reviewing, proofreading, documentation, manuals, guides, web content, user guides, operations manuals, procedure manuals, processes, procedures, training guides. (Woman/AA, estab 2007, empl 2, sales , cert: State, NMSDC)

3096 United Geo Technologies LLC
7715 Mainland Dr, Ste 110
San Antonio, TX 78250
Contact: Patricia Ingram President
Tel: 210-684-2147
Email: pingram@unitedgeotech.com
Website: www.unitedgeotech.com
Softcopy photogrammetric mapping, digital orthophotography, GIS services, geospatial database architecture, raster/vector data layer production, CAD to GIS data integration, remotely updating of GIS layers & solution development. (Woman, estab 2011, empl 6, sales , cert: State)

Utah

3097 Avalon Business Engineering Services
908 W Gordon Ave, Ste 6
Layton, UT 84041
Contact: Lorraine Peart CEO
Tel: 801-668-5823
Email: lpeart@avalonbes.com
Website: www.avalonbes.com
Engineering Services, Aerospace Engineering (Weapons System Sustainment), Finite Element Analysis, Structural Analysis, Computer Aided Design (CAD), Environmental Engineering, Technical/Functional Writing & Analysis. (Woman/AA, As-Ind, estab 2010, empl 21, sales , cert: 8a)

Virginia

3098 AccuWrit Inc.
118 Primrose Dr
Blacksburg, VA 24060
Contact: Eileen Y. Ivasauskas Presdient
Tel: 540-961-1611
Email: eileen@accuwrit.com
Website: www.accuwrit.com
Editorial consulting — Editorial specialist in medical, scientific, and technical information and communication materials. Custom writing services and editorial support for the preparation of manuscripts, monographs, abstracts, critiques. (Woman, estab 1984, empl 1, sales , cert: State)

3099 Alpha Construction and Engineering Corporation
21351 Ridgetop Cir Ste 200
Dulles, VA 20166
Contact: Philios Angelides Sr VP
Tel: 703-450-0800
Email: pangelides@alphacorporation.com
Website: www.alphacorporation.com
Project management, construction management & professional engineering svcs: scheduling, cost estimating, project controls, construction inspection, condition inspections, constructibility reviews, value engineering, claims avoidance. (Minority, estab 1979, empl 197, sales $29,609,371, cert: State)

3100 Ashe Consultants, PLLC
950 Herndon Pkwy Ste 320
Herndon, VA 20170
Contact: President
Tel: 703-230-2500
Email:
Website: www.asheconsultants.com
Mechanical, electrical & plumbing engineering design services for buildings. (Woman, estab 2008, empl 5, sales $130,660, cert: State, WBENC)

3101 INTERSPEC, LLC
464 S Independence Blvd Ste C-104
Virginia Beach, VA 23452
Contact: Sean Murphy Business Devel Dir
Tel: 757-622-6299
Email: murphys@interspecllc.net
Website: www.interspecllc.net
Tank, piping & pressure vessel inspections, STI storage tank inspections, Non-Destructive Examination/Testing steel structures, Spill Prevention Control & Countermeasure (SPCC) plans, Oil Discharge Control Plans (ODCP. (Nat Ame, estab 2001, empl 22, sales $1,200,000, cert: State, 8a)

3102 Lu Smith Engineers
4604 Sadler Grove Way
Glen Allen, VA 23060
Contact: Dawen Lu President
Tel: 804-519-9306
Email: dlu6838@gmail.com
Website: www.lsengineers.net
Building system commissioning services, energy modeling/audit services, geothermal system study & design, sustainable design/LEED consultation & administration, mechanical, electrical, plumbing & fire protection system design. (As-Pac, estab 2012, empl 12, sales $1,400,000, cert: State)

3103 MKAssociates, Inc.
6593 Commerce Ct, Ste 100
Warrenton, VA 20187
Contact: Presdient
Tel: 540-428-3550
Email:
Website: www.mkassociates.com
Land surveying coordination. (Woman, estab 1998, empl 12, sales $350,000,000, cert: WBENC)

3104 Raul V. Bravo + Associates, Inc.
1889 Preston White Dr Ste 202
Reston, VA 20191
Contact: Claudio Bravo VP
Tel: 703-326-9092
Email: procurement@rvba.com
Website: www.RVBA.com
Rail Car Design, Mechanical, CADD, Electrical schematics, Telecommunication Design, Security Design, Electrical Diagrams Wiring, Smoke Detector Layout, CCTV & MATV Design, Power Supplies. (As-Pac, Hisp, estab 1979, empl 63, sales , cert: State)

3105 T3 Design Corporation
10340 Democracy Ln, Ste 305
Fairfax, VA 22030
Contact: Tandrumn Reid WBENC Liaison
Tel: 770-813-0882
Email: treid@t3design.us
Website: www.streetsmarts.us
Transportation engineering, civil/site engineering, transportation planning, intelligent transportation systems, traffic engineering, survey services, subsurface utility engineering, data collection, geographic information systems & public involvement. (Woman, estab , empl , sales $9,500,000, cert: State)

3106 Unified Industries Inc.
6551 Loisdale Ct Ste 400
Springfield, VA 22150
Contact: Tom Callahan
Tel: 703-922-9800
Email: callahan@uii.com
Website: www.uii.com
Metrology & calibration services, life cycle logistics planning, supply chain support, ship outfitting, distance support, obsolescence analysis. (AA, estab 1970, empl 200, sales $16,045,000, cert: State)

Washington

3107 CS3W Associates, Inc.
2821 167th Ave NE
Bellevue, WA 98008
Contact: Christopher Sims Presdient
Tel: 425-922-5900
Email: csims@cs3w.com
Website: http://cs3w.com
Engineering & management services, electrical & structural/seismic engineering services, project management & analysis support. (AA, estab 1999, empl 8, sales $671,000, cert: State)

3108 Garry Struthers Associates, Inc.
3150 Richards Rd
Bellevue, WA 98005
Contact: Garry Struthers President
Tel: 425-519-0300
Email: garrys@gsassoc-inc.com
Website: www.gsassoc-inc.com
Engineering, construction, environmental science, facilities maintenance. (AA, estab 1988, empl 106, sales $21,000,000, cert: NMSDC)

3109 GeoTest Services, Inc.
741 Marine View Dr
Bellingham, WA 98225
Contact: Jeremy Wolf VP
Tel: 360-733-7318
Email: jeremyw@geotest-inc.com
Website: http://geotest-inc.com
Geotechnical engineering, environmental services, special inspection & materials testing, facilities, structures, roads, bridges & all types of infrastructure. (Woman, estab 1993, empl 33, sales $6,000,000, cert: State)

3110 Land Development Consultants, Inc.
14201 NE 200th St Ste 100
Woodinville, WA 98072
Contact: Frank Lemos Presdient
Tel: 425-806-1869
Email: flemos@ldccorp.com
Website: www.ldccorp.com
Civil Engineering, Land Survey, Land Use Planning/Permitting, A/E Design, Commercial Site Design, Roadway Design, Drainage Design and Reporting, GIS ESRI Mapping, Water Systems. (Hisp, estab 2003, empl 40, sales $5,354,378, cert: State, NMSDC)

3111 Professional CAD Services, Inc. dba PCSI Design
18916 N Creek Pkwy Ste 103
Bothell, WA 98011
Contact: Carlos Veliz CEO
Tel: 425-485-3420
Email: carlos@pcsidesign.com
Website: www.pcsidesign.com
Product design & engineering services focused on assisting companies to translate conceptual design into market-ready production products. Our product & solution offerings extend to many industries. (Hisp, estab 1997, empl 5, sales $1,116,889, cert: NMSDC)

3112 WHPacific, Inc.
12100 NE 195th St Ste 300
Bothell, WA 98011
Contact: Carl Romig Dir ICS
Tel: 425-951-4000
Email: cromig@whpacific.com
Website: http://WHPacific.com
Accessibility/Universal Access, Aviation Planning & Design, Bridge Design and Rehabilitation, Civil Engineering, Commissioning, Community & Urban Design, Construction Inspection, Construction Management, Construction Management. (Nat Ame, estab 1981, empl 351, sales $55,249,100, cert: NMSDC)

Wisconsin

3113 Datasyst Engineering & Testing
S14 W33511 Hwy 18
Delafield, WI 53018
Contact: Rose Hoisington CFO
Tel: - -
Email: mhoisington@datasysttest.com
Website: www.datasysttest.com
Mechanical & electrical equipment testing & engineering: medical, telecommunications, construction, mining & process, industrial, automotive. (Woman/Hisp, estab 1990, empl 11, sales , cert: NMSDC)

3114 Fusion Integrated Solutions LLC
416 Security Blvd
Green Bay, WI 54313
Contact: Seaphes Miller CEO
Tel: 920-593-4200
Email: solutions@fusion-etc.com
Website: www.fusion-etc.com
Mechanical, civil & structural, electrical & process engineering & design svcs, project management, materials procurement, construction field supervision, electrical panel construction & custom machine design & manufacture. (AA, estab 2004, empl 60, sales $9,113,000, cert: State, NMSDC)

3115 K. Singh & Associates, Inc.
3636 N 124th St
Wauwatosa, WI 53222
Contact: Pratap Singh CEO
Tel: 262-821-1171
Email: gmiller@ksaconsultants.com
Website: www.ksaconsultants.com
Environmental engineering & management services, transportation, structural, environmental & civil engineering, land surveying & construction management. (As-Ind, estab 1987, empl 33, sales $3,000,000, cert: State)

3116 PSJ Engineering, Inc.
7665 N Port Washington Rd
Milwaukee, WI 53217
Contact: Parmjit Jaspal CEO
Tel: 414-352-2211
Email: jesse@psjengineering.com
Website: www.psjengineering.com
Consulting engineering svcs: heating, ventilation, air conditioning, plumbing & fire protection. (As-Pac, estab 1986, empl 13, sales $1,186,006, cert: State, City)

<table>
<tr><td>

ENVIRONMENTAL SERVICES
Firms are engaged in underground and above ground storage tank removal and installation, assessment and remediation, lead and asbestos abatement, hazardous waste management, pollution, etc. NAICS Code 54

</td></tr>
</table>

Alabama

3117   Hygieneering, Inc.
       7575 Plaza Court, Ste B
       Willowbrook, AL 35222
       Contact: George Guidarelli VP Sales
       Tel: 630-654-2550
       Email: gguidarelli@hygieneering.com
       Website: www.hygieneering.com
Environmental consulting. (Woman, estab 1987, empl 42, sales $2,750,000, cert: WBENC)

3118   One Stop Environmental, LLC
       4800 Division Ave
       Birmingham, AL 35222
       Contact: Elizabeth Hinson Marketing Dir
       Tel: 205-595-8188
       Email: ehinson@onestopenv.com
       Website: www.onestopenv.com
Hazardous waste transport & disposal, confined space entry, industry cleaning, emergency response, remediation, oil/water separator, lead/asbestos abatement, environmental consulting. (Woman, estab 1999, empl 42, sales $4,000,000, cert: WBENC)

3119   Orrs Environmental, LLC
       515 Sparkman Dr
       Huntsville, AL 35756
       Contact: Debra Sanders Mgr
       Tel: 256-556-1220
       Email: orrsenvironmental@gmail.com
       Website: www.orrsenvironmental.com
Rail, air, water, trucking multimodal service, general & climate control warehousing, waste management assessments, spill response supplies & PPE, safety training, haz mat disposal & recycling services. (Woman/AA, estab 2004, empl 12, sales $268,000, cert: State)

3120   Slade Land Use, Environmental & Transportation
       Planning LLC
       1500 1st Ave N, Unit 54
       Birmingham, AL 35203
       Contact: L'Tryce Slade Owner
       Tel: 205-413-4685
       Email: lslade@sladellc.com
       Website: www.sladellc.com
General Contracting, Environmental Consulting, Geotechnical Services, Construction Material Testing, Urban Planning. (Woman/AA, estab 2006, empl 6, sales $644,986, cert: NMSDC, WBENC, 8a)

3121   Vulcan Industrial Contractors Co., LLC
       4625-A Valleydale Rd
       Birmingham, AL 35242
       Contact: Kristi Lawler CEO
       Tel: 205-313-4766
       Email: KLawler@vindco.com
       Website: www.vindco.com
Asbestos & lead removal. (Woman, estab 1949, empl 727, sales $68,000,000, cert: WBENC)

Arizona

3122   Archaeological Consulting Services, Ltd.
       424 W Broadway Rd
       Tempe, AZ 85282
       Contact: Margerie Green President
       Tel: 480-894-5477
       Email: mgreen@acstempe.com
       Website: www.acstempe.com
Cultural resource services, class I to class III studies, testing, & data recovery, environmental services, biological assessments/evaluations, environmental project management, paleo environmental analysis, GIS mapping. (Woman, estab 1977, empl 34, sales $1,945,942, cert: State, City, CPUC)

3123   Beck Environmental and Remediation, Ltd.
       772 S Holmes Rd
       Apache Junction, AZ 85119
       Contact: Julie Beck President
       Tel: 480-671-1365
       Email: julie.beck@earthlink.net
       Website: www.beckenvironmental.com
Environmental assessments, site characterizations, remediation, air monitoring, hazardous materials management, environmental impact statements, health & safety, environmental engineering, mitigation modeling. (Woman, estab 1998, empl 5, sales $292,915, cert: WBENC, 8a)

3124   Darling Geomatics
       9040 S Rita Rd, Ste 2350
       Tucson, AZ 85747
       Contact: Mary Darling CEO
       Tel: 520-298-2725
       Email: marydarling@darlingltd.com
       Website: www.darlingltd.com
Environmental consulting. (Woman, estab 1997, empl 15, sales $2,000,000, cert: City, CPUC)

3125   Gutierrez-Palmenberg, Inc.
       2922 W Clarendon Ave
       Phoenix, AZ 85017
       Contact: Jason Weed Engineer
       Tel: 602-234-0696
       Email: jason.w@gpimail.com
       Website: www.gpieng.com
Environmental consulting & engineering support services, site characterizations, design, identifying potential environmental impacts of planned operations, remediation, monitoring and protecting valued resources. (Hisp, estab 1980, empl 25, sales $2,250,273, cert: NMSDC)

3126   Harris Environmental Group, Inc.
       650 N 6th Ave
       Tucson, AZ 85705
       Contact: Lisa Harris Presdient
       Tel: 520-628-7648
       Email: lharris@heg-inc.com
       Website: www.heg-inc.com
Natural & cultural resources consulting: archaeologists, cultural resource management specialists, wildlife biologists, environmental compliance specialists, environmental scientists, plant ecologists, landscape & historic architects. (Minority, estab 1992, empl 15, sales $800,000, cert: 8a)

3127 The Green Way Environmental Group, LLC.
      P.O. Box 5705
      Scottsdale, AZ 85261
      Contact: Chris McNally Business Dev Mgr
      Tel: 480-639-0389
      Email: chris@gweg-az.com
      Website: http://greenway-environmental.com
Environmental, construction & restoration, sampling &
clearance sampling of asbestos, lead based paint &
microbial, environmental compliance, consulting, industrial hygiene & occupational safety. (Woman, estab 2010,
empl 5, sales $616,000, cert: WBENC)

California

3128 B & B Environmental Safety, Inc.
      17416 Murphy Pkwy
      Lathrop, CA 95330
      Contact: Kenneth S. Baugh President & CEO
      Tel: 209-858-4447
      Email: ken@bbensafety.com
      Website: www.bbensafety.com
Health Physics consulting svcs: decommissioning surveys,
industrial radiography protection svcs, radiological lab
audits, radioactive & mixed waste remediation & disposal
svcs, dose assessments. (AA, estab 2005, empl 10, sales
$3,672,515, cert: State)

3129 BC Laboratories, Inc.
      4100 Atlas Court
      Bakersfield, CA 93308
      Contact: Mark Ellis Business Devel Dir
      Tel: 800-878-4911
      Email: mark.ellis@bclabs.com
      Website: http://bclabs.com
Analytical Services for Groundwater, Drinking Water,
Wastewater, Soils & Air, Certified Testing Services, Sam-
pling & Monitoring. (Woman, estab 1949, empl 97, sales
$1,000,000,000, cert: CPUC)

3130 CAL INC.
      2040 Peabody Rd
      Vacaville, CA 95687
      Contact: David Esparza President
      Tel: 707-446-7996
      Email: desparza@cal-inc.com
      Website: www.cal-inc.com
General contracting: Asbestos & Lead Abatement, Demolition, Remediation Services & Environmental & Safety
Training. (Hisp, estab 1979, empl 40, sales $4,786,000,
cert: CPUC)

3131 California Hazardous Services Inc
      1431 E St Andrew PL
      Santa Ana, CA 92705
      Contact: Tammy Taylor Sales Mgr
      Tel: 714-434-9995
      Email: bids@calhaz.com
      Website: www.calhaz.com
Fuel tank service, cleaning, waste disposal, water intrusion
pump-outs, environmental compliance tank testing, tank
removals, tank installations, tank upgrades. (Woman, estab
1988, empl 24, sales $4,960,000, cert: CPUC, WBENC)

3132 Del Mar Environmental & Construction Services,
      Inc
      629 Del Mar Ave
      Chula Vista, CA 91910
      Contact: Juan Diez de Bonilla Presdient
      Tel: 619-638-3679
      Email: jdiezdebonilla@dmecservices.com
      Website: www.dmecservices.com
Environmental Consulting & Remediation, Stormwater
Management/Erosion Control, Range Maintenance /
Lead Recovery, Habitat Restoration, Demolition, Facility
Maintenance & Tenant Improvements. (Hisp, estab
2005, empl 10, sales $500,000, cert: 8a)

3133 Desert Environmental Services, Inc.
      12563 Caballero Ct
      Victorville, CA 92392
      Contact: Fernando Nieves Project Mgr
      Tel: 760-949-1110
      Email: desertfr@verizon.net
      Website:
Transportation & disposal of hazardous waste, lab
packing, emergency response,
spill remediation, hazardous waste container supplies.
(Hisp, estab 1999, empl 5, sales $351,745, cert: State)

3134 EFR Environmental Services Inc.
      P.O. Box 2669
      Alpine, CA 91903
      Contact: Laura L Harris Presdient
      Tel: 619-722-6781
      Email: accounting@efrenviro.com
      Website: www.efrenviro.com
Transport hazardous waste and non-hazardous waste,
Drum, Rolloff Services, Bulk Services, Vacuum Services,
Site Cleanups and Waste Categorization and Profiling.
(Woman, estab 1999, empl 17, sales $2,506,684, cert:
State, CPUC)

3135 Engineering/Remediation Resources Group, Inc.
      4585 Pacheco Blvd Ste 200
      Martinez, CA 94553
      Contact: Tyson Appel Sr Project Mgr
      Tel: 925-969-0750
      Email: tyson.appel@errg.com
      Website: www.errg.com
Engineering & remediation services, environmental, civil
& geotechnical engineers, geologists, soil physicists,
scientists, construction managers, construction superintendents, equipment operators, certified hazardous
waste technicians. (Woman/As-Pac, estab 1997, empl
175, sales $81,494,792, cert: CPUC)

3136 Future Power Corporation
      66 Franklin St Ste 300
      Oakland, CA 94607
      Contact: Dahlia Moodie Presdient
      Tel: 510-647-8450
      Email: dahlia@ecoptions.biz
      Website: www.ecoptions.biz
Facility energy audits, energy savings solution recom-
mendation & technology solution implementation.
(Woman/AA, Hisp, estab 2008, empl 7, sales $1,175,198,
cert: CPUC)

3137   G2RJ Inc. dba Trevet
       9888 Carroll Centre Rd, Ste 228
       San Diego, CA 92126
       Contact: Don Peters Project Mgr
       Tel: 858-578-8859
       Email: dpeters@trevetinc.com
       Website: www.trevetinc.com
Engineering services, environmental remediation & waste
management services. (As-Ind, estab 2005, empl 26, sales
$8,371,299, cert: State)

3138   GGG Demolition Inc.
       1130 W Trenton Ave
       Orange, CA 92867
       Contact: President
       Tel: 714-699-9350
       Email:
       Website: www.gggdemo.com
Structural Demolition, Asbestos/Lead Abatement, Mold
Remediation, Soil Remediation.
Selective Demolition. (Woman, estab 2013, empl 150,
sales $12,000,000, cert: CPUC, WBENC)

3139   Global Transloading, LLC
       16209 Paramount Blvd Ste 203
       Paramount, CA 90723
       Contact: Shannon Griego President
       Tel: 949-307-4148
       Email: shannongriego@globaltransloading.com
       Website:
Hazardous waste transportation & disposal, hazardous
waste management, logistics. (Woman/Nat Ame, Hisp,
estab 2004, empl 6, sales $1,424,695, cert: State)

3140   Greenway Solid Waste & Recycling, Inc.
       P.O. Box 1453
       Claremont, CA 91711
       Contact: Charles Elias VP
       Tel: 909-518-7943
       Email: celias@greenwayrecyclinginc.com
       Website: www.greenwayrecyclinginc.com
Electronic waste recycling, nonhazardous waste treatment
& disposal. (Woman/Hisp, estab 2006, empl 3, sales
$321,000, cert: State, 8a)

3141   H2O Engineering, Inc.
       189 Granada Dr
       San Luis Obispo, CA 93401
       Contact: Jeff Cedillos Sales Coord
       Tel: 866-987-0303
       Email: marketing@h2oengineering.com
       Website: www.h2oengineering.com
Create tailored water treatment solutions for industrial
process water, ultra-pure water, water reuse, and groundwater remediation. (Hisp, estab 2000, empl 16, sales
$4,200,000, cert: NMSDC)

3142   Impact Absorbents, Inc.
       5255 Traffic Way
       Atascadero, CA 93422
       Contact: Tammy Rayner Dir of Corporate Sales
       Tel: 800-339-7672
       Email: trayner@spillhero.com
       Website: spillhero.com
Mfr & dist granular absorbents, sorbent pads, sorbents
socks, spill clean up programs and products, non-hazard-
ous, earth friendly, cost effective. XSORB, FiberDuck,
FiberLink, Spill Station, Spill Caddy, Spill Rack, Biohazard
Kit. (Woman, estab 1992, empl 30, sales $5,300,000, cert:
State)

3143   Integrated Science Solutions (ISSI)
       1777 N California Blvd Ste 305
       Walnut Creek, CA 94596
       Contact: Cecelia Mccloy President
       Tel: 925-979-1535
       Email: info@issi-net.com
       Website: www.issi-net.com
Earth & environmental science, engineering, regulatory
compliance, occupational safety & health, homeland
security, emergency response, & energy, water & natural
resource development. (Woman, estab 1999, empl 40,
sales $5,035,703, cert: CPUC, WBENC)

3144   New World Environmental, Inc.
       448 Commerce Way
       Livermore, CA 94551
       Contact: Mark Davis VP Business Devel
       Tel: 949-833-7113
       Email: commercialdept@newworld.org
       Website: www.newworld.org
Nuclear & hazardous materials, site remediation,
characterization surveys, facility decontamination &
decommissioning, unrestricted release surveys. (Nat
Ame, estab 1988, empl 53, sales $8,245,469, cert: State)

3145   Ninyo & Moore
       5710 Ruffin Rd.
       San Diego, CA 92123
       Contact: Elizabeth Brooks Corp Business Develop
       Mgr
       Tel: 858-576-1000
       Email: ebrooks@ninyoandmoore.com
       Website: www.ninyoandmoore.com
Geotechnical & environmental sciences consulting:
geotechnical engineering, engineering geology, engineering geophysics, hydrogeology, soil & materials
testing & environmental sciences. (Hisp, estab 1986,
empl 492, sales $80,020,000, cert: City, NMSDC, CPUC)

3146   Northstar Environmental Remediation
       26225 Enterprise Ct
       Lake Forest, CA 92630
       Contact: Katherine Tweidt President
       Tel: 949-580-2800
       Email: ktweidt@cox.net
       Website: www.northstarremediation.com
Environmental consulting & remediation of soil &
groundwater, equipment fabrication, installation, &
operation, permitting, consulting, soil & groundwater
characterization, well installation, reporting, compliance
activities. (Woman, estab 2002, empl 6, sales
$1,250,000, cert: CPUC)

3147   Orange Coast Analytical, Inc.
       3002 Dow Ave, Ste 532
       Tustin, CA 92780
       Contact: Cindy Noorani President
       Tel: 714-832-0064
       Email: cindyn@ocalab.com
       Website: www.ocalab.com
Environmental & analytical testing laboratory, organic &
inorganic testing-water, waste water, soil, air, industial,
chemical & food products. (Woman, estab 1990, empl
15, sales $1,450,178, cert: State, CPUC)

3148 OST Trucks and Cranes, Inc.
      2951 N Ventura Ave
      Ventura, CA 93002
      Contact: L. Dennis Zermeno Presdient
      Tel: 805-643-9963
      Email: ostcranes@aol.com
      Website: www.ostcranes.com
General & hazardous substance removal & remedial
action, hydraulic cranes 5 to 140. (Hisp, estab 1947, empl
69, sales $ 0, cert: City, NMSDC, CPUC)

3149 Pari & Gershon Inc.
      2053 Lincoln Ave Ste A
      San Jose, CA 95125
      Contact: Romena Jonas Presdient
      Tel: 408-966-7184
      Email: rjonas@pgiinc.net
      Website: www.pgicompany.com
Environmental Consulting, Engineering Design & Construc-
tion. (Woman, estab 2009, empl 5, sales $100,000, cert:
State, WBENC)

3150 Piper Environmental Group, Inc.
      11600 California St
      Castroville, CA 95012
      Contact: Jane Piper CEO
      Tel: 831-632-2700
      Email: jpiper@peg-inc.com
      Website: http://peg-inc.com
Design ozone solutions, turn-key ozone trailer systems,
ozone sparging systems. (Woman, estab 1992, empl 3,
sales $1,483,616, cert: CPUC, WBENC)

3151 Pivox Corporation
      3240 El Camino Real Ste 230
      Irvine, CA 92602
      Contact: Sean Shahin VP
      Tel: 949-727-1400
      Email: sean@pivox.com
      Website:
Remediation of soil & groundwater, demolition, project &
construction management, permitting, design, feasibility
study, treatment system installation (civil, mechanical,
electril, and instrumentation). (Woman, estab 2004, empl
20, sales $8,000,000, cert: CPUC)

3152 Raibon & Colbert Associates, Inc.
      50 California St, Ste 1500
      San Francisco, CA 94111
      Contact: Regina Colbert President
      Tel: 415-951-4709
      Email: grcolbert@comcast.net
      Website:
Environmental health & safety services, hazardous
materials management, construction safety, stormwater
management, consulting & transportation. (Woman/AA,
estab 1997, empl 1, sales $157,000, cert: State, CPUC)

3153 RORE, Inc.
      5151 Shoreham Place
      San Diego, CA 92122
      Contact: Gita Murthy
      Tel: 858-404-7393
      Email:
      Website: www.roreinc.com
General & hazardous waste contracting, environmental
investigation & remediation. (Woman/As-Ind, estab 2003,
empl 70, sales $15,000,000, cert: State)

3154 SCA Environmental, Inc.
      320 Justin Dr
      San Francisco, CA 94112
      Contact: Christina Codemo Presdient
      Tel: 415-882-1675
      Email: ccodemo@sca-enviro.com
      Website: www.sca-enviro.com
Environmental consulting services, O & M plans.
(Woman, estab 1992, empl 11, sales $ 0, cert: WBENC)

3155 Spring Rivers Ecological Sciences LLC
      P.O. Box 153
      Cassel, CA 96016
      Contact: Maria Ellis Aquatic Ecologist
      Tel: 530-335-5446
      Email: maria@springrivers.com
      Website: www.springrivers.com
Aquatic ecology & resources consulting. (Woman, estab
1994, empl 15, sales $ 0, cert: CPUC)

3156 TERRA Solutions & Services, LLC
      3478 Buskirk Ave Ste 100
      Pleasant Hill, CA 94523
      Contact: Bruce Borup Owner
      Tel: 925-651-6388
      Email: bborup@sircorporation.com
      Website: www.terras2.com
Environmental engineering, Phase I & Phase II property
assessment & site investigation,
underground storage tank assessment, removal, & site
restoration services, environmental construction &
remediation system installation. (Nat Ame, estab 2011,
empl 11, sales $664,000, cert: CPUC)

3157 Thomas Land Clearing Company
      2170 W Esther St
      Long Beach, CA 90813
      Contact: Bernice Antimo Presdient
      Tel: 562-436-6025
      Email: tlc.demo@verizon.net
      Website: www.jesdbes.com
Demolition, asbestos abatement, lead based paint
removal & general land clearing. (AA, estab 1985, empl
5, sales $1,700,000, cert: State, CPUC)

3158 Three Squares International Inc.
      1507 7th St, Ste 05
      Santa Monica, CA 90401
      Contact: Jaime Nack Presdient
      Tel: 310-403-6225
      Email: jnack@threesquaresinc.com
      Website: www.threesquaresinc.com
Environmental consulting, strategy, planning & implementation of sustainability initiatives. (Woman, estab
2008, empl 4, sales $500,000, cert: State, City, CPUC)

3159 Tycho Services, Inc.
      3906 W. Burbank Blvd.
      Burbank, CA 91505
      Contact: Raj Chhina Presdient
      Tel: 818-840-9404
      Email: raj@tychoservices.com
      Website: www.tychoservices.com
Pre & post event clean-up & biohazard waste removal
and clean-up. (As-Ind, estab 2009, empl 81, sales
$1,600,000, cert: NMSDC, CPUC)

3160   UltraViolet Devices, Inc.
26145 Technology Dr
Valencia, CA 91355
Contact: Kathi Million Inside Sales Mgr
Tel: 661-295-8140
Email: marys@uvdi.com
Website: www.uvdi.com
Mfr & dist ultraviolet sanitation devices that purify
surfaces, air and water. UV-C Disinfection. (Hisp, estab ,
empl , sales $ 0, cert: State, NMSDC)

3161   Veridian Environmental, Inc.
425 Merchant St, Ste 101
Vacaville, CA 95688
Contact: Charlotte R. Symms Presdient
Tel: 707-449-4400
Email: csymms@veridianenv.com
Website: www.veridianenv.com
Quality assurance environmental chemistry consulting
services: human health & ecological risk assessment, lab
audits, lab data validation, environmental data mgmt,
technical liaison services, QA/QC programs & documents,
litigation. (Woman, estab 2001, empl 5, sales $210,000,
cert: State, CPUC)

3162   West Coast Environmental Solutions
2650 Lime Ave
Signal Hill, CA 90755
Contact: Beatriz Esparza Business Dev Mgr
Tel: 562-448-9510
Email: beaesparza@westcoastes.com
Website: www.westcoastes.com
24-hour hazardous & non-hazardous emergency response
spill cleanup; pipeline, facility, marine, rail, highway,
container spills, river, stream, harbor, shoreline, drug lab,
containment & protective booming, product skimming/
recovery & storage. (Woman, estab 2010, empl 35, sales
$5,768,900, cert: CPUC)

3163   Wildscape Restoration, Inc.
2500 Channel Dr Ste A-1
Ventura, CA 93003
Contact: Noreen Cabanting Principal
Tel: 805-644-6852
Email: noreen@wildscaperestoration.com
Website: www.wildscaperestoration.com
Environmental consulting & contracting: habitat restora-
tion, non-native invasive species removal, biological
surveys & monitoring, permitting & environmental
planning. (Woman/As-Pac, estab 2006, empl 8, sales
$415,369, cert: State)

Colorado

3164   Colorado's Advanced Restoration Experts, LLC
P.O. Box 1592
Lyons, CO 80540
Contact: Theodore Pangilinan Presdient
Tel: 303-588-6796
Email: theo@restorationwithcare.com
Website: http://restorationwithcare.com
Water damage mitigation, mold remediation, carpet
cleaning, fire & smoke restoration, odor control & uphol-
stery cleaning. (As-Pac, estab 2015, empl 12, sales
$350,000, cert: State)

3165   Diamond T Services Inc.
112 N Rubey Dr Ste 101
Golden, CO 80403
Contact: Vanessa Ingalls CEO
Tel:
Email: vanessa.ingalls@dtservices.com
Website: www.diamondtservices.com
Soil stabilization & welding solutions, access & environmental matting, primary & secondary containment,
surface rentals, certified welding services for pipeline &
well sites, fabrication, roustabout, heavy equipment,
trucking & environmental services. (Woman, estab 2009,
empl 30, sales $7,434,245, cert: WBENC)

3166   Impact Mitigation Consultants LLC.
9851 Castleridge Cir
Highlands Ranch, CO 80129
Contact: James Balman Owner
Tel: 720-285-9918
Email: james@imcnow.com
Website: www.imcnow.com
Environmental testing. Air quality, asbestos, mold, lead.
Mitigation consulting Construction services not exceed-
ing 2MMPlastic mold injection & design, IT develop-
ment. (Nat Ame, estab 2016, empl 5, sales , cert: State)

3167   Marketing Data Solutions
36424 Forest Trail
Elizabeth, CO 80107
Contact: CEO
Tel: 720-474-7604
Email:
Website:
Environmental Remediation, RCRA Hazardous waste
packaging, transportation & disposal, TSCA waste,
Soils Excavation, Environmental services,
Hazardous waste profiling, Hazardous waste collection,
transfer and transportation. (Nat Ame, estab 2012, empl
1, sales , cert: 8a)

3168   Munchiando Excavating, Inc.
5040 Tabor St
Wheat Ridge, CO 80033
Contact: Linda Munchiando Presdient
Tel: 303-940-6642
Email: munchexc@aol.com
Website:
Environmental clean-up, excavation & transportation,
excavation & earthwork, UST removal, underground
utilities, vacuum tanker, roll-off trailers, end-dumps, van
trailers & flatbed trailers. (Woman, estab 1987, empl 6,
sales $958,000, cert: State, City)

3169   Property Doctors Inc.
14700 W 66th Place Unit 7
Arvada, CO 80004
Contact: Nancy Rees Presdient
Tel: 888-456-0911
Email: information@property-drs.com
Website: www.property-drs.com
Asbestos abatement & removal, asbestos testing,
asbestos consulting, carpet cleaning. (Woman, estab
2005, empl 12, sales $17,000,000, cert: City, WBENC)

3170 RDS Environmental, Inc.
11603 Teller St
Broomfield, CO 80020
Contact: Tammy Linton President
Tel: 303-444-5253
Email: tammy@rdsenvironmental.com
Website: www.rdsenvironmental.com
Environmental consulting, asbestos testing, mold testing, mold remediation/removal, radon testing, radon mitigation installation. (Woman, estab 1978, empl 6, sales $1,032,000, cert: WBENC)

3171 RMC Consultants, Inc.
12345 W Alameda Pkwy Ste 205
Lakewood, CO 80228
Contact: Richard Valdez President
Tel: 303-980-4101
Email: rvaldez@rmc-consultants.com
Website: www.rmc-consultants.net
Environmental services consulting: science & engineering, project mgmt, planning & documentation, compliance, mine reclamation, heavy equipment operation, waste mgmt, remediation services. (Hisp, estab 1990, empl 56, sales $3,980,000, cert: State, City)

District of Columbia

3172 Windjammer Environmental
1001 G St NW Ste 800
Washington, DC 20001
Contact: Damien Hammond Presdient
Tel: 888-270-8387
Email: hammond@wjenviro.com
Website: www.wjenviro.com
Industrial Hygiene Services: Indoor air Quality Surveys, Mold & Moisture Investigation, General Air & Waterborne Contaminate Sampling, Asbestos Management Services & Lead Management Services, Environmental Health & Occupational Safety Services. (AA, estab 2012, empl 5, sales $350,000, cert: State, City, 8a)

Delaware

3173 BrightFields, Inc.
801 Industrial St
Wilmington, DE 19801
Contact: Donald Short CFO
Tel: 302-656-9600
Email: dshort@brightfieldsinc.com
Website: www.brightfieldsinc.com
Environmental consulting svcs: phase I & II investigations, multi-media sampling, above & underground storage tanks, soil & groundwater remediation, brownfield redevelopment, asbestos & lead svcs. (Woman, estab 2003, empl 35, sales $5,907,000, cert: WBENC)

Florida

3174 Advantage Environmental Services, Inc.
2325 5th Ave N
St. Petersburg, FL 33713
Contact: project dir
Tel: 727-323-1902
Email:
Website: www.aesenv.com
Remediation, waste management & construction services. (Woman/AA, estab 1994, empl 3, sales $1,351,000, cert: State, City)

3175 Advisory Environmental Technologies, Inc.
4240 William Dr
Gulf Breeze, FL 32563
Contact: Gary Butler Business Dev Mgr
Tel: 850-356-2365
Email: gbutler@aet-environmental.com
Website: www.aet-environmental.com
Environmental Remediation Services, Indoor Air Quality Remediation, Asbestos Abatement, Lead Abatement, Laboratory Services, Environmental & Safety Training Services, Problem Solving. (Woman/Hisp, estab 2007, empl 4, sales $2,169,158, cert: 8a)

3176 AirQuest Environmental, Inc.
6851 SW 45th St
Fort Lauderdale, FL 33314
Contact: Presdient
Tel: 954-792-4549
Email:
Website: www.airquestinc.com
Environmental consulting: due diligence investigations, Phase I & II site assessments, mold & asbestos surveys, abatement mgmt, indoor air quality surveys, soil & groundwater assessment & remediation, etc. (Woman, estab 2002, empl 28, sales $600,000, cert: State, WBENC)

3177 Ambient Technologies, Inc.
4610 Central Ave
St. Petersburg, FL 33711
Contact: Carlos Lemos President
Tel: 727-328-0268
Email: ambtec@aol.com
Website: www.ambienttech.com
Environmental & geotechnical drilling, geophysics & utility designating services. (Hisp, estab 1992, empl 30, sales $3,000,000, cert: State, NMSDC)

3178 Clark Environmental, Inc.
755 Prairie Industrial Pkwy
Mulberry, FL 33860
Contact: Beth Clark Presdient
Tel: 863-425-4884
Email: bclark@clarkenvironmental.com
Website: www.ThermalTreatment.com
Thermal treatment facility: dispose petroleum contaminated soil, waste processing, hazardous & non-hazardous waste disposal & transportation services. (Woman, estab 1991, empl 23, sales $ 0, cert: State)

3179 Meryman Environmental, Inc.
10408 Bloomingdale Ave
Riverview, FL 33578
Contact: Charles CEO
Tel: 813-626-9551
Email: meryman@merymanenvironmental.com
Website: www.merymanenvironmental.com
Environmental consulting services: scientists, geologists, ecologists, forestry experts, & laboratory scientists. (Nat Ame, estab 1974, empl 9, sales $928,261, cert: State)

3180 Pinnacle Environmental Management Support
2001 W Sample Rd, Ste 101
Pompano Beach, FL 33064
Contact: Cynthia Williams CEO
Tel: 954-977-3775
Email: nhaddy@pinnacleems.com
Website: https://pinnacleems.com
Environmental claims management and cost-control services for petroleum-impacted sites. (Woman, estab 1995, empl 65, sales , cert: WBENC)

3181 Progressive Engineering & Construction, Inc.
12402 N. 56th St
Tampa, FL 33617
Contact: Jill Doyle Office Admin
Tel: 813-930-0669
Email: jdoyle@progressiveec.com
Website: www.progressiveec.com
Environmental engineering, construction management
services, environmental feasibility/technology evaluations,
remedial/closure strategy development, remedy construc-
tion & enhancement. (Woman, estab 1999, empl 9, sales
$2,811,000, cert: WBENC)

3182 Pure Air Control Services, Inc.
4911 Creekside Dr, Ste C
Clearwater, FL 33760
Contact: Alan Wozniak President & CEO
Tel: 800-422-7873
Email: awozniak@pureaircontrols.com
Website: www.pureaircontrols.com
Indoor environmental svcs: IEQ training, building & home
diagnostics, mold identification, industrial hygiene svcs,
forensic IEQ testimony, environmental lab svcs, environ-
mental project mgmt, IAQ-screen test kits, HVAC cleaning.
(Hisp, estab 1982, empl 35, sales $2,500,000, cert: State,
NMSDC)

3183 Spaulding Decon, LLC
9420 Lazy Lane, E-9
Tampa, FL 33614
Contact: Laura Spaulding Owner
Tel: 813-298-7122
Email: spaulding911@yahoo.com
Website: www.spauldingdecon.com
Bio-hazard clean up svcs: blood, vomit, feces, urine
removal, odor abatement, dead animal removal. (Woman,
estab 2005, empl 7, sales $1,500,000, cert: City, WBENC)

3184 Stone Environmental Services
6151 Lake Osprey Dr
Sarasota, FL 33946
Contact: Anna Milantoni Owner
Tel: 941-628-5693
Email: amilantoni@stoneenvironmentalservices.com
Website: www.stoneenvironmentalservices.com
Dist metal/plastic cleaning chemistry, refrigerants, disposal
of non-hazardous & hazardous waste disposal, cleaning
equipment. (Woman, estab 2001, empl , sales $446,000,
cert: WBENC)

3185 Urban E Consulting, Inc.
5630 E Powhatan Ave
Tampa, FL 33610
Contact: Dellinda Rabinowitz Presdient
Tel: 813-512-6998
Email: dell@urbanerecycling.com
Website: http://urbanerecycling.com
Provide, pick up, data destruction, recycling, and certifica-
tion. (Woman, estab 2012, empl 24, sales $2,556,300, cert:
WBENC)

Georgia

3186 Basha Services, LLC
2336 Wisteria Dr Ste 510
Snellville, GA 30078
Contact: Neville Anderson President
Tel: 678-344-1161
Email: nanderson@bashaservices.com
Website: http://bashaservices.com/
Environmental services: remediation, emergency & spill
response, soil remediation, excavation & restoration,
groundwater remediation, UST/AST closure, cleaning,
inspection & installation. (AA, estab 2007, empl 11, sales
, cert: State, NMSDC)

3187 Cape Environmental Management Inc.
500 Pinnacle Court, Ste 100
Norcross, GA 30071
Contact: Michael Healy Business Develop Mgr
Tel: 610-470-1189
Email: mhealy@cape-inc.com
Website: www.cape-inc.com
Environ remediation & consulting: base closures, USTS,
ASTS, assessments, lead based paint, radon, asbestos,
environ communication programs, hazardous wastes,
soil & groundwater. (Hisp, estab 1985, empl 455, sales
$128,148,143, cert: NMSDC)

3188 Corporate Environmental Risk Management
1990 Lakeside Pkwy Ste 300
TUCKER, GA 30084
Contact: Al Edwards Managing Dir
Tel: 678-999-0173
Email: certification@cerm.com
Website: www.cerm.com
Environmental mgmt & remediation, civil engineering &
site dev, water resources mgmt, program & construction
mgmt. (AA, estab 1995, empl 112, sales $2,960,000,
cert: State)

3189 Kemron Environmental Services, Inc.
1359-A Ellsworth Industrial Blvd
Atlanta, GA 30318
Contact: John Dwyer Exec VP
Tel: 404-636-0928
Email: mbe@kemron.com
Website: www.kemron.com
Environ svcs: consulting, site remediation, environ
assessment, investigation & engineering, analytical svcs,
geotechnical testing, treatability studies & technology
evaluation. (Hisp, estab 1975, empl 165, sales
$47,127,478, cert: NMSDC)

Idaho

3190 Wynsor, LLC
3605 Sycamore Circle
Idaho Falls, ID 83402
Contact: Lea Ann Rodriquez President
Tel: 208-681-7969
Email: leaann@wynsorenv.com
Website: www.wynsorenv.com
Environmental Remediation Services: decontamination,
decommissioning & demolition, Site characterization &
hazardous assessment, Site restoration & closure,
Environmental engineering services. (Woman, estab
2007, empl 6, sales $541,458, cert: 8a)

Illinois

3191 All Service Contracting Corp.
2024 E Damon Ave
Decatur, IL 62526
Contact: CEO
Tel: 217-233-3018
Email:
Website: www.allservice.com
Dist, remove & install filter media, water & waste water plants, industial & municipal. (Woman, estab 1996, empl 12, sales $ 0, cert: WBENC)

3192 Anderson & Egan, Co.
124 N Water St Ste 206
Rockford, IL 61107
Contact: Jennifer Anderson President
Tel: 815-962-9000
Email: janderson@andersonenveng.com
Website: www.andersonenveng.com
Air monitoring, asbestos abatements, environmental consulting & engineering, permitting assistance, underground storage tank removals, environmental site assessments. (Woman, estab 2003, empl 5, sales $469,000, cert: State, City)

3193 Endure, Inc.
360 Beinoris Dr
Wood Dale, IL 60191
Contact: Angelia Hopson Enviro Safety/Training
Tel: 630-616-9700
Email: ahopson@endure-inc.com
Website: www.endureinc.com
Safety, health & environmental consulting, training for regulatory compliance to OSHA, EPA & DOT requirements. (Woman/AA, estab 2010, empl 17, sales $1,845,500, cert: City, NMSDC)

3194 NES Incorporated
19015 Jodi Rd Unit B
Mokena, IL 60448
Contact: Kyla Lawson Secretary
Tel: 708-478-5497
Email: klawson@nesincorp.com
Website: www.nesincorp.com
Asbestos abatement, operations & maintenance, inspections & sampling, lead removal, mitigation, sampling & testing, mold remediation, inspections & sampling, hazardous materials clean-up & infrared investigations. (Hisp, estab 2000, empl 10, sales $1,800,000, cert: State, NMSDC)

Indiana

3195 Gurman Container & Supply Co.
800 N 3rd St
Terre Haute, IN 47807
Contact: Michael Roberts Sales Mgr
Tel: 800-448-7626
Email: mike@gurmancontainer.com
Website: www.gurmancontainer.com
Removal of used or damaged drums for reconditioning or disposal. (Woman, estab 1922, empl 13, sales $1,654,920, cert: State, WBENC)

3196 Hoosier Equipment Service, Inc.
8149 Network Dr
Plainfield, IN 46168
Contact: Anne DaVega VP Business Dev
Tel: 317-838-8988
Email: adavega@hoosierequipment.com
Website: www.hoosierequipment.com
Environmental services, underground & aboveground storage tank work (removals, installs, repairs), oil/water separator cleanouts, & environmental remediation work, excavate contaminated soil. (Woman, estab 1978, empl 13, sales $3,169,000, cert: WBENC)

3197 Keramida Environmental, Inc.
401 N College Ave
Indianapolis, IN 46202
Contact: Tim Higgins VP
Tel: 317-414-9862
Email: thiggins@keramida.com
Website: www.keramida.com
Environmental, health & safety engineering & consulting, remediation, site assessments, permitting. (Woman, estab 1988, empl 92, sales $15,049,406, cert: WBENC)

Kansas

3198 EMR, Inc.
2110 Delaware, Ste B
Lawrence, KS 66046
Contact: VP Marketing
Tel: 785-842-9013
Email:
Website: www.emr-inc.com
Environmental consulting: compliance, industrial hygiene, mold, asbestos, lead paint, UST/AST investigation, hazardous waste mgmt, recycling, soil & groundwater remediation. (Woman/Nat Ame, estab 1988, empl 250, sales $44,000,000, cert: WBENC)

Kentucky

3199 Evergreen Environmental
7416 Hwy 329
Crestwood, KY 40014
Contact: Hollis Flora Project Mgr
Tel: 502-241-4171
Email: hflora@evgusa.com
Website: www.evgusa.com
Compliance plan dev, environmental process & RCRA audits, property audits, UST mgmt, hazard risk analysis, OSHA training & consulting, soil & groundwater remediation, permitting & closure plans, industrial cleaning, hazardous & waste mgmt, etc. (Woman, estab 1986, empl 26, sales $4,300,000, cert: WBENC)

3200 Specific Waste Industries
3600 Chamberlain Lane, Ste 104
Louisville, KY 40241
Contact: Victor Anderson Presdient
Tel: 502-425-2770
Email: vanderson@a-solutionsinc.com
Website: www.specificwaste.com
Regulated Medical Waste Removal & Treatment, Pharmaceutical Waste (Haz and Non-Haz), Sharps Waste (Reusable Sharps Program). (AA, estab , empl , sales $500,000, cert: NMSDC)

Louisiana

3201 Quaternary Resource Investigations, LLC
13588 Florida Blvd
Baton Rouge, LA 70819
Contact: Mary Ruiz VP Sales
Tel: 225-292-1400
Email: info@qri.com
Website: www.qri.com
Litigation & strategy support; environmental sampling & lab data mgmt; groundwater geophysical svcs; remediation implementation; regulatory compliance; coastal & wetlands svcs. (Woman, estab 1986, empl 18, sales $31,000,000, cert: WBENC)

Massachusetts

3202 Capaccio Environmental Engineering Inc.
293 Boston Post RdWest
Marlborough, MA 01752
Contact: Lisa Wilk President
Tel: 508-970-0033
Email: lwilk@capaccio.com
Website: www.capaccio.com
Environmental engineering & consulting services, environmental compliance & permitting, occupational safety & health consulting services, environmental, health & safety management systems. (Woman, estab , empl , sales $3,139,945, cert: State, WBENC)

3203 Corporate Environmental Advisors, Inc.
127 Hartwell St
West Boylston, MA 01583
Contact: Scott Soucy Health, Safety & Compliance
Tel: 800-358-7960
Email: contactus@cea-inc.com
Website: http://cea-inc.com/
Environmental engineering, consulting & contracting firm. (Woman, estab 1985, empl 20, sales $3,878,000, cert: State)

3204 CR Environmental Inc
639 Boxberry Hill Road
East Falmouth, MA 02536
Contact: Charlotte Cogswell Presdient
Tel: 508-563-7970
Email: charlotte@crenvironmental.com
Website: www.crenvironmental.com
Ecological risk assessments & characterizations of terrestrial, wetland & aquatic habitats. (Woman, estab 1994, empl 7, sales $1,826,063, cert: State, City)

3205 Essex Newbury North Contracting Corporation
65 Parker St, Unit 5
Newburyport, MA 01950
Contact: Delano Brooks Presdient
Tel: 978-463-5414
Email: delano_br@yahoo.com
Website: www.essexnewburynorth.com
General Contracting, construction management, commercial & industrial construction, lead abatement & asbestos remediation, finish carpentry, commercial & institutional bldg construction, painting & wall coverings, site preparation. (AA, estab 1997, empl 400, sales $31,000,000, cert: State, City, NMSDC)

3206 Strategic Environmental
362 Putnam Hill Rd
Sutton, MA 01590
Contact: Ross Hartman Exec VP
Tel: 508-757-7782
Email: info@strategic-es.com
Website: www.strategic-es.com
Transportation & disposal management svcs: environmental testing & on-site field svcs, site clean-up & remediation, groundwater mgmt. (Woman, estab 2001, empl 48, sales $26,000,000, cert: WBENC)

Maryland

3207 C&R Environmental Associates, Inc.
1415 Bush St 2nd Fl
Baltimore, MD 21230
Contact: Rudy Scipio President
Tel: 410-727-8762
Email: rscipio@crdemoinc.com
Website: www.crdemoinc.com
Hazardous materials remediation & demolition services, construction/renovation services & design/build services. (AA, estab 1997, empl 15, sales $5,000,000, cert: State)

3208 Environmental Health and Safety Solutions, LLC
13 Pheasant View Place
Parkton, MD 21120
Contact: Frank Damato Dir of Safety/Training
Tel: 904-556-6422
Email: fdamato@ehssgroup.com
Website: www.EHSSGroup.com
Environmental services, industrial hygiene monitoring services, air & noise monitoring surveys. (Woman, estab 2011, empl 5, sales $760,000, cert: State)

3209 Turtle Wings Inc.
1771 Olive St
Capitol Heights, MD 20743
Contact: Elizabeth Wilmot Presdient
Tel: 301-583-8399
Email: info@datakillers.com
Website: www.datakillers.com
Environmental services. (Woman, estab 2005, empl 13, sales $1,200,000, cert: State, WBENC)

Maine

3210 Credere Associates, LLC
776 Main St
Westbrook, ME 04092
Contact: Rip Patten, PE VP
Tel: 207-828-1272
Email: rpatten@crederellc.com
Website: www.crederellc.com
Environmental consulting & engineering, cleanup, construction, adaptive reuse & Brownfields Redevelopment projects. (Woman, estab 2007, empl 11, sales $2,000,000, cert: 8a)

Michigan

3211 Advanced Environmental Management Group, LLC
44339 Plymouth Oaks Blvd
Plymouth, MI 48170
Contact: Linda Leonard Office Admin
Tel: 734-354-9070
Email: admin@aemgroup.biz
Website: www.aemgroup.biz
Environmental permitting, compliance assessments, dispersion modeling, stack & ambient air testing, due diligence & remediation svcs, ISO 14001 EMS svcs, facility closure & decommissioning services, spill & contingency plans. (As-Ind, estab 1998, empl 11, sales $ 0, cert: NMSDC)

3212 A-Global Solution, LLC DBA Environmental Services
of North America, In
10455 Ford Rd
Dearborn, MI 48126
Contact: Joe Coelho Owner
Tel: 313-945-7400
Email: jcoelho@esnainc.com
Website: www.esnainc.com
Facility svcs: waste disposal & recycling, snow removal, parking lot sweeping, power washing, janitorial services & supplies, landscaping, onsite & offsite document shredding, asbestos, lead based paint & mold, waste containers. (AA, estab , empl , sales $ 0, cert: NMSDC)

3213 Atier
24074 Gibson Dr
Warren, MI 48089
Contact: Patricia Schrenk Acct Mgr
Tel: 586-759-4240
Email: patti.schrenk@atierpro.com
Website: www.atierpro.com
Total Quality Management & Engineering Consulting, Quality & Industrial Engineering, Containment, Supplier Representation, ISO & TS Implementation Audits, Quality Inspection, Launch support, Scrap Reduction, Project Management. (AA, estab 2012, empl 100, sales $4,700,000, cert: NMSDC)

3214 Cadena, LLC.
1099 Highland Dr, Ste A
Ann Arbor, MI 48108
Contact: Armando Ojeda CEO
Tel: 734-418-1977
Email: aojeda@cadenaco.com
Website: www.cadenaco.com
Environmental services, lab data, Level II & Level IV validations, environmental laboratory audits, archiving environmental data. (Hisp, estab 2013, empl 2, sales $384,654, cert: NMSDC, CPUC)

3215 EKS Services Incorporated
7451 Third St
Detroit, MI 48202
Contact: Clarence E. Carpenter III CEO
Tel: 313-963-1433
Email: clarencecarpenter@eksservices.com
Website: www.eksservices.com
Environmental consulting & construction mgmt. (AA, estab 2000, empl 20, sales $1,500,000, cert: NMSDC)

3216 Environmental Compliance Office Inc.
3011 W Grand Blvd, Ste 420
Detroit, MI 48202
Contact: Vimala Anishetty, Ph.D. President
Tel: 313-285-8401
Email: vanishet@ecomain.com
Website: www.ecomain.com
Environmental engineering & consulting svcs: air, water, waste, auditing, reporting & training. (Woman/As-Pac, estab 2007, empl 4, sales $310,000, cert: WBENC)

3217 Environmental Testing and Consulting Inc.
38900 W Huron River Dr
Romulus, MI 48174
Contact: Patricia Stephen Contract Mgr
Tel: 734-955-6600
Email: sales@2etc.com
Website: http://2etc.com
Environmental consulting firm, asbestos, lead based paint, mold surveys, risk assessments, clearances, O&M plans, project management and training, indoor air quality assessments. (Woman, estab 1989, empl 75, sales $3,270,519, cert: WBENC)

3218 Infiniti Group International, LLC
241 Keelson Dr
Detroit, MI 48215
Contact: Melvin Gilmer Member
Tel: 586-995-5331
Email: mg@infinitigroup.us
Website: www.infinitigroupinternational.org
Environmental Products and Services. (AA, estab 2014, empl 2, sales , cert: NMSDC)

3219 Integrated Recycling Industries
P.O. Box 581
Wyandotte, MI 48192
Contact: Richard Pacheco Presdient
Tel: 734-818-9835
Email: rpacheco.iri@gmail.com
Website: www.integratedrecyclingindustries.com
Recycle Ferrous and Non-Ferrous scrap metals, Cardboard and Plastics. (Hisp, estab 2015, empl 2, sales $100,000, cert: NMSDC)

3220 McDonald & Assoc. Quality Management &
Environment
17561 Westhampton
Southfield, MI 48075
Contact: Sherman McDonald President
Tel: 248-559-5197
Email: mcdonaldquality@msn.com
Website: www.qltyenvsys.com
Leadership development, problem solving, 6 Sigma & 8D problem solving, waste management, environmental site assessment & environmental remediation. (AA, estab 1999, empl 10, sales , cert: State)

3221 Merit Laboratories, Inc.
2680 E Lansing Dr
East Lansing, MI 48823
Contact: Maya Murshak Presdient
Tel: 517-332-0167
Email: mayamurshak@meritlabs.com
Website: www.meritlabs.com
Environmental testing laboratory, RCRA remediation analytical, testing for soil, water & waste. We work with large and small industries, engineering firms, municipalities (Woman, estab 1987, empl , sales $ 0, cert: WBENC)

3222 MPS Group, Inc.
      38755 Hills Tech Dr
      Farmington Hills, MI 48331
      Contact: Bryon Lawrence Dir of Sales & Marketing
      Tel: 313-841-7588
      Email: blawrence@mpsgrp.com
      Website: www.mpsgrp.com
Environmental Consulting & Engineering. (AA, estab 1995,
empl 495, sales $46,200,000, cert: NMSDC)

3223 RTI Laboratories, Inc.
      33080 Industrial Rd
      Livonia, MI 48150
      Contact: Kae Trojanowski Presdient
      Tel: 734-422-8000
      Email: ktrojanowski@rtilab.com
      Website: www.rtilab.com
Analytical testing laboratory: environmental, chemical &
metallurgical testing, environmental compliance field
sampling services. (As-Ind, estab 1986, empl 40, sales
$5,000,000, cert: NMSDC, SDB)

3224 VMX International, LLC
      3011 W Grand Blvd Ste 2401
      Detroit, MI 48202
      Contact: Vickie Lewis CEO
      Tel: 313-875-9450
      Email: vlewis@vmxi.com
      Website: www.vmxi.com
International waste management & recycling services.
(Woman/AA, estab 2001, empl 54, sales $3,140,800, cert:
NMSDC, WBENC)

Minnesota

3225 EnviroBate, Inc.
      3301 E 26th Sttreet
      Minneapolis, MN 55406
      Contact: Dana Krakowski VP of Sales and Marketing
      Tel: 612-437-5797
      Email: dkrakowski@envirobate.com
      Website: www.envirobate.com
Environmental remediation, asbestos & lead abatement,
mold remediation & Indoor Air Quality (Duct Cleaning),
hazardous waste disposal to include mercury, lead &
PCB's. (Woman, estab 1991, empl 80, sales $14,000,000,
cert: City, WBENC)

Missouri

3226 Ahrens Contracting, Inc.
      140 Lafayette Ave
      St. Louis, MO 63104
      Contact: Patricia Ahrens Presdient
      Tel: 314-631-7799
      Email: pahrens@ahrenscontracting.com
      Website: www.ahrenscontracting.com
Hauling Dirt, Rubbish, Trash, Special Waste, Hazardous
Waste, Clean Fill, etc. (Woman, estab 0, empl , sales $ 0,
cert: WBENC)

3227 Cardinal Environmental Operations Corp.
      4518 Woodson Rd
      Saint Louis, MO 63134
      Contact: Paula Milligan President
      Tel: 314-890-2088
      Email: pmilligan@callcardinal.com
      Website:
Asbestos abatement, lead abatement, environmental
remediation, mold remediation, soil/water remediation,
UST/AST removal & installation, duct cleaning services,
consulting services, site assessments, demolition.
(Woman, estab 1993, empl 25, sales $2,000,000, cert:
State, City)

3228 CCI Environmental, Inc.
      6913 Noble Dr
      Hazelwood, MO 63024
      Contact: Mark Briguglio President
      Tel: 314-974-3893
      Email: marksbriguglio@gmail.com
      Website: www.ccienv.info
Asbestos abatement, inspections, testing, project
management & estimating to air monitoring & project
consulting. (Nat Ame, estab 1994, empl 7, sales
$930,000, cert: State)

3229 Global Environmental, Inc.
      6439 Plymouth Ave Ste 119
      Wellston, MO 63133
      Contact: John Dingus Project Mgr
      Tel: 314-875-9501
      Email: john@globalabatement.com
      Website: www.globalabatement.com
Environmental remediation & consulting. (Woman/Nat
Ame, estab 1991, empl 10, sales $10,500,000, cert:
State, 8a)

3230 Haz-Waste, Inc.
      12951 Gravois Rd Ste 110
      St. Louis, MO 63127
      Contact: Kimberly Medlock VP
      Tel: 800-429-9783
      Email: kmedlock@haz-waste.com
      Website: www.haz-waste.com
Air pollution permitting, asbestos, abatement,
byproduct mgmt, environmental audits, field service,
industrial compliance, OSHA compliance, Phase I & II site
work, plant closures, pollution prevention. (Woman,
estab 1993, empl 34, sales $6,200,000, cert: WBENC)

3231 Tehama, LLC
      1600 Genessee Ste 318
      Kansas City, MO 64102
      Contact: David Brewer GM
      Tel: 816-678-7510
      Email: david.brewer@tehamallc.com
      Website: www.tehamallc.com
Engineering/Architectural design, Environmental
Consulting Services & Construction Support Services.
(Nat Ame, estab 2009, empl 2, sales , cert: 8a)

3232 The Kiesel Company
4801 Fyler Ave
St. Louis, MO 63166
Contact: Larry Gooden VP
Tel: 314-351-5500
Email: larry.gooden@kieselco.com
Website: www.thekieselcompany.com
Dist fuels & lubricants, emergency response services to chemical & petroleum product releases, railroad tank car cleaning, barge cleaning, non-hazardous & hazardous waste disposal, demolition & petroleum-contaminated waste water treatment & disposal. (Woman, estab , empl 48, sales $75,010,000, cert: City)

North Carolina

3233 Environmental Process Solutions, PLLC
7000 Stinson Hartis Rd Ste F
Indian Trail, NC 28079
Contact: CEO
Tel: 980-202-2377
Email:
Website: www.EPSCharlotte.com
Environmental Consulting, Industrial wastewater treatment, engineering services. (Woman, estab 2010, empl 5, sales $103,000, cert: WBENC)

3234 Environmental Service Systems, LLC
5550 77 Center Dr. Ste 160
Charlotte, NC 28217
Contact: Ciara Lilly VP of Diversity and Inclusion
Tel: 704-527-4099
Email: clilly@environmentalss.com
Website: www.environmentalss.com
Facility maintenance & janitorial services. (AA, estab 1998, empl 10000, sales $250,000,000, cert: NMSDC)

3235 FireWater CleanUp Crew Corp.
P.O. Box 78145
Greensboro, NC 27427
Contact: Jamal Mention Presdient
Tel: 336-666-1913
Email: jamalmention@firewatercleanupcrew.com
Website: http://firewatercleanupcrew.com
Remediation/restoration services for smoke, fire & water damage. Trauma scene cleanup. (AA, estab 2016, empl 3, sales , cert: State)

3236 Porter Scientific Inc.
P.O. Box 1359
Pembroke, NC 28372
Contact: Freda Porter President & CEO
Tel: 910-521-0549
Email: fporter@porterscientific.com
Website: www.porterscientific.com
Environmental consulting services, assessments, remediation & cleanup, pollution prevention, regulatory compliance, water, sewer & solid waste project management. (Woman/Nat Ame, estab 1997, empl 18, sales $3,458,000, cert: City)

3237 Reliable Solutions Construction, LLC dba Reliable Restorations
8201 Arrowridge Blvd Ste 147
Charlotte, NC 28273
Contact: Johanna Suarez Operations Mgr
Tel: 704-909-7616
Email: johanna@reliablerestorations.net
Website: https://reliablerestorations.net
Disaster emergency response services, board ups, water extraction, fire & water damage restoration, odor & mold remediation, contents clean up & pack-outs, Non-Destructive Mold Remediation, Smoke & odor deodorization, Removal. (Woman/Hisp, estab 2009, empl 15, sales $1,426,000, cert: State)

Nebraska

3238 Inspection Experts, Inc.
808 P St Ste 318
Lincoln, NE 68508
Contact: Maureen Faulconer VP
Tel: 410-715-3939
Email: mfaulconer@ieinc.net
Website: www.ieinc.net
Environmental services, health & safety consulting, industrial hygiene, facilities & asset management & development. (Woman/As-Ind, estab 2004, empl 16, sales $3,365,268, cert: State)

New Hampshire

3239 Absolute Resource Associates, LLC
124 Heritage Ave Unit 16
Portsmouth, NH 03801
Contact: Susan Sylvester Presdient
Tel: 603-436-2001
Email: sues@absoluteresourceassociates.com
Website: www.absoluteresourceassociates.com
Environmental laboratory testing & indoor air quality assessments. (Woman, estab 1994, empl 25, sales $ 0, cert: WBENC)

New Jersey

3240 BGI Resources International Corporation
205 Barclay Pavilion W
Cherry Hill, NJ 08034
Contact: Bassey Akpan CEO
Tel: 856-888-2396
Email: info@bgiresourcesintl.com
Website: www.BGIResourcesIntl.com
Air, Water Soil Sampling, Phase I, II, III Projects, GIS Mapping, Preliminary Assessments. (AA, estab 2010, empl 3, sales , cert: State)

3241 Brinkerhoff Environmental Services, Inc.
1805 Atlantic Ave
Manasquan, NJ 08736
Contact: Laura Brinkerhoff CEO
Tel: 732-223-2225
Email: lbrinkerhoff@brinkenv.com
Website: www.brinkenv.com
Environmental services, Environmental Engineering, Environmental Site assessments, NEPA Evaluation Reports, Environmental Planning & Permitting, Wetland Services, Brownfield Redevelopment, Underground Storage Tank management, Geologic and Hydrogeologic. (Woman, estab 1989, empl 40, sales $7,505,209, cert: State, WBENC)

3242 Cornerstone EHS, LLC
P.O. Box 1102
Mullica Hill, NJ 08062
Contact: Marianne Payne Presdient
Tel: 856-776-0455
Email: mpayne@cornerstoneehs.com
Website: www.cornerstoneehs.com
Environmental, health, safety consulting & services, EHS program development & management; comprehensive EHS compliance & management system auditing; EHS related training, management systems development & implementation. (Woman, estab 2011, empl 1, sales $332,065, cert: WBENC)

3243 Environmental Industrial Services Corp. of NJ
288 Oak Grove Rd
Swedesboro, NJ 08085
Contact: Robert Feller Business Dev Mgr
Tel: 856-467-5001
Email: rfeller@eisco4service.com
Website: www.eisco4action.com
Environmental remediation services, soil remediation, capping, stabilization, UST & AST cleaning & closure, subsurface exploratory/test pits, groundwater remediation, install systems, pump & treat, vapor extraction, vacuum enhanced recovery. (Woman, estab 1990, empl 55, sales $3,211,964, cert: State)

3244 Fortune Metal Inc. of RI
900 Leesville Ave
Rahway, NJ 07065
Contact: Rick Gosselin Natl Sales Dir
Tel: 401-725-9100
Email: rickgosselin@fortunegroup.net
Website: www.fortunegroup.net
Buy & recycle scrap metals & plastics. (As-Pac, estab 1998, empl 128, sales $110,856,318, cert: NMSDC)

3245 Matrix New World Engineering, Land Surveying and Landscape Architectur
26 Columbia Turnpike 2nd Fl
Florham Park, NJ 07932
Contact: Jayne Warne, PE Presdient
Tel: 973-240-1800
Email: jwarne@mnwe.com
Website: www.matrixneworld.com
Environmental, geotechnical, civil engineering, survey & building facility consulting & engineering firm. (Woman, estab 1990, empl 200, sales $28,899,396, cert: State, City, WBENC)

3246 Prestige Environmental, Inc.
220 Davidson Ave Ste 307
Somerset, NJ 08873
Contact: Girish Mehta President
Tel: 908-757-9700
Email: girish.mehta@prestige-environmental.com
Website: www.prestige-environmental.com
Environmental consulting & contracting svcs: site assessments & feasibility studies; removal & installation of petroleum tanks; soil & groundwater investigations; site remediation; design, installation & operation of remediation systems. (As-Ind, estab 1993, empl 6, sales $1,092,700, cert: State)

3247 Sovereign
111 A North Gold Dr
Robbinsville, NJ 08691
Contact: Michael Hanlon Mgr
Tel: 609-259-8200
Email: mhanlon@sovcon.com
Website: www.sovcon.com
Environmental consulting & remediation services, environmental, civil & geotechnical engineering; remediation system evaluation, optimization, design & construction/installation; environmental, land use & natural resources permitting. (As-Pac, estab 1999, empl 165, sales $35,466,433, cert: NMSDC)

Nevada

3248 The Westmark Group
2430 N Decatur Blvd Ste 140
Las Vegas, NV 89108
Contact: Leslie Mujica Dir of BD & gov affairs
Tel: 702-839-2960
Email: marketing@westmarkgroup.net
Website: www.westmarkgroup.net
Consulting & project management, environmental consulting, occupational safety & health services & waste management services. (Hisp, estab 1999, empl 25, sales $5,000,000, cert: State)

New York

3249 Abtron Associates Corp.
60A Corbin Ave
Bay Shore, NY 11706
Contact: Robert Green President
Tel: 631-392-1330
Email: rgreen@abtronassociatescorp.com
Website: www.abtronassociatescorp.com
Environmental hazards/non-hazards services. (AA, estab 1997, empl 30, sales $1,055,000, cert: NMSDC, 8a)

3250 American Environmental Assessment & Solutions, Inc
679 Lafayette Ave, 3rd Fl
Brooklyn, NY 11216
Contact: Antoinette Ollivierre Principal
Tel: 718-209-0653
Email: aollivierre@aeasinc.com
Website: www.aeasinc.com
Environmental services: Phase I, II and III Environmental Site Assessments (ESA), soil & groundwater investigation, remediation of contaminated sites, NYC E-designation investigation and compliance. (Woman/AA, estab 2006, empl 9, sales , cert: State, City)

3251 Atlantic Testing Laboratories, Limited
6431 US Highway 11
Canton, NY 13617
Contact: Eric M. Van Alstyne Business Develop Mgr
Tel: 315-386-4578
Email: evanalstyne@atlantictesting.com
Website: www.ATlanticTesting.com
Subsurface investigations, water-based investigations, geotechnical engineering, construction materials engineering & testing, special inspection services, pavement engineering, nondestructive testing & environmental services. (Woman, estab 1967, empl 260, sales $16,190,692, cert: State, City)

3252 CSA Central, Inc.
55 Broadway, 14th Fl
New York, NY 10006
Contact: Frederik Riefkohl Sr VP
Tel: 305-461-5484
Email: friefkohl@csagroup.com
Website: www.csagroup.com
Program & project mgmt, environmental services, architecture & engineering, Construction Management, Operation & Maintenance. (Hisp, estab 1995, empl 55, sales $4,963,359, cert: NMSDC)

3253 Environmental Design & Research, DPC
217 Montgomery St Ste 1000
Syracuse, NY 13202
Contact: Joanne Stewart Associate
Tel: 315-471-0688
Email: jstewart@edrdpc.com
Website: www.edrdpc.com
Landscape architecture, civil engineering, community planning, visualization, environmental regulatory, ecological, geographic information systems mapping & analysis, historic preservation, cultural resources, archeology. (Woman, estab 1979, empl 38, sales $4,500,000, cert: State)

3254 Foit-Albert Associates, Architecture, Engineering and Surveying, P.C.
215 W 94th St, Ste 517
New York, NY 10025
Contact: Gregory Carballada Presdient
Tel: 716-856-3933
Email: cstoebe@foit-albert.com
Website: www.foit-albert.com
Architecture, Engineering, Environmental & Land Surveying Consulting. (Hisp, estab 1977, empl 70, sales $10,000,000, cert: State, City)

3255 LEADCARE, Inc.
10-25 44th Ave
Long Island City, NY 11101
Contact: Sarah Attias-Dunn President
Tel: 718-706-8383
Email: dunn@leadcare.com
Website: www.leadcare.com
Environmental testing, consultating & remediation project management, asbestos, lead, mold & indoor air quality investigations. (Woman, estab 1992, empl 10, sales $1,100,000, cert: State, City)

3256 Mechanical Testing, Inc.
70 Lake Ave.
Saratoga Springs, NY 12866
Contact: CEO
Tel: 518-450-7292
Email:
Website: www.mechtest.com
Testing, Adjusting & Balancing of HVAC Systems, Indoor Air Quality Testing, Performance Tests for HVAC Equipment, Sound Testing, In Room/Space Pressure Relationship Testing, Duct Pressurization, SMACNA. (Woman, estab 1967, empl 27, sales $3,800,000, cert: State, WBENC)

3257 NPTS, Inc.
2060 Sheridan Dr
Buffalo, NY 14223
Contact: Hormoz Mansouri Presdient
Tel: 716-876-8066
Email: rbroman@eiteam.com
Website: www.npts.net
Engineering consulting: nuclear, fossil, petrochem, risk assessment, thermohydraulic, design, outage mgmt, technical support svcs, etc. (As-Ind, estab 1983, empl 15, sales $1,521,462, cert: NMSDC)

3258 Sienna Environmental Technologies, LLC
350 Elmwood Ave
Buffalo, NY 14222
Contact: Susanne Kelley President
Tel: 716-332-3134
Email: skelley@siennaet.com
Website: www.siennaet.com
Asbestos inspections & contamination assessments, lead-based paint inspection & risk assessment, indoor air quality, microbial & radon testing & investigative services, air, soil, dust, water & solid waste sampling. (Woman/Hisp, estab 2000, empl 17, sales $2,000,000, cert: State, City)

3259 Universal Environmental Consulting, Inc.
900 Merchants Concourse Ste 214
Westbury, NY 11590
Contact: Operations
Tel: 800-552-0309
Email:
Website: www.uecny.com
Collection management of solid waste & recyclables. (Woman, estab 1995, empl 20, sales $33,785,084, cert: WBENC)

Ohio

3260 Ace Healthy Products LLC
907 W Fifth St
Dayton, OH 45402
Contact: Anthony Watson CEO
Tel: 866-891-5338
Email: acehealthyproducts11@gmail.com
Website: www.eaglewatchproducts.com/
Mfr unique and patented environmentally friendly products globally. (AA, estab 2015, empl 8, sales $200,000, cert: City)

3261 CTL Engineering, Inc.
2860 Fisher Rd
Columbus, OH 43204
Contact: C.K. Satyapriya President
Tel: 614-276-8123
Email: ctl@ctleng.com
Website: www.ctleng.com
Geotechnical, construction inspection, environmental, mining engineering, analytical chemistry, forensic science, metallurgy, product testing, research & development, roof engineering, existing structure evaluation, asbestos inspection. (Minority, estab 1928, empl 187, sales $ 0, cert: NMSDC)

3262 Environmental and Safety Solutions, Inc.
      544 Tohatchi Dr
      Cincinnati, OH 45215
      Contact: Cindy Tomaszewski President & CEO
      Tel: 513-383-7703
      Email: ctomaszewski@theessinc.com
      Website: www.essinc.info
Enviromental, health & safety services. (AA, estab 2002,
empl 9, sales $3,034,000, cert: State, NMSDC)

3263 Iron Eagle Enterprises, LLC
      4991 Belmont Ave
      Youngstown, OH 44505
      Contact: Business Development
      Tel: 330-759-2760
      Email:
      Website: www.IronEagleEnt.com
Custom frac & storage tank rentals, Vacuum truck service—wet & dry materials, Professional cleaning—disposal
wells, drains, holding tanks, frac tanks, Solid waste disposal
& hauling—rentals of vac boxes & sealed top boxes.
(Woman, estab 2010, empl 14, sales $4,500,000, cert:
WBENC)

3264 MCFS Enterprises, Inc.
      P.O. Box 30207
      Middleburg Heights, OH 44130
      Contact: Carrie Scaravelli Owner
      Tel: 440-888-0497
      Email: cscaravelli@cox.net
      Website: www.rainbowintl.com/cleveland
Water & fire restoration, smoke & odor remediation, mold,
lead & asbestos testing & abatement, hazardous waste
specialist. (Minority, Woman, estab 2007, empl 5, sales
$798,000, cert: State, City)

3265 Property & Environmental Management, Inc.
      6161 Busch Blvd, Ste 255
      Columbus, OH 43229
      Contact: Thomas Zwick VP
      Tel: 614-210-7202
      Email: tzwick@paeminc.com
      Website: http://paeminc.com
Environmental consulting Services, Remediation Services,
Facility Support Services, Residential Property Managers.
(As-Ind, estab 2010, empl 8, sales $2,000,000, cert: 8a)

3266 Stone Environmental Engineering & Science, Inc.
      748 Green Crest Dr
      Westerville, OH 43081
      Contact: Mary Sharrett Presdient
      Tel: 614-865-1874
      Email: marysharrett@stoneenvironmental.com
      Website: www.StoneEnvironmental.com
Assessment, Permitting, Design & Compliance, air, water,
soil, waste streams, hazardous materials, storm water,
natural resources, site civil, utilities, and structures.
(Woman, estab 1989, empl 17, sales $1,400,000, cert:
State, City, WBENC)

3267 Superior Environmental Corp.
      1132 Luschek Dr
      Cincinnati, OH 45241
      Contact: Michael Weinstein Sr Project Mgr
      Tel: 513-923-9000
      Email: m.weinstein@superiorenvironmental.com
      Website: www.superiorenvironmental.com
Environmental consulting: remedial design & implementation, property transfers. (Woman, estab 1989, empl 83,
sales $12,200,000, cert: WBENC)

Oregon

3268 Paul Carlson Associates, Inc.
      5775 Jean Rd. Ste 101
      Lake Oswego, OR 97035
      Contact: Joel McCarthy industrial hygienist
      Tel: 503-652-6040
      Email: joelm@pcasafety.com
      Website: http://pcasafety.com
HAZsolutions designed to manage hazardous materials
and waste in retail. (Woman, estab 1988, empl 12, sales
, cert: State)

Pennsylvania

3269 Environmental Data Validation, Inc.
      1326 Orangewood Ave
      Pittsburgh, PA 15216
      Contact: Maxine Wright-Walters Presdient
      Tel: 412-341-5281
      Email: mwalters@edv-inc.com
      Website: www.edv-inc.com
Chemical & radiochemical data validation, environmental health & safety training, occupational health & safety
consulting, industrial hygienist services, building
inspections, environmental site assessments, risk
assessment, hazard assessment. (Woman/AA, estab
1990, empl 8, sales $350,000, cert: State)

3270 Environmental Equipment + Supply, LLC
      491-L Blue Eagle Ave, Ste L
      Harrisburg, PA 17112
      Contact: Lisa Reeves Presdient
      Tel: 717-901-8891
      Email: reevesl@envisupply.com
      Website: www.envisupply.com
Environmental equipment rental and sales. (Woman,
estab 2018, empl 9, sales $1,260,211, cert: WBENC)

3271 Keating Environmental Management, Inc.
      835 Springdale Dr
      Exton, PA 19341
      Contact: Keith Choper President
      Tel: 484-876-2200
      Email: kchoper@kempartners.com
      Website: www.kempartners.com
Engineering, environmental engineering and consulting,
brownfields redevelopment, groundwater studies,
subsurface evaluations, geology, remediation management, asbestos, site assessments and environmental
auditing. (Woman, estab 1988, empl 13, sales
$2,250,000, cert: State, City, WBENC)

3272 Niche Waste Reduction and Recycling Systems, Inc
      P.O. Box 245246
      Philadelphia, PA 19119
      Contact: Maurice Sampson II CEO
      Tel: 267-269-6912
      Email: msampson@nicherecycling.com
      Website: www.nicherecycling.com
Waste Management & recycling planning & consultation
svcs: site survey/waste assessments, Waste Audits,
Architectural Design Consultation for Waste Management, In-house container, brochure, poster training &
orientation. (AA, estab 1995, empl 1, sales , cert: State)

3273 Novel Geo-Environmental, LLC
171 Montour Run Rd
Moon Township, PA 15108
Contact: Grace Aiken Office Mgr
Tel: 412-722-1970
Email: gaiken@ngeconsulting.com
Website: www.ngeconsulting.com
Environmental & geotechnical engineering consulting,
Multi- Media Compliance Auditing, Permitting, Reporting
& Plan Development, Environmental Management Systems
Design & Implementation. (Woman, estab 2002, empl 34,
sales $5,579,823, cert: State)

3274 Polaris Engineering, Inc.
5015 Preakness Pl
Bethlehem, PA 18020
Contact: Fidel Gonzalez President
Tel: 610-698-7185
Email: fidel@polarisengineeringinc.com
Website: www.polarisengineeringinc.com
Civil engineering: feasibility studies, roadways, storm
water management facilities, water line design, sanitary
sewer design, site layout & site grading. (Hisp, estab 2007,
empl 2, sales , cert: State)

3275 W. K. Merriman, Inc.
7038 Front River Rd
Pittsburgh, PA 15225
Contact: Mary Ann Merriman CEO
Tel: 412-262-7024
Email: m.merriman@wkmerriman.com
Website: www.wkmerriman.com
Dist commodity chemicals & environmental technology,
neutralize wastewater, reduce sluge & cost saving alterna-
tives. (Woman, estab 1986, empl 6, sales $6,377,400, cert:
WBENC)

Puerto Rico

3276 RAC Enterprises, Inc.
Road 1, KM 24.8
Caguas, PR 00726
Contact: Vivian Carballo President
Tel: 787-789-9338
Email: rac@racsteeldrums.com
Website: www.racsteeldrums.com
Mfr steel drums, dist plastic, steel & stainless containers,
sorbent products, secondary containment: spill pallets,
drain seals. Stormwater management products, PPE &
material handling, monitors. (Hisp, estab 1995, empl 15,
sales $2,300,000, cert: NMSDC)

Rhode Island

3277 Full Circle Recycling
23 Green Hill Rd
Johnston, RI 02919
Contact: Maria Vinagro Presdient
Tel: 401-464-5996
Email: maria@fullcircleri.com
Website: www.fullcirclerecyclingri.com
Full service recycling facility for metal, plastic, paper, fiber,
and electronic post-industrial and post-consumer scrap
materials and components. (Woman/AA, estab 2007, empl
30, sales , cert: WBENC)

South Carolina

3278 Air Hub, LLC
P.O. Box 2535
Mount Pleasant, SC 29465
Contact: Terri Sciarro Owner
Tel: 843-343-3618
Email: tls@airhubllc.com
Website: www.airhubllc.com
Air permitting, air modeling, noise modeling & studies,
stormwater pollution prevention plans (SWPPP), spill
prevention control & countermeasure (SPCC), environ-
mental consulting. (Woman, estab 2011, empl 1, sales ,
cert: State)

Tennessee

3279 EGSE Holdings, LLC. dba Emergency Response
Team
195 Omohundro Pl, Unit H
Nashville, TN 37210
Contact: Kevin Seats Sales Assoc
Tel: 615-525-9075
Email: kseats@ertnashville.com
Website: http://fireandfloodexperts.com
Water Restoration, Fire & Smoke Mitigation, Mold
Remediation. (AA, estab 2004, empl 5, sales $470,000,
cert: State, NMSDC)

3280 iSustain Inc.
12249 Wildlife Place
Soddy Daisy, TN 37379
Contact: Presdient
Tel: 423-668-0111
Email: huberda@me.com
Website: www.isustain.expert
Recycling & Waste Management. (Woman, estab 2014,
empl 4, sales $2,653,697, cert: WBENC)

3281 Microbial Insights, Inc.
10515 Research Dr
Knoxville, TN 37932
Contact: Anita Biernacki VP Operations
Tel: 865-573-8188
Email: info@microbe.com
Website: www.microbe.com
Environmental biotechnology, bioremediation of
chlorinated hydrocarbons, biofilm formation in drinking
water systems. (Woman, estab 1992, empl 15, sales
$2,951,477, cert: WBENC)

3282 Tioga Environmental Consultants, Inc.
357 North Main St
Memphis, TN 38112
Contact: Larkin Myers VP
Tel: 901-791-2432
Email: lmyers@tiogaenv.com
Website: www.tiogaenv.com
Lead based paint inspections, mold sampling, IAQ
investigations, asbestos inspections, environmental
sampling, soil & groundwater sampling, environmental
compliance, SWPPP, SPCC Plans, waste water studies,
erosion control. (Woman, estab 2009, empl 7, sales
$730,000, cert: State, City)

Texas

3283 ALPHA Facilities Solutions, LLC
11503 NW Military Hwy, Ste 300
San Antonio, TX 78231
Contact: Cassandra Garcia Marketing Mgr
Tel: 210-262-2634
Email: cassy.garcia@alpha-fs.com
Website: www.alphafacilities.com/
Capital planning, facility condition assessments (FCA), maintenance management, environmental assessments, hazardous materials management planning, investment strategy & space planning services. (Hisp, estab 2007, empl 68, sales $9,000,000, cert: 8a)

3284 Architect for Life - A Professional Corporation
2450 Louisiana St, Ste 400-233
Houston, TX 77006
Contact: Lolalisa King
Tel: 888-986-7771
Email: lking@architectforlife.com
Website: www.architectforlife.com
Green consulting professional services, develop & manage energy efficient strategies, programs, & projects, retrofit strategies, benchmarking building energy performance, long-term energy management & water saving goals assessment. (Woman/AA, estab 1995, empl , sales $108,000, cert: City)

3285 Bocci Engineering, LLC
12709 Pine Dr.
Cypress, TX 77429
Contact: Lianne Lami Presdient
Tel: 832-304-2295
Email: marketing_bid_notice@bocciengineering.com
Website: www.BocciEngineering.com
Efficiency & Optimization, Renewable Resources, Combined Heat & Power, Distributed Generation, Central Plant Projects, Emissions Reduction, Waste Recovery, & Sustainability. Expect Engineering Excellence. (Woman, estab 2002, empl 7, sales $129,378, cert: WBENC, SDB)

3286 Dougherty Sprague Environmental, Inc.
3902 Industrial St Ste A
Rowlett, TX 75088
Contact: John Dougherty VP of Marketing
Tel: 972-412-8666
Email: jdougherty@dsei.com
Website: www.dsei.com
Environmental consulting, phase I & II site assessments, groundwater modeling, industrial compliance, UST removal & site clean-up, litigation support & expert witness testimony. (Woman, estab 1998, empl 25, sales $2,000,000, cert: State, WBENC)

3287 Lynx Ltd
P.O. Box 591540
Houston, TX 77259
Contact: Darlene Sanchez VP
Tel: 281-797-2546
Email: darlene.sanchez@lynxltd.com
Website: www.lynxltd.com
Environmental compliance & mechanical svcs: hazardous waste mgmt, hazardous waste permit compliance, environmental training, NPDES compliance, air quality compliance, spill response, NEPA review & compliance, asbestos & lead. (Hisp, estab 1998, empl 2, sales $119,640, cert: State, City)

3288 Nation Waste Inc.
12006 Proctor St
Houston, TX 77038
Contact: Brendan Goodnough Chief mktg officer
Tel: 713-649-7776
Email: bgood@nationwaste.us
Website: www.nationwaste.us
Commercial waste disposal: Construction, Demolition, Commercial & Industrial Non-Hazardous Waste Removal, Portable Toilets & Recycling services. (Woman/Hisp, estab 1997, empl 24, sales $3,200,000, cert: State, City)

3289 RNDI Companies, Inc.
2255 Ridge Rd, Ste 216
Rockwall, TX 75087
Contact: Diana Cross President
Tel: 214-771-3977
Email: diana@rndicompanies.com
Website: http://rndicompanies.com
Environmental services: asbestos, lead, mold remediation & abatement, demolition. (Woman/Hisp, estab 2005, empl 20, sales $2,000,000, cert: State)

3290 Separation Systems Consultants, Inc.
17041 El Camino Real, Ste 200
Houston, TX 77058
Contact: Helen Hodges Presdient
Tel: 281-486-1943
Email: ssci@sscienvironmental.com
Website: www.sscienvironmental.com
Risk-based corrective action, remediation & closure, engineering & consulting, waste mgmt, petroleum storage tank, environmental site assessments, health, safety & environmental compliance audits, plans, permits & training. (Woman, estab 1986, empl 23, sales $4,000,000, cert: State, WBENC)

3291 SIA Solutions, LLC
17171 Park Row Ste 370
Houston, TX 77084
Contact: Mark Knight Program Mgr
Tel: 866-768-4625
Email: mjknight@siasolutions.com
Website: www.siasolutions.com
Environmental Consulting & Engineering • Asset Management and Energy Consulting • Environmental Remediation • Radiological Services • Hazardous, Toxic & Radioactive Waste (HTRW) Management. (As-Ind, estab 2012, empl 49, sales $2,100,000, cert: City, 8a)

3292 TGE Resources, Inc.
8048 Northcourt Rd
Houston, TX 77040
Contact: Robin Franks Presdient
Tel: 713-744-5800
Email: melanie.rivas@tgeresources.com
Website: www.tgeresources.com
Full Service Environmental and Consulting & Managment Services (Woman, estab 1994, empl 20, sales $2,360,000, cert: State, City, WBENC)

Virginia

3293 Aegis Environmental, Inc.
11511 Allecingie Pkwy
Richmond, VA 23235
Contact: Lori Bonds Presdient
Tel: 804-378-6015
Email: lbonds@aegisenv.com
Website: www.aegisenv.com
Air permitting & compliance, air dispersion modeling analyses, pollution control technology analyses, emissions estimates, environmental training & compliance, contingency planning, environmental mgmt systems dev & auditing. (Woman, estab 1996, empl 20, sales $ 0, cert: State)

3294 CMMD Enterprises, Inc.
7001 Loisdale Rd Ste C
Springfield, VA 22150
Contact: Carolyn Marina CEO
Tel: 703-646-2900
Email: carolyn.m@cmmdinc.com
Website: www.cmmdinc.com
Critical maintenance management & distribution, rotating process plant systems, wastewater treatment systems, potable water systems, chemical processes. (Woman/AA, estab 2001, empl 5, sales $483,000, cert: State, NMSDC)

3295 Environmental Waste Specialists, Inc.
4451 Brookfield Corporate Dr Ste 206
Chantilly, VA 20151
Contact: Dawn Walker Recycling Mgr
Tel: 703-502-0100
Email: dawn@ewsihazmat.com
Website: www.EWSIhazmat.com
Package, transport, dispose & recycle hazardous & non-hazardous materials. (Woman, estab 1994, empl 4, sales $1,700,000, cert: State)

3296 Froehling & Robertson, Inc.
3015 Dumbarton Rd
Richmond, VA 23228
Contact: Jackie Clingenpeel Exec Asst to the CEO
Tel: 804-264-2701
Email: jclingenpeel@fandr.com
Website: www.fandr.com
Environmental services: phase I & II ESAs, EIRs, EIS, wetland & stream delineations, hazardous materials assessments, industrial hygiene svcs, asbestos & lead testing, environmental planning, property condition assessments. (Woman/Nat Ame, estab , empl 400, sales $ 0, cert: State)

3297 INTERSPEC, LLC
464 S Independence Blvd Ste C-104
Virginia Beach, VA 23452
Contact: Sean Murphy Business Devel Dir
Tel: 757-622-6299
Email: murphys@interspecllc.net
Website: www.interspecllc.net
Tank, piping & pressure vessel inspections, STI storage tank inspections, Non-Destructive Examination/Testing steel structures, Spill Prevention Control & Countermeasure (SPCC) plans, Oil Discharge Control Plans (ODCP. (Nat Ame, estab 2001, empl 22, sales $1,200,000, cert: State, 8a)

3298 J. R. Caskey, Inc.
P.O. Box 305
Oilville, VA 23129
Contact: Ginger Caskey Presdient
Tel: 804-784-8001
Email: gec@jrcaskey.com
Website: www.jrcaskey.com
Engineering, Layout & Surveying, Clearing & Demolition, Earthwork, Grading & Excavation, Erosion & Sediment Control, Traditional Stormwater Management Systems, Low-Impact Development Systems, Underground Water & Sanitary Sewer Utilities. (Woman, estab 1985, empl 42, sales $6,630,000, cert: State)

3299 LaRock Associates, Inc.
1816 Upper James Court
Virginia Beach, VA 23454
Contact: Joan LaRock President
Tel: 202-438-1920
Email: joan.larock@verizon.net
Website:
Environmental & energy consulting, green building certification, energy efficient light bulbs. (Woman, estab 1998, empl 1, sales $138,000, cert: State)

3300 Mac-Par Services, LLC
20 B Research Dr
Hampton, VA 23666
Contact: David Parham Presdient
Tel: 866-622-7271
Email: dparham@macparservices.com
Website: www.macparservices.com
Interior demolition, material & debris hauling, lead paint & asbestos abatements, mold remediation & HVAC duct cleaning. (AA, estab 1999, empl 3, sales $370,000, cert: State)

3301 Sea Consulting Group
325 Mason Ave
Cape Charles, VA 23310
Contact: Ann Hayward Walker Presdient
Tel: 757-331-1787
Email: ahwalker@seaconsulting.com
Website: www.seaconsulting.com
Environmental consulting. (Woman/Hisp, estab 1983, empl 10, sales $ 0, cert: WBENC)

3302 Service Disabled Contracting Group, Inc.
1108 Tidwater Dr
Norfolk, VA 23504
Contact: Terry Penn Presdient
Tel: 757-965-8496
Email: tpenn@sdcgroup.net
Website: www.sdcgroup.net
Environmental Remediation/Consulting. (AA, estab 2005, empl 27, sales $16,000,000, cert: 8a)

Washington

3303 Dunkin & Bush, Inc.
P.O. Box 97080
Kirkland, WA 98083
Contact: Deidre Dunkin President
Tel: 425-885-7064
Email: ddunkin@dunkinandbush.com
Website: www.dunkinandbush.com
Industrial painting, scaffolding, insulation, rigging, containment, lead abatement, shop coating aplication, concrete restoration, plural applied tank linings, abrasive blasting, specialty blasting, water jetting, high heat coating applications. (Woman, estab 2008, empl 300, sales $ 0, cert: WBENC)

3304 EHS-International, Inc.
1011 SW Klickitat Way, Ste 104
Seattle, WA 98134
Contact: Nancy Yee Marketing
Tel: 425-455-2959
Email: nancyy@ehsintl.com
Website: www.ehsintl.com
Environmental engineering & industrial hygiene svcs: workplace & environmental health & safety, hazards identification & removal, assessments & remediation, employee training & abatement management. (Hisp, estab 1996, empl 21, sales $1,489,983, cert: State)

3305 Environmental Assessment Services, LLC
350 Hills St Ste 112
Richland, WA 99354
Contact: Brett Tiller
Tel: 509-375-4212
Email: brett.tiller@easbio.com
Website: www.easbio.com
Environmental characterization, Spill Response & Natural Resource Damage Assessments, Hazardous Waste Site Remedial Investigations, Risk Assessments, & Environmental Surveillance, Ecological Characterization & Restoration. (Nat Ame, estab 2005, empl 44, sales $2,700,000, cert: NMSDC)

3306 GeoTest Services, Inc.
741 Marine View Dr
Bellingham, WA 98225
Contact: Jeremy Wolf VP
Tel: 360-733-7318
Email: jeremyw@geotest-inc.com
Website: http://geotest-inc.com
Geotechnical engineering, environmental services, special inspection & materials testing, facilities, structures, roads, bridges & all types of infrastructure. (Woman, estab 1993, empl 33, sales $6,000,000, cert: State)

Wisconsin

3307 K. Singh & Associates, Inc.
3636 N 124th St
Wauwatosa, WI 53222
Contact: Pratap Singh CEO
Tel: 262-821-1171
Email: gmiller@ksaconsultants.com
Website: www.ksaconsultants.com
Environmental engineering & management services, transportation, structural, environmental & civil engineering, land surveying & construction management. (As-Ind, estab 1987, empl 33, sales $3,000,000, cert: State)

3308 OGC Construction, LLC
w171 n10330 Wildrose Ln
Germantown, WI 53022
Contact: Michael Owens President
Tel: 414-383-4205
Email: mowens@ogcconstruction.com
Website: www.ogcconstruction.com
Hazardous waste removal remediation, construction lead asbestos abatement. (AA, estab 2005, empl , sales $117,000, cert: NMSDC)

3309 White Glove Environmental
8326 N Stevens Rd
Milwaukee, WI 53223
Contact: London Thomas President
Tel: 414-760-1733
Email: london@wgginc.net
Website: www.wgginc.net
Environmental services, safe abatement & removal. (AA, estab 2005, empl , sales $125,000, cert: NMSDC)

3310 White Glove Group, Inc.
8326 N Stevens Rd
Milwaukee, WI 53223
Contact: Joseph Njuguna Sales Dir
Tel: 414-760-1733
Email: joe@wgginc.net
Website: www.wgenvironmental.com
Environmental services, facility maintenance, demolition, construction & demolition waste recycling program mgmt, green construction final cleaning, LEED consulting, sustainable product procurement for new construction & existing buildings. (AA, estab 2003, empl 25, sales $700,000, cert: State)

DIR Products and Services

Diversity Information Resources, Inc. (DIR) helps corporations build the best possible supplier diversity programs through verified and validated data, data management and other managed services, educational seminars and trusted print resources. Our exceptional products and services support both corporations and suppliers, facilitating the advancement of corporate diversity as a whole.

DIR's Supplier Diversity Resource Services include:

- Data Scrubbing, Validation and Reporting
- Sourcing Diverse Suppliers: Online database
- Sourcing Requests: DIR conducts specific supplier searches for upcoming opportunities, RFI's, etc.
- National Minority & Women Owned Business Directory
- The Business of Supplier Diversity: A Handbook of Essential Contacts and Information for Navigating the Industry
- Corporate Supplier Diversity Seminars: Building Strategic Phases of a Supplier Diversity Process and Best Practices in Supplier Diversity Strategies & Initiatives

Data Scrubbing and Validation

DIR's data scrubbing/validation service allows you to classify your current suppliers that fall into diverse categories and accurately analyze and report spend. Categories include: Small, Minority, Women, Veteran, Service-disabled Veteran, LGBT, HUBZone, 8a and Disability-Owned Business Enterprises. Diverse certifications are also classified. Certifications include: National Minority Supplier Development Council (NMSDC); Women Business Enterprise National Council (WBENC); Small Business Administration SDB, 8(a) and HUBZone; National LGBT Chamber of Commerce (NGLCC); State and City Agencies (DOT, Dept. of Commerce, Economic Development, etc.) DIR offers competitive pricing and quick turn-around. Contact DIR for additional information and pricing.

Sourcing Diverse Suppliers

Access to a high-quality database of certified and personally validated diverse suppliers: Small, Minority, Women, Veteran, Service-disabled Veteran, LGBT, HUBZone, 8a and Disability-Owned Business Enterprises certified by NMSDC, WBENC, NWBOC, CPUC, 8(a), NGLCC, USBLN, WEConnect, CAMSC, State and City, MSDUK and more. Monthly or annual subscriptions available. DIR can also conduct specific supplier searches for upcoming opportunities, RFI's, etc.

Corporate Supplier Diversity Seminars

DIR's sought-after educational seminars are designed to give supplier diversity professionals valuable insight they can then leverage to improve the performance of their own programs. Presented by experienced supplier diversity practitioners with world-class programs, these seminars share best practices, current trends and issues impacting supplier diversity programs today.

Client/Membership Packages Available

For more information and pricing please call DIR at (612) 781-6819 or email info@diversityinforesources.com. Business hours are M-F 8:30-4:30 CST

FOOD PRODUCTS AND SERVICES
Products include coffees, teas, bottled water, water filtration units, milk and milk products, juices, soft drinks, candies, cookies, jellies, pastries, snacks, dressings, flavorings, sauces, spices, syrups, ethnic foods, fish, seafood & prepared meats, fruits & vegetables. NAICS Code 31

Alabama

3311 The Widget Development & Trading Company, LLC
10 S Perry St
Montgomery, AL 36104
Contact: David Martin Presdient
Tel: 404-695-0141
Email: davidmartin@widgetdtc.com
Website: www.widgetdtc.com
Dist nuts, meats, sauces, baked goods. (Woman/AA, estab 2011, empl 2, sales , cert: NMSDC)

Arkansas

3312 My Brother's Salsa LLC
P.O. Box 922
Bentonville, AR 72712
Contact: Helen Lampkin Founder
Tel: 479-271-9404
Email: helen@mybrotherssalsa.com
Website: www.mybrotherssalsa.com
Produce 9 salsa varieties some available in multiple heat levels. Salsas range from smooth to textured consistencies with flavor profiles the span from earthy to smoky to sweet and savory. (Woman, estab 2003, empl 5, sales , cert: WBENC)

Arizona

3313 Sir Aubrey's Tea Company, Ltd
15941 N 77th St Ste 3
Scottsdale, AZ 85260
Contact: Kathryn Petty Presdient
Tel: 480-607-5300
Email: kpetty@whiteliontea.com
Website: http://whiteliontea.com
White Lion Tea offers a collection of rare & beautiful teas from the world's finest gardens. (Woman, estab 1998, empl 8, sales $998,470, cert: WBENC)

3314 Strategic Nutrition Alliance Brokers, LLC
1710 N Higley Road Ste 106
Mesa, AZ 85205
Contact: Ronald Coleman Managing Member
Tel: 480-299-2399
Email: sales@snabrokers.com
Website: www.snabrokers.com
Dairy Commodities, Nutritional Ingredients, sweeteners & flavors, Turn-key Private Label Contract Manufacturing services. (AA, estab 2010, empl 1, sales $250,788, cert: State)

California

3315 AG Commodties, Inc.
12815 Stevens Dr
Tustin, CA 92782
Contact: Theresa Bailey VP Business Dev
Tel: 612-839-3385
Email: ach112350@gmail.com
Website: www.agcommoditiesinc.com
Natural sweeteners & natural maltodextrins, rice maltodextrin, tapioca maltodextrin, rice syrups: brown & clarified, medium invert sugar cane syrup, clear tapioca syrups, organic sugar cane, organic glycerin, organic acacia powder, etc. (As-Ind, estab 2006, empl 10, sales $3,500,000, cert: NMSDC)

3316 American Food Ingredients, Inc.
2521 Oceanside Blvd, Ste I
Oceanside, CA 92054
Contact: Karen Koppenhaver President
Tel: 760-967-6287
Email: amerfood@aol.com
Website:
Dist dehydrated & freeze dried vegetables. (Woman/As-Pac, estab 1993, empl 15, sales , cert: State)

3317 Asiana Cusine Enterprises (ACE Sushi)
22771 S. Western Ave
Torrance, CA 90501
Contact: Gary Chin CFO
Tel: 310-327-2223
Email: gary.chin@acesushi.com
Website: www.acesushi.com
Dist Sushi. (As-Pac, estab 1998, empl 35, sales , cert: City)

3318 Bellrose, LLC
2340 Powell St, Ste 127
Emeryville, CA 94608
Contact: Onezime Biagas Jr Mgr
Tel: 925-628-1738
Email: bellrose.llc@gmail.com
Website:
Dist fresh roasted whole bean or ground coffee: bulk, pre-measured, pillow pack, k-cup. (AA, estab 2005, empl 6, sales $120,000, cert: NMSDC)

3319 Cacique, Inc.
14940 Proctor Ave
City of Industry, CA 91746
Contact: Bob Cashen Dir of Sales
Tel: 626-961-3399
Email: rcashen@caciqueinc.com
Website: www.caciqueinc.com
Mfr & dist food (dairy) products. (Hisp, estab 1973, empl 350, sales , cert: NMSDC)

3320 Carlos Steffens, Inc.
3061 Independence Dr, Ste E
Livermore, CA 94550
Contact: Carlos Steffens President
Tel: 925-838-2336
Email: carlos@steffenscorp.com
Website: www.steffenscorp.com
Industrial ingredient brokers, concentrated fruit juice products. (Hisp, estab 2000, empl 6, sales , cert: NMSDC)

3321   Creative Research Management
       P.O. Box 7843
       Stockton, CA 95267
       Contact: Cheryl R. Mitchell Presdient
       Tel: 209-598-7565
       Email: cheryl@crmcorp.net
       Website: www.crmcorp.net
Produce Sucramask™, RiceLife® Brown Rice-Milk syrups,
TherMoPectin and our line of GrainLife™ products including RiceLife® and CornLife™. (Woman, estab 2000, empl 3,
sales $5,000,000, cert: NWBOC)

3322   C-Shore International Inc.
       1010 N Central Ave
       Glendale, CA 91202
       Contact: Jacques Isaac CEO
       Tel: 818-909-4684
       Email: mirline@aol.com
       Website: www.beantrader.com
Peas, beans, lentils, pre cooked flour, bread flour, wheat
flour, dried malt extract roasted barley. (AA, estab 1988,
empl 3, sales , cert: NMSDC)

3323   Encore Fruit Marketing, Inc.
       120 W Bonita Ave, Ste 204
       San Dimas, CA 91773
       Contact: Kandi Ashcraft VP Finance
       Tel: 909-394-5640
       Email: kashcraft@encorefruit.com
       Website: www.encorefruit.com
Acai, Acerola, Agave, Apple, Apricot, Aronia, Banana,
Bilberry, Blackberry, Black Currant, Blueberry, Boysenberry,
Cherry, Cranberry, Date (domestic), Dragon Fruit, Elder-
berry, Fig, Gac Fruit, Goji Berry, Grape, etc. (Woman, estab
1989, empl 15, sales $16,050,000, cert: WBENC)

3324   F. Gavina & Sons, Inc.
       2700 Fruitland Ave
       Vernon, CA 90058
       Contact: Tiffany Masterson Exec Admin
       Tel: 323-582-0671
       Email: tiffany.masterson@gavina.com
       Website: www.gavina.com
Coffee roasting, new blend development or matching of
your current blend, brand & marketing support, brewing &
espresso service & training. (Hisp, estab 1967, empl 265,
sales $127,485,828, cert: NMSDC)

3325   Frieda's Inc.
       4465 Corporate Center Dr
       Los Alamitos, CA 90720
       Contact: Karen Caplan CEO
       Tel: 714-826-6100
       Email: karen.caplan@friedas.com
       Website: www.friedas.com
Specialty Fruits (including Fresh Tropicals and Dried Fruits),
Specialty Vegetables (including cooking vegetables and
leafy greens), Hispanic Fruits & Vegetables (including fresh
& dried chile peppers), Asian Fruits & Vegetables.
(Woman, estab 1962, empl 75, sales $46,000,000, cert:
WBENC)

3326   Fusion Ranch, Inc. dba Fusion Jerky
       405 S Airport Blvd
       South San Francisco, CA 94080
       Contact: Kaiyen Mai CEO
       Tel: 650-589-8899
       Email: kaiyen@fusionranch.com
       Website: http://fusionjerky.com
Jerky, Sausage, Ham, Shredded Pork. (Woman/As-Pac,
estab 2014, empl 46, sales , cert: NMSDC, WBENC)

3327   Got Broccoli, Inc.
       6201 Progressive Ave Ste 400
       San Diego, CA 92154
       Contact: Art Sanchez Director
       Tel: 619-661-0909
       Email: art@gotbroccoli.com
       Website: http://frugo.com.mx
IQF Vegetables, Asparagus, Broccoli, Cauliflower, Celery,
Cucumber, Jalapeno, Spinach, Kale. (Hisp, estab 2010,
empl , sales $10,000,000, cert: NMSDC)

3328   Kruger Foods Inc.
       18362 E Hwy 4
       Stockton, CA 95215
       Contact: Kara Kruger CEO
       Tel: 209-941-8518
       Email: k.kruger@krugerfoods.com
       Website: www.krugerfoods.com
Pickles, Sweet Pickle Relish, Dill Pickle Relish, Hot Pepper
Relish, Jalapeno Peppers (sliced, diced, whole), Banana
Wax Peppers, Peppers, Giardinera. (Woman, estab 1930,
empl 158, sales $65,400,000, cert: WBENC)

3329   Laxmi's Delights
       98 Brevensville Dr
       San Ramon, CA 94583
       Contact: Laxmi Hiremath Owner
       Tel: 925-833-0115
       Email: laxmihiremath@gmail.com
       Website: www.laxmisdelights.com
Organic flaxseed spreads. (Woman/As-Ind, estab 2000,
empl 1, sales $100,000, cert: WBENC)

3330   National Raisin Company
       P.O. Box 219
       Fowler, CA 93625
       Contact: Joe Leon VP Business Dev
       Tel: 559-834-5981
       Email: jleon@nationalraisin.com
       Website: www.nationalraisin.com
High industrial specifications for confection, cereal &
baking, using the California grown Natural Seedless
Select and Small raisins, sugar coated raisins, glycerin
infused raisins, juice concentrates, pastes and purees.
(Woman, estab 1969, empl 450, sales , cert: WBENC,
NWBOC)

3331   NC Moving & Storage Solutions
       3146 Corporate Pl
       Hayward, CA 94545
       Contact: Johanna Lobation Business Develop Mgr
       Tel: 510-385-4441
       Email: jlobaton@ncmss.com
       Website: www.ncmss.com
NC Moving & Storage Solutions is a full service household goods provider for both domestic and international
moving services. We are an agent for North American
Van Lines. (Woman/As-Pac, estab 2006, empl 19, sales
$1,165,000, cert: NMSDC, CPUC, WBENC)

3332   P.S. Let's Eat Inc.
       3943 Irvine Blvd, Ste 610
       Irvine, CA 92602
       Contact: Preya Patel Bhakta President
       Tel: 855-998-3554
       Email: preya@elliquark.com
       Website: www.elliquark.com
Produce German style Quark products. (Woman/As-Pac,
estab 2011, empl 2, sales , cert: WBENC)

3333   Peas of Mind LLC
       2339 3rd St Unit 53-3R
       San Francisco, CA 94107
       Contact: Jill Litwin CEO
       Tel: 415-504-2556
       Email: jill@peasofmind.com
       Website: www.peasofmind.com
Mfr healthy eating options. (Woman, estab 2005, empl 4, sales $2,800,000, cert: WBENC)

3334   Planet Popcorn, Inc.
       1616 E Wilshire Ave
       Santa Ana, CA 92705
       Contact: Sharla Gandy-Caldaronello CEO
       Tel: 949-278-1312
       Email: sharla@planetpopcorn.com
       Website: www.planetpopcorn.com
Hand-crafted gourmet popcorn. (Woman, estab 2005, empl 23, sales $2,009,000, cert: WBENC)

3335   Somax Inc.
       339 S Notre Dame Ave
       Orange, CA 92869
       Contact: Grace Knight Owner
       Tel: 714-633-6614
       Email: graceknight@sanluissausage.com
       Website: http://sanluissausage.com
Healthy, preservative free pork & chicken gourmet sausages. (Woman, estab 1991, empl 2, sales $2,200,286, cert: WBENC, NWBOC)

3336   The French Patisserie
       1080 Palmetto Ave
       Pacifica, CA 94044
       Contact: Sales Support
       Tel: 650-738-4990
       Email:
       Website: http://frenchpatisserie.com
Mfr gourmet frozen desserts: macarons, individual mousse cakes, tarts, petits fours, cakes and briques. (Woman, estab 1989, empl 130, sales $8,200,000, cert: WBENC)

3337   Valley Lahvosh Baking Co.
       502 M St
       Fresno, CA 93721
       Contact: Lori Miller President & CEO
       Tel: 559-485-2700
       Email: customerservice@valleylahvosh.com
       Website: www.valleylahvosh.com
Mfr valley lahvosh crackerbreads & pita breads. (Woman, estab , empl , sales $8,578,874, cert: WBENC)

3338   Zego LLC
       912 Cole St, Ste 294
       San Francisco, CA 94117
       Contact: CEO
       Tel: 415-622-8115
       Email:
       Website: http://zegofoods.com
Mfr & dist Oats, Muesli, Sacha Inchi Protein Powder, Nutrition Bars, and Mix-Ins Trail Mix all free of the top 12 most common allergens and gluten. (Woman, estab 2013, empl 3, sales $410,000, cert: WBENC)

Colorado

3339   All American Seasonings, Inc.
       10600 E 54th Ave, Unit B & C
       Denver, CO 80239
       Contact: Andy Rodriguez President
       Tel: 303-623-2320
       Email: andyr@allamericanseasonings.com
       Website: www.allamericanseasonings.com
Custom blenders of food ingredients. (Hisp, estab 1968, empl 40, sales $18,000,000, cert: NMSDC)

3340   Mona's Granola and Cookies, Inc.
       651 Eldorado
       Broomfield, CO 80021
       Contact: Mona Gale CEO
       Tel: 727-420-0707
       Email: mona@monasinc.com
       Website: www.monasinc.com
All natural no white sugar nutrient rich granola cereal & ice cream toppings. (Woman, estab 1981, empl 27, sales $600,000, cert: WBENC)

Connecticut

3341   Aurora Product Inc.
       205 Edison Road
       Orange, CT 06477
       Contact: Stephanie Blackwell Business Devel
       Tel: 203-375-9956
       Email: sblackwell@auroraproduct.com
       Website: www.auroranatural.com
Natural & organic snacks: almonds, cashews, mixed nuts & peanuts, salted, unsalted & raw, dried fruits. (Woman, estab 1998, empl 225, sales $60,000,000, cert: WBENC)

3342   Carla's Pasta, Inc.
       50 Talbot Lane
       South Windsor, CT 06074
       Contact: Sandro Squatrito VP Business Dev
       Tel: 860-436-4042
       Email: abiel@carlaspasta.com
       Website: www.carlaspasta.com
Produce pasta & pesto products, Cheeseburger Ravioli, Buffalo Chicken Ravioli & Stromboli Ravioli. (Woman, estab 1978, empl 182, sales , cert: NWBOC)

3343   Frescobene Foods, LLC
       120 Treasure Rd
       Fairfield, CT 06824
       Contact: Ann Marie Riffice Co-Founder
       Tel: 203-610-4688
       Email: orders@frescobene.com
       Website: www.frescobene.com
Dist super premium, frozen artisan sauces in heat and serve pouches for peak freshness and utmost convenience. Marinara (vegan), Vodka Sauce (vegetarian), Amatriciana (pancetta based). (Woman, estab 2015, empl 2, sales , cert: WBENC)

3344   Gelato Giuliana, LLC
       240 Sargent Dr
       New Haven, CT 06511
       Contact: Deborah Cairo Mktg
       Tel: 203-772-0607
       Email: dcbottega@sbcglobal.net
       Website: www.gelatogiuliana.com
Mfr & dist gelato under our label Gelato Giuliana. (Woman, estab 2006, empl 10, sales $882,662, cert: State)

3345 Heidi's Real Food LLC
47 Hillside Rd
Greenwich, CT 06830
Contact: Heidi Matonis Owner
Tel: 203-219-4202
Email: heidi@heidisrealfood.com
Website: www.heidisrealfood.com
Heidi's Meatless "Meat"balls also available in bulk for food service and prepared foods. (Woman, estab 2013, empl 1, sales , cert: WBENC)

3346 The Bites Company
P.O. Box 122
Westport, CT 06881
Contact: Dina Upton Owner
Tel: 203-296-2482
Email: sales@thebitescompany.com
Website: http://thebitescompany.com
All natural, round, bite size pieces of Biscotti in 5 flavors; almond, orange, lemon, cocoa & coffee. (Woman, estab 2011, empl 1, sales , cert: State)

District of Columbia

3347 Hard Light Consulting Group
2119 First St NW
Washington, DC 20001
Contact: Don Smith Exec VP
Tel: 202-232-0355
Email: don@hlcg.biz
Website:
Dist imported sugars & fruits. (Woman/AA, estab 2002, empl 2, sales , cert: City)

3348 Tribes-A-Dozen, LLC
P.O. Box 42063
Washington, DC 20015
Contact: Leah Hadad Presdient
Tel: 202-684-8256
Email: leah@tribesadozen.com
Website: http://tribesadozen.com
Mfr three all-natural & kosher (OU) Voil! Hallah Egg Bread Mixes: Traditional, Wholey Wheat & Simply Spelt. (Woman, estab 2012, empl 1, sales , cert: WBENC)

3349 Village Tea Company Distribution Inc.
1342 Florida Ave., NW Ste 225-B
Washington, DC 20009
Contact: Janon Costley CEO
Tel: 888-406-1138
Email: janon@villageteaco.com
Website: www.villageteaco.com
100% organic & natural tea in biodegradable packaging, foodservice tea, bulk tea, tea dispensers, tea machines, packaged tea, tea in bags, loose leaf tea, loose tea, organic tea, natural tea. (AA, estab 2008, empl , sales $125,000, cert: NMSDC)

Florida

3350 Base Culture LLC
4509 George Rd
Tampa, FL 33634
Contact: CEO
Tel: 727-667-5086
Email:
Website: www.baseculture.com
Natural, gluten free bakery that provides paleo baked goods and snacks to wholesale and distributor accounts nation wide. Our products are shipped, stored and sold frozen. (Woman, estab 2012, empl 7, sales , cert: WBENC)

3351 Brisk/RCR Coffee Company
507 N. 22nd St
Tampa, FL 33605
Contact: Richard Perez CEO
Tel: 813-248-6264
Email: customer@briskcoffee.com
Website: www.briskcoffee.com
Coffee importing, roasting, grinding, packaging & shipping. (Hisp, estab 1968, empl 30, sales , cert: State)

3352 COEX Coffee International Inc.
525 NW 27th Ave
Miami, FL 33125
Contact: Robert Menos Sr Trader
Tel: 305-459-5180
Email: lmones@coexgroup.com
Website: www.coexgroup.com
Coffee trading, importing green coffee from all major global coffee producing countries. (Hisp, estab 1980, empl 45, sales $415,000,000, cert: NMSDC)

3353 Delina Inc.
1068 Pine Branch Dr
Weston, FL 33326
Contact: President
Tel: 954-306-0628
Email:
Website: www.delinainc.com
Dist asparagus spears, green pickled asparagus spears, cornichons, roasted red peppers, artichoke hearts, hearts of palm & organic coffee. (Woman/Hisp, estab 1998, empl 2, sales , cert: City)

3354 Emerald Cove Gourmet Products,Inc.
P.O. Box 380
Shalimar, FL 32579
Contact: CEO
Tel: 850-651-4216
Email:
Website: www.susansmarinade.com
Mfr & dist gourmet marinade sauces for meats, poultry, fish & seafood. (Woman, estab 1992, empl 1, sales , cert: WBENC)

3355 GFIS
2525 Ponce de Leon Blvd Ste 300
Coral Gables, FL 33134
Contact: Andrea Cordova Mgr
Tel: 305-521-9094
Email: acordova@foodingredientsolution.com
Website: http://foodingredientsolution.com
Frozen, Aseptic, No pasteurized, Unpasteurized, IQF, Fruitm Vegetables, Puree, Juice, Concentrate, NFC, Single Straight, Organic, Conventional, Acai, Acerola, Apple, Blackberry, Blueberry, Cherry, Grapefruit, Guava, Kiwi, Lemon, Lime, Mango, and more. (Woman/Hisp, estab 2016, empl 4, sales $1,500,000, cert: State)

3356 Henry Roberts BBQ Sauce
2001 Art Museum Dr
Jacksonville, FL 32207
Contact: Anthony Ammons VP
Tel: 904-591-8102
Email: anthony.ammons@gmail.com
Website: http://HenryRoberts.com
Bottle & distribute barbecue sauce & chow chow. (Woman/AA, estab 1985, empl 4, sales $160,000, cert: City)

3357 M&G Expresso, Inc
13311 SW 132 Ave, Unit 3
Miami, FL 33186
Contact: Gabriel Cortina VP
Tel: 786-200-9802
Email: mgexpressinc@gmail.com
Website: www.ladybeehoney.net
Dist Lady Bee Honey. (Woman/Hisp, estab 2009, empl 3, sales , cert: NMSDC)

3358 MH Food Group LLC
1800 Sunset Harbour Dr, Ste P
Miami Beach, FL 33139
Contact: Calvin Harris Presdient
Tel: 954-501-6215
Email: charris@mhfoodgroup.com
Website: www.mhfoodgroup.com
Pack & dist frozen fruit & industrial food ingredients. (Woman/Hisp, estab 2014, empl 4, sales $1,000,000, cert: NMSDC)

3359 Quirch Foods Co.
2701 S. LeJeune Rd.
Miami, FL 33134
Contact: Elijah Davis Natl Acct Sales Mgr
Tel: 305-691-3535
Email: elijah.davis@quirchfoods.com
Website: www.quirchfoods.com
Dist & export meat & seafood. (Hisp, estab 1967, empl 500, sales $747,373,931, cert: NMSDC)

3360 Sweet Additions, Inc.
4440 PGA Blvd, Ste 600
Palm Beach Gardens, FL 33410
Contact: Ken Valdivia President
Tel: 561-472-0178
Email: kvaldivia@sweetadditions.com
Mfr & dist cane & grain based sweeteners. (Hisp, estab 2004, empl 3, sales $5,000,000, cert: NMSDC)

3361 The Best Direct Marketing Group LLC
250 N Orange Ave Ste 990
Orlando, FL 32801
Contact: Latif Qadri
Tel: 407-730-6569
Email: latif@bestdirectgroup.com
Website: www.bestdirectgroup.com
Direct mail & staffed event company that can fulfill all print needs ad creative design. (As-Ind, estab 2012, empl 4, sales $112,000, cert: NMSDC)

Georgia

3362 82's, LLC
1475 Buford Dr Ste 403-227
Lawrenceville, GA 30043
Contact: Reginald Kelly Owner
Tel: 770-402-2226
Email: contact@kyvan82.com
Website: www.kyvan82.com
All Natural Honey Apple Salsa (Hot & Mild), Sesame Garlic BBQ Sauce, Sweet BBQ Sauce, Hot Sauce. (AA, estab 2008, empl 7, sales $100,000, cert: NMSDC)

3363 Diaz Foods
5501 Fulton Industrial Blvd SW
Atlanta, GA 30336
Contact: Jorge Antona EVP
Tel: 404-344-5421
Email: jorge.antona@diazfoods.com
Website: www.diazfoods.com
Hispanic grocery distributor, grocery, frozen, dairy, meats & produce. (Hisp, estab 1980, empl 323, sales $168,000,000, cert: NMSDC)

3364 Fire & Flavor Grilling Co.
1160 S Milledge Ave, Ste 230
Athens, GA 30605
Contact: Davis Knox CEO
Tel: 706-369-9466
Email: davis@fireandflavor.com
Website: www.fireandflavor.com
Dist spices, seasonings, sauces, brines, grilling planks, wood chips, charcoal & fire starters. (Woman, estab 2003, empl 6, sales $5,000,000, cert: WBENC)

3365 H. Walker Enterprises, LLC
22 E Montgomery Crossroads
Savannah, GA 31406
Contact: Herschel Walker CEO
Tel: 912-961-0002
Email: hwrmi34@aol.com
Website: www.34promotions.com
Mfr & dist poultry, beef & pork food products. (AA, estab 2002, empl 4, sales , cert: NMSDC)

3366 JCPG LLC DBA Popbar
4573 Bogan Meadows Ct
Buford, GA 30519
Contact: Charel Palmer Owner
Tel: 678-783-9688
Email: alpharetta@pop-bar.com
Website: www.pop-bar.com
Hand crafted, all natural and preservative free gelato, yogurt, vegan gelato and sorbet in a new way, on a stick! With 5 chocolate dippings. (AA, estab 2017, empl 15, sales $200,000, cert: NMSDC)

3367 Seeds of Nature, LLC
1456 Lechemin Dr
Snellville, GA 30078
Contact: Patricia Nowell Managing Member
Tel: 877-277-9260
Email: pnowell@prodigy.net
Website: www.seedsofnature.com
Premium Cocoa Beans sourced from Ivory Coast, Nigeria & Ghana. (Woman/AA, estab 2009, empl 3, sales $300,000, cert: NMSDC)

Iowa

3368 Young G's Barbecue Sauce, LLC
8211 Brookview Dr.
Urbandale, IA 50322
Contact: Gerald Young Presdient
Tel: 515-331-8001
Email: youngsbbq@gmail.com
Website: http://ygsbbq.com
Young G's is a gluten free low sodium content with no high fructose corn syrup. (AA, estab 2010, empl 1, sales , cert: NMSDC)

Illinois

3369 Baldwin Richardson Foods Co.
One Tower Lane Ste 2390
Oakbrook Terrace, IL 60181
Contact: Cara Hughes Dir of Sales & Marketing
Tel: 630-607-1780
Email: chughes@brfoods.com
Website: www.brfoods.com
Mfr custom sauces, condiments, syrups, toppings & fillings. (AA, estab 1997, empl 287, sales , cert: NMSDC)

3370 Bell Marketing, Inc.
10135 S Roberts Rd
Palos Hills, IL 60465
Contact: Mary Ann Bell President
Tel: 708-598-8873
Email: maryann@bellmarketing.com
Website: www.bellmarketing.com
Fruit concentrates, purees, puree concentrates IQF frozen fruit, all natural colors from fruit & vegetable juice concentrates, extracts, ice cream inclusions. (Woman, estab 1986, empl 5, sales $10,000,000, cert: WBENC)

3371 CBC Sales, Inc.
5117 S Normandy Ave
Chicago, IL 60638
Contact: Desiree Alonzo Presdient
Tel: 773-218-9563
Email: desiree@cbcsalesinc.com
Website: www.cicerobloodymary.com
Gourmet beverages, Craft Sodas & Bloody Mary Mixes, Salted Caramel Root beer, Bacon Bloody Mary Mix. (Woman, estab 2008, empl 1, sales $400,000, cert: WBENC)

3372 Chapin LLC
1350 N Wells St Ste F109
Chicago, IL 60610
Contact: Jennifer Alexander Monzón
Tel: 312-493-6976
Email: jennifer@chapincoffee.com
Website: www.ChapinCoffee.com
Specialty coffee, whole bean, ground & single serve (k-cup). (Hisp, estab 2013, empl 2, sales , cert: NMSDC)

3373 Compact Industries
3945 Ohio Ave
St Charles, IL 60174
Contact: Dan Matyus VP bus dev
Tel: 630-513-9600
Email: matyus@compactind.com
Website: www.compactind.com
Contract manufacturer of dry food products. (Woman, estab 1963, empl 120, sales $98,000,000, cert: WBENC)

3374 Cornfields, Inc.
3898 Sunset Ave
Waukegan, IL 60087
Contact: JB Weiler VP Sales
Tel: 847-263-7000
Email: info@cornfieldsinc.com
Website: www.cornfieldsinc.com
Mfr natural & organic snacks. (Woman, estab 1991, empl 60, sales $12,000,000, cert: WBENC)

3375 Cristina Foods, Inc.
4555 S Racine Ave
Chicago, IL 60609
Contact: Cesar Dovalina Presdient
Tel: 312-829-0360
Email: cdovalina@cristinafoods.com
Website: www.cristinafoods.com
Dist fresh produce, frozen foods, spices, grocery & canned goods, meats, dairy, poultry, seafood, disposable paper & plastics. (Hisp, estab 1989, empl 42, sales $21,750,000, cert: NMSDC)

3376 DAMRON Corporation
4433 W Ohio St
Chicago, IL 60624
Contact: Amariah Bradford Marketing Media Specialist
Tel: 773-826-6000
Email: amariahbradford@damroncorp.com
Website: www.damroncorp.com
Healing Tea Leaves of the World brand of Specialty Tea - 25 ct. teabag cartons (25% more than National Brands), quality fully equal to or better than National Brands. (AA, estab 1985, empl 50, sales $5,800,000, cert: City, NMSDC)

3377 Frey Produce
RR 1 Box 89
Keenes, IL 62851
Contact: Renee Mattingly VP Sales/Mktg
Tel: 618-835-2536
Email: reneemattingly@freyproduce.com
Website: www.freyproduce.com
Grow, pack & dist fresh fruits & vegetables: watermelons, cantaloupe, green bell peppers, sweet corn, pumpkins, squash, soybeans, wheat. (Woman, estab 1996, empl 20, sales $50,000,000, cert: WBENC)

3378 Harris Ice Company
3927 W 5th Ave
Chicago, IL 60624
Contact: Walker Harris Presdient
Tel: 773-826-3110
Email: harrisice1@sbcglobal.net
Website: http://harrisicechicago.com
Harris Ice Company manufactures and delivers ice throughtout the City of Chicago and surrounding suburbs. (AA, estab 1970, empl 15, sales $1,423,175, cert: City, NMSDC)

3379 Jakpan Enterprises, Inc.
41 Northfiled Terrace
Wheeling, IL 60090
Contact: harold triche Presdient
Tel: 312-925-5289
Email: haroldtriche@yahoo.com
Website:
Snack foods: package peanuts & dry fruit. (AA, estab 2001, empl 4, sales $150,000, cert: NMSDC)

3380 Mullins Food Products, Inc.
2200 S 25th Ave
Broadview, IL 60155
Contact: Andy Camp Dir of Sales
Tel: 708-344-3224
Email: acamp@mullinsfood.com
Website: www.mullinsfood.com
Custom mfr & package liquid condiments: sauces, salad dressings, ketchup, mayonnaise, picante sauce, salsa sauce, pizza sauce, asian style sauces, flavored syrups, icing. (Woman, estab 1934, empl 350, sales , cert: WBENC)

3381 Navisource Holdings LLC dba Golden Hill Foods LLC
851 W Grand Ave 2nd Fl
Chicago, IL 60642
Contact: Demetrio Garcia VP Business Dev
Tel: 312-226-5900
Email: dgarcia@goldenhillfoods.com
Website: www.goldenhillfoods.com
Import & dist dehydrated vegetables & spices. (Hisp, estab 2005, empl 6, sales $2,500,000, cert: NMSDC)

3382   Reggios' Pizza, Inc.
340 W 83rd St
Chicago, IL 60620
Contact: Darryl Humphrey Sales & Marketing Dir
Tel: 773-488-1411
Email: dhumphrey@reggiospizzainc.com
Website: www.reggios.com
Chicago Style Famous Buttercrust Pizza. (AA, estab 1972, empl 42, sales , cert: City)

3383   Stern Ingredients, Inc.
1030 N State St #10BC
Chicago, IL 60610
Contact: Joni Stern Presdient
Tel: 773-472-0301
Email: joni@sterningredients.com
Website: www.sterningredients.com
Dist ingredients: confectionery, bakery, nutritional & snack food products. (Woman, estab 1990, empl 2, sales $434,255, cert: WBENC)

3384   Subco Foods
1150 Commerce Dr
West Chicago, IL 60185
Contact: Mas Khan President & CEO
Tel: 630-231-0003
Email: mkhan@subcofoods.com
Website: www.subcofoods.com
Dist dry food products: randed, private label & contract packaging, drink mixes, gelatin & puddings, coffee creamer, hot chocolate, cappuccino, cake mixes, gravy mixes, seasonings, pancake mixes, soup bases, rice products, nutraceuticals. (As-Ind, estab 1994, empl 150, sales , cert: NMSDC)

3385   Sulpice Better Bites
P.O. Box 70
Barrington, IL 60011
Contact: Anne Shaeffer Founder
Tel: 630-301-2345
Email: anne@sulpicechocolat.com
Website: www.sulpicechocolat.com
Milk chocolate with salt and almonds; dark chocolate with cinnamon and cayenne pepper; dark chocolate with ginger and lemon; 70% dark chocolate with sea salt; white chocolate with cake batter. (Woman, estab 2009, empl 2, sales $300,000, cert: WBENC)

3386   Suzy's Swirl
703 Rockland Rd
Lake Bluff, IL 60044
Contact: Founder
Tel: 224-544-5189
Email:
Website: http://suzysswirl.com
Frozen desserts, liquor-infused frozen yogurts and sorbets. (Woman, estab 2012, empl 8, sales $350,000, cert: WBENC)

3387   The Edlong Corporation
225 Scott St
Elk Grove Village, IL 60007
Contact: Gail Scott Exec Asst
Tel: 847-631-6775
Email: diversity@edlong.com
Website: www.edlong.com
Dairy: cheese, butter, milk & cream, cultured, sweet & functional dairy. (Woman, estab 1914, empl 100, sales , cert: WBENC)

3388   Thomas Imports LLC
1327 W. Washington BLVD Ste 3D
Chicago, IL 60607
Contact: Chris Cottrell Sales
Tel: 312-929-2699
Email: ccottrell@isiahinternational.com
Website: www.isiahimports.com
Corn tortillas, flour tortillas, flavored tortilla flour wraps; jalapeno wrap, tomato basil wrap, chipotle wrap, roasted garlic wrap, cheese, wraps corn chips, spices, chile peppers, canned sauces, frozen foods. (AA, estab 2016, empl 8, sales , cert: NMSDC)

3389   V&V Supremo Foods Inc.
2141 S Throop St
Chicago, IL 60608
Contact: John Brandley Natl Sales Mgr
Tel: 312-421-1020
Email: johnb@vvsupremo.com
Website: http://vvsupremo.com
Produce Hispanic cheese, creams & Chorizo. (Hisp, estab 1964, empl 184, sales $67,142,000, cert: NMSDC)

Indiana

3390   Williams, West & Witt's Product Co.
3501 W Dunes Hwy
Michigan City, IN 46360
Contact: Joanne Tica Steiger Natl Dir Business Development
Tel: 219-879-8236
Email: jtsteiger@integrativeflavors.com
Website: www.cooksdelight.com
Mfr healthy soup bases & innovative food flavor additives for the institutional, food service, corporate and government user channels. (Woman, estab 1938, empl 19, sales $2,500,000, cert: State, WBENC)

Louisiana

3391   Bridge Foods, Inc.
P.O. Box 58698
New Orleans, LA 70158
Contact: Henry Chigbu President
Tel: 504-254-9770
Email: hchigbu@bridgefoods.com
Website: www.ashantifoods.com
Condiments: hot sauce, wing sauce, steak sauce, worcestershire sauce, etc. (AA, estab 1993, empl 5, sales $15,000,000, cert: NMSDC)

Massachusetts

3392   600 lb Gorillas, Inc.
558 Washington St
Duxbury, MA 02332
Contact: Paula White CEO
Tel: 781-452-7273
Email: paula@600lbgorillas.com
Website: www.600lbgorillas.com
Dist premium frozen cookie dough. (Woman, estab 2000, empl 2, sales $3,000,000, cert: WBENC)

3393 Adonai Spring Water Inc.
      31 West St, Ste 4
      Randolph, MA 02368
      Contact: Gloria Olatunji Presdient
      Tel: 844-273-7672
      Email: gloolat@aol.com
      Website: www.adonaisprings.com
Bottled water 5 Gallons, Bottled Water Coolers, Point of
Use Coolers, Drinking Water Fountains, Biodegradable &
Compostable hot and cold cups, lids, straws, trays, nap-
kins, plates, trays clamshells.Woman/AA, estab 2014, empl
2, sales , cert: State, WBENC)

3394 Boston Baking, Inc.
      101 Sprague St
      Boston, MA 02136
      Contact: Julee Robey-Boschetto Presdient
      Tel: 617-364-6900
      Email: julee@bostonbaking.com
      Website: www.bostonbaking.com
Wholesale manufacturer of baked goods. (Woman, estab
2004, empl 54, sales $4,900,000, cert: City)

3395 Cape Cod Select LLC
      73 Tremont St
      Carver, MA 02330
      Contact: Cindy Rhodes Owner
      Tel: 508-866-1149
      Email: crhodes@capecodselect.com
      Website: www.capecodselect.com
Harvest, pack & dist cranberries. (Woman, estab 2009,
empl 3, sales , cert: WBENC)

3396 Harbar LLC
      320 Turnpike St
      Canton, MA 02021
      Contact: Keith Brennan Retail Sales Mgr
      Tel: 800-881-7040
      Email: kbrennan@harbar.com
      Website: www.harbar.com
Mfr corn & flour tortillas. (Woman/Hisp, estab 1986, empl
140, sales , cert: NMSDC)

3397 HimalaSalt - Sustainable Sourcing, LLC
      1375 Boardman St
      Sheffield, MA 01257
      Contact: melissa kushi CEO
      Tel: 413-446-8927
      Email: melissa@himalasalt.com
      Website: www.himalasalt.com
Dist pink Himalayan sea salt produced in our owned facility
that is certified organic, Non-GMO, Gluten-Free, Kosher for
Passover & powered by 156 solar panels. (Woman, estab
2006, empl 12, sales $2,500,000, cert: State)

3398 Jensay Co.
      61 Maple St
      Acton, MA 10720
      Contact: Stephen Chen Presdient
      Tel: 978-929-9797
      Email: stephenchen@joycechenfoods.com
      Website: www.joycechenfoods.com
Asian, Chinese cooking sauces, oils, comdiments, spices &
Asian frozen prepared food products. (As-Pac, estab 2006,
empl , sales $950,000, cert: State)

3399 Monsoon Kitchens, Inc.
      165 Memorial Dr Unit F
      Shrewsbury, MA 01545
      Contact: Presdient
      Tel: 508-842-0070
      Email:
      Website: www.monsoonkitchens.com
Mfr Indian style frozen chicken entrees, vegetarian
entress & appetizers. (As-Ind, estab 2003, empl 6, sales
$5,000,000, cert: NMSDC)

3400 R Square Desserts LLC
      P.O. Box 990031
      Boston, MA 02199
      Contact: Susie Parish Co-Owner
      Tel: 857-263-8833
      Email: susie@batchicecream.com
      Website: www.batchicecream.com
Ice cream made from real ingredients & without additives. (Woman, estab 2009, empl 5, sales , cert: WBENC)

3401 Signature Breads, Inc.
      100 Justin Dr
      Chelsea, MA 02150
      Contact: Heidi Keathley VP Sales/Mktg
      Tel: 617-819-3105
      Email: heidi.keathley@signaturebreads.com
      Website: www.signaturebreads.com
Mfr par-baked breads: dinner rolls, sandwich rolls,
baguettes, ciabattas, breadsticks, pieggas & artisan
breads, individual & bulk packaging, frozen or par-baked.
(Hisp, estab 2006, empl 280, sales $48,000,000, cert:
NMSDC)

3402 SJB Bagel Makers of Boston
      77 Rowe St
      Newton, MA 02466
      Contact: Jeff Malich Dir of Sales
      Tel: 617-213-8400
      Email: jeff@finagleonline.com
      Website: www.finagleabagel.com/
Artisan all natural bagel baker. We product 2 oz - 5 oz
premium bagels. (Woman, estab 1992, empl 130, sales
$12,000,000, cert: State, WBENC)

3403 VSR Enterprise, LLC
      1675 Dorchester Ave
      Boston, MA 02121
      Contact: Vernon Barsatee CEO
      Tel: 617-514-4711
      Email: vernon@vsrenterprise.com
      Website: http://vsrenterprise.com
Food Brokerage, Import & Export of consumer sized
packaged (CPG), frozen foods, spices, dairy products,
meats, health & beauty aids. (As-Pac, estab 2012, empl
2, sales , cert: NMSDC)

Maryland

3404 Better and Best Corporation
      1601 Knecht Ave
      Halethorpe, MD 21227
      Contact: Patricia Lobel President
      Tel: 410-902-5701
      Email: patricia.lobel@avenuegourmet.com
      Website: www.avenuegourmet.com
Dist natural/organic products: sauces, marinades, fruit
butters & spreads, cookies, crackers, cooking oils,
vinegars, snacks, condiments & beverages. (Woman,
estab 2000, empl 20, sales , cert: State)

3405   Caribbean Blue Organic Foods, LLC
         6701 Democracy Blvd Ste 300
         Bethesda, MD 20817
         Contact: Lenore Travers Presdient
         Tel: 301-564-4322
         Email: sales@caribbeanbluewater.com
         Website: http://CaribbeanBlueWater.com
Caribbean Blue Natural Spring Water. (AA, estab 2011,
empl 1, sales $185,000, cert: State)

3406   CharmedBar, LLC
         120 Canfield Hill Dr
         Gaithersburg, MD 20878
         Contact: Debbi Ascher Presdient
         Tel: 202-430-5637
         Email: debbi@charmedbar.com
         Website: www.charmedbar.com
CharmedBars are kosher, baked fruit & nut bars (nutrition/
energy bars) that are certified gluten free and free of
grains, dairy, soy, egg, refined sugars, GMOs, preservatives
& artificial ingredients. (Woman, estab 2013, empl 2, sales
$188,000, cert: WBENC)

3407   Collaborative Food & Beverage, LLC (DBA Mayorga
         Coffee)
         15151 Southlawn Ln
         Rockville, MD 20850
         Contact: Martin Mayorga Presdient
         Tel: 301-315-8093
         Email: martin@mayorgacoffee.com
         Website: www.mayorgacoffee.com
Roasted whole bean specialty coffees, ground "portion
packed" specialty coffees, custom blends, private labeling.
(Woman/Hisp, estab 1997, empl 87, sales $17,500,000,
cert: State)

3408   Demeter's Pantry (dba): GreenFood Associates LLC
         419 Greenbrier Dr
         Silver Spring, MD 20910
         Contact: Maria Kardamaki Robertson Managing
         Partner
         Tel: 301-587-0048
         Email: maria@demeterspantry.com
         Website: www.thegreektable.net
Dist ethnic foods, Mediterranean (Greek prepared foods,
entrées, side dishes & bean salad dishes. (Woman, estab
2003, empl 2, sales $490,058, cert: State)

3409   MAS Foods International, LLC
         P.O. Box 2886
         Montgomery Village, MD 20886
         Contact: Michael Short Chief Managing officer
         Tel: 301-591-9728
         Email: mshort@masfi.com
         Website: www.masfi.com
Gourmet chicken sausage & personal chicken pizza made
from halal products. (AA, estab 2004, empl 2, sales , cert:
NMSDC)

3410   SoFine Food
         4825 Cordell Ave, Ste 200
         Bethesda, MD 20814
         Contact: Sophia Maroon CEO
         Tel: 301-979-9555
         Email: sophia@sofinefood.com
         Website: www.dressitupdressing.com
Produce all-natural, shelf-stable vinaigrettes, called Dress
It Up Dressing, gluten-free, sugar-free & vegan. (Woman,
estab 2012, empl 2, sales , cert: WBENC)

3411   Soft Stuff Distributors, Inc.
         8200 Preston Court Ste L
         Jessup, MD 20794
         Contact: Lois Gamerman President & CEO
         Tel: 301-604-3300
         Email: loisg@gosoftstuff.com
         Website: www.gosoftstuff.com
Dist breads, bagels, cakes, cheesecakes, muffin batters &
baked muffins, frozen doughs, preproofed danish &
croisants, cookies-frozen doughs & prebaked, pizzas,
soups fresh & frozen, catering dessert items. (Woman,
estab 1989, empl 35, sales $10,500,000, cert: State,
WBENC)

Maine

3412   Blue Sky Produce
         243 Tory Hill Rd
         Phillips, ME 4966
         Contact: Lynn Thurston Owner
         Tel: 207-684-2172
         Email: hope@tdstelme.net
         Website: www.blueskyproduce.com
Pesticide Free & Conventionally grown Frozen Wild
Blueberries packed in 14 oz containers. (Woman, estab
1987, empl 6, sales , cert: WBENC)

Michigan

3413   Dual Sales & Associates, Inc.
         P.O. Box 725
         Grand Blanc, MI 48480
         Contact: Donna Bromm Owner
         Tel: 248-505-7128
         Email: donna@dualsales.com
         Website: www.dualsales.com
Dist shelled walnuts & pecans, specialty dried fruits.
(Woman, estab 1993, empl 1, sales , cert: WBENC)

3414   Ebonex
         18400 Rialto
         Melvindale,, MI 48122
         Contact: Shelly Toenniges Principal
         Tel: 313-388-0063
         Email: stoenniges@ebonex.com
         Website: www.keystoneuniversal.com
Dist baking ammonium carbonate: lump, chip or
powder. (Woman, estab , empl , sales , cert: WBENC)

3415   Flamm Pickle & Packing Co., Inc.
         4502 Hipps Hollow Rd
         Eau Claire, MI 49111
         Contact: Dorothy Munao Presdient
         Tel: 269-461-6916
         Email: dorothymunao@flammpickle.com
         Website: www.flammpickle.com
Mfr dill pickles & sweet pickle relishes. (Woman, estab
1917, empl 16, sales $1,885,000, cert: WBENC)

Minnesota

3416   Aarthun Enterprises, LLC dba Taste of Scandinavia
         111 E County Rd F
         Vadnais Heights, MN 55127
         Contact: CFO
         Tel: 651-483-9242
         Email:
         Website: www.tasteofscandinavia.com
Hand crafted Cakes & Tortes, Cupcakes & Cookies both
traditional & custom request. (Woman, estab 2004,
empl 118, sales $7,062,388, cert: WBENC)

3417 Healthy America, LLC
      13570 Grove Dr#372
      Maple Grove, MN 55311
      Contact: Sunil Kumar Presdient
      Tel: 651-666-0375
      Email: sunil.kumar@theamazingchickpea.com
      Website: www.theamazingchickpea.com
Produce Chickpea Spread that tastes like peanut butter but
does not contain any Nuts, Gluten Free and Dairy Free.
"The Amazing Chickpea - Creamy", "The Amazing Chickpea
- Crunchy","The Amazing Chickpea - Traditional". (As-Pac,
estab 2016, empl 5, sales $200,000, cert: NMSDC)

3418 Sweet Harvest Foods Management Company
      15100 Business Parkway
      Rosemount, MN 55068
      Contact: Joel Rengel Sales Dir
      Tel: 507-263-8599
      Email: jrengel@sweetharvestfoods.com
      Website: www.sweetharvestfoods.com
Mfr honey, ingredient honey, pancake syrup (table syrup),
corn syrup & branded peanut butter. (Woman, estab 1923,
empl 50, sales , cert: WBENC)

North Carolina

3419 Calvine's Coffee LLC
      P.O. Box 3005
      Matthews, NC 28106
      Contact: John Williamson Presdient
      Tel: 800-545-8553
      Email: john@cadprinting.biz
      Website: www.calvinescoffee.com
Gourmet specialty roast blend of coffee beans from many
origins around the world, including small farms and
farmers. Our beans are roasted in small batches in a San
Franciscan Artisan Roaster. (Woman/AA, estab 2015, empl
1, sales , cert: State)

3420 FDY, Inc.
      2459 Wilkinson Blvd Ste 300
      Charlotte, NC 28208
      Contact: Keith Haywood VP Sales/Mktg
      Tel: 704-523-6605
      Email: khaywood@fdyinc.com
      Website: www.fdyinc.com
Food service mgmt: cafeteria, dining services, vending,
catering, design. (Woman/AA, estab 1983, empl 275, sales
$10,870,702, cert: City)

3421 High Country Springs LLC
      P.O. Box 238
      Pilot Mountain, NC 27041
      Contact: Linda Tucker Partner
      Tel: 336-374-7474
      Email: ltucker@highcountrysprings.com
      Website: www.highcountrysprings.com
Provide 5-gallon, 3-gallon & 1-gallon Spring, Distilled, RO
(Reverse Osmosis), Deionized, and Fluoride Water, water
dispensers & coffee service. (Woman, estab 1992, empl
10, sales $605,431, cert: State)

3422 MyThreeSons Gourmet, LLC
      2309 Lafayette Ave
      Greensboro, NC 27408
      Contact: Cheryl Barnett President
      Tel: 336-324-5638
      Email: mtsgourmet@gmail.com
      Website: www.mtsgourmet.com
Mfr natural gourmet pimento cheese spread. (Woman,
estab 2010, empl 10, sales $645,000, cert: WBENC)

3423 The Busha Group LLC
      302 Lord Court
      Cramerton, NC 28032
      Contact: Julie Busha CEO
      Tel: 704-879-4411
      Email: jbusha@slawsa.com
      Website: www.slawsa.com
Mfr Slawsa, slaw-salsa hybrid condiment, all natural, fat-
free, cholesterol-free, gluten-free, low in sodium &
kosher. (Woman, estab 2013, empl 1, sales $363,320,
cert: WBENC)

3424 Tropical Nut & Fruit Co
      1100 Continental Blvd
      Charlotte, NC 28273
      Contact: Angela Bauer Owner
      Tel: 704-588-0400
      Email: abauer@tropicalfoods.com
      Website: www.tropicalfoods.com
Mfr & dist nuts, seeds, dried fruit, snack mixes, candy &
specialty foods. (Woman, estab 1977, empl 150, sales
$88,000,000, cert: WBENC)

New Hampshire

3425 Healthy Solutions Spice Blends, LLC
      P.O. Box 1094
      Hampton, NH 03843
      Contact: Shelly Wolcott Mgr
      Tel: 603-622-8744
      Email: shelly@spiceblends.com
      Website: www.spiceblends.com
Produce all natural, high quality, recipe ready spice
blends. (Woman, estab 2013, empl , sales , cert: WBENC)

3426 Homefree, LLC
      P.O. Box 491
      Windham, NH 03087
      Contact: Jill Robbins President
      Tel: 603-898-0172
      Email: info@homefreetreats.com
      Website: www.homefreetreats.com
Mfr all natural or organic, ready-to-eat whole grain
baked goods free of gluten & common food allergens.
(Woman, estab 2009, empl 18, sales $624,408, cert:
WBENC)

New Jersey

3427 Advanced Food Systems
      21 Roosevelt Ave
      Somerset, NJ 08863
      Contact: Al Rose midwest sales Mgr
      Tel: 732-873-6776
      Email: ajrose@charter.net
      Website: www.afsnj.com
Food ingredients: gums, starches, proteins, spices,
flavors, lab services. (As-Pac, estab 1980, empl 40, sales
$50,000,000, cert: NMSDC)

3428 Crispy Green Inc.
      10 Madison Rd
      Fairfield, NJ 07004
      Contact: Angela Liu President
      Tel: 973-679-4515
      Email: angela@crispygreen.com
      Website:
Crispy Green Fruit product line is created using a
sophisticated freeze-drying process where water is
removed from the fresh fruit in a cold (freezing) vacuum
condition, leaving behind the true essence of the fruit in
a light and crispy texture. (Woman/As-Pac, estab 2004,
empl 10, sales , cert: State)

3429   Groezinger Provisions, Inc.
1200 Seventh Ave
Neptune, NJ 07753
Contact: President & CEO
Tel: 800-927-9473
Email:
Website: www.alexianpate.com
Perishable prepared food mfg: meat, sausages, pates & prepared meats. (Woman, estab 1982, empl 20, sales , cert: WBENC)

3430   Harris Freeman & Co LP
344 New Albany Rd
Moorestown, NJ 08057
Contact: Steve Sernka Natl Sales Mgr
Tel: 856-793-0290
Email: steve.sernka@harrisfreeman.com
Website: www.HarrisTea.com
Manufacturer tea. (As-Ind, estab 1997, empl 129, sales , cert: NMSDC)

3431   JK Enterprise Solutions LLC
1000 Delsea Dr Building I Unit 1
Westville, NJ 08093
Contact: Abdul Ahad Butt Owner
Tel: 856-228-5934
Email: ahad@jkens.com
Website: www.jkens.com
Dist snack food products: Bud's Best Cookies, Uncle AL's Cremes, Lil Dutch maid wirecut cookies, Mayfair Candy Carnival, Select Sweets Candy, Daddy Rays fruit bars, Marco Polo Preserves, Caribbean Ice pops, Kisko Freezies. (As-Ind, estab 2014, empl 1, sales $187,000, cert: NMSDC)

3432   JVM Sales Corp.
3401a Tremley Point Rd
Linden, NJ 07036
Contact: Justin Tomasino Owner
Tel: 908-862-4866
Email: justintomasino@aol.com
Website: http://jvmsales.com
Provide Grated, Shredded & Shaved Cheeses, Hard Italian Cheese, Custom blended cheeses. (Woman, estab 1983, empl 200, sales $50,000,000, cert: WBENC)

3433   Soul Sisters Foods, Inc.
41 Prince St, Ste B11
Paterson, NJ 07505
Contact: Betty Dixon Presdient
Tel: 973-742-8255
Email: betty.dixon@unilever.com
Website: www.soulroll.com
Retail frozen food, Soul Rolls: collard greens, marinated meats, cheddar cheese, onions, green peppers, and tomatoes, seasoned to perfection in a crispy flour tortilla. (Woman/AA, estab 2006, empl 2, sales , cert: WBENC)

Nevada

3434   Tortillas Inc.
2912 N Commerce St
North Las Vegas, NV 89030
Contact: Gustavo Gutierrez President
Tel: 702-399-3300
Email: gus@tortillasinc.com
Website: www.tortillasinc.com
Corn tortillas, flour tortillas, flavored tortilla flour wraps; jalapeno wrap, tomato basil wrap, chipotle wrap, roasted garlic wrap, cheese, wraps corn chips, spices, chile peppers, canned sauces, frozen foods. (Hisp, estab 1979, empl 76, sales $8,000,000, cert: NMSDC)

New York

3435   Allie's GF Goodies, LLC
1B W Village Green
Hicksville, NY 11801
Contact: Owner
Tel: 516-216-1719
Website: www.AlliesGFG.com
Certified gluten free & certified kosher pareve bakery: breads, bagels, cookies, brownies, blondies, muffins, cupcakes, cakes, cheesecakes & pies. (Woman, estab 2012, empl 8, sales , cert: WBENC)

3436   Chocolate Promises, Inc.
P.O. Box 694
Merrick, NY 11566
Contact: Zakalik Cindy Presdient
Tel: 516-299-6400
Email: cindy@chocolatepromises.com
Website: www.chocolatepromises.com
Personalized chocolate with edible images. We'll custom print your full color logo, picture, design and/or special message directly on delicious chocolate coins, lollipops, Belgian truffles and more. (Woman, estab 2012, empl 2, sales , cert: State, City, WBENC)

3437   Golden Glow Cookie Co. Inc.
1844 Givan Ave
Bronx, NY 10469
Contact: Joan Florio Mgr
Tel: 718-379-6223
Email: ggcookies@aol.com
Website: www.thecookiefactory.com
Wholesale bakery, cookies & other related bakery items in bulk , plastic clamshells & individually wrapped. (Woman, estab 1954, empl 15, sales , cert: City)

3438   IMK Products, Inc.
244 Fifth Ave Ste D146
New York, NY 10001
Contact: Ilona Kovacs Presdient
Tel: 914-500-8127
Email: imkproductsinc@gmail.com
Website: www.truetastebar.com
Dist nutritional bars, organic/non gmo, no added sugar, vegan, gluten free, soy free, dairy free. (Woman, estab 2011, empl 2, sales , cert: WBENC)

3439   Lugo Nutrition Inc.
51 N Broadway, Ste 2B
Nyack, NY 10960
Contact: Nick Lugo VP
Tel: 302-573-2301
Email: nlugo@lugonutrition.com
Website: www.lugonutrition.com
Gelatin, beta carotene. Bitterness masking, sweetness enhancing, natural preservative/flavoring. (Hisp, estab 2010, empl 5, sales $4,500,000, cert: NMSDC)

3440   SFR&R Inc.
9 Soundview Lane
Sands Point, NY 11050
Contact: Giovannina Bellino Owner
Tel: 516-767-7286
Email: goddess6x8@aol.com
Website: www.flavorbombs.net
Mfr frozen cooking bases & foods. Low Sodium, Gluten Free, All Natural products. (Woman, estab 2008, empl 1, sales , cert: WBENC)

3441 Thunder Island Coffee Roasters, L.L.C.
P.O. Box 1275
Southampton, NY 11969
Contact: Benjamin Haile CEO
Tel: 631-204-1110
Email: info@thunderislandcoffee.com
Website: www.thunderislandcoffee.com
Coffee roasting and packaging. (Nat Ame, estab 2005, empl 4, sales , cert: State)

Ohio

3442 ABC Cookie Co., Inc.
3 Nationwide Plaza
Columbus, OH 43215
Contact: Dee Tolber CEO
Tel: 614-221-4442
Email: dee@ablessedcookie.com
Website: http://ablessedcookie.com
Fresh baked cookies, muffins, coffee cake, custom shaped, logo design cookies & custom gift items. (Woman/AA, estab 1990, empl 4, sales $185,000, cert: NMSDC)

3443 Safety Services & Supply, Inc.
14373 Rd. 23-M
Cloverdale, OH 45827
Contact: Andrea Vorst Presdient
Tel: 419-615-9923
Email: andreavorst@hotmail.com
Website:
Grow & manufacture popcorn. (Woman, estab 2013, empl 5, sales , cert: State, WBENC)

3444 Super Bakery
1667 E 40th St, Ste 1D3
Cleveland, OH 44103
Contact: Karen Cahill Corporate Admin
Tel: 216-426-8989
Email: karen.cahill@superbakery.com
Website: www.superbakery.com
Baked goods. (AA, estab 1989, empl 27, sales , cert: NMSDC)

3445 Urban Food Concepts LLC
852 E Highland Rd
Macedonia, OH 44056
Contact: Claude Booker President
Tel: 330-908-0493
Email: claude@simplysouthernsides.com
Website: www.simplysouthernsides.com
Fully cooked & seasoned vegetables & side dishes. (Woman/AA, estab 2007, empl 3, sales $4,000,000, cert: State, NMSDC, WBENC)

3446 Whitehall, Inc.
4760 Paddock Rd
Cincinnati, OH 45229
Contact: Shawn Higgins Dir of Natl Sales
Tel: 513-242-1004
Email: shiggins@klostermanbakery.com
Website: www.klostermanbakery.com
Restaurant quality bread, buns & rolls in a unique, handy and more compact retail package. (Minority, Woman, estab , empl 560, sales $295,400,000, cert: WBENC)

Oregon

3447 Hood River Juice Company
550 Riverside Dr
Hood River, OR 97031
Contact: David Ryan President
Tel: 541-386-3003
Email: davidr@hrjco.com
Website: www.ryansjuice.com
Natural & organic apple juice, single strength, not from concentrate. (Hisp, estab 1982, empl 113, sales $35,000,000, cert: NMSDC)

3448 Lucky Foods, LLC
7774 SW Nimbus Ave, Bldg 10
Beaverton, OR 97008
Contact: Tammy Jo Presdient
Tel: 503-641-6602
Email: tammyjo@luckyfood.com
Website: www.luckyfood.com
Asian foods. (Woman/As-Pac, estab 1985, empl 16, sales $1,547,000, cert: State)

Pennsylvania

3449 A.S.K. Foods Inc.
71 Hetrick Ave
Palmyra, PA 17078
Contact: Liz Burkholder Reg Sales Mgr
Tel: 717-838-6356
Email: ldurr@askfoods.com
Website: www.askfoods.com
Mfr prepared deli salads, entrees, side dishes, soups with no preservatives added. (Woman, estab 1947, empl 175, sales $42,200,000, cert: WBENC)

3450 Casalingo LLC
6321 S Highlings Circle
Harrisburg, PA 17111
Contact: Monette Roberto Member
Tel: 717-805-5088
Email: monetteroberto@yahoo.com
Website: http://casalingofoods.com
Four Generation homemade local pasta sauce. (Woman, estab 2013, empl 2, sales , cert: WBENC)

3451 Dutch Gold Honey, Inc.
2220 Dutch Gold Dr
Lancaster, PA 17601
Contact: Jill Clark
Tel: 717-393-1716
Email: jclark@dutchgoldhoney.com
Website: www.dutchgoldhoney.com
Honey & maple syrup processing & packaging. (Woman, estab 1946, empl 75, sales , cert: WBENC)

3452 Enchanted Acres Farm, Inc.
200 N 8th St Ste 500
Reading, PA 19601
Contact: Kelley Huff President
Tel: 877-707-3833
Email: quality@enchantedacresfarm.net
Website: www.enchantedacresfarm.net
Mfr beverages: tea, coffee, cocoa. (Woman, estab 2002, empl 15, sales $700,000, cert: State)

3453   Fallon Trading Co., Inc.
3897 Adler Pl, Ste C150
Bethlehem, PA 18017
Contact: Michele Rossi Office Mgr
Tel: 610-867-5527
Email: michele@fallontrading.com
Website: www.fallontrading.com
Dist conventional and organic fruit and vegetable juice concentrates, purees, NFC, IQF, essences, powders, oils, flavors, colors, and extracts. (Woman, estab 1998, empl 4, sales , cert: WBENC)

3454   Gourmail Inc.
300 Elmwood Ave
Sharon Hill, PA 19079
Contact: Business Mgr
Tel: 610-522-2650
Email:
Website: www.jyotifoods.com
Ready to serve vegetarian entrees, soups and sauces for at-home cooking, packed in cans. Indian Dals (Legumes), in pouches. (Woman/As-Pac, estab 1979, empl 25, sales $30,000,000, cert: NMSDC)

3455   Sweet Street Desserts
722 Hiesters Lane
Reading, PA 19605
Contact: Anthony DiGirolamo CFO
Tel: 610-921-8113
Email: cathy.bitler@sweetstreet.com
Website: www.sweetstreet.com
Mfr frozen gourmet desserts: cakes, pies, cheesecakes, dessert bars, bundt cakes, loaf cakes, cookies, scones, cupcakes & mousses. (Woman, estab , empl , sales , cert: WBENC)

South Carolina

3456   Charleston Gourmet Burger Company
4206 Sawgrass Dr
North Charleston, SC 29420
Contact: chevalo wilsondebriano Owner
Tel: 843-847-8369
Email: chevalo@charlestongourmetburger.com
Website: http://charlestongourmetburger.com
Charleston Gourmet Burger Marinade -blend of nine herbs & spices. (Woman/AA, Hisp, estab 2012, empl 2, sales $1,000,000, cert: NMSDC)

3457   Chef Belinda LLC dba Chef Belinda Spices
6 Mooney Court
Trenton, SC 29847
Contact: Belinda Smith-Sullivan Presdient
Tel: 803-552-6450
Email: belinda@chefbelinda.com
Website: http://chefbelindaspices.com
Produce all-natural artisan spice blends. (Woman/AA, estab 2009, empl 3, sales , cert: NMSDC)

3458   Pino Gelato, LLC
1000 William Hilton Pkwy, Ste G-1
Hilton Head Island, SC 29928
Contact: Jessica Scott CEO
Tel: 843-842-2822
Email: marketing@pinogelato.com
Website: http://pinogelato.com
Premium gelato & sorbetto. (Woman, estab 2004, empl 6, sales $1,748,000, cert: WBENC)

3459   Spartanburg Meat Processing Co., Inc.
3003 N Blackstock Rd
Spartanburg, SC 29301
Contact: Business Development
Tel: 864-621-1520
Email:
Website: www.eatbbqribs.com
Meat processing plant, pork, beef & chicken. Baby Back Ribs w/Sauce, Back Ribs, Pulled Pork w/Sauce, Pulled Chicken w/Sauce, Custom Proteins & Sauces. (Woman, estab 1999, empl 51, sales $17,128,586, cert: State, WBENC)

3460   Sweet Bottom Cookies
P.O. Box 355
Mt. Pleasant, SC 29466
Contact: Michele Lewis Presdient
Tel: 843-693-7366
Email: mlewis@sweetbottomcookies.com
Website: www.SweetBottomCookies.Com
Privately brands & wholesales jumbo (3.5oz), soft, individually wrapped, fudge covered bottom cookies. (Woman, estab 2010, empl 4, sales , cert: WBENC)

3461   The Muffin Mam, Inc.
3129 N Industrial Dr
Simpsonville, SC 29681
Contact: Greg Marshall VP Sales/Mktg
Tel: 800-948-4268
Email: gmarshall@muffinmam.com
Website: http://muffinmam.com
Mfr custom baked CrÄ¨me Cakes, Pound Cakes, Coffee Cakes, Gourmet Muffins, & Brownies. Use recycled & recycle able packaging. (Woman, estab 1990, empl 70, sales $24,500,000, cert: WBENC)

South Dakota

3462   Native American Natural Foods LLC
287 Water Tower Rd
Kyle, SD 57752
Contact: Mark Tilsen President
Tel: 605-455-2187
Email: mtilsen@tankabar.com
Website: http://tankabar.com
Gluten free, nitrate free, MSG free & hormone free Tanka Bar, Tanka Bites, and Tanka Sticks. (Woman/Nat Ame, estab 2007, empl 12, sales $1,525,000, cert: NMSDC)

Texas

3463   Artesia Springs LLC
8130 Interchange Pkwy
San Antonio, TX 78218
Contact: Rudy Ramon Presdient
Tel: 210-637-5554
Email: rudy@artesiasprings.com
Website: www.artesiasprings.com
Bottled water in all sizes from 16.9 liters, 3 and 4 gallon disposable and 5 gallon recycable, Private label options, water coolers, water filtration options. (Woman/Hisp, estab 2004, empl 19, sales $1,400,000, cert: State, NMSDC)

3464 Behrnes Pepper Salts
5313 E Side Ave
Dallas, TX 75214
Contact: Jan Olavarri Owner
Tel: 214-724-0581
Email: jan@behrnes.com
Website: www.behrnes.com
Mfr pepper salts blends using Chipotle, Cayenne & Green Jalapeno. (Woman, estab 2012, empl 1, sales , cert: WBENC)

3465 Cadeco Industries, Inc.
5610 Clinton Dr
Houston, TX 77020
Contact: Carlos deAldecoa President
Tel: 713-670-0700
Email: carlos@cadeco.cc
Website: www.cadeco.cc
Bulk coffee processing, storage & distribution services. (Hisp, estab 1995, empl 45, sales $40,000,000, cert: State, NMSDC)

3466 Clint's Picante Inc.
12 Thornhurst
San Antonio, TX 78218
Contact: Keri Poulter CFO
Tel: 210-274-5916
Email: keripoulter@yahoo.com
Website: www.clintspicante.com
Mfr Salsa & BBQ sauce. (Woman, estab 1996, empl , sales $29,990,000, cert: State, City)

3467 Cookies by Design
1865 Summit Ave Ste 607
Plano, TX 75074
Contact: Darylyn Phillips Natl Sales Coord
Tel: 800-347-3110
Email: dphillips@cookiesbydesign.com
Website: www.cookiesbydesign.com
Customized, hand-decorated cookie baskets, cookie bouquets, cookie cakes, individual logo cookies, gourmet cookies, cupcakes, gluten free & sugar free. (Woman, estab 1983, empl 54, sales $28,000,000, cert: State, WBENC)

3468 Ezbake Technologies
P.O. Box 270527
Flowermound, TX 75027
Contact: Rita Tolvanen CEO
Tel: 888-287-8447
Email: rita@ezbake.net
Website: http://ezbaketechnologies.com
Dist baking ingredients, enzyme based dough conditioners, shelf life extenders & specialty conditioners for cookies, cakes, donuts, English muffins & low moisture products. (Woman, estab 1993, empl 4, sales $1,000,000, cert: WBENC)

3469 Global Coffee Company
6161 Savoy Dr, Ste 821
Houston, TX 77236
Contact: Shaheed Momin Presdient
Tel: 713-222-2291
Email: shaheed@globalcoffeecompany.com
Website: www.javatogo.com
Coffee, cappuccino, slushy, iced tea, juices, soda, water, paper goods, etc. (As-Ind, estab 2007, empl 4, sales $1,596,400, cert: State, City, NMSDC)

3470 Sociologie Wines Vintage LLC
3901 Arlington Highlands Blvd Ste 200
Arlington, TX 76018
Contact: Mark Hansen Owner
Tel: 832-871-7917
Email: mark@sociologiewine.com
Website: www.sociologiewine.com
Refreshing blends of delicious fruits & natural ingredients, Red Berry & Blushing Rose wine. (Woman/AA, estab 2012, empl 3, sales , cert: NMSDC)

3471 Twang Partners, Ltd.
6255 WT Montgomery Rd
San Antonio, TX 78252
Contact: Patrick Trevino VP Business Dev
Tel: 603-498-7078
Email: ptrevino@twang.com
Website: www.twang.com
Mfr premium-flavored salts, sugars & seasonings. (Hisp, estab 1986, empl 65, sales , cert: State, NMSDC)

Utah

3472 Amboseli Foods, LLC
320 W. 1550 N, Ste L
Salt Lake City, UT 84041
Contact: Sylvia Kapsandoy CEO
Tel: 801-471-4250
Email: sylvia@amboselifoods.com
Website: www.usimplyseason.com
Custom seasoning manufacturing services. (AA, estab 2013, empl 4, sales $250,000, cert: NMSDC)

Virginia

3473 A M King LLC
13241 Otto Rd
Woodbridge, VA 22193
Contact: Adima Aniteye CEO
Tel: 703-855-9822
Email: amkingllc@gmail.com
Website: www.queenvictoriaspunch.com
Mfr & dist fruit punches: The Queen-Grapefruit, Pineapple, Apple, Orange, The Duchess— Lemon, Pineapple, Apple, Orange, The Baroness—Pomegranate, Pineapple, Lemon, Lime, Agave. (Woman/AA, estab 2012, empl 2, sales , cert: State)

3474 Amelia Distributing Company
3420 Pump Rd Box 159
Henrico, VA 23233
Contact: Eve Painter President
Tel: 804-840-0228
Email: evepainter@msn.com
Website:
Seltzer water in liters and cans, distilled water in gallons (Woman, estab 1994, empl 3, sales , cert: State)

3475 Grandmas Garden
7044 Sauvage Ln
Gainesville, VA 20155
Contact: Amy Weaver President
Tel: 571-244-1443
Email: amyweaver@grandmasgarden.us
Website: www.grandmasgarden.us
All natural "Sweet" & "Spicy Sweet" gourmet relish: cabbage, peppers, tomatoes, onions & spices. (Woman, estab 2011, empl 2, sales , cert: State)

3476 Greenberry's Coffee Roasters
1610 Quail Run
Charlottesville, VA 22911
Contact: COO
Tel: 434-964-1655
Email:
Website: www.greenberrys.com
Hand-roasted premium artisan coffees: Single Origin, Signature Blends, Fair Trade Organic & Flavored. (Woman, estab 2001, empl 10, sales $1,845,350, cert: State)

3477 Savaspice LLC
6247 Glen Wood Loop
Manassas, VA 20112
Contact: Lova Mitchell Owner
Tel: 703-895-4800
Email: savaspice@gmail.com
Website: www.savaspice.com
Madagascar vanilla & spices. (Woman/As-Ind, estab 2015, empl 1, sales , cert: State)

Washington

3478 Kylie B's Pastry Case LLC
4114 B Place NW, Ste 100
Auburn, WA 98001
Contact: Sabrina Bacungan Chief Marketing Officer
Tel: 253-217-6131
Email: sabrina@kyliebbakery.com
Website: www.kyliebbakery.com
Hand-made traditional shortbread. (Woman/As-Pac, estab 2016, empl 4, sales , cert: WBENC)

3479 Lanier's Fine Candies
5710 S Bangor St
Seattle, WA 98178
Contact: Herman Lanier CEO
Tel: 206-723-6465
Email: herman@laniersfinecandies.com
Website: www.laniersfinecandies.com
Brittle candies: almond, cashew, peanut, pecan & macadamia, hand dipped in dark & milk chocolate. (AA, estab 2013, empl 2, sales , cert: NMSDC)

3480 Lynnae's Gourmet Pickles LLC
3024 S Mullen #F
Tacoma, WA 98466
Contact: Lynnae Schneller President
Tel: 253-226-2370
Email: lynnae@lynnaesgourmetpickles.com
Website: www.lynnaesgourmetpickles.com
Mfr all natural, high quality pickles with unique flavor combinations. (Woman, estab 2011, empl 3, sales $285,000, cert: State)

Wisconsin

3481 Asenzya, Inc.
7616 S 6th St
Oak Creek, WI 53154
Contact: Chris Anderson VP Sales
Tel: 414-764-1220
Email: chris.anderson@asenzya.com
Website: www.asenzya.com
Custom dry seasoning product development, custom dry seasoning blending & custom bulk & batch-specific-weight packaging services. (Woman, estab 1953, empl 140, sales $46,000,000, cert: WBENC)

3482 Fair Oaks Farms, LLC
7600 95th St
Pleasant Prairie, WI 53158
Contact: Michael Thompson Natl Acct Sales Mgr
Tel: 262-947-0320
Email: mthompson@osigroup.com
Website: www.fairoaksfarms.com
Dist meats. (AA, estab 1985, empl 260, sales , cert: NMSDC)

3483 Jeneil Biotech, Inc.
400 N Dekora Woods Blvd
Saukville, WI 53080
Contact: Stephen Beaver Sales
Tel: 262-268-6815
Email: s.beaver@jeneilbiotech.com
Website: www.jeneilbiotech.com
Mfr natural dairy flavors in pastes & powders, natural flavor aroma chemicals, soymilk powder, soy-cream cheese, fermentation, enzymolysis & distillation. (As-Ind, estab 1998, empl 43, sales $17,000,000, cert: NMSDC)

3484 Nanland LLC
5959 N Shore Acres Rd
New Franken, WI 54229
Contact: Nan Bush Presdient
Tel: 920-562-9822
Email: nan@nanlandllc.com
Website: www.nanlandllc.com
Provides premium, single origin, organic coffee, 100% Arabica coffees from Peru, Nicaragua, Sumatra and Colombia packaged in 12 or 42 single serve cup boxes. (Woman, estab 2016, empl 2, sales , cert: WBENC)

Wyoming

3485 Smart Fords LLC
34 Franklin Ave, Ste 687
Pinedale, WY 82941
Contact: Sara Ford Marketing
Tel: 917-791-2818
Email: Fords1903@gmail.com
Website: www.smartfords.com
Dist soft drinks, energy drinks and anti aging mineral water. (Woman, estab 2021, empl 1, sales , cert: State)

FURNISHINGS

Manufacturers, distributors or importers of furniture for office and home. Also floor and window coverings, light fixtures, household and kitchen accessories such as wastebaskets, planters, dishes, vases, brooms, dustpans, etc. (See also GIFTWARE, ARTS & CRAFTS and OFFICE SUPPLIES categories. NAICS Code 42

Alabama

3486 E.S. Robbins Corp.
2802 E Avalon Ave
Muscle Shoals, AL 35661
Contact: Bonnie Donato Channel Marketing Mgr
Tel: 256-248-2494
Email: badonato@esrobbins.com
Website: www.esrchairmats.com
Dist office products & furnishings. Mfr polymer products. (Woman, estab 1967, empl 187, sales , cert: WBENC)

Arkansas

3487 Burris Inc.
113 S Arkansas Ave
Russellville, AR 72801
Contact: Presdient
Tel: 479-968-4888
Email:
Website: www.burrisinc.com
Office supplies & office furniture, panel systems, custom millwork, office layout & design. (Woman, estab 1953, empl 15, sales $3,374,600, cert: WBENC)

Arizona

3488 Dave Scott & Associates, Inc.
P.O. Box 22115
Phoenix, AZ 85028
Contact: David R Scott Owner
Tel: 602-971-1600
Email: dave.scott@davescottassociates.com
Website: www.davescottassociates.com
Office Furniture: Systems, Case Goods, Seating, Specialty; Health Care Furniture; Benches, receptacles, bike racks, ash urns; Millwork; Cell phone Charging Station Kiosks, Playgrounds, Design/space planning, Installation. (AA, estab 1999, empl 6, sales $1,360,539, cert: State, City, NMSDC)

3489 Elontec
5502 W Buckeye Rd, Ste 100
Phoenix, AZ 85043
Contact: Jessica Chappell Inside Sales Mgr
Tel: 602-759-5500
Email: jchappell@elontec.com
Website: http://elontec.com
Office furniture: cubicles, case goods, private offices, ect. Planning, design, procurement & installation. (Woman, estab 1997, empl 65, sales $5,200,000, cert: State, WBENC)

California

3490 Alternative Office Solutions
140 San Pedro Ave, Ste 110
Morgan Hill, CA 95037
Contact: Kevin Collier Sales Dir
Tel: 408-776-2036
Email: kevin@alt-office.com
Website: http://alt-office.com
Office space planning & installation of remanufactured Herman Miller AO1 and AO2 cubicles. (Woman, estab 1998, empl 19, sales $2,091,446, cert: CPUC)

3491 American Dawn Inc.
401 W Artesia Blvd
Compton, CA 90220
Contact: Mike Maloney Corp Secretary
Tel: 310-609-3222
Email: mmaloney@americandawn.com
Website: www.americandawn.com
Mfr & dist industrial & hospitality items: linens, towels, etc. (As-Ind, estab 1975, empl 200, sales , cert: NMSDC)

3492 Compact International
16161 Ventura Blvd, Ste 382
Encino, CA 91436
Contact: Robert Paul mktg/sales
Tel: 818-585-1374
Email: robert.paul@compactintl.com
Website: www.compactintl.com
Design, mfr & dist commercial furniture, folding chairs & tables. (AA, estab 1998, empl 4, sales $2,050,000, cert: State)

3493 Dawn Medical Inc.
844 Jury Court
San Jose, CA 95112
Contact: Gaylene McIntosh Presdient
Tel: 408-280-7676
Email: caremed.products@yahoo.com
Website:
Anesthesia,& critical care equipment and supplies: blood pressure cuffs ,cables & lead wires laryngoscopes blades, airways, electrodes, labor & delivery/Nursery/NICU products, Bio Medical engineering products (Woman, estab 1996, empl 3, sales $375,175, cert: NWBOC)

3494 Decor Interior Design
2937 E 4th St
Los Angeles, CA 90033
Contact: Principal
Tel: 310-289-2186
Email:
Website: www.designsbydecor.com
Interior Design, Custom Furniture, Window Treatments, Project Management, Interior Landscaping. (Woman/AA, estab 1997, empl 28, sales $552,000, cert: State, NMSDC, CPUC, WBENC)

3495 Environments Plus, Inc.
1700 1st St
San Fernando, CA 91340
Contact: REGINA CORDELL Owner
Tel: 866-865-8120
Email: rcordell@epi-usa.com
Website: www.Environmentsplus.com
Office Furniture Installation, Office Reconfiguration, Office Moves, Office Furniture Liquidation, Furniture Storage, Project Manager,
Design Services, Furniture Lifting. (Woman, estab 1992, empl 45, sales $6,500,000,000, cert: CPUC, WBENC)

3496 HSE USA, Inc.
      5709 E 61st St
      Commerce, CA 90040
      Contact: Nelson Yip President
      Tel: 323-278-0888
      Email: nelson.yip@hseusa.com
      Website: www.hseusa.com
We carry a large selection of candles for the food-service
and hospitality industries. (As-Pac, estab 2008, empl 10,
sales $4,100,000, cert: NMSDC)

3497 Media Management Systems
      3525 Del Mar Heights Rd, Ste 440
      San Diego, CA 92130
      Contact: Chita McCollum Owner
      Tel: 858-792-0029
      Email: mediamgmts@aol.com
      Website: http://mediamgmtsystems.com
Dist office, computer & industrial furniture; file & storage
surveys, tool cabinets. (Woman/Hisp, estab 1986, empl 1,
sales , cert: State)

3498 Metro Contract Group
      1111 Broadway Ste 1650
      Oakland, CA 94607
      Contact: Dwight Jackson Presdient
      Tel: 510-254-4281
      Email: dwight@metrocontractgroup.com
      Website: www.metrocontractgroup.com
Contract furniture dealer & design firm. (AA, estab 1993,
empl 30, sales $3,010,000, cert: State, NMSDC, CPUC)

3499 MikaPak Inc.
      P.O. Box 4276
      Walnut Creek, CA 94596
      Contact: Helen Ma Presdient
      Tel: 800-579-0880
      Email: helen@mikapak.com
      Website: www.mikapak.com
Sustainable, compostable products from plate wares,
utensils, drink cups, food containers to packaging labels
using renewable plant base raw materials. (Woman/As-
Pac, estab 1995, empl 1, sales $279,000, cert: NMSDC)

3500 Southwest Country
      17940 Ventura Blvd
      Encino, CA 91316
      Contact: Fred Fuchs Mgr
      Tel: 818-345-3900
      Email: webmaster@swcountry.com
      Website: www.cowboyindian.com
Mfr & dist southwest, western & country furniture, art &
accessories. (Woman/Hisp, estab 1989, empl 5, sales , cert:
State, City)

3501 Systems Source Inc.
      4685 MacArthur Blvd. Ste 100
      Newport Beach, CA 92660
      Contact: Rosemarie Smith CEO
      Tel: 949-852-0920
      Email: bvente@systemsource.com
      Website: www.systemsource.com
Office furniture, modular furniture systems, demountable
walls, design, installation, refinishing, reupholstery &
service. (Woman, estab 1982, empl 215, sales
$164,000,000, cert: CPUC, WBENC)

3502 Systems Source, Inc.
      2100 Main St, Ste 100
      Irvine, CA 92614
      Contact: Rosemarie Correia Presdient
      Tel: 949-224-0488
      Email: rcorreia@systemsource.com
      Website: www.systemsource.com
Contract office furniture, design, installation & service.
(Woman, estab 2000, empl , sales , cert: WBENC)

3503 Uniworld Omniport
      690 Garcia Ave Ste A
      Pittsburg, CA 94565
      Contact: Chris Smead Dir of Operations
      Tel: 925-439-3070
      Email: chris@bbopokertables.com
      Website: www.BBOPokerTables.com
Mfr & dist folding leg & furniture/dining/conference
solid wood poker tables. (As-Pac, estab 2006, empl 5,
sales $1,302,000, cert: NMSDC)

Colorado

3504 Premier Commercial Interiors, Inc.
      6830 N Broadway, Unit H
      Denver, CO 80221
      Contact: Brenda Jones Presdient
      Tel: 303-466-8575
      Email: brendaj@pciwindowcoverings.com
      Website: www.pciwindowcoverings.com
Furnish & install window treatments (blinds, roller
shades etc.) and projection screens. Clean & repair
existing window treatments. (Woman, estab 2004, empl
9, sales , cert: WBENC)

3505 Workplace Elements LLC
      2501 Blake St
      Denver, CO 80205
      Contact: Cameron Gilbreath Controller
      Tel: 303-471-4334
      Email: cgilbreath@workplaceelements.com
      Website: www.workplaceelements.com
Office furniture, furniture storage, flooring, carpet,
demountable walls, private office furniture. (Woman,
estab 2008, empl 60, sales $38,000,000, cert: WBENC)

Connecticut

3506 De Clercq Office Group
      85 Willow St
      New Haven, CT 6511
      Contact: Deborah Hopewell Declercq Presdient
      Tel: 203-230-9380
      Email: deb@dog-office.com
      Website: www.dog-office.com
Furniture related consulting services, pre-owned
furniture & furniture rescue. (Woman, estab 2001, empl
6, sales $11,311,190, cert: WBENC)

3507 People Places and Spaces, LLC
      225 Asylum St
      Hartford, CT 6103
      Contact: Mark Nisbett CEO
      Tel: 860-386-8600
      Email: markn@pps-ct.com
      Website: www.pps-ct.com
Commercial office furniture, adaptable workspaces, and
architectural interiors. (AA, estab 2018, empl 3, sales
$8,280,210, cert: State, NMSDC)

3508   Workspace Consulting Group, LLC
       2777 Summer St, 2nd Fl
       Stamford, CT 6902
       Contact: Paulina Ribadeneyra Owner
       Tel: 203-548-0305
       Email: paulina@workspacecg.com
       Website: www.workspacecg.com
Office furniture and related consulting services. (Woman/
Hisp, estab 2010, empl 4, sales $1,591,348, cert: NMSDC)

Florida

3509   Above the Sill
       745 C Shamrock Blvd
       Venice, FL 34293
       Contact: Phillip Barone VP Sales/Mktg
       Tel: 941-492-3101
       Email: phil@abovethesill.net
       Website: www.abovethesill.net
Cubicle Curtains and track fabrication and installation,
vertical blinds, roller shades, solar shades, mini blinds, faux
wood blinds, solar panels, shutters, venetian blinds, etc.
(Woman, estab 2004, empl 4, sales , cert: State)

3510   Berwin, Inc.
       3501 Commerce Pkwy
       Miramar, FL 33025
       Contact: Nancy Wolfe A/R Specialist
       Tel: 954-499-6677
       Email: nancy.wolfe@jcwhite.com
       Website: www.jcwhite.com
Design, dist, install & service office furniture, walls &
floors. (Woman, estab 1978, empl 103, sales $43,000,000,
cert: State, WBENC)

3511   Business Interior Group, Inc.
       93 Rosehill Crescent Ct
       Debary, FL 32713
       Contact: John North President
       Tel: 386-668-9387
       Email: big32779@aol.com
       Website:
Office furniture & installation, cubicles, seating,
casegoods, etc. (AA, estab 2003, empl 2, sales , cert: State)

3512   Cadence Keen Innovations d/b/a CKI Solutions
       1645 Palm Beach Lakes Blvd #210
       West Palm Beach, FL 33401
       Contact: Gregg Saxton
       Tel: 561-249-2219
       Email: gregg.s@ckisolutions.us
       Website: www.ckisolutions.us
Bed doubling systems, mattress & pillow protectors,
mattress protection systems, disposable luggage protection systems. (Woman, estab 1996, empl 6, sales
$2,211,409, cert: NWBOC)

3513   Cubicle Curtain Factory
       7810 S Dixie Hwy
       West Palm Beach, FL 33405
       Contact: Stephanie Serio CEO
       Tel: 800-588-9296
       Email: stephanie@cubiclecurtainfactory.com
       Website: www.cubiclecurtainfactory.com
Mfr & dist hospital cubicle curtains, window draperies, bed
covers, shower curtains, blackout & disposable curtains.
(Woman, estab 2004, empl 23, sales $2,673,550, cert:
State)

3514   Furniture Installation Solution Inc
       4740 NW 15th Ave Ste D
       Fort Lauderdale, FL 33309
       Contact: Donovan Williams Operations Mgr
       Tel: 954-638-2432
       Email: info@myfis.biz
       Website: http://myfis.biz
Install, reconfigure & relocate panel (cubicle) system &
case good furniture. (AA, estab 2008, empl 10, sales
$2,400,000, cert: NMSDC)

3515   HNM Global Logistics
       9603 Satellite Boulevard Ste 150
       Orlando, FL 32837
       Contact: CEO
       Tel: 407-472-7576
       Email:
       Website: www.gohnm.com
Dist & install furniture supplies, furniture, fixtures &
equipment. (Minority, estab 2004, empl 10, sales
$5,600,000, cert: NMSDC)

Georgia

3516   Contract Business Interiors, Inc.
       3455 N Desert Dr, Bldg 3, Ste 103
       East Point, GA 30344
       Contact: Michael Murphy
       Tel: 404-684-0800
       Email: michael@contractbusinessinteriors.com
       Website:
Contract furniture dealer: office case goods, modular
systems, seating, auditorium, lecture hall/training room,
dormitory, lockers & signage, interior design, space
layout, specification, installation, reconfiguration,
furniture restoration. (AA, estab 2001, empl 5, sales
$1,200,000, cert: State)

3517   Corporate Environments of GA, Inc.
       1636 Northeast Expressway
       Atlanta, GA 30329
       Contact: Sr Acct Mgr
       Tel: 404-679-8999
       Email: rstandard@ceofga.com
       Website: www.corporateenvironments.com
Dist office furniture. (Woman, estab 1973, empl 37, sales
$47,200,000, cert: WBENC)

3518   Nance Carpet & Rug Inc.
       201 Nance Road
       Calhoun, GA 30701
       Contact: Trenna Smith Natl Accts Specialist
       Tel: 706-629-7731
       Email: trenna.smith@nancecarpet.com
       Website: http://nancefloors.com
Dist area rugs, carpet remnants, carpet by the roll,
carpet tiles & carpet base. (Woman, estab 1972, empl
300, sales $19,000,000, cert: WBENC)

3519   Table Decor International Inc.
       2748 S Cobb Industrial Blvd
       Smyrna, GA 30082
       Contact: Lynn Wells President
       Tel: 770-432-1156
       Email: tdi@tabledecor.com
       Website: www.tabledecor.com
Design & mfr specialty table lighting & unique center-
pieces & table accessory items. (Woman, estab 1984,
empl 5, sales $750,000, cert: WBENC)

3520 White Howard Brands
2282 Defoor Hills Ave Ste 180
Atlanta, GA 30318
Contact: Principal
Tel: 404-789-5573
Email:
Website: www.whitehowardbrands.com
Office furniture, panel systems, workstations, cubicles, chairs, task chair, desks, furniture, installation, contract sales. (Woman/AA, estab 2017, empl 4, sales , cert: WBENC)

3521 Zig Zag Inc.
4300 Westpark Dr, SW
Atlanta, GA 30336
Contact: Gokul Nair CEO
Tel: 347-558-6767
Email: gokul@zzincorporation.com
Website: www.zzincorporation.com
Mfr patio cushions, rugs, door mats & general safety items. (As-Ind, estab 2008, empl 10, sales $16,000,000, cert: NMSDC)

Illinois

3522 Phoenix Woodworking Corporation
P.O. Box 459
Woodstock, IL 60098
Contact: President
Tel: 815-338-9338
Email:
Website: http://phoenixwoodworking.com
Custom & commercial cabinetry & casework, reception centers, filing cabinets, wooden lockers & millwork, custom desks & wooden store fixtures. (Woman, estab 1996, empl 10, sales , cert: State, WBENC)

3523 Resource One
321 E Adams
Springfield, IL 62701
Contact: Cynthia Davis President
Tel: 217-753-5742
Email: cdavis@resourceoneoffice.com
Website: www.resourceoneoffice.com
Dist office furniture, carpet, wallcovering, window treatments, refurbishment services, furniture, space-planning & interior design, furniture installation. (Woman, estab 1987, empl 22, sales $8,000,000, cert: State, WBENC)

Indiana

3524 Commercial Office Environments Inc.
7301 Zionsville Road
Indianapolis, IN 46268
Contact: James Bednarski Acct Exec
Tel: 317-876-9200
Email: james@coeindy.com
Website: www.coeindy.com
Furniture & storage equipment, design, install furniture & storage solutions. (Woman, estab 1989, empl 29, sales $13,000,000, cert: State)

3525 Lapsley Inc.
1002 E Rudisill Blvd
Fort Wayne, IN 46806
Contact: Donita Mudd President
Tel: 260-745-3265
Email: dmudd@lapsleyinc.com
Website: www.lapsleyinc.com
Furnish & install window treatments: blinds, shades, draperies, manual or motorized, projection screens, cubicle curtains & cubicle tracks. (Woman/AA, estab 2003, empl 4, sales $140,000, cert: State, 8a)

3526 Office and Business Resources LLC
244 McConnell Dr
New Albany, IN 47150
Contact: Kahy Brown Presdient
Tel: 502-333-8907
Email: kbrown@officeandbusinessresources.com
Website: www.officeandbusinessresources.com
Office furniture assembly & installation, furniture systems (cubicles), office relocations & interoffice relocations, space planning & design. (Woman, estab 2012, empl 4, sales , cert: NWBOC)

3527 TLS by Design, LLC
10737 Sand Key Circle
Indianapolis, IN 46256
Contact: Jeff Day Dir
Tel: 765-683-1971
Email: sales@tlsbydesign.com
Website: www.tlsbydesign.com
Mfr custom furniture. (Woman, estab 2002, empl 12, sales $780,000, cert: State, WBENC)

Kentucky

3528 Munson Business Interiors
2307 River Rd
Louisville, KY 40206
Contact: Susan Lewis Acct Rep
Tel: 502-588-7368
Email: susan@mbifurniture.com
Website: www.mbifurniture.com
Office furnishings, space planning, design, delivery, installation, project management, warehousing & inventory reports, repair & refinishing, reupholstery panels, chairs & custom furniture. (Woman, estab 1986, empl 21, sales $6,376,824, cert: NWBOC)

Louisiana

3529 Contract Furniture Group, LLC
201 James Dr E James Business Park
Saint Rose, LA 70087
Contact: Julio Rodriguez President
Tel: 504-412-0080
Email: julio@contractfurnituregroup.com
Website: www.contractfurnituregroup.com
Design & install furniture systems modular furniture, freestanding casegoods, conference room furniture, break rooms, training rooms, healthcare furniture & high density filing systems. (Hisp, estab 2000, empl 20, sales , cert: NMSDC)

Massachusetts

3530 McElroy Scenic Services LLC
P.O. Box 145
Ashley Falls, MA 1222
Contact: Presdient
Tel: 413-229-9920
Email:
Website: www.mcelroyscenic.com
Decor fabrication, set design & fabrication, custom displays, architectural models, exterior & interior signage, custom corporate furniture & staging, museum exhibits. (Woman, estab 1999, empl 7, sales $1,200,000, cert: State, WBENC)

3531 Wholesale Distribution
P.O. Box 1497
Cotuit, MA 2635
Contact: Linda Sharp Presdient
Tel: 800-345-4027
Email: linda@facilitiesfurniture.com
Website: www.facilitiesfurniture.com
Dist folding, stack, office & classroom chairs, training & computer, cafeteria & classroom tables & desks, restroom fixtures & components, lockers, flags, communication boards. (Woman, estab 2001, empl 3, sales , cert: State, WBENC)

Maryland

3532 Contemporary Business Interiors, LLC
1369 D Brass Mill Rd
Belcamp, MD 21017
Contact: Member
Tel: 410-272-5559
Email:
Website: www.cbillc.com
Dist business furniture: office, hospitality, bar & restaurant, medical, school, space planning & design, project mgmt, installation. (Woman, estab 2006, empl 3, sales $1,300,000, cert: State)

Michigan

3533 Airea
3000 Town Center Ste 80
Southfield, MI 48075
Contact: Yulanda Trout Exec Asst
Tel: 248-226-3971
Email: ytrout@pistongroup.com
Website: www.aireainc.com
Modular walls & ceiling systems, raised-access flooring, floor covering, furniture & lighting. (AA, estab 1995, empl 28, sales $12,000,000, cert: NMSDC)

3534 Designer Installation Services, Inc.
9685 Harrison St, Ste 200
Romulus, MI 48174
Contact: Robert Corona Presdient
Tel: 313-582-9310
Email:
danielle.smith@designerinstallationservicesin.com
Website: www.designerinstallationservicesin.com
Dist commercial office furniture, flooring & ancillary items, installation, warehousing, asset management, delivery. (Hisp, estab 1979, empl 25, sales $4,000,000, cert: NMSDC)

3535 Hercules & Hercules, Inc.
19055 W Davison
Detroit, MI 48223
Contact: Belinda Jefferson Presdient
Tel: 313-933-6669
Email: bjefferson@herculesandherculesinc.com
Website: www.herculesandherculesinc.com
Dist maintenance supplies & equip, office supplies & equip, office furniture. (AA, estab , empl , sales $7,000,000, cert: NMSDC)

3536 ISCG
612 N Main St
Royal Oak, MI 48067
Contact: Stephanie Chyz Presdient
Tel: 248-399-1600
Email: schyz@iscginc.com
Website: www.iscginc.com
Contract furnishings (Haworth Preferred Dealer) & Floorcoverings, Facility Asset Management, Project & Move Management, Union & Non. (Woman, estab 1976, empl 21, sales $14,000,000, cert: WBENC)

3537 Remco Storage Systems, Inc.
2328 Livernois Road Ste 1070
Troy, MI 48083
Contact: Donna Tamburo-Wilson President & CEO
Tel: 248-362-0500
Email: donna@remcoequipment.com
Website: www.remcoequipment.com
Storage & retrieval systems: vertical lifts & carousels, electric lateral filing systems, movable shelving, rotary files, cabinets, records mgmt systems, color coded labels, custom filing systems, folders & indexes. (Woman, estab 1976, empl 7, sales $2,000,000, cert: WBENC)

Minnesota

3538 AIM Global Trading, LLC
11209 Commerce Dr N
Champlin, MN 55316
Contact: Mahtab Khan CEO
Tel: 612-305-8021
Email: linenbay3@gmail.com
Website: www.aimglobaltrading.com
Mfr & dist 100% cotton terry towel & Polyester/Cotton Blended Bath Towels, Hand Towels, Wash Cloths, Bath Mats, Pool Towels, & Bar Mops. (As-Pac, estab 2014, empl 3, sales , cert: NMSDC)

3539 Electronic Office Environments, Inc.
264 East Lafayette Frontage Road
Saint Paul, MN 55107
Contact: Presdient
Tel: 651-224-0344
Email:
Website: www.EOEergo.com
Ergonomic seating, ESD seating, cleanroom seating, specialized seating, height adjustable table frames, office furniture, lounge furniture, cafeteria furniture, panel systems & accessories. (Hisp, estab 1983, empl 4, sales , cert: NMSDC)

3540   Ideal Commercial Interiors LLC
      740 Portland Ave. Ste 1418
      Minneapolis, MN 55414
      Contact: Rick Harris CEO
      Tel: 612-759-0955
      Email: rick@icinteriors.net
      Website: www.icinteriors.net
Office furniture, flooring, fixtures, design, space planning, installation, delivery & project management. (AA, estab 2012, empl 3, sales , cert: NMSDC)

3541   Kelly Computer Supply
      2042 Wooddale Dr Ste 250
      Woodbury, MN 55125
      Contact: Bob Kelly Presdient
      Tel: 651-773-1109
      Email: bobkelly@kellyrest.com
      Website: www.kellyrest.com
Ergonomic equip; mfr "KellyRest" computer products: wrist & foot rests, adjustable copy holders, keyboard drawers & articulating keyboard trays; workstations. (Nat Ame, estab 1983, empl 10, sales , cert: State, NMSDC, CPUC)

3542   R and L Woodcraft, Inc
      823 Industrial Park Dr SE
      Lonsdale, MN 55046
      Contact: Randall Rivers Business Dev Mgr
      Tel: 507-744-2318
      Email: randall@randlwoodcraft.com
      Website: www.randlwoodcraft.com
Mfr commercial millwork & casework: cabinets, countertops, workstations, service counters, point of service counters, tables, booths, upholstered seating, running trim, trash recepticles, lockers & toilet partitions. (Woman, estab 1986, empl 22, sales $3,600,000, cert: WBENC)

Mississippi

3543   Commercial Interiors, Inc.
      4277 Espy Ave
      Long Beach, MS 39560
      Contact: Presdient
      Tel: 228-452-9540
      Email:
      Website: www.cidesigns.net
Commercial FF&E contractor. (Woman, estab 1990, empl 3, sales $555,647, cert: State)

3544   Durfold Corporation
      102 Upton Dr
      Jackson, MS 11111
      Contact: Dawn Warren
      Tel: 601-922-4144
      Email: dwarren@durfold.com
      Website: www.durfold.com
Mfr upholstered healthcare furniture: sleeper chairs & sofas, trendelenberg recliners, incliners, rocking chairs, gliders, bariatric seating, patient & guest seating, lounge seating, lobby furniture & ganged & tandem seating. (Woman, estab , empl , sales $3,200,000, cert: WBENC)

North Carolina

3545   DARRAN Furniture Industries, Inc.
      2402 Shore St
      High Point, NC 27263
      Contact: Jennifer Hollingsworth President
      Tel: 800-334-7891
      Email: jlhollingsworth@darran.com
      Website: www.darran.com
Mfr high quality, mid-market wood desk collections, conferencing solutions, reception stations & seating. (Woman, estab 1977, empl 195, sales $25,559,279, cert: WBENC)

New Jersey

3546   Concepts Office Furnishings, Inc.
      280 N Midland Ave, Bldg J Unit 204
      Saddle Brook, NJ 07663
      Contact: Aida DeSoto Presdient
      Tel: 201-727-9110
      Email: adesoto@conceptsoffice.com
      Website: www.conceptsoffice.com
Contract office furniture & equipment, project management, furniture installations & re-configurations, refinishing & reupholstery. (Woman/Hisp, estab 1973, empl 15, sales $3,200,000, cert: City)

3547   Global Installation Resources LLC
      18 Robert St
      Clifton, NJ 07014
      Contact: Krista Korinis Presdient
      Tel: 973-494-9680
      Email: kkorinis@gi-resources.com
      Website: www.gi-resources.com
Installation services: office furniture, demountable walls, signage & laboratory case work installations & project management services. (Woman, estab 2002, empl 10, sales $1,345,540, cert: State, WBENC)

3548   Image Office Environments, LLC
      1122 Route 22 W
      Mountainside, NJ 07092
      Contact: Tricia Patricco President
      Tel: 908-301-0074
      Email: tpatricco@image-office.com
      Website: www.image-office.com
Interior constructions, raised flooring, moveable walls & furniture. (Woman, estab 2005, empl 6, sales $9,000,000, cert: State, WBENC)

3549   JC Office Consultants,LLC
      242 Union Ave
      Somerville, NJ 08876
      Contact: Jackie Orlando CEO
      Tel: 908-842-2150
      Email: jackie@jcofficeconsultants.com
      Website: www.jcofficeconsultants.com
Dist office furniture, installation & reconfiguration services. Space planning & CAD design. (Woman/Hisp, estab 2009, empl 5, sales $1,900,000, cert: State, WBENC)

New York

3550 Alianza Services LLC
74 N Broadway 2nd Fl S
Nyack, NY 10960
Contact: Dawn Cannon VP
Tel: 845-675-7337
Email: dcannon@alianzacorp.com
Website: www.alianzacorp.com
Dist furniture, budgeting, refurbishing, storage & asset management, rental solutions, service & repair. (Hisp, estab 2006, empl 6, sales $5,100,000, cert: NMSDC)

3551 Architectural Flooring Resources, Inc.
135 W 27th St
New York, NY 10001
Contact: Mercedes Montano Project Coord
Tel: 212-290-0200
Email: mercedes@afrny.com
Website: www.afrny.com
Carpet, carpet tile, vinyl, composition tile, wood (varies by species), cork, linoleum & specialty flooring. (Woman/Hisp, estab 1993, empl 19, sales $7,896,224, cert: City, NMSDC, WBENC)

3552 Golden Group International, Ltd.
305 Quaker Rd
Patterson, NY 12563
Contact: Presdient
Tel: 845-440-5220
Email:
Website: www.GoldenGroupInternational.com
Mfr & dist bags, dispensers, receptacles and cabinets. (Woman, estab 2009, empl 8, sales , cert: WBENC)

3553 Meadows Office Supply Co., Inc.
885 3rd Ave, 29th Fl
New York, NY 10022
Contact: Dina Radoncic Exec VP
Tel: 212-741-0333
Email: mofwbe@meadowsoffice.com
Website: www.meadowsofficeinteriors.com
Dist Haworth furniture products. (Woman, estab 1967, empl 76, sales $81,500,000, cert: City, WBENC)

3554 Seating Inc.
P.O. Box 898
Hunda, NY 14517
Contact: Emily J Hart Special Projects Coord
Tel: 585-468-2875
Email: emily@seatinginc.com
Website: www.seatinginc.com
Mfr office seating: ergonomic task, executive, multi-purpose, stools, stacking & nesting chairs. (Woman, estab 1987, empl 25, sales , cert: WBENC)

3555 Waldner's Business Environments, Inc.
125 Route 110
Farmingdale, NY 11735
Contact: Meredith Stern Presdient
Tel: 631-844-9342
Email: mstern@waldners.com
Website: www.waldners.com
Dist & install office furniture. (Woman, estab 1939, empl 107, sales $92,800,000, cert: City, WBENC)

Ohio

3556 APG Office Furnishings
P.O. Box 631850
Cincinnati, OH 45263
Contact: Connie L. Goins Presdient
Tel: 513-239-6814
Email: cgoins@apgde.com
Website: www.apgof.com
Dist office furniture, space planning, design, project management services & product solutions. (Woman, estab 1969, empl , sales $50,000,000, cert: State, WBENC)

3557 Budget Office Interiors LLC
1771 E. 30th St
Cleveland, OH 44114
Contact: Presdient
Tel: 216-566-1540
Email:
Website: www.budgetofficeinteriorsllc.com
New furniture, used furniture & refinished furniture: cubicles, workstations, space planning, desks, seating, conference rooms, training rooms, break rooms, home offices, telemarketing areas, reception areas, lateral & vertical filing. (Woman, estab 2005, empl 4, sales $292,229, cert: City)

3558 Clara I. Brown Interiors, Inc. (CIBI)
5305 Courtney Pl
Columbus, OH 43235
Contact: Clara I. Brown Presdient
Tel: 614-224-9180
Email: jim@cibiinc.com
Website: http://cibiinc.com
Office Furniture, Carpet & Hard Flooring, Carpet Cleaning, Re-upholstery, Mill Work, De-mountable Walls, Wall Coverings, Window Treatments, Interior Design/Space Planning, Furniture Moves, Warehousing. (Woman/Hisp, estab 1993, empl 12, sales $3,828,904, cert: NMSDC)

3559 Interior Services Incorporated dba Enriching Spaces
1360 Kemper Meadow Dr
Cincinnati, OH 45240
Contact: Dawn Schwartzman President & CEO
Tel: 513-851-0933
Email: dawn@enrichingspaces.com
Website: www.enrichingspaces.com
Office Furniture, Healthcare Furniture, School & University Furniture, Art & Accessories, Carpet Tile, Signage, Interior Design, Branding, Ergonomic Accessories, Ergonomic Chairs, Desks, Workstations, Conference Room. (Woman, estab 1982, empl , sales , cert: WBENC)

3560 King Business Interiors
1400 Goodale Blvd, Ste 102
Columbus, OH 43212
Contact: Darla King Owner
Tel: 614-430-0020
Email: darlaking@kbiinc.com
Website: www.kbiinc.com
Office furniture dealer. (Woman, estab 1998, empl , sales , cert: WBENC)

3561 Master Manufacturing Co, Inc.
      9200 Inman Ave
      Cleveland, OH 44105
      Contact: Bob Ptacek V.P. Sales
      Tel: 800-323-5513
      Email: bptacek@mastermfgco.com
      Website: www.mastermfgco.com
Mfr furniture casters & self-stick wheels; felt pads, surface
protectors, wobble stoppers; furniture movers; door stops;
ergonomic support cushions & wire mgmt channels &
grommets. (Woman, estab , empl , sales , cert: CPUC,
WBENC)

3562 RCF Group
      6454 Centre Park Dr
      West Chester, OH 45069
      Contact: Carl Satterwhite Presdient
      Tel: 513-612-7303
      Email: damian.thomas@thercfgroup.com
      Website: www.thercfgroup.com
Design office layout, new furniture, installation, move
management & asset management. (AA, estab 2003, empl
104, sales $67,344,541, cert: NMSDC)

3563 Vocon Partners, LLC
      3142 Prospect Ave
      Cleveland, OH 44115
      Contact: Karen Lipnick Finance Asst
      Tel: 216-588-0800
      Email: karen.lipnick@vocon.com
      Website: www.vocon.com
Furniture coordination, graphic design. (Woman, estab
1987, empl , sales $30,000,000, cert: WBENC)

3564 Williams Interior Designs, Inc
      4449 Easton Way, 2nd Floor
      Columbus, OH 43219
      Contact: Carolyn Williams Francis CEO
      Tel: 614-418-7250
      Email: carolyn@williamsinteriordesigns.com
      Website: www.williamsinteriordesigns.com
Interior design, office furniture, office supplies & window
treatments. (Woman/AA, estab 1985, empl 4, sales
$2,000,000, cert: NMSDC)

Oregon

3565 Carriage Works, Inc.
      1877 Mallard Ln
      Klamath Falls, OR 97601
      Contact: Barbara Evensizer President
      Tel: 541-882-0700
      Email: info@carriageworks.com
      Website: www.carriageworks.com
Mfr carts: food, espresso, kiosks, beverage, bar, vending &
display items. (Woman/Nat Ame, estab 1971, empl 30,
sales $4,000,000, cert: State)

Pennsylvania

3566 Alpha Office Supplies, Inc.
      4950 Parkside Ave Ste 500
      Philadelphia, PA 19131
      Contact: Chester Riddick CEO
      Tel: 215-226-2690
      Email: chet.riddick@alphaos.com
      Website: www.alphaos.com
Dist office furniture & supplies, paper, computers &
accessories; desktop delivery, installation, space planning
& project mgmt. (AA, estab 1985, empl 29, sales
$26,000,000, cert: NMSDC)

3567 Corporate Facilities of New Jersey, LLC
      2129 Chestnut St
      Philadelphia, PA 19103
      Contact: Amanda Chevalier Principal
      Tel: 215-279-9999
      Email: achevalier@cfinj-knoll.com
      Website: www.cfi-knoll.com
Office furniture. (Woman/As-Pac, estab 2004, empl 26,
sales , cert: NMSDC, WBENC)

3568 Peerless Wall and Window Coverings, Inc.
      3490 William Penn Hwy
      Pittsburgh, PA 15235
      Contact: Bob Cherry Mgr
      Tel: 412-823-7660
      Email: sales@peerlesswallpaperandblinds.com
      Website: www.peerlesswallpaperandblinds.com
Dist & install wallcoverings, window coverings, blinds,
shades, shutters & draperies. (Woman, estab 1993, empl
6, sales $761,857, cert: State)

3569 Telrose Corporation
      3801 Ridge Ave
      Philadelphia, PA 19132
      Contact: CEO
      Tel: 215-229-0500
      Email:
      Website: www.telrosecorp.com
Dist office supplies, equipment & furniture. (AA, estab
1995, empl 19, sales $8,000,000, cert: City, NMSDC)

Puerto Rico

3570 Integrated Design Solutions
      90 Carr 165, Ste 405
      Guaynabo, PR 00968
      Contact: Marlen Diaz VP
      Tel: 787-706-0201
      Email: mdiaz@ids-pr.com
      Website: www.ids-pr.com
Office furniture dealer. (Hisp, estab 1999, empl 17, sales
$5,800,000, cert: NMSDC)

South Carolina

3571 Skutchi Designs Inc.
      171 Gardner Lacy Rd
      Myrtle Beach, SC 29579
      Contact: Jeff Little Ecommerce
      Tel: 843-410-0605
      Email: jeff@skutchi.com
      Website: www.skutchi.com
Mfr Office Furniture, Panels Systems, Wall Systems,
Conference Tables, Acrylic Screens, Acoustical products,
and Desks. We space plan, design and install nationwide.
(Woman, estab 2005, empl 30, sales $5,000,000, cert:
WBENC)

Tennessee

3572 Norris Design, LLC
      751 Fox Ridge Lane
      Caryville, TN 37714
      Contact: Liz Salem Principal
      Tel: 865-712-9658
      Email: liz@norrisdesignco.com
      Website: www.norrisdesignco.com
Contract furniture, single office contracts to multi-floor
buildings. (Woman/As-Pac, estab 2004, empl 5, sales
$2,500,000, cert: State)

Texas

3573 B&H Total Office Solutions
120 Sam Bass Ridge Rd
Southlake, TX 76092
Contact: Jeannie Norris Presdient
Tel: 817-430-8345
Email: jeannie@bhofficesolutions.com
Website: http://bhofficesolutions.com
New & used Furniture, refurbished cubicles, Space
Planning, Furniture Moves. (Woman, estab 2006, empl 6,
sales $650,000, cert: State)

3574 Business Interiors
1111 Valley View
Irving, TX 75061
Contact: Sally Smith Presdient
Tel: 817-858-2000
Email: ssmith@businessinteriors.com
Website: www.businessinteriors.com
Office furniture sales & services: rental, used sales,
installation, reconnfiguration, repair, touch up, carpet
sales & installation, relocations, storage, design & space
planning. (Woman, estab 1968, empl 151, sales
$48,000,000, cert: WBENC)

3575 Facilitech Inc. dba Business Interiors
1111 Valley View Ln
Irving, TX 75061
Contact:
Tel: 817-858-2024
Email:
Website: www.businessinteriors.com
Office furniture: space planning & design, project mgmt,
installation, relocation, work process consulting, refurbish-
ing, asset management & rental. (Woman, estab 1970,
empl 140, sales $51,517,000, cert: WBENC)

3576 Facilities Connection, Inc.
240 E Sunset Rd
El Paso, TX 79922
Contact: Patty Holland Branch CEO
Tel: 915-833-8303
Email: phbranch@facilitiesconnection.com
Website: www.facilitiesconnection.com
Interior design, furniture layout, space planning, project
management, office furniture installation, reconfiguration,
relocation, interiors, assets maintenance. (Woman/Hisp,
estab 1987, empl 25, sales $27,000,000, cert: State)

3577 Facilities Resource Inc.
9737 Great Hills Trail, Ste 305
Austin, TX 78759
Contact: Business Dev Mgr
Tel: 512-371-1232
Email:
Website: www.fri-texas.com
Office furniture furnishings. Move services & move
coordination & planning. Furniture installation, interior
design & space planning. (Woman, estab 1997, empl 13,
sales $1,800,000, cert: State, City)

3578 Facility Interiors Inc.
P.O. Box 201828
Dallas, TX 75320
Contact: Charles Griggsby Presdient
Tel:
Email: charlesg@fiinc.com
Website: www.facilityinteriors.com
Furniture installation, design, project management,
move services, reconfigurations services. (AA, estab ,
empl , sales $80,000,000, cert: State, NMSDC)

3579 Houston Modular Installation
245 Brookhill Dr, Ste 9
Houston, TX 77087
Contact: Robert Garza Owner
Tel: 713-847-7666
Email: rgarza.houstonmodular@yahoo.com
Website:
Modular furniture installation: new installations. re-
configurations inner office moves, re-location moves &
deliveries. (Hisp, estab 1999, empl 18, sales , cert: State)

3580 Intelligent Interiors, Inc.
16837 Addison Rd Ste 500
Addison, TX 75001
Contact: Mindy Casas Presdient
Tel: 214-239-9886
Email: mcasas@intelligentinteriors.net
Website: www.intelligentinteriors.net
Contract office furniture, design, installation, repair
refurbishing, carpet, window covering. (Woman/Hisp,
estab 1996, empl 12, sales $800,000, cert: State,
NMSDC)

3581 Modular Installation Services, Inc.
8606 Wall St Ste 150
Austin, TX 78754
Contact: Monica Gould VP
Tel: 512-835-7706
Email: mpgould@modularinstall.com
Website: www.modularinstall.com
Commercial office furniture installation &
reconfiguration services. (Hisp, estab 1996, empl 30,
sales $1,300,000, cert: State)

3582 Neutral Posture, Inc.
3904 N. Texas Ave
Bryan, TX 77803
Contact: Rebecca Boenigk CEO
Tel: 979-778-0502
Email: rboenigk@np-us.com
Website: www.neutralposture.com
Mfr ergonomic, multipurpose, industrial seating &
accessories. (Woman, estab 1989, empl 65, sales , cert:
WBENC, SDB)

Virginia

3583 Alpha Stone Solutions
2251 Dabney Rd, Ste H
Richmond, VA 23230
Contact: Shion Fenty Acct Exec
Tel: 804-622-2068
Email: shion@alphastone.us
Website: www.alphastone.us
Dist granite products, furniture, fixtures & equipment
for hotel industry. (Woman/As-Pac, estab 2000, empl 20,
sales $2,800,000, cert: State)

3584 Finial Showcase, Inc.
      720 Third St
      Vinton, VA 24179
      Contact: Whitney Snyder Corp acct Mgr
      Tel: 540-982-3593
      Email: sales@finialshowcase.com
      Website: www.finialshowcase.com
Dist accent tables, plant stands, quilt racks, coat racks,
dvd/cd cabinets, stacking tables, umbrella stands, waste
baskets, desks for home office, magazine racks, luggage
racks, mirrors and wall decor, vases, decorative accessories, table lamps. (Woman, estab 1982, empl 5, sales
$650,000, cert: WBENC)

3585 Votum Enterprises, LLC
      3530 Post Office Rd Ste 5104
      Midlothian, VA 23112
      Contact: Mark Walton Dir Business Dev
      Tel: 804-317-9660
      Email: mark@votument.com
      Website: http://votument.com
Provides cubicle, modular & systems furniture & related
services, installations, reconfigurations, disassembly,
moving & storage. (AA, estab 2009, empl 3, sales
$257,000, cert: State, NMSDC)

Washington

3586 Home and Travel Solutions, LLC dba BedVoyage
      18915 142nd Ave NE, Ste 230
      Woodinville, WA 98072
      Contact: CEO
      Tel: 425-949-8216
      Email:
      Website: www.bedvoyage.com
Mfr eco-luxury bamboo bed linens, towels & blankets.
(Woman, estab 2008, empl 7, sales $1,200,000, cert:
NWBOC)

Wisconsin

3587 Laacke & Joys LLC
      3205 N 124th St
      Brookfield, WI 53005
      Contact: Joel Vento VP Sales/Mktg
      Tel: 800-892-5563
      Email: jsvento@conceptseating.com
      Website: http://conceptseating.com
Mfr 24/7 intensive use ergonomic office chairs used for
dispatch, security, control rooms, surveillance. (Woman,
estab , empl 100, sales $9,000,000, cert: WBENC)

GIFTWARES, ARTS & CRAFTS
Manufacture, distribute and import merchandise as well as cooperatives which produce jewelry, carvings, baskets, greeting cards, etc. NAICS Code 42

California

3588 The Corporate Gift Service, Inc.
4120 W Burbank Blvd
Burbank, CA 91505
Contact: Lydia Eltringham Accounting Dept
Tel: 818-845-9500
Email: accounting@corpgiftservice.com
Website: www.thecorporategiftservice.com
Handmade Custom Gift Baskets, Embroidered Corporate Apparel, High End Corporate Gifts, Branded Promotional Products & Advertising Specialties. (Woman, estab 1990, empl 7, sales $1,600,000, cert: WBENC)

Florida

3589 Floral Group, Inc.
2291 NW 82 Ave
Miami, FL 33122
Contact: Dornett Mullings President
Tel: 305-477-5008
Email: dornett@floralgroup.net
Website: www.floralgroup.net
Fresh floral products to supermarket chains, foam arrangements, vase arrangements, hand-tied bouquets, rose bouquets, mixed bouquets. (Woman/AA, estab 2003, empl 12, sales $990,000, cert: NMSDC)

Georgia

3590 Barazzo, LLC
2221 Peachtree Rd NE Ste D357
Atlanta, GA 30309
Contact: Quiana Lloyd Member
Tel: 888-716-5785
Email: quiana@barazzo.com
Website: www.barazzo.com
Custom gift & accessory solutions, corporate brand identity & marketing solutions. (Woman/AA, estab 2009, empl , sales , cert: State, NMSDC, SDB)

3591 Gratitude Goodies, LLC
433 Canton Rd Ste 315
Cumming, GA 30040
Contact: Diane Campbell Owner
Tel: 770-886-9598
Email: diane@gratitudegoodies.com
Website: www.GratitudeGoodies.com
Gift basket with chocolate, savory & gift items. (Woman, estab 2009, empl 4, sales , cert: WBENC, NWBOC)

Illinois

3592 Pearl's Girl Sweet Treats
15222 S LaGrange
Orland Park, IL 60463
Contact: Jacqueline Jackson Owner
Tel: 708-460-3960
Email: gojackiejackson@aol.com
Website: http://kilwins.com
Corporate gift baskets: gourmet caramel apples, handmade fudge, carmel corn, brittles, fine chocolates, dipped strawberries & confectins & 32 flavors of koshers icecream. (Woman/AA, estab 2007, empl , sales $160,000, cert: NMSDC)

3593 Planet Canit, LLC
843 Kimball Rd
Highland Park, IL 60035
Contact: Virginia Price
Tel: 847-433-1619
Email: vprice@planetcanit.com
Website: www.planetcanit.com
Custom decorative tin-ware packaging. (Woman, estab 2000, empl 1, sales , cert: WBENC)

Indiana

3594 Trans-Plants Inc.
1260 S Senate Ave
Indianapolis, IN 46225
Contact: Christine Ernst Presdient
Tel: 317-972-6760
Email: admin@trans-plantsindy.com
Website: http://transplants-indy.com
Interior plants & maintenance, design & installation. Floral arrangements, gift baskets, corporate & individual gifts. (Woman, estab 1986, empl 10, sales $360,786, cert: City)

Kentucky

3595 Wall Street Greetings, LLC
3265 Pincakrd Pike
Versailles, KY 40383
Contact: Susan Rice Natl Accts Specialist
Tel: 859-873-0877
Email: april@wallstreetgreetings.com
Website: http://wallstreetgreetings.com
Corporate greeting cards. (Woman, estab 1992, empl 33, sales $2,628,121, cert: WBENC)

Massachusetts

3596 Madison Floral, Inc.
63B Innerbelt Rd
Somerville, MA 02143
Contact: Edison Chae Presdient
Tel: 781-648-2000
Email: edison@madisonfloral.com
Website: www.madisonfloral.com
Floral design: corporate functions, annual meetings, dinner affairs. (As-Pac, estab 2000, empl 5, sales $180,000, cert: State)

Maryland

3597 Copiosity, LLC
8230 Georgia Ave, 2nd Fl
Silver Spring, MD 20910
Contact: Dianne Harrison Principal
Tel: 301-608-9102
Email: dcharrison@copiosityllc.com
Website: www.copiositygreetings.com
Greeting products: holiday gift wrapping paper, bags, tags, and decorations; holiday greeting cards; graphic & decorative wall decals; celebration yard signs; and stylish seasonal garden products such as disposable table liners. (Woman/AA, estab 2010, empl 2, sales , cert: NMSDC)

3598 Main Street Embroidery
85 Main St
Reisterstown, MD 21136
Contact: Carol Payne President
Tel: 410-833-0414
Email: mse@marylandtowns.com
Website: www.marylandtowns.com
Embroidery, screen printing, heat press, gift card printing. (Woman, estab 1992, empl 2, sales , cert: State)

Minnesota

3599 Schaaf Floral
6554 University Ave NE
Minneapolis, MN 55432
Contact: Marcia Schaaf Owner
Tel: 763-571-4600
Email: flowers@schaaffloral.com
Website: www.schaaffloral.com
Floral arrangement, gifts, etc. (Woman, estab 1970, empl 13, sales $806,748, cert: WBENC)

New York

3600 Chocolate Promises, Inc.
P.O. Box 694
Merrick, NY 11566
Contact: Zakalik Cindy Presdient
Tel: 516-299-6400
Email: cindy@chocolatepromises.com
Website: www.chocolatepromises.com
Personalized chocolate with edible images. We'll custom print your full color logo, picture, design and/or special message directly on delicious chocolate coins, lollipops, Belgian truffles and more. (Woman, estab 2012, empl 2, sales , cert: State, City, WBENC)

Ohio

3601 Independence Flowers & Gifts
6495 Brecksville Rd
Independence, OH 44131
Contact: Laura Gmitro Owner
Tel: 216-524-2800
Email: indyflowers@yahoo.com
Website: www.independenceflorist.com
Florist & gift shop, fruit baskets, gourmet baskets, custom baskets, floral arrangements & gifts. (Woman, estab 2009, empl 4, sales $280,000, cert: City)

3602 Uniquely Lisa Designs dba Our Favorite Things Boutique
12730 Larchmere Blvd
Shaker Heights, OH 44120
Contact: Lisa McGuthry CEO
Tel: 216-536-7928
Email: info@ourfavoritethingscle.com
Website: www.ourfavoritethingscle.com
Boutique that features fine gift items and body products. (AA, estab 2019, empl 5, sales $139,000, cert: NMSDC)

Texas

3603 Dessert Gallery Bakery & Cafe
P.O. Box 981034
Houston, TX 77098
Contact: Sara Brook CEO
Tel: 713-960-4400
Email: sara@dessertgallery.com
Website: www.dessertgallery.com
Custom photo & logo cookies & cakes, catering- box lunches, office birthday cakes, corporate gifts. (Woman, estab 1995, empl 35, sales , cert: WBENC)

HARDWARE & TOOLS DIST.
Distribute hardware: screw machine products, plumbing supplies, safety apparel, ladders, etc. (See also HYDRAULIC & COMPRESSED AIR EQUIPMENT and INDUSTRIAL EQUIPMENT & SUPPLIES). NAICS Code 42

Alabama

3604 Ram Tool & Supply Co., Inc.
4500 5th Ave South Bldg A
Birmingham, AL 35222
Contact: Ashley Cato Accts Receivable Rep
Tel: 205-599-7085
Email: ashley.cato@ramtool.com
Website: www.ram-tool.com
Dist construction material, supplies & tools. (Woman, estab 1985, empl 804, sales , cert: WBENC)

Arizona

3605 Machine Works, LLC
3832 E Illini St
Phoenix, AZ 85040
Contact: carter Trisha Sales/Office Mgr
Tel: 602-426-1035
Email: trisha.c@mworkllc.com
Website: http://machineworksllc.com
Dist aerospace components & assemblies. (As-Pac, estab 1997, empl 12, sales $900,000, cert: NMSDC)

California

3606 ACF Components & Fasteners, Inc.
31012 Huntwood Ave
Hayward, CA 94544
Contact: Bob Henriquez Exec VP
Tel: 510-487-2100
Email: bobh@acfcom.com
Website: www.acfcom.com
Dist industrial fasteners, electronic component hardware, wire, industrial supplies, vmi, kitting, kits, fastener plating, fastener patching, fuses, screws, bolts, terminals. (As-Pac, estab 1976, empl 50, sales $13,000,000, cert: CPUC)

3607 B&B Socket Products, Inc.
1919 Nancita Cir
Placenta, CA 92870
Contact: Robert Huke GM
Tel: 714-985-4360
Email: rchuke@bbsocket.com
Website: www.bbsocket.com
Dist fasteners, hardware & electronic components. (Woman, estab 1976, empl 17, sales , cert: WBENC)

3608 Cordova Bolt, Inc.
5601 Dolly Ave
Buena Park, CA 90621
Contact: Moses E. Cordova President
Tel: 714-739-7500
Email: info@cordovabolt.com
Website: www.cordovabolt.com
Dist nuts, bolts, screws, washers, anchors, A325, A490, GR 2-5-8-L9, etc. (Hisp, estab 1975, empl 34, sales , cert: NMSDC, CPUC)

3609 Mackenzie Aircraft Parts, Inc.
1400 Decision St
Vista, CA 92081
Contact: Toni Mackenzie Presdient
Tel: 760-727-3775
Email: toni@macairparts.com
Website: www.macairparts.com
Dist hardware, screws, nuts, bolts, rivets, washers, bearings & electrical parts. (Woman, estab 1979, empl 11, sales $2,500,000, cert: NWBOC)

3610 Satori Seal, Inc.
8455 Utica Ave
Rancho Cucamonga, CA 91730
Contact: Anne Houlihan Presdient
Tel: 909-987-8234
Email: anne@satoriseal.com
Website: www.satoriseal.com
Dist o-rings, seals, custom molded seals, rotary shaft seals, PTFE seal tape, worm drive hose clamps, gaskets, washers, die cut gaskets, lathe cut gaskets. (Woman, estab 1971, empl 8, sales $2,749,793, cert: WBENC)

3611 STX, Inc. DBA Alta Industries
418 Aviation Blvd, Ste E
Santa Rosa, CA 95403
Contact:
Tel: 800-788-0302
Email:
Website: www.altaindustries.com
Mfr & dist protective knee pads & elbow pads, tool belts for industrial, construction, safety, military & tactical markets. (Woman, estab , empl , sales $3,800,000, cert: NWBOC)

3612 Vampire Tools, Inc.
47 Peters Canyon Rd
Irvine, CA 92606
Contact: Farooqui Ali Administrator
Tel: 949-449-5724
Email: ali@vampiretools.com
Website: www.vampiretools.com
Unique pliers for rusted, damaged, stripped screws/nuts/bolts extraction. (Woman/As-Pac, estab 2010, empl 7, sales $400,000, cert: NMSDC, CPUC)

3613 Widespread Industrial Supplies, Inc.
1220 S Boyle Ave
Los Angeles, CA 90023
Contact: Josh Dorfman President
Tel: 310-793-7315
Email: josh.dorfman@widespreadind.com
Website: www.widespreadind.com
Dist industrial supplies: fasteners, cutting tools, electrical, welding, chemical & safety related supplies, hand & power tools. (Woman, estab 2002, empl 4, sales $820,341, cert: State, City)

Florida

3614 Arrowhead Global, LLC
22033 US 19 N
Clearwater, FL 33765
Contact: Anthony Terranova Sales Mgr
Tel: 727-497-7340
Email: tony@arrowheadglobal.com
Website: www.arrowheadglobal.com
Dist aerospace, military & commercial fasteners, hardware, connectors, electronic components, aircraft parts, adhesives & information technology products & services. (Nat Ame, estab 2013, empl 10, sales $3,100,000, cert: NMSDC, 8a)

3615 Consolidated Cordage Corp Inc.
1707 Avenida Del Sol
Boca Raton, FL 33432
Contact: Mike Perry Sales Mgr
Tel: 561-347-7247
Email: info@consolidatedcordage.com
Website: www.consolidatedcordage.com
Dist rope, cord, pull cord, twine, elastic shockcord, fall protection safety equip, multe tape, riggings, hoistings, etc. (Woman, estab 1993, empl 8, sales , cert: State, WBENC, NWBOC)

3616 Limitless Investigative Solutions, L.L.C.
11160 Lost Creek Terrace #205
Bradenton, FL 34211
Contact: Miguel Caraballo Presdient
Tel: 678-458-8538
Email: miguel@limitlessinv.com
Website: http://limitlessinv.com
Solid carbide end mills, drills, reamers, burrs, inserts & specials, in house research & development, custom tool design for various applications, ools simulation software. (Hisp, estab 2017, empl 1, sales , cert: State)

3617 Pelican Sales, Inc.
2825 Business Center Blvd Ste C9
Melbourne, FL 32940
Contact: Callena Spearman Sales Professional
Tel: 321-254-9569
Email: sales@pelican-sales.com
Website: www.pelican-direct.com
Dist industrial hardware equipment & supplies. (Woman, estab 1993, empl 15, sales $13,000,000, cert: State)

3618 The Bernd Group Inc.
1251 Pinehurst Rd
Dunedin, FL 34698
Contact: Pilar Bernd Presdient
Tel: 727-733-0122
Email: businessdevelopment@berndgroup.com
Website: www.berndgroup.com
Material handling equip, safety products, hand & power tools, pumps & compressors, motors, generators, electrical hardware, batteries, lighting fixtures, lockers, bins, shelving, lab equip. (Woman/Hisp, estab 1992, empl 66, sales , cert: NMSDC)

3619 Tropic Fasteners LLC
255 Semoran Comerce Pl
Apopka, FL 32703
Contact: Judy Watson Presdient
Tel: 407-703-1582
Email: judy@tropicfast.com
Website: www.tropicfast.com
Dist fastener products. (Woman, estab 1995, empl 50, sales , cert: WBENC)

Illinois

3620 Alin Machining Co, Inc. dba Power Plant Services
3131 W Soffel Ave
Melrose Park, IL 60160
Contact: Sonia Gandhi Sales Team Lead
Tel: 708-345-8600
Email: sonia@ppsvcs.com
Website: www.ppsvcs.com
Dist fasteners, studs, nuts, washers, bolts & pins, turbine valve parts, stems, discs & bushings, turbine blade mfg, turbine seals & packing, erosion shields. (As-Ind, estab 1998, empl 142, sales $42,000,000, cert: NMSDC)

3621 Hacha Products Corporation
801 North Main St
Wheaton, IL 60187
Contact: Kimberly Meek CEO
Tel: 630-347-6093
Email: kmeek@hachaproducts.com
Website: www.hachaproducts.com
Wire management devices: cable ties, wire nuts, clamps, nuts, bolts, fasteners, shrink tubing. (Woman/Hisp, estab 2015, empl 2, sales $750,000, cert: NMSDC, WBENC)

Indiana

3622 Impex International Inc.
7114 Innovation Blvd
Fort Wayne, IN 46818
Contact: Nagin Shah Presdient
Tel: 260-489-3030
Email: nshah@impexint.com
Website: www.impexint.com
Dist fasteners. (As-Ind, estab 1985, empl 6, sales , cert: NMSDC)

3623 Powell Tool Supply Co., Inc.
1338 Mishawaka Ave
South Bend, IN 46615
Contact: Cari Eaton CEO
Tel: 574-289-4811
Email: ceaton@powelltool.com
Website: www.powelltool.com
Dist industrial supplies: cutting tools, abrasives, chemicals, MRO supplies, material handling, janitorial, etc. (Woman, estab 1948, empl 20, sales $5,500,000, cert: WBENC)

3624 Quest Safety Products, Inc.
1414 S West St, Ste 200
Indianapolis, IN 46225
Contact: Sudhansu (Sam) Yadav Presdient
Tel: 317-594-4500
Email: ar@questsafety.com
Website: www.QuestSafety.com
Dist safety products. (As-Pac, estab 1997, empl 34, sales $13,600,000, cert: NMSDC)

3625 Thompson Distribution Company
2225 N College Ave
Indianapolis, IN 46205
Contact: John Thompson President
Tel: 317-923-2581
Email: johnt@thomdist.com
Website: www.thomdist.com
Dist pipes, valves, pumps, fittings; plumbing, electrical & industrial supplies; fasteners, stainless steel. (AA, estab 2001, empl 14, sales , cert: State, NMSDC)

Kentucky

3626 America's Finest Filters
2910 W Jefferson St
Louisville, KY 40212
Contact: Charles Houston Sales Mgr
Tel: 502-587-1937
Email: cahou65@aol.com
Website:
Dist filters. (AA, estab 1999, empl 5, sales $1,500,000, cert: NMSDC)

3627 Com Serv LLC
10201 Bunsen Way
Louisville, KY 40299
Contact: Shiva Dhanapal Presdient
Tel: 502-553-1770
Email: sdhanapal@component-supply.com
Website: http://component-supply.com
Specialty screws & customs hardware, engineering special fasteners,tubing, plastic parts, plastic injection molds, packaging supply, jigs for paint line applications, jigs & fixtures, returnable containers/totes, stamping. (As-Ind, estab 2000, empl 7, sales $5,435,800, cert: NMSDC)

3628 Sandy Valley Fasteners, LLC
528 Broadway St
Paintsville, KY 41240
Contact: Christy Henry-Gregory CEO
Tel: 606-788-0222
Email: christy@sandyvalleyfasteners.com
Website: www.sandyvalleyfasteners.com
Dist commercial & aerospace fasteners & supplies: AN, MS, NAS washers, nuts, bolts, screws, rivets, nutplates, electrical connectors & backshells, tools, raw materials, fittings, tubing, bushings, etc. (Woman, estab 1999, empl 13, sales , cert: WBENC)

Louisiana

3629 Best Bolt & Nut Corp.
2726 Lexington Ave
Kenner, LA 70062
Contact: Jason Mangiaracina GM
Tel: 504-469-3585
Email: jason@bestboltandnut.com
Website: www.bestboltandnut.com
Dist hardware. (Hisp, estab 1988, empl 20, sales , cert: NMSDC)

3630 Lightning Bolt and Supply
10626 S Choctaw Dr
Baton Rouge, LA 70815
Contact: Wesley Valverde VP Business Dev
Tel: 225-272-6200
Email: sharon@lightningboltandsupply.com
Website: www.lightningboltandsupply.com
Dist fasteners, nuts, bolts, hex bolts, lock nuts, lock washers, flat washers, fender washers, clips, retaining rings, hex head bolts, socket head cap screws, buttons, lug nuts, studs, double end studs, latches. (Woman, estab 1994, empl 15, sales , cert: WBENC)

Massachusetts

3631 CDP Fastener Group, Inc.
15 Jonathan Dr, Unit 6 Unit 6
Brockton, MA 02301
Contact: Peter A Cheney Sales / Quality Mgr
Tel: 508-580-5323
Email: petec@cdpfastener.com
Website: www.cdpfastener.com
Dist fasteners & mechanical products, vendor managed inventory svcs & kitting. (Minority, estab 1993, empl 12, sales , cert: State)

Maryland

3632 American General Contractor Inc.
1 Research Ct, Ste 450
Rockville, MD 20850
Contact: Linward Hope VP
Tel: 301-202-4511
Email: americangeneralmd@yahoo.com
Website: http://americangeneralmd.com
Dist construction materials, thermostats, tools, cement, sheet rock, led lights, hardware nails, screws, toilets, tile, all flooring, hand towels, paper towels. (Woman/As-Ind, estab 2012, empl 2, sales $107,000, cert: State)

3633 Atlantic Hardware Supply
8389 Ardwick Ardmore Rd
Hyattsville, MD 20785
Contact: Jon Gray VP
Tel: 240-249-6047
Email: jgray@atlantic-supply.com
Website: www.atlantic-supply.com
Dist hardware. (Woman, estab 2009, empl 6, sales , cert: State)

3634 B & B Lighting Supply, Inc.
P.O. Box 68084
Baltimore, MD 21215
Contact: Sharon Bradford CEO
Tel: 410-523-7300
Email: sbradford@bnblightingsupply.com
Website: www.bnblightingsupply.com
Dist lamps, relamping & energy mgmt, const mgmt & svcs, provision & professional. (Woman/AA, estab 1994, empl 2, sales $525,000, cert: State)

3635 JarCo-Fasteners
7909 Marlboro Pike
Forestville, MD 20747
Contact: Bill Todd Dir Sales/Marketing
Tel: 301-420-0146
Email: jrrco@aol.com
Website:
Dist fastener products: fasteners, washers, rivets & screws, bolts & nuts, anchors. (AA, estab 1999, empl 4, sales , cert: State)

Michigan

3636   Ewie Co., Inc.
       1099 Highland Dr
       Ann Arbor, MI 48108
       Contact: Shoki Mullick Dir of diversity
       Tel: 734-971-6265
       Email: shoki.mullick@ewie.com
       Website: www.ewie.com
Dist cutting tools, abrasives, special tools, chemical/
lubricants. (As-Ind, As-Pac, estab 1981, empl 253, sales
$122,000,000, cert: NMSDC)

3637   Extreme Tooling LLC
       48750 Structural Dr
       Chesterfield, MI 48051
       Contact: Kurt Schill Presdient
       Tel: 586-232-3618
       Email: kschill@extremetooling.com
       Website: www.extremetooling.com
Dist metal removal & industrial supplies, milling, drilling &
industrial products. (Woman, estab 2003, empl 5, sales
$3,683,821, cert: WBENC)

3638   Marshall Sales Inc
       14359 Meyers Road
       Detroit, MI 48227
       Contact: Paul Allar
       Tel: 248-761-8937
       Email: paul@allarse.com
       Website: www.marshallsales.com
Dist fasteners, rivets, screws, bolts, etc. (Woman/AA, estab
1958, empl 9, sales $7,000,000, cert: WBENC)

3639   Marshall Sales Inc.
       14359 Meyers Rd
       Detroit, MI 48227
       Contact: Brian Tupiak Acct Mgr
       Tel: 313-491-1700
       Email: btupiak@marshallsales.com
       Website: http://marshallsales.com
Fasteners & fastener installation, tooling. (Woman, estab ,
empl , sales , cert: State, WBENC)

3640   Materials Management Services Inc.
       13691 Girardin St
       Detroit, MI 48212
       Contact: Jack Long Presdient
       Tel: 313-365-1290
       Email: jlong@mms-inc.com
       Website: www.mms-inc.com
Mfr & dist industrial work gloves of fabric & leather in a
variety of styles. Also dist tools, tape, coolant, etc. (AA,
estab 1994, empl 11, sales , cert: NMSDC)

3641   Mer Wil Industries, Inc.
       328 S Saginaw St, Ste 902
       Flint, MI 48502
       Contact: Deborah Love Sales Rep
       Tel: 810-239-0600
       Email: mwilliams@merwil.com
       Website: www.merwil.com
Dist hardware & building supplies. (AA, estab 1983, empl
2, sales , cert: State)

3642   National Industrial Supply Co.
       1201 Rochester Rd
       Troy, MI 48083
       Contact: Kathryn Harper Presdient
       Tel: 248-588-1828
       Email: kathybrett@nischain.com
       Website: www.nischain.com
Dist chain, wire rope, nylons, hardware supplies, etc.
(Woman/Hisp, estab 1981, empl 20, sales $2,000,000,
cert: NMSDC, WBENC)

3643   New Eagle, LLC
       3588 Plymouth Rd, Ste 271
       Ann Arbor, MI 48105
       Contact: Mickey Swortzel CEO
       Tel: 734-929-4557
       Email: mswortzel@neweagle.net
       Website: www.neweagle.net
Controls system solutions, tools, products & services.
(Woman, estab 2008, empl 25, sales $3,874,600, cert:
WBENC)

3644   Northern Industrial Products Corp.
       20380 Cornillie Dr
       Roseville, MI 48066
       Contact: Andrew Wilson VP
       Tel: 586-293-9544
       Email: awilson@nipcorp.com
       Website: www.nipcorp.com
Dist industrial fasteners, tools, rack & shelving, etc. (AA,
estab 1976, empl 17, sales $5,000,000, cert: NMSDC)

3645   Reggie Mckenzie Industrial Materials, Inc.
       34401 Schoolcraft Rd Ste 200
       Livonia, MI 48150
       Contact: Dan Kapp Office Mgr
       Tel: 734-261-0844
       Email: dkapp@rmimi.com
       Website: www.reggiemckenzieindustrial.com
Dist MRO, Cutting Tools, Abrasives, Industrial Supplies,
Industrial Materials. (AA, estab 2000, empl 3, sales
$6,000,000, cert: NMSDC)

3646   Suburban Bolt and Supply Co.
       27670 Groesbeck
       Roseville, MI 48066
       Contact: Frank Woch Sales
       Tel: 586-775-8900
       Email: defense@suburbanbolt.com
       Website: www.suburbanbolt.com
Fasteners - Socket Products, Bolts, Screws, Pins, NAAMS,
Nuts, Washers, Anchors, Cutting Tools - Drills, Taps,
Counter Bores, Countersinks, Dies, Reamers, End Mills,
Saw Blades, Abrasives- Coated Abrasives, Cut off Wheels,
Flap Wheels and Discs. (Minority, estab 1971, empl 77,
sales $14,004,169, cert: NMSDC)

Minneosta

3647   Bredemus Hardware Co Inc.
       1285 Sylvan St
       St. Paul, MN 55117
       Contact: Betty Bredemus CEO
       Tel: 651-489-6250
       Email: betty@bredemus.com
       Website: www.bredemus.com
Dist hardware, hollow metal doors, frames & wood
doors. (Minority/Woman, estab 1955, empl 29, sales
$5,000,000, cert: State, City)

Missouri

3648 AMC Industries, LLC
       4251 N Kentucky Ave
       Kansas City, MO 64117
       Contact: Adam French Dir of Sales
       Tel: 816-833-4249
       Email: adam@amc-industries.net
       Website: www.amc-industries.net
Dist pipes, valves, fittings, plumbing fixtures, HVAC
equipment, HVAC accessories, toilet partitions & wash-
room accessories. (AA, estab 2001, empl 5, sales
$4,400,000, cert: State, City, NMSDC)

North Carolina

3649 ARTU-USA, Inc.
       330 Fields Dr.
       Aberdeen, NC 28315
       Contact: Beverly Tate-Cooper Presdient
       Tel: 910-944-1883
       Email: beverly@artu.com
       Website: www.artu.com/
Cutting tools, Multi-Purpose Drill Bits, PORC+ Drill Bits,
Cobalt Drill Bits, Tungsten Carbide Grit Hole Saws & Saw
Blades, SDS Drill Bits, Precision Multi-Purpose Drill Bits &
Spline Shanks. (Woman, estab 1989, empl 6, sales
$1,636,453, cert: State, CPUC, NWBOC)

3650 C & D Industrial Tools & Supplies Inc.
       2415 Penny Road Ste 101
       High Point, NC 27265
       Contact: Jerry Camp Presdient
       Tel: 336-885-6675
       Email: jerry@cdi-tools.com
       Website: www.cdi-tools.com
Dist cutting tools: drills, end mills, reamers, taps & dies,
precision tools, etc. (AA, estab 1988, empl 4, sales
$2,500,000, cert: NMSDC)

3651 Southern Fasteners & Supply, Inc.
       2421 W Clemmonsville Rd
       Winston-Salem, NC 27127
       Contact: Gene Yates VP
       Tel: 336-765-1790
       Email: gyates@southernfasteners.com
       Website: www.southernfasteners.com
Dist fasteners. (Woman/Nat Ame, estab , empl , sales
$20,000,000, cert: NMSDC)

New Jersey

3652 Edwards & West, Inc. dba Divspec
       605 Springfield Rd
       Kenilworth, NJ 07033
       Contact: Doug Burke NC Sales Mgr
       Tel: 908-688-2550
       Email: dougb@divspec.com
       Website: www.divspec.com
Dist threaded rod, strut, strut fittings, and fasteners.
(Woman, estab 1980, empl 12, sales $5,913,389, cert:
WBENC)

3653 Fastenation, Inc.
       120 Bright Rd Unit 2
       Clifton, NJ 07012
       Contact: Stephanie Cherepinsky Sales Rep
       Tel: 973-591-1277
       Email: stephanie@fastenation.com
       Website: www.fastenation.com
Distributor & Converter of VELCRO(R) Brand Fasteners
(Die-Cutting, Packaging, Printing, etc.) (Woman, estab
1997, empl 28, sales $9,000,000, cert: WBENC)

3654 Lightning Supply, Inc.
       87 Chadwick Rd Ste 200
       Teaneck, NJ 07666
       Contact: Benjamin JonesPresident
       Tel: 800-724-9976
       Email: bjones@lightningsupply.com
       Website: www.lightningsupply.com
Dist safety equip, supplies & protective apparel &
fabrics. (AA, estab 1993, empl 4, sales , cert: State)

3655 MF Supply Corp.
       164 Garibaldi Ave
       Lodi, NJ 07644
       Contact: Robin Lieberman Presdient
       Tel:
       Email: robin@mfsupply.com
       Website: www.mfsupply.com
Dist fasteners, Stainless Steel, Inserts & Keenserts,
Socket products, Standoffs & Spacers & Mil-Spec
fasteners. (Woman, estab 1974, empl 5, sales $823,000,
cert: State)

New York

3656 Global Connection Co. of America, Inc.
       150-123 Powells Cove Blvd
       Whitestone, NY 11357
       Contact: Grace King President
       Tel: 718-767-5168
       Email: gk@madeinchina.net
       Website: www.glocoamerica.com
Dist hardware & tools. (Woman/As-Pac, estab 1992,
empl 3, sales $2,107,046, cert: State, NMSDC)

3657 Henssgen Hardware Corporation
       P.O. Box 2078
       Queensbury, NY 12804
       Contact: Rachel Novak Presdient
       Tel: 518-793-3593
       Email: rachel@henssgenhardware.com
       Website: www.henssgenhardware.com
Sources rigging hardware, Snap Hooks, Pulleys (both
Fixed Eye and Swivel with Single Sheave and Double
Sheave), Quick Links, Shackles, Wire Rope Clips, Drop
Forged Clevis Grab & Clevis Slip Hooks. (Woman, estab
2000, empl 3, sales $548,000, cert: WBENC)

3658 NY Plumbing Wholesale & Supply, Inc.
       933 Columbus Ave
       New York, NY 10025
       Contact: Derek Price Presdient
       Tel: 212-678-4900
       Email: derek@nyps1.com
       Website: http://nyps1.com
Dist plumbing fittings, fixtures, pipe, tools & accessories.
(AA, estab 2009, empl 23, sales , cert: City)

3659 South Atlantic Marine Services
      342 Cold Spring Rd
      Syosset, NY 11791
      Contact: Linda Allen Presdient
      Tel: 516-449-9000
      Email: southatlantic15@yahoo.com
      Website: www.southatlantic-services.com
Dist lubricants, greases, additives, hardware, bolts fasteners, tools, fittings, safety products, ropes, chains, hoses,
twine, clamps rivet, cables, pumps, valves, bearings,
tubing, welding supplies, cutting tools. (Woman, estab
2000, empl 2, sales $889,255, cert: State, City)

Ohio

3660 CJ Industrial Supply Inc.
      15326 Waterloo Rd
      Cleveland, OH 44110
      Contact: Tom Frohwerk VP Sales
      Tel: 216-481-4448
      Email: tom@cjindustrial.com
      Website: http://cjindustrial.com
Industrial hardware, Valves Pumps Steel Fabrication, OSHA
Products, Plumbing, Electrical, Cutting Tools, Machine
Shop Services, Abrasives, Hand Tools, Power Tools, VOC
Compliant Chemicals & Paints, Steel. (Woman, estab 1995,
empl 8, sales $2,000,000, cert: State, City)

3661 CryoPlus, Inc.
      2429 N Millborne Rd
      Wooster, OH 44691
      Contact: Kathi Bond President
      Tel: 330-683-3375
      Email: kathicryo@aol.com
      Website: www.cryoplus.com
Cutting tools, blades, knives, dies & punches. (Woman,
estab 1994, empl 3, sales , cert: NWBOC)

3662 General Factory/ WD Supply
      4811 Winton Rd
      Cincinnati, OH 45232
      Contact: Pat Priko Sales
      Tel: 513-681-6300
      Email: patp@gfwdsupply.com
      Website: www.gfwdsupply.com
Dist MRO, welding, cutting tools, hand tools & safety.
(Woman, estab 2007, empl 32, sales $12,500,000, cert:
WBENC)

3663 Power Tool & Supply Co., Inc.
      3699 Leharps Rd
      Youngstown, OH 44515
      Contact: Linda Richardson Dir Business Devel
      Tel: 330-792-1487
      Email: linda@powertoolandsupply.com
      Website: http://powertoolandsupply.com
Dist power tools & supplies. (Woman, estab 1961, empl
18, sales , cert: State, WBENC)

3664 Queensgate Hardware & Security, Inc.
      1025 Dalton Ave
      Cincinnati, OH 45203
      Contact: Sarah Back President
      Tel: 513-929-0062
      Email: sarah@queensgatehardware.com
      Website: www.queensgatehardware.com
Dist commercial grade hardware, wood doors & frames,
hollow metal doors & frames, access control systems,
toilet partitions & accessories. (Woman, estab 2010, empl
3, sales $768,000, cert: WBENC)

3665 River City Building Solutions, LLC
      19885 Detroit Rd, Ste 173
      Cleveland, OH 44116
      Contact: Peggy Powers Presdient
      Tel: 216-333-1491
      Email: peggy@rivercitybuildingsolutions.com
      Website: www.rivercitybuildingsolutions.com
Dist building materials, sustainable materials, paintings
& coatings, roofing materials, flooring, HVAC, plumbing
materials, electrical / telecommunications wiring.
(Woman, estab 2011, empl 2, sales , cert: State, City)

Pennsylvania

3666 Hardware & Supply Company of Chester Inc.
      Fourth & Edgmont Ave
      Chester, PA 19013
      Contact: CEO
      Tel: 610-876-6116
      Email:
      Website: www.hschester.com
Dist maintenenance repair, operational, safety, janitorial,
material handling. (Woman, estab 1942, empl 11, sales ,
cert: State)

3667 Keystone Industrial Sales & Service, Inc.
      808 N Fourth Ave
      Altoona, PA 16601
      Contact: Tina McMullen President
      Tel: 814-949-5900
      Email: tmcmullen@keystoneindustrialss.com
      Website:
Dist power tools, hand tools, tool storage, industrial
vacuums, filters & floor matting/carpet. (Woman, estab
1997, empl 1, sales $251,120, cert: WBENC)

Puerto Rico

3668 Industrial Fittings & Valves
      P.O. Box 2329
      Toa Baja, PR 00951
      Contact: Jose Merino President
      Tel: 787-251-0840
      Email: jmerino@infiva.com
      Website: www.infiva.com
Dist industrial valves & fittings. (Hisp, estab 1985, empl
30, sales $6,093,000, cert: NMSDC)

South Carolina

3669 GT Industrial LLC Co.
      846 Royle Rd
      Ladson, SC 29456
      Contact: Teresa Gore Presdient
      Tel: 843-873-0290
      Email: teresag@gtindustrial.net
      Website: http://gtindustrial.com/
Dist tools, cert kits, tape, adhesives, dust masks, respira-
tors, marking crayons, flashlights, batteries, light bulbs.
(Nat Ame, estab 1998, empl 6, sales $5,111,180, cert:
NMSDC)

3670 Janeice Products Inc. Co.
      1084 Williston Road
      Aiken, SC 29803
      Contact: Valeria Castillo Cstmr Service
      Tel: 803-652-3025
      Email: sales@janeiceproducts.com
      Website: www.janeiceproducts.com
Dist MRO products: abrasives, cutting tools, fans, hand
tools, hardware, ladders, lawn & garden, material handling
equip & safety prods. (AA, Hisp, estab 1994, empl 5, sales ,
cert: NMSDC)

Tennessee

3671 D & J Tool Supply, LLC
      P.O. Box 9601
      Knoxville, TN 37940
      Contact: Deanna Maurer Owner
      Tel: 865-546-0744
      Email: deanna@djtoolsupply.com
      Website: www.djtoolsupply.com
Dist metalworking & fabricating machinery, machine tool
accessories, cutting tools, hand & power tools, metalworking fluids, abrasives, safety supplies, welding consumables.
(Woman, estab 1999, empl 2, sales $386,641, cert: State)

3672 Industrial Supply Solutions, LLC
      108 Jasmine Ct
      Henderson, TN 37072
      Contact: Tonya Martinek Managing Partner
      Tel: 615-461-7433
      Email: iss.martinek@gmail.com
      Website:
Power Tools & Metalworking; Cutting Tools; Precision
Measuring; Inserts; Abrasives; Pneumatics & Hydraulics;
Pumps & Plumbing; HVAC; Electrical; Lighting; Test
Instruments; Hand Tools, Power Tools & Fleet/Vehicle
Maintenance. (Woman, estab 2005, empl 2, sales , cert:
WBENC)

Texas

3673 Power Tool Service Co., Inc.
      3718 Polk St
      Houston, TX 77003
      Contact: JB Robertson VP
      Tel: 713-228-0100
      Email: sales@powertoolservice.com
      Website: www.powertoolservice.com
Dist, rent & repair tool & equipment, calibration. (Woman/
Hisp, estab 1969, empl 18, sales , cert: State)

3674 PowerOne and Associates, LLC
      12320 Barker Cypress Rd Ste 600-300
      Cypress, TX 77429
      Contact: Gus Guerrero BDM
      Tel: 713-955-7888
      Email: gus@power-one-usa.com
      Website: www.powerone-usa.com
Dist High Temperature Pipe, Hose & Cable Wraps (Safety),
MRO products, Hand Tools, Personal Safety Equipment
(PSE), Power transmission equipment (Safety Couplings,
Metal Bellows Coupling, Locking assemblies). (Hisp, estab
2008, empl 10, sales , cert: NMSDC)

3675 Powr-Guardian, Inc.
      1607 Falcon Dr, Ste 101
      DeSoto, TX 75115
      Contact: Von Miller President
      Tel: 972-228-9029
      Email: info@powrguardian.com
      Website: www.powrguardian.com
Dist & service batteries. (AA, estab 1988, empl 11, sales
$1,375,000, cert: State)

3676 Trinity Tape & Marking LLC
      3573 Bennett Rd
      Howe, TX 75459
      Contact: Dir of Sales
      Tel: 903-532-6068
      Email:
      Website: http://trinity-tape.com
Marking flags, inverted marking paint, barricade tape,
underground detectable & non-detectable tape,
surveyors flagging, safety vests, hard hats, hearing
protection, fall protection, safety glasses, first aid kits,
conduit, adhesive tapes, whiskers. (Woman, estab 2007,
empl 10, sales $1,200,000, cert: State, WBENC)

Virginia

3677 Apollo Energy Components Inc. t/a Apollo Supply
      2711 Lowesville Rd
      Arrington, VA 22922
      Contact: Christine Manley Presdient
      Tel: 434-277-5556
      Email: apollonrg2711@aol.com
      Website: http://apolloenergycomponents.com
Dist fasteners, pipe fittings, valves, high pressure tube
fittings, abrasives, grinding wheels, cutting tools, saw
blades, aerosols. (Woman, estab 2009, empl 3, sales
$122,080, cert: State)

3678 Machine Tools of Virginia, Inc.
      8147 Shady Grove Rd
      Mechanicsville, VA 23111
      Contact: Cindy Waddell President
      Tel: 804-569-6147
      Email: machinetoolsofva@hotmail.com
      Website: www.machinetoolsofvirginia.com
Dist machine tools: lathes & mills, CNC & standard, lathe
& mill accessories, carbide cutting tools, compressors,
grinders, drills, saws & fabrication equipment. (Woman,
estab 2001, empl 4, sales , cert: State)

HARDWARE & TOOLS MFG.
Manufacture fasteners and other screw machine products. Many manufacture tools and hand tools (See also HYDRAULIC & COMPRESSED AIR EQUIPMENT and INDUSTRIAL EQUIPMENT & SUPPLIES). NAICS Code 42

Arizona

3679   B&T Tool & Engineering Inc.
2618 E Washington St
Phoenix, AZ 85034
Contact: William Meras Presdient
Tel: 602-267-1481
Email: bnttool@aol.com
Website: http://bnttool.us
Mfr & dist precision cutting tools. (Hisp, estab 1992, empl 21, sales $3,701,273, cert: NMSDC)

3680   Special Carbide Tools
3153 E 36th St
Tucson, AZ 85713
Contact: Jerry Gamboa CEO
Tel: 520-624-0007
Email: jerry@specialcarbide.com
Website: www.specialcarbide.com
Mfr special custom carbide cutting tools: standard drills, endmills & reamers. (Hisp, estab 1999, empl 18, sales $2,000,000, cert: NMSDC)

California

3681   Blue Sky Industries
595 Monterey Pass Rd
Monterey Park, CA 91754
Contact: Denis Gagnier Outside Sales Mgr
Tel: 213-620-9950
Email: dgagnier@blueskyindustries.com
Website: www.blueskyindustries.com
Cherry & Monogram blind rivets & blind bolts, Shear Pins & Collars Hi-locks, Standard Aerospace Bolts, Screws, Nuts & Washers, Single & Double Oversize fasteners, Bushings, Bearings, Spacers, & Shims. (As-Pac, estab 1995, empl 52, sales $15,000,000, cert: NMSDC)

3682   D-Unique Tools
5744 International
Oakland, CA 94621
Contact: Nanette Hunter Presdient
Tel: 510-569-9961
Email: nanette@universalsquare.com
Website: www.universalsquare.com
Mfr & dist tools. (Woman/AA, estab 1991, empl 4, sales $125,536, cert: NMSDC)

Connecticut

3683   Chapman Manufacturing Company
471 New Haven Rd
Durham, CT 06422
Contact: Jason Camassar VP
Tel: 860-349-9228
Email: jason@chapmanmfg.com
Website: www.chapmanmfg.com
Mfr screwdriver kits. (Woman, estab 1936, empl 13, sales $683,000, cert: CPUC)

Florida

3684   AAW Products Inc.
825 Brickell Bay Dr Ste 246
Miami, FL 33131
Contact: Andre Woolery CEO
Tel: 305-330-6863
Email: andre@magnogrip.com
Website: www.magnogrip.com
Mfr magnetic work gear "MagnoGrip." MagnoGrip: wristbands, hammer holders, tool pouches & tool belts. (AA, estab 2005, empl 3, sales $4,500,000, cert: NMSDC)

3685   Limitless Investigative Solutions, L.L.C.
11160 Lost Creek Terrace #205
Bradenton, FL 34211
Contact: Miguel Caraballo Presdient
Tel: 678-458-8538
Email: miguel@limitlessinv.com
Website: http://limitlessinv.com
Solid carbide end mills, drills, reamers, burrs, inserts & specials, in house research & development, custom tool design for various applications, ools simulation software. (Hisp, estab 2017, empl 1, sales , cert: State)

3686   Raisman Corporation
5543 NW 72nd Ave
Miami, FL 33166
Contact:
Tel: 786-581-3820
Email: sales@raisman.com
Website: www.raisman.com
Mfr trimmer heads, spindles, primer bulbs, fuel filters, oil pumps, spark plugs, shock absorbers, mufflers, carburetors, carburetor kits, etc. (Hisp, estab 1998, empl 120, sales $15,000,000, cert: State)

Illinois

3687   Foreman Tool & Mold Company
3850 Swenson Ave
St. Charles, IL 60174
Contact: Jeff Gardner Sales Mgr
Tel: 630-377-6389
Email: jgardner@foremantool.com
Website: www.foremantool.com
Complete 3D part design, Pro-E mold design & layout. (Hisp, estab 1984, empl 80, sales $ 0, cert: NMSDC)

3688   Pioneer Service Inc. - Addison, IL
542 W Factory Rd
Addison, IL 60101
Contact: Beth Swanson VP Sales/Mktg
Tel: 630-628-0249
Email: bswanson@pioneerserviceinc.com
Website: www.pioneerserviceinc.com/
Contract mfr screw machine products & centerless grinding services: shafts, axles, bolts, bushings, dowels, pins, rods, spacers, valve stems, deburring, drilling, flatting, grinding, knurling, slotting, tapping, threading, heat treating. (Woman, estab 1990, empl 40, sales $5,000,000, cert: CPUC, WBENC)

3689 Tag Tool Services, Inc.
      3303 N Main St
      East Peoria, IL 61611
      Contact: Vonda Jones Presdient
      Tel: 309-694-2400
      Email: vonda@countyline-tool.com
      Website: www.countyline-tool.com
Cutting tool manufacturing & tool refurbishment, regrind
Hobs, Shaper Cutters, Broach Bars, Drills, Rota Broaches,
Port Tools, Gun Drills, End Mills, Taps, Reamers, Chamfer
Tools, Special Form Tools. (Woman, estab 1984, empl 14,
sales $1,200,000, cert: WBENC)

Massachusetts

3690 Electrical Safety Products LLC
      375 Main St
      Woburn, MA 01801
      Contact: Tom Wilkie Dir of Sales
      Tel: 781-249-5007
      Email: tom.wilkie@electricalsafety-usa.com
      Website: www.electricalsafety-usa.com
Mfr ASTM F-1505 certified insulated tools. (Woman, estab
2009, empl 4, sales , cert: WBENC)

Michigan

3691 2K Tool LLC
      3025 Madison Ave SE
      Wyoming, MI 49548
      Contact: Kevin Smith Engineering Mgr
      Tel: 616-452-4927
      Email: kevin@2ktool.com
      Website: www.2ktool.com
Moldmaker, machining, tooling, plastic injection molds,
compression tooling, composite machining, casting
machining, small part Injection molding. (Woman, estab
2004, empl 19, sales $2,269,151, cert: WBENC)

3692 Anderson Express, Inc.
      580 W Sherman Blvd
      Muskegon Heights, MI 49444
      Contact: Angel Ball HR Mgr
      Tel: 231-733-6001
      Email: aball@andersonexpressinc.com
      Website: www.andersonexpressinc.com
Rapid tooling & tooling prototypes for small & medium
projects. (Woman, estab 2011, empl 17, sales $ 0, cert:
WBENC)

3693 Ideal Machine Tool Technologies, LLC
      675 E Big Beaver Rd, Ste 105
      Troy, MI 48083
      Contact: Vincent H. Hylton Owner
      Tel: 248-792-9061
      Email: v.hylton@e-imtt.com
      Website: www.e-imtt.com
Commodity management services, program management,
engineering services, field services in the machine tool
industry. (AA, estab 2010, empl 2, sales $ 0, cert:
NMSDC)

3694 Micro Fixtures, Inc.
      20448 Lorne
      Taylor, MI 48180
      Contact: SUE RADER Office Mgr
      Tel: 313-382-9781
      Email: microfixtures@msn.com
      Website: www.MicroFixtures.com
Design & mfr tools, fixtures, gauges, prototype products.
(Nat Ame, estab 1993, empl 4, sales $514,590, cert:
NMSDC)

3695 T&D Machine, Inc.
      2485 E Monroe Rd
      Tecumseh, MI 49286
      Contact: Debra Fowle President
      Tel: 517-423-0778
      Email: tdmachine@lni.net
      Website: http://tdmachineinc.net
Precision machined products: steel, aluminum, brass &
plastic parts, hand tools, scribers, torque, screwdriver,
pliers, mirrors, telescoping tools, magnet hand tools,
spark plug pliers. (Woman/Hisp, estab 1985, empl 3,
sales $200,000, cert: State)

3696 Universal Tool Equipment & Controls, Inc.
      6525 Center Dr
      Sterling Heights, MI 48312
      Contact: Bill Bartolotta VP
      Tel: 586-268-4380
      Email: bbartolotta@universaltecinc.com
      Website: www.universaltecinc.com
Automation & welding systems, robotics, weld guns,
vision systems, sealant systems, drawn arc welders,
projection welders, material handling end effectors &
welding fixtures. (Woman/AA, estab 2009, empl 29,
sales $10,000,000, cert: WBENC)

Minnesota

3697 Carbide Tool Services, Inc.
      1020 Lund Blvd
      Anoka, MN 55303
      Contact: Julie Reiling Presdient
      Tel: 763-421-2210
      Email: julie@carbidetool.com
      Website: www.carbidetool.com
Mfr & repair indexable cutting tools, live tooling.
(Woman/Hisp, estab 1988, empl 40, sales $3,493,686,
cert: WBENC)

North Dakota

3698 Posi Lock Puller, Inc.
      805 Sunflower Ave
      Cooperstown, ND 58425
      Contact: Tamara Somerville VP
      Tel: 701-797-2600
      Email: t.somerville@posilock.com
      Website: www.posilock.com
Mfr gear & bearing pullers. (Woman, estab 1977, empl
45, sales $3,900,000, cert: City)

New Jersey

3699 JDV Products, Inc.
22-01 Raphael St.
Fair Lawn, NJ 07410
Contact: Ron Vradenburg Sales Mgr
Tel: 201-796-1720
Email: ron@jdvproducts.com
Website: www.jdvproducts.com
Mfr & dist telecom tools: wire wrap & unwrap tools, semi-automatic wire wrap machines, wire strippers, hand & pneumatic power tools, industrial power bits, hand screwdrivers, tool balancer, torque wrenches & accessories, wire & plastics cutting tools. (Woman, estab 1995, empl 19, sales , cert: WBENC)

3700 SMG Services, LLC
462 W Lookout Ave
Hackensack, NJ 07601
Contact: CEO
Tel: 201-937-5378
Email: sweintraub@svcmgmt.com
Website: www.smgdiamondtools.com
Mfr Diamond Drill Bits, Diamond Plated drill Bits, Diamond Grinding Tools, Cutting Blades, Impregnated Inserts, Brazed Diamond Products, Diamond Core Drills, Diamond Solid Tools, Cstmr specs. (Woman/AA, estab 2009, empl , sales $765,000, cert: State)

3701 SYSMIND LLC
38 Washington Rd
Princeton Junction, NJ 08550
Contact: Business Devel Specialist
Tel: 609-897-9670
Email:
Website: www.sysmind.com
Fabricate plastic components & fasteners for computer, aerospace, electronic, instrumentation, etc. applications. Prototype to production. Also stock molded nylon fasteners. (Woman/As-Ind, estab 1999, empl 456, sales $45,000,000, cert: NMSDC, WBENC)

New York

3702 American Pride Fasteners, LLC
195 S Fehr Way
Bay Shore, NY 11706
Contact: Lynda Zacpal President
Tel: 631-940-8292
Email: lynda@americanpridefasteners.com
Website: www.americanpridefasteners.com
Engineering & mfr miniature screws & miniature fasteners. (Woman/Hisp, estab 2004, empl 24, sales $4,200,000, cert: City)

3703 Burnett Process, Inc.
545 Colfax St
Rochester, NY 14606
Contact: Melissa Shea-Brooks Marketing Dev Mgr
Tel: 585-254-8080
Email: burnettprocesscsr@cannonind.com
Website: www.burnettprocessinc.com
Mfr & dist ozone, pleated, particulate & HEPA filters. (AA, estab 1957, empl 39, sales $6,000,000, cert: NMSDC)

Ohio

3704 AKKO Fastener, Inc.
6855 Cornell Rd
Cincinnati, OH 45242
Contact: Art Huge Sales Mgr
Tel: 513-489-8300
Email: arthuge@comcast.net
Website: www.akkofastener.com
Mfr fastening products: machine screws, tapping screws, plascrews, thread cutting screws, & cold formed metal products. (Woman/Hisp, estab 1967, empl 40, sales $7,000,000, cert: NMSDC)

3705 Cold Headed Fasteners & Assemblies, Inc.
1875 Harsh Ave SE
Massillon, OH 44646
Contact: Oscar Lee President
Tel: 330-833-0800
Email: o.lee@coldheaded.us
Website: www.coldheaded.us
Mfr fasteners & assemblies, sorting & packaging (As-Pac, estab 2002, empl 15, sales $ 0, cert: State)

3706 Custom Millcraft Corp.
9092 Le Saint Dr
Fairfield, OH 45014
Contact: Jody Corbett Presdient
Tel: 513-874-7080
Email: jcorbett@custommillcraft.com
Website: www.custommillcraft.com
Mfr wood & plastic laminate store fixtures. (Woman, estab 1983, empl 45, sales $4,000,000, cert: WBENC)

3707 M.O.M. Tools, LLC
3659 Green Road Ste 304
Cleveland, OH 44122
Contact: Anthony Lockhart
Tel: 216-464-2992
Email: axlockhart@toolsbymom.com
Website: http://toolsbymom.com/
Mfr dual-head piercing tools & dies. (AA, estab 2003, empl 2, sales $ 0, cert: NMSDC)

3708 Master Manufacturing Co, Inc.
9200 Inman Ave
Cleveland, OH 44105
Contact: Bob Ptacek V.P. Sales
Tel: 800-323-5513
Email: bptacek@mastermfgco.com
Website: www.mastermfgco.com
Mfr furniture casters & self-stick wheels; felt pads, surface protectors, wobble stoppers; furniture movers; door stops; ergonomic support cushions & wire mgmt channels & grommets. (Woman, estab , empl , sales , cert: CPUC, WBENC)

3709 Midwest Ohio Tool Company, Inc.
215 Tarhe Trail
Upper Sandusky, OH 43351
Contact: Stephanie Kettels Presdient
Tel: 419-294-1987
Email: skettels@midwestohio.com
Website: www.midwestohio.com
Mfr custom cutting tools, metal cutting tools, milling cutters, specialized cutting tools, boring bars, tool holders, industrial tools. (Woman, estab 1954, empl 9, sales $500,000, cert: WBENC)

3710 RB Tool & Mfg Co.
2680 Civic Center Dr
Cincinnati, OH 45231
Contact: Scott Schaeper Sales/Marketing Mgr
Tel: 513-521-8292
Email: scott@rbtoolandmfg.com
Website: www.rbtoolandmfg.com
Mfr mills-horizontal and vertical, lathes-CNC and manuals, EDM-wire and sinker, welding, painting. (Woman, estab 1957, empl 40, sales $6,000,000, cert: WBENC)

3711 Steam Turbine Alternative Resources
116 LATOURETTE ST
MARION, OH 43302
Contact: Ken Kubinski Sales Mgr
Tel: 740-387-5535
Email: ken@starturbine.com
Website: www.starturbines.com
Mfr steam seals, packing, spill strips hardware, oil seals & deflectors, on-site field installation & machining sevices. (Woman, estab 1986, empl 40, sales $5,610,000, cert: WBENC)

3712 Stelfast Inc.
22979 Stelfast Pkwy
Strongsville, OH 44149
Contact: Todd McRoberts Sales
Tel: 877-619-8231
Email: toddm@stelfast.com
Website: www.stelfast.com
Import & manufacture fasteners. (As-Pac, estab 1973, empl 80, sales $31,500,000, cert: NMSDC)

3713 Talent Tool & Die, Inc.
777 Berea Industrial Pkwy
Berea, OH 44017
Contact: Mylynh Vu Presdient
Tel: 440-239-8777
Email: mylynh@talent-tool.com
Website: www.talent-tool.com
Mfr dies, tools & fixtures; metal stamping & laser cutting. (As-Pac, estab 1989, empl 44, sales $ 0, cert: NMSDC)

3714 The M.K. Morse Company
1101 11th St SE
Canton, OH 44707
Contact: Ryan Rhodes Cstmr Service
Tel: 330-453-8187
Email: rhodesr@mkmorse.com
Website: www.mkmorse.com
Mfr saw blades, band saws, reciprocating saws, hole saws, hack saws and frames, wood boring bits, portable band saws, metal cutting circular saws & machines. Made from bimetal, carbon steel, carbide tipped & carbide grit. (Woman, estab 1963, empl 500, sales $84,000,000, cert: WBENC)

Oklahoma

3715 Hover Group, LLC
416 Heritage Green Rd
Edmond, OK 73003
Contact: Nicole Hover CEO
Tel: 405-437-8691
Email: Nicole@hovergroup.net
Website: www.hovergroup.net
Manufacturing and providing composite components, oil and gas downhole tools. (Woman, estab 2016, empl 5, sales $473,000, cert: WBENC)

Texas

3716 Arise Solutions Inc.
5862 Cromo Ste 149
El Paso, TX 79912
Contact: Daniel Laing President
Tel: 915-345-9134
Email: sales@arisesolutions.biz
Website: www.arisesolutions.biz
Custom designed wire harness, cable assembly, bulk wire, signal cable, specialty bolts, screws, Nut Rivets, Inserts, Fasteners, Spacers, Connectors & Fittings for automotive industry. (As-Pac, estab 2012, empl 5, sales $1,000,000, cert: State, NMSDC)

3717 BiTech Tool & Die Inc.
5240 Tetons
El Paso, TX 79904
Contact: Maria Castillo
Tel: 915-757-8001
Email: mcastillo@bitech.net
Website:
Mfr precision tools, crimping applicator die & crimp tooling. (Hisp, estab 1995, empl 35, sales $615,000, cert: NMSDC)

3718 Danrick Industries Inc.
850 Kastrin St
El Paso, TX 79907
Contact: Marco Herrera Presdient
Tel: 915-599-2988
Email: marcoherrera@danrick.net
Website: www.danrick.net
Mfr tooling & precision machining parts, fabrication of parts & components of terminal crimping. (AA, estab 2002, empl 22, sales $ 0, cert: State, NMSDC)

3719 EZKutter Company
3617 Rabbit Lane
Bryan, TX 77808
Contact: Dora Loria Owner
Tel: 979-778-0825
Email: ezkutter@suddenlink.net
Website: http://ezkutter-usa.com
Mfr hand held cutting tools used for cutting heavy plastic straps, strings & shrink wrapping. (Woman, estab 1992, empl 2, sales , cert: State)

3720 Versatech, LLC
315 N Park Dr
San Antonio, TX 78216
Contact: Diana Grinman Admin
Tel: 210-979-2823
Email: dgrinman@pmtool.com
Website: www.versatech-mfg.com
Advanced tooling, plastic injection molds, tools & dies fields. (Hisp, estab 2006, empl 5, sales , cert: NMSDC)

Virginia

3721   Master Gage & Tool Company
       112 Maplewood St
       Danville, VA 24543
       Contact: Debbye Lyle President
       Tel: 434-836-4243
       Email: debbyel@mastergt.com
       Website: www.mastergt.com
Calibration, specialized tooling & gaging products.
(Woman, estab 1986, empl 26, sales $12,010,000, cert:
WBENC)

Wisconsin

3722   R.J. Zeman Tool & Mfg. Co., Inc.
       W228 N575 Westmound Dr
       Waukesha, WI 53186
       Contact: Spencer Schreindl Presdient
       Tel: 262-549-4400
       Email: sschreindl@zemantool.com
       Website:
Machining, design, mfr & inspect fixtures, special machines, gages, die cast dies, plastic injection molds,
permanent molds, core boxes, patterns for sand casting &
short and long-run production parts. (Woman, estab 1966,
empl 48, sales $9,600,000, cert: WBENC)

HYDRAULIC & COMPRESSED AIR EQUIPMENT

Manufacturers and distributors of compressed air equipment, valves, gaskets, fittings, pumps, meters, hoses, special tools, pipe, etc. (See also HARDWARE & TOOLS, INDUSTRIAL EQUIPMENT & SUPPLIES, INDUSTRIAL MACHINES and MATERIAL HANDLING EQUIPMENT). NAICS Code 42

Alabama

3723 Elle Waterworks Supply, LLC
P.O. Box 205
Leeds, AL 35094
Contact: Courtney Myrick Owner
Tel: 205-352-3240
Email: cmyrick@ellewws.com
Website: www.ellewws.com
Dist process valves, air valves, control valves, ductile iron pipe, steel pipe, pipe supports & hangers, couplings, adapters, pvc pipe & fittings, ductile iron fittings, hydrants, valve boxes, hardware, bolts, nuts, gaskets, safety equipment. (Woman, estab 2011, empl 2, sales $3,800,000, cert: State, WBENC)

Arizona

3724 Stenzel Sealing Solutions, LLC
16809 N 53rd Ave, Ste 5
Glendale, AZ 85306
Contact: Linda Stenzel Owner
Tel: 602-903-1250
Email: linda@azstenzel.com
Website: www.stenzelsealingsolutions.com
Fluid sealing solutions: Gaskets, Seals, Pump/Valve Packing, Duct/Pipe Expansion Joints, Valves, Pipe, Fittings, Flanges & Steam Traps. (Woman, estab 2012, empl 4, sales $1,925,914, cert: CPUC, WBENC)

California

3725 CLEAR Solutions, Inc.
942 Calle Amanecer, Ste D
San Clemente, CA 92673
Contact: Judy McMacking VP
Tel: 949-429-8922
Email: judy@clearsolutionscorp.com
Website: www.clearsolutionscorp.com
Dist filters, filter housings, water purification, filtration, separation, process liquid filtration, HVAC, compressed air & gas filtration, sanitary gaskets, flange gaskets, screen gaskets, hose assemblies, tubing, quick disconnect fittings. (Woman, estab 2010, empl 6, sales , cert: WBENC)

3726 Dexen Industries, Inc.
9220 Norwalk Blvd
Santa Fe Springs, CA 90670
Contact: Yu-Shan Teng President
Tel: 562-699-8490
Email: info@dexen.com
Website: www.dexen.com
Mfr gas valves. (As-Pac, estab 1988, empl 17, sales $11,000,000, cert: CPUC)

3727 The Valve Shop
6070-A Corte Del Cedro
Carlsbad, CA 92024
Contact: Ray Herrera President
Tel: 760-438-4840
Email: rherrera@thevalveshop.com
Website: www.thevalveshop.com
Dist on/off & flow control valves: butterfly valves, check valves, diaphragm valves, float valves, gate valves, globe valves, plug valves, pressure regulators, relief valves, solenid valves, strainers, water valves. (Hisp, estab 2000, empl 7, sales $3,050,985, cert: State)

3728 VIAIR Corporation
15 Edelman
Irvine, CA 92618
Contact: Alan Basham Dir of Operations
Tel: 949-585-0011
Email: alanb@viaircorp.com
Website: www.viaircorp.com
Dist Air Compressor, Air Tank, LED Light, Air accessories for automotive industry. (As-Pac, estab 1998, empl 32, sales $22,000,000, cert: NMSDC)

Colorado

3729 Die Cut Technologies/Denver Gasket
10943 Leroy Dr
Northglenn, CO 80233
Contact: Evelyn Meyers CEO
Tel: 303-452-4600
Email: evelyn@diecuttech.com
Website: www.diecuttech.com
Mfr gaskets, die cut parts & converted non-metallic materials. Also dist sponge, foam tapes rubber, bridge bearing pads, expansion joints, impact attenuators & adhesives, contract assembly & packaging svcs. (Hisp, estab 1961, empl 20, sales $2,524,000, cert: NMSDC, SDB)

Florida

3730 Amazon Hose and Rubber Company
4105 Seaboard Rd
Orlando, FL 32808
Contact: Jim Donlin Presdient
Tel: 407-843-8190
Email: jimdonlin@amazonhose.com
Website: www.amazonhose.com
Dist industrial & hydraulic hoses & related fittings. (Woman, estab 1919, empl 60, sales $12,698,846, cert: City, WBENC)

3731 Industrial Hose & Hydraulics, Inc.
2450 N Powerline Rd
Pompano Beach, FL 33069
Contact: Joanne R. Heckman controller
Tel: 954-960-0311
Email: joeyheckman@industrialhose.com
Website: www.industrialhose.com
Dist hoses, fittings, clamps, adapters, fuel hose, hose reels, check valves, lubrication supplies, garden hose & pumps. (Woman, estab , empl , sales $ 0, cert: WBENC)

3732 The Bernd Group Inc.
1251 Pinehurst Rd
Dunedin, FL 34698
Contact: Pilar Bernd Presdient
Tel: 727-733-0122
Email: businessdevelopment@berndgroup.com
Website: www.berndgroup.com
Material handling equip, safety products, hand & power tools, pumps & compressors, motors, generators, electrical hardware, batteries, lighting fixtures, lockers, bins, shelving, lab equip. (Woman/Hisp, estab 1992, empl 66, sales $ 0, cert: NMSDC)

Illinois

3733 Bearings & Industrial Supply
431 Imen Ave
Addison, IL 60101
Contact: Sejal Khandwala Acct Exec
Tel: 630-628-1966
Email: Sejal@BearingsNow.Com
Website: www.bearingsnow.com
Dist bearings & power transmission products; pump & pump repair parts, HVAC & electrical parts. (As-Pac, estab , empl , sales $ 0, cert: NMSDC)

3734 Chambers Gasket & Manufacturing Co.
4701 W Rice St
Chicago, IL 60651
Contact: Heide Kenny Presdient
Tel: 773-626-8800
Email: hkenny@chambersgasket.com
Website: www.chambersgasket.com
Gaskets; Washers; Strips; Spiral Wound Gaskets; Molded Gaskets; Waterjet cut parts; pressure sensitve adhesive added; kitting; special packaging. (Woman, estab 0, empl , sales $ 0, cert: WBENC)

3735 Cylinders Inc.
580 W 5th Ave
Naperville, IL 60563
Contact: Cynthia Crawford Presdient
Tel: 630-357-5649
Email: cindy@cylindersinc.com
Website: www.cylindersinc.com
Repair & recondition hydraulic & pneumatic cylinders. (Woman, estab , empl 7, sales $1,440,992, cert: WBENC)

Indiana

3736 MIDpro Fluid Power and Automation
444 Johnson Ln
Brownsburg, IN 46112
Contact: Cynthia Torrance Presdient
Tel: 317-852-5920
Email: ctorrance@midprofluidpower.com
Website: www.midprofluidpower.com
Pnuematic, hydraulic, electronic & air systems, conveyors, blowers, pumps, dryers, filtration, air tools, cylinders, valves, fittings, power units, PLC controllers, monitors & touch screens. (Woman, estab 1986, empl 11, sales $5,200,000, cert: WBENC)

Kentucky

3737 SealingLife Technology
1141 Red Mile Rd Ste 201
Lexington, KY 40504
Contact: Danette Wilder CEO
Tel: 859-977-6640
Email: wilderdj@sealinglife.com
Website: www.sealinglife.com
Fabricate, mfr & dist sealing, shielding & coating solutions, O-rings, gaskets, molded parts, extrusions, RFI/EMF shielding, vacuum coating & encapsulating. (Woman/AA, estab 2008, empl 9, sales $1,200,000, cert: NMSDC, SDB)

Louisiana

3738 Treco Stainless Solutions, LLC
366 Technology Lane
Gray, LA 70359
Contact: Brenna Treland Owner
Tel: 985-858-2880
Email: brenna@trecostainless.com
Website: http://trecostainless.com
Stainless Steel Compression fittings, Stainless Steel Instrumentation fittings, Tubing & Piping, Autoclave fittings (up to 60K PSI), Gauges, Hydraulic Hoses, Quick Connects. (Woman, estab 2014, empl 3, sales , cert: WBENC)

Maryland

3739 Phelps Industrial Products
6300 Washington Blvd
Elkridge, MD 21075
Contact: Gina Lehman CEO
Tel: 410-796-2222
Email: gmlehman@phelpsgaskets.com
Website: www.phelpsgaskets.com
Mfr, fabricator & dist Gaskets, Compression Packing, O' Rings, Molded Parts & Sealing Devices. (As-Pac, estab 1945, empl 15, sales , cert: State)

Michigan

3740 Chippewa Systems, Ltd.
32663 Coach
Chesterfield, MI 48047
Contact: Brian Barr VP
Tel: 586-772-1783
Email: chippewasystemsltd@gmail.com
Website: www.chippewasystems.com
Dist vacuum pumps, compressors, blowers, filters, air knives. (Woman/Nat Ame, estab 1986, empl 3, sales $668,000, cert: NMSDC)

3741 Fluid Line Components, Inc.
638 S Rochester Rd
Clawson, MI 48017
Contact: Mary Schmitt CEO
Tel: 248-583-9070
Email: mary@fluidlinecomponents.com
Website: www.fluidlinecomponents.com
Dist air cylinders, air valves, air fittings, air filters, air gauges, air hoist, air hose, air manifolds, air motors, air drills, air presses, air tanks, air-oil tanks, anti-tie down, balancers, ball valves, ball vibrators, blow guns, brass pipe fittings (Woman, estab 1972, empl 4, sales $1,102,252, cert: WBENC)

3742 MCEM LLC
31153 Plymouth Rd
Livonia, MI 48150
Contact: BK Masti Presdient
Tel: 517-881-1226
Email: bkm@mcem.co
Website: www.mcem.co
Lubricants, valves, conduit fittings. (As-Pac, estab 2011, empl 5, sales , cert: NMSDC)

3743 Service Manufacturing & Supply Co.
33380 Groesbeck Hwy
Fraser, MI 48026
Contact: Ryan Maggio GM
Tel: 586-415-0455
Email: sales@servicemanufacturing.com
Website: www.servicemanufacturing.com
Hydraulic & pneumatic components & accessories, brass, steel, stainless steel, malleable & galvanized fittings, JIC 37 degree flare, push-on barbs, adaptors, solid & union barbs, pipe els & extension adaptors, hydraulic tubing. (Woman, estab 1957, empl 7, sales $1,154,683, cert: WBENC)

Minnesota

3744 Chrom Tech, Inc.
P.O. Box 240248
Apple Valley, MN 55124
Contact: Jessica Kolsky Technical Sales Rep
Tel: 952-431-6000
Email: jessica@chromtech.com
Website: www.chromtech.com
Dist HPLC & GC instrumentation, supplies & accessories: autosampler vials, columns, filters, fittings, PEEK tubing & fittings, solid phase extraction cartridges, protein crash plates, positive pressure manifolds, evaporators, syringes, tubing. (Woman, estab 1985, empl 12, sales $10,538,000, cert: WBENC)

3745 Unique Contracting Service Corp.
20531 156th St NW
Elk River, MN 55330
Contact: Angel Perez Presdient
Tel: 763-218-9385
Email: angelpeppy1@izoom.net
Website:
LPGas & NH3 equipment, Fittings, Pipes, High pressure Hoses, Pumps, Valves, tanks. (Hisp, estab 1987, empl 3, sales $156,000, cert: State, NMSDC)

3746 Water Technology Resources
9201 E Bloomington Fwy, Ste Z
Bloomington, MN 55420
Contact: Sally Waldor President
Tel: 952-641-9004
Email: sallywaldor@wtrvalves.com
Website: www.wtrvalves.com
Mfr industrial valves. (Woman, estab 2009, empl 5, sales $1,000,000, cert: State)

North Carolina

3747 Raleigh-Durham Rubber & Gasket Co., Inc.
P.O. Box 90397
Raleigh, NC 27675
Contact: Judy Hooks President
Tel: 919-781-6817
Email: judyh@raleighdurhamrubber.com
Website: www.raleighdurhamrubber.com
Mfr & dist rubber gaskets. (Woman, estab , empl , sales , cert: WBENC)

3748 Smith Seal of NC
8441 Garvey Dr
Raleigh, NC 27616
Contact: Gertraud Smith Presdient
Tel: 919-790-1000
Email: judysmith@smithseal.com
Website: www.smithseal.com
Dist hydraulic seals, gaskets & packings. (Woman, estab 1976, empl 13, sales $ 0, cert: WBENC)

New Jersey

3749 Liquid-Solids Separation Corp.
25 Arrow Rd
Ramsey, NJ 07446
Contact: Stacey Painter COO
Tel: 201-236-4833
Email: spainter@nafilter.com
Website: www.leemfiltration.com
Mfr pressure leaf filters and their components for oil seed processing, bio diesel fuel production, chemical processing and water treatment applications. (Woman, estab 1994, empl 42, sales $13,000,000, cert: WBENC)

3750 Sur-Seal, Inc.
12 Edgeboro Rd Unit 6
East Brunswick, NJ 08816
Contact: Donna King Accountant
Tel: 732-651-7070
Email: donnak@sur-sealinc.com
Website: www.sur-sealinc.com
Dist gaskets, gashet sheet, roll material, mechanical packing, compression packing, mechanical seals (new & repairs), pressure gauges & thermometers (new and repairs), hydraulic packings, o-rings, lantern rings, extrusions. (Woman, estab 1979, empl 11, sales $2,263,945, cert: State)

Ohio

3751 Triad Technologies LLC
985 Falls Creek Dr
Vandalia, OH 45377
Contact: Bruno Amicci Presdient
Tel: 419-878-9647
Email: sales@triadtechnologies.com
Website: www.triadtechnologies.com
Dist hydraulics, pneumatics, fluid connectors, hose products, automation, sensors, electromechanical, lubrication, etc. (Hisp, estab 2002, empl 187, sales , cert: State)

3752 Trident Fluid Power, LLC
P.O. Box 368
Middletown, OH 45042
Contact: Sandy Ewen GM
Tel: 513-217-4999
Email: sewen@tridentfluidpower.com
Website: www.Tridentfluidpower.com
Replace, overhaul, manufacture, fluidpower components (cylinders, pumps, valves, systems), field service, trouble shoot, design, engineer, all coke oven equipment & operations, machine, welding, fabricating. (Woman, estab 2006, empl 17, sales $2,000,000, cert: WBENC)

Oklahoma

3753   PT Coupling Co.
P.O. Box 3909
Enid, OK 73702
Contact: James Matthew Parrish Presdient
Tel: 580-237-4033
Email: credit03@ptcoupling.com
Website: www.ptcoupling.com
Mfr industrial hose couplings used in the transfer of fluid & dry products at medium to low pressure. (Nat Ame, estab 1951, empl 390, sales $60,000,000, cert: NMSDC)

South Carolina

3754   Eastern Power Technologies, Inc.
11 Caledon Court
Greenville, SC 29615
Contact: Chet Chea Legal Counsel
Tel: 864-312-3840
Email: chet.chea@easternfirst.com
Website: www.easternpowertech.com
Dist industrial & commercial pipes, valves, fittings & commercial plumbing fixtures. (Woman, estab 2014, empl 15, sales $250,000, cert: WBENC)

3755   Filters South, Inc.
656 Wraggs Ferry Rd
Georgetown, SC 29440
Contact: Deborah Powell Presdient
Tel: 843-833-1042
Email: dwillspowell@earthlink.net
Website: www.filterssouth.com
Dist filters: Air, HVAC, Oil, Hydraulic, Dust Collection, Water, Liquid, etc. (Minority, Woman, estab 1997, empl 2, sales $ 0, cert: State, City)

3756   Greenville Fluid System Technologies
2516 River Rd
Piedmont, SC 29673
Contact: Greg Farley Sales Mgr
Tel: 864-295-6700
Email: greg.farley@swagelok.com
Website: www.swagelok.com/columbiasc
Dist compression & pipe fittings, valves, hoses, tubing, pumps, gauges & regulators, Orbital welding equipment, tube benders, hydraulic swaging units. (Woman, estab 2001, empl 18, sales $3,200,000, cert: WBENC)

3757   SeherIhde LLC dba Freedom Air Filtration
2600 Needlegrass Dr
Beaufort, SC 29902
Contact: Mary Beth Seher Sales Mgr
Tel: 312-560-7788
Email: marybeth@freedomairfiltration.com
Website: https://freedomairfiltration.com
Dist Air Scrubbers, Ashrae, Cartridges, Domange, Filter Bags, Filters, Fleetguard, Gemicidal Lights, Hepa, Hvac Filters, Hydraulic, Merv 13, Pleats, UV Lights, Vcell, Dust Cartridges. (Woman, estab 2006, empl 3, sales $500,000, cert: WBENC)

3758   Wallace Mechanical Supply, Inc.
635 State Rd
Cheraw, SC 29520
Contact: Wallace Funderburck, Jr Presdient
Tel: 843-537-4277
Email: inc_wallace@bellsouth.net
Website:
HVAC/Plumbing , Pipe, Valves, and Pipe fittings (AA, estab 1985, empl 2, sales $1,375,463, cert: State, NMSDC)

Tennessee

3759   Pioneer Air Systems, Inc.
210 Flat Fork Rd
Wartburg, TN 37887
Contact: Sam Basseen CEO
Tel: 423-346-6693
Email: sam@pioneerair.com
Website: www.pioneerair.com
Convert CO to CO2 in compressed air to make it suitable for breathing air purposes, clean & dry Nitrogen, Natural Gas, Hydrogen, Helium, Ethylene, Seal Gas, OxyPurge (with MONEL vessels & Teflon lined piping) etc. (As-Ind, estab 1980, empl 25, sales , cert: NMSDC)

Texas

3760   Asociar, LLC
2800 E Plano Pkwy #400
Plano, TX 75074
Contact: Betty Manetta CEO
Tel: 214-918-1013
Email: bmanetta@asociar1.com
Website: www.asociar1.com
Streamline Supply Chain Management
Total Equipment Rack Integration & Testing
Procure, Rack, Integrate, Deliver, Engineer
Warehousing & Logistics (Woman/Hisp, estab 2012, empl 15, sales $185,000,000,000, cert: State, NMSDC, WBENC)

3761   Carrco Painting Contractors, Inc.
10944 Alder Cir
Dallas, TX 75238
Contact: RUDY COX Business Dev Mgr
Tel: 214-624-7560
Email: rcox@carrcopainting.com
Website: www.carrcopainting.com
Painting, pressure cleaning, wallcovering, drywall repair, epoxy and urethane floor, specialty coating, wall and ceiling coating, protective coating, Cool Seal Roof Coating and Industrial Painting (Hisp, estab 1994, empl 250, sales $8,000,000, cert: State, City)

3762   Corley Gasket Company
P.O. Box 271124
Dallas, TX 75227
Contact: Jody Anderson Office Mgr
Tel: 214-388-7437
Email: janderson@corleygasket.com
Website: www.corleygasket.com
Mfr gaskets. (Woman, estab 1975, empl 19, sales $1,941,386, cert: CPUC)

3763   CVAL Innovations LLC
9701 Raven Ln
Irving, TX 75063
Contact: Jinen Adenwala President
Tel: 214-699-1326
Email: jinen@cvalinnovations.com
Website: www.cvalinnovations.com
Energy Consumption for Industrial and Commercial customers. We conduct Energy Efficiency Audits, recommend and implement the efficiency measures. (Woman/AA, As-Ind, estab 2009, empl 5, sales $1,093,000, cert: State, NMSDC, SDB)

3764   El Paso Industrial Supplies
       119 N Cotton
       El Paso, TX 79901
       Contact: Antonio Herrera Sales Mgr
       Tel: 915-533-5080
       Email: sales@epis-usa.com
       Website: www.epis-usa.com
Dist pneumatic equipment & parts, sensors, sensors for
safety, hydraulic equipments & parts, filters, HEPA filters,
work mats, signal towers. (Hisp, estab 1988, empl 16, sales
$4,000,000, cert: NMSDC)

3765   Industry Junction, Inc.
       3427 W. Kingsley Rd., Ste # 6 & 7
       Garland, TX 75041
       Contact: Rogelio Cabello Presdient
       Tel: 972-926-3526
       Email: contact@industryjunction.com
       Website: http://industryjunction.com/
Dist fluid power valves, industrial Valves, mallable gittings,
stainless steel fittings, hydra-sanitary products. (Hisp,
estab 2011, empl 4, sales $4,400,000, cert: State, NMSDC)

3766   iSTAFF Solutions, Inc.
       P.O. Box 118440
       Carrollton, TX 75011
       Contact: Wanda Young Director
       Tel: 972-251-9877
       Email: wanda.young@istaffsolutions.org
       Website: http://istaffsolutions.org
IT Staffing,
Light Warehouse
Admin. (Woman/AA, estab 2010, empl , sales $100,000,
cert: State)

3767   MARS Industries, LLC
       P.O. Box 560
       Cedar Creek, TX 78612
       Contact: Alvino Rosales Presdient
       Tel: 512-303-4413
       Email: arosales@marsindustries.us
       Website: www.marsindustries.us
Dist pipe, fittings, valves, etc.for the construction of water
& wastewater treatment facilities & water & wastewater
utilities. (Hisp, estab 2001, empl 1, sales , cert: State, City)

3768   OG Energy Solutions LLC
       1836 Snake River Rd Ste A
       Katy, TX 77449
       Contact: Federico Zamar Reg Sales Mgr
       Tel: 832-644-0121
       Email: fzsales@ogenergys.com
       Website: www.ogenergys.com
Pipes, tubes, fitting, flanges; Valves; Automation &
Instrumentation (transducers, sensors, transmitters,
panels); Heat Exchanger Equipment & Parts; Seals &
Gaskets; Non-toxic, environmentally-safe cleaners,
degreasers & solvents. (Woman/Hisp, estab 2010, empl 8,
sales $600,000, cert: WBENC)

3769   OnPoint, LLC
       13155 Noel Rd, Ste 900
       Dallas, TX 75240
       Contact: Amber B D'Amico Partner
       Tel: 972-918-5154
       Email: amber@onpointlighting.com
       Website: www.onpointlighting.com
Energy-efficient LED lighting, surveys, ROI analysis, best-
of-breed American-made products, lighting design,
installation & financing. (Hisp, estab 2011, empl 2, sales
$750,000, cert: State)

3770   Petroleum Accessories, Inc.
       12500 Oxford Park Dr
       Houston, TX 77077
       Contact: Anna de Chabannes Technical Sales Dir
       Tel: 281-589-9337
       Email: hydraulics@paihouston.com
       Website: www.paihouston.com
Dist hydraulic components: filters, high pressure micro
pumps & valves. (Woman, estab 1980, empl 5, sales
$2,930,802, cert: WBENC)

3771   Piping Technology and Product Inc.
       3701 Holmes Rd
       Houston, TX 77051
       Contact: Michael Rucker Business Develop Mgr
       Tel: 713-731-0030
       Email: info@pipingtech.com
       Website: www.pipingtech.com
Custom Engineered Hot/Cold Insulated Pipe Shoes and
Supports, Fabric Expansion Joints/Metal Bellows, ASME
Certified Pressure Vessels, and ASME-U-Stamp rated
Hydraulic and Mechanical Snubbers, Custom Engineered
(As-Ind, As-Pac, estab 1978, empl 750, sales
$60,000,000, cert: NMSDC)

3772   Professional Choice Fire & Security Systems
       1815 N. Hampton Road
       DeSoto, TX 75115
       Contact: Dwanald Walker Presdient
       Tel: 972-298-2303
       Email: dwanald@professionalchoicefire.com
       Website: http://professionalchoicefire.com
Installation, service and repair for fire sprinkler, fire
pump, fire alarm systems in the Dallas-Fort Worth
metropolitan areas. Testing, inspection and maintenance
for fire alarm, sprinkler, fire pumps and backflow
detetion equipment. 24 hour central (AA, estab 2004,
empl 6, sales $500,000, cert: State, NMSDC)

3773   Texas Seal Supply Co, Inc.
       606 N Great Southwest Pkwy
       Arlington, TX 76011
       Contact: Carol Gallegos Ortega Mgr
       Tel: 817-640-1193
       Email: carols@texasseal.com
       Website: www.texasseal.com
Dist seals: hydraulic, pneumatic, aerospace, oilfield.
(Hisp, estab 1971, empl 13, sales, cert: NMSDC)

Virginia

3774   E&R Minority Supplier LLC
21290 Hedgerow Terr
Ashburn, VA 20147
Contact: Esvith Palomino-Quillama Presdient
Tel: 703-932-5045
Email: epalomino@erminoritysupplier.com
Website: www.erminoritysupplier.com
Heavy highway material & industrial hydraulic hoses &
fittings. (Hisp, estab 2011, empl 1, sales , cert: State)

Wisconsin

3775   Anderson Seal Inc.
16555 W Lincoln
New Berlin, WI 53151
Contact: Jennifer Hansen President
Tel: 262-821-0344
Email: jennifer@andersonseal.com
Website: www.andersonseal.com
Dist rubber o-rings, custom molded shapes, gaskets, oil
seals, kit assemblies, inventory management. (Woman,
estab 1990, empl 50, sales $27,000,000, cert: WBENC)

3776   Central Wisconsin Flex
8510 Enterprise Way
Weston, WI 54476
Contact: Carmen Sauer VP
Tel: 715-355-4344
Email: cenflex@cenflex.com
Website: www.cenflex.com
Flexible metal hose, braided metal hose, expansion
joints, exhaust tubing and assemblies, laser cutting,
plate rolling, fab shop, Teflon hoses, machining.
(Woman/Hisp, estab 1992, empl 37, sales $8,394,000,
cert: NMSDC)

3777   Husco Automotive, LLC
2239 Pewaukee Rd
Waukesha, WI 53188
Contact: Jonathan Hassert Acct Mgr
Tel: 262-953-6400
Email: jon.hassert@huscoauto.com
Website: www.huscoauto.com
Design, develop & mfr electro-hydraulic solenoid valves
& electro-magnetic solenoid actuators. (Hisp, estab
1946, empl 1015, sales $238,000,000, cert: NMSDC)

3778   Roeming Industries, Inc.
1133 W Liebau Rd
Mequon, WI 53092
Contact: Owner
Tel: 262-243-5800
Email:
Website: www.roeming.com
Contract sewing on vinyl, leather, Kevlar, fiberglass,
plastics and fabric. Distributor of hydraulic packing,
seals, and packing. Gasket cutting. Rubber to metal
bonding. (Woman, estab 1955, empl 13, sales
$1,600,000, cert: WBENC)

DIVERSITY INFORMATION **RESOURCES**

DIVERSITY 411

excerpts from DIR's Blog: www.diversityinforesources.blogspot.com

DIR works directly with diverse-owned suppliers, and helps to bring them to the procurement discussion table. Using this book is a fantastic first step. Keep in mind that these contacts and information are best used:

- to establish business relationships
- reinforce business matchmaking

After years of discussions with people on both sides of the procurement "fence," we offer our Top 10 Ways to make the most out of this resource:

#10: Don't send information blindly: Let the buyer ask you for samples, line cards and other company specific information.

#9: Let corporate contacts know what you've done and ask about the best next steps ("I've registered," "I've researched your products/services." etc.). Use references within their industry.

#8: Keep track of conversations: What was said. With whom. What to do next. Schedule follow-ups.

#7: Ask about a corporation's "prime suppliers". You may not be able to work directly with a global conglomerate, but you most likely are able to work with one of their prime suppliers ... ask about them!

#6: Take advantage of any "personal" time you can get. Utilize business events to their fullest potential, reconnecting face-to-face with contacts you meet locally or at national business fairs.

#5: Do your homework about regional outreach groups: Chambers of Commerce, Economic Development Agencies, state or regional divisions of national organizations. Check them all out and be tenacious about following up with their matchmaking opportunities.

#4: Practice your introductions, and have more than one 'ready'. Know what you're going to say to someone experienced or inexperienced in your industry. Educate efficiently!

#3: Do your due diligence in researching what a Supplier Diversity contact needs to bring your information forward to their procurement department. You'll often find their preferences and needs listed on their Web site's supplier diversity page.

#2: Develop targeted marketing lists, and be specific when following up ("Good to meet you at NMSDC on Monday," etc.). Recall a piece of information that distinguishes you from everyone else ("Thank you for commenting on the effectiveness of my capabilities brochure.").

#1: Use names and titles and use them correctly in all your correspondence. If you send an email that says "Dear Ray" to a Ramona, it'll be deleted at first glance.

INDUSTRIAL EQUIPMENT & SUPPLIES
Manufacturers and distributors of food service and restaurant equipment, drive belts, aircraft parts, motors, industrial batteries, underground mining equipment, heaters, bearings, spark plug cleaner, traffic control signs, etc. (See also HARDWARE & TOOLS, HYDRAULIC & COMPRESSED AIR EQUIPMENT, INDUSTRIAL MACHINES and MATERIAL HANDLING EQUIPMENT). NAICS Code 42

Alabama

3779 Alabama Safety Products Inc.
150 Supply Room Rd
Oxford, AL 36203
Contact: Tracy Rouse Presdient
Tel:
Email: tracyr@alabamasafety.com
Website: www.alabamasafety.com
Dist safety supplies, safety audits, hand protections surveys, respirator fit-testing. (Woman/Nat Ame, estab 1992, empl 8, sales , cert: NMSDC)

3780 Cornerstone Supply, Inc.
340 Production AVe
Madison, AL 35758
Contact: Bonnie Powers Presdient
Tel: 256-461-4147
Email: bonnie@cornerstone-supply.com
Website: www.cornerstone-supply.com
Dist military fasteners, electronic components, MRO equipment & supplies. (Woman, estab 1986, empl 11, sales , cert: WBENC)

3781 Elle Waterworks Supply, LLC
P.O. Box 205
Leeds, AL 35094
Contact: Courtney Myrick Owner
Tel: 205-352-3240
Email: cmyrick@ellewws.com
Website: www.ellewws.com
Dist process valves, air valves, control valves, ductile iron pipe, steel pipe, pipe supports & hangers, couplings, adapters, pvc pipe & fittings, ductile iron fittings, hydrants, valve boxes, hardware, bolts, nuts, gaskets, safety equipment. (Woman, estab 2011, empl 2, sales $3,800,000, cert: State, WBENC)

Arizona

3782 Air Energy Systems & Services
4202 E Superior Ave, Ste 3
Phoenix, AZ 85040
Contact: Patricia Bewley Owner
Tel: 602-454-0210
Email: pbewley@aesas.com
Website: www.aesas.com
Dist & install commerical, industrial & HVAC air filters, energy products, IAQ products, UVC producst, energy audits. (Woman/Nat Ame, estab 1997, empl 15, sales $2,300,000, cert: NMSDC, WBENC)

3783 Diversified Diamond Products
4634 E Mountain View Ct
Phoenix, AZ 85028
Contact: Mary Dillon CEO
Tel: 480-443-4899
Email: mdillon@diversifieddiamond.com
Website: www.diversifieddiamond.com
Dist safety supplies & equipment, vests, gloves, respirators, test meters, locks, cable protection, prescription safety glasses, fall protection, ear protection, face masks, cutting tools, abrasives, work holding, metal working. (Woman, estab 1989, empl 5, sales $1,295,404, cert: WBENC)

3784 Industrial Specialties Supply, Inc.
3941 E 29th St, Ste 606
Tucson, AZ 85711
Contact: Alan Davila Mgr
Tel: 520-745-5800
Email: indussupply@live.com
Website: www.indussupplyinc.com
Solenoid valves, PLC components, Conveyor belts, Steam traps, High Pressure Valves, Sanitary/Food grade fittings, valves & tubing, industrial concrete coatings, personal safety equipment, Gas detectors. (Hisp, estab 2001, empl 2, sales $1,438,845, cert: State, City)

California

3785 Able Industrial Products, Inc.
2006 S Baker
Ontario, CA 91761
Contact: Courtney Salvidar Sales/Marketing Mgr
Tel: 909-930-1585
Email: courtneys@able123.com
Website: www.able123.com
Mfr & convert thermal management materials: gap pads, interface pads & various non-metallic gaskets. (Woman/Hisp, estab 1974, empl 40, sales $3,800,000, cert: NMSDC)

3786 Brandon Supply Corporation
14120 Gannet St, Unit 101
Santa Fe Springs, CA 90670
Contact: Clarence D. Scott Presdient
Tel: 562-921-0407
Email: cdavis@brandonsupplycorp.com
Website: www.brandonsupply.com
Dist pipes, valves, fittings, waterworks, material handling, safety line, industrial supplies. (AA, estab 1980, empl 9, sales $1,500,000, cert: State)

3787 Empire Safety & Supply
10624 Industrial Ave
Roseville, CA 95678
Contact: Monette Crawford CEO
Tel: 800-995-1341
Email: monette@empiresafety.com
Website: www.empiresafety.com
Dist environmental health & safety products. (Woman, estab 1992, empl 14, sales $6,000,000, cert: CPUC)

3788 FTG, Inc.
12750 Center Court Dr S Ste 280
Cerritos, CA 90703
Contact: Pino Pathak Presdient
Tel: 562-865-9200
Email: pino@ftginc.com
Website: www.ftginc.com
Mfr air filters, oil filters, fuel filters, filtration products, custom engineered parts. (As-Pac, estab 1992, empl 20, sales $3,000,000, cert: NMSDC)

3789 Harris Industrial Gases
8475 Auburn Blvd
Citrus Heights, CA 95610
Contact: Tim Lettich GM
Tel: 916-725-2168
Email: tlettich@harrisgas.com
Website: www.harrisgas.com
Dist welding & industrial equipment & industrial gases.
(Woman, estab 1936, empl 20, sales $5,000,000, cert:
State, CPUC)

3790 Jeyco Products, Inc.
1221 Cushman Ave
San Diego, CA 92110
Contact: Sales Mgr
Tel: 619-260-1075
Email:
Website: www.jeyco.com
Dist industrial MRO supplies: cutting tools, abrasives,
fittings, fasteners, aerosol & bulk chemicals, electrical
maintenance supplies, janitorial cleaning supplies &
equipment, stainless steel food grade products, food grade
chemicals. (Woman, estab 1977, empl 10, sales
$3,500,000, cert: CPUC)

3791 Liberty Glove, Inc.
433 Cheryl Lane
City of Industry, CA 91789
Contact: Ken Tran Natl Sales Mgr
Tel: 800-327-8333
Email: kentran@libertyglove.com
Website: www.libertyglove.com
Dist safety industrial products. (Woman/As-Pac, estab
1988, empl 70, sales , cert: NMSDC)

3792 Paramount Safety Supply
14516 Crenshaw Blvd
Gardena, CA 90249
Contact: Joel Pulgarin Presdient
Tel: 866-200-2975
Email: info@paramountsafetysupply.com
Website: www.paramountsafetysupply.com
Personal Protective Equipment, Fall Protection Systems,
Gas Monitors/Sniffers, Disaster Preparedness, Emergency
Response Supplies, Confined Space Entry/Rescue, Rescue
& Descent Systems, Construction Safety. (Hisp, estab 2015,
empl , sales $500,000, cert: State, CPUC)

3793 R.J. Safety Supply Company Inc.
7320 Convoy Court
San Diego, CA 92111
Contact: Diane Rodriguez VP
Tel: 858-541-2880
Email: drodriguez@rjsafety.com
Website: www.rjsafety.com
Dist safety supplies: PPE products, respiratory, confined
space, fall protection, blowers, first aid, gloves, boots,
rainwear, protective clothing, hazardous material contain-
ers, signs, traffic control, safety cabinets, gas detectors.
(Woman, estab 1959, empl 17, sales , cert: CPUC)

3794 Safetyvibe
2530 Corporate Pl, Ste A105
Monterey Park, CA 91754
Contact: Lila Don Owner
Tel: 626-281-8444
Email: bidops@safetyvibe.com
Website: www.safetyvibe.com
Dist industrial equipment & supplies. (Woman/Hisp, estab
2003, empl 5, sales $1,950,000, cert: State)

3795 Widespread Industrial Supplies, Inc.
1220 S Boyle Ave
Los Angeles, CA 90023
Contact: Josh Dorfman President
Tel: 310-793-7315
Email: josh.dorfman@widespreadind.com
Website: www.widespreadind.com
Dist industrial supplies: fasteners, cutting tools, electri-
cal, welding, chemical & safety related supplies, hand &
power tools. (Woman, estab 2002, empl 4, sales
$820,341, cert: State, City)

Connecticut

3796 IBC - Industrial Supply Plus
2 Creamery Brook
East Granby, CT 06026
Contact: Ron Nunez CEO
Tel: 860-246-1618
Email: rnunez@industrialbuyers.com
Website: www.industrialbuyers.com
Dist maintenance, repair, operations, production,
bearing & power transmission supplies, technical
support, inventory control & mgmt, product support &
service, consolidated invoicing & sales reporting,
minority credits, standardization & rationalization. (Hisp,
estab 1999, empl 15, sales $90,000,000, cert: NMSDC)

Florida

3797 Arroyo Process Equipment Inc.
1550 Centennial Blvd
Bartow, FL 33830
Contact: Diane Schleicher President
Tel: 863-533-9700
Email: diane@arroyoprocess.com
Website: www.arroyoprocess.com
Dist pumps, tanks, mixers, meters, filters, water treat-
ment equip. (AA, As-Pac, Hisp, estab 1968, empl 32,
sales $15,576,805, cert: NMSDC)

3798 O.T. Trans Inc.
201 Babock St
Melbourne, FL 32901
Contact: Dean Danner Business Dev Mgr
Tel: 321-259-9880
Email: ddanner@ottrans.com
Website: www.ottrans.com
Industrial machinery & equip, material handling, hand
tools, wiring supplies, industrial supplies safety & rescue
equip, tool & hardware boxes, abrasive materials,
cabinets, lockers, bins & shelving, winches, hoists,
cranes & derricks. (Hisp, estab 1993, empl 15, sales
$5,000,000, cert: NMSDC)

3799 Pelican Sales, Inc.
2825 Business Center Blvd Ste C9
Melbourne, FL 32940
Contact: Callena Spearman Sales Professional
Tel: 321-254-9569
Email: sales@pelican-sales.com
Website: www.pelican-direct.com
Dist industrial hardware equip & supplies. (Woman,
estab 1993, empl 15, sales $13,000,000, cert: State)

3800 Silver Wings Aerospace
25400 SW 140th Ave
Princeton, FL 33032
Contact: Eduardo Montalvo Presdient
Tel: 305-258-5950
Email: eddie@silverwingsaerospace.com
Website: www.silverwingsaerospace.com
Dist & repair aircraft parts. (Hisp, estab 2007, empl 16,
sales $12,765,527, cert: NMSDC)

Georgia

3801   A.D.A. Supplies & Leasing Services, Inc.
205 Old Perry Rd
Bonaire, GA 31005
Contact: Ima McLean Business Dev Mgr
Tel: 478-329-8896
Email: ima.mclean@adasupply.com
Website: www.adasupply.com
Dist safety supplies & equip: respiratory protection, fall protection gear, eye & ear plugs & muffs protection, welding equipment & fire safety, gloves. (Woman/As-Pac, estab 0, empl , sales $2,500,000, cert: State)

3802   Control Specialties, Inc.
2503 Monroe Dr
Gainesville, GA 30507
Contact: Janice Moody CSR
Tel: 770-532-7736
Email: janice@control-specialties.com
Website: www.control-specialties.com
Dist pumps, instrumentation, filtration, controls, valves, energy audits, utility consultations. (Woman, estab 1987, empl 4, sales $1,965,970, cert: WBENC)

3803   Covenant Distributors, Inc.
1227 Augusta West Pkwy
Augusta, GA 30909
Contact: Mark Pugh Contract Admin
Tel: 706-610-2207
Email: mark@ecovenant.net
Website: www.ecovenant.net
Dist valves, pumps, element filters. (AA, estab 1999, empl 7, sales $360,000, cert: State)

3804   DBS Manufacturing, Inc.
45 SouthWoods Pkwy
Atlanta, GA 30354
Contact: Nicole McDermott NWBOC Admin
Tel: 404-768-2131
Email: nwboc@dbsmfg.com
Website: www.dbsmfg.com
Water & Waste Water Treatment Clarifiers & Thickener; Water & Waste Water Treatment Clarifiers & Thickeners Bolt-In Retrofit Drive Units; Trickling Filters; Aeration Equipment; Mixing Equipment. (Woman, estab 1975, empl 30, sales $9,000,000, cert: State)

3805   H&S Supply Co., Inc.
528 N Main St
Moultrie, GA 31768
Contact: Mgr
Tel: 229-985-4575
Email:
Website: www.hssupplyco.com
Dist plumbing & HVAC supplies, drilling supplies. (Nat Ame, estab 1969, empl 10, sales $40,000,000, cert: State)

3806   HeatRep, LLC
400 Galleria Pkwy, Ste 1500
Atlanta, GA 30339
Contact: Owner
Tel: 404-989-5457
Email:
Website: www.heatrep.com
Industrial equipment supplies, heat exchangers, fired heaters, electric heaters, economizers, condensers, liquid filtration, gas filtration, strainers, automatic strainers, filter separators, knockout tanks, reactors, pulsation bottles, custom fabrication (Woman, estab 2011, empl 1, sales , cert: WBENC)

3807   KACO Supply Company
1950 Lois Pointe Smyrna
Georgia, GA 30080
Contact: Kay Williams Presdient
Tel: 770-435-8902
Email: kay.williams@kacosupplycompany.com
Website: www.kacosupplycompany.com
Dist institutional food, paper & plastic products, janitorial supplies, kitchenwares & equipment. (Woman/AA, estab , empl , sales $1,449,460, cert: City, NMSDC)

3808   Stag Enterprise, Inc.
383 Wilbanks Dr
Ball Ground, GA 30107
Contact: Rachel Niederer VP Operations
Tel: 770-720-8888
Email: racheln@stagenterprise.com
Website: www.stagenterprise.com
Dist industrial supplies, slitting tapes. (Woman/As-Pac, estab 1993, empl 21, sales $22,000,000, cert: NMSDC, WBENC)

Iowa

3809   Molded Products, Inc.
1112 Chatburn Ave
Harlan, IA 51537
Contact: Sheri Tyrrel Mktg/Sales Mgr
Tel: 800-435-8957
Email: mpc@moldedproducts.com
Website: www.moldedproducts.com
Dist ancillary supplies, access sites, luer lock caps, transducer protectors, tube occluding forceps, hansen connectors, recirculation sets, patented tandem dialysis supplies, specialty connectors, dialyzer holders, fistula pressure clamps. (Woman, estab 1986, empl 46, sales $4,030,797, cert: State)

Illinois

3810   AMSYSCO, Inc.
1200 Windham Pkwy
Romeoville, IL 60446
Contact: Neel Khosa VP
Tel: 630-296-8383
Email: nkhosa@amsyscoinc.com
Website: www.amsyscoinc.com
Dist post-tensioning tendons used in concrete reinforcement, barrier cable used in parking garage restraint systems. (As-Pac, estab 1981, empl 30, sales $18,697,191, cert: NMSDC)

3811   Emergent Safety Supply
1055 Kingsland Dr
Batavia, IL 60510
Contact: Jerry Hill VP
Tel: 630-406-9666
Email: jhill@emergentsafety.com
Website: www.Emergentsafety.com
Dist PPE, FR Clothing, Traffic Safety Products, Safety Signage, Spill Containment, Repertory Products. (Woman, estab 1985, empl 28, sales $12,200,000, cert: State, WBENC)

3812   Equity Industrial
2000 S 25th Ave Unit A
Broadview, IL 60155
Contact: Robert Butler Presdient
Tel: 708-450-0000
Email: kevindonnelly@equityind.com
Website: www.equityind.com
Dist industrial supplies. (Woman/AA, estab 1996, empl 7, sales $4,675,276, cert: NMSDC)

3813 Freedom Air Filtration Inc.
1712 Arden Place
Joliet, IL 60435
Contact: Linda Freveletti Presdient
Tel: 877-715-8999
Email: linda@freedomairfiltration.com
Website: www.freedomairfiltration.com
HVAC supplies & services. (Woman, estab 2004, empl 5, sales $850,000, cert: WBENC)

3814 Howe Corporation
1650 N Elston Ave
Chicago, IL 60642
Contact: VP Finance & Treasurer
Tel: 773-235-0200
Email:
Website: www.howecorp.com
Mfr Flake ice makers, refrigeration & ammonia pump out compressors & refrigeration pressure vessels. (Woman, estab 1912, empl 37, sales $10,000,000, cert: WBENC)

3815 Inter-City Supply Co
8830 S Dobson Ave
Chicago, IL 60619
Contact: Jackie Dyess Presdient
Tel: 773-731-8007
Email: intercity@ameritech.net
Website: www.intercity-supply.com
Dist janitorial, safety & food service. (AA, estab , empl , sales $11,000,000, cert: State, City, NMSDC)

3816 International Filter Manufacturing Corporation
713 W Columbian Blvd
Litchfield, IL 62056
Contact: Cecilia Ewing Hayes Presdient
Tel: 217-324-2303
Email: ifmpres@consolidated.net
Website: www.ifm-corp.com
Mfr air filters for heavy-duty equip: transit vehicles, coal mining. Also dist HVAC, industrial & specailty filters. (Woman/AA, estab 1987, empl 35, sales $ 0, cert: NMSDC)

3817 ITA, Inc.
150 Pierce Road, Ste 550
Itasca, IL 60143
Contact: Ritu Agrawal Dir of Marketing
Tel: 281-712-7608
Email: ragrawal@itaoffice.com
Website: www.itaoffice.com
Dist Industrial Equipment, Printers, Production Simulation Software, Hazardous & remote sensing robots, Oil filtration equipment, R&D Equipment, Chemiluminesent Oxidation Analyzers, Ferro Magnetic Detector, Automation MRO Products. (As-Pac, estab 1980, empl 10, sales $2,500,000, cert: NMSDC)

3818 JM Industrial Supply
2323 Lakeshore
Pekin, IL 61554
Contact: Daniel Whitford Sales
Tel: 309-346-5796
Email: daniel@jmindsupply.com
Website: www.jmindsupply.com
Dist MRO mill supplies company. (AA, estab 1986, empl 11, sales $10,500,000, cert: State)

3819 One Way Safety, LLC
418 Shawmut Ave
LaGrange, IL 60525
Contact: Anne Callaghan Sales Mgr
Tel: 708-579-0229
Email: anne@onewaysafety.com
Website: www.onewaysafety.com
Dist PPE, gas detection, fall protection, supplied air, respiratory equipment & uniforms, rescue teams, respiratory fit testing, safety training, safety equipment repair & rental, safety supervisors. (Woman, estab 2013, empl 20, sales $2,500,000, cert: WBENC)

3820 Permatron
2020 Touhy Ave
Elk Grove Village, IL 60007
Contact: Leslye Sandberg President
Tel: 847-434-1421
Email: lsandberg@permatron.com
Website: www.permatron.com
Mfr air filters, air intake filters, equipment protection filters. (Woman, estab 1957, empl 40, sales , cert: WBENC)

3821 Production Distribution Companies
9511 S Dorchester ave
Chicago, IL 60628
Contact: Cleo Downs President
Tel: 708-489-0195
Email: cleo@pdcompanies.org
Website: www.pdcompanies.org
Dist electrical, industrial supplies, tools & equipment. (AA, estab 2004, empl 9, sales $5,400,272, cert: City, NMSDC)

3822 Supplied Industrial Solutions, Inc.
1635 West 1st St Ste 151
Granite City, IL 62040
Contact: Stephen Brock President
Tel: 618-452-8151
Email: sbrock@supplied-industrial.com
Website: www.supplied-industrial.com
Dist industrial supplies: hose, fittings, valves, safety supplies. (AA, estab 2003, empl 5, sales $240,000, cert: State)

3823 Wabash Transformer (PowerVolt and Ensign Corp)
300 W. Factory Rd.
Addison, IL 60101
Contact: Ajay Sharma VP Sales/Mktg
Tel: 630-628-9999
Email: ajays@wabashtransformer.com
Website: www.wabashtransformer.com
Mfr power transformers: medical, dental, HVAC, controls, packaging & automation equipment. (As-Pac, estab 1966, empl 33, sales $3,200,000, cert: NMSDC)

Indiana

3824 Courtney Material Handling, Inc.
P.O. Box 6925
South Bend, IN 46660
Contact: Beth Courtney Presdient
Tel: 574-231-0094
Email: beth@cmhionline.com
Website: www.cmhionline.com
Dist safety items: hard hats, vests, safety glasses, gloves, tools, fire & detection, bins, cabinets, carts, casters, chairs & stools. (Woman, estab 2003, empl 2, sales $213,673, cert: State)

3825 GM Supply Company, Inc.
      6321 E 30th St Ste 205
      Indianapolis, IN 46219
      Contact: Steven Batts Business Dev Mgr
      Tel: 317-898-3510
      Email: steveb@gmsupplyco.com
      Website: www.gmsupplyco.com
Integrated supply services, commodity management
services, component assembly services, distribution of
cutting tools, abrasives, safety supplies, MRO, packaging,
tools, janitorial, electrical, plumbing, power transmission,
bearings. (AA, estab 1992, empl 12, sales $22,000,000,
cert: NMSDC)

3826 Powell Tool Supply Co., Inc.
      1338 Mishawaka Ave
      South Bend, IN 46615
      Contact: Cari Eaton CEO
      Tel: 574-289-4811
      Email: ceaton@powelltool.com
      Website: www.powelltool.com
Dist industrial supplies: cutting tools, abrasives, chemicals,
MRO supplies, material handling, janitorial, etc. (Woman,
estab 1948, empl 20, sales $5,500,000, cert: WBENC)

3827 Rfs Group
      P.O. Box 68506
      Indianapolis, IN 46268
      Contact: Ramon Morrison Principal
      Tel: 317-507-3165
      Email: rmorrison@meticulousdb.com
      Website: www.meticulousdb.com
Dist maintenance, janitorial & cleaning supplies, equipment & accessories. Also wholesale distributes office,
foodservice and safety supplies. (AA, estab 2007, empl 6,
sales $ 0, cert: State, City)

3828 Team Cruiser Supply LLC
      P.O. Box 88255
      Indianapolis, IN 46208
      Contact: Christopher Barney Presdient
      Tel: 317-423-2430
      Email: mbarney@teamcruiser.com
      Website: www.tcsupplylogistics.com
Dist industrial products. (AA, estab 2013, empl 5, sales
$3,345,000, cert: NMSDC)

3829 Worldwide Filters, LLC
      3318 Pagosa Court
      Indianapolis, IN 46201
      Contact: Dawn Codozor Sales Mgr
      Tel: 317-808-3719
      Email: frank@worldwidefilters.com
      Website: www.worldwidefilters.com
Dist filters: commercial, industrial & residential, HEPA
filters, air, oil, hydraulic & fuel vehicle filters, water
filtration systems. (AA, estab 2004, empl 5, sales $250,000,
cert: NMSDC)

Kansas

3830 Touch Enterprises LLC
      117 N Cooper St
      Olathe, KS 66061
      Contact: Camilo Fernandez Sales Admin
      Tel: 913-440-0770
      Email: cfernandez@touchenterprises.com
      Website: www.touchenterprises.com/shop
Dist industrial products, safety products, medical supplies,
vet supplies, MRO supplies. (As-Pac, estab 2007, empl 15,
sales $3,000,000, cert: NMSDC)

Kentucky

3831 Industrial Electronics LLC dba Indel-USA
      10312 Bluegrass Pkwy
      Louisville, KY 40299
      Contact: Vadim Nazarenko Owner
      Tel: 888-499-4877
      Email: indel@indel-usa.com
      Website: www.indel-usa.com
Repair, troubleshooting, retrofitting & design services for
industrial electronic equipment. (Minority, Woman,
estab 2005, empl 4, sales , cert: State)

3832 United American Supply, LLC
      100-C Dewey Dr
      Nicholasville, KY 40356
      Contact: Albert Taylor Managing Partner
      Tel: 859-881-1850
      Email: al@unitedamericansupply.com
      Website: www.unitedamericansupply.com
Dist safety supplies (PPE), machined parts & sanitary
maintenance supplies. (AA, estab 2008, empl 8, sales
$1,600,000, cert: NMSDC)

Louisiana

3833 Brewster Procurement Group, Inc.
      401 W Main St
      Lafayette, LA 70501
      Contact: V. Janet Brewster CEO
      Tel: 337-291-9009
      Email: janet@brewsterprocurement.com
      Website: www.brewsterprocurement.com
Dist MRO, mill & industrial supplies, electrical, tools,
safety products, buyout services. (Woman/Hisp, estab
1999, empl 8, sales $113,609,858, cert: NMSDC,
WBENC)

3834 Precision Air & Liquid Solutions, LLC
      1905 W Thomas St, Ste D271
      Hammond, LA 70401
      Contact: Cynthia Bourg Chief Exec Mgr
      Tel: 504-208-1525
      Email: cyndibourg@precisionair-liquid.com
      Website: www.precisionair-liquid.com
Dist ventilation fans, fan parts, filtration, replacement
filters, cartridges, housings, compressors, turbines &
engines, dust, fume & mist control products & flow
monitoring equipment. (Woman, estab 2003, empl 2,
sales $550,000, cert: State, WBENC)

Massachusetts

3835 New England Die Cutting, Inc.
      96 Milk St
      Methuen, MA 01844
      Contact: Kimberly L Abare Presdient
      Tel: 978-374-0789
      Email: kabare@nedc.com
      Website: www.nedc.com
Mfr gaskets, seals & insulators, die cutting, waterjet
cutting & laser etching. (Woman, estab 1982, empl 28,
sales $3,900,000, cert: WBENC)

Michigan

3836 Choctaw-Kaul Distribution Company
3540 Vinewood
Detroit, MI 48208
Contact: Caitlin Johnson Customer Dev Mgr
Tel: 313-895-3165
Email: cjohnson@choctawkaul.com
Website: www.choctawkaul.com
Mfr gloves & safety products, mgmt svcs, janitorial svcs,
industrial specialty cleaning, paint booth cleaning,
chemical mgmt, recycling, filter maintenance, truck repair,
construction mgmt, parking lot maintenance, temp
manpower, etc. (Nat Ame, As-Ind, As-Pac, estab 1998,
empl 350, sales $107,000,000, cert: NMSDC)

3837 Extreme Tooling LLC
48750 Structural Dr
Chesterfield, MI 48051
Contact: Kurt Schill Presdient
Tel: 586-232-3618
Email: kschill@extremetooling.com
Website: www.extremetooling.com
Dist metal removal & industrial supplies, milling, drilling &
industrial products. (Woman, estab 2003, empl 5, sales
$3,683,821, cert: WBENC)

3838 IMC Products, Inc.
2743 Henry St, Ste 130
Muskegon, MI 49441
Contact: Irmgard Cooper Presdient
Tel: 877-625-8743
Email: irmgard.cooper@imc-products.com
Website: www.imc-products.com
Assembly & kit packaging, contract administration,
warehouse & distribution. (AA, estab 1990, empl 12, sales
$1,900,000, cert: NMSDC)

3839 JISI Group, LLC
6043 18 Mile Rd
Sterling Heights, MI 48314
Contact: Amber Amato Presdient
Tel: 586-239-9016
Email: a.amato@jisisupply.com
Website: www.jisisupply.com
Concrete construction & repair products. (Woman, estab
2014, empl 2, sales $446,000, cert: WBENC)

3840 Mahar Tool Supply Company, Inc.
7105 Nineteen MIle Rd
Sterling Heights, MI 48314
Contact: Dave Plosky Exec VP of Sales
Tel: 586-997-2584
Email: dp@mahartool.com
Website: www.mahartool.com
Dist industrial products & MRO supplies, commodity
management, integrated supply, technical staffing,
engineering support. (Woman, estab 1947, empl 142,
sales $115,200,000, cert: WBENC)

3841 Master Pneumatic Detroit, Inc.
6701 Eighteen Mile Road
Sterling Heights, MI 48314
Contact: Wendy Goscenski Mgr
Tel: 586-254-1000
Email: wgoscenski@aol.com
Website: www.masterpneumatic.com
Mfr filters, regulators & lubrication systems for com-
pressed air systems. (Woman, estab 1950, empl 56, sales
$6,500,000, cert: WBENC)

3842 Midwest Safety Products of Michigan
4929 E Paris SE
Grand Rapids, MI 49512
Contact: Vanh Miller CEO
Tel: 616-554-5155
Email: vanhm@midwestsafety.com
Website: www.midwestsafety.com
Dist safety, first aid, janitorial, packaging supplies,
Personal Protective Equipment, Gloves, Safety Glasses,
Ear Plugs, Disposable Clothing, Respirators, Welding
Supplies, Hardhats. (As-Pac, estab 1978, empl 32, sales
$10,010,000, cert: NMSDC)

3843 Safety Services, Inc.
5286 Wynn Rd
Kalamazoo, MI 49048
Contact: Kathryn Bowdish CEO
Tel: 269-382-1052
Email: info@safetyservicesinc.com
Website: www.safetyservicesinc.com
Dist industrial safety equipment: personal protective
equipment, gloves, first aid, fall protection, confined
space equipment, handling, storage, instrumentation,
spill control. (Woman/As-Pac, estab 1948, empl 28, sales
$ 0, cert: WBENC)

3844 The Safety Source, LLC
35320 Forton Court
Clinton Township, MI 48035
Contact: Elizabeth VanSickle Presdient
Tel: 866-688-7233
Email: elizabeth@safetysourcellc.com
Website: www.safetysourcellc.com
Dist industrial safety supplies, first aid supplies &
miscellaneous MRO supplies. (Woman, estab 2006, empl
6, sales $2,200,000, cert: WBENC)

Minnesota

3845 Allied Electrical & Industrial Supply Company Inc.
6112 14th St W
St. Louis Park, MN 55416
Contact: Valerie McKissack Presdient
Tel: 763-544-3600
Email: vmckissack@allied-electrical.com
Website: www.allied-electrical.com
Dist medical, industrial, electrical, safety, janitorial &
construction supplies. (Woman/AA, estab 1994, empl 6,
sales $832,000, cert: NMSDC)

3846 AMKA Global, LLC
6441 Cecilia Circle
Edina, MN 55439
Contact: Bocar Kane CEO
Tel: 952-495-4492
Email: sales@amkasafety.com
Website: www.amkasafety.com
Personal Protective products and work zone safety cones
and equipment. (AA, estab 2006, empl 2, sales
$129,000, cert: City)

3847 Northern Traffic Supply Inc.
2740 N Ferry St
Anoka, MN 55303
Contact: Brent Gummert CEO
Tel: 763-576-1200
Email: brentg@ntsindustries.com
Website: www.ntsindustries.com
Dist traffic control devices, mfr road, building & parking
lot signage, safety vests, safety signs, ear protection, eye
protection, safety gloves. (Nat Ame, estab 1998, empl
14, sales $1,400,000, cert: State)

3848   Safety Signs
19784 Kenrick Ave
Lakeville, MN 55044
Contact: Sue Blanchard President
Tel: 952-469-6700
Email: sueblanchard@safetysigns-mn.com
Website: www.safetysigns-mn.com
Traffic safety equipment and svcs specializing in traffic control, permanent signs, pavement striping, pavement stripe removals & safety apparel. (Woman, estab 1993, empl 28, sales , cert: State, City)

Missouri

3849   Alliance Industries LLC
2959 N. Martin Ave
Springfield, MO 65803
Contact: Brenda Ryan Presdient
Tel: 417-863-6315
Email: bryan@allianceind.com
Website: www.allianceind.com
Remanufacture OEM torque converters. (Woman/AA, estab 2002, empl 20, sales $ 0, cert: NMSDC, WBENC)

3850   King Filtration Technologies, Inc.
1255 Research Blvd
Saint Louis, MO 63132
Contact: Michael Miossi Energy Acct Mgr
Tel: 800-999-8441
Email: michael.miossi@kingfiltration.com
Website: www.kingfiltration.com
Dist filtration products. (Woman, estab 1964, empl 20, sales $ 0, cert: WBENC)

3851   Millennium Industrial Equipment, LLC
1475 Legacy Circle
Fenton, MO 63026
Contact: Tony Estopare Presdient
Tel: 314-574-2047
Email: testopare@miequipment.com
Website: www.millennium-industrial-equipment.com
Manufacturer's Rep, Bulk Solids (Dry) Material Handling, Air Handling, and Air Pollution Control Equipment. (As-Pac, estab 2002, empl 4, sales $630,862, cert: State)

3852   National Material Supply Co, LLC
2206 Sidney St
St. Louis, MO 63104
Contact: Kevie Hendrix
Tel: 314-865-1644
Email: sales@nmsupply.com
Website: www.nmsupply.com
Dist industrial supplies, products & safety equipment. (AA, estab 1997, empl 5, sales $1,500,000, cert: State)

3853   Stainless Integrity
3431 E Bluff Point Dr
Ozark, MO 65721
Contact: Presdient
Tel: 417-773-6383
Email:
Website: www.stainlessintegrity.com
Dist stainless steel nickel alloy ASME pressure vessels & tanks; bioreactor & fermenter skids; field repair; field modification & field erection, tank cleaning & inspection, powder hoppers & bins. (Woman, estab 2010, empl 1, sales $ 0, cert: WBENC)

Mississippi

3854   MS Rubber Company
715 E McDowell Rd
Jackson, MS 39204
Contact: Susan Foster GM
Tel: 601-948-2575
Email: sfoster@msrubber.com
Website: www.msrubber.com
Dist rubber hoses, hydraulic hoses, belting, plastic, gaskets, safety supplies, o'rings, general hoses, hose fittings, clamps, rubber tubing, matting, sheet packing, rainsuit, gloves & boots. (Woman, estab 1963, empl 14, sales $1,300,000, cert: CPUC, WBENC)

North Carolina

3855   EMI Supply
5502 Cannon Dr
Monroe, NC 28110
Contact: Susan Richardson CEO
Tel: 704-721-3641
Email: srichardson@emisupply.com
Website: www.emisupply.com
Dist electrical & industrial supplies: abrasives, adhesives, chemicals, cutting tools, safety, tapes. (Woman, estab 1990, empl 7, sales , cert: WBENC)

3856   GP Supply Company
501 E Washington St
Greensboro, NC 27401
Contact: Antonio Wallace CEO
Tel: 336-274-7615
Email: awallace@gpsupplycompany.com
Website: www.gpsupplycompany.com
Dist mechanical supplies, industrial supplies, commercial plumbing supplies, pipe, valves, fittings, fixtures. (AA, estab , empl , sales $14,000,000, cert: State, NMSDC)

New Hampshire

3857   Quintana Associates, Inc.
8 Puzzle Lane
Newton, NH 03858
Contact: Jorge Cruz Sales and Acct Rep
Tel: 978-689-4411
Email: jorgec@qaisupply.com
Website: www.quintanasupply.com
Dist industrial supplies: safety, janitorial, packaging, material handling equip, office & clean room supplies. (Hisp, estab 1991, empl 20, sales $8,717,183, cert: NMSDC)

New Jersey

3858   Automotive and Industrial Equipment LLC
43 Wilkeshire Blvd
Randolph, NJ 07869
Contact: Vijay Srinivasan President
Tel: 973-343-6432
Email: autoandindustrialinc@gmail.com
Website: www.ai-equip.com
Dist materials, tools, equipment & supplies to laboratories, government facilities & private facilities. (As-Pac, estab 2011, empl 1, sales $375,891, cert: State)

3859   BKC Industries, Inc.
       3288 Delsea Dr Ste B
       Franklinville, NJ 08322
       Contact: Karen Harrison-Carter Presdient
       Tel: 856-694-9400
       Email: bkcindustrial@comcast.net
       Website: http://bkcindustries.com
Dist industrial plant supplies, safety supplies, packaging
materials & construction materials. (Woman/AA, estab
1998, empl 3, sales $1,200,000, cert: State, 8a)

3860   Centryco Inc.
       300 W Broad St
       Burlington, NJ 08016
       Contact: Mary Gordon Presdient
       Tel: 609-386-6448
       Email: mtg@centryco.com
       Website: www.centryco.com
Mfr point of operation barriers for machinery & equipment: bellows, way covers, telescoping covers, flat bellows
& screens, spring guards/covers. (Woman, estab 1949,
empl 35, sales $3,910,958, cert: WBENC)

3861   Forty Nine Corp.
       P.O. Box 2325
       Paterson, NJ 07509
       Contact: Michael Temkin VP
       Tel: 201-791-0584
       Email: mct@49corp.com
       Website: http://49corp.com
Mfr safety, warning & protective flags, tapes & tarpaulins
for electric utilities & telephone companies. (Woman,
estab , empl , sales $500,000, cert: State, WBENC)

3862   Turtle & Hughes, Inc.
       1900 Lower Rd
       Linden, NJ 07036
       Contact: Jayne Millard Co-CEO
       Tel: 732-574-3600
       Email: info@turtleintegrated.com
       Website: www.turtle.com
Dist MRO, industrial & electrical supplies & equipment.
(Woman, estab 1923, empl 1000, sales $760,000,000, cert:
WBENC)

New York

3863   Active Fire Extinguisher Co., Inc.
       5-16 47th Ave
       Long Island City, NY 11101
       Contact: President
       Tel: 718-729-0450
       Email:
       Website: www.activefire.com
Dist fire extinguishers, pre-engineered automatic kitchen
range hood systems, cabinets, fire hoses. (Woman, estab
1942, empl 13, sales $2,600,000, cert: City)

3864   AMKO Trading
       129-09 26th Ave Unit D
       Flushing, NY 11354
       Contact: Tae S Rim Sales Mgr
       Tel: 718-505-8401
       Email: trim@amkotrading.com
       Website: www.amkotrading.com
Dist commercial kitchen equipment. Electric & Gas Rice
cookers, Electric rice warmer, Steam pans, PC food pans,
Noodle making machines, Stock pots. (Woman/As-Pac,
estab 2001, empl 8, sales $1,000,000, cert: NMSDC)

3865   J.T. Systems, Inc.
       8132 Oswego Rd, Rt 57
       Liverpool, NY 13090
       Contact: Jit Turakhia President
       Tel: 315-622-1980
       Email: info@jtsystemsinc.com
       Website: www.jtsystemsinc.com
Mfr air pollution control equipment: cyclones, scrubbers
& baghouses, fans, ventilation, blowers, etc. (As-Pac,
estab 1980, empl 5, sales $ 0, cert: State)

3866   JHP Industrial Supply Co., Inc.
       312 W Taylor St
       Syracuse, NY 13202
       Contact: Robert Jenkins Sales Rep
       Tel: 315-422-0050
       Email: j.robert3@verizon.net
       Website:
Dist plumbing & heating supplies, industrial & construction related products. (AA, estab 1981, empl 7, sales $
0, cert: State)

3867   Legacy Construction, LLC
       85 Milton Ave
       Sag Harbor, NY 11963
       Contact: Stephen Watson CFO
       Tel: 917-560-5593
       Email: swatson@twcurban.com
       Website: www.twcurban.com
Dist construction material & supplies. (AA, estab 2004,
empl 2, sales , cert: State)

3868   Mechanical Heating Supply, Inc.
       476 Timpson Pl
       Bronx, NY 10455
       Contact: Frank Rivera Presdient
       Tel: 718-402-9765
       Email: frank@mechheat.com
       Website: www.mechheat.com
Dist heating equipment & supplies. (Hisp, estab 1989,
empl 11, sales $12,800,000, cert: State)

3869   R. Kraft, Inc.
       129 Shorecliff Dr
       Rochester, NY 14612
       Contact: Ralph Kraft President
       Tel: 585-621-6946
       Email: clnrmsrvs@aol.com
       Website: www.cleanroomservices.com
Dist cleanroom systems, components, furnishings,
cleanroom cert, personnel training, consulting, design
assistance, troubleshooting. (Nat Ame, estab 1977, empl
1, sales $ 0, cert: State)

3870   Strategic Procurement Group
       36 Harbor Park Dr
       Port Washington, NY 11050
       Contact: Donna Kay Presdient
       Tel: 516-479-3778
       Email: kayd@strategicprocurement.us
       Website: http://strategicprocurement.us
Dist MRO supplies. (Woman/As-Pac, estab 2002, empl
10, sales $13,000,000, cert: NMSDC, WBENC)

3871   Wats International Inc.
       200 Manchester Rd
       Poughkeepsie, NY 12603
       Contact: Josh Andelmo President
       Tel: 845-473-2106
       Email: josh.anselmo@watsinternational.com
       Website: www.watsinternational.com
Dist janitorial, office & MRO supplies. (AA, estab 1980,
empl 8, sales $ 0, cert: State, City, NMSDC)

Ohio

3872 All Contractors Supply LLC
8671 Tyler Blvd. Unit D
Mentor, OH 44060
Contact: Presdient
Tel: 440-290-0703
Email:
Website: http://allcontractorssupply.com
Dist plastic pipe, concrete, sealers, coatings, rebar, concrete cure, structural steel, expansion joint materials, drainage pipe, epoxy, grouts and waterproofing. (Minority, estab 2011, empl 1, sales $400,000, cert: City)

3873 Benchmark Industrial Supply, LLC
1913 Commerce Rd
Springfield, OH 45504
Contact: Ron Tenkman Natl Sales Mgr
Tel: 937-325-1001
Email: rtenkman@benchmarkindustrial.com
Website: www.benchmarkindustrial.com
Dist safety products & industrial supplies. (Woman, estab 2003, empl 18, sales $5,000,000, cert: State, WBENC)

3874 Hydro Dyne Inc.
225 Wetmore Ave SE
Massillon, OH 44646
Contact: Kevin Boone Business Develop Mgr
Tel: 330-832-5076
Email: kevin@hydrodyneinc.com
Website: www.hydrodyneinc.com
Design, mfr & repair shell & tube heat exchangers, condensers, evaporators & feedwater heaters. (Woman, estab 1967, empl 30, sales $ 0, cert: WBENC)

3875 IPS Group LLC
3254 Hill Ave
Toledo, OH 43607
Contact: Michele Bighouse CEO
Tel: 419-241-5955
Email: ipsti@ipstreatment.com
Website: www.ipsgroupllc.com
Derusting, degreasing, washing, deburring, demagnetizing, descaling, pickling, rust inhibiting, surface passivation, chemical paint stripping, bonding removal, assembly, sorting & inspecting, repackaging & shipping. (Woman/As-Ind, estab 1994, empl 30, sales $900,000, cert: State, WBENC)

3876 National Access Design, LLC
1924 Losantiville Ave
Cincinnati, OH 45237
Contact: Cheryl White Presdient
Tel: 513-351-3400
Email: cheryl@nationalaccessdesign.com
Website: www.nationalaccessdesign.com
Mfr double acting traffic/impact doors, strip doors, door jambs, blast cell doors, industrial/divider curtains, dock seals & equipment, dist FRP doors, cold storage doors, and air curtains. (Woman, estab 2011, empl 12, sales $ 0, cert: WBENC)

3877 Niche Consumer Products, LLC
2600 Civic Center Dr
Cincinnati, OH 45231
Contact: Benjamin Moore Presdient
Tel: 513-807-4174
Email: info@nicheconsumerproducts.com
Website: www.nicheconsumerproducts.com
Licenses, distributes and manufactures non-woven consumer products. (AA, estab 2007, empl 5, sales $330,000, cert: State, NMSDC)

3878 Norfleet Distributors LLC
32493 Jefferson Dr
Solon, OH 44139
Contact: Garrick Norfleet Owner
Tel: 216-832-2038
Email: garrick.norfleet@norfleetdistributors.com
Website: www.norfleetdistributors.com
Construction safety equipment including hard hats, safety vests etc. (AA, estab 2020, empl 2, sales $229,000, cert: NMSDC)

3879 PenCo Industrial Supply, Inc.
300 Industrial Pkwy, Unit D
Chagrin Falls, OH 44022
Contact: Penny Scocos President
Tel: 440-893-9506
Email: penny@pencosupply.com
Website: www.pencosupply.com
Dist MRO, safety & janitorial supplies: fasteners, cutting tools, abrasives, chemicals, eye & ear protection, gloves, respirators, toilet paper, paper towels, cleaning supplies & chemicals. (Woman, estab 2005, empl 5, sales $1,000,000, cert: WBENC)

3880 Quality Building Supplies For Industry, Inc.
17485 Saylor Ln
Grand Rapids, OH 43522
Contact: Edward haynes CEO
Tel: 419-832-2202
Email: qualitybldginc@aol.com
Website: www.qualitybuildingsupplies.com
Dist construction & industrial products: rebar, structural steel, piling, tools & hardware. (AA, estab 1978, empl 5, sales $2,300,000, cert: NMSDC)

3881 Superior Industrial Supply & Services Inc.
1717 Indianwood Circle Ste 200
Maumee, OH 43537
Contact: Stan McCormick President
Tel: 419-697-3700
Email: stan.mccormick@siss.cc
Website: http://superiorindustrialsupply.com
Dist janitorial chemicals & equipment, packaging supplies & equipment, paper supplies, mill & crib. (AA, estab 1972, empl 3, sales $ 0, cert: NMSDC)

3882 Tradex International Inc.
5300 Tradex Pkwy
Cleveland, OH 44102
Contact: Philip A. Baseil COO
Tel: 216-651-4788
Email: pab@tradexgloves.com
Website: www.tradexgloves.com
Dist gloves, aprons, shoe covers, bouffant caps, toilet seat covers & wipers. (As-Ind, As-Pac, estab 1988, empl 70, sales $ 0, cert: NMSDC)

Oklahoma

3883 Omni Packaging Corporation
12322 E 55th St
Tulsa, OK 74146
Contact: Roberta Jones President
Tel: 918-461-1700
Email: ar@omnipackaging.com
Website: www.omnipackaging.com
Dist adhesives/sealants, hose clamps, expansion joints, gaskets, matting, urethane, protective clothing, plastic, etc. (Woman/Nat Ame, estab 1988, empl 65, sales $ 0, cert: NMSDC)

Pennsylvania

3884 Aquatech International Corporation
1 Four Coins Dr
Canonsburg, PA 15317
Contact: Francis D'sa Reg Sales Mgr
Tel: 724-746-5300
Email: aic@aquatech.com
Website: www.aquatech.com
Mfr water & waste water treatment equip & systems.
ASME tank & piping fabricators. (Woman/As-Ind, As-Pac,
estab 1981, empl 450, sales $80,000,000, cert: NMSDC)

3885 Arbill Industries, Inc.
10450 Drummond Rd
Philadelphia, PA 19154
Contact: Renee Millett Sales Admin
Tel: 215-501-8246
Email: rmillett@arbill.com
Website: www.arbill.com
Mfr & dist industrial safety products. (Woman, estab 1957,
empl 76, sales $ 0, cert: WBENC)

3886 Electrical Systems & Construction Supplies
5131-37 N 2nd St, Bldg 12
Philadelphia, PA 19120
Contact: Bernard Hopewell CEO
Tel: 215-324-3291
Email: bhopewell@escsinc.net
Website: www.escsinc.net
Dist electrical equipment, construction supplies, wire &
cable & lighting. (AA, estab 2003, empl 3, sales
$1,440,000, cert: State, City)

3887 General Fire Equipment Company, Inc.
220 Broadway Ave
Aston, PA 19014
Contact: Kim McDonnell Exec Asst
Tel: 610-485-8200
Email: kmcdonnell@generalfireequipment.net
Website: http://GeneralFireEquipment.Net
Dist, Service & Inspect Fire Extinguishers, Fire Equipment
& Fire Surpession Systems. (Minority, Woman, estab 1975,
empl 23, sales $ 0, cert: City)

3888 Industrial Piping Systems, Inc.
1250 Toronita St.
York, PA 17402
Contact: Christine Wardrop President
Tel: 717-846-7473
Email: christine.wardrop@ipspipe.com
Website: www.ipspipe.com
Dist pipes, valves, fittings, pumps, heat exchangers, tube,
industrial coatings, lubricants. (Woman, estab 1982, empl
56, sales $17,574,304, cert: WBENC)

3889 Shah Industrial Sales Inc.
5824 Library Rd
Bethel Park, PA 15102
Contact: Barbara Shah President
Tel: 412-831-1224
Email: kara@shahind.com
Website: www.shahind.com
Dist fasteners, seals, o-rings, gaskets. (As-Ind, estab 1988,
empl 2, sales $280,000, cert: State, NMSDC)

Puerto Rico

3890 Interport Trading Corp.
P.O. Box 51958
Toa Baja, PR 00950
Contact: Antonio Cruz GM
Tel: 787-788-8650
Email: acruz@interportpr.com
Website: www.interportpr.com
Dist & service fire prevention equipment: extinguisher,
hose, supresion systems, fire alarms, safety equipment:
gloves,coveralls,eye protection, ear protection, showers,
boots, caps, etc. (Hisp, estab 1989, empl 10, sales
$1,448,600, cert: NMSDC)

3891 New York Wiping & Industrial Products, Inc.
698 Calle B
San Juan, PR 00920
Contact: Dr. Mario Julia President
Tel: 787-273-6363
Email: jsantos@nywiping.com
Website: www.nywiping.com
Dist industrial supplies. (Hisp, estab 1989, empl 5, sales ,
cert: NMSDC)

South Carolina

3892 Atlan-Tec, Inc. (Atlantic Technical Sales & Svc)
3215 Bryson Dr
Florence, SC 29501
Contact: Grace Patterson Presdient
Tel: 843-661-0415
Email: atlreceivables@aol.com
Website: www.atlan-tec.net
Dist industrial equipment. (Woman, estab 1991, empl 6,
sales $3,156,683, cert: State)

3893 Bullzeye Equipment & Supply
1383 Old Hwy 52
Moncks Corner, SC 29461
Contact: Kristie Collins Owner
Tel: 843-499-2226
Email: kcollins@bullzeyeequipment.com
Website: www.bullzeyeequipment.com
Dist industrial products, welding supplies, janitorial
supplies, safety supplies, packaging supplies, material
handling supplies & construction supplies. (Woman,
estab 2012, empl 1, sales , cert: State, SDB)

3894 Charleston's Rigging and Marine Hardware Inc
P.O. Box 21255
Charleston, SC 29413
Contact: Jessica Sage President
Tel: 843-723-7145
Email: jsage@charlestonsrigging.com
Website: www.charlestonsrigging.com
Dist rigging & material handling equipment, industrial &
safety products, fabricates custom wire rope, chain, &
nylon slings. (Woman, estab 1982, empl 47, sales
$10,000,000, cert: City)

3895 Indcon Inc.
105 Ben Hamby Dr., Ste E
Greenville, SC 29601
Contact: Collin Atkins Corporate Counsel
Tel: 864-298-8300
Email: collin@indconinc.com
Website: www.indconinc.com
Dist industrial maintenance products, lubrication
quality, general equipment maintenance, equipment
installation, concrete & industrial repair, maintenance
tools & hardware. (Woman, estab 1998, empl 10, sales
$6,000,000, cert: WBENC)

3896   Munaco Sealing Solutions, Inc.
5 Ketron Ct
Greenville, SC 29607
Contact: Jeff Adams Business Dev Mgr
Tel: 864-676-2055
Email: jeff@munaco-online.com
Website: www.munacosealing.com
Sealing solutions & precision components: gaskets, custom gaskets, metal seals, piston rings, metal gaskets, fiber gaskets, spiral-wound gaskets, rubber gaskets, silicone gaskets, elastomer o-rings, rubber o-rings, FKM, PTFE. (Woman, estab 1995, empl 13, sales $13,050,000, cert: WBENC)

Tennessee

3897   Dixon Services, Inc.
1315 Farmville Rd
Memphis, TN 38122
Contact: Charles Dixon Presdient
Tel: 901-345-6608
Email: charlesrdixon@dixonservicesinc.com
Website: www.dixonservicesinc.com
Dist safety & industrial supplies. (Woman/AA, estab 2000, empl 10, sales , cert: City, NMSDC)

3898   eSpin Technologies, Inc.
7151 Discovery Dr
Chattanooga, TN 37416
Contact: Jay Doshi Presdient
Tel: 423-267-6266
Email: jdoshi@exceedfilters.com
Website: www.eSpintechnologies.com
Mfr & dist low energy consuming, high performance HVAC air filters. (As-Ind, estab 1999, empl 27, sales $ 0, cert: NMSDC, 8a)

3899   Government & Industrial Supply, Inc.
401 Leatherwood Creek Rd
Pulaski, TN 38478
Contact: Kris Garner Presdient
Tel: 931-424-6067
Email: kris@gisupplyinc.com
Website: www.gisupplyinc.com
Dist industrial supplies, material handling supplies, safety supplies, security supplies, hardware items, tools, abrasives, office furniture & office supplies. (Nat Ame, estab 1993, empl 10, sales $4,200,000, cert: State)

3900   Porter-Walker LLC
115 Dyer St Ste 3
Columbia, TN 38401
Contact: Terrence Bybee strategic accts Mgr
Tel: 931-560-2428
Email: tbybee@porter-walker.com
Website: www.porter-walker.com
Dist safety, industrial & MRO supplies, supply chain mgmt. (AA, estab 1907, empl 41, sales $35,000,000, cert: State, NMSDC)

3901   Sportsdrive LLC
115 Horne Dr
Vonore, TN 37885
Contact: Jennifer Miller
Tel: 423-884-6189
Email: jmiller.sportsdrive@tds.net
Website:
Mfr felt seals & distribution warehousing of rollled goods to ISO standards; master scheduling- MRP, cutting, sewing, inventory control and logistics of product delivery; dist nonwovens & fire retardants- squeakstop, rayon/carbon precursor, breather. (As-Pac, estab 2010, empl 40, sales $1,200,000, cert: NMSDC, 8a)

3902   Superior Industrial Supply Co.
2675 Whitman Ave
Memphis, TN 38182
Contact: Rita Montesi CEO
Tel: 901-327-0450
Email: info@superiorindsupply.com
Website: www.superiorindsupply.com
Dist safety, industrial, janitorial, first aid supplies, fire protection & AED's. (Woman, estab 1981, empl 13, sales $2,500,000, cert: NWBOC)

3903   T G Inc.
615 Main St
Nashville, TN 37206
Contact: Joseph Towner VP Sales
Tel: 615-620-5100
Email: jtowner@t-g-inc.com
Website: www.t-g-inc.com
Dist industrial & electrical products, construction supplies, materials & equipment. (Woman/AA, estab 1999, empl 8, sales $2,000,000, cert: NMSDC)

Texas

3904   All-Tex Pipe & Supply, Inc.
9743 Brockbank
Dallas, TX 75220
Contact: Paul Borham Exec Asst
Tel: 214-389-2201
Email: paulb@alltexsupply.com
Website: www.alltexsupply.com
Dist pipe, valves & fittings: acid waste, carbon steel, cast iron, copper, CPVC, PVC, drainage, stainless steel. (Woman, estab 1973, empl 120, sales $78,039,000, cert: State, WBENC)

3905   Battery Consulting
4020 Christopher Way
Plano, TX 75024
Contact: MuMu Moorthi Owner
Tel: 214-929-6790
Email: mumu@battery-consulting.com
Website: www.battery-consulting.com
Dist batteries. (As-Pac, estab 2001, empl 2, sales $181,000, cert: State)

3906   CASADA Industrial
P.O. Box 203161
Austin, TX 78720
Contact: Ernest Anguiano Owner
Tel: 800-828-0934
Email: ernest@casada-industrial.com
Website: www.casada-industrial.com
Dist industrial supplies. (Hisp, estab 1993, empl 8, sales $ 0, cert: State)

3907   Dow-Caide Industrial, Inc.
1534 Sunset Lane
Duncanville, TX 75137
Contact: Michael Downs Presdient
Tel: 972-421-8662
Email: dewaye@sbcglobal.net
Website: www.dowcaidesupply.com
Dist industrial supplies, industrial equipment, safety supplies, plastic wrap/sheeting, trashbags, corrugated boxes, lights/ballasts, food products, chemicals, paper products, tape, labels, packaging supplies & materials etc. (AA, estab 2011, empl 2, sales $424,660, cert: State, NMSDC)

3908 Evco Partners dba Burgoon Company
P.O. Box 1168
Galveston, TX 77553
Contact: Donna Hanson Presdient
Tel: 409-766-1900
Email: office@burgooncompany.com
Website: www.burgooncompany.com
Dist industrial supplies & equipment, laboratory & medical supplies, heavy equipment. (Woman, estab 1988, empl 17, sales $20,981,530, cert: State, WBENC)

3909 Guardian Industrial Supply, LLC
10629 Metric Blvd
Austin, TX 00000
Contact: Christina Duncan Managing Member
Tel: 512-973-3500
Email: sales@guardian-industrial.com
Website: www.guardiancatalog.com
Dist industrial supplies: circuit breakers, motor starters, motor control products, transformers, fuses, safety switches, wiring devices, plug, receptacles, softstarters, variable frequency drives, transfer switches, controls, enclosures, contactors, etc. (Woman, estab 2006, empl 10, sales $3,193,459, cert: WBENC)

3910 HLF Distributing, Inc.
1213-B N Post Oak Rd
Houston, TX 77055
Contact: update
Tel: 713-932-9320
Email: info@huskybicycles.com
Website: www.huskybicycles.com
Dist industrial & commercial bicycles & tricycles: wheels, tires, tubes, chains, tools & lubricants. (Woman, estab 1993, empl 7, sales $2,600,000, cert: WBENC)

3911 I AM Safety
4565 FM 466
Seguin, TX 78155
Contact: Lynda Presdient
Tel: 832-715-0375
Email: lynda@iamsafetytx.com
Website: www.iamsafetytx.com
Safety Training (OSHA), Fire, First Aid/CPR/BBP/AED, Safety Products. (Woman, estab 2011, empl 2, sales , cert: State, City)

3912 Industrial Water Services
4500 Turf Rd
El Paso, TX 79938
Contact: Ruben Diaz President
Tel: 915-849-0401
Email: rdiaz@industrialwaterservice.com
Website: www.industrialwaterservice.com
Industrial water equipment parts & service. (Hisp, estab 1997, empl 17, sales $3,800,000, cert: NMSDC)

3913 MagRabbit-Alamo Iron Works, LLC
P.O. Box 2341
San Antonio, TX 78298
Contact: Wayne Dennis Diversity Coord
Tel: 210-704-8520
Email: wdennis@aiwnet.com
Website: www.magrabbit-aiw.com
Dist industrial supplies, steel service & fabrication, hand & power tools, equipment repair & installation, logistics, transportation & freight forwarding. (As-Pac, estab 2004, empl 150, sales $1,573,543, cert: NMSDC)

3914 Mavich LLC
525 Commerce St.
Southlake, TX 76092
Contact: Vincent Manfredini Operations
Tel: 682-503-4484
Email: vincent.manfredini@mavich.com
Website: www.mavich.com
Dist MRO & industrial supplies: electronic components, connectors, passives, resistors, etc. (Woman/Hisp, estab 2010, empl 10, sales $3,000,000, cert: State)

3915 Romar Supply
2468 Fabens
Dallas, TX 75229
Contact: Ron Adair VP Operations
Tel: 214-357-2020
Email: rona@romarsupply.com
Website: www.romarsupply.com
Dist pipe, valves, fittings, steam controls, valve actuation, stainless piping products, sanitary stainless piping. (Woman, estab 1983, empl 42, sales $17,000,000, cert: State, WBENC)

3916 Safety Supply, Inc.
12050 Crownpoint, Ste 160
San Antonio, TX 78233
Contact: Crystal Turner Presdient
Tel: 800-873-9033
Email: crystal@safetysupplyinc.com
Website: www.safetysupplyinc.com
Dist industrial safety apparel & equipment, fire service & rescue equipment, environmental & health products. (Woman, estab 1983, empl 11, sales $6,400,000, cert: State, WBENC)

3917 Supply Innovations Co, LLC
200 Chihuahua St, Ste 100
San Antonio, TX 78207
Contact: Nancy Flack Mgr
Tel: 210-225-3194
Email: nancy@supplyinnovationsllc.com
Website: www.supplyinnovationsllc.com
Dist industrial supplies: tapes, safety , tools , abrasives, packaging, material handling, hardware, janitorial, adhesive & aircraft supplies. (Woman, estab 2007, empl 4, sales $1,673,122, cert: State, WBENC)

3918 TKC Enterprises Inc. dba Batteries Plus
2703 N Beltline Rd
Irving, TX 75062
Contact: Miguel Yan Owner
Tel: 972-256-2073
Email: miguel@battplus.net
Website: www.batteriesplus.com
Dist batteries. (As-Pac, estab , empl , sales $100,000,000, cert: State, NMSDC)

3919 Track Trading Co./ dba Exaco USA., Exaco Trading
4209 Greystone Dr
Austin, TX 78731
Contact: Kim Cook President & CEO
Tel: 512-345-1900
Email: kim@exaco.com
Website: www.exaco.com
Dist metal mixing blades, mixing paint & drywall. (Woman, estab 1987, empl 18, sales $10,000,000, cert: State, WBENC)

3920 V M Graphic Packaging & Safety Products LLC
4413 Fairlake Dr
Garland, TX 75043
Contact: Verna Melton CEO
Tel: 972-303-9102
Email: vmgraph@flash.net
Website: https://
vmgraphicpkgandsafetyproducts.espwebsite.c
Dist style bags & textile bags, industrial supplies, part bags, brooms, trash containers, tilt trucks. (Woman/AA, estab 1988, empl 5, sales $2,015,489, cert: State)

Virginia

3921 Can See Fire Service Co Inc. t/a Fire Solutions
205 Haley Rd
Ashland, VA 23005
Contact: Edward Caldas VP Sales
Tel: 804-752-2366
Email: edward@firesolutionsinc.com
Website: www.firesolutionsinc.com
Install, maintain, service, inspects, relocate & repair fire protection equipment. (Woman/Hisp, estab 1987, empl 53, sales $4,901,793, cert: State, NMSDC, WBENC)

3922 Encompass Supply
8000 Towers Crescent Dr Ste 1350
Vienna, VA 22182
Contact: Presdient
Tel: 804-716-0546
Email: info@encompasssupply.net
Website: www.encompasssupply.net
Electrical and industrial supplies, electrical construction & industrial supplies. (AA, estab 2013, empl 3, sales $2,500,000, cert: State)

3923 Parker Battery, Inc.
208 South St
Franklin, VA 23851
Contact: Shaun Parker Sales
Tel: 800-569-6084
Email: shaun@parkerbattery.com
Website: www.parkerbattery.com
Dist batteries, starters & alternators for automotive, commercial & industrial applications. (Woman, estab 1990, empl 9, sales $2,000,000, cert: State)

Washington

3924 Birch Equipment Rental & Sales
P.O. Box 30918
Bellingham, WA 98228
Contact: Cara Buckingham Information Director
Tel: 360-734-5744
Email: planning@birchequipment.com
Website: www.birchequipment.com
Dist & rent equipment & machines: aerators, carpet cleaners, boom ifts, large excavators & forklifts. (Woman, estab 1972, empl 75, sales $15,000,000, cert: WBENC)

3925 Emerald, Inc.
P.O. Box 14227
Seattle, WA 98168
Contact: President
Tel: 206-767-8909
Email:
Website: http://emeraldinc.net
Kitchen Hood Cleaning, Fire Extinguisher Sales/Service, Kitchen Hood Fire System Sales/Service, Safety Equipment Sales. (Hisp, estab 1989, empl 5, sales $300,000, cert: State, City)

3926 Excel Gloves & Safety Supplies, Inc.
6808 26th St E, Ste 102
Fife, WA 98424
Contact: Irene Reyes CEO
Tel: 253-896-1195
Email: glovelady@excelgloves.com
Website: www.excelgloves.com
Import & dist gloves, safety, medical, janitorial & packaging supplies, (Woman/As-Pac, estab 1993, empl 8, sales $2,000,000, cert: State, NMSDC)

3927 Rohtek Automation LLC
9223 NE 174th Pl
Bothell, WA 98011
Contact: Oscar Rojas Presdient
Tel: 425-318-2179
Email: orojas@rohtek.com
Website: www.rohtekautomation.com
Dist high tech mfg, operating & monitoring solutions. (Hisp, estab 2011, empl 2, sales , cert: State)

3928 E. R. Abernathy Industrial Inc.
2000 Pewaukee Rd, Ste 0
Waukesha, WI 53188
Contact: Edna Abernathy President
Tel: 262-446-3377
Email: edna@abernathyco.com
Website: www.abernathyco.com
Dist safety, construction, electrical & industrial supplies. (Woman/AA, estab 1991, empl 10, sales $1,354,000, cert: NMSDC)

3929 First American Engineered Solutions, LLC
136 Jackson St, Ste C
Oshkosh, WI 54901
Contact: Gerald Morris President
Tel: 920-231-8501
Email: gmorris@firstamericanllc.com
Website: www.firstamericanllc.com
Dist electronics, electrical equipment, industrial equipment & supplies, office equipment & supplies & ordnance. (Nat Ame, estab 1997, empl 12, sales $4,500,000, cert: NMSDC, 8a)

INDUSTRIAL MACHINES
Manufacturers and distributors of ovens, vacuum cleaners, air compressors, blasting machines, food processing equipment, paint mixers, tube flaring machines, etc. (See also HARDWARE & TOOLS, HYDRAULIC & COMPRESSED AIR EQUIPMENT, INDUSTRIAL MACHINES and MATERIAL HANDLING EQUIPMENT). NAICS Code 42

Arizona

3930   STRATCO, Inc.
       14821 N 73rd St
       Scottsdale, AZ 85260
       Contact: Diane Graham CEO
       Tel: 480-991-0450
       Email: supplier.diversity@stratcoglobal.com
       Website: www.stratcoglobal.com
Design blending & reaction equipment for grease, lubricants, bio-diesel & petrochemical industries. (Woman, estab 1928, empl 16, sales $5,621,643, cert: WBENC)

California

3931   Combustion Associates, Inc.
       555 Monica Circle
       Corona, CA 92880
       Contact: Preeti Chandan Sales/Marketing Mgr
       Tel: 951-272-6999
       Email: pchandan@cai3.com
       Website: www.cai3.com
Food processing systems; integrated skid-mounted process systems; lube oil & gas systems; water heaters & industrial burners; modular aeroderivative power generation systems; packaged. (Woman/As-Ind, estab 1991, empl 45, sales $9,100,000, cert: NMSDC, CPUC)

3932   Lucio Family Enterprises, Inc.
       2150 Prune Ave
       Fremont, CA 94539
       Contact: Sandra Garcia
       Tel: 510-623-2323
       Email: sgarcia@compactormc.com
       Website: http://compactormc.com
Mfr waste & recycling equipment: compactors, containers, balers (all sizes), custom fabrication requests. (Woman/Hisp, estab 2006, empl 18, sales $2,500,000, cert: NMSDC)

Florida

3933   New England Machinery, Inc.
       2820 62nd Ave E
       Bradenton, FL 34203
       Contact: Hans Weiden Sales Mgr
       Tel: 941-755-5550
       Email: hweiden@neminc.com
       Website: www.neminc.com
Packaging equipment, Unscramblers, Orienters, Cappers, Retorquers, Pluggers, Pump Placers, Lidding. (Woman, estab 1974, empl 55, sales $15,000,000, cert: WBENC)

3934   Supergreen Inc.
       4051 107th Circle N, Ste 1
       Clearwater, FL 33762
       Contact: Hoang Mai President
       Tel: 727-459-3130
       Email: mike.hoang@supergreenusa.com
       Website: www.supergreenusa.com
Mfr Tankless Water Heaters. (As-Pac, estab 2013, empl 4, sales , cert: NMSDC)

Illinois

3935   AM Manufacturing Company
       14151 Irving Ave
       Dolton, IL 60419
       Contact: Edward Mentz President
       Tel: 708-841-0959
       Email: lserafin@ammfg.com
       Website: www.ammfg.com
Mfr dough processing equipment: dough dividers, dough rounders, pizza / tortilla presses, pizza crust dockers, proofers, cooling conveyors, bagel forming equipment. (Woman, estab 1961, empl 30, sales $7,000,000, cert: City)

3936   Apex Beverage Equipment Distribution Group, LLC.
       450 Tower Blvd, Ste 200
       Carol Stream, IL 60188
       Contact: Christie Tierney President
       Tel: 877-901-2739
       Email: ctierney@totalapex.com
       Website: www.totalapex.com
Dist beverage equipment, replacement parts & installation products. (Woman, estab 2008, empl 11, sales $14,000,000, cert: WBENC)

Indiana

3937   Cici Boiler Rooms Inc.
       7811 Baumgart Rd
       Evansville, IN 47711
       Contact: Penny Duncan Admin Asst
       Tel: 812-867-0810
       Email: penny@ciciboilers.com
       Website: www.ciciboilers.com
Boilers, HVAC, Deareators, Water Heaters, Air Conditioning, New Equipment, Parts, Service, (Minority, Woman, estab 1965, empl 14, sales $4,900,000, cert: State)

3938   Harriman Material Handling
       511 N Range Line Rd
       Morristown, IN 46161
       Contact: Ashley Larochelle President
       Tel: 765-763-8985
       Email: ashlar@harrimanmaterialhandling.com
       Website: www.HarrimanMaterialHandling.com
Overhead Cranes, Hoists, Jib Cranes, Monorails, Gantry Cranes, Custom Lifting Devices, Slings/Rigging, Fall Protection Equipment, Crane Components & Parts, Dock Equipment, Storage Equipment, Drum Handling Equipment (Woman, estab 2004, empl 5, sales $3,528,300, cert: WBENC)

Michigan

3939   Manufacturers/Machine Builders Services Co.
13035 Wayne Rd
Livonia, MI 48150
Contact: Glen Neal Managing Partner
Tel: 734-748-3706
Email: mmbswork2@sbcglobal.net
Website: www.mmbscorp
Build & service automated machines: pipe, wire, debug &
install machines. (Woman/Nat Ame, As-Pac, estab 2002,
empl 16, sales $800,000, cert: NMSDC)

3940   Quality Design Services, Inc.
3914 Highwood Pl
Okemos, MI 48864
Contact: Ashish Manek Business Dev Mgr
Tel: 614-946-4749
Email: ashish.manek@qdsautomation.com
Website: www.qdsautomation.com
System Integration: Engine Assembly Lines, Transmission
Assembly Lines, Axle Assembly Lines, Transfer Machines,
Test Systems, Washers, Conveyor Systems, Hydraulic
Systems, Lubrication Systems. (As-Ind, estab 1990, empl ,
sales $250,000, cert: NMSDC)

3941   Tillman Industries dba MEDBIO, Inc.
630 S Division
Grand Rapids, MI 49503
Contact: Roosevelt Tillman CEO
Tel: 616-245-0214
Email: rt@medbioinc.com
Website: www.medbioinc.com
Clean room assembly services, injection molding &
medical device mfg. (AA, estab 2002, empl 1, sales , cert:
State)

3942   Ultimation Industries LLC
27930 Groesbeck Hwy
Roseville, MI 48066
Contact: Jacqueline Canny CEO
Tel: 586-771-1881
Email: jcanny@ultimationinc.com
Website: http://ultimationinc.com
Design, mfr & install assembly line equipment & services,
automation devices & conveyor systems, tire & wheel
mounting & inflation devices, tire processing lines, TPMS &
soaping machines. (Woman, estab 1989, empl 14, sales
$4,855,120, cert: WBENC)

Minnesota

3943   DV Roland Enterprises, Inc.
15171 Freeland Ave N
Hugo, MN 55038
Contact: Kenny Scamp GM
Tel: 651-429-9012
Email: ken@jtservicesinc.com
Website: www.jtservicesinc.com
Dist & service industrial diesel engines & diesel engine
parts. Supporting diesel engines for aerial lifts, air com-
pressors, backhoes, dozers, excavators, forklifts, genera-
tors, light towers, rollers, skid steer loaders, tractors,
welders. (AA, estab 2004, empl 6, sales $1,433,333, cert:
City, NMSDC)

Missouri

3944   Erb Equipment Co., Inc.
200 Erb Industrial Dr
Fenton, MO 63026
Contact: Gregg Erb Dir of Sales
Tel: 636-349-0200
Email: greggerb@erbequipment.com
Website: www.erbequipment.com
Construction equipment, rent new & used equipment &
repair parts, repair & maintenance, Backhoe, Wheel
Loaders, Front loaders, excavators, dozers, crawler
loaders, skid steer (bobcat), mini excavators & material
handlers. (Woman, estab 1943, empl 230, sales
$134,737,841, cert: WBENC)

3945   Productive Automoated Systems Corp. (PASCO)
2600 S Hanley Rd, Ste 450
St. Louis, MO 63144
Contact: Nate Mahoney Dir Finance & IT
Tel: 314-781-2212
Email: nmahoney@pascosystems.com
Website: www.pascosystems.com
Design & Mfr rugged robotic automation systems and
palletizers. (Woman, estab 1976, empl 50, sales
$13,332,000, cert: State)

3946   TSA Sales Associates, LLC
3466 Bridgeland Dr
Bridgeton, MO 63044
Contact: Pamela Sanders Owner
Tel: 314-291-4400
Email: psanders@tsasales.com
Website: www.tsasales.com
Air pollution control equipment, dry bulk solids, han-
dling equipment & storage silos & bins. Design dust,
fume & mist collecion systems. (Woman, estab 2001,
empl 5, sales $374,087, cert: State)

New Jersey

3947   Ana M Fisher dba A & A Glove & Safety Co.
20 Richey Ave
West Collingswood, NJ 08107
Contact: Ashton Goerge Sales
Tel: 800-854-0060
Email: ashton@aaglove.com
Website: www.aasafetyindustrial.com
Safety consulting & sourcing, industrial equipment.
(Woman/Hisp, estab 1990, empl 5, sales $400,000, cert:
State, City)

3948   Hop Industries Corp.
1251 Valley Brook Ave
Lyndhurst, NJ 07071
Contact: Melanie Harkin Sales Rep
Tel: 201-438-6200
Email: mharkin@hopindustries.com
Website: www.hopindustries.com
Laminating Supplies & Equipment: laminating rolls,
laminating pouches, pouch laminators, roll laminators,
Binding Supplies & Equipment: binding combs, twin wire
binding, plastic coil binding. (As-Pac, estab 1977, empl
70, sales $43,697,760, cert: NMSDC)

Ohio

3949   ASD - Automation Systems & Design
         6222 Webster St
         Dayton, OH 45414
         Contact: Sunny Kullar CEO
         Tel: 937-387-0351
         Email: sunny@asddayton.com
         Website: www.asddayton.com
Build, design & integrate custom machines. (As-Ind, estab 2000, empl 14, sales $1,500,000, cert: NMSDC)

3950   OCS Process Systems
         24142 Detroit Rd
         Westlake, OH 44145
         Contact: Beth Kloos CEO
         Tel: 440-871-6009
         Email: bkloos@ocsprocess.com
         Website: www.ocsprocess.com
Engineer, design & install food processing systems: liquid & dry powder processing systems, heat transfer, mixing, batching systems, metering systems, distribution systems, COP, CIP, piping, pumps, valves, welding, fabrication & installation. (Woman, estab , empl 40, sales $7,500,000, cert: WBENC)

3951   Taner Crane & Equipment, LLC
         540 E 105th St, Ste 206A
         Cleveland, OH 44108
         Contact: Bobby Hale Operations Mgr
         Tel: 216-681-1990
         Email: tanerequipment@sbcglobal.net
         Website:
Equipment rental: cranes, lifts, forklifts & light to heavy contruction equipment. (AA, estab 2008, empl 3, sales , cert: State, City)

Pennsylvania

3952   American Kitchen Machinery and Repair Co., Inc.
         204 Quarry St
         Philadelphia, PA 19106
         Contact: Andrea Mahon President
         Tel: 215-627-7760
         Email: service@akmco.com
         Website: www.akmco.com
Parts & service to commercial kitchen equipment: cooking equipment, sanitation & dishwashing equipment, preparation equipment & mixers, refrigeration equipment & ice machines. (Woman, estab 1953, empl 45, sales $7,000,000, cert: WBENC)

3953   Gottscho Printing Systems, Inc.
         740 Veterans Circle
         Warminster, PA 18974
         Contact: Aimee Hasson President
         Tel: 267-387-3005
         Email: sales@gottscho.com
         Website: www.gottscho.com
Printing machines, marking machines, bar code printing, ink jet, coding & printing, blister pack printing, hot stamp, thermal printer, T1J printer, C1J printer, flexographic printer, platen printer, UV printer, digital coder, digital printer. (Woman, estab 2009, empl 12, sales , cert: WBENC)

Texas

3954   Epcon Industrial Systems
         P.O. Box 7060
         The Woodlands, TX 77387
         Contact: Shan Jamaluddin COO
         Tel: 936-273-3300
         Email: epcon@epconlp.com
         Website: www.epconlp.com
Design, engineer & mfr air pollution control systems, oxidizers, afterburners, deoilers, washlines, spray booths, ovens & furnaces. (As-Pac, estab 1977, empl 99, sales $14,000,000, cert: State, NMSDC)

3955   PLP Enterprises, Inc.
         P.O. Box 578
         Blue Ridge, TX 75424
         Contact: Phillip Pulliam VP
         Tel: 972-752-4837
         Email: ppulliam@aps-plp.com
         Website: www.aps-plp.com
Build Plastic & Stainless Steel Chemical Delivery Systems, Valve Manifold Boxes, Chemical Process Tanks, Process Hoods, Drain Pans, Chemical Carts, Storage Cabinets. PLC Control Systems, Electrical Panels, Sump Systems. (Woman, estab 2000, empl 6, sales $1,100,000, cert: WBENC)

3956   RECS, Inc.
         P.O. Box 520
         Prosper, TX 75078
         Contact: Elaine Underwood President
         Tel: 972-346-3226
         Email: recsmaterials@windstream.net
         Website: www.recsinc.com
Heavy construction rental equipment: excavators, rock chrushers, bulldozers, motorgraders, dumptrucks, backhoes, wheel loader/w bucket & forks, dredging machines, automobile & pickup rental, truck & trailer rental, generators lightplants. (Woman, estab 1982, empl 25, sales $5,000,000, cert: State)

Virginia

3957   Century Sales, Inc.
         P.O. Box 11743
         Roanoke, VA 24022
         Contact: Herbert Chappelle Owner
         Tel: 540-562-0847
         Email: keymike5120@aol.com
         Website:
Commercial foodservice equipment, cooking equipment, refrigeration, blast chillers, microwaves, coffee urns, flatware, tables, chairs, salad bars, china, table linen, etc. (AA, estab 1988, empl 2, sales $175,000, cert: State)

3958   Crest Foodservice Equipment Company
         605 Jack Rabbit Rd
         Virginia Beach, VA 23451
         Contact: Karen Ricketts Business Dev Mgr
         Tel: 757-425-8883
         Email: karen@cresteq.com
         Website: www.crestfoodservice.com
Dist commercial kitchen equipment & ancillary items. (Woman, estab 1984, empl 36, sales $11,531,745, cert: State)

3959 E2C Group, LLC
      1418 Jacquelin St
      Richmond, VA 23220
      Contact: Denise Fields Principal
      Tel: 804-358-3334
      Email: dif1@aol.com
      Website: www.e2cgroup.com
Dist & install commercial foodservice equipment. (AA, estab 2004, empl 6, sales $2,200,000, cert: State)

3960 VMEK Group LLC
      2719 Oak Lake Blvd
      Midlothian, VA 23112
      Contact: Adriana Lovvorn Operations Mgr
      Tel: 804-349-9001
      Email: adriana@vmek.com
      Website: www.vmek.com
Build & support high speed industrial machines powered by advanced vision technology & machine design. (Woman/As-Pac, estab 2012, empl 9, sales , cert: NMSDC)

Wisconsin

3961 Accuracy Machine
      201 Stange St.
      Merrill, WI 54452
      Contact: Kevin Keiser Project Mgr
      Tel: 715-722-0825
      Email: kevin.keiser@accuracymachine.com
      Website: www.accuracymachine.com
Mfr machines & specialty parts: converting, printing, coating, paper, material handling, packaging, food grade machine, performance automotive, performance marine, aerospace & powertrain industries. (As-Pac, estab 1994, empl 10, sales , cert: State)

3962 Memmert USA, LLC
      W355 S9075 Godfrey Ln
      Eagle, WI 53119
      Contact: Tina M. Binder CEO
      Tel: 262-594-3941
      Email: tslaboven@memmertusa.com
      Website: http://memmertusa.com
Dist ovens, incubators, climate chambers, humidity chamber, vacuum ovens, water baths, oil baths, CO2 incubators, Paraffin Ovens, Climatic test chambers, sterilizers, glassware washers. (Woman, estab 2006, empl 4, sales $2,242,000, cert: WBENC)

3963 Quintec Integration, Inc.
      1600 Paramount Dr
      Waukesha, WI 53186
      Contact: Tony Storniolo President
      Tel: 262-754-5900
      Email: tstorniolo@quintecconveyor.com
      Website: www.quintecconveyor.com
Layout engineering, conveyor hardware, mechanical equipment, electrical controls & programming, mechanical & electrical installation, project management, field training of equipment. (Hisp, estab 1999, empl 7, sales $10,000,000, cert: State)

3964 Trester Hoist Equipment, Inc.
      W136 N4863 Campbell Dr, Ste 6
      Menomonee Falls, WI 53051
      Contact: Robyn Vaupel President
      Tel: 262-790-0700
      Email: robyn@tresterhoist.com
      Website: http://tresterhoist.com
Overhead lifting equipment & service. (Woman, estab 1995, empl 11, sales $5,000,000, cert: WBENC)

West Virginia

3965 Sisterville Tank Works, Inc.
      1942 McCoy St
      Sisterville, WV 26175
      Contact: Jason Morgan Owner
      Tel: 304-652-3011
      Email: sales@stwinc.com
      Website: www.stwinc.com
Fabricate pressure vessels, heat exchangers, boilers, condensers, cryogenics, evaporators, hoppers, reactors, stills, strippers, tanks, towers, vaporizers, nitrators, columns, autoclaves. (Woman, estab , empl 50, sales , cert: WBENC)

Alaska

3966   Tuknik Government Services, LLC
       3800 Centerpoint Dr Ste 502
       Anchorage, AK 99503
       Contact: Navid Nekoui
       Tel: 301-802-3114
       Email: nnekoui@koniag.com
       Website: www.tuknikgs.com
Outsourced computer related services, IT support, software installation & security, physical security, program management. (Nat Ame, estab 2014, empl 2, sales , cert: NMSDC)

Alabama

3967   Aetos Systems, Inc.
       1525 Perimeter Pkwy, Ste 115
       Huntsville, AL 35806
       Contact: Donna Coleman CEO
       Tel: 256-527-7821
       Email: donna.coleman@aetossystems.com
       Website: www.aetossystems.com
IT, information management, IT systems architecture, business management & engineering services. (Woman/Nat Ame, estab 2007, empl 18, sales $6,346,796, cert: 8a)

3968   Ariel Information Technology Corporation
       1 Chase Corporate Center Ste 400
       Birmingham, AL 35244
       Contact: Terry Pennington
       Tel: 205-705-3100
       Email: tpennington@ariel-it.com
       Website: www.ariel-it.com
Information technology consulting & services, technology staff augmentation, business analysis, requirements management, software design, system design, software development, quality assurance testing, hardware & software procurement. (AA, estab 2009, empl 1, sales , cert: NMSDC)

3969   C E Fallin & Company, LLC
       3814 Meridian St N
       Huntsville, AL 35811
       Contact: Carl Fallin CEO
       Tel: 256-489-4600
       Email: cefallincpa@comcast.net
       Website: http://6sigmaindustries.com
Management Consulting, Fabrication, Software Development, IT Integration Subject Matter Experts. (AA, estab 1984, empl 10, sales $350,000, cert: State)

3970   Daten System Consulting
       8225 Old Pascagoula Road
       Theodore, AL 36582
       Contact: Catina Short
       Tel: 866-388-3856
       Email: cshort@datensys.com
       Website: www.datensystemconsulting.com
Information technology data centric consulting organization. (Woman/AA, estab 2013, empl 5, sales $396,000, cert: State, NMSDC, WBENC)

3971   HCI Management Services
       6767 Old Madison Pike Ste 250
       Huntsville, AL 35806
       Contact: Bruce Ricker Director
       Tel: 256-763-6671
       Email: bricker@allnativegroup.com
       Website: www.allnativegroup.com
Information Technology, IT, Telecommunications, Network Administration, Help Desk, Database, Video Teleconferencing, Health Services, Logistics, Technical Manuals, Financial Management, Program Management, Public Affairs. (Nat Ame, estab 1994, empl 700, sales $24,000,000, cert: 8a)

3972   Horizon Services Corporation
       4898 Valleydale Rd Ste B-3
       Birmingham, AL 35242
       Contact: CEO
       Tel: 205-249-8033
       Email:
       Website: www.horizonamerica.net
Technical products & services. (AA, estab 2001, empl 30, sales $5,200,000, cert: NMSDC)

3973   M2 Connections, a JKM Consulting, Inc. division
       P.O. Box 3250
       Oxford, AL 36203
       Contact: Janine Moses President
       Tel: 256-405-0613
       Email: jkmoses@jkmconsultinginc.com
       Website: www.m2connections.com
Telecom audit detail, network design & support, project management, data management & process engineering. (Minority, Woman, estab 1998, empl 5, sales , cert: State)

3974   Never Ending Technology, Inc.
       4900 University SQ STE 14
       Huntsville, AL 35816
       Contact: Laquita Nelson CEO
       Tel:
       Email: lnelson@net-incorporated.com
       Website: www.net-incorporated.com
IT management & technical experts in supporting network, servers, software, distance learning system, end user computer & mobile devices, A/V in conference rooms & help desk. (Woman/Nat Ame, estab 2012, empl 6, sales , cert: 8a)

3975   Safety Research Corporation of America, LLC
       133 Research Lane
       Dothan, AL 36305
       Contact: Susan Crump CEO
       Tel: 334-678-7722
       Email: scrump@srca.net
       Website: www.srca.net
Information technology services: software design & development database applications, websites & graphic design services. (Woman, estab 1993, empl 20, sales $2,200,000, cert: State)

3976   The Computer Consulting Group
       445 Dexter Ave, Ste 4050
       Montgomery, AL 36104
       Contact: Kendra Jenkins Chief Sales/Mktg Officer
       Tel:
       Email: info@ccg-al.com
       Website: www.ccg-al.com
A Service Disabled Veteran Owned Small Business. More
than 60 years of combined IT security industry and
management experience mission to ensure that we serve,
secure, and protect our client's information, intelligence,
and physical location to the best o (Woman/AA, estab
2013, empl 5, sales , cert: State)

Arkansas

3977   Celerit
       2200 N Rodney Parham, Ste 205
       Little Rock, AR 72212
       Contact: Terry Rothwell President
       Tel: 501-312-2900
       Email: info@celerit.com
       Website: www.celerit.com
IT consulting: full time personnel and custon application
development. (Woman, estab 1985, empl 50, sales , cert:
WBENC)

3978   Inteliblue
       15300 Governors Lake Dr
       Little Rock, AR 72223
       Contact: Priyanka kothakanti Mgr
       Tel: 501-251-8918
       Email: priya@inteliblue.com
       Website: www.inteliblue.com
IT Consulting/Staffing. (Woman, estab 2012, empl 1, sales ,
cert: State)

Arizona

3979   Business Partner Solutions Inc.
       7362 E Rovey Ave
       Scottsdale, AZ 85250
       Contact: Katherine Bluma CEO
       Tel: 858-337-9020
       Email: kat@businesspartnersolutions.com
       Website: www.businesspartnersolutions.com
Asset intelligence, encryption, strong authentication &
application security & access control. (Woman, estab 2005,
empl 7, sales $2,800,000, cert: WBENC, SDB)

3980   Centacor, Inc.
       135 Chilton Dr
       Chandler, AZ 85225
       Contact: Troy Bryan Mgr
       Tel: 480-899-9500
       Email: info@centacor.com
       Website: www.centacor.com
IT products & services. (AA, estab 2009, empl 4, sales ,
cert: NMSDC)

3981   Clutch Solutions LLC
       2152 S Vineyard Ave, Building 1, Ste 120
       Mesa, AZ 85210
       Contact: Damien Norwood Strat Diversity Partner
       Tel: 888-725-8824
       Email: damien.norwood@clutchsolutions.com
       Website: www.clutchsolutions.com
Information technology: IT Hardware and Software Value
Added Reseller, Solution Architect/engineering, Cyber-
Security, Unified Communications. (Nat Ame, estab 2017,
empl 58, sales $200,000,000, cert: NMSDC)

3982   Cutting Edge Technologies & Solutions
       7406 E Nora St
       Mesa, AZ 85207
       Contact: Wilbert Johnson President
       Tel: 888-832-2090
       Email: wjohnson@cetechs.net
       Website: www.cetechs.net
Software Development, Systems Engineering, IV&V,
Training & Information Technology, real-time systems,
embedded systems and application development to
include C++, Java, Ada, UML, C, Fortran, Perl, Python,
Corba, VME, Linux, Solaris. (AA, estab 2009, empl 4,
sales $250,000, cert: 8a)

3983   EDB Warehousing and Logistics, LLC
       P.O. Box 11363
       Chandler, AZ 85248
       Contact: Eric Bell Owner
       Tel: 800-370-8670
       Email: eric.bell@edbwarehousing.com
       Website: www.edbwarehousing.com
Inventory Management. (AA, estab 2015, empl 2, sales
$100,000, cert: NMSDC)

3984   Executive Technology Inc.
       4809 E Thistle Landing Dr Ste 100
       Phoenix, AZ 85044
       Contact: Linda Perkins Controller
       Tel: 480-346-7041
       Email: lperkins@exectechdirect.com
       Website: www.exectechdirect.com
Information technology products & services. (AA, estab
2001, empl 16, sales , cert: NMSDC)

3985   Indidge Systems
       130 N Central Ave Ste 201
       Phoenix, AZ 85004
       Contact: President
       Tel: 480-829-0479
       Email:
       Website: www.itsone.net
IT consulting: enterprise application dev, database dev,
web solutions, re-engineering & testing. (As-Ind, estab
1999, empl 30, sales $1,000,000, cert: NMSDC)

3986   Native Technology Solutions Inc.
       7065 W Allison Rd
       Chandler, AZ 85226
       Contact: Mabel Tsosie
       Tel: 480-639-1234
       Email: mtsosie@gilarivertel.com
       Website: http://native-tech.net
Cabling & computing services, structured cabling,
phone, security systems, video conferencing, & technology solutions. (Nat Ame, estab 2007, empl 14, sales
$4,000,000, cert: State)

3987   QCM Technologies, Inc.
       9060 E Via Linda Ste 220
       Scottsdale, AZ 85258
       Contact: Lenny Aupperlee Sales Exec
       Tel: 602-412-3539
       Email: laupperlee@qcmtech.com
       Website: www.qcmtech.com
IT solutions & services, hardware, software & professional services, design, implement & support enterprise-
wide IT solutions. (Hisp, estab 2001, empl 20, sales
$12,651,000, cert: NMSDC)

3988 TDR Consulting Inc
951 N Forest Ct
Chandler, AZ 85226
Contact: Dean Rosales
Tel: 480-293-4959
Email: deanrosales@tdrconsultinginc.com
Website: www.tdrconsultinginc.com
Engineering consulting, systems engineering, specification development, requirements traceability, derived requirements, schedule development, milestone tracking, performance tracking & metrics reporting. (Hisp, estab 2013, empl 1, sales , cert: NMSDC)

3989 Tec Global
9674 E Vantage Point Rd
Scottsdale, AZ 85262
Contact: Richard Stanford President
Tel: 480-575-4333
Email: richard.stanford@tecglobalinc.com
Website: www.tecglobalinc.com
Global Supply Chain optimization Company. (AA, estab 1996, empl 3, sales $150,000, cert: NMSDC)

3990 TIPS Consultants LLC
1412 E Michelle Dr
Phoenix, AZ 85022
Contact: Dr. Charles Fisher CFO
Tel: 713-307-3362
Email: cfisher@tipsconsultants.com
Website: http://tipsconsultants.squarespace.com
Engineering consultant & training services, Enterprise Project Management (EPM) & Earned Value Management (EVM) solutions. (Woman/AA, estab 2015, empl 3, sales , cert: State)

3991 XL Technology Group, LLC
6895 E Camelback Rd Ste 118
Scottsdale, AZ 85251
Contact: Michael Brown Director
Tel: 602-324-7474
Email: michael@xltechnologygroup.com
Website: www.xltechnologygroup.com
IT staffing resources for IT implementations & staff augmentation (contract, contract to hire, & direct hire) . (AA, As-Pac, estab 2010, empl 20, sales $2,600,000, cert: NMSDC)

California

3992 24-Hour Medical Staffing Services, LLC
21700 East Copley Dr Ste 270
Diamond Bar, CA 09765
Contact: Linda Stone VP, Sales & Client Delivery
Tel: 909-895-8960
Email: linda@24-hrmed.com
Website: www.24-hrmed.com
24-Hour Medical Staffing provides temporary healthcare staffing services to clients on permanent, per diem, travel, and local contract assignment. Services provided are Registered Nurses, Allied, Laboratory, and Administrative staff. 24- Hour Medical is (Woman/As-Pac, estab 2000, empl 150, sales $8,678,030, cert: NMSDC)

3993 360 IT Professionals, Inc.
3031 Tisch Way, 110 Plaza West
San Jose, CA 95128
Contact: Manmeet Manace Business Devel Exec
Tel: 510-254-3300
Email: manmeet@360itpro.com
Website: www.360itpro.com/
Programming Languages, .net, Java, PHP, Android, IOS, Python, Ruby, Enterprise Resource Planning SAP, Oracle, Microsoft AX & GP, Functional IT Positions, Program Managers, Project Managers, Business Analysts & Data. (As-Pac, estab 2013, empl 93, sales $8,948,501, cert: State, NMSDC, SDB)

3994 3K Technologies LLC
161 Mission Falls Ln Ste 201
Fremont, CA 94539
Contact: Krishna Chittabathini CEO
Tel: 408-716-5900
Email: krishna@3ktechnologies.com
Website: www.3ktechnologies.com
Information technology consulting services & staffing. (Woman/As-Ind, estab 2002, empl 65, sales $5,106,000, cert: CPUC)

3995 3S Global Business Solutions
7923 Nita Ave
Canoga Park, CA 91304
Contact: Sam Mookerjee Dir Corp affairs
Tel: 818-453-4403
Email: sam.mookerjee@3sgbs.com
Website: www.3sgbs.com
Information technology resources, staff augmentation, project management, IT training, IT development/ maintenance outsourcing. (As-Ind, estab 2007, empl 12, sales $895,000, cert: State, City, CPUC)

3996 4WardTech Inc.
7317 El Cajon Blvd, Ste 111, La Mesa, CA 91942
La Mesa, CA 91942
Contact: Andrew Parker President
Tel: 757-876-1735
Email: andrew@4ward.tech
Website: www.4ward.tech
Information Technology (IT) solutions & services, Cloud Computing, Internet of Things (IoT), Bluetooth Low Energy (BLE) & Beacons, Machine Learning, Chatbots, Blockchain and DevOps.
Other Technical Expertise: Mobility Platform. (AA, estab 2016, empl 2, sales $100,000, cert: NMSDC, SDB)

3997 AccountSight
19925 Stevens Creek Blvd Ste 100
Cupertino, CA 95014
Contact: Anita Bist VP Business Devel
Tel: 408-560-3900
Email: abist@accountsight.com
Website: www.accountsight.com
AccountSight time tracking & resource planning software, SaaS solution, eSign Genie esignature software. (Woman/As-Ind, estab 2013, empl 20, sales $250,000, cert: NMSDC)

3998   Adroit Resources Inc.
        39500 Stevenson Place, Ste 202
        Fremont, CA 94539
        Contact: Prashant Sharma Sr. Director
        Tel: 510-573-6102
        Email: prashant@adroitresources.com
        Website: www.adroitresources.com
Information Technology services. (Woman/As-Pac, estab
2011, empl 75, sales $7,000,000, cert: NMSDC, CPUC)

3999   Agama Solutions Inc.
        39159 Paseo Padre Pkwy Ste 216
        Fremont, CA 94538
        Contact: Peter Kalra VP
        Tel: 510-377-9959
        Email: peter@agamasolutions.com
        Website: www.agamasolutions.com
IT Consulting services in terms of Project based
consulting and Staffing Services of various technical hard
to find skills in the area of Information technology. (As-Pac,
estab 2006, empl 200, sales $3,000,000, cert: State)

4000   Agile Global Solutions, Inc.
        13405 Folsom Blvd, Ste 515
        Folsom, CA 95630
        Contact: Raja Krishnan President
        Tel: 916-353-1780
        Email: raja@agileglobal.com
        Website: www.agileglobal.com
IT services (staffing) & turnkey solutions. (Woman/As-Ind,
estab 2003, empl 62, sales $8,300,000, cert: State,
NMSDC, CPUC)

4001   AgileTalent, Inc.
        1900 S Norfolk Ave.
        San Mateo, CA 94403
        Contact: Jay Singh
        Tel: 650-931-2572
        Email: jay.singh@agiletalentinc.com
        Website: www.agiletalentinc.com
IT contract staffing & recruiting. (As-Ind, estab 2011, empl
48, sales $4,600,000, cert: NMSDC, CPUC)

4002   Agilis Group Inc.
        7968 Arjons Dr Ste 105
        San Diego, CA 92126
        Contact: Joyce Tang President
        Tel: 888-832-4858
        Email: jtang@agilisit.com
        Website: http://agilisit.com
Managed IT Services: Consultation, Design, Development,
Deployment, Staffing, Training, Remote Monitoring and
Software Licensing, IT hardware & software products.
(Woman/As-Pac, estab 2006, empl 20, sales $500,000,
cert: 8a)

4003   AgreeYa Solutions, Inc.
        605 Coolidge Dr
        Folsom, CA 95630
        Contact: Ajay Kaul Managing Partner
        Tel: 916-294-0075
        Email: sales_americas@agreeya.com
        Website: www.agreeya.com
IT consulting services, staff or project based. (Woman/As-
Pac, estab 1999, empl 1800, sales $110,000,000, cert:
NMSDC, CPUC)

4004   Ahtna Contractors, LLC
        3680 Industrial Blvd Ste 600H
        West Sacramento, CA 95691
        Contact: Jessica Vela Admin Asst
        Tel: 916-329-1591
        Email: jvela@ahtna.net
        Website: www.ahtnacontractors.com
IT Support (Nat Ame, estab 2005, empl 1, sales
$376,178, cert: 8a)

4005   AKRAYA, Inc.
        2901 Tasman Dr Ste 106
        Santa Clara, CA 95054
        Contact: Sonu Ratra President
        Tel: 408-907-6400
        Email: sonu.ratra@akraya.com
        Website: www.akraya.com
IT consulting - Java, Microsoft, databases, Peoplesoft,
Oracle, Siebel, SAP, data warehousing. (Woman/As-Ind,
estab 2001, empl 390, sales $33,430,000, cert: NMSDC,
CPUC, WBENC)

4006   Alicon Group, Inc.
        5405 Alton Pkwy, Ste 5A514
        Irvine, CA 92604
        Contact: Chris Metzger Operations Coord
        Tel: 949-294-9634
        Email: chris@alicongroup.com
        Website: www.alicongroup.com
Oracle applications technology consulting. (Woman/Nat
Ame, estab 2001, empl 4, sales $3,980,000, cert:
NMSDC, NWBOC)

4007   Allfon LLC
        2746 Glendon Ave
        Los Angeles, CA 90064
        Contact: Roya Hosseinion President
        Tel: 310-470-7868
        Email: roya@allfon.com
        Website: www.allfon.com
Systems integration, offshore development, outsourcing
services. (Woman, estab 2000, empl 50, sales
$5,390,928, cert: WBENC)

4008   Alpha Omega Solutions, Inc.
        3070 Saturn St, Ste 200
        Brea, CA 92821
        Contact: Benny Wong President
        Tel: 714-996-8760
        Email: bennywong@aosolutions.com
        Website: www.aosolutions.com
Computer software, computer consulting, financial
consulting, automotive business consulting. (As-Pac,
estab 1993, empl 8, sales $1,000,000, cert: NMSDC)

4009   AMBCO Electronics Corporation
        15052 Redhill Ave, Ste D
        Tustin, CA 92780
        Contact: ADA XIONG
        Tel: 714-259-7930
        Email: ada@ambco.com
        Website: www.ambco.com
Audiometer Manufacturer. 5 year warranty on all Ambco
Audiometers from date of purchased. We repair, service,
and calibrate all makes of audiometers. (Woman/As-Pac,
estab 1941, empl 4, sales $914,803, cert: State)

4010   Amick Brown LLC
           2500 Old Crow Canyon Road Ste 425
           San Ramon, CA 94583
           Contact: Karen Gildea Principal
           Tel: 925-820-2000
           Email: admin@amickbrown.com
           Website: www.amickbrown.com
SAP BI Implementation, SAP HANA, SAP BI, Strategy and
Roadmaps, SAP BI Production Support, SAP BI Installations
and Upgrade, Reporting, Analytics & Dashboards, SAP BI
Training Workshops, SAP BI Security. (Woman/As-Ind,
estab 2010, empl 31, sales $7,000,000, cert: State, CPUC,
WBENC, SDB)

4011   Apex Computer Systems, Inc.
           13875 Cerritos Corporate Dr Unit A
           Cerritos, CA 90703
           Contact: Ira Klein Dir Partner Alliance
           Tel: 562-926-6820
           Email: sales@acsi2000.com
           Website: www.acsi2000.com
Computer hardware maintenance & support, managed
services, project management, accounting/ERP, EDI, data
warehousing, (As-Pac, estab 1984, empl 52, sales
$17,010,000, cert: State, NMSDC, CPUC, SDB)

4012   Applied Computer Solutions
           15461 Springdale St.
           Huntington Beach, CA 92649
           Contact: Cathy Fancher Operations Mgr
           Tel: 714-861-2200
           Email: cathy.fancher@acsacs.com
           Website: www.acsacs.com
System integration, strategic solutions, enterprise infra-
structure, Sun Microsystems, Cisco Systems, HDS, Veritas,
Oracle, Network Appliance, Checkpoint, Symantec,
StorageTek. (Woman, estab 1989, empl 25, sales
$119,476,000, cert: CPUC, WBENC)

4013   Ashunya Inc
           642 n. eckhoff St
           orange, CA 92868
           Contact: Melanie Merchant CEO
           Tel: 714-385-1900
           Email: melaniem@ashunya.com
           Website: www.ashunya.com
Information technology: hardware & software, LAN/WAN
wiring, project mgmt, post implementation svcs. (Woman/
As-Ind, estab 1993, empl 8, sales $3,000,000, cert:
WBENC)

4014   Automae
           7111 Garden Grove Blvd
           Garden Grove, CA 92841
           Contact: Mbuyi Khuzadi CEO
           Tel: 714-816-3000
           Email: mbuyi@mail.automae.com
           Website: www.automae.com
Technical services: hardware design, systems engineering,
software engineering, system safety & health management. (AA, estab 1997, empl 3, sales , cert: City)

4015   Aviana Global Technologies, Inc.
           915 W Imperial Highway Ste 100
           Brea, CA 92821
           Contact: Donna Sanchez staffing consultant
           Tel: 714-256-9756
           Email: donnas@avianaglobal.com
           Website: www.avianaglobal.com
Enterprise planning, reporting, OLAP analysis, dashboards,
scorecards, analytics & statutory regulations. (As-Pac,
estab 1994, empl 30, sales $53,822,829, cert: CPUC)

4016   Axelliant LLC
           21250 Hawthorne Blvd, Ste 500
           Torrance, CA 90503
           Contact: Mohsin Khan Procurement Mgr
           Tel: 310-377-2881
           Email: mohsin.khan@axelliant.com
           Website: www.axelliant.com
IT Solutions, Cyber Security, Date Center/ Networking,
to Mobility, Cloud Life Cycle Management & UC /
Collaboration. (As-Ind, As-Pac, estab 2016, empl 10,
sales , cert: NMSDC)

4017   Axiom Global Technologies, Inc.
           220 North Wiget Lane
           Walnut Creek, CA 94598
           Contact: Adam Ireland
           Tel: 925-393-5800
           Email: adam.ireland@axiomglobal.com
           Website: www.axiomglobal.com
Application development, staff augmentation, document management. (Woman/As-Ind, estab 2001, empl
70, sales $6,000,000, cert: NMSDC)

4018   Axxera Inc
           5251 California Ave, Ste 140
           Irvine, CA 92617
           Contact: Laura Pichardo Sr Mgr
           Tel: 949-534-3000
           Email: rfp@axxerainc.com
           Website: www.axxerainc.com
Cyber Security, SIEM, anti-trojan, anti-malware, Security
Software. (As-Ind, estab 2007, empl 10, sales
$3,000,000, cert: State)

4019   Bay Systems Consulting, Inc.
           610 16 St, Ste 409
           Oakland, CA 94612
           Contact: Jasmine Ali CEO
           Tel: 800-510-7754
           Email: jasmine@baycareers.com
           Website: www.baysyst.com
Custom software dev, sytem integration, IT / datacenter
operations, IT security, application support, system
admin, domain svcs, web hosting, data entry & transcription, etc. (Woman/As-Ind, estab 1997, empl 7, sales
$240,000, cert: State)

4020   BayInfotech LLC
           11501, Dublin Blvd Ste 200
           Dublin, CA 94568
           Contact: Maulik Shyani Sr. Acct Mgr
           Tel: 408-480-8501
           Email: maulik@bay-infotech.com
           Website: http://bay-infotech.com
Contingent Staffing, Beeline, Infrastructure Manage-
ment: End-to-End Management, Application, Network,
Security, Data Center, Service Desk. (Woman/As-Pac,
estab 2011, empl 15, sales $1,101,000, cert: NMSDC,
CPUC, WBENC)

4021   BayOne Solutions
           4637 Chabot Dr Ste 250
           Pleasanton, CA 94588
           Contact: Mohammed Ismail Sr Mgr MSP/VMS
           Program
           Tel: 925-399-0595
           Email: mismail@bayone.com
           Website: www.bayonesolutions.com
IT & Engineering - Development, testing, Mobile Apps,
infrastructure, Analytics, Creative/Product & Data
Science/Machine Learning. (Nat Ame, As-Ind, estab
2012, empl 187, sales $54,000,000, cert: NMSDC)

4022 Beta Soft Systems Inc.
      42808 Christy St Ste 101
      Fremont, CA 94538
      Contact: Bob Hemnani Sr Sales Mgr
      Tel: 510-744-1700
      Email: bob@betasoftsystems.com
      Website: www.betasoftsystems.com
IT Services & solutions, recruitment, business development, software development & service delivery. (As-Pac,
estab 2005, empl 300, sales , cert: State)

4023 BeyondCurious, Inc.
      3767 Overland Ave, Ste 115
      Los Angeles, CA 90034
      Contact: Nikki Barua CEO
      Tel: 310-210-1907
      Email: nbarua@beyondcurious.com
      Website: www.beyondcurious.com
Design & technology, mobile interfaces. (Woman/As-Ind,
estab 2011, empl 9, sales $2,289,210, cert: NMSDC)

4024 California Electronic Asset Recovery
      3678 LeMay St
      Mather, CA 95655
      Contact: Stacey Henrikson Corporate Acct Mgr
      Tel: 916-952-1711
      Email: shenrikson@cearinc.com
      Website: www.cearinc.com
Electronic asset recovery & recycling, Total Solution IT
Asset Management & Disposition, E-Waste/E-Asset, ITAD,
Data Sanitization, Recovery, Destruction/Shred
Remarketing, Test, Repair, Reporting. (As-Pac, estab 2000,
empl 58, sales $11,000,000, cert: CPUC)

4025 Celer Systems, Inc.
      1024 Iron Point Rd, Ste 100
      Folsom, CA 95630
      Contact: Sree Gaddam VP
      Tel: 916-220-2093
      Email: sree.gaddam@celersystems.com
      Website: www.celersystems.com
IT consulting services, project management, end to end,
application development, testing services, database
management, data warehouse, staff augmentation.
(Woman/As-Pac, estab 2007, empl 25, sales $3,000,000,
cert: NMSDC)

4026 Central Computer Systems Inc.
      3777 Stevens Creek Blvd
      Santa Clara, CA 95051
      Contact: Heidi Co CEO
      Tel: 408-248-5888
      Email: heidi@centralcomputer.com
      Website: www.CentralComputers.com
Custom-build computer systems, repair services, IT
services, networking, notebook repair, corporate sales,
local government sales, education sales & retail consumer
sales. (Woman/As-Pac, estab 1986, empl 80, sales
$25,000,000, cert: NMSDC, WBENC)

4027 Cerna Solutions, LLC
      3304 Febo Ct
      Carlsbad, CA 92009
      Contact: Michelle Yu CEO
      Tel: 442-222-0303
      Email: michelle@cernasolutions.com
      Website: www.cernasolutions.com
IT consulting services. (Woman/As-Pac, estab 2012, empl
6, sales , cert: NMSDC)

4028 Certified Independent Adjusters, Inc.
      25000 Ave Stanford Ste 224
      Valencia, CA 91390
      Contact: Roosevelt Jackson Owner
      Tel: 800-501-6032
      Email: rosey@gociai.com
      Website: www.gociai.com
Certified Independent Adjusters, Inc. is a nationwide
independent adjusting firm. Our adjusters have over 50
years of experience in Insurance industry.

ï¿½Daily Claims
ï¿½Auto Claims
ï¿½Catastrophes
ï¿½Commercial Claims
ï¿½Li (AA, estab 2010, empl 350, sales $2,300,000, cert:
NMSDC)

4029 Citrus Studios, Inc
      2450 Colorado Ave, Ste 100E
      Santa Monica, CA 90404
      Contact: CEO
      Tel: 310-717-8201
      Email: HELLO@CITRUSSTUDIOS.COM
      Website: www.citrusstudios.com
Web design & development. (Woman/As-Pac, estab
1999, empl 6, sales $1,300,000, cert: State)

4030 Connexus Hub
      14252 Culver Dr, Ste #257
      Irvine, CA 92604
      Contact: Daniel Jung Managing Partner
      Tel: 949-415-4364
      Email: dan@connexushub.com
      Website: www.connexushub.com
IT solutions products & services that encompass data
storage, mobile, cloud technologies, security & networking solutions, IT hardware & software solutions.
(Woman/As-Pac, estab 2014, empl 20, sales $1,700,000,
cert: CPUC, 8a, SDB)

4031 Consult Our Sorce, LLC
      2121 26th St, Ste 202
      San Francisco, CA 94107
      Contact: Bruin Gerber Business Develop Exec
      Tel: 937-925-1336
      Email: Bruin@consultoursource.com
      Website: www.consultoursource.com
ITIL (Information Technology Infrastructure Library),
TOGAF (The Open Group Architecture Framework),
Project Management (PMP, Agile), Management
Consulting Services, Information Security Consulting,
Managed Services. (Hisp, estab 2014, empl 5, sales
$937,564, cert: NMSDC)

4032 CPAC Inc.
      4749 E. Wesley Dr
      Anaheim, CA 92807
      Contact: Kara Mack Natl Acct Mgr
      Tel: 800-778-2722
      Email: kmack@cpacinc.com
      Website: www.cpacinc.com
Technical support, IT solutions. (Woman, estab 1993,
empl 30, sales $20,000,000, cert: CPUC)

4033   Cyber Professionals Inc. DBA Encore Software
       2025 Gateway Pl, Ste 385
       San Jose, CA 95110
       Contact: Radha Krishnan Managing Partner
       Tel: 408-573-7337
       Email: rkrishnan@encoress.com
       Website: www.encoress.com
Mobility, social commerce, Cloud & analytics IT services.
(As-Ind, estab 1998, empl 500, sales $10,679,387, cert:
NMSDC)

4034   Danta Technologies
       561 Rush Dr
       San Marcos, CA 92078
       Contact: President
       Tel: 619-862-3415
       Email:
       Website: www.dantatechnologies.net
IT applications, Infrastructure, IBM WebSphere, Oracle,
Sales Force, IOS developer, Network engineer, Big Data,
Hadoop, Java, Angular JS, Node JS, etc. (As-Pac, estab
2013, empl 25, sales $864,000, cert: NMSDC)

4035   Delta Computer Consulting, Inc.
       25550 Hawthorne Blvd Ste 106-108
       Torrance, CA 90505
       Contact: Acct Exec
       Tel: 310-541-9440
       Email:
       Website: www.deltacci.com
Human Capital Recruiting & Deployment, IT Staff Recruiting & Augmentation. (Woman, estab 1987, empl 165, sales
$28,000,000, cert: WBENC, NWBOC)

4036   Dew Software, Inc.
       983 Corporate way
       Fremont, CA 94539
       Contact: Suresh Deopura President
       Tel: 510-490-9995
       Email: suresh@dewsoftware.com
       Website: www.dewsoftware.com
Provide software consultants for short/long term in latest
technology as well in legacy systems, develop projects at
offsite or offshore. (Minority, estab 1997, empl 25, sales
$3,400,000, cert: CPUC)

4037   DFI Technologies, LLC
       1065 National Dr Ste 1
       Sacramento, CA 95834
       Contact: Vieng Phouthachack Technical Sales
       Engineer
       Tel: 916-568-1234
       Email: vieng@dfitech.com
       Website: www.dfitech.com
High performance computing solutions: Digital Signage,
Interactive Kiosk, Gaming, Industrial Automation, Medical
Device/Healthcare, Transportation. (As-Pac, estab 1985,
empl 70, sales , cert: State)

4038   Digital Mountain
       4633 Old Ironsides Dr Ste 401
       Santa Clara, CA 95054
       Contact: Julie Lewis CEO
       Tel: 866-344-3627
       Email: supplierdiversity@digitalmountain.com
       Website: www.digitalmountain.com
Web-based filtering & review (FileQuest), electronic
evidence collection, electronic discovery, computer
forensics, data breach management & expert witness
services. (Woman, estab 2003, empl 5, sales $2,006,316,
cert: State, CPUC, WBENC)

4039   Digital World Alliance, Corp.
       2030 Main St, Ste 1300
       Irvine, CA 92614
       Contact: Ken Riley Sr systems & bus Mgr
       Tel: 949-260-9106
       Email: kriley@digitalworldalliance.com
       Website: www.digitalworldalliance.com
Custom system design, programming, database architec-
tures, security, encryption, VPNs & systems integration.
(Woman/As-Pac, Hisp, estab 2003, empl 10, sales
$2,000,000, cert: State)

4040   ECommerce Holdings, Inc.
       201 Los Gatos Saratoga Rd, Ste 230
       Los Gatos, CA 95030
       Contact: Purnima Nandkishore President
       Tel: 866-465-3294
       Email: purnima@babychangingstations.com
       Website: www.babychangingstations.com
IT services. (Woman/As-Ind, estab 2009, empl 2, sales
$840,866, cert: NMSDC, CPUC)

4041   eJangar, Inc.
       13700 Altin Pkwy, Ste 154
       Irvine, CA 92618
       Contact: Ayesh Natekal President
       Tel: 800-259-9578
       Email: ayesha@ejangar.com
       Website: http://ejangar.com
IT services: staffing, project mgmt, Cloud architect, SFDC
Consultants, Sharrepoint Developers, Salesforce devel-
opers, .Net, Java, Offshore Development from India,
Onsite Services. (Woman/As-Ind, estab 2009, empl 25,
sales $250,000, cert: CPUC)

4042   En Pointe IT Solutions, LLC
       2121 Rosecrans Ave, Ste 4310 #4310
       El Segundo, CA 90245
       Contact: Paul Rayburn Field Acct Mgr
       Tel: 424-220-6700
       Email: anthony.spino@enpointeits.com
       Website: www.enpointeits.com
Provides software, hardware and IT Services. (Woman/
As-Ind, estab 2016, empl 24, sales $150,000,000, cert:
NMSDC, WBENC)

4043   En Pointe Technologies Sales, Inc.
       18701 S Figueroa St
       Gardena, CA 90248
       Contact: Michael Rapp VP Sales/Mktg
       Tel: 310-337-5200
       Email: helpdesk@enpointe.com
       Website: www.enpointe.com
IT products & professional services. (Woman/As-Ind,
estab 1993, empl 1200, sales $347,000,000, cert:
NMSDC, WBENC)

4044   eTouch Systems
       6627 Dumbarton Circle
       Freemont, CA 94555
       Contact: Amit Shah VP
       Tel: 510-795-4800
       Email: ashah@etouch.net
       Website: www.etouch.net
Information technology services - QA, Automation,
Manual, Functional, Performance, Specialized testing,
Mobile testing, etc. (As-Ind, estab 1997, empl 700, sales
$70,000,000, cert: NMSDC)

4045 EUS IT Solutions, LLC
19327 Broadacres Ave
Carson, CA 90746
Contact: Donald Hale CEO
Tel:　562-731-2244
Email: donhale@eusitsolutions.com
Website: http://eusitsolutions.com
IT consulting, IT Support, pc/laptop/workstation support, Hardware/Software support, smartphone support, tablet support, network support, printer support, cloud support, do projects. (AA, estab 2012, empl 5, sales , cert: NMSDC)

4046 EYP, Inc.
235 E Broadway Ste 800-B
Long Beach, CA 90802
Contact: Troy DuCre CEO
Tel:　310-684-3022
Email: tducre@eypinc.com
Website: www.eypinc.com
Workforce Management - IT and engineering contract services, Software as a Service (SaaS), Talent Management and Learning Management,
Management Consulting - Business Process Improvement. (AA, estab 2011, empl 3, sales $146,000, cert: NMSDC)

4047 Flexon Technologies Inc.
7901 Stoneridge Dr, Ste 390
Pleasanton, CA 94588
Contact: Sandeep Singh VP - Sales
Tel:　510-648-8878
Email: ken@flexontechnologies.com
Website: www.flexontechnologies.com
Our offerings are designed to cater to the entire range of clients' technology needs. (As-Ind, estab 2015, empl 52, sales $1,500,000, cert: NMSDC)

4048 Flight Light Inc.
2708 47th Ave
Sacramento, CA 95822
Contact: isabel martin President
Tel:　916-394-2800
Email: isabel.martin@flightlight.com
Website: www.flightlight.com
We are manufacturer and distributor of Airfield, Heliport and Obstruction lighting equipment as well as spare parts for all the equipment (Nat Ame, estab 1993, empl 18, sales $5,825,000, cert: State)

4049 Future State
2101 Webster St, Ste 520
Oakland, CA 94612
Contact:　Office Mgr
Tel:　877-614-0222
Email:
Website: www.futurestate.com
Training svcs, technical writing & information technology consulting svcs. (Woman, estab , empl , sales $16,000,000, cert: NWBOC)

4050 Gemini Associates Inc.
33 Musick
Irvine, CA 92618
Contact: Robert Manciet President
Tel:　949-830-8858
Email: sales@federalsales.com
Website: www.federalsales.com
Networking & data communications, air blown fiber optics, CAT5 wireless networks, ruggedized CPU, monitor & keyboard. (Hisp, estab 1975, empl 35, sales , cert: State)

4051 Global IT Services
180 Promenade Circle, Ste 300
Sacramento, CA 95834
Contact: Shavinder (Shawn) Phagura President
Tel:　916-414-0311
Email: sphagura@globalitsvcs.com
Website: www.globalitsvcs.com
IT Staffing Services, Cloud & IT Consulting, and Skilled Staffing Solutions. (As-Ind, estab 2014, empl 15, sales $910,000, cert: State, NMSDC, SDB)

4052 Global Software Resources, Inc.
4447 Stoneridge Dr
Pleasanton, CA 94588
Contact: Keith Granucci Dir
Tel:　925-249-2200
Email: keith@gsr-inc.com
Website: www.gsr-inc.com
Engineering services, plant floor operations. (As-Pac, estab 2003, empl 45, sales $4,000,000, cert: CPUC)

4053 GoAhead Solutions LLC.
400 Oyster Point Blvd Ste 407
South San Francisco, CA 94080
Contact: Jaime Mendoza CEO
Tel:　650-873-7255
Email: jaime@goaheadsolutions.com
Website: www.goaheadsolutions.com
IT Staff Augmentation, Consulting Services, Oracle Software Resell & Oracle Audit Representation. (Hisp, estab 2001, empl 46, sales $12,469,516, cert: NMSDC)

4054 Grove Technical Resources
9035 Rosewood Ave
West Hollywood, CA 90048
Contact:　President
Tel:　786-390-7119
Email:
Website: www.grovetechnicalresources.com
Technical staffing & consulting services. (Woman, estab 2005, empl 2, sales , cert: CPUC, WBENC)

4055 HB Computers, Inc.
17131 Beach Blvd, Ste B
Huntington Beach, CA 92647
Contact: MADIHA RAJPUT CEO
Tel:　714-916-9294
Email: amir@hbcomputerz.com
Website: www.hbcomputerz.com
Test & manage networks cables. (Woman/As-Ind, estab 2005, empl 10, sales $268,089, cert: WBENC)

4056 Heritage Global Solutions, Inc.
230 N Maryland Ave Ste 202
Glendale CA, CA 91206
Contact: Jeff Estep President
Tel:　949-501-1038
Email: jeff.estep@heritageglobal.com
Website: www.heritageglobal.com
Information technology solutions, staff augmentation. (Nat Ame, estab 2003, empl 19, sales $2,000,000, cert: State)

4057 Horologiii, Inc.
270 Corte Colina
Novato, CA 94949
Contact: Rod Nash President
Tel:　510-764-8500
Email: rod@horologiii.com
Website: www.horologiii.com
Energy Consulting Services & Information Technology. (AA, estab 2002, empl 1, sales , cert: CPUC)

4058 IGIS Technologies Inc.
10393 San Diego Mission Rd Ste 212
San Diego, CA 92108
Contact: Andres Abeyta CEO
Tel: 619-640-2330
Email: abeyta@igist.com
Website: www.igist.com
GIS consulting, training & application development for the geospatial community. (Hisp, estab 1997, empl 11, sales $1,000,000, cert: CPUC)

4059 IMPEX Technologies, Inc.
880 Apollo St Ste 315
El Segundo, CA 90245
Contact: Rajiv Shah President
Tel: 310-320-0280
Email: rshah@impextechnologies.com
Website: www.impextechnologies.com
Systems integration: computer hardware, software, consulting & project management, enterprise storage systems & mgmt, enterprise backup, regulatory compliance, business continuance & disaster recovery, security solutions & networking. (As-Ind, estab 1992, empl 10, sales $3,000,000, cert: NMSDC)

4060 IMS
7755 Center Ave Ste 1100
Huntington Beach, CA 92647
Contact: Kristi Newman Dir Client Services
Tel: 714-840-3775
Email: knewman@imssvs.com
Website: www.imssvs.com
IT Contract, Consulting, Contract-to-Hire & Full Time placement services. (Woman, estab 1973, empl 35, sales $7,600,293, cert: State)

4061 Information Design Consultants, Inc.
222 W 6th St, Ste 400
San Pedro, CA 90731
Contact:
Tel: 310-707-2532
Email:
Website: www.idcinc.net
Project Management; Systems Integration (Woman/AA, estab 2002, empl 1, sales , cert: CPUC, WBENC)

4062 Information Management Resources, Inc.
85 Argonut, Ste 200
Aliso Viejo, CA 92656
Contact: Martha Daniel CEO
Tel: 949-215-8889
Email: jmiller@imri.com
Website: www.imri.com
Business process mgmt, application integration, systems integration, data mgmt, operations & network support, outsourcing, training, programming, etc. (Woman/AA, estab 1992, empl 60, sales , cert: State)

4063 Infosoft Inc.
7891 Westwood Dr, Ste 113
Gilroy, CA 95020
Contact: Raj Chopra VP
Tel: 408-659-4326
Email: rchopra@infosoft-inc.com
Website: www.infosoft-inc.com
Information technology staffing & consulting. (As-Ind, estab 2000, empl 130, sales $16,330,000, cert: NMSDC)

4064 Infoyogi LLC
2320 #A Walsh Ave
Santa Clara, CA 95051
Contact: Sriram Sundaravaradan Mktg Mgr
Tel: 408-850-1700
Email: info@infoyogi.com
Website: www.infoyogi.com
Information technology, custom computer programming services, systems design services. (As-Ind, estab 1995, empl 15, sales , cert: CPUC)

4065 Integrated Spatial Solutions, Inc.
13879 Penn St
Whittier, CA 90602
Contact: Julie Henry COO
Tel: 562-693-2253
Email: jhenry@issi-gis.com
Website: www.issi-gis.com
Application devel, internet map services, systems integration, strategic planning, needs assessment, data conversion, database design, GIS mapping. (Woman, estab 1999, empl 7, sales $841,279, cert: CPUC)

4066 Intelliswift Software, Inc.
39600 Balentine Dr
Newark, CA 94560
Contact: Payal Kanaiya VP - Strategic Initiatives
Tel: 510-370-2619
Email: payal.kanaiya@intelliswift.com
Website:
Systems integration & software services. (As-Pac, estab 2001, empl 1100, sales $80,224,959, cert: NMSDC)

4067 International Word Processing Services, Inc.
P.O. Box 5053
Downey, CA 90241
Contact: Mary Jones CEO
Tel: 562-900-8359
Email: mary.jones@intlword.com
Website: www.intlword.com
Technical word processing, transcription & employment placement. (Woman/AA, estab 1994, empl 2, sales , cert: State, City, CPUC)

4068 Intrinsyx Technologies
350 N Akron Rd, Bldg.19-102
Moffett Field, CA 94035
Contact: Nabil Afifi Business Dev Mgr
Tel: 510-266-2721
Email: nabil@intrinsyx.com
Website: www.intrinsyx.com
Information technology solutions. (Woman/As-Ind, estab 2000, empl 50, sales $7,137,776, cert: State, NMSDC)

4069 IP International, Inc.
1510 Fashion Island Blvd, Ste 104
San Mateo, CA 94404
Contact:
Tel: 650-403-7840
Email:
Website: www.infoplusintl.com
IT consulting services: project mgmt & PMO, ERP, help desk & contact center, cost mgmt savings, bill audit & mgmt, ordering & provisioning, business case development, RFP & RFI creation, vendor mgmt & selection. (Woman, estab 1986, empl 50, sales $15,000,000, cert: CPUC, WBENC)

4070 IsComp Systems Inc.
5777 W Century Blvd, Ste 560
Los Angeles, CA 90045
Contact: Joshlyn Black Sr. Acct Exec
Tel: 310-641-3260
Email: jblack@iscompsystems.com
Website: www.iscompsystems.com
Unix system integration, systems engineering, software develop, database mgmt. (AA, estab 1986, empl 20, sales , cert: CPUC)

4071 iTalent Corporation
27 Devine St Ste 20
San Jose, CA 95110
Contact: Silvia Quintanilla Director
Tel: 408-428-2641
Email: silvia@italentdigital.com
Website: www.italentdigital.com
Global technology consulting services, Software Development Solutions, Innovative & Flexible Consulting Project Resource Solutions, Specialized Practices, Managed Services, Social Knowledge Management, Change Management. (Woman/Hisp, estab 2005, empl 150, sales $25,000,000, cert: NMSDC, WBENC)

4072 JAUST Consulting Partners Inc.
3150 Almaden Exprwy Sutie 215
San Jose, CA 95118
Contact: Gail D'Silva Founder
Tel: 408-805-0901
Email: gail@jaustpartners.com
Website: www.jaustpartners.com
IT solutions, ERP, CRM, SCM, Analytics & Web services, development & application integration. (As-Ind, Hisp, estab 2005, empl 8, sales , cert: NMSDC)

4073 JE Components Inc.
8709 Aviation Blvd
Inglewood, CA 90301
Contact: Joni Paulo President
Tel: 310-645-6021
Email: joni@jecom.com
Website: www.jecom.com
Resell PC & network hardware. (Woman/AA, As-Ind, estab 1995, empl 7, sales , cert: NMSDC, NWBOC)

4074 Kaygen, Inc.
15420 Laguna Canyon Road Ste 270
Irvine, CA 92618
Contact: Rashmi Chaturvedi President
Tel: 949-203-5100
Email: rashmi.chaturvedi@kaygen.com
Website: www.kaygen.com
Oracle Enterprise Resource Planning (ERP). (Woman/As-Ind, As-Pac, estab 2003, empl 45, sales $13,000,000, cert: State, City, NMSDC, WBENC)

4075 KT Consulting, Inc.
2545 W 10th St Ste A
Antioch, CA 94509
Contact: Acct Mgr
Tel: 972-734-5128
Email:
Website: www.ktconsultinginc.com
Information technology & management consulting: IT operations support, project & program mgmt, outsourcing, strategy, performance & operations mgmt, technical writing, IT security, planning, analysis, design, configuration, implementation. (AA, estab 2001, empl 25, sales $39,814,191, cert: State)

4076 Kutir Corporation
37600 Central Ct, Ste 280
Newark, CA 94560
Contact: Prathiba Kalyan Sr. Business Mgr
Tel: 510-870-0227
Email: prathiba@kutirtech.com
Website: www.kutirtech.com
Contract & permanent staffing, custom software development, business & technology consulting, systems integration, technical support, admin, testing & support, data warehousing, business intelligence. (As-Ind, estab 2003, empl 40, sales $3,400,000, cert: NMSDC, CPUC, 8a)

4077 Laboratory Data Consultants, Inc.
2701 Loker Ave. West Ste 220
Carlsbad, CA 92010
Contact: Laura Soeten Exec Admin
Tel: 760-827-1100
Email: Lsoeten@lab-data.com
Website: www.lab.data.com
Data validation and data management services. (As-Pac, estab 1991, empl 36, sales $3,940,313, cert: State)

4078 LocalBizNetwork
3141 Stevens Creek Blvd, Ste 358
San Jose, CA 95117
Contact: Indu Jayakumar President
Tel: 408-741-8184
Email: info@localbiznetwork.com
Website: www.localbiznetwork.com
Custom software applications: Internet, Internet based online survey forms, computation of survey data, Internet marketing, SEO, Internet publishing, blogging, website development & hosting. (Woman/As-Ind, estab 2002, empl 22, sales $300,000, cert: CPUC)

4079 LogixService, Inc.
1383 Calle Avanzado
San Clemente, CA 92673
Contact: Van Boone CEO
Tel: 949-400-6083
Email: vboone@amtek.net
Website: www.amtek.net
Computer Maintenance and Support Services: IBM, HP, DELL, Compaq, Gateway, EMC, NetApp, Cisco, etc. Samsung, Brother Canon, Okidata, etc. (AA, estab 1980, empl 12, sales $2,100,000, cert: State, NMSDC)

4080 Luminous Tec LLC
15481 Red Hill Ave, Ste B
Tustin, CA 92780
Contact: Uma Sharma Dir new business devel
Tel: 949-630-0448
Email: usharma@luminoustec.com
Website: www.luminoustec.com
IT & non IT staffing & consulting services: project managers, business & technical architects, business analysts, applications development resources, systems integration specialists. (Woman/As-Pac, estab 2006, empl 5, sales $750,000, cert: CPUC)

4081   Magellan Solutions USA
       100 Old County Rd Ste H
       Brisbane, CA 94005
       Contact: Dee Mark Anthony CEO
       Tel: 650-897-5147
       Email: mark.dee@magellansolutionsusa.com
       Website: www.magellansolutionsusa.com
Call Center, Business Process Outsourcing,
Inbound/Outbound Call Center, E-Commerce Support,
Data Entry/Processing, Financial/Billing Support, Business
Process Management. (As-Pac, estab 2005, empl 600, sales
$3,004,000, cert: State)

4082   Meijun LLC
       9888 Carroll Centre Rd Ste#210
       San Diego, CA 92126
       Contact: Huy Ly
       Tel: 619-333-8698
       Email: hly@meijun.cc
       Website: http://meijun.cc
Web development & marketing agency, custom software
solutions, web & mobile development, design & strategy,
digital marketing services, SEO, content marketing &
marketing automation integration. (As-Pac, estab 2011,
empl 5, sales , cert: NMSDC, CPUC)

4083   Metabyte Inc.
       39350 Civic Center Dr Ste 200
       Fremont, CA 94538
       Contact: Unni Krishnan Business Dev Mgr
       Tel: 510-494-9700
       Email: unnik@metabyte.com
       Website: www.metabyte.com
IT Services, High Technology & ISV, Life Sciences &
Healthcare, Manufacturing & Logistics, Banking & Financial
Services, Speciality Retail, Telecom & Media. (As-Pac, estab
1993, empl 235, sales , cert: NMSDC)

4084   Mission Critical Technologies, Inc.
       2041 Rosecrans Ave Ste 220
       El Segundo, CA 90245
       Contact: Patti Converse
       Tel: 310-246-4455
       Email: patti_converse@mctinc.com
       Website: www.mctinc.com
Technology solutions: relational database, application
design & implementation, custom software dev,
outsourcing, offsite dev projects, graphic design & development. (Woman, estab 1993, empl 50, sales , cert:
WBENC)

4085   MSRCOSMOS LLC
       6200 StoneRidge Mall Rd, Ste 300
       Pleasanton, CA 94588
       Contact: Rajkumar Bogam Lead Sales
       Tel: 321-332-6344
       Email: rajj@msrcosmos.com
       Website: www.msrcosmos.com
IT services, mobile application, web applications, cloud
solutions, analytics, infrastructure management & offshore
consulting. (Woman, estab 2008, empl 84, sales
$6,000,000, cert: WBENC)

4086   NexInfo Solutions, Inc.
       1851 E First St Ste 900
       Santa Ana, CA 92705
       Contact: Kate Duffy Client Relations
       Tel: 714-955-6970
       Email: kate.duffy@nexinfo.com
       Website: www.nexinfo.com
ERP solutions, PLM solutions, Supply Chain Planning,
Software implementations, Manged Services, Technical
consulting, Functional consulting, Techno Functional
Consulting, business process design, Global order
promising. (As-Ind, estab 1999, empl 300, sales , cert:
NMSDC)

4087   Omni2max, Inc.
       1202 Morena Blvd, Ste 100
       San Diego, CA 92110
       Contact: Javonda Franklin Business Dev Mgr
       Tel: 619-269-1663
       Email: javonda.franklin@omni2max.com
       Website: www.omni2max.com
Information Assurance, Information Technology,
Logistics, Engineering, Contract Management, Help Desk
Management & CRM, Systems Engineering, Program
Management & Performance Based Acquisition. (AA,
estab 2009, empl 25, sales $1,500,000, cert: State, 8a)

4088   Omnikron Systems Inc.
       20920 Warner Center Lane Ste A
       Woodland Hills, CA 91367
       Contact: Robin Borough President
       Tel: 818-223-4115
       Email: robin.borough@omnikron.com
       Website: www.Omnikron.com
Applications development (ERP), database, reporting,
business intelligence, operations, infrastructure, security
& business personnel. (As-Pac, estab 1980, empl 50,
sales $8,000,000, cert: CPUC)

4089   OrangePeople
       300 Spectrum Dr Ste 400
       Irvine, CA 92618
       Contact: Natasha Myers VP
       Tel: 949-667-1762
       Email: natasha.myers@orangepeople.com
       Website: www.orangepeople.com
OrangePeople is one of the fastest growing Technology
Leadership Services company in America. Our team of
consultants bring tremendous hands-on experience in
business strategy, architecture, and program management. (As-Pac, estab 2006, empl 70, sales $1,800,000,
cert: NMSDC)

4090   Partner Engineering and Science, Inc.
       1990 E Grand Ave, Ste 100
       El Segundo, CA 90245
       Contact: Sean Rakhshani Principal
       Tel: 800-419-4923
       Email: srakhshani@partneresi.com
       Website: www.partneresi.com
Software engineering, modeling & simulation, research
& development & consulting services. (Woman, estab
2006, empl 120, sales $22,700,000, cert: WBENC)

4091 Perlinski & Company
      30025 Alicia Pkwy, Ste 107
      Laguna Niguel, CA 92677
      Contact: Isabel Perlinski CEO
      Tel: 949-481-5482
      Email: isabel.perlinski@perlinskico.com
      Website: www.perlinskico.com
Perlinski & Company is the culmination of the experience,
leadership, skills and capabilities of its founders, partners,
board members and strategic partners. Founded in 1989,
Perlinski & Company specializes in providing management
consulting (Woman/Hisp, estab 1989, empl 2, sales
$244,250, cert: NMSDC, WBENC, 8a)

4092 Pinpoint Resource Group, LLC
      1960 E Grand Ave Ste 1260
      El Segundo, CA 90245
      Contact: Felix Lin President
      Tel: 310-356-8123
      Email: felix@pinpoint.jobs
      Website: www.pinpoint.jobs
Information technology staffing: consultants & direct hire,
systems analysts, project managers & management
personnel. (As-Pac, estab 2004, empl 15, sales $4,500,000,
cert: NMSDC)

4093 Plan b Solutions, Inc.
      29222 Rancho Viejo Rd
      San Juan Capistrano, CA 92675
      Contact: CEO
      Tel: 949-221-9301
      Email:
      Website: www.planbsolutions.com
IT staffing & professional services, contract, contract-to-
hire & permanent placement staffing, process consulting.
(Woman, estab 2000, empl 20, sales $4,800,000, cert:
WBENC)

4094 PM Business Holdings LLC
      733 Hindry Ave, Ste C205
      Inglewood, CA 90301
      Contact: Derrick Ferguson CEO
      Tel: 310-242-3171
      Email: pmbh14@gmail.com
      Website: www.brilliantmindssolutions.com
Computer Systems Design Services, employment placement & executive search services (AA, estab 2012, empl 1,
sales , cert: NMSDC)

4095 Premium Technologies, Inc.
      P.O. Box 757
      Palm Desert, CA 92261
      Contact: Stanway Wong President
      Tel: 760-340-4603
      Email: stanwong@premium-technologies.com
      Website: www.premium-technologies.com/
Computer software design & development, data integration, physical asset mgmt, computerized maintenance
mgmt system (CMMS) & enterprise asset mgmt (EAM) &
asset tracking. (As-Pac, estab 1993, empl 1, sales , cert:
NMSDC, CPUC)

4096 Progressive Technology Solutions
      500 E Calaveras
      Milpitas, CA 95035
      Contact: Rumi Bordoloi Acct/Relationship Mgr
      Tel: 408-507-7106
      Email: hr@ptsol.com
      Website: www.ptsol.com
Business, Functional Technical consultants and perma-
nent staff/workforce, SAP, Oracle, Internet Technology,
Data Management and Analysis, ETL and
Datawarehousing, Release and Change Management.
(Woman/As-Ind, estab 2002, empl 50, sales $6,650,000,
cert: NMSDC)

4097 Propane Studio
      1153 Mission St
      San Francisco, CA 94103
      Contact: Neil Chaudhari CXO
      Tel: 415-902-7958
      Email: neil@propanestudio.com
      Website: https://propanestudio.com
Websites & Applications, Responsive Websites, Tech
Arch Consulting, E-Commerce Development, UX
Prototyping & Testing, Mobile Applications, Online
Applications, Content Strategy & Migration, CMS
Consulting, Strategic Digital Consulting. (As-Ind, estab
2003, empl 20, sales $5,000,000, cert: NMSDC)

4098 Prosum, Inc.
      2201 Park Place, Ste 102
      El Segundo, CA 90245
      Contact: Ravi Chatwani CEO
      Tel: 310-426-0609
      Email: ravi.chatwani@prosum.com
      Website: www.prosum.com
Technology staffing services, technology consulting
services, technology product sales. (As-Ind, estab 1996,
empl 250, sales $38,000,000, cert: NMSDC, CPUC)

4099 Qsolv Inc.
      1735 N First St, Ste 302
      San Jose, CA 95112
      Contact: President
      Tel: 408-429-0918
      Email:
      Website: www.qsolv-inc.com
Cloud Automation Services, Network management and
Networking products, virtualization, automation and
orchestration solutions. (Woman/As-Pac, estab 1999,
empl 150, sales , cert: NMSDC, WBENC)

4100 QualityWorks Consulting Group, LLC
      6018 S Citrus Ave
      Los Angeles, CA 90043
      Contact: Stacy Kirk CEO
      Tel: 310-467-5122
      Email: skirk@qualityworkscg.com
      Website: http://qualityworkscg.com
Automated & manual web testing, Automated & manual
mobile testing, Integrated automation test frameworks
for web & mobile, DevOps/Continuous Integration
Support, API/microservices testing, Agile QA coaching &
training. (Woman/AA, estab 2010, empl 34, sales
$1,295,000, cert: NMSDC, WBENC)

4101   RaviG Inc. dba Salient Global Technologies
       510 Garcia Ave, Ste E
       Pittsburg, CA 94565
       Contact: Ravikanth Ganapavarapu President
       Tel: 925-526-1234
       Email: rganapa@salientglobaltech.com
       Website: www.salientglobaltech.com
End-to-end business applications & IT infrastructure. (As-Pac, estab 1999, empl 45, sales $8,323,350, cert: NMSDC)

4102   Raycom Data Technologies, Inc.
       1320 E Imperial Ave
       El Segundo, CA 90245
       Contact: Ayaz Pandhiani President
       Tel: 310-322-5113
       Email: ayaz@raycomdtech.com
       Website: www.raycomdtech.com
Document archiving software, document management services, document scanning, conversion services, microfiche & microfilm. (As-Pac, estab 1978, empl 10, sales $1,165,000, cert: State)

4103   Related Technologies, Inc.
       81 Blue Ravine Rd Ste 230
       Folsom, CA 95630
       Contact: Cheryl Borgonah Mgr
       Tel: 916-357-5902
       Email: cherylb@relatedtech.com
       Website: www.relatedtech.com/
Technical & Functional SAP consultants & Subject Matter Experts, implementations, upgrades, enhancements & support. (Woman/As-Ind, estab 2002, empl 150, sales $1,500,000, cert: CPUC)

4104   RJT Compuquest
       222 N Sepulveda Blvd. Ste 2250
       El Segundo, CA 90245
       Contact: Vivek Bhatia Sr. Accts Exec
       Tel: 310-421-1297
       Email: vivek@rjtcompuquest.com
       Website: www.rjtcompuquest.com
IT solutions, SAP, Oracle, WB, web development, CRM & archiving solutions, staff augmentation. (As-Pac, estab 1996, empl 300, sales $46,000,000, cert: NMSDC)

4105   RKG Technologies Inc
       11 Antietam
       Irvine, CA 92620
       Contact: Raju Gottimukkala President
       Tel: 949-910-1262
       Email: grkraju@hotmail.com
       Website: www.rkgtech.com
Strategic consulting, staffing and staff augmentation, training, vendor management and outsourcing services. (As-Ind, estab 2004, empl 20, sales $465,000, cert: City, NMSDC, CPUC)

4106   RPM Engineers, Inc.
       102 Discovery
       Irvine, CA 92618
       Contact: Raymond Phua Principal
       Tel: 949-450-1229
       Email: marisolv@rpmpe.com
       Website: www.rpmpe.com
RPM Engineers, Inc. was established 1993 in Irvine, California. An engineering firm under the direction of Mr. Raymond Phua, a registered professional engineer in state of California, providing air conditioning (As-Pac, estab 1993, empl 17, sales $1,727,000, cert: State)

4107   SA Technologies Inc.
       5201 Great America Pkwy, Ste #441 Ste 441
       Santa Clara, CA 95054
       Contact: Priyanka Joshi President
       Tel: 408-986-0152
       Email: priyanka.joshi@satechglobal.com
       Website: www.satechglobal.com
Information technology consulting & staffing. (Woman/As-Ind, estab , empl , sales $10,800,000, cert: NWBOC)

4108   SD Shredding, Inc.
       7263 Engineer Rd Ste C
       San Diego, CA 92111
       Contact: Todd M Hoover CFO
       Tel: 858-492-9600
       Email: todd.hoover@proshred.com
       Website: http://proshred.com
On-site document & computer hard drive shredding. (Woman, estab 2010, empl 3, sales $200,000, cert: WBENC)

4109   Sidebench Studios
       10317 Washington Blvd.
       Culver City, CA 90232
       Contact: Nate Schier Dir of Staff & Co-Founder
       Tel: 808-294-5948
       Email: nate@sidebench.com
       Website: www.sidebench.com
App design, development & strategy. (As-Pac, estab 2012, empl 13, sales $1,342,459, cert: NMSDC, CPUC)

4110   Sigmaways, Inc
       39737 Paseo Padre Parkway
       Fremont, CA 94538
       Contact: Prakash Sadasivam CEO
       Tel: 510-713-7800
       Email: info@sigmaways.com
       Website: www.sigmaways.com
Software product, technology innovation & staff augmentation. (As-Ind, estab 2006, empl 85, sales $8,300,000, cert: NMSDC)

4111   Sohum Inc
       1055 Minnesota Ave, Ste 6
       San Jose, CA 95125
       Contact: Vandana Patil President
       Tel: 408-265-2391
       Email: marketing@sohum.biz
       Website: www.sohum.biz
Software UX design, web & mobile, Software Design & Development, Cloud based software deployment & monitoring. (Woman/As-Ind, estab 1998, empl 5, sales $300,000, cert: State)

4112   Solugenix Corporation
       7700 Irvine Center Dr Ste 800
       Irvine, CA 92618
       Contact: Director
       Tel: 949-266-0938
       Email:
       Website: www.solugenix.com
Application Lifecycle Management: Project & Requirements Management, Custom Application Development, Testing & Quality Assurance, Change & Release Management, Level 2 & Level 3 Production Support. (As-Ind, estab 2004, empl 52, sales $27,583,910, cert: NMSDC)

4113 Source Diversified, Inc.
      1206 Vista Cantora
      San Clemente, CA 92672
      Contact: Alfred Ortiz President
      Tel: 949-940-0450
      Email: aortiz@sourced.com
      Website: www.sourced.com
Command & control systems, security alerting systems,
flight test support svcs, aircraft system integration,
software dev, construction automation software, network
installation, mission control room support svcs. (Hisp,
estab 1987, empl 3, sales , cert: State)

4114 SPK and Associates, LLC
      5011 Scotts Valley Dr
      Scotts Valley, CA 95030
      Contact: Michael Roberts VP Sales/Mktg
      Tel: 888-310-4540
      Email: mroberts@spkaa.com
      Website: www.spkaa.com
Information Technology (IT), Infrastructure, IT Services
(implementation, support, training, data migration), IT
Staffing through a MSP, Large Data Storage/Management,
Network Management, Product Development, Software
Programming, Web Administrators (Woman, estab 2003,
empl 17, sales $2,882,705, cert: WBENC)

4115 SRS Consulting Inc.
      39465 Paseo Padre Pkwy, Ste 1100
      Fremont, CA 94538
      Contact: Aswath Panduranga Business Dev Mgr
      Tel: 510-252-0625
      Email: aswath@srsconsultinginc.com
      Website: www.srsconsultinginc.com
IT Development, Custom Software Development, R&D/
Product Development/Re-engineering, Testing and Quality
Assurance, Network Security Services, ERP/EAI consulting
& implementation, CRM, SCP, BPM, CMS, DMS, e-Gover-
nance, Mobile Security. (Woman/As-Ind, estab 2002, empl
250, sales $46,000,000, cert: NMSDC, WBENC)

4116 Stealth Network Communication
      6900 Koll Center Pkwy, Ste 413
      Pleasanton, CA 94566
      Contact: Dave Drews Dir
      Tel: 925-846-7018
      Email: ddrews@stealthnetwork.com
      Website: www.stealthnetwork.com
Voice, network & security, telcom technologies, call center
efficiencies information, switching systems, project mgmt,
technical project mgmt, IP telephony & VOIP design.
(Woman/Nat Ame, estab 2001, empl 32, sales
$15,000,000, cert: State)

4117 Stratitude
      6601 Koll Center Pkwy, Ste 132
      Pleasanton, CA 94566
      Contact: Khannan Sankaran CEO
      Tel: 510-461-3981
      Email: khannan@stratitude.com
      Website: www.stratitude.com
IT services, implementation & staffing, software advisory,
design, development & testing services, SAP, Microsoft,
Java, Salesforce.com , Netsuite, Pega BPM, Guidewire
Temenos, Veeva. (As-Ind, estab 2006, empl 36, sales
$3,600,000, cert: NMSDC)

4118 Sun MicroSolutions Inc.
      29 Avanzare St
      Irvine, CA 92606
      Contact: Ruchi Mitra CEO
      Tel: 949-387-9878
      Email: ruchi@sunmicrousa.com
      Website: www.sunmicrousa.com
IT consulting, staffing & training. (Woman/As-Pac, estab
2000, empl 5, sales $540,000, cert: City)

4119 Sunny City Enterprises, Inc.
      959 Mount Whitney Ct
      Chula Vista, CA 91913
      Contact: Francisco Esparza President
      Tel: 619-250-5970
      Email: francisco.esparza@sbcitpros.com
      Website: www.sbcitpros.com
IT & Telecom services, Technology Services, Software
Solutions & Applications, Staffing Augmentation. (Hisp,
estab 2007, empl 10, sales $1,500,000, cert: NMSDC,
CPUC)

4120 SysIntelli, Inc.
      9466 Black Mountain Road, Ste. 200
      San Diego, CA 92126
      Contact: CEO
      Tel: 858-271-1600
      Email:
      Website: http://sysintelli.com
Software Development Life Cycle, Re-engineering &
Legacy Migration, Database Administration, Quality
Assurance Testing & Validation, E-Commerce, Data
Processing, Software Maintenance & Support. (As-Ind,
estab 2005, empl 55, sales $16,690,351, cert: NMSDC)

4121 Systems Integration Solutions, Inc.
      1255 Treat Blvd. Ste 100
      Walnut Creek, CA 94597
      Contact: Nick Bata Reg Acct Dir
      Tel: 952-220-7549
      Email: nbata@sisinc.com
      Website: www.sisinc.com
IT consulting & executive search services. (As-Pac, Hisp,
estab 1990, empl 150, sales $30,000,000, cert: CPUC)

4122 Tap3Solutions
      2279 Eagle Glen Pkwy, Ste 112-444
      Corona, CA 92883
      Contact: Catrina Snell-Rehder President
      Tel: 949-229-1910
      Email: catrina@tap3solutions.com
      Website: www.Tap3Solutions.com
Information technology & human capital solutions.
(Woman/AA, estab 2015, empl 2, sales , cert: State, City)

4123 TechLink Systems, Inc.
      2 Embarcadero Center Ste 2240
      San Francisco, CA 94111
      Contact: Shannon Proverbs Mgr, Business Dev
      Tel: 415-732-7580
      Email: sproverbs@techlinksystems.com
      Website: www.techlinksystems.com
Information technology, engineering, scientific & biotech, application development. (Woman/As-Pac, estab
1998, empl 141, sales $23,560,181, cert: NMSDC,
WBENC)

4124　Technology Integration Group
　　　10240 Flanders Court
　　　San Diego, CA 92121
　　　Contact: Bruce Geier CEO
　　　Tel:　858-566-1900
　　　Email: bruce.geier@tig.com
　　　Website: www.tig.com
System integration, engineering, programming, computer software, hardware & furniture, cabling, telephony, help desk. (As-Pac, estab , empl , sales $325,000, cert: NMSDC, CPUC)

4125　Technossus LLC
　　　4000 MacArthur Blvd Ste 100
　　　Newport Beach, CA 92660
　　　Contact: Dave LaJeunesse Dir of Sales
　　　Tel:　949-769-3522
　　　Email: info@technossus.com
　　　Website: www.technossus.com
Custom software development, Microsoft technology stack, application development, desktop, enterprise & web-based, mobile applications, SharePoint & Dynamics CRM, proprietary systems development & enhancement. (As-Ind, estab 2008, empl 25, sales $4,700,000, cert: NMSDC)

4126　Tellus Solutions, Inc
　　　3350 Scott Blvd 34A
　　　Santa Clara, CA 95054
　　　Contact:　HR/Business Development
　　　Tel:　408-850-2942
　　　Email:
　　　Website: www.tellussol.com
Information technology services. (Woman/As-Pac, estab 2005, empl 67, sales $5,320,000, cert: NMSDC, WBENC, 8a)

4127　The LSC Group, Inc.
　　　200 Spectrum Center Dr 3rd Fl
　　　Irvine, CA 92618
　　　Contact: Troy Humphrey CEO
　　　Tel:　800-572-9280
　　　Email: troy.humphrey@yourlscgroup.com
　　　Website: www.yourlscgroup.com
Electronic Discovery, Data Collection, Data Processing, Data Production, Forensic Date Discovery, Litigation Support, Records Management, Early Case Assessment, Webhosting, Project Management, Consulting. (AA, estab 2007, empl 1, sales $125,000, cert: NMSDC, CPUC)

4128　Thoughtpowers LLC
　　　1919 Williams St Ste 215
　　　Simi Valley, CA 93065
　　　Contact: Surendra Kulkarni President
　　　Tel:　805-433-4950
　　　Email: surendra@thoughtpowers.com
　　　Website: www.thoughtpowers.com
Custom Application IT development & management, IT consulting services, IT resources, technical resources. (Minority, estab 2008, empl 1, sales , cert: NMSDC)

4129　Trident Consulting
　　　2410 Camino Ramon, Ste 183
　　　San Ramon, CA 94583
　　　Contact: Shabana Siraj CEO
　　　Tel:　925-683-5166
　　　Email: Farhaan@Tridentconsultinginc.com
　　　Website: www.Tridentconsultinginc.com
IT staffing and technology company. (Woman/As-Ind, estab 2005, empl 80, sales $12,908,447, cert: State, NMSDC, WBENC)

4130　Trinus Corporation
　　　225 South Lake Ave, Ste 1080
　　　Pasadena, CA 91101
　　　Contact: Harshada Kucheria President
　　　Tel:　818-246-1143
　　　Email: harshada_kucheria@trinus.com
　　　Website: www.trinus.com
IT consulting & implementation services, business consulting, systems integration & outsourcing. (Woman/As-Ind, estab 1995, empl 250, sales , cert: NMSDC, CPUC, WBENC, SDB)

4131　Two Shea Consulting, Inc.
　　　1009 Oak Hill Rd, Ste 202
　　　Lafayette, CA 94549
　　　Contact: Maureen Shea CEO
　　　Tel:　925-962-7432
　　　Email: maureen@twoshea.com
　　　Website: www.twoshea.com
IT consulting & recruiting services. (Woman, estab 2000, empl 25, sales $5,000,000, cert: City, WBENC)

4132　United Support Services, Inc.
　　　713 Mission Ave, Ste C
　　　Oceanside, CA 92054
　　　Contact: Michael Fernandez President
　　　Tel:　760-688-0115
　　　Email: sales@usscompany.com
　　　Website: www.usscompany.com
Training & Education, Information Technology (IT) & Networks, Cyber Security, Software Devel & Professional Support, Custom Software Design, Online Education & Training Programs, Custom Designed Computer Based Training. (Hisp, estab 2002, empl 8, sales , cert: 8a)

4133　Versa Shore Inc.
　　　1999 S Bascom Ave Ste 700
　　　Campbell, CA 95008
　　　Contact: Shawn Rao CEO
　　　Tel:　408-874-8330
　　　Email: shawnrao@versashore.com
　　　Website: www.versashore.com
Consulting, staffing & headhunting, Microsoft APS, Data warehousing, big data, business intelligence, Oracle, Birst, Tableau, Sql Server, Hadoop, MongoDB, Database, Java & IT management skills. (As-Ind, estab 2003, empl 10, sales $3,000,000, cert: NMSDC)

4134　Vertisystem Inc.
　　　39300 Civic Center Dr, Ste 230
　　　Fremont, CA 94538
　　　Contact: Shaloo Jeswani Sr. BDM
　　　Tel:　702-241-5131
　　　Email: shaloo@vertisystem.com
　　　Website: www.vertisystem.com
Staff Augmentation, Full-Time Placements, contract to Hire, IT Projects & Consulting. (Woman/As-Pac, estab 2008, empl 120, sales $20,000,000, cert: City, CPUC)

4135　Volante Enterprise Consulting
　　　3863 Millbrae Terr
　　　Perris, CA 92571
　　　Contact: Sheila Volante CEO
　　　Tel:　310-256-9639
　　　Email: sheilavolante@volantenc.com
　　　Website: www.volantenc.com
Scheduling Management, Risk Management, Systems Consulting, Microsoft Project Server, Microsoft Project Professional, Configuration, Office 365 + SharePoint Configuration, Project Management Office Setup & Maintenance. (Woman/AA, estab 2014, empl 2, sales , cert: State)

4136 VXI Global Solutions, LLC
220 W 1st St 3rd Floor
Los Angeles, CA 90012
Contact: Annette Timmins Marketing Solutions &
Sales Support
Tel: 213-637-1300
Email: annette.timmins@vxi.com
Website: www.vxi.com
Business process & information technology outsourcing,
call center & BPO services, software development, quality
assurance testing & infrastructure outsourcing. (As-Pac,
estab 1998, empl 30000, sales , cert: NMSDC)

4137 Webbege, Inc.
7851 Mission Center Ct Ste 108
San Diego, CA 92108
Contact: Francis Geraci President
Tel: 619-786-7075
Email: frank.geraci@webbege.com
Website: www.webbege.com
Web Design, Development, and Online Marketing. (Hisp,
estab 2011, empl 7, sales $300,000, cert: NMSDC)

4138 WINTEC Software Corporation
3333 Bowers Ave, Ste 189
Santa Clara, CA 95054
Contact: Narender Ramarapu CEO
Tel: 408-988-1600
Email: narender@winteccorp.com
Website: www.winteccorp.com
Information technology consulting & staffing, contract
computer programming, software application develop-
ment & training, system & database administration. (As-
Ind, As-Pac, estab 1998, empl 56, sales $3,320,000, cert:
8a)

4139 WMBE Payrolling, dba TargetCW
9475 Chesapeake Dr
San Diego, CA 92123
Contact: Dave Bakkeby SVP, Business Developmen
Tel: 858-810-8038
Email: dave.bakkeby@targetcw.com
Website: www.targetcw.com
Payrolling of contingent workers identified by our clients.
Employer of record for temporary workers and contractors
already sourced across the US and overseas. (Woman,
estab 2009, empl 12, sales $200,000, cert: State)

4140 Xavient Information Systems, Inc.
2125 Madera Rd, Ste B
Simi Valley, CA 93065
Contact: Melissa Montejano Dir Admin
Tel: 805-955-4140
Email: melissa@xavient.com
Website: www.xavient.com
Application development & integration, testing & quality
assurance, IT infrastructure support, application support,
core telecom engineering services. (As-Pac, estab 2003,
empl 2200, sales $40,000,000, cert: NMSDC)

4141 Xinnovit Inc.
21001 San Ramon Valley Blvd, Ste A4-103
San Ramon, CA 94583
Contact: Client Relations Mgr
Tel: 925-236-2310
Email:
Website: www.xinnovit.com
Information technology services: application development,
systems & database management, data warehousing &
quality assurance. (Woman/As-Ind, estab 2002, empl 165,
sales $12,000,000, cert: NMSDC)

4142 Yadari Enterprises
728 Texas St, Ste 3
Fairfield, CA 94533
Contact: Tara Lynn Gray President
Tel: 707-398-6478
Email: tara@yadari.com
Website: www.yadari.com
Web development, databasese, report writing, business
intelligence, visual data displays, management consult-
ing, graphic design, electronic health record, diagnostic
imaging systems, laboratory systems, pharmacy systems.
(Woman/AA, estab 2004, empl 3, sales $310,000, cert:
State, CPUC)

Colorado

4143 Advance IT Network Solutions LLC
4600 S Syracuse St Ste 900
Denver, CO 80237
Contact: Dwight Cunningham CEO
Tel: 303-846-3071
Email: dwight@advanced-it-solutions.com
Website: www.advanced-it-solutions.com
Computer Systems Design Services, Computer Facilities
Management Services, Security Consulting Services,
Computer & Computer Peripheral Equip & Software. (AA,
estab 2005, empl 3, sales $800,000, cert: State)

4144 Aspen Capital Company, Inc.
530 North Jefferson Ave Unit A
Loveland, CO 80537
Contact: Peggy Tomcheck
Tel: 303-716-2898
Email: plapp@aspencapitalcompany.com
Website: www.aspencapitalcompany.com
Custom asset tracking & invoicing solutions, educational
laptop program lease structures, unique iPad refresh
programs, consignment solutions, electronic invoicing &
billing processes, web based equipment stores. (Woman,
estab 2001, empl 8, sales $10,385,908, cert: WBENC)

4145 Aureus Tech Systems, LLC
17593 E Euclid Ave
Aurora, CO 80016
Contact: Sujata Bhattarai CEO
Tel: 816-373-1979
Email: sujata@aureustechsystems.com
Website: http://aureustechsystems.com
Customized & needs-based reporting dashboard, Web-
based, & and near real-time reporting tools, overall
performance optimization reducing lag times & frivolous
resource allocation. (Woman/As-Ind, estab 2008, empl
35, sales $2,316,830, cert: WBENC)

4146 BCM Global Technologies Consultants, Inc.
9457 S University Blvd, Ste 329
Highlands Ranch, CO 80126
Contact: President
Tel: 866-761-8880
Email:
Website: www.bcmglobaltech.com
Provide technical resources & solutions. (Woman/AA,
estab 2008, empl 20, sales $1,550,000, cert: NMSDC,
WBENC, NWBOC, 8a)

4147 Bross Group LLC
      200 Union Blvd, Ste 200
      Lakewood, CO 80228
      Contact: Cathy Fligger Sr. Acct Exec
      Tel: 303-945-2700
      Email: sales@brossgroup.com
      Website: www.brossgroup.com
Information technology consulting & staffing. (Woman,
estab 2004, empl 50, sales $3,094,000, cert: WBENC,
NWBOC)

4148 Daniels & Patterson Corporate Search Inc.
      1732 Marion St
      Denver, CO 80218
      Contact: Ruby Chavez Patterson President
      Tel: 303-830-1230
      Email: dpsearch@nilenet.com
      Website: www.dp-search.com
Permanent & temp human resources providing EDP, MIS,
IS, telecommunications, clerical/office support & contract
personnel. (Woman/Hisp, estab 1985, empl 25, sales , cert:
State)

4149 DCM Technology Solutions, Inc.
      17011 Moorside Dr
      Parker, CO 80134
      Contact: Leslie Kleyweg President
      Tel: 303-325-5202
      Email: info@dcmsolution.com
      Website: www.dcmsolution.com
IT services: staffing, low voltage wiring, networking &
computer repair/maintenance. (Woman, estab 2002, empl
5, sales $550,000, cert: WBENC)

4150 HD Communications LLC
      2140 S Platte River Dr
      Denver, CO 80223
      Contact: Michael Dominguez President
      Tel: 303-756-4388
      Email: mikeh@hdcom.org
      Website: http://hdcom.org
Audio Video Design & Installation. (Hisp, estab 2003, empl
10, sales $2,000,000, cert: 8a)

4151 Istonish
      5500 Greenwood Plaza Blvd
      Greenwood Village, CO 80108
      Contact: Shannon Hickey Business Devel Exec
      Tel: 720-529-4550
      Email: shickey@istonish.com
      Website: www.istonish.com
Technical resources: staff augmentation, perm placement,
vendor mgmt svcs, IT solutions, project based svcs,
customer call ctr svcs. (Woman/Nat Ame, Hisp, estab
1990, empl 100, sales $6,883,874, cert: NMSDC, WBENC)

4152 Jenco Technologies
      3720 Sinton Rd, Ste 203
      Colorado Springs, CO 80907
      Contact: Dan McOmber Acct Mgr
      Tel: 719-471-1200
      Email: dan@jencotech.com
      Website: www.jencotech.com
Hardware & software procurement, LAN connectivity,
maintenance & monitoring, computer configurations &
maintenance. (Woman, estab 2000, empl 5, sales
$1,595,000, cert: State)

4153 Managed Business Solutions
      12325 Oracle Blvd, Ste 200
      Colorado Springs, CO 80921
      Contact: Jane Kovalik Marketing Mgr
      Tel: 719-314-3400
      Email: diversity@mbshome.com
      Website: www.mbshome.com
IT managed svcs: IT infrastructure support, multi-
vendor/platform system admin, storage mgmt & admin,
SAN engineering & design, server consolidation, open
view service desk support, project mgmt, data center
operations & mgmt. (Nat Ame, estab 1993, empl 101,
sales $14,491,000, cert: NMSDC)

4154 Maven Companies
      1880 Office Club Pointe
      Colorado Springs, CO 80920
      Contact: Manish Kochhar President
      Tel: 719-884-0102
      Email: diversity@mavenco.com
      Website: www.mavenco.com
IT consulting, Project Management & Business Analysis
(PM Coordination, Change and Release Management,
Process Analysis), ERP Development & Support (Oracle,
PeopleSoft, SAP),Business Intelligence (Business Objects,
Cognos, Microstrategy, Crystal Reports). (As-Pac, estab
2003, empl 30, sales $3,000,000, cert: NMSDC)

4155 netRelevance LLC
      4865 Hidden Rock Rd
      Colorado Springs, CO 80908
      Contact: Dir Business Dev
      Tel: 719-488-5742
      Email:
      Website: www.netrelevance.com
Wireless Network Site Surveys, Design, Installation &
Support, Network Equipment Installations and Startup,
Computer Room and Data Center Design and Installation, Copper and Fiber Cabling, Performing Network
refresh/upgrades, IP Surveillance. (Hisp, estab 2007,
empl 9, sales $2,679,948, cert: NMSDC)

4156 Rearden Logic Inc.
      2010 E 17th Ave Unit 1
      Denver, CO 80206
      Contact: Kristopher Schehr Principal
      Tel: 720-515-3289
      Email: kschehr@reardenlogic.com
      Website: www.reardenlogic.com
Offensive Cyber, Defensive Cyber, Networks, Reverse
Engineering, TS//SCI, Software Defined Radio SDR,
FPGA, TCP/IP, Coding, C++, Assembly ASM, Training, RF,
Radio Frequency, Ettus, USRP, LTE, GSM, GPS, Satellite,
IoT, GNURadio, Xmidas. (Hisp, estab 2013, empl 5, sales
$537,000, cert: 8a)

4157 RTL Networks
      1391 Speer Blvd #850
      Denver, CO 80204
      Contact: Jason Sand Sr Sales Associate
      Tel: 303-757-3100
      Email: jsand@rtl-networks.com
      Website: www.rtl-networks.com
Resell hardware & software, network architecture
planning, design & implementation, network security,
framework dev, program & project mgmt, cable splicing
& installation. (AA, estab 2002, empl 50, sales
$1,500,000, cert: State)

4158   Sedulus Group LLC
19511 Good Life View
Calhan, CO 80808
Contact: Julian Candia CEO
Tel: 719-505-8419
Email: julian.candia@cyberlogistix.com
Website: https://cyberlogistix.com
Cybersecurity expertise and operations. (Hisp, estab 2019, empl 3, sales , cert: NMSDC)

4159   Source One Management Inc.
1225 Seventeenth St, Ste 1500
Denver, CO 80202
Contact: Larry Woodburn Business Dev Mgr
Tel: 303-832-8600
Email: lwoodburn@sourceone.com
Website: www.sourceone.com
Contract mgmt admin support svcs: records mgmt, document mgmt, correspondence control, litigation support, information technology, data mgmt, copy & print ctr mgmt, meeting svcs, video conferencing, call ctr, shipping & receiving, bar coding. (Hisp, estab 1985, empl 270, sales $12,758,000, cert: State)

4160   Systems Research Group
740 Wooten Rd, Ste 108
Colorado Springs, CO 80915
Contact: Ken Sandoval Dir Business Dev
Tel: 719-596-0737
Email: ksandoval@srgcorp.com
Website: www.srgcorp.com
IT systems operations & administrative support, reprographics in-house operations. (Hisp, estab 1986, empl 78, sales $7,000,000, cert: State)

4161   The 'Apps' Consultants Inc.
6909 S Holly Circle Ste 350
Centennial, CO 80112
Contact: Kiran Pingali President
Tel: 303-502-5407
Email: kiran@appsconsultants.com
Website: www.appsconsultants.com
IT consulting, ERP/ CRM & Business Intelligence. (Woman/As-Ind, estab 2005, empl 4, sales $546,846, cert: City)

4162   Tukuh Technologies
5045 List Dr
Colorado Springs, CO 80919
Contact: Dan Beard Dir Business Devel
Tel: 210-383-5839
Email: dan.beard@tepa.com
Website: www.tukuh.com
Information technology, Unmanned aerial systems (UAS) for data collection, Survey support, Remote sensing, GIS, Mapping, GPS, Simulation, Visualization, Analytics, 3D-printed terrain models, GIS-embedded video. (Nat Ame, estab 2013, empl 18, sales $478,000, cert: 8a)

4163   Y2Fox, Inc
7900 E Union Ave, Ste 1100
Denver, CO 80237
Contact: Managing Dir
Tel: 720-436-2288
Email:
Website: www.y2fox.com
Strategic software development, Cloud Computing, Cyber Security, OEM (Microsoft, Oracle, and others) Hardware, and Software licensing reseller. Information Technology application support, Big data management. (AA, estab 2008, empl 25, sales , cert: 8a)

Connecticut

4164   Agilus Global Services, LLC
35 E Main St, Ste 352
Avon, CT 06001
Contact: Dennis Williams CEO
Tel: 860-404-0476
Email: dwilliams@agilusglobal.com
Website: www.agilusglobalservices.com
IT consulting/staffing & recruiting services. (AA, estab 2015, empl 1, sales , cert: NMSDC)

4165   Aquinas Consulting, LLC
154 Herbert St
Milford, CT 06460
Contact: Dir of HR
Tel: 203-876-7822
Email:
Website: www.aquinasconsulting.com
IT & engineering consulting & staffing. (Woman/As-Pac, estab 2000, empl 27, sales $3,045,910, cert: State)

4166   Aspire Systems
36 Mill Plain Rd
Danbury, CT 06811
Contact: Laura Del Corpo VP Business Dev
Tel: 732-406-4284
Email: laura@aspiresystem.com
Website: www.aspiresystem.com
Information Technology, Staff Augmentation, Technology Deployment & Enterprise support. (As-Pac, estab 2002, empl 45, sales $5,000,000, cert: NMSDC)

4167   Dudas IT Resources & Advisory, Inc.
117 Butternut Lane
Stamford, CT 06903
Contact: Liz Chait CEO
Tel: 203-653-2739
Email: liz@zarit.com
Website: http://zarit.org
Information technology staffing & consulting services. (Woman, estab 2005, empl 8, sales $6,389,623, cert: WBENC)

4168   eRichards Consulting LLC
1381 Burr St Ste 390
Fairfield, CT 06824
Contact: Doreen F. Gebbia President
Tel: 203-944-0816
Email: dgebbia@erichards.com
Website: www.eRichards.com
IT consulting: strategic assessment, internet strategy, application development, project management, IT governance, web development & staff augmentation. (Woman, estab 1996, empl 3, sales , cert: WBENC)

4169   InfoLynx Services, Inc.
325 Danbury Rd
New Milford, CT 06776
Contact: Uelysee Scantling Dir of Sales
Tel: 860-210-1203
Email: contact@infolynx.com
Website: www.infolynx.com
Technical services: project mgmt, technical configuration, system & application engineering, performance tuning, desktop support. (AA, estab 1994, empl 75, sales $6,200,000, cert: State)

4170 iTech Solutions, Inc.
20 Stanford Dr
Farmington, CT 06032
Contact: Salil Sankaran President
Tel: 703-638-1346
Email: salil.sankaran@itechsolutions.com
Website: www.itechsolutions.com
Information technology staffing, consulting & recruting
services. (Minority, Woman, estab 1995, empl 115, sales
$14,092,608, cert: NMSDC, WBENC)

4171 JANUS Software, Inc. (d/b/a JANUS Associates)
2 Omega Dr
Stamford, CT 06907
Contact: Patricia Fisher President & CEO
Tel: 203-251-0200
Email: patfisher@janusassociates.com
Website: www.janusassociates.com
Information & telecommunications security solutions; risk
analysis & disaster recovery planning; computer forensics
& fraud investigations; information mgmt strategies;
identity authentication software. (Woman, estab 1988,
empl 20, sales , cert: WBENC)

4172 Nadicent Technologies LLC
2389 Main St
Glastonbury, CT 06033
Contact: Frank Gomes Director
Tel: 860-659-2600
Email: frank.gomes@nadicent.com
Website: www.nadicent.com
Advanced Managed Security, Conferencing, Video, Web &
Audio, Cloud Services, Disaster Recovery, Help Desk
Services, Microsoft Azure, Office 365 Enterprise Suites,
Data Centers, Colocation, Infrastructure. (As-Pac, estab
2003, empl 10, sales $9,000,000, cert: NMSDC)

4173 OutSecure Inc.
Shelton Pointe, 2 Trap Falls Rd Ste 401
Shelton, CT 06484
Contact: Pamela Gupta President
Tel: 203-816-8061
Email: pamela.gupta@outsecure.com
Website: www.outsecure.com
Cyber Security assessment & security programs, risk
assessments. (As-Pac, estab 2003, empl 7, sales $300,000,
cert: NMSDC)

4174 PCC Technology Group
2 Barnard Lane
Bloomfield, CT 06002
Contact: Jo Gumbs Marketing Coord
Tel: 860-466-7261
Email: jomal.gumbs@pcctg.com
Website: www.pcctg.com
Software development. (AA, As-Pac, estab 1995, empl 50,
sales , cert: NMSDC)

4175 PCNet, Inc.
100 Technology Dr
Trumbull, CT 06611
Contact: VP Finance/Operations
Tel: 203-452-8559
Email: teric@pcnet-inc.com
Website: www.pcnet-inc.com
Network systems integrator; e-commerce, Internet/
Intranet; resell of personal computer products & svcs.
(Hisp, estab 1993, empl 65, sales $26,000,000, cert:
NMSDC)

4176 Safety Management Systems, Inc.
5 Eversley Ave, Ste 306
Norwalk, CT 06851
Contact: Business Dev Mgr
Tel: 203-838-8877
Email:
Website: www.sms360.com
Develop SMS360, an industry-changing, cost effective
software tool that enables any organization, large or
small, to manage its EHS program on a par with the
biggest and the best. (Woman, estab 2004, empl 9, sales
$451,000, cert: State, WBENC)

4177 Saisystems International
5 Research Dr
Shelton, CT 06484
Contact: Chirag Modi VP, Technology Services
Tel: 203-929-0790
Email: cmodi@saisystems.com
Website: www.saisystems.com
Informatation technology consulting: disaster recovery
planning, dataware & database mgmt systems, quality
assurance svcs. (Woman/As-Ind, estab 1987, empl 350,
sales $12,306,249, cert: State, NMSDC)

4178 Source IT Technologies, LLC
24 East Ave, Ste 244
New Canaan, CT 06840
Contact: Serica King CEO
Tel: 203-252-0439
Email: sking@sourceittech.com
Website: www.sourceittech.com
Technology solutions. (Woman, estab 2012, empl 7,
sales $8,696,000, cert: WBENC)

4179 Stratoserve LLC
18 Colonial Ct
Cheshire, CT 06410
Contact: Subroto Roy President
Tel: 203-768-5690
Email: subroto.roy@stratoserve.com
Website: www.stratoserve.com
consulting, research and training for the following
NAICS codes:541720,541613,611430 and is committed
to provide quick and measurable value to its clients.
(As-Pac, estab 2005, empl 1, sales , cert: NMSDC)

4180 Technosteps LLC
3 Hayes Ave Unit B
Norwalk, CT 06855
Contact: Narayan Venugopal President
Tel: 703-864-4848
Email: narayan.venugopal@technosteps.com
Website: http://technosteps.com
IT Staffing. (As-Ind, estab 2012, empl 3, sales $189,000,
cert: State)

4181 Terrelonge Mastercopy Inc.
45 Church St
Suite 302, CT 06906
Contact: Renee Lunchana CMO
Tel: 203-325-4408
Email: rlt@cdmastercopy.com
Website: www.cdmastercopy.com
CD ROM/DVD ROM replication & duplication services.
(Woman/AA, estab 2000, empl 5, sales $800,000, cert:
State)

4182   The Computer Company, Inc.
15 Commerce Dr
Cromwell, CT 06416
Contact: Eileen Hasson President
Tel: 860-635-0500
Email: ehasson@www.computercompany.net
Website: www.computercompany.net
Network engineering, internet connectivity, system firewalls & security, remote system monitoring, IT outsourcing, custom programming & integration. (Minority/Woman, estab 1995, empl 22, sales $3,750,000, cert: State, NMSDC)

4183   The Computer Support People, LLC
16 River St Upper Level
Norwalk, CT 06850
Contact: Cassandre Jean Business Development
Tel: 203-653-4643
Email: cassandre.jean@tcsp360.com
Website: http://tcsp360.com
Managed Computer Services. Computer Software & Hardware support. (Hisp, estab 2005, empl 8, sales $419,362, cert: State, NMSDC)

4184   Transcend Business Solutions, LLC
30 Grassy Plain St, Unit 5A
Bethel, CT 06801
Contact: Linda Rowan President
Tel: 203-790-5222
Email: info@transcendbus.com
Website: www.transcendbus.com
IT consulting firm & employment recruiting. (Woman, estab 2003, empl 10, sales $850,000, cert: WBENC)

4185   Virpie Inc
1449 Old Waterbury Rd
Southbury, CT 06488
Contact: Shre Thammana President
Tel: 203-264-0999
Email: shre@virpietech.com
Website: www.virpietech.com
Information technology staffing, storage area network design, architecture & administration, disaster recovery, database developers & administrators, senior & project management. (As-Pac, estab 1997, empl 150, sales $4,725,000, cert: State, NMSDC)

4186   VisionPoint LLC
152 Rockwell Rd
Newington, CT 06111
Contact: Louise Mastroianni Acct Mgr, Diversity Champion
Tel: 860-436-9673
Email: visionpointct@gmail.com
Website: www.visionpointllc.com
Technology acquisition, integration, design, installation, technical meeting support & service. (Woman, estab 2003, empl 24, sales $7,002,015, cert: WBENC)

District of Columbia

4187   A&A
20 F St NW Ste 700
Washington, DC 20001
Contact: Aditya Dahagam VP - Business & Strategy
Tel: 202-505-1431
Email:
Website: www.adincorp.com
ITSM & ITIL process improvement, Software/Application Development, IT Business Analytics, BPR, Quality Assurance, Systems Engineering, IT & Organizational Strategy. (As-Ind, estab , empl , sales , cert: State, NMSDC, 8a, SDB)

4188   Centricity Technology Partners, Inc.
621 Quackenbos St NW
Washington, DC 20011
Contact: CEO
Tel: 202-696-5270
Email:
Website: www.centricity-us.com
Cloud, Mobile & SOA Application Development, Enterprise Architecture, Program/Project Mgmt, Architecture & Engineering, Business Process Reengineering, Operations & Maintenance, IT Governance, Independent Validation & Verification. (Woman/AA, estab 2012, empl 4, sales $1,661,362, cert: WBENC, 8a)

4189   E-Logic, Inc.
1025 Connecticut Ave NW Ste 1000
Washington, DC 20036
Contact: Luis F Padilla CEO
Tel: 202-499-7837
Email: lpadilla@e-logic.us
Website: www.e-logic.us
IT Hardware, Software, System Integration, IT Services. (Hisp, estab 2007, empl 20, sales $8,500,000, cert: 8a, SDB)

4190   FWG Solutions, Inc.
1725 I St, NW Ste 520
Washington, DC 20006
Contact: Vincent L. Dixon Capture Exec
Tel: 202-391-0058
Email: vince.dixon@fwgsolutions.com
Website: www.fwgsolutions.com
Information Technology (IT) solutions, Cyber Security, Wireless Systems, and Distributed Antenna Solutions. (AA, estab 2010, empl 75, sales $5,000,000, cert: 8a)

4191   Logistics Systems Incorporated
1100 G St, NW Ste 410
Washington, DC 20005
Contact: Henry Jennings Sr VP business devel
Tel: 202-347-0821
Email: henry.jennings@logistics-sys.com
Website: www.logistics-sys.com
Integrated logistics management and life cycle support, information technology services, and program management support (AA, estab 2002, empl 125, sales $15,000,000, cert: 8a)

4192   MSys Inc.
1025 Connecticut Ave, NW Ste 1000
Washington, DC 20036
Contact: Raj Thiyagarajan Director
Tel: 202-629-0353
Email: register@msysinc.com
Website: www.msysinc.com
Software consulting, custom programming & development, web development. (As-Ind, estab 1994, empl 67, sales $5,787,890, cert: NMSDC)

4193   Optimus Technologies, LLC
700 12th St NW Ste 700
Washington, DC 20005
Contact: Donald Jones CEO
Tel: 202-263-7370
Email: djones@optimustech.net
Website: www.optimustech.net
Document scanning, black & white copy, color copy, records mgmt & retention, electronic data processing, computer forensics, foreign language document conversion, web hosting, backup tape restoration, document printing. (AA, estab 2005, empl 20, sales $8,000,000, cert: NMSDC)

4194 Peak Technology Solutions, Inc.
1627 K St, NW, Ste 400
Washington, DC 20006
Contact: Mohammad Tariq President
Tel: 202-776-7196
Email: mtariq@peaktsinc.com
Website: www.peaktsinc.com
COTS implementation, system integration, database design & application development services, Geographic Information System (GIS) solutions, and web enabled automation. (As-Ind, estab 2002, empl 9, sales $645,948, cert: State)

4195 SupreTech, Inc.
7600 Georgia Ave, NW Ste LL
Washington, DC 20012
Contact: Ignatius Ogu CEO
Tel: 202-726-7200
Email: ig.ogu@supretech.com
Website: www.supretech.com
Database development, internet/intranet solutions, custom application devel, switches, routers install, configure & support, information security engineering, LAN/WAN install & configure, Wi-Fi solutions, document mgmt. (AA, estab 2003, empl 3, sales $1,531,432, cert: 8a)

4196 The ELOCEN Group
1341 H St, NE Ste 301
Washington, DC 20002
Contact: Taryn Lewis Dir of Operations
Tel: 202-644-8500
Email: tarynl@elocengroup.com
Website: www.elocengroup.com
Program & Project Management, Construction Management, Interior Design, Information Technology, Facilities/Logistics, and Healthcare Facilities/Logistics/Management. (Woman/AA, estab 2007, empl 62, sales $20,089,894, cert: State, City, WBENC, 8a)

4197 The Training Institute of Washington DC
1801 10 St NW
Washington, DC 20001
Contact: Belinda Pirtle Business Dev Mgr
Tel: 202-797-9099
Email: bpirtle@traindc.com
Website: www.traindc.com
Customized training, network security & project mgmt certification training, facility rentals & contract trainers. (AA, estab 2001, empl 2, sales $100,000, cert: State)

4198 VIRE Consulting Inc.
730 Quincy St NW
Washington, DC 20011
Contact: Raj Bandi Program Dir
Tel: 703-688-3008
Email: raj.bandi@vireconsulting.com
Website: www.vireconsulting.com
IT services & solutions, emerging technologies, rapid mobile application development, business intelligence & data analytics. (Hisp, estab 2008, empl 49, sales $7,000,000, cert: 8a, SDB)

4199 vTech Solution Inc
1100 H St NW Ste 750
Washington, DC 20005
Contact: Client Relation Specialist
Tel: 202-919-8964
Email:
Website: www.vtechsolution.com
IT staffing, permanent & temporary. (Woman/As-Pac, estab 2006, empl 60, sales $16,000,000, cert: State, NMSDC, SDB)

4200 vTech Solution Inc.
1100 H St, NW, Ste 750
Washington, DC 20005
Contact: Associate Mgr
Tel: 202-894-8884
Email:
Website: www.vtechsolution.com
Cloud solutions, Network Services, Security Solutions, Customized Application Services, System Integration and Professional IT Services, Project Management, Staff Augmentation and IT Infrastructure. (Nat Ame, As-Pac, estab 2006, empl 49, sales $38,800,000, cert: State, 8a)

Delaware

4201 Alpha Technologies USA, Inc.
704 N King St
Wilmington, DE 19801
Contact: Amrit Gurung COO
Tel: 302-304-8421
Email: amrit@alphait.us
Website: www.alphaIT.us
Information technology staffing & consulting, project mgmt, software devel, systems integration, datacenter mgmt. (Woman/Hisp, estab 1997, empl 200, sales $42,000,000, cert: NMSDC)

4202 DecisivEdge LLC
131 Continental Dr Ste 409
Newark, DE 19713
Contact: Michele Frayler
Tel: 302-299-1570
Email: michele.frayler@decisivedge.com
Website: www.decisivedge.com
Business consulting & technology services, business architecture & performance, business analytics, data warehouse strategy, design, development & governance, marketing analytics development. (As-Ind, estab 2007, empl 41, sales $4,739,862, cert: NMSDC)

4203 Frontier Technologies, Inc.
1521 Concord Pike Ste 302
Wilmington, DE 19803
Contact: President
Tel: 302-225-2530
Email:
Website: www.ftiusa.com
Develop & deploy integrated business solutions: front office apps, IT staff augmentation, CRM, supply chain mgmt & computer telephony. (Woman/As-Ind, estab 1989, empl 15, sales $20,000,000, cert: NMSDC, WBENC)

4204 LiivData Inc.
1201 N Orange St Ste 7065
Wilmington, DE 19801
Contact: Dominic Francis Oguejiofo CEO
Tel: 302-235-3040
Email: dom.francis@liivdata.com
Website: www.liivdata.com
Information & systems integration, communications services, Voip technology. (AA, estab 2010, empl 15, sales $3,850,000, cert: State)

Florida

4205 A. Harold and Associates, LLC
7595 Baymeadows Way
Jacksonville, FL 32256
Contact: President
Tel: 904-535-2290
Email:
Website: www.aha-llc.com
Engineering, training, e-learning, software development, aviation systems, V-22, H-60, project & program mgmt, technical publications, custom application dev, CBT, WBT. (AA, estab 2003, empl 260, sales $27,521,267, cert: SDB)

4206 Action 9-A, Inc.
10416 New Berlin Rd
Jacksonville, FL 32226
Contact: William Valentino President
Tel: 904-696-9191
Email: action9a@earthlink.net
Website: www.action9astorage.com
Moving totes/dollies rentals; specialized equipment for modular furniture; breakdown and reconfiguration for modular furniture systems; corporate moving and storage (Hisp, estab 1999, empl 12, sales $800,000, cert: NMSDC)

4207 Advanced IT Concepts, Inc.
1351 Sundial Point
Winter Springs, FL 32708
Contact: Gabriel Ruiz President
Tel: 407-914-2484
Email: eve.maldonado@aitcinc.com
Website: www.aitcinc.com
Telecommunications & Information Technology services. (Hisp, estab 2006, empl 51, sales $24,860,693, cert: City, 8a)

4208 Advanced Systems Design, Inc.
2450 Tim Gamble Pl Ste 200
Tallahassee, FL 32308
Contact: John Adams VP
Tel: 850-385-5129
Email: john.adams@asd-web.com
Website: www.asd-web.com
Operational support services, help desk & call centers, staff augmentation, web-based disease surveillance applications, network support, design & development, implementation, monitoring & management. (Nat Ame, estab 1979, empl 80, sales $7,570,227, cert: State)

4209 Almond Consulting Group
5472 Baytowne Place
Oviedo, FL 32765
Contact: Derrick Henry President & CEO
Tel: 407-602-8540
Email: derrick.henry@almondconsulting.com
Website: www.almondconsulting.com
Information technology consulting solutions: Project Management, Information Assurance, Certification & Accreditation & Process Improvement. (AA, estab 2001, empl 1, sales , cert: State, City, NMSDC)

4210 Amzur Technologies, Inc.
405 N Reo St Ste 110
Tampa, FL 33609
Contact: Bala Nemani CEO
Tel: 813-600-4060
Email: supplier@amzur.com
Website: www.amzur.com
Information technology, information security, anti-virus, firewalls, operating systems, IT services, Web e-commerce, LAN / WAN, network management, staff augmentation, servers, workflow, imaging, asset management. (Woman/As-Pac, estab 2004, empl 200, sales $22,173,714, cert: State, NMSDC)

4211 Auritas
4907 International Pkwy Ste 1051
Sanford, FL 32771
Contact: Anne Cross Dir of Mktg
Tel: 407-834-8324
Email: rfp@auritas.com
Website: www.auritas.com
SAP Consulting Services & Project Management services, Data Lifecycle Management. (Woman, estab 2003, empl 75, sales $7,400,000, cert: WBENC)

4212 Beacon Systems, Inc.
3928 Coral Ridge Dr
Coral Springs, FL 33065
Contact: Brian Tupiak Contracts Administrator
Tel: 954-426-1171
Email: info@beacongov.com
Website: www.beacongov.com
Information technology training & support, security systems, program management, performance consulting, software & program training, systems security, systems & networking engineering support, web design & development. (Woman/As-Ind, estab 2005, empl 20, sales $500,000, cert: State, NMSDC)

4213 BlueStreak Learning, LLC
P.O. Box 110435
Naples, FL 34108
Contact: President
Tel: 630-842-1865
Email:
Website: www.bluestreaklearning.com
Technology-based training programs: needs assessments, e-learning strategy, LMS selection, course development svcs, evaluation/ROI analysis. (Woman, estab 2003, empl 3, sales $500,000, cert: WBENC)

4214 Braille Works International, Inc.
941-942 Darby Lake St
Seffner, FL 33584
Contact: Marketing
Tel: 813-654-4050
Email:
Website: www.brailleworks.com
Braille, large print, audio & computerized documents. (Woman, estab 1994, empl 12, sales $1,250,000, cert: WBENC)

4215 Business Information Technology Solutions.Com
100 S. Orange Ave Ste 800
Orlando, FL 32801
Contact: Amy Seaman Acct Exec
Tel: 407-363-0024
Email: amy@abtsolutions.com
Website: www.abtsolutions.com
IT staffing. (Woman, estab 2000, empl 25, sales $4,700,000, cert: State, City)

4216 C&C International Computers and Consultants, Inc.
7777 N Davie Rd Ext Ste 100 A
Hollywood, FL 33024
Contact: Bill James President
Tel: 954-450-0023
Email: bjames@ccintercomputers.com
Website: www.ccintercomputers.com
Value Added Reseller (VAR) Services, Support Services & IT
Staffing, Computer Installations, Product Rollouts &
Deployments, Consulting Services & Project Management,
Onsite & Remote Help Desk Support. (Woman/AA, estab
1995, empl 27, sales , cert: State, City, NMSDC)

4217 Corpotel, Inc
2800 Glades Circle Ste. 146
Weston, FL 33327
Contact: Elias Benaim Sales
Tel: 954-364-7045
Email: ebenaim@corpotel.com
Website: www.corpotel.com
Telecom expense mgmt, call accounting, multi-store
telecom svcs, call center software dev, bilingual call center
outsourcing. (Hisp, estab 2001, empl 15, sales $1,000,000,
cert: NMSDC)

4218 Craig Technical Consulting, Inc.
150 N Sykes Creek Pkwy
Merritt Island, FL 32952
Contact: Greg Sheppard Dir Business Devel
Tel: 321-613-5620
Email: greg.sheppard@craigtechinc.com
Website: www.craigtechinc.com
Software Design and Development, Systems Engineering
and Integration, Multidisciplinary Engineering, Training
and Courseware Development, Modeling and Simulation,
Information Technology Support and Integrated Logistics
Support. (Woman/Hisp, estab 1999, empl 300, sales
$30,000,000, cert: NMSDC, WBENC, SDB)

4219 Curia Document Solutions LLC
815 North Homestead Blvd. Ste #646
Homestead, FL 33030
Contact: Lourdes Cox President
Tel: 888-516-5193
Email: sales@curiausa.com
Website: www.curiausa.com
On-site & Off-site Document Production & Reprographics,
Imaging Services, On-site & Offsite Scanning & Data
Conversion, Document Utilization & Coding, Document
Clustering for Review Prioritization, Auto Coding. (Woman/
Hisp, estab 2011, empl 5, sales $100,000, cert: State)

4220 Damasco Design Inc
7136 Crescent Creek Way
Coconut Creek, FL 33073
Contact: Jorge Castillo President
Tel: 954-361-6600
Email: jorge@damascodesign.com
Website: www.damasco.io
Web Application solutions & Cloud systems integration.
(Hisp, estab 2013, empl 1, sales , cert: State)

4221 Dbsys Inc.
5224 W State Rd 46, Ste 369
Sanford, FL 32771
Contact: Matthew Hudson Field Tech/Mktg
Tel: 497-322-7832
Email: matt@dbsys.com
Website: http://dbsys.com
Hardware Solutions, PCs, Notebooks, Storage & File
Servers Networking Solutions, Certified Novell Engineer,
staff Supporting Windows, Sales Solutions. (Woman,
estab 1990, empl 13, sales $2,200,000, cert: State)

4222 Digital Hands
400 N Tampa St 17th Fl
Tampa, FL 33602
Contact: Karen Krymski Dir strategic initiatives
Tel: 877-229-8020
Email: kkrymski@digitalhands.com
Website: www.digitalhands.com
Outsourced IT managed services: IT security, enterprise
data security, data loss prevention, endpoint security,
infrastructure security & management. (Woman, estab
2001, empl 25, sales $2,225,000, cert: WBENC)

4223 Easy Verification Inc.
7050 W Palmetto Park Rd Ste 15-256
Boca Raton, FL 33433
Contact: Lisa Bruno President
Tel: 877-904-7770
Email: lbruno@easyverification.com
Website: https://easyverification.com
4506-T Fulfillment, IRS Tax Transcript Verification.
Income Verification, SSN & ID Validation. Web-based
verification application. (Woman, estab 2006, empl 3,
sales , cert: State, SDB)

4224 Ebyte Technologies, Inc.
7855 NW 12th St Ste 214 & 212
Miami, FL 33126
Contact: Mgr, business devel
Tel: 786-358-9300
Email:
Website: www.ebytetechnologies.com
Technology staffing, placing contract, project solutions &
permanent placement opportunities. (Woman/As-Ind,
estab 2009, empl 70, sales $5,400,000, cert: City)

4225 Employer Management Solutions, Inc.
5550 W Executive Dr Ste 450
Tampa, FL 33609
Contact: Jennifer Johnston
Tel: 813-287-2486
Email: jjohnston@consultems.com
Website: www.consultems.com
Info technology svcs: enterprise wide initiatives; vendor
selection, software implementation & project planning
svcs. (Woman, estab 1998, empl 30, sales $4,000,000,
cert: WBENC)

4226 Enterprise Risk Management, Inc.
800 S Douglas Rd, North T s940
Coral Gables, FL 33134
Contact: Suzanne Siberon Sr Business Devel
Tel: 305-447-6750
Email: ssiberon@emrisk.com
Website: www.emrisk.com
IT Security Design and Implementation
Vulnerability Assessments Penetration Testing Social
Engineering Incident Response Planning Business
Continuity Planning Disaster Recovery (Woman/Hisp,
estab 1998, empl 18, sales $2,543,700, cert: State, City,
8a)

4227 ExecuSys, Inc.
551 S Apollo Blvd, Ste 104
Melbourne, FL 32901
Contact: Eddie Haralson President
Tel: 321-253-0077
Email: eharalson@execusys.com
Website: www.execusys.com
Software engineering & information technology services, financial management systems support & range operations cost modelling solutions. (AA, estab 1993, empl 20, sales $2,155,571, cert: State)

4228 FermiTron, Inc.
440 Plumosa Ave Ste 1020
Casselberry, FL 32707
Contact: Guilford Cantave President & CEO
Tel: 407-513-2716
Email: gcantave@fermitron.com
Website: https://fermitron.com
Commercial, industrial, medical & military/aerospace development; R&D, Analog & Digital Circuit Design, Firmware Development & Implementation, Schematic Capture, PCB Layout, RF, Wireless, Circuit Prototyping & Assembly. (AA, estab 2012, empl 6, sales $310,000, cert: State)

4229 Freedom Solutions LLC
19046 Bruce B Downs Blvd, Ste 108
Tampa, FL 33647
Contact: Kelli Covel Dir Business Dev
Tel: 404-713-7777
Email: kcovel@freedomsolutionsllc.com
Website: www.freedomsolutionsllc.com
IBM Business partner, dist IBM software & hardware, aintenance, programming services & installation services. (AA, estab 2002, empl 18, sales $12,000,000, cert: NMSDC)

4230 GDKN Corporation
9700 Stirling Road Ste 110
Cooper City, FL 33024
Contact: Gary Dhir VP
Tel: 954-985-6650
Email: gdhir@gdkn.com
Website: www.gdkn.com
Staffing: information technology, engineering, professional, administrative & clerical, IT consulting, custom application development. (As-Ind, estab 1993, empl 400, sales $18,000,000, cert: NMSDC)

4231 Global Information Technology
8905 Regents Park Dr Ste 210
Tampa, FL 33647
Contact: Aruna Ajjarapu VP
Tel: 813-973-1061
Email: araj@git-org.com
Website: www.git-org.com
IT developers, DBA's, project managers & architects. (Woman/As-Pac, estab 1995, empl 300, sales $36,000,000, cert: State)

4232 ICG Software Corporation
2860 W State Rd 84 Ste 113
Fort Lauderdale, FL 33312
Contact: Tiffany Nutt Office Mgr
Tel: 305-933-9100
Email: info@icgsoftware.us
Website: www.icgsoftware.us
Mfr Point of Sale Software & Hardware for the retail and restaurant industry. (Woman/Hisp, estab 2010, empl 5, sales $200,000, cert: State)

4233 ITG Global, LLC
11235 St. Johns Industrial Pkwy N Ste 2A
Jacksonville, FL 32246
Contact: Joseph Lukowski CEO
Tel: 904-425-4760
Email: almaferrante@itgtec.com
Website: www.itgtec.com
Automation Design, PLC Programming, Software Development, Technologies Consulting, Motion Design, Robot programming, Data Analytics, Condition Monitoring, Control System Design, Control Panel. (Woman/Hisp, estab 2003, empl 27, sales $3,000,000, cert: NMSDC)

4234 ITTConnect Inc.
9021 Southern Orchard Rd N
Davie, FL 33328
Contact: Fabio Back CEO
Tel: 954-732-8277
Email: fabio.back@ittconnect.com
Website: www.ittconnect.com
IT Recruiting / Direct Hire / Placement, IT Staffing / Temporary Contractors. (Hisp, estab 2017, empl 2, sales , cert: State, NMSDC)

4235 Kolter Solutions
175 Middle St
Lake Mary, FL 32746
Contact: Kim Carr Partner
Tel: 407-583-9483
Email: kcarr@koltersolutions.com
Website: www.koltersolutions.com
Information Technology Staff Augmentation, Project Teams, Application Design and Development (Java, C/C++, .NET/C#), Business Analysis/Project Management/Program Management, Quality Assurance, Infrastructure/Network/Security. (Woman, estab 2010, empl 28, sales $1,300,000, cert: WBENC)

4236 Lancesoft, Inc.
8804 FAZIO CT Ste 120
TAMPA, FL 33647
Contact: Philip J Kalafut VP Healthcare Advisory
Tel: 813-449-1301
Email: phil.kalafut@lancesoft.com
Website: www.lancesoft.com
IT software, staffing & project execution. (Woman/As-Ind, As-Pac, estab 2000, empl 2000, sales $90,000,000, cert: NMSDC)

4237 LebenTech Innovative Solutions Inc.
P.O. Box 670832
Coral Springs, FL 33067
Contact: Lennox Bennett President
Tel: 954-796-7107
Email: lennox_bennett@lebentech.com
Website: www.lebentech.com
Technology consultation svcs: CAD designs, product development, RAMS analysis, R&D, FRACAS implementation, product validation, reliability testing. (AA, estab 2004, empl 6, sales $106,250, cert: State)

4238 Lodestar Solutions, Inc.
3212 W Harbor View Ave
Tampa, FL 33611
Contact: Heather Cole President
Tel: 813-415-2910
Email: hcole@lodestarsolutions.com
Website: www.lodestarsolutions.com
IBM business analytics/Cognos reseller & IBM support renewals, IBM Cognos licenses, TM1, Cognos business intelligence, FSR, SPSS, Varicent & Cognos planning. (Woman, estab 2004, empl 11, sales $3,949,751, cert: WBENC)

4239 Loricca, Inc.
      10711 Shady Preserve Dr
      Tampa, FL 33579
      Contact: Michael Whitcomb President
      Tel: 813-600-3005
      Email: mwhitcomb@loricca.com
      Website: www.loricca.com
IT Solutions for business and government, is committed to maintaining customer satisfaction, trust, and integrity. (As-Pac, estab 2004, empl 8, sales $650,000, cert: State)

4240 N2 Services Inc
      13241 Bartram Park Blvd Ste 2301
      Jacksonville, FL 32258
      Contact: Neminathan Ammaiyappan President
      Tel: 904-703-4245
      Email: nemi@n2sglobal.com
      Website: www.n2sglobal.com
Software design, development, analysis a& nd consulting services, internet application development, E-Commerce solutions, Web 2.0, n-tier architecture & rapid application development environments. (As-Pac, estab 2004, empl 140, sales $6,580,000, cert: NMSDC)

4241 Noise Consulting Group, Inc.
      9280 Bay Plaza Blvd Ste 705
      Tampa, FL 33619
      Contact: Gina Hannah CEO
      Tel: 315-491-0771
      Email: gina.hannah@noisetcd.com
      Website: www.noisetcd.com
IT staffing, consulting & systems integration, technology solutions & systems integration & implementation services. (Woman/AA, estab 2007, empl 38, sales $1,900,000, cert: State)

4242 Ospro Systems, LLC
      1327 LaFayette St Ste C
      Cape Coral, FL 33904
      Contact: Prasad Kasireddy BDM-Recruitment
      Tel: 239-309-0319
      Email: prasad@osprosys.com
      Website: www.osprosys.com
Software Implementations, Software Changes, Custom Software Development, Software validation/Testing, Maintenance and Support, Project Management, E-commerce, B2B, B2C, Custom Web Development, Application Web. (Woman/As-Ind, estab 2004, empl 70, sales $2,000,000, cert: State, NMSDC)

4243 Professional Translating Services, Inc.
      44 W Flagler St, Ste 1800
      Miami, FL 33130
      Contact: Alexandra Hunt Natl Business Dev
      Tel: 305-371-7887
      Email: ahunt@protranslating.com
      Website: www.protranslating.com
Translate documents, films & websites, interpreting services & equipment for multilingual meetings. (Woman/Hisp, estab 1973, empl 100, sales $8,800,000, cert: NMSDC)

4244 Qualex Consulting Services, Inc.
      1111 Kane Concourse Ste 320
      Bay Harbor Island, FL 33154
      Contact: Mark Miller Govt Sales
      Tel:
      Email: mark.miller@qlx.com
      Website: www.qlx.com
Software solutions & consulting services. (Woman/Hisp, estab 1995, empl 26, sales $4,700,000, cert: State, WBENC)

4245 RADgov Inc.
      6750 N Andrews Ave, Ste 200
      Fort Lauderdale, FL 33309
      Contact: Mark Smith Sr Business Mgr
      Tel: 954-691-4588
      Email: msmith@radgov.com
      Website: www.radgov.com
IT planning services, system planning, development & implementation, electronic commerce, training & support, program management. (Woman/As-Pac, estab 2005, empl 247, sales $2,900,000, cert: NMSDC, WBENC)

4246 Readix Inc.
      4134 SW 131 Ave
      Davie, FL 33330
      Contact: Javier Abuabara CFO
      Tel: 954-636-6983
      Email: javier.ab@readixtechnologies.com
      Website: www.readixtechnologies.com
Engineering svcs: electronic design, software development, mechanical design, system integration, embedded telecommunication, consulting. (Hisp, estab 2003, empl 3, sales $394,375, cert: State)

4247 RIK Data Solutions Inc.
      8875 Hidden River Pkwy Ste 300
      Tampa, FL 33637
      Contact: Chris Kambhampati Principal Architect
      Tel: 941-527-1464
      Email: krk@rds-us.com
      Website: http://rds-us.com
Datacenter Systems Integration, Cloud Brokerage Services, Software Development, Graphic Art and Design Services (for Web and Promotional products). (Woman/As-Pac, estab 2012, empl 6, sales $1,540,000, cert: NMSDC)

4248 Riley Technology Solutions, Inc.
      3030 N Rocky Point Dr W
      Tampa, FL 33607
      Contact: John Riley President
      Tel: 813-908-4190
      Email: jerile1@rileyts.com
      Website: www.rileyts.com
Managed IT equipment & services: LAN/WAN, computing design, custom software solutions & integrating systems, web-based data mining & reporting. (AA, estab 2002, empl 10, sales $7,500,000, cert: State)

4249 Rudram Engineering, Inc.
      845 Executive Lane Ste 200
      Rockledge, FL 32955
      Contact: Patel Alkesh President
      Tel: 321-735-4159
      Email: alkesh.patel@rudramengineering.com
      Website: www.rudramengineering.com
System design, development, verification & validation, EMI analysis, Concept analysis, trade studies, emerging technology research, Software development, embedded system support, Interface identification, definition, design and system safety. (As-Ind, estab , empl 20, sales $1,454,900, cert: State, NMSDC, 8a, SDB)

4250 SDI International Corp
      2500 N Military Trail,STE. 318
      Boca Raton, FL 33431
      Contact: Carmen Castillo President & CEO
      Tel: 561-288-4079
      Email: sdidiversity@sdintl.com
      Website: www.sdintl.com
Staffing & business solutions, staff augmentation, e-vendor
mgmt services. (Woman/Hisp, estab 1992, empl 1500,
sales $600,000,000, cert: NMSDC, WBENC)

4251 Securance LLC
      13904 Monroes Business Park
      Tampa, FL 33635
      Contact: Paul Ashe President
      Tel: 877-578-0215
      Email: supplydiv@securanceconsulting.com
      Website: www.securanceconsulting.com
Independent technology risk consulting & IT auditing
services. (AA, estab 2002, empl 12, sales , cert: NMSDC)

4252 SGF US Inc.
      501 Golden Isles Dr, Ste 205
      Hallandale Beach, FL 33009
      Contact: Kevin Cabrera Acct Mgr
      Tel: 954-454-7676
      Email: kcabrera@sgfglobal.com
      Website: www.sgfglobal.com
Technical recruiting & staffing. (Hisp, estab 1997, empl 90,
sales $21,929,723, cert: NMSDC)

4253 SGS Technologie
      6817 Southpoint Pkwy, Ste 2104
      Jacksonville, FL 32216
      Contact: Arun Venkatesan CEO
      Tel: 904-332-4534
      Email: bids@sgstechnologies.net
      Website: www.sgstechnologies.net
Custom Software Applications Development, Mobile Apps
Development, Website Design, Digital Marketing, SEO,
Salesforce Implementation, CRM, SharePoint Develop-
ment. (As-Pac, estab 2003, empl 150, sales $15,000,000,
cert: State, NMSDC)

4254 Simplified Technologies, LLC
      6310 Techster Blvd, Ste 2
      Fort Myers, FL 33966
      Contact: Darius Joseph Owner
      Tel: 239-210-9645
      Email: darius@simplifiedtech.biz
      Website: www.simplifiedtech.biz
Network & systems integration, Windows Servers, Small
Business Server, SQL Server, Exchange Server, Windows
Desktop, Microsoft Office & Office 365. (AA, estab 2010,
empl 10, sales , cert: State)

4255 Sonoi Solutions LLC
      800 6th St N
      St. Petersburg, FL 33701
      Contact: Vienggeun Gertsch President
      Tel: 727-341-5100
      Email: vienggeun.gertsch@sonoisolutions.com
      Website: www.sonoisolutions.com
IT aggregation, logistics & technical services for supply
chain diversification. (Woman/As-Pac, estab 2013, empl 2,
sales , cert: NMSDC, WBENC)

4256 Southeastern Aerospace Services, LLC
      1816 SW 7th Ave
      Pompano Beach, FL 33060
      Contact: Julian Tucker Acctability Mgr
      Tel: 305-992-8257
      Email: sales@southeasternaerospace.com
      Website: www.southeasternaerospace.com
Southeastern Aerospace Services, LLC., is a certified FAA
Repair Station, FAA 145 Cert 8SIR251C. As an independent MRO facility, we provide repair and overhaul of
military and commercial aircraft power generating units,
ranging from regional to wide/nar (AA, estab 2016, empl
4, sales , cert: NMSDC)

4257 SpendCheQ, Inc.
      3171 Jasmine Dr
      Delray Beach, FL 33483
      Contact: Mary Ellen Mitchell President
      Tel: 561-870-3171
      Email: mmitchell@spendcheq.com
      Website: www.spendcheq.com
Integrated supply chain & procurement solutions,
Catalog Management, Inventory Data Management,
Supplier Information Management & Spend Analysis.
(Woman, estab 2014, empl 19, sales $321,000, cert:
State, WBENC)

4258 SRR International, Inc.
      6649 Indian Trail Dr
      Loxahatchee, FL 33470
      Contact: Rekha Jadala President
      Tel: 561-228-8349
      Email: rekha@srrintl.com
      Website: www.srrintl.com
Systems Architecture Design, Mobile & Web App
Development, Information Architecture, Hardware and
Software Maintenance. (Woman/As-Ind, estab 2001,
empl 5, sales $750,000, cert: 8a)

4259 SurfBigData LLC
      4474 Foxtail Ln
      Weston, FL 33331
      Contact: Andrew Li CEO
      Tel: 954-353-5599
      Email: service@surfbigdata.com
      Website: www.surfbigdata.com
Enterprise Workflow Analysis, Information Technology,
Architecture & System Integration, Dev/Ops & Agile
Scrum Plan & Management, Web Application Develop-
ment, Central Information Repository Design, Big Data
Platform design. (As-Pac, estab 2015, empl 6, sales
$480,000, cert: State)

4260 Synergy Technologies, LLC
      9600 W Sample Rd, Ste 207
      Coral Springs, FL 33065
      Contact: Srikaanth Bollampally Program Mgr
      Tel: 954-775-0064
      Email: sri.b@synergytechs.net
      Website: http://synergyteks.com
Synergy Technologies has excellent domain competen-
cies in verticals such as Banking & Financial Service,
Insurance & Healthcare, and Manufacturing. As a diverse
end-to-end IT solutions provider, offers a range of
expertise aimed at helping customers re-en (Woman/As-
Ind, estab 2006, empl 65, sales $5,000,000, cert:
NMSDC, WBENC)

4261   System Soft Technologies, Inc
3000 Bayport Dr Ste 840
Tampa, FL 33607
Contact: Sreedhar Veeramachaneni CEO
Tel: 727-723-0801
Email: v.sreedhar@sstech.us
Website: www.sstech.us
Software development & IT services. (As-Pac, estab 2000, empl 800, sales $67,964,203, cert: State, NMSDC)

4262   SYSTEMiQ Solutions
101 S Garland Ave Ste 108
Orlando, FL 32801
Contact: Troy Woods President
Tel: 407-607-0080
Email: troy.woods@systemiqsolutions.com
Website: www.systemiqsolutions.com
DoDAF, Systems Engineering, Requirements Management, Engineering Standards, Modeling and Simulation, Testing. (AA, estab 2016, empl 3, sales , cert: SDB)

4263   Tech Army, LLC
7777 Davie RdExtension Ste 303B
Hollywood, FL 33024
Contact: Jay Narang CEO
Tel: 954-372-2698
Email: sales@techarmy.com
Website: www.techarmy.com
IT consulting and staffing augmentation. (As-Ind, estab 2016, empl 18, sales , cert: NMSDC, 8a)

4264   Techno-Transfers of Florida, Inc.
4609 NW 26th Ave
Boca Raton, FL 33434
Contact: Virginia Mendiola Director
Tel: 561-212-2383
Email: vmendiola@techno-transfers.com
Website: http://techno-transfers.com
IT personnel for temporary contract, temp-to-perm roles & full-time positions. (Woman/Hisp, estab 1992, empl 6, sales $350,000, cert: State)

4265   Tec-Link
16350 BB Downs Blvd, Ste 48942
Tampa, FL 33646
Contact: Derek Holmes President
Tel: 813-929-3222
Email: derek@tec-link.com
Website: www.tec-link.com
Information technology professional services & consulting. (AA, estab 1999, empl 20, sales $2,000,000, cert: NMSDC)

4266   Tenosar Corportation
3259 Progress Dr Ste 142
Orlando, FL 32826
Contact: Negron Raymond President
Tel: 407-347-2333
Email: raymondnegron@tenosar.com
Website: www.Tenosar.com
Software Engineering, customized & legacy system integration. (Hisp, estab 2012, empl 8, sales $160,000, cert: 8a, SDB)

4267   Tropical Surveillance & Investigations, Inc.
1813 N Tampa St
Tampa, FL 33602
Contact: JC Dominguez
Tel: 813-282-0074
Email: jc@tsilegal.com
Website: www.tsilegal.com
Process serving & document repoduction. (Woman/Hisp, estab 2003, empl 15, sales $1,100,000, cert: NMSDC)

4268   Vitaver and Associates, Inc.
401 East Las Olas Boulevard Ste 1400
Fort Lauderdale, FL 33301
Contact: Pablo Vitaver CEO
Tel: 954-382-0075
Email: pablo@vitaver.com
Website: www.vitaver.com
IT staff augmentation & software outsourcing. (Hisp, estab 1993, empl 15, sales $8,309,079, cert: State)

4269   Widescope Consulting And Contracting Services LLC
14466 Kandi Ct
Largo, FL 33774
Contact: Donald Jackson VP Operations
Tel: 813-374-5205
Email: donald.jackson@widescopeccs.com
Website: http://widescopeccs.com/
IT, Cyber Security, Submarine Fiber optic cable route survey, engineering, professional services and consulting to government entities and large corporations. (AA, estab 2014, empl 6, sales , cert: 8a)

Georgia

4270   1Source International, LLC
925 Woodstock Rd Ste 150
Roswell, GA 30075
Contact: Margaret Tinsley VP Operations
Tel: 770-733-1202
Email: mtinsley@1source-intl.net
Website: www.1sourceinternational.com
Audio, video & conferencing solutions. (Woman, estab 2000, empl 11, sales $6,000,000, cert: WBENC)

4271   24X7SYSTEMS, Inc.
1080 Holcombe Bridge Rd Bldg 200, Ste 150
Roswell, GA 30076
Contact: Ranjan Dattagupta EVP
Tel: 678-234-2711
Email: ranjan@24x7systems.com
Website: www.24x7systems.com
Information technology solutions, Resource Sourcing, PM, Entr Arch, Application Software Development, Systems Integration & developing SCAM (Security, Cloud, Analytics Mobility) emerging solutions. (As-Ind, estab 2000, empl 20, sales $4,000,000, cert: 8a)

4272   3i People, Inc.
5755 N Point Pkwy Ste 234
Alpharetta, GA 30022
Contact: Buvi Raj CMO
Tel: 678-628-4810
Email: rbuvi@3ipeople.com
Website: www.3ipeople.com
IT consulting, application dev, project mgmt & contract staffing. (As-Pac, estab 2002, empl 220, sales $12,300,000, cert: NMSDC)

4273   Accretive Technologies, Inc.
330 Research Ct Ste 250
Norcross, GA 30092
Contact: Claire Ehrhardt President
Tel: 678-328-2440
Email: claire@accretive.com
Website: www.accretive.com
Information technology consulting & placement services. (Woman, estab 1997, empl 17, sales $1,857,679, cert: WBENC)

4274 ACS Solutions
2400 Meadowbrook Pkwy
Duluth, GA 30096
Contact: Akshay Reddy Dir Business Dev
Tel: 630-605-4731
Email: akshay.reddy@acsicorp.com
Website: www.acsicorp.com
IT services: staffing, payrolling, vendor management services, consulting & business solutions. (As-Ind, estab 1998, empl 17000, sales $683,000,000, cert: NMSDC)

4275 Adroix Corp DBA CodeForce 360
3970 Old Milton Parkway, Ste 200 Ste 200
Alpharetta, GA 30005
Contact: Dickson-Lemond VP Sales
Tel: 470-407-4189
Email: amandad@codeforce.com
Website: www.codeforce.com/
IT Staffing & Talent Management. (As-Ind, estab 2010, empl 250, sales $30,000,000, cert: NMSDC)

4276 All Points Logistics, Inc.
2567 Athens Hwy
Gainesville, GA 30507
Contact: Phil Monkress Dir info tech
Tel: 770-503-7474
Email: pmonkress@allpointslogistics.com
Website: www.allpointslogistics.com
Logistics, supply chain mgmt, inventory control, hardware & software procurement, integration, maintenance & warranty, help desk & computer center technical support, systems admin & mgmt support. (Nat Ame, estab 1997, empl 110, sales $21,000,000, cert: State)

4277 Analysts International Corporation (AIC)
2400 Meadowbrook Parkway
Duluth, GA 55435
Contact: Vicki Bien Sr Director - Marketing and Sales Enablement
Tel: 800-800-5044
Email: diversitysupplier@aictalent.com
Website: www.analysts.com
Information technology (IT) services. (As-Ind, estab 1966, empl 350, sales $695,000,000, cert: NMSDC)

4278 Arete Technology Solutions, Inc. dba STATEMENT
3379 Peachtree RdNE Ste 555
Atlanta, GA 30326
Contact: Kendall Flagg Principal
Tel: 800-640-5589
Email: kendall.flagg@statementcorp.com
Website: www.statementcorp.com
Software & IT consulting, Architecture Custom software development Automated Testing Continuous Development and Integration Oracle Database Development noSql Development Services Native tablet/mobile iOS. (AA, estab 2007, empl 12, sales $1,641,519, cert: NMSDC)

4279 Arion Systems, Inc.
2741 Calloway Ct
Duluth, GA 30097
Contact: Michael Brewington II President
Tel: 770-569-3434
Email: michael.brewington@arioncorp.com
Website: www.ArionCorp.com
Implementation & systems integration consulting: business applications & ERP products, PeopleSoft, SAP, Oracle, Siebel, technology solutions, financials, supply chain mgmt, human capital mgmt, enterprise performance mgmt. (Woman/AA, estab 2003, empl 10, sales $2,000,000, cert: NMSDC)

4280 ASAP Solutions Group, LLC
3885 Holcomb Bridge Rd
Norcross, GA 30092
Contact: Nancy Williams CEO
Tel: 770-246-1718
Email: nancy@myasap.com
Website: www.myasap.com
IT staff augmentation. (Woman, estab 1989, empl 800, sales $60,000,000, cert: CPUC, WBENC)

4281 Blaze Information Systems Inc.
13026 Dartmore Ave
Alpharetta, GA 30005
Contact: Smita Deshpande CEO
Tel: 877-877-5293
Email: smita.deshpande@blazeinfosys.com
Website: www.blazeinfosys.com
Onsite Technical Support, Onsite Temporary Technology Staffing, Remote Temporary Technology Staffing, End-To-End e-Business Solutions. (Woman/As-Pac, estab 2009, empl 5, sales $116,000, cert: State)

4282 BlueFletch LLC
621 North Ave NE Ste A-150
Atlanta, GA 30308
Contact: Richard Makerson Managing Partner
Tel: 855-529-6349
Email: invoices@bluefletch.com
Website: https://bluefletch.com
Mobile software development, program leadership, business analysis, mobile web application development, legacy integration, MDM management & cloud infrastructure integration. (AA, estab 2008, empl 34, sales $2,906,767, cert: NMSDC)

4283 Capricorn Systems, Inc.
3569 Habersham At Northlake Bldg K
Tucker, GA 30084
Contact: Charles Goldman VP Sales
Tel: 678-514-1080
Email: cgoldman@capricornsys.com
Website: www.capricornsys.com
Software consulting: staff augmentation, turnkey custom application develpment & permanent placements, on site, offsite & off-shore. (As-Ind, As-Pac, estab 1991, empl 155, sales $3,250,000, cert: NMSDC)

4284 Cellworx LLC
1005 Alderman Ste 110
Alpharetta, GA 30005
Contact: Chandrasekhar Anchala
Tel: 678-254-9094
Email: csanchala@celworx.com
Website: www.celworx.com
Wireless & wireline technology design, development, validation & realization, Software Defined Network, Cloud & Virtualization. (As-Ind, estab 2008, empl 10, sales $500,000, cert: NMSDC, CPUC)

4285 Charter Global Inc.
One Glenlake Parkway Ste 525
Atlanta, GA 30328
Contact: Dev Shah Client Engagement Mgr
Tel: 770-326-9933
Email: dshah@charterglobal.com
Website: www.charterglobal.com
Software consulting svcs: client server, web based, e-commerce. (As-Ind, As-Pac, estab 1994, empl 1100, sales $45,000,000, cert: NMSDC)

4286   CI² Aviation, Inc.
       9 Dunwoody Park Dr, Ste 104
       Dunwoody, GA 30338
       Contact: Michael Baylis CEO
       Tel: 770-425-2267
       Email: mbaylis@ci2.com
       Website: www.ci2.com
CI² Aviation aspires to be one of the nations leading and
award winning aerospace companies. Among areas of
involvement in the aerospace industry, CI² Aviation
operates 21 Air Traffic Control Towers on behalf of the FAA
and other government entities. Th (Woman/AA, estab
1993, empl 160, sales , cert: NMSDC)

4287   CI2, Inc.
       200 Galleria Pkwy, Ste 1200
       Atlanta, GA 30339
       Contact: Sharon Mendon VP bus devel
       Tel: 770-425-2267
       Email: info2@ci2.com
       Website: www.ci2.com
Systems integration & engineering, telecommunications
mgmt. (Woman/AA, estab 1993, empl 83, sales
$25,000,000, cert: State, City, NMSDC)

4288   CIYIS LLC
       5 Concourse Parkway Ste 3046
       Atlanta, GA 30328
       Contact: Christian Sellu CEO
       Tel: 678-619-1980
       Email: christian.sellu@ciyis.net
       Website: http://ciyis.net
SAP ECC, SAP HANA, Program Management, Technical
Advisory, (AA, estab 2013, empl 4, sales , cert: 8a)

4289   Competent Systems Inc.
       4080 McGinnis Ferry Rd Ste 1504
       Alpharetta, GA 30005
       Contact: Sridhar Konkala Mgr
       Tel: 678-691-7120
       Email: skonkala@competentsystems.com
       Website: http://competentsystems.com
Information Technology Consulting, Development,
Outsourcing & Technology Staffing. (As-Pac, estab 2004,
empl 150, sales $15,000,000, cert: NMSDC)

4290   Concept Software & Services Inc
       11600 Atlantis Place Ste E
       Alpharetta, GA 30022
       Contact: Ravindra Bhave CEO
       Tel: 770-300-9486
       Email: ravi@concept-inc.com
       Website: www.concept-inc.com
Software solutions, IT consulting, application outsourcing
& enterprise consulting services. (As-Ind, estab 1998, empl
57, sales $7,682,520, cert: NMSDC)

4291   Corpnet Consulting LLC
       2300 Lakeview Pkwy, Ste 700
       Alpharetta, GA 30009
       Contact: Faisal Ansari Managing Principal
       Tel: 678-795-1612
       Email: corpnet@corpnetconsulting.com
       Website: www.corpnetconsulting.com
Information security & risk management consultancy
services, IT platform integration services. (Woman/As-Pac,
estab 2008, empl 15, sales $1,300,000, cert: WBENC)

4292   Datamatics Consultants Inc.
       3505 Duluth Park Ln Ste 200
       Duluth, GA 30096
       Contact: Frank Kulendran Business Dev Mgr
       Tel: 770-232-9460
       Email: frank@datamatics.us
       Website: www.datamatics.us
Business process management, financial management,
CRP, ERP, consulting & strategy, architecture & integration, custom systems dev, supply chain mgmt, knowledge mgmt, IT strategy, re-engineering & migration
services, maintenance. (As-Ind, estab 1993, empl 95,
sales $10,000,000, cert: NMSDC)

4293   Dataset, Inc.
       145 Noble Ct Ste 100
       Alpharetta, GA 30005
       Contact: Azhar Syed President
       Tel: 678-240-0771
       Email: azhar_syed@dataset-inc.com
       Website: www.datasetcorp.com
Professional consulting services, software & hardware
installation, software training & temporary contractors.
(As-Ind, estab 1994, empl 7, sales $3,009,031, cert:
NMSDC)

4294   Dominus Gray, LLC
       1273 Mackintosh Park NW
       Atlanta, GA 30318
       Contact: Odie Gray CEO
       Tel: 404-360-7453
       Email: odie.gray@dominusgray.com
       Website: www.dominusgray.com
Cybersecurity & IT Diversity Staffing Services as well as
the development and administration of cyber security
workforce development. (AA, Hisp, estab 2020, empl 1,
sales , cert: NMSDC)

4295   DW Practice, LLC
       5901 Peachtree Dunwoody Rd Ste C-160
       Atlanta, GA 30328
       Contact: Rajani Koneru President
       Tel: 678-999-8197
       Email: raj.koneru@dwpractice.com
       Website: www.dwpractice.com
Software development services, product development
services & IT staffing services. (As-Pac, estab 1998, empl
30, sales $4,000,000, cert: NMSDC)

4296   Edge Solutions, LLC
       131 Roswell St C-101
       Alpharetta, GA 30009
       Contact: Julie Ison Haley CEO
       Tel: 888-861-8884
       Email: jhaley@edge-solutions.com
       Website: www.edge-solutions.com
Data center solutions, Application dev tools, cloud
computing, virtualization, network security, data
storage, backup and recovery, archiving, professional &
managed services. (Woman, estab 2008, empl 32, sales
$50,000,000, cert: WBENC)

4297   Enrich Inc
       3655 Brookside Pkwy Ste 265
       Alpharetta, GA 30022
       Contact: Paul Herron VP-Sales & Marketing
       Tel: 770-667-0510
       Email: info@enrich.com
       Website: www.enrich.com
Software deployment lifecycle in Oracle EBS. (Woman/
As-Pac, estab 2004, empl 200, sales $17,624,212, cert:
NMSDC)

4298   Entellimetrix LLC
       445 Victorian Lane
       Johns Creek, GA 30097
       Contact: Magha Devan Partner
       Tel: 678-779-7673
       Email: mdevan@entellimetrix.com
       Website: www.entellimetrix.com
Data Management, Business Intelligence and Analytics
Services, Teradata, Informatica, DataStage. (Woman/As-Ind,
estab 2012, empl 17, sales $2,450,000, cert: State, City,
CPUC)

4299   Exalt Integrated Technologies LLC
       P.O. Box 888161
       Atlanta, GA 30356
       Contact: Donald Maycott VP
       Tel: 678-920-3019
       Email: dmaycott@exaltit.com
       Website: www.exaltit.com
Network business consulting, organizational assessment, IT
strategic planning, telecommunications services, security
assessment, intrusion detection, firewall & DMZ implementation & management. (Woman/AA, estab 2004, empl 15,
sales $1,750,000, cert: NMSDC)

4300   Fabulous Sites, Inc.
       160 Clairemont Ave, Ste 555
       Decatur, GA 30030
       Contact: Laron Walker President
       Tel: 404-478-2050
       Email: walkerla@sciberus.com
       Website: www.sciberus.com
Information technology consulting & software develop-
ment. (AA, estab 2006, empl 5, sales $1,447,158, cert:
NMSDC, 8a)

4301   Firmament Solutions
       510 Plaza Dr
       College Park, GA 30349
       Contact: Adrian Andrews
       Tel: 770-742-0385
       Email: aandrews@firmamentsolutions.com
       Website: www.firmamentsolutions.com
Managed IT Services, Network Services, CAT3 & CAT6
Install, Hosting Software Service, Break FIX, Fiber Patch
Panel, Cloud Services, ISP Services, Conduit/Surface Mount,
IT Asset Management, Application Support, Voice/Mobile.
(AA, estab 2013, empl 10, sales , cert: State, City, NMSDC)

4302   Fulcher Interactive Group, Inc.
       2132 Weldon St
       Savannah, GA 31415
       Contact: Eric Fulcher CEO
       Tel: 912-398-3739
       Email: fulcher2132@hotmail.com
       Website:
Applications development, IT staffing, logistics support.
(AA, estab 2001, empl 2, sales $1,540,000, cert: State)

4303   Global Resource Manangement, Inc.
       5400 Laurel Springs Pkwy Ste 902
       Suwanee, GA 30024
       Contact: Naheed Syed CEO
       Tel: 678-456-6992
       Email: naheed1@grmi.net
       Website: www.grmi.net
IT consulting, telecommunications & staff augmentation.
(Woman/As-Pac, estab 1993, empl 70, sales $2,600,000,
cert: NMSDC, WBENC)

4304   Global Technology Services Group, Inc.
       2850 Barrett Lakes Blvd NW Ste 500
       Kennesaw, GA 30144
       Contact: Jacqueline Holland CEO
       Tel: 404-551-5189
       Email: jacqui@gtservices.net
       Website: www.gtservices.net
IT Asset Mgmt, Auditing, Inventory Mgmt, Warehouse &
Logistics, Project Mgmt & Deployment, Reverse Logistics
& Asset Recovery, NSA Level Data Security, Depot
Technology Hardware Repair & Refurbishment. (Woman,
estab 2010, empl 44, sales $8,947,059, cert: State,
WBENC)

4305   GSquared Group, LLC
       3180 Northpoint Pkwy, Ste 301
       Alpharetta, GA 30005
       Contact: Joan Guillory CEO
       Tel: 404-698-1810
       Email: contactus@gsquaredgroup.com
       Website: www.gsquaredgroup.com
Technology Talent Solutions for contract, contract-to-
hire & direct hire positions, Technology Consulting
Solutions for short-term, high-touch, high-value engage-
ments. (Woman, estab 2010, empl 25, sales , cert:
WBENC)

4306   Heagney Logan Group, LLC
       2002 Summit Blvd Ste 300
       Atlanta, GA 30319
       Contact: Jeannette Weigelt Principal
       Tel: 404-267-1351
       Email: info@heagneylogan.com
       Website: www.heagneylogangroup.com
Management Consulting, IT Consultant Staffing, Project
Management, ERP Consulting, Remote Development,
Contract Technical Staffing. (AA, estab 2009, empl 3,
sales $924,954, cert: State, NMSDC)

4307   HireGenics, Inc.
       2400 Meadowbrook Pkwy
       Duluth, GA 30096
       Contact: Nancy Budmayr Program Director
       Tel: 651-470-5240
       Email: nancy.budmayr@hiregenics.com
       Website: www.hiregenics.com
Technology consulting & solutions: onsite, near-shore,
off-shore, business intelligence, e-business, database
technologies, ERP, CRM. (As-Ind, estab 1998, empl
10000, sales $683,000,000, cert: NMSDC)

4308   HI-TEC Professional Solutions, Inc.
       2501 E Piedmont Rd Ste 103
       Marietta, GA 30062
       Contact: Acct Mgr
       Tel: 770-575-5855
       Email:
       Website: www.hi-tecsolutions.com
Technical staffing solutions: engineering, information
technology & professional services. (Woman/AA, estab
2004, empl 10, sales $5,200,000, cert: 8a)

4309   IBEX IT Business Experts LLC
       3295 River Exchange Dr, Ste 550
       Sandy Springs, GA 30092
       Contact: Maggie Carter Sales Dir
       Tel: 678-752-7542
       Email: mcarter@ibexexperts.com
       Website: www.ibexexperts.com
IT Service Management, Enterprise Governance, Project
Management, IT Security Management. (Woman/AA,
estab , empl , sales $7,500,000, cert: NMSDC, WBENC,
8a)

4310   Impel Professional Consulting, LLC
        7058 Wind Run Way
        Stone Mountain, GA 30082
        Contact: Jerome Potts Business Develop Dir
        Tel: 678-410-9245
        Email: info@impelprofessional.com
        Website: www.impelprofessional.com
Design & develop end-to-end integrated IT Solutions in
ERP (SAP, SAP S/4 HANA, PeopleSoft,Oracle, Workday), BI,
CRM Assessment for ERP systems and Business process
improvements for SAP IT Road Maps and Best Practices.
(Woman/AA, estab 2016, empl 2, sales , cert: State,
WBENC)

4311   INDU LLC dba intiGrow
        2760 Peach tree Ind. Blvd, Ste D
        Duluth, GA 30097
        Contact: Mike Evans Business Develop Exec
        Tel: 678-666-4365
        Email: mike@intigrow.com
        Website: www.intigrow.com
Managed Security Services, Identity & Access Management, Federated Identity Management, Single Sign On (E-
SSO and SSO), Intrusion Detection & Prevention, Vulnerability Assessment & Penetration Testing. (As-Pac, estab
2006, empl 580, sales $13,000,000, cert: NMSDC)

4312   Information Technology Consulting Company
        190 Bluegrass Valley Parkway Ste B7
        Alpharetta, GA 30005
        Contact: Gary Kallenbach Sr Procurement Advisor
        Tel: 614-207-9475
        Email: gkallenbach@itc2.net
        Website: www.itc2.net
IT resource & infrastrucute consulting. (Hisp, estab 2006,
empl 15, sales , cert: NMSDC)

4313   InfoSmart Technologies Inc.
        5400 Laurel Springs Pkwy Ste 706
        Suwanee, GA 30024
        Contact: Karun Kevin Reddy President
        Tel: 678-584-5635
        Email: kevin@infosmarttech.com
        Website: http://infosmarttech.com
Software consulting business, project management,
participation & subcontracting, partnership, staff
augumentation, software programming, design & area.
(As-Ind, estab 1998, empl 75, sales $6,700,000, cert:
NMSDC)

4314   Intellectual Concepts LLC
        3300 Buckeye Rd, Ste 601
        Atlanta, GA 30341
        Contact: DeLois Babiker CEO
        Tel: 202-321-4560
        Email: dbabiker@intellectualconcepts.net
        Website: www.intellectualconcepts.com
Information management technology, full life-cycle IT
services, communication, content, collaboration &
conferencing, contract administration, asset management
& IT acquisition services. (Woman/AA, estab 2004, empl 7,
sales $817,000, cert: City, NMSDC, WBENC, 8a)

4315   IT Division, Inc.
        5955 Parkway North Blvd Unit A
        Cumming, GA 30040
        Contact: Jamie Crosby Dir of Sales
        Tel: 678-649-3022
        Email: jamiec@itdivisioninc.com
        Website: www.itdivisioninc.com
IT staffing & services, application development, application testing & infrastructure services. (Woman/As-Pac,
estab 2006, empl 165, sales $9,332,282, cert: State)

4316   K.L. Scott & Associates LLC
        235 Peachtree St NE Ste 400
        Atlanta, GA 30303
        Contact: Keith Scott CEO
        Tel: 404-692-5552
        Email: keith.scott@klscottassociates.com
        Website: http://klscottassociates.com
Information technology & management consulting, data
analytics, analysis, and business growth strategy,
Business Process Management (BPM) & (Re)engineering.
(AA, estab 2013, empl 10, sales , cert: NMSDC)

4317   Kavi Software Inc.
        250 Gladeside Path
        Suwanee, GA 30024
        Contact: Jegannathan Mehalingam President
        Tel: 678-358-4861
        Email: mjegann@kavisoft.net
        Website: www.kavisoft.net
IT services & temporary staffing: application security
implementation. (As-Ind, estab 1999, empl 25, sales
$1,500,000, cert: NMSDC)

4318   Komplete Systems Integrators, Inc. (Kompsys)
        3300 Cumberland Blvd, Ste 500
        Atlanta, GA 30339
        Contact: Kevin Doby President
        Tel: 770-690-4272
        Email: kevin.doby@kompsys.com
        Website: www.kompsys.com
IP telephony, network design & implementation, LAN/
WAN, wireless, IP communication solutions, remote
network operations services, staff augmentation,
disaster recovery. (AA, estab 2001, empl 60, sales
$7,400,000, cert: State)

4319   Lanin Technologies
        730 Stuart Ct
        Alpharetta, GA 30004
        Contact: Mariano Saldana VP Operations
        Tel: 678-620-8210
        Email: msaldana@lanintech.com
        Website: www.lanintech.com
Software development, IT services, custom software
development; primarily web, mobile applications & SAP.
(Hisp, estab 2015, empl 3, sales , cert: NMSDC)

4320   LNKE Technologies Inc.
        236 Auburn Ave NE Ste 103B
        Atlanta, GA 30303
        Contact: Nate Jones Owner
        Tel: 404-919-5653
        Email: najones@lnketech.com
        Website: www.LNKETECH.com
Cloud Services, Web Development, Web Design, Strate-
gic IT Consulting, Mobile Dev, Project Mgm, Endpoint
Support, Software Development, Managed Services,
Programming Services, System Engineering, Network
Engineering. (AA, estab 2011, empl 4, sales , cert: 8a)

4321   Management Decisions, Inc. - MDI Group
        35 Technology Pkwy S Ste 150
        Norcross, GA 30092
        Contact: Joel McCreight Client Mgr/Business Devel
        Tel: 770-416-7949
        Email: jmccreight@mdigroup.com
        Website: www.mdigroup.com
IT staffing & contracting, project mgmt, vendor mgmt,
direct hire, IT staffing. (Woman, estab , empl , sales
$45,800,000, cert: WBENC, NWBOC)

4322   Megasys Inc.
        200 Lazy Shade Ct
        Duluth, GA 30097
        Contact: Vandana Raman President
        Tel: 770-573-0745
        Email: vandanaraman@megasysinc.org
        Website: www.megasysinc.org
Software consulting services, staff augmentation services.
(Woman/As-Ind, As-Pac, estab 1995, empl 2, sales
$200,000, cert: State)

4323   Metasys Technologies
        3460 Summit Ridge Pkwy, #401
        Duluth, GA 30096
        Contact: Romeen Sheth President
        Tel: 678-523-1798
        Email: info@metasysinc.com
        Website: www.metasysinc.com
Information technology svcs: e-business application devel &
integration, staff augmentation. (Nat Ame, As-Ind, estab
2000, empl 495, sales $40,900,000, cert: NMSDC)

4324   Milletech Systems Inc.
        11539 Park Woods Cir, Ste 201
        Alpharetta, GA 30005
        Contact: Nasir Mujawar VP
        Tel: 770-619-0095
        Email: nmujawar@milletechinc.com
        Website: www.milletechinc.com
IT services: staffing & consultants, outsourcing, ERP
solutions & implementation, application support, upgrades,
custom application devel, training, QA & testing, systems
integration. (Woman/As-Ind, estab 2000, empl 46, sales
$3,900,000, cert: NMSDC)

4325   Next Level Business Services Inc.
        11340 LAKEFIELD DR STE 200
        JOHNS CREEK, GA 30097
        Contact: Theresa Jackson Mgr, Strategic Business
        Tel: 678-438-0195
        Email: theresa.jackson@nlbservices.com
        Website: www.nlbservices.com
IT Consultancy and BPO Services. (As-Ind, estab 2007, empl
6000, sales $305,000,000, cert: NMSDC)

4326   Nineteen Eleven Solutions Inc.
        12850 Hwy 9 Ste 600-247
        Alpharetta, GA 30004
        Contact: Daud Haseeb Principal
        Tel: 404-644-3702
        Email: daud@1911solutions.com
        Website: http://nineteenelevensolutions.com/
IT Staffing, ERP (Oracle, PeopleSoft, & SAP), Open Source &
Big Data (Hadoop). (AA, estab 2010, empl 9, sales $275,000,
cert: NMSDC)

4327   Nutech Systems Inc.
        2675 Paces Ferry Rd Ste 460
        Atlanta, GA 30339
        Contact: Nachu Anbil President
        Tel: 770-434-7063
        Email: nanbil@nutech-inc.com
        Website: www.nutech-inc.com
IT staff augmentation, IT solutions, software development life cycle, support & infrastructure. (As-Ind, estab
1995, empl 120, sales $20,400,000, cert: NMSDC)

4328   Ocher Technology Group
        130 Prospect Pl
        Alpharetta, GA 30005
        Contact: vijay vasudevan CEO
        Tel: 678-521-6329
        Email: vijay_vasudevan@ochertech.com
        Website: www.ochertech.com
IT consulting & staffing. (As-Ind, estab 2007, empl 55,
sales $4,945,175, cert: NMSDC)

4329   Olivine LLC
        970 Peachtree Industrial Blvd. Ste 100
        Suwanee, GA 30024
        Contact: Rajeev Maddur Sr Acct Mgr
        Tel: 770-596-5155
        Email: rajeevm@olivinellc.com
        Website: www.olivinellc.com
IT Consulting Services, Contract, Contract to Hire and
Direct hire placements. (As-Ind, estab 2006, empl 20,
sales $235,000, cert: NMSDC)

4330   Open Systems Inc.
        6495 Shiloh Rd, Ste 310
        Alpharetta, GA 30005
        Contact: Karen Ashley Sr. Recruiting Mgr
        Tel: 770-752-8600
        Email: karen.ashley@opensystemsinc.com
        Website: www.opensystemsinc.com
IT consulting & custom software development. (As-Ind,
As-Pac, estab 1994, empl 300, sales $15,165,059, cert:
NMSDC)

4331   Paramount Software Solutions, Inc
        4030 Old Milton Parkway
        Alpharetta, GA 30005
        Contact: Srinivas Kumar Business Develop Mgr
        Tel: 770-872-7829
        Email: srinivas@paramountsoft.net
        Website: www.paramountsoft.net/
IT Staffing, IT Consulting, Software outsourcing %
development services. (As-Ind, estab 1997, empl 120,
sales $178,777,000, cert: NMSDC)

4332   Paramount Software Solutions, Inc.
        4030 Old Milton Pkwy
        Alpharetta, GA 30005
        Contact: Lokesh Shiv Sr Business Exec
        Tel: 704-565-5707
        Email: lokesh@paramountsoft.net
        Website: www.paramountsoft.net
Research and Emerging Technologies. (Nat Ame, As-Ind,
estab 1997, empl 200, sales , cert: NMSDC)

4333 PIE Technology Consulting
559 Commons Park Lane
Tucker, GA 30084
Contact: Wesner Charlotin Dir of Operations
Tel: 877-866-2677
Email: wesnerc@pietconsulting.com
Website: www.pietconsulting.com
Planning, design, and implementation services for Microsoft products: Active Directory, Exchange, Lync/Skype for Business, SharePoint, and Office 365. (AA, estab 2014, empl 7, sales $554,276, cert: NMSDC)

4334 Precedent Technologies LLC
3330 Cumberland Blvd SE, Ste 500
Atlanta, GA 30339
Contact: Patrick Carley
Tel: 770-303-0223
Email: pfcarley@precedent-tech.com
Website: www.precedent-tech.com
Strategic IT consulting & project management, voice over IP telephone systems installation & support, web services, network design, installation and support, internet security software/services. (AA, estab 2006, empl 3, sales $196,000, cert: NMSDC)

4335 Premier Software Solutions
3707 Main St, Ste 201
College Park, GA 30337
Contact: Paul Gupta President
Tel: 678-643-3034
Email: pgupta@presoftsolutions.com
Website: www.presoftsolutions.com
IT solutions and services provider in the Healthcare IT, Cyber Security, Data Analytics, and Custom Software Development. (Woman/As-Ind, estab 2008, empl 5, sales $3,050,000, cert: 8a)

4336 Primus Software Corporation
3061 Peachtree Industrial Blvd Ste 110
Duluth, GA 30097
Contact: Satish Anand President, Project Sevices
Tel: 678-336-1871
Email: supplier.diversity@primussoft.com
Website: www.primussoft.com
J2EE technology implementation, web services, IBM Websphere, MS .NET Web svcs, data warehousing, Oracle & SYBASE, project management, ERP, CRM and SCM technologies. (Woman/As-Pac, estab 1996, empl 220, sales $27,000,000, cert: NMSDC, WBENC)

4337 Prosys Information Systems
6025 The Corners Parkway Ste 120
Norcross, GA 30092
Contact: Becky Brown Acct Exec
Tel: 404-663-1403
Email: becky.brown@prosysis.com
Website: www.prosysis.com
IP telephony & wireless, network integration, outsourcing solutions & technical staff augmentation. (Woman, estab 1997, empl 425, sales $776,000,000, cert: WBENC)

4338 PSR Associates, Inc.
3350 Riverwood Parkway Ste 1900
Atlanta, GA 30339
Contact: Ernest Ball SVP
Tel: 404-618-0206
Email: eball@psrassociates.com
Website: www.psrassociates.com
Information technology, program management, project management, staff augmentation, web portal, customer relationship management, IT resources, program testing. (As-Pac, estab 2003, empl 43, sales $7,900,000, cert: NMSDC)

4339 Pyramid Consulting, Inc.
3060 Kimball Bridge Rd Ste 200
Alpharetta, GA 30022
Contact: Lara Lundy Exec VP, Client Relations
Tel: 678-514-3500
Email: pcistaffing@pyramici.com
Website: www.pyramidci.com
Information technology consulting: staff augmentation, turnkey IT projects. (As-Ind, estab 1996, empl 1150, sales $283,000,000, cert: NMSDC)

4340 Rapid IT, Inc.
4080 McGinnis Ferry Rd, Ste 1206
Atlanta, GA 30005
Contact: Goutham Goli President
Tel: 678-366-3820
Email: contracts@rapiditinc.com
Website: www.rapiditinc.com
Information Technology. (As-Ind, estab 2006, empl 120, sales , cert: NMSDC)

4341 Renovo Data, Inc.
3121 Maple Dr Ste 200
Atlanta, GA 30305
Contact: Charlotta Vinson President
Tel: 404-935-6363
Email: cvinson@renovodata.com
Website: www.renovodata.com
Data backup & disaster recovery solutions: replication services, virtualization, consulting services. (Woman/As-Pac, estab 2005, empl 9, sales $2,000,000, cert: NMSDC, NWBOC)

4342 ResiliEnt Business Solutions, LLC
11175 Cicero Dr, Ste 100
Alpharetta, GA 30022
Contact: CEO
Tel: 678-242-5242
Email:
Website: www.resilientbiz.com
SDLC, Business Intelligence, Enterprise Data Management/Reporting, Data Modeling, Governance, warehousing, cleansing, WebFOCUS, WebQuery, ScoreCards, Dashboards Cognos, MicroStrategy, Mobile Development. (Woman, estab 2004, empl 6, sales $1,153,725, cert: WBENC)

4343 RiVi Consulting Group LLC
2475 Northwinds Pkwy, Ste 200
Alpharetta, GA 30009
Contact: Bhushan Mocherla CIO/partner
Tel: 678-643-8133
Email: bmocherla@rivigroup.com
Website: www.rivigroup.com
Technology solutions: SAP, Peoplesoft & Oracle. (Woman/As-Ind, estab 2002, empl 45, sales $6,217,522, cert: NMSDC, WBENC, 8a)

4344 RTX Technology Partners, LLC
400 Perimeter Center Terr NE Ste 900
Atlanta, GA 30346
Contact: M. Hans Delly Managing Dir
Tel: 404-551-5609
Email: m.hans.delly@rtxpartners.com
Website: www.rtxpartners.com
Global management & technology consulting: business strategy, technology planning & architecture & business process optimization. (AA, estab 2007, empl 25, sales $6,500,000, cert: NMSDC)

4345   Scintel Technologies Inc.
6340 Sugarloaf Pkwy Ste 200
Duluth, GA 30097
Contact: Shailesh Patel Acct Mgr
Tel: 678-775-6874
Email: s.patel@scintel.com
Website: www.scintel.com
Application outsourcing & enterprise consulting solutions.
(As-Ind, estab 2003, empl 400, sales $17,500,000, cert:
NMSDC)

4346   Scope IT Consulting
3235 Satellite Blvd Bldg 400, Ste 300
Duluth, GA 30096
Contact: Nadir Noorani Principal, Consultant
Tel: 912-580-5929
Email: nadir.noorani@scopeitconsulting.com
Website: www.scopeitconsulting.com
Business Process Management, Project Management,
Mobility Solutions, BigData Solutions, Cloud Solutions.
(Woman/As-Ind, estab 2015, empl 16, sales $200,000, cert:
NMSDC, WBENC)

4347   Serenity Infotech, Inc.
950 Scales Rd, Ste 104
Suwanee, GA 30024
Contact: Srini Vangimalla Partner
Tel: 770-242-9966
Email: srini@serenityinfotech.com
Website: www.serenityinfotech.com
Software solutions & consulting services. (As-Pac, estab
1997, empl 120, sales $13,000,000, cert: NMSDC)

4348   Six Consulting, Inc.
5900 Windward Pkwy, Ste 230
Alpharetta, GA 30005
Contact: Sam Yehya VP
Tel: 470-395-0200
Email: sa@sixconsultingcorp.com
Website: www.sixconsultingcorp.com
Custom Application Development & Maintenance, Business
Intelligence & Data Warehousing, Enterprise Resource
Planning, Business Process Management, Enterprise
Content Management. (As-Ind, estab 2007, empl 72, sales
$5,472,009, cert: NMSDC)

4349   SJ Technologies Inc.
5024 Meadowbrook Circle
Suwanee, GA 30024
Contact: Patrick Henson
Tel: 404-386-7376
Email: patrick.henson@sjtechcorp.com
Website: www.sjtechcorp.com
Oracle technology consulting, staffing & implementation of
comprehensive IT solutions for both private and public
sector. (Woman/As-Pac, estab 2005, empl 1, sales
$120,000, cert: 8a)

4350   Smartecute LLC
1266 Wt Paces ferry Rd Ste 196
Atlanta, GA 30327
Contact: Sheldon Mundle CEO
Tel: 404-939-6303
Email: sheldon@smartecute.com
Website: www.smartecute.com
IT Consulting, IT Advisory, IT Network & Wireless Access
Points, IT Unified Communications, Voice Communications
& Data, PeopleSoft ERP Consulting, Telecommunications, IT
Project Management. (AA, estab 2010, empl 2, sales , cert:
NMSDC)

4351   Softech Int'l Resources, Inc.
3300 Holcomb Bridge Rd, Ste 216
Norcross, GA 30092
Contact: Balaji HR
Tel: 770-447-8002
Email: supplier@softintl.com
Website: www.softintl.com
IT consulting, project mgmt, analysis, architectural
design, object modeling, application devel. (Woman/As-
Ind, estab 1995, empl 40, sales $7,415,369, cert:
NMSDC)

4352   Softpath System, LLC
3985 Steve Reynolds Blvd Bldg C
Norcross, GA 30093
Contact: Sushumna Roy Jalajam President
Tel: 404-315-1555
Email: supplier@softpath.net
Website: www.softpath.net
IT services: business intelligence & data warehousing.
(Woman/As-Pac, estab 1999, empl 500, sales
$40,000,000, cert: NMSDC, CPUC, WBENC)

4353   Stellar Consulting Solutions, LLC
2475 NorthWinds Pkwy, Ste 200
Alpharetta, GA 30009
Contact: Varun Jhanjee CEO
Tel: 678-777-7411
Email: varun@stellarconsulting.com
Website: http://stellarconsulting.com
Onsite Technology Staff Augmentation, Contract,
Contract to Hire & Permanent Placements, C Level
executive search. (As-Ind, estab 2015, empl 11, sales
$2,500,500, cert: NMSDC)

4354   Strategic Systems & Technology Corporation
3325 Paddocks Pkwy Ste 250
Suwanee, GA 30024
Contact: Magan McQuiston CEO
Tel: 678-389-7200
Email: magan.mcquiston@sstid.com
Website: www.sstid.com
Computer database, peripherals, printers, application
systems, terminals, network interface hardware,
terminal remote job entry. (Woman, estab , empl 29,
sales $6,200,000, cert: WBENC)

4355   Sun Technologies, Inc.
3700 Mansell Road Ste 220
Alpharetta, GA 30022
Contact: Heather Johnston Business Develop Mgr
Tel: 770-418-0434
Email: supplierdiversity@suntechnologies.com
Website: www.suntechnologies.com
IT staffing & IT projects. (Woman/Nat Ame, As-Ind, As-
Pac, estab 1996, empl 793, sales $32,000,000, cert:
NMSDC, WBENC)

4356   Symbioun Technologies, Inc.
4501 Circle 75 Pkwy D4200
Atlanta, GA 30339
Contact: Raj Muppalla Relationship Mgr
Tel: 408-385-1078
Email: srinik@symbiountech.com
Website: www.symbiountech.com
Information technology consulting, staffing services. (As-
Ind, estab 1993, empl 140, sales $7,900,000, cert:
NMSDC)

4357   Synergy America, Inc.
       6340 Sugarloaf Pkwy, Ste 200
       Duluth, GA 30097
       Contact: Mike Williams CEO
       Tel: 770-923-9300
       Email: mike@synergyamerica.com
       Website: www.synergyamerica.com
IT services: BPO, healthcare, ERP, e-business, & client
server environments. (As-Ind, estab 1993, empl 50, sales ,
cert: NMSDC, 8a)

4358   TechBios, Inc.
       11800 Amberpark Dr, Ste 130
       Alpharetta, GA 30004
       Contact: Larry Parker President
       Tel: 770-569-2721
       Email: lparker@techbios.com
       Website: www.techbios.com
Information technology contract & permanent staffing;
professional, administrative & clerical staffing, help desk &
customer svc, software engineering, LAN/WAN installation, maintenance, & support, configuration mgmt &
desktop deployment. (AA, estab 2000, empl 18, sales
$1,466,970, cert: State, NMSDC)

4359   The Danby Group, LLP
       3060-A Business Park Dr
       Norcross, GA 30071
       Contact: Genie Ragin Managing Partner
       Tel: 770-416-9844
       Email: genie@danbygroup.com
       Website: www.danbygroup.com
Automatic identification technology (AIT) design &
integration, bar code printing stations. (Woman, estab
1982, empl 11, sales $10,000,000, cert: WBENC)

4360   The Ian Thomas Group, LLC
       2870 Peachtree Rd, Ste 417
       Atlanta, GA 30305
       Contact: Exec operations Mgr
       Tel: 404-993-5698
       Email:
       Website: www.ianthomasgroup.com
Software performance engineering (SPE) services &
solutions: software performance testing, engineering
analysis & optimization, database analysis & tuning &
operational support. (AA, estab 2007, empl 15, sales
$1,451,588, cert: NMSDC, 8a)

4361   The REIA Corporation
       3348 Fieldwood Dr
       Smyrna, GA 33080
       Contact: Darnell Clarke CEO
       Tel: 770-432-6974
       Email: darnell@reiacorp.com
       Website: www.reiacorp.com
Systems software application dev & integration, security
mgmt & compliance, custom development, help desk & IT
support project & risk management. (Woman/AA, estab
1992, empl 46, sales $5,868,000, cert: State, City, 8a)

4362   Think Development Systems
       6000 Live Oak Pkwy, Ste 102
       Norcross, GA 30093
       Contact: P I Joy President
       Tel: 770-723-7777
       Email: joy@thinkdevelopment.com
       Website: www.thinkdevelopment.com
Software development & IT consulting, offshore development, wireless application. (Woman/As-Ind, estab 1998,
empl 47, sales $3,085,109, cert: City, NMSDC)

4363   Unicorn Technologies, LLC
       4080 McGinnis Ferry Rd Ste 1203
       Alpharetta, GA 30005
       Contact: Sunil Savili President
       Tel: 678-825-8143
       Email: sales@unicorntek.com
       Website: www.unicorntek.com
IT solutions & staffing services, Fit Gap Analysis, Application Development, Implementation, Upgrades, Quality
Assurance, Maintenance & Support, Project Management. (Woman/As-Ind, estab 2012, empl 60, sales
$3,700,000, cert: State, WBENC, SDB)

4364   Universal Business Solutions, LLC
       4080 McGinnis Ferry Rd Ste 803
       Alpharetta, GA 30005
       Contact: Jan O'Brien VP of Recruitment & Sales
       Tel: 770-416-9900
       Email: jobrien@ubsolutions.com
       Website: www.ubsolutions.com
Information technology svcs & solutions: ERP & CRM
systems, application systems, web systems, e-business,
security & threat evaluation, telecommunications,
telephony consulting, call & contact centers, infrastructure design, project mgmt. (Nat Ame, estab 1995, empl
34, sales , cert: SDB)

4365   VDart Inc
       11180 State Bridge Road Ste 302
       Alpharetta, GA 30022
       Contact: Bruce Hay VP Business Dev
       Tel: 309-657-8528
       Email: supplier.registration@vdartinc.com
       Website: www.vdartinc.com
Global IT staffing: SAP FICO Functional, SAP ABAP,
Abinitio, Microstrategy, Oracle Applications (SCM, FIN,
MFG, WMS) Functional/Technical, Microsoft,
Middleware, etc. (As-Ind, estab 2007, empl 2400, sales
$132,000,000, cert: NMSDC)

4366   VDart Inc.
       11180 State Bridge Rd, Ste 302
       Alpharetta, GA 30022
       Contact: Sanaan Mohamed Business Dev Mgr
       Tel: 800-371-1664
       Email: mohamed.s@vdartinc.com
       Website: www.vdart.com
High growth, global digital solutions, product develop-
ment and professional services Firm with 23% CAGR,
Headquartered in Atlanta, GA, USA with global presence
in Canada, Mexico, Belgium, UK, Japan, Australia and
India. (As-Ind, estab 2007, empl 3500, sales
$158,580,118, cert: NMSDC)

4367   Virtue Group
       5755 N Point Pkwy, Ste 85
       Alpharetta, GA 30022
       Contact: Lakshmi Manthena President
       Tel: 678-578-4554
       Email: lmanthena@virtuegroup.com
       Website: www.virtuegroup.com
IT professionals: contract, contract-to-hire & direct hire
basis. (Woman/As-Ind, estab 2002, empl 250, sales
$23,400,000, cert: NMSDC)

4368 Whitty IT Solutions LLC
260 Peachtree St, NW Ste 2200
Atlanta, GA 30303
Contact: Mrs. Charlie Whitfield CEO
Tel: 404-823-6955
Email: charlie@whittyapps.com
Website: www.whittyit.solutions
Software engineering & integration, architecture, design, development & project mgmt, mobile software solutions. (Woman/AA, estab 2011, empl 2, sales , cert: WBENC, 8a)

4369 XentIT, LLC
5425 Peachtree Pkwy
Norcross, GA 30092
Contact: Tariq Alvi President
Tel: 678-906-4046
Email: talvi@xentit.com
Website: www.xentit.com
Value Added Reseller, System Integrator & Cloud Managed Service provider. (As-Ind, estab 2006, empl 7, sales $2,247,000, cert: NMSDC)

4370 Xtreme Solutions, Inc.
1170 Peachtree St, Ste 1875
Atlanta, GA 30309
Contact: Phyllis Newhouse Project Mgr
Tel: 404-883-2000
Email: pnewhouse@xtremesolutions-inc.com
Website: www.xtremesolutions-inc.com
Engineering & technology services. (Woman/AA, estab 2002, empl 140, sales $800,000, cert: NMSDC)

Hawaii

4371 In the Middle dba HTS Information Systems
99-1285 Halawa Valley St Ste A7
Aiea, HI 96701
Contact: Stanley Lau President
Tel: 808-535-9700
Email: slau@hitechsupport.net
Website: www.hitechsupport.net
Technology products & solutions, virtual computing, secure communications, mobile computing, managed network services, technical staffing, IT equipment procurement. (As-Pac, estab 2004, empl 6, sales $1,100,000, cert: State)

4372 Premier Solutions Hi, LLC
7391 Makaa St, Ste A
Honolulu, HI 96825
Contact: Rob Hardisty VP
Tel: 808-396-4444
Email: rob@premiersolutionshi.com
Website: www.premiersolutionshi.com
Information technology & and solutions, design, build & support applications & networks, data security. (Woman/As-Pac, estab 2007, empl 13, sales $1,600,000, cert: 8a)

Iowa

4373 Certintell, Inc.
317 6th Ave Ste 901
Des Moines, IA 50309
Contact: Benjamin Lefever Sales
Tel: 515-802-1281
Email: benjamin@certintell.com
Website: www.certintell.com
Online & on-demand healthcare delivery services, software & remote monitoring that benefit patients, hospitals, employers, payers, physician practice groups & accountable care orgs. (AA, estab 2014, empl 6, sales , cert: NMSDC)

4374 ePATHUSA
1075 Jordan Creek Pkwy, Ste 295
West Des Moines, IA 50266
Contact: Hari Nallure VP
Tel: 515-974-6778
Email: hnallure@epathusa.net
Website: https://epathusa.net
IT services, Cyber Security, Cloud Services, Data Science, Legacy Modernization and Advanced Software Development. (As-Ind, estab 2005, empl 48, sales $7,500,000, cert: 8a)

4375 Nguyen Information Consulting Inc.
3636 Westown Pkwy Ste 217
West Des Moines, IA 50266
Contact: Trich Mullane Sr Business Dev Mgr
Tel: 515-457-3174
Email: tmullane@nicwdm.com
Website: www.nicwdm.com
Information technology consulting svcs: staff augumentation, technical resources, outsourcing, contract programming, staffing, web applications, e-business, network & system admin, system engineering, technical writing, technical support. (As-Pac, estab 1993, empl 31, sales $2,455,000, cert: State)

4376 PC Pitstop LLC
2515 W 22nd St
Sioux City, IA 51103
Contact: Scott Palmer Sales Consultant
Tel: 712-233-4015
Email: scottp@pcpitstop.com
Website: www.pcpitstop.com/
Security optimization software, PC Matic. (As-Pac, estab 1999, empl 32, sales $11,913,000, cert: NMSDC)

Illinois

4377 3Core Systems, Inc.
75 Executive Dr, Ste 401I
Aurora, IL 60504
Contact: Shyam Reganti Dir PreSales
Tel: 630-748-8800
Email: shyam.reganti@3coresystems.com
Website: www.3coresystems.com
Information Technology services, solutions & consulting, ERP (Enterprise Resource Planning), CRM (Customer Relationship Management), DW/BI (Data Warehousing & Business Intelligence), Application Development & Management. (As-Ind, As-Pac, estab 2004, empl 45, sales $9,064,920, cert: State)

4378 A1PlusSoft, Inc.
222 W Merchandise Mart Plaza, Ste 1212
Chicago, IL 60654
Contact: Balaji Rengamannar CEO
Tel: 630-935-6938
Email: brengamannar@a1plussoft.com
Website: www.a1plussoft.com
PCI Compliance assessment, Staff Augmentation, Information & Cloud security consulting, Legacy system transformation/modernization, Data & EMV Migration, Testing & Technical Writing. (As-Ind, estab 2002, empl 5, sales $296,000, cert: State, City, NMSDC)

4379 About Xtreme LLC
      401 N Michigan Ave Ste 1200
      Chicago, IL 60611
      Contact: Yasoob Ahmed Dir Business Devel
      Tel: 815-603-5521
      Email: yasoob.ahmed@axtcorp.com
      Website: https://axtcorp.com
Cloud IT Consulting, Microsoft Azure, Amazon AWS, and
SalesForce, Office 365, Dynamics 365, SharePoint, SCCM,
AI Chatbots, Knowledge Mining, Big Data, and Analytics,
Azure and AWS IAAS. (As-Ind, estab 2016, empl 12, sales
$1,000,000, cert: NMSDC)

4380 Accede Solutions Inc.
      164 Ela Rd
      Inverness, IL 60067
      Contact: Garvita Sethi Managing Partner
      Tel: 844-522-2333
      Email: garvita@accedesol.com
      Website: www.accedesol.com
IT, Healthcare, Finance & HR staffing & consulting. Enterprise Resource Planning (ERP) Customer relationship
management (CRM) Human Resource Management
System (HRMS) Software configuration Management (SCM
) System. (Woman/As-Ind, estab 2005, empl 32, sales ,
cert: City, WBENC)

4381 Advantech Solutions Inc.
      2340 S Arlington Heights Rd Ste 270
      Arlington Heights, IL 60005
      Contact: Michelle Advaney Operations Mgr
      Tel: 847-690-0255
      Email: aa@atsus.net
      Website: www.atsus.net
Information technology consulting. (Woman, estab 1999,
empl 38, sales $4,498,633, cert: State)

4382 Ageatia Technology Consultancy Services Inc
      949 N Plum Grove Road
      Schaumburg, IL 60173
      Contact: Chuck Srinivasan President
      Tel: 847-517-8415
      Email: csrinivasan@ageatia.com
      Website: www.ageatia.com
e-gov, systems integration, database admin, software,
implementation, software services, Legacy data, conversions, software devel, custom devel, web devel, systems
outsourcing & support, technical support, enterprise,
Oracle, Microsoft, PeopleSoft, SAP. (Woman/As-Ind, As-
Pac, estab 2005, empl 300, sales $30,000,000, cert: City,
NMSDC)

4383 Aloha Document Services
      60 E Van Buren St Ste S-1502
      Chicago, IL 60605
      Contact: Ginger Peak President
      Tel: 312-542-1300
      Email: gpeak@alohadocs.com
      Website: www.alohadocs.com
Litigation copying, oversize & digital imaging, presentation,
marketing & training materials, multi-media duplication &
electronic archiving. (Woman, estab 2002, empl 35, sales
$2,600,000, cert: City, WBENC)

4384 Ameex Technologies Corp.
      1701 E Woodfield Rd, Ste 710
      Schaumburg, IL 60173
      Contact: Arockia Preethi Marketing Analyst
      Tel: 847-563-3064
      Email: vendor.registration@ameexusa.com
      Website: http://ameexusa.com/
Develop content management solutions, web development, maintenance & enhanced services. (As-Pac, estab
2007, empl 180, sales $8,000,000, cert: NMSDC)

4385 AmorServ LLC
      2340 W Touhy Ave Ste B
      Chicago, IL 60645
      Contact: Otse Amorighoye CEO
      Tel: 312-414-0430
      Email: o.amorighoye@amorserv.com
      Website: www.amorserv.com
Turn-key technology service and solutions, white
labelled on-demand / on-site solutions. (AA, estab 2016,
empl 10, sales $593,000, cert: City, NMSDC)

4386 Aonsoft International, Inc
      1600 Golf Rd, Ste 1270
      Rolling Meadows, IL 60008
      Contact: Siddiq Ahmed President
      Tel: 847-999-4060
      Email: siddiq@aonsoft.com
      Website: www.aonsoft.com
IT Consulting Services & Staff Augmentation Services.
(As-Ind, estab 2007, empl 14, sales $661,000, cert:
NMSDC)

4387 Aptude, Inc.
      1601 North Bond St, Ste 316
      Naperville, IL 60563
      Contact: Guy De Rosa Principal
      Tel: 630-692-6700
      Email: accounts@aptude.com
      Website: www.aptude.com
Remote data capturing applications, ebusiness solutions,
customer relationship mgmt solutions, data warehousing & business intelligence, content svcs, CAD/CAM
integration, knowledge mgmt solutions. (As-Ind, estab
2001, empl 100, sales $15,300,000, cert: State, City)

4388 ARBA Technology, Inc.
      2760 Forgue Dr Ste 104
      Naperville, IL 60564
      Contact: Kathy de la Torre Dir Sales/Marketing
      Tel: 630-620-8566
      Email: kathy@arbapro.com
      Website: www.arbapro.com
Point of Sale (POS), inventory management & cashless
payment solutions. (Woman/As-Pac, estab 2007, empl
17, sales $881,670, cert: NMSDC)

4389 Ascent Innovations, LLC
      475 N Martingale Rd Ste 820
      Schaumburg, IL 60173
      Contact: Sohena Hafiz President
      Tel: 847-572-8000
      Email: solutions@ascent365.com
      Website: www.ascent365.com
Dynamics AX & Dynamics CRM Consulting, Implementa-
tion, Development, Integration, Support, Upgrades, Data
Migration, Implementation & Integration, ERP/CRM
Integration. (Woman/As-Ind, estab 2009, empl 32, sales
$780,000, cert: State, WBENC, 8a)

4390 Asset Management Concepts
4654 N Kenmore St
Chicago, IL 60640
Contact: Tommy Thompson President
Tel: 773-878-5150
Email: thomacce@aol.com
Website:
Design LAN networks, help desk, call center support, custom design systems, IT staffing, dist PCs. (AA, estab 1991, empl 5, sales , cert: State)

4391 Aura Innovative Technology
223 W Jackson Blvd, Ste 1112
Chicago, IL 60606
Contact: James Chen President
Tel: 312-342-4292
Email: mmrcela@aurachicago.com
Website: http://aurachicago.com
Microsoft & AWS consulting & custom software/integration development. (As-Pac, estab 2011, empl 15, sales , cert: City, NMSDC)

4392 Aurora Solutions, Inc.
1051 Perimeter Dr, Ste 510
Schaumburg, IL 60173
Contact: Sanjeev Srivastava Business Development
Tel: 847-274-7777
Email: sanjeev@auroraworldwide.com
Website: www.auroraworldwide.com
Data Mining & Business Analytics, ECommerce & Custom Application Development. (Woman/As-Ind, As-Pac, estab 1997, empl 30, sales $3,500,000, cert: NMSDC, 8a)

4393 Bourntec Solutions, Inc.
1701 E Woodfield Rd Ste 636
Schaumburg, IL 60173
Contact: Srujana Gudur President
Tel: 224-232-5090
Email: ssurya@bourntec.com
Website: www.bourntec.com
Information technology remote Oracle support services, on-site Oracle implementation & application development services. (Woman/As-Ind, estab 1994, empl 33, sales $4,500,000, cert: State, NMSDC, 8a)

4394 BTR Solutions, LLC
1300 Thorndale
Elk Grove Village, IL 60007
Contact: Business Dev Mgr
Tel: 630-594-2011
Email: JOEP@SIPIAR.COM
Website: www.sipiar.com
IT Asset Disposition, remarket, redeploy, perform DOD level Data Security. (Woman, estab 1988, empl 300, sales , cert: WBENC, NWBOC)

4395 Clerysys Incorporated
10600 W Higgins Rd, Ste 711
Rosemont, IL 60018
Contact: Nicole Lim Business Develop Exec
Tel: 847-768-0314
Email: info@clerysys.com
Website: www.clerysys.com
Application design & devel, ERP, business intelligence, systems integration, quality assurance, content mgmt & web-based applications,SAP R/3 implementation svcs, ERP, CRM, SRM, PLM, BI & data warehousing. (As-Pac, estab 2005, empl 450, sales $10,000,000, cert: NMSDC)

4396 Cogent Data Solutions LLC
2500 W Higgins Rd Ste 1165
Hoffman Estates, IL 60169
Contact: Sumanth Yalavarthy VP IT
Tel: 866-666-1877
Email: sumanth@cogentdatasolutions.com
Website: www.cogentdatasolutions.com
IT services, IT project base & contract staff augmentation, Information management, Infrastructure Management, Data Warehousing, Business Intelligence, QA Testing, Web Development, EHR & EMR. (Woman/As-Ind, estab 2007, empl 89, sales $5,400,000, cert: State, NMSDC, WBENC)

4397 Compact Solutions, LLC.
Two TransAm Plaza Dr Ste 400
Oakbrook Terrace, IL 60181
Contact: Pankaj Agrawal President
Tel: 312-493-9911
Email: pankaj.agrawal@compactsolutionsllc.com
Website: www.compactsolutionsllc.com
Enterprise wide data integration, data management & quality initiatives, data migration/consolidation, data synchronization, master data management & cross-enterprise information integration. (As-Ind, estab 2002, empl 54, sales $5,550,000, cert: NMSDC)

4398 Complex Network Solutions
7747 W 96th Pl
Hickory Hills, IL 60457
Contact: Eduardo Lopez President
Tel: 708-233-6222
Email: elopez@complexnetwork.com
Website: www.complexnetwork.com
IT services, routing switching & wireless, desktop & server support. (Hisp, estab 2005, empl 7, sales , cert: NMSDC)

4399 CosaTech, Inc.
1415 W 22nd St, Tower Fl
Oak Brook, IL 60523
Contact: Ann Le VP
Tel: 630-684-2331
Email: ann.le@cosatech.com
Website: www.cosatech.com
Information technology services: systems integration & applications, development, quality assurance, managed services, IT staff augmentation, onsite, offsite & offshore applications dev & maintenance. (Woman/As-Pac, estab 1988, empl 350, sales $25,000,000, cert: NMSDC)

4400 CRSGroup, Inc.
One Pierce Place Ste 325 West
Itasca, IL 60143
Contact: YOLANDA GAINES Business Solutions Mgr
Tel: 630-202-5348
Email: YGAINES@CRSCORP.COM
Website: www.crscorp.com
Information technology consulting. (AA, estab 1994, empl 311, sales $17,500,000, cert: State, City, NMSDC)

4401 Cube Hub Inc.
600 N Commons Dr Ste 109
Aurora, IL 60504
Contact: Sunil Bakhshi Business Develop Mgr
Tel: 630-746-1239
Email: sunil@cube-hub.com
Website: www.cube-hub.com
Technology, Training, Staffing & Professional Services, Staffing/Recruiting services, Software Development, IT, Engineering, Professional, Marketing, Healthcare, Clinical, Scientific, Finance/Audit, Telecommunication, etc. (Woman/AA, As-Ind, estab 2014, empl 28, sales $3,580,640, cert: NMSDC)

4402 Cyberbridge Intl. Inc. dba Creospan Inc.
1515 E Woodfield Rd, Ste 350
Schaumburg, IL 60173
Contact: Praj Shah President
Tel: 847-598-1101
Email: praj.shah@creospan.com
Website: www.creospan.com
Software solutions consulting. (Woman/As-Ind, estab 1999, empl 125, sales $12,500,000, cert: NMSDC)

4403 Data Defenders, LLC
10 W 35th St, Ste 9F5-1
Chicago, IL 60616
Contact: Lester McCarroll Business Develop Mgr
Tel: 312-224-8831
Email: lester.mccarroll@data-defenders.com
Website: www.data-defenders.com
Information Security, Managed Technology, Applied Computer Forensics & Professional Services solutions. (AA, estab 2005, empl 14, sales $400,000, cert: City)

4404 DivIHN Integration Inc.
2800 W Higgins Rd Ste 240
Hoffman Estates, IL 60169
Contact: Shantanoo A Govilkar VP
Tel: 224-704-1704
Email: sgovilkar@divihn.com
Website: www.divihn.com
Computer software consulting, staff augmentation, custom software design & development, data management solutions & services. (As-Ind, estab 2002, empl 55, sales $11,200,000, cert: NMSDC)

4405 E Gen Solutions Inc.
One Energy Center Ste 302
Naperville, IL 60532
Contact: Allison Reed govt acct Mgr
Tel: 630-299-4433
Email: adr@egeni.com
Website: www.egeni.com
Information technology consulting, project management, staffing & on-site customized IT programming. (As-Ind, estab 2000, empl 92, sales $1,000,000, cert: 8a)

4406 Edgilent Corp.
700 Cooper Ct Ste AF
Schaumburg, IL 60173
Contact: Raj Ponnuswamy President
Tel: 847-839-7388
Email: rponnuswamy@edgilent.com
Website: www.edgilent.com
Information technology svcs: application development, outsourcing & consulting. (As-Pac, estab 2003, empl 20, sales $2,500,000, cert: NMSDC)

4407 Edify Technologies, Inc.
1952 Mc Dowell Rd, Ste 112
Naperville, IL 60563
Contact: Acct Exec
Tel: 630-932-9308
Email:
Website: www.edifytech.com
Software development & consulting, business process automation, SharePoint consulting, custom .NET solutions, testing & quality assurance, project management, staffing, offshore development. (As-Pac, estab 2002, empl 65, sales $4,000,000, cert: State, NMSDC)

4408 Electronic Knowledge Interchange, Co.
33 W Monroe St, Ste 1050
Chicago, IL 60603
Contact: Jose Cruz
Tel: 312-762-0129
Email: jcruz@eki-consulting.com
Website: www.eki-consulting.com
Technology solutions: web portals, e-commerce, knowledge management, employee intranets, workgroup collaboration & process automation technologies. (AA, estab 1996, empl 91, sales $17,105,910, cert: State, City, NMSDC)

4409 Enterprise Solutions Inc
500 E. Diehl Road Ste 130
Naperville, IL 60563
Contact: Ishrat Jan VP
Tel: 408-385-1731
Email: ishratjan@enterprisesolutioninc.com
Website: www.enterprisesolutioninc.com
IT & engineering staffing, direct hire, contract to hire & contract positions. (As-Ind, estab 2000, empl 350, sales $83,874,697, cert: NMSDC, CPUC)

4410 Evanston Technology Partners, Inc.
56 East 47th St
Chicago, IL 60653
Contact: Emmanuel Jackson President
Tel: 312-348-5122
Email: ejackson@evanstontec.com
Website: www.evanstontec.com
Implement & integrate object storage data (partner to Cleaversafe). Unified & Real Time Communications platform including Telehealth. (AA, estab , empl , sales $120,000, cert: NMSDC)

4411 Evolutyz Corp.
1560 Wall St Ste 105
Naperville, IL 60563
Contact: Adriana Perez Dir of Sales
Tel: 312-275-5735
Email: adriana@evolutyz.com
Website: www.evolutyz.com
Application Development, ERP, Mobile Apps, ETL/ BI/ DW, Quality Assurance & Testing, Professional Services, Staff Augmentation. (Woman/As-Pac, estab 2011, empl 25, sales $6,051,748, cert: NMSDC)

4412 Excelsior Consulting Services
P.O. Box 325
Clarendon Hills, IL 60514
Contact: Dileta Sapokaite Business Mgr
Tel: 973-447-2575
Email: dileta@excelsiorconsulting.net
Website: www.excelsiorconsulting.net
IT staff & contracting resources. (Woman/As-Ind, estab 2004, empl 2, sales $790,000, cert: State, WBENC, 8a)

4413   Frontier Technologies LLC
       1601 Bond St, Ste 305
       Naperville, IL 60563
       Contact: Richard Ewbank Sales Exec
       Tel: 630-687-1606
       Email: richard@frontiertechllc.com
       Website: http://frontiertechllc.com/
IT consulting services. (Woman/As-Pac, estab 2002, empl
146, sales , cert: State)

4414   Galmont Consulting, LLC
       70 W Madison St, Ste 1400
       Chicago, IL 60602
       Contact: Jeri Smith President
       Tel: 312-214-3261
       Email: jerig@galmont.com
       Website: www.galmont.com
Software quality assurance, testing & tool automation.
(Woman, estab 2000, empl 50, sales $5,700,000, cert:
WBENC)

4415   Genius Business Solutions, Inc.
       1711 5TH AVE STE 2
       Moline, IL 61265
       Contact: Sarthak Joshi CEO
       Tel: 309-269-2551
       Email: Shivaji@GeniusBSI.com
       Website: www.GeniusBSI.com
Information Technology & Engineering Services Consulting,
Software licensing, Implementation & Support SAP, Oracle
& Windchill, Custom software dev, Quality assurance &
Testing, End User Training, Strategic Staffing. (As-Ind, estab
2004, empl 70, sales $6,015,657, cert: NMSDC)

4416   Harrington Technology & Associates, Inc dba HTA
       Technology Security
       30 S Wacker Dr, 22 Fl
       Chicago, IL 60606
       Contact: Michelle Chaudry CEO
       Tel: 708-862-6348
       Email: mchaudry@hta-inc.com
       Website: www.hta-inc.com
Technology & information security consulting: risk assessments, protection, independent verification & validation,
vulnerability assessments & penetration testing, computer
forensics, network & security remediation. (Woman/AA,
estab 2001, empl 29, sales $2,778,000, cert: WBENC)

4417   HOBI International, Inc.
       1202 Nagel Blvd
       Batavia, IL 60510
       Contact: CEO
       Tel: 630-761-0500
       Email:
       Website: http://hobi.com
Recycle electronics, reverse logistics, IT & cellular asset
management, resale & re-marketing, data security, data
erasure, equipment removal & environmentally safe
recycling. (Woman, estab 1992, empl 250, sales
$42,000,000, cert: WBENC)

4418   Indusa Technical Corp.
       1 TransAm Plaza Dr Ste 350
       Oakbrook Terrace, IL 60181
       Contact: Hemant Shah Dir Business Dev
       Tel: 865-769-0715
       Email: hemant.shah@indusa.com
       Website: www.indusa.com
Information technology consulting & software solutions.
(As-Ind, estab 1989, empl 100, sales , cert: NMSDC)

4419   Innovative Systems Group, Inc.
       799 Roosevelt Rd Ste 109
       Glen Ellyn, IL 60137
       Contact: Jordan Myers Acct Mgr
       Tel: 312-861-1745
       Email: jordanm@innovativesys.com
       Website: www.innovativesys.com/
Information systems consulting, full life cycle systems,
application dev & support, project mgmt, business
systems analysis, staff augmentation, QA & testing svcs,
database architecture & admin, network & systems
admin, CRM & enterprise systems. (As-Pac, estab 1991,
empl 250, sales $20,000,000, cert: City)

4420   Intellisys Technology, LLC
       1000 Jorie Blvd Ste 200
       Oak Brook, IL 60523
       Contact: Raju Iyer Managing Partner
       Tel: 630-928-1111
       Email: riyer@intellisystechnology.com
       Website: www.intellisystechnology.com
IT consulting: system integration, application development, QA & testing, embedded system technology &
staff augmentation. (As-Ind, estab 1998, empl 300, sales
$6,000,000, cert: State)

4421   JRE & Associates Inc.
       46 E 26th St
       Chicago, IL 60616
       Contact: Jeffrey Edwards CEO
       Tel: 312-326-4327
       Email: jedwards@jreitsolutions.com
       Website: www.jreitsolutions.com
Logical Identity Controls
Logical Access Control Systems
Telecommunications and Network Security
Computer Operations Security Management
Cryptography & PKI Infrastructure Support (AA, estab
2009, empl 3, sales $150,000, cert: State)

4422   Kaizen Technologies, Inc.
       2339 N Kildare Ave
       Chicago, IL 60639
       Contact: Usman Hafeez President
       Tel: 773-934-3010
       Email: usman@kaizeninc.co
       Website: http://kaizeninc.co
Project Management Consulting & Software Development. (As-Ind, estab 2010, empl 1, sales , cert: 8a)

4423   KBS
       12549 S Laramie Ave
       Alsip, IL 60803
       Contact: Anthony R. Kitchens President
       Tel: 708-720-5981
       Email: tonyk@kbs.us.com
       Website: www.kbs.us.com
Technology products & svcs: desktop & notebook
support, network admin, voice, video, data & electricity
cabling, RFID tagging, WLAN, LAN, wireless cameras,
help desk & end-user technical support. (AA, estab 1992,
empl 22, sales $16,710,521, cert: NMSDC)

4424 Kristine Fallon Associates, Inc.
      11 E Adams St, Ste 1100
      Chicago, IL 60603
      Contact: Angelica Martinez Marketing Coord
      Tel: 312-360-9600
      Email: amartinez@kfa-inc.com
      Website: www.kfa-inc.com
Information technology consulting services, Building
Information Modeling (BIM / COBie), electronic project
management & collaboration systems, Facility Management Systems & Transit Asset Management database
solutions. (AA, estab 1993, empl 11, sales , cert: City)

4425 LCS Entertainment LLC
      4545 S Drexel
      Chicago, IL 60653
      Contact: Chrishon Lampley CEO
      Tel: 773-330-2440
      Email: chrishon@lovecorkscrew.com
      Website: www.lovecorkscrew.com
LCS Entertainment, LLC offers Love Cork Screw wine to
provide consumers a diverse line of
varietals. Regionally produced, and distributed in Illinois,
each sleek wine bottle offers a colorful, whimsical and fun
experience. (Woman/AA, estab 2014, empl 5, sales , cert:
NMSDC, WBENC)

4426 Lead IT Corporation
      1999 Wabash Ste 210
      Springfield, IL 62704
      Contact: Ira Neuman Sales Mgr
      Tel: 217-726-7250
      Email: ira.neuman@leaditgroup.com
      Website: www.leaditgroup.com
IT staffing & HR, executive search, consulting, computer
programming, IT management, technical consulting.
(Woman/As-Ind, estab 2005, empl 232, sales $23,712,000,
cert: State)

4427 LG Associates Inc. dba Asen Computer Associates
      900 N National Pkwy, Ste 155
      Schaumburg, IL 60173
      Contact: Liza Brigham Acct Mgr
      Tel: 847-995-1300
      Email: lbrigham@asen.com
      Website: www.asen.com/
Information technology & engineering consulting.
(Woman, estab 1975, empl 137, sales $5,985,000, cert:
WBENC)

4428 Midwest Solution Providers, Inc.
      21720 W Long Grove Rd, Ste C-227
      Deer Park, IL 60010
      Contact: Raj Andathode Principal Consultant
      Tel: 224-520-1510
      Email: raj@midwest-sp.com
      Website: www.midwest-sp.com
IT Consulting, Database design, database programming,
ETL, solutions using Informatica, Oracle, Teradata, Java,
Web-Services & custom applications. (As-Ind, estab 2004,
empl 1, sales , cert: NMSDC)

4429 Mirage Software Inc
      1701 E Woodfield Rd Ste 200
      Schaumburg, IL 60173
      Contact: Tori Johnstin Business Development
      Tel: 224-232-5090
      Email: tjohnstin@bourntec.com
      Website: www.bourntec.com
ERP implementation (Oracle, SAP, Microsoft, Infor &
others), ERP upgrades, successful Cloud migration, E-
business, Big Data, BI, IT Security & Managed IT.
(Woman/As-Ind, estab 1994, empl 35, sales , cert:
NMSDC, 8a)

4430 MVC Consulting Inc.
      203 N LaSalle St
      Chicago, IL 60601
      Contact: Greg Mummert Recruiting Mgr
      Tel: 312-606-5555
      Email: greg.mummert@mvc-consulting.com
      Website: www.mvc-consulting.com
IT consulting svcs: business intelligence/data warehous-
ing, compliance, ERP, CRM sales force automation,
change mgmt & project based consulting projects.
(Woman, estab 1981, empl 30, sales $2,800,000, cert:
WBENC)

4431 MZI Group Inc.
      1937 W Fulton St
      Chicago, IL 60612
      Contact: Nicole Klimenko VP
      Tel: 312-492-8740
      Email: nicole@mzigroup.com
      Website: www.mzigroup.com
Electrical, Mechanical, and Building Services Contractor
(Hisp, estab 1999, empl 110, sales $35,877,000, cert:
City, NMSDC)

4432 Netrion Global Solutions, Inc
      451 Dunham Rd Ste 202
      St. Charles, IL 60174
      Contact: Heather Thompson VP business ops
      Tel: 630-510-3000
      Email: heather.thompson@netrion.com
      Website: www.netrion.com
IT svcs: ERP implimentation, e-commerce solutions,
database development, project mgmt. (As-Ind, estab
1989, empl 21, sales $1,950,000, cert: NMSDC)

4433 Next Generation, Inc.
      800 West 5th Ave Ste 202
      Naperville, IL 60563
      Contact: Darrell Higueros President & CEO
      Tel: 312-739-0520
      Email:
      Website: www.nxtgeninc.com
Customizations, implementation & support Enterprise
Resource Planning software. (Hisp, estab 2001, empl 15,
sales $2,100,000, cert: State)

4434 On the Job Consulting, Inc, DBA Pixo
      110 W Main Strett
      Urbana, IL 61801
      Contact: CEO
      Tel: 217-344-0444
      Email:
      Website: pixotech.com
Information technology consulting services. (Woman,
estab 1998, empl 25, sales $565,000, cert: State)

4435 OnShore Technology Group, Inc.
505 N Lake Shore Dr Ste 220
Chicago, IL 60611
Contact: Valarie King- Bailey CEO
Tel: 312-321-6400
Email: vkbailey@onshoretech.com
Website: www.onshoretech.com
Applied technology products & svcs: engineering, e-govt support, advanced strategic & tactical mktg svcs, digital media production, enterprise business intelligence solutions, digital home networking. (Woman/AA, estab 2004, empl 6, sales $1,534,540, cert: City, NMSDC, WBENC)

4436 Pace Systems, Inc
2040 Corporate Ln
Naperville, IL 60563
Contact: Nick Taylor
Tel: 630-395-2191
Email: ntaylor@pace-systems.com
Website: www.pace-systems.com
Information technology services & sales. Citrix networking design & consulting. Physical & network security consulting. (As-Pac, estab 1983, empl 32, sales $30,000,000, cert: State, City, NMSDC)

4437 Pinnakle Technologies, Inc.
424 Fort Hill Dr, Ste 134A
Naperville, IL 60540
Contact: Ajay Kshatriya President
Tel: 630-352-0070
Email: ajay.kshatriya@pinnakle.net
Website: www.pinnakle.net
IT project management, staff augmentation, ERPs, web development, databases, business intelligence, infrastructure, etc. (As-Ind, estab 2009, empl 22, sales $4,500,000, cert: 8a)

4438 Plego Technologies
5002 Main St Ste 203
Downers Grove, IL 60515
Contact: Dir of Business Dev
Tel: 630-796-2074
Email:
Website: http://Plego.com
Web apps development, enterprise web design, systems integration, mobile app development, business intelligence & staff augmentation. (As-Ind, As-Pac, estab 2002, empl 20, sales $1,890,332, cert: NMSDC)

4439 Premier Systems, Inc
14489 John Humphrey Ste 202 Ste 202
Orland Park, IL 60462
Contact: Tariq Khan Acct Mgr
Tel: 708-349-9200
Email: tkhan@premiersystemsinc.com
Website: www.premiersystemsinc.com
IT consulting & staffing, project mgmt, systems programming & admin: IBM mainframe midrange, client server, PeopleSoft, SAP & Microsoft based systems; e-commerce devel. (As-Pac, estab 1993, empl 30, sales $2,713,000, cert: City, NMSDC)

4440 PTS Consulting Services LLC
1700 Park St, Ste 212
Naperville, IL 60563
Contact: Reshma Multani Client Servicing Mgr
Tel: 630-635-8328
Email: reshma.multani@ptscservices.com
Website: www.ptscservices.com
IT consulting and Business Consulting Services. (As-Pac, estab 2012, empl 50, sales $7,000,000, cert: State)

4441 Purple Consulting
2539 Lexington Lane
Naperville, IL 60540
Contact: Purnima Parashar Principal
Tel: 630-303-2706
Email: purnima@consultpurple.com
Website: www.consultpurple.com
Permanent placement of Software Engineers, Network Engineers, Analysts. Positions like Systems Engineers, Project Managers, Trading Engineers, IT Analysts, Business Analysts, Software Engineers, Sales. (Woman/As-Ind, estab 2014, empl 5, sales , cert: City)

4442 Quinnox Inc.
400 N. Michigan Ave Ste 1300
Chicago, IL 60611
Contact: Amar Sowani Sr. Mgr
Tel: 312-219-6517
Email: amars@quinnox.com
Website: www.quinnox.com
Information technology consulting & staff augmentation services. (As-Ind, estab 0, empl , sales $52,000,000, cert: NMSDC)

4443 RK Management Consultants, Inc.
One Tower Lane Ste 2540
Oakbrook Terrace, IL 60181
Contact: Nidhi Kapoor President
Tel: 630-202-3768
Email: nidhi@rkmcinc.com
Website: www.rkmcinc.com
Information technology solutions & professional consulting services, e-commerce & web dev, network infrastructure & support, software mgmt svcs, client server & mainframe computing environments. (Woman/As-Ind, As-Pac, estab 1988, empl 70, sales $8,200,000, cert: NMSDC, WBENC)

4444 RL Canning Inc.
8700 W. Bryn Mawr Ste 120N
Chicago, IL 60631
Contact: Rachel Canning President
Tel: 773-693-1900
Email: rachel@rlcanning.com
Website: www.rlcanning.com
Information technology consulting & staffing services. (Woman/Hisp, estab 1999, empl 48, sales $5,000,000, cert: State, City, WBENC)

4445 S & F Software Solutions Inc.
285 Victor Lane
Lake Zurich, IL 60047
Contact: Asma Farhin
Tel: 847-726-2571
Email: afarhin@sandfbizsolutions.com
Website: www.sandfbizsolutions.com
Project Management, Program/Project Management Office (PMO), Enterprise Risk Management, Business Process Re-engineering (BPR), Strategic Business Analysis, Data Management, Enterprise Quality Management. (Woman/As-Ind, estab 2011, empl 2, sales , cert: State, NMSDC, WBENC)

4446 SDA Consulting, Inc.
3011 W 183rd St
Homewood, IL 60430
Contact: Shawn Anderson President
Tel: 708-372-8809
Email: sda@sdaci.com
Website: http://sdaci.com
Technical consulting, staffing, support, development &
training, business software, Oracle EBS, PeopleSoft, JDE,
Siebel, Hyperion,
Microsoft, SAP, custom software. (Woman/AA, estab 2004,
empl 66, sales $9,185,610, cert: State, NMSDC)

4447 SDI Presence LLC
200 East Randolph, Ste 3550
Chicago, IL 60601
Contact: Dawn Pfeiffer Sr. Proposal Mgr
Tel: 312-580-7563
Email: dpfeiffer@sdipresence.com
Website: http://sdipresence.com
Traditional or cloud-based systems life-cycle, concept
development, systems integration & long-term support.
(As-Ind, estab 2015, empl 250, sales , cert: State, NMSDC)

4448 Senryo Technologies
387 Shuman Blvd, 208e
Naperville, IL 60563
Contact: Nick Georgelos Research Analyst
Tel: 630-355-7429
Email: nick.georgelos@senryo.com
Website: www.senryo.com
Consulting services: project management, systems
delivery, management consulting, technology consulting,
quality assurance, value management, application integra-
tion & business intelligence. (As-Ind, estab 2001, empl 20,
sales , cert: 8a)

4449 SNtial Technologies, Inc.
150 N. Michigan Ave Ste 2800
Chicago, IL 60601
Contact: Leon Francisco President
Tel: 630-452-4735
Email: leon.francisco@sntialtech.com
Website: www.sntialtech.com
Information technology services, custom software devel-
opment, systems integration & re-engineering. (As-Pac,
estab 2001, empl 8, sales $1,000,000, cert: City, NMSDC)

4450 Software Tech Enterprises, Inc.
19730 Governors Hwy Ste 5
Flossmoor, IL 60422
Contact: Rolland Craig Business Dev Mgr
Tel: 708-922-9008
Email: rcraig@software-tec.com
Website: www.software-tec.com
IT management consulting, IT planning, IT governance,
enterprise architecture, service oriented architecture, ERP
strategy & health information technology. (AA, estab 2001,
empl 55, sales $8,000,000, cert: 8a)

4451 Swoon Group
300 South Wacker Dr Ste 300
Chicago, IL 60606
Contact: Joseph Matalone EVP
Tel: 312-450-8700
Email: joe.matalone@swoonstaffing.com
Website: www.swoonstaffing.com
Technical staffing. (Woman, estab , empl , sales
$80,000,000, cert: WBENC)

4452 Synchronous Solutions, Inc.
211 W Wacker Dr Ste 300
Chicago, IL 60606
Contact: John Sterling CEO
Tel: 312-252-3700
Email: jsterling@synch-solutions.com
Website: www.synch-solutions.com
Implementations, integrations & upgrades, ERP software
products, Oracle-PeopleSoft & SAP, functional & techni-
cal Consulting, database admin, application integration,
training, project mgmt, strategic IT outsourcing. (AA,
estab 1998, empl 75, sales $14,000,000, cert: State, City)

4453 Synectics Inc.
135 S LaSalle St Ste 2050
Chicago, IL 60603
Contact: Melissa Lounds Dir of Global Accts
Tel: 312-629-1020
Email: m_lounds@synectics.com
Website: www.synectics.com/
Information technology consulting, staff augmentation.
(Woman, estab 1984, empl 300, sales $19,300,000, cert:
CPUC, WBENC)

4454 System Solutions, Inc.
3630 Commercial Ave
Northbrook, IL 60062
Contact: Oliver Patterson Sr Acct Mgr
Tel: 847-272-6160
Email: oliver.patterson@thessi.com
Website: www.THESSI.COM
Information technology: enterprise solution products &
architecture, consulting, staffing, network design &
implementation, hardware & software procurement,
onsite installation services. (As-Pac, estab 1987, empl
20, sales $24,000,000, cert: State, NMSDC)

4455 TechCircle, Inc.
500 N Michigan Ave Ste 600
Chicago, IL 60611
Contact: Aakash Gajera President
Tel: 312-767-5653
Email: agajera@techcircleinc.com
Website: www.techcircleinc.com
Information technology consulting & staff augmentation
services, project/program mgmt, business system
analysis, quality assurance, verification & validation. (As-
Ind, estab 2015, empl 4, sales $300,000, cert: State,
NMSDC)

4456 Technical Source, Inc.
1447 E Rosita Dr
Palatine, IL 60074
Contact: President
Tel: 847-705-1730
Email:
Website: www.computerrelocation.com
Project Management Information Technology, IT
Management, Help Desk & Support Disaster Recovery.
(Woman, estab 1999, empl 54, sales $1,025,201, cert:
City, WBENC)

4457 Total Response Technology, LLC
1921 Richfield Ave
Highland Park, IL 60035
Contact: Sandra Bast President
Tel: 312-513-0478
Email: sandra@trt-llc.com
Website: www.totalresponsetechnology.com
Implement or maintain IT investments. (Woman/Hisp,
estab 2009, empl 20, sales $1,400,000, cert: City,
WBENC)

4458   Tranzact Technologies, Inc.
       360 W Butterfield Rd Ste 400
       Elmhurst, IL 60126
       Contact: LeAnn DeFalco Sales Assoc
       Tel: 630-833-0890
       Email: diversity@tranzact.com
       Website: www.tranzact.com
Sourcing and Spend Management, Constellation TMS,
Supply Chain Edge, Risk Monitoring, Advanced Data mining
& reporting. (Woman, estab 1984, empl 250, sales
$74,228,000, cert: WBENC)

4459   Von Technologies, LLC
       1193 Old Creek Ct
       Woodridge, IL 60517
       Contact: Michelle Vondrasek President
       Tel: 630-985-8474
       Email: vondrasek.michelle@vontechnologies.com
       Website: www.vontechnologies.com
Network solutions: infrastructure design, implementation,
management, refresh, software & hardware configuration,
wireless solutions. (Woman, estab 2006, empl 23, sales ,
cert: State, WBENC)

Indiana

4460   Alliance Group Technologies Co-Calumet, Inc.
       911 Broad Ripple Ave, Ste B
       Indianapolis, IN 46220
       Contact: Michael Weir Dir Business Development
       Tel: 317-254-8285
       Email: mweir@alliancegrouptech.com
       Website: www.alliancegrouptech.com
Engineering consulting & technical staffing solutions. (As-
Pac, estab 1975, empl 215, sales , cert: NMSDC)

4461   Anchor Point Technology Resources, Inc
       9510 N Meridian StSte 200
       Indianapolis, IN 46260
       Contact: Rachael Schatko President
       Tel: 317-225-4141
       Email: rachael.schatko@anchorpointtr.com
       Website: www.anchorpointtr.com/
Engineering & IT solutions, IT staffing, contract, C2D,
Permanent Placement, Engineering Staffing & Executive
Placement. (Woman, estab 2004, empl 140, sales
$15,500,000, cert: State)

4462   Bottom-Line Performance, Inc.
       P.O. Box 155
       New Palestine, IN 46163
       Contact: Kirk Boller President
       Tel: 317-861-5935
       Email: kirk_boller@bottomlineperformance.com
       Website: www.bottomlineperformance.com
E-learning, classroom-based training. (Woman, estab , empl
, sales $1,500,000, cert: WBENC)

4463   CIMCOR Inc.
       8252 Virginia St
       Merrillville, IN 46410
       Contact: Robert Johnson President
       Tel: 219-736-4400
       Email: johnson.robert@cimcor.com
       Website: www.cimcor.com
Protect critical IT infrastructure from malicious exposure.
(AA, estab 1997, empl 15, sales $1,359,269, cert: NMSDC)

4464   Data Integration Consulting, Inc.
       7399 N. Shadeland Ave Ste 312
       Indianapolis, IN 46250
       Contact: Tim Thompson President
       Tel: 317-894-2623
       Email: tthompson@dataic.com
       Website: www.dataic.com
IT consulting, web application development, desktop
application development, computer programming,
network design & administration, database design &
administration. (AA, estab 2003, empl 1, sales , cert:
State)

4465   GuideSoft Inc. dba Knowledge Services
       5875 Castle Creek Parkway N Dr Ste 400
       Indianapolis, IN 46250
       Contact: Cindy Davis Director
       Tel: 317-578-1700
       Email: cindyd@knowledgeservices.com
       Website: www.knowledgeservices.com
IT staffing; IT training development. project mgmt,
application development, tier I-III help desk & desktop
support. (Woman, estab 1994, empl 130, sales
$13,186,909, cert: State)

4466   Guilford Group LLC
       615 W Carmel Dr, Ste 130
       Carmel, IN 46032
       Contact: Rajan Kapur Director
       Tel: 317-814-1060
       Email: rajkapur@guilfordgroup.com
       Website: http://guilfordgroup.com
Information technology consulting, IT project management, enterprise application development, mobile
development, data management, staffing, cloud storage,
systems integrations, web development & graphic
design resources. (As-Ind, estab 2003, empl 30, sales
$2,922,823, cert: State, NMSDC)

4467   GyanSys Inc.
       702 Adams St
       Carmel, IN 46032
       Contact: Padmaja Una Chairman
       Tel: 317-332-3290
       Email: padma.una@gyansys.com
       Website: www.gyansys.com
Global systems integration: SAP & Microsoft products,
mobile platforms. (Woman/As-Ind, estab , empl , sales
$17,000,000, cert: State, WBENC)

4468   JumpStart Point of Arrival, LLC
       9801 Fall Creek Rd, Ste 410
       Indianapolis, IN 46256
       Contact: Ek-Leng Chua-Miller CEO
       Tel: 317-777-1995
       Email: ek-leng@jumpstartpoa.biz
       Website: www.jumpstartpoa.biz
Statistical analysis, data analysis, database marketing,
data mining, statistical modeling, regression analysis
(Woman/As-Pac, estab 2005, empl 2, sales $442,000,
cert: State, NMSDC, WBENC)

4469 LHP Software, LLC
1888 Poshard Dr
Columbus, IN 47203
Contact: Kandace Yamcharern Mgr Payment Process
Tel: 812-418-6331
Email: kandace.y@lhpes.com
Website: www.lhpsoftware.com
Custom software solutions: embedded software, communication software, internet software, testing. (As-Pac, estab 2001, empl 210, sales $26,893,359, cert: NMSDC)

4470 Lucidia IT
6525 E 82nd St, Ste 103
Indianapolis, IN 46250
Contact: Janet Stiller CEO
Tel: 317-953-9800
Email: anikirk@lucidiait.com
Website: www.lucidiait.com/
Data Center Technologies, Cloud Connectivity, Collaboration, End User Technology, Enterprise Networking, Cybersecurity and Project Management. (Woman, estab 2018, empl 11, sales $5,000,000, cert: WBENC)

4471 Morse Communications Inc.
8207 Linden Ave
Munster, IN 46321
Contact: Tim Kerrick Sr Acct Mgr
Tel: 219-314-6029
Email: tkerrick@morsecom.com
Website: www.morsecom.com
Systems integration, communications, networking & electronic safety & security. (Woman, estab 1994, empl 75, sales $17,000,000, cert: State)

4472 Phelco Technologies, Inc.
9801 Fall Creek Rd #131
Indianapolis, IN 46256
Contact: Tasha Phelps CEO
Tel: 317-898-0334
Email: tasha@phelco.com
Website: www.phelco.com
Network infrastructure, disaster recovery, off-site data backup, web development. (Woman/AA, estab 1997, empl 1, sales , cert: State)

4473 Pinnacle Mailing Products, LLC
7701 W Kilgore Ave, Ste 5
Yorktown, IN 47396
Contact: Kimberly Laffoon Owner
Tel: 765-405-1194
Email: kimlaffoon@pinnaclemailing.com
Website: www.pinnaclemailingproducts.net
Address correction & shipping software solutions. (Woman, estab 2009, empl 6, sales $195,000, cert: State)

4474 RCR Technology Corporation
251 N Illinois St Ste 1150, North Tower
Indianapolis, IN 46204
Contact: Robert Reed CEO
Tel: 317-624-9500
Email: rreed@rcrtechnology.com
Website: www.rcrtechnology.com
Information technology consulting, network design, application services & project management. (AA, estab 1997, empl 150, sales $18,000,000, cert: State, City, NMSDC)

4475 Ryan Consulting Group, Inc.
7914 North Shadeland Ave, Ste 200
Indianapolis, IN 46250
Contact: Aisha Washington proposal Mgr
Tel: 317-541-9300
Email: awashington@consultrcg.com
Website: www.consultrcg.com
Information technologies, systems integration, design & consulting. (AA, estab 2001, empl 106, sales $15,604,064, cert: State, City, NMSDC)

4476 STLogics
1119 Keystone Way Ste 301
Carmel, IN 46032
Contact: Priya Prasad President
Tel: 800-505-0357
Email: hr@stlogics.com
Website: www.stlogics.com
IT consulting, staff augmentation, managed IT solutions, project management, web & software development, quality assurance, Java applications, sharepoint, SAP, ERP, datawarehouse & network administration. (Woman/As-Ind, estab 2004, empl 120, sales $750,000, cert: NMSDC)

Kansas

4477 3 Fuerzas Technology Solutions, LLC
14013 Outlook
Overland Park, KS 66223
Contact: Shawn Hashmi VP, Program Management
Tel: 913-744-1163
Email: shashmi@edzsystems.com
Website: www.edzsystems.com
Software Development, IT Consulting Services, Intelligent Resource Management System (Intelligent RMS. (Woman/Hisp, estab 2015, empl 5, sales $201,000, cert: NMSDC, WBENC)

4478 Evolv Solutions, LLC.
7300 West 110th St Ste 700
Overland Park, KS 66210
Contact: Eric Harland VP
Tel: 913-469-8900
Email: eharland@evolvsolutions.com
Website: www.evolvsolutions.com
IT & document mgmt solutions, project mgmt & outsourcing, enterprise solutions, web devel, system integration, tech communication, office assessment, asset mgmt, etc. (AA, estab 2001, empl 8, sales $7,849,351, cert: NMSDC)

4479 IT Consulting Services, Inc.
901 Kentucky St Ste 105
Lawrence, KS 66044
Contact: Kishor Gohel COO
Tel: 913-972-2321
Email: kgohel@itcscorp.net
Website: http://itcscorp.net
Software Engineering: Application Development (Web, non-Web, Mobile, SharePoint, e-commerce), Legacy systems & data migration, System Integration (SOA based & FOSS Custom Solutions). (Woman/As-Ind, estab 2004, empl 6, sales $156,456, cert: State, 8a)

4480 JMA Chartered
      10551 Barkley St Ste 400
      Overland Park, KS 66212
      Contact: Sanjay Chopra Dir of Western Region
      Tel: 913-722-3252
      Email: schopra@jmait.com
      Website: www.jma-it.com
Infomration technology: systems integration, IT infrastructure planning, IT facilities management, network design & implementation, IT security audits & staff supplementation. (As-Pac, estab 1994, empl 250, sales $13,900,000, cert: NMSDC, CPUC)

4481 Perfect Output, LLC
      9200 Indian Creek Pkwy Ste 400
      Overland Park, KS 66210
      Contact: Angela Pease VP Business Dev
      Tel: 913-317-8400
      Email: apease@perfectoutput.com
      Website: www.perfectoutput.com
Document output devices: printers, fax machines, & digital multi-functional devices, develop & implement document management strategies. (AA, estab 1997, empl 70, sales , cert: State, NMSDC, CPUC)

4482 Saicon Consultants, Inc.
      9300 W 110th St Ste 650
      Overland Park, KS 66210
      Contact: Kristalle Ulrich Strategic Accts Mgr
      Tel: 214-705-1825
      Email: kristalleu@staffingtechnologies.com
      Website: www.saicon.com/index.php
IT consulting: ERP, client server devl, & admin. (Woman/As-Ind, estab 1998, empl 550, sales $65,000,000, cert: NMSDC, WBENC)

4483 Technology Group Solutions, LLC
      8551 Quivira Road
      Lenexa, KS 66215
      Contact: Lenora Payne CEO
      Tel: 913-451-9900
      Email: lpayne@tgs-mtc.com
      Website: www.tgs-mtc.com
Information technology soutions. (Woman/AA, estab 2005, empl 79, sales $87,407,949, cert: NMSDC, WBENC)

4484 Veracity Consulting, Inc.
      15516 W 81st St, Ste 195
      Lenexa, KS 66219
      Contact: Angela Hurt CEO
      Tel: 913-579-9242
      Email: angela.hurt@engageveracity.com
      Website: http://veracityconsulting.us
IT contracting services: process improvement, PMO, project Mgt, custom computer programming, systems administration & information security. (Woman/Nat Ame, estab 2006, empl 26, sales , cert: WBENC)

Kentucky

4485 AnITConsultant, LLC
      P.O. Box 22998
      Owensboro, KY 42304
      Contact: Whaylon Coleman Owner
      Tel: 270-883-1450
      Email: it@anitconsultant.com
      Website: www.anitconsultant.com
IT solutions & consulting services, Game Development (Unity3d), Social Media Consulting (Facebook, LinkedIn, & Twitter), Microsoft Application Development (Sharepoint, Office, Microsoft Dynamics), Mobile & Tablet Apps. (AA, estab 2010, empl 1, sales , cert: State)

4486 CEEJS Software
      3406 Greentree Rd
      Lexington, KY 40517
      Contact: Eddie Sanford President
      Tel: 859-576-6790
      Email: esanford@ceejs.com
      Website: www.ceejs.com
Information technology: design, development, maintenance & support software applications. (AA, estab 1996, empl 11, sales $6,404,000, cert: State)

4487 Etisbew Technology Group Inc.
      7031 Glen Arbor Dr
      Florence, KY 41042
      Contact: Raj Pakala CEO
      Tel: 502-386-4999
      Email: bizteam@etisbew.com
      Website: www.etisbew.com
E-Business solutions, e-business strategy, architecture & process automation, web based applications development & maintenance. (As-Pac, estab 2000, empl 150, sales $5,321,106, cert: NMSDC)

4488 V-Soft Consulting Group Inc.
      101 Bullitt Lane Ste 205
      Louisville, KY 40222
      Contact: Vincel Anthony Natl Business Dev Mgr
      Tel: 502-425-8425
      Email: vanthony@vsoftconsulting.com
      Website: www.vsoftconsulting.com
Information technology staffing & consulting services: temporary, contract & permanent placement. (Woman/As-Pac, estab 1997, empl 230, sales , cert: NMSDC)

Louisiana

4489 A-B Computer Solutions, Inc.
      P.O. Box 1851
      Mandeville, LA 70470
      Contact: Jason Brady President
      Tel: 985-624-3092
      Email: jasonb@a-bcomputers.com
      Website: www.a-bcomputers.com
Information technology solutions & consulting. (Woman, estab 1997, empl 13, sales $3,060,000, cert: WBENC)

4490 Barrister Global Services Network Inc
      42548 Happywoods Road
      Hammond, LA 70403
      Contact: Melissa Dobson Dir of Service Solutions
      Tel: 985-365-0806
      Email: mdobson@barrister.com
      Website: www.barrister.com
Information technology services. (Woman, estab , empl 147, sales , cert: WBENC)

4491 ComTec Consultants Inc.
2400 Veterans Memorial Blvd Ste 205
Kenner, LA 70062
Contact: Vijay Saradhi VP
Tel: 972-338-3533
Email: vijay@comtecinfo.com
Website: www.comtecinfo.com
Information technology & business process services.
(Woman/As-Ind, estab 1996, empl 635, sales $62,550,319,
cert: NMSDC)

4492 Morine Networking, Inc.
P.O. Box 363
Opelousas, LA 70570
Contact: Rodney Morine VP
Tel: 337-942-1790
Email: rodney@morinetrucking.com
Website: www.morinenetworking.com
We are a freight brokering company providing 3rd party
property logistics (Woman/AA, estab 2007, empl 2, sales ,
cert: State, NMSDC)

4493 MSF Global Solutions, LLC
201 St. Charles Ave, Ste 2500
New Orleans, LA 70170
Contact: Marseyas Fernandez CEO
Tel: 504-872-0641
Email: marseyas@msfglobal.net
Website: www.msfglobal.net
Geospatial & location based software & data development,
mobile website & app development, staffing & training
support services, data & business intelligence services,
web & custom software design & development services.
(AA, estab 2003, empl 5, sales $400,000, cert: NMSDC)

4494 Trendsic Corporation
311 Veterans Blvd Ste A
Denham Springs, LA 70726
Contact: Jelani Clark President
Tel: 225-490-9505
Email: jelani@trendsic.com
Website: www.Trendsic.com
Software engineers, application support, integration,
testing, deployment & software management systems
(applications) & system software tools. (AA, estab 2006,
empl 9, sales $976,415, cert: State)

4495 VINFORMATIX L.L.C.
801 North Boulevard Ste 120
Baton Rouge, LA 70802
Contact: Kelli Cagle Dir Business Devel
Tel: 504-401-0533
Email: kcagle@vinformatix.com
Website: www.vinformatix.com
Custom-built software applications for web & mobile
platforms (including OS/Android/Windows mobile apps),
software lifecycle services, requirements analysis, design,
coding, testing, QA/QC, training & maintenance. (Woman/
As-Ind, estab 2008, empl 27, sales $1,073,605, cert:
WBENC)

Massachusetts

4496 Advans IT Services, Inc.
65 Boston Post Rd W Ste 390
Marlborough, MA 01752
Contact: Paul Angelo CRM Mgr
Tel: 508-624-9900
Email: pangelo@advansit.com
Website: www.AdvansIT.com
IT infrastructure, project management & software
development & offshore support. (As-Pac, estab 2009,
empl 205, sales $21,000,000, cert: State, NMSDC)

4497 Advoqt, LLC
10 Guest St Ste 290
Boston, MA 02135
Contact: Reinier Moquete CEO
Tel: 617-307-7770
Email: info@advoqt.com
Website: www.advoqt.com
Systems integration & technology advisory firm focused
on Hybrid Cloud Computing. (Hisp, estab 2012, empl 10,
sales , cert: State)

4498 Aquent LLC
501 Boylston St Third Fl
Boston, MA 02116
Contact: Jennifer Cousins Dir Staffing Solutions
Development
Tel: 202-808-0557
Email: jcousins@aquent.com
Website: www.aquent.com
Graphic designers, web designers, production artists,
presentation graphics experts, writers & project manag-
ers: freelance, permanent & temporary-to-permanent
basis. (Woman/As-Ind, As-Pac, estab 1986, empl 890,
sales $500,000,000, cert: NMSDC)

4499 AVCO Consulting, Inc.
38 Front St, Unit #4
Worcester, MA 01608
Contact: Sukesh Kunduru Operations Mgr
Tel: 508-450-1075
Email: partnerships@avcoconsulting.com
Website: www.avcoconsulting.com
Customer software development, technology consult-
ing, staffing consulting, business automation, systems
integration, business intelligence, big data and data
analytics solutions. (As-Ind, estab 1999, empl 1000,
sales $45,000,000, cert: NMSDC)

4500 Cambridge Computer Services, Inc.
271 Waverley Oaks Ste 301
Waltham, MA 02452
Contact: Business Operations Customer Advocate
Tel: 781-250-3000
Email: bizops@cambridgecomputer.com
Website: http://cambridgecomputer.com
Data storage & data protection solutions: SAN, NAS,
backup, cloud, solid state, archiving solutions, research
data management, scientific workflow, metadata, tiered
storage, chargebacks, archiving & cloud storage.
(Woman, estab , empl , sales , cert: State, WBENC)

4501   CTS Services Inc.
       260 Maple St
       Bellingham, MA 02019
       Contact: Michelle Carlow President
       Tel: 508-528-7720
       Email: mcarlow@ctsservices.com
       Website: www.ctsservices.com
Computer, printer & peripheral repair: touch screen
displays, barcode scanning equipment, receipt printer.
(Woman, estab 1989, empl 22, sales $2,775,000, cert:
State)

4502   Cube Intelligence Corporation
       12 Brattle Lane
       Arlington, MA 02474
       Contact: Hemant Verma President
       Tel: 617-275-8254
       Email: hsverma@cubeic.com
       Website: www.cubeic.com
IT consulting and Staffing augmentationsvcs: data warehousing, data integration, data profiling, data quality,
master data management, ODS, Operational Data Stores,
Data Mart, Star Schema. (As-Ind, estab 2001, empl 2, sales
$178,654, cert: State, NMSDC, 8a)

4503   Deerwalk, Inc.
       430 Bedford St
       Lexington, MA 02420
       Contact: Jeffrey Gasser President
       Tel: 781-325-1775
       Email: jgasser@deerwalk.com
       Website: www.deerwalk.com
Global data analytics, big data technology & web based
data analytics applications, healthcare data analytics,
population management & controlling healthcare costs.
(As-Ind, estab 2010, empl 400, sales $7,450,000, cert:
NMSDC)

4504   Distributed Technology Associates
       1740 Massachusetts Ave
       Boxborough, MA 01719
       Contact: Sanjay Tikku President
       Tel: 978-274-0462
       Email: office@dtainc.us
       Website: www.dtainc.us
Database & systems services, database & systems, Oracle &
SQL Server databases, Linux, Solaris & Windows platforms.
(As-Ind, estab 1997, empl 7, sales $2,114,602, cert: State,
NMSDC)

4505   Dnutch Associates, Inc.
       301 Broadway
       Methuen, MA 01844
       Contact: Stephen Payne CEO
       Tel: 978-687-1500
       Email: spayne@dnutch.com
       Website: www.dnutch.com
Networking & systems integration solutions. (Woman/AA,
estab 1993, empl 8, sales $550,000, cert: State, WBENC)

4506   Executive Analytics & Design, Inc.
       10 Malcolm X Blvd
       Boston, MA 02119
       Contact: Josie Haywood
       Tel:
       Email: eadtech@msn.com
       Website: www.eadtech.com
Network installation, maintenance & external client
interfaces, training, support & outsourcing, project mgmt,
web site hosting, etc. (Woman/AA, estab 1998, empl 3,
sales , cert: State)

4507   Fenco Global Industries Corp.
       1 Federal St
       Springfield, MA 01105
       Contact: Fenella Sitati President
       Tel: 413-308-8800
       Email: fenella@winningtek.com
       Website: www.winningtek.com
Technology hardware for application security,
datacenters & cloud virtualization, F5 Networks,
VMware, Palo Alto, Cisco Networks, RedHat, Microsoft,
NetApp, EMC, HP, IBM, Dell & ExtraHop. (Woman/AA,
estab 2009, empl 5, sales $450,000, cert: NMSDC)

4508   Hawkins Point Partners LLC
       7 Technology Dr
       North Chelmsford, MA 01863
       Contact: Heather Morris Kyer Sr Principal
       Tel: 781-640-0893
       Email: hmorriskyer@hawkinspointpartners.com
       Website: http://hawkinspointpartners.com
IT consulting, outsourcing reset, application modernization, information management, mobile solutions &
enterprise architecture & integration. (Woman, estab
2012, empl 5, sales , cert: State, WBENC)

4509   IntePros Incorporated
       750 Marrett Road Ste 301
       Lexington, MA 02421
       Contact: Jeffrey Anderson Branch Mgr
       Tel: 612-916-7387
       Email: janderson@intepros.com
       Website: www.intepros.com
Contracted IT consultants, software development
lifecycle, network infrastructure & security. (Woman,
estab 1996, empl 350, sales $55,400,000, cert: WBENC)

4510   Interactive Tactical Group
       55 Wallace St
       Somerville, MA 02144
       Contact: Michael Quan President
       Tel: 617-500-7520
       Email: mike@tacticalvr.com
       Website: www.tacticalvr.com
Interactive panoramic imaging for military, security &
industrial organizations. DotProduct3D hand held 3D
scanner, DotProduct3D hand held 3D scanner, DPI-7,
uses Android tablet & Kinect sensor. (As-Pac, estab 2000,
empl 1, sales $150,500, cert: State, NMSDC)

4511   Iterators LLC
       50 Milk St, Fl 16
       Boston, MA 02109
       Contact: Jill Willcox Managing Member
       Tel: 617-909-0564
       Email: jwillcox@iteratorstesting.com
       Website: https://Iteratorstesting.com
Accessibility Testing, Website and Mobile App Testing:
Manual, Accessibility, Automation • Manual Functional
and Regression Testing • Automated Regression Testing.
(Woman, estab 2017, empl 5, sales $264,000, cert:
WBENC)

4512 Martindale Associates, Inc.
      65 Avco Rd, Unit M
      Bradford, MA 01835
      Contact: Laurie Hall President
      Tel: 978-372-2120
      Email: lmh@martindaleassoc.com
      Website: www.martindaleassoc.com
Automated machine & process control systems, data
acquisition systems, barcode data collection, inventory &
asset tracking, RFID, mobile device management,
handheld computers & systems integration.
(Woman/Nat Ame, estab 1976, empl 7, sales $1,525,041,
cert: State)

4513 On Track Consulting
      317 Eliot St
      Milton, MA 02186
      Contact: Janet McCloskey President
      Tel: 617-653-1409
      Email: jmccloskey@ontrackconsult.com
      Website: www.ontrackconsult.com
Information management services, big data, data ware-
housing, business intelligence & data management.
(Woman, estab 1997, empl , sales $3,157,077, cert: State,
WBENC)

4514 Online Computer Prodcuts, Inc.
      672 Pleasant St
      Norwood, MA 02062
      Contact: Harry Butters Acct Mgr
      Tel: 781-255-9100
      Email: hbutters@online-computer.com
      Website: www.online-computer.com
Information technology support products, services &
solutions. (Woman, estab 1987, empl 24, sales
$14,075,000, cert: WBENC)

4515 Onyx Spectrum Technology, Inc. dba Shearwater EM
      78 Fisher Ave
      Boston, MA 02120
      Contact: Adrienne R. Benton President & CEO
      Tel: 617-407-2826
      Email: abenton@onyxspectrum.com
      Website: www.onyxspectrum.com
Technical consulting services: data analysis, information
security, business process improvement & regulatory
concerns. (Woman/AA, estab 2004, empl 5, sales
$726,000, cert: State)

4516 ResourceSoft, Inc.
      33 Boston Post Rd W Ste 230
      Marlborough, MA 01752
      Contact: Pyi Phyo VP
      Tel: 508-787-0882
      Email: pyi@resourcesoft.com
      Website: www.resourcesoft.com
Custom computer programming svcs: MS .NET, JAVA/J2EE,
quality assurance. (Woman/As-Pac, estab 1999, empl 55,
sales $5,711,183, cert: State, NMSDC)

4517 Scitics Inc.
      436 Central St
      Acton, MA 01720
      Contact: Joan Yu President
      Tel: 978-844-1258
      Email: jyu@sciticsinc.com
      Website: www.sciticsinc.com
Data analytic services, data exploration & discovery, data
processing, hosting & related services, custom computer
programming services, dashboard & customized business intelligence reports, predictive modeling. (Woman/
As-Pac, estab 2010, empl 3, sales $128,170, cert: State,
WBENC)

4518 Shred King Corporation
      60 McGrath Hwy
      Quincy, MA 02169
      Contact: Donald Cornell GM
      Tel: 617-221-1600
      Email: info@shred-king.com
      Website: www.shred-king.com
Document destruction services. (Woman, estab 2006,
empl 10, sales $160,200, cert: State)

4519 Sigma Systems, Inc.
      5 Mt Royal Ave Ste 100
      Marlborough, MA 01752
      Contact: Shama Nannapaneni President
      Tel: 508-925-3200
      Email: nfischer@sigmainc.com
      Website: www.sigmainc.com
IT consulting, project mgmt, application dev, network
mgmt, database mgmt & support, staffing services,
custom application dev, data warehousing, business
intelligence, CRM, ERP, EAI, quality assurance, systems
admin, web dev & custom MIS. (Woman/As-Ind, estab
1994, empl 97, sales $4,000,000, cert: State, NMSDC)

4520 SJB Enterprises, Inc. dba Sandra Network
      25 Goodale St
      Peabody, MA 01960
      Contact: Sandra Batakis President
      Tel: 978-535-0202
      Email: wbe@sandranetwork.com
      Website: www.sandranetwork.com
IT consulting: PC repair, training & networks. (Woman,
estab 1998, empl 5, sales $671,895, cert: State, WBENC)

4521 Softlinx, Inc.
      100 Riverpark Dr
      North Reading, MA 01864
      Contact: Helen Kim Contract Mgr
      Tel: 978-881-0575
      Email: hkim@softlinx.com
      Website: www.softlinx.com
Software, IT development, consulting & training.
(Woman/As-Pac, estab 1993, empl 15, sales $1,530,000,
cert: NMSDC, WBENC)

4522 Solidus Technical Solutions, LLC
      17 Forsythia Rd
      Leominster, MA 01453
      Contact: Jill Blagsvedt Business Develop Mgr
      Tel: 866-765-4387
      Email: solidussmallbd@solidus-ts.com
      Website: www.solidus-ts.com
Software & systems engineering, life cycle, radar,
sensors, fault tolerant, mission planning, intelligence
systems, embedded software, networking, integration &
test. (Woman, estab 2001, empl 95, sales , cert: WBENC)

4523   Soltrix Technology Solutions Inc.
860 Worcester Road Ste 215
Framingham, MA 01702
Contact: Raghu Nandan President
Tel: 774-293-1293
Email: raghu.nandan@soltrixsolutions.com
Website: www.soltrixsolutions.com
Custom software application design & development services. (Woman/As-Ind, estab 2007, empl 3, sales , cert: State)

4524   Stellar Corporation
594 Marrett Rd
Lexington, MA 02421
Contact: Swapan Roy
Tel: 781-863-0101
Email: sroy@stlr.net
Website: www.stlr.net
software - custom application development, reengineering, database
engineering - structural engineering (As-Pac, estab 2002, empl 7, sales $614,678, cert: State)

4525   Stemac Inc
30 Evergreen Dr
Bridgewater, MA 02324
Contact: Jane McCarthy President
Tel: 508-331-1410
Email: jane@stemacinc.com
Website: www.stemacinc.com
IT placement, pre screened Supply Chain & SAP Talent, Customer Service & Consultative. (Woman, estab 2013, empl 2, sales $400,000, cert: WBENC)

4526   TalentBurst, Inc
679 Worcester Road
Natick, MA 01760
Contact: Jamie Jacobs Dir of Strategic Partnerships
Tel: 614-382-8840
Email: jamie.jacobs@talentburst.com
Website: www.talentburst.com
Information technology staff augmentation, lifesciences, business & regulatory compliance, accounting, finance & IT solutions services. (Nat Ame, As-Pac, estab 2002, empl 1405, sales $84,700,000, cert: NMSDC)

4527   Tanisha Systems Inc.
75 Federal St Ste 1330
Boston, MA 02110
Contact: Gorav Aggarwal VP
Tel: 617-729-0260
Email: gaggarwal@tanishasystems.com
Website: www.tanishasystems.com
Custom application development & end-to-end IT services. (As-Ind, estab 2002, empl 80, sales $9,700,000, cert: State)

4528   tCognition, Inc.
70 Kemble St Ste 201
Boston, MA 02119
Contact: Manoj Shinde CEO
Tel: 617-552-5002
Email: manoj.shinde@tcognition.com
Website: www.tCognition.com
IT/software consulting & outsourcing services. (As-Ind, estab 2003, empl 65, sales $3,159,484, cert: State, NMSDC)

4529   Vernance, LLC
745 Atlantic Ave
Boston, MA 02111
Contact: Pedro Marcano CEO
Tel: 936-647-3376
Email: pmarcano@vernance.com
Website: www.vernance.com
Cyber & Physical Security Risk Management consulting services. (Hisp, estab 2014, empl 3, sales $350,000, cert: State, NMSDC)

Maryland

4530   5 Star Consulting Group, LLC.
3261 Old Washington Rd Ste 2020
Waldorf, MD 20602
Contact: Lethia Dargin President & CEO
Tel: 301-216-3839
Email: ldargin@5starconsultinggrp.com
Website: www.5StarConsultingGrp.com
Systems Integration & Design, Computer Integration, SCCM, Software deployment, Software packaging, Server maintenance, troubleshooting, configuration & build. IT Consulting, software & hardware support. (Woman/AA, estab 2013, empl 5, sales , cert: State, SDB)

4531   Acela Technologies, Inc.
5115 Pegasus Ct, Ste A
Frederick, MD 21704
Contact: Carole Derringer CEO
Tel: 301-846-9060
Email: cderringer@acelatechnologies.com
Website: www.acelatechnologies.com
Wireless solutions engineering & integration, wireless internet services, VoIP, VoWiFi, wireless video surveillance. (AA, estab 2002, empl 20, sales $3,834,797, cert: State)

4532   Advanced Engineering Design, Inc.
6525 Belcrest Road Ste 426
Hyattsville, MD 20782
Contact: Reginald Waters CEO
Tel: 301-683-2112
Email: rwaters@aedworld.com
Website: www.aedworld.com
Central office & data center engineering services: site surveys, computer-aided-design drafting, equipment inventories & assessments, records development & space planning. (AA, estab 1991, empl 60, sales $2,480,000, cert: State, NMSDC)

4533   Alliance Technology Group, LLC
7010 Hi Tech Dr
Hanover, MD 21076
Contact: Corporate Admin
Tel: 410-712-0270
Email: Lauren.Russ@alliance-it.com
Website: www.alliance-it.com
End-to-end storage technology solutions, computer, monitor & printer repair, network peripherals, system upgrades, backup & recovery engineering, data storage assessments. (Woman, estab 1987, empl 83, sales $36,903,666, cert: WBENC)

4534 Alphatech Systems And Consulting Inc.
762 Perthshire Place
Abingdon, MD 21009
Contact: Deepak Sharma CEO
Tel: 269-274-7877
Email: deepak.sharma@alphatechglobal.com
Website: http://alphatechglobal.com
Information Technology Managed Services, Business Process Management, System Engineering, Big Data Analytics & Field Communication Technologies. (As-Ind, estab 2006, empl 20, sales , cert: 8a)

4535 ALTEK Information Technology, Inc.
241 E Fourth St, Ste 205
Frederick, MD 21701
Contact: Anne Lipman CEO
Tel: 301-695-4440
Email: cardinalhealth@al-tekinc.com
Website: www.al-tekinc.com
Information technology staffing & project management: contract, contract to hire or direct hire. (Woman, estab 2004, empl 150, sales $15,000,000, cert: State, WBENC)

4536 Altus Technology Solutions
1121 Annapolis Rd, Ste 211
Odenton, MD 21113
Contact: David Brashear President
Tel: 443-321-2069
Email: dbrashear@altusts.com
Website: www.altusts.com
Mission-critical services & IT solutions. (AA, estab 2004, empl 32, sales $5,618,000, cert: 8a)

4537 Apex IT Services
5999 Harpers Farm Rd Ste E250
Columbia, MD 21044
Contact: Nagesh Gorantla President
Tel: 508-863-2733
Email: nagesh@apex-its.com
Website: www.apex-its.com
IT service solution provider, responsive customer service, innovative technical solutions & targeted risk management strategies. (As-Ind, estab 2005, empl 25, sales $2,354,343, cert: 8a)

4538 Applications Alternatives, Inc.
P.O. Box 4238
Upper Marlboro, MD 20775
Contact: David Kiasi-Barnes
Tel: 301-350-4752
Email: david.kiasi@appalt.com
Website: http://appalt.com
Information technology applications consulting in the area of informational survey processing. (AA, estab 1987, empl 2, sales , cert: State)

4539 Applied Development LLC
7 S Front St Ste 200
Baltimore, MD 21202
Contact: Kimberly Citizen
Tel: 410-571-4016
Email: kcitizen@applied-dev.com
Website: www.applied-dev.com
Process improvement, automation, analytics & cyber security, project management, business process improvement, strategic communications, cybersecurity & administrative support. (Woman/AA, estab 2011, empl 12, sales $687,000, cert: State, City, NMSDC, WBENC, 8a)

4540 A-Team Solutions
12507 Marlow Rd
Fulton, MD 20759
Contact: Craig Chung Operations Coord
Tel: 702-224-8243
Email: cchung@a-teamsolutions.com
Website: www.a-teamsolutions.com
Mission oriented business integrated services, management consulting, training, professional support, administrative & information technology. (As-Pac, estab 2004, empl 60, sales , cert: State)

4541 Avance IT Solutions LLC
7 Gondola View Court
Woodstock, MD 21163
Contact: Antoinette Gardner CEO
Tel: 443-955-5107
Email: partner@avanceits.com
Website: www.avanceitsolutions.com
IT consulting services, project management, training, technology assessments, programming, helpdesk, testing & deployment. (Woman/AA, estab 2007, empl 5, sales , cert: State)

4542 BITHGROUP Technologies, Inc.
113 W Monument St
Baltimore, MD 21201
Contact: Robert Wallace President & CEO
Tel: 410-962-1188
Email: robertwallace@bithgroup.com
Website: www.bithgroup.com
Information Technology Consulting, Network Engineering, Application Development, Wireless Infrastructure Development, e-learning (AA, estab 1992, empl 60, sales , cert: State)

4543 Brooks Logic LLC
4640 Forbes Blvd Ste 320
Lanham, MD 20706
Contact: Tchikaya Brooks Sr Partner
Tel: 301-358-2600
Email: tbrooks@brookslogic.com
Website: www.brookslogic.com
Custom developed IT solutions. (AA, estab 1996, empl 3, sales $5,265,000, cert: State)

4544 Business Integra Technology Solutions, Inc.
6550 Rock Spring Dr Ste 600
Bethesda, MD 20817
Contact: Yashika Prabhakar Business Develop Mgr
Tel: 301-474-9600
Email: bistates@businessintegra.com
Website: www.businessintegra.com
Staff augmentation services, information technology consulting. (Woman/As-Pac, estab 2001, empl 450, sales $63,000,000, cert: WBENC)

4545 CAEI Inc.
9256 Bendix Rd, Ste 102
Columbia, MD 21045
Contact: Derrick Burnett Sr. Business Devel. Exec
Tel: 443-319-5381
Email: dburnett@caeiinc.com
Website: www.caeiinc.com
Help Desk and Customer Service call center Personnel and management, in addition to our Help Desk Tier I, Tier II and Tier III experience and past performance. (AA, estab 2011, empl 125, sales $6,500,000, cert: State, NMSDC)

4546 Carson Solutions, LLC
16701 Melford Blvd. Ste. 431
Bowie, MD 20715
Contact: Eugene Carson President
Tel: 800-480-7132
Email: eugene@carsonsolutionsllc.com
Website: www.carsonsolutionsllc.com
Information technology solutions & administrative support.
(AA, estab 2000, empl 10, sales $1,850,000, cert: State)

4547 Cinnity LLC
10809 Boswell Lane
Potomac, MD 20854
Contact: Aboje Jay Ameh President
Tel: 301-642-6595
Email: jay@cinnity.com
Website: www.cinnity.com
Design, develop & implement user-centered software
solutions: web-based applications, Content Management
Systems, Graphical User Interfaces, Interactive Training
Software & data visualization. (AA, estab 2007, empl 2,
sales $130,000, cert: 8a)

4548 Cyber Management Systems
11504 Eastern Red Cedar Ave
Clinton, MD 20735
Contact: Cory Coleman CEO
Tel: 301-613-3717
Email: corycoleman@cybermss.com
Website: www.cybermanagementsystems.com
Information Technology consulting, Enterprise IT Systems
Monitoring, Management Consulting & IT Consulting. (AA,
estab 2014, empl 1, sales , cert: State)

4549 Cybern Consulting Group, LLC
13615 Triadelphia Mill Rd
Clarksville, MD 21029
Contact: Serif Mumuney President
Tel: 410-379-0545
Email: serif.mumuney@cyberngroup.com
Website: www.cyberngroup.com
Develop applications using Business Process Management
tools running on finely tuned Databases. (AA, estab 2004,
empl 8, sales $400,050, cert: State, 8a)

4550 Dakota Consulting Inc.
1110 Bonifant St, Ste 310
Silver Spring, MD 20910
Contact: Lori Renner CEO
Tel: 240-839-7812
Email: lori.renner@dakota-consulting.com
Website: www.Dakota-Consulting.com
Information technology management, telecommunications
& networking. (Woman, estab 2004, empl 93, sales
$10,834,069, cert: State)

4551 Davis Unlimited Information Technologies, Inc.
9532 Whitehurst Dr
Owings Mills, MD 21117
Contact: Howard Marcellas CEO
Tel: 301-637-5411
Email: MRHoward@duit.us
Website: www.duit.us
IT modernization & Software Engineering, secure software,
vulnerability analysis, custom modular code that is scalable,
reusable & maintainable for UNIX, LINUX & Microsoft
platforms, GOTs & COTS, requirements analysis. (Woman/
AA, estab 2010, empl 10, sales $1,200,000, cert: 8a)

4552 DB Commercial Group LLC
8401 Colesville Rd Ste 310
Silver Spring, MD 20910
Contact: Kim Harwell CEO
Tel: 301-363-2790
Email: kim.harwell@dbcommercialgroup.com
Website: www.dbcommercialgroup.com
IT Services, Staff Augmentation, Systems Engineering,
Cyber Security, Application Development, Cloud Com-
puting & Multimedia Services. (AA, estab 2014, empl 20,
sales $10,000,000, cert: NMSDC)

4553 Dhaivat Maharaja Enterprises Inc.
6 Latimore Ct
Reisterstown, MD 21136
Contact: Dhaivat Maharaja CEO
Tel: 443-650-8287
Email: dhaivat.maharaja@dhaivat.com
Website: www.dhaivat.com
Enterprise resource planning (ERP), customer relation-
ship management (CRM), Cloud architecture, unified
computing system (UCS), online course development,
service-oriented architecture (SOA). (As-Pac, estab 2006,
empl 3, sales , cert: State)

4554 Diverse Concepts, Inc.
1131 Benfield Blvd, Ste K
Millersville, MD 21108
Contact: CEO
Tel: 443-698-1052
Email:
Website: www.dciits.com
Web Development and Design, System Engineering,
Network Engineering, Information Assurance, Disaster
Recovery, Program Management, (AA, estab 2002, empl
20, sales $1,520,000, cert: State)

4555 DK Consulting, LLC
8955 Guilford Road Ste 240
Columbia, MD 21046
Contact: CEO
Tel: 443-552-5851
Email:
Website: www.dkconsult.net
Management & technological solutions services.
(Woman, estab 2003, empl 9, sales $818,570, cert: State,
City, WBENC)

4556 Douglas Consulting & Computer Services, Inc.
3108 Timanus Ln, Ste 100
Baltimore, MD 21244
Contact: James Douglas President
Tel: 410-298-3812
Email: jdouglas@douglasccs.com
Website: www.douglasccs.com
Computer systems integration, ecommerce, web &
database design, LAN/WAN/MAN & sec, document
imaging & data capture, auto workflow, custom applica-
tion dev. (AA, estab 1985, empl 45, sales , cert: State)

4557 Eigennet LLC
13508 Wisteria Dr
Germantown, MD 20874
Contact: Godfrey Pereira President
Tel: 240-476-5094
Email: gpereira@eigennet.com
Website: www.eigennet.com
IT supplier diversity programs and staffing models. (Nat
Ame, estab 2016, empl 25, sales , cert: State, NMSDC)

4558 Encore Solutions Inc.
12300 Twinbrook Parkway, Ste 330
Rockville, MD 20852
Contact: Gary Lewis President & CEO
Tel: 301-998-6191
Email: glewis@encore-solu.com
Website: www.encore-solu.com
Technology solutions: systems engineering, acquisition & logistics support, program management & administrative services, records information management. (Woman/AA, estab 2001, empl 3, sales $502,789, cert: State, NMSDC, WBENC)

4559 ERPMatrix LLC
3620 Turbridge Dr
Burtonsville, MD 20866
Contact: Shams Abedin Managing Partner
Tel: 240-396-4380
Email: sa@erpmatrix.com
Website: www.erpmatrix.com
Staffing, enterprise architecture/integration, software devel, database & IT support. (As-Ind, estab 2005, empl 4, sales $178,191, cert: State)

4560 GenRev Technologies, LLC
7620 Serenade Circle
Clinton, MD 20735
Contact: CEO
Tel: 202-528-3082
Email:
Website: www.GenRevTechnologies.com
Network installation of CAT 5e/CAT6/Fiber/Copper cabling, cisco switch installation, IP address schemas, IP subnetting, ACAS scanning, HBSS, IAVA/IAVM patch management, help desk support, windows server mgmt. (AA, estab 2006, empl 2, sales , cert: 8a)

4561 Infinite Computer Solutions Inc.
15201 Diamondback Dr Ste 125
Rockville, MD 20850
Contact: John Stritzl Dir of Sales
Tel: 215-262-8027
Email: partnership@infinite.com
Website: www.infinite.com
Applications development, network engineering/operations, help desk support; e-business, client/server & mainframe solutions; network & system migrations; LAN/WAN/MAN svcs. (As-Ind, estab 2001, empl 5400, sales , cert: NMSDC)

4562 Information Protection Solutions
1997 Annapolis Exchange Pkwy Ste 300
Annapolis, MD 21401
Contact: Todd Chamberlain CEO
Tel: 240-345-4212
Email: info@ips314.com
Website: http://ips314.com
Cyber Security • Cloud security • Continuous Monitoring Strategies • Cyber Security Policy Development • System Hardening Implementation • Vulnerability Analysis Information Assurance: • FedRAMP compliance • NIST 800-53 Rev 4 to Rev 5 Prep • Risk Mgmt. (AA, estab 2014, empl 3, sales , cert: State, NMSDC, 8a)

4563 Information Security Enterprise Consulting, LLC
6701 Democracy Blvd
Bethesda, MD 20814
Contact: Jason Peterson CEO
Tel: 301-337-2527
Email: jpeterson@isec-cybersecurity.com
Website: www.isec-cybersecurity.com
Cyber security, design, develop, deploy, operate & maintain defensive security measures. (AA, estab 2007, empl 20, sales $2,500,200, cert: State, NMSDC)

4564 ITnova
108 Old Solomons Island Rd Ste L10
Annapolis, MD 21401
Contact: Sandra Seldes CEO
Tel: 443-906-6073
Email: cseldes@itnovaconsulting.com
Website: www.itnovaconsulting.com
IT and Engineering consulting, Software Development Life Cycle (SDLC), project management, cybersecurity, business re-engineering, organizational change management, quality assurance. (Woman/Hisp, estab 2014, empl 20, sales , cert: 8a)

4565 JuneGem Technologies, Inc.
3601 Hamilton St Ste 201
Hyattsville, MD 20782
Contact: Stephanie Thomas Business Develop Mgr
Tel: 301-864-2321
Email: hr@junegemtech.com
Website: www.junegemtech.com
Information Technology and Enterprise Resource Planning (ERP) solutions, project management, business process engineering, and software & systems development. (Woman/AA, estab 2011, empl 10, sales $333,686, cert: State)

4566 Jupiter LLC
12021 Eaglewood Ct
Silver Spring, MD 20902
Contact: E Alex Jupiter President
Tel: 240-316-2943
Email: alexj@jupitercybsec.com
Website: http://jupitercybsec.com
Risk assessment, analysis & management; control vulnerability assessment, data & functional specification; IS/IT security scope management, features, architecture & design; cyber incident response planning; software
capability maturity assessment. (AA, estab 2013, empl 3, sales , cert: State, City)

4567 MASAI Technologies Corporation
201B Broadway St
Frederick, MD 21701
Contact: Masai Troutman CEO
Tel: 301-694-2751
Email: masai@masai-tech.com
Website: www.masai-tech.com
Specialized Staffing & Enterprise Resource Planning (ERP) SAP Software System Integration, implementation & operational services. (AA, estab 1997, empl 15, sales $2,000,000, cert: State, NMSDC)

4568 MORI Associates, Inc.
      3202 Tower Oaks Blvd, Ste 200
      Rockville, MD 20852
      Contact: Michael Robertson Operations Mgr
      Tel: 301-468-6674
      Email: mrobertson@moriassociates.com
      Website: www.moriassociates.com
Internet svcs & total system solutions: client server, e-commerce, hardware, networking, programming, software, system reengineering, web technology. (Minority, Woman, estab 1997, empl 105, sales $14,000,000, cert: State)

4569 Neo Technologies, Inc.
      2901 Druid Park Dr, Ste C104
      Baltimore, MD 21215
      Contact: Ronald Curry CEO
      Tel: 410-728-9104
      Email: rcurry@neotechs.com
      Website: www.neotechs.com
Network svcs, routers, bridges, gateways, transmitting equip, analysis, programming LAN integration, software engineering. (AA, estab 1990, empl 8, sales $800,000, cert: State)

4570 NucoreVision, Inc
      4601 Forbes Blvd, Ste 310
      Lanham, MD 20706
      Contact: Yolanda Murphy
      Tel: 301-577-3999
      Email: ymurphy@nucorevision.com
      Website: www.nucorevision.com
Cybersecurity, Agency IT Operations, IT Program / Project Management, Management Consulting, IT Services & Solutions. (AA, estab 1996, empl 25, sales $1,900,000, cert: NMSDC)

4571 Nu-Pulse Technologies, Inc.
      21 Industrial Park Dr Ste 101
      Waldorf, MD 20602
      Contact: E. Renee Ingram President
      Tel: 301-374-2534
      Email: ringram@nu-pulse.com
      Website: www.nu-pulse.com
Information technology svcs: software design & devel, LAN/WAN design & implementation, database design & devel, project mgmt. IT security, fire protection engineering, voice guidance exit systems, electronic door locks. (AA, estab 1998, empl 39, sales $3,000,000, cert: State)

4572 Omega Micro Services
      P.O. Box 1271
      Bowie, MD 20721
      Contact: Paulson Obiniyi CEO
      Tel: 240-602-8624
      Email: info@omicroservices.com
      Website: www.omicroservices.com
Technical Services and Consulting, Enterprise Architecture, Data & Media Sanitization, Web site Design and development, Project and Program Management, Staffing Augmentation, Content Production, Enterprise Content Management. (AA, estab 2007, empl 2, sales , cert: State)

4573 Pa Na Solutions Inc.
      3504 Waterford Mill Rd
      Bowie, MD 20721
      Contact: Brahim Zahar VP
      Tel: 703-348-6436
      Email: bzahar@panasolutions.com
      Website: www.panasolutionas.com
IT Svcs: Program Management, Finance, Scheduling, Methodology, Tools, Network Engineering, Strategy & Planning, Assessment, Architecture & design services, Integration & deployment, Optimization, & Device Support, Video Engineering. (AA, estab 2006, empl 28, sales $4,218,518, cert: State, 8a)

4574 Peyak Solutions, Inc.
      9250 Bendix Rd N, Ste 150
      Columbia, MD 21045
      Contact: Leah Conover CEO
      Tel: 800-958-2188
      Email: leah.conover@peyaksolutions.com
      Website: www.peyaksolutions.com
IT consulting & support services: network design, procurement & installation, desktop, internet & database application dev, project & program management, hardware recycling & confidential data destruction. (Woman/Nat Ame, estab 2007, empl 2, sales $195,000, cert: State, City, 8a)

4575 Planned Systems International, Inc.
      10632 Little Patuxent Pkwy, Ste 200
      Columbia, MD 21044
      Contact: Terry Lin CEO
      Tel: 410-964-8000
      Email: tlin@plan-sys.com
      Website: www.plan-sys.com/
Providing Healthcare IT, management consulting, IT solutions & services. (As-Pac, estab 1988, empl 350, sales $105,101,730, cert: State)

4576 Pn Automation
      1521 S Edgewood St
      Baltimore, MD 21227
      Contact: Nitin Baviskar COO
      Tel: 410-409-6730
      Email: nitin@pnautomation.com
      Website: www.pnautomation.com
Software development & IT service. (As-Ind, estab 2004, empl 25, sales $600,000, cert: State)

4577 Pramac Engineering LLC
      2000 Astilbe Way
      Odenton, MD 21113
      Contact: Kevin Ruffin CEO
      Tel: 410-409-9772
      Email: kfruffin@pramacengineering.com
      Website: www.pramacengineering.com
Java and C/C++ object oriented design and development, web applications Model/View/Controller (MVC) development, Niagara Files development, Commercial Off the Shelf (COTS) Integration, Systems Integration and 508 Compliance application implementation. (AA, estab 2017, empl 1, sales $121,000, cert: State)

4578   ProSync Technology Group, LLC
        6021 University Blvd, Ste 300
        Ellicott City, MD 21043
        Contact: Keith Slack VP Business Dev
        Tel: 410-772-7969
        Email: keith.slack@prosync.com
        Website: www.prosync.com
Information technology & infrastructure, enterprise
information systems services & solutions, adaptive
engineering products & svcs, data & signal processing
products. (As-Pac, estab 2000, empl 45, sales $4,000,000,
cert: State)

4579   Qlaire Systems Incorporated
        11002 Veirs Mill Rd Ste 700
        Silver Spring, MD 20902
        Contact: Uma Subramanian President
        Tel: 301-873-1972
        Email: umas@qlaire.com
        Website: www.qlaire.com
Web Application, Web design, E-Business, BPR, Search &
Analytics Services, Portal Services, PMO Support, Process
Improvement, IV&V, Enterprise Architecture, ERP solu-
tions, CRM applications, 508 compliance, C&A, Security.
(Woman/As-Ind, estab 2008, empl 8, sales $420,000, cert:
8a)

4580   Reliable Government Solutions Inc.
        3002 Gazebo Ct
        Silver Spring, MD 20904
        Contact: Chieu Le President
        Tel: 800-767-0896
        Email: chieule@rgsfederal.com
        Website: www.rgsfederal.com
Data warehouse, development, architecture & admin,
financial applications, IT audits, JCIDS documentation,
network admin & security, testing, program & project
mgmt, equirements analysis, SME, training, web development. (As-Pac, estab 2001, empl 5, sales $317,842, cert:
City)

4581   Rescon Inc.
        4526 Cheltenham Dr,
        Bethesda, MD 20814
        Contact: Prem Singh CEO
        Tel: 301-330-5265
        Email: resconinc@aol.com
        Website: www.resconisit.com
IT technology consulting & staffing, project management,
software architects, programmers, systems admin,
network engineers, software quality assurance. (As-Ind,
estab 1998, empl 14, sales $2,000,000, cert: State)

4582   Right Choice Computers & Networks, LLC
        P.O. Box 5324
        Capitol Heights, MD 20791
        Contact: Pamela Mitchell President
        Tel: 301-839-4905
        Email: contactus@rchoicecn.com
        Website: www.rchoicecn.com
Software & applications, mainframe Legacy Systems,
networks topologies, computer hardware & accessories,
help desk & support, network installation. (Woman/AA,
estab 1994, empl 1, sales , cert: State)

4583   RTH Solutions LLC
        10320 Little Patuxent Pkwy, Ste 200
        Columbia, MD 21044
        Contact: Tanisha Lockett COO
        Tel: 240-638-1222
        Email: tanisha.lockett@rthsolutions.com
        Website: www.rthsolutions.com
Management consulting, staffing & training, business &
IT Service Management process consulting, ITIL, Project
Management, Cyber Resilia, DevOps, Lean IT, and Scrum.
(Woman/AA, estab 2006, empl 2, sales , cert: State,
WBENC, NWBOC)

4584   Secure Technologies LLC
        5160 Squawroot Ct
        Indian Head, MD 20640
        Contact: James Hoxsie Business Dev Mgr
        Tel: 301-613-6605
        Email: jim.hoxsie@securetechnologiesllc.net
        Website: http://securetechnologiesllc.net
IT consulting & solutions. (Woman/AA, estab 2007, empl
6, sales $575,000, cert: 8a)

4585   Shakthy Information Systems, Inc.
        13910 Falconcrest Rd
        Germantown, MD 20874
        Contact: Susheela Palaniswamy CEO
        Tel: 240-355-6184
        Email: hr@shakthy.com
        Website: www.shakthy.com
Custom software development services & solutions.
(Minority/Woman, estab 2000, empl 5, sales $350,000,
cert: State)

4586   Sustainable Approach Consulting
        9319 Kendal Circle
        Laurel, MD 20723
        Contact: Carol Morgan President
        Tel: 240-696-3000
        Email: cmorgan@sustainac.com
        Website: https://sustainac.com
Project Management Enterprise Infrastructure Setup
And Maintenance Technology And Business Strategy
Migrations And Upgrades Business Intelligence Big Data
SAP Applications Cloud Application Solution Manager
Configuration. (Woman/AA, estab 2009, empl 5, sales ,
cert: 8a)

4587   Sympora Technologies
        5431 Woodland Blvd Ste B
        Oxon Hill, MD 20745
        Contact: Dean Matthews President
        Tel: 800-568-9965
        Email: dean.matthews@sympora.com
        Website: www.sympora.com
Software development, information technology, web-
based training & information security services. (AA,
estab 2000, empl 3, sales $158,325, cert: State)

4588   TASA Information Technology Group
        9111 Edmonston Rd, Ste 402
        Greenbelt, MD 20770
        Contact: Jamar Spruill
        Tel: 240-599-7030
        Email: contracts@tasait.com
        Website: www.tasait.com
IT Systems Design & Integration, IT architecture, LAN,
hardware & software requirements, system cost,
acquisition, implementation & maintenance. (AA, estab
2006, empl 13, sales $3,607,578, cert: 8a)

4589   Technology Engineering Associates, LLC
       2275 Research Blvd, Ste 500
       Rockville, MD 20850
       Contact: Lloyd Tang President
       Tel: 240-603-6563
       Email: lloyd.tang@tea-llc.com
       Website: www.tea-llc.com
Software development, data management, operations
management & technical leadership. (As-Pac, estab 2006,
empl 4, sales $850,000, cert: 8a)

4590   The Aspen Group, Inc.
       1100 Wayne Ave Ste 1200
       Silver Spring, MD 20910
       Contact: Christina Fitts Exec VP
       Tel: 410-308-0629
       Email: cfitts@theaspengroupinc.com
       Website: www.theaspengroupinc.com
Information technology consulting & services. (Woman/AA,
estab 1988, empl 400, sales $38,481,357, cert: NMSDC,
WBENC)

4591   The net.America Corporation
       16201 Trade Zone Ave, Unit 112
       Upper Marlboro, MD 20774
       Contact: Yasmin Hines business devel Asst
       Tel: 301-218-4559
       Email: yasmin.hines@netamerica.net
       Website: www.discovernetamerica.com
Information technology solutions, contact centers & help
desk, information technology, health services, program
management, peer review & grants management. (Woman/
AA, estab 2000, empl 51, sales $8,226,437, cert: State,
WBENC)

4592   The Squires Group
       128 Lubrano Dr, Ste 102
       Annapolis, MD 21401
       Contact: Nancy Squires CEO
       Tel: 410-224-7779
       Email: nancy@squiresgroup.com
       Website: www.squiresgroup.com
ERP staffing & consulting svsc: process reengineering,
change mgmt, implementation, upgrades & web-enabled
integration. (Woman, estab 1994, empl 75, sales , cert:
WBENC)

4593   Thomas & Herbert Consulting LLC
       1010 Wayne Ave, Ste 460
       Silver Spring, MD 20910
       Contact: Frederick Schaefers business support Mgr
       Tel: 301-578-4004
       Email: fred.schaefers@thcllc.com
       Website: www.thcllc.com
Enterprise architecture, e-government, business realignment, managed services. (AA, estab 1996, empl 100, sales ,
cert: State)

4594   TISTA Science and Technology Corporation
       1201 Seven Locks Rd Ste 350
       Rockville, MD 20850
       Contact: Ahmed Ali CEO
       Tel: 301-968-3435
       Email: aali@tistatech.com
       Website: www.tistatech.com
Information technology & professional services, cyber
security, software & database development, engineering
support, network & critical infrastructure protection, IT
operations & maintenance. (As-Pac, estab 2005, empl 150,
sales $22,000,000, cert: State)

4595   TMCS, LLC
       6910 Wade Ave Ste A
       Clinton, MD 20735
       Contact: Tynnetta McBeth CEO
       Tel: 301-686-8417
       Email: tmcbeth@tmcsllc.com
       Website: www.tmcsllc.com
Technical & management consulting, design & implementation of LAN/WAN solutions, security,
communicatons & mobility, virtual data center solutions,
hardware & software resales. (Minority/Woman, estab
2008, empl 3, sales $160,000, cert: State, 8a)

4596   Unatek, Inc.
       1100 Mercantile Lane Ste 115-A
       Largo, MD 20774
       Contact: Charles Iheagwara Dir
       Tel: 301-583-4629
       Email: ciheagwara@unatek.com
       Website: www.unatek.com
Information technology consulting. (AA, estab 1996,
empl 15, sales $1,860,000, cert: State, 8a)

4597   Vangel Inc.
       3020 Nieman Ave
       Baltimore, MD 21230
       Contact: Valerie Androutsopoulos Principal
       Tel: 410-644-2600
       Email: valerie@vangelinc.com
       Website: www.vangelinc.com
Data destruction & recycling services: on-site & off-site
paper shredding, off-site non-paper storage, media
shredding. (Woman, estab 1988, empl 15, sales
$1,642,150, cert: State)

4598   Victory Global Solutions, Inc.
       5950 Symphony Woods Rd, Ste 211
       Columbia, MD 21044
       Contact: Angela Brown CEO
       Tel: 410-884-9310
       Email: abrown@victorygs.com
       Website: www.victorygs.com
Information technology & networking integration
services, systems engineering, integration & consulting.
(Woman/AA, estab 2001, empl 30, sales $26,000,000,
cert: State, WBENC)

4599   VVL Systems & Consulting, LLC
       8840 Stanford Blvd Ste 1550
       Columbia, MD 21045
       Contact: Vinnie Lima Managing Dir
       Tel: 410-864-8659
       Email: vlima@vvlsystems.com
       Website: www.vvlsystems.com
Information technology & consulting, cloud services,
infrastructure & end-user optimization. (Hisp, estab
2008, empl 6, sales $950,000, cert: State, 8a)

4600   Web Traits, Inc.
       9423 Eagleton Lane
       Montgomery Village, MD 20886
       Contact: Bhaskar Roy President
       Tel: 240-731-6120
       Email: bhaskar.roy@web-traits.com
       Website: www.web-traits.com
Information systems security & operations (ISSO), cyber
security, network operations management,
virtualization, certification & accreditation (C&A),
independent verification & validation (IV&V). (As-Ind,
estab 2007, empl 7, sales $960,000, cert: State, 8a)

4601 Williams Consulting, LLC
5523 Research Park Dr Ste 310
Baltimore, MD 21228
Contact: Antoinette Williams CEO
Tel: 855-597-9666
Email: awilliams@williamsconsultingllc.com
Website: www.williamsconsultingllc.com/
Healthcare Policy, Planning, Health Plan Operations & large scale enterprise transformational IT Projects. (Woman/AA, estab 2013, empl 6, sales $280,000, cert: 8a)

4602 WITS, LLC
5070 Wabash Ave Blg A, Ste 201
Baltimore, MD 21225
Contact: Vijay Williams CEO
Tel: 443-919-0113
Email: vwilliams@witsbusiness.com
Website: www.witsbusiness.com
IT services, Software Engineering, Systems Engineering, Systems Administration, Database Management, Virtualization, Project management, Systems Integration, Information Assurance, and Cyber analysis. (AA, estab 2007, empl 5, sales , cert: 8a)

Maine

4603 CST2000 dba iCST IT Solutions
100 Brickhill Ave Ste C, Lower Level
South Portland, ME 04106
Contact: Sasha Asdourian Finance Mgr
Tel: 207-221-2952
Email: finance@i-cst.com
Website: www.i-cst.com
Software testing & IT solutions: ASP, client server, database, IT staffing, .NET, internet, Java, network admin, mainframe, migration, etc. (As-Pac, estab 1997, empl 70, sales $6,050,000, cert: State)

Michigan

4604 Acro Service Corporation
39209 W. Six Mile Rd.
Livonia, MI 48152
Contact: Todd Kearns Marketing & Proposal Mgr
Tel: 734-591-1100
Email: acrocorp@acrocorp.com
Website: www.acrocorp.com
Staff augmentation: engineering, information technology, light industrial, clerical. Outsourcing; offshore application dev; IT, engineering, project mgmt consulting. (As-Ind, estab 1982, empl 8693, sales $371,000,000, cert: NMSDC)

4605 All About Technology
6450 Michigan Ave
Detroit, MI 48210
Contact: Willie Brake Mgr
Tel: 313-965-5543
Email: isupply@all-about-technology.com
Website: www.all-about-technology.com
Computer Sales, Service, Training & Upgrades. Data Backup & Recovery, Wireless Networking, Microsoft, Adobe, Quicken, Value Added Reseller, Computer Insurance, Website Maintenance & Design. (AA, estab 2001, empl 7, sales $210,000, cert: State, NMSDC, SDB)

4606 Allegiance Technologies Inc.
140 Edgelake Dr
Waterford, MI 48327
Contact: Matthew Montpas President
Tel: 248-425-0252
Email: matt.montpas@allegiance-tech.com
Website: www.allegiance-tech.com
SAP consulting & implementation. (Hisp, estab 1998, empl 10, sales $594,447, cert: NMSDC)

4607 Alliance Technology Solutions, LLC
540 N.Lapeer Road #379
Lake Orion, MI 48359
Contact: Margie Garza-Carlson President
Tel: 248-364-2195
Email: mcarlson@ats.biz
Website: www.ats.biz
Ebusiness infrastructure solutions: server consolidation, high availability, Tivoli storage mgr, firewall & security, enterprise storage & networks. (Woman/Hisp, estab 2002, empl 7, sales $5,862,867, cert: State)

4608 AltaFlux Corporation
3250 W Big Beaver Rd Ste 342
Troy, MI 48084
Contact: John Morrison Natl Sales Mgr
Tel: 248-850-2298
Email: john.morrison@altaflux.com
Website: www.altaflux.com
Business Transformation Consulting, Complete SaaS Solutions, Cloud Computing Solutions, Specialized Technology Staffing, SAP, Oracle, Google Apps, Dell Boomi, OrangeScape (Woman/As-Ind, estab 2006, empl 48, sales $5,000,000, cert: NMSDC)

4609 Blue Chip Talent
43252 Woodward Ave, Ste 240
Bloomfield Hills, MI 48302
Contact: Steve Gaura Sr. Dir of IT Services
Tel: 248-630-7170
Email: steveg@bctalent.com
Website: www.bctalent.com
Information technology project based services, project management, staff augmentation services & security consulting. (Woman, estab 1994, empl 220, sales $26,500,000, cert: WBENC)

4610 Broadgate Inc.
830 Kirts Blvd, Ste 400
Troy, MI 48084
Contact: Kashi Kotha Director
Tel: 248-918-0110
Email: kashi@broadgateinc.com
Website: www.broadgateinc.com
IT Profetional services, consulting, project services & software development. (Woman/As-Ind, estab 2006, empl 70, sales $5,000,000, cert: NMSDC)

4611 BSC Solutions, Inc.
1000 John R. Rd, Ste 203
Troy, MI 48083
Contact: Jody Kapale Business Develop Mgr
Tel: 810-449-3640
Email: jody@bsc-us.com
Website: www.BSCSolutionsInc.com
ERP Implementation & support PeopleSoft, Oracle, SAP, CRM - Siebel & Salesforce, Staff Augmentation/Custom Application Development, Java, .Net, C#, EDI, Data Warehousing, BI, Big Data, Cloud based applications. (As-Ind, estab 1999, empl 200, sales $11,143,000, cert: NMSDC)

4612 CADworks Solutions, Inc.
43422 W Oaks Dr, Ste 326
Novi, MI 48377
Contact: James Vaughn Jr. President
Tel: 248-910-9988
Email: jamesv@cadwrx.com
Website: www.cadwrx.com
CAD systems integration, lifecycle mgmt consulting. (AA, estab 1995, empl 5, sales $153,000, cert: NMSDC)

4613 CAEtech International, Inc.
43000 W 9 Mile Rd, Ste 305
Novi, MI 48375
Contact: Vic Havele President
Tel: 248-342-7661
Email: havelev@caetech.com
Website: www.caetech.com
Contract & direct placement staffing svcs, engineering svcs, IT svcs. (As-Ind, estab 1989, empl 55, sales , cert: NMSDC)

4614 Ciber Global, LLC
3270 West Big Beaver Road
Troy, MI 48084
Contact: Neal King Sr Client Partner
Tel: 603-661-0146
Email: nking@ciber.com
Website: www.ciber.com
Software Eng., Systems Eng., Software and Systems Test, Configuration Mgmt, Systems Anaylsis, Intelligence, Data Warehousing, Business Intelligence, Network Security, Network Engineering, Information Technology (As-Ind, estab 1974, empl 11000, sales , cert: NMSDC)

4615 CnC Controls
5745 W Maple #217
West Bloomfield, MI 48322
Contact: Abizer Rasheed President
Tel: 248-681-7722
Email: arasheed@cnccontrolsusa.com
Website: www.cnccontrolsusa.com
Information technology: installation, repairs & maintenance services. (Woman/As-Ind, estab 1983, empl 10, sales $2,102,000, cert: NMSDC, WBENC)

4616 Cogent Integrated Business Solutions, Inc.
2855 Coolidge Hwy Ste 112
Troy, MI 48084
Contact: Srini Thonta Dir SAP Solutions
Tel: 248-649-4444
Email: sthonta@cogentibs.com
Website: www.cogentIBS.com
IT services & solutions, SAP services. (Woman/As-Pac, estab 2005, empl 30, sales $3,795,325, cert: WBENC)

4617 Communications Professionals, Inc.
2265 Livernois Rd
Troy, MI 48083
Contact: Andrew Wallace CEO
Tel: 248-557-0100
Email: awallace2@cpgp.com
Website: www.cpgp.com
Information technology: development, implementation & application, hardware, software & technological analysis. (AA, estab 1997, empl 15, sales $15,000,000, cert: NMSDC)

4618 CompuSoft Integrated Solutions, Inc.
31500 W 13 Mile Rd Ste 200
Farmington Hills, MI 48334
Contact: Pratap Koganti CEO
Tel: 248-538-9494
Email: pkoganti@compusoft-is.com
Website: www.compusoft-is.com
Internet & intranet, e-commerce dev, ERP, Oracle, SAP, PeopleSoft, client/server software. (As-Ind, estab 1997, empl 80, sales $8,500,000, cert: State, NMSDC)

4619 Computech Corporation
W 100 Kirby St
Detroit, MI 48202
Contact: Sai Kancharla Project Mgr
Tel: 248-622-1420
Email: sai.kancharla@computechcorp.com
Website: www.computechcorp.com
Information technology staffing & project svcs: custom programming, enterprise resource planning, CRM, ebusiness, database programming. (As-Ind, As-Pac, estab 1996, empl 250, sales $1,200,000, cert: NMSDC)

4620 Dechen Consulting Group, Inc.
37000 Grand River Ave Ste 330
Farmington Hills, MI 48335
Contact: Raj Dechen President
Tel: 248-722-2817
Email: ritaa@dcg-us.com
Website: www.dcg-us.com
IT professional staffing & project-based implementation, PeopleSoft, SAP & Oracle software application packages, staff augmentation services, design, develop & implement Business Intelligence. (As-Ind, estab 1998, empl 30, sales $4,100,000, cert: NMSDC)

4621 DPM Consulting Services, Inc.
5440 Corporate Dr Sutie 125
Troy, MI 48098
Contact: Gary Gozdor Business Develop Mgr
Tel:
Email: ggozdor@dpmcs.com
Website: www.dpmcs.com
Program & project managers, business intelligence & data mgmt, Legacy, business analysts, executive search, network & technical support, database dev & admin, ebusiness & offshore staffing resources. (Woman, estab 1992, empl 120, sales , cert: WBENC)

4622 Emergent Systems Corp.
3 Parklane Blvd Ste 1120 West
Dearborn, MI 48126
Contact: Saleem Qureshi VP - Engineering
Tel: 313-996-8285
Email: saleemq@emergentsys.com
Website: www.EmergentSys.com
Engineering, design, product dev& styling, CAD/CAM/ CAE consulting, software dev, engineering design staffing, tooling design, offshore capability, engineering software products, KBE, knowledge mgmt. (As-Ind, estab 1997, empl 40, sales $7,000,000, cert: NMSDC)

4623 Epitec
24800 Denso Dr Ste 150
Southfield, MI 48033
Contact: Kelleen Young
Tel: 469-454-3649
Email: businessdevelopment@epitec.com
Website: www.epitec.com
IT staff augmentation. (AA, estab 1978, empl 1000, sales $75,000,000, cert: NMSDC)

4624　ESM Group LLC
43422 W Oaks Dr, Ste 298
Novi, MI 48377
Contact: Jayme Rossiter President
Tel:　248-921-7452
Email: jrossiter@esmonline.com
Website: www.esmonline.com
Information technoly services & staffing. (Woman, estab 1992, empl 23, sales $1,800,000, cert: WBENC)

4625　Excel Technical Services, Inc.
200 Kirts Blvd Ste A
Troy, MI 48084
Contact: Pat Kirby Managing Dir
Tel:　248-310-9413
Email: patkirby@exceltechnical.com
Website: www.exceltechnical.com
Technical staffing & document management svcs, supplier quality & development. (Hisp, estab 1998, empl 30, sales $2,500,000, cert: NMSDC)

4626　GDI Infotech, Inc.
3775 Varsity Dr
Ann Arbor, MI 48108
Contact: Vishal　Chaubal Dir
Tel:　734-477-6900
Email: vishal@gdii.com
Website: www.gdii.com
Enterprise information technology consulting & services. (As-Ind, estab 1993, empl 125, sales $10,200,000, cert: NMSDC)

4627　HRU Technical Resources
3451 Dunckel Road Ste 200
Lansing, MI 48911
Contact: Todd Briggs V.P. Business Development
Tel:　517-272-5888
Email: briggs.todd@hru-tech.com
Website: www.hru-tech.com
Engineering, IT, design, mfg, technical staffing services: contract or direct hire. (Woman, estab 1980, empl 215, sales $20,500,517, cert: WBENC)

4628　HTC Global Services Inc.
3270 W Big Beaver
Troy, MI 48084
Contact: Gary Gozdor Director
Tel:　763-245-0746
Email: kevin.kraft@htcinc.com
Website: www.htcinc.com
Information technology services and solutions, Business Process Services. (As-Pac, estab 1990, empl 11000, sales $450,000,000, cert: NMSDC)

4629　ICONMA, LLC
850 Stephenson Hwy Ste 612
Troy, MI 48083
Contact: Lauren Diener Sales Operations Mgr
Tel:　888-451-2519
Email: rfp@iconma.com
Website: www.iconma.com
IT consultant staffing: contract, contract to hire & fulltime. (Woman, estab 2000, empl 2092, sales $142,700,000, cert: WBENC)

4630　IGI Detroit dba Villc, LLC
1020 Metro Dr
Commerce, MI 48390
Contact: Pat Hernandez President
Tel:　248-624-6520
Email: pat@werigi.com
Website: www.werigi.com
Large scale, ultra high resolution systems for advanced visualization applications and commercial AV systems. Automotive engineering and design, military collaboration and intelligence, oil and gas exploration, command and control room. (Hisp, estab 2003, empl 1, sales , cert: NMSDC)

4631　Iknowvate Technologies, Inc.
17197 N Laurel Park Dr, Ste 307
Livonia, MI 48152
Contact: Sriram Rajakumar Sales Dir
Tel:　734-432-0634
Email: rkumar@iknowvate.com
Website: www.iknowvate.com
IT staff augmentation, application dev, maintenance & support, project mgmt, real time embedded systems, e-strategize, portals, implement & deploy SCM, CRM, ERP packaged solutions, business intelligence solutions, etc. (As-Pac, estab 2001, empl 40, sales $2,000,000, cert: NMSDC)

4632　Infomatics Inc.
31313 Northwestern Hwy, Ste 219
Farmington Hills, MI 48334
Contact: Ragan Raghunathan Founder
Tel:　248-865-0300
Email: rajan@infomatinc.com
Website: www.infomatinc.com
Information technology staffing, web technologies, Java, J2EE , ERP/CRM-Oracle, SAP, database administration, Oracle, DB2 SQL Server, content management. (Woman/As-Ind, estab 1998, empl 225, sales $25,000,000, cert: NMSDC)

4633　Information Systems Resources
1800 BAILEY ST
Dearborn, MI 48124
Contact: Eric Levy Business Develop Mgr
Tel:
Email: elevy@is-resources.com
Website: www.is-resources.com
Computer asset mgmt services, professional services, lifecycle mgmt, dist hardware & software.
(AA, estab 1989, empl 48, sales $4,856,426, cert: NMSDC, CPUC)

4634　Internet Operations Center, Inc.
200 Galleria Officentre Ste 109
Southfield, MI 48034
Contact: Rhonda Hall Business Dev Mgr
Tel:　248-204-8800
Email: thayward@iocenter.net
Website: www.iocenter.net
Managed internet service provider, web development, help center, EDI, TPP appilcation development. (As-Pac, estab 1996, empl 56, sales , cert: NMSDC)

4635 IP Consulting, Inc.
3635 29th St
Kentwood, MI 49512
Contact: Cherri Mosey VP
Tel: 616-855-9967
Email: cherri.mosey@ipconsultinginc.com
Website: www.ipconsultinginc.com
Information technology solutions, design, implementation & support services. (Hisp, estab 2006, empl 10, sales $1,400,000, cert: NMSDC, 8a)

4636 IPS Technology Services
363 W Big Beaver Rd Ste 100
Troy, MI 48084
Contact: Pradip Sengupta CEO
Tel: 248-835-9895
Email: info@ipstechnologyservices.com
Website: www.ipstechnologyservices.com
Information technology services: customer systems development, CAD/CAM/CAE/PDM svcs, systems integration, HR technology implementation, consulting, & ERP implementation. (As-Pac, estab 2000, empl 22, sales $1,200,000, cert: NMSDC)

4637 JRD Systems, Inc.
42450 Hayes Rd Ste 3
Clinton Township, MI 48038
Contact: Melissa Husmillo
Tel: 586-416-1500
Email: contact@jrdsi.com
Website: www.jrdsi.com
Information technology solutions, services, & staffing. (As-Ind, As-Pac, estab 2000, empl 80, sales $5,500,000, cert: State, NMSDC)

4638 Logic Solutions, Inc.
2929 Plymouth Rd Ste 207
Ann Arbor, MI 48105
Contact: Grace Lee CFO
Tel: 734-930-0009
Email: grace@logicsolutions.com
Website: www.logicsolutions.com
Custom web based software development & integration. (As-Pac, estab 1995, empl 104, sales $8,261,867, cert: NMSDC)

4639 Millennium Software Inc.
2000 Town Center Dr Ste, 300
Southfield, MI 48075
Contact: Anu Anand President
Tel: 248-213-1800
Email: anu@webmsi.com
Website: www.webmsi.com
IT consulting, project developemnt, contract programming, web designing. (Woman/As-Pac, estab 1996, empl 165, sales $23,129,824, cert: NMSDC, WBENC)

4640 Miracle Software Systems
45625 Grand River Ave
Novi, MI 48374
Contact: Pandu Byroj IT Sales Lead
Tel: 234-233-1851
Email: pbyroj@miraclesoft.com
Website: www.miraclesoft.com/
IT consulting: SAP, Oracle, PeopleSoft, JDEdwards, Solaris, J2EE. webMethods, MQ, EAI, Cognos, MicroStrategy, VB, ASP,.Net, SQL, Siebel, Informatica, TIBCO, Vitria, etc. (As-Ind, As-Pac, estab 1994, empl 2750, sales $100,000,000, cert: NMSDC)

4641 Netlink Software Group
999 Tech Row
Madison Heights, MI 48071
Contact: Bob Pniewski Exec Dir NA Sales
Tel: 248-535-3250
Email: bpniewski@netlink.com
Website: www.netlink.com
IT Business solutions: Automotive, High Tech, Health Care. Education. Solutions experience in Portals, Intranet/Extranet, Software Applications, Exchanges Wireless, eLearning, Program Management (As-Ind, estab 1997, empl 112, sales , cert: NMSDC)

4642 Ocean Inc. dba Omega Systems
5324 Plainfield Ave NE
Grand Rapids, MI 49525
Contact: Nadeem Hamid President
Tel: 616-361-6677
Email: nadeem.hamid@oceaninc.com
Website: www.oceaninc.com
Computer solutions, components, notebooks, printers, assembly, packing & configuration, web development, web hosting, surveillance camera solutions & installation. (As-Ind, estab 1984, empl 8, sales $600,000, cert: NMSDC)

4643 Ojibway, Inc.
3720 High St
Ecorse, MI 48229
Contact: James Richardson Acct Exec
Tel: 248-526-0555
Email: jrichardson@theojibwaygroup.com
Website: www.theojibwaygroup.com
Information technology, leasing & financial services, computer equipment & services. (Nat Ame, estab 1988, empl 13, sales $3,500,000, cert: NMSDC)

4644 OpenLogix Corporation
28345 Beck Rd Ste 308
Wixom, MI 48393
Contact: Rick Pardy Acct Mgr
Tel: 919-200-4333
Email: mbe@open-logix.com
Website: www.open-logix.com
SOA, business integration, portals & business intelligence, SAP, WebSphere, web svcs, webMethods, Java/J2EE, Informatica, business objects.. (As-Ind, estab 2006, empl 45, sales $18,000,000, cert: NMSDC)

4645 Paskon, Inc.
25899 W 12 Mile Rd Ste 380
Southfield, MI 48034
Contact: Sharath Konanur CEO
Tel: 248-440-2334
Email: sharath@paskon.com
Website: www.paskon.com
Business & Technology Consulting, SAP Development Implementations. (As-Pac, Hisp, estab 1999, empl 50, sales $3,530,000, cert: NMSDC)

4646 Peer Solutions Group, Inc.
30777 Northwestern Hwy Ste 107
Farmington Hills, MI 48334
Contact: Mohamed Irfan Peeran CEO
Tel: 248-522-7767
Email: mpeeran@peersolutionsgroup.com
Website: www.peersolutionsgroup.com
IT Consulting Staffing, Recruiting, Project Management, Technology Consulting. (As-Ind, estab 2002, empl 60, sales $5,412,715, cert: NMSDC)

4647 PeoplePlus software Inc.
      3131 South State St. Ste 250
      Ann Arbor, MI 48108
      Contact: Tom Bastian Solutions Consultant
      Tel: 734-531-6620
      Email: tbastian@peopleplussoftware.com
      Website: http://peopleplussoftware.com
Software design & dev, SaaS cloud supply chain software.
IT staffing, Mobile app development. (Woman/As-Ind,
estab 2007, empl 35, sales $1,500,000, cert: NMSDC)

4648 Preferred Data Systems, LLC
      39100 Country Club Dr Ste 200
      Farmington Hills, MI 48331
      Contact: Chad Muncy
      Tel: 248-522-4442
      Email: cmuncy@pdsnetworking.com
      Website: www.pdsnetworking.com
IT networking infrastructure & consulting services.
(Woman/Nat Ame, estab 1982, empl 12, sales $510,000,
cert: NMSDC)

4649 Prince Technology Solutions, Inc.
      51221 Schoenherr, Ste 106
      Shelby Township, MI 48315
      Contact: Tigi Duraku CEO
      Tel: 810-512-4253
      Email: jessica@princetechnology.com
      Website: www.princetechnology.com
IT consulting services, contract & permanent positions.
(Woman, estab 1998, empl 50, sales $4,500,000, cert:
WBENC)

4650 PROLIM Global Corporation
      30445 Northwestern Hwy Ste 380
      Farmington Hills, MI 48334
      Contact: Prabhu Patil President
      Tel: 248-522-6959
      Email: prabhu.patil@prolim.com
      Website: www.prolim.com
IT & PLM solutions & consulting services. (As-Ind, estab
2005, empl 350, sales , cert: NMSDC)

4651 Pro-Motion Technology Group
      29755 Beck Rd
      Wixom, MI 48393
      Contact: Brian Flewelling Acct Mgr
      Tel: 248-668-3100
      Email: hello@promotion.tech
      Website: promotion.tech
Audiovisual technology solutions. (Woman, estab 2002,
empl 45, sales $25,000,000, cert: WBENC)

4652 Pure Data Services LLC
      4459 13th St
      Wyandotte, MI 48192
      Contact: Owner
      Tel: 734-283-3000
      Email:
      Website: www.puredataservices.com
Document destruction services. (Woman, estab 2014,
empl 5, sales , cert: WBENC)

4653 Ragha Systems, LLC
      8390 Warwick Groves Ct
      Grand Blanc, MI 48439
      Contact: Veera R Thota CEO
      Tel: 810-694-6551
      Email: vthota@raghasys.com
      Website: www.raghasys.com
IT solutions. (Woman/As-Ind, estab 2002, empl 4, sales
$240,000, cert: NMSDC, WBENC)

4654 Ramsoft Systems, Inc..
      29777 Telegraph Rd Ste 2250
      Southfield, MI 48034
      Contact: Rama Gudivada COO
      Tel: 248-354-0100
      Email: rama@ramsoft.net
      Website: www.ramsoft.net
IT solutions, staff augmentation: onsite, offsite,
nearshore, offshore projects. (Woman/As-Pac, estab
1993, empl 100, sales , cert: NMSDC)

4655 Rapid Global Business Solutions, Inc.
      1200 Stephenson Hwy
      Troy, MI 48083
      Contact: Vivek Thakur Business Dev Mgr
      Tel: 248-589-1135
      Email: vt@rgbsi.com
      Website: www.rgbsi.com
Engineering svcs: staffing, mechanical, electrical &
electronics, mfg, automotive, design & release, embedded systems, systems modeling & simulation, CAD/CAM/
CAE/PIM svcs, software dev, contract & permanent. (As-
Ind, As-Pac, estab 1997, empl 1800, sales $80,000,000,
cert: NMSDC)

4656 Real World Technologies Inc.
      28423 Orchard Lake Rd Ste 203
      Farmington Hills, MI 48334
      Contact: Vishnu Jampala President
      Tel: 248-987-6008
      Email: vishnujam@rwts.net
      Website: www.rwts.net/
Information Technology Solutions & Business Analyst
solutions, Application development, Enterprise resource
planning, Data-Warehousing, Customer Relationship
Management, Business Analysis, Project Management.
(As-Pac, estab 2005, empl 40, sales $3,155,012, cert:
State, NMSDC, SDB)

4657 Rumba Solutions, LLC
      44648 Mound Rd, Ste 190
      Sterling Heights, MI 48314
      Contact: Jibu Joseph Managing Dir
      Tel: 248-978-3674
      Email: jibu.joseph@rumbasolutions.com
      Website: www.rumbasolutions.com
Application development, staff augmentation & consult-
ing services, Mobile, Web Applications (Cloud and On
premise), IoT, Identity & Access Management, Portal
Development. (As-Ind, estab 2010, empl 50, sales , cert:
NMSDC)

4658 Skansoft Inc.
      4681 Amberwood Ct
      Rochester, MI 48306
      Contact: Srividya Sadasivam President
      Tel: 248-276-4770
      Email: srividya@skandasoftinc.com
      Website: www.skandasoftinc.com
Integrated information technology consulting & placement services, IT professionals. (Woman/As-Ind, estab
2006, empl 11, sales $1,118,340, cert: NMSDC)

4659 SoftCorp International, Inc.
2838 E Long Lake Ste 236
Troy, MI 48085
Contact: Raja Puli President
Tel: 248-918-2224
Email: vinod@softcorpinc.com
Website: www.softcorpinc.com
Staff augmentation, permanent & temporary IT resources. (As-Ind, estab 1997, empl 87, sales $6,100,000, cert: NMSDC)

4660 SoftPath Technologies LLC
16801 Newburgh Rd, Ste 112
Livonia, MI 48154
Contact: Rohith Thumma Reg Sales Mgr
Tel: 248-522-7011
Email: supplier@softpathtech.com
Website: http://softpathtech.com
Global Staffing, Technology, Services & Consulting. (As-Ind, estab 2006, empl 150, sales $6,012,589, cert: NMSDC)

4661 SunSoft Technologies Inc.
21772 Manchester Ct
Farmington Hills, MI 48335
Contact: Rashmi Upadhyaya President
Tel: 248-426-9805
Email: rashmiu@sunsoft.us
Website: www.sunsofttechnologies.com
Engineering & IT staffing. (Woman/As-Pac, estab 2000, empl 45, sales $3,705,233, cert: NMSDC, WBENC)

4662 Synergy Computer Solutions, Inc,
30700 Telegraph Rd Ste 2615
Bingham Farms, MI 48025
Contact: Ruslan Avshalumov Accountant
Tel: 248-723-7220
Email: ravshalumov@synergycom.com
Website: www.synergycom.com
Information techology & engineering consulting & staffing: implementation & integration, infrastructure support, web solutions, project mgmt, data warehousing, EDI, off shore devel. (As-Pac, estab 1995, empl 250, sales $16,000,000, cert: NMSDC)

4663 Synova Inc.
1000 Town Center Ste 700
Southfield, MI 48075
Contact: Iain McKendrick Dir of Automotive & Mfg
Tel: 248-281-2500
Email: imckendrick@synovainc.com
Website: www.synovainc.com
IT Staffing, Managed Programs, Offshore, Creative Technical Outsourcing, Projects and Solution Service offerings. (As-Pac, estab 1998, empl 1800, sales $117,000,000, cert: NMSDC)

4664 Syntel Inc.
525 E Big Beaver Third Fl
Troy, MI 48083
Contact: ShyamSundar Dittakavi Dir Lifesciences
Tel: 602-391-8868
Email: vendor_registration@syntelinc.com
Website: www.syntelinc.com
IT lifecycle solutions, applications outsourcing, development, enhancements, maintenance, integration & technology transformation & support. (Minority, estab , empl , sales $923,828,000, cert: NMSDC)

4665 Systems Technology Group, Inc. (STG)
3001 W Big Beaver Rd Ste 500e
Troy, MI 48084
Contact: Anup Popat CEO
Tel: 248-712-6702
Email: apopat@stgit.com
Website: www.stgit.com
Application software development outsourcing svcs: onsite & offshore. (As-Ind, As-Pac, estab 1985, empl 600, sales $102,000,000, cert: NMSDC)

4666 Systems Technology International, Inc.
39555 Orchard Hill Pl, Ste 530
Novi, MI 48375
Contact: Rodney Tesarz Dir of Sales
Tel: 248-735-3900
Email: rodney.tesarz@sti-world.com
Website: www.sti-world.com
Information technology & engineering: contract staffing, off shore services, software development & testing, engineering design & diagnostics. (AA, estab 0, empl , sales $7,500,000, cert: NMSDC)

4667 Technosoft Corporation
1 Towne Square 6th Fl
Southfield, MI 48076
Contact: Radhakrishnan Gurusamy CEO
Tel: 248-603-2666
Email: supplierdiversity@technosoftcorp.com
Website: www.technosoftcorp.com
Information technology staffing, IT consulting, system integration & business process outsourcing. (Woman/As-Pac, estab 1996, empl 4000, sales $123,867,758, cert: NMSDC)

4668 Tekshapers Inc.
2018 Harbor Village Ave
Keego Harbor, MI 48320
Contact: Nalini Kolli President
Tel: 248-470-5733
Email: nalini@tekshapers.com
Website: www.tekshapers.com
Software development, consulting services. (Minority, Woman, estab 0, empl , sales , cert: NMSDC)

4669 Touch World, Inc.
31500 W 13 Mile Rd Ste 101
Farmington Hills, MI 48334
Contact: Gordon McKenna President
Tel: 248-539-3700
Email: gordon.mckenna@touchworld.com
Website: www.touchworld.com
Computer software consulting & staff agumentation svcs: ERP, Client Server, Microsoft, UNIX, workflow, supply chain mgmt, ILVS, EDI , barcoding, RFID, Gentran, Future 3, Harbinger, Mercator, Trinary, AS 400, mainframe products. (As-Pac, estab 1996, empl 17, sales $1,550,000, cert: NMSDC)

4670 Trillium Teamologies Inc.
219 S Main St
Royal Oak, MI 48067
Contact: Greg Stanalajczo COO
Tel: 248-584-2080
Email: stano@trilliumteam.com
Website: www.trilliumteam.com
IT solutions: 2D & 3D animations, web dev, flash animations, IT consulting, e-commerce, project mgmt, systems integration & software dev, etc. (Woman, estab 1996, empl 63, sales , cert: WBENC)

4671   TTi Global
       6001 N. Adams Road Ste 185
       Bloomfield Hills, MI 48304
       Contact: April Bousamra Controller, NAO
       Tel: 248-853-5550
       Email: abousamra@tti-global.com
       Website: www.tti-global.com
Training design, development & delivery, outsourcing
services, staffing services. (Woman, estab 1976, empl 780,
sales $38,100,000, cert: WBENC)

4672   Unified Business Technologies Inc.
       315 Indusco Ct
       Troy, MI 48083
       Contact: Allyssia Gutierrez Sales Rep
       Tel: 248-677-9550
       Email: allyssia.gutierrez@ubtus.com
       Website: www.emd.ubtus.com
Software consulting services & staffing. (Woman/As-Ind,
As-Pac, estab 1997, empl 150, sales , cert: WBENC)

4673   V2Soft Inc.
       300 Enterprise Court
       Bloomfield Hills, MI 48302
       Contact: Varchasvi Shankar President & CEO
       Tel: 248-904-1702
       Email: vs@v2soft.com
       Website: www.v2soft.com
Software business solutions, consulting, contract services
& staff augmentation, project outsourcing, offshore
development. (As-Ind, As-Pac, estab 1998, empl 1200,
sales $37,000,000, cert: NMSDC)

4674   Vision Information Technologies, Inc.
       3031 W Grand Blvd, Ste 600
       Detroit, MI 48202
       Contact: Christine Rice President
       Tel: 313-420-2000
       Email: info@visionit.com
       Website: www.visionit.com
IT staffing, e-business consulting & web application dev.
(Hisp, estab 1997, empl 1000, sales $209,000,000, cert:
NMSDC)

4675   Vivek Systems, Inc.
       2163 Avon Industrial Dr
       Rochester Hills, MI 48309
       Contact: Bose Vivek President
       Tel: 248-293-1070
       Email: bvivek@viveksystems.com
       Website: www.viveksystems.com
CAD/engineering solution company. (As-Ind, estab 0, empl
, sales $1,080,000, cert: NMSDC)

4676   WebRunners, Inc. dba W3R Consulting
       1000 Town Center Ste 1150
       Southfield, MI 48044
       Contact: CEO
       Tel: 248-358-1002
       Email: info@w3r.com
       Website: www.w3r.com
Infrastructure planning & design, custom hosting solutions, directory svcs design, systems admin, middleware &
database support, metrics tools, monitoring & reporting,
firewall mgmt & security, VPN architecture, application
integration. (AA, estab 1995, empl 400, sales $36,500,000,
cert: NMSDC)

4677   Weldon Enterprise Global IT, LLC
       3031 W Grand Blvd, Ste 695
       Detroit, MI 48202
       Contact: Markeith Weldon CEO
       Tel: 313-687-4990
       Email: mweldon@weglobalit.com
       Website: www.weglobalit.com
IT managed services, technical staffing & non technical
staffing. (AA, estab 2011, empl 10, sales $1,000,000,
cert: NMSDC)

4678   WIT Inc.
       900 Tower Dr Ste 325
       Troy, MI 48098
       Contact: Quaid Saifee President
       Tel: 248-641-5900
       Email: quaid@witinc.com
       Website: www.witinc.com
Web site design & development, internet branding,
graphic design, content management solutions, database design & consulting, web application development,
training, web collaboration. (As-Ind, estab 1996, empl
20, sales $2,500,000, cert: NMSDC)

4679   Youngsoft Inc.
       49197 Wixom Tech Dr Ste B
       Wixom, MI 48393
       Contact: Chris Reaume Dir of Sales Operations
       Tel: 248-675-1200
       Email: chrisr@youngsoft.com
       Website: www.youngsoft.com
Information technology services: staffing support,
consulting, solution design & development. (As-Ind,
estab 1996, empl 130, sales $11,690,000, cert: NMSDC)

Minnesota

4680   Active-Duty
       12996 Eastview Ct
       Apple Valley, MN 55124
       Contact: Gregory St.James President
       Tel: 952-322-3662
       Email: gstjames@active-duty.us
       Website: www.active-duty.us
Project management, information technology, research
& development. (Woman/AA, Nat Ame, estab 2001,
empl 1, sales , cert: State)

4681   Analytiks International, Inc.
       10 S Fifth St Ste 720
       Minneapolis, MN 55402
       Contact: Mike Regan Marketing & Sales
       Tel: 612-305-4312
       Email: mregan@aii-3.com
       Website: www.aii-3.com
SAS consulting & resource placement services. (As-Ind,
estab 2004, empl 6, sales $200,000, cert: NMSDC)

4682   Arrowhead Promotion & Fulfillment Co., Inc.
       1105 SE 8th St
       Grand Rapids, MN 55744
       Contact: Katie Prokop Christmas CEO
       Tel: 218-327-1165
       Email: katie@apfco.com
       Website: www.apfco.com
Software development, customized reporting, fulfillment activities. (Woman, estab 1983, empl 300, sales
$14,250,000, cert: WBENC)

4683   Backbone Consultants
      50 S 6th St Ste 1360
      Minneapolis, MN 55402
      Contact: Operations & Acct Mgr
      Tel: 612-568-7167
      Email:
      Website: www.backboneconsultants.com
IT Audit Outsource & Co-source, IT Risk Assessment &
Advisory, IT Sourcing Risks, Information Security Risk
Assessment, Financial Institutions Data Privacy (GLBA)
Reviews. (As-Pac, Hisp, estab 2008, empl 13, sales
$1,897,914, cert: State)

4684   Barnes Business Solutions, Inc.
      4857 Island View Dr
      Mound, MN 55364
      Contact: Maria Barnes President
      Tel: 630-715-4452
      Email: mbarnes@barnesbusinesssolutions.com
      Website: www.BarnesBusinessSolutions.com
Core competency: Custom programming services, Microsoft
Access databases, SQL Server databases, Microsoft Excel
tools & macros,
Microsoft Office integration, Windows-based software
solutions. (Woman, estab 2008, empl 1, sales $139,235,
cert: WBENC)

4685   BCforward
      7701 France Ave S, Ste 325
      Edina, MN 55435
      Contact: Kortney Cartwright District Branch Mgr
      Tel: 954-540-4064
      Email: kortney.cartwright@bcforward.com
      Website: www.bcforward.com
IT consulting & staffing. (AA, estab , empl , sales
$2,500,000, cert: NMSDC)

4686   BPK Inc.
      12800 Whitewater Dr, Ste 100
      Minnetonka, MN 55439
      Contact: Rajeev Bhatia CEO
      Tel: 612-293-7585
      Email: rajeev@bpktech.com
      Website: www.bpktech.com
IT Consulting, Agile, Software Development, IT Services,
Financial consulting, Staff augmentation, Staffing solutions,
Java, .Net, Project Manager, Sap, SQ, Investment manage-
ment, Wealth management. (As-Ind, estab 2006, empl 10,
sales $4,000,000, cert: NMSDC)

4687   BTM Global Consulting LLC
      330 S Second Ave Ste 450
      Minneapolis, MN 55401
      Contact: Lesli Hines President
      Tel: 612-238-8801
      Email: lesli.hines@btmgcs.com
      Website: www.btmgcs.com
Custom application development, software development,
integration, implementation. (As-Pac, estab 2004, empl 85,
sales $5,100,000, cert: NMSDC)

4688   Business Technology Solutions, Inc.
      7441 Windmill Dr
      Chanhassen, MN 55317
      Contact: Brian Hugh President & CEO
      Tel: 612-208-7287
      Email: brian.hugh@btsbiz.com
      Website: www.btsbiz.com
Information systems integration/development, project
management, business/system analysis, large-scale
application/infrastructure upgrades, packaged software
evaluation/selection & database performance analysis &
tuning. (As-Pac, estab 1996, empl 2, sales $290,804,
cert: State)

4689   Clarity Tek, Inc.
      2859 Aspen Lake Dr NE
      Blaine, MN 55449
      Contact: Abida Banu President
      Tel: 612-567-0835
      Email: abida.banu@claritytek.com
      Website: http://claritytek.com/
Placement, Recruiting, IT Consulting, IT Services, Staff
augmetation, IT Contractor Services, Software development services, Software maintenance services. (Woman/
As-Pac, estab 2012, empl 4, sales , cert: City)

4690   Crown CyberSystems
      160 Birchwood Ave
      St. Paul, MN 55110
      Contact: Austin Kasper Mgr of Client Partnerships
      Tel: 612-207-7423
      Email: akasper@crowncybersystems.com
      Website: http://crowncybersystems.com/
IT Solutions, managed IT Department Services. (Woman,
estab 2010, empl 10, sales $6,000,000, cert: WBENC)

4691   CS Solutions, Inc.
      7525 Mitchell Road Ste 106
      Eden Prairie, MN 55344
      Contact: Sonia Stephen Staffing Mgr
      Tel: 651-271-4477
      Email: sonia@cssoln.com
      Website: www.cssolutionsinc.com
IT consulting, staff augmentation, project outsourcing,
solution design & develop, data warehousing & admin,
e-commerce security, web develop. (As-Ind, estab 1996,
empl 30, sales $1,200,000, cert: NMSDC)

4692   Denysys Corporation
      2400 Blaisdell Ave Ste 202
      Minneapolis, MN 55404
      Contact: Philip Denny President
      Tel: 612-869-7617
      Email: philip.denny@denysys.com
      Website: www.denysys.com
Information technology, administrative & management
consulting services. (AA, estab 1991, empl 35, sales
$4,100,540, cert: State)

4693   E-Comm Systems, Inc.
      1728 Ashland Ave
      St. Paul, MN 55104
      Contact: President
      Tel: 612-875-5531
      Email:
      Website: www.e-commsystems.com
IT security, risk mgmt, security assessment reports,
remediation efforts, identification of mitigating controls
& security planning, implement security policies. (Hisp,
estab 1999, empl 5, sales $120,001, cert: NMSDC)

4694   Enclipse Corp.
       331 2nd Ave S Ste 703
       Minneapolis, MN 55401
       Contact: Mohammed Halim Client Relationship Mgr
       Tel: 612-360-4713
       Email: halimm@enclipse.com
       Website: www.enclipse.com
Professional consulting svcs, managed svcs & solutions
design & development: identifying organizational strategies & objectives, design, develop & implement end-to-
end software solutions. (As-Pac, estab 2002, empl 128,
sales $10,000,000, cert: NMSDC)

4695   Genisys Technologies, Inc.
       3545 Plymouth Blvd, Ste 115
       Plymouth, MN 55447
       Contact: MOHAN DHAVILESWARAPU CEO
       Tel: 763-205-4883
       Email: mohan@genisystechnologies.com
       Website: www.genisystechnologies.com
Management, IT staffing & solutions, business information, system design, planning, development & implementation. (As-Ind, estab 2013, empl 15, sales $2,000,000,
cert: NMSDC)

4696   Horizontal Integration, Inc.
       1660 Hwy 100 Ste 200
       St. Louis Park, MN 55416
       Contact: Craig Blake Dir Staffing Operations
       Tel: 612-392-7581
       Email: finance@horizontalintegration.com
       Website: www.horizontalintegration.com
Information technology staff augmentation , software
design & devel, e-commerce, crm apps, enterprise
arcitecture & enterprise app integration, business performance mgmt app, custom business apps, web app information architecture & creative design. (As-Pac, estab 2003,
empl 632, sales $101,000,000, cert: NMSDC)

4697   Icon IT Group
       3025 Hatbor Ln N, Ste 324
       Plymouth, MN 55447
       Contact: Shaik Ahmed President
       Tel: 612-207-4778
       Email: ahmed@iconitgroup.com
       Website: www.iconitgroup.com
E-verify Software Development, Web Technologies, ERP
Packages, Data Warehousing, Business Intelligence,
Business Analysis & Quality Assurance. (As-Ind, estab
2013, empl 11, sales $1,200,000, cert: NMSDC)

4698   Ideal System Solutions, Inc.
       5610 Rowland Rd Ste 150
       Minnetonka, MN 55343
       Contact: Elise M Hernandez President
       Tel: 888-696-1044
       Email: sales@idealssi.com
       Website: www.idealssi.com
Dist servers, workstations, pcs, parts, upgrades, memory,
storage, networking components & peripherals, consulting, system planning & integration, network design & set
up, maintenance & training. (Woman/Hisp, estab , empl
25, sales $25,500,000, cert: State)

4699   ILM Professional Services, Inc.
       5221 Viking Dr Ste 300
       Edina, MN 55435
       Contact: Lee Ann Villella Acct Exec
       Tel: 952-960-2220
       Email: leeann.villella@ilmservice.com
       Website: www.ilmservice.com
Integrated, custom web & mobile applications, consulting, project outsourcing on & offsite. (Woman/As-Ind,
estab 2002, empl 30, sales $4,100,000, cert: NMSDC,
WBENC)

4700   Infinity Systems, Inc.
       P.O. Box 43925
       Brooklyn Park, MN 55443
       Contact: Michael Perkins Dir of Business Devel
       Tel: 612-819-3940
       Email: mperknoll@aol.com
       Website: www.isimetrics.com
Internet security software. (AA, estab 1993, empl 10,
sales , cert: NMSDC)

4701   IPCS
       600 S Hwy 169 Ste 1595
       Minneapolis, MN 55426
       Contact: Kuldeep Dhar Sr VP
       Tel: 952-541-4888
       Email: kuldeep@ipcs.net
       Website: www.ipcs.net
Software development & consulting: on-site, off-site &
off-shore IT contract programming, e-commerce
applications, data warehousing, application development, database admin, package implementations.
(Woman/As-Pac, estab 1996, empl 51, sales
$10,000,000, cert: State)

4702   Jeevtek Inc.
       7160 Cahill Rd, Ste 238
       Edina, MN 55439
       Contact: President
       Tel: 612-440-0123
       Email:
       Website: www.jeevtek.com/
IT staff augmentation & custom software development
services, Java, J2EE, web applications, eCommerce,
databases, SQL, ERP (Oracle, SAP), .NET, Cloud etc.
(Woman/As-Ind, estab 2015, empl 2, sales $230,000,
cert: City, WBENC)

4703   JOBMA LLC
       13911 Ridgedale Dr, Ste 230
       Minnetonka, MN 55305
       Contact: Krishna Kant Head of Global Business
       Tel: 952-546-3300
       Email: krishnak@jobma.com
       Website: www.jobma.com/
Cloud based video interview platform, artificial intelligence recruiting, video resumes, and automated
recruiting, (Nat Ame, estab 2013, empl , sales $200,000,
cert: NMSDC)

4704   KCS
       2395 Ariel St N, Ste A
       Saint Paul, MN 55109
       Contact: Dorothy C. Richburg CEO
       Tel: 651-777-9119
       Email: drichburg@keystonecs.com
       Website: www.keystonecs.com
IT consulting, technical services, IT training. (Woman/AA,
estab 1987, empl 45, sales $9,894,985, cert: State)

4705   Net Anchor, Inc.
202 N 22nd Ave
Minneapolis, MN 55411
Contact: Keni Fegbeboh
Tel: 612-425-2200
Email: kenfegb@netanchor.com
Website: www.netanchor.com
Software & hardware procurement, Help desk support, IT Managed Services, IT Staff Augmentation, Remote monitoring, IT Network Architecture, Network Design & Installation, IT Infrastructure & Data Center, Custom hardware software app dev. (AA, estab 2006, empl 1, sales , cert: NMSDC)

4706   New Horizons Computer Learning Center Minnesota
2915 Commers Dr Ste 500
Eagan, MN 55121
Contact: Sammy Peterson Dir of Operations
Tel: 651-900-7203
Email: speterson@newhorizonsmn.com
Website: www.newhorizonsmn.com
IT training. (Woman, estab 2010, empl 18, sales $3,554,749, cert: WBENC)

4707   Performix
7400 Metro blvd Ste 390
Edina, MN 55439
Contact: Sunil Bafna Owner
Tel: 952-893-0143
Email: priya@performixbiz.com
Website: www.performixbiz.com
Software consulting, application integration, database integration, ecommerce application, enterprise application. (As-Ind, As-Pac, estab 1997, empl 13, sales $1,650,000, cert: State, NMSDC)

4708   Pinnacle Consulting Solutions
17761 Cascade Dr
Eden Prairie, MN 55347
Contact: Ranja Tarafder CEO
Tel: 952-292-4556
Email: ranja@pinnacleconsultingsolutions.com
Website: www.pinnacleconsultingsolutions.com
IT staffing & consulting, Project/Program Management, ITIL Process Management, Application Development, Software Development Life Cycle, Database Design & Development, Business Intelligence, Business Analysis/Data Analysis. (Woman/As-Ind, estab 2014, empl 2, sales $150,000, cert: NMSDC, WBENC)

4709   Pleasant Consulting, LLC
9145 Lyndale Ave S
Bloomington, MN 55420
Contact: Marty Pleasant President
Tel: 952-484-4373
Email: marty@pleasantconsulting.com
Website: www.pleasantconsulting.com
Contract & temporary IT staff, contract to hire staff. (Woman, estab 2012, empl 17, sales $900,000, cert: WBENC)

4710   Procellis Technology Inc.
901 Marquette Ave Ste 1500
Minneapolis, MN 55402
Contact: Damian Young
Tel: 612-430-9505
Email: damian.young@procellis.com
Website: www.procellis.com
IT services, servers, storage, virtualization, backup, disaster recovery & cloud services. (AA, estab 2013, empl 6, sales , cert: NMSDC)

4711   SDK Software Inc aka Sudhko Inc.
810 Lilac Dr North Ste #116
Golden Valley, MN 55422
Contact: Hema Arumilli President
Tel: 763-657-7272
Email: sdkhr@sdksoft.com
Website: www.sdksoft.com
Software development svcs, staff augmentation & project mgmt. (Woman/As-Ind, estab 1993, empl 100, sales $13,350,000, cert: City, NMSDC)

4712   Select Source International
13911 Ridgedale Dr, Ste 230
Minnetonka, MN 55305
Contact: Mandeep Sodhi CEO
Tel: 952-546-3300
Email: sales@selectsourceintl.com
Website: www.SelectSourceIntl.com
Temporary Staffing, Information Technology Staffing, Information Technology Services, Engineering Services, Financial Services, Govtt Services, Retail Services, Energy & Utility Services, Application Dev, Mobile Development. (Nat Ame, estab 2000, empl 771, sales , cert: NMSDC)

4713   TAJ Technologies, Inc.
7900 International Dr Ste 405
Bloomington, MN 55425
Contact: K.C. Sukumar President & CEO
Tel: 651-405-7411
Email: kcs@tajtech.com
Website: www.tajtech.com
E-business solutions, e-commerce applications, client/server programming, on-site, off-site & offshore. (As-Ind, estab 1987, empl 208, sales $22,829,532, cert: NMSDC)

4714   Tartan Marketing, Inc.
10467 93rd Ave N
Maple Grove, MN 55369
Contact: Margie MacLachlan CEO
Tel: 763-391-7575
Email: info@tartanmarketing.com
Website: http://tartanmarketing.com
We are a full service B2B agency that specializes in helping food, technology and service companies energize their brands and grow their businesses. We employ a completely integrated marketing approach where strategy drives creative execution (Woman, estab 1999, empl 14, sales $2,038,340, cert: WBENC)

4715   Technical Information & Professional Solutions Inc
15600 35th Ave N Ste 203
Plymouth, MN 55447
Contact: Adnan (AJ) Jalil Sales/Mktg Mgr
Tel: 763-557-7010
Email: aj@tips2e.com
Website: www.tips2e.com
Technical staffing: short & long term contract, contract to hire & direct placement staff. (As-Ind, estab 1995, empl 89, sales $9,374,046, cert: NMSDC)

4716   Technology Solutions Group LLC
60 S 6th St Ste 2800
Minneapolis, MN 55402
Contact: Alexandra Farnsworth CEO
Tel: 888-733-4599
Email: ali@tsg-mn.com
Website: http://tsg-mn.com/
BI/Data Mining, IoT & Software Development, Business Intelligence, BI/Data mining, Analytics, Internet of Things, Mobile App Development, Software Development, Web Development, QA/testing. (Woman, estab 2013, empl , sales $616,140, cert: WBENC)

4717   The Macro Group, Inc.
       1200 Washington Ave S Ste 350
       Minneapolis, MN 55415
       Contact: Dawn Kuzma Marketing Dir
       Tel: 612-206-3382
       Email: dkuzma@macrogroup.net
       Website: www.macrogroup.net
Project/Program Management, Business Analysis,
Process Improvement, Web Application Devel, Application
Integration, Electronic Content Management/Electronic
Document Management, Technical Analysis & Design,
Client/Service Application Devel. (Woman, estab 1987,
empl 35, sales $3,700,000, cert: City)

4718   Titan Data Group Inc.
       6043 Hudson Rd, Ste 399-E
       Woodbury, MN 55125
       Contact: Viswanathan Subramanian President
       Tel: 651-493-0039
       Email: vish@titandata.com
       Website: www.titandata.com
Business strategy, IT consulting, process improvement &
technology development. (Woman/As-Ind, estab 2002,
empl 20, sales $3,917,883, cert: NMSDC)

4719   Transcomp Inc. DBA: Evolve Systems
       2974 Rice St
       St Paul, MN 55113
       Contact: CEO
       Tel: 651-628-4000
       Email:
       Website: www.evolve-systems.com
Web development, shopping carts, event management
interfaces, Content Management Systems (CMS) &
payment forms. (Woman, estab 1993, empl 15, sales
$1,128,000, cert: WBENC)

4720   TSG Server and Storage
       10 2nd St NE, Ste 214
       Minneapolis, MN 55413
       Contact: Mike DuBois COO
       Tel: 612-465-0800
       Email: info@tsg-usa.com
       Website: www.tsg-usa.com
Solution Integrator & infrastructure, Hyper-converged
infrastructure, cloud and security, networking, storage,
server & software, cloud storage, back up & recovery,
cybersecurity, IBM Power Systems, IBM Storage. (As-Pac,
estab 2001, empl 11, sales , cert: State, City)

4721   Twin Cities Solutions, Inc.
       P.O. Box 21975
       Eagan, MN 55121
       Contact: Scott Miller CFO
       Tel: 952-583-0367
       Email: smiller@twincs.com
       Website: www.twincs.com
IT consulting: .Net developers, Java developers, business
analysts & project managers. (Woman, estab 2000, empl
10, sales $970,000, cert: State)

4722   UpNet Technologies, Inc.
       7825 Washington Ave S Ste 450
       Minneapolis, MN 55439
       Contact: Kevin Amys Controller
       Tel: 952-944-2345
       Email: kevin.amys@upnettec.com
       Website: www.upnettec.com
Information technologies: EDI, XML, CIDX , EDIFACT and
Rosetta net. (Woman/As-Pac, estab 2000, empl 25, sales
$3,200,000, cert: WBENC)

4723   Virtelligence, Inc
       6216 Baker Road Ste 100
       Eden Prairie, MN 55346
       Contact: Akhtar Chaudhri CEO
       Tel: 952-548-6600
       Email: achaudhri@virtelligence.com
       Website: www.virtelligence.com
Management consulting & technology solutions: project
mgmt, enterprise software dev & integration, business
intelligence & data warehousing, application
outsourcing, staffing. (As-Ind, As-Pac, estab , empl , sales
$27,100,000, cert: NMSDC)

4724   Virtual Matrix Corporation (dba 1 Source, Inc.)
       7200 France Ave S Ste 324
       Edina, MN 55435
       Contact: Bill Hohn Director
       Tel: 952-835-6400
       Email: hohnb@vmatrixcorp.com
       Website: www.1Source.net
IT staffing/consulting, SAP, ABAP, Java, PHP, Oracle,
Microsoft products (.NETs). (As-Ind, estab 2002, empl
78, sales $3,500,000, cert: State, City, NMSDC)

4725   Visual Consultants, Inc.
       4900 Hwy 169 N, Ste 307
       New Hope, MN 55428
       Contact: Bala Akkina VP
       Tel: 763-533-1000
       Email: bala@visual-consultants.com
       Website: www.visual-consultants.com
IT solutions, enterprise IT applications development & IT
consulting services. (Woman/As-Pac, estab 2003, empl
42, sales $3,500,000, cert: NMSDC)

4726   Word Tech Secretarial Service Inc.
       6825 York Place N
       Minneapolis, MN 55429
       Contact: Patty Mesenbrink President
       Tel: 612-349-9214
       Email: patty@wordtechtranscription.com
       Website: http://wordtechtranscription.com
Audio Transcription, Digital transcription, Video transcription, transcription, document preparation, audio
and video transcription. (Woman, estab 1986, empl 3,
sales , cert: State, City, SDB)

4727   Xylo Technologies Inc.
       2434 Superior Dr NW Ste 105
       Rochester, MN 55901
       Contact: Dharani Ramamoorthy President
       Tel: 507-289-9956
       Email: dharani@xylotechnologies.com
       Website: www.xylotechnologies.com
IT consulting, web & client/server technolgies, custom
software development & system integration services.
(As-Pac, estab 2000, empl 60, sales $7,043,821, cert:
NMSDC)

4728   YFI Technologies
       1422 Thomas Ave
       Saint Paul, MN 55104
       Contact: Reynaldo Lyles President
       Tel: 651-645-4987
       Email: rlyles@yourfutureimage.com
       Website: www.YFItechnologies.com
Mobile & wireless solutions: PDA's, palm devices,
custom software design, mobile database synchronization, IT consulting & staff augmentation. (AA, estab
1994, empl 8, sales $183,000, cert: NMSDC)

Missouri

4729 Advanced Resources Group, Inc.
687 Trade Center Blvd Ste 110
Chesterfield, MO 63005
Contact: Sonya Gotto CEO
Tel: 636-777-4141
Email: tgeolat@advr.com
Website: www.advr.com
Contract engineers & IT consultants. (Woman, estab 2002, empl 450, sales $15,100,000, cert: WBENC)

4730 Applications Engineering Group
12300 Old Tesson Rd, Ste 100-G
St. Louis, MO 63128
Contact: Chris Rakel VP Operations
Tel: 314-842-9110
Email: chris.rakel@aeg-inc.com
Website: www.aeg-inc.com
Provide contract, contract to hire & direct hire IT employment services. (Hisp, estab 1992, empl 35, sales , cert: State)

4731 Ares Construction Co, LLC
4900 Lawn Ave
Kansas City, MO 64130
Contact: Quinton Fears CEO
Tel: 816-285-5933
Email: qfears@aresconst.com
Website: www.aresconst.com
Electrical contracting, satellite dishes, computer consulting, network design & installation, web design, data recovery, customer training, structured cabling & phone systems. (AA, estab 2002, empl 7, sales , cert: State, City)

4732 Byrne Software Technologies, Inc.
16091 Swingley Ridge Rd Ste 200
Chesterfield, MO 63017
Contact: Tom Allen VP
Tel: 636-537-2505
Email: tra@byrnesoftware.com
Website: www.byrnesoftware.com
IT consulting & software development; custom applications, web sites, Windows applications. (Woman, estab 1985, empl 55, sales $6,538,000, cert: State)

4733 C-Edge Software Consultants LLC
655 Craig Rd Ste 220
Creve Coeur, MO 63141
Contact: Sekhar Prabhakar CEO
Tel: 314-254-7551
Email: sekhar@cedgecorp.com
Website: www.cedgecorp.com
Project mgmt, software application development, infrastructure consolidation, database mgmt, systems integration. (As-Ind, estab 2004, empl 40, sales $5,000,000, cert: 8a)

4734 Communitronics Corp.
970 Bolger Court
Fenton, MO 63026
Contact: Rita Leitensdorfer CEO
Tel: 314-771-7160
Email: rital@communitronics.com
Website: www.communitronics.com
Audio Visual Systems, VTC Systems, Secure/Non-Secure VTC, Enterprise Collaboration, Video/Media Walls, Project Engineering, Custom AV Applications, Service Contracts, FTEs, Information Assurance Compliance (Woman, estab 1969, empl 11, sales $2,000,000, cert: State, NWBOC)

4735 Data Dynamics, Inc.
500 Oak Leaf Manor Court Ste 1
St. Louis, MO 63021
Contact: Thomas Van Cleave Mgr Business Devel
Tel: 314-607-3758
Email: thomas.vancleave@datadynamics-inc.com
Website: www.datadynamics-inc.com
IT consulting, software development, web applications, mobile apps, web sites& custom software development, infrastructure, PCs, server, networks, routers, etc. (Woman/As-Ind, estab 1996, empl 2, sales $195,836, cert: State)

4736 Digital Partners Incorporated
8008 Carondelet Ave Ste 103
Saint Louis, MO 63105
Contact: Matina Koester President
Tel: 314-863-8008
Email: matina@dpipro.com
Website: www.dpipro.com
System Integration. (Woman, estab 1994, empl 11, sales $8,500,000, cert: WBENC)

4737 Document Imaging Systems of St. Louis
1463 S Vandeventer Ave
St. Louis, MO 63110
Contact: Adrienne Williams President
Tel: 314-531-0167
Email: awilliams@disrepro.com
Website: www.disrepro.com
blueprint document reproduction, project collaboration & document management solutions. (Woman/AA, estab 1995, empl 8, sales $4,095,761, cert: State, City, NMSDC)

4738 ECCO Select Corporation
1601 Iron St, Ste 200
North Kansas City, MO 64116
Contact: Jeanette Prenger President
Tel: 816-960-3800
Email: registrations@eccoselect.com
Website: www.eccoselect.com
Project management, security consulting, network security admin, system security audits. (Woman/Hisp, estab , empl , sales $28,172,000, cert: State, NMSDC, WBENC)

4739 Ferguson Consulting Inc.
1350 Timberlake Manor Pkwy Ste 450
Chesterfield, MO 63017
Contact: Paul Woolverton VP, Govt Sector
Tel: 636-728-4408
Email: pwoolverton@fergcons.com
Website: www.fergusonconsultinginc.com
IT solutions. (Woman, estab 1993, empl 110, sales , cert: State)

4740 Geodata IT
555 Washington Ave, Ste 310
St. Louis, MO 63101
Contact: Justin Bennett President
Tel: 217-390-8085
Email: justin@geodatait.com
Website: www.geodatait.com
Agile Software Development, Data Center Consolidation & Cloud Services, Big Data & Data Analytics, Systems Engineering & Integration, Program & Project Management, Enterprise Content Management, Data & Information Engineering. (Hisp, estab 2012, empl 4, sales $120,000, cert: NMSDC, 8a)

4741   Information Solutions Design
       2122 Kratky Rd Ste 250
       St. Louis, MO 63114
       Contact: Timothy Slater CEO
       Tel: 314-429-3311
       Email: tim.slater@newhorizonsstl.com
       Website:
Information technology svcs: network & server consolidation, web & portal development, application & database
development. (AA, estab 2005, empl 35, sales $1,500,000,
cert: NMSDC)

4742   Ingenuity Consulting Partner, Inc.
       410 B SE 3rd St, Ste 102
       Lee's Summit, MO 64081
       Contact: Brenda Riggs CEO
       Tel: 816-272-8145
       Email: briggs@ingenuityconsulting.com
       Website: www.ingenuityconsulting.com
Software development & application integration, web &
mobile applications. (Woman, estab 2002, empl 22, sales
$1,155,578, cert: State)

4743   Kelly Mitchell Group, Inc.
       8229 Maryland Ave
       Clayton, MO 63105
       Contact: Cassandra Sanford
       Tel: 314-727-1700
       Email: cassandra.sanford@kellymitchell.com
       Website: www.kellymitchell.com
Technology consulting: staff augmentation, project
solutions, managed outsourcing & strategic consulting.
(Woman, estab 1998, empl 2000, sales $90,000,000, cert:
CPUC, WBENC)

4744   NextGen Information Services Inc.
       906 Olive St Ste 600
       Saint Louis, MO 63101
       Contact: Christy Herschbach Admin Asst
       Tel: 314-588-1212
       Email: supplierdiversity@nextgen-is.com
       Website: www.nextgen-is.com
IT consulting services: project mgmt, custom application
dev, legacy transition svcs & staff augmentation, staff
augmentaion. (Woman/Hisp, estab 1997, empl 300, sales ,
cert: State, City, WBENC)

4745   Pace Solutions, Inc.
       1065 Executive Parkway Ste 225
       St. Louis, MO 63141
       Contact: Clint Kleinsorge Dir Business Devel
       Tel: 314-560-9641
       Email: clint@pacesi.com
       Website: www.pacesi.com
Information Technology staffing & consulting services.
(Woman/As-Ind, estab 2011, empl 55, sales $5,000,000,
cert: NWBOC)

4746   PSRI TecHnologies LLC
       113 Eastland Dr
       Jefferson City, MO 65101
       Contact: Natasha Conley President
       Tel: 573-636-9696
       Email: cconley@psritech.com
       Website: www.psritech.com
Information technology/staff augmentation, project
management & call center/help desk operations. (Woman/
AA, estab 2001, empl 5, sales $197,053, cert: State)

4747   Quanteq, Inc.
       10 Strecker Rd, Ste 1170
       Ellisville, MO 63011
       Contact: Juan Kuanfung CEO
       Tel: 314-329-7799
       Email: jkuanfung@quantequsa.com
       Website: www.quantequsa.com
Software service solutions: information systems &
technology life-cycle, project mgmt, requirement &
business studies, package evaluation, system design &
dev, system & software integration, database admin,
custom programming svcs. (Hisp, estab 1997, empl 1,
sales , cert: State, City)

4748   Rose International, Inc.
       16401 Swingley Ridge Road Ste 300
       Chesterfield, MO 63017
       Contact: Jonnie Gray VP of Finance
       Tel: 636-812-4000
       Email: sales@roseint.com
       Website: www.roseint.com
Information systems consulting, software devlopment,
computer programming & maintenance. (Woman/As-
Ind, As-Pac, estab 1993, empl 4500, sales $332,000,000,
cert: State, NMSDC, WBENC)

4749   Saigan Technologies Inc.
       2300 Main St Ste 900
       Kansas City, MO 64108
       Contact: Julie Robertson Client Engagement Mgr
       Tel: 816-303-1301
       Email: diversity@saigantech.com
       Website: www.saigantech.com
Information technology IT services & solutions.
(Woman/As-Pac, estab 2004, empl 31, sales $1,701,826,
cert: State, NMSDC, WBENC)

4750   ServeKool Technologies LLC
       287 Arbor Trails Dr
       Ballwin, MO 63021
       Contact: Lovelina Bhagat President
       Tel: 636-207-8055
       Email: info@servekool.com
       Website: www.servekool.com
Custom software development, application support
outsourcing & staffing services. (Woman/As-Ind, estab
2013, empl 2, sales , cert: NMSDC)

4751   Strategic Staffing Solutions
       120 S. Central Ave
       St. Louis, MO 63105
       Contact: Denice Olson VP
       Tel: 630-546-1784
       Email: gscharf@strategicstaff.com
       Website: www.strategicstaff.com
Information technology consulting. (Woman, estab
1990, empl 2700, sales $642,000,000, cert: WBENC)

4752   TechGuard Security LLC
       28 Hawk Ridge Blvd, Ste 107
       Lake St. Louis, MO 63367
       Contact: CEO
       Tel: 636-489-2230
       Email:
       Website: www.techguard.com
IT networking & security services: vulnerability assessments; policy development; secure network infrastructure design; security awareness training; intrusion
detection; business continuity/disaster recovery; 24x7
incident response. (Woman, estab 2000, empl 45, sales
$7,550,000, cert: State)

4753   TechnoSmarts, Inc.
16090 Swingley Ridge Rd Ste 330
St. Louis, MO 63017
Contact: Rao Vallabhaneni President
Tel: 636-519-0814
Email: rao@technosmarts.com
Website: www.technosmarts.com
IT consulting & staffing services. (As-Ind, estab 1997, empl 30, sales , cert: NMSDC)

4754   The Newberry Group, Inc.
2440 Executive Dr, Ste 208
St. Charles, MO 63303
Contact: Brenda Newberry President
Tel: 636-928-9944
Email: bnewberry@thenewberrygrp.com
Website: www.thenewberrygrp.com
Information systems consulting, software devel, LAN/WAN planning, installation & support, & permanent placement. (Woman/AA, estab 1996, empl 78, sales $3,100,000, cert: State)

4755   TurnGroup Technologies, LLC
2811 Locust St
St. Louis, MO 63103
Contact: Kim St. Onge Business Dev Mgr
Tel: 314-289-8734
Email: kim@turngroup.com
Website: www.turngroup.com
Database development, hardware/software support, internet solutions, LAN/WAN, programming, website development. (AA, estab 2002, empl 9, sales $225,000, cert: City)

4756   Unitech Consulting, LLC dba Chameleon
3207 Washington Ave
St. Louis, MO 63103
Contact: Mary Burgess Business Develop Mgr
Tel: 314-773-7200
Email: sales@chameleonis.com
Website: www.chameleonis.com
Program management, software development & integration & infrastructure support services. (Hisp, estab 2003, empl 75, sales $7,742,000, cert: NMSDC)

Mississippi

4757   Applied Geo Technologies, Inc.
404 Industrail Rd
Choctaw, MS 39350
Contact: Tim Magnusson GM
Tel: 601-663-7415
Email: tmagnusson@appliedgeotech.com
Website: www.appliedgeotech.com
Digital mapping services: conversion, parcel mapping, feature extraction, aerial & satellite image orthophotography production. (Nat Ame, estab 2001, empl 26, sales $4,545,061, cert: State)

4758   Omni Sourcing, Inc.
1230 Raymond Road; Box 6
Jackson, MS 39204
Contact: John Perkins President
Tel: 713-628-6929
Email: jperkins@omnisourcing.net
Website: www.omnisourcing.net
Systems integration & quality management, service assurance mgmt & testing, sourcing value creation, business & technology performance improvement, program & project mgmt. (AA, estab 2012, empl 30, sales $3,600,000, cert: NMSDC)

Montana

4759   S & K Global Solutions, LLC
145 S Lake Crest, Ste 2
Polson, MT 59860
Contact: Barbara DeBernardo President
Tel: 281-709-1080
Email: bdeberrnardo@skgs-llc.com
Website: www.skglobalsolutions.com
Logistics, engineering, telecommunications, and information technology (IT). (Nat Ame, estab 2005, empl 250, sales $21,000,000, cert: 8a)

4760   S & K Technologies
63066 Old Hwy 93
St. Ignatius, MT 59865
Contact: Sr VP IT Ops
Tel: 406-745-7500
Email:
Website: www.sktcorp.com
Information technology engineering svcs, software dev, technical manuals, software integration, web site design, web application dev, internet mgmt, program mgmt, logistical support, systems mgmt, integration, installation & training. (Nat Ame, estab 1999, empl 300, sales $67,403,178, cert: State)

North Carolina

4761   3 Birds Marketing, LLC
505-B W Franklin St
Chapel Hill, NC 27516
Contact: Layton Judd President
Tel: 919-913-2750
Email: layton@3birdsmarketing.com
Website: www.3birdsmarketing.com
Technology, software, integrated marketing platform, marketing, digital marketing, multichannel marketing, email marketing, email newsletters, digital newsletters, social media management, social media marketing. (Woman, estab 2009, empl 60, sales $3,769,500, cert: WBENC, NWBOC)

4762   Active Ergonomics, Inc.
6501 Creedmoor Rd Ste 101
Raleigh, NC 27613
Contact: Shannon A Powell President
Tel: 919-676-8211
Email: spowell@actergo.com
Website: www.actergo.com
Office ergonomic software to help increase worker productivity and reduce repetitive stress injuries. (Woman/Hisp, estab 1997, empl 4, sales $934,000, cert: NMSDC, WBENC)

4763   Alliance of Professionals & Consultants, Inc.
8200 Brownleigh Dr
Raleigh, NC 27617
Contact: Troy Roberts
Tel: 919-510-9696
Email: mgmt@apcinc.com
Website: www.apcinc.com
Requirements analysis, network architecture definitions & enhancements, information technology, hardware & software upgrades, modifications, installation, operation & maintenance. (Nat Ame, estab 1993, empl 724, sales $65,872,532, cert: NMSDC)

4764   Banerasoft Inc.
        5710 W Gate City Blvd Ste K, #279
        Greensboro, NC 27407
        Contact: Brenda Zamzow Sales & Customer Rela-
        tions Mgr
        Tel: 864-787-5408
        Email: akshata@banerasoft.biz
        Website: www.banerasoft.com
Technology Consulting/Outsourcing, Software Develop-
ment, App Development for all iOS & Android devices,
Data Analytics & Business Intelligence, QA & Solutions
Integration. (As-Ind, estab 2012, empl 35, sales $310,000,
cert: NMSDC)

4765   Barrchin, Inc.
        326 Morgan Brook Way
        Rolesville, NC 27571
        Contact: Janet Barrett President
        Tel: 919-630-5128
        Email: jbarrett@barrchin.com
        Website: www.barrchin.com
Information Technology (IT) & Management consulting.
(Woman/AA, estab 2013, empl 4, sales , cert: State, City)

4766   Carolina IT Professionals, Inc.
        243 W Catawba Ave
        Mount Holly, NC 28120
        Contact: VP Marketing
        Tel: 704-827-8102
        Email: gus.brown@citpinc.com
        Website: www.citpinc.com
Information technology staff augmentation, solutions &
consulting, permanent placements. (Woman, estab 2001,
empl 160, sales $19,009,811, cert: WBENC)

4767   Clark-Powell Associates, Inc.
        920 Blairhill Rd
        Charlotte, NC 28217
        Contact: C. Gibson Sales
        Tel: 704-525-4223
        Email: cgibson@clark-powell.com
        Website: www.clark-powell.com
Design, integration & maintenance of AV systems for
presentation, videoconferencing, video broadcast &
production. (Woman, estab 1983, empl 62, sales
$20,000,000, cert: State)

4768   Clinton Gaddy Inc.
        717 Green Valley Rd Ste 200
        Greensboro, NC 27408
        Contact: Gaddy Will CEO
        Tel: 336-355-8708
        Email: Wmgaddy@gsostaffing.com
        Website: www.gsostaffing.com
Contract IT Staffing/Temporary Labor: Systems Analyst, API
Development, Data Analyst, Software Developers, DevOps,
Lead Architects, IT Audit Managers, Change Management,
Incident/Change Management, Technical Lead, IT Direc-
tors, Solution Architect. (AA, estab 2017, empl 8, sales
$319,000, cert: State)

4769   COMNet Group, Inc.
        301 McCullough Dr, Ste 400
        Charlotte, NC 28262
        Contact: Ana Sai President & CEO
        Tel: 704-323-7762
        Email: ana@comnetgroup.com
        Website: www.comnetgroup.com
IT Technology & training services: ERP, offshoring/
outsourcing, agile program management & complex
software development & delivery. (Woman/As-Ind,
estab 2005, empl 20, sales $400,000, cert: NMSDC,
WBENC)

4770   Data Bridge Consultants LLC
        101 N Tryon St, Ste 1260
        Charlotte, NC 28246
        Contact: Sola Daves Principal Partner
        Tel: 980-319-7635
        Email: sola.daves@databridgeconsultants.com
        Website: www.databridgeconsultants.com
Big data and Artificial Intelligence Consulting, staffing/
BPO. (AA, estab 2013, empl 8, sales $11,300,000, cert:
NMSDC)

4771   DD Consulting and Management
        13016 Eastfield Rd Ste 200-272
        Huntersville, NC 28078
        Contact: Walter Great
        Tel: 704-909-2970
        Email: walter@ddconsultingservice.com
        Website: www.DDConsultingservice.com
IT consulting, data storage, data backup, physical
surveillance data, digital evidence & security-sensitive
digital data. (AA, estab 2001, empl 3, sales , cert:
NMSDC)

4772   DynPro
        7412 Chapel Hill Rd
        Raleigh, NC 27607
        Contact: Michael Kallam VP-Business Develop-
        ment
        Tel: 919-747-7114
        Email: mkallam@dynpro.com
        Website: www.dynpro.com
Design & implement internet applications & web-
enable, enterprise solutions, SAP, People Soft & Oracle
application mgmt outsourcing, technical svcs, staff
augmentation, project mgmt, help desk support. (As-
Ind, As-Pac, estab 1996, empl 90, sales $3,695,000, cert:
NMSDC)

4773   Empores LLC
        11020 David Taylor Dr
        Charlotte, NC 28262
        Contact: Satish Prasad Ramamurthy VP Business
        Dev
        Tel: 703-409-4945
        Email: satish@emporesllc.com
        Website: http://emporesllc.com
Voltage optimization, intelligent PF correction, KVAR
improvements, cloud based energy monitoring &
automatic techniques. (As-Ind, As-Pac, estab 2012, empl
5, sales , cert: State, City)

4774　GrimeGuru Janitorial Service
　　　1531 Westbrook Plaza Dr, Ste A
　　　Winston-Salem, NC 27103
　　　Contact: Brigitte Hampton President
　　　Tel:　336-710-4406
　　　Email: brigitte@grimeguru.com
　　　Website: www.grimeguru.com
GrimeGuru Janitorial Services is a Service Disabled Veteran Owned Small Business (SDVOSB), Woman-Owned Small Business (WOSB), and minority-owned green cleaning company located in Winston-Salem, North Carolina. With a focus on general janitorial cleaning f (Woman/AA, estab , empl , sales , cert: State, WBENC)

4775　IBG Global Consulting
　　　333 W Trade St
　　　Charlotte, NC 28202
　　　Contact: Diondre Lewis President
　　　Tel:　866-611-3604
　　　Email: ellie@ibgsoftware.com
　　　Website: http://ibgsoftware.com
I.T. Resource Procurement / Application Development / Software Architecture / Project Mangement / I.T Training & Education / Federal/State government technical solutions / Block Chain Solutions / Architecting. Engineering/Developing/Middleware Systems. (AA, estab 2008, empl 50, sales $10,850,000, cert: NMSDC)

4776　Infestus Inc.
　　　P.O. Box 222
　　　McLeansville, NC 27301
　　　Contact: Glasco Taylor CEO
　　　Tel:　202-794-7280
　　　Email: glasco.taylor@calibertec.com
　　　Website: http://calibertec.com/
IT staffing: Cyber Security, Data Center(Virtualization, Storage, SAN, Networking, Server Hardware, Linux, etc), Infrastructure Networking. (AA, estab 2014, empl 5, sales $200,000, cert: NMSDC)

4777　IT People Corporation
　　　One Copley Pkwy. Ste 216
　　　Morrisville, NC 27560
　　　Contact: Sai Nidamarty Business Dev Mgr
　　　Tel:　919-806-3535
　　　Email: sai@itpeoplecorp.com
　　　Website: www.itpeoplecorp.com
Information technology staffing, consulting & outsourcing services. (Woman/As-Ind, As-Pac, estab 1999, empl 153, sales $7,459,294, cert: State, NMSDC, WBENC)

4778　J2 Associates, LLC
　　　900 S. Wilmington St, Ste 207
　　　Raleigh, NC 27601
　　　Contact: John Johnston President
　　　Tel:　919-949-4707
　　　Email: jjohnston@j2assoc.com
　　　Website: www.j2assoc.com
Information Technology, Systems Integration & Professional Services: audio visual systems, cabling, VTC, network engineers, sharepoint, cyber security, help desk, systems administration & web development. (AA, estab 2008, empl 18, sales $2,800,000, cert: 8a)

4779　Marketing Resource Solutions LLC
　　　725 W Main St, Ste E
　　　Jamestown, NC 27282
　　　Contact: Melita Vick Natl Accts Svc Mgr
　　　Tel:　336-510-7523
　　　Email: info@marketingresourcesolutions.com
　　　Website: www.marketingresourcesolutions.com
Remote Executive Assistance, Database & CRM support, Basic Internet Research, Data mgmt, Website content management, Sales & Customer support, Social Media Optimization Services, Office management. (Minority, Woman, estab 2003, empl 160, sales , cert: NMSDC)

4780　Paula P. White and Associates, Inc dba
　　　DataMasters
　　　P.O. Box 14548
　　　Greensboro, NC 27415
　　　Contact: Dana White Dir Operations
　　　Tel:　336-373-1461
　　　Email: dwhite@datamasters.com
　　　Website: www.datamasters.com
IT staffing, contract, staff augmentation & permanent or direct hire positions. (Woman, estab 1971, empl 25, sales $2,500,000, cert: State)

4781　QCentric Consultants, LLC
　　　624 Tyvola Rd, Ste 103-177
　　　Charlotte, NC 28217
　　　Contact: Nuradin Kariye Managing Partner
　　　Tel:　800-260-5728
　　　Email: admin@qcentricconsultants.com
　　　Website: www.qcentricconsultants.com
IT staffing & technology solutions. (AA, estab 2009, empl 45, sales , cert: State)

4782　Quantum Technology Group, LLC
　　　P.O. Box 762
　　　Cornelius, NC 28031
　　　Contact: Adam Jones President
　　　Tel:　800-918-3510
　　　Email: amjones@qtg-llc.com
　　　Website: www.qtg-llc.com
Information technology, cabling infrastructure, IP converged telephony systems, voice mail solutions, access control, paging systems, mass notification systems, video teleconferencing, CATV. (AA, estab 2007, empl 16, sales $338,454, cert: 8a)

4783　Refulgent Technologies Inc.
　　　112 South Tryon St Ste 1270
　　　Charlotte, NC 28284
　　　Contact: Horace Worley President
　　　Tel:　704-405-4238
　　　Email: horace.worley@refulgent-tech.com
　　　Website: www.refulgent-tech.com
IT consulting & staffing services, application development & staffing. (Woman/As-Pac, estab 2005, empl 22, sales $1,157,433, cert: NMSDC)

4784　Sajiton LLC
　　　301 McCullough Dr Ste 400
　　　Charlotte, NC 28262
　　　Contact: Nicole Williams Managing Dir
　　　Tel:　888-828-7991
　　　Email: nicole.williams@sajiton.com
　　　Website: www.sajiton.com
Custom Mobile & Web Application Development, Big Data, Data Analytics, Data Engineering, Data Integration, Master Data Management. Data Encryption, Data Security in the Cloud & On Premise - CyberSecurity. (Woman/AA, estab 2014, empl 1, sales , cert: NMSDC, WBENC)

4785 Saponi Industries, Inc.
      3229 Goslen Dr
      Pfafftown, NC 27040
      Contact: Deborah Bare Owner
      Tel: 336-770-5321
      Email: lynn@saponi-industries.com
      Website: www.saponi-industries.com
IT services. (Woman/Nat Ame, estab 2010, empl 2, sales ,
cert: NMSDC)

4786 STATProg Inc.
      421 Fayetteville St, Ste 1100
      Raleigh, NC 27601
      Contact: Dany Guerendo Christian President
      Tel: 919-987-2015
      Email: statprogadmin@statproginc.com
      Website: www.statproginc.com
Research and Development, and/or Life Sciences departments. Statistical Programming and Analysis using SAS as
software. (Woman/AA, estab 2012, empl 2, sales
$162,000, cert: NMSDC, WBENC)

4787 Technology Concepts & Design, Inc.
      4510 Weybridge Ln
      Greensboro, NC 27407
      Contact: Lisa Cain CFO
      Tel: 336-232-5800
      Email: l_cain@tcdi.com
      Website: www.tcdi.com
Advanced application & system design services,
eDiscovery, review & production & large-scale case
management products & services to help effectively
manage and reduce costs associated with significant
litigation and investigations. (As-Pac, estab 1988, empl 69,
sales , cert: NMSDC)

4788 Telecom Sales & Marketing, Inc.
      P.O. Box 1454
      High Point, NC 27261
      Contact: Don Taylor President
      Tel: 336-882-6113
      Email: don@tsmtelecom.com
      Website: www.tsmtelecom.com
Dist telecommunications parts & equipment, telephone
headsets. (AA, estab 1979, empl 6, sales $1,380,000, cert:
State)

4789 Third Law Enterprises, LLC
      517 S Front St
      Wilmington, NC 28401
      Contact: Michael Gilbert Managing Partner
      Tel: 910-477-3772
      Email: mgilbert@thirdlawenterprises.com
      Website: www.thirdlawenterprises.com
Data Center Solutions (Computer hardware, software,
implementation services), Servers, Storage, Networking,
Cloud solutions (on premise, off premise) and Hybrid
Cloud Solutions, Personal Computing (PCs, Notebooks,
Backup drives). (Hisp, estab 2004, empl 2, sales $220,000,
cert: State)

4790 VDC Technologies
      202 Clear Brooks Ct
      Jacksonville, NC 28546
      Contact: Vactronia Russell CEO
      Tel: 910-353-1492
      Email: support@vdctechs.com
      Website: http://vdctechs.com
IT solutions. (Woman/AA, estab , empl , sales , cert: State)

North Dakota

4791 Laducer & Associates, Inc.
      201 Missouri Dr
      Mandan, ND 58554
      Contact: James Laducer President
      Tel: 701-667-1980
      Email: boston@laducer.com
      Website: http://laducer.com
Data input & comprehensive processing; mgmt & admin
computer based work environments; business devel &
consulting svcs. (Nat Ame, estab 1985, empl 175, sales
$8,136,389, cert: State)

Nebraska

4792 Client/Server Software Solutions
      5069 S 108th St
      Omaha, NE 68137
      Contact: Lisa Wolford CEO
      Tel: 402-393-8059
      Email: lisa@csss.net
      Website: www.csss.net
Technology consulting & IT solutions, short long term,
contract-to-hire & permanent placement. (Woman,
estab 1997, empl 15, sales , cert: State)

4793 Coltcam, LLC
      1130 N Riverside Blvd Ste 100
      Norfolk, NE 68701
      Contact: Troy Jones Sales Rep
      Tel: 402-316-3379
      Email: troy.jones@coltcam.com
      Website: www.coltcam.com
Information technology solutions to small, medium and
large businesses and government facilities. (Woman/
Hisp, estab 2012, empl 11, sales $7,000,000, cert: SDB)

New Hampshire

4794 Advanced Presentation Systems dba CCS
      132 Northeastern Blvd
      Nashua, NH 03062
      Contact: Chris Gamst VP
      Tel: 978-256-2001
      Email: cgamst@ccsprojects.com
      Website: www.ccsnewengland.com
Audio visual system design, integration, sales, service &
installation for boardrooms, conference rooms, training
rooms & auditoriums. (Woman/As-Ind, estab 1998, empl
23, sales , cert: State)

4795 Apollo Professional Solutions, Inc.
      29 Stiles Rd Ste 302
      Salem, NH 03079
      Contact: Bruce Thomason VP
      Tel: 866-277-3343
      Email: bthomason@apollopros.com
      Website: www.apollopros.com
Recruited & payrolled engineering & information
technology temporary personnel. (Woman, estab 1983,
empl 20, sales $12,000,000, cert: State, WBENC)

4796 Dataservinc
      1 Tara Blvd, Ste 102
      Nashua, NH 03062
      Contact: Anil Kumar VP Business Dev
      Tel: 603-557-0600
      Email: contact@dataservinc.com
      Website: www.dataservinc.com
IT staffing & IT software development. (Woman/As-Ind,
estab 2005, empl 100, sales $7,000,000, cert: State)

4797　Digital Prospectors Corp.
　　　100 Domain Dr Ste 103
　　　Exeter, NH 03833
　　　Contact: Chris Roos Principal
　　　Tel:　　603-772-2700
　　　Email: croos@dpcit.com
　　　Website: www.dpcit.com
Permanent & temporary IT staffing. (Woman, estab 1999, empl 120, sales $50,201,563, cert: WBENC)

4798　Paramount Technology Solutions LLC
　　　63 Emerald St, Ste 442
　　　Keene, NH 03431
　　　Contact: Beth Wright Dir of Finance
　　　Tel:　　281-617-1400
　　　Email: beth.wright@acuitycloudsolutions.com
　　　Website: http://acuitycloudsolutions.com
Computer software consulting services. (Woman, estab 2008, empl 25, sales , cert: WBENC)

4799　Patriot Cyber Defense
　　　80 Winkley Farm Lane
　　　Rochester, NH 03867
　　　Contact: Jennifer Caron CEO
　　　Tel:　　603-231-7000
　　　Email: jennifer.caron@patriotcyberdefense.com
　　　Website: https://patriotcyberdefense.com
DFARS Cyber Compliance, Cyber Security Consulting, Security Program Deployments, Managed Security Monitoring Services, CISO Support, Security Staff Augmentation, Security Gap Analysis & Needs Assessment. (Woman, estab 2017, empl 4, sales , cert: State)

4800　SCA Technica, Inc.
　　　P.O. Box 3148
　　　Nashua, NH 03061
　　　Contact: David Murotake President
　　　Tel:　　603-321-6536
　　　Email: dmurotak@scatechnica.com
　　　Website: www.scatechnica.com
Research & development, high assurance & secure software defined radio, wireless computing system, develop embedded communications software systems. (As-Pac, estab 2002, empl 5, sales $611,320, cert: State)

4801　Universal Software Corporation
　　　20 Industrial Park Dr
　　　Nashua, NH 03062
　　　Contact: Sonu Khanna Sr Mgr
　　　Tel:　　603-324-4004
　　　Email: sonuk@universal-sw.com
　　　Website: www.universal-sw.com
Information technology: staff augmentation, project mgmt, project & offshore outsourcing, embedded systems & hardware design, Oracle/MS SQL, .Net framework, open source tools, WinNT, Solaris, Unix, Linux. (As-Pac, estab 1992, empl 58, sales , cert: State)

New Jersey

4802　1st Choice Financial Group LLC
　　　1121 Asbury Ave
　　　Asbury Park, NJ 07712
　　　Contact: Kathrina Nease CEO
　　　Tel:　　717-599-1907
　　　Email: knease@1stchoicefg.com
　　　Website: www.1stchoicefg.com
Information technology solutions & program/project management. (Woman, estab 2006, empl 10, sales $500,000, cert: State)

4803　20/20 Solutions, Inc.
　　　33 Wilson Dr Unit D
　　　Sparta, NJ 07871
　　　Contact: Jody Torre President
　　　Tel:　　973-383-8703
　　　Email: j.torre@20-20solutions.com
　　　Website: www.20-20solutions.com
Website dev & mgmt, search engine optimization, website design, website hosting, programming, computer repair, computer training, computer equip, computer maintenance, computer support. (Woman, estab 1999, empl 10, sales $450,000, cert: WBENC)

4804　22nd Century Staffing, Inc.
　　　1 Executive Dr Ste 285
　　　Somerset, NJ 08873
　　　Contact: Eva Gaddis-McKnight Contracts Administrator
　　　Tel:　　732-537-9191
　　　Email: com@tscti.com
　　　Website: www.tscti.com
Staffing services, IT staffing & workforce management services, contract or permanent positions. (Woman/As-Pac, estab 2013, empl 191, sales $2,907,117,800, cert: State, NMSDC)

4805　Actuan Global LLC
　　　4 Debra Ct
　　　Scotch Plains, NJ 07076
　　　Contact: Talib Morgan President
　　　Tel:　　908-443-1180
　　　Email: talib.morgan@actuanglobal.com
　　　Website: www.actuanglobal.com
Digital innovation & technology consulting, mobile, personalization, marketing automation, content management, social media, data & digital systems. (AA, estab 2011, empl 1, sales , cert: NMSDC)

4806　Adaptive Tech Resources Inc.
　　　4400 Route 9 South Ste 1000
　　　Freehold, NJ 07728
　　　Contact: Roland Williams CEO
　　　Tel:　　732-683-0800
　　　Email: roland.williams@atrstaffing.com
　　　Website: www.atrstaffing.com
IT consulting/contract & full time staffing services. (AA, estab 1996, empl 3, sales $862,000, cert: NMSDC)

4807　Advanced Technology Solutions, Inc.
　　　251 Monmouth Road, Ste 1-A
　　　Oakhurst, NJ 07755
　　　Contact: Jeffrey Wean VP Operations
　　　Tel:　　732-918-4664
　　　Email: JCWean@atsolutions.com
　　　Website: www.atsolutions.com
IT consulting: software devel, system & network engineers, project managers, etc. (Woman, estab 1995, empl 85, sales $3,233,188, cert: State, City, WBENC, SDB)

4808　Agnosco Technologies Inc.
　　　6 Thornhill Dr
　　　Lumberton, NJ 08048
　　　Contact: Kiran Khan Operations Mgr
　　　Tel:　　877-933-5439
　　　Email: kiran@agnoscotech.com
　　　Website: www.agnoscotech.com
Information technology recruitment consultancy services: permanent, temporary & contract positions, executive search & outplacement services & solutions. (Woman/As-Pac, estab 2013, empl 50, sales , cert: State)

4809 AIT Global Inc.
228 Route 34
Matawan, NJ 07747
Contact: Mittal Shah VP
Tel: 732-997-9917
Email: mittals@aitglobalinc.com
Website: www.aitglobalinc.com
IT Staffing & Solutions, Contract, Contract to Hire or Full-time Placements. (Woman/As-Ind, estab 2003, empl 135, sales $14,800,000, cert: NMSDC, WBENC)

4810 AITA Consulting Services Inc.
6-80 Towne Center Dr
North Brunswick, NJ 08902
Contact: Aisha Thomas Business Develoment Mgr
Tel: 732-658-4471
Email: hello@aishathomas.com
Website: www.aitacs.com
IT staffing services, Corp To Corp, W2, 1099, contract, full time, contract to hire, Business Intelligence, Big Data, Web development, J2EE, Microsoft technologies, Quality Assurance & Oracle Applications, SAP, Mobile Apps. (Woman/As-Ind, estab 2006, empl 182, sales , cert: NMSDC, WBENC)

4811 Alliance Sourcing Network Inc
40 Galesi Dr Ste 2
Wayne, NJ 07470
Contact: CEO
Tel: 201-438-2005
Email:
Website: www.asn-corp.com
IT consulting services: application design, client server design, database admin & hardware design & support, network admin. (Woman, estab 2006, empl 26, sales $10,893,853, cert: WBENC)

4812 AppliedInfo Partners, Inc.
28 World's Fair Dr
Somerset, NJ 08873
Contact: Betty Lau CEO
Tel: 732-507-7316
Email: blau@appliedinfo.com
Website: www.appliedinfo.com
Software & web dev, computer & IT products & services, marketing communications. (Woman/As-Pac, estab 1990, empl 50, sales $10,000,000, cert: NMSDC, WBENC)

4813 APTIVA Corp.
100 Franklin Square Dr, Ste 210
Somerset, NJ 08873
Contact: Paula Philip Sr VP
Tel: 732-391-1055
Email: info@applesandorangespr.com
Website: www.aptivacorp.com
IT Solutions and services. (As-Ind, estab 2007, empl 80, sales $8,000,000, cert: NMSDC)

4814 Arborsys Group
3131 Princeton Pike, Bldg 4, Ste 210
Lawrenceville, NJ 08648
Contact: Vasu Ranganathan Partner/President
Tel: 609-843-0225
Email: vranganathan@arborsys.com
Website: www.arborsys.com
Business & IT consulting, content lifecycle management, collaboration, business process management, portal solutions & electronic records management. (Woman/As-Pac, estab 2004, empl 20, sales $5,300,000, cert: State, NMSDC)

4815 Artech L.L.C.
360 Mt. Kemble Ave Ste 2000
Morristown, NJ 07960
Contact: Vinu Varghese Dir New Business Development
Tel: 973-998-2500
Email: rfp@artech.com
Website: www.artech.com
Network infrastructure mgmt, web applications dev, content mgmt, design, internet infrastructure design devel & maintenance, multitier architecture, client server, software applications, systems devel & support. (Woman/As-Ind, As-Pac, estab 1992, empl 10500, sales $725,000,000, cert: State, NMSDC, WBENC)

4816 Astir IT Solutions
50 Cragwood Rd Ste 219
South Plainfield, NJ 07080
Contact: Robert Markowitz Exec VP
Tel: 908-279-8670
Email: bobm@astirit.com
Website: www.astirit.com
IT consulting, staffing & outsourced software development. (Woman/As-Ind, estab 2001, empl 300, sales $30,700,000, cert: State, NMSDC)

4817 Atlas Data Systems DBA Atlas
400 Connell Dr Ste 6000
Berkeley Heights, NJ 07922
Contact: Lisa Wickey Acct Exec
Tel: 908-519-8013
Email: lisa.wickey@chooseatlas.com
Website: www.chooseatlas.com
Information technology consulting: internet, e-commerce, infrastructure & RDMS consulting. (Woman, estab 1998, empl 350, sales $31,900,000, cert: State, WBENC)

4818 Atlas Systems, Inc.
5 Independence Way Ste 309
Princeton, NJ 08540
Contact: Robin Grossman Business Develop Mgr
Tel: 609-452-0101
Email: robin.grossman@atlassystems.com
Website: www.atlassystems.com
IT Services Solutions, Product Development, Maintenance, Data Base Management, BI, Spend Analytics, Sourcing, Supplier/Vendor Management, Contract Management, P2P- iBuy- Order management. (Nat Ame, estab 2007, empl 300, sales , cert: NMSDC)

4819 Aumtech, Inc.
710 Old Bridge Turnpike
East Brunswick, NJ 08816
Contact: Tom Porter COO
Tel: 732-254-1875
Email: tporter@aumtech.com
Website: www.aumtech.com
IVR & VoIP network solution: speech recognition, touchtone input, VXML programming tools. (As-Ind, As-Pac, estab 1988, empl 38, sales $2,120,000, cert: NMSDC)

4820   Avenues International Inc.
       4 Restrick Court
       Princeton Junction, NJ 08550
       Contact: Anupam Gupta Director
       Tel: 609-945-1160
       Email: anupam@avenuesinc.com
       Website: http://avenuesinc.com
IT consulting services: Data Analytics, Business Intelligence, Data Warehousing, Big Data Solution & Management Reporting Solutions. (As-Ind, estab 1994, empl 15, sales $1,870,000, cert: NMSDC)

4821   Blue Planet Solutions Inc.
       36 Route 10 W, Ste E
       East Hanover, NJ 07936
       Contact: Pradeep Darbhe Resource Mgr
       Tel: 973-581-1500
       Email: pradeep@blueplanetsolutions.com
       Website: www.blueplanetsolutions.com
Outsource software development & maintenance, contract programmers, offshore programming. (Woman/As-Ind, estab 1997, empl 20, sales , cert: State)

4822   BNG Consulting, Inc.
       12 Sandhill Ct
       Jamesburg, NJ 08831
       Contact: Biswatosh Guha VP
       Tel: 732-631-0003
       Email: guha@bngconsulting.com
       Website: www.bngconsulting.com
Business intelligence, data warehousing, reporting/ ETL tools, database admin, support, development, maintenanance, enhancements, architecture & design, data modeling. (As-Pac, estab 2003, empl 65, sales $7,000,000, cert: State)

4823   Brillio, LLC
       100 Town Square Pl, Ste 308
       Jersey City, NJ 07310
       Contact: Gautam Arni VP Sales
       Tel: 201-744-5759
       Email: gautam@brillio.com
       Website: www.brillio.com
Business Technology Consulting | PROGRAM MANAGEMENT | ANALYTICS | Application PORTFOLIO | COST OPTIMIZATION | CHANGE MANAGEMENT | Mobility | VISUALIZATION | ANALYTICS | BIG DATA (As-Ind, estab 2013, empl 2000, sales $1,000,000, cert: NMSDC)

4824   Cardinal Technology Solutions Inc.
       1100 Cornwall Rd, Ste 113
       Monmouth Junction, NJ 08852
       Contact: Director
       Tel: 732-821-7400
       Email:
       Website: www.cardinaltsinc.com
IT and Engineering Staffing and consulting services. (As-Ind, estab 2004, empl 22, sales $8,000,000, cert: NMSDC)

4825   Caresoft Inc.
       220 Lincoln Blvd Ste 300
       Middlesex, NJ 08846
       Contact: Dhaval Desai Business Dev Mgr
       Tel: 732-764-9500
       Email: ddesai@caresoftinc.com
       Website: www.caresoftinc.com
Information technology staff augmentation. (As-Ind, estab 1994, empl 189, sales $9,000,000, cert: NMSDC)

4826   Cavalier Workforce, Inc
       379 Thornall St 6th Fl
       Edison, NJ 08837
       Contact: Parag Shroff VP - Delivery
       Tel: 201-215-2160
       Email: parag@cavalierworkforce.com
       Website: http://cavalierworkforce.com/
Technology staffing & consulting. (As-Pac, estab 2007, empl , sales $13,000,000, cert: State, NMSDC)

4827   CBS Technologies
       191 Main St
       Hackensack, NJ 07601
       Contact: President
       Tel: 201-843-8070
       Email:
       Website: https://cbstechnologies.com
Business analysis, software & hardware architectures, vendor software selection, hosting, application, database support, security, business processes, portals, intranets & extranets. (AA, estab 1996, empl 12, sales $800,000, cert: City)

4828   Chenoa Information Services, Inc.
       10 Parsonage Rd Ste 312
       Edison, NJ 08837
       Contact: Michael Fortino EVP Client Solutions
       Tel: 732-549-6800
       Email: mfortino@chenoainc.com
       Website: www.chenoahealth.com
Information technology solutions & staff augmentation. (As-Ind, estab 1998, empl 600, sales $17,000,000, cert: State, NMSDC)

4829   Client Solution Architects
       142 W Upper Ferry Rd
       West Trenton, NJ 08628
       Contact: Neftali Arroyo CEO
       Tel: 609-638-3304
       Email: larroyo@csaassociates.com
       Website: www.csaassociates.com
Information technology: Manugistics, SAP, Logility, i2. (Hisp, estab 2003, empl 28, sales $3,390,000, cert: State)

4830   CNC Consulting
       50 E Palisades Ave Ste 422
       Englewood, NJ 07631
       Contact: Business Develop Mgr
       Tel: 201-541-9122
       Email:
       Website: www.cncconsulting.com
IT professionals for consulting contracts. (AA, estab 1996, empl 25, sales $3,000,000, cert: State)

4831   Cognixia Inc.
       110 Allen Rd
       Basking Ridge, NJ 00007
       Contact: Irina Borovitskaya Associate VP
       Tel: 973-559-9121
       Email: irina.borovitskaya@cognixia.com
       Website: www.cognixia.com
IT and business training courses. (Nat Ame, As-Pac, estab 2018, empl 20, sales , cert: NMSDC)

4832   Collab USA, LLC
       9 Haypress Rd
       Cranbury, NJ 08512
       Contact: VP
       Tel: 609-488-6400
       Email:
       Website: www.collabclinical.com
IT consulting, software development & technology
services. (Woman/As-Ind, estab 2009, empl 47, sales
$4,470,000, cert: NMSDC)

4833   Combined Computer Resources, Inc.
       120 Wood Ave S, Ste 408
       Iselin, NJ 08830
       Contact: Laura Palamara Controller
       Tel: 732-632-2502
       Email: laurap@combinedcomputer.com
       Website: www.combinedcomputer.com
Information technology consulting: data processing, right-
to-hire & full time placement services. (Woman, estab
1994, empl 107, sales $16,500,000, cert: State)

4834   Communication Experts, Inc.
       51 Cragwood Rd Ste 304
       South Plainfield, NJ 07080
       Contact: Shirish R. Nadkarni CEO
       Tel: 908-512-9129
       Email: srn@comexpinc.com
       Website: http://comexpinc.com
I help clients identify and solve problems using analytical
abilities I have developed through management education,
decades of working with small and large companies and
from my own experience of founding and running software product and service companie (As-Ind, estab 2003,
empl 8, sales $1,704,000, cert: NMSDC)

4835   Compunnel Software Group, Inc.
       103 Morgan Lane Ste 102
       Plainsboro, NJ 08536
       Contact: Lalitha Reddy AVP - Finance & Legal
       Operations
       Tel: 609-606-9010
       Email: contracts@compunnel.com
       Website: www.compunnel.com
IT Staffing, eLearning, Application Development, Off shore
DEvelopment Facility in India. (Nat Ame, As-Ind, estab
1994, empl 1028, sales $262,418,117, cert: NMSDC)

4836   CompuPlus International Inc.
       94 Lilac Lane
       Paramus, NJ 07652
       Contact: David Wei President
       Tel: 626-755-0607
       Email: davidw@cp-intl.com
       Website: www.cp-intl.com
IT staffing & IT consulting, recruitment & service. (As-Pac,
estab 1990, empl 7, sales $1,625,219, cert: State)

4837   Comrise Technology, Inc.
       90 Woodbridge Center Dr Ste 360
       Woodbridge, NJ 07730
       Contact: Michael Ferrara Dir of Operations
       Tel: 732-203-6236
       Email: mferrara@comrise.com
       Website: www.comrise.com
Staff supplementation, IT mgmt consulting, project
outsourcing & recruiting svcs. (As-Pac, estab 1984, empl
150, sales $19,000,000, cert: NMSDC)

4838   Connexions Data Inc.
       241 Main St, Ste 206
       Hackensack, NJ 07601
       Contact: Raghu Menon CFA
       Tel: 201-210-8938
       Email: raghu.menon@cdatainc.com
       Website: www.cdatainc.com
Information technology consulting & integration
services, SAP, Oracle & Cloud computing. (As-Ind, estab
2004, empl 48, sales , cert: State)

4839   Consolidated Energy Design, Inc.
       1933 Hwy 35 Ste 105, No. 367
       Wall, NJ 07719
       Contact: Rey Montalvo President
       Tel: 732-681-8800
       Email: reym@cedinternational.com
       Website: www.cedinternational.com
Smart Grid and Smart Micro Grid technology (Hisp,
estab 1987, empl 2, sales $101,432, cert: NMSDC)

4840   Corporate Training Group, Inc.
       120 Wood Ave S Ste 405
       Iselin, NJ 08830
       Contact: Kathleen Harvey Sr Acct Exec
       Tel: 732-635-9033
       Email: kharvey@ctgtraining.com
       Website: www.ctgtraining.com
Technical & business end user training on Microsoft,
Java, J2EE, Linux, Oracle solutions. (Woman, estab 1991,
empl 8, sales $2,000,000, cert: State, WBENC)

4841   Cosmic Software Technology, Inc.
       14 Benedek Rd
       Princeton, NJ 08540
       Contact: Ranvir Sinha CEO
       Tel: 609-430-8284
       Email: ranvir@cosmic-usa.com
       Website: www.cosmic-usa.com
System programming, database analysis, design, dev &
admin, documentation & content mgmt, software
analysis & design, system analysis & architecture,
systems integration, interface design & dev, ERP/CRM
implementations. (As-Ind, estab 1999, empl 15, sales
$950,000, cert: State)

4842   Crave InfoTech LLC
       15 Corporate Place S Ste 104
       Piscataway, NJ 08854
       Contact: President
       Tel: 253-310-5371
       Email:
       Website: www.craveinfotech.com
Global software and technology services. (Woman/As-
Ind, estab 2007, empl 75, sales $2,439,000, cert: State,
NMSDC, CPUC, WBENC)

4843   Crescens Inc.
       1200 Route 22 East, Ste 2000-2176
       Bridgewater, NJ 08807
       Contact: Sophia Samuel President & CEO
       Tel: 732-305-2858
       Email: supplier@crescensinc.com
       Website: www.crescensinc.com
IT consulting, application development, maintenance,
product engineering services, testing, business intelli-
gence, packaged applications & staffing. (Woman/As-
Ind, estab 2002, empl 25, sales $550,000, cert: State,
NMSDC)

4844   Crystal Data LLC
       1 Eves Dr Ste 145
       Marlton, NJ 08053
       Contact: CEO
       Tel: 732-766-9292
       Email:
       Website: www.crystaldatasystems.net
IT Staffing & Services. (Woman/As-Ind, estab 2008, empl
40, sales $3,009,933, cert: State, City, WBENC)

4845   CSF Technologies Inc.
       1427 Cranleigh Ln
       Williamstown, NJ 08094
       Contact: Curtis Freeman President
       Tel: 888-495-7561
       Email: cfreeman@csftechnologies.com
       Website: www.csftechnologies.com
IT staffing solutions. (AA, estab 2002, empl 2, sales
$110,000, cert: State)

4846   Cyber Security Consulting Ops
       309 Fellowship Rd, East Gate Center, Ste 200
       Mt. Laurel, NJ 08054
       Contact: Tony Wittock Dir /CTO
       Tel: 888-588-9951
       Email: tonyw@cybersecurityconsultingops.com
       Website: http://cybersecurityconsultingops.com/
Hardware and software security services. (AA, estab 2017,
empl 5, sales , cert: NMSDC)

4847   cyberThink, Inc.
       685 Route 202/206 Ste 101
       Bridgewater, NJ 08807
       Contact: Raj Thind Director
       Tel: 908-429-8008
       Email: rajveer.thind@cyberthink.com
       Website: www.cyberthink.com
IT auditing & assessment, project mgmt, app devel &
integration, infrastructure architecture & deployment,
database modeling, data warehousing, business intelligence, quality assurance, ebusiness, collaboration &
knowledge mgmt, network & sys admin. (As-Ind, As-Pac,
estab 1996, empl 407, sales $42,800,000, cert: State,
NMSDC)

4848   DataEdge Consulting, Inc.
       101 Morgan Ln Ste 203B
       Plainsboro, NJ 08536
       Contact: Shiv Kolli VP, Operations
       Tel: 609-275-4500
       Email: Shiv@DataEdgeConsulting.com
       Website: www.DataEdgeConsulting.com
Provide broad-based ERP, Web technology and management consulting services. (As-Ind, estab 2007, empl 30,
sales $4,000,000, cert: NMSDC)

4849   Datanomics, Inc.
       991 US Hwy 22 West Ste 201
       Bridgewater, NJ 08807
       Contact: Lori Vail CEO
       Tel: 908-707-8200
       Email: vail@datanomics.com
       Website: www.datanomics.com
IT staffing, helpdesk, desktop support,
administration, technical writers, validation specialists,
business/systems
analysts, programmers, mainframe, client/server, & web.
(Woman, estab 1982, empl 100, sales , cert: State)

4850   Decentxposure LLC
       75 Gorge Rd
       Edgewater, NJ 07020
       Contact: Joseph Confreda VP of Finance
       Tel: 201-313-1100
       Email: jconfreda@dxagency.com
       Website: www.dxagency.com
IT services. (Woman/Hisp, estab 2004, empl 45, sales
$15,300,000, cert: NMSDC, WBENC)

4851   EmployVision, Inc.
       1100 Cornwall Road Ste 115
       Monmouth Junction, NJ 08854
       Contact: Ash Geria Managing Dir
       Tel: 732-422-7100
       Email: ash@emplolyvision.com
       Website: www.employvision.com
Information technology, recruitment, RPO, IT consulting,
staffing. (Woman/As-Pac, estab 2005, empl 10, sales
$15,000,000, cert: State, City)

4852   Enin Systems, Inc.
       666 Plainsboro Rd
       Plainsboro, NJ 08536
       Contact: Raj Vendra VP
       Tel: 615-710-8582
       Email: su@eninsystems.com
       Website: www.eninsystems.com/
IT Services, Consulting and Business Solutions. (Woman/
As-Pac, estab 2019, empl 60, sales $311,788, cert: State,
NMSDC, WBENC)

4853   Entrophase Solutions
       19 Washington Rd
       Princeton Junction, NJ 08550
       Contact: Mark Conover business devel Exec
       Tel: 732-734-9119
       Email: mark.conover@entrophase.com
       Website: www.entrophase.com
SAP, SharePoint, CFR compliance, Regulatory and
compliance services, cGMP, GLP, GCP, Systems Engineer-
ing, IT Infrastructure Support, Enterprise Support, and
Data Center Support , Program/Project Management.
(As-Ind, estab 2005, empl 15, sales $2,000,000, cert: 8a)

4854   eTeam, Inc.
       1001 Durham Ave Ste 201
       South Plainfield, NJ 07080
       Contact: Ann Thakur Dir Strategic Accts
       Tel: 732-248-1900
       Email: rfp@eteaminc.com
       Website: www.eteaminc.com
IT, Business Consulting, Management Consulting. (As-
Ind, estab 1999, empl 1300, sales $93,586,862, cert:
State, NMSDC, CPUC)

4855   Evergreen Technologies, LLC
       2050 Route 27 Ste 202
       North Brunswick, NJ 08902
       Contact: Elan Kling Sr Acct Mgr
       Tel: 732-422-1500
       Email: elank@evergreentechnologies.com
       Website: http://evergreentechnologies.com
Provides top-notch IT talent with a depth of knowledge
in the latest cutting-edge technologies. (Woman/As-Ind,
estab 1998, empl 80, sales $3,154,475, cert: State,
NMSDC, WBENC)

4856   ExterNetworks Inc.
       10 Corporate Place S, Ste 1-05
       Piscataway, NJ 08854
       Contact: Abdul Moiz Sr Director
       Tel: 908-751-0875
       Email: mmoiz@externetworks.com
       Website: www.externetworks.com
Staff augumentation, IT professional services, managed
services. (Woman/As-Pac, estab 2001, empl 205, sales
$20,000,000, cert: CPUC, WBENC)

4857   Fabergent, Inc.
       63 Ramapo Valley Rd, Ste 214
       Mahwah, NJ 07430
       Contact: Ratna Silpa Gorantla President
       Tel: 201-378-0036
       Email: ratna@fabergent.com
       Website: www.fabergent.com
Contract & full-time positions IT staffing in Java, .Net,
SharePoint, SAP, Oracle, BI, Analytics, networking & IT
security. (Woman/As-Pac, estab 2005, empl 125, sales ,
cert: State)

4858   Fortidm Technologies LLC
       103 Carnegie Center Ste 300
       Princeton, NJ 08540
       Contact: Hariram Hari President
       Tel: 609-851-7190
       Email: chari@fortidm.com
       Website: www.fortidm.com
IT Program management, information security advisory,
identity & access management, secured SDLC, vulnerability
management services. (Woman/As-Ind, estab 2005, empl
9, sales $900,000, cert: State, City, 8a, SDB)

4859   Fourth Technologies Inc.
       1816 Springdale Road
       Cherry Hill, NJ 08003
       Contact: Ravi Shankar CEO
       Tel: 856-751-4848
       Email: ravi@fortek.com
       Website: www.fortek.com
IT Solutions & Staffing; Customized, cost-effective, reliable
solutions; SEI-CMM assessed & quality conscious; Resource Management Group. (As-Ind, estab 1987, empl
200, sales , cert: NMSDC)

4860   Futran Solutions Inc.
       2025 Lincoln Hwy STE 110, Edison, NJ 08817 Ste
       110
       Edison, NJ 08817
       Contact: Jyoti Vazirani President
       Tel: 908-279-3112
       Email: apankaj@futransolutions.com
       Website: www.futransolutions.com
IT services, information technology services. (As-Ind, estab
2010, empl 150, sales $7,000,000, cert: State, NMSDC)

4861   FYI Systems Inc.
       3799 Route 46 E
       Parsippany, NJ 07054
       Contact: Mindy Zaziski
       Tel: 973-909-0390
       Email: colleen.luzaj@fyisolutions.com
       Website: www.fyisolutions.com
IT solutions: corporate performance mgmt, business
intelligence, analytics, data warehousing, web dev,
systems integration, project mgmt, applications support,
testing, etc. (Woman, estab 1984, empl 100, sales
$14,500,000, cert: WBENC)

4862   Global IT Solutions, Inc.
       200 Centennial Ave Ste 200
       Middlesex, NJ 08846
       Contact: William Moore President
       Tel: 732-667-3578
       Email: info@globalitsolutionscorp.com
       Website: www.globalitsolutionscorp.com
Software development life cycle. (AA, estab 2008, empl
2, sales , cert: State, NMSDC)

4863   Global World Solutions
       1 Phoenix Dr
       Lincoln Park, NJ 07035
       Contact: President
       Tel: 551-206-4432
       Email:
       Website: http://globalworldstaffing.com
Network deployment life cycle, cabling and security
system. (AA, estab 2004, empl 3, sales $600,000, cert:
NMSDC)

4864   Globalnest LLC
       281 State Route 79, Ste 208
       Morganville, NJ 07751
       Contact: Durga P Mikkilineni Partner
       Tel: 732-333-1901
       Email: durgam@globalnest.com
       Website: www.globalnest.com
IT staffing, software development & design. (As-Ind, As-
Pac, estab 2005, empl 170, sales $12,000,000, cert:
NMSDC, CPUC)

4865   Government Systems Technologies, Inc.
       3159 Schrader Rd
       Dover, NJ 07801
       Contact: Prashanth Kalnad Mgr, Finance and
       Contracts
       Tel: 973-361-2627
       Email: accounting@gstiusa.com
       Website: www.gstiusa.com
Consulting services, software products, full service SAP
implementations & offshore development and support.
(Woman/As-Ind, estab 2002, empl 46, sales
$16,367,405, cert: NMSDC)

4866   Hired by Matrix, Inc.
       266 Harristwon Rd Ste 202
       Rochelle Park, NJ 07452
       Contact: Jennifer Catanese Supplier Diversity &
       Business Devel
       Tel: 201-587-0777
       Email: jcatanese@hiredbymatrix.com
       Website: www.hiredbymatrix.com
IT consulting svcs & permanent placements. (Woman,
estab 1986, empl 275, sales $23,000,000, cert: WBENC)

4867   Ideal Data Inc.
       420 River Rd
       North Arlington, NJ 07031
       Contact: President
       Tel: 201-998-9440
       Email:
       Website: www.idealdata.com
Data processing svcs: data entry, inventory, word
processing, mailing lists, surveys, tax rebates, traffic
studies, etc. (Woman/Hisp, estab 1987, empl 5, sales
$350,000, cert: NMSDC)

4868 iii Technologies Inc.
      100 Horizon Center Blvd, Ste 100
      Hamilton, NJ 08691
      Contact: Deepak Mandrekar President
      Tel: 609-901-8000
      Email: drman@iiitech.com
      Website: www.iiitech.com
IT & SAP transformation projects, SAP program management, project management, architecture & implementation consulting. (As-Ind, estab 2005, empl 1, sales $150,000, cert: State, NMSDC)

4869 InfoQuest Consulting Group Inc.
      68 Culver Road Ste 106
      Monmouth Junction, NJ 08852
      Contact: Vinita Lobo Business Mgr
      Tel: 609-409-5151
      Email: vinita@infoquestgroup.com
      Website: www.infoquestgroup.com
IT contract staffing: ERP, CRM, business intelligence, infrastructure management, industry verticals. (Woman/As-Ind, As-Pac, estab 1994, empl 40, sales , cert: City, NMSDC)

4870 Inforeem
      One Quality Pl
      Edison, NJ 08820
      Contact: Bhal Deshpande CEO
      Tel: 732-494-4100
      Email: bhal@inforeem.com
      Website: www.inforeem.com
IT consulting services. (As-Pac, estab 2004, empl 40, sales $3,000,000, cert: State)

4871 Innospire Systems Corporation
      281 State Route 79
      Morganville, NJ 07751
      Contact: Raj Durai President
      Tel: 732-858-1740
      Email: vrm@innospire.com
      Website: www.innospire.com
IT consulting, custom application development & advanced analytics solutions, Predictive Analytics, Enterprise Performance Management, Mobile & Custom Application development. (As-Ind, estab 1996, empl 5, sales $355,480, cert: NMSDC)

4872 Instaknow.com, Inc.
      180 Talmadge Rd, Ste 32
      Edison, NJ 08817
      Contact: Paul Khandekar CEO
      Tel: 908-650-9598
      Email: pkhandekar@instaknow.com
      Website: www.instaknow.com
Artificial Intelligence software solutions. (As-Ind, estab 1999, empl 3, sales $293,478, cert: NMSDC, CPUC)

4873 Integration International Inc.
      1081 Parsippany Blvd, Ste#101
      Parsippany, NJ 07054
      Contact: Rahul Chitte
      Tel: 973-796-2300
      Email: rahul.chitte@i3intl.com
      Website: www.i3intl.com
IT infrastructure planning & implementation, software dev, ERP design & deployment, offshore software development & network monitoring. (As-Ind, As-Pac, estab 2000, empl 400, sales $23,000,000, cert: NMSDC)

4874 Intellyk Inc.
      15 Corporate Place South Ste 450
      Piscataway, NJ 08854
      Contact: Vineet Kumar CEO
      Tel: 732-399-9510
      Email: vineet@intellyk.com
      Website: www.intellyk.com
IT consulting and technology professional services. (As-Ind, estab 2007, empl 200, sales $13,000,000, cert: State)

4875 International Digital Systems
      400 Kelby St, 6th Fl
      Fort Lee, NJ 07024
      Contact: Anthony Han CEO
      Tel: 201-983-7700
      Email: ahan@idigitalsystems.com
      Website: www.idigitalsystems.com
Server, Network management, Helpdesk, Desktop Support. Microsoft .Net C# based system development. Data Cabling, Data Center build up, SAN, NAS, Server & Network Hardware Resell. (As-Pac, estab 2005, empl 20, sales $1,883,584, cert: State)

4876 International Information Technology Team
      45 Campus Dr
      Edison, NJ 08837
      Contact: Balaji Ravi President
      Tel: 732-417-9301
      Email: balaji.ravi@i2t2.com
      Website: www.i2t2.com
IT Consulting, HRIS services, software implementation & staffing support services. (As-Ind, estab 1997, empl 36, sales $3,005,097, cert: State)

4877 International Technology Solutions, Inc.
      2000 Cornwall Road Ste 220
      Monmouth Junction, NJ 08852
      Contact: Brian Armstrong Dir Business Devel
      Tel: 732-754-7019
      Email: brian@itcsolutions.com
      Website: www.itcsolutions.com
Information technology consulting & software development services. (As-Ind, As-Pac, estab 1998, empl 165, sales , cert: NMSDC)

4878 Intuity Technologies, LLC
      One Gateway Center Ste 2600
      Newark, NJ 07102
      Contact: Max Bhavnani VP, Operations
      Tel: 201-880-0774
      Email: mbhavnani@intuitytech.com
      Website: www.intuitytech.com
IT Services, Oracle Hyperion tool-set (Essbase, Planning, HFM, DRM/MDM Financial Reporting) & Oracle Business Intelligence (OBIEE, Staff Augmentation, Implementations, Infrastructure, Performance Tuning. (As-Ind, estab 2005, empl 12, sales $1,100,000, cert: State)

4879 iQuanti, Inc.
      111 Town Square Place Ste 710
      Jersey City, NJ 07310
      Contact: Vish Sastry CEO
      Tel: 718-223-3403
      Email: supplier@iquanti.com
      Website: www.iquanti.com/
Web analytics, web development, web design, online marketing, search engine optimization, pay per click. (As-Ind, estab 2008, empl 205, sales $5,867,132, cert: NMSDC)

4880 Iris Software Inc.
      200 Metroplex Dr, Ste 300
      Edison, NJ 08817
      Contact: Jonathan Fabros Director
      Tel: 732-393-0034
      Email: jfabros@irissoftinc.com
      Website: www.irissoftware.com
Information technology services. (As-Ind, As-Pac, estab
1994, empl 200, sales $180,000,000, cert: NMSDC)

4881 ISES, Inc
      372 Rte 22 West
      Whitehouse Station, NJ 08889
      Contact: Kathleen Sullivan Director
      Tel: 800-447-4737
      Email: ksullivan@isesincorporated.com
      Website: www.isesincorporated.com
Information technology consulting: esolutions &
ecommerce, B2B, knowledge mgmt, customer relationship
mgmt, application dev & support, database dev & admin,
data warehousing, telecommunications, systems support
& admin. (Woman, estab 1980, empl 142, sales
$20,000,000, cert: WBENC)

4882 IT by Design
      120 Wood Ave S Ste 608
      Iselin, NJ 08830
      Contact: Kam Attwal CEO
      Tel: 646-380-0688
      Email: kkaila@itbd.net
      Website: www.itbd.net
Infrastructure management, virtualization/cloud computing, data center hosting, managed backups, implementa-
tions/migrations & 24x7x365 Live Help Desk. (Woman/As-
Ind, estab 2003, empl 100, sales $3,000,000, cert: WBENC)

4883 IT Staffing, Inc.
      5 Bliss Court Ste 200
      Woodcliff Lake, NJ 07677
      Contact: Jerry G. Myers Dir Business Devel
      Tel: 201-505-0493
      Email: jerry.myers@itstaffinc.com
      Website: www.itstaffinc.com
Strategic contract sourcing, consulting, staff augmentation,
managed teams & outsourcing. (Minority/Woman, estab
1998, empl 78, sales $11,500,000, cert: State)

4884 IT Trailblazers
      2050 Route 27, Ste 203
      North Brunswick, NJ 08902
      Contact: Chris Jones Business Head
      Tel: 732-227-1772
      Email: chris@ittblazers.com
      Website: www.ittblazers.com
Information Technology Consulting, onsite and offshore
capabilities. (As-Ind, estab 1999, empl 100, sales
$37,000,000, cert: State)

4885 ITM Information & Technology Management
      6 Kilmer Rd
      Edison, NJ 08817
      Contact: Jeffrey Snow Business Develop Mgr
      Tel: 732-339-9801
      Email: jeffs@itmsys.com
      Website: www.itmsys.com
Computer consulting, applications development, QA,
infrastructure support, SAP implimentation, database
administration, maintanance & support, data warehousing, technical support. (Woman/As-Ind, estab 1989, empl
40, sales $2,750,000, cert: State, NMSDC)

4886 Kavayah Solutions Inc.
      5 Independence Way, Ste 360
      Princeton, NJ 08540
      Contact: Vivek Casula Principal
      Tel: 609-919-9797
      Email: vivek.casula@kavayahsolutions.com
      Website: www.kavayahsolutions.com
Enterprise application management (development and
maintenance) & project management services, technology solutions, staff augmentation. (As-Ind, estab 2006,
empl 10, sales $1,224,316, cert: State)

4887 LexHarbor, LLC
      1974 State Route 27
      Edison, NJ 08817
      Contact: Akshat Tewary Director
      Tel: 626-427-2674
      Email: info@lexharbor.com
      Website: http://lexharbor.com
Information technology services. (As-Ind, estab 2007,
empl 2, sales $100,000, cert: NMSDC)

4888 Link2consult, Inc.
      1 Bridge Plaza Ste 275
      Fort Lee, NJ 07024
      Contact: PETER MCCREE President
      Tel: 201-308-9101
      Email: peter.mccree@link2consult.com
      Website: www.link2consult.com
Information technology consulting: PeopleSoft, human
resources & finance solutions. (AA, estab 1992, empl 35,
sales $5,800,000, cert: State, NMSDC, CPUC)

4889 Logistic Solutions Inc.
      216 Stelton Rd Ste 2
      Piscataway, NJ 08854
      Contact: Al Limaye President
      Tel: 732-743-2300
      Email: al.limaye@logistic-solutions.com
      Website: www.logistic-solutions.com
Information technologies, Mobile (iPhone, Android,
Blackberry/RIM) content aggregation services. (As-Pac,
estab 1990, empl 715, sales $140,000,000, cert: NMSDC)

4890 Maestro Technologies, Inc.
      510 Thornall St Ste 375
      Edison, NJ 08837
      Contact: Kamal Bathla Managing Dir
      Tel: 908-458-8600
      Email: kamal.s.bathla@maestro.com
      Website: www.maestro.com
Actuarial Sciences, Big Data & and Technologies, Data
Science, IT Services. (Woman/As-Ind, estab 2003, empl
63, sales $6,800,000, cert: State, City, NMSDC)

4891 Makro Technologies, Inc.
      One Washington Park, Ste 1303
      Newark, NJ 07102
      Contact: Pritesh Dholakia Business Development
      Tel: 973-481-0100
      Email: pritesh.dholakia@makrocare.com
      Website: www.makrocare.com
Information technology, IT staffing services. (As-Ind,
estab 1996, empl 650, sales $45,000,000, cert: State)

4892   Marlabs Inc.
       One Corporate Place S
       Piscataway, NJ 08854
       Contact: Danielle Jennings Assoc Business Develop-
       ment Mgr
       Tel: 732-694-1000
       Email: danielle.jennings@marlabs.com
       Website: www.marlabs.com
Information technology services & solutions: IT strategy
consulting, resources & staff augmentation, application
dev, business intelligence solutions, SAP & Oracle, ERP/
CRM systems, data warehousing. (As-Pac, estab 1996,
empl 2100, sales $92,000,000, cert: NMSDC)

4893   MARVEL INFOTECH Inc.
       45 Knightsbridge Rd Ste 101
       Piscataway, NJ 08854
       Contact: President
       Tel: 732-906-0444
       Email:
       Website: www.marvelinfotech.com
Information technology staffing, consulting. (As-Pac, estab
2000, empl 25, sales $1,850,000, cert: NMSDC)

4894   MashPoint, LLC
       100 Wood Ave S Ste 109
       Iselin, NJ 08830
       Contact: KJ Saini President
       Tel: 732-515-7171
       Email: kjsaini@mashpoint.com
       Website: www.mashpoint.com
Staffing services, data management, data quality, data
security, business intelligence, web & mobile development
& internet marketing services. (As-Ind, estab 2011, empl
55, sales $797,510, cert: NMSDC)

4895   Masterex Technologies, Inc.
       379 Princeton-Hightstown Rd, Bldg 2
       Cranbury, NJ 08512
       Contact: Sunny Gupta Business Dev Mgr
       Tel: 302-632-9532
       Email: info@masterexinc.com
       Website: www.Masterexinc.com
IT staffing , application development, project management, framework, on-shore & offshore testing & QA
services. (Woman/As-Ind, estab 2002, empl 60, sales
$5,000,000, cert: State)

4896   Mercury Systems, Inc.
       5 Independence Way Ste 140
       Princeton, NJ 08540
       Contact: Wing Li Admin Mgr, VP
       Tel: 609-937-2801
       Email: wli@mercurysystemsinc.com
       Website: www.mercurysystemsinc.com
Consulting, IT Staffing & IT Placement services. (As-Pac,
estab 1999, empl 170, sales $10,000,000, cert: State)

4897   microMEDIA Imaging Systems, Inc.
       300-2 Route 17 South, Ste 4
       Lodi, NJ 07644
       Contact: Joseph Wise President
       Tel: 973-685-5164
       Email: jwise@imagingservices.com
       Website: www.imagingservices.com
Document conversion & scanning services, Data Capture,
Data Migration, Document Hosting. (Woman, estab 1993,
empl 85, sales $3,200,000, cert: State, City)

4898   Millennium Info Tech. Inc.
       101 Morgan Lane Ste 204
       Plainsboro, NJ 08536
       Contact: Ramana Krosuri President
       Tel: 609-750-7120
       Email: ramana@mitiweb.com
       Website: www.mitiweb.com
Application Development, Business Analysis/Project
Management, Business Intelligence, Data/Database
Management,
 Document Management, ERP, ETL, Information Secu-
rity/Compliance, Migration Services. (As-Ind, estab 1999,
empl 150, sales $9,500,000, cert: State)

4899   Mindlance, Inc.
       1095 Morris Ave, Unit 101A
       Union, NJ 07083
       Contact: Vikram Kalra President
       Tel: 201-386-5400
       Email: vik@mindlance.com
       Website: www.mindlance.com
IT contigent staffing, offshore recruitment, IT permanent
placement, software, semiconductor, finance & insurance. (As-Ind, As-Pac, estab 1999, empl 3300, sales
$225,000,000, cert: NMSDC)

4900   MKI Group, LLC dba IS3 Solutions
       740 Broad St Ste 1
       Shrewsbury, NJ 07702
       Contact: John Marshall President
       Tel: 732-945-0403
       Email: sraffetto@is3sol.com
       Website: www.is3sol.com
Information technology solutions, Services & Staffing
programs. (AA, estab 2010, empl 220, sales , cert:
NMSDC)

4901   Momento USA LLC
       440 Benigno Blvd Unit A, 2nd Fl
       Bellmawr, NJ 08031
       Contact: Hasheem Himmati Director
       Tel: 856-432-4774
       Email: info@momentousa.com
       Website: www.momentousa.com
Project Mgmt, Application Development, Business
Analysis, Systems Analysis, System Design, ERP, Database
Administration, Systems Engineering, Systems Mainte-
nance, Systems Testing, Systems Architecture, Systems
Administration. (As-Pac, estab 2009, empl 28, sales
$2,128,413, cert: NMSDC)

4902   MSquare Systems Inc.
       35 Journal Sq, Ste 415
       Jersey City, NJ 07306
       Contact: Muthu Natarajan President
       Tel: 201-290-6728
       Email: info@msquaresystems.com
       Website: www.msquaresystems.com
IT consulting services. (As-Pac, estab 2005, empl 5, sales
$403,967, cert: NMSDC)

4903   Mutex Systems Inc.
       50 Cragwood Rd Ste 224
       South Plainfield, NJ 07080
       Contact: Bill Scharnikow BDM
       Tel: 908-822-8515
       Email: bill.scharnikow@mutexsystems.com
       Website: www.mutexsystems.com
IT staff augmentation & consulting services. (Woman/As-
Ind, estab 1999, empl 100, sales $10,000,000, cert:
State)

4904 NatSoft Corporation
      27 WORLDS FAIR DR
      SOMERSET, NJ 08873
      Contact: Rakesh Kotha Business Develop Mgr
      Tel: 732-939-2969
      Email: rakeshkv@natsoft.us
      Website: www.natsoft.us
Software development, IT consulting, Enterprise application development, ERP implementation & support, Quality assurance services on offshore/Onsite/Nearshore model. (As-Pac, estab 2004, empl 300, sales , cert: State)

4905 NCS Technologies, Inc.
      15 Corporate Place South Ste 200
      Piscataway, NJ 08854
      Contact: Michael Giannotti Sales
      Tel: 732-562-8880
      Email: mgiannotti@ncstech.com
      Website: www.ncstech.com
Data warehousing, business intelligence, enterprise architecture, process engineering & enterprise security. (Hisp, estab 1984, empl 155, sales $29,000,000, cert: NMSDC)

4906 Neo Tech Solutions, Inc.
      1 Cragwood Rd Ste 301
      South Plainfield, NJ 07080
      Contact: CEO
      Tel: 917-385-8717
      Email:
      Website: www.neotechusa.com
IT, telecommunications, program & project management: ASP.NET, ASP, HTML, DHTML, VBScript, JavaScript, SOAP, ADO.NET, ActiveX, ADO, RDO, DAO, MTS, ODBC, OLEDB, MSOffice, MS-Visual Source Safe, VB.NET, C#, C++, Cobol, VB 6.0,XML, XSLT, SQL. (As-Ind, estab 1996, empl 63, sales , cert: NMSDC)

4907 NetTarius Technology Solutions, LLC
      35 College Dr
      East Orange, NJ 07017
      Contact: Derrick Law President
      Tel: 973-788-1955
      Email: sdiversity@nettarius.net
      Website: www.nettarius.com
Business Strategy, Technology Design & Integration, Fiber Wireless Broadband, Data Network, Video Technology, Web & Application Development, Cloud Services, Installation & Support. (AA, estab 2003, empl 5, sales $300,000, cert: NMSDC)

4908 New Instruction, LLC
      615 Valley Rd
      Upper Montclair, NJ 07043
      Contact: Dir of Training
      Tel: 973-744-3339
      Email:
      Website: www.newinstruction.com/
Instructor-led technology training: systems & software engineering, project management, programming languages, internet security, telecommunications & networking, management & leadership skills. (Woman, estab 1978, empl 4, sales $1,000,000, cert: WBENC)

4909 New Millenium Consulting, LLC
      21 Merry Lane
      East Hanover, NJ 07936
      Contact: Aleksandra Moore Diversity Coord
      Tel: 973-386-5580
      Email: aleksandra.moore@nmcus.com
      Website: www.nmcus.com
Global IT Staffing & Consulting Services- Onsite, Offsite, Near Shore, and Offshore. (Woman, estab 2016, empl 10, sales $3,000,000, cert: State)

4910 NewAgeSys, Inc.
      4390 US-1, Ste 110
      Princeton, NJ 08540
      Contact: Greeshma Digi Sales Coord
      Tel: 609-919-9800
      Email: contact@newagesys.com
      Website: www.newagesys.com
Validation & quality mgmt svcs, custom application devel, SAP upgrade & support svcs, information security, infrastructure services. (Woman/As-Ind, estab 1994, empl 190, sales $21,000,000, cert: NMSDC, WBENC)

4911 NexAge Technologies USA Inc.
      75 Lincoln Hwy Ste 104
      Iselin, NJ 08830
      Contact: Suresh Kumar CEO
      Tel: 732-494-4944
      Email: minoritymanager@nexageusa.com
      Website: www.nexageusa.com
IT staffing & consulting, software applications. (As-Pac, estab 2001, empl 65, sales , cert: State, NMSDC)

4912 NIKSUN Inc.
      100 Nassau Park Blvd 3rd Fl
      Princeton, NJ 08540
      Contact: Christopher Dervishian VP Operations
      Tel: 609-936-9999
      Email: cdervish@niksun.com
      Website: www.niksun.com
Develop real time & forensics-based cybersecurity, network performance management & mobility solutions. (As-Ind, estab 1997, empl 175, sales , cert: NMSDC)

4913 NPD Global Inc.
      3 Lincoln Hwy Ste 102
      Edison, NJ 07018
      Contact: Nagesh Davuluri President
      Tel: 732-902-6342
      Email: ndavuluri@npdglobal.com
      Website: www.npdglobal.com
IT staffing & recruiting services. (Nat Ame, estab 2006, empl 30, sales $6,000,000, cert: NMSDC)

4914 Optima Global Solutions, Inc.
      3113 Princeton Pike Bldg. 3, Ste 207
      Lawrenceville, NJ 08648
      Contact: Rajesh Sinha Federal Business Specialist
      Tel: 609-586-8811
      Email: rajesh@optimags.com
      Website: www.optimags.com
IT staffing, BPM, Data Warehousing, Business Intelligence, Microsoft & Enterprise Mobility. (As-Ind, estab 2001, empl 10, sales $3,186,483, cert: NMSDC, 8a)

4915 Paxton Consultants Limited Liability Company
50 Brandywine Rise
Green Brook, NJ 08812
Contact: Anand Emmanuel CEO
Tel: 831-210-8850
Email: anand.emmanuel@paxtonconsultants.com
Website: www.paxtonconsultants.com
Information Technology (IT) Consulting & Staffing Solutions. (As-Ind, estab 2007, empl 2, sales , cert: State)

4916 Peri Software Solutions
570 Broad St
Newark, NJ 07102
Contact: Rosemarie Lederer Sr. Acct Mgr
Tel: 973-735-9500
Email: rlederer@perisoftware.com
Website: www.perisoftware.com
Open source solutions, IT staff augmentation, offshore business outsourcing, custom application development. (Woman/As-Pac, estab 1999, empl 700, sales $12,631,398, cert: NMSDC)

4917 Pioneer Data Systems, Inc.
379 Thornall St
Edison, NJ 08837
Contact: Naushad Mulji Director
Tel: 732-603-0001
Email: nmulji@pioneerdata.com
Website: www.pioneerdata.com
Client-server, e-business, data warehousing, CRM & ERP. (As-Ind, estab 1995, empl 100, sales $5,000,000, cert: NMSDC)

4918 Platys Group
100 Franklin Square Dr
Somerset, NJ 08873
Contact: Darren Cobb VP Business Dev
Tel: 908-888-6007
Email: dcobb@platysgroup.com
Website: www.platygroup.com
IT consulting & software solutions. (Woman/As-Pac, estab 2008, empl 140, sales $10,000,000, cert: State)

4919 Presafe Technologies, LLC
P.O. Box 5872
Somerset, NJ 08875
Contact: Robert V Jones CEO
Tel: 732-887-2442
Email: rvjones@presafetech.com
Website: www.presafetech.com
Cybersecurity architecture & design; Secure network planning & design, enterprise system design, network builds, migration upgrades; Data center planning design, consolidation migrations & relocations; network & performance mgmt. (AA, estab 2010, empl 2, sales , cert: State)

4920 Princeton Web Systems Inc.
1901 N Olden Ave Ext, Ste 8A
Ewing, NJ 08618
Contact: Bhavesh Senedhun CEO
Tel: 888-485-9040
Email: bhavesh@princetonwebsystems.com
Website: www.princetonwebsystems.com
Custom software development, software & application development, website design, mobile app development, IT staff augmentation, staffing & networking solutions. (As-Ind, As-Pac, estab 2014, empl 25, sales $1,000,000, cert: State)

4921 Prudentia Group, LLC
101 Hudson St Ste 2100
Jersey City, NJ 07302
Contact: Vladimir Laguerre
Tel: 201-479-2372
Email: vlaguerre@prudentia-grp.com
Website: www.prudentia-grp.com
Pharmacovigilance (PV) process & technology services, operational improvements, inspection readiness, system selection, upgrades (for both ARISg and Argus), data migrations & managed services. (AA, As-Ind, estab 2012, empl 22, sales $5,800,000, cert: NMSDC)

4922 Rang Technologies Inc.
15 Corporate Place South, Ste #356
Piscataway, NJ 08854
Contact: Jigar Patel Exec VP
Tel: 732-947-4119
Email: sales@rangtech.com
Website: www.rangtech.com/
Analytics & Data Science solutions & comprehensive IT staffing services. (As-Ind, As-Pac, estab 2005, empl 388, sales $18,964,631, cert: State, NMSDC)

4923 Rangam Consultants Inc.
270 Davidson Ave Ste 103
Somerset, NJ 08873
Contact: Hetal Parikh President
Tel: 908-704-8843
Email: rci@rangam.com
Website: www.rangam.com
IT staffing & outsourced web application development services. (Woman/As-Ind, As-Pac, estab 1995, empl 900, sales $33,400,000, cert: State, City, NMSDC, WBENC)

4924 Rapid Response Computer Service Inc.
2313 Route 33
Robbinsville, NJ 08691
Contact: Terry Ikey Owner
Tel: 609-945-2389
Email: tikey@rapidresponsecs.com
Website: www.rapidresponsecs.com
Software development, website design, network installation & support & compuer repair. (Woman, estab 2004, empl 12, sales $750,000, cert: State)

4925 RCI Technologies
1133 Green St
Iselin, NJ 08830
Contact: Gereld Boffa Exec VP
Tel: 732-382-3000
Email: gereld@rci-technologies.com
Website: www.rci-technologies.com
Custom software development & IT staffing, consulting services. (Woman/As-Pac, estab 1983, empl 63, sales $8,000,000, cert: State, City, WBENC)

4926 Real Soft Inc.
68 Culver Road Ste 100
Monmouth Junction, NJ 08852
Contact: Joel Jerva VP
Tel: 609-409-3636
Email: joel@realsoftinc.com
Website: www.realsoftinc.com
Software development, consulting & staffing, offshore resources, turnkey dev, voice solutions, IVR, VXML. (As-Ind, As-Pac, estab 1991, empl 450, sales $30,000,000, cert: NMSDC)

4927 RedSalsa Technologies, Inc.
      12 Roszel Rd Ste A-204
      Princeton, NJ 08540
      Contact: Kiran Vallurupalli CEO
      Tel: 609-243-9603
      Email: k_vallurupalli@redsalsa.com
      Website: www.redsalsa.com
IT consulting services: internet & e-business consulting,
system integration, custom application development &
application management. (As-Ind, As-Pac, estab 1993,
empl 120, sales , cert: NMSDC)

4928 Reliant Tech., Inc.
      2137 Route 35 Ste 365
      Holmdel, NJ 07733
      Contact: Subhash Kothari President
      Tel: 732-583-6244
      Email: skothari@relianttech.com
      Website: www.relianttech.com
Application development, technical training, Sun Solaris,
HP UX certified. (As-Ind, As-Pac, estab 1985, empl 30, sales
$3,000,000, cert: State)

4929 Resource Logistics, Inc.
      39 Milltown Rd
      East Brunswick, NJ 08816
      Contact: Scott Adams VP Client Services
      Tel: 609-934-5089
      Email: scottadams@resource-logistics.com
      Website: www.resource-logistics.com
IP Services with following industry verticals,ie: Banking and
Finance, Clinical Databases and Bioinformatics. (As-Ind, As-
Pac, estab 2002, empl 150, sales $28,000,000, cert: State)

4930 Revision Technologies Inc.
      10 Station Place, Ste 3
      Metuchen, NJ 08840
      Contact: Raja Balan President
      Tel: 732-261-9239
      Email: raja.balan@revisiontek.com
      Website: www.revisiontek.com
Data Center Design, support, maintenance.Networking, IP
and SAN products, Project management, Storage Area
Networking architect, planning, implementation, system
analysis, Big Data, Cloud implementation & support
services. (As-Ind, estab 2006, empl 4, sales $17,792,057,
cert: NMSDC)

4931 Samiti Technologies, Inc.
      2 Lincoln Highway Ste 401
      Edison, NJ 08820
      Contact: Akash Kulshrestha Client Relationship
      Specialist
      Tel: 732-516-0066
      Email: rfp@samitimail.com
      Website: www.samititechnology.com
Software development & consulting services. (Woman/As-
Pac, estab 2003, empl 70, sales $11,796,921, cert: State,
NMSDC)

4932 Satnam Data Systems, Inc.
      220 Davidson Ave Ste 318
      Somerset, NJ 08873
      Contact: Parita Patel Dir Business Dev
      Tel: 732-961-8383
      Email: parita@satnam.com
      Website: www.satnam.com
Technology Consulting, Professional & Outsourcing, Staff
Augmentation, Custom Dev , Software Integration, Custom
Solution. (Woman/As-Pac, estab 1994, empl 23, sales
$6,500,000, cert: State, NMSDC, CPUC)

4933 Scadea Solutions Inc
      100 Franklin Square Dr Ste 304
      Somerset, NJ 08873
      Contact: Sreekanth Akkapalli CEO
      Tel: 609-937-6699
      Email: sreekanth@scadea.net
      Website: www.scadea.net
ERP, Consulting & Outsourcing Services. (Woman/As-Ind,
estab 2011, empl 150, sales $9,000,000, cert: WBENC)

4934 Scalable Systems Inc.
      15 Corporate Place South Ste 222
      Piscataway, NJ 08854
      Contact: Suman Bajaj Acct Mgr
      Tel: 732-333-3191
      Email: sumanb@scalable-systems.com
      Website: www.scalable-systems.com
Software consulting, development & IT outsourcing,
offshore & onshore software solutions & integration
services. (As-Ind, estab 2005, empl 30, sales $3,000,000,
cert: State, NMSDC)

4935 Scalar Solutions, LLC.
      330 Changebridge Rd, Ste 101
      Pinebrook, NJ 07058
      Contact: Mariana C Mgr Sales
      Tel: 973-767-3260
      Email: sales@scalarsol.com
      Website: www.scalarsol.com
IT consulting/staffing, end-to-end IT consulting services,
Software Development Services (Java, Dot Net Platform),
Database & Data warehouse development (SQL Server,
Oracle, MPP Systems, Cloud, Hadoop Big data), Database
Administration. (As-Ind, estab 2013, empl 2, sales , cert:
State)

4936 SEAL Consulting Inc.
      105 Fieldcrest Ave 4th FL, Raritan Plaza 3
      Edison, NJ 08837
      Contact: John Beaumont VP
      Tel: 732-947-4901
      Email: info@sealconsult.com
      Website: www.sealconsult.com/
Systems integration, implementation services & staffing:
ERP, APO, SEM, BW and SRM. (As-Ind, estab 1996, empl
400, sales $50,000,000, cert: NMSDC)

4937 Seven Seven Softwares, Inc.
      217 E Main St
      Rockaway, NJ 07866
      Contact: Adela Sering VP / Global HR Director
      Tel: 973-586-1817
      Email: dsering@77soft.com
      Website: www.77soft.com
Information technology, business process outsourcing &
call center services. (Woman/As-Pac, estab 1996, empl
335, sales , cert: NMSDC)

4938 Silicon Alley Group, Inc.
      1 Austin Ave. 2nd Fl
      Iselin, NJ 08830
      Contact: Terrance L Sprinkle Business Develop
      Mgr
      Tel: 732-326-1600
      Email: tsprinkle@sag-inc.com
      Website: http://sag-inc.com
Information technology services & solutions. (Woman/
As-Pac, estab 2003, empl 30, sales $1,901,608, cert:
State, 8a)

4939   Smart Source Technologies, Inc.
       622 Georges Rd Ste 203
       North Brunswick, NJ 08902
       Contact: Shaan Kelly Acct Rep
       Tel: 732-729-7700
       Email: subcontract@smartsourcetec.com
       Website: http://smartsourcetec.com
IT staffing, application & web dev, database administration & development, data warehousing & systems administration, business analyst & project management. (Woman/As-Ind, estab 1999, empl 52, sales $6,000,000, cert: State)

4940   Software Synergy, Inc.
       151 Highway 33 E Ste 252
       Manalapan, NJ 07726
       Contact: Rose Oxley CEO
       Tel: 732-617-9300
       Email: rmo@ssi-corp.com
       Website: www.ssi-corp.com
Information technology: automate key business processes, modernize legacy systems, integrate multi system & technology environments, data translations. (Woman, estab 1990, empl 10, sales $1,500,000, cert: WBENC)

4941   Software Technology, Inc.
       100 Overlook Center Ste 200
       Princeton, NJ 08540
       Contact: Scott Mandel VP Sales
       Tel: 609-858-0630
       Email: scott.mandel@stiorg.com
       Website: www.stiorg.com
IT staffing services. (Woman/As-Ind, estab 2004, empl 45, sales , cert: NMSDC)

4942   Solutions3 LLC
       637 Wyckoff Ave PMB 352
       Wyckoff, NJ 07481
       Contact: Dianne McKim Exec Business Administrator
       Tel: 845-365-0675
       Email: dianne.mckim@solutions3llc.com
       Website: www.solutions3llc.com
Enterprise Network & Systems Management (architecture and implementation), IT Service Management, Service Desk & associated process definitions (Incident & Problem Management, Change & Configuration Management). (Woman, estab 2003, empl 18, sales $2,707,834, cert: State)

4943   SPHERE Technology Solutions
       525 Washington Blvd. Ste 2635
       Jersey City, NJ 07310
       Contact: Director
       Tel: 201-659-6204
       Email:
       Website: www.sphereco.com
Data Governance, Security & Compliance centering on structured & un-structured data. (Woman, estab 2009, empl 22, sales $6,448,680, cert: State, WBENC)

4944   Spruce Technology, Inc.
       1149 Bloomfield Ave Ste G
       Clifton, NJ 07012
       Contact: Srini Penumella CEO
       Tel: 781-413-5527
       Email: spenumella@sprucetech.com
       Website: www.sprucetech.com
Information technology consulting svcs: systems deployment, server infrastructure, technology deployment, network infrastructure, executive, management & general support. (As-Ind, estab 2006, empl 69, sales $42,000,000, cert: State, NMSDC)

4945   Sunrise Systems, Inc.
       105 Fieldcrest Ave, Ste 504
       Edison, NJ 08837
       Contact: Sandy Baldino Sr Acct Exec
       Tel: 732-395-4446
       Email: sandy@sunrisesys.com
       Website: www.sunrisesys.com
IT systems integration, systems integration. (As-Ind, estab 1990, empl 500, sales , cert: NMSDC)

4946   Synergem, Inc.
       2323 Randolph Ave
       Avenel, NJ 07001
       Contact: Amy Silverman President
       Tel: 732-225-0001
       Email: amysilverman@synergem.com
       Website: www.synergem.com
Duplicate DVD's, CD's & USBs, custom packaging, custom printing, fulfillment & distribution. (Woman, estab 1985, empl 26, sales $7,344,330, cert: WBENC)

4947   Systemart, LLC
       140 Littleton Rd, Ste 303
       Parsippany, NJ 07054
       Contact: Nitin Shah President
       Tel: 973-917-4834
       Email: mbe@systemart.com
       Website: www.systemart.com
IT related services, custom software dev, business process mgmt svcs. (Woman/As-Ind, estab 1999, empl 75, sales $5,000,000, cert: NMSDC)

4948   SystemGuru,Inc.
       900 Rte 9 N Ste 205
       Woodbridge, NJ 07095
       Contact: Nitin Sohal Business Dev Mgr
       Tel: 732-326-3951
       Email: nitin.sohal@systemguru.com
       Website: www.systemguru.com
Web enabled application development, data modeling & enterprise data architecture, application design & architecture. (As-Pac, estab 2000, empl 100, sales $8,907,001, cert: City)

4949   Technology Concepts Group International, LLC
       150 Maple Ave #306
       Somerset, NJ 08873
       Contact: Elizabeth Shelton Office Mgr
       Tel: 732-659-6035
       Email: eshelton@technologyconcepts.com
       Website: www.technologyconcepts.com
E-business solutions, web design & hosting, systems integration, desktop support. (Woman/AA, estab 2008, empl 7, sales $21,000,000, cert: NMSDC, WBENC)

4950   Technovision, Inc.
       10 Stuyvesant Ave
       Lyndhurst, NJ 07071
       Contact: Anju Aggarwal President
       Tel: 732-381-0200
       Email: anju@etechnovision.com
       Website: www.etechnovision.com
IT Consulting. (Woman/As-Ind, estab 1995, empl 35, sales $3,000,000, cert: State, WBENC)

4951   The Roy Consulting Group, LLC
       103 Carnegie Center Ste 300
       Princeton, NJ 08540
       Contact: Managing Dir
       Tel: 609-955-3549
       Email:
       Website: www.process-stream.com
Life Sciences IT Solutions, Quality Management & Custom
Development Systems. (As-Ind, estab 2008, empl 25, sales
, cert: NMSDC)

4952   The Sourcium Group
       833 Blanch Ave
       Norwood, NJ 07648
       Contact: Gabriella Lombardi CEO
       Tel: 201-447-1777
       Email: gabriella.lombardi@sourcium.net
       Website: www.sourcium.net
IT procurement, project management, desktop svcs, staff
augmentation. (Woman, estab 2002, empl 12, sales , cert:
WBENC)

4953   Twintron Data Systems Inc.
       26 Woodbrook Rd
       Voorhees, NJ 08043
       Contact: Dayal Nagasuru President
       Tel: 856-952-8506
       Email: dayal.nagasuru@twintron.com
       Website: www.twintron.com
IT services (Java, C++, SQL, Big Data, .NET, Web Applica-
tions). (As-Ind, estab 2004, empl 5, sales $500,000, cert:
NMSDC)

4954   Urooj LLC
       301 Route 17N Ste 800
       Rutherford, NJ 07070
       Contact: Salman Mohammed CEO
       Tel: 201-966-7861
       Email: salman@urooj.net
       Website: www.urooj.net
IT solutions, IT staffing, project architecture, design &
analysis, project admin & mgmt, web paradigm, e-commerce & web applications, networking & system administration, RF engineering, database admin & management.
(As-Ind, estab , empl , sales $2,154,929, cert: City, NMSDC)

4955   US Tech Solutions, Inc.
       10 Exchange Place
       Jersey City, NJ 07302
       Contact: Michelle Vanetti Legal/Compliance Mgr
       Tel: 201-719-9953
       Email: Michelle@ustechsolutions.com
       Website: www.ustechsolutions.com
IT solutions: consulting, outsourcing, software development, engineering, systems integration, ERP, customer
relationship management, supply chain mngt, product
development, & electronic commerce. (Nat Ame, As-Ind,
As-Pac, estab 2000, empl 9000, sales $530,000,000, cert:
NMSDC)

4956   Vedicsoft Solutions Inc.
       100 Wood Ave, Ste 200
       Iselin, NJ 08830
       Contact: Sam Vaghela Strat Business Alliance Mgr
       Tel: 732-906-3200
       Email: sam@vedicsoft.com
       Website: www.vedicsoft.com
IT technologies: ERP, data warehousing, web & client/
server technologies. (As-Ind, estab 1999, empl 300, sales
$54,000,000, cert: NMSDC)

4957   Ventures Unlimited Inc.
       309 Fellowship Rd, Ste 200
       Mount Laurel, NJ 08054
       Contact: Rajesh Varma President
       Tel: 201-377-5954
       Email: rvarma@vui-inc.com
       Website: www.vui-inc.com
IT consulting services: enterprise application services,
product life cycle management, business process
modeling. (As-Ind, estab 2004, empl 162, sales
$4,500,000, cert: State, NMSDC, 8a)

4958   Vichara Technologies Inc.
       5 Marine View Plaza Ste 312
       Hoboken, NJ 07030
       Contact: Atul Jain CEO
       Tel: 201-850-1912
       Email: payables@vichara.com
       Website: http://vichara.com
Software development services for financial institutions,
banks & asset management firms, hedge funds, private
equity firms. (As-Pac, estab 2000, empl 15, sales
$7,259,788, cert: NMSDC)

4959   VNB Consulting Services, Inc.
       100 Menlo Park Ste 302B
       Edison, NJ 08837
       Contact: Nirav Shah Dir HR & Finance
       Tel: 732-474-0700
       Email: info@vnbconsulting.com
       Website: www.vnbconsulting.com
IT services, Business Intelligence, Analytics, CRM,
Marketing & Application Integration solutions. (As-Ind,
estab 2007, empl 25, sales $2,000,000, cert: State)

4960   XL Impex Inc DBA Atika Technologies
       5 Independence Way Ste 300
       Princeton, NJ 08540
       Contact: Ashish Dua President
       Tel: 732-907-9001
       Email: ash@atikaservices.com
       Website: www.atikatech.com
CRM recruiting, staff augmentation, IT services & Digital
Marketing. (As-Pac, estab 2008, empl 22, sales
$1,770,777, cert: NMSDC)

4961   Xybion Corporation & Subsidiaries
       2000 Lenox Dr, Ste 101
       Lawrenceville, NJ 08648
       Contact: Rose Ann McBride Personnel Admin
       Tel: 609-512-5790
       Email: rmcbride@xybion.com
       Website: www.xybion.com
Preclinical Data Management and Analysis Software
(Pristime); Quality & Process Management software;
Enterprise Content Management Software, Data
Migration & Federation. (As-Ind, As-Pac, estab 1975,
empl 109, sales , cert: NMSDC)

4962   Xybion Medical Systems Corporation
       2000 Lenox Dr Ste 101
       Lawrenceville, NJ 08648
       Contact: Nagraj Lanka Business Develop Dir
       Tel: 609-512-5790
       Email: nlanka@xybion.com
       Website: www.xybion.com
Compliance/software & services solutions, data migration, data content & compliance mgmt, enterprise asset
mgmt, pre-clin/R&D, quality mgmt, validation/software
testing & IT consulting services. (As-Ind, estab 1977,
empl 33, sales $7,751,400, cert: State, NMSDC)

4963   York Telecom Corporation
81 Corbett Way
Eatontown, NJ 07724
Contact: Rebecca Kane Contracts Specialist
Tel: 732-413-6000
Email: mbe@yorktel.com
Website: www.yorktel.com
Visual communications applications: videoconferencing, streaming media, distance learning, consulting, integration, design, training, project mgmt, on-site & remote support services. (As-Pac, estab 1985, empl 402, sales $125,000,000, cert: NMSDC)

4964   Z&A Infotek Corporation
35 Waterview Blvd 2nd Fl
Parsippany, NJ 07054
Contact: John Pezzullo EVP
Tel: 917-751-2299
Email: johnp@znainc.com
Website: www.znainc.com
Information technology, consulting & software, ERP & CRM, web enabling applications, RDBMS, project management, network infrastructure tools & management. (As-Ind, estab 2003, empl 90, sales $7,500,000, cert: NMSDC, 8a)

New Mexico

4965   Westwind Computer Products
5655 Jefferson St NE, Ste B
Albuquerque, NM 87109
Contact: Brigetta Koepke Supplier Diversity AE
Tel: 505-345-4720
Email: diversity@wwcpinc.com
Website: www.wwcpinc.com/
Mobility & End User Computing, Enterprise Storage Solutions, Blade and Rack Server Integration, Large Deployment Rollouts, VDI design and pilots, Cyber Security, Control & Command Solutions, AV Solutions, VOIP / VTC. (Hisp, estab 1992, empl 56, sales $173,704,356, cert: NMSDC)

Nevada

4966   A.R. Acosta, Ltd. dba Alisa Acosta Business Conslt
18124 Wedge Pkwy
Reno, NV 89511
Contact: Alisa Acosta President
Tel: 702-203-4382
Email: alisaa@earthlink.net
Website: www.AlisaAcostaConsulting.com
Business consulting: process reengineering, documentation, process mapping, project management, develop training curriculum & conducting training. (Woman/Hisp, estab 1998, empl 1, sales , cert: State, 8a)

4967   Agilea Solutions, Inc.
6671 S.Las Vegas Blvd Ste D, Ste 210
Las Vegas, NV 89119
Contact: Marce Roth CEO
Tel: 866-800-1897
Email: contact@agileasolutions.com
Website: http://agileasolutions.com
IT consulting firm, systems integration, implement & support enterprise software applications. (Woman/As-Pac, estab 2005, empl 75, sales $14,110,000, cert: NMSDC, WBENC)

4968   American Project Management LLC
11700 W Charleston Blvd, Ste 170-315
Las Vegas, NV 89135
Contact: Jane Lee Managing Partner
Tel: 702-220-4562
Email: jlee@apmlasvegas.com
Website: www.apmlasvegas.com
Project Scheduling & Cost Control, Earned Value Management System (EVMS) Implementation, Computer Programming & Embedded Software Development Services & Staff Augmentation. (Woman/As-Pac, estab 2003, empl 2, sales , cert: NMSDC, NWBOC)

4969   Blue Fields Digital LLC
3172 N Rainbow Blvd, Ste 1120
Las Vegas, NV 89108
Contact: Akilah Kamaria Data Security Consultant
Tel: 949-344-2996
Email: akilahk@bluefieldsdigital.com
Website: www.bluefieldsdigital.com
Cybersecurity solutions, security risk assessments, third-party risk management, security engineering & cyber security awareness training. (Woman/AA, estab 2015, empl 2, sales , cert: City)

4970   ECF Data LLC
6149 S Rainbow Blvd, Ste 400
Las Vegas, NV 89118
Contact: Joseph Henderson
Tel: 702-664-0075
Email: jhenderson@ecfdata.com
Website: www.ecfdata.com
Polycom telephones & video equipment, Audio Codes, Dialogic, Acme Packet voice gateways, HP, Dell, Lenovo Server Hardware, Cisco, Juniper, HP network switches and Routers, Contact Center, Voice Response Applications. (AA, estab 2010, empl 4, sales $220,000, cert: NMSDC, 8a)

4971   Ingenarius, Inc.
29 N 28th St, Ste 14E
Las Vegas, NV 89101
Contact: Ishmael Thomas President
Tel: 702-763-1419
Email: ishmaellthomas@ingenarius.com
Website: http://solutions.oracle.com/scwar/scr/Partner/SCP
Software product life cycle (SPLC) services & enterprise Java software development services, embedded, mobile, big data & the Internet of Things (IoT), analysis, design, construction, operation, configuration & maintenance. (AA, estab 2013, empl 1, sales , cert: State)

4972   Intelligent Image Management Inc.
2850 W Horizon Ridge Pkwy Ste 200
Henderson, NV 89052
Contact: Shuvo Rahman VP Business Dev
Tel: 801-906-9517
Email: shuvo@iimdirect.com
Website: www.capturedata.com
Business Process Outsourcing (BPO) & document management, data entry, indexing, data conversion, data mining, call center, post scan processing, back office. (As-Ind, estab 1999, empl 3, sales $5,000,000, cert: NMSDC)

4973 OCAA Solutions LLC
      170 S Green Valley Pkwy, Ste 300
      Henderson, NV 89012
      Contact: Foma Odje
      Tel: 702-900-2733
      Email: odje@ocaasolutions.com
      Website: www.ocaasolutions.com
Identity Management Solutions, Single Sign-On Solutions,
Custom Software Development, Enterprise Architecture
Design, Technical Writing, Remote DBA Services, Business
Analysis, Personal GPS Trackers. (AA, estab 2011, empl 3,
sales $500,446, cert: NMSDC)

4974 Spartacus Consulting, Inc.
      7521 W Lake Mead Blvd Ste 300
      Las Vegas, NV 89128
      Contact: Henry Lowery Managing Dir
      Tel: 702-997-4132
      Email: henry@scicpa.com
      Website: www.scicpa.com
AGILE Project Management Methodology for Software
Development Lifecycle, design, configuration, develop-
ment & support. (Woman/AA, estab 2003, empl 18, sales
$13,000,000, cert: State)

4975 XIOSS, Inc.
      4730 S. Fort Apache Rd Ste 300
      Las Vegas, NV 89147
      Contact: Susie Galyardt Founder, President & CEO,
      XIOSS
      Tel: 952-941-4000
      Email: susie.galyardt@xioss.com
      Website: www.xioss.com
IT storage solutions: data & network architecture, data
management, infrastructure management, systems
architecture & disaster recovery. (Woman, estab 2008,
empl 11, sales $1,100,000, cert: WBENC)

New York

4976 A-1 Technology Inc.
      115 Broadway, 13th Fl
      New York, NY 10006
      Contact: Ishwari Singh President
      Tel: 212-397-7481
      Email: ishwari.singh@a1technology.biz
      Website: www.a1technology.com
Website design, iPhone programming, mobile programming, application development, database , networking,
quality assurance. (As-Ind, estab 2001, empl 45, sales
$4,500,000, cert: City)

4977 Aimssoft Consultants Inc.
      13760 45th Ave Ste- 6 -C
      Flushing, NY 11355
      Contact: Ambreen Imran President
      Tel: 718-762-2370
      Email: imran@aimssoftconsultant.net
      Website: www.aimssoftconsultant.net
Aimssoft serves the business clients by locating a professional candidates, Interviewing and screening candidates,
setting up interviews if necessary Administering all hiring
paperwork. (As-Pac, estab 2013, empl 45, sales $357,809,
cert: NMSDC)

4978 American Technical Services, Inc.
      59,Hilldale Rd
      New York, NY 11507
      Contact: Nitin Dave President
      Tel: 347-282-7137
      Email: atscorp@gmail.com
      Website:
Information Technology staffing, consulting &
outsourcing services. (As-Pac, estab 1997, empl 3, sales ,
cert: State, City, NMSDC)

4979 ASI System Integration, Inc.
      48 W 37th St
      New York, NY 10018
      Contact: RICK LISKER Dir
      Tel: 212-736-0111
      Email: rlisker@asisystem.com
      Website: www.asisystem.com
IT technology sourcing/procurement, support services,
consulting & integration, asset disposition & recycling,
technical staffing. (As-Pac, estab 2005, empl 625, sales ,
cert: City, NMSDC)

4980 Ask IT Consulting Inc
      33 Peachtree St., Ste 100
      Holtsville, NY 11742
      Contact: President
      Tel: 631-649-1313
      Email:
      Website: www.askitc.com
Information technology services. (Woman/As-Ind, estab
2008, empl 10, sales , cert: State, City, SDB)

4981 Bell Services Group, Inc.
      88 Hunns Lake Rd
      Stanfordville, NY 12581
      Contact: Justin Macedonia President
      Tel: 800-645-8191
      Email: jmacedonia@bellservicesgroup.com
      Website: www.bellservicesinc.com
converting words into various types of tangible media.
Specifically, Bell provides Transcription, Closed
Captioning, Foreign Language Subtitling and Court
Reporting services on a national basis. (AA, estab 2003,
empl 68, sales $2,100,000, cert: State)

4982 BruteForce Solutions Inc
      545 8th Ave, Ste 540
      New York, NY 10018
      Contact: Khurshedur Rahman President
      Tel: 212-658-0277
      Email: info@bruteforcesolution.com
      Website: http://bruteforcesolution.com/bfs/
Staffing & consulting, Information Technology (IT)
solutions. (As-Ind, estab 2010, empl 14, sales
$1,093,686, cert: State)

4983 Compulink Technologies, Inc.
      214 W 29th St Ste 201
      New York, NY 10001
      Contact: RAFAEL ARBOLEDA CEO
      Tel: 212-695-5465
      Email: rafael@compu-link.com
      Website: www.compu-link.com
Cabling, network consulting, wireless networks, fiber
optic cabling, LAN/WAN, computer hardware, software.
(Woman/Hisp, estab 1989, empl 15, sales $5,000,000,
cert: State, City)

4984   Connect Technology Solutions
       550 W Old Country Rd, Ste 307
       Hicksville, NY 11801
       Contact: Donna Chaimanis President
       Tel: 516-433-7707
       Email: donnac@connectts.com
       Website: www.connectts.com
Information technology consulting & staffing services:
technical staffing, executive recruiting, project mgmt,
process reengineering, networking& system admin,
software development & web design. (Woman, estab
1998, empl 30, sales $1,084,139, cert: State)

4985   Controls and Automation Consultants LLC
       100 N Main St, Ste L06
       Elmira, NY 14901
       Contact: Tangela Nixon CEO
       Tel: 800-430-4021
       Email: tnixon@controls-automation.com
       Website: www.controls-automation.com
IT Staffing
Hybrid Technical Staffing TM
Project Management & Control
Electrical Engineering
Automation Engineering (AA, estab 2005, empl 4, sales
$1,000,000, cert: State, NMSDC)

4986   Corporate Computer Solutions
       55 Halstead Ave
       Harrison, NY 10528
       Contact: Larry Grippo VP Sales
       Tel: 914-835-1105
       Email: lgrippo@corporatecomputersol.com
       Website: www.corporatecomputersol.com
Computer-based business solutions. (Woman, estab 1986,
empl 18, sales $12,000,000, cert: State, City, WBENC)

4987   Crossfire Consulting
       1940 Commerce St
       Yorktown Heights, NY 10598
       Contact: Paul Byrne VP Sales
       Tel: 914-302-2900
       Email: jessica@crossfireconsulting.com
       Website: www.crossfireconsulting.com
IT Consulting, Development & Staff Augmentation,
consulting, development, program management &
onshore outsourcing. (Woman, estab 2000, empl 25, sales
, cert: State, City, CPUC, WBENC, NWBOC)

4988   Datrose
       660 Basket Rd
       Webster, NY 14580
       Contact: Eunice Sonneville Operations Business
       Partner
       Tel: 585-217-0225
       Email: esonneville@datrose.com
       Website: www.datrose.com
Facilities support mgmt svcs: mailing-repro & steno;
computer hardware & software; programming; data
processing; systems design. (AA, estab 1976, empl 219,
sales $14,765,522, cert: NMSDC)

4989   Deltronix Technologies Inc.
       251 New Karner Road
       Albany, NY 12205
       Contact: Snekalatha Jegadeesan President
       Tel: 518-713-5140
       Email: hr@deltronixtech.com
       Website: www.deltronixtech.com
IT Staff Augmentation: Java, .NET, Siebel, SAP, Peoplesoft,
CRM, Database, Kofax, Testing etc. (Woman/As-Pac, estab
2012, empl 15, sales $888,071, cert: State)

4990   Derive Technologies
       40 Wall St
       New York, NY 10005
       Contact: Bill Eggers Sr VP
       Tel: 212-363-1111
       Email: beggers@derivetech.com
       Website: www.derivetech.com
Hardware fullfillment, computer integration service,
iinfrastructure, desktop & printer support. (As-Ind, estab
1986, empl 110, sales $85,000,000, cert: NMSDC)

4991   Doddi Information Technologies
       24 Picture Lane
       Hicksville, NY 11801
       Contact: David Trotman Dir Business Devel
       Tel: 646-330-5354
       Email: david.trotman@dodditech.com
       Website: www.dodditech.com
Professional Services and Software development. (As-
Ind, estab 2013, empl 10, sales , cert: NMSDC)

4992   Donnelly & Moore Corporation
       75 Carolina Dr
       New City, NY 10956
       Contact: TRACY STEIN CEO
       Tel: 845-304-8344
       Email: tracys@donmor.com
       Website: www.donmor.com
IT consulting & full time IT staffing: GUI dev, internet &
intranet application dev, quality assurance testing, help
desk & desk top support, database dev & administration.
(Woman/Hisp, estab 1997, empl 50, sales $10,000,000,
cert: State, City, NMSDC)

4993   Eclaro International
       450 Seventh Ave Ste 1102
       New York, NY 10123
       Contact: Rick CAFIERO VP
       Tel: 212-258-2626
       Email: rcafiero@eclaroit.com
       Website: www.eclaroit.com
Information technology staffing & software development services. (As-Pac, estab , empl , sales $23,100,000,
cert: State, City, NMSDC)

4994   eiWorkflow Solutions, LLC
       125 Wolf Rd
       Albany, NY 12205
       Contact: John Andrew CEO
       Tel: 518-240-1155
       Email: info@eiworkflowsolutions.com
       Website: www.eiworkflowsolutions.com/
Cloud software consulting, Workflow Management,
Customer Service Management, Customer Relationship
Management & Human Resource Management. (As-Ind,
estab 2006, empl 7, sales $450,000, cert: NMSDC)

4995   Elite Technical Services, Inc.
       3281 Veterans Memorial Hwy Ste E17
       Ronkonkoma, NY 11779
       Contact: Donna Keller President
       Tel: 631-256-1399
       Email: dkeller@elitetechnical.com
       Website: www.elitetechnical.com
Technical consultants & staff augmentation services:
information technology, networking & engineering.
(Woman, estab 1992, empl 88, sales $14,500,000, cert:
State, WBENC)

4996 emedia, LLC
274 Madison Ave Ste 1202
New York, NY 10017
Contact: Shari Lowsky Dir Client Relations
Tel: 212-774-6100
Email: slowsky@emediaweb.com
Website: http://emediaweb.com
Design, build, integrate & maintain custom software applications, Enterprise Resource Planning (ERP) systems, Enterprise Content Management (ECM) systems, Customer Relationship Management (CRM) systems. (Woman, estab 1996, empl 8, sales $1,000,000, cert: State, City, WBENC)

4997 Episerve Corp.
266 Midwood St
Brooklyn, NY 11225
Contact: Sony Titus President
Tel: 917-921-2644
Email: info@episervecorp.com
Website: www.episervecorp.com
Training, consulting, system integration & managed services. (Woman/AA, estab 2003, empl 6, sales $245,000, cert: City)

4998 Espirit Systems, LLC
14 Penn Plaza Ste 2105
New York, NY 10122
Contact:
Tel: 212-631-0188
Email: amcclean@eliteconsulting.com
Website: www.eliteconsulting.com
Application architect & dev, database dev, network admin & architects, systems admin, business analysts, mainframe. (AA, estab 1997, empl 10, sales $5,000,000, cert: State)

4999 Expinfo, Inc.
1621 Central Ave
Albany, NY 12205
Contact: CEO
Tel: 518-459-4100
Email: nys@expinfo.com
Website: www.expinfo.com
Information technology staffing, HR consulting, custom computer programming, computer systems design, web development & graphic design, custom application development. (Woman/As-Pac, estab 2005, empl 21, sales $1,800,000, cert: State, City)

5000 Fair Pattern Inc.
1460 Broadway
New York, NY 10036
Contact: Simon Islam Managing Dir
Tel: 800-906-1656
Email: simon@fairpattern.com
Website: www.fairpattern.com
IT staffing, web & mobile application, software engineering & project management. (As-Ind, estab 2015, empl 22, sales $650,000, cert: NMSDC)

5001 Fast Lane Interactive
P.O. Box 987
New York, NY 11225
Contact: Shalonda Hunter Founder
Tel: 646-389-8495
Email: contactus@flitimes.com
Website: www.flitimes.com
Digital Media & Advertising, Content Development, Web, Mobile, Tablet Device Development & Services, Software Development, Web Security, Information Security, Cloud Services (Email, Web Storage, Telecomm, Data Center Migration). (Woman/AA, estab 2015, empl 5, sales , cert: NMSDC)

5002 Financial Technologies Inc
305 Madison Ave, Ste 4600
New York, NY 10165
Contact: Young Lee CEO
Tel: 212-485-9842
Email: hlee@sciostrategy.com
Website: www.ScioStrategy.com
IT consulting services, web/mobile applications & back end data management & integration solutions. (Woman/As-Pac, estab 2006, empl 3, sales $527,935, cert: State)

5003 Galica, LLC
620 Park Ave, Ste 216
Rochester, NY 14607
Contact: Carlos Perez Principal
Tel: 585-319-9301
Email: galicaehs@gmail.com
Website: www.galicalean.com
Galica LLC provides bilingual (Spanish/English) Strategy Support and Lean Facilitation using The Toyota KATA teachings. We specialize in: Rapid Improvement Event Facilitation Lean Program development Training on Strategy development (Hisp, estab 2009, empl 1, sales , cert: State, NMSDC)

5004 GCom Software, Inc.
24 Madison Ave
Albany, NY 12203
Contact: Rebecca Fischer Acct Mgr
Tel: 518-869-1671
Email: PreSales@gcomsoft.com
Website: www.gcomsoft.com
IT Staff Augmentation, fixed cost deliverable, project based services, Web based application development, Data warehousing, Network support, server , security, virtualization, Quality/Testing. (As-Ind, estab 2005, empl 130, sales , cert: State)

5005 GENESYS Consulting Services, Inc.
1 Marcus Blvd, Ste 102
Albany, NY 12205
Contact: Leo Pfohl VP
Tel: 518-459-9500
Email: leo@genesysonline.com
Website: www.genesysonline.com
Information Technology consulting services, design, develop, implement & maintain technology solutions. (Woman, estab 1987, empl 84, sales $12,500,717, cert: State, City)

5006 Globalquest
435 Lawrence Bell Dr, Ste 7
Williamsville, NY 14221
Contact: Lynn Dearmyer Business Develop Mgr
Tel: 716-635-9820
Email: ldearmyer@globalquestinc.com
Website: www.globalqueststaffing.com
IT staffing: contract, contract-to-hire, direct & payroll.
(Woman, estab 1994, empl 120, sales $24,000,000, cert:
State, City)

5007 Granwood Inc
61-43 186th St
Fresh Meadows, NY 11365
Contact: Glen Greene Managing Dir
Tel: 718-640-2828
Email: ggreene@granwoodinc.com
Website: www.granwoodinc.com
Information technology consulting & staffing. (AA, estab
2005, empl 11, sales $1,200,000, cert: State, City, NMSDC)

5008 ImageWork USA LLC
170 Hamilton Ave, Ste 301
White Plains, NY 10601
Contact: President
Tel: 914-681-0700
Email:
Website: www.imagework.com
Full life Cycle Recruitment - IT services - Information
Technology; Documentation Scanning; Printing; Comput-
ing. (Woman/Hisp, estab 2009, empl 1, sales , cert: State,
City)

5009 Indotronix International Corporation
687 Lee Rd, Ste 250
Rochester, NY 14606
Contact: Venkat S Mantha President
Tel: 845-473-1137
Email: bd@iic.com
Website: www.iic.com
Software applications, e-business initiatives, IT consulting,
customer interaction management. (Nat Ame, As-Ind,
estab 1986, empl 1000, sales $70,000,000, cert: State,
NMSDC, CPUC)

5010 InnoSoul, Inc.
24 Fairfield Ave
Albany, NY 12205
Contact: Rashi Shamshabad President
Tel: 518-400-0425
Email: innosoul@gmail.com
Website: www.innosoul.com
Software Product Development & IT Consulting Services, IT
Staffing. (Woman/As-Ind, estab 2003, empl 20, sales
$4,000,000, cert: State, City, WBENC)

5011 Integrated Systems Management
303 S Broadway, Ste 101
Tarrytown, NY 10591
Contact: Business Dev Mgr
Tel: 914-332-5590
Email:
Website: www.ismnet.com
IT solution services & IT staffing: network security, ERP,
CRM softwares. (Woman/As-Pac, estab 1989, empl 35,
sales $5,550,000, cert: State)

5012 Integrity Communications
130 Route 209
Port Jervis, NY 12771
Contact: Wayne Murray President
Tel: 845-649-5387
Email: wmurray@integritycom.net
Website: www.integritycom.net
Systems integration & installation, troubleshooting,
structured network cabling for computer, LAN networks,
voice/data. (AA, estab 2003, empl 2, sales , cert: State)

5013 Jasper Solutions Inc.
21 Melville Rd
Huntington Station, NY 11746
Contact: Anshuman Patel President
Tel: 631-514-8106
Email: contracts@jaspersolutions.com
Website: www.jaspersolutions.com
Enterprise storage, network monitoring, security, private
& public Cloud, networking, disaster recovery, applica-
tion integration, data warehousing, data mining,
database implementation, virtualization, hybrid Cloud,
Cisco. (As-Ind, estab 2002, empl 3, sales $300,000, cert:
State)

5014 Jean Martin Inc.
551 Fifth Ave, Ste 1425
New York, NY 10176
Contact: Shawn Kumar CEO
Tel: 212-883-1000
Email: shawnk@jeanmartin.com
Website: www.jeanmartin.com
Information technology consulting services. (As-Ind,
estab 1997, empl 150, sales $16,000,000, cert: City)

5015 JSL Computer Services, Inc.
447 E Allen St
Hudson, NY 12534
Contact: Ed Grossman VP
Tel: 518-828-7761
Email: ed@jslinc.com
Website: www.jslinc.com
E-commerce, web design & dev, JAVA, systems program-
ming, analysis & business requirements, project mgmt,
software testing & quality assurance, documentation,
database design, data modeling & warehousing, net-
work engineering. (Woman, estab 1978, empl 33, sales
$3,610,079, cert: City, WBENC)

5016 KDI Technology Solutions, Inc
412 Broadway 2nd Fl
New York, NY 10113
Contact: John Thomas President
Tel: 646-724-0875
Email: jthomas@kditek.com
Website: www.kditek.com
Database design & development, mobile applications,
web development, business & systems analysis. (AA,
estab 2007, empl 1, sales $100,000, cert: State, City)

5017 Maureen Data Systems, Inc.
307 W 38th St Ste 1801
New York, NY 10018
Contact: Robert Irvin Dir govt channels
Tel: 646-744-1000
Email: rirvin@mdsny.com
Website: www.mdsny.com
Systems integrator & VAR, UC, Cloud computing,
virtualization & storage, networking & security. (Woman,
estab 1994, empl 24, sales $8,500,000, cert: State, City,
WBENC)

5018 Mola Group Corporation
      401 Park Ave S, 10th Fl
      New York, NY 10016
      Contact: Rhiannon Callahan Business Support
      Associate
      Tel: 866-977-6655
      Email: contact@molaprise.com
      Website: http://molaprise.com
Cybersecurity Solutions, Threat Detection. (AA, estab 2014, empl 15, sales $5,000,000, cert: State, City)

5019 Motivate Design, LLC
      111 John St, Ste 450
      New York, NY 10038
      Contact: Laura Haykel Client Experience Dir
      Tel: 646-400-5108
      Email: laura@motivatedesign.com
      Website: http://motivatedesign.com
Motivate Design is a user experience (UX) research, design, and staffing* agency in New York City. We know that great customer experience doesn't just happen. It is the result of deep and empathetic thinking, research and design. We help companies shape t (Woman/As-Ind, estab 2009, empl 15, sales $4,000,000, cert: NMSDC, WBENC)

5020 Navatar Consulting Group Inc.
      44 Wall St, 12 Fl
      New York, NY 10005
      Contact: Mgr operations
      Tel: 212-461-2140
      Email: billing@navatargroup.com
      Website: www.navatargroup.com
On-demand CRM, ERP & supply chain. (As-Pac, estab 2002, empl 25, sales $820,000, cert: State)

5021 Netfast Technology Solutions Inc.
      589 8th Ave 22nd Fl
      New York, NY 10018
      Contact: Navid Nawaz Mgr
      Tel: 212-792-5200
      Email: nnawaz@netfast.com
      Website: www.netfast.com
Information security consulting & network integration. (As-Pac, estab 1994, empl 25, sales $13,800,000, cert: City, NMSDC)

5022 New York Technology Partners
      332 Jefferson Rd
      Rochester, NY 14623
      Contact: VP
      Tel: 585-300-4720
      Email:
      Website: www.nytp.com
Software consulting, onsite, offsite, and offshore, IT & Business Consulting, IT Integration, Project Management. (As-Pac, estab 1999, empl 280, sales $4,000,000,000, cert: NMSDC)

5023 Panther Solutions, LLC
      1001 Lee Rd
      Rochester, NY 14606
      Contact: Robert Kleinschmidt Dir Natl Accts
      Tel: 414-336-8217
      Email: robert_kleinschmidt@panthersolutions.com
      Website: www.flowercitygroup
Account management, custom data programming. (AA, estab 2005, empl 45, sales $32,000,000, cert: NMSDC)

5024 Perpetual Solutions LLC
      134 W 29th St, 607
      New York, NY 10001
      Contact: Amish Gandhi CEO
      Tel: 212-904-1497
      Email: b2bsales@perpetualny.com
      Website: www.perpetualny.com
Software User Experience Mobile Development Computer Services, Technology & Engineering Services. (As-Ind, estab 2012, empl 8, sales $1,650,000, cert: NMSDC)

5025 Quantilus Inc.
      115 Broadway Ste 1202
      New York, NY 10006
      Contact: Debarshi Chaudhury Dir Business Devel
      Tel: 212-768-8900
      Email: debarshi.chaudhury@quantilus.com
      Website: www.quantilus.com
IT Strategy, Implementation, Custom Development, Machine Vision, Publishing, Education, Artificial Intelligence, Natural Language Processing3. (As-Ind, estab 2004, empl 22, sales $7,213,447, cert: State, City, NMSDC)

5026 RMK Consulting, Inc.
      2 Oregon Hollow Rd
      Armonk, NY 10504
      Contact: Debra DeWitt Acct Exec
      Tel: 914-765-0075
      Email: info@rmkconsulting.com
      Website: http://rmkconsulting.com
BPO & IT consulting, outsourcing & consulting services for staff augmentation, managed services & project sourcing solutions, on-site, near-site & off-shore staffing/delivery models. (Woman, estab 1998, empl 127, sales $30,000,000, cert: WBENC)

5027 SD Services Inc.
      3149 Wilmarth Pl
      Wantagh, NY 11793
      Contact: President
      Tel: 516-633-5229
      Email:
      Website: www.sdservicesinc.us
Custom software dev, website design & dev, application dev, website optimization. (Woman/As-Ind, estab 2001, empl , sales $700,000, cert: State, City, WBENC)

5028 Sharp Decisions, Inc.
      1040 Ave of the Americas 9th Fl
      New York, NY 10018
      Contact: Edward McCann Managing Dir
      Tel: 212-403-7557
      Email: hdteam@sharpdecisions.com
      Website: www.sharpdecisions.com
Computer consulting: staff augmentation & contract programming, systems integration, data networks design, development & implementation, business continuity planning, security & firewall design & dev, vendor product evaluation. (Woman, estab 1990, empl 330, sales $60,000,000, cert: NWBOC)

5029   Siwel Consulting, Inc.
       213 W 35th St Ste 12 W
       New York, NY 10001
       Contact: Michael LaPayower Sr Acct Exec
       Tel: 212-691-9326
       Email: mlapayower@siwel.com
       Website: www.siwel.com
Information technology: contract & fulltime staffing, IBM
Premier VAR, ELA & software license, asset management,
Linux, VOIP, VMware, server, storage & networking.
(Woman, estab 1992, empl 30, sales $52,780,000, cert:
WBENC)

5030   Softpath Systems Inc.
       75 Maiden Lane, Ste 903
       New York, NY 10038
       Contact: Shiv Mgr
       Tel: 212-405-1894
       Email: shiv@softpathsystems.com
       Website: www.softpathsystems.com
IT & supply chain staffing. (As-Pac, estab 1997, empl , sales
$300,000, cert: State)

5031   Software Guidance & Assistance, Inc.
       200 White Plains Road
       Tarrytown, NY 10591
       Contact: Craig Rydell Business Develop Mgr
       Tel: 914-366-5950
       Email: craigr@sgainc.com
       Website: www.sgainc.com
IT professionals: programmers, analysts, senior project
managers, operating systems, programming, networking,
application software & hardware skills & certifications.
(Woman, estab 1981, empl 652, sales $78,218,000, cert:
City, WBENC)

5032   Source Of Future Technology (SOFT), Inc.
       333 Hudson St Ste 202
       New York, NY 10013
       Contact: Cathy Grubiak President
       Tel: 212-633-1515
       Email: cgrubiak@soft-inc.com
       Website: www.softinc.com
Computer technology solutions: project life cycle.
 (Woman, estab 1981, empl 75, sales $6,000,000, cert:
State, WBENC)

5033   Sphynx Software Solutions LLC
       59 Lafayette Ave Ste 2D
       Brooklyn, NY 11217
       Contact: Yonas Keflemariam CEO
       Tel: 917-705-5548
       Email: yonas@sphynxsoftware.com
       Website: www.sphynxsoftware.com
Technology solutions, enterprise architecture, local &
offshore software development resources & technical staff
augmentation. (AA, estab 2007, empl 3, sales , cert: City,
NMSDC)

5034   Sutherland Global Services
       1160 Pittsford-Victor Rd
       Pittsford, NY 14534
       Contact: Steve Sandt Business Develop Mgr
       Tel: 585-586-5757
       Email: sandts@sutherlandglobal.com
       Website: www.sutherlandglobal.com
Business process outsourcing & call ctr svcs: technical &
customer support, systems integration & application
development. (As-Ind, estab 1986, empl 33000, sales
$500,500,000, cert: NMSDC)

5035   SVAM International Inc.
       233 East Shore Rd, Ste 201
       Great Neck, NY 11023
       Contact: Manav Bhasin Managing Dir
       Tel: 516-466-6655
       Email: manav@svam.com
       Website: www.svam.com
IT staff augmentation, custom software dev, web
enabling technologies, workflow automation, content
management. (As-Pac, estab 1994, empl 600, sales
$40,919,959, cert: State, NMSDC)

5036   Sygma Technology Solutions, Inc.
       300 W 135th St, Ste 5J
       New York, NY 10030
       Contact: Stuart Holland President
       Tel: 917-507-1500
       Email: stuart.holland@sygmatechnology.com
       Website: www.sygmatechnology.com
Custom software development, integrated technology,
technology system solutions, application software
development, business information technology, business
software development. (AA, estab 2005, empl , sales
$165,000, cert: State, NMSDC, 8a)

5037   Techolution LLC
       3 World Financial Center 24th Fl
       New York, NY 10281
       Contact: Zachary Kissel Office Mgr
       Tel: 201-417-7240
       Email: zak@techolution.com
       Website: http://techolution.com
Digital transformation: web & mobile, migrating server
farms & applications to the cloud (public or private). (As-
Pac, estab 2014, empl 50, sales $1,500,000, cert:
NMSDC)

5038   Trivision Group Inc.
       118-21 Queens Blvd Ste 401
       Forest Hills, NY 11375
       Contact: Vijay Shenoy CEO
       Tel: 212-869-5455
       Email: contracts@trivisioninc.com
       Website: www.trivisioninc.com
Contract staffing solutions, Project Management and
Information Technology Consulting Services, system
design, programming, and testing, to post-implementa-
tion support and maintenance. (As-Pac, estab 2003,
empl 17, sales $1,000,000, cert: State, City)

5039   Ubiqus
       601 Bangs Ave
       Asbury Park, NY 07712
       Contact: TTI of USA CEO
       Tel: 646-495-9019
       Email: LK@TTIOFUSA.COM
       Website: www.ttiofusa.com
IT staff augmentation. (Woman, estab 1996, empl 240,
sales $20,182,200, cert: WBENC)

5040   URimagination, Inc.
       18 E 41st St Ste 1703
       New York, NY 10017
       Contact: Alf Baez CEO
       Tel: 212-729-9558
       Email: info@urimagination.com
       Website: www.urimagination.com
Information technology solutions: custom application
development, systems integration, maintenance span-
ning. (Hisp, estab 2007, empl 7, sales $500,000, cert:
City, NMSDC)

5041   Vernalis Group Inc
       353 Lexington Ave, Ste 1604
       New York, NY 10016
       Contact: Nanda Rajasek COO
       Tel: 647-923-1903
       Email: nanda.rajasek@vernal.is
       Website: www.vernalisengg.com
Global software & engineering solutions, Microsoft, IBM,
JEE, openSource, Mobile, Business Intelligence, Enterprise
Application Integration. (As-Ind, estab 2012, empl 300,
sales $4,440,000, cert: NMSDC)

5042   VQV Services LLC
       204 Forrest Pointe Dr
       East Greenbush, NY 12061
       Contact: Khuhsbooben Patel President
       Tel: 201-920-6170
       Email: khush@vqvservices.com
       Website: www.vqvservices.com
Quality Engineer, Validation Engineer, Qualification
Specialist, Information Technology consultants. (Woman/
As-Pac, estab 2016, empl 2, sales , cert: State)

5043   Xperteks Computer Consultancy, Inc.
       132 West 36th St
       New York, NY 10018
       Contact: Marcial Velez CEO
       Tel: 212-206-6262
       Email: mvelez@xperteks.com
       Website: www.xperteks.com
Apple, PC & network managed services, IT services. (Hisp,
estab 2002, empl 17, sales $2,500,000, cert: City, NMSDC)

Ohio

5044   Accelerated Business Results an A Fox Corporation
       1530 Sycamore Ridge Dr
       Maineville, OH 45039
       Contact: Amy Fox Owner
       Tel: 513-774-8608
       Email: amy.fox@acceleratedbr.com
       Website: http://acceleratedbr.com/what-we-do/
Customized content development, design & develop
instructor-led training programs, e-Learning solutions &
blended learning solutions. (Woman, estab 2002, empl 11,
sales $1,678,119, cert: WBENC)

5045   AespaTech, LLC
       23800 Commerce Park, Ste A
       Beachwood, OH 44122
       Contact: President
       Tel: 216-928-1919
       Email:
       Website: www.aespatech.com
Information Technology Consulting & Training Services.
(Woman/As-Pac, estab 2014, empl , sales $750,000, cert:
State, City, WBENC, 8a)

5046   Alego Health
       24651 Center Ridge Rd Ste 400
       Westlake, OH 44145
       Contact: Jonathan Levoy VP
       Tel: 440-617-6516
       Email: jlevoy@alegohealth.com
       Website: www.alegohealth.com
Healthcare IT, EMR Training, EMR Implementation, EMR
Analysts, Hardware Support, Hardware, Software, IT
Analysts, IT, Mobile Technology (Woman, estab 2004, empl
127, sales $11,500,000, cert: WBENC)

5047   American Business Solutions, Inc.
       8850 Whitney Dr
       Lewis Center, OH 43035
       Contact: Nitin Sharma Sr Mgr, Business Devel
       Tel: 614-888-2227
       Email: nitin@absi-usa.com
       Website: www.absi-usa.com
Technology Services & Solutions, Business Intelligence &
Database Mgmt, Organizational Change Mgmt, Mobile
Application Dev, Project gmt & Support, Quality Assur-
ance & Testing, Cloud Computing Services. (As-Ind, estab
1998, empl 85, sales $19,000,000, cert: State, NMSDC)

5048   Ardent Technologies Inc.
       6234 Far Hills Ave
       Dayton, OH 45459
       Contact: Vas Appalaneni President
       Tel: 937-312-1345
       Email: ohbids@ardentinc.com
       Website: www.ardentinc.com
ITservices & project management, software development & maintenance, systems
analysis, turnkey project implementations, data services
(modeling, management and migration),
project outsourcing services. (As-Ind, estab 2000, empl
60, sales $7,300,000, cert: State, SDB)

5049   ASC Associates, Inc.
       110 Clearbrook Lane
       Aurora, OH 44202
       Contact: Shashi Jina President
       Tel: 216-496-2773
       Email: sjina@ascassociates.com
       Website: www.ascassociates.com
IT services, custom systems development (COBAL, JAVA,
.NET), ERP implementations. Oracle, SAP & related
databases (Oracle 9, 10g, SQL). (As-Ind, estab 2001,
empl 15, sales $300,000, cert: State)

5050   Ascendum
       10290 Alliance Rd
       Cincinnati, OH 45242
       Contact: Tara Heiner Business Devel Exec
       Tel: 513-792-5100
       Email: tara.heiner@ascendum.com
       Website: http://ascendum.com
IT solutions, technology-inspired solutions to business-
driven challenges. (As-Ind, estab 2008, empl 1500, sales
$80,000,000, cert: State, NMSDC)

5051   Avantia, Inc.
       9655 Sweet Valley Dr, Ste 1
       Valley View, OH 44125
       Contact: Jeff Ladd Controller
       Tel: 216-901-9366
       Email: jladd@avantia-inc.com
       Website: www.avantia-inc.com
Information technology consulting & systems development. (Woman, estab 2000, empl 35, sales $9,240,331,
cert: WBENC)

5052   Barcode Industrial Systems, Inc.
       8044 Montgomery road Ste 700
       Cincinnati, OH 45236
       Contact: Juan Merchan Business Develop Mgr
       Tel: 513-772-5252
       Email: contracts@bislabels.com
       Website: www.BISLabels.com
Mobile data transaction systems, wireless & batch data
capture applications: inventory, shipping, receiving &
warehouse mgmt via Internet. (AA, Hisp, estab 1990,
empl 16, sales $1,010,000, cert: NMSDC)

5053 Cadre Computer Resources Co.
      201 E 5th St, Ste 1800
      Cincinnati, OH 45202
      Contact: Kristen Norris Marketing
      Tel: 513-762-7350
      Email: kristen.norris@cadre.net
      Website: www.cadre.net
Network & information security solutions, design, assessment, installation, training & support of information security systems. (Woman, estab 2001, empl 47, sales $43,383,000, cert: WBENC, NWBOC)

5054 CB Tech
      1491 Polaris Pkwy Ste 291
      Columbus, OH 43240
      Contact: Josh Harris Sr Dir of Business Development
      Tel: 614-339-8550
      Email: info@cbtechnow.com
      Website: www.cbtechnow.com
IT services & document management solutions. (AA, estab 1990, empl 15, sales $25,770,000, cert: NMSDC)

5055 CDO Technologies, Inc.
      5200 Springfield St Ste 320
      Dayton, OH 45431
      Contact: Valerie Smith contracts Admin
      Tel: 937-258-0022
      Email: valerie.smith@cdotech.com
      Website: www.cdotech.com
Information engineering; computer networks; network mgmt; design; software engineering; programming; communications; telecommunications; system engineering & admin; bar codes; biometric authentication, etc. (AA, estab 1995, empl 185, sales $36,136,518, cert: State)

5056 CGB Tech Solutions Inc
      2310 Superior Ave Ste 105
      Cleveland, OH 44114
      Contact: Jennifer Brunkow Owner
      Tel: 216-373-9449
      Email: jen@cgbtech.com
      Website: http://cgbgtech.com
Network Infrastructure planning, procurement, installation & troubleshooting, server monitoring, evaluation, troubleshooting and repair, User endpoint (desktop/laptop) troubleshooting, remote or in-person
Help Desk services. (Minority, estab 2003, empl 17, sales $1,000,000, cert: City)

5057 Chagrin Consulting Services Inc.
      1795 South Belvoir Blvd.
      South Euclid, OH 44121
      Contact: Ann Allard President
      Tel: 216-514-3301
      Email: ahallard@chagrinconsulting.com
      Website: www.chagrinconsulting.com
Information technology consulting & staffing. (Woman, estab 1993, empl 12, sales $2,451,851, cert: WBENC)

5058 ClemCorp
      714 E Monument Ave
      Dayton, OH 45402
      Contact: Kevin Clemons CEO
      Tel: 937-531-6645
      Email: kevin.clemons@clemcorp.com
      Website: www.ClemCorp.com
IT solution & services: rational capabilities, enterprise architecture, GCSS, web dev, graphic design, document mgmt, network design & admin, software dev, project mgmt, system design, life cycle application support. (AA, estab 2005, empl 12, sales $300,000, cert: State, 8a)

5059 Corbus, LLC
      1129 Miamisburg Centerville Rd
      West Carrollton, OH 45449
      Contact: Jerry Teuschler Dir Strategic Sales Development
      Tel: 513-703-2929
      Email: corbusconnects@corbus.com
      Website: www.corbus.com
Software development, offshore IT support, testing & quality solutions, staff augmentation. (As-Ind, As-Pac, estab 1994, empl 600, sales , cert: NMSDC)

5060 Cybervation, Inc.
      4150 Tuller Rd, Ste 204
      Dublin, OH 43017
      Contact: Purba Majumder President
      Tel: 614-818-9061
      Email: pmajumder@cybervationinc.com
      Website: www.cybervationinc.com
Technology Services, Website Dev, custom Software Programming, Graphics Design, Animation, Video, Transcription, Data Entry & Internet Marketing. (Woman/As-Pac, estab 1998, empl 32, sales , cert: State, NMSDC, WBENC)

5061 Cynergies Solutions Group
      26301 Curtiss-Wright Pkwy Ste 400
      Richmond Heights, OH 44143
      Contact: Debbie Holy President
      Tel: 440-565-0168
      Email: debbie_holy@cynergies.net
      Website: www.cynergies.net
Information technology staffing: consulting, contracting, permanent, executive placement, contract-to-hire, software devel & training. (Woman, estab 1997, empl 62, sales , cert: WBENC)

5062 Dedicated Tech Services, Inc.
      545 Metro Place S Ste 100
      Dublin, OH 43017
      Contact: President
      Tel: 614-309-0059
      Email:
      Website: www.dtsdelivers.com
Application Design & Dev Service Oriented Architecture (SOA), Database Design & Dev, Client/Server & N-Tier Development, Web & Web Service Development, Data Warehousing Solutions. (Woman/As-Ind, estab 2008, empl 30, sales $1,930,000, cert: WBENC, NWBOC)

5063 Deemsys Inc.
      800A Cross Pointe Rd
      Columbus, OH 43230
      Contact: RT Rajan
      Tel: 614-322-9929
      Email: raj@deemsysinc.com
      Website: www.deemsysinc.com
Application design, development & implementation, Systems integration/consolidation, Re-engineering, Implementation, Feasibility & requirement analysis. (Woman/As-Ind, estab 2004, empl 82, sales $7,550,000, cert: State, NMSDC)

5064 DevCare Solutions
      131 N High St Ste 640
      Columbus, OH 43215
      Contact: Ron Vogel Dir Business Devel
      Tel: 614-285-2714
      Email: rvogel@devcare.com
      Website: www.devcare.com
On-site/offshore development of software solutions &
Staff Augmentation consultants. (Woman/As-Pac, estab
1995, empl 380, sales $22,000,000, cert: State, WBENC)

5065 Echo Imaging Inc.
      2645 Wooster Rd
      Rocky River, OH 44116
      Contact: Barbara Milloy President
      Tel: 440-356-4720
      Email: barbara@echoimg.com
      Website: www.echoimg.com
Replication svcs: CD-R, CD-ROM, DVD-R, mini CD's,
business card CD's & diskette duplication, full color custom
printed packaging. (Woman, estab 1997, empl , sales
$801,642, cert: WBENC)

5066 ERP Analysts, Inc
      425 Metro Place N Ste 510
      Dublin, OH 43017
      Contact: Cory Drescher Director
      Tel: 727-424-4427
      Email: jvyas@erpagroup.com
      Website: www.erpagroup.com
Project management, ERP Application Implementations
and Major/Minor
Upgrades in PeopleSoft,Oracle, and SAP. Database Management and Administration, Performance Tuning. (AA, As-
Pac, estab 2003, empl 500, sales $88,000,000, cert: State,
8a)

5067 Evanhoe & Associates, Inc.
      5089 Norman Blvd.
      Dayton, OH 45431
      Contact: Marty Pendergrass VP for Contracts &
      Admin
      Tel: 937-528-5806
      Email: marty.pendergrass@evanhoe.com
      Website: www.evanhoe.com
Data management, software development, business
process reengineering & modeling & simulation. (As-Pac,
estab 1996, empl 35, sales $6,051,297, cert: State)

5068 EXCEL Management Systems, Inc.
      691 N High St, 2nd Fl
      Columbus, OH 43215
      Contact: Curtis Jewell
      Tel: 614-224-4007
      Email: curtis@emsi.com
      Website: www.emsi.com
Project mgmt, BPR/BPI, document imaging, EC/EDI,
systems design development & legacy data conversion
services. (AA, estab 1989, empl 130, sales $13,000,000,
cert: State)

5069 Expeed Software LLC
      659 Lakeview Plaza Blvd, Ste K
      Worthington, OH 43085
      Contact: Rao Chejarla President
      Tel: 614-371-4791
      Email: rao.chejarla@expeedsoftware.com
      Website: www.expeedsoftware.com
Custom Application Dev, Mobile Application Dev,
Application Integration, Data Warehousing and Business
Intelligence, Independent Software, Verification/Quality
Assurance, Project Management. (As-Pac, estab 2008,
empl 35, sales $735,000, cert: State, NMSDC)

5070 Fiducia TechneGroup LLC
      3838 Eileen Dr
      Cincinnati, OH 45209
      Contact: Alma Bartos CEO
      Tel: 513-418-8217
      Email: amartinez@fiduciatg.com
      Website: www.fiduciatg.com
Engineering Services, Reliability (Products, Processes
and Software), Implement Reliability Life Cycle Management & Benchmarking. (Woman/Hisp, estab 2014, empl
2, sales $100,000, cert: NMSDC, WBENC)

5071 Flairsoft, LTD
      7720 Rivers Edge Dr Ste 200
      Columbus, OH 43235
      Contact: Sharon Fraley Sr Business Devel Mgr
      Tel: 614-207-0764
      Email: sharon.fraley@flairsoft.net
      Website: www.flairsoft.net
Information Technology, e-Business, Professional
Services, Systems Integration & Business Process Re-
Engineering. (As-Ind, estab 2001, empl 100, sales
$8,000,000, cert: NMSDC)

5072 Global Associates, Inc.
      7160 Corporate Way
      Dayton, OH 45459
      Contact: Kevin Toshok Dir Solutions Sales
      Tel: 937-312-1204
      Email: ktoshok@gassociates.com
      Website: www.gassociates.com
IT Consulting, Staff Augmentation, Project Outsourcing
& Offshore software design & testing. (Woman/As-Ind,
As-Pac, estab 1996, empl 8, sales $15,000,000, cert:
NMSDC)

5073 IdentiPhoto Company Ltd.
      1810 Joseph Lloyd Pkwy
      Willoughby, OH 44094
      Contact: Pamela Johnson GM
      Tel: 440-306-9000
      Email: pam@identiphoto.com
      Website: www.identiphoto.com
Badging, tracking, verification systems, photo ID systems
ID badges, ID software ID supplies, ID badge attachments, ID cards, visitor management software/systems,
card printers, perimeter management systems, smart
cards, proximity. (Woman, estab 1969, empl 15, sales
$2,252,840, cert: WBENC)

5074 Integrated Solutions and Services
      4055 Executive Park Dr, Ste 450
      Cincinnati, OH 45241
      Contact: Clarence McGill
      Tel: 513-769-3913
      Email: rmcgill@iss-unlimited.com
      Website: www.iss-unlimited.com
Information technology hardware integration, network
server mgmt, help desk svcs, LAN/WAN, database dev &
mgmt, system application support. (AA, estab 1999,
empl 5, sales , cert: State)

5075   JASStek, Inc.
       555 Metro Place N Ste 100
       Dublin, OH 43017
       Contact: Praveen Tummalla Business Develop Mgr
       Tel: 614-808-3600
       Email: praveen@jasstek.com
       Website: www.jasstek.com
Information technology consulting, project staffing, IT staffing, contract programming, contract consultants, technology consultants & contract to hire consultants. (Woman/As-Pac, estab 2012, empl 9, sales , cert: State, NMSDC, WBENC)

5076   Lightwell Inc.
       565 Metro Place S Ste 220
       Columbus, OH 43017
       Contact: Bryan Scott Acct Exec
       Tel: 614-310-2700
       Email: bryan.scott@lightwellinc.com
       Website: www.lightwellinc.com
EDI, B2B integration, order management, ecommerce, business management, and supply chain management services. (Woman, estab 1998, empl 225, sales $39,000,000, cert: WBENC)

5077   Logic Soft, Inc.
       5900 Sawmill Rd, Ste 200
       Dublin, OH 43017
       Contact: Louis Viciedo Business Dev Mgr
       Tel: 614-884-5544
       Email: louis.viciedo@logicsoftusa.com
       Website: www.logicsoftusa.com
IT Managed Services, monitor program activity, detailed program analysis & benchmarking, invoicing, robust supplier management & total workforce solutions. (As-Ind, estab 1997, empl 50, sales $15,000,000, cert: State)

5078   LRSolutions, LLC
       5743 Edgepark Dr
       Brook Park, OH 44142
       Contact: Linda Gutekunst CEO
       Tel: 440-476-9492
       Email: linda@lrsolutions.net
       Website: www.LRSolutions.net
IT staffing & solutions: permanent placement, staff augmentation & project-based solutions. (Woman, estab 2006, empl 8, sales $500,000, cert: State, NWBOC)

5079   Marinar Technology Co LLC dba VantageOne
       Software
       33801 Curtis Blvd, Ste 112
       Eastlake, OH 44095
       Contact: Erica Martin CEO
       Tel: 440-354-1458
       Email: erica.francis@vantageonesoftware.com
       Website: www.vantageonesoftware.com
IT service engineers & technicians, infrastructure expansion, data migration, system security, disaster planning or basic workstation & server optimization. (Woman, estab 1994, empl 14, sales $975,000, cert: WBENC)

5080   Marketing & Engineering Solutions
       625 Bear Run Lane
       Lewis Center, OH 43035
       Contact: Hiten Shah President
       Tel: 740-201-8112
       Email: hshah@mesinc.net
       Website: www.mesinc.net
Information technology, outsourcing, customer survey processing, database maintenance, OCR & ICR data processing, call center, data processing, data entry, rebate processing. (AA, As-Ind, estab 1999, empl 110, sales $2,700,000, cert: NMSDC)

5081   MAX Technical Training Inc.
       4900 Parkway Dr
       CINCINNATI, OH 45040
       Contact: Patricia Miller CEO
       Tel: 513-322-8888
       Email: patricia@maxtrain.com
       Website: www.maxtrain.com
IT programmers & developers training. (Woman, estab 1998, empl 12, sales $1,950,556, cert: WBENC)

5082   MCB Consulting, Inc.
       501 Evans Ln
       Dayton, OH 45459
       Contact: B. Michael Bennett III CEO
       Tel: 937-291-2751
       Email: michaelbennett@ameritech.net
       Website:
Information technology solutions, Oracle, DB2, IBM 360, software process, software methodology, program mgmt, enterprise architecture, logistics, education, analysis, design, testing, implementation, installation, data modeling, database admin. (Woman/AA, estab 1998, empl 10, sales , cert: State, 8a)

5083   MEDIASCRIPT, LLC
       3982 Powell Rd, Ste 235
       Powell, OH 43065
       Contact: Angela Horne CEO
       Tel: 614-551-3549
       Email: angela@mediascriptllc.com
       Website: https://mediascriptllc.com
Media webinar technology: distance education, online learning & training. (Woman, estab 2009, empl 3, sales $175,000, cert: WBENC)

5084   MurTech Consulting LLC
       4807 Rockside Rd, Ste 250
       Independence, OH 44131
       Contact: Ailish Murphy President
       Tel: 216-328-8580
       Email: amurphy@murtechconsulting.com
       Website: www.murtechconsulting.com
Information technology consulting & placement services. (Woman, estab 2000, empl 25, sales $14,200,000, cert: WBENC)

5085   Myca Multimedia and Training Solutions, LLC
       4555 Lake Forest Dr Ste 650
       Cincinnati, OH 45242
       Contact: Patricia Massey President
       Tel: 513-608-6033
       Email: pmassey@mycagroup.com
       Website: www.mycalearning.com
Interactive & engaging eLearning tools, computer & cloud-based eLearning courseware on harassment prevention, culture & inclusion, bullying. (Woman, estab 1991, empl 15, sales $984,166, cert: WBENC)

5086   Net Activity
       9535 Midwest Ave, Ste 114
       Garfield Heights, OH 44125
       Contact: John Marion CFO
       Tel: 216-503-5150
       Email: info@netactivity.us
       Website: www.netactivity.us
Hardware & Software reseller, VoIP Phone Systems; hosted & on-site, Connectivity; dedicated data & voice communication, Cloud Back-up; proprietary infrastructure & Microsoft Azure, Remote network & hardware managed services. (As-Ind, estab 2002, empl 11, sales $1,377,695, cert: 8a, SDB)

5087   N-ovation Technology Group
       10 W. 2nd St Ste 2201
       Dayton, OH 45402
       Contact: Dwayne Coker CEO
       Tel: 937-886-4850
       Email: sales@n-ovationtech.com
       Website: http://n-ovationtech.com
Network Design, Architecture & Integration services, Data
Center Solutions, Cyber Security, Wireless DAS deployment, Cloud strategy, Infrastructure Program Management, Process Management & Quality Assurance, Vendor
Management. (AA, estab 2015, empl 5, sales $10,000,000,
cert: City, NMSDC)

5088   Precise Infotech Inc.
       7315 Royal Portrush Dr
       Solon, OH 44139
       Contact: Kashifa Ahmed President
       Tel: 440-265-0402
       Email: kahmed@preciseinfotech.com
       Website: www.preciseinfotech.com
Software development & consulting. (Woman/As-Pac,
estab 2004, empl 2, sales $274,121, cert: State)

5089   Professional Consulting Technology, LLC
       526 South Main St Ste 230
       Akron, OH 44311
       Contact: President
       Tel: 404-433-4677
       Email:
       Website: www.procon-technologies.com
Information Technology & Security, Network Design,
Installation, Operation & Maintenance, Governance Risk
Management & Compliance, Managed Services, Informa-
tion Technology Staff Augmentation. (AA, estab 2011,
empl 5, sales $201,850, cert: State)

5090   Promark Custom Solutions LLC
       8 Prestige Plaza, Ste 110
       Springboro, OH 45342
       Contact: Lisa Johnson President
       Tel: 937-557-0333
       Email: ljohnson@promarkcs.com
       Website: www.promarkcs.com
Office Productivity, Cyber Security, Security Certifications,
IT Certifications, IT Skills, and Business Skills. (Woman,
estab 1995, empl 1, sales , cert: WBENC)

5091   R.Dorsey & Company, Inc.
       400 W Wilson Bridge Rd Ste 105
       Worthington, OH 43085
       Contact: Joyce Dorsey CEO
       Tel: 614-486-8900
       Email: jcdorsey@dorseyplus.com
       Website: www.dorseyplus.com
Network Architecture, Application Architecture, Service
Oriented Architecture, Data Warehouse, Hosting, Security,
Data Backup, Outsourcing (Woman, estab 1996, empl 30,
sales , cert: WBENC, 8a)

5092   Record Express, LLC
       4295 Armstrong Blvd
       Batavia, OH 45103
       Contact: Nadine Albenze-Smith CEO
       Tel: 513-685-7329
       Email: nalbenze@recordexpressllc.com
       Website: www.recordexpressllc.com
Record retrieval & document management: insurance
defense, personal injury, medical malpractice, tobacco,
product liability, construction, asbestos, finance & banking, toxic tort, environmental. (Woman, estab 2003, empl
33, sales $1,500,000, cert: State)

5093   Solutions For You Inc.
       470 Olde Worthington Rd Ste 200
       Westerville, OH 43082
       Contact: Robert Johnson
       Tel: 614-410-6648
       Email: robertj@sfyi.com
       Website: www.sfyi.com
Information Technology consulting: Full cycle product
development, Business Analysis, Quality Assurance,
Project Management, Security (data, network, database), Open Source (language, tools, software), data
analysis, Electronic Data Interchange. (Woman/AA, estab
1999, empl 4, sales $423,027, cert: State, City, NMSDC)

5094   StarTech Consulting, Inc.
       6746 Rivercrest Dr, Ste 100
       Cleveland, OH 44141
       Contact: Joe Bains President
       Tel: 440-546-9500
       Email: jbains@startech-consult.com
       Website: www.startech-consult.com
Staff Augmentation, Web applications, Mobile applica-
tions, Database development/administrators, Project
Managers, Business Analysts, Quality Assurance, etc.
(As-Ind, estab 1998, empl 6, sales $2,107,771, cert:
State)

5095   Strategic Systems, Inc.
       475 Metro Place South #450
       Dublin, OH 43017
       Contact: Kaushal Vadada Dir of Operations
       Tel: 614-973-7979
       Email: kaushal@strsi.com
       Website: https://strsi.com
Staff Augmentation for Information Technology, Project
Management, Hybrid Staff Aumentation, Contract to
Hire, and Platform Development/Delivery. (Woman/As-
Ind, estab 2004, empl 175, sales $19,000,000, cert:
State, NMSDC)

5096   SYSTEMIAN LLC
       555 Metro Place N, Ste 100
       Plain City, OH 43064
       Contact: Wilson Fernando President
       Tel: 614-390-9660
       Email: wilson@systemian.com
       Website: www.systemian.com
IT services, Enterprise Architecture, Intelligent Automation, Cloud Adoption and Migration, Talent Management. (As-Pac, estab 2020, empl 12, sales , cert: NMSDC)

5097   TechSoft Systems, Inc.
       10296 Springfield Pike Ste 400
       Cincinnati, OH 45215
       Contact: Clifford A. Bailey President & CEO
       Tel: 513-772-5010
       Email: cabailey@techsoftsystems.com
       Website: www.techsoftsystems.com
IT Consultants/Staffing, On-Site Support (desktop,
network, help desk), Remot Support, Manages Services,
Hardware & Software purchasing. (AA, estab 1983, empl
10, sales $904,328, cert: City, NMSDC)

5098   Texcel, Inc.
       4415 Euclid Ave
       Cleveland, OH 44103
       Contact: Herman Atkins President
       Tel: 216-514-1818
       Email: batkins@texcelinc.net
       Website: www.texcelinc.net
Digital document rendering. IBM cloud solutions. (AA,
estab , empl , sales $6,000,000, cert: State, City, NMSDC)

5099　TMH Solutions LLC
　　　4176 Menderes Dr
　　　Powell, OH 43065
　　　Contact: Theresa Harris President & CEO
　　　Tel:　614-581-4450
　　　Email: theresa@tmhsolutions.com
　　　Website: www.tmhsolutions.com
Resell software & services, management & information technology solutions. (Woman/AA, estab 2010, empl 5, sales $5,100,000, cert: State, NMSDC, WBENC)

5100　TPSi, LLC
　　　11590 Century Blvd
　　　Cincinnati, OH 45246
　　　Contact: Matt Bender President
　　　Tel:　877-682-5300
　　　Email: mbender@tpsinc.com
　　　Website: www.tpsinc.com
Technical staffing & engineering services. (Woman, estab 2000, empl 25, sales $2,300,000, cert: WBENC)

5101　UNICON International, Inc.
　　　241 Outerbelt St
　　　Columbus, OH 43213
　　　Contact: Bobby Cameron Dir Client Services
　　　Tel:　614-861-7070
　　　Email: bcameron@unicon-intl.com
　　　Website: www.unicon-intl.com
Information technology solutions. (Woman/As-Pac, estab 1990, empl 300, sales $31,000,000, cert: City, NMSDC, WBENC)

5102　Vertex Computer Systems, Inc.
　　　25700 Science Park Dr, Ste 280
　　　Beachwood, OH 44122
　　　Contact: Ganesh Iyer President
　　　Tel:　216-702-4849
　　　Email: vertex.rfp@vertexcs.com
　　　Website: www.vertexcs.com
IT development & outsourced services: web, database & middleware. (Woman/As-Ind, estab 1989, empl 200, sales $16,000,000, cert: State, WBENC)

5103　Warwick Communications, Inc.
　　　405 Ken Mar Parkway
　　　Broadview Heights, OH 44147
　　　Contact: Heidi Murphy Principal
　　　Tel:　216-787-0300
　　　Email: hmurphy@warwickinc.com
　　　Website: www.warwickinc.com
Information technology managed services, telephone systems, VOIP systems, cloud/hosted systems, wireless systems, data switching equipment, call recording software, support desk services, call accounting systems, call center software. (Woman, estab 1960, empl 40, sales $6,245,000, cert: State)

Oklahoma

5104　Aero Tech Service Associates, Inc.
　　　909 S Meridian Ave, Ste 200
　　　Oklahoma City, OK 73108
　　　Contact: John Howard CEO
　　　Tel:　405-946-2872
　　　Email: atsa@atsainc.com
　　　Website: www.atsainc.com
Aviation systems requirements, systems engineering & operations, information technology, communications, technical training, technical & administrative svcs & support. (AA, estab 1991, empl 180, sales , cert: State)

5105　Delaware Resource Group of Oklahoma LLC
　　　3220 Quail Springs Parkway
　　　Oklahoma City, OK 73134
　　　Contact: Meredith Kemp Program Management Asst
　　　Tel:　405-721-7776
　　　Email: meredith.kemp@drgok.com
　　　Website: www.drgok.com/
Contract instruction services, computer based training, curriculum development & maintenance, computer training materials devel & contract operations maintenance svcs. (Nat Ame, estab 2002, empl 200, sales $21,569,317, cert: NMSDC)

5106　Muscogee International LLC.
　　　1018 S Wood Dr
　　　Okmulgee, OK 74447
　　　Contact: Mike Duke Business Develop Mgr
　　　Tel:　918-752-3150
　　　Email: mduke@muscogeeinternational.com
　　　Website: http://muscogeeinternational.com/
IT, telecom, data, security, audio video, low voltage specialty, cyber security, consulting, programming, engineering, design, procurement, management, support (Nat Ame, estab 2011, empl 24, sales $10,161,321, cert: 8a)

5107　Muscogee Nation Business Enterprise
　　　P.O. Box 147
　　　Okmulgee, OK 74447
　　　Contact: Woody Anderson Sales Mgr
　　　Tel:　918-752-3150
　　　Email: wanderson@mnbe.com
　　　Website: www.mnbe.com
Program mgmt, system engineering & integration, information technology, project admin & mgmt, architectural design & engineering, telecommunications, fire & security total integrated systems, surveillance, CCTV & access control. (Nat Ame, estab 1999, empl 100, sales $19,000,000, cert: State)

5108　Xyant Technology, Inc.
　　　710 ASP Ave Ste 500
　　　Norman, OK 73069
　　　Contact: Sowmya Sridhar President
　　　Tel:　405-209-7371
　　　Email: sowmyas@xyant.com
　　　Website: www.xyant.com
IT consulting & staff augmentation solutions: application implementation & deployment, maintenance & support, networking svcs, migration upgrades. (As-Pac, estab 1995, empl 50, sales $2,000,000, cert: NMSDC)

Oregon

5109　Cayuse Technologies, LLC
　　　72632 Coyote Rd
　　　Pendleton, OR 97801
　　　Contact: Heather Collins Dir Business Development
　　　Tel:　541-278-8200
　　　Email: heather.collins@cayusetechnologies.com
　　　Website: www.cayusetechnologies.com
Technology Platforms: Java and .NET-Operating Systems: UNIX and Windows-Programming Languages: Java, J2EE, PL/SQL, ASP, C, C+, C++, C#, VB, COBOL, TAL, TACL-Open Source Frameworks; Hibernate, Spring. (Nat Ame, estab 2006, empl 240, sales $15,063,354, cert: State, NMSDC)

5110   Everest Consultants, Inc.
        1500 NW Bethany Blvd Ste 235
        Beaverton, OR 97006
        Contact: Ranya Edupuganti President
        Tel: 503-643-3990
        Email: ranya@everestinc.com
        Website: www.everestinc.com
Software consulting, offshore software dev, systems
integration & IS/IT staff augmentation. (Woman/As-Ind,
estab 1993, empl 65, sales $9,500,000, cert: NMSDC)

5111   iBridge LLC
        12725 SW Millikan Way, Ste 300
        Beaverton, OR 97005
        Contact: Desh Urs President & CEO
        Tel: 503-906-3930
        Email: bids@ibridgellc.com
        Website: www.ibridgellc.com/
Digitizing, converting, data processing all forms of information, electronic, paper, microfilm, voice or video, e cleanse,
format & verify data. (As-Ind, estab 2004, empl 16, sales ,
cert: State)

5112   Martin's Got You Covered
        P.O. Box 3764
        Portland, OR 97208
        Contact: Donald Martin President
        Tel: 503-289-0278
        Email: donald@martinsgotyoucovered.com
        Website: www.martinsgotyoucovered.com/
Computer hardware & software, custom-build laptops,
notebooks, tablet pcs, monitors, modems, presentation
equipment, servers. (AA, estab 2002, empl 1, sales , cert:
State)

5113   Mavensoft Technologies
        15248 NW Greenbrier Pkwy
        Beaverton, OR 97006
        Contact: Acct Mgr
        Tel: 503-629-4855
        Email:
        Website: http://mavensoft.com
IT services, software development, QA, Cloud Engineering,
Project Management, Java, .NET, PHP, Angular JS, HP ALM,
Selenium, BI Analytics, E-commerce, IBM Websphere, SAP
Hybris, Oracle ATG, Magento. (As-Ind, estab 2004, empl 30,
sales $2,400,000, cert: NMSDC)

5114   Protech Excellens Inc.
        1500 NW Bethany Blvd Ste 200
        Beaverton, OR 07006
        Contact: Ben Condol CEO
        Tel: 866-688-8843
        Email: ben@protechexcellens.com
        Website: www.protechexcellens.com
Oracle Databases, Oracle Middleware, Oracle applications,
Oracle Engineered Systems, Oracle storage, Oracle support. PeoleSoft, Fusion, EBS, CRM. (Woman/As-Pac, estab
2007, empl 2, sales $170,000, cert: State)

5115   Rapid External Solutions, Inc.
        9450 SW Gemini Dr Ste 61944
        Beaverton, OR 97008
        Contact: Vic Gupta Dir
        Tel: 617-616-0986
        Email: info@r-e-s.com
        Website: www.r-e-s.com
ERP Applications staffing: Oracle, SAP, PeopleSoft, JDE,
Siebel, Microsoft. (As-Ind, estab 2009, empl 13, sales
$11,000,000, cert: NMSDC)

5116   Triad Technology Group
        10300 SW Greenburg Rd, Ste 560
        Portland, OR 97223
        Contact: Regina Shapiro Acct Mgr
        Tel: 503-293-9547
        Email: kelley@go2triad.com
        Website: www.triadtechnology.com
Information technology staffing & recruiting services.
(Hisp, estab 1989, empl 30, sales $3,700,000, cert: State)

Pennsylvania

5117   Abator Information Services, Inc.
        615 South Ave
        Pittsburgh, PA 15221
        Contact: Joanne Peterson CEO
        Tel: 412-271-5922
        Email: joanne@abator.com
        Website: www.abator.com
Information technology & systems projects. (Woman,
estab 1983, empl 9, sales $1,297,485, cert: State,
WBENC)

5118   ABOUT-Consulting LLC
        330 Kennett Pike, Ste 205
        Chadds Ford, PA 19317
        Contact: Frances Gatto CEO
        Tel: 610-388-9455
        Email: fgatto@about-consulting.com
        Website: www.about-consulting.com
Project mgmt, internet, intranet & extranet design &
dev, business apps & databases, help desk, network
systems engineering, architecture & admin, operations
& technical svcs. (Woman, estab 2002, empl 20, sales
$3,000,000, cert: WBENC)

5119   AptoTek Inc.
        2026 Milta Hill Rd
        Romansville, PA 19320
        Contact: Joe Johnbosco CEO
        Tel: 610-241-2603
        Email: joe.johnbosco@aptotek-inc.com
        Website: www.aptotek-inc.com
Custom Application Development, CRM Solutions, IT
staff augmentation, IT outsource Services, Application/
software support & maintenance contracts, IT strategy
solutions. (As-Ind, estab 2015, empl 1, sales , cert:
NMSDC)

5120   Aspect Consulting, Inc.
        20140 Valley Forge Cir
        King of Prussia, PA 19406
        Contact: Nicole Gantzhorn Business Develop Mgr
        Tel: 610-783-0600
        Email: ngantzhorn@aspect-consulting.com
        Website: www.aspect-consulting.com
Technical Staffing, Data Management, Business Intelligence, Configuration, Data Warehouse Development,
Database Administration, Oracle, SQL Server, Custom
Software Development, Application Design & Architecture. (Woman, estab 1994, empl 40, sales $5,300,000,
cert: WBENC)

5121   Cogent Infotech Corporation
       1035 Boyce Rd Ste 108
       Pittsburgh, PA 15241
       Contact: Manu Mehta President
       Tel: 412-835-2700
       Email: manu.mehta@cogentinfo.com
       Website: www.cogentinfo.com
Information technology services, systems integration, technical/functional IT consulting, staff augmentation. (As-Ind, As-Pac, estab 2003, empl 120, sales $7,100,000, cert: State, NMSDC)

5122   Cognis IT Advisors LLC
       1735 Market St Ste A-485
       Philadelphia, PA 19103
       Contact: Mike Thomas CEO
       Tel: 215-557-4455
       Email: mthomas@cognisit.com
       Website: www.cognisit-advisors.com
Information Technology (IT) Services. (AA, estab 2007, empl 4, sales $489,000, cert: NMSDC)

5123   Computer Enterprises, Inc.
       1000 Omega Dr Ste 1150
       Pittsburgh, PA 15205
       Contact: Joe Esposito Solutions Sales Director
       Tel: 412-680-4880
       Email: jesposito@ceiamerica.com
       Website: www.ceiamerica.com
Software consulting & system integration services, custom applications & systems software programming services & Internet systems consulting services. (AA, As-Pac, estab , empl 620, sales $71,947,000, cert: NMSDC)

5124   ConnectedSign, LLC
       120A W Airport Rd
       Lititz, PA 17543
       Contact: Loren Bucklin President
       Tel: 866-833-2723
       Email: lbucklin@connectedsign.com
       Website: www.connectedsign.com
Digital Signage Software, Navori Tycoon Software, Digital Signage Hardware, Digital Signage Content, Website Development and Content, Kiosks Software, Kiosks Hardware, Kiosks Content. (Woman, estab 2003, empl 12, sales $1,000,000, cert: WBENC)

5125   CREDO Technology Solutions, Inc.
       110 Sunset Ave Ste 101
       Harrisburg, PA 17112
       Contact: Missy Flexman Dir of Marketing & Communications
       Tel: 717-657-7017
       Email: mflexman@credotsinc.com
       Website: www.credotsinc.com
IT project solutions, ERP software implementations & upgrades. (As-Ind, estab 2010, empl 42, sales $3,130,000, cert: State, NMSDC)

5126   Eminent Group, Inc
       2 Walnut Grove Rd Ste 130
       Horsham, PA 19044
       Contact: Katherine Moore CEO
       Tel: 267-387-6487
       Email: kmoore@egiusa.com
       Website: www.egiusa.com
Transportation Management Systems Implementation, Global Trade Management Systems Implementation. Woman, estab 2002, empl 38, sales $7,104,089, cert: WBENC)

5127   Genzeon
       559 W Uwchlan Ave Ste 120
       Exton, PA 19341
       Contact: Brendan OHayre COO
       Tel: 203-516-1109
       Email: brendan.ohayre@genzeon.com
       Website: www.genzeon.com
Technology solutions, custom application development, performance engineering & human capital solutions. (As-Ind, As-Pac, estab 2009, empl 50, sales $10,000,000, cert: NMSDC)

5128   Genzeon Corporation
       559 W Uwchlan Ave, Ste 120
       Exton, PA 19341
       Contact: Frank Clement Sr Business Dev Exec
       Tel: 484-302-0474
       Email: frank.clement@genzian.com
       Website: www.genzeon.com
Application development and integration – cloud, on-prem, or hybrid, Application modernization, Data and predictive analytics, Cloud migration to Azure, Chat Bots, Virtual Assistants. (As-Ind, estab 1999, empl 150, sales $17,500,000, cert: NMSDC)

5129   Hanabi Networks Systems, LLC
       150 N Radnor Chester Rd, Ste F200
       Radnor, PA 19087
       Contact: Tariq Yusufzai VP Business Dev
       Tel: 484-381-0698
       Email: tyusufzai@ehanabi.com
       Website: www.ehanabi.com
Analyze, design, install, configure, manage & repair global network infrastructure & application components. (As-Pac, estab 2016, empl 2, sales $120,000, cert: NMSDC)

5130   I&I Software, Inc.
       2571 Baglyos Circle, B-32
       Bethlehem, PA 18020
       Contact: VP Marketing
       Tel: 610-882-9699
       Email:
       Website: www.iandisoft.com
IT Services on COTS products, ERP, CRM, Business Intelligence, Network & Systems Administration, DBA, Project Management Services & Application Development. (As-Pac, estab 2001, empl 48, sales $8,343,201, cert: State)

5131   iBusiness Solution, LLC
       5000 Lenker St
       Mechanicsburg, PA 17050
       Contact: Narendra Ghuge
       Tel: 717-724-7865
       Email: sales@ibusinesssolution.com
       Website: www.ibusinesssolution.com
IT consulting, technology services, staffing & outsourcing. (As-Ind, estab 2000, empl 54, sales $9,000,000, cert: State, NMSDC)

5132   ImageTech Systsems, Inc.
       3913 Hartzdale Dr
       Camp Hill, PA 17011
       Contact: RJ Oommen Principal
       Tel: 717-761-5900
       Email: rjo@imagetechsys.com
       Website: www.imagetechsys.com
Enterprise Content Management (ECM) & Business Process automation technologies. (As-Ind, estab 1994, empl 7, sales $2,000,000, cert: State, NMSDC)

5133 Independent Computer Consulting Group, Inc.
      1 Ivybrook Blvd Ste 177
      Warminster, PA 18974
      Contact: Mihir Shah Sr Business Dev Mgr
      Tel: 215-675-9149
      Email: mshah@iccg.com
      Website: www.iccg.com
LX, SA, M3 products implementation, upgrades & support,
WMS/PkMS, WMOS, SCALE, DOM implementations,
upgrades & support, Business Intelligence, Qlik, Cognos &
Micro Strategy, SAP suite of applications. (Woman/As-Ind,
estab 1988, empl 100, sales , cert: WBENC)

5134 Iron Lady Enterprises Inc.
      1943 Poplar St, 2nd Fl
      Philadelphia, PA 19130
      Contact: Dianna Montague CEO
      Tel: 267-973-8626
      Email: dianna.montague@ironladyenterprises.com
      Website: www.ironladyenterprises.com/
IT services. (Woman/AA, estab 2011, empl 2, sales , cert:
City, NMSDC)

5135 JCW Computer Consulting, LLC
      7478 Rhoads St, Ste C
      Philadelphia, PA 19151
      Contact: Carl Johnson Sales Assoc
      Tel: 215-879-6701
      Email: carl@jcwcc.com
      Website: www.jcwcc.com
Computer consulting: Microsoft, IBM & Compaq solutions,
workstation & server product lines. (AA, estab 1992, empl
3, sales , cert: City, NMSDC)

5136 KORYAK Consulting, Inc.
      2003 Kinvara Dr
      Pittsburgh, PA 15237
      Contact: Suresh Ramanathan CEO
      Tel: 412-364-6600
      Email: sramanathan@koryak.com
      Website: www.koryak.com
Management & IT consulting: business & IT strategy dev,
supply chain enhancement, E-business integration, Oracle
app implementation & outsourcing, systems dev &
integration. (As-Ind, estab 2000, empl 25, sales
$3,000,000, cert: State, NMSDC)

5137 Lim, Norris & Associates
      12 Fox Hunt Cir
      Plymouth Meeting, PA 19462
      Contact: Yvonne Norris President
      Tel: 610-825-6730
      Email: ynorris@limnorris.com
      Website: www.limnorris.com
Information technology, strategic planning & organization
design. (Woman/AA, As-Ind, estab 1994, empl 3, sales
$953,000, cert: City)

5138 Logix Guru LLC
      3821 Old William Penn Hwy
      Murrysville, PA 15668
      Contact: Singh Ajmani Business Develop Mgr
      Tel: 724-733-4500
      Email: ajmani@logixguru.com
      Website: www.logixguru.com
IT consulting & staff augmentation, engineering, administrative, information technology. (As-Ind, estab 2000, empl
20, sales $4,200,000, cert: State, NMSDC)

5139 M.A.P. Consulting Services, Inc.
      520 South 3rd St
      Philadelphia, PA 19147
      Contact: CEO
      Tel: 215-315-4175
      Email:
      Website: www.mapconsult.com
IT staffing & consulting, ERP & EDI specialists, project
mgmt expertise, data warehousing. (Woman, estab
1997, empl 2, sales $201,000, cert: WBENC)

5140 Mastech Digital Technologies, Inc.
      1305 Cherrington Parkway Bldg 210, Ste 400
      Moon Township, PA 15108
      Contact: Michael Kosar Dir of MSP
      Tel: 412-787-9559
      Email: Michael.kosar@mastechdigital.com
      Website: www.mastechdigital.com
IT services: usiness intelligence, data warehousing,
architecture & web svcs, enterprise resource planning,
custom applications, dev & maintenance, migration, re-
engineering, project mgmt, ebusiness solutions. (Nat
Ame, As-Ind, estab , empl 750, sales $123,400,000, cert:
NMSDC)

5141 Momentum, Inc.
      2120 Market St Ste 100
      Camp Hill, PA 17011
      Contact: Scott Reilly Exec Director
      Tel: 717-214-8000
      Email: momentum@m-inc.com
      Website: www.m-inc.com
IT & management consulting, process improvement,
project management & implementation support.
(Woman, estab 1998, empl 54, sales $9,304,338, cert:
State, City)

5142 MWIDM Inc.
      1445 City Ave Ste 10B
      Wynnewood, PA 19096
      Contact: Briana James AVP Staffing Solutions
      Tel: 302-298-0101
      Email: briana.j@mwidm.com
      Website: mwidm.com
IT services, staffing, consulting and product implementation. (Woman/AA, estab 2004, empl 3600, sales
$327,550,000, cert: State)

5143 Ohm Systems, Inc.
      955 Horsham Rd Ste 205
      Horsham, PA 19044
      Contact: Praful Patel President
      Tel: 215-309-6233
      Email: ppatel@ohmsysinc.com
      Website: www.ohmsysinc.com
Software development, support, maintenance, R&D,
web, consulting, FAA, telecom, protocols, client/server,
java. (As-Ind, estab 1998, empl 65, sales $6,500,000,
cert: NMSDC)

5144 OPTiMO Information Technology LLC
      240 Market St, Ste 112
      Bloomsburg, PA 17815
      Contact: Michael Miguelez CEO
      Tel: 877-564-8552
      Email: mmiguelez@optimo-it.com
      Website: http://optimo-it.com
Web / Mobile application development, UI/UX system
integration, database development, agile project/
program management, digital forensic investigations,
eDiscovery processing & hosted review. (Hisp, estab
2008, empl 50, sales $5,000,000, cert: 8a)

5145 Partner's Consulting, Inc.
       2004 Sproul Road, Ste 206
       Broomall, PA 19008
       Contact: Delivery & Engagement Mgr
       Tel: 215-939-6294
       Email:
       Website: http://partners-consulting.com
Information technology recruiting for full-time, temp-to-
perm & contract positions. (Woman, estab 2006, empl 40,
sales $6,000,000, cert: State, WBENC)

5146 PC Network Inc.
       1315 Walnut St Ste 1402
       Philadelphia, PA 19107
       Contact: General Counsel
       Tel: 267-236-0015
       Email:
       Website: www.pcn-inc.com
IT Staffing Services, Managed Service Delivery & Business
Process Outsourcing, Technology Deployments, Deskside
Support, Help desk, Data Center Operations. (Woman,
estab 1988, empl 76, sales $7,340,000, cert: State,
WBENC)

5147 Pierson Computing Connection, Inc.
       6 N Frederick St
       Mechanicsburg, PA 17055
       Contact: Debra Pierson President
       Tel: 717-796-0493
       Email: dpierson@piersoncci.com
       Website: www.piersoncci.com
Project mgmt, multi-site IT & related installations, printers,
cash registers, PC equipment, cabling, networking equipment, etc. (Woman, estab 1993, empl 47, sales
$4,250,000, cert: State, WBENC)

5148 Probitas Technology Inc.
       3544 N Progress Ave Ste 104
       Harrisburg, PA 17110
       Contact: Benjamin Williams President & CEO
       Tel: 717-773-4208
       Email: sales@probitastek.com
       Website: www.probitastek.com
Computer networking design, installation & maintenance,
electronic security. (AA, estab 2004, empl 8, sales
$600,000, cert: State, City)

5149 PRWT Services, Inc.
       1835 Market St Ste 800
       Philadelphia, PA 19103
       Contact: Rose Braverman SVP, Strategic Planning &
       Operations
       Tel: 215-569-8810
       Email: rose.braverman@prwt.com
       Website: www.prwt.com
Information & document processing; lockbox processing;
call ctr customer care & service; facilities mgmt; web &
telephone-based fulfillment; telecommunications construction; help desk functions & toll collections operations.
(AA, estab 1988, empl 1000, sales $69,800,000, cert: City,
NMSDC)

5150 Relevante, Inc
       1235 Westlakes Dr Ste 280
       Berwyn, PA 19312
       Contact: William Brassington CEO
       Tel: 484-403-4100
       Email: wbrassington@relevante.com
       Website: www.relevante.com
Accounting & technology consultants. (As-Ind, estab 2002,
empl 130, sales $6,100,000, cert: NMSDC)

5151 River Development Corporation
       2005 Garrick Dr
       Pittsburgh, PA 15235
       Contact: Cheryl McAbee
       Tel: 412-243-2005
       Email: crmcabee@riverdevcorp.com
       Website:
Records storage: off site, web access inventory, media
vault storage & delivery, scan & index, data vaulting,
shredding. (Woman/AA, Nat Ame, estab 1996, empl 4,
sales , cert: State, City, NMSDC)

5152 RST Solutions Inc.
       1005 Azlen Lane Ste 114
       Chalfont, PA 18914
       Contact: Rajan Kaistha VP
       Tel: 610-613-8699
       Email: rajan@rstsolutions.com
       Website: www.rstsolutions.com
ERP services, implementations, upgrade, integrations,
JDE Mobile Apps, FRICE/COMLI, etc. (Woman/As-Ind,
estab 2003, empl 18, sales $5,000,000, cert: WBENC)

5153 Sigma Resources LLC
       7950 Saltsburg Rd
       Pittsburgh, PA 15239
       Contact: VP consulting
       Tel: 412-712-1019
       Email:
       Website: www.sigma-resources.com/
IT consulting services. (Woman/As-Pac, estab 1998,
empl 24, sales $9,000,000, cert: State, WBENC)

5154 SoftNice Inc.
       5050 Tilghman St, Ste 115
       Allentown, PA 18104
       Contact: Zubin Pardiwala Mgr, Business Dev
       Tel: 201-603-2635
       Email: zubin@softnice.com
       Website: www.softnice.com
Global Consulting and IT services. (As-Pac, estab 2001,
empl 600, sales $18,007,269, cert: NMSDC)

5155 SoftSages, LLC
       17 Mystic Lane, Ste 2A
       Malvern, PA 19355
       Contact: Jiraj Ruparelia VP
       Tel: 484-604-0603
       Email: jiraj@softsages.com
       Website: www.softsages.com
Software Development Consultants, programming,
Database Developments, Networking & mobile develop-
ment, custom software & security solutions. (Woman/
As-Pac, estab 2005, empl 25, sales $8,000,000, cert:
State, NMSDC, WBENC)

5156 solutions4networks, Inc.
       1501 Reedsdale St Ste 2001
       Pittsburgh, PA 15233
       Contact: Michele McGough CEO
       Tel: 412-638-4341
       Email: michele@s4nets.com
       Website: www.s4nets.com
Data, voice, wireless & network security consulting:
network assessments & design, security assessments,
IPv6 planning, MPLS, QoS, project mgmt, product
selection, RFP devel. (Woman, estab 2000, empl 25,
sales $8,430,000, cert: State, WBENC)

5157   Strother Enterprises Inc.
       100 S Broad St Ste 2130
       Philadelphia, PA 19110
       Contact: Ernest L Strother CEO
       Tel: 215-564-5538
       Email: elstrother@strotherenterprises.com
       Website: www.strotherenterprises.com
Food Service Management; Facilities Management;
Commissary Services; Staffing and Training. Knowledge of
government contracts, knowledge of compliance and
regulatory standards and long-standing (AA, estab 1990,
empl 26, sales $3,409,222, cert: State, City, NMSDC)

5158   SwitchLane Inc.
       5 Christy Dr Ste 303
       Chadds Ford, PA 19317
       Contact: Meera Kalyani President
       Tel: 267-297-0790
       Email: meera@switchlane.com
       Website: www.switchlane.com
IT staffing & consulting services. (Woman, estab 2010,
empl 10, sales $1,312,407, cert: State, WBENC)

5159   Symphony Enterprises LLC
       P.O. Box 16140
       Pittsburgh, PA 15242
       Contact: Head Sales & Business Development
       Tel: 412-212-0135
       Email:
       Website: www.symphonyenterprises.com
IT staffing & consulting services. (Woman/As-Ind, As-Pac,
estab 2004, empl 4, sales , cert: State)

5160   Synergy EnterPrize, LLC
       1150 First Ave, Ste 501
       King of Prussia, PA 19406
       Contact: Jonathan Ngah Principal
       Tel: 610-945-1737
       Email: information@synergy-ia.com
       Website: www.synergy-ia.com
Audit Support, Information Technology Management &
Governance, Business Process Improvement, Project
Management, Fraud Risk & Vulnerability Assessment
solutions. (AA, estab 2011, empl 10, sales $1,500,000, cert:
NMSDC, 8a)

5161   Systems Staffing Group   Inc.
       910 E. Main St Ste 201
       Norristown, PA 19401
       Contact: Beth Verman CEO
       Tel:
       Email: bverman@systemsstaffinggroup.com
       Website: www.systemsstaffinggroup.com
Information technology staffing: consultants & permanent
employees. (Woman, estab 2000, empl 30, sales
$15,000,000, cert: WBENC)

5162   Tan Check Consolidated, Inc.
       2 Silver Trail Circle Ste 101
       Newtown, PA 18940
       Contact: Rebecca Smith Sr Acct Mgr
       Tel: 215-860-5031
       Email: rsmith@tcci.com
       Website: www.tcci.com
IT Staffing, Information Technology Management, Consulting, Permanent Placement, Temp to Perm, Executive
Search, Software Development. (Woman, estab 2001,
empl 75, sales $6,850,000, cert: State, WBENC)

5163   Techwave Consulting Inc.
       1 E Uwchlan Ave
       Exton, PA 19341
       Contact: Jalpesh Thaker Mgr
       Tel: 484-873-4602
       Email: infona@techwave.net
       Website: https://techwave.net/
Software consulting & staffing services: SAP (BI, BO, BPC,
BPM & BW), Oracle (OBIEE), Cognos & BPM products &
services. (Woman/As-Ind, estab 2004, empl 150, sales
$11,000,000, cert: State)

5164   The United Solutions Group Inc.
       1101 W Hamilton St Ste 351
       Allentown, PA 18101
       Contact: Sri Vadi Dir Govt Relations
       Tel: 267-401-1300
       Email: gov@tusgi.com
       Website: www.usgit.com
Database Design and Development, Data Warehouse
Design, WEB Based Application Development, WEB
Administration, Legacy Migration Strategies, Facility
Management,Software Development. (As-Ind, estab
2002, empl 24, sales $2,535,000, cert: State, NMSDC,
SDB)

5165   Trecom System Group, Inc.
       700 E Township Line Rd Ste 205
       Havertown, PA 19083
       Contact: Phil Gring COO
       Tel: 610-328-7971
       Email: pgring@trecomsystems.com
       Website: www.trecomsystems.com
Internet Services, Network Services and Support, Help-
Desk Management, Data Entry, Computer Facility
Operations, Staff Augmentation, Program Management
Support, Documentation, Software Application Develop-
ment. (AA, estab 2009, empl 37, sales , cert: State,
NMSDC)

5166   TreCom Systems Group
       99 November Dr
       Camp Hill, PA 17011
       Contact: Phillip Gring COO
       Tel: 717-319-0711
       Email: pgring@trecomsystems.com
       Website: www.trecomsystems.com
Information technology consulting svcs: software dev &
design, enterprise architecture, training, help desk,
programming, networking, documentation, software
testing, staff augmentation, contract programming,
Oracle authorized reseller. (AA, estab 2009, empl 58,
sales $7,000,000, cert: State, NMSDC)

5167   Tri-force Consulting Services Inc.
       650 North Cannon Ave
       Lansdale, PA 19446
       Contact: Manish Gorawala President & CEO
       Tel: 215-362-2611
       Email: mgorawala@triforce-inc.com
       Website: https://triforce-inc.com/
Information technology consulting: Java, J2EE, .NET, QA
& open source technologies based business applications
solutions. (As-Ind, estab 2000, empl 45, sales
$6,533,943, cert: State, City, NMSDC)

5168 TriLogic Corporation
161 Hillpointe Dr
Canonsburg, PA 15317
Contact: Gary Grabowski Operations Mgr
Tel: 724-745-0200
Email: ggrabowski@tri-logic.com
Website: www.tri-logic.com
Design, install & maintain LAN/WANs; wireless networking, IP telephony, virtual private networks. (AA, estab 1981, empl 35, sales , cert: NMSDC)

5169 Urban Harvest Partnership, LLC
6050 Osage Ave
Philadelphia, PA 19143
Contact: Jonathan Ford Principal
Tel: 610-482-4284
Email: ford@uhpwireless.com
Website: http://uhpwireless.com/
Technology services: desktop & network services, secure wireless networking, cabling services, voice, data & audio/video installations. (AA, estab 2003, empl 7, sales $960,000, cert: State, NMSDC)

5170 YIKES, Inc.
204 E Girard Ave
Philadelphia, PA 19125
Contact: Mia Levesque Co-Owner
Tel: 215-238-8801
Email: info@yikesinc.com
Website: https://yikesinc.com
Web design & development services, WordPress, Custom web design, website maintenance, ecommerce, web/database integration, ColdFusion, custom-built web-based applications, content management systems. (Woman/Nat Ame, As-Pac, Hisp, estab 1996, empl 5, sales $664,693, cert: City, WBENC)

5171 ZIOS Corporation
211 N Camac St
Philadelphia, PA 19107
Contact: Eileen Hing CEO
Tel: 215-988-9467
Email: ec.hing@zios3.com
Website: www.zios3.com
Information technology: software, hardware & wireless telecom services. (Woman/As-Pac, estab 1999, empl 1, sales , cert: State)

5172 Zodiac Solutions Inc.
270 Lancaster Ave Ste h-2
Malvern, PA 19355
Contact: VP Operations
Tel: 484-550-6482
Email:
Website: www.zodiac-solutions.com
IT staff augmentation , IT solutions services, managed services, project management, software development, knowledge process outsourcing, management consulting. (As-Ind, estab 2011, empl 70, sales $4,751,993, cert: NMSDC)

Puerto Rico

5173 Beryllium Corporation
P.O.Box 5938
Caguas, PR 00726
Contact: Jorge Normandia CEO
Tel: 787-744-5729
Email: info@berylliumpr.com
Website: www.berylliumpr.com
Custom Software Design & Development, Pharmaceutical/Medical Devices Industries, Manufacturing Execution Systems Integrators. (Hisp, estab 1998, empl 8, sales $756,288, cert: NMSDC)

5174 Integrated Services for Productivity & Validation
Acuarela St, Ste 3A Urb Munoz Rivera
Guaynabo, PR 00969
Contact: Luis Baez Principal
Tel: 787-789-4778
Email: lmbaez@is-pv.com
Website: www.is-pv.com
Technology, Management, Systems & Productivity Improvement projects. (Hisp, estab 2007, empl 25, sales $2,280,441, cert: NMSDC)

5175 Integrated Technology & Compliance Services
PMB 470 Box 4956
Caguas, PR 00726
Contact: Ismael Aviles COO
Tel: 939-579-3846
Email: ismael.aviles@itcspr.com
Website: www.itcspr.com
Information Technology Consulting & cGMP Validation Consulting & Compliance services. (Hisp, estab 2005, empl 10, sales $977,456, cert: NMSDC)

5176 JC Automation, Corp.
Calle D #27-C Urb. Los Maestros
Humacao, PR 00791
Contact: Juan Senquiz GM
Tel: 787-719-7315
Email: jsenquiz@jcapr.cmom
Website: www.jcapr.com
IT Management, Compliance & Manufacturing System Services, Application Design & Development, Systems Integration. (Hisp, estab 1997, empl 40, sales $4,700,000, cert: NMSDC)

5177 Mirus Consulting Group Corp
P.O. Box 851
Humacao, PR 00792
Contact: Giovanni Gomez Dir
Tel: 787-285-0992
Email: ggomez@miruspr.com
Website: www.miruspr.com
Computer system validation & information technology consulting services. (Hisp, estab 2001, empl 25, sales $2,900,000, cert: NMSDC)

5178 PharmaBioServ US, Inc. (PBSV)
545 West Germantown Pike
Dorado, PR 00646
Contact: Armando Morales US Operations Director
Tel: 787-278-2709
Email: info@pharmabioserv.com
Website: www.pharmabioserv.com
Data Processing, Hosting, and related Services, Internet Publishing and Broadcasting and Web Search Portals, Engineering Services. (Hisp, estab 1993, empl 150, sales $14,000,000, cert: NMSDC)

5179   Real Physics, Inc.
       1056 Munoz Riviera Ave Ste 903
       San Juan, PR 00927
       Contact: Pedro Torres President
       Tel: 787-469-1359
       Email: ptorres@realphysics.net
       Website: www.realphysics.net
Project management, IT consulting, outsourcing, appraisal, validation, aerial photography, scheduling services,
quality & logistics audits. (Hisp, estab 2007, empl 3, sales ,
cert: NMSDC)

5180   Weil Group, Inc.
       Urb. Villa Blanca Calle Aquamarina #78 Ste 1
       Caguas, PR 00725
       Contact: Milagros del R Gonzalez GM
       Tel: 787-633-0025
       Email: clopez@weilgroup.com
       Website: www.weilgroup.com
Temporary employment agency, outsourcing IT & automation services: management and/or admin, help desk,
servers, WAN, email system, desktop, maintenance,
backup & restore. (Hisp, estab 1994, empl 215, sales
$12,000,000, cert: NMSDC)

South Carolina

5181   Artifex Technology Consulting, Inc.
       614 George Washington Hwy
       Lincoln, RI 02865
       Contact: Jenna Schmidt President
       Tel: 401-723-6644
       Email: jenna@artifextech.com
       Website: www.artifextech.com
Custom software solutions & graphic design. (Woman,
estab 2002, empl 13, sales $2,380,350, cert: WBENC)

5182   CSG
       98 Slope Ave
       Wakefield, RI 02879
       Contact: Meridith Voshell Acct Exec
       Tel: 770-377-8955
       Email: mvoshell@csg-llc.co
       Website: http://csg-llc.co
Information Technology strategies. (Woman, estab 2017,
empl 2, sales , cert: WBENC)

5183   Granger Warburton Consulting, LLC
       79 West St
       East Greenwich, RI 02818
       Contact: Bethany Warburton Principal Consultant
       Tel: 401-965-1288
       Email: bethany@grangerwarburton.com
       Website: www.grangerwarburton.com
Learning management system design & deployment,
elearning creation, software application development,
project management, business analysis, change management, documentation & process design. (Woman, estab
2013, empl 2, sales $127,000, cert: State)

5184   AQuate II, LLC
       508 Hampton St, Ste 204
       Columbia, SC 29201
       Contact: Deveda Hunter GM
       Tel: 256-837-1774
       Email: dhunter@aquate2.com
       Website: www.aquate2.com
IT, engineering, base operations support, logistics, administrative, and technical support services. (Nat Ame, estab
2013, empl 80, sales , cert: 8a)

5185   Blue Eye Soft Corp.
       44 Parkway Commons Way
       Greer, SC 29650
       Contact: Srikanth Kodeboyina Managing Partner
       Tel: 864-479-0888
       Email: sri@blueyesoft.com
       Website: www.blueyesoft.com
IT Consulting Software solutions, BI Analytics, CRM,
Scalable Architecture, Health IT, Program& Project
Management, Human Resource Consulting. (As-Pac,
estab 2017, empl 14, sales $479,000, cert: NMSDC)

5186   Datasoft Technologies Inc.
       34 Parkway Commons Way
       Greer, SC 29650
       Contact: Manyapu Alka President
       Tel: 864-849-9022
       Email: amanyapu@datasoft-tech.com
       Website: www.datasoft-tech.com
Software devel & consulting: system integration,
engineering & architecture, project mgmt, analysis &
design. (As-Ind, As-Pac, estab 1994, empl 45, sales
$4,000,000, cert: State, NMSDC)

5187   Globalpundits Technology Consultancy Inc.
       4715D Sunset Blvd
       Lexington, SC 29072
       Contact: Manoj Devulapalli President
       Tel: 803-354-9400
       Email: manoj@globalpundits.com
       Website: www.globalpundits.com
Computer programming services, software design
services, project mgmt, business analysts, database
administrations, contract engineering, mechanical
engineers, stress engineers, electrical engineers,
aeronautical engineers, CAD. (As-Ind, As-Pac, estab
2000, empl 106, sales $13,000,000, cert: State, NMSDC)

5188   Ishpi Information Technologies, Inc.
       496 Bramson Court
       Mt. Pleasant, SC 29464
       Contact: Pat Stanton Dir of Operations
       Tel: 843-329-4100
       Email: pat.stanton@ishpi.net
       Website: www.ishpi.net
System engineering & integration, information &
assurance & enterprise architecture. (Nat Ame, estab
2006, empl 58, sales $550,000, cert: State)

5189   Synesis International, Inc.
       30 Creekview Ct
       Greenville, SC 29615
       Contact: Ricardo Studart President
       Tel: 864-288-1550
       Email: rstudart@synesisintl.com
       Website: www.synesisintl.com
Information technology: ERP, MES, business analytics,
EDI, bar code & quality control systems. (Hisp, estab
1994, empl 28, sales $3,500,000, cert: NMSDC)

Tennessee

5190   Conch Technologies, Inc.
       6750 Poplar Ave, Ste 711
       Memphis, TN 38138
       Contact: Ray Scott VP Natl Accts
       Tel: 901-827-5183
       Email: contact@conchtech.com
       Website: www.conchtech.com
IT consultants & contract programming, pc/client
servers, internet/intranet, B2B & e-commerce. (Woman/
As-Pac, estab 2004, empl 55, sales $1,700,000, cert:
State)

5191 MCH Corporation
P.O. Box 720
Sweetwater, TN 37874
Contact: President
Tel: 865-388-2727
Email:
Website: www.visualc.com
Data extraction & conversion, document scanning, OCR & ICR processing, litigation support svcs, reverse engineering , data transformation, data capturing & harvesting. (Nat Ame, estab 1998, empl 3, sales $372,000, cert: State)

5192 Redbird Technology Inc.
2505 Blair Blvd
Nashville, TN 37212
Contact: Dir Business Dev
Tel: 404-386-3073
Email:
Website: www.rbti.com
Develops software technologies used in the aerospace & defense industry. (Nat Ame, As-Pac, estab 1993, empl 3, sales $220,000, cert: State)

5193 Stragistics Technology
6263 Poplar Ave, Ste 603
Memphis, TN 38119
Contact: Scott Swanson Business Develop Mgr
Tel: 901-799-0402
Email: sswanson@stragistics.com
Website: www.stragistics.com
Technology solutions, data integration, migration, eCommerce, infrastructure mgmt, proprietary software, SDLC, systems integration. (Woman/AA, estab 1997, empl 8, sales $379,010, cert: State, City, NMSDC, WBENC)

5194 Zycron, Inc.
413 Welshwood Dr
Nashville, TN 37211
Contact: Rochelle Taylor VP Operations
Tel: 615-251-9588
Email: rtaylor@zycron.com
Website: www.zycron.com
System integration,technical consulting, supplemental staffing, configuration mgmt, software analysis, system design & facilities mgmt. (AA, estab 1991, empl 300, sales $29,245,696, cert: State)

Texas

5195 A1 Shredding Inc.
P.O. Box 460085
Houston, TX 77056
Contact: Christopher Passmore President
Tel: 832-545-3949
Email: cpassmore@a1shreddinginc.com
Website: www.a1shreddinginc.com
Document shredding, paper recycling, paper destruction & shredding, IT/computer services. (AA, estab 2007, empl 1, sales , cert: State)

5196 AACANN Mechanical, Inc.
12718 Robert E. Lee
Houston, TX 77044
Contact: Larry Cannon President
Tel: 281-458-2258
Email: aacann@ymail.com
Website: www.aacann.com
Service, repair, installation, maintenance and zone comfort controls/design of HVACR systems. (AA, estab 1982, empl 4, sales $642,000, cert: NMSDC)

5197 Accolite Inc.
16479 Dallas North Pkwy, Ste 350
Addison, TX 75001
Contact: Matthew McKinley VP Business Dev
Tel: 469-235-9316
Email: matthew.mckinley@accolite.com
Website: www.accolite.com
Contingent staffinng services: contract, contract to hire & permanent candidates for IT. (As-Pac, estab 2006, empl 280, sales $12,000,000, cert: State, NMSDC)

5198 Addison Stuart
566 Homewood Dr
Coppell, TX 75019
Contact: Christina Kolassa Owner
Tel: 847-707-0429
Email: ckolassa@addisonstuart.com
Website: www.addisonstuart.com
Information technology, PPM implementation using CA Clarity & Oracle PPM tools. (Woman, estab 2012, empl 4, sales $200,000, cert: WBENC)

5199 Advent Global Solutions, Inc
12777 Jones Rd, Ste 445
Houston, TX 77070
Contact: Chet Mann VP - Client Services
Tel: 281-640-8934
Email: chet.mann@adventglobal.com
Website: www.adventglobal.com/
ERP implementation, IT development & systems integration, SAP technology. (As-Ind, estab 1997, empl 1500, sales $182,000,000, cert: NMSDC)

5200 Akorbi (Elahi Enterprises dba Akorbi)
6010 W Spring Creek Pkwy Ste 238
Plano, TX 75024
Contact: President
Tel: 214-256-9222
Email:
Website: www.akorbi.com
IT consulting & recruitment: information technology, telecommunications, professional services & language solutions, technical staffing, professional placements, custom application development & business communications. (Woman/AA, estab 2003, empl 964, sales $34,000,000, cert: State, NMSDC, WBENC)

5201 Alphaworks LLC
1600 10th St, Ste B
Plano, TX 75074
Contact: Don R Joe Operations Mgr
Tel: 972-509-8837
Email: rodney.joe@alphaworksnow.com
Website: www.alphaworksnow.com
IT hardware, software & services: HP, Oracle, SAP, Cisco & TDi. (As-Pac, estab 2010, empl 16, sales $3,000,000, cert: NMSDC)

5202 Al-Razaq Computing Services
6001 Savoy, Ste 505
Houston, TX 77036
Contact: Vicki Semander contract vehicle spec
Tel: 713-839-9613
Email: vsemander@al-razaqcomputing.com
Website: www.al-razaqcomputing.com
Database mgmt, systems network integration, computer hardware & software, educational product dev & training, financial mgmt, budget dev & execution package, software dev & computer programming. (AA, estab 1993, empl 48, sales $3,167,414, cert: State, NMSDC)

5203   American Unit, Inc.
         2901 N Dallas Pkwy Ste 333
         Plano, TX 75093
         Contact: Ramana Mgr
         Tel:
         Email: ramana@americanunit.com
         Website: www.americanunit.com
Enterprise & e-business implementation, upgrade, &
production support services. (As-Pac, estab 2003, empl
365, sales $30,000,000, cert: State, NMSDC)

5204   Amtek Consulting LLC
         18170 Dallas Pkwy Ste 104
         Dallas, TX 75287
         Contact: Satya Movva President
         Tel: 214-680-6111
         Email: smovva@amtekconsulting.com
         Website: www.amtekconsulting.com
IT consulting services, system design & implementation,
client-Server solutions, application development, systems
maintenance/operations support. (As-Ind, estab 2004,
empl 47, sales $155,000, cert: City, NMSDC)

5205   Applied Training Resources Inccorporated
         6405 Cypresswood Dr, Ste 250
         Spring, TX 77379
         Contact: Rose Bradshaw Controller
         Tel: 281-370-9540
         Email: rbradshaw@atrco.com
         Website: www.atrco.com
Lifecycle management systems: procedure & policy
management, editing, procedure workflow (MOC), periodic
review, incident investigation, action tracking & integrated
learning management. (Woman, estab 1990, empl 43, sales
$6,580,266, cert: WBENC)

5206   Argus Talent, LLC
         11739 Willcrest
         Houston, TX 77031
         Contact: Zeyn Patel President
         Tel: 713-465-5985
         Email: info@argustalent.com
         Website: www.argustalent.com
Document Management, Records Management and
Electronic Content Management (ECM) systems, custom
computing services, system design services, and staff
augmentation services. (As-Ind, Hisp, estab 1989, empl 20,
sales $500,000, cert: State, NMSDC)

5207   Armstrong Archives LLC
         1515 Crescent Dr
         Carrollton, TX 75006
         Contact: Sherri Taylor President
         Tel: 972-242-7179
         Email: staylor@aarchives.com
         Website: www.armstrongarchives.com
Secure & Reliable Record Storage, Document Storage,
Document Management, Document Scanning, Paper
Shredding & Distribution. (Woman, estab 1996, empl 13,
sales , cert: WBENC)

5208   Aspiryon, LLC
         711 Nolana, Ste 103-F
         McAllen, TX 78504
         Contact: Neil Crisman GM
         Tel: 919-900-8622
         Email: sales@aspiryon.net
         Website: www.aspiryon.net
Plan & implement information security solutions. (Woman/
Hisp, estab 2011, empl 12, sales $2,000,000, cert: State)

5209   Assent Solutions LLC
         27311 Bentridge Park Ln
         Katy, TX 77494
         Contact: Venkata Reka VP
         Tel: 713-853-9288
         Email: reka@assentsolutions.com
         Website: www.assentsolutions.com
Information Technology Consulting, Staffing Augmentation, IT Staffing Services, Custom Software Application
Development, Web Development. (Woman/As-Ind,
estab 2009, empl 10, sales $588,751, cert: City)

5210   Associates Systems LLC
         750 S Mac Arthur Blvd Ste 100
         Coppell, TX 75019
         Contact: Pavan Akula Dir of Sales
         Tel: 972-241-4436
         Email: pavan.akula@associatessystems.com
         Website: www.associatessystems.com
Information technology solutions & services. (Woman/
As-Pac, estab 2002, empl 40, sales , cert: State, NMSDC)

5211   Austin Tele-Services Partners, LP dba Genesis ATS
         4209 S Industrial Dr Ste 300
         Austin, TX 78744
         Contact: Patrick Manning VP Business Devel
         Tel: 512-437-3041
         Email: pmanning@genesis-ats.com
         Website: www.genesis-ats.com
IT, Networking, Telecommunications & Computer related
equipment & services. (Hisp, estab 2003, empl 45, sales
$25,000,000, cert: State, NMSDC)

5212   AustinCSI LLC
         7950 Legacy Dr Ste 750
         Plano, TX 75024
         Contact: Karen Moree CEO
         Tel: 972-677-6464
         Email: karen.moree@austincsi.com
         Website: www.austincsi.com
Project & Portfolio Delivery (Organizational Change
Management, Agile Transformation, DevOps Transfor-
mation, Digital Transformation, Big Data, Internet of
Things (IoT), Cybersecurity, Process Innovation, Gover-
nance, Metrics & Exec Dashboards, Data Center.
(Woman, estab 2007, empl 201, sales $31,000,000, cert:
WBENC)

5213   Axis Technologies
         5904 Chapel Hill Blvd Ste 205
         Plano, TX 75093
         Contact: Dana Bower CEO
         Tel: - -
         Email: dbower@axistec.com
         Website: www.axistec.com
Contract consulting: PLM, PDM, CRM/ERP Seibel, SAP,
Peoplesoft. (Minority, Woman, estab , empl , sales
$1,675,000, cert: NMSDC)

5214   Bastion Technologies, Inc.
         17625 El Camino Real
         Houston, TX 77058
         Contact: Jorge Hernandez President
         Tel: 281-283-9330
         Email: jhernandez@bastiontechnologies.com
         Website: www.bastiontechnologies.com
Engineering design, analysis, systems engineering,
information technology applications, engineering
research, mechanical engineering, structural engineering, safety & reliability engineering, systems safety,
hazard analysis. (Hisp, estab 1998, empl 400, sales
$42,711,000, cert: State, NMSDC)

5215   Bestica, Inc.
          3463 Magic Dr Ste 303
          San Antonio, TX 78229
          Contact: Harvinder Singh CEO
          Tel: 210-614-4198
          Email: harvinder@bestica.com
          Website: www.bestica.com
IT consulting & staffing firm. (As-Ind, estab 2005, empl
198, sales $7,500,000, cert: NMSDC, 8a)

5216   Bravo Technical Resources, Inc.
          5301 Alpha Road Ste 80-37
          Dallas, TX 75204
          Contact: Bettina Jones Strategic Acct Mgr
          Tel: 214-422-3620
          Email: bjones@bravotech.com
          Website: www.bravotech.com
IT & engineering staffing: contract, contract to hire, direct
hire. (Woman, estab 1996, empl 180, sales $28,500,000,
cert: WBENC)

5217   BroadAxis Inc.
          2591 Dallas Pkwy Ste 300
          Frisco, TX 75034
          Contact: Nazish Imran Technical Recruiter
          Tel: 215-280-1992
          Email: nazish@broadaxis.com
          Website: www.broadaxis.com
Technology solutions, infrastructure & security projects, IT
projects & staffing. (As-Ind, estab 2014, empl 5, sales ,
cert: State, NMSDC)

5218   Broadmoor Consulting, LLC
          P.O. Box 896
          Roanoke, TX 76262
          Contact: CEO
          Tel: 888-383-0380
          Email:
          Website: www.broadmoor.io
Top Secret and Secret eligible, JavaScript, Python, C/CPP,
PHP, Swift, Ruby, SQL, Perl, Node JS, React (Woman, estab
2018, empl 5, sales , cert: WBENC)

5219   Calpion Inc.
          4835 Lyndon B Johnson Freeway Ste 515
          Dallas, TX 75244
          Contact: Thomas John President
          Tel: 469-242-6056
          Email: thomas@calpion.com
          Website: www.calpion.com
IT consulting & staffing, software development, SAP
testing & consulting, Cloud based server
& IT resources. (As-Ind, estab 2004, empl 50, sales
$2,400,000, cert: State, NMSDC)

5220   Can-Am Wireless LLC dba Can-Am IT Solutions
          1333 Corporate Dr, Ste 110
          Irving, TX 75038
          Contact: Johan Rahardjo Dir of Engineering
          Tel: 866-976-4177
          Email: johan.rahardjo@canamitsolutions.com
          Website: www.canamitsolutions.com
Telecommunications and Information Technology Hardware & Software. (As-Pac, estab 2001, empl 7, sales
$1,020,000, cert: NMSDC)

5221   Caravan Consulting, LLC
          16947 Old Pond Dr
          Dallas, TX 75248
          Contact: Richard Bird Mgr
          Tel: 469-525-6518
          Email: rbird@caravanconsulting.com
          Website: www.caravanconsulting.com
Infrastructure Architecture, Data Modeling, Database
Management, ETL Architecture & Development, Data
Warehouse Architecture & Development. (AA, estab
2009, empl 1, sales $318,000, cert: NMSDC)

5222   Castillo & Associates
          6942 FM 1960 E., Ste 290
          Humble, TX 77346
          Contact: Mike Castillo President
          Tel: 281-852-7487
          Email: mike.a.castillo@cainfotech.com
          Website: www.cainfotech.com
Engineering & technical support services: network
infrastructure, telecommunications systems & services,
enterprise application support & IT risk analysis. (Hisp,
estab 1998, empl 16, sales $3,200,000, cert: State, City)

5223   CBI Consulting Group
          9609 Asheboro St
          Frisco, TX 75035
          Contact: Heriberto Estrada President
          Tel: 956-559-0454
          Email: heriberto.estrada@cbiconsultinggroup.com
          Website: www.cbiconsultinggroup.com
IT professional services, SAP solutions, implementation,
system upgrades, education, support, and custom
development. (Hisp, estab 2014, empl 5, sales $350,000,
cert: State, NMSDC)

5224   CES Network Services, Inc.
          P.O. Box 810256
          Dallas, TX 75381
          Contact: Enrique Flores President
          Tel: 972-241-3683
          Email: ehflores@cesnetser.com
          Website: www.cesnetser.com
Network engineering services, LAN, WAN & MAN, cell
site planning & desig, RFI / EMI analysis, CADD services,
satellite design, microwave radio, topographic map
studies, digital terrain studies. (Nat Ame, Hisp, estab
1988, empl 11, sales $6,200,000, cert: State, City)

5225   CESCO, Inc.
          11969 Plano Rd Ste 130
          Dallas, TX 75243
          Contact: Billie Bryant Schultz CEO
          Tel: 214-824-8741
          Email: bbryant@cesco-inc.cm
          Website: www.cesco-inc.net
Dist & service fax, printers & copiers, pens, paper,
furniture, etc. (Woman, estab , empl , sales $6,874,952,
cert: State, WBENC)

5226   Cima Solutions Group, Ltd.
          118 Lynn Ave Ste 300
          Lewisville, TX 75057
          Contact: John Alday President
          Tel: 972-499-8261
          Email: jalday@cimasg.com
          Website: www.cimasg.com
IT optization & business continuity. (Hisp, estab 2005,
empl 11, sales $2,374,624, cert: State, City, NMSDC)

5227 CIS Cenergy International Services
      12650 Crossrroads Park Dr
      Houston, TX 77065
      Contact: June Ressler President
      Tel: 713-965-6200
      Email: christine.lujan@cenergyintl.com
      Website: www.cenergyintl.com
Information technology consulting services: outsourcing,
software development, PC repairs & network support,
training, project mgmt, GIS consulting, web development,
system support, repair & maintenance. (Woman, estab
2006, empl , sales $100,000, cert: WBENC)

5228 ClearRES LLC
      800 E Campbell Rd Ste 170
      Richardson, TX 75081
      Contact: Dhanya Yalamanchi CEO
      Tel: 214-455-7860
      Email: dhanya@clearres.com
      Website: www.ClearRES.com
IT services & solutions, fixed priced projects, strategic
staffing, onshore, offshore developed centers. (Nat Ame,
estab 2015, empl 3, sales $100,000, cert: State, NMSDC)

5229 Cognitive Technologies, Inc.
      115 Wild Basin Rd S Ste 104
      Austin, TX 78746
      Contact: Karen McGraw CEO
      Tel: 512-380-1204
      Email: kmcgraw@cognitive-technologies.com
      Website: www.cognitive-technologies.com
Project management, project recovery, business process
redesign, implementation planning, change management,
testing. (Woman, estab 2001, empl 10, sales $800,000,
cert: City)

5230 CompQsoft, Inc.
      505N Sam Houston Pkwy East Ste 682
      Houston, TX 77060
      Contact: Franklin Benjamin Business Develop Mgr
      Tel: 832-932-8732
      Email: franklinb@compqsoft.com
      Website: www.compqsoft.com
Mobile computing solutions, custom programming,
network support, e-commerce solutions, QA testing svcs,
staffing, on-site training. (As-Ind, estab 1997, empl 170,
sales $12,000,000, cert: NMSDC)

5231 Coptic Communications, Inc. dba Wave Technology
      2340 E Trinity Mills Rd Ste 240
      Carrollton, TX 75006
      Contact: Phillip Radcliff VP Business Devel
      Tel: 972-820-6950
      Email: pradcliff@wavehitech.com
      Website: www.wavehitech.com
Voice, data, cabling, inside & outside plant design, PC's,
network appliances, servers, printers, routers, switches &
network design, systems integration, network admin &
configuration mgmt, database dev, email & calendaring,
systems upgrades & support. (Minority, Woman, estab
1990, empl 12, sales $3,000,000, cert: State)

5232 Corporate Records Management Inc.
      3141 Hansboro Ave
      Dallas, TX 75233
      Contact: Denise Chadima Owner
      Tel: 214-333-3453
      Email: denise@crmfiles.com
      Website: www.crmfiles.com
Record storage, archiving, secured shredding, back up tape
rotation. (Woman, estab 1998, empl 12, sales $764,220,
cert: State)

5233 Critical Start LLC
      6100 Tennyson Pkwy Ste 250
      Plano, TX 75024
      Contact: Tera Davis Managing Dir
      Tel: 214-810-6760
      Email: tera.davis@criticalstart.com
      Website: www.criticalstart.com
Network security products & services: risk, compliance,
governance; threat management & incident response.
(Woman, estab 2012, empl 10, sales , cert: State)

5234 CRV, Inc.
      3407 Northeast Pkwy, Ste 170
      San Antonio, TX 78218
      Contact: Glenda Anzualda Project Mgr
      Tel: 210-828-8552
      Email: glendaa@crvinc.com
      Website: www.crvinc.com
Network consulting, resell Cisco, Dell, Hewlett Packard/
Compaq, IBM & Minolta/QMS, printer repair & maintenance agreements, voice & data circuits, audio visual
integration & rental svcs. (Hisp, estab 1993, empl 15,
sales $8,858,797, cert: State)

5235 Dallas Digital Services, LLC
      5316 Bransford Dr
      Colleyville, TX 76034
      Contact: Howie Evans VP
      Tel: 817-577-8794
      Email: howie.evans@ddserv.com
      Website: www.ddserv.com
IT storage products: Fibre Channel & iSCSI devices, data
center design solutions, Quantum, OverlandStorage,
EMC, SUN, Tek-Tools, Qlogic, Legato, Cisco, NEOScale.
(Woman, estab 1996, empl 14, sales $10,000,000, cert:
State, WBENC)

5236 Decca Consulting LLC
      14090 SW Freeway Ste 300
      Sugar Land, TX 77478
      Contact: Nayeem Amin Managing Partner
      Tel: 832-561-0634
      Email: amin@deccaconsulting.com
      Website: www.deccaconsulting.com
IT staffing & solutions. (Woman/As-Ind, estab 2007,
empl 25, sales $1,850,000, cert: State, NMSDC)

5237 Decision Tree Technologies
      306 Thunderbird Ln
      El Paso, TX 79912
      Contact: Bryyan Ritter Client Mgr
      Tel: 512-294-0604
      Email: ritter@dtreetech.com
      Website: www.dtreetech.com
Data center, contact center, IT security, networking &
related IT technologies. (Woman, estab 1989, empl 10,
sales $8,100,000, cert: State)

5238 Defense Support Services, Inc.
      3212 Bishop Dr
      Arlington, TX 76010
      Contact: Deon Moses President
      Tel: 817-261-0233
      Email: dmoses@dss-inc.net
      Website: www.dss-inc.net
Aircraft hardware logistics & distribution, IT design &
services, communications. (AA, estab 1998, empl 15,
sales $3,000,000, cert: NMSDC)

5239 Digital Consulting & Software Services, Inc.
2277 Plaza Dr Ste 275
Sugar Land, TX 77479
Contact: Patricia Patterson CEO
Tel: 713-982-8034
Email: pmpatter@dcss.com
Website: www.dcss.com
Management consulting, professional technical serivces. (Woman, estab , empl , sales $30,241,907, cert: WBENC)

5240 Direct Line To Compliance, Inc.
9555 W Sam Houston Pkwy S, Ste 333
Houston, TX 77099
Contact: Micha Adeeko Business Dev Mgr
Tel: 713-777-3522
Email: michael.adeeko@dl2c.com
Website: www.dl2c.com
Software & consulting (ColorCodeIT and ChameleonDocs), form automation, electronic document handling & compliance program software. (Woman/AA, estab 2008, empl 17, sales $1,363,745, cert: State, NMSDC)

5241 doc2e-file,Inc.
4500 S. Wayside Dr, Ste 102
Houston, TX 77087
Contact: Sherry McManus President & CEO
Tel: 713-649-2006
Email: sherrymcmanus@doc2e-file.com
Website: www.doc2e-file.com
Document scanning & indexing, e-records mgmt, systems & equipment. (Woman, estab , empl , sales $4,600,000, cert: State, WBENC)

5242 Doyensys, Inc.
2591 Dallas Pkwy, Ste 300
Frisco, TX 75034
Contact: Chithra Gopalan President
Tel: 972-992-4220
Email: sales@doyensys.com
Website: www.doyensys.com
Information Technology Staffing and Services in technologies inlcuding but not limited to SAP, Oracle , Siebel, peoplesoft, Java, Dot net, IBM Mainframe (Woman/As-Pac, estab 2006, empl 4, sales $185,000, cert: City)

5243 Dynamic Computing Services
3307 Northland Dr, Ste 250
Austin, TX 78731
Contact: Jenelle Thomas Dir Business Devel
Tel: 800-345-1275
Email: jenelle@dcshq.com
Website: www.dcshq.com
Information technology placements services. (Woman, estab 1990, empl 152, sales $13,926,270, cert: WBENC)

5244 ECOM Consulting, Inc.
2828 W Parker Rd Ste 224
Plano, TX 75075
Contact: Baku Kshatriya President
Tel: 972-578-0191
Email: baku@ecomconsultinginc.com
Website: www.ecomconsultinginc.com
Technical consulting services & staff augmentation. (As-Ind, estab 1995, empl 72, sales , cert: State, NMSDC)

5245 eConsulting Partners Global, Inc
10000 North Central Exprwy Ste 400
Dallas, TX 75231
Contact: Jade Tran Principal
Tel: 214-680-0982
Email: jade.tran@ecpgi.com
Website: http://ecpgi.com
System Integration, Enterprise Application Architecture, Service-Oriented Architecture, and IT Security (Cyber Security, Information Assurance, Computer Forensics). (Woman/As-Pac, estab 2006, empl 20, sales $300,000, cert: State)

5246 eDataWorld LLC
2770 Main St Ste 229
Frisco, TX 75033
Contact: Bhujang Karakavalasa Director
Tel: 206-504-8739
Email: bhujang.k@edataworld.com
Website: www.edataworld.com
IT consulting, software development & service. (Woman/As-Pac, estab 2005, empl 100, sales $2,000,000, cert: NMSDC)

5247 ElectroSystems Engineers Inc.
4141 Pinnacle St, Ste 208
El Paso, TX 79902
Contact: Benita R Munoz Dir of Operations
Tel: 915-587-7902
Email: brmunoz@esei.com
Website: www.esei.com
Information technology, integrated solutions, telecommunications engineering, software design, management & consulting, test & evaluation support & intelligence training. (Hisp, estab 1994, empl 20, sales $1,441,208, cert: NMSDC)

5248 Elise Resources, Inc.
950 Echo Lane Ste 200
Houston, TX 77024
Contact: Nadia Clark CEO
Tel: 281-313-4422
Email: nadia@eliseresources.com
Website: www.eliseresources.com
call center that specializes in the handling of inbound and outbound customer service and sales related calls. We do this by employing quality staff and by utilizing the best technology available related to training (AA, estab 2015, empl 1, sales , cert: State)

5249 Endata Corporation
3217 Thorne Hill Ct
Richardson, TX 75082
Contact: Ricardo Rossi CTO
Tel: 214-603-4456
Email: ricardo@endata.com
Website: www.endata.com
Information Technology Professional Services, machine learning, sentiment analysis, predictive data analytics, web & app development, artificial intelligence for web, mobile & cloud applications. (Woman/Hisp, estab 1997, empl 2, sales $370,808, cert: State, NMSDC)

5250 Enovox Technical Group, LLC
1775 St. James Place, Ste 120
Houston, TX 77584
Contact: Michael Wilson President
Tel: 832-736-5869
Email: mike@enovox.com
Website: www.enovox.com
IT consulting & technology services, telecommunication services, telecommunication/network equipment, program/project management & outsourcing. (AA, estab 2011, empl 2, sales $100,000, cert: State, City)

5251 Enterprise IT Experts LLC dba EITE LLC
4017 Duclair Dr
McKinney, TX 75070
Contact: Ravi Vegesna Managing Partner
Tel: 248-494-7474
Email: ravi@eitellc.com
Website: www.enterpriseitexperts.com
Information Technology & Computer Software services: Enterprise Architecture, SAP Implementations, Upgrades, Technology Upgrades, Microsoft Technologies - Sharepoint & Office 365, Cloud Architecture, Integration & Custom development. (As-Ind, estab 2011, empl 228, sales $8,700,000, cert: State, NMSDC)

5252 Enterprise Logic, Inc.
7457 Harwin Dr, Ste 208
Houston, TX 77036
Contact: Ajay Thomas CEO
Tel: 832-489-1851
Email: admin@enterprise-logic.com
Website: www.enterprise-logic.com
Staffing company that focuses on staffing all types of IT Skills. (As-Ind, estab 2000, empl 200, sales $1,000,000, cert: City, NMSDC)

5253 ERP Logic
7423 Las Colinas Blvd Ste 103
Irving, TX 75063
Contact: Caldwell Velnambi CEO
Tel: 972-401-3771
Email: caldwell@erplogic.com
Website: www.erplogic.com
SAP-ERP Implementation, Customization, Integration, Business Process, Re-Engineering, Application Development, Management and Staff Augmentation (As-Ind, estab 2009, empl 45, sales $3,000,000, cert: NMSDC)

5254 Expedien Inc.
2925 Richmond Ave Ste 1200
Houston, TX 77098
Contact: Jiten K Agarwal Director
Tel: 832-607-5335
Email: jkumar@expedien.net
Website: www.expedien.net/
Business Intelligence, Data Warehousing, Data Integration, Data Migration, Data conversion, Master Data Management, SAP, SAP BW, EAI, SAP Netweaver, SAP Portal, Oracle Financials, Application Development, Business Objects. (Woman/As-Ind, estab 2002, empl 72, sales $15,873,000, cert: NMSDC)

5255 Feuji, Inc.
105 Decker Ct, Ste 850
Irving, TX 75062
Contact: Ruchi Bindra Director
Tel: 972-514-1949
Email: info@feuji.com
Website: www.feuji.com
IT services, cloud solutions, proposal management, analytics, emerging technologies, managed services and strategic staffing. (As-Ind, As-Pac, estab 2014, empl 250, sales $15,000,000, cert: State)

5256 Fidelis Companies
2800 N Dallas Pkwy Ste 250
Plano, TX 75093
Contact: Bryce Shields Business Dev Mgr
Tel: 972-392-9230
Email: bshields@fideliscompanies.com
Website: www.fideliscompanies.com
IT Consulting for Oracle, PeopleSoft, Hyperion, SAP. (Woman, estab 2000, empl 50, sales $4,000,000, cert: State, WBENC)

5257 Fuel7 Inc.
11910 Greenville Ave, Ste 275
Dallas, TX 75243
Contact: Steven Pratt
Tel: 888-669-4009
Email: steven@fuel7.com
Website: www.fuel7.com
Fuel7 provides embedded development services, both hardware and software, specializing in new embedded Linux projects. From design and architecture through development and board bringup (Hisp, estab 2004, empl 12, sales $2,200,000, cert: NMSDC)

5258 Fuse Solutions Inc.
4100 Midway Rd Ste 2120
Carrollton, TX 75007
Contact: Jay Jordan COO
Tel: 214-687-7393
Email: jay@fusesolutions.com
Website: www.fusesolutions.com
Strategic consulting, enterprise service delivery, vendor & asset management. (Woman, estab 2014, empl 25, sales , cert: State, WBENC)

5259 Genesis Networks Enterprises, LLC
600 N Loop 1604 E
San Antonio, TX 78232
Contact: Jason McGinnis Dir Vendor Engagements
Tel: 770-329-6538
Email: jason.mcginnis@genesisnet.com
Website: www.genesisnet.com
Software development, software testing, systems integrator, proto-type development, security, system application mgmt, application mgmt, business process flow, event mgmt, exception mgmt. (Hisp, estab 2001, empl 771, sales $1,100,000,000, cert: State, NMSDC, CPUC)

5260 Genesis Networks Integration Services, LLC
600 N. Loop 1604 East
San Antonio, TX 78232
Contact: Nicole Nash supplier diversity Asst
Tel: 210-489-6600
Email: nicole.nash@genesisnet.com
Website: www.genesisnet.com
Provides engineering, furnish & installation services for data & phone networks, network management architecture, implementation & support, information systems security management, server & virtualization management. (Hisp, estab 2010, empl 77, sales $16,526,811, cert: State, NMSDC)

5261   GeoPropel, LLC
        16225 Park Ten Place Ste 500
        Houston, TX 77084
        Contact: Aditya Tadakaluru Managing Member
        Tel: 713-338-3441
        Email: aditya@geopropel.com
        Website: www.geopropel.com
Technology solutions, staffing & recruiting, enterprise GIS, application development & geospatial solutions. (As-Pac, estab 2011, empl 3, sales $1,240,270, cert: State)

5262   Gill Digital Services, LLC
        4100 Spring Valley Road, Ste 920
        Dallas, TX 75244
        Contact: Barbara Gill President
        Tel: 214-653-8352
        Email: bgill@gilldigital.com
        Website: www.gilldigital.com
Document Scanning, Database Software, Disaster Recovery Services, Court Reporting (Woman, estab 0, empl , sales , cert: State, WBENC)

5263   Global IT, Inc.
        1303 W Walnut Hill Ln Ste 360
        Irving, TX 75038
        Contact:
        Tel: 972-871-9292
        Email: info@globalitinc.com
        Website: www.globalitinc.com
Information technology: ERP packages, SAP, Oracle Apps & PeopleSoft. (As-Ind, estab 1999, empl 182, sales $13,400,000, cert: State)

5264   GS Infovision LLC dba Global Systems LLC
        1200 Walnut Hill Lane, Ste 2220
        Irving, TX 75038
        Contact: Shekhar Gupta VP
        Tel: 214-717-4344
        Email: account@globalsyst.com
        Website: www.globalsyst.com
IT Consulting, Staffing, BPO, IT Consulting, temporary, contract, temp to perm & permanent staffing solutions. (Woman/As-Pac, estab 2005, empl 110, sales $11,000,000, cert: NMSDC)

5265   Guardian Zone LLC
        4843 Colleyville Blvd Ste 251-155
        Colleyville, TX 76034
        Contact: CEO
        Tel: 866-866-8731
        Email:
        Website: www.guardianzone.com
Security & protection software, wireless software, security services. (Woman/AA, estab 2016, empl 5, sales , cert: State, WBENC)

5266   Hacware, Inc.
        1212 E Arapaho Rd Ste 204
        Richardson, TX 75081
        Contact: CEO
        Tel: 214-662-8332
        Email:
        Website: www.hacware.com
Mobile applications and emerging technology solutions. (Woman/AA, estab 2017, empl 8, sales , cert: WBENC)

5267   Hy-Density Imaging
        1850 Hunter Dr, Ste 108
        El Paso, TX 79915
        Contact: Steve Madrid Owner
        Tel: 915-593-7007
        Email: steve_hdcpr@sbcglobal.net
        Website:
Service/Sales: Computers & Printers, IT equipment sales, Data & Voice Cabling, Remove viruses, General Computer and Printer repair, Data recovery, Laptop repair (power Jacks, Lcd screen replacements. (Hisp, estab 1994, empl 3, sales $187,000, cert: State)

5268   iBizSoft
        9300 Wade Blvd Ste 301
        Frisco, TX 75035
        Contact: Sandeep Kuttiyatur President
        Tel: 214-705-3623
        Email: vendor@ibizsoftinc.com
        Website: www.ibizsoftinc.com
Enterprise application services: system integration & solution development for Oracle ERP, CRM, Endeca & ATG implementation. (As-Ind, estab 2001, empl 100, sales $6,000,000, cert: State)

5269   ICC Software
        4837 Frost Hollow Dr
        Plano, TX 75093
        Contact: Anthony Johnson President
        Tel: 214-227-9559
        Email: ajohn@iccsoftware.net
        Website: www.iccsoftware.net
Document management, biometrics & document conversion software, programming, risk analysis, & project management. (AA, estab 2001, empl 3, sales , cert: State)

5270   Imagetek Office Systems
        630 Westway Place, Ste 500
        Arlington, TX 76018
        Contact: Jim Grady Customer Care Coord
        Tel: 817-465-2450
        Email:
        Website: http://imagetekos.com
Extensive managed document, print services and software solutions. (Woman, estab , empl , sales , cert: State, WBENC)

5271   Independent Professional Management
        9525 Katy Freeway, Ste 435
        Houston, TX 77024
        Contact: VP - Resource Mgmt
        Tel: 713-973-7400
        Email:
        Website: www.ipm-inc.com
IT Staffing, SAP programers, developers & consultants. (Woman, estab 1992, empl 9, sales , cert: State, WBENC)

5272   Infobeam Technologies LLC
        1333 Corporate Dr, Ste 262
        Irving, TX 75038
        Contact: Jay Gajavelli Director
        Tel: 972-365-9928
        Email: jay.gajavelli@infobeamtech.com
        Website: www.infobeamtech.com
IT consulting. (As-Pac, estab 2009, empl 15, sales , cert: State)

5273　Infolob Solutions, Inc.
　　　909 Lake Carolyn Parkway Ste 120
　　　Irving, TX 75039
　　　Contact: Vijay Cherukuri CEO
　　　Tel:　972-535-5559
　　　Email: vijay@infolob.com
　　　Website: www.infolob.com
Database services, RAC, Exadata, SOA, Oracle Fusion,
Ebusiness, OBIEE, BI, DW, OLTP, networking, J2EE, replica-
tion. (Woman/As-Ind, estab 2009, empl 130, sales
$50,000,000, cert: State, NMSDC)

5274　Inoditech LLC, dba Camino Information Services
　　　14340 Torrey Chase Blvd Ste 210
　　　Houston, TX 77014
　　　Contact: Lam Nguyen CEO
　　　Tel:　281-742-9560
　　　Email: lam.nguyen@caminois.com
　　　Website: www.caminois.com
Custom software development & mobile applications.
(Woman/As-Pac, estab 2012, empl 22, sales $1,273,000,
cert: State, NMSDC)

5275　Instant Data Technologies
　　　85 NE Loop 410, Ste. 405
　　　San Antonio, TX 78216
　　　Contact: Bede Ramcharan CEO
　　　Tel:　210-344-0012
　　　Email: bramcharan@indatatech.com
　　　Website: www.indatatech.com
Physical inventory, RFID technology, asset valuation &
tracking, supplier integration, barcoding, asset procure-
ment, tagging & management, inventory mgmt software.
(AA, As-Pac, estab 2001, empl 31, sales $11,999,837, cert:
State, NMSDC, SDB)

5276　Intras LLC
　　　101 E Park Ste 769
　　　Plano, TX 75074
　　　Contact: Elvan Jones
　　　Tel:　972-422-1022
　　　Email: elvanj@intras-it.com
　　　Website: www.intras-it.com
Global integrator of technology solutions, technology
hardware & applications develop, IT products, IT Services,
IT Consulting & IT Managed services. (AA, estab 2010,
empl 10, sales $3,000,000, cert: State, NMSDC)

5277　IPM Asset Solutions, Inc.
　　　9525 Katy Freeway Ste 435
　　　Houston, TX 77024
　　　Contact: Andy Bishop VP - Resource Management
　　　Tel:　713-973-7400
　　　Email: andy.bishop@ipm-inc.com
　　　Website: www.ipmasset.com
Asset management & tracking utilizing bar code & Radio
Frequency Identification (RFID) technology. (Woman, estab
2006, empl 9, sales , cert: State, WBENC)

5278　JB Software and Consulting, Inc.
　　　333 E. Bethany Dr Ste J130
　　　Allen, TX 75002
　　　Contact: VP
　　　Tel:　469-878-3639
　　　Email:
　　　Website: www.jbsac.com
Information technology services & staff augmentation.
(Woman/As-Ind, estab 2004, empl 38, sales $6,000,000,
cert: NMSDC, CPUC, WBENC)

5279　JG Haney & Associates LLC
　　　9711 Haven Crossing Court
　　　Houston, TX 77065
　　　Contact: Joyce Haney CEO
　　　Tel:　281-653-2441
　　　Email: haney@jghaneyassociates.com
　　　Website: www.jghaneyassociates.com
Telecommunications Services, IT products & services,
data acquisition systems, telemetry products, circuit
card assemblies, shipping containers, test set cases,
special nonmetallic, preformed packing material &
acquisition program management. (Woman/AA, estab
2011, empl 2, sales $300,000, cert: 8a)

5280　KEDAR Integration Services, Inc.
　　　405 State Hwy 121 Bypass Ste A250
　　　Lewisville, TX 75067
　　　Contact:
　　　Tel:　972-317-3577
　　　Email: charles@kedarit.com
　　　Website: http://kedarit.com
IT financial management, cost optimization; business
process management; lean transformation; and training.
(AA, estab , empl , sales $586,858, cert: State)

5281　Kreative Zeno Systems, Inc.
　　　12019 Colwick
　　　San Antonio, TX 78216
　　　Contact: Thomas Dooley VP
　　　Tel:　877-768-1574
　　　Email: tomd@kreativesystemsinc.com
　　　Website: www.kreativesystemsinc.com
Provide SCSI disk drive assemblies. (Woman, estab 2010,
empl 7, sales $160,000, cert: State)

5282　LMG Technology Services, LLC
　　　134 Vintage Park Blvd, Ste A-791
　　　Houston, TX 77070
　　　Contact: Lloyd Gauthier CEO
　　　Tel:　832-465-4641
　　　Email: Lloyd@Lmgtechnology.com
　　　Website: www.lmgtechnology.com
Information technology. (AA, estab 2006, empl 2, sales ,
cert: State, City, NMSDC)

5283　Managed Staffing Inc
　　　15851 Dallas Parkway | Ste 450, Addison
　　　Dallas, TX 75001
　　　Contact: Mark Miller Sr Mgr
　　　Tel:　469-608-7015
　　　Email: mark@managedstaffing.com
　　　Website: www.managedstaffing.com
IT consulting: contract, contract to hire, or direct
placement, outsourcing. (Woman/As-Ind, estab 2007,
empl 300, sales $39,300,000, cert: NMSDC, WBENC)

5284　MB Five Consulting LLC
　　　8013 Blue Hole Ct
　　　McKinney, TX 75070
　　　Contact: Andre Ketter Mgr
　　　Tel:　972-895-2414
　　　Email: aketter@mb5consulting.com
　　　Website: www.mb5consulting.com
IT Services & Industrial Automation services, desktop &
server support, Networking & software development.
(AA, estab 2014, empl 1, sales $220,000, cert: State,
NMSDC)

5285 Milner & Schooley LLC
14000 S Hwy 95
Coupland, TX 78615
Contact: Sheri Milner Mgmt Svcs
Tel: 512-914-4061
Email: slmilner@milnerschooley.com
Website: www.milnerschooley.com
Information technology svcs: ERP CIS/CRM. (Woman, estab 2005, empl 2, sales $165,000, cert: State)

5286 MRI Technologies
17047 El Camino Real Ste 200
Houston, TX 77058
Contact: Debbie Kropp CEO
Tel: 281-786-2000
Email: dkropp@mricompany.com
Website: www.mricompany.com
Information systems, engineering, planning & integration, logistics, configuration & data management & project management. (Woman, estab 1988, empl 110, sales $9,957,839, cert: State)

5287 Mshana Group LLC dba AriesPro
19901 Southwest Frwy
Sugar Land, TX 77479
Contact: Shivani Sangari Dir Business Dev
Tel: 281-410-6930
Email: shivani.sangari@ariespro.com
Website: www.ariespro.com
Information technology consulting: SAP, HANA, BW, ERP, CRM, SCM, Business Objects, FICO, Oracle, Teradata, Big Data, Microsoft, IBM, Java, Microstrategy, Cognos, Hadoop, DB2, DataStage, Informatica, Netezza, Tivoli, Unix, WebSphere. (Woman/As-Ind, estab 2011, empl 5, sales $460,000, cert: City)

5288 MTech Partners, LLC
1464 E. Whitestone Blvd
Cedar Park, TX 78613
Contact: Tommy Hodinh President & CEO
Tel: 512-993-5730
Email: tommy.hodinh@mtechpartners.net
Website: http://mtechpartners.net
Global Digital Transformation services, Legacy Modernization to Distributed Platform, ERP Integration and DevOps Support, SalesForce Cloud Development and Migration, IOT Engineering Design. (AA, estab 2019, empl 1001, sales $23,245,423, cert: NMSDC)

5289 New Renewable Energy Technologies, LLC dba NERETEC
4102 Amhurst Dr
Highland Village, TX 75077
Contact: Phil Fosso Principal
Tel: 217-299-7789
Email: fosso@neretec.com
Website: www.neretec.com
Project Management, Application Development, Technology Migration/Upgrade, Application Maintenance and Support, IT Assessments/Planning, Independent Verification and Validation, Business Intelligence/Data Warehouse, Service Oriented, Architecture (SOA). (AA, estab 2010, empl 2, sales $154,000, cert: State)

5290 NewData Strategies
5339 Alpha Rd Ste 200
Dallas, TX 75240
Contact: Kristen Scott Dir of Sales
Tel: 972-735-0001
Email: tpope@newdata.com
Website: www.newdata.com
Information technology consulting, placement & education. (Woman, estab 1989, empl 70, sales $7,384,599, cert: WBENC)

5291 Next Generation Technology Inc.
6060 N Central Exprwy, Ste 560
Dallas, TX 75206
Contact: Ray Richardson President & CEO
Tel: 214-800-2893
Email: rrichardson@nexgentech.us
Website: www.nexgentech.us
Resell Hewlett Packard products, UPS back-up power for Liebert, APC & Powerware, digital video surveillance systems, IT consulting. (AA, estab 2003, empl 5, sales , cert: State, SDB)

5292 Nomotion Software, LLC
6243 Cypress Cir
San Antonio, TX 78240
Contact: Orlando Padilla President
Tel: 210-710-2800
Email: opadilla@nomotion.net
Website: www.nomotion.net
Information security consulting & software development, application security design, assessment, and remediation. (Hisp, estab 2012, empl 4, sales $400,000, cert: 8a)

5293 Object Information Services, Inc.
1755 North Collins Blvd #220
Richardson, TX 75080
Contact: Mohammad Hafizullah President
Tel: 214-335-6632
Email: mhafiz@objectinformation.com
Website: www.objectinformation.com
Information technology recruiting. (As-Ind, estab 1995, empl 42, sales $3,449,325, cert: NMSDC)

5294 ObjectWin Technology, Inc.
19219 Katy Freeway, Ste 275
Houston, TX 77094
Contact: Pete Adams Sales
Tel: 832-485-1566
Email: mbe@objectwin.com
Website: www.objectwin.com
IT services & staffing, Partners with Microsoft, Oracle SAP. (As-Ind, As-Pac, estab 1997, empl 220, sales $28,000,000, cert: NMSDC)

5295 Omega Business Systems
P.O. Box 8297
Fort Worth, TX 76124
Contact: Norman Labrosse President
Tel: 817-492-4249
Email: norman@omegabiz.com
Website: www.omegabiz.com
Network solutions & technical services. (As-Ind, estab 1992, empl 6, sales $2,000,000, cert: State, City, NMSDC, SDB)

5296   On Air Solutions, Inc.
5415 Chevy Chase
Houston, TX 77056
Contact: Dir
Tel: 713-961-3990
Email:
Website: www.onairsol.com
Wireless infrastructure projects & telecommunications svcs: in-building wireless system engineering & installation, tower erection/construction; site maintenance, site acquisition, project management. (Woman, estab 2003, empl 6, sales , cert: State)

5297   Oveana
123 W Mills Ave, Ste 400
El Paso, TX 79901
Contact: Bill Randag Business Development
Tel: 915-533-0549
Email: bill.randag@oveana.com
Website: www.oveana.com
Document mgmt, data processing, mail room processing, scanning, data storage, data entry, data capture & destruction, call center. (Woman/Hisp, estab 2013, empl 2200, sales , cert: State)

5298   OverNite Software Inc.
1212 N Velasco, Ste 110
Angleton, TX 77515
Contact: David Stark Mktg Dir
Tel: 979-849-2002
Email: david.stark@overnitecbt.com
Website: http://overnitecbt.com
Computer-based performance systems. (Hisp, estab 1995, empl 55, sales , cert: State)

5299   Pinnacle Technical Resources, Inc.
5501 Lyndon B. Johnson Frwy, Ste 600
Dallas, TX 75240
Contact: Monica Watkins Managing Dir
Tel: 214-995-6648
Email: monica.watkins@pinnacle1.com
Website: www.pinnacle1.com
Nearshore software development in latin america. (Woman/Hisp, estab 1996, empl 3606, sales $1,890,058,695, cert: WBENC)

5300   Principle Information Technology
9301 Southwest Fwy Ste 475
Houston, TX 77074
Contact: Nickell Cheruku President
Tel: 832-434-4016
Email: reddy@principleinfotech.com
Website: www.principleinfotech.com
SAP Services, Oracle Service, Big Data, Cloud Mobility, Luxon. (As-Pac, estab 2009, empl 157, sales , cert: State, City, NMSDC, 8a)

5301   Promacsolution Inc.
9916 Bundoran Dr
Austin, TX 78717
Contact: Srinivas Ande Director
Tel: 310-733-3076
Email: srinivas@promacsolution.com
Website: www.promacsolution.com
IT consulting, SOA Architecture, Web Services, ERP, Data warehousing, SAP, Oracle HRMS, .NET,J2EE etc. (Woman/As-Ind, estab 2004, empl 5, sales $143,086, cert: State)

5302   Prudent Technologies and Consulting Inc.
1505 LBJ Freeway Ste 327
Dallas, TX 75234
Contact: Mario Guerra VP
Tel: 414-491-9056
Email: mguerra@prudentconsulting.com
Website: www.prudentconsulting.com
IT consultants & staffing: Oracle, SAP, PeopleSoft, .Net, Java, Hyperion, Documentum, Clarity, Crystal Reports, Testing, Mercury Tools, Compuware Tools, .Net, C#, Oracle, Oracle ERP, SQL, etc. (As-Ind, estab 1998, empl 70, sales $5,000,000, cert: NMSDC)

5303   Pure Business Solutions, LLC
219 Gessner Rd
Houston, TX 77024
Contact: Andrea Hite CEO
Tel: 713-750-9500
Email: ahite@purebizsolns.com
Website: www.purebizsolns.com
IT Operations Management Software, IT Service Management, Discovery, Configuration Management Database, Application & Service Modeling, IT Operations & Business Analytics, Performance and Availability Management. (Woman, estab 2015, empl 1, sales , cert: State, WBENC)

5304   Quality High-Tech Services, Inc.
11807 Forestgate Dr
Dallas, TX 75243
Contact: Mary Rogers President
Tel: 972-231-6696
Email: m.rogers@qht.com
Website: www.QHT.com
IT services and repairs. (Woman, estab 1987, empl 17, sales $2,492,492, cert: State)

5305   RD Data Solutions
2340 E Trinity Mills Ste 349
Carrollton, TX 75006
Contact: Reuben D'Souza CEO
Tel: 972-899-2334
Email: reuben.dsouza@rddatasolutions.com
Website: www.rddatasolutions.com
Technology staffing: SAP & ERP. (Woman/As-Pac, estab 2002, empl 26, sales $25,000,000, cert: State, NMSDC)

5306   Remedy Technological Services, L.P.
501 N 4th St
Killeen, TX 76541
Contact: Christopher Walton VP & Legal Counsel
Tel: 254-213-4740
Email: cwalton@centextech.com
Website: www.centextech.com
Information Technology, Software Engineering, Project Management, Database Management, ERP Solutions, Data Warehouse & Business Intelligence, Web & App Development, Internet Marketing & Network Administration. (As-Ind, estab 2006, empl 50, sales $1,300,000, cert: State, 8a)

5307   Research Analysis and Maintenance, Inc.
9440 Viscount Blvd, Ste 200
El Paso, TX 79925
Contact: Richard Jones Contracts Admin
Tel: 915-592-7047
Email: jonesr@ramincorp.com
Website: www.ramincorp.com
IT services, networking & telecommunications, software development, systems integration & information management. (Woman, estab 1982, empl 650, sales $62,000,000, cert: State)

5308   Resolve Tech Solutions
15851 Dallas Pkwy, Ste 1103
Addison, TX 75001
Contact: Business Dev Mgr
Tel: 703-995-7377
Email:
Website: http://resolvetech.com/
Information Technology Staffing, Consulting Services and Implementation. (As-Ind, estab 1996, empl 25, sales $3,000,000, cert: State)

5309   RSI Solutions Inc.
3607 Summer Ranch Dr
Katy, TX 77494
Contact: Principal
Tel: 832-506-0868
Email:
Website: www.rsisolutions.net
Enterprise Resource Planning (ERP) based solutions to both public and private sector entities, SAP BW, HANA. (As-Ind, estab 2011, empl 2, sales $254,000, cert: State, SDB)

5310   Saratoga Software Solutions, Inc.
555 Republic Dr. Ste 200
Plano, TX 75074
Contact: Arlene Carter President
Tel: 469-301-1515
Email: arlene.carter@teamsaratoga.com
Website: www.saratogasoftwaresolutions.com
IT staff augmentation: contract, contract-to-hire & permanent. (Woman, estab , empl , sales $1,400,000, cert: State)

5311   Sasaki Evolutionary Integration Services, LLC
P.O. Box 340562
Austin, TX 78734
Contact: CEO
Tel: 512-263-7347
Email:
Website: www.TeamSEIS.com
Business automation & modeling/simulation for decision support & project/program management. (As-Pac, estab 2009, empl 6, sales $452,500, cert: 8a)

5312   Shirley Hollywood & Associates, Inc.
17585 State Hwy 19 Ste 100
Canton, TX 75103
Contact: Stacie Hollywood-Baber President
Tel: 972-287-8834
Email: stacie@shirleyhollywoodinc.com
Website: www.shirleyhollywoodinc.com
SAP curriculum devel & training delivery resources. (Woman, estab 1996, empl 5, sales $5,000,000, cert: State, WBENC)

5313   Simplistek, LLC
5050 Quorum Dr, Ste 700
Dallas, TX 75254
Contact: Xavier Hurd VP of Talent Acquisition
Tel: 469-675-3594
Email: xhurd@simplistekit.com
Website: www.simplistekit.com
ERP Implementation & support, business process improvement, utilities business consulting & staff augmentation for all areas of Information Technology (IT). (Minority, estab 2014, empl 3, sales $1,200,000, cert: State, NMSDC)

5314   Skylla Engineering Ltd.
316 Main St
Humble, TX 77338
Contact: Tim Brogdon Exec VP
Tel: 228-344-5449
Email: brogdont@skyllaeng.com
Website: www.skyllaeng.com
Systems engineering, software & hardware design, systems integration, configuration control, program mgmt, acquisition planning & mgmt, program planning, scheduling & resource mgmt. (Hisp, estab 2004, empl 110, sales $12,800,000, cert: State)

5315   SMART IT PROS INC
506 N Goliad st Ste 200
Rockwall, TX 75087
Contact: David Thomas Dir Sales
Tel: 734-238-1553
Email: dave.thomas@smartitpros.com
Website: www.smartitpros.com
IT & Business Services, Application & Business process services. (Woman/AA, estab 2012, empl 65, sales $3,456,787, cert: WBENC)

5316   SOAL Technologies, LLC
10900 Research Blvd, Ste. 160C-40
Austin, TX 78759
Contact: Ahmed Moledina CEO
Tel: 512-270-6700
Email: amoledina@soaltech.com
Website: www.soaltech.com
Information technology development & consulting. (As-Ind, estab 2009, empl 40, sales $10,600,000, cert: City)

5317   Software Professionals, Inc.
1029 Long Prairie Road Ste A
Flower Mound, TX 75022
Contact: Reena Batra CEO
Tel: 972-355-0054
Email: reena@spius.net
Website: www.spius.net
Systems integration & computer programming svcs: client/server & mainframe environ; facilities mgmt, help desk support & training; business re-engineering & total quality mgmt. (Woman/As-Ind, As-Pac, estab 1992, empl 100, sales $15,000,000, cert: NMSDC, WBENC)

5318   Softway Solutions, Inc.
7324 Southwest Frwy Ste 1600
Houston, TX 77074
Contact: Robert Goady VP Client Services
Tel: 281-914-4381
Email: robert@softwaysolutions.com
Website: www.softway.com
Website design & development, Internet marketing services, graphics design & multimedia. (As-Pac, estab 2003, empl 65, sales $5,800,000, cert: NMSDC)

5319   Sontesa Technologies Inc.
2101 Cedar Springs Rd, Ste 1050
Dallas, TX 75201
Contact: Jewel Hale CEO
Tel: 972-534-2023
Email: procurement@sontesa.com
Website: www.sontesa.com
Telecom Network and System Design. (Woman/AA, estab 2007, empl 4, sales , cert: NMSDC, WBENC)

5320   SPAR Information Systems
       7800 Dallas Pkwy, Ste 120
       Plano, TX 75024
       Contact: Abraham Regan VP, IT Talent Acquisition
       Tel: 201-528-5324
       Email: abraham.regan@sparinfosys.com
       Website: www.sparinfosys.com
IT Services. (Minority/Woman, estab 2012, empl 380, sales
$30,000,000, cert: State)

5321   Storage Assessments LLC
       P.O. Box 864017
       Plano, TX 75086
       Contact: Carolyn Chambers CEO
       Tel: 972-578-2708
       Email: cc@storageassessments.com
       Website: www.storageassessments.com
Resell, design & support computer storage related products: database, backup & recovers, disaster recovery & file
management. (Woman, estab 2003, empl 6, sales
$4,774,271, cert: State, WBENC)

5322   STS Systems Integration, LLC
       1077 Central Pkwy S Bldg A, Ste 150
       San Antonio, TX 78232
       Contact: Dan Beard Sr Program Mgr
       Tel: 210-888-2631
       Email: daniel.beard@ssi-anc.com
       Website: www.ssi-anc.com
System engineering, performance, mission readiness &
sustainment for weapon systems, propulsion systems &
information systems. (Nat Ame, estab 2011, empl 143,
sales $13,000,000, cert: 8a)

5323   Swift Pace Solutions, Inc
       600 E John Carpenter Frwy Ste 175
       Irving, TX 75062
       Contact: Pratima Upadhya Client Partner
       Tel: 972-714-0000
       Email: pratima@spsolinc.com
       Website: www.spsolinc.com
IT Services Consulting, Oracle Gold Partner, SAP Partner,
Horton Works Partner Migrate, Integrate & Build Custom
Apps. (Woman/As-Ind, estab 2013, empl 12, sales
$2,000,000, cert: State, NMSDC)

5324   Talent Logic Inc.(formerly Sai People Solutions, Inc.)
       2313 Timber Shadows Dr Ste 200
       Kingwood, TX 77339
       Contact: Hilda Roper VP
       Tel: 281-358-1858
       Email: hroper@talentlogic.com
       Website: www.talentlogic.com
Computer consulting & programming svcs. (As-Ind, estab
1984, empl 300, sales $17,500,000, cert: NMSDC)

5325   Taylor Smith Consulting, LLC
       16800 Greenspoint Park Dr, STE 155N
       Houston, TX 77060
       Contact: Tracy Smith CEO
       Tel: 713-937-3111
       Email: staylor@taylorsmithconsulting.com
       Website: www.taylorsmithconsulting.com
Business Development Training, Call/Customer Service
Center Operations, Staffing, Contracting Services (Woman/
AA, estab 2006, empl 1200, sales $18,001,317, cert: State,
City, NMSDC)

5326   Technology Asset LLC
       789 N Grove Rd, Ste 103
       Richardson, TX 75081
       Contact: Tom Earley Reg Sales Mgr
       Tel: 972-318-2600
       Email: tearley@globalassetonline.com
       Website: www.globalassetonline.com
Eco-Friendly IT lifecycle management. (Woman/Nat
Ame, estab 2010, empl 40, sales $12,500,000, cert:
State)

5327   Technology for Education
       658 Alliance Pkwy
       Hewitt, TX 76643
       Contact: Brandy Mynar-Olson Sales Mgr
       Tel: 254-741-2450
       Email: sales@tfeconnect.com
       Website: http://tfe-wordpress.tfeconnect.com
Structured cabling & networking, Data Center, IP
Communications, Audio Visual & Physical Security.
(Woman, estab 1998, empl 50, sales $31,709,451, cert:
State, WBENC)

5328   Techway Services
       12880 Valley Branch Ln Ste 120
       Farmers Branch, TX 75234
       Contact: Cathi Coan CEO
       Tel: 855-832-4929
       Email: cathi@techwayservices.com
       Website: www.techwayservices.com
E-data destruction services & used computer asset
remarketing. (Woman, estab 2004, empl 52, sales
$607,751,300, cert: State, WBENC)

5329   TekFokus Inc.
       1950 N Stemmons, Ste 2062
       Dallas, TX 75207
       Contact: Steve Lindley Business Dev Mgr
       Tel: 214-800-5643
       Email: slindley@tekfokus.com
       Website: www.tekfokus.com
Microsoft IT training & consulting. (Hisp, estab 2003,
empl 12, sales $1,650,000, cert: State)

5330   TELA Technologies, Inc.
       10310 Harwin Dr.
       Houston, TX 77036
       Contact: Jaime Flores President
       Tel: 713-863-1411
       Email: jflores@telatechnologies.com
       Website: www.telatechnologies.com
Document management solutions, electronic document
storage & retrieval solutions. (Hisp, estab 2003, empl 15,
sales $1,050,000, cert: State, NMSDC)

5331   Telecopy, Inc.
       2280 Springlake Rd Ste 104
       Dallas, TX 75234
       Contact: President
       Tel: 972-432-8384
       Email:
       Website: www.telecopy.com
CD, DVD, video & audio duplication. (Woman, estab
1979, empl 6, sales $717,000, cert: State, WBENC)

5332 The Ternio Group LLC
      8285 El Rio Ste 120
      Houston, TX 77054
      Contact: Principal
      Tel: 210-519-7933
      Email:
      Website: www.terniogroup.com
Consulting & project management services: supply chain,
logistics, distribution, medical-surgical & pharmacy
inventory management, consignment, resource management, data processing, data cleansing, e-commerce, ERP.
(Hisp, estab 2012, empl 10, sales $1,960,000, cert: State)

5333 Themesoft Inc.
      13601 Preston Rd, Ste W860
      Dallas, TX 75240
      Contact: Pascal Vinoth Director
      Tel: 972-474-8787
      Email: vinoth@themesoft.com
      Website: www.themesoft.com
Custom Software Development & Consulting, Java, J2EE,
SAP, Networking, Infrastructure, QA, Project Management.
(Woman/As-Ind, estab 2004, empl 200, sales $42,845,261,
cert: State, NMSDC, WBENC)

5334 Third Term Inc.
      6 Meadowridge Pl
      the Woodlands, TX 77381
      Contact: Carolina Denkler Project Mgr
      Tel: 713-357-6666
      Email: carolina.denkler@thirdtermlearning.com
      Website: www.thirdtermlearning.com
eLearning, computer based training, web based Training,
Learning Management Systems, LMS. (Hisp, estab 2013,
empl 2, sales $266,000, cert: NMSDC)

5335 Thurstfield Roman
      6113 Covington Dr
      Rowlett, TX 75089
      Contact: Courtney Davis President
      Tel: 214-335-2806
      Email: cdavis@thurstfieldroman.biz
      Website:
Secure on-site/off-site document shreddiing services. (AA,
estab 2001, empl 3, sales , cert: State)

5336 Traveling Coaches Inc.
      2805 Dallas Pkwy Ste 150
      Dallas, TX 75093
      Contact: Lyndi Lockhart Acct Mgr
      Tel: 214-742-6224
      Email: llockhart@travelingcoaches.com
      Website: www.travelingcoaches.com
Software, consulting, integration & training. (Woman,
estab 1995, empl 35, sales $10,637,000, cert: State,
WBENC)

5337 Tunabear, Inc.
      13155 Noel Rd Ste 900
      Dallas, TX 75240
      Contact: James Knowles
      Tel: 888-923-8889
      Email: james@tunabear.com
      Website: www.tunabear.com
Staff Augmentation, Project Management, Upgrades,
Implementation, Development, Strategy Development,
Infrastructure Planning, Training / Change Management,
Technologies, Peoplesoft, Hyperion / Data Warehousing.
(As-Pac, estab 2010, empl 6, sales $1,444,000, cert: City)

5338 Unified Services of Texas, Inc.
      2110 Greenbriar Dr
      Southlake, TX 76092
      Contact: Marshall Ryan President
      Tel: 817-481-9510
      Email: mryan@ust-inc.com
      Website: www.ust-inc.com
Retail and fleet Fuel system design and installation,
including tanks, piping, dispensers, canopies, electrical
and concrete (Nat Ame, estab 1991, empl 18, sales
$4,100,000, cert: State)

5339 VCM Technologies, Inc.
      25 Highland Park Village, Ste 100-149
      Dallas, TX 75205
      Contact: CEO
      Tel: 817-571-6335
      Email:
      Website: www.beaconsystems.com
Information technology staff augmentation, SAP
consultants. (Woman, estab 2002, empl 6, sales
$14,200,000, cert: WBENC)

5340 Vensiti Inc
      300 East Royal Lane Ste 104
      Irving, TX 75039
      Contact: Vijaya Saradhi Sr.Director Staffing
      Tel: 972-887-7995
      Email: saradhi.v@vensiti.com
      Website: www.vensiti.com
Information tehcnology staffing & consulting services.
(Woman/As-Ind, estab 2004, empl 52, sales $4,340,000,
cert: State)

5341 Verge Information Technologies, Inc.
      1305 Cheyenne Trail
      Corinth, TX 76210
      Contact: Mark McLaughlin Operations Mgr
      Tel: 940-279-1390
      Email: mark@vergeit.com
      Website: www.vergeit.com
Information technology & IS consulting & staff augmentation. (Nat Ame, estab 2000, empl 25, sales $5,342,852,
cert: State, NMSDC)

5342 Virtuo Group Corporation
      6700 Woodlands Pkwy Ste 230-322
      The Woodlands, TX 77382
      Contact: Theresa Blackwell CEO
      Tel: 281-298-8571
      Email: tblackwell@virtuogroup.com
      Website: www.virtuogroup.com
PMO, Cyber Security, application modernization,
migration & consolidation technology services.
(Woman/AA, estab 2001, empl 35, sales , cert: City,
NMSDC)

5343 VKNetworks IT Solutions
      638 Quail Run Dr
      Murphy, TX 75094
      Contact: Dr. Rajan Subramanian President
      Tel: 469-323-3345
      Email: drrajs@vknetworks.com
      Website: www.vknetworks.com
IT/SAP STAFFING & Consulting, SAP Projects, AM, AD.
Big Data, SAP HANA, S/4 HANA, SAP Vistex, EDI, Business
Intelligence and Analytics, BW4HANA, ERP, BPC, HCM,
SAP Fiori, RDS, POC, HEC, BI Reporting (Webi, Crystal
Reports, Dash Boards. (Woman/As-Ind, estab 1999, empl
10, sales , cert: State)

5344   Wise Men Consultants Inc
        1500 S Dairy Ashford Ste 285
        Houston, TX 77077
        Contact: Rosa Delgado-Batchan Dir of Operations
        Tel: 281-953-4511
        Email: rosa.batchan@wisemen.com
        Website: www.wisemen.com
IT staffing, project mgmt, team leads, onshore & offshore
custom software development. (Woman/As-Ind, estab
1997, empl 220, sales , cert: NMSDC, WBENC)

5345   XBI Tech Corporation
        7670 Woodway Dr, Ste 370
        Houston, TX 77063
        Contact: Trieu Nguyen CEO
        Tel: 713-999-1286
        Email: trieu.nguyen@xbitech.com
        Website: www.xbitech.com
Comprehensive web dev & management services: web
design & development, accessibility, web content management, web training, maintenance & support, web applica-
tion/software development & business intelligence. (As-
Pac, estab 2007, empl 5, sales $1,300,000, cert: State)

5346   Xpediant Solutions
        2425 W Loop South
        Houston, TX 77027
        Contact: Suparna Mahesri Director
        Tel: 713-335-5550
        Email: qusai@xpediantsolutions.com
        Website: www.xpediantsolutions.com
Digital experience consulting and systems integration,
Cloud installation, configuration and staffing support. (As-
Ind, estab 2001, empl 25, sales $4,800,000, cert: City)

5347   XTGlobal, Inc.
        2701 N Dallas Pkwy, Ste 550
        Plano, TX 75093
        Contact: Ananth Ramaswamy President
        Tel: 972-755-1800
        Email: ananth@xtglobal.com
        Website: www.xtglobal.com
Professional design, development, integration & support
services: Microsoft. NET, SQL, BizTalk, SharePoint, .NET
Web-based & Desktop Application development. (As-Ind,
estab 1998, empl 170, sales $26,500,000, cert: State,
NMSDC)

5348   YASME Soft Inc.
        1212 Corporate Dr Ste 150
        Irving, TX 75038
        Contact: Sandeep Kilaru President
        Tel: 214-529-3693
        Email: sam@yasmesoft.com
        Website: www.yasmesoft.com
IT consulting solution services: Oracle, SAP, Microsoft & IT
staff augmentation. Application devel, maintenance &
support, enterprise applications, practices, consulting. (As-
Ind, estab 2007, empl 70, sales $6,000,000, cert: State,
NMSDC)

Utah

5349   Global Consulting International Inc.
        270 East 100 South
        Salt Lake City, UT 84111
        Contact: Michelle Dennis Mgr, Business Devel
        Tel: 801-707-4463
        Email: michelle.dennis@gci-usa.com
        Website: www.GCI-USA.com
Oracle's e-business solutions. (As-Ind, estab 2005, empl
210, sales $10,662,180, cert: State)

5350   Rylex Consulting LLC
        1785 East 1450 South Ste 140
        Clearfield, UT 84015
        Contact: Steven Noyce Exec VP
        Tel: 801-820-5221
        Email: steven.noyce@rylex.com
        Website: www.rylex.com
IT help desk management support, Network design &
administration, System / server administration, Software
engineering & development (ASP.net, C#, C++) Hill AFB,
Web application development. (Woman/As-Pac, estab
2004, empl 45, sales $5,000,000, cert: State)

5351   Toyakoi Ventures, LLC
        95 Bridger Cir
        Woodland Hills, UT 84653
        Contact: Elliot Collins President
        Tel: 801-634-4194
        Email: ecollins@toyakoi.com
        Website: www.toyakoi.com
SAP consulting & full-service background checks. (Nat
Ame, estab 2010, empl 12, sales $664,000, cert: 8a)

Virginia

5352   Aarisha Inc.
        11890 Sunrise Valley Dr Ste 201
        Reston, VA 20191
        Contact: Shailesh Akhouri President
        Tel: 703-579-8510
        Email: supplier@aarisha.com
        Website: www.aarisha.net
Software dev life cycle, Oracle Fusion Middle ware
Administration, Oracle Fusion Middle ware Dev, Oracle
Database Administration, Business Intelligence and Data
warehousing, Software Development. (As-Pac, estab
2005, empl 6, sales $1,059,708, cert: NMSDC)

5353   ACI Solutions Inc.
        131 E Broad St
        Falls Church, VA 22046
        Contact: Jovan Silva Business Develop Mgr
        Tel: 703-766-4070
        Email: jsilva@acisolutions.net
        Website: www.acisolutions.net
Information technology, data & voice networking
products & services. (AA, As-Pac, estab 2001, empl 25,
sales $125,000, cert: NMSDC)

5354   Advanced Computer Concepts
        7927 Jones Branch Dr Ste 600
        Mclean, VA 22102
        Contact: Mark Braxton Sr Acct Exec
        Tel: 571-395-4117
        Email: bill@acconline.com
        Website: www.acconline.com
IT hardware, software sales & network engineering
services, wireless network design & implementation, IT
security, IT storage systems, VOIP design & implementation. (Woman, estab 1982, empl 45, sales $55,000,000,
cert: WBENC)

5355   Advinti Technical Solutions, Inc.
        P.O. Box 37
        Bealeton, VA 22712
        Contact: Maurice Nowlin President
        Tel: 702-261-7090
        Email: maurice@advinti.com
        Website: www.advinti.com
Information technology systems integration, consulting
& technical training. (AA, estab 2006, empl 2, sales ,
cert: State)

5356 AEi International LLC
7686 Richmond Hwy, Ste 118
Alexandria, VA 22306
Contact: Jenna Reese CEO
Tel: 410-988-3966
Email: jenna.reese@aeiintl.com
Website: www.aeiintl.com
Management consulting & technology, strategic consulting, digital experience & enterprise technology related-services, staff augmentation. (Woman/AA, estab 2007, empl 12, sales $1,200,000, cert: 8a)

5357 Affigent, LLC
13873 Park Center Rd Ste 127
Herndon, VA 20171
Contact: Joe Clagett Acct Exec
Tel: 301-305-9513
Email: joe.clagett@affigent.com
Website: www.affigent.com
Dist IT product & systems integration. (Nat Ame, estab 2004, empl 5, sales , cert: NMSDC)

5358 AhaApps LLC
11608 Timberton Ct
Glen Allen, VA 23060
Contact: Satish Reddy CEO
Tel: 804-366-9979
Email: satish@ahaapps.com
Website: www.ahaapps.com
Design & build mobile applications for iOS (iPhone, iPad), Android phone & tablets, web applications, ASP.NET, ASP.NET MVC, Ruby on Rails, Java, Salesforce.com implementation & integration. (As-Pac, estab 2010, empl 15, sales $245,146, cert: State, NMSDC)

5359 All Native, Inc.
1229 King St 2nd Fl
Alexandria, VA 22314
Contact: Joe Harrison Exec Director
Tel: 703-838-8902
Email: jharrison@allnativegroup.com
Website: www.allnativeinc.com
Information Technology & Infrastructure, transport Systems, Network Administration, IT Infrastructure Installation, LAN/WAN Services, Database Administration, Help Desk, Asset Management, Information Assurance. (Nat Ame, estab 2008, empl 488, sales , cert: 8a)

5360 Alliant Global Strategies Inc.
4607 W. Broad St
Richmond, VA 23230
Contact: James Wallace
Tel: 804-283-2203
Email: jwallace@alliantglobalstrategies.com
Website: www.alliantglobalstrategies.com
Business process outsourcing (BPO) & technology training solutions. (AA, estab 2011, empl 5, sales $137,000, cert: State, NMSDC)

5361 Ampcus Inc.
14900 Conference Center Dr, Ste 500
Chantilly, VA 20151
Contact: Donna Howell Sr VP
Tel: 703-429-0550
Email: donna.howell@ampcus.com
Website: www.ampcus.com
Information technology and application development services that are aligned with our clients business objectives. (Woman/As-Ind, As-Pac, estab 2004, empl 1350, sales $77,550,031, cert: State, NMSDC, CPUC, WBENC)

5362 Apex CoVantage
198 Van Buren St Ste 200
Herndon, VA 20170
Contact: MIKE LOHNEIS Dir Proposal & Contract
Tel: 703-709-3000
Email: mlohneis@apexcovantage.com
Website: www.apexcovantage.com
Process engineering, knowledge & content management, imaging, document management, forms processing & digital assets creation, engineering: data conversion, purification & conflation, work order posting, inspections, audits. (As-Ind, estab 1988, empl 2500, sales , cert: State, NMSDC)

5363 Applied Integrity Consulting, LLC
40646 Weaver Ct
Leesburg, VA 20175
Contact: Loan Clarke CEO
Tel: 703-868-3886
Email: lclarke@aic-llc.us
Website: www.aic-llc.us
Enterprise IT & Software Engineering support and services. Expertise in Microsoft technologies. (Woman/As-Pac, estab 2011, empl 2, sales , cert: State)

5364 Archura, LLC
673 Potomac Station D, Ste 808
Leesburg, VA 20176
Contact: Kurt McHenry COO
Tel: 703-728-1302
Email: kurt.mchenry@archura.com
Website: www.archura.com
lifecycle requirements of wire-line, wireless and optical networks, design, deploy, maintain and manage large and small scale public & private network infrastructures. (AA, estab 2005, empl 85, sales $7,200,000, cert: State)

5365 Astyra Corporation
411 East Franklin St, Ste 105
Richmond, VA 23219
Contact: Lee Rattigan VP, Strategy & Development
Tel: 804-433-1117
Email: lrattigan@astyra.com
Website: www.astyra.com
IT staff augmentation & IT solutions: Medicaid & HIPAA application development & project management. (AA, estab 1997, empl 150, sales $15,000,000, cert: State, NMSDC, SDB)

5366 Atlantic Resource Group, Inc.
4880 Cox Rd, Ste 105
Glen Allen, VA 23060
Contact: President
Tel: 804-262-4400
Email:
Website: www.atlanticresource.com
Information technology, staff augmentation & project mgmt. (Woman, estab 1990, empl 45, sales , cert: WBENC)

5367 BAI, Inc.
4600 Duke St, Ste 303
Alexandria, VA 22304
Contact: Mindy Cookmeyer VP
Tel: 703-461-4713
Email: cookmeyerm@bai-inc.net
Website: www.bai-inc.net
Program mgmt & policy, implementation, security & info technology. (Hisp, estab 1999, empl 70, sales , cert: State)

5368 Balance Technology Group, Inc.
8136 Old Keene Mill Rd Ste A207
Springfield, VA 22152
Contact: Tracy Betts CEO
Tel: 703-451-8675
Email: tracy.betts@balanceinteractive.com
Website: www.balanceinteractive.com
Web design & development agency. (Woman, estab 1997, empl 13, sales $1,600,000, cert: WBENC)

5369 Benten Technologies
13996 Parkeast Circle
Herndon, VA 20171
Contact: President
Tel: 703-788-6560
Email:
Website: www.bententech.com
IT consulting. (As-Pac, estab 2000, empl 4, sales $2,050,615, cert: State)

5370 Biswas Information Technology Solutions Inc.
2612 Litchfield Dr
Herndon, VA 20171
Contact: Sumita Biswas
Tel: 202-203-0982
Email: sbiswas@b-itsinc.com
Website: www.b-itsinc.com
Database centric applications, dbase mgmt & development. (Woman/As-Ind, estab 2006, empl 5, sales $383,733, cert: NMSDC, WBENC, 8a)

5371 BP International, LLC
5885 Trinity Pkwy, Ste 100
Centreville, VA 20120
Contact: Thomas Orlowski Mktg Dir
Tel: 703-815-4644
Email: torlowski@bpintl.com
Website: www.bpintl.com
IT & physical security, enterprise & solutions architecture, IT & mgmt consulting, business process reengineering & change mgmt, organizational devel & strategy implementation, IT acquisition, project & logistical mgmt. (As-Pac, estab 1995, empl 40, sales , cert: State)

5372 Burke Consortium, Incorporated
5500 Cherokee Ave, Ste 510
Alexandria, VA 22312
Contact: Thomas Nodeen COO
Tel: 703-941-0600
Email: tnodeen@bcinow.com
Website: www.bcinow.com
Information technology solutions, software development, cyber security, independent verification & validation. (Woman, estab 1982, empl 44, sales $10,500,000, cert: WBENC)

5373 Capital Legal Solutions dba Capital Novus
10521 Rosehaven St Ste 300
Fairfax, VA 22030
Contact: Ramesh Purohit Business Dev Mgr
Tel: 703-226-1500
Email: rpurohit@capitalnovus.com
Website: www.capitalnovus.com
Forensic data collection from project sites around the world, data preservation, processing, and presentation, web hosting services & loading (Woman/As-Ind, As-Pac, estab 2002, empl 250, sales $21,560,000, cert: State, WBENC)

5374 Centurion Consulting Group, LLC
13800 Coppermine Rd Ste 190
Herndon, VA 20171
Contact: Krampf Jacob Principal Owner
Tel: 571-375-8179
Email: jacob@centurioncg.com
Website: www.centurioncg.com
IT/Professional staffing. (Woman, estab 2016, empl 65, sales $4,409,535, cert: State)

5375 CEXEC Inc.
11440 Commerce Park Dr Ste 600
Reston, VA 20191
Contact: Mike Klazas Dir of Mktg
Tel: 703-766-8489
Email: mike.klazas@cexec.com
Website: www.cexec.com
Information technology svcs, telecommunications, LAN/WANs, networking. (Nat Ame, estab 1976, empl 144, sales , cert: State)

5376 Cheshil Consultants, Inc.
8136 Old Keene Mill Rd, Ste B-201
Springfield, VA 22152
Contact: Chet Bhimani President
Tel: 703-569-8763
Email: cvbhimani@ccione.com
Website: www.ccione.com
Information technology consulting. (As-Ind, estab 1991, empl 13, sales $1,226,303, cert: State)

5377 Citadel Logic
26 Town Center Way, Ste 236
Hampton, VA 23666
Contact: VP plans/programs
Tel: 757-864-0905
Email:
Website: www.citadellogic.com
Cyber security, IT, intelligence, command & control, UAS/RPA operations & support, energy security/management, logistics & emergency management support. (AA, estab 2009, empl 6, sales $400,000, cert: State)

5378 Commonwealth Copy Products dba Commonwealth Digital Office Solutions
21205 Ridgetop Circle
Sterling, VA 20166
Contact: Dir Major Accts
Tel: 240-401-4776
Email:
Website: http://commonwealthdigital.com
Document management systems managed network services, managed print services, records retention, systems integration hardware and software. (Minority, estab 1977, empl 80, sales $21,000,000, cert: State)

5379 Conviso Inc.
312 E Main St, Ste 200
Luray, VA 22835
Contact: Uday Malhan President
Tel: 703-980-7074
Email: umalhan@convisoinc.com
Website: www.convisoinc.com
Application Development & Maintenance lication security & applications portfolio rationalization, .NET, Java, PeopleSoft, Systems Integration. (As-Ind, estab 2010, empl 18, sales $1,590,000, cert: State)

5380 CoreLogix Consulting Inc.
1900 Campus Commons Dr Ste 100
Reston, VA 20191
Contact: Inderbir Singh President
Tel: 703-665-0813
Email: inder@clx-inc.com
Website: www.clx-inc.com
IT & management consulting services. (As-Ind, estab 2011, empl 25, sales $1,400,000, cert: State)

5381 Corporate Leads, Inc.
2009 Mara Park Pl
Williamsburg, VA 23185
Contact: Luis Long President
Tel: 757-220-8215
Email: longl@corporateleads.com
Website: http://CorporateLeads.com
Corporate Leads, Inc. is a contingency search firm specializing in the global placement of Junior Military Officers and business experienced managers, supervisors, engineers, and technicians. (Hisp, estab 1997, empl 2, sales $462,000, cert: State)

5382 CurtMont Global Services, Inc.
9501 Hull St Rd, Ste D
Richmond, VA 23236
Contact: Curtiss Stancil President
Tel: 804-982-9349
Email: cstancil@curtmont.com
Website: www.curtmontglobalservices.com
Contracted foodservices, facility management, and transportation support services through our operating companies (CurtMont Foodservices and TransitServcorp). We are minority owned certified in 20 states in the USA. (AA, estab 2014, empl 105, sales $2,000,000, cert: State)

5383 Cyber Clarity Inc.
15722 Ryder Court
Haymarket, VA 20169
Contact: Ed Kraemer VP
Tel: 571-982-6710
Email: ed@cyberclarity.com
Website: www.cyberclarity.com
Cyber Intelligence, Operational Continuity, Computer network Defense, Incident Response & Compliance. (Woman, estab 2011, empl 12, sales $1,700,000, cert: State, City)

5384 Cynet Systems Inc.
21000 Atlantic Blvd #700
Sterling, VA 20166
Contact: Arpit Paul AVP - Strategy & Partnerships
Tel: 571-645-5910
Email: arpitp@cynetsystems.com
Website: www.cynetsystems.com
IT & engineering staffing consulting, direct/full time hiring, contract (temp hiring) or contract to hire services. (As-Ind, As-Pac, estab 2010, empl 1012, sales $56,000,000, cert: NMSDC)

5385 Data Concepts
4405 Cox Rd Ste 140
Glen Allen, VA 23060
Contact: Dennis Woomer Dir Business Dev
Tel: 804-968-4700
Email: dennis.woomer@dataconcepts-inc.com
Website: www.dataconcepts-inc.com
Application development, Microsoft, Java & Mobile technologies.. (Woman, estab 1997, empl 20, sales $15,000,000, cert: State)

5386 Dataline Inc.
9830 Mayland Dr Ste J
Richmond, VA 23233
Contact: John Cumberland Sr Acct Mgr
Tel: 804-270-4900
Email: john.cumberland@dataline.com
Website: www.dataline.com
Applications development, collaborative tools & help desk consulting. (Hisp, estab 1960, empl 450, sales , cert: State)

5387 Deque Systems, Inc.
2121 Cooperative Way Ste 210
Reston, VA 20191
Contact: Preety Kumar CEO
Tel: 703-225-0380
Email: preety.kumar@deque.com
Website: www.deque.com
IT consulting & services. (Woman/As-Ind, estab 1999, empl 25, sales $1,745,001, cert: State, WBENC)

5388 DESKTOP SERVICE CENTER, INC.
111 N 17th St
Richmond, VA 23219
Contact: Philise Conein CEO
Tel: 804-249-8720
Email: info@techead.com
Website: www.techead.com
IT staff augmentation svcs, web & graphics training, website devel, Linux platform. (Woman, estab 1988, empl 100, sales $7,000,000, cert: State, WBENC)

5389 Digilent Consulting, LLC
2612 Amanda Ct
Vienna, VA 22180
Contact: Vinny Raj Managing Dir
Tel: 412-657-2219
Email: vinnyraj@digilentconsulting.com
Website: www.digilentconsulting.com
SMAC (Social, Mobile, Analytics and Cloud), Cyber Security expertise/capabilities. (Woman/As-Ind, estab 2006, empl 5, sales $450,000, cert: State, NMSDC)

5390 Digital Intelligence Systems, LLC
8270 Greensboro Dr Ste 1000
McLean, VA 22102
Contact: Jessica Ocello MSP Client Partner
Tel: 703-752-7900
Email: broadridge@disys.com
Website: www.disys.com
Information technology service, staff augmentation & recruitment, hardware & software, wireless & mobile systems design, implementation & mgmt. (As-Ind, As-Pac, estab 1994, empl 5348, sales $427,400,000, cert: NMSDC)

5391 DISYS Solutions, Inc.
4151 Lafayette Center Dr Ste 600
Chantilly, VA 20151
Contact: Vinu Luthra COO
Tel: 703-802-0500
Email: supplier.diversity@disyssolutions.com
Website: www.disyssolutions.com
Information technology products & services. (As-Ind, estab 2010, empl 45, sales $62,000,000, cert: State)

5392   Diverse Solutions Group Inc.
       12185 Balls Ford Rd
       Manassas, VA 20109
       Contact: Steve ForUs President
       Tel: 571-921-4801
       Email: sforus@dsginc-usa.com
       Website: www.diversesolutionsgrp.com
Industrial Security Services, Security Management and
Support Services utilizing the latest technologies and
proven practices to comply with HSPD-12 and FIPS 201-2
compliance. (Woman/Hisp, estab 2010, empl 6, sales
$474,000, cert: 8a, SDB)

5393   Dorkin Inc.
       1103 W Broad St
       Falls Church, VA 22046
       Contact: Stephanie Juniel President
       Tel: 202-657-9907
       Email: sjuniel@dorkin.net
       Website: www.dorkin.net/
Project Management Software, HR staffing software, Data
Encryptions software, Access Development, Asset Manage-
ment, Business Intelligence, Cloud & Virtualization,
Content Management Systems, Custom Software.
(Woman/AA, estab 2012, empl 11, sales , cert: 8a)

5394   E&E Enterprises Global Inc.
       2017 Cunningham Dr, Ste 213
       Hampton, VA 23666
       Contact: Ernest Green CEO
       Tel: 757-826-9532
       Email: egreen@eeenterprisesinc.com
       Website: www.eeenterprisesinc.com
Broadband internet satellite communications systems,
digital satellite television, web based & computer based
training products & programs, IT solutions, WiFi & wireless
technologies. (AA, estab 1997, empl 11, sales $2,000,000,
cert: State)

5395   END TO END COMPUTING
       1800 Diagonal Rd Ste 600
       Alexandria, VA 22150
       Contact: Esteve Mede Principal
       Tel: 833-720-7770
       Email: emede@eecomputing.com
       Website: www.eecomputing.com
Vendor agnostic solutions, infrastructure solution, network
architectureand design, network security architecture,
unified communications, data center design, Cloud data
center design, information assurance, policy implementation & procedure. (Minority, estab 2012, empl 31, sales
$3,800,000, cert: State)

5396   Enterprise Architecture and Information Manage-
          ment
       9220 Treasure Oak Ct
       Lorton, VA 22079
       Contact: Arulkumar Selvappan President
       Tel: 703-725-3801
       Email: aselvappan@eaaim.com
       Website: www.eaaim.com
Enterprise architecture solutions, actionable enterprise
architecture, information & data architecture, application
architecture, metadata management, repository support.
(As-Ind, estab 2006, empl 2, sales $350,000, cert: 8a)

5397   Enterprise ITech Corp.
       10014 Manor Pl
       Fairfax, VA 22032
       Contact: Pals Nagaraj
       Tel: 703-731-7881
       Email: pnagaraj@enterpriseitech.com
       Website: www.enterpriseitech.com
Full Software Development Lifecycle, Business Analytics,
Business Intelligence, Enterprise Web Development,
Enterprise Legacy System Modernization, Mobile
application development, Database Design, Data
Warehouse ETL. (As-Ind, estab 2000, empl 2, sales
$300,000, cert: State, NMSDC)

5398   ESC, Inc.
       2451 Crystal Dr Ste 775
       Arlington, VA 22202
       Contact: Maggie Harris President & CEO
       Tel: 703-291-6706
       Email: harris_maggie@escinc1.com
       Website: www.escinc1.com
Information Technology, Information Security & Assurance, Cyber Security, Network Security, Certifications &
Accreditation, Access Control, Investigative & Adjudica-
tion, Information Sharing, Portfolio Management.
(Woman/AA, estab 1992, empl 110, sales $10,000,000,
cert: State)

5399   EsteemLogic
       722 E Market St
       Leesburg, VA 20176
       Contact: CEO
       Tel: 571-235-9284
       Email:
       Website: www.esteemlogic.com
IT consulting and training firm that implements sustainable, scalable solutions to ensure organizations optimize
engagement with its people, customers and the commu-
nities they serve. (Woman/AA, estab 2017, empl 2, sales
, cert: State, WBENC)

5400   ETELIC Inc.
       5388 Twin Hickory Rd
       Glen Allen, VA 23059
       Contact: Mark Murphy President
       Tel: 866-240-3395
       Email: mark.murphy@etelic.com
       Website: www.etelic.com
Computer programming svcs: systems design, facilities
management, consulting, database & data warehouse.
(As-Pac, estab 2004, empl 20, sales $2,400,000, cert:
State, NMSDC)

5401   EvereTech LLC
       2705 Main Sail Ct
       Henrico, VA 23233
       Contact: Andrew Everett Principal
       Tel: 804-986-9998
       Email: andrew.everett@everetech.com
       Website: www.everetech.com
Systems Administration & Engineering , Network Design,
Network Administration & Network Engineering,
Software Development & Engineering, Project Manage-
ment, COTS/GOTS Systems Integration & Configuration.
(AA, estab 2014, empl 7, sales $300,000, cert: State)

5402　eWaste Tech Systems, LLC
501 E Franklin St Ste 726
Richmond, VA 23219
Contact: Felipe Wright Managing Member
Tel:　804-716-3577
Email: fwright@ewastetech.com
Website: www.ewastetech.com
Green Information technology sustainability & asset mgmt, data destruction & disposition services, electronic waste disposal. (AA, estab 2012, empl 16, sales $225,000, cert: State, NMSDC)

5403　Eyak Technology
22980 Indian Creek Dr Ste 400
Dulles, VA 20166
Contact: Susan Stepanski Business Dev Mgr
Tel:　703-481-0050
Email: susan.stepanski@eyaktek.com
Website: www.eyaktek.com
IT products, information assurance, help desk, networking, storage solutions, satellite & LMR communications, wireless, physical security, critical infrastructure design & construction, medical staffing, enironmental mediation. (Nat Ame, estab 2002, empl 170, sales $225,000,000, cert: 8a)

5404　Force 1 Global, LLC
1050 Temple Ave Ste 214
Colonial Heights, VA 23834
Contact: DeAlteman Beasley CEO
Tel:　804-723-1164
Email: dbeasley@force1global.com
Website: www.force1global.com
Staffing, outsourcing & technology integration. (AA, estab 2014, empl 1, sales , cert: State, NMSDC)

5405　G2 Global Solutions, LLC
202 Church St SE Ste 538
Leesburg, VA 20176
Contact: Elizabeth Lauren Galati CEO
Tel:　703-349-7787
Email: lgalati@g2gs.net
Website: www.g2gs.net
Cyber Exploitation, Information Technology Services, Intelligence. (Woman/Hisp, estab 2012, empl 86, sales $8,000,000, cert: State, 8a, SDB)

5406　G2 Ops Inc.
205 Business Park Dr
Virginia Beach, VA 23462
Contact: Robert Gregorio COO
Tel:　757-965-8330
Email: bobg@g2-ops.com
Website: www.g2-ops.com
Model based systems engineering & cybersecurity, acquiring data, modeling systems & processes, identifying cyber vulnerabilities, performing analysis. (Woman, estab 2005, empl 15, sales $2,200,000, cert: State, WBENC)

5407　Geologics Corporation
5285 Shawnee Rd, Ste 300
Alexandria, VA 22312
Contact: John Hildreth Dir Consulting Services
Tel:　978-524-8152
Email: jhildreth@geologics.com
Website: www.geologics.com
Technical services: systems engineering, spacecraft, space systems, software dev, science applications. (Hisp, estab 1989, empl 500, sales $79,434,480, cert: NMSDC)

5408　Global Geographic Inc.
11511 Cavalier Landing Ct
Fairfax, VA 22030
Contact: Sameer Chandra VP
Tel:　703-594-5181
Email: schandra@globalgeographic.com
Website: www.globalgeographic.com
IT Services. (As-Pac, estab 2006, empl 3, sales , cert: State, NMSDC)

5409　Global Technology Solutions, LLC
108 E Grace St, Ste 01
Richmond, VA 23219
Contact: Anthony Long
Tel:　804-343-7400
Email: aelong@gtsnetwork.com
Website: www.gtsnetwork.com
Systems design & implementation, project mgmt, network security & mgmt, business transformation outsourcing, software design & implementation. (AA, estab 2003, empl 10, sales $600,000, cert: State)

5410　Gupton & Associates, Inc.
901 N Pitt St Ste 230
Alexandria, VA 22314
Contact: Clara Lee Client Engagement Mgr
Tel:　703-419-3048
Email: clarablee@guptonassociates.com
Website: http://guptonassociates.com
Program/Project Management; Application Architecture; Information Assurance/Cyber Security; Network Services; Virtualization & Consolidation; Cloud Computing; Engineering Services; Data Analysis & Generation. (Woman, estab 2002, empl 5, sales $19,200,000, cert: State)

5411　Hanusoft Inc.
7206 Impala Dr, Ste 214
Richmond, VA 23228
Contact: Bala Kamuju President
Tel:　804-484-2400
Email: kamuju@hanusoftinc.com
Website: www.hanusoftinc.com
Computer related services, implementation requirements, computer applications, implementing customize hardware systems, updating & modifying existing programs. (As-Ind, estab 2005, empl 46, sales $4,816,708, cert: State)

5412　HarmonyTech
2010 Corporate Ridge Ste 700
McLean, VA 22102
Contact: Nat Vinod President
Tel:　703-405-4587
Email: nat.vinod@harmonytech.com
Website: http://harmonytech.com
SQL/NoSQL/XML development, Microsoft Dynamics, Sharepoint, Secure Enterprise Search, Azure, AWS, 508 accessibility,mobile apps,enterprise architecture, server & desktop hardening, Agile/Scrum, Native Xamarin, Program Management. (As-Ind, estab 1995, empl 30, sales $3,500,000, cert: 8a)

5413　HyperGen Inc.
7810 Carvin St
Roanoke, VA 24019
Contact: Sherry Dyer VP Sales
Tel:　540-992-6500
Email: sales@hypergeninc.com
Website: www.hypergeninc.com
PeopleSoft® functional & technical consulting svcs: implementation, upgrade, system analysis, custom developed. (Woman, estab 1992, empl 25, sales $5,000,000, cert: State, WBENC)

5414 ILM Corporation
       1551 Jefferson Davis Hwy, Ste 200
       Fredericksburg, VA 22401
       Contact: Jason Cohen President
       Tel: 540-898-1406
       Email: bids@ilmcorp.com
       Website: www.ilmcorp.com
Document & data capture services. (As-Pac, estab 1976,
empl 15, sales $3,000,000, cert: State)

5415 INADEV Corporation
       1651 Old Meadow Rd Ste 205
       McLean, VA 22102
       Contact: Scott Armstrong Chief Strategy Officer
       Tel: 703-286-0860
       Email: scott.armstrong@inadev.com
       Website: www.inadev.com
Application Modernization & Development, cloud &
mobile enablement, Software Architecture, Design,
Implementation, & Integration, Native & Hybrid Apps,
Content Management Systems, Dashboard. (As-Ind, estab
2001, empl 65, sales $6,000,000, cert: State, 8a)

5416 Inficare, Inc.
       22375 Broderick Dr Ste 225
       Dulles, VA 20166
       Contact: VP
       Tel: 703-945-1800
       Email:
       Website: www.inficaretech.com
IT consulting, staff augmentation. (As-Ind, estab 2001,
empl 465, sales $29,000,000, cert: State)

5417 Infomatics Corporation
       23465 Rock Haven Way, Ste 100
       Dulles, VA 20166
       Contact: Shahil Shariff CEO
       Tel: 703-786-4824
       Email: jeff@infomaticscorp.com
       Website: www.infomaticscorp.com
Digital Transformation, Application Modernization.
(Woman/As-Ind, estab 2005, empl 67, sales $15,000,000,
cert: State)

5418 Innovative Computing & Applied Technology
       11490 Commerce Park Dr, Ste 530
       Reston, VA 20191
       Contact: Bruce Freedman VP of Corporate Devel
       Tel: 703-391-1600
       Email: bruce.freedman@incatech-corp.com
       Website: www.incatech-corp.com
Web Design & Development, Enterprise Web Content
Management, User Interface (UI)/User Experience (UX)
Design, Full Life Cycle Software Devel, Microsoft
SharePoint Development & Administration. (Woman, estab
2007, empl 20, sales , cert: 8a)

5419 Innovative Technology Application, Inc. (ITA)
       6551 Loisdale Ct
       Springfield, VA 22150
       Contact: Jim Clifford strat bus dev
       Tel: 703-924-9200
       Email: jimc@itapages.com
       Website: www.itapages.com
Computer based training; multimedia presentations;
interactive full motion video training; PC; multimedia
graphics applications; CD-ROM production; simulations;
3D imagery devel; full text search & retrieval databases;
etc. (As-Pac, estab 1995, empl 113, sales $25,000,000,
cert: State)

5420 Inoventures, LLC/SciMetrika, LLC
       7601 Lewinsville Road Ste 101
       McLean, VA 22102
       Contact: Meena Krishnan CEO
       Tel: 703-917-6622
       Email: meenak@inoventures.com
       Website: www.inoventures.com
Information Technology, Big Data, Software Engineering
and Development, Systems Integration, Cloud Migration,
and Talent Acquisition. (Woman/As-Ind, estab 2008,
empl 53, sales $4,550,315, cert: WBENC)

5421 Inscope Internatioinal, Inc.
       12018 Sunrise Valley Dr Ste 100
       Reston, VA 20191
       Contact: Acct Exec
       Tel: 703-480-3280
       Email:
       Website: www.inscopeinternational.com
IT strategy, deployment & operations, enterprise
application, integration, data & COTS solutions. (AA,
estab 1997, empl 100, sales $33,301,501, cert: NMSDC)

5422 Integrated Support Systems Inc (ISSi)
       P.O. Box 2402
       Arlington, VA 22202
       Contact: Frank Duron CEO
       Tel: 703-892-6100
       Email: fduron@integratedsupport.com
       Website: www.integratedsupport.com
Web design, develop & content mgmt, imaging, form
conversion, records & docuemnt mgmt, workflow &
litigation solutions, systems integration & custom
solutions. (Hisp, estab 1984, empl 22, sales $2,334,042,
cert: NMSDC)

5423 IntellecTechs, Inc.
       195 S Rosemont Rd
       Virginia Beach, VA 23455
       Contact: Jeri Prophet CEO
       Tel: 757-962-2487
       Email: accounting@intellectechs.com
       Website: www.intellectechs.com
Information technology (IT), logistics, program management, training & testing & professional services.
(Woman, estab 2008, empl 30, sales $1,500,000, cert:
8a)

5424 IntellectFaces, Inc.
       23397 Minerva Dr
       Ashburn, VA 20148
       Contact: Kishore Kochi CEO
       Tel: 703-340-6445
       Email: kkochi@intellectfaces.com
       Website: www.intellectfaces.com
IT and managed services. (Woman/As-Pac, estab 2011,
empl 10, sales $854,791, cert: NMSDC, WBENC)

5425 iQuasar, LLC
       6 Pidgeon Hill Dr Ste 305
       Sterling, VA 20165
       Contact: Amin Bhat Chief Business Officer
       Tel: 703-962-6001
       Email: amin.bhat@iquasar.com
       Website: www.iQuasar.com
Information technology solutions & services, IT consulting, staffing & recruitment services. (As-Pac, estab 2004,
empl 15, sales $2,070,152, cert: State, NMSDC)

5426   Iron Horse Computers, Inc.
8328-A Traford Ln
Springfield, VA 22152
Contact: Office Mgr
Tel: 703-866-6413
Email:
Website: www.ih-online.com
LAN/WAN; network utilities, CAD, GIS, hardware, software, parts, supplies, system integration, consulting, telephone integration, imaging, repairs. (Hisp, estab 1990, empl 3, sales $1,600,000, cert: State)

5427   IT Data Consulting LLC
11951 Freedom Dr, Ste 1300
Reston, VA 20190
Contact: Benny Asnake CEO
Tel: 202-999-9184
Email: benny@it-dc.com
Website: www.it-dc.com
Enterprise Business Solutions, Enterprise Data Management, Cloud/Web/Mobile/Database Solution Development. (AA, estab 2010, empl 8, sales $570,000, cert: 8a, SDB)

5428   iWorks Corporation
1889 Preston Shite Dr Ste 100
Reston, VA 20191
Contact: Jothi Radhakrishnan Sr. VP
Tel: 571-485-2004
Email: jradhakrishnan@iworkscorp.com
Website: www.iworkscorp.com
Information technology consulting & staff augmentation. (As-Ind, estab 2005, empl 9, sales $8,000,000, cert: State)

5429   JPI Technology LLC
9720 Capital Court, Ste 301
Manassas, VA 20155
Contact: Haris Perwaiz VP
Tel: 703-828-5651
Email: harris@jpitechnology.com
Website: www.jpitechnology.com
Information consulting, contracting, application development, e-commerce/ERP, application integration, infrastructure & staff augmentation. (Woman/As-Ind, estab 2011, empl 9, sales $1,300,000, cert: State)

5430   Key Concepts Knowledgebase LLC
4031 University Dr
Fairfax, VA 22030
Contact: Kim de Peiza President
Tel: 703-966-1364
Email: kdepeiza@keyknowledgebase.com
Website: www.keyknowledgebase.com
Technical and customer centric documentation, SOPsService Desk supportLAN/WAN Infrastructure and Systems Administration supportSoftware Web Development, SOA development, mobile computing, Web 2.0 (AA, estab 2004, empl 10, sales $450,000, cert: NMSDC, 8a)

5431   Knowledge Connections, Inc.
610 Herndon Pkwy Ste 900A
Herndon, VA 20170
Contact: Marion Bonhomme-Knox President
Tel: 571-203-9120
Email: marion.bk@theknowledgeconnection.com
Website: www.knowledgeconnector.com
Systems engineering & telecommunications. (Woman/AA, estab 1996, empl 150, sales $4,000,000, cert: State)

5432   Knowledge Information Solutions, Inc.
227 South Rosemont Road
Virginia Beach, VA 23452
Contact: Terry Kreamer CFO
Tel: 757-463-0033
Email: terry.kreamer@kisinc.net
Website: www.kisinc.net
Information technology products & services: inside/outside plant cabling & wireless solutions, security systems, telephone systems, computer products & services, web development, data base dev & mgmt, network architecture & engineering. (Woman/Hisp, estab 1983, empl 100, sales $30,200,000, cert: State)

5433   Logistics Applications Inc.
2760 Eisenhower Ave, Ste 302
Alexandria, VA 22314
Contact: Thomas Walker Dir Business Dev
Tel: 703-317-9800
Email: twalker@logapp.com
Website: www.logapp.com
Facilities mgmt: warehouses & clearinghouses, mailroom & delivery services, inventory management; information svcs: contract close-out svcs, adverse event reporting, bookwriting, information dissemination; training svcs. (AA, estab 1986, empl 250, sales , cert: State)

5434   Loyola Enterprises Inc.
2984 S Lynnhaven Rd Ste 101
Virginia Beach, VA 23452
Contact: Benito Loyola President
Tel: 757-498-6118
Email: benito@loyola.com
Website: www.loyola.com
TS/SCI, Modeling & Simulation Information Technology, Web Portal and Multimedia. (Hisp, estab 1991, empl 30, sales $7,325,312, cert: State)

5435   MAI Enterprises, Inc.
P.O. Box 1194
Annandale, VA 22003
Contact: Bonnie Norem President
Tel: 703-750-2228
Email: bonnie@maienterprises.com
Website: www.maienterprises.com
System engineering, graphic illustration, desktop publishing, proposals, tech editing & writing, computer hardware & software products. (Woman, estab 1986, empl 15, sales $763,400, cert: State)

5436   Management Support Technology, Inc. (MSTI)
3701 Pender Dr Ste 505
Fairfax, VA 22030
Contact: Norris Middleton President & CEO
Tel: 703-385-5841
Email: nmiddleton@msti-net.com
Website: www.msti-net.com
Information Management Support Incident Management, Problem Management, Change Management, Configuration Management, Asset Management, enterprise desktop Systems (AA, estab 1989, empl 125, sales $115,798,643, cert: State)

5437   Maven Inc
161 Fort Evans Rd, NE Ste 205
Leesburg, VA 20176
Contact: Venkat Mallasani President
Tel: 202-888-7159
Email: vm@maven-federal.com
Website: www.maven-federal.com
Computer Programming Services, Systems Design Services, Facilities Management Services, Management Consulting Services. (As-Pac, estab 2010, empl 10, sales $1,400,000, cert: 8a)

5438 McKinney & McKinney Technical Services, Inc.
3122 Golansky Blvd Ste 202
Woodbridge, VA 22192
Contact: Michelle McKinney CEO
Tel: 703-580-1995
Email: mmckinney@mmtsi.com
Website: www.mmtsi.com
Engineering, systems engineering, software development, and Tier I, II, and III Help Desk Support. We provide systems engineering support for FAA Air Traffic Management systems (Woman/AA, estab 1989, empl 15, sales $1,600,000, cert: State)

5439 Meta Dimensions Inc.
7115 Leesburg Pike, Ste 213
Falls Church, VA 22043
Contact: Amit Prakash
Tel: 571-969-4140
Email: amit@metadim.com
Website: www.metadim.com
Analytics service, Big Data Lake, Data Visualization, Enterprise Info Mgmt, Intelligent Enterprise Roadmap, Master Data Mgmt. (Woman/As-Ind, estab 2007, empl 85, sales $2,064,955, cert: State, NMSDC, WBENC)

5440 MicroAutomation, Inc.
5870 Trinity Pkwy, Ste 600
Centreville, VA 20120
Contact: Suresh Gursahaney CEO
Tel: 703-543-2100
Email: Sgursahaney@microautomation.com
Website: www.microautomation.com
Computer telephony integration, speech recognition, interactive voice response, reporting, workforce mgmt & digital recording. (As-Ind, estab 1991, empl 34, sales $7,900,000, cert: NMSDC)

5441 MicroHealth, LLC
8245 Boone Blvd, Ste 706
Vienna, VA 22182
Contact: Jutta Whitfield Business Develop Mgr
Tel: 855-294-3547
Email: jutta.whitfield@microhealthllc.com
Website: www.microhealthllc.com
Health information technology & health information mgmt. (As-Pac, estab 2010, empl 71, sales , cert: 8a)

5442 MicroTechnologies, LLC
8330 Boone Blvd, Ste 600
Vienna, VA 22182
Contact: Aaron Drabkin SVP of Contracts
Tel: 703-891-1073
Email: adrabkin@microtech.net
Website: www.MicroTech.net
Program mngt, database mgnt & admin, change mgmt & process re-engineering, sys eng svcs, info sys sustainment & support, IT svcs & solns, collaboration svcs & info sharing apps, network solns & sys modernization, & IT enterprise transformation. (Hisp, estab 2004, empl 420, sales $780,000,000, cert: State, NMSDC)

5443 Mindseeker, Inc.
20130 Lakeview Center Plaza, Ste 320
Ashburn, VA 20147
Contact: Cassie Kelly VP, Client Services & Ops
Tel: 304-549-9281
Email: ckelly@mindseeker.com
Website: www.mindseeker.com
Information Technology, Financial, Clerical and Enterprise Performance Management services and solutions. (Woman/AA, estab , empl 234, sales $2,000,000, cert: State, WBENC)

5444 Mosaic Solutions, Inc.
209 Elden St, Ste 204
Herndon, VA 20170
Contact: Vikash Nangalia Program Mgr
Tel: 703-707-1680
Email: vikash@mosaic-us.com
Website: www.mosaic-us.com/
Systems integration, program mgmt, enterprise resource mgmt, customer relationship mgmt, data mgmt, database admin & warehousing, knowledge mgmt, networking, desktop & help desk svcs, business process outsourcing & supply chain mgmt. (As-Ind, estab 1996, empl 17, sales $1,170,660, cert: NMSDC)

5445 NETHOST, Inc.
1750 Tysons Blvd. Ste 1500
McLean, VA 22102
Contact: Ikram Koreshi CEO
Tel: 571-236-0781
Email: ikoreshi@nethostus.com
Website: http://nethostus.com
Network systems & data communication, engineering, business processes, ERP & CRM functional areas & technical consulting. (As-Ind, estab 2002, empl 3, sales $300,000, cert: State)

5446 NetVision Resources
2201 Cooperative Way Ste 600
Herndon, VA 20171
Contact: Sunny Nangia Dir Resource Management
Tel: 703-342-4284
Email: snangia@netvisionresources.com
Website: www.netvisionresources.com
Information technology svcs: staff augmentation, on-site, off-site & off-shore software development. (As-Ind, estab 1999, empl , sales $180,000, cert: NMSDC)

5447 NexThreat
7686 Richmond Hwy Ste 116
Alexandria, VA 22306
Contact: Ruben Gavilan CEO
Tel: 202-796-1676
Email: ruben@nexthreat.com
Website: www.Nexthreat.com
Cyber Security. Emerging SIEM Tool Optimization (Splunk, Qradar, Arcsight Partner), Insider Threat Detection, Incident Response, SOC/NOC Support Services, Continuous Data Analytics, IA, IT Security, Vulnerability Assessments. (Hisp, estab 2016, empl 15, sales $1,000,000, cert: State)

5448 Nirvana International Inc.
2108 Gunnell Farms Dr
Vienna, VA 22181
Contact: Pritish Nawlakhe President
Tel: 571-215-0072
Email: pritish@nirvana-international.com
Website: http://nirvana-international.com
Oracle EBS/ERP Solutions, INFOR Solutions, Program & Project Management, Staff Augmentation, PCI Compliant Credit Card Solutions, Business Intelligence & Analytics solutions, Social Media Integration. (Woman/As-Ind, estab 2012, empl 5, sales $158,000, cert: State)

5449   OSI Federal Technologies, Inc.
     42020 Village Center Plaza, Ste 120-154
     Stone Ridge, VA 20105
     Contact: Sales
     Tel: 703-940-5879
     Email:
     Website: www.osifederal.com
Information Technology, Systems Integration. (Woman, estab 1988, empl 9, sales $9,000,000, cert: State)

5450   Pan Asia Resources Pte Ltd.
     44031 Pipeline Plaza Ste 305
     Ashburn, VA 20147
     Contact: Aparnaa Vinod President
     Tel: 571-269-2778
     Email: aparnaa@panasiagroup.net
     Website: www.panasiaresources.com
Information Technology, Marketing & Telecommunications. (Woman/As-Ind, estab 2003, empl 35, sales , cert: State)

5451   Pantheon Inc.
     1801 Robert Fulton Dr, Ste 160
     Reston, VA 20191
     Contact: Anna Bogdanova Business Dev Mgr
     Tel: 571-276-1130
     Email: annab@pantheon-inc.com
     Website: www.pantheon-inc.com/index.php/
     services-sit
Technology consulting services, Cloud engineering services. SAP services, Salesforce consulting services, Cyber Security services, Web development services, IT staff augmentation services, TaaS services, Customer Technology Solutions. (As-Pac, estab 1997, empl 1200, sales $247,000,000, cert: NMSDC, NWBOC)

5452   PeopleNTech LLC
     8133 Leesburg Pike, Ste 220
     Vienna, VA 22182
     Contact: Chandra Sharma Dir Business Dev
     Tel: 703-982-7034
     Email: chandra.sharma@email.peoplentech.com
     Website: www.peoplentech.com/index.php
IT & Engineering solutions, Development, Outsourcing & Consulting. (Woman/As-Pac, estab 2005, empl 57, sales $9,600,000, cert: State, City, NMSDC)

5453   Pioneer Corporate Services Inc.
     44345 Premier Plaza, Ste 120
     Ashburn, VA 20147
     Contact: Purna Dokku CEO
     Tel: 703-726-1653
     Email: purna@pcservicesinc.com
     Website: www.pcservicesinc.com/contactus.php
Software Integration, Database Services, Managed Services, IT Consulting Services. (As-Ind, estab 2002, empl 90, sales , cert: 8a)

5454   PL Systems LLC
     14570 Woodland Ridge Dr
     Centreville, VA 20121
     Contact: Donald Jung President
     Tel: 703-598-2333
     Email: jung.donald@plsystems.net
     Website: www.plsystems.net
IT services: infrastructure support, applications development, web services, Cloud based tools, CMMI level II, PMI & PMP certified staff, Global IT deployments, advanced systems design & delivery. (As-Pac, estab 2004, empl 25, sales $2,000,000, cert: 8a)

5455   Pretek Corporation
     800 Corporate Dr Ste 301
     Stafford, VA 22554
     Contact: Exec Director
     Tel: 703-855-7148
     Email:
     Website: www.pretek.com
Enterprise architecture, agile application development, DevOps, enterprise data management, IT infrastructure, systems engineering, and security. (As-Ind, estab 2002, empl 25, sales $2,800,000, cert: State, 8a)

5456   Protege LLC
     12359 Sunrise Valley Dr Ste 260
     Reston, VA 20191
     Contact: Shyam Monaysar Sr Business Devel Mgr
     Tel: 703-953-2535
     Email: shyam@protegellc.com
     Website: www.protegellc.com
Web/Application Development (.Net, Java, J2EE, JSP, HTML, DHTML, CSS, Ajax, Flash, C#, C++, C), Web Services(WebLogic, WebSphere, Apache, TeamSite, Windows Administration), SharePoint. (Woman/As-Ind, estab 2004, empl 60, sales $3,500,000, cert: State)

5457   Qassurance Technology Inc.
     5821 Maybrook Court
     Glen Allen, VA 23059
     Contact: Gurushyam Mony CEO
     Tel: 814-441-9634
     Email: support@qassurancetechnology.com
     Website: www.qassurancetechnology.com
Information technology consulting services. (As-Ind, estab 2012, empl 2, sales $145,000, cert: State)

5458   QSACK & Associates, Inc.
     2111 Wilson Blvd, Ste 700
     Arlington, VA 22201
     Contact: C. Anthony Cusack CEO
     Tel: 703-351-5035
     Email: cac@qsack1.com
     Website: www.qsack1.com
Professional, information technology & business support services, systems integration; information assurance; systems security services; information technology services, program & project management. (AA, estab 2001, empl 35, sales $3,879,000, cert: State)

5459   RazorX2, LLC
     403 Old Dominion Ave
     Herndon, VA 20170
     Contact: Mary Flaherty Business Develop Mgr
     Tel: 703-464-9829
     Email: mflaherty@razorx2.net
     Website: www.razorX2.net
Full-cycle Software Development, Tier 1, 2 & 3 level Help Desk Support, IT Program Management & Support, Technologies & Methodologies. (Woman/As-Pac, estab 2004, empl 30, sales , cert: 8a)

5460   Red Jacket Systems, LLC
     13912 Cristo Ct
     Centreville, VA 20120
     Contact: Rex Lallmang President
     Tel: 703-623-9982
     Email: rex@redjacketsystems.com
     Website: www.redjacketsystems.com
IT professional svcs: software engineering, IVV&V, project management, QA, CM, training, helpdesk, web development. (Nat Ame, estab 2002, empl 4, sales $210,000, cert: State)

5461   Reed Integration, Inc.
       7007 Harbour View Blvd Ste 117
       Suffolk, VA 23435
       Contact: Steve Waddell VP strategy
       Tel: 757-638-3238
       Email: swaddell@reedintegration.com
       Website: www.reedintegration.com
Systems engineering & project management. (Woman, estab 2002, empl 40, sales $5,000,000, cert: State)

5462   Savi Solutions, Inc.
       8200 Greensboro Dr, Ste 900
       McLean, VA 22102
       Contact: CEO
       Tel: 571-258-7602
       Email:
       Website: www.savisolutions.biz
Strategic Planning, Program/Project Management, Merger & Acquisition Support, Systems Implementation (ERP/CRM/SCM), Cloud Based Implementation Solutions, Business Requirement Analysis, System Design and Development. (Woman/As-Ind, estab 2010, empl 3, sales $552,551, cert: WBENC)

5463   Secured Network Solutions, Inc.
       929 Ventures Way Ste 113
       Chesapeake, VA 23320
       Contact: President
       Tel: 757-819-7647
       Email:
       Website: www.eamsns.com
Telecommunications & information technology: cabling, design, install, fiber optics single/multi-strand, fiber fusion & splicing, LAN/WAN/wireless network engineering, drafting & information systems security. (AA, estab 2006, empl 11, sales , cert: State)

5464   Shivan Technologies, Inc.
       12818 Owens Glen Dr
       Fairfax, VA 22030
       Contact: Rekha Bathula President
       Tel: 703-595-6879
       Email: contact@stgxinc.com
       Website: www.stgxinc.com
Information Technology (IT), Network Management, Computer Facilities Management, Program Management, Consulting, Administrative & Professional Support Services, Information Assurance, Enterprise Architecture, Cloud. (Woman/As-Pac, estab 2007, empl 4, sales , cert: State, 8a)

5465   SilTek, Inc.
       13454 Sunrise Valley Dr Ste 250
       Herndon, VA 20171
       Contact: Silvia M. Park President
       Tel: 703-620-9130
       Email: info@siltek.com
       Website: www.siltekinc.com
Computer hardware, IT svcs, systems integration, computer training. (Woman/As-Pac, estab 1997, empl 1, sales , cert: State)

5466   Simba Enterprises LLC
       21 Fort Evans Rd, Ste F
       Leesburg, VA 20176
       Contact: Ali Sajjad CEO
       Tel: 703-782-4042
       Email: asajjad@simbacom.net
       Website: www.simbacom.net
Satellite-based telecommunications & information technology solutions worldwide. (As-Ind, estab 2005, empl 10, sales $3,500,000, cert: State)

5467   Solvitur Systems LLC
       202 Church St SE Ste 526
       Leesburg, VA 20176
       Contact: Ade Odutola Managing Dir
       Tel: 703-348-3544
       Email: aodutola@solvitursystems.com
       Website: www.solvitursystems.com
Regulatory Compliance & Security Assessments, Privacy Impact Analysis, Cloud Security Services, FedRAMP, CSA, Assessment & Authorization: FISMA, FISCAM, DIACAP, FFIEC, PCI, HIPAA, ISO 27001/27002, Independent Verification & Validation. (AA, estab 2007, empl 5, sales $230,000, cert: State, 8a)

5468   Spurgetech, LLC
       21580 Atlantic Blvd, Ste 220B
       Sterling, VA 20166
       Contact: Susetha Balabishegan President
       Tel: 703-652-6576
       Email: susetha@spurgetech.com
       Website: www.spurgetech.com
Information Technology Consulting, contract & permanent staffing solutions, On-site, off-site or remote, ERP Resources, SAP, Oracle & Peoplesoft. (Woman/As-Pac, estab 2006, empl 5, sales $900,000, cert: State, WBENC)

5469   Stanton Secure Technologies, LLC
       2054 S Shirlington Rd
       Arlington, VA 22204
       Contact: Lisa Wallace CEO
       Tel: 703-568-0553
       Email: johnson@sst-llc.com
       Website: www.sst-llc.com
Information Assurance services, training & security management, Cyber Security Program Management, Assessment & Authorization, Security Engineering, Remediation Solutions, Security Awareness & Training. (Woman/AA, estab 2005, empl 2, sales $180,000, cert: State)

5470   Strategic Operational Solutions, Inc.
       8391 Old Courthouse Rd Ste 300
       Vienna, VA 22182
       Contact: Brennan Reif Business Operations Analyst
       Tel: 703-942-8590
       Email: brennan.reif@stopso.com
       Website: www.stopso.com
Acquisition Support & Logistics, Biometrics & Identity Management, Information Assurance & Cybersecurity, Information Technology, Policy & Analysis Support, Intelligence, Security, Critical Infrastructure, Force Protection/Anti-Terrorism. (As-Pac, estab 2006, empl 250, sales $24,000,000, cert: State)

5471   Summit Information Solutions, Inc.
       3957 Westerre Pkwy Ste 120
       Richmond, VA 23233
       Contact: Vickie Quigg Communications & Marketing Mgr
       Tel: 804-201-4356
       Email: vickie.quigg@summitis.com
       Website: www.summitis.com
Enterprise Architecture; Change Management; Information Technology; SCORM; Virtual; 3D; Training; Atomic Layering; ALD; Banking; Finance; Aerospace Engineering; Big Data; Data Analytics; Resource Management; Portfolio Management; Cloud; Procurement; AGIL. (Woman/As-Ind, estab 2002, empl 37, sales $8,326,000, cert: NMSDC)

5472 Sygna Technologies Inc
4000 Legato Rd Ste 1100
Fairfax, VA 22033
Contact: Paul Shakya President
Tel: 571-445-4800
Email: paul@sygnatechnologies.com
Website: www.sygnatechnologies.com
Temporary contract IT Staffing. (As-Ind, estab 2014, empl 1, sales , cert: State)

5473 Symposit LLC
4809 Eisenhower Ave Ste B3
Alexandria, VA 22304
Contact: President
Tel: 571-224-4739
Email:
Website: www.symposit.com
Cloud Solutions & Applications, Cloud Office Productivity Integration, Email Migration Services, Virtual Machines / Virtual Desktop Infrastructure, Windows & Linux Servers, Network & Wireless Infrastructure, Business Applications, Content Management. (Hisp, estab 2009, empl 6, sales $400,000, cert: 8a)

5474 Synapse Business Systems
11350 Random Hills Rd, Ste 800
Fairfax, VA 22030
Contact: Sales Head
Tel: 703-782-0007
Email:
Website: www.synapsebsystems.com
Staff Augmentation, Experienced, dedicated and qualified core staffs, Network of IT Professional, Systematic and well-defined process to recruit and hire new talent. (Woman/As-Ind, estab 2013, empl 63, sales $2,911,046, cert: City, NMSDC, WBENC)

5475 Synaptein Solutions Inc.
1568 Spring Hill Road Ste 402
Mclean, VA 22102
Contact: Sharad Dayma CEO
Tel: 703-209-2350
Email: sharad.d@synap-one.com
Website: www.synapteinsolutions.com
Staff Augmentation & Resource Planning Services, BPM Solutions, Product Dev, Customer Support, Professional Services, Enterprise Solutions Provider, Business Intelligence & DSS, Off-& and On-site. (As-Ind, estab 2011, empl 15, sales $1,196,000, cert: State, NMSDC, 8a)

5476 Talteam,Inc
13800 Coppermine Rd Ste 120
Herndon, VA 20171
Contact: Bobby Toe Exec VP-Partner
Tel: 571-315-4958
Email: bobbyt@talteam.com
Website: www.talteam.com
IT professional Services, Salesforce & Java technologies. (Woman/As-Ind, estab 2011, empl 100, sales $9,000,000, cert: WBENC)

5477 Team Askin Technologies, Inc
13135 Lee Jackson Memorial Hwy Ste 340
Fairfax, VA 22033
Contact: steve askin COO
Tel: 703-230-0111
Email: steve.askin@teamaskin.com
Website: www.teamaskin.com
Software engineering & development, electronic commerce, Java Applets, XML, Graphical User Interface (GUI), Front Page, Cold Fusion, Dreamweaver. (Woman/Hisp, estab 1992, empl 50, sales $9,000,000, cert: State, WBENC)

5478 Technalink, Inc.
8000 Towers Crescent Dr Ste 600
Vienna, VA 22182
Contact: Alka Dhillon CEO
Tel: 703-627-1916
Email: adhillon@technalink.net
Website: www.technalink.net
Informaiton technology staffing solutions. (Woman/As-Ind, estab 2000, empl 20, sales , cert: WBENC)

5479 Technatomy Corporation
3900 Jermantown Rd Ste 420
Fairfax, VA 22030
Contact: Nadeem Butler Managing Dir
Tel: 703-268-5525
Email: nbutler@technatomy.com
Website: www.technatomy.com
Information technology, program mgmt, logistics & engineering. (As-Ind, estab 2000, empl 11, sales $2,900,000, cert: State)

5480 Technical Expert Consulting LLC
5765-F Burke Centre Pkwy, Ste 182
Burke, VA 22015
Contact: Al Bradley President
Tel: 202-905-2392
Email: al.bradley@tecincorp.com
Website: www.tecincorp.com
Data Management, Business Intelligence & Systems Integration services. (AA, estab 2002, empl 6, sales $2,226,378, cert: 8a)

5481 Technogems Inc.
14039 Compton Heights Ct
Clifton, VA 20124
Contact: Jean Meslie President
Tel: 703-856-3350
Email: jean.meslie@technogemsinc.com
Website: www.technogemsinc.com
Android application dev, web application dev & maintenance, mobile applications & wireless protocols, business intelligence & data analysis, interactive application dev,
database design & implementation. (As-Pac, estab 2007, empl 3, sales $253,000, cert: 8a)

5482 Technology Assurance Group, Inc.
2114 Tomlynn St
Richmond, VA 23230
Contact: Angela Taylor CEO
Tel: 804-323-7480
Email: ahtaylor@tagva.com
Website: www.tagva.com
Systems integration: LAN/WAN, VP & wireless networks, bandwidth mgmt tools, file & directory svcs, storage, messaging, databases, IP telephony, desktop support. (Woman, estab 2002, empl 10, sales $850,000, cert: State)

5483 The Mt. Olivet Group, LLC
P.O. Box 56415
Virginia Beach, VA 23456
Contact: Jon McGlothian President
Tel: 757-271-8681
Email: jon@tmogllc.com
Website: www.tmogllc.com
Power, lighting, security and data products. (AA, estab 2007, empl 2, sales , cert: State)

5484 Total System Services US, Inc.
      1900 Campus Commons Dr #100
      Reston, VA 20191
      Contact: Aniths Paalepu
      Tel: 703-732-6063
      Email: anithapaalepu@tsysus.com
      Website: www.tsysus.com
IT consulting solutions, distributed operating & computing
systems, storage, networking, systems knowledge.
(Woman/As-Pac, estab 2012, empl 3, sales , cert: NMSDC)

5485 True Information Assurance, LLC
      7790 Abbey Oaks Court
      Manassas, VA 20112
      Contact: Steven Covey CEO
      Tel: 703-795-0535
      Email: coveys@true-ia.com
      Website: www.true-ia.com
IT, Cybersecurity, Management Consulting, Cybersecurity
program management, certification & accreditation (e.g.,
FISMA, DIACAP, FIPS, NIST, RMF), security engineering, risk
assessment & management. (AA, estab 2007, empl 30,
sales $12,000,000, cert: 8a)

5486 Unicom Government, Inc.
      2553 Dulles View Dr Ste 100
      Herndon, VA 20171
      Contact: Margaret Dooley Systems Int Client Exec
      Tel: 703-502-2937
      Email: maggie.dooley@unicomgov.com
      Website: http://unicomgov.com
Integration, Logistics, Warehouse Warehousing, Cloud
Computing, IT Products Computers, laptops Desktops
Servers Switches Cables Software, Supply Chain
Outsourcing, procurement, Financial Services Leasing. (As-
Pac, estab 1986, empl 199, sales $193,000,000, cert:
NMSDC)

5487 US Websoft Corp.
      2430 Birch Cove Rd
      Herndon, VA 20171
      Contact: Guru Nagaraja VP
      Tel: 703-318-0103
      Email: gnagaraja@us-websoft.com
      Website: http://us-websoft.com
Information technology products & services. (Woman/As-
Pac, estab 2000, empl 3, sales , cert: State)

5488 USM Business Systems, Inc.
      14175 Sullyfield Circle Ste 400
      Chantilly, VA 20151
      Contact: USM Business Systems SVP Business
      Development
      Tel: 832-881-7903
      Email: joshuar@usmsystems.com
      Website: www.usmsystems.com
Staffing & implementation solutions, computer software
programming, application dev, web dev, data warehouse
dev & ERP implementations. (As-Ind, estab 1999, empl
400, sales $45,000,000, cert: State)

5489 Vigintis LLC
      4000 Legato Rd, Ste 1100
      Fairfax, VA 22033
      Contact: President
      Tel: 703-395-3044
      Email:
      Website: www.vigintis.us
Agile Program & Project Management, Software Engineering & Product Development, Solution Architecture
& Technology Consulting, System & Application Integration, Cloud Solutions & Services. (As-Pac, estab 2004,
empl 3, sales $460,000, cert: 8a)

5490 Weiatech, LLC
      22584 Hammersmith Pl
      Ashburn, VA 20148
      Contact: Akomala Akouete Operation Director
      Tel: 703-665-9603
      Email: aakouete@weiatech.com
      Website: www.weiatech.com
Information technology equipment, solutions, and
services. (AA, estab 2016, empl 5, sales , cert: State)

5491 Wiltex Incorporated
      1012 Oaklawn Ave
      Norfolk, VA 23504
      Contact: Lois S. Williams CEO
      Tel: 757-961-3734
      Email: lwilliams@wiltexinc.com
      Website: http://wiltexinc.com
Desktop, server & network mgmt, LAN/WAN, database
mgmt, application development. (Woman/AA, estab
1999, empl 5, sales $2,039,000, cert: State)

5492 Worldgate, LLC
      1760 Reston Pkwy Ste 312
      Reston, VA 20190
      Contact: Dir Client Services
      Tel: 703-349-0493
      Email:
      Website: www.worldgatellc.com
IT systems integration consulting, technology platforms,
operating systems & infrastructures, data warehouse,
business intelligence, ERP, project managment, call
center/service desk. (Woman, estab 2002, empl 20, sales
$1,200,000, cert: State, WBENC)

5493 Zeva Inc
      10300 Eaton Place Ste 305
      Fairfax, VA 22030
      Contact: Sam I Shihadeh Dir Inside Sales- Diversity
      and Inclusion
      Tel: 301-518-3705
      Email: sshihadeh@zeva.us
      Website: www.zevainc.com
Cloud Services, Public Key Ennoblement (PKE), Identity,
Credentialing and Access Management. (Woman, estab
2005, empl 55, sales $10,500,000, cert: WBENC)

5494 Zillion Technologies, Inc.
      45189 Research Pl Ste 150
      Ashburn, VA 20147
      Contact: Kimberlee Sours Business Develop Mgr
      Tel: 703-592-6949
      Email: kimberlee@zilliontechnologies.com
      Website: www.zilliontechnologies.com
Business consulting & technology solutions, strategic
outsourcing & application management. (As-Ind, estab
2002, empl 350, sales $38,000,000, cert: State, NMSDC,
SDB)

5495 Zirtex Systems Corporation
7371 Atlas Walk Way, Ste 152
Gainesville, VA 20155
Contact: Rajeev Jessani President
Tel: 800-536-4982
Email: rjessani@zirtexsystems.com
Website: www.zirtexsystems.com
Management consulting & technology services. (As-Ind, estab 2006, empl 2, sales $328,832, cert: NMSDC)

5496 Zolon Tech Solutions, Inc.
13921 Park Center Rd, Ste 500
Herndon, VA 20171
Contact: Goutham Amarneni President
Tel: 703-636-7370
Email: supplier.diversity@zolon.com
Website: www.zolontech.com
Information technology consulting services: integration, modification, unification, secure & customized, applications & enterprise software solutions. (As-Ind, As-Pac, estab 1998, empl 623, sales $66,000,000, cert: NMSDC)

Vermont

5497 iTech US, Inc.
20 Kimball Ave, Ste 303N
South Burlington, VT 05403
Contact: Kishore Khandavalli CEO
Tel: 802-383-1500
Email: kk@itechus.com
Website: www.itechus.com
Software consulting services, application development, business process outsourcing solutions & offshore project development. (As-Pac, estab 2001, empl 1150, sales $53,000,000, cert: NMSDC)

Washington

5498 Advanced Technology Computers, Inc.
824 Grimes Rd
Bothell, WA 98012
Contact: Andre Tyson Owner
Tel: 425-486-6045
Email: andre@atcdirect.com
Website: www.atcdirect.com
Information technology systems integration, networking & information security. (AA, estab 1996, empl 3, sales , cert: 8a)

5499 Amreli Technology Solutions, LLC
17530 NE Union Hill Rd, Ste 290
Redmond, WA 98052
Contact: Atul Hirpara CEO
Tel: 425-881-6971
Email: atul@amrelitech.com
Website: www.amrelitech.com
IT intelligence, dashboards & scorecards, software, integration of disparate systems & applications. (As-Pac, estab 2004, empl 32, sales $3,400,000, cert: State, NMSDC)

5500 Axelerate
13401 Bel Red Rd, Ste B8
Bellevue, WA 98005
Contact: Sr Client Services Mgr
Tel: 425-429-6720
Email:
Website: http://axelerate.com
IT consulting & staffing. (Woman, estab 2003, empl 5, sales , cert: WBENC)

5501 BiSoft Consultancy Services
16310 NE 80th St, Ste 104
Redmond, WA 98052
Contact: Balaji Udayshankar CEO
Tel: 401-450-1672
Email: bala@bisoftllc.com
Website: www.bisoftllc.com
Information technology svcs, website design, wed development & maintenance, SEO optimization, application software. (As-Ind, estab 2015, empl , sales $2,000,000, cert: NMSDC)

5502 Dynamics Intelligence Inc.
8201 164th Ave NE, Ste 200
Redmond, WA 98052
Contact: CEO
Tel:
Email:
Website: www.dynamicsintelligence.us
Cloud technologies, Microsoft Dynamics and Microsoft Azure, PowerApps, SharePoint, SQL Server, and Cognitive Services such as (Face API, Speech to Text, Text Translation, Bot Framework. (Nat Ame, estab 2015, empl 2, sales , cert: State)

5503 Eastside Groups LLC
P.O. Box 165
Mercer Island, WA 98040
Contact: Jessie Wang Owner
Tel: 206-466-6649
Email: main@catandena.com
Website: www.catandena.com
Software solutions, financial applications, web sites & web services, from stand-alone scale to enterprise scale. (Woman/As-Pac, estab 2014, empl 1, sales , cert: State)

5504 ELYON International Inc.
1111 Main St, Ste 405
Vancouver, WA 98660
Contact: Carmen Nazario President
Tel: 360-696-5892
Email: carmen@elyoninternational.com
Website: www.elyoninternational.com
Consulting & technology svcs: software devel, systems integration, offshore solutions delivery, etc. (Woman/Hisp, estab 1997, empl 148, sales $23,000,000, cert: State, NMSDC, WBENC)

5505 Hansell Tierney, Inc.
2955 80th AVE SE #103
Mercer Island, WA 98040
Contact: Acct Mgr
Tel: 206-232-3080
Email:
Website: www.hanselltierney.com
IT consulting services & recruiting. (Woman, estab 2001, empl 35, sales $2,800,000, cert: State)

5506 i9 Systems, Inc.
16928 NE 38th Place
Bellevue, WA 98008
Contact: Sukhjot Basi CEO
Tel: 206-412-7918
Email: basi@i9systems.com
Website: www.i9systems.com
Staffig, consulting, software development & testing, program/project management, database & network administrations, business requirements, full software development life cycle. (Woman/As-Ind, estab 1999, empl 16, sales $500,000, cert: State)

5507 Idea Entity Corporation
16625 Redmond Way Ste M 009
Redmond, WA 98052
Contact: John Strathy CFO
Tel: 425-454-2905
Email: john.strathy@ideaentity.com
Website: www.ideaentity.com
Project, staff, development, testing, onsite, offsite, offshore, application developmen, custom application development & packaged solution integration. (As-Ind, estab 2006, empl 45, sales $706,000, cert: State, NMSDC)

5508 InConsulting Inc.
12901 181st Ave NE
Redmond, WA 98052
Contact: Aparna Mahadevan CEO
Tel: 425-281-7284
Email: services@inconsultinginc.com
Website: www.inconsultinginc.com
Information staffing & placement, IT services, Consulting, Systems planning, Web Design & development. (Woman/As-Ind, estab 2010, empl 40, sales , cert: State)

5509 Kaasm, LLC
900 1st Ave S, Ste 302
Seattle, WA 98134
Contact: Shawn Sandoval President
Tel: 206-735-3882
Email: shawns@kaasm.com
Website: http://kaasm.com
SCADA software, Industrial computers, networking components, alarm notification software & Enterprise Asset Management. (Hisp, estab 2013, empl 3, sales $150,000, cert: City, NMSDC)

5510 Kathcart Open Systems & Consulting, Inc.
17311 135th Ave NE, Ste B500
Woodinville, WA 98072
Contact: CEO
Tel: 425-402-0258
Email:
Website: www.dimension-systems.com
Information technology consulting services. (Woman, estab 1993, empl 20, sales $42,000,000, cert: WBENC)

5511 Martirx Infotech LLC
1017 4th Ave E Ste 6
Olympia, WA 98506
Contact: Narasimha Varakantham CEO
Tel: 360-545-4089
Email: reddy@matrixinf.com
Website: www.matrixinf.com
Information technology services, contingent workforce staffing solutions, technology support, consulting & development, software to hardware. (Woman/As-Ind, estab 2014, empl 3, sales $105,253, cert: State)

5512 Nvelup Consulting
19125 North Creek Parkway Ste 120
Bothell, WA 98011
Contact: Chris Barrios CEO
Tel: 206-419-2584
Email: chris@nvelupconsulting.com
Website: www.nvelupconsulting.com
Performance Management (Budgeting, Planning & Forecasting) & Business Intelligence (Data Analysis & Reporting) solutions. (Nat Ame, Hisp, estab 2014, empl 15, sales $936,000, cert: State, NMSDC, SDB)

5513 Online Training Solutions, Inc.
P.O. Box 951
Bellevue, WA 98009
Contact: Joan Preppernau President
Tel: 888-308-6874
Email: biz@otsi.com
Website: www.otsi.com
Publishing & programming services. (Woman, estab 1987, empl 13, sales $1,120,873, cert: WBENC)

5514 P2 Solutions Group LLC
2296 W Commodore Way, Ste 300
Seattle, WA 98199
Contact: Tonjia Borland
Tel: 206-226-8433
Email: tborland@p2solutionsgroup.com
Website: http://p2solutionsgroup.com
Technical, system administrator, programming, developer, engineering, finance, marketing & project management staff. (Hisp, estab 2002, empl 120, sales $10,600,000, cert: City, NMSDC)

5515 S3Global Consulting Services, LLC
10532 82nd Ave Court SW
Lakewood, WA 98498
Contact: Morris Sterling III, MBA CEO
Tel: 877-470-1900
Email: morris.sterling@s3goglobal.com
Website: www.s3goglobal.com
Information technology & business-based enterprises, project, program & product management, technical writing & communications, continuous process improvement, business analysis & intelligence. (Woman/AA, estab 2012, empl 5, sales , cert: State, City)

5516 ScrumPoint
1110 112th Ave Northeast Ste 350
Bellevue, WA 98052
Contact: Michael Mpare President
Tel: 509-714-4842
Email: michael@scrumpoint.com
Website: www.scrumpoint.com
Custom software applications, SSIS & SSRS management, SharePoint portals, custom web applications, Windows Azure Cloud Services. (AA, estab 2011, empl 6, sales , cert: NMSDC)

5517 Synergistics, Inc.
114 Columbia Point Dr Ste A
Richland, WA 99352
Contact: Kim DeTienne VP
Tel: 800-875-7921
Email: kim@syngt.com
Website: www.syngt.com
Customized software & project management. (Hisp, estab 2003, empl 12, sales $1,010,000, cert: State)

5518 Tam Partners Consulting, LLC
18350 204th Ave NE
Woodinville, WA 98077
Contact: Lisa Tam Founder
Tel: 425-998-8401
Email: lisatam@tpartnerscg.com
Website: http://tpartnerscg.com
Engineering: Power BI, Excel Power Pivot, ETL, SSIS, SSAS, T-SQL, Data Marts, Data Warehouse, SQL Server Management Studio, Business Intelligence Development StudioBig Data Analytics: JSon, HiveQL, Microsoft Azure HDInsight | Cloud Hadoop, Azure Managem (Woman, estab 2016, empl 1, sales $114,784, cert: WBENC)

5519 TripleNet Technologies, Inc.
1122 E Pike St, Ste 509
Seattle, WA 98122
Contact: Hans Gomez President
Tel: 206-260-8998
Email: hansgomez@triplenettech.com
Website: www.triplenettech.com
IT staffing, network architecture & design, software development, wireless network design & implementation, data storage plan, disaster recovery. (Hisp, estab 1997, empl 18, sales $500,000, cert: State, City, NMSDC)

5520 TSS Redmond
8461 154th Ave NE, Bldg G
Redmond, WA 98052
Contact: Lisa Roeder CEO
Tel: 425-749-3030
Email: lroeder@tssredmond.com
Website: www.tssredmond.com
Software, computer, technical development, soft skills, project management, business development & leadership training. (Woman, estab 2000, empl 20, sales $700,000, cert: State)

5521 ZONES LLC
15th St SW, Ste 102. Auburn, WA 98001
Washington, WA 98001
Contact: Zack Wheeler Acct Mgr
Tel: 253-545-3100
Email: zack.wheeler@zones.com
Website: www.zones.com
Information technology products & services, resell computer hardware & software. (As-Ind, As-Pac, estab 1986, empl 2223, sales $230,000,000,000, cert: NMSDC)

Wisconsin

5522 Abaxent LLC
N28 W23050 Roundy Dr. Ste 200
Pewaukee, WI 53072
Contact: Adonica Randall President
Tel: 414-587-2950
Email: arandall@abaxent.com
Website: www.abaxent-global.com
Information technology services, project management, software development, network engineering & consulting/design. (Woman/AA, estab 2002, empl 10, sales , cert: State, NMSDC, WBENC)

5523 Comcentia, LLC
1025 W Glen Oaks Lane Ste 211
Mequon, WI 53092
Contact: Darrell Caldwell President
Tel: 414-871-1100
Email: info@comcentia.com
Website: www.comcentia.com
IT Consulting, Custom Applications & Database Development, Custom web based or windows desktop application development, Application Management of Existing Systems, Ongoing & and ad hoc changes. (AA, estab 2006, empl 6, sales $612,112, cert: NMSDC, 8a)

5524 CTL Resources (Caribou Thunder)
8558 N County Rd K
Hayward, WI 54843
Contact: Rita Peterson Owner
Tel:
Email: rita@ctlresources.com
Website: www.ctlresources.com
Project Management, Process Re-engineering, Process Change, Enterprise application integration, Engineering (Woman/Nat Ame, estab , empl , sales $10,000,000, cert: NMSDC)

5525 Excel Global Solutions Inc.
2727 N Grandview Blvd Ste 117
Waukesha, WI 53188
Contact: Jerry Sorci VP
Tel: 262-347-4911
Email: jerry.sorci@excelglobalsolution.com
Website: www.excelglobalsolution.com
IT services, solutions & products, Big Data Predictive intelligence Product, Automated Application Testing Product, Vehicle Maintenance Management Product. (Woman/As-Pac, estab 2010, empl 250, sales $2,100,000, cert: State)

5526 Malleswari Inc.
11512 N Port Washington Rd, Ste 101-I
Mequon, WI 53092
Contact: Trinadha Pattem
Tel:
Email: trinadha@malleswari.com
Website: www.malleswari.com
End to End SAP ERP/SRM/BI/Mobile Technology Solutions. (Woman/As-Ind, estab 2004, empl 5, sales $2,350,227, cert: State, City, NMSDC)

5527 Valicom Corp
2923 Marketplace Dr Ste 104
Fitchburg, WI 53719
Contact: Marketing
Tel: 800-467-7226
Email:
Website: www.valicomcorp.com
IT & telecom invoice audit & management: RFP facilitation, contract negotiation & management, network design & engineering, help desk, invoice payment & general ledger coding. (Woman, estab 1991, empl 20, sales , cert: State, WBENC)

5528 Wissen Infotech Inc
2325 Parklawn Dr Ste G
Waukesha, WI 53186
Contact: Upendra Rachupaly Operations Mgr
Tel: 262-510-2900
Email: upendra.rachupally@wisseninfotech.com
Website: www.wisseninfotech.com
IT services, onsite, offsite & offshore service, End to end
Mobility application, development, Analytics, Cloud
Management, Media & Entertainment, Embedded Systems, Big data & Hadoop.
Enterprise Resource Planning, Remote Infrastructure
Management (As-Ind, estab 2001, empl 800, sales
$12,000,000, cert: State)

West Virginia

5529 Fusion Plus Solutions Inc.
17 Cherokee Dr
Moundsville, WV 26041
Contact: Mark Thomas Director
Tel: 732-250-9048
Email: mark@fusionplusinc.com
Website: www.fusionplusinc.com
IT Staff Augmentation, Information Technology Solutions,
Consulting/Staffing Services, System Integration, Software
Products. (Woman/As-Pac, estab 2009, empl 1000, sales
$3,000,000, cert: State)

INFORMATION TECHNOLOGY: Supplies
Manufacture or distribute magnetic media supplies such as , disketts, paper, printers, fascimilies, toner cartridges, keyboards, computer peripherials. NAICS Code 42

Arizona

5530 Centacor, Inc.
135 Chilton Dr
Chandler, AZ 85225
Contact: Troy Bryan Mgr
Tel: 480-899-9500
Email: info@centacor.com
Website: www.centacor.com
IT products & services. (AA, estab 2009, empl 4, sales , cert: NMSDC)

5531 Cybergear, Inc.
4711 E Falcon Dr Ste 202
Mesa, AZ 85215
Contact: President
Tel: 480-926-6470
Email:
Website: www.cybergearusa.com
Dist computer hardware, consumer electronics, electronic test & measurement, computer software & software licensing, POS/bar code equipment, wireless voice/data products & services. (Woman, estab 1998, empl 2, sales , cert: City, WBENC)

5532 ESI Ergonomic Solutions, LLC
4030 E Quenton Dr Ste 101
Mesa, AZ 85215
Contact: Carol Keogh CEO
Tel: 480-517-1871
Email: ckeogh@esiergo.com
Website: www.esiergo.com
Mfr & dist articulating arms, keyboard platforms, flat screen monitor arms & ergonomic accessories. (Woman, estab 1988, empl 25, sales $15,000,000, cert: NWBOC)

5533 Herco Technology div. of Hernandez Companies
3734 E Anne St
Phoenix, AZ 85040
Contact: Mike Pena Acct Exec
Tel: 602-438-7825
Email: info@hernandezcompanies.com
Website: www.hernandezcompanies.com/
Dist computer & networking cable & cable accessories: fiber optic cables, coaxial, custom assemblies, racks, shelving, wire mgmt, Cat5E patch cables. (Woman/Hisp, estab 1975, empl 75, sales $150,000, cert: NMSDC)

5534 LEEO Industries
6868 N 7th Ave Ste 205
Phoenix, AZ 85013
Contact: Pierre Tousant GM
Tel: 800-584-5554
Email: sales@leeo-industries.com
Website: www.leeo-industries.com
Dist office & information technology products: bar-coding equipment & printers, cables, network hubs & interface cards, power supplies, CPUs. (AA, estab 2002, empl 6, sales $200,000, cert: State)

5535 Swift Office Solutions
2429 W 12th St Ste#6
Tempe, AZ 85281
Contact: Edward Swift President
Tel: 480-966-2100
Email: eswift@sosnet.com
Website: www.sosnet.com
Dist computers, hardware, software, and office products. (Minority, estab 1981, empl 9, sales $5,000,000, cert: NMSDC)

California

5536 Alliant Event Services
196 University Pkwy
Pomona, CA 91768
Contact: Heather Milianak Sr sales Mgr
Tel: 909-354-4469
Email: hmilanak@asn-corp.com
Website: www.AlliantEvents.com
Rental technology & event production solutions: laptop & desktop computers, printers, copiers, audio-visual, sound & lighting products. (As-Ind, estab 2003, empl 38, sales $4,150,000, cert: State)

5537 CDCE Inc.
22755-G Savi Ranch Pkwy
Yorba Linda, CA 92887
Contact: Kim Hufford Natl Sales Mgr
Tel: 714-282-8881
Email: khufford@cdce.com
Website: www.cdce.com
Wireless, computer vehicle installations, ruggedized notebooks & tablets. (Woman, estab 1984, empl 25, sales , cert: CPUC, WBENC)

5538 Computer 1 Products of America, Inc.
11135 Rush St, Unit A
South El Monte, CA 91733
Contact: Robert Edwards Small Business Coordinator
Tel: 626-213-2407
Email: robert@computer1products.com
Website: www.c1psolutions.com
Dist computer hardware, software, networking, electronic components, audio visual, printers & supplies. (Woman/Hisp, estab 1992, empl 25, sales $10,000,000, cert: 8a)

5539 ComputerSuppliers.Com
7377 Convoy Court, Ste A
San Diego, CA 92111
Contact: Jay Satpute bids specialist
Tel: 858-268-7370
Email: bids@computersupplies.com
Website: www.computersupplies.com
Dist inks, toners, monitor filters, furniture, pens, printers, ribbons, and storage media such as DVD, CD, LTO, SDX, AIT, 4mm & 8mm cartridges. (Woman/As-Ind, estab 2002, empl 7, sales $6,000,000, cert: City)

5540 Conversions Technology
1740 Emerson Ave
Oxnard, CA 93033
Contact: Kevin Williams VP Sales
Tel: 800-596-2037
Email: kevin@conversionstechnology.com
Website: www.ConversionsTechnology.com
Mfr & dist cable accessory & PC peripheral components. (Woman/Nat Ame, estab 2006, empl 25, sales $1,000,000, cert: CPUC)

5541 GC Micro Corporation
      3910 Cypress Dr
      Petaluma, CA 94954
      Contact: Ashley Kidd Acct Mgr
      Tel: 800-426-4276
      Email: bg@gcmicro.com
      Website: www.gcmicro.com
Dist personal computers, microcomputer hardware, software, peripherals, IBM, HP, AST, Epson authorized dealer. (Woman/Hisp, estab 1986, empl 35, sales , cert: State, NMSDC, WBENC)

5542 Kambrian Corporation
      2707 E Valley Blvd
      West Covina, CA 91792
      Contact: Cathy Hsieh CEO
      Tel: 626-374-3933
      Email: cathyh@kambrian.com
      Website: www.kambrian.com
Resell IT products: software, hardware & services. (Woman/As-Pac, estab 2009, empl 7, sales $10,469,102, cert: NMSDC, WBENC, 8a)

5543 MelroseMAC, Inc.
      6614 Melrose Ave
      Hollywood, CA 90038
      Contact: Jonathan Strayhorn CEO
      Tel: 323-937-4600
      Email: jon@mac330.com
      Website: www.melrosemac.com
Resell Apple products. (Woman, estab 2003, empl 80, sales $55,000,000, cert: CPUC, WBENC)

5544 Mobile ID Solutions, Inc.
      1574 N Batavia St, Ste 1
      Orange, CA 92867
      Contact: Rick Fahilga Acct Exec
      Tel: 714-922-1134
      Email: rfahilga@mobileidsolutions.com
      Website: www.mobileidsolutions.com
Mobile Computers, printers. Barcode Printers, Scanners, verifiers. ID Card Printers and supplies. IP Cameras. Cellular Routers, modem, POS Equipment, Satellite phones. (As-Pac, estab 2004, empl 9, sales $4,800,000, cert: NMSDC)

5545 Mobilematics, Inc.
      2528 Qume Dr, Ste 2
      San Jose, CA 95131
      Contact: Dominick Borrello Business Dev Mgr
      Tel: 408-609-1220
      Email: dominick@mobilematics.us.com
      Website: www.mobilematics.us.com
IT hardware & software, training, configuration, etc. (Woman/As-Ind, estab 2012, empl 15, sales $100,000,000, cert: NMSDC, CPUC, WBENC)

5546 New Century Technologies Inc.
      4290 Kendall St
      San Diego, CA 92109
      Contact: Peter Steiner COO
      Tel: 800-457-4313
      Email: peter@nctsolution.com
      Website: www.nctsolution.com
Toner cartridges, office supplies/products, office equipment, office furniture, janitorial supplies, breakroom supplies, industrial supplies/products, hard drive, memory, IT products that offers hardware, software, related services. (Woman/As-Pac, estab 2006, empl 3, sales $1,391,800, cert: 8a)

5547 On-Site LaserMedic Corp.
      21540 Prairie St, Unit D
      Chatsworth, CA 91311
      Contact: Gail Solomon CEO
      Tel: 818-772-6911
      Email: sd@onsitelasermedic.com
      Website: www.onsitelasermedic.com
Laser printer, fax & deskjet service & repair, dist toner. (Woman, estab 1992, empl 46, sales $5,318,472, cert: WBENC)

5548 Performance Designed Products
      14144 Ventura Blvd Ste 200
      Sherman Oaks, CA 91423
      Contact: Theresa Harrell Natl Sales Mgr
      Tel: 479-445-8612
      Email: theresa.harrell@pdp.com
      Website: http://pdp.com
Design & mfr video game peripherals & accessories: PS2, PS3, PSP PS Vita, Xbox, Xbox 360, Wii, Wii U, 3DS, DS Lite. (Woman, estab 1990, empl 200, sales , cert: WBENC)

5549 PNH Technology, Inc.
      15375 Barranca Pkwy Ste F-108
      Irvine, CA 92618
      Contact: Thacher Grauer Office Mgr
      Tel: 949-614-4102
      Email: thacher@pnhtech.com
      Website: http://pnhtech.com
Dist servers, rack, tower, blades, memory, hard drives, server accessories, storage (SAN, NAS, DAS), storage accessories. networking switches, routers, firewalls, network accessories, desktops, PCs & laptops. (As-Pac, estab 2008, empl 6, sales $3,000,000, cert: State)

5550 RC & JT Inc. dba Computer Masters
      6185 Cornerstone Court Ste 103
      San Diego, CA 92121
      Contact: Jessie Thorell Acct Mgr
      Tel: 858-444-2966
      Email: jthorell@computermastersinc.com
      Website: www.computermastersinc.com
Dist computer hardware, software, printers, supplies & networking products & services. (Woman/Hisp, estab 1990, empl 4, sales , cert: State)

5551 Saitech Inc.
      42640 Christy St
      Fremont, CA 94538
      Contact: Ernesto Juarez Business Development
      Tel: 510-440-0256
      Email: ernesto@esaitech.com
      Website: https://saitechincorporated.com/
Dist telecom, network & computer components & equipment. (As-Ind, As-Pac, estab 2002, empl 18, sales $18,721,958, cert: NMSDC, CPUC)

5552 Source Graphics
      1530 N. Harmony Circle
      Anaheim, CA 92807
      Contact: Sy Hussaini Sr Acct Mgr
      Tel: 714-701-1500
      Email: sy.h@sourcegraphics.com
      Website: www.sourcegraphics.com
Dist & svc plotter scanners, printers & digitizers. (As-Pac, estab 1989, empl 10, sales , cert: State)

5553　Southland Technology Inc.
　　　8053 Vickers St
　　　San Diego, CA 92111
　　　Contact: Jack Lowrey Acct Exec
　　　Tel:　858-634-4136
　　　Email: jlowrey@southlandtechnology.com
　　　Website: www.southlandtechnology.com
Computer, computer hardware, software, cables, peripherals, IT, information technology, audio, video, A/V, sound systems, servers, storage, virtualization, fiber cables, workstations, notebooks, voip, projectors, monitors. (Woman/As-Pac, estab 2001, empl 43, sales $45,000,000, cert: CPUC)

5554　Varitek, Inc.
　　　1100 E. Orangethorpe Ave Ste 195
　　　Anaheim, CA 92801
　　　Contact: Moe Moalemi VP
　　　Tel:　714-224-0361
　　　Email: moalemi@varitekinc.com
　　　Website: www.varitekinc.com
Dist & service network solutions, computers, printers, barcode printers, plotters, point of sale, copiers, faxes, office equipment consumables. (Woman/Nat Ame, estab 1982, empl 12, sales $1,030,000, cert: State)

5555　ViewSonic Corporation
　　　381 Brea Canyon Rd
　　　Walnut, CA 91789
　　　Contact: Julie Yao Legal Asst
　　　Tel:　909-444-8613
　　　Email: legal@viewsonic.com
　　　Website: www.viewsonic.com
Dist visual display technology products: liquid crystal displays, LCD, monitors, cathode ray tube, CRT, monitors, projectors, LCD TVs, plasma displays, tablet personal computers & PCs, wireless monitors. (As-Pac, estab 1987, empl 700, sales $1,093,000,000, cert: NMSDC)

5556　Vision Specialties, Inc.
　　　10330 Regis Ct
　　　Rancho Cucamonga, CA 91730
　　　Contact: Donn DeMarzio VP
　　　Tel:　800-499-8176
　　　Email: donn.demarzio@visionspecialties.com
　　　Website: www.visionspecialties.com
Mfr & dist Category Cable, HDMI Cable, Audio/Video Cable, Batteries, Injection Molding products & services. (Woman, estab 1995, empl 14, sales $6,000,000, cert: CPUC)

5557　Zetta Pros - Total IT Solutions
　　　2201 E Willow St, Ste D232
　　　Signal Hill, CA 90755
　　　Contact: Sarom Hong CEO
　　　Tel:　562-252-3673
　　　Email: sarom.hong@zettapros.com
　　　Website: www.zettapros.com
Computers, hardware, software, printers, computer peripherals, cables. (Woman/As-Pac, estab 2005, empl 4, sales $600,000, cert: NMSDC, CPUC, 8a)

Colorado

5558　Image Projections West, Inc.
　　　14135 E 42nd Ave Ste 40
　　　Denver, CO 80239
　　　Contact: Kedar Morarka CEO
　　　Tel:　888-576-9477
　　　Email: josephf@ipwusa.com
　　　Website: www.ipwusa.com
Mfr advance technology toner cartridges. (As-Ind, estab 1996, empl 172, sales $31,200,000, cert: NMSDC)

5559　SK&T Integration Inc.
　　　10495 S Progress Way
　　　Parker, CO 80112
　　　Contact: Kathy Lawson President
　　　Tel:　720-851-9108
　　　Email:
　　　Website: www.skandt.com
Dist stock & custom labels, ribbons, bar code & specialty printers, asset tracking & inventory management systems, bar coding software, scanners, mobile computers & wireless switches. (Woman, estab , empl , sales $3,200,000, cert: WBENC)

5560　Systec101
　　　1027 Fenwick Dr
　　　Fort Collins, CO 80524
　　　Contact: Murat Yildirim Owner
　　　Tel:　970-646-2706
　　　Email: murat.yildirim@systec101.com
　　　Website: www.systec101.com
Dist networking equipment, manufacture & resell, cat5e, cat6, cat6a cables & accessories. (Minority, estab 2012, empl 3, sales $277,000, cert: State)

Connecticut

5561　Hartford Toner & Cartridge
　　　6 Wapping Rd
　　　Broad Brook, CT 06016
　　　Contact: Timothy Golubeff Sr sales
　　　Tel:　860-292-1280
　　　Email: tgolubeff@hartfordtoner.com
　　　Website: www.hartfordtoner.con
Hp authorized service center, repair laser printers & supplies. (Woman, estab 1998, empl 9, sales $1,000,100, cert: State)

District of Columia

5562　Borrowed Time Enterprises, Inc.
　　　4460 Alabama Ave, SE
　　　Washington, DC 20019
　　　Contact: Vanessa Brooks CEO
　　　Tel:　202-581-0406
　　　Email: borrowedte@rcn.com
　　　Website: www.btenterprise.us
Dist computers, parts, software & hardware, office supplies, digital signage & content management software installation & services. (Woman/AA, estab 1999, empl 1, sales $127,000, cert: State, City)

5563　Mall Lobby.com, Inc.
　　　1775 Eye St, NW Ste 1150
　　　Washington, DC 20006
　　　Contact: Lang Maith CEO
　　　Tel:　301-807-2422
　　　Email: lang.maith@malllobby.com
　　　Website: www.malllobby.com
Dist computers, software, network equipment, office products, electronics, cellular phones, pagers, merchant accounts, microfilm/microfiche, CD/DVD production, etc. (AA, estab 1995, empl 15, sales $500,000, cert: State)

Florida

5564   American Data & Computer Products, Inc.
4505 Town N Country Blvd
Tampa, FL 33615
Contact: Robert Castro President
Tel: 800-367-2461
Email: rcastro@adcpi.com
Website: www.adcpi.com
Dist computer systems, software & peripheral compo-
nents. (Hisp, estab 1988, empl 15, sales $25,000,000, cert:
State)

5565   BIT DIRECT
2202 N Westshore Blvd, Ste 200
Tampa, FL 33607
Contact: Duane Turner Sr VP & GM
Tel: 813-343-0879
Email:
Website: www.bitdirect.com
Dist audio & headsets, digital cameras, LCD & plasma TV's
& projectors, handheld computers, removable media,
optical dives, keyboards & mice, software & licenses, flash
drives, cables, hard drives, media tapes, computer furniture. (Woman, estab 2002, empl 11, sales $700,000,000,
cert: City, WBENC)

5566   Card Quest, Inc.
6630 Rowan Rd
New Port Richey, FL 34655
Contact: Shannon Capshaw President
Tel: 727-816-8401
Email: sales@cardquest.com
Website: www.cardquest.com
Dist proximity cards, readers, photo ID printers, ribbons,
accessories, cards. (Woman, estab 2001, empl 4, sales
$750,000, cert: State)

5567   Chilcott, Inc.
15751 Sheridan St, Ste 3158
Fort Lauderdale, FL 33331
Contact: Allyson Ameideiras VP
Tel: 786-351-8298
Email: admin@chilcottinc.com
Website: http://chilcottinc.com
Computer hardware, software, peripherals,   Mobile
Command Centers, Satellite Service & Equipment, Helicop-
ter Training & Equipment/Parts & Mutualink
Interoperability Systems. (Hisp, estab 2012, empl 8, sales ,
cert: 8a)

5568   Innovative Software Solution
3762 NW 124th Ave
Coral Springs, FL 33065
Contact: Kareline Duverge Office Mgr
Tel: 954-800-7552
Email: kduverge@isoftwaresolution.com
Website: www.isoftwaresolution.com
Mfr ink & toner cartridges. Authorized distributors of HP,
Lexmark & Ricoh products & supplies, general office
supplies, toner & ink cartridges. (Woman/AA, estab 2012,
empl 15, sales $1,590,000, cert: State, NMSDC)

5569   Keiki Enterprises LLC
200 Crandon Blvd Ste 327
Key Biscayne, FL 33149
Contact: Karina Diaz VP
Tel: 305-361-0623
Email: karina@dsignage.net
Website: http://dsignage.net
Software and hardware manufacturers in the digital
signage (Woman/Hisp, estab , empl , sales $441,317, cert:
City)

5570   Laser Products, Inc.
11975 SW 142nd Terrace Unit 105
Miami, FL 33186
Contact: Wendy K. Rudman President
Tel: 305-235-9544
Email: laser@laser-products.com
Website: www.laser-products.com
Digital imaging products, parts & supplies: copier, fax,
printer, wide-format, high speed, ink, toner, ribbons,
software, registration & warranty. (Woman, estab 1990,
empl 4, sales $801,011, cert: State)

5571   LRE Inc. dba Lee Ryder Lamination
6187 NW 167th St Unit H-10
Miami, FL 33015
Contact: Lee Ryder President
Tel: 305-893-2762
Email: office@leeryder.com
Website: www.leeryder.com
Computerized photo id systems & supplies: Hid Global,
Edisecure, Magicard, Eltron, Fargo, Nisca, Zebra, Evolis,
Datacard. retractable id badge reels, laminator, pouch
laminator, roll laminator, laminating pouches, laminating
roll (Minority, Woman, estab 1980, empl 2, sales
$350,000, cert: State, City)

5572   R&D Systems Group, Inc.
19140 SW 24th St
Miramar, FL 33029
Contact: patricia Garcia Acct Exec
Tel: 305-528-9402
Email: pgarcia@rdsgi.com
Website: www.rdsgi.com
Resell IBM software & hardware. (Woman/Hisp, estab
2004, empl 6, sales $400,000, cert: NMSDC)

5573   Solares Electrical Services, Inc.
10421 NW 28th St Ste D105
Miami, FL 33172
Contact: A. Solares President
Tel: 305-717-6184
Email: asolares@solareselectrical.com
Website: www.solareselectrical.com
Electrical, Communication, Lightning Protection, Utilites.
Experience in Toll Collection Equipment, wiring and
testing. (Hisp, estab 1997, empl 40, sales $3,500,000,
cert: State)

Georgia

5574   Eastern Data, Inc.
4386 Park Dr
Norcross, GA 30093
Contact: JoAnn Pfeiffer Natl Accts Mgr
Tel: 770-279-8888
Email: jo.pfeiffer@ediatlanta.com
Website: www.ediatlanta.com
Dist computer systems, components & peripherals.
(Woman/As-Pac, estab 1997, empl 27, sales
$20,906,578, cert: NMSDC, WBENC)

5575   Worldwide Audio Visual Services Inc
5040 Bakers Ferry Rd SW
Atlanta, GA 30336
Contact: Bradford McWhorter CEO
Tel: 404-745-9842
Email: brad@atlanta-audiovisual.com
Website: www.atlantaav.com
Audio visual equipment, audio reinforcement, video
production, lighting design & corporate set design. (AA,
estab 2005, empl 8, sales $374,970, cert: NMSDC)

5576   XentIT, LLC
       5425 Peachtree Pkwy
       Norcross, GA 30092
       Contact: Tariq Alvi President
       Tel: 678-906-4046
       Email: talvi@xentit.com
       Website: www.xentit.com
Value Added Reseller, System Integrator & Cloud Managed
Service provider. (As-Ind, estab 2006, empl 7, sales
$2,247,000, cert: NMSDC)

Illinois

5577   Data Media Products, Inc.
       1946 Lehigh Ave, Ste B
       Glenview, IL 60025
       Contact: President
       Tel: 847-729-2020
       Email:
       Website: www.datamediaproducts.com
Dist blank audio/video tapes, dvds, cds, data backup tapes,
printer & toner cartridges. (Minority, Woman, estab , empl
, sales $5,569,000, cert: State, City)

5578   Flexaco, Inc.
       936 W Lake St
       Roselle, IL 60172
       Contact: President
       Tel: 630-529-4510
       Email:
       Website: www.flexaco.com
Dist flexographic & rotogravure printers: 10 color printing,
2 color backside printing, surface & reverse printing,
laminating, shrink sleeves, lidding material, paper, poly,
foil & poly. (Woman, estab 1981, empl 5, sales $1,000,000,
cert: WBENC)

5579   GACC Video Electronics Inc.
       700 Nicholas Blvd Ste 103
       Elk Grove Village, IL 60007
       Contact: Jennifer Chang Secretary
       Tel: 312-733-5774
       Email: jennifer@gaccvideo.com
       Website: www.gaccvideo.com
Audio and Video Service and repair. Dist microphones,
cameras, decks, monitors, (Woman/As-Pac, estab 2000,
empl 3, sales $450,000, cert: City)

5580   Mercommbe Inc.
       2101 Estes Ave
       Elk Grove Village, IL 60007
       Contact: Eric Moe Sales
       Tel: 847-290-0368
       Email: eric@mercommbe.com
       Website: http://mercommbe.com
Dist datacom & networking products; fiber optic, struc-
tured wiring, low voltage cable & connectors. (Woman/
Hisp, estab 1989, empl 7, sales $5,686,000, cert: State,
City, NMSDC, WBENC)

5581   MNJ Technologies Direct, Inc.
       1025 Busch Pkwy
       Buffalo Grove, IL 60089
       Contact: Susan Kozak President
       Tel: 847-634-0700
       Email: skozak@mnjtech.com
       Website: www.mnjtech.com
Dist computer hardware, software & peripheral products.
(Woman, estab 2002, empl 85, sales $25,000,000, cert:
WBENC)

5582   RPT Toner LLC
       475 Supreme Dr
       Bensenville, IL 60106
       Contact: Jamie Sr VP sales/mktg
       Tel: 630-694-0400
       Email: jamie@rpttoner.com
       Website: www.rpttoner.com
Re-manufacture laser toner cartridges. (As-Ind, estab ,
empl , sales $10,770,000, cert: NMSDC)

Indiana

5583   ASAP Identification Security, Inc.
       212 W 10th St, Ste F-100
       Indianapolis, IN 46202
       Contact: Sheila Brown President
       Tel: 317-488-1030
       Email: sbrown@asapident.com
       Website: www.asapident.com
Photo ID printers, supplies, service, software and
accessories. (Woman, estab 1982, empl 3, sales , cert:
State, WBENC)

5584   Convenient Tape & Supplies LLC
       545 Industrial Dr
       Carmel, IN 46032
       Contact: Jennifer Pippen President
       Tel: 317-846-0335
       Email: jencts1@sbcglobal.net
       Website: http://sundsales.com
Distributors of point-of-sale (pos) paper rolls, cash
register rolls, printer ribbons, toner cartridges, ink-jet
cartridges, printer cleaning supplies, scale labels,
industrial bar code labels, pos printers to small computer printer users. (Woman, estab 2002, empl 3, sales
$244,000, cert: State)

Kansas

5585   Inland Associates, Inc.
       18965 W 158th St
       Olathe, KS 66062
       Contact: Peggy Meader President
       Tel: 913-764-7977
       Email: pmeader@inlandassoc.com
       Website: www.inlandassoc.com
Dist computer peripherals, data communications
equipment. (Woman, estab 1969, empl 7, sales
$4,000,000, cert: WBENC)

Louisiana

5586   Dempsey Business Systems of Louisiana
       1321 Second St, Ste B
       Alexandria, LA 71301
       Contact: Freddie Price, Sr. President
       Tel: 318-604-6061
       Email: fprice@dempseybus.com
       Website: www.dempseybus.com
Dist Computer & Computer Peripheral equipment &
software, custom computer programing services,
computer systems design services, computer facilities
management services, information technology value
added reseller. (AA, estab 2004, empl 1, sales $278,789,
cert: NMSDC)

5587   The Lazers Edge LLC
       2168 Airline Dr, Ste C
       Bossier City, LA 71111
       Contact: Sandra Nix Owner
       Tel: 318-742-6232
       Email: nix@lazers-edge.com
       Website: www.lazers-edge.com
Remanufactured Toner cartridges, laser printer service & repair. (Woman, estab 1989, empl 7, sales , cert: City)

Massachusetts

5588   Encore Images
       21 Lime St
       Marblehead, MA 01945
       Contact: Laurel Mervis President
       Tel: 781-631-4568
       Email: laurel.mervis@encoreimages.com
       Website: www.encoreimages.com
Remanufacture toner cartridges: monochrome & color laser printers, copiers & facsimile machines. (Woman, estab 1989, empl 14, sales $2,020,000, cert: State)

5589   Pro AV Systems, Inc.
       275 Billerica Road Ste 3
       Chelmsford, MA 01824
       Contact: President
       Tel: 978-692-5111
       Email:
       Website: www.proavsi.com
Dist audiovisual products & installation services. (Woman/As-Ind, estab 2006, empl 58, sales $16,100,000, cert: State)

Maryland

5590   Cartridge Technologies, Inc. dba CTI
       15738 Crabbs Branch Way
       Rockville, MD 20855
       Contact: Kevin Brooks Federal Acct Mgr
       Tel: 301-417-8057
       Email: kevinb@ctimd.com
       Website: www.ctimd.com
Laser/Color Printers and Fax Machines, Maintenance/Warranty Service and manufactures the Optima brand Toner Cartridge. (Woman/Hisp, estab 1989, empl 25, sales , cert: WBENC)

5591   Laser Printers Plus
       P.O. Box 264
       Greenbelt, MD 20768
       Contact:
       Tel: 301-933-9007
       Email: info@laserprintersplus.com
       Website: www.laserprintersplus.com
Dist new & remanufactured laser & toner cartridges, drum units, fusers, ribbons, developers, parts. (As-Ind, estab 1998, empl 4, sales $500,000, cert: State)

Michigan

5592   AVE Solutions
       1155 Brewery Park Blvd., #350
       Detroit, MI 48207
       Contact: Carol Kirkland Exec VP
       Tel:
       Email: carol@avesolutions.net
       Website: www.avesolutions.net
Dist office supplies, office furniture, office equipment, audio visual equipment, computer equipment & supplies, printer equipment & supplies, paper, janitorial supplies, first aid supplies. (Woman/AA, estab 1990, empl 6, sales , cert: NMSDC, WBENC)

5593   Computer Group, Inc.
       41252 Vincenti Court Ste 200
       Novi, MI 48375
       Contact: Beverly Ricci VP Sales
       Tel: 248-888-6900
       Email: bev@compgroup.com
       Website: www.compgroup.com
Dist micro computer hardware, software, peripherals & supplies, MS Access databases programming. (AA, estab 1982, empl 10, sales $800,000, cert: NMSDC)

5594   Data Ranger Computer Products
       507 E Main St
       Manchester, MI 48158
       Contact: Andrea Ranger Owner
       Tel: 734-428-8551
       Email: andrea@datarangercomputerproducts.com
       Website: www.datarangercomputerproducts.com
Dist computer, pos, barcoding & imaging supplies, hardware/equipment & peripherals, toner, ink, ribbons, back-up media, paper, labels, custom forms, printers, cables, scanners, networking hardware, monitors, computers, etc. (Woman, estab 2002, empl 2, sales , cert: WBENC)

5595   JEM Tech Group
       23537 Lakepointe Dr.
       Clinton Township, MI 48036
       Contact: Shelley Deane Sr Technology Consultant
       Tel: 586-783-3400
       Email: s.deane@jemtechgroup.com
       Website: www.jemtechgroup.com
Dist IT products: toners, tape backup media, printers, cables, monitors, bar code readers, backup libraries, furniture, switches, hubs, racks, projectors, hardware & software, etc. (Woman, estab 1979, empl 14, sales $10,400,000, cert: WBENC)

5596   M.O.R.E. Computer Supplies, LLC
       384 Park
       Troy, MI 48083
       Contact: Jim Williams CEO
       Tel: 248-733-9011
       Email: steve@more-office.biz
       Website: www.more-office.biz
Dist computer supplies. (AA, estab 0, empl , sales $16,000,000, cert: NMSDC)

5597   Micro Wise, Inc.
       21421 Hilltop Dr, Unit 4
       Southfield, MI 48034
       Contact: Dan Mamman Sales Mgr
       Tel: 248-350-0066
       Email: dan@microwise.net
       Website: www.microwise.net
Resell computers, servers & networking gear, POS, access-control, PC repairs, upgrades, service, leasing & disposal. (Woman/As-Ind, estab 1989, empl 9, sales , cert: NMSDC)

5598   Mikan Corporation
       1271 Industrial, Ste 3
       Saline, MI 48176
       Contact: Maggie Stevens President
       Tel: 734-944-9447
       Email: maggie@mikancorp.com
       Website: www.mikancorp.com
Remanufacture laser toner cartridges. (Woman, estab 1990, empl 7, sales $1,726,617, cert: WBENC)

5599 More Computer Supplies
14132 10 Mile Rd
Warren, MI 48089
Contact: Steve Llorens Dir
Tel: 586-771-4030
Email: moresupplies@aol.com
Website: http://more-office.biz
Office supplies, printer supplies, bar code labels, furniture, printers, fax machines and supplies. (As-Ind, estab 2001, empl 9, sales $9,800,000, cert: NMSDC)

5600 PFA Recycling, Inc.
50150 E Russell Schmidt
Chesterfield, MI 48051
Contact: Peter Feamster VP Business Dev
Tel: 586-949-5788
Email: pfeamster92@gmail.com
Website: www.pfa-recycling.com
Recycle plastic consumer goods, ink jet cartridges. (Hisp, estab 1991, empl 20, sales $3,306,104, cert: NMSDC)

5601 The Computer Group, Inc.
32985 Hamilton Ct Ste 135
Farmington Hills, MI 48331
Contact: Phillip Ingram President
Tel: 248-888-6900
Email: phil@compgroup.com
Website: www.compgroup.com
Computer systems, copy machines, computer peripherals, computer software networking products. (AA, estab 1982, empl 9, sales $525,000, cert: NMSDC)

Minnesota

5602 All Media Supplies Inc.
4902 NE Tri Oak Cir S
Wyoming, MN 55092
Contact: Rita Morse President
Tel: 763-413-1907
Email: rita@allmediasuppliesinc.com
Website: www.allmediasuppliesinc.com
Dist computer media supplies. (Woman, estab 1997, empl 5, sales $729,000, cert: WBENC)

5603 Best Datacom, Inc.
8405 First Ave NE
Stacy, MN 55079
Contact: Doug Anderson Acct Mgr
Tel: 715-398-0342
Email: doug@best-datacom.com
Website: www.best-datacom.com
Computer & network hardware & peripheral products, copper & fiber cable assemblies, cabinets/racks & computer/network enclosures. (Woman/As-Pac, estab 2007, empl 3, sales $264,000, cert: NMSDC)

5604 CaDan Technologies
4131 Old Sibley Memorial Hwy Ste 200
Eagan, MN 55122
Contact: Tom Kreiling Sales
Tel: 952-278-0560
Email: sales@cadan.com
Website: www.cadan.com
Computer hardware, software & services, new & refurbished hardware, hardware/software installations, new site setups or site tear downs. (Woman, estab 1992, empl 32, sales $9,300,000, cert: WBENC)

5605 Kelly Computer Supply
2042 Wooddale Dr Ste 250
Woodbury, MN 55125
Contact: Bob Kelly President
Tel: 651-773-1109
Email: bobkelly@kellyrest.com
Website: www.kellyrest.com
Ergonomic equip; mfr "KellyRest" computer products: wrist & foot rests, adjustable copy holders, keyboard drawers & articulating keyboard trays; workstations. (Nat Ame, estab 1983, empl 10, sales , cert: State, NMSDC, CPUC)

5606 Magnetic Products and Services, Inc.
7600 Boone Ave N. Ste 1
Minneapolis, MN 55428
Contact: Michelle Morey VP
Tel: 800-447-1277
Email: mmorey@mpsinc.org
Website: www.mpsinc.org
Dist electrical products & computer supplies: magnetic tapes, cartridges, optical disks, etc. (Woman, estab 1989, empl 14, sales $9,520,000, cert: WBENC)

Missouri

5607 Desktop Color Systems
1675 Larkin Williams Rd
Fenton, MO 63122
Contact: Maryann Gephardt CEO
Tel: 636-343-4600
Email: info@dtcolor.com
Website: www.dtcolor.com
Resell imaging supplies & office equipment hardware, service agreements, break-fix & warranty service. (Woman, estab 1993, empl 5, sales $1,546,000, cert: WBENC)

5608 Huber & Associates, Inc.
1400 Edgewood Dr
Jefferson City, MO 65109
Contact: Elizabeth Huber CEO
Tel: 573-634-5000
Email: ehuber@teamhuber.com
Website: www.teamhuber.com
Dist IBM hardware, software, maintenance & services. (Woman, estab 1986, empl 80, sales , cert: WBENC)

5609 Missouri Office Systems & Supplies, Inc.
941 W 141st Terrace Ste B
Kansas City, MO 64145
Contact: Virgie Dillard President
Tel: 816-761-5152
Email: vld@8asupplier.com
Website: www.8asupplier.com
Dist office supplies, furniture, ethernet, media, printers, software, hardware, ribbons, fax, scanners, computers, typewriters, routers, hubs, toners, servers. (Woman/AA, estab 1993, empl 9, sales $8,775,113, cert: State, City, NMSDC)

North Carolina

5610 Carolina Cartridge Systems, Inc.
516 E Hebron St
Charlotte, NC 28273
Contact: CEO
Tel: 704-347-2447
Email:
Website: www.ccsinside.com
Mfr toner cartridges. (Woman, estab 1991, empl 35, sales $2,200,000, cert: State, WBENC)

5611 Key Services, Inc.
      3921 Westpoint Blvd
      Winston-Salem, NC 27103
      Contact: Lisa Hodges VP & Quality Assurance Mgr
      Tel: 336-397-2129
      Email: arice@key-services.com
      Website: www.key-services.com
Dist & repair computer hardware & software, displays, touchscreens, printers, scanners, barcoding products & networking equipment. (Woman, estab 1976, empl 35, sales $2,749,120, cert: WBENC)

5612 Stay Online Corp.
      3301 Bramer Dr
      Raleigh, NC 27604
      Contact: Jim Higgins GM
      Tel: 919-510-5464
      Email: jim@stayonline.com
      Website: http://stayonline.com/
Power and data products. (Woman/Hisp, estab 1987, empl 13, sales $6,050,000, cert: NMSDC)

Nebrasksa

5613 The EW Armstrong Industries Inc.
      3702 Burr Oak Dr
      Bellevue, NE 68123
      Contact: Carole Armstrong CEO
      Tel: 402-291-4982
      Email: carolea@ewaindustries.com
      Website: www.ewaindustries.com
Computer equipment, supply sales & services. (AA, estab 2012, empl 3, sales , cert: State)

New Hampshire

5614 110 Technology LLC
      27 Technology Way Millyard Technology Park
      Nashua, NH 03060
      Contact: Gary Nicoll Sales Mgr
      Tel: 603-886-2800
      Email: sales@110technology.com
      Website: www.110technology.com
Resell information technology products: Hewlett Packard, IBM, Dell, Apple, Microsoft, Cisco, 3Com, APC, Philips, Xerox, NEC, Infocus, Intel, Viewsonic. (Woman/Hisp, estab 2004, empl 8, sales $11,000,000, cert: NMSDC, WBENC)

5615 Tape Services, Inc.
      15 Londonderry Rd, Unit 11
      Londonderry, NH 03053
      Contact: Bryan Webb Sales Mgr
      Tel: 603-425-2202
      Email: bwebb@tapeservices.com
      Website: www.tapeservices.com/
Pro Audio; Videotape; Back Up Tape; Data Media;Hard Drives; CD;Computer Media; Digital Media; Pro Tape; Professional Media; Recording Media; Computer Media; Data Migration; DBeta; DVCam; DVCPro; DVD; Glyph; G-Tech. (Woman, estab 1989, empl 8, sales $4,314,589, cert: WBENC)

New Jersey

5616 Baanyan Software Services, Inc.
      399 Thornall St First Fl
      Edison, NJ 08837
      Contact: VP Sales
      Tel: 732-595-9006
      Email: nshah@baanyan.com
      Website: www.baanyan.com
IT staffing, ERP, BI, Data Warehousing, Cloud and Mobile Computing, and Big Data. (Woman/As-Ind, estab 2009, empl 100, sales $7,091,695, cert: City, NMSDC)

5617 DATA Inc. USA
      72 Summit Ave
      Montvale, NJ 07645
      Contact: Deepali Schwarz Dir Corporate Affairs
      Tel: 201-802-9800
      Email: dschwarz@dataincusa.com
      Website: www.datainc.biz
IT solutions: staff augmentation & custom application development solutions. (As-Pac, estab 1983, empl 400, sales $49,079,601, cert: State, NMSDC)

5618 First Call Services, Inc.
      121 Chestnut St
      Roselle Park, NJ 07204
      Contact: Fred Bonda President
      Tel: 908-620-1240
      Email: firstcallsvcs@live.com
      Website: www.firstcallservicesinc.com
Repair & service office machines, fax machines, typewriters, scanners, micro-graphics, computers, printers & shredders. dist toners, ribbons, drums, fuser units & additional parts. (Hisp, estab 1995, empl 10, sales , cert: State)

New York

5619 BXI Consultants, Inc.
      33 Peuquet Pkwy
      Tonawanda, NY 14150
      Contact: Ingrid Charlton President
      Tel: 716-693-0343
      Email: icharlton@bxiconsultants.com
      Website: www.bxiconsultants.com
Xerox copying, printing & scanning. (Woman/As-Pac, estab 1993, empl 15, sales , cert: State)

5620 Empress Media, Inc.
      306 W 38th St, 4 Fl
      New York, NY 10018
      Contact: David Miller President
      Tel: 212-643-4898
      Email: empressmedia@cs.com
      Website:
Dist recording media, video, audio & data. (Woman/As-Pac, estab 1998, empl 25, sales , cert: State)

5621 Garic, Inc.
      26 Broadway Ste 961
      New York, NY 10004
      Contact: Patrick O'Keefe Principal
      Tel: 646-487-0103
      Email: patrick@garicinc.com
      Website: www.garicinc.com
Technology leasing & computer remarketing, financial services, computer & telecommunications equipment, computers, telephone systems, switches, networks, peripherals, etc. (AA, Hisp, estab 2000, empl 7, sales $5,000,000, cert: State, City, NMSDC)

5622 Gholkar's, Inc.
      7321 State Rt 251
      Victor, NY 14564
      Contact: Preeya Gholkar President
      Tel: 585-924-2050
      Email: info@gholkars.com
      Website: www.gholkars.com
Dist computer supplies: magnetic media, CAD plotter paper, ribbons, barcode labels, & ribbons. (As-Ind, estab 1988, empl 7, sales $3,400,000, cert: State)

5623   GT Business Supplies LLC
     115-13 Linden Blvd
     South Ozone park, NY 11420
     Contact: Jodhan Basanta Managing Dir
     Tel: 718-659-9165
     Email: jodhanb@gttoner.com
     Website: www.gttoner.com
Dist printers, ink cartridges & toners. (Hisp, estab 2003, empl 4, sales $400,000, cert: City)

5624   Hugo Neu Recycling, LLC
     249 E Sandford Blvd
     Mount Vernon, NY 10550
     Contact: Joseph Claiborne Dir sourcing
     Tel: 917-566-8464
     Email: info@hugoneu.com
     Website: www.hugoneurecycling.com
IT asset disposal & advance electronic e-waste recycler. (Woman/As-Pac, estab 2009, empl 90, sales , cert: NMSDC, WBENC)

5625   Minoria Tech LLC
     326 Broad St
     Utica, NY 00000
     Contact: President
     Tel: 315-628-0021
     Email:
     Website: www.minoriatech.com/
We are a computer, hardware, software, and peripherals value added reseller. (Woman/Hisp, estab 2017, empl 3, sales $854,026, cert: State, City, WBENC)

5626   New Computech, Inc.
     39 Broadway Ste 1630
     New York, NY 10006
     Contact: President
     Tel: 212-406-1801
     Email:
     Website: www.newcomputech.com
Resell computer hardware & software products. (Woman/AA, estab 1996, empl 12, sales $1,500,000, cert: City, WBENC)

5627   Pioneer Business Systems
     165 W 29th St
     New York, NY 10001
     Contact: James Breland Dir Business Devel
     Tel: 212-594-2614
     Email: jamesb@pioneercopier.com
     Website: www.pioneercopier.com
Lease, rentals, purchase copiers, prints, scanners, MFP equipment, wide format printers. Service copiers, printers, fax & MFP equipment. (As-Pac, estab , empl , sales $13,500,000, cert: City, NMSDC)

5628   Sidewinder Holdings, Inc.
     245 Mineola Blvd
     Mineola, NY 11501
     Contact: Stacey Rose President
     Tel: 516-742-1700
     Email: srose@cartridgeworldusa.com
     Website: www.cartridgeworldusa.com/store76
Dist laser, toner & inkjet cartridges for printers, copiers & fax machines. (Woman/AA, estab 2005, empl 5, sales $211,429, cert: City, NMSDC)

Ohio

5629   Integrated Business Supplies Inc.
     17381 Old Tannery Trail
     Chagrin Falls, OH 44023
     Contact: Judy Wardley VP
     Tel: 440-498-3888
     Email: judyw@misibs.com
     Website: www.askibs.com
Dist computers & equipment, office machines, supplies, paper, furniture, vellum. (Woman, estab 1990, empl 5, sales $546,600, cert: State, City)

5630   SpaceBound, Inc.
     280 Opportunity Way
     LaGrange, OH 44050
     Contact: Cindi Duesler Sales Mgr
     Tel: 440-355-8008
     Email: govtbids@spaceboundsolutions.com
     Website: http://spaceboundsolutions.com
Computer hardware, software, peripherals, accessories, electronics, office supplies, office equipment, audio, video, cameras, phones telephone, etc. (Woman, estab 1987, empl 49, sales $34,000,000, cert: WBENC)

5631   WMG, LLC
     P.O. Box 3115
     Dayton, OH 45401
     Contact: William Michael Green CEO
     Tel: 937-268-0773
     Email: info@wmgreensales.com
     Website: http://WMGreensales.com
Office equipment, hardware & doftware multifunctional devices, copiers, scanners, plotters & faxes. (AA, estab 2011, empl , sales $1,250,000, cert: State, City, NMSDC)

Oklahoma

5632   Miami Business Services, Inc.
     28 N Main
     Miami, OK 74354
     Contact: Gary Shelton Econ Dev Mgr
     Tel: 918-541-2195
     Email: gshelton@mn-e.com
     Website: http://mbs.mn-e.com
Dist office products, remanufactured & compatible imaging products. (Nat Ame, estab 1987, empl 5, sales $263,158, cert: State)

Pennsylvania

5633   Parmetech, Inc.
     137 W Eagle Ave
     Havertown, PA 19083
     Contact: Ana Fernandez-Parmet President
     Tel: 610-446-4000
     Email: afparmet@parmetech.com
     Website: www.parmetech.com
Dist printers, scanners, multifuction machines & storage devices. (Woman/Hisp, estab 1991, empl 23, sales $4,900,000, cert: NMSDC, WBENC)

Rhode Island

5634   NetCablesPlus Inc.
       P.O. Box 7815
       Cumberland, RI 02864
       Contact: John Rodrigues President
       Tel: 401-475-6040
       Email: sales@netcablesplus.com
       Website: www.netcablesplus.com
Network & PC cables & accessories, ethernet, fiber optic,
USB, firewire. (Hisp, estab 2004, empl 3, sales $135,000,
cert: State)

Tennessee

5635   Columbia Data Systems, Inc.
       2002 Oakland Pkwy
       Columbia, TN 38401
       Contact: Julie Baker President
       Tel: 931-381-4660
       Email: julie.baker@edge.net
       Website: www.cdsmicro.com
Dist & service computer & peripherals. (Woman, estab
1983, empl 3, sales $308,690, cert: State)

5636   Guy Brown, LLC
       7111 Commerce Way
       Brentwood, TN 37027
       Contact: Lauren Dooros Sales & Marketing Mgr
       Tel: 615-777-1500
       Email: lauren.dooros@guybrown.com
       Website: www.guybrown.com
Mfr recycled laser toner cartridges & office products.
(Woman/AA, As-Pac, Hisp, estab 1997, empl 76, sales
$204,877,006, cert: NMSDC, WBENC)

5637   Laser Recharge Inc.
       485 E South St Ste 100
       Collierville, TN 38017
       Contact: John Ferris VP
       Tel: 901-853-0742
       Email: jferris@laser-recharge.com
       Website: www.laser-recharge.com
Laser Printers, Ink Jet Printers, Copiers, Fax, Machines,
Multi Function Machines, Scanners, Digital Senders,
Plotters, Printer & Copier Supplies, Printer Repair Service.
(Woman, estab 1986, empl 11, sales $2,780,000, cert:
State)

5638   Unistar-Sparco Computers, Inc.
       7089 Ryburn Dr
       Millington, TN 38053
       Contact: SooTsong Lim CEO
       Tel: 901-872-2272
       Email: lim@sparco.com
       Website: www.sparco.com
IT solutions, hardware, computer systems, desktops,
notebooks, thin clients, tablet PCs, PDAs, workstations,
rack-mount servers, blade servers, monitors, displays,
Plasma TVs, LCD monitors, flat-screen monitors, LCD TVs.
(As-Pac, estab 1992, empl 35, sales $38,700,641, cert:
NMSDC)

Texas

5639   ARDETECH Industries, Inc.
       11526 Pagemill Rd
       Dallas, TX 75243
       Contact: Sales Rep
       Tel: 800-821-5678
       Email:
       Website: www.ardetech.com
Dist IT products, cable assemblies, computer peripherals, data & telecomm supplies. (Woman, estab 1996,
empl 14, sales $2,415,008, cert: State, WBENC)

5640   CompuPro Global
       15720 Park Row Ste 400
       Houston, TX 77084
       Contact: Randy Pfeiffer VP Business Dev
       Tel: 713-934-9633
       Email: ginnib@compuproglobal.com
       Website: www.compuproglobal.com
Dist computer tape, computer media, computer
accessories, hardware, toner, wide format printer
supplies (Woman, estab 1999, empl 9, sales $5,600,000,
cert: State, WBENC)

5641   Designs That Compute
       1778 N Plano Rd, Ste 211B
       Richardson, TX 75081
       Contact: Gregg Coapman technical sales consult-
       ant
       Tel: 214-276-0124
       Email: sales@visionality.com
       Website: http://visionality.com
Videoconferencing & audio/visual solutions, digital
signage, interactive whiteboards & displays, video walls,
projectors/screens, audio/speakers, recording, streaming video. (Woman, estab 1986, empl 14, sales
$5,400,000, cert: State)

5642   ELP Enterprises, Inc.
       9346 Rosstown Way
       Houston, TX 77080
       Contact: Martha Ceballos CEO
       Tel: 832-969-9947
       Email: mceball@aol.com
       Website: www.elpenterprisesinc.com
Dist computer supplies. (Woman/Hisp, estab 1999, empl
2, sales $813,923, cert: City, NMSDC, WBENC)

5643   JHJ Computer Supplies, Inc.
       3901 Arlington Highlands Blvd. Ste 200
       Arlington, TX 76018
       Contact: Jessie Jones President
       Tel: 817-861-0888
       Email: jhampton@jhjcs.com
       Website: www.jhjcs.com
Dist computer supplies: printers, keyboards, flash drives,
ink & toner cartridges, magnetic media, media storage,
anti-glare screens, mouse pads, optical mouse devices,
wireless devices, computer bags, USB cables. (Woman/
AA, estab 2007, empl 3, sales $116,336, cert: State)

5644 Meridian Office Systems, Inc.
4113 Lindbergh Dr
Addison, TX 75001
Contact: Jeff Emery Mgr
Tel: 972-690-3661
Email: jemery@meridianoffice.com
Website: www.meridianoffice.com
Sell, lease, rent, repair, service & maintenance office copiers, laser printers & multifunction color copiers. (Woman/As-Pac, estab 1994, empl 15, sales $3,200,000, cert: State)

5645 OAS Computer Supplies
3333 Earhart Dr, Ste 120
Carrollton, TX 75006
Contact: Sales Exec
Tel: 972-267-8020
Email:
Website: www.oas-supplies.com
Resell office supplies & computer supplies. (Woman, estab 1986, empl 12, sales $150,500,000, cert: State)

5646 Patriot Group, Ltd.
5000 Terminal St
Bellaire, TX 77401
Contact: Lois Livingston Acct Mgr
Tel: 713-664-1172
Email: llivingston@patriotgroup.com
Website: www.patriotgroup.com
Dist business equipment, equipment supplies, service and support. (Woman, estab 1979, empl 22, sales $5,137,000, cert: State)

5647 RLS Interests, Inc.
10402 Harwin Dr
Houston, TX 77036
Contact: Michael Chang
Tel: 713-933-0934
Email: directron@globalxlr.com
Website: www.directron.com
DIY computer components, CPUs, memory, hard drives, optical drives, hardware & software, pre-built systems, notebooks, netbooks, tablets, peripherals & accessories. (As-Pac, estab 1990, empl 157, sales $51,100,000, cert: NMSDC)

5648 Southwest Office Systems, Inc.
13960 Trinity Blvd
Fort Worth, TX 76040
Contact: Debbie Sorrells COO
Tel: 817-730-8000
Email: rjasper@sostexas.com
Website: www.sostexas.com
Copiers, printers, print management, plotters, digital white boards. (Hisp, estab , empl , sales $10,819,775, cert: State, City, NMSDC)

5649 TAPEANDMEDIA.COM, LLC
450 Colorado Dr
Cedar Creek, TX 78612
Contact: Bennie Wallace VP
Tel: 877-938-0901
Email: bennie@tapeandmedia.com
Website: www.tapeandmedia.com
Dist blank media: computer back-up tapes, video tapes, audio tapes, DVD's, CD's, DVD/CD cases. (Woman, estab 2000, empl 6, sales $5,000,000, cert: State)

Virginia

5650 Advanced Business Software Consulting dba NCN
11890 Sunrise Valley Dr, Ste 515
Reston, VA 20191
Contact: Sharon Muniz CEO
Tel: 703-298-2468
Email: sharon@ncntechnology.com
Website: http://ncntechnology.com
Mobile & web application development, SharePoint services. (Woman/Hisp, estab 2006, empl 3, sales $520,000, cert: State, WBENC, 8a)

5651 Computer Upgrade King, LLC
1555 Standing Ridge Dr Ste A-1
Powhatan, VA 23139
Contact: Robert Robinson VP
Tel: 800-985-9364
Email: sales@computerupgradeking.com
Website: http://cukusa.com/
Computers (laptops, desktops), Custom Desktops, Components, Cases, Laser Etching. (Woman/As-Pac, estab 2008, empl 45, sales $846,956, cert: State)

5652 Metropolitan Technology Solutions Corp.
3633 Brockenbrough Dr
Dumfries, VA 22026
Contact: Russell Henderson CEO
Tel: 703-946-6565
Email: hendersonr@mts2003.com
Website: www.mtsitcorp.com
Dist hardware & software products, office supplies, IT consulting. (Woman/AA, estab 2003, empl 11, sales $169,000, cert: State)

Washington

5653 EC Corporation Export
22307 Marine View Dr S
Des Moines, WA 98198
Contact: Patricio Mendoza Mgr
Tel: 206-878-3321
Email: patricio@eccomputer.com
Website: www.eccomputer.com
Computers Peripherals, Cartridges, Office Supply, External hard drives, Keyboard, Mouse, Monitors, Software, Licenses, Office Supplies, PC'S. (Hisp, estab 1991, empl 4, sales $250,000, cert: State)

5654 Evergreen Computer Products Inc
2720 1st Ave S
Seattle, WA 98134
Contact: Barbara Anderson VP
Tel: 206-624-3722
Email: banderson@evergreencomp.com
Website: www.evergreencomp.com
Printer repair services. (Woman/AA, estab 1977, empl 10, sales $10,116,295, cert: State, NMSDC)

Wisconsin

5655 Cartridge Savers, Inc.
2801 Coho St Ste 206
Madison, WI 53713
Contact: Thomas Wangard President
Tel: 608-663-5126
Email: tom.w@cartridgesavers.com
Website: www.cartridgesavers.com
Dist remanufactured & new laser printer toner cartridges, laser printers. (Hisp, estab 1994, empl 8, sales $6,843,995, cert: State, NMSDC)

INFORMATION TECHNOLOGY: Systems/Machines
Design, manufacture, lease and/or distribute information processing systems, machines and components. Many of these firms also distribute information processing supplies. (See also INFORMATION TECHNOLOGY: Services and INFORMATION TECHNOLOGY: Supplies). NAICS Code 33

California

5656 CB Technologies, Inc.
750 The City Dr South Ste 225
Orange, CA 92868
Contact: Dwanna Lynch Dir Corporate Relations
Tel: 714-573-7733
Email: dwanna.lynch@cbtechinc.com
Website: www.cbtechinc.com
Information technology hardware. (Woman/Hisp, estab 2001, empl 40, sales $1,400,000, cert: CPUC, WBENC)

5657 CCIntegration, Inc.
2060 Corporate Ct
San Jose, CA 95131
Contact: Stephanie Stoller Dir Business Dev
Tel: 408-228-1314
Email: stephanie.stoller@ccintegration.com
Website: www.ccintegration.com
Technology, Computer, Server, Storage, Networking, Rack, On-site Service, Integration, Global Logistics, Hardware Engineering Support, Life Cycle Management, Appliance, System Platform, Dell, Lenovo, Supermicro, HPe. (Woman/As-Pac, estab 1985, empl 81, sales $108,000,000, cert: WBENC)

5658 DuraTech USA, Inc.
6765 Westminster Blvd Ste 314
Westminster, CA 92683
Contact: Skip Howland Govt Business Devel
Tel: 831-419-8179
Email: showland@duratechusa.com
Website: www.Duratechusa.com
Dist semi rugged & MIL-STD 810F laptops, rugged & submersible tablet pc's. (Woman/As-Pac, Hisp, estab 2005, empl 3, sales $2,500,000, cert: State)

5659 Elgin Micro
14271 Jeffrey Rd Ste 247
Irvine, CA 92620
Contact: Daniel Laterneau Sales Dir
Tel: 949-878-7461
Email: dan@elginmicro.com
Website: www.elginmicro.com
Dist HP, IBM, SUN Microsystems (Oracle), Dell, Cisco, Emulex, Qlogic, Juniper, EMC, NetApp, Nortel, Lenovo, Toshiba, Acer, Operating systems, Security, Applications, Design, Accounting, Training & Utilities. (Woman/Hisp, estab 2012, empl 8, sales , cert: NMSDC)

5660 JE Components Inc.
8709 Aviation Blvd
Inglewood, CA 90301
Contact: Joni Paulo President
Tel: 310-645-6021
Email: joni@jecom.com
Website: www.jecom.com
Resell PC & network hardware. (Woman/AA, As-Ind, estab 1995, empl 7, sales , cert: NMSDC, NWBOC)

5661 Performance Designed Products
14144 Ventura Blvd Ste 200
Sherman Oaks, CA 91423
Contact: Theresa Harrell Natl Sales Mgr
Tel: 479-445-8612
Email: theresa.harrell@pdp.com
Website: http://pdp.com
Design & mfr video game peripherals & accessories: PS2, PS3, PSP PS Vita, Xbox, Xbox 360, Wii, Wii U, 3DS, DS Lite. (Woman, estab 1990, empl 200, sales , cert: WBENC)

5662 RICOM
26062 Merit Circle Bldg. 108
Laguna Hills, CA 92653
Contact: Isaac Buchanan Acct Exec
Tel: 949-788-9939
Email: isaac@ricom.net
Website: www.shopricom.com
Computers: Cisco; IBM; Hewlett Packard; Emulex; Sun Microsystems; Dell; EMC; Nimble Storage; F5 Networks; VMware; citrix. (Woman/Hisp, estab 1998, empl 9, sales $13,000,000, cert: NMSDC, CPUC, WBENC)

Colorado

5663 SF&B, LLC
9585 Niwot Rd
Longmont, CO 80504
Contact: Mgr
Tel: 703-297-7447
Email:
Website: www.sfbllc.com
Dist top-tier computer hardware. (Woman, estab 2011, empl 4, sales , cert: WBENC)

Connecticut

5664 PCNet, Inc.
100 Technology Dr
Trumbull, CT 06611
Contact: VP Finance/Operations
Tel: 203-452-8559
Email: teric@pcnet-inc.com
Website: www.pcnet-inc.com
Network systems integrator; e-commerce, Internet/Intranet; resell of personal computer products & svcs. (Hisp, estab 1993, empl 65, sales $26,000,000, cert: NMSDC)

Florida

5665 United Data Technologies
8825 NW 21 Terrace
Doral, FL 33172
Contact: Mariana Lugaro Mgr Sales Operations
Tel: 305-882-0435
Email: sales.operations@udtonline.com
Website: www.udtonline.com
Dist, install & repair IT equipment: desktops, laptops, servers, printers, switches, peripherals, & audio visual equipment. (Hisp, estab 1995, empl 94, sales , cert: State)

Georgia

5666 American Megatrends Inc.
      5555 Oakbrook Pkwy, Ste 200
      Norcross, GA 30093
      Contact: Srivatsan Ramachandran Dir Business Dev
      Tel: 770-246-8600
      Email: srivatsanr@ami.com
      Website: www.ami.com
Mfr key hardware & software solutions, StorTrends, IP
Storage Area Network (IP-SAN) and Network Attached
Storage (NAS) solutions, Aptio and AMIBIOS system
software and firmware, MegaRAC remote management
software & firmware. (As-Ind, estab 1985, empl 1345, sales
$10,000,000, cert: NMSDC)

5667 Eastern Data, Inc.
      4386 Park Dr
      Norcross, GA 30093
      Contact: JoAnn Pfeiffer Natl Accts Mgr
      Tel: 770-279-8888
      Email: jo.pfeiffer@ediatlanta.com
      Website: www.ediatlanta.com
Dist computer systems, components & peripherals.
(Woman/As-Pac, estab 1997, empl 27, sales $20,906,578,
cert: NMSDC, WBENC)

Illinois

5668 Hagerman & Company Inc.
      505 Sunset Ct
      Mount Zion, IL 62549
      Contact: Sandy Hagerman President & CEO
      Tel: 217-972-7268
      Email: sandyhagerman@hagerman.com
      Website: www.hagerman.com
Platinum Autodesk Reseller, System Integrator and
Consultant. (Woman, estab 1985, empl 89, sales
$43,800,000, cert: WBENC)

5669 Koi Computers Inc.
      200 W North Ave
      Lombard, IL 60148
      Contact: Ayde Chavez Acct Rep
      Tel: 630-627-8811
      Email: ayde@koicomputer.com
      Website: www.koicomputer.com
Dist computers, servers, printers, copiers, digital imaging &
networking equipments. (Woman/As-Ind, As-Pac, estab
1995, empl 6, sales $7,500,000, cert: State)

Indiana

5670 Professional Information Systems
      232 S Linda St
      Hobart, IN 46342
      Contact: Paulette Hill President
      Tel: 219-947-4349
      Email: paulette@proinfosys.com
      Website: www.proinfosys.com
Hardware & software, build customize computers or
prebuilt computers. (Woman, estab 1992, empl 4, sales
$172,000, cert: State, 8a)

5671 Qumulus Solutions LLC
      101 N Michigan St Ste 300
      South Bend, IN 46601
      Contact: Russell Ford President & CEO
      Tel: 574-208-6772
      Email: rford@qumulussolutions.com
      Website: www.qumulussolutions.com
Resell servers, storage, data backup hardware & soft-
ware. (AA, estab 2010, empl 7, sales $644,000, cert:
State, NMSDC)

Kansas

5672 ProActive Solutions Inc.
      5625 Foxridge Dr
      Shawnee Mission, KS 66202
      Contact: Dean Thiede Exec VP
      Tel: 913-948-8000
      Email: dthiede@proactivesolutions.com
      Website: www.proactivesolutions.com
IBM Hardware Power, System i, AS400, System p,
RS6000, System x, Storage, SAN, Lotus, Domino, Notes,
Websphere, Tivoli, TSM, VMWare, virtualization,
Disaster Recovery, DR, High Availability, HA, Business
Continuity, BC, Linux, (Woman, estab 1996, empl 30,
sales $45,029,277, cert: CPUC, WBENC)

Massachusetts

5673 Concord Information Systems, LLC
      165 Middlesex Turnpike Ste 201
      Bedford, MA 01730
      Contact: Suzanne Hiniker Partner
      Tel: 781-863-7200
      Email: suzy@concordinfo.com
      Website: www.concordinfo.com
Computers, laptops, tablets, servers, monitors, printers,
networking hardware, cloud & email services & technical consulting services. (Woman, estab 1994, empl 10,
sales $10,000,000, cert: State)

5674 Fenco Global Industries Corp.
      1 Federal St
      Springfield, MA 01105
      Contact: Fenella Sitati President
      Tel: 413-308-8800
      Email: fenella@winningtek.com
      Website: www.winningtek.com
Technology hardware for application security,
datacenters & cloud virtualization, F5 Networks,
VMware, Palo Alto, Cisco Networks, RedHat, Microsoft,
NetApp, EMC, HP, IBM, Dell & ExtraHop. (Woman/AA,
estab 2009, empl 5, sales $450,000, cert: NMSDC)

5675 Pyramid Technology Services, Inc.
      10 Riverbank Rd, Ste 200
      Maynard, MA 01754
      Contact: President
      Tel: 877-289-7874
      Email:
      Website: www.pyramiddec.com
Resell new, used & refurbished computer equipment:
Sun, HP, Digital & Compaq systems, Cisco, Enterasys &
Cabletron networking lines. (Woman, estab 1989, empl
12, sales , cert: State)

Michigan

5676 Dynamic Computer Corporation
      23400 Industrial Park Court
      Farmington Hills, MI 48335
      Contact: Tami Schultz VP Business Dev
      Tel: 248-473-2200
      Email: tschultz@dynamictech.solutions
      Website: https://dynamictech.solutions
Dist IT equipment: HP/Compaq, Dell, IBM, Microsoft,
Symantec & Gateway. (Woman/As-Ind, estab 1979, empl
24, sales $29,500,000, cert: NMSDC, WBENC)

Minnesota

5677 Vaske Computer Inc
      2310 W County Rd D Ste 110
      St. Paul, MN 55112
      Contact: Shaun Stefano CEO
      Tel: 651-633-6446
      Email: smstefano@collier-it.com
      Website: www.collier-it.com
Computer maintenance; HP & Sun Microsystems computer
equipment. (Woman, estab 1993, empl 22, sales
$17,000,000, cert: State)

New Jersey

5678 CPI (USA) Inc.
      6 Doreen Court
      Edison, NJ 08820
      Contact: Deepak Advani
      Tel: 732-494-0007
      Email: dadvani@cpiusainc.com
      Website: www.cpiusainc.com
Workstations, Laptops, Servers, Tablets, Multifunction
Printers, Held Workstations, CCTV
Phone Systems (Panasonic, Mitel), Enterprise Business,
Industry Standard Servers and Options
Routers & Add On, Switches & Add On, UPS & Generators.
(Woman/As-Pac, estab 1997, empl 2, sales $375,000, cert:
NMSDC)

New York

5679 Empire Electronics Inc.
      103 Fort Salonga Rd
      Northport, NY 11768
      Contact: Krista Fisher
      Tel: 631-544-9111
      Email: kfisher@empireusa.com
      Website: www.empireusa.com
Dist information technology equip, computer hardware &
components. (Woman, estab 1983, empl 6, sales
$10,400,000, cert: City, WBENC)

5680 Ergonomic Group, Inc.
      609-3 Cantiague Rock Rd
      Westbury, NY 11590
      Contact: Keith Trotte Sr. Acct Director
      Tel: 516-746-7777
      Email: keith.trotte@ergogroup.com
      Website: www.ergogroup.com
Resell computer equipment, peripherals & computer
related services. (Woman, estab 1984, empl 139, sales ,
cert: WBENC)

Ohio

5681 Northern Technical Group LLC
      14500 Industrial Ave N
      Maple Heights, OH 44137
      Contact: Mary Fink President
      Tel: 216-662-0561
      Email: mfink@northerntechnicalgroup.com
      Website: http://northerntechnicalgroup.com
IT Asset Management, removal, audit, sanitizing,
remarketing & recycling of computer related asset.
(Woman, estab 2003, empl 17, sales $921,316, cert:
NWBOC)

Texas

5682 Computize Inc.
      80 E. McDermott Dr.
      Allen, TX 75002
      Contact: Bennie Moore Sr Sales Dir
      Tel: 972-437-3100
      Email: benniem@computize.com
      Website: www.computize.com
Resell computers. (Woman/As-Pac, estab 1982, empl
125, sales $4,000,000, cert: WBENC)

5683 Cytec Software Systems Inc.
      10877 Sanden Dr
      Dallas, TX 75238
      Contact: Oscar De Leon President
      Tel: 214-349-8881
      Email: oscar@cytecsys.com
      Website: www.cytecsys.com
Mfr & integrate industrial network computers, RAID
servers & rugged portable computers, custom hardware
& software devel. (Hisp, estab 1984, empl 18, sales ,
cert: State)

5684 M&A Technology Inc.
      2045 Chenault Dr
      Carrollton, TX 75006
      Contact: Donna Shepard Exec VP
      Tel: 469-767-6657
      Email: dshepard@macomp.com
      Website: www.macomp.com
Custom intergration, servers, workstation, high performance intergrating, data center, on line back up, disater
recovery. (AA, estab 1984, empl 55, sales $75,000,000,
cert: State)

Virginia

5685 US21, Inc.
      2721 Prosperity Ave, Ste 300
      Fairfax, VA 22031
      Contact: Bassel Shubassi Business Dev Mgr
      Tel: 703-560-0021
      Email: info@us21.com
      Website: www.us21.com
Dist IT hardware: SMB & Enterprise. (Woman, estab
1998, empl 20, sales $10,000,000, cert: State)

5686   Video & Telecommunications, Inc.
       5427-A Backlick Rd
       Springfield, VA 22151
       Contact: Justin Larkin Sr Acct Mgr
       Tel: 703-658-0304
       Email: justinl@vti2.com
       Website: www.vti2.com
Dist PCs, ATs, microcomputers, laptops, printers, modems,
multiplexers, fiber optics, ASCII & ANSI terminals, disk
drives, etc. (Nat Ame, estab 1982, empl 20, sales , cert:
State)

INSURANCE COMPANIES
Firms carry life, accident, auto and health insurance policies. Most are licensed in several states. NAICS Code 52

California

5687   Merriwether & Williams Insurance Services
550 Montgomery St Ste 550
San Francisco, CA 94111
Contact: Donna Hart CEO
Tel: 415-986-3999
Email: dhart@imwis.com
Website: www.imwis.com
Commercial insurance marketing & placements, surety bonding, OCIP, third party administration. (Woman/AA, estab 1997, empl 35, sales $2,292,090, cert: NMSDC, CPUC)

5688   Mudrasys Inc.
6200 Stoneridge Mall Rd, Ste 300
Pleasanton, CA 94588
Contact: Narsi Ayyagari CEO
Tel: 925-353-3888
Email: narsi@mudrasys.com
Website: www.mudrasys.com
AgeAlert is the first thermal age sensor for use in predicting remaining thermal life of propellants as well as other thermally degradable components in ordnance and aircraft and other aerospace platforms. These sensors, weighing less than 1/4 gram, elim (Woman/As-Ind, estab 2009, empl 59, sales $4,200,000, cert: NMSDC, CPUC)

5689   Sovereign Employee Benefits, Inc.
10630 Town Center Dr, Ste 113
Rancho Cucamonga, CA 91730
Contact: Katie King Owner
Tel: 909-948-7779
Email: melissadickson@sebins.com
Website: www.sebins.com
Insurance brokerage services: group medical, customized employee benefit packages, liability, workers' comp & consulting services. (AA, estab 1982, empl 10, sales , cert: CPUC)

Florida

5690   Epiphany Insurance Company LLC
6073 NW 167 St, Ste C7
Hialeah, FL 33015
Contact: Martine Miller Mgr
Tel: 305-783-1487
Email: epiphanyinsures@gmail.com
Website: www.epiphanyinsures.com
Health and Life Insurance, Group Benefits, Supplemental Benefits, Dental & Vision. (Woman/AA, estab 2017, empl 4, sales , cert: State, SDB)

Georgia

5691   AEGIAS Corporation
3500 Lenox Rd, Ste 1500
Atlanta, GA 30326
Contact: Mary L Beachum President
Tel: 404-419-2173
Email: mbeachum@aegias.com
Website: www.aegias.com
Employee benefits & financial risk consulting: group health & dental insurance, self-funded plans, life and AD&D, short & long term disability, vision plans, employee assistance programs. (AA, estab 2003, empl 11, sales $392,902, cert: State)

5692   Atlanta Life Insurance Company
191 Peachtree St. Ste 2500
Atlanta, GA 30303
Contact: Howard Stephenson
Tel: 404-654-8842
Email: hstephenson@atlantalife.com
Website: https://atlantalife.com
Financial services, employee benefits, reinsurance, asset mgmt, etc. (AA, estab 1905, empl 5, sales $7,481,269, cert: NMSDC)

5693   Benalytics Consulting Group, LLC
1850 Parkway Place SE Ste 730
Marietta, GA 30067
Contact: Charles Atkinson Principal
Tel: 770-420-0525
Email: catkinson@benalytics.com
Website: www.benalytics.com
Benefit consulting & insurance brokerage services. (AA, estab 2005, empl 12, sales , cert: NMSDC, 8a, SDB)

5694   JLM Risk Management Group
201 17th St Ste 300
Atlanta, GA 30363
Contact: Joseph L Moore
Tel: 404-874-2929
Email: jmoore@jlmriskmgmt.com
Website: www.jlmriskmanagementgroup.com
Property, casualty, life & employee benefits insurance brokerage. Risk management, claims management & loss control consultation. (AA, estab 1996, empl 7, sales $600,000, cert: NMSDC)

5695   Premier Benefit Consultants, Inc.
2470 Windy Hill Rd Ste 300
Marietta, GA 30068
Contact: Maureen Jurgelas President
Tel: 678-794-8104
Email: maureen@premierbenefit.com
Website: www.Premierbenefit.com
Insurance agency & consulting: group medical, dental, vision plans, LTD, STD, life insurance, AD&D, etc. (Woman, estab 2000, empl 4, sales $240,000, cert: WBENC)

Illinois

5696 CS Insurance Strategies
542 S Dearborn St
Chicago, IL 60605
Contact: Charles Smith CEO
Tel: 312-566-9700
Email: csmith@csstrategy.com
Website: www.csstrategy.com
Comprehensive risk management, commercial insurance & group employee benefit solutions. (AA, estab 2006, empl 4, sales $500,000, cert: City)

5697 Insurers Review Services, Inc.
225 N Michigan Ave Ste 902
Chicago, IL 60601
Contact: Alvin Robinson President
Tel: 312-938-0900
Email: arobin3172@aol.com
Website: http://insurersreviewservices.com
Insurance coverages, employee benefits, property coverages, special events, travel accident insurance & expatriate benefits. (AA, estab 1983, empl 5, sales $450,000, cert: State, City, NMSDC)

5698 Lambent Risk Management Services, Inc.
33 N. La Salle St Ste 1150
Chicago, IL 60602
Contact: Shirley Evans-Wofford CEO
Tel: 866-419-1415
Email: shirley_evans@lambent-rms.com
Website: www.lambent-rms.com
Insurance brokerage: property & casualty, third party theft, construction builders risk, insurance bonding, travel accident, healthcare & life, 401(k). (Woman/AA, estab 2000, empl 21, sales $2,433,496, cert: State, City)

Louisiana

5699 1st Team Insurance Agency
3745 Choctaw Dr
Baton Rouge, LA 70805
Contact: Harold Williams Owner
Tel: 225-806-6923
Email: hwilliams@1stteaminsurance.com
Website: www.1stteaminsurance.com
Property & casualty insurance, property management, public relations, lobbying. (AA, estab 2005, empl 3, sales $350,000, cert: State)

Michigan

5700 Brownrigg Companies LTD
840 W Long Lake Rd Ste 100
Troy, MI 48098
Contact: Nancy Brownrigg CEO
Tel: 248-373-5580
Email: nbrownrigg@brownrigg.com
Website: www.brownrigg.com
Specialty insurance. (Woman, estab 1990, empl 14, sales $11,000,000, cert: WBENC)

5701 Custom Results Corporate Consulting LLC
101 W Big Beaver Rd Ste 115
Troy, MI 48084
Contact: Diane Christensen President
Tel: 248-572-1160
Email: diane@customresults.com
Website: www.customresults.com
Insurance, design, implementation, service & communication of Employee Benefit Plans & Retiree Medicare Advantage plans. (Woman, estab 2001, empl 6, sales , cert: WBENC)

5702 Employee Solve
725 S Adams Ste L-140
Southfield, MI 48009
Contact: Kenneth Hurtt, RHU, REBC President
Tel: 248-438-0096
Email: info1@employeesolve.com
Website: www.employeesolve.com
Health & welfare plans for employer groups. (AA, estab 1987, empl 6, sales $3,000,000, cert: NMSDC)

5703 GOSS LLC
600 Renaissance Ctr, Ste 1200
Detroit, MI 48243
Contact: Vincent Davis Dir of Mktg
Tel: 313-446-9636
Email: vdavis@gossllc.com
Website: www.gossllc.com
Commercial risk & risk consulting svcs: group benefits, property, casualty, liability, E&O, D&O, workers comp, business auto, etc. (AA, estab 2001, empl 7, sales $37,150,000, cert: NMSDC)

5704 Laurie Sall & Associates
201 West Big Beaver Rd#300
Troy, MI 48084
Contact: Laurie Sall President
Tel: 248-641-2755
Email: laurie@lauriesall.com
Website: www.lauriesall.com
Life, disability & health insurance. (Woman/Hisp, estab 1980, empl 3, sales $8,532,047, cert: NMSDC, WBENC)

5705 ReviewWorks
21500 Haggerty Rd Ste 250
Northville, MI 48167
Contact: Carolyn Lahousse President
Tel: 248-848-5067
Email: carolyn_lahousse@reviewworks.com
Website: www.reviewworks.com
Medical cost containment solutions & disability services for workers' compensation, LTD & auto injury related claims & claimants. (Woman, estab 1989, empl 70, sales $11,650,921, cert: WBENC)

5706 The Dearborn Agency
22691 Michigan Ave
Dearborn, MI 48124
Contact: Wendy Beaver Sales Mgr
Tel: 313-562-8373
Email: wendyb@dearbornagency.com
Website: www.dearbornagency.com
Insurance. (Woman, estab 1924, empl 10, sales , cert: WBENC)

5707 The Goss Group, Inc.
600 Renaissance Center Dr Ste 1200
Detroit, MI 48243
Contact: Cindy Smith Sr VP
Tel: 313-446-9636
Email: csmith@gossllc.com
Website: www.gossllc.com
Commercial insurance agency. (AA, estab 1995, empl 3, sales $333,876, cert: City)

5708 Yee & Associates LLC
20789 Harper
Harper Woods, MI 48225
Contact: Matthew Yee Member
Tel: 313-886-6770
Email: matthew@bakerhopp.com
Website: www.bakerhopp.com
Property & casualty life and health insurance agency. (As-Pac, estab 2002, empl 1, sales , cert: NMSDC)

Minnesota

5709 Integrated Benefits Group, Inc.
601 Carlson Pkwy Ste 1097
Hopkins, MN 55305
Contact: Deborah J. Dybdahl CEO
Tel: 952-449-5290
Email: deborah@integratedbenefitsgroup.com
Website: www.integratedbenefitsgroup.com
Auto/home, legal, long term care, critical illnesss, supplemental disability, retirement planning, PET, etc. (Woman, estab 1992, empl 16, sales $550,000, cert: WBENC)

Ohio

5710 Pinkney-Perry Insurance Agency, Inc.
2143 Stokes Blvd
Cleveland, OH 44106
Contact: Patricia L. Welcome VP
Tel: 216-795-1995
Email: pwelcome@pinkney-perry.com
Website: www.pinkney-perry.com
Insurance. (AA, estab 0, empl , sales , cert: NMSDC)

Rhode Island

5711 Axiom Actuarial Consulting
26 Knapton St
Barrington, RI 02806
Contact: Carlos Fuentes President
Tel: 860-550-0740
Email: carlos-fuentes@axiom-actuarial.com
Website: http://axiom-actuarial.com
Actuarial consulting: dental & vision coverages, pension, life insurance, employee benefits, special risk insurance, reinsurance, investment, finance & strategy. (Hisp, estab 2008, empl 4, sales , cert: 8a)

Tennessee

5712 Diversity Benefits
230 N 4th Ave, Ste 162
Nashville, TN 37219
Contact: David Carter President
Tel: 615-515-3329
Email: davidc@diversitybenefits.net
Website: www.diversitybenefits.net
Health insurance/self-funded health plans, Prescription drug coverage, Reinsurance ,Dental insurance, Vision insurance, Life and AD&D insurance, Disability insurance, Voluntary benefits, Retirement plans. (AA, estab 2012, empl 2, sales , cert: NMSDC)

Texas

5713 CPR Insurance Group LLC
600 E John Carpenter Frwy Ste 365
Irving, TX 75062
Contact: Les Titus President
Tel: 972-887-3660
Email: ltitus@cprins.com
Website: www.cprins.com
Insurance claims: property, liability/casualty & auto claims. (AA, Hisp, estab 2013, empl 19, sales $1,200,000, cert: State)

LABORATORY/SCIENTIFIC SUPPLIES & SERVICES
Manufacture or distribute products or provide services for scientific laboratories. Products include glassware, disposables, chemicals, safety items. etc.
NAICS Code 33

California

5714　Accurate C&S Services, Inc.
8105 Edgewater Dr #225
Oakland, CA 94621
Contact: Regina Jones President
Tel:　510-387-0324
Email: rjones@accuratemgmt.com
Website: www.accureatecsservices.com
Drug & alcohol testing. (Woman/AA, estab 2006, empl 15, sales $1,500,000, cert: State, NMSDC, WBENC)

5715　BC Laboratories, Inc.
4100 Atlas Court
Bakersfield, CA 93308
Contact: Mark Ellis Business Devel Dir
Tel:　800-878-4911
Email: mark.ellis@bclabs.com
Website: http://bclabs.com
Analytical Services for Groundwater, Drinking Water, Wastewater, Soils & Air, Certified Testing Services, Sampling & Monitoring. (Woman, estab 1949, empl 97, sales $1,000,000,000, cert: CPUC)

5716　BIO PLAS, Inc.
4340 Redwood Hwy Ste A1
San Rafael, CA 94903
Contact: Jeananne McGrath VP
Tel:　415-472-3777
Email: jam@bioplas.com
Website: www.bioplas.com
Mfr disposable laboratory supplies. (Woman, estab 1977, empl 10, sales , cert: State)

5717　Brylen Technologies
275 Orange Ave
Santa Barbara, CA 93117
Contact: Barbara Tzur President
Tel:　805-692-9300
Email: barbara.tzur@brylen.com
Website: www.brylen.com
Calibration & testing laboratory, clean room & clean bench certifications, calibration is electro-magnetic, thermodynamics, dimensional, angle, & mechanical areas, calibrate equipment. (Woman, estab 1985, empl 10, sales $571,850, cert: State)

5718　Comprehensive Drug Testing, Inc. (CDT, Inc.)
P.O. Box 11869
Santa Ana, CA 92711
Contact: Kim Jasper President
Tel:　800-440-3784
Email: kimj@cdtsolutions.com
Website: www.cdtsolutions.com
Substance abuse program management, drug testing, collections, laboratory, education. (Woman, estab 1985, empl 13, sales $2,400,000, cert: State, CPUC)

5719　Core Diagnostics
3535 Breakwater Ave
Hayward, CA 94545
Contact: Krishnamurthy Balachandran CEO
Tel:　650-532-9500
Email: balachandran@corediagnostics.net
Website: http://corediagnostics.net
Laboratory offering biomarker analysis & translational research support for studies ranging from early discovery to analyses of Phase III clinical trial samples. (As-Ind, estab 2009, empl 12, sales $3,259,000, cert: NMSDC)

5720　CP Lab Safety
14 Commercial Blvd, Ste 113
Novato, CA 94949
Contact: Jessica Kurtz Cstmr Service
Tel:　415-883-2600
Email: info@cplabsafety.com
Website: www.calpaclab.com
Mfr environmentally conscious laboratory safety products & dist leading lab supply brands. (Woman, estab 1996, empl 6, sales $3,069,391, cert: State, 8a)

5721　Discount Lab Supplies
3201 Verdant Way
San Jose, CA 95117
Contact: Stacey Blanding President
Tel:　408-246-4024
Email: stacey@discountlabs.com
Website: www.discountlabs.com
Dist lab products: cryogenic storage vessels, DI water systems, furnaces, harvey sterilizers, incubators, NANOpure water systems, ovens, rotators & rockers, spectrophotometers, turner fluorometers, ultrasonic cleaners. (Minority/Woman, estab 2004, empl 1, sales , cert: NMSDC)

5722　Fulgent Therapeutics LLC
4978 Santa Anita Ave Ste 205
Temple City, CA 91780
Contact: Joe Roach VP
Tel:　626-350-0537
Email: joeroach@fulgentdiagnostics.com
Website: http://fulgentdiagnostics.com
Hereditary genetic testing. (As-Pac, estab 2013, empl 30, sales $1,000,000, cert: NMSDC)

5723　InterWorking Labs, Inc.
P.O. Box 66190
Scotts Valley, CA 95067
Contact: Judy Jones Marketing Mgr
Tel:　831-460-7010
Email: info@iwl.com
Website: https://iwl.com
Network Emulation for testing Products. (Woman, estab 1993, empl 10, sales $800,000, cert: WBENC)

5724　Orange Coast Analytical, Inc.
3002 Dow Ave, Ste 532
Tustin, CA 92780
Contact: Cindy Noorani President
Tel:　714-832-0064
Email: cindyn@ocalab.com
Website: www.ocalab.com
Environmental & analytical testing laboratory, organic & inorganic testing-water, waste water, soil, air, industial, chemical & food products. (Woman, estab 1990, empl 15, sales $1,450,178, cert: State, CPUC)

5725 Pure Lab Solutions, Inc.
4901 Morena Blvd, Ste 118
San Diego, CA 92117
Contact: Pam Wammes President
Tel: 619-840-5858
Email: pwammes@purelabsolutions.com
Website: www.purelabsolutions.com
Dist Sartorius lab equipment, ultrapure water purification
& lab bench scales. (Woman, estab 2012, empl 2, sales ,
cert: WBENC)

5726 The Andwin Corp.
6636 Variel Ave
Canoga Park, CA 91303
Contact: Arnie Shedlow Sr VP sales
Tel: 818-999-2828
Email: jpalaganas@andwin.com
Website: www.andwinsci.com
Dist medical & lab supplies & product kits: boxes, labels,
bar codes, instruction inserts & kit components. (Woman,
estab 1950, empl 98, sales $32,000,000, cert: WBENC)

Connecticut

5727 PRO Scientific Inc.
99 Willenbrock Rd
Oxford, CT 06478
Contact: Holly Archibald Sales Dir
Tel: 203-267-4600
Email: sales@proscientific.com
Website: www.proscientific.com
Mfr PRO Scientific laboratory equipment, PRO homogeniz-
ers, mixers, shakers & stirrers. Dist Andreas Hettich
Centrifuges. (Woman, estab 1992, empl 15, sales , cert:
State)

Florida

5728 Algon Corporation
12000 SW 132 Court
Miami, FL 33186
Contact: Eduardo Suarez-Troconis Director
Tel: 305-253-6901
Email: edal@algon.com
Website: www.algon.com
Chemical raw materials, laboratory supplies & machine
parts. (Woman/Hisp, estab 1989, empl 24, sales
$20,570,883, cert: NMSDC)

5729 Kramer Laboratories, Inc.
400 University Dr Ste 400
Coral Gables, FL 33134
Contact: Myrna Patterson Sales Mgr
Tel: 800-824-4894
Email: mpatterson@kramerlabs.com
Website: www.kramerlabs.com
Fungi Nail Brand, Safetussin CD Cough Relief/Nasal
Decongestant Formula, Safetussin DM Cough Formula.
(Woman/Hisp, estab 1987, empl 14, sales , cert: NMSDC,
WBENC)

5730 VetMeds, Inc.
8950 SW 74th Court Ste 2201
Miami, FL 33156
Contact: President
Tel: 786-220-3634
Email:
Website: www.vetmedsinc.biz
Dist medical equipment, medical apparel, wound care
supplies, medical furniture, exam room supplies,
extrication-patient transport equipment, surgical gloves,
IV therapy & laboratory supplies. (Woman/AA, estab
2012, empl 5, sales , cert: State)

Massachusetts

5731 Cross-Spectrum Acoustics Inc
P.O. Box 90842
Springfield, MA 01139
Contact: Herbert Singleton Managing Partner
Tel: 413-315-5770
Email: dbe@csacoustics.com
Website: www.csacoustics.com
Acoustical consulting, noise and vibration control, sound
measurements, noise & vibration mitigation. (AA, estab
2003, empl 1, sales , cert: State)

Maryland

5732 Quality Biological, Inc.
7581 Lindbergh Dr
Gaithersburg, MD 20879
Contact: Basile Whitaker VP, Operations
Tel: 301-840-9331
Email: whitakerb@qualitybiological.com
Website: www.qualitybiological.com
Mfr tissue culture & molecular biology products,
bacteriological plates, dist Corning glass & plastics,
Corning lab equipment, Microflex gloves & JT Baker
chemicals. (Woman/AA, estab 1983, empl 24, sales ,
cert: NMSDC)

5733 The Perara Group Inc.
1610 Professional Blvd Stes E & F
Crofton, MD 21114
Contact: Yancey Brown telecomm dir
Tel: 410-451-4141
Email: ybrown@peraragroup.com
Website: www.peraragroup.com
DNA research support, genetic models, bio-analytical
chemistry models, metabolism & pharmacokinetics,
oncology models, toxicology
lab diagnostics, vaccine & vector safety, bio-safety
testing. (Woman/AA, estab 2001, empl 7, sales
$1,700,000, cert: State)

5734 Trinity Sterile, Inc.
201 Kiley Dr
Salisbury, MD 21801
Contact: Crystal Lutz VP, Sales
Tel: 410-860-5123
Email: crystal.lutz@trinitysterile.com
Website: www.trinitysterile.com
Production & sterilization equipment: clinical kits, trays
or instruments. (As-Ind, estab , empl , sales , cert:
NMSDC)

Michigan

5735   Forensic Fluids Laboratories Inc.
      225 Parsons St
      Kalamazoo, MI 49007
      Contact: Bridget Lemberg CEO
      Tel: 269-492-7700
      Email: blemberg@forensicfluids.com
      Website: www.Forensicfluids.com
Drug testing & screening. (Woman, estab 2005, empl 60, sales $19,861,000, cert: WBENC)

5736   RTI Laboratories, Inc.
      33080 Industrial Rd
      Livonia, MI 48150
      Contact: Kae Trojanowski President
      Tel: 734-422-8000
      Email: ktrojanowski@rtilab.com
      Website: www.rtilab.com
Analytical testing laboratory: environmental, chemical & metallurgical testing, environmental compliance field sampling services. (As-Ind, estab 1986, empl 40, sales $5,000,000, cert: NMSDC, SDB)

5737   Structural Testing Laboratory
      397 Washington St, Ste B
      Brighton, MI 48116
      Contact: Tracy LaCroix Owner
      Tel: 734-476-9882
      Email: sales@stlbrighton.com
      Website: www.stlbrighton.com
Vibration & shock testing services for automotive, aerospace & defense, transportation & packaging & military. (Nat Ame, estab 2005, empl 3, sales , cert: NMSDC)

Minnesota

5738   LKT Laboratories, Inc.
      545 Phalen Blvd
      Saint Paul, MN 55130
      Contact: Luke Lam President
      Tel: 651-644-8424
      Email: llam@lktlabs.com
      Website: www.lktlabs.com/
Mfr biochemicals for life science research, inhibitors, activators, modulators, and many other high purity small molecules, phytochemical isolation and analysis. (As-Pac, estab 1990, empl 11, sales $1,300,000, cert: NMSDC)

Missouri

5739   HERA Laboratory Planners
      411 N. Tenth St, Ste 400
      St. Louis, MO 63101
      Contact: Laurie Sperling President
      Tel: 314-289-9202
      Email: lauries@herainc.com
      Website: www.herainc.com
Laboratory planning, design, programming & equipment planning. (Woman, estab 1996, empl 22, sales $8,113,716, cert: State, WBENC)

North Carolina

5740   Clinical Choice, LLC
      204 Muirs Chapel Rd, Ste 334
      Greensboro, NC 27410
      Contact: Minerva Loran President
      Tel: 336-841-0919
      Email: mloran@clinicalchoice.com
      Website: www.clinicalchoice.com
Lab supplies, cleaning brushes, bite blocks, filters for the reprocessing scope washing machines, Endo supplies, SafeCap Endoscope Transport Trays, ScopeVault Endoscope Storage Cabinets, OneTab Powder and Liquid detergent. (Woman/Hisp, estab 2001, empl 5, sales $3,751,424, cert: NMSDC)

5741   LJP Lab LLC
      495-S Arbor Hill Rd
      Kernersville, NC 27284
      Contact: Thomas Stith President
      Tel: 336-992-3902
      Email: tstith@ljplab.com
      Website: www.ljplab.com
Urine drug screen & confirmation services. (As-Pac, estab 2017, empl 6, sales $500,000, cert: State)

Nebraska

5742   Midland Scientific Inc.
      10651 Chandler Rd, Ste 102
      La Vista, NE 68128
      Contact: Shane Hanzlik
      Tel: 402-346-8352
      Email: shanzlik@midlandsci.com
      Website: www.midlandsci.com
Dist lab supplies & equipment. (Woman, estab , empl , sales $48,000,000, cert: WBENC)

New Jersey

5743   AGC Products Inc.
      3740 NW Blvd
      Vineland, NJ 08360
      Contact: Subu Natesan CEO
      Tel: 856-692-4435
      Email: snatesan@andrews-glass.com
      Website: http://andrews-glass.com
Manufacture specialty and precision glass products for industrial and scientific applications. (As-Ind, estab 1948, empl 40, sales $4,000,000, cert: State, NMSDC)

5744   BioRepository Resources, LLC
      755 Central Ave, Unit 3
      New Providence, NJ 07974
      Contact: Catherine Chin CEO
      Tel: 908-790-8890
      Email: cchin@brr.us.com
      Website: www.brr.us.com
Long term storage of biological & clinical trial samples: blood, plasma, urine, tissue, biomarkers, retain drug product, API, pathology slides, blocks. (Woman/As-Pac, estab 2008, empl 2, sales , cert: State)

5745 Laboratory Disposable Products
1 Como Court
Towaco, NJ 07082
Contact: Cindy Beatty President
Tel: 973-335-2966
Email: mail@labdisposable.com
Website: www.labdisposable.com
Laboratory Disposable Products. (Woman, estab 1979, empl 10, sales $3,549,720, cert: City, WBENC)

5746 NETA Scientific Inc.
4206 Sylon Blvd
Hainesport, NJ 08036
Contact: Winfred Sanders, PhD President
Tel: 609-265-8210
Email: sales@netascientific.com
Website: www.netascientific.com
Dist laboratory instruments & supplies safety & environmental supplies. (Woman/AA, estab 1999, empl 45, sales , cert: State, NMSDC, WBENC)

5747 Sarchem Laboratories, Inc.
5012 Industrial Rd
Farmingdale, NJ 07727
Contact: Arun Kumar VP
Tel: 732-938-2777
Email: arun.kumar@sarchemlabs.com
Website: http://sarchemlabs.com
Custom Synthesis, Process development from concept to lab scale preparation, Contract Research and Development. Supply small scale diagnostic reagents, chemical reagents and EPA samples in customer required ampules. (Woman/As-Ind, estab 1984, empl 6, sales $1,215,000, cert: NMSDC)

Ohio

5748 Crawford & Associates Services, LLC
100 E Campus View Blvd Ste 250
Columbus, OH 43235
Contact: Troy Crawford Principal
Tel: 614-557-1498
Email: tcrawford@cas-associates.com
Website: www.cas-associates.com
Commercial & Industrial Commissioning of Mechanical/Electrical/Plumbing Systems, including Heating, Ventilating and Air Conditioning Systems and Building Automatic Temperature Control Systems. (AA, estab 2007, empl 5, sales $293,055, cert: 8a)

5749 DHDC Engineering Consulting Services, Inc.
2390 Advanced Business Center Dr
Columbus, OH 43228
Contact: Savvas Sophocleous President
Tel: 614-527-7656
Email: sophocleous@dhdcinc.com
Website: www.dhdcinc.com
Laboratory testing services, geotechnical (engineering, drilling, and laboratory) & subsurface utility engineering (SUE). (As-Pac, estab 2012, empl 15, sales $500,000, cert: State)

5750 Midtown Scientific, Inc.
4415 Euclid Ave, Ste 343
Cleveland, OH 44103
Contact: Darlene Darby Baldwin CEO
Tel: 216-431-0110
Email: ddarbywatt@aol.com
Website: www.midtownscientific.com
Dist scientific laboratory research supplies & equipment, chemicals. (Woman/AA, estab 2002, empl 4, sales , cert: City)

5751 Nnodum Pharmaceuticals Corp.
483 Northland Blvd
Cincinnati, OH 45240
Contact: Nnodum Iheme President
Tel: 513-861-2329
Email: n.iheme@nnodumpharma.com
Website: www.nnodumpharma.com
Research, development & mfg over the counter & generic pharmaceuticals: prenatal Vitamins, dialysis vitamins, topical analgesics, lotions & creams for diabetic patients. (AA, estab 1997, empl 10, sales $30,000,000, cert: State, 8a)

Pennsylvania

5752 Hayes
157 S Broad St, Ste 200
Lansdale, PA 19446
Contact: Glenn Phillips Dir Provider Sales
Tel: 215-855-0615
Email: gphillips@hayesinc.com
Website: http://hayesinc.com
Devices, procedures, drugs/biologics, laboratory equipment & genetic tests. (Woman, estab 1989, empl 60, sales , cert: WBENC)

5753 MB Research Laboratories
1765 Wentz Rd
Spinnerstown, PA 18968
Contact: Betty Salyer Accts Receivable
Tel: 215-536-4110
Email: blandis@mbresearch.com
Website: www.mbresearch.com
Contract Research Toxicology Laboratory. (Woman/Hisp, estab 1972, empl 28, sales , cert: WBENC)

Puerto Rico

5754 Instrumed Services Corp.
10th St O 14 Castellana G
Carolina, PR 00983
Contact: Luis Peña President
Tel: 787-257-9249
Email: luis.pena@instrumed.net
Website: www.instrumed.net
Sales, Service, Validation and Calibration of Laboratory Equipments. (Woman/Hisp, estab 1999, empl 10, sales $138,603, cert: NMSDC)

5755 J.C. Gonzalez, Inc.
2 St KM 178.2 Interior BO. Minillas Alto
San German, PR 00683
Contact: Julio C. Gonzalez Santiago CEO
Tel: 787-892-0047
Email: sales@jcgonzalezinc.com
Website: www.jcgonzalezinc.com
Dist & service scientific & research equipment, laboratory equipment & consumables, microscopes, stereoscopes, freezers, refrigerators. (Hisp, estab 2001, empl 6, sales $865,047, cert: NMSDC, SDB)

Tennessee

5756 Safety Plus, LLC
P.O. Box 2549
Chattanooga, TN 37409
Contact: Alexa Wardlaw VP/Member
Tel: 423-822-0487
Email: alexa@safetyplusllc.com
Website: www.safetyplusllc.com
Safety solutions: fume hood, biosafety cabinet & clean air bench testing & maintenance, employee training, lab design & equipment recommendations. (Woman, estab 2005, empl 7, sales $284,017, cert: WBENC)

5757 Scientific Sales, Inc.
130 Valley Court St
Oak Ridge, TN 37830
Contact: Ember Murphy President
Tel: 865-483-9332
Email: emurphy@scisale.com
Website: www.scisale.com
Dist laboratory supplies, equipment, chemicals, safety, industrial & environmental products. (Woman/Nat Ame, estab 1987, empl 30, sales , cert: State, NMSDC)

5758 The Premier Group
4600 Cromwell Ave, Ste 101
Memphis, TN 38118
Contact: JW Gibson CEO
Tel: 901-346-9002
Email: jwgibson@gibsoncompanies.com
Website: www.gibsoncompanies.com
Dist medical supplies, laboratory & scientific equipment & related supplies. (AA, estab 1991, empl 7, sales $8,692,576, cert: NMSDC)

Texas

5759 Food Safety Net Services, Ltd.
199 W Rhapsody
San Antonio, TX 78216
Contact: Kelby Harke Purchasing/Distribution Team
Tel: 210-308-0675
Email: Kelby.harke@fsns.com
Website: www.fsns.com
Microbiological testing & chemical analysis. (Woman, estab , empl , sales , cert: WBENC)

5760 Fox Scientific, Inc.
8221 East FM 917
Alvarado, TX 76009
Contact: Jetta Lewis Sales
Tel: 800-369-5524
Email: paisleyg@foxscientific.com
Website: www.foxscientific.com
Dist laboratory supplies, equipment & chemicals. (Hisp, estab 1988, empl 21, sales $5,420,000, cert: State, City, NMSDC)

5761 Products Unlimited, Inc.
P.O. Box 339
Justin, TX 76247
Contact: Raithel Susan Sales Mgr
Tel: 940-648-3073
Email: sraithel@products-unlimited.com
Website: www.products-unlimited.com
Dist medical, lab & safety supplies & equipment. (Woman, estab 1992, empl 7, sales $5,020,000, cert: State)

Virginia

5762 United Lab Company
103 Arrow Ct Ste B
Yorktown, VA 23693
Contact: Wendy Wood VP
Tel: 757-806-6230
Email: wendy.wood@unitedlabco.com
Website: www.unitedlabco.com
Laboratory appliances & instruments. (Woman, estab 2008, empl 2, sales $1,962,425, cert: State)

Wisconsin

5763 Scientific Molding Corporation, Inc.
330 SMC Dr
Somerset, WI 54025
Contact: Rochelle Livingston Paralegal
Tel: 715-247-3500
Email: rochelle.livingston@smcltd.com
Website: www.smcltd.com
Design, molding & assembly enterprise, project integration, validation & quality controls, packaging & labeling & sterilization management. (As-Ind, estab 1988, empl 1200, sales , cert: NMSDC)

California

5764 Banker's Hill Law Firm, A.P.C.
160 Thorn St, Ste 200
San Diego, CA 92103
Contact: Carlos Alvarez Tostado Marketing Rep
Tel: 619-230-0330
Email: carlosa@bhlflaw.com
Website: www.bhlflaw.com
Personal injury, immigration law, criminal defense, bankruptcy, and family law. (AA, estab 1991, empl 12, sales $3,154,988, cert: NMSDC)

5765 Behmke Reporting & Video Services
160 Spear St Ste 300
San Francisco, CA 94105
Contact: Paula Behmke Owner
Tel: 415-597-5600
Email: paula.behmke@behmke.com
Website: http://www.behmke.com
Court reporting, realtime reporting, legal videography, litigation support services with local, state, and nationwide coverage. Cetralized scheduling and billing. (Woman, estab 1989, empl 7, sales $2,168,392, cert: CPUC, WBENC)

5766 Ben Hyatt Corporation
17835 Ventura Blvd Ste 310
Encino, CA 91316
Contact: Mitch Hyatt VP
Tel: 888-272-0022
Email: mhyatt@benhyatt.com
Website: http://www.benhyatt.com
Court reporting, litigation support services. (Woman, estab 1998, empl 10, sales $3,300,000, cert: WBENC)

5767 California Deposition Reporters
599 S Barranca Penthouse
Covina, CA 91723
Contact: Jamie Kirk President
Tel: 800-274-1996
Email: jamie@caldepo.com
Website: http://caldepo.com
Court reporting, deposition transcription, videography for depositions, legal depositions, civil trial reporting, video conferencing. (Woman, estab 1979, empl 15, sales $1,687,887, cert: State, CPUC)

5768 Carol Nygard & Associates
2295 Gateway Oaks Dr, Ste 170
Sacramento, CA 95833
Contact: John Nygard VP Business Dev
Tel: 877-438-7787
Email: john@walnutcreekcourtreporter.com
Website: http://www.nygardreporting.com
Full-service court reporting agency specializing in complex litigation 24/7. (Woman, estab 2000, empl 5, sales $1,257,000, cert: State)

5769 EcoTeal, Inc.
18685 Main St, 101-144
Huntington Beach, CA 92648
Contact: Maria Tettman President
Tel: 714-375-5700
Email: mtettman@ecoteal.com
Website: http://www.ecoteal.com
Accident Investigation and Reporting, Acquisitions & Divestitures, Construction Safety, Emergency Preparedness & Response, Energy Efficiency & Conservation. (Woman, estab 2012, empl 1, sales $100,000, cert: City, CPUC)

5770 Kupferstein Manuel LLP
865 S Figueroa St Ste 3338
Los Angeles, CA 90017
Contact: Phyllis Kupferstein Managing Partner
Tel: 213-988-7531
Email: pk@kupfersteinmanuel.com
Website: www.kupfersteinmanuel.com
Trial law firm specializing in employment and general business litigation. (Woman, estab 2014, empl 3, sales $1,406,238, cert: WBENC)

5771 Kusar Court Reporters & Legal Services, Inc.
111 W Ocean Blvd Ste 1200
Long Beach, CA 90802
Contact: Amber Kusar contract Mgr
Tel: 800-282-3376
Email: info@kusar.com
Website: http://www.kusar.com
Court reporters specializing in complex litigation & medmal, and they are professional, accurate, on time, accommodating, friendly, andhelpful. (Woman, estab 1983, empl 12, sales $3,600,000, cert: City, CPUC, WBENC)

5772 Lafayette & Kumagai LLP
1300 Clay St Ste 810
Oakland, CA 94612
Contact: Clara Marigmen Office Admin
Tel: 415-357-4600
Email: cmarigmen@lkclaw.com
Website: https://www.lkclaw.com
Civil litigation law firm, motion practice, jury trials, appeals, mediations, arbitrations, other ADR procedures and hearings. (AA, As-Pac, estab 1994, empl 15, sales $3,285,704, cert: NMSDC, CPUC)

5773 Livingston Law Firm, A Professional Corporation
1600 S Main St, Ste 280
Walnut Creek, CA 94596
Contact: Renee Livingston President
Tel: 925-952-9880
Email: rlivingston@livingstonlawyers.com
Website: http://www.livingstonlawyers.com
Liability litigation. (Woman, estab 2000, empl 11, sales $1,976,196, cert: CPUC, WBENC)

5774 Parker Law Group, Inc.
27815 Barbate
Mission Viejo, CA 92692
Contact: Claudia Parker CEO
Tel: 949-916-9910
Email: cparker@parkerlawgroup.com
Website: http://www.parkerlawgroup.com
Transactional business legal services to publicly traded, private companies in the manufacturing and technology sectors as well as to non-profit companies covering general business law, technology law. (Woman/As-Pac, Hisp, estab 2008, empl 2, sales $ 0, cert: NMSDC)

5775   Urrabazo Law, P.C.
      2029 Century Park E Ste 400
      Los Angeles, CA 90067
      Contact: Donald Urrabazo President
      Tel: 310-388-9099
      Email: durrabazo@ulawpc.com
      Website: http://www.ulawpc.com
Full range of complex litigation matters, contractual and commercial disputes in federal and state courts through-out California. (Hisp, estab 2011, empl 6, sales $1,500,000, cert: NMSDC, CPUC)

5776   Wang & Chang
      255 California St Ste 525
      San Francisco, CA 94111
      Contact: Justin Chang Partner
      Tel: 415-599-2828
      Email: justin@wangchanglaw.com
      Website: http://www.wangchanglaw.com
Litigation matters, complex commercial cases, class actions, and civil lawsuits. (As-Pac, estab 2011, empl 4, sales $1,300,000, cert: NMSDC)

5777   Wilson Turner Kosmo LLP
      550 West C St, Ste 1050
      San Diego, CA 92101
      Contact: Robin Wofford Partner
      Tel: 619-236-9600
      Email: rwofford@wilsonturnerkosmo.com
      Website: http://www.wilsonturnerkosmo.com
Legal services: employment law, product liability, contract disputes, real property litigation, health care, warranty, first amendment, trade secret and trust litigation. (Woman/AA, estab 1991, empl 55, sales $11,770,943, cert: CPUC, WBENC)

5778   Yang Professional Law Corporation
      80 S. Lake Ave, Ste 820 91101
      Pasadena, CA 91101
      Contact: Rey Shung President
      Tel: 626-921-4300
      Email: ryang@yangpc.com
      Website: http://www.yangpc.com
Civil litigation, insurance defense, personal injury, pre-mises liability, product liability, insurance, subrogation, indemnity, employment, automobile, labor, transporta-tion. (As-Pac, estab 2014, empl 3, sales $350,000, cert: NMSDC, CPUC)

Colorado

5779   Campbell Litigation, P.C.
      730 17th St, Ste 740
      Denver, CO 80202
      Contact: Michelle Campbell VP Operations
      Tel: 303-536-1833
      Email: michelle@campbell-litigation.com
      Website: http://www.campbell-litigation.com/
Employment, labor and commercial litigation defense trial lawyers. (AA, estab 2015, empl 5, sales $1,000,000, cert: NMSDC)

5780   Fair Measures, Inc.
      P.O. Box 22939
      Denver, CO 80222
      Contact: Jo-Ann Birch President
      Tel: 800-458-2778
      Email: jbirch@fairmeasures.com
      Website: https://www.fairmeasures.com
Legal services and training on management law for line Mgrs, business owners, Human Resource professionals and lawyers. (Woman, estab 1900, empl , sales $640,000, cert: WBENC)

5781   Gibson Arnold & Associates, Inc.
      518 17th St, Ste 1125
      Denver, CO 80202
      Contact: Elizabeth Dahill Exec VP
      Tel: 303-595-3655
      Email: denver@gibsonarnold.com
      Website: http://www.gibsonarnold.com
Natl legal recruiting firm with offices in Denver, Houston, and Los Angeles. We have over 29 years experience in placing attorneys, paralegals, and legal support staff. (Woman, estab 1981, empl 16, sales $5,228,089, cert: WBENC)

5782   Wells, Anderson & Race, LLC
      1700 Broadway, Ste 1020
      Denver, CO 80290
      Contact: Jaime Heveron CFO
      Tel: 303-830-1212
      Email: jheveron@warll.com
      Website: http://www.warllc.com
Litigation and appeals for local, regional and national clients. (Woman, estab 1995, empl 28, sales , cert: WBENC)

Connecticut

5783   Reardon Scanlon LLP
      45 S Main St, Ste 305
      Hartford, CT 06107
      Contact: Katherine Scanlon Managing Partner
      Tel: 860-955-9450
      Email: katherine.scanlon@reardonscanlon.com
      Website: http://www.reardonscanlon.com
Insurance industry litigation boutique. (Woman, estab 2012, empl 3, sales $899,950, cert: WBENC)

5784   Varunes & Assocaites, P.C.
      5 Grand St
      Hartford, CT 06106
      Contact: Anita Varunes President
      Tel: 860-541-1675
      Email: avarunes@varuneslaw.com
      Website: http://www.varuneslaw.com
Liability defense litigation and workers' compensation defense litigation. The attorneys in our office handle all aspects of civil lititgation from inception, discovery and trials before a jury or judge. (Woman, estab 2006, empl 9, sales $996,810, cert: WBENC)

District of Columbia

5785   Garrison & Sisson, Inc.
      1620 Eye St, NW Ste 501
      Washington, DC 20006
      Contact: Kathy Charlwood
      Tel: 202-429-5630
      Email: kcharlwood@g-s.com
      Website: http://g-s.com
Attorney Referral and Placement. (Woman, estab 1986, empl 8, sales $1,565,495, cert: WBENC)

5786   Livesay IP Law, PLLC
      888 16th St, NW, Ste 800
      Washington, DC 20006
      Contact: Margo Livesay Owner
      Tel: 202-684-8685
      Email: Margo@Livesay-IP.com
      Website: http://www.Livesay-IP.com
Patent attorney services - patent prosecution, opinion work, due diligence, litigation support, software-related inventions, systems, architectures. (Woman, estab 2009, empl 1, sales $186,590, cert: WBENC)

Florida

5787 Alvin K. Brown, P.A.
1001 3rd Ave West Ste 375
Bradenton, FL 34203
Contact: Alvin Brown President
Tel: 941-953-2825
Email: alvin@akbrownlaw.com
Website: http://brownandbrown.legal/
Security assessments, risk assessments, security training,
investigation & litigation svcs. (AA, estab 2002, empl 1,
sales $ 0, cert: State)

5788 DeMahy Labrador & Drake PA (DLD Lawyers)
806 Douglas Rd 12th Fl
Coral Gables, FL 33134
Contact: Greg Victor Partner
Tel: 305-443-4850
Email: gvictor@dldlawyers.com
Website: http://www.dldlawyers.com
Trial practice for large corporations. Our lawyers have over
1,000 completed jury trials. (Hisp, estab 1984, empl 56,
sales $10,000,000, cert: NMSDC)

5789 Hudson & Calleja LLC
355 Alhambra Circle Ste 801
Coral Gables, FL 33134
Contact: Alexis Calleja Attorney
Tel: 305-444-6628
Email: acalleja@hudsoncalleja.com
Website: http://www.hudsoncalleja.com
Legal services. (Woman/Hisp, estab 2011, empl 20, sales
$1,700,000, cert: NMSDC, WBENC)

5790 Leon Cosgrove, LLC
255 Alhambra Circle, Ste 800
Coral Gables, FL 33134
Contact: Maricarmen Ortega Firm Admin
Tel: 305-740-1975
Email: mortega@leoncosgrove.com
Website: http://www.leoncosgrove.com
Complex litigation with offices in Miami, FL, Washington,
DC and Dallas, Texas. (Hisp, estab 2013, empl 23, sales ,
cert: NMSDC)

5791 Levi G. Williams, Jr., P.A.
12 SE 7th St Ste 700
Fort Lauderdale, FL 33301
Contact: Levi Williams President
Tel: 954-463-1626
Email: levi@leviwilliamslaw.com
Website: http://www.leviwilliamslaw.com
Business Consulting, Litigation, Mediation, Administrative
Hearings, Employment, Wage, Civil Rights, Sexual Harass-
ment, Contracts, Negligence, Third Party Litigation,
Premises Liability, Negotiations, Bonds, Mergers. (AA,
estab 2011, empl 2, sales $300,000, cert: NMSDC)

5792 Losey PLLC
450 S Orange Ave, Ste 550
Orlando, FL 32801
Contact: M. Catherine Losey Managing Partner
Tel: 407-986-0406
Email: closey@losey.law
Website: http://www.losey.law
Legal services, litigations, arbitrations, and negotiations,
manage cybersecurity risks, manage data breach response.
(Woman, estab 2016, empl 5, sales $949,437, cert:
WBENC)

5793 Marrero & Wydler
2600 Douglas Rd, PH-4
Coral Gables, FL 33113
Contact: Oscar Marrero President
Tel: 305-446-5528
Email: oem@marrerolegal.com
Website: http://www.marrerolegal.com
Litigation management. (Hisp, estab 2002, empl 6, sales
$833,348, cert: State, NMSDC)

5794 Mint Legal Solutions
150 South Pine Island Rd Ste 300
Plantation, FL 33324
Contact: Zully Vergel President
Tel: 954-241-1300
Email: zully@mintlegalsolutions.com
Website: http://www.mintlegalsolutions.com
Electronic discovery and litigation support. Services
include data identification, collection, processing (and
culling for review), managed review/document review
including but not limited to, physical facilities, review
software, contractor staffing. (Woman/Hisp, estab 2017,
empl 5, sales , cert: State, WBENC)

5795 Orange Legal Inc.
633 E Colonial Blvd
Orlando, FL 32803
Contact: Kim Henderson Corporate Account Mgr
Tel: 404-400-6289
Email: kim.henderson@orangelegal.com
Website: http://www.orangelegal.com
Litigation support and unmatched customer service to
the legal community, court reporting, process service,
interpreting, videography. (Woman, estab 1900, empl ,
sales $15,542,932, cert: State, City)

5796 Phipps Reporting, Inc.
1615 Forum Place, Ste 500
West Palm Beach, FL 33401
Contact: Christine Phipps Owner
Tel: 888-811-3408
Email: christine@phippsreporting.com
Website: http://www.phippsreporting.com
Court reporting. (Woman, estab 2010, empl 10, sales
$2,862,699, cert: NWBOC)

5797 Roig Lawyers
1255 S Military Trail Ste 100
Deerfield Beach, FL 33442
Contact: Michael Rosenberg Managing Partner
Tel: 954-462-0330
Email: mrosenberg@roiglawyers.com
Website: www.roiglawyers.com
defense law firm that has been defending claims for
numerous insurers and self-insureds for more than 12
years. Our areas of practice include but are not limited
to: premises liability; workers' compensation; wrongful
death (Hisp, estab 2000, empl 300, sales $19,452,441,
cert: NMSDC)

5798 Sanchez-Medina, Gonzalez, Quesada, et al.
201 Alhambra Circle Ste 1205
Miami, FL 33134
Contact: Emilia Quesada Partner
Tel: 305-377-1000
Email: equesada@smgqlaw.com
Website: http://www.smgqlaw.com
Legal services. (Hisp, estab 2007, empl 40, sales $ 0,
cert: NMSDC)

5799 Steven C. Fraser, P.A.
221 W Hallandale Beach Blvd, Ste 201
Hallandale Beach, FL 33009
Contact: Steve Fraser Managing Dir
Tel: 305-809-6781
Email: sfraser@fraserlawfl.com
Website: http://www.fraserlawfl.com
Civil trial lawyers. We handle all kinds of claims, defense
and liability cases throughout Florida in county, state and
federal. (AA, estab 2008, empl 2, sales , cert: State)

5800 Torricella Law, PLLC
4551 Ponce de Leon Blvd
Coral Gables, FL 33146
Contact: Roberto A. Torricella, Jr. Managing Member
Tel: 786-693-6644
Email: Robert@TorricellaPastor.com
Website: http://www.TorricellaLaw.com
Civil and commercial litigation firm that practices in the
areas of business, insurance, aviation, real estate, profes-
sional liability, employment and general liability litigation.
(Hisp, estab 2014, empl 4, sales , cert: NMSDC)

5801 Van Ness Law Firm, PLC
1239 E Newport Center Dr, Ste 110
Deerfield Beach, FL 33442
Contact: John Van President
Tel: 954-571-2031
Email: compliance@vanlawfl.com
Website: www.vanlawfl.com
Law Firm, Commercial and Real Estate Litigation. (AA,
estab 2004, empl 75, sales , cert: NMSDC)

Georgia

5802 Benefits Law Group, PK Keesler, PC
945 E Paces Ferry Rd Ste 2515
Atlanta, GA 30326
Contact: Patricia Keesler Owner
Tel: 404-995-9505
Email: pkeesler@benefitslawgroup.com
Website: http://www.benefitslawgroup.com
Law firm: employee benefits & executive compensation
matters. (Woman, estab 1996, empl 8, sales $ 0, cert:
WBENC)

5803 Lee, Hong, Degerman, Kang & Waimey, APC
133 Main St
LaGrange, GA 30240
Contact: Bernard Ham Partner
Tel: 706-298-0134
Email: bham@lhlaw.com
Website: http://www.lhlaw.com
intellectual property, business and corporate transactions,
commercial litigation, products liability, labor & employment, international arbitration, banking & financial
services, and real estate. (As-Pac, estab 1991, empl 70,
sales $17,290,000, cert: NMSDC, CPUC)

5804 Moser Law Co LLC
112 Krog St NE, Ste 26
Atlanta, GA 30307
Contact: Theresia Moser Owner
Tel: 404-537-5339
Email: tmoser@moserlawco.com
Website: http://www.moserlawco.com
Employment Lawyers & Litigators (Woman, estab 2014,
empl 5, sales $250,000, cert: WBENC, NWBOC)

5805 Patrick Law Group, LLC
3705 Canyon Ridge Ct, NE
Atlanta, GA 30319
Contact: Founder
Tel: 404-437-6731
Email:
Website: http://www.patricklawgroup.com
Construction Law and Commerical Contracting. We have
prepared and negotiated hundreds of design, architect,
construction, procurement and other contracts.
(Woman, estab 2006, empl 4, sales $1,281,125, cert:
WBENC)

5806 Rutherford & Christie LLP
225 Peachtree Street South Tower, Ste 1750
Atlanta, GA 30303
Contact: Carrie Christie Managing Partner
Tel: 404-522-6888
Email: clc@rclawllp.com
Website: http://www.rutherfordchristie.com
Defense litigation in the areas of general liability,
employment, construction, contracts, constitutional law,
aviation, products liability and workers's compensation.
(Woman, estab 1999, empl 12, sales $2,600,000, cert:
WBENC)

Hawaii

5807 Carlsmith Ball LLP
1001 Bishop St, Ste 2100
Honolulu, HI 96809
Contact: Michael Dolan COO
Tel: 808-523-2500
Email: mdolan@carlsmith.com
Website: http://carlsmith.com
Law firm providing legal advise in Hawaii and California.
Specialize in real estate and land use, corporate,
litigation, energy and environmental. (Woman/As-Pac,
estab 1900, empl 180, sales $32,450,000, cert: CPUC)

Iowa

5808 Goosmann Law Firm, PLC
410 5th St
Sioux City, IA 51101
Contact: Legal Exec
Tel: 712-226-4000
Email:
Website: www.goosmannlaw.com
Goosmann Law Firm is a Small Business Administration
certified woman owned business serving clients in IA,
NE, SD, ND, and MN. Our team of professionals brings a
strategic, high quality, and collaborative approach to
business (Woman, estab 2009, empl 22, sales
$3,000,000, cert: WBENC)

5809 MWH Law Group LLP
1501 42nd St Ste 465
West Des Moines, IA 50266
Contact: Kerrie Murphy Managing Partner
Tel: 515-453-8509
Email: kerrie.murphy@mwhlawgroup.com
Website: http://www.mwhlawgroup.com
Corporate & Transactional, Real Estate, Contract Sup-
port, Employment and Labor Law, Litigation, Intellectual
Property. (AA, estab 2016, empl 14, sales $2,563,000,
cert: NMSDC)

Illinois

5810   Advitam IP, LLC
       160 N Wacker Dr, 2nd Fl
       Chicago, IL 60606
       Contact: Michele Katz Founding Partner
       Tel: 312-332-7700
       Email: MKatz@AdvitamIP.com
       Website: http://www.advitamip.com
Legal services in the field of intellectual property, patent
and trademark prosecution and litigation, copyright and
domain name registration. (Woman, estab 2012, empl 4,
sales , cert: WBENC)

5811   Chico & Nunes, P.C.
       333 W. Wacker Dr. Ste 1420
       Chicago, IL 60606
       Contact: Marcus Nunes Partner
       Tel: 312-463-1000
       Email: mnunes@chiconunes.com
       Website: http://www.chiconunes.com
Legal Services, Government Relations Services. (Hisp, estab
2004, empl 33, sales , cert: NMSDC)

5812   Clayborne, Sabo, and Wagner LLP
       525 W Main St Ste 105
       Belleville, IL 62220
       Contact: John Sabo Partner
       Tel: 618-239-0187
       Email: jsabo@cswlawllp.com
       Website: http://www.cswlawllp.com
The Firm consists of attorneys independently recognized
by the Leading Lawyers Network and Martindale-Hubble
as being in the top 5% of lawyers in their state in their
fields of practice. (AA, estab 2013, empl 10, sales
$1,580,000, cert: State, NMSDC)

5813   Grant Law, LLC
       230 W Monroe St Ste 240
       Chicago, IL 60606
       Contact: Maurice Grant Principal
       Tel: 312-551-0111
       Email: Mgrant@grantlawllc.com
       Website: http://www.grantlawllc.com
Commercial and Corporate Litigation: Real Estate, Com-
mercial Lending and Corporate Services, Employment Law,
Estate Planning. (Woman/AA, estab 2004, empl 6, sales
$315,000, cert: NMSDC)

5814   Heavner Beyers & Mihlar LLC
       P.O. Box 740
       Decatur, IL 62525
       Contact: Faiq Mihlar Managing Member
       Tel: 217-422-1719
       Email: faiqmihlar@hsbattys.com
       Website: http://www.hsbattys.com
Law firm representing leading financial corporations, as
well as middle and small-market clients in the default
space. (Woman, estab 1978, empl 143, sales $11,771,967,
cert: WBENC)

5815   Johnson Blumberg & Associates
       230 W Monroe Ste 1125
       Chicago, IL 60606
       Contact: Kenneth Johnson Sr Partner
       Tel: 312-541-9713
       Email: ken@johnsonblumberg.com
       Website: http://www.johnsonblumberg.com
Legal services. (Minority, estab 0, empl , sales $ 0, cert:
NMSDC)

5816   McClain & Canoy, LLC
       10 S Riverside Plaza Ste 875
       Chicago, IL 60606
       Contact: Salina Canoy Managing Member
       Tel: 312-474-6030
       Email: salina@mcclaincanoy.com
       Website: https://www.mcclaincanoy.com
Comprehensive legal services to businesses for transactional matters concerning health care, regulatory
compliance, information privacy and security, health
care information technology, government affairs, public
policy. (Woman/AA, estab 2015, empl 5, sales $702,892,
cert: State, NMSDC)

5817   McCormack Schreiber Legal Solutions Inc.
       303 W Madison St Ste 1725
       Chicago, IL 60606
       Contact: Amy McCormack Co-President
       Tel: 312-827-6470
       Email: amy@mslegalsolutions.com
       Website: www.thelawrecruiters.com
Contract attorney staffing firm. (Woman, estab 2007,
empl 12, sales $458,579, cert: WBENC)

5818   Reyes Kurson, Ltd.
       328 S Jefferson St Ste 909
       Chicago, IL 60661
       Contact: Amy Kurson Managing Partner
       Tel: 312-332-0055
       Email: akurson@rkchicago.com
       Website: http://rkchicago.com
Boutique law firm. (AA, As-Pac, Hisp, estab 2005, empl
14, sales , cert: NMSDC)

5819   Valentine Austriaco & Bueschel, P.C.
       105 W Adams St 35th Fl
       Chicago, IL 60603
       Contact: Aurora Austriaco Partner
       Tel: 312-288-8285
       Email: aaustriaco@vablawfirm.com
       Website: http://www.vablawfirm.com
Experience resolving and litigating business disputes and
handling real estate related matters, employment law,
commercial litigation, contract dispute. (Woman, estab
2016, empl 8, sales $500,000, cert: WBENC)

5820   Victoria Legal + Corporate Services
       2 N. LaSalle Street Ste 1615
       Chicago, IL 60602
       Contact: Victoria Rock CEO
       Tel: 312-443-1025
       Email: victoria@victorialcs.com
       Website: http://www.VictoriaLCS.com
Court reporting, complex litigation, accurate, verbatim
transcripts, comprehensive services. (Woman, estab
1981, empl 4, sales $1,034,478, cert: State, WBENC)

Indiana

5821   Delaney & Delaney LLC
       3640 N Washington Blvd
       Indianapolis, IN 46205
       Contact: Kathleen Delaney President
       Tel: 317-920-0400
       Email: kathleen@delaneylaw.net
       Website: http://www.delaneylaw.net
Law Firm (Woman, estab 0, empl , sales $1,500,000,
cert: State)

Louisiana

5822 Courington Kiefer & Sommers, LLC
650 Poydras St Ste 2105
New Orleans, LA 70130
Contact: Valerie Matherne Member
Tel: 504-524-5510
Email: vmatherne@courington-law.com
Website: http://www.courington-law.com
Defending cases in Louisiana, Mississippi, and Texas.
(Woman, estab 2011, empl 29, sales $3,854,117, cert:
WBENC)

Massachusetts

5823 Fitzhugh & Mariani LLP
155 Federal St, Ste 1700
Boston, MA 02110
Contact: Amy Crowley Partner
Tel: 617-695-2330
Email: acrowley@fitzhughlaw.com
Website: http://www.fitzhughlaw.com
Environmental law, employment law, products liability,
personal injury and general corporate litigation. (Woman/
AA, estab 1986, empl 22, sales $1,700,000, cert: NMSDC)

5824 Schwartz Hannum PC
11 Chestnut Street Ste 11
Andover, MA 01810
Contact: Sara Goldsmith Schwartz President
Tel: 978-623-0900
Email: schwartz@shpclaw.com
Website: http://shpclaw.com
Labor and Employment law firm representing employers
with respect to a full spectrum of labor and employment
issues, including Immigration-related matters. (Woman,
estab 1995, empl 24, sales $5,639,572, cert: State,
WBENC)

5825 West Hill Technology Counsel, Inc.
900 Cummings Center Ste 206-T
Beverly, MA 01915
Contact: Louise Kennedy President
Tel: 978-338-4082
Email: llkennedy@westhillcounsel.com
Website: http://www.westhillcounsel.com
Boutique business and technology law firm. (Woman,
estab 2008, empl 9, sales $563,930, cert: State, WBENC)

Maryland

5826 For The Record, Inc.
10760 Demarr Rd
White Plains, MD 20695
Contact: Sara Vance CFO
Tel: 800-921-5555
Email: svance@ftrinc.net
Website: http://www.ftrinc.net
Court reporting, transcription, legal video and litigation
support. (Woman, estab 1991, empl 12, sales $2,265,600,
cert: State, WBENC)

5827 Law Offices of Grady L. White, LLC
10605 Concord Street, Ste 207 The Concord Building
Kensington, MD 20895
Contact: Grady White Owner, Principal Attorney
Tel: 240-813-7500
Email: accountspayable@patentrep.com
Website:
Provides advice, counseling, and legal opinions on a
variety of intellectual property matters, including patents,
trademarks and copyrights. (AA, estab 2003, empl 1, sales
$703,522, cert: NMSDC)

5828 Rahman LLC
10025 Governor Warfield Pkwy Ste 212
Columbia, MD 21044
Contact: Mohammad Rahman Owner
Tel: 443-283-7000
Email: rahman@rahmanllc.com
Website: www.rahmanllc.com
Intellectual property, patents, trademarks, copyrights,
trade secrets, legal, strategy, valuation, IP (As-Ind, estab
2008, empl 3, sales , cert: State, NMSDC)

5829 Taylor & Ryan, LLC
1777 Reisterstown Rd CommereCenter E, Ste 265
Pikesville, MD 21208
Contact: Frances Taylor Member
Tel: 410-486-5800
Email: ftaylor@taylor-ryan.com
Website: http://www.taylor-ryan.com
Immigration legal services to employers of all sizes.
(Woman, estab 2005, empl 6, sales $851,000, cert:
State)

Michigan

5830 A.K.Adams, PLC dba A|Squared Legal Group, PLC
615 Griswold Ste 714
Detroit, MI 48226
Contact: Alari Adams Managing Member
Tel: 313-702-2222
Email: aa@asquaredlegal.com
Website: http://www.asquaredlegal.com
Provide legal counseling to businesses for litigation and
transactional matters pertaining to business law, labor/
employment law, and human resources management.
(Woman/AA, estab 2014, empl 2, sales $100,000, cert:
NMSDC, WBENC)

5831 Americlerk, Inc. dba Lumen Legal
1025 N. Campbell Rd
Royal Oak, MI 48067
Contact: Iris Dalfrey VP Southern Region
Tel: 281-853-9295
Email: idalfrey@lumenlegal.com
Website: http://www.lumenlegal.com
Contract Legal Services, Secondments, Process Assess-
ment, Spend Optimization, Document Review, Six Sigma
Project Management, Lumen Review Center, Legal
Spend Analysis with Sky Analytics, Document Automa-
tion. (Woman, estab 1993, empl 25, sales $8,000,000,
cert: WBENC)

5832 Apis LLC
2216 Northlawn Blvd
Birmingham, MI 48009
Contact: Turkia Mullin CEO
Tel: 313-468-4932
Email: tmullin@apisconsultinggroup.com
Website: www.apisconsultinggroup.com
Corporate transactional attorney providing legal,
financial and business consulting advice and support,
drafting and negotiating all aspects of a deal, including
all agreements for such transactions. (Woman, estab
2013, empl 1, sales , cert: WBENC)

5833 Banas and Associates PLLC
330 Hamilton Ste 350
Birmingham, MI 48009
Contact: Leslie Banas Managing Member
Tel: 248-203-5400
Email: leslie.banas@banaslegal.net
Website: http://www.banaslegal.net
Commercial real estate and corporate legal services; negotiation and documentation of office leases; sales and purchases of manufacturing and warehouse facilities; construction contracts and tenant build. (Woman, estab 2009, empl 4, sales $400,000, cert: WBENC)

5834 Bush Seyferth PLLC
3001 W Big Beaver Rd
Troy, MI 48084
Contact: Cheryl Bush President
Tel: 248-822-7800
Email: bush@bsplaw.com
Website: http://www.bsplaw.com
Law Firm; legal services (Woman, estab 0, empl , sales $5,344,367, cert: WBENC)

5835 LegalEase Solutions LLC
2301 Platt Rd, Ste 20
Ann Arbor, MI 48104
Contact: Teri Whitehead VP Global Strategy
Tel: 866-534-6177
Email: teri.whitehead@lgles.com
Website: http://www.legaleasecorporate.com
Customized legal support, including legal research and drafting service, compliance support, contract lifecycle management, transactional and litigation support. (Minority, estab 2005, empl 6, sales $80,000,000, cert: NMSDC)

5836 Lewis & Munday
2490 First Natl Bldg 660 Woodward Ave
Detroit, MI 48226
Contact: Gerald W. Helms Controller
Tel: 313-961-2550
Email: ghelms@lewismunday.com
Website: www.lewismunday.com
Law firm, legal services. (AA, estab 1972, empl 31, sales $0, cert: NMSDC)

5837 Rona M. Lum, P.C., dba Law Offices of Rona M. Lum
691 N Squirrel Rd Ste 185
Auburn Hills, MI 48326
Contact: Rona Lum, Esq. President
Tel: 248-340-1854
Email: rlum@corpimmigration.us
Website: www.corpimmigration.us
Immigration Law - corporate and business immigration related matters. (Woman, estab 0, empl , sales $ 0, cert: WBENC)

5838 Skye Suh, PLC.
32000 Northwestern Hwy, Ste 260
Farmington Hills, MI 48334
Contact: Skye Suh Managing Member
Tel: 248-932-8844
Email: ssuh@skyesuhplc.com
Website: www.skyesuhplc.com
Law firm, legal services. (Woman/As-Pac, estab 2002, empl 8, sales $ 0, cert: NMSDC)

Minnesota

5839 Blackwell Burke P.A.
431 S 7th St Ste 2500
Minneapolis, MN 55415
Contact: Kandy Branch FIRM Admin
Tel: 612-343-3200
Email: info@blackwellburke.com
Website: http://www.blackwellburke.com
Law Firm (AA, estab 2006, empl 34, sales $6,250,000, cert: NMSDC)

5840 Depo International
1330 Jersey Ave South
Minneapolis, MN 55426
Contact: CEO
Tel: 763-591-0535
Email:
Website: http://www.depointernational.com
Court reporting, videography, digital litigation tools, online repository, trial consulting, videoconferencing on a national/international level. (Woman, estab 2008, empl 15, sales $2,420,000, cert: WBENC)

5841 Fondungallah & Kigham, LLC
2499 Rice St, Ste 145
Saint Paul, MN 55113
Contact: Mike Essien Attorney
Tel: 651-482-0520
Email: messien@fondlaw.com
Website: http://www.fondlaw.com
Legal services: Intellectual property; immigration & nationality law; business & corporate law; business & commercial litigation; employment issues; international law. (AA, estab 2005, empl 3, sales $650,000, cert: State, NMSDC)

5842 Hollingsworth Davis, LLC
8500 Normandale Lake Blvd Ste 320
Minneapolis, MN 55437
Contact: Tracey Dotter Exec Dir
Tel: 952-854-2700
Email: info@hdpatlaw.com
Website: http://www.hdpatlaw.com
U.S. and international patent procurement, strategic patent portfolio Devel and management, legal analysis and opinion work, pre-litigation and M&A due diligence, litigation support. (Woman, estab 2005, empl 12, sales $2,600,000, cert: WBENC)

5843 Igbanugo Partners Int'l Law Firm, PLLC
250 Marquette Ave Ste 1075
Minneapolis, MN 55401
Contact: Herbert Igbanugo CEO
Tel: 612-746-0360
Email: higbanugo@igbanugolaw.com
Website: http://www.igbanugolaw.com
U.S. Immigration & Nationality Law and International Trade Law limited to Sub-Saharan Africa. (AA, estab 2006, empl 13, sales $1,011,828, cert: NMSDC)

5844 J. Selmer Law, P.A.
500 Washington Ave S Ste 2010
Minneapolis, MN 55415
Contact: James Selmer Managing Partner
Tel: 612-338-6005
Email: jselmer@jselmerlaw.com
Website: www.jselmerlaw.com
Defense law firm specializing in litigation and appellate practice, civil litigation process, from initial case evaluation through appellate proceedings. (AA, estab 1983, empl 10, sales $747,769, cert: NMSDC)

5845   Kelly & Berens, P.A. dba Berens & Miller, P.A.
       3720 IDS Center 80 S Eighth St
       Minneapolis, MN 55402
       Contact: President
       Tel: 612-349-6171
       Email:
       Website: www.berensmiller.com
Law firm, legal services. (Woman, estab 1989, empl 10, sales $2,280,000, cert: WBENC)

5846   Nightowl Document Management Services, Inc.
       724 N First St
       Minneapolis, MN 55401
       Contact: Andrea Wallack CEO
       Tel: 612-337-0448
       Email: awal2652@msn.com
       Website: http://www.nightowldiscovery.com
Full service litigation support, single-source solution for both paper and electronic document collections. (Woman, estab 1991, empl 100, sales $3,800,000, cert: WBENC)

Missouri

5847   Boggs, Avellino, Lach & Boggs
       9326 Olive Blvd Ste 200
       St. Louis, MO 63131
       Contact: Beth Boggs Managing Partner
       Tel: 314-726-2310
       Email: bbblawyers@aol.com
       Website: http://www.balblawyers.com
Legal services in Missouri & southern Illinois. (Woman/AA, estab 1999, empl 45, sales $5,000,000, cert: City, WBENC)

5848   Optitek, Inc.
       2001 S Hanley Rd Ste 250
       Brentwood, MO 63144
       Contact: Ricki McGuire President
       Tel: 314-644-2880
       Email: ricki@optitek.com
       Website: www.optitek.com
Electronic remittance processing, electronic lockbox services, forms processing, legal services & electronic document management systems. (Woman, estab 1992, empl 30, sales $1,796,300, cert: WBENC)

5849   Taylor and Associates, Inc.
       711 N 11th St
       St. Louis, MO 63101
       Contact: Deborah Weaver CEO
       Tel: 314-644-2191
       Email: dweaver@alaris.us
       Website: https://alaris.us/
Court Reporting, Video Depositions, Video Conferencing, digital video services, video-to-text synchronization in multiple formats, photo, document scanning, real time reporting, on-line scheduling, repository for depositions and exhibits. (Woman, estab 1985, empl 63, sales , cert: State, WBENC)

New Jersey

5850   Hudson Reporting & Video Inc.
       90 Woodbridge Center Dr Ste 240
       Woodbridge, NJ 07095
       Contact: Geeta Sundrani Communications Spec
       Tel: 732-906-2078
       Email: geeta@hudsonreporting.com
       Website: http://www.hudsonreporting.com
Boutique court reporting agency servicing the legal industry. (Woman/As-Ind, estab 1998, empl 6, sales $2,541,000, cert: NMSDC, WBENC)

5851   Johnson & Associates
       280 Amboy Ave
       Metuchen, NJ 08840
       Contact: Al Gil VP of Business Devel
       Tel: 848-229-2254
       Email: agil@johnsonlegalpc.com
       Website: http://www.johnsonlegalpc.com
Law Firm, Corporate & Business Law, Litigation, Immigration, Appeals, Real Estate, Bankruptcy, Municipal Court. (AA, estab 2012, empl 42, sales $600,000, cert: NMSDC)

5852   Kim Winston LLP
       1307 White Horse Rd, Ste 601
       Voorhees, NJ 08043
       Contact: Jae Kim Partner
       Tel: 856-520-8991
       Email: yjaekim@kimwinston.com
       Website: http://kimwinston.com
Intellectual property law firm, legal services for patents, patent prosecution, patent procurement, trademarks, trademark prosecution, copyright, intellectual property litigation, patent litigation, trademark litigation, copyright litigation, trademark. (As-Pac, estab 2013, empl 14, sales $850,000, cert: NMSDC)

5853   Love and Long, LLP
       108 Washington Street
       Newark, NJ 07102
       Contact: Lisa Love Partner
       Tel: 215-546-8433
       Email: llove@lovandlonglaw.com
       Website: http://www.loveandlonglaw.com
Law firm specializing in commercial transactions. (Woman/AA, estab 1992, empl 5, sales $500,000, cert: State, NMSDC)

5854   Rosenberg & Associates
       425 Eagle Rock Ave, Ste 201
       Roseland, NJ 07068
       Contact: Catherine Kane VP of Operations
       Tel: 973-618-2101
       Email: ckane@trantech.net
       Website: http://
       www.rosenbergandassociates.com
Court reporting, litigation support, trial presentation, stenographic transcription services, audiography, videography, video conferencing, interpreting, database consulting. (Woman, estab 1973, empl 48, sales $450,000, cert: WBENC)

5855   RVM Enterprises, Inc.
       525 Washington Blvd. 25th Fl
       Jersey City, NJ 07310
       Contact: Cheryl A. Brunetti Executive Chairwoman
       Tel: 212-693-1525
       Email: cbrunetti@rvminc.com
       Website: http://www.rvminc.com
Litigation, litigation support, ediscovery, e-discovery, Information Governance, Managed Review, document review , ESI Processing , ESI Hosting, data hosting, Kcura, Relativity, clearwell, Predictive Coding, Legal, Litigation Consulting (Woman, estab 1989, empl 116, sales $28,000,000, cert: City, WBENC)

5856 Wall & Tong, LLP
      25 James Way
      Eatontown, NJ 07724
      Contact: Robert Traina Business Mgr
      Tel: 732-542-2280
      Email: rtraina@walltong.com
      Website: http://www.walltong.com
Patent, Trademark and related Intellectual Property Legal
Services. (As-Pac, estab 2009, empl 15, sales $3,993,003,
cert: CPUC)

5857 Wong Fleming
      821 Alexander Rd, Ste 200
      Princeton, NJ 08540
      Contact: Linda Wong CEO
      Tel: 609-951-9520
      Email: lwong@wongfleming.com
      Website: www.wongfleming.com
Employment Law, Civil Rights, Commercial Law, Real
Estate, Education Law, Intellectual Property, and Interna-
tional Law. (Woman/As-Pac, estab 1994, empl 65, sales
$2,590,897, cert: NMSDC, WBENC)

New Mexico

5858 Ortiz & Lopez, LLC
      P.O. Box 4484
      Albuquerque, NM 87196
      Contact: Kermit Lopez Patent Attorney
      Tel: 505-314-1312
      Email: klopez@olpatentlaw.com
      Website: http://www.olpatentlaw.com
Patent and other intellectual property legal services. (Hisp,
estab 2001, empl 8, sales $1,000,000, cert: NMSDC)

New York

5859 A. Kershaw, PC//Attorneys & Consultants
      161 Grove St, Ste 200
      Tarrytown, NY 10591
      Contact: Anne Kershaw Owner
      Tel: 914-332-0438
      Email: anne.kershaw@akershaw.com
      Website: www.akershaw.com
Litigation management consulting, providing innovative
and impartial analysis and recommendations for the
management of all aspects of volume litigation. (Woman,
estab 1999, empl 1, sales $ 0, cert: WBENC)

5860 B&N Legal Interpreting, Inc.
      350 Fifth Ave, 59th Floor
      New York, NY 10118
      Contact: Livingston Buchanan President
      Tel: 866-661-1053
      Email: lbuchanan@bninterpreting.com
      Website: http://www.bninterpreting.com
Provides interpreting, translation and sign language
services to court reporting agencies, law firms, fortune 100
& 500 companies, individuals for all language needs. (AA,
estab 2004, empl 2, sales , cert: City)

5861 Complete Discovery Source Inc.
      345 Park Ave Level B
      New York, NY 10154
      Contact: Bibi Bacchus
      Tel: 212-813-7005
      Email: bbacchus@cdslegal.com
      Website: http://cdslegal.com
eDiscovery services, litigation support, and software
supporting planning, early case assessment, information
governance, processing and production, software, data
analytics, review hosting, managed review, and cross-
border. (As-Ind, estab 1900, empl , sales $39,601,399,
cert: City, NMSDC)

5862 Drohan Lee LLP
      489 Fifth Ave
      New York, NY 10017
      Contact: Vivian Drohan Partner
      Tel: 212-710-0000
      Email: vdrohan@dlkny.com
      Website: http://www.dlkny.com
Boutique law firm with capabilities to provide legal
services in corporate, contract transactions and litigation. (As-Pac, Hisp, estab 2007, empl 5, sales $1,400,000,
cert: State, City)

5863 Frank, Frank, Goldstein & Nager, PC
      330 West 38th Street Ste 701
      New York, NY 10018
      Contact: Jocelyn Nager President
      Tel: 212-686-0100
      Email: jnager@ffgnesqs.com
      Website: http://www.ffgnesqs.com
Law Firm devoted exclusively to the collection of bad
debt, commercial and consumer. (Woman, estab 2000,
empl 12, sales $1,405,280, cert: City)

5864 Green Point Technology Services LLC
      555 Theodore Fremd Ave Ste A102
      Rye, NY 10580
      Contact: Shirley Sharma President
      Tel: 212-913-0500
      Email: shirley@greenpointglobal.com
      Website: www.greenpointglobal.com/
Legal and Compliance, Regulatory Tracking, Publishing &
Editorial services, Software Development, Professional
development. (Woman/As-Ind, estab 2001, empl 350,
sales $3,200,000, cert: State)

5865 JG Advisory Services LLC
      200 E 27th St
      New York, NY 10016
      Contact: Judith Gross Principal
      Tel: 917-375-6852
      Email: judy@jgadvisory.com
      Website: http://www.jgadvisory.com
Specialty consulting related to hedge funds, particularly
on legal/regulatory/compliance issues. Devel of technology in this area. "Industry intelligence" on hedge funds,
and analysis of market. (Woman, estab 2005, empl 1,
sales $200,000, cert: City)

5866 Johnson Liebman, LLP
      305 Broadway Ste 801
      New York, NY 10007
      Contact: Robert Johnson Partner
      Tel: 212-619-6744
      Email: robert.johnson@johnsonliebman.com
      Website: http://johnsonliebman.com
Insurance defense firm, handle defense and subrogation
cases for various insurers for flat fees. (AA, estab 1999,
empl 6, sales $875,000, cert: City)

5867 Law Office of Marian Polovy
      192 Lexington Ave, Ste 903
      New York, NY 10016
      Contact: Marian Polovy Owner
      Tel: 212-696-0133
      Email: marianpolovy@aol.com
      Website: http://www.lawofficeofmarianpolovy.com
Law firm-trial attorneys, defense negligence, product
liability, general liability, defense medical malpractice,
employment law and general civil litigation. (Woman,
estab 1983, empl 4, sales $635,382, cert: State, City)

5868 Lee Anav Chung White Kim Ruger & Richter LLP
      156 Fifth Ave Ste 303
      New York, NY 10010
      Contact: Annie Chen Legal Asst
      Tel: 212-271-0664
      Email: anniechen@lacwkrr.com
      Website: www.leeanavchung.com
Sophisticated legal advice and representation on complex
legal matters. (As-Pac, estab 2003, empl 30, sales
$3,100,000, cert: NMSDC)

5869 Pittleman & Associates
      336 E 43rd St
      New York, NY 10017
      Contact: Linda Pittleman chrmn
      Tel: 212-370-9600
      Email: lindap@pittlemanassociates.com
      Website: http://www.pittlemanassociates.com
Placement of attorneys. Our candidates span the full range
of legal specialties and levels of expertise. At least 50% of
our search activity is for in-house law departments.
(Woman/Hisp, estab 1993, empl 7, sales $1,625,000, cert:
NMSDC)

5870 QuisLex
      126 E 56th St
      New York, NY 10022
      Contact: Adam Beschloss Exec Dir Client Solutions
      Tel: 917-512-4447
      Email: adam.beschloss@quislex.com
      Website: http://www.quislex.com
Premier legal services provider founded by attorneys from
Skadden Arps, Shearman & Sterling and Sidley Austin
QuisLex offers multi-shore capabilities through execution
centers in Chicago and Hyderabad, India. (As-Ind, estab
2004, empl 9, sales $30,500,000, cert: NMSDC)

5871 Rozario & Associates, P.C.
      55 Broadway 20th Fl
      New York, NY 10006
      Contact: Rovin Rozario Managing Partner
      Tel: 212-301-2770
      Email: rrozario@rozariolaw.com
      Website: www.rozariolaw.com
Superior client service, high-quality legal services. (AA,
estab 2005, empl 9, sales $821,000, cert: NMSDC)

5872 Schoeman Updike Kaufman & Gerber LLP
      551 Fifth Ave 12th Fl
      New York, NY 10176
      Contact: Beth L. Kaufman Managing Partner
      Tel: 212-661-5030
      Email: bkaufman@schoeman.com
      Website: http://www.schoeman.com
Law firm specializing in litigation (employment, commercial, personal injury and product liability) and real estate
(commercial transactions and leasing, financing).
(Woman/As-Pac, Hisp, estab 1969, empl 39, sales
$5,054,048, cert: State, City)

5873 Silverman Shin & Byrne PLLC
      88 Pine St, 22nd Fl
      New York, NY 10005
      Contact: Gerard Crowe Partner
      Tel: 212-779-8600
      Email: gcrowe@silverfirm.com
      Website: www.silverfirm.com
Corporate/Commercial realm, we represent small startup companies to multinationals alike in both
tranactional & litigation. (Woman/AA, As-Pac, Hisp,
estab 1986, empl 46, sales $9,188,231, cert: NMSDC)

5874 Yorkson Legal, Inc.
      800 2nd Ave 804, 8th Fl
      New York, NY 10017
      Contact: Gail Reichwald Managing Dir
      Tel: 212-265-1400
      Email: greichwald@yorkson.com
      Website: http://www.yorkson.com
Legal staffing and recruiting serves. We deal with
contract attorneys and legal support staff, and both
temporary and permanent paralegals. (Woman, estab
2003, empl 10, sales $6,207,569, cert: WBENC)

Ohio

5875 Curtin & Associates, LLP
      159 S Main St, Ste 920
      Akron, OH 44308
      Contact: Cynthia K. Curtin President
      Tel: 330-376-7245
      Email: dbudny@curtinlawfirm.com
      Website: http://www.curtinlawfirm.com
Tort Litigation; emphasis on defense. (Woman, estab
2003, empl 9, sales $1,200,000, cert: WBENC)

5876 DCR Denmark Court Reporting Agency, LLC
      810 Sycamore St, 3rd Fl
      Cincinnati, OH 45202
      Contact: Angela Denmark CEO
      Tel: 513-254-8753
      Email: angela@dcragency.com
      Website: http://www.dcragency.com
Independent, freelance court reporting agency. Are
services are typically requested by legal professionals,
educational, business and government entities.
(Woman/AA, estab 2006, empl 1, sales , cert: State)

5877 Giffen & Kaminski, LLC
      1300 E Ninth St Ste 1600
      Cleveland, OH 44114
      Contact: Karen Giffen Partner
      Tel: 216-621-5161
      Email: kgiffen@thinkgk.com
      Website: http://www.thinkgk.com
Legal Services; Arbitration; Mediation; Creditor's Rights;
Business Torts; Criminal Defense; White Collar Criminal
Defense; Employment Law; Employment Litigation;
Immigration Law; Product Liability; Real Estate. (Woman,
estab 2004, empl , sales $ 0, cert: WBENC)

5878 Litigation Management, Inc.
6000 Parkland Blvd
Mayfield Heights, OH 44124
Contact: Megan Pizor Executive Dir
Tel: 440-484-2000
Email: megan.pizor@lmiweb.com
Website: http://www.lmiweb.com
Comprehensive management and analysis of medical information for the defense of claims, individual lawsuits, mass torts or class actions where health, illness or injury . (Woman, estab 1984, empl 300, sales , cert: WBENC)

5879 Perez & Morris LLC
8000 Ravine's Edge Ct, Ste 300
Columbus, OH 43235
Contact: Juan Jose Perez Partner
Tel: 614-431-1500
Email: jperez@perez-morris.com
Website: http://www.perez-morris.com
Legal services. (Hisp, estab 1997, empl 29, sales $2,350,000, cert: NMSDC)

5880 Thacker Martinsek LPA
2330 One Cleveland Ctr 1375 E 9th St
Cleveland, OH 44114
Contact: John Larger President
Tel: 216-456-3840
Email: jlarger@TMLPA.com
Website: http://www.thackermartinsek.com
Law firm specializing in business & commercial litigation, insurance recovery, litigation management, employment law, intellectual property and civil rights. (Woman, estab 2010, empl 33, sales $6,590,743, cert: WBENC)

Oregon

5881 Gordon & Polscer LLC
9755 SW Barnes Rd Ste 650
Portland, OR 97225
Contact: Diane Polscer Managing Partner
Tel: 503-242-2922
Email: dpolscer@gordon-polscer.com
Website: http://www.gordon-polscer.com
Represent insurers, corporate, business clients for: Insurance Coverage Advice & Litigation; Civil Litigation; Extra-contractual Claim Advice & Litigation; Class-Action Defense. (Woman, estab 0, empl , sales $5,253,027, cert: WBENC)

Pennsylvania

5882 Assigned Counsel Inc.
950 W Valley Rd Ste 2600
Wayne, PA 19087
Contact: Bob Murphy President
Tel: 610-964-8300
Email: NABRAMS@ASSIGNEDCOUNSEL.COM
Website: http://www.assignedcounsel.com
Provide attorneys on a temporary, temp-to-perm and direct hire basis to corporate law departments, nonprofit organizations, federal agencies, and law firms. (AA, estab 1900, empl , sales $5,084,003, cert: NMSDC)

5883 Ellen Freeman Immigration Law Group
303 Timber Court
Pittsburgh, PA 15238
Contact: Ellen Freeman Managing Partner
Tel: 412-822-6500
Email: efreeman@freemanimmigration.com
Website: http://freemanimmigration.com
A full-service immigration law firm. (Woman, estab 2019, empl 4, sales $750,000, cert: WBENC)

5884 Griesing Law, LLC
1880 John F. Kennedy Boulevard Ste 1800
Philadelphia, PA 19103
Contact: Francine Griesing Managing Member
Tel: 215-618-3720
Email: fgriesing@griesinglaw.com
Website: http://www.griesinglaw.com
Represent public Fortune 1000 corporations and closely held companies in complex business transactions and high stakes litigation, as well as advises its clients on how to reduce risk and contain litigation costs. (Woman, estab 2010, empl 15, sales , cert: WBENC)

5885 Parrish Law Offices
788 Washington Rd
Pittsburgh, PA 15228
Contact: Debra Parrish Partner
Tel: 412-561-6250
Email: debbie@dparrishlaw.com
Website: www.dparrishlaw.com
Legal support for provider and beneficiary appeals of denied claims by payers, including Medicare through the administrative process up to and including Federal court litigation; appeals of post-payment overpayment determinations (Woman, estab 2000, empl 4, sales $833,635, cert: WBENC)

5886 Summit Court Reporting, Inc.
1500 Market St 12th Fl - East Tower
Philadelphia, PA 19102
Contact: Yvette Samuel President
Tel: 215-665-5633
Email: ysamuel@summitreporting.com
Website: http://www.summitreporting.com
Court Reporting & Legal Video & Videoconference Services for legal proceedings held in depositions, hearings, meetings, video depositions, video playbacks at trial. (Woman, estab 1993, empl 4, sales $958,498, cert: State)

5887 Tiagha & Associates, Ltd.
2112 Walnut St
Philadelphia, PA 19103
Contact: Kahiga Tiagha Attorney At Law
Tel: 215-543-7970
Email: info@tiaghalaw.com
Website: http://www.tiaghalaw.com
Law firm providing tailored solutions in Corporate and Real Estate transactional services. (AA, estab 2009, empl 7, sales $ 0, cert: NMSDC)

5888　Walker Nell Partners Inc.
　　　1515 Market St, Ste 820
　　　Philadelphia, PA 19102
　　　Contact: Wayne Walker CEO
　　　Tel:　215-569-1660
　　　Email: WalkerNell@walkerNell.com
　　　Website: http://www.WalkerNell.com
Litigation Support and Insolvency, Restructuring, Valuation
and Fiduciary Services; Accounting; Management and
Technology Governance, Risk and Compliance; Forensic
and Dispute. (AA, estab 2004, empl 7, sales $249,000, cert:
City, NMSDC)

Puerto Rico

5889　Del Toro & Santana
　　　Plaza 273, Ste 900
　　　San Juan, PR 00917
　　　Contact: Roberto Santana Sr Partner
　　　Tel:　787-754-8700
　　　Email: rsantana@dtslaw.com
　　　Website: www.dtslaw.com
Litigation and counseling representing a number of
industrial and commercial firms, (Hisp, estab 1984, empl
12, sales $1,400,000, cert: NMSDC)

5890　Fiddler Gonzalez & Rodriguez, PSC
　　　P.O. Box 363507
　　　San Juan, PR 00936
　　　Contact: Kenneth Bury General Admin
　　　Tel:　787-759-3145
　　　Email: kcbury@fgrlaw.com
　　　Website: http://www.fgrlaw.com
Full-service law firm with well established practice areas
encompassing nearly all areas of law. With over 100
lawyers, the firm is one of the largest in the Caribbean and
Latin America. (Hisp, estab 1932, empl 209, sales $　0,
cert: NMSDC)

Texas

5891　Bennett Law Office, PC
　　　132 W Main St
　　　Lewisville, TX 75057
　　　Contact: Tamera H. Bennett President
　　　Tel:　972-436-8141
　　　Email: info@tbennettlaw.com
　　　Website: http://www.tbennettlaw.com
Intellectual Property Law, Trademark Law, Copyright Law,
Entertainment Law. (Woman, estab 2001, empl 2, sales ,
cert: State)

5892　Brewer & Lormand, PLLC
　　　5910 N Central Expressway, Ste 730
　　　Dallas, TX 75206
　　　Contact: Ruth Brewer Managing Partner
　　　Tel:　214-420-6001
　　　Email: rbrewer@brewerlormand.com
　　　Website: http://brewerlormand.com
Legal Services, Attorneys, Lawyers. (Woman, estab 2008,
empl 11, sales $1,140,687, cert: State, WBENC)

5893　Callier & Garza, L.L.P.
　　　4900 Woodway, Ste 700
　　　Houston, TX 77056
　　　Contact: Bernardo Garza Partner
　　　Tel:　713-439-0248
　　　Email: garza@callierandgarza.com
　　　Website: www.callierandgarza.com
The firm specializes in representing large entities,
private and government, insured and self insured, in
State and Federal co urtsin the following areas: (1)
Employment Litigation (including age, gender, race, ADA
and FLA (AA, Hisp, estab 1985, empl 8, sales $1,650,000,
cert: State, NMSDC)

5894　Carter Scholer Arnett Hamada & Mockler PLLC
　　　8150 N Central Expressway Ste 500
　　　Dallas, TX 75206
　　　Contact: Helen Gilliland Partner
　　　Tel:　214-550-8188
　　　Email: helen@carterscholer.com
　　　Website: www.carterscholer.com
Legal Services (Woman/AA, As-Ind, As-Pac, estab 2012,
empl 14, sales $6,000,000, cert: NMSDC)

5895　Cluso Investigation LLC
　　　4500 Mercantile Plaza Dr Ste 106
　　　Fort Worth, TX 76137
　　　Contact: Sharon Sutila CEO
　　　Tel:　817-422-2289
　　　Email: ssutila@cluso.com
　　　Website: http://www.cluso.com
Provides comprehensive reports for fraud prevention,
asset recovery, collection, skip tracing, litigation &
employment screening. (Woman, estab 2008, empl 10,
sales $923,433, cert: State, WBENC)

5896　ELS ESQ. LLC
　　　400 N Ervay Street No. 131612
　　　Dallas, TX 75201
　　　Contact: E. Lynette Stone Attorney
　　　Tel:　972-383-9499
　　　Email: inquire@elsesq.com
　　　Website: http://www.elsesq.com
Legal services (commercial litigation). (Woman/AA, estab
2008, empl 1, sales $150,000, cert: WBENC)

5897　Henjum Goucher Reporting Services, LP
　　　2777 N Stemmons Fwy, Ste 1025
　　　Dallas, TX 75207
　　　Contact: Kristin Neerhof Dir Business Dev
　　　Tel:　214-521-1188
　　　Email: kneerhof@hglitigation.com
　　　Website: http://www.hglitigation.com
Deposition provider with over 35 years in the litigation
support industry. (Woman, estab 1979, empl 33, sales ,
cert: WBENC)

5898　Lehtola & Cannatti PLLC
　　　5001 Spring Valley Rd, Ste 400 E
　　　Dallas, TX 75244
　　　Contact: Patricia Lehtola Managing Member
　　　Tel:　972-383-1515
　　　Email: plehtola@lc-lawfirm.com
　　　Website: http://www.lc-lawfirm.com
Legal services. (Minority, Woman, estab 0, empl , sales $
0, cert: NMSDC)

5899 Lindsay Law
      11700 Preston Rd, Ste 660-167
      Dallas, TX 75230
      Contact: John Lindsay Principal Attorney
      Tel: 214-736-4306
      Email: supplier@inventiveiplaw.com
      Website: http://www.inventiveiplaw.com
Provides intellectual property law services, namely patent,
copyright, trademark, and technology services. The firm
focuses on the legal aspects of analysis, protection. (AA,
estab 2009, empl 2, sales , cert: CPUC)

5900 Owens Hervey PLLC
      Bank of America Plaza 901 Main St, Ste 3612
      Dallas, TX 75202
      Contact: Maurice Owens Jr Member
      Tel: 214-741-2288
      Email: mowens@owenshervey.com
      Website: http://www.owenshervey.com
Civil litigation and trial experience. (AA, estab 2008, empl
3, sales $254,446, cert: State)

5901 Reeves & Brightwell LLP
      221 W 6th St
      Austin, TX 78701
      Contact: Beverly Reeves President
      Tel: 512-334-4501
      Email: breeves@reevesbrightwell.com
      Website: http://www.reevesbrightwell.com
Commercial Litigation firm. (Woman, estab 0, empl , sales
$ 0, cert: WBENC)

5902 State Tax Group, LLC
      5050 Quorum Dr, Ste 700
      Dallas, TX 75254
      Contact: Richard Fleming
      Tel: 972-492-9841
      Email: rfleming@statetaxgroup.com
      Website: www.statetaxgroup.com
State audit representation, sales tax compliance review,
tax refund reviews, litigation support, dispute resolution,
sampling analysis & evaluation, voluntary disclosures. (AA,
estab 2005, empl 4, sales $518,000, cert: NMSDC)

5903 Stratos Legal Services
      4299 San Felipe, Ste 350
      Houston, TX 77027
      Contact: Bert Farris Exec. VP
      Tel: 713-481-2180
      Email: bfarris@stratoslegal.com
      Website: http://www.stratoslegal.com
Litigation support: court reporting, videography, interpreters, records retrieval, process serving, and electronic
discovery. (Woman/Hisp, estab 2005, empl 40, sales
$8,100,000, cert: WBENC)

5904 The Law Office of Kathryn N Karam
      2200 Southwest Frwy Ste 400
      Houston, TX 77098
      Contact: Kathryn Karam President
      Tel: 832-582-0620
      Email: katie@immisolver.com
      Website: www.immisolver.com
Law firm: internal I-9 audit, immigration liabilities of a
merger or acquisition by reviewing all employees' immigration documentation. (Woman, estab 2013, empl 4,
sales , cert: WBENC)

5905 The Marker Group, Inc.
      13105 Northwest Frwy
      Houston, TX 77040
      Contact: Hillary Johnson GM
      Tel: 713-460-9070
      Email: supplierdiversity@marker-group.com
      Website: http://www.marker-group.com
Litigation support services, medical record (MR) collection, MR retrieval, MR review, record analysis, reprographics, scanning, subpoenas, litigation management,
chronologies, oral despositions, evidentiary chain of
custody, real time reporting. (Woman, estab 1985, empl
197, sales $22,021,460, cert: WBENC)

5906 We Muv U, LLC
      3948 Legacy Dr Ste 106, PMB 185
      Plano, TX 75023
      Contact: Jessica Oliver Dir
      Tel: 214-208-1313
      Email: jessica@wmull.com
      Website: http://www.wmull.com
Manage trial logistics for corporations in a manner that
minimizes cost and maximizes desired productivity. (AA,
estab 2014, empl 5, sales $225,000, cert: NMSDC)

Virginia

5907 Gavin Law Offices, PLC
      2500 Gaskins Rd, Ste B
      Richmond, VA 23238
      Contact: Pamela Gavin Managing Member
      Tel: 804-784-4427
      Email: pgavin@gavinlawoffices.com
      Website: http://www.gavinlawoffices.com
Legal services, intellectual property (transfers, licensing,
protection, enforcement, commercial transactional
services, entertainment focused legal services, litigation,
trademark preclearance and prosecution, managing
trademark portfolios. (Woman, estab 2004, empl 9, sales
$1,345,216, cert: State, WBENC)

5908 Guidance Law Firm, P.C.
      440 Monticello Ave, Ste 1834
      Norfolk, VA 23510
      Contact: Lamont Maddox President
      Tel: 757-454-2045
      Email: lmaddox@guidancelaw.com
      Website: www.guidancelaw.com
Legal services, contract review, contract drafting,
document review, regulatory compliance, corporate
governance, policy drafting, policy review, corporate
transactions, general business law, negotiations,
settlements, consulting. (AA, estab 2010, empl 1, sales ,
cert: State, NMSDC)

5909 PCT Law Group, PLLC
      330 John Carlyle St Ste 300
      Alexandria, VA 22314
      Contact: Raymond Millien Owner
      Tel: 703-881-9141
      Email: rmillien@pctlg.com
      Website:
PCT Law Group, PLLC is a law firm with offices in
Washington, D.C., Northern Virginia, and Jacksonville, FL
that provides legal services and representation in the
complementary core areas of corporate (AA, estab 2007,
empl 3, sales $1,095,270, cert: State)

Washington

5910   Focal PLLC
       900 1st Ave S, Ste 201
       Seattle, WA 98134
       Contact: Venkat Balasubramani Owner
       Tel: 206-718-4250
       Email: info@focallaw.com
       Website: www.focallaw.com
Focal is a boutique law firm specializing in internet and
technology-related issues. (AA, As-Ind, estab 2009, empl
11, sales $666,153, cert: NMSDC)

5911   Mayner Business Law, P.S.
       19495 SE 57th Pl
       Issaquah, WA 98027
       Contact: Andrea Mayner Owner
       Tel: 425-996-7335
       Email: andrea@maynerlaw.com
       Website: www.maynerlaw.com
Provides exceptional value and personal services. (Woman,
estab 2008, empl 1, sales $287,385, cert: WBENC)

Wisconsin

5912   Bell & Manning, LLC
       2801 W Beltline Hwy Ste 210
       Madison, WI 53713
       Contact: Callie Bell Shareholder
       Tel: 608-661-3590
       Email: cbell@bellmanning.com
       Website: http://www.bellmanning.com/
Intellectual property, with an emphasis on U.S. and
international patents. (Woman, estab 2010, empl 6, sales
$1,312,916, cert: WBENC)

5913   JAC Consulting LLC dba The Champagne Group
       2233 N Summit Ave Ste 315
       Milwaukee, WI 53202
       Contact: Jacquie Champagne President
       Tel: 414-704-0602
       Email: jacquie@champagnegrp.com
       Website: www.champagnegrp.com
Executive search, legal services. (Woman, estab 2015,
empl 1, sales , cert: WBENC)

5914   Midwest Legal and eData Services, Inc.
       7625 S Howell Ave
       Oak Creek, WI 53154
       Contact: Shawn Olley Owner
       Tel: 414-764-2772
       Email: solley@mwedata.com
       Website: http://www.mwedata.com
Provides experienced paralegals on an as-needed basis
charged at an hourly rate. (Woman, estab 1989, empl ,
sales $ 0, cert: WBENC)

MATERIAL HANDLING EQUIPMENT

Manufacturers or distributors of handtrucks, hoists, dollies, conveyors, racks, forklifts, etc. (See also HARDWARE & TOOLS, HYDRAULIC & COMPRESSED AIR EQUIPMENT, INDUSTRIAL EQUIPMENT & SUPPLIES and INDUSTRIAL MACHINES. NAICS Code 42

Alabama

5915   Southeastern Conveyor Services, Inc.
       870 Minor Pkwy
       Birmingham, AL 35224
       Contact: Stephanie Weeks President
       Tel: 205-785-6884
       Email:
       stephanie.weeks@southeasternconveyorservices.com
       Website: www.southeasternconveyorservices.com
Conveyor solutions for all types of conveyor systems, belt sales, belt vulcanizing, change-outs and replacement, mechanical splices, new installations, wiper replacements, roller change-outs. (Woman, estab 2014, empl 15, sales $1,800,000, cert: WBENC)

5916   Springer Equipment Co., Inc.
       4263 Underwood Industrial Dr
       Birmingham, AL 35210
       Contact: Annette Springer CEO
       Tel: 205-951-3675
       Email: annettes@springerequip.com
       Website: www.SpringerEquipment.com
New & used forklift equipment sales, service, parts rentals & leasing. (Woman, estab 1992, empl 52, sales $19,225,692, cert: WBENC)

California

5917   Bench-Tek Solutions, LLC
       525 Aldo Ave
       Santa Clara, CA 95054
       Contact: Maria Castellon CEO
       Tel: 408-653-1100
       Email: mcastellon@bench-tek.com
       Website: www.bench-tek.com
Custom workbenches, materials handling & storage. (Woman/Hisp, estab , empl , sales $4,000,000, cert: NMSDC, WBENC)

5918   Can Lines Engineering
       9839 Downey-Norwalk Rd
       Downey, CA 90241
       Contact: Erik Koplien
       Tel: 800-233-4597
       Email: erik.koplien@canlines.com
       Website: www.canlines.com
Engineer, design, fabricate, install & service container & material operational & conveying systems. (Hisp, estab 1960, empl 100, sales , cert: NMSDC)

5919   ELA Enterprises
       1813 Lexington Dr
       Fullerton, CA 92835
       Contact: President
       Tel: 714-738-0397
       Email:
       Website: www.elaent.com
Design & mfr custom material handling solutions: dollies, service carts, platform trucks, hand trucks, electric tugs, tow vehicles, trailers, food containers, packaging for transportation & storage solutions. (Woman/Hisp, estab 2006, empl 2, sales $115,000, cert: CPUC, WBENC)

Colorado

5920   Advanced Manufacturing Technology For Bottles
       3920 Patton Ave
       Loveland, CO 80538
       Contact: Jamie Maier Accountant
       Tel: 970-612-0315
       Email: jmaier@amtcolorado.com
       Website: www.amtcolorado.com
Mfr conveyor systems, integrated systems, conveyors, controls & mechanical & electrical installation services, primarily for the packaging industry. (Woman, estab 1996, empl 57, sales , cert: WBENC)

Connecticut

5921   Warner Specialty Products, Inc.
       40-B Montowese Ave
       North Haven, CT 06473
       Contact: Jack Norton VP
       Tel:
       Email: amy@warnerspecialty.com
       Website: www.warnerspecialty.com
Dist material handling & ergonomic equipment solutions. (Woman, estab 1991, empl 8, sales $4,228,000, cert: WBENC)

Florida

5922   Teknia Networks & Logistics, Inc.
       10451 66th St N
       Pinellas Park, FL 33782
       Contact: Jorge Monsalve President
       Tel: 813-918-8417
       Email: laura@teknialogistics.com
       Website: www.teknialogistics.com
Teknia Networks and Logistics provides rental of machinery, copiers, printers, material handling machines like Toyota foklifts, racking systems, power generators (Hisp, estab 2010, empl 10, sales $5,000,000, cert: NMSDC)

5923   The Bernd Group Inc.
       1251 Pinehurst Rd
       Dunedin, FL 34698
       Contact: Pilar Bernd President
       Tel: 727-733-0122
       Email: businessdevelopment@berndgroup.com
       Website: www.berndgroup.com
Material handling equip, safety products, hand & power tools, pumps & compressors, motors, generators, electrical hardware, batteries, lighting fixtures, lockers, bins, shelving, lab equip. (Woman/Hisp, estab 1992, empl 66, sales , cert: NMSDC)

Georgia

5924   Atlanta Caster & Equipment
       1810-E Auger Dr
       Tucker, GA 30084
       Contact: John Brumbaugh Govt Sales Mgr
       Tel: 770-492-0682
       Email: atlantacaster@atlantacaster.com
       Website: www.atlantacaster.com
Dist casters, wheels & non-powered material handling equipment. (Woman, estab 1986, empl 8, sales $2,010,000, cert: WBENC)

5925 Material Handling Inc.
P.O. Box 1045
Dalton, GA 30722
Contact: William Gleaton CFO
Tel: 706-278-1104
Email: billgleaton@mhiusa.net
Website: www.mhiusa.net
New & used lift trucks, lift truck parts, service, mainte-
nance, rental & leasing. (As-Ind, estab 1975, empl 93, sales
$33,707,229, cert: NMSDC)

Illinois

5926 Midway Industrial Equipment Inc.
660 Heartland Dr
Sugar Grove, IL 60554
Contact: Dawn Adams President
Tel: 630-466-7700
Email: dawn@midwaylift.com
Website: www.midwaylift.com
Material Handling Services, sales, service, rental & parts
for forklifts, scrubbers, aerial. (Woman, estab 2003, empl
42, sales $11,200,000, cert: State)

5927 Stevenson Crane Service, Inc.
410 Stevenson Dr
Bolingbrook, IL 60440
Contact: John Edmonson President
Tel: 630-972-9199
Email: john@stevensoncrane.com
Website: www.stevensoncrane.com
Material handling equipment: truck cranes, carrydeck
cranes, crawler cranes, rough terrain cranes, material &
personnel hoists, material handlers, scissor lifts & boom
lifts. (Woman, estab 1989, empl 85, sales $17,779,999,
cert: WBENC)

Indiana

5928 Courtney Material Handling, Inc.
P.O. Box 6925
South Bend, IN 46660
Contact: Beth Courtney President
Tel: 574-231-0094
Email: beth@cmhionline.com
Website: www.cmhionline.com
Dist safety items: hard hats, vests, safety glasses, gloves,
tools, fire & detection, bins, cabinets, carts, casters, chairs
& stools. (Woman, estab 2003, empl 2, sales $213,673,
cert: State)

5929 Handling Technologies, Inc.
51024 Portage Road
South Bend, IN 46628
Contact: Scott Fowler VP
Tel: 866-518-8108
Email: sfowler@handlingtechnologies.com
Website: www.HandlingTechnologies.com
Dist material handling products - shelving, racking systems,
decking, conveyor systems, shop equipment (i.e., carts,
bins, tables, hoists). (Woman, estab 0, empl 12, sales ,
cert: WBENC)

5930 Harriman Material Handling
511 N Range Line Rd
Morristown, IN 46161
Contact: Ashley Larochelle President
Tel: 765-763-8985
Email: ashlar@harrimanmaterialhandling.com
Website: www.HarrimanMaterialHandling.com
Overhead Cranes, Hoists, Jib Cranes, Monorails,
Gantry Cranes, Custom Lifting Devices, Slings/Rigging,
Fall Protection Equipment, Crane Components & Parts,
Dock Equipment, Storage Equipment, Drum Handling
Equipment (Woman, estab 2004, empl 5, sales
$3,528,300, cert: WBENC)

5931 Meyer Material Handling Products Inc.
P.O. Box 47366
Indianapolis, IN 46247
Contact: Carolyn F. Meyer Chairman
Tel: 317-786-9214
Email: cfmeyer@meyermat.com
Website: www.meyermat.com
Material handling equipment. (Woman, estab 1974,
empl 11, sales , cert: WBENC)

Michigan

5932 Brooks & Perkins, Inc. d/b/a B&P Manufacturing
8051 E Boon Rd
Cadillac, MI 49601
Contact: Lia K. Lipar Dir Military Sales & Contracts
Tel: 231-306-3828
Email: lia.krantz@bpmfg.com
Website: www.bpmfgdefense.com
Mfr heavy duty aluminum material handling equipment:
hand trucks, convertible dollies & brake trucks, dock
boards & dock plates. (Woman, estab 1995, empl 65,
sales $11,747,633, cert: State)

5933 Dynamic Conveyor Corp
5980 Grand Haven Rd
Muskegon, MI 49441
Contact: Tracy Powers Business Dev Mgr
Tel: 800-640-6850
Email: tpowers@dynamicconveyor.com
Website: www.dynamicconveyor.com
Quality built radius turns, metal detection, clean room,
water tanks, cooling fans, box filling, split belt, ergo-
nomic tilt, etc. (Woman, estab 1991, empl 24, sales
$5,700,000, cert: WBENC)

5934 ECI Unlimited, Inc.
110 Trealout Dr Ste 102
Fenton, MI 48430
Contact: Lance Stokes President
Tel: 810-354-2775
Email: powertrain@ecienv.com
Website: www.ecipowertrain.webs.com
Install & refurbish material handling & machine loading
& unloading equipment: chain conveyors, roller convey-
ors, pallet conveyors, accumulating conveyors, overhead
conveyors, inverted conveyors, skillet conveyors,
assembly machines. (AA, estab 1993, empl 4, sales , cert:
NMSDC)

5935 Econobuild, LLC
21060 Bridge St
Southfield, MI 48033
Contact: Ramiro Salazar Managing Member
Tel: 248-799-7500
Email: rsalazar@econobuild.com
Website: www.econobuild.com
Material handling equip: flow-thru racks, rack systems, industrial carts, fork-free environment, plant engineering, facility improvements. (As-Pac, estab 1999, empl 15, sales $3,100,000, cert: NMSDC)

5936 Jarvis Handling Equipment Co.
P.O. Box 140767
Grand Rapids, MI 49514
Contact: Susan Smith President
Tel: 616-363-9847
Email: ssmith@jarvishandling.com
Website: www.jarvishandling.com
Dist material handling equipment: racks, containers, modular offices mezzanines, and all basics and essentials, i.e. pallet trucks, carts, drum dumpers, lockers, work benches, etc. (Woman, estab 1966, empl , sales $650,520, cert: WBENC)

5937 Kenowa Industries
11405 E Lakewood Blvd
Holland, MI 49424
Contact: Dan Houle Sales Mgr
Tel: 616-392-7080
Email: dan.houle@kenowa.com
Website: www.kenowa.com
Fabricate material handling racks, baskets, workstations, containers, work-in-process carts, dollies, signboards, mezzanines, steel containers, tubs, steel skids, steel pallets, stands, shelf units. (Hisp, estab 1979, empl 26, sales $3,964,542, cert: NMSDC)

5938 Technical Conveyor Group, Inc.
5918 Meridian Blvd, Ste 2
Brighton, MI 48116
Contact: Rob Tarrien President
Tel: 810-229-5811
Email: rtarrien@tcginc.org
Website: www.tcginc.org
Material handling systems: floor conveyors, overhead/inverted power & free systems, chain-on-edge systems, AGV, electrified monorails, indexing systems, AS/AR systems. (Nat Ame, estab 2000, empl 5, sales $650,956, cert: NMSDC)

5939 Ultimation Industries LLC
27930 Groesbeck Hwy
Roseville, MI 48066
Contact: Jacqueline Canny CEO
Tel: 586-771-1881
Email: jcanny@ultimationinc.com
Website: http://ultimationinc.com
Design, mfr & install assembly line equipment & services, automation devices & conveyor systems, tire & wheel mounting & inflation devices, tire processing lines, TPMS & soaping machines. (Woman, estab 1989, empl 14, sales $4,855,120, cert: WBENC)

5940 Valmec Inc.
1274 S Holly Rd
Fenton, MI 48430
Contact: Krystn Tatus CEO
Tel: 810-629-8750
Email: valmec@comcast.net
Website: http://valmecinc.com
Material handling & packaging, conveyors, returnable packaging, installation, tear-outs & complete system integration. (Woman, estab 1971, empl 5, sales $1,344,664, cert: WBENC)

Minnesota

5941 J & B Equipment Company, Inc.
8200 Grand Ave S
Bloomington, MN 55420
Contact: David Heggem VP/COO
Tel: 952-884-2040
Email: office@jbeq.com
Website: www.jbeq.com
Design & sell engineered overhead crane & monorail systems; hoists; lift tables; specialty carts; and engineered ergonomic material handling systems. (AA, As-Pac, estab 1961, empl 10, sales , cert: NMSDC)

Missouri

5942 C&B Lift Truck Service, Inc.
6250 Knox Industrial Dr
High Ridge, MO 63049
Contact: Owner
Tel: 314-781-5438
Email:
Website: www.cbforklift.com
Dist & service forklifts, aerial/scissor lifts, sweepers, scrubbers, golf carts, dollies, dock equipment, warehouse & distribution equipment (Woman, estab 1976, empl 12, sales $1,000,000, cert: State)

North Carolina

5943 Guna Enterprises, Inc.
1104 Commercial Ave
Charlotte, NC 28205
Contact:
Tel: 704-358-8787
Email: info@gandrcasters.com
Website: www.gandrcasters.com
Mfr industrial, institutional, special & custom made casters, wheels & floor locks. (Woman/As-Ind, estab 1994, empl 60, sales $2,400,000, cert: State)

5944 MYCA Material Handling Solutions, Inc.
223 E Chatham St, Ste 102
Cary, NC 27511
Contact: Maria Ezell CFO
Tel: 919-378-9409
Email: mezell@mycagroup.com
Website: www.mycamaterialhandling.com
Material handling equipment, lift trucks, safety programs & safety equipment, training, warehouse systems, conveyor systems. (Woman, estab , empl , sales $4,600,000, cert: WBENC)

5945   WARP Services, LLC
1316 Providence Rd
Charlotte, NC 28207
Contact: Dr. Patrick LaRive CEO
Tel: 888-547-9277
Email: patrick@warprobotics.com
Website: www.warprobotics.com
Intall, repair & replace conveyors, motors, compressors, electrical safety equipment, material handling, industrial robotics, laser navigation, anything mechanical or electrical. (Woman/AA, estab 2005, empl 4, sales $298,000, cert: State, NWBOC)

New Jersey

5946   Hu-Lift Equipment
400 Apgar Dr, Unit F
Somerset, NJ 08873
Contact: Ming Gang Guo Mgr
Tel: 908-874-5585
Email: mgguo@hu-liftusa.com
Website: www.hu-liftusa.com
Dist material handling products: lift table, cart, platform trucks, furniture movers, skid lifters, highlifts, scale jacks, hydraulic jacks, skates,
pallet trucks, industrial class portable air conditioners, pallet tilters, forklift jacks. (As-Pac, estab 1999, empl 5, sales , cert: State)

5947   JDB Equipment Company, Inc.
116 W Almond St
Vineland, NJ 08360
Contact: Jennifer Sexton President
Tel: 856-264-0314
Email: jdbequipment@hotmail.com
Website:
Rent scissor lifts, boom lifts, aerial lifts, man lifts, forklifts & aerial work platforms. (Woman, estab 2001, empl 3, sales $592,000, cert: WBENC)

Ohio

5948   Caster Connection, Inc.
2380 International St
Columbus, OH 43228
Contact: Joe Lyden Dir of Sales
Tel: 800-544-8978
Email: joe.lyden@casterconnection.com
Website: www.casterconnection.com
Mfr & dist institutional & industrial casters and wheels, hand trucks, pallet jacks, dollies & manual materials handling products. (Woman, estab 1987, empl 36, sales , cert: WBENC)

5949   Darana Hybrid
345 High St, STE 510
Hamilton, OH 45011
Contact: Darryl Cuttell CEO
Tel: 513-785-7540
Email: development@daranahybrid.com
Website: www.daranahybrid.com
Industrial electrical & mechanical installations of processing, packaging, and conveyor equipment systems and machinery for the food & beverage industry. (Nat Ame, estab 1995, empl 50, sales , cert: NMSDC)

5950   WHM Equipment Co.
11775 Enterprise Ave
Cincinnati, OH 45241
Contact: Joan Morgan President
Tel: 513-771-3200
Email: joan@whmequipment.com
Website: www.whmequipment.com
Design, fabricate & assemble conveyors & material handling systems. (Woman, estab 1968, empl 12, sales $1,920,869, cert: WBENC)

Pennsylvania

5951   Shingle Belting
420 Drew Ct
King of Prussia, PA 19406
Contact: Bob Frasetto
Tel: 610-239-6667
Email: bfrasetto@shinglebelting.com
Website: www.shinglebelting.com
Dist industrial conveyors & power transmission belting. (Woman, estab 1979, empl 31, sales , cert: WBENC)

Tennessee

5952   Kenco Material Handling Solutions
2001 Riverside Dr
Chattanooga, TN 37406
Contact: LIndsey Shrader Business Dev Mgr
Tel: 706-766-9554
Email: lindsey.shrader@kencogroup.com
Website: www.kencogroup.com
Fleet management program, material handling fleet, regardless of OEM, we offer battery and charger maintenance. (Woman, estab 1950, empl 4000, sales $615,000,000, cert: WBENC)

5953   Southfork Lift Truck, Inc.
3070 Sidco Dr
Nashville, TN 37204
Contact: Marketing Mgr
Tel: 615-647-9615
Email:
Website: www.SouthforkLiftTruck.com
Forklift & material handling equipment sales, service, parts, rentals & leasing. (Woman, estab 2014, empl 10, sales $1,700,000, cert: State, WBENC)

Texas

5954   Casters of Amarillo Inc.
1520 S Polk St
Amarillo, TX 79101
Contact: Karen Hicks President
Tel: 806-373-2884
Email: karenh@casterama.com
Website: www.casterama.com
Dist material handling equipment: casters & industrial wheels, freight, dock & warehouse equipment, drum handling equipment, wire & steel shelving & pallet rack, steel & aluminum hand trucks, appliance trucks & specialty hand trucks. (Woman, estab 1974, empl 5, sales $649,054, cert: State)

5955 Design Associates International, Inc
11615 Forest Central Dr, Ste 101
Dallas, TX 75243
Contact: Lucia Fredenburgh President
Tel: 214-720-6083
Email: luciaf@daiinc.com
Website: www.daiinc.com
Dist materials handling equipment: casters, wheels, carts, dollies, hand trucks, facilities planning & design. (Woman/Hisp, estab 1994, empl 8, sales $1,250,000, cert: State)

5956 Mighty Lift Inc.
P.O. Box 14998
Houston, TX 77221
Contact: Helen Fu President
Tel: 713-668-0263
Email: helenfu@mightylift.com
Website: www.mightylift.com
Dist pallet jacks, lifting tables, hand trucks, casters and wheels, wire containers, wire partitions, pallet racks & guard rails, electric personnel & burden carriers & scooters. (Woman/As-Pac, estab 2002, empl 15, sales $4,042,931, cert: State, NMSDC, WBENC)

5957 Permian Machinery Movers Inc.
2200 W Interstate 20
Odessa, TX 79763
Contact: Robert M. Chavez President
Tel: 432-333-1777
Email: robert@permianmachineryinc.com
Website: www.permianmachineryinc.com
Dist, rent & lease forklifts. (Hisp, estab 1981, empl 45, sales $11,100,000, cert: State)

5958 Texas Storage Systems
P.O. Box 751632
Houston, TX 77075
Contact: Karen Cato Owner
Tel: 713-991-1089
Email: tssinc@ymail.com
Website: www.catoindustries.com
Material handling & warehouse equipment. (Woman/AA, estab 2010, empl 5, sales $100,000, cert: State)

5959 Walter Terry Distributor, Inc.
2420 Louisiana A111
Houston, TX 77006
Contact: President
Tel: 713-227-6369
Email:
Website: www.wtstraps,com
Material Handling Equipment, Cargo Control Systems, vending trucks, appliance trucks, dollies, ramps, bars, nets, furniture pads, plastic mattress & furniture bags, packaging items, Load Control/Protection items & Wheelchair Restraint. (Woman, estab 1965, empl 3, sales $863,762, cert: State, City)

Utah

5960 Conveyors & Equipment, Inc.
3580 S 300 W
Salt Lake City, UT 84115
Contact: Ginger Goyzueta President
Tel: 801-263-1843
Email: goyzuetag@conveyequip.com
Website: www.conveyequip.com
Conveyor design, service & installation, Conveyor belt supply, service & installation, Material handling equipment, Ergonomic solutions. (Woman, estab 1972, empl 32, sales $6,600,000, cert: State)

Washington

5961 Washington Liftruck
700 S Chicago
Seattle, WA 98108
Contact: Jeff Darling VP
Tel: 206-762-2040
Email: darling@forkliftsamerica.com
Website: www.washingtonlift.com
Dist forklifts & material handling equipment. (Woman, estab 1973, empl 34, sales $21,260,000, cert: City, WBENC)

MEASURING INSTRUMENTS
Manufacturers and distributors of counters and timers, X-ray spectrometers, voltage and frequency indicators, gas analyzers, thermocouples, thermometers, etc. (See also ELECTRONIC categories and
HARDWARE & TOOLS). NAICS Code 42

California

5962   Technical Maintenance, Inc.
     117 Jetplex Circle, Ste C4
     Madison, AL 35758
     Contact: Scott Chamberlain Quality Mgr
     Tel: 256-772-4115
     Email: scott.chamberlain@tmicalibration.com
     Website: www.tmicalibration.com
Calibrate test & measurement equipment (Woman, estab
1991, empl 162, sales $22,700,000, cert: WBENC)

5963   Alloy Valves and Control
     3210 S Susan St
     Santa Ana, CA 92704
     Contact: Phyllis Abrams Dir of Sales & Marketing
     Tel: 714-427-0877
     Email: pabrams@avcovalve.com
     Website: www.avcovalve.com
Design & mfr ball valves & flow measurement products,
manual & automated ball valve assemblies. (Woman, estab
2000, empl 15, sales , cert: CPUC)

5964   Brylen Technologies
     275 Orange Ave
     Santa Barbara, CA 93117
     Contact: Barbara Tzur President
     Tel: 805-692-9300
     Email: barbara.tzur@brylen.com
     Website: www.brylen.com
Calibration & testing laboratory, clean room & clean bench
certifications, calibration is electro-magnetic, thermodynamics, dimensional, angle, & mechanical areas, calibrate
equipment. (Woman, estab 1985, empl 10, sales $571,850,
cert: State)

5965   RHF, Inc.
     16202 Keats Circle
     Westminster, CA 92683
     Contact: Robert Friesen President
     Tel: 714-848-9367
     Email: rhf.radar@earthlink.net
     Website: www.radaretc.com
Repair & calibration of speed radar & lidar equipment.
(Woman, estab 1983, empl 3, sales $300,000, cert: State)

5966   STB Electrical Test Equipment, Inc.
     1666 Auburn Ravine Rd
     Auburn, CA 95603
     Contact: Patricia Tavare President
     Tel: 530-823-5111
     Email: pat@stbinc.com
     Website: www.stbinc.com
Mfr phasing voltmeters, voltage detectors, voltage
sensors, ground detectors, clamp-on ammeters, phase
rotation meters, ground cable testers, drain tools.
(Woman, estab 1979, empl 6, sales $1,329,220, cert:
State, CPUC)

5967   Vanguard Instruments Company, Inc.
     1520 S. Hellman Ave
     Ontario, CA 91761
     Contact: Timm Smith Natl Sales Mgr
     Tel: 513-477-2965
     Email: timm.s@vanguard-instruments.com
     Website: www.vanguard-instruments.com
Mfr measuring & testing electricity & electrical signal
instruments. (As-Pac, estab 1993, empl 11, sales , cert:
CPUC)

Connecticut

5968   Environics, Inc.
     69 Industrial Park Rd E
     Tolland, CT 06084
     Contact: Cathy Dunn CEO
     Tel: 860-872-1111
     Email: cdunn@environics.com
     Website: www.environics.com
Design, mfr, dist & service computerized gas flow
instruments, gas mixing systems, gas on-demand
systems, gas calibration systems, gas dilution systems,
gas flow management systems. (Woman, estab 1986,
empl 20, sales $3,000,000, cert: State)

Florida

5969   Diverse Services USA, Inc.
     11111 N 46th St
     Tampa, FL 33617
     Contact: Michael Schmidt VP
     Tel: 813-988-6000
     Email: michael.schmidt@diverseservicesusa.com
     Website: www.diverseservicesusa.com
Mfr & install all signs: interior, exterior, graphics, LED
message centers, millwork (counters, cabinetry),
architectural imaging (ACM panel systems, awnings) and
lighting (general illumination, specialty/accent, energy
savings (Hisp, estab 2009, empl 650, sales $152,000,000,
cert: NMSDC)

Georgia

5970 Georgia Time Recorder Co., Inc.
      722 Collins Hill Rd Ste H-283
      Lawrenceville, GA 30046
      Contact: Andrea Drath President
      Tel: 770-441-2879
      Email: andrea@georgiatime.com
      Website: http://gtrbusinesssystems.com
Time & Attendance, Time clocks, Wireless Synchronized
clocks & master clocks, Temperature Sensors, temp/
humidity sensors, CO2 sensors, emergency lighting, event
monitoring. (Woman, estab 1982, empl 6, sales $550,000,
cert: WBENC)

Illinois

5971 B&B Instruments, Inc.
      145 W Taft Dr
      South Holland, IL 60473
      Contact: BobSamoska Owner
      Tel: 708-596-1700
      Email: bobsamoska@bbinstruments.com
      Website: www.bbinstruments.com
Dist pressure, temperature, level, flow, humidity gauges &
instrumentation, NiST shop calibrations, testing type
calibrators. (As-Pac, estab 1972, empl 8, sales , cert:
NMSDC)

5972 Connor-Winfield Corp.
      2111 Comprehensive Dr
      Aurora, IL 60505
      Contact: Gordon Olp Reg Sales Mgr
      Tel: 630-851-4722
      Email: golp@conwin.com
      Website: www.conwin.com
Quartz crystals, oscillators & timing synchronization
modules. (Woman, estab 1963, empl 250, sales
$20,050,000, cert: CPUC)

Indiana

5973 AFC International Inc
      P.O. Box 894
      DeMotte, IN 46310
      Contact: Pamela Seneczko President
      Tel: 219-987-6825
      Email: pjseneczko@afcintl.com
      Website: www.afcintl.com
Gas detectors, respiratory protection, detector tubes, self
contained breathing apparatus, heat stress monitors, CO
detectors, toxic gas detectors. (Woman, estab 1992, empl
6, sales $3,000,000, cert: WBENC)

5974 The CREW Corporation
      P.O. Box 254
      Brownsburg, IN 46112
      Contact: President
      Tel: 317-713-7777
      Email:
      Website: www.crewcorp.com
Validation services: qualification testing & validation,
change control, FAT & SAT, IQ/OQ/PQ protocols &
execution, instrument calibration, supporting documentation. (Woman, estab 1995, empl 38, sales $2,970,000,
cert: WBENC)

Louisiana

5975 A-T Specialties, LLC
      P.O. Box 4157
      New Orleans, LA 70178
      Contact: Tony Asberry, Jr President
      Tel: 504-828-1424
      Email: tony.asberry@atspecialties.com
      Website: www.atspecialties.com
Dist measurement & controls, level, pressure, temperature, flow & position. (AA, estab 2002, empl 2, sales
$1,350,000, cert: State)

Michigan

5976 Hines Industries, Inc.
      793 Airport Blvd.
      Ann Arbor, MI 48108
      Contact: Beverly Monge Sales Admin
      Tel: 734-769-2300
      Email: ddonall@hinesindustries.com
      Website: www.hinesindustries.com
Balancing machines, rebuild balancing equipment &
balancing instrumentation services, balancing equipment design innovation & manufacturing process
improvement. (Woman, estab 1971, empl 25, sales
$8,400,000, cert: WBENC)

5977 M & B Holdings, LLC
      5594 E Ten Mile Rd
      Warren, MI 48091
      Contact: Brian McMillan GM
      Tel: 586-427-9971
      Email: bmcmillan@gsnscorp.com
      Website: www.gsnscorp.com
Gage Commodity Management, Gage Purchasing, Gage
Design & Manufacturing. (As-Ind, estab 2005, empl 31,
sales $4,420,017, cert: NMSDC)

5978 Omni-Tech Sales, Inc.
      31189 Schoolcraft Rd
      Livonia, MI 48150
      Contact: Deborah Denne CEO
      Tel: 734-425-5730
      Email: omnitech_sales@ameritech.net
      Website: www.omnitech-sales.com
Dist precision measuring equipment, CMM's, Vision
Systems, Roundness & Form Measurement, Surface Finish
equipment & fixturing, Hardness Testers, Optical Compara-
tors. (Woman, estab 1988, empl 6, sales $3,975,637, cert:
WBENC)

5979 River City Metrology LLC
      2215 29th St SE, Ste B1
      Grand Rapids, MI 49508
      Contact: Victor Barker Owner
      Tel: 616-530-4899
      Email: vbarker@rcmetrology.com
      Website: www.rcmetrology.com
Dimensional Inspection, CMM calibration & sales, Dimensional inspection product sales. (As-Pac, estab 2004, empl
5, sales , cert: NMSDC)

5980 Standard Scale & Supply Co.
      25421 Glendale
      Redford, MI 48239
      Contact: John Bowman GM
      Tel: 313-255-6700
      Email: jbowman@standardscale.com
      Website: www.standardscale.com
Dist & service weight-based measuring equipment &
accessories. (Hisp, estab 1946, empl 12, sales , cert:
NMSDC)

5981 Universal Tool Equipment & Controls, Inc.
      6525 Center Dr
      Sterling Heights, MI 48312
      Contact: Bill Bartolotta VP
      Tel: 586-268-4380
      Email: bbartolotta@universaltecinc.com
      Website: www.universaltecinc.com
Automation & welding systems, robotics, weld guns, vision
systems, sealant systems, drawn arc welders, projection
welders, material handling end effectors & welding
fixtures. (Woman/AA, estab 2009, empl 29, sales
$10,000,000, cert: WBENC)

North Carolina

5982 Measurement Controls, Inc.
      P.O. Box 562775
      Charlotte, NC 28256
      Contact: Paresh Patel President
      Tel: 704-921-1101
      Email: sales@measurementcontrols.com
      Website: www.measurementcontrols.com
Refurbish, mfr & dist rotary, diaphragms & turbine gas
meters, meter sets with regulators, filters & by-pass,
install index, connections, swivels, nuts, & washers,
electro mechanical correctors, dust caps & blind disc.
(As-Ind, estab 1999, empl 9, sales $400,000, cert: State,
City, NMSDC)

Ohio

5983 AVM Industries
      30505 Bainbridge Rd, Ste 100
      Solon, OH 44139
      Contact: Linda Holt Dir
      Tel: 440-349-1849
      Email: lholt@hawthornmc.com
      Website: www.avminc.com
Mfr & dist climate control actuators & counterbalancing
systems for the automotive, commercial & aftermarket
industries. (As-Pac, estab 2006, empl 376, sales
$34,000,000, cert: NMSDC)

5984 Cincinnati Control Dynamics Inc.
      4924 Para Dr
      Cincinnati, OH 45237
      Contact: Jeff Bao President
      Tel: 513-242-7300
      Email: jbao@ccdi1.com
      Website: www.airflowmachines.com
Non-destructive air flow test equipment for
turbine engines, customized air flow solutions, nacelle
testing, leak testing & pressure testers. (As-Pac, estab
1977, empl 10, sales $1,900,000, cert: State)

5985 Cooper Atkins
      11353 Reed Hartman Hwy Ste 110
      Cincinnati, OH 45241
      Contact: Sr VP sales
      Tel: 847-373-2033
      Email: gmarcus@cooper-atkins.com
      Website: www.cooper-atkins.com
Wireless temperature / environmental monitoring
systems, software, hardware, installation & support.
(Woman, estab , empl , sales , cert: WBENC)

5986 Intek, Inc.
751 Intek Way
Westerville, OH 43082
Contact: Audrey Myers Cstmr Service
Tel: 614-895-0301
Email: amyers@intekflow.com
Website: www.intekflow.com
Mfr & dist thermal low flow meters & switches, measures
liquid flow rates, also mfr RheoVac line of vacuum moni-
toring equipment. (As-Pac, estab 1976, empl 17, sales ,
cert: City)

Pennsylvania

5987 RNDT, Inc.
228 Maple Ave
Johnstown, PA 15901
Contact: VP Technical Dir
Tel: 814-535-5448
Email:
Website: www.rndt.net
Nondestructive testing services, radiographic, magnetic
particle, liquid penetrant, ultrasonic and visual testing
services. Also offer Positive Material Identification (PMI),
remote video, certified welding inspector services (CWI).
(Woman, estab 2002, empl 35, sales $5,800,000, cert:
WBENC)

Puerto Rico

5988 American Test & Balance
P.O. Box 366584
San Juan, PR 00936
Contact: David Rosa President
Tel: 787-781-7654
Email: d.rosa@american-test.com
Website: www.american-test.com
Testing, adjusting and balancing (TAB) services for heating,
ventilating and air conditioning systems. We also provide
Cleanroom Performance Testing (CPT) services. (Hisp,
estab 1994, empl , sales $167,000, cert: NMSDC)

5989 Instrumentation Corps, Inc.
P.O. Box 2116
Barceloneta, PR 00617
Contact: Juan Oliveras President
Tel: 787-970-0746
Email: jaoliver@instrumentationcorps.com
Website: www.instrumentationcorps.com
Process instrumentation & weight scales sales, installation,
configuration, calibration & certification svcs, equipment
repair & technical services. (Hisp, estab 1998, empl 40,
sales $4,851,214, cert: NMSDC)

5990 PAS Technologies, Inc.
9 Pedro Arzuaga W
Carolina, PR 00984
Contact: Alfredo Agelviz President
Tel: 787-752-2370
Email: alfredo.agelviz@pastechnologies.com
Website: http://pastechnologies.com
Dist & service instrumentation & control products. (Hisp,
estab 1993, empl 3, sales $1,300,000, cert: NMSDC)

Texas

5991 DDLS Group, LLC
5734 Trowbridge
El Paso, TX 79925
Contact: Dalia De Los Santos Owner
Tel: 915-881-0281
Email: dalia@fas-tes.com
Website:
Drug & Alcohol Policy Development, Workplace Drug
Screen Programs, Random Drug Screen Programs, Urine
& Saliva Drug Screens. (Woman/Hisp, estab 2012, empl
1, sales , cert: State)

Wisconsin

5992 Precision Metrology, Inc.
7350 N Teutonia Ave
Milwaukee, WI 53209
Contact: Carol Shipley President
Tel: 414-351-7420
Email: carol@precisionmetrology.com
Website: www.precisionmetrology.com
Calibrate & repaire precision measuring instruments.
(Woman, estab , empl , sales , cert: WBENC)

MEDICAL SUPPLIES & SERVICES
Manufacturers and distributors of over the counter drugs, dental supplies, diagnostic equipment and supplies, glass containers, labwear, veterinary products, latex, hospital supplies & apparel, etc. NAICS Code 32

Alabama

5993 Hygia Health Services
434 Industrial Lane
Birmingham, AL 11111
Contact: Glenn Chenot Natl Business Dir
Tel: 865-755-3181
Email: glenn.chenot@hygia.net
Website: www.hygia.net
Reprocessed, non-invasive, non-critical medical devices. (Minority, estab , empl , sales , cert: State)

5994 Medical Place
350 Industial Park Blvd
Montgomery, AL 36117
Contact: Shanavian Strickland
Tel: 334-241-0807
Email: sstrickland@medicalplace.net
Website: www.medicalplace.net
Dist medical, laboratory, respiratory, scientific, telemedicine equipement & supplies. (AA, estab , empl , sales $45,627,571, cert: State)

5995 NuAngel Inc.
14717 Friend Rd
Athens, AL 35611
Contact: President
Tel: 256-729-5000
Email:
Website: www.NuAngel.com
Mfr breastfeeding & infant items: washable nursing pads, biodegradable disposable nursing pads, burp cloths, washable baby wipes, receiving blankets, bra extenders. (Woman, estab 1990, empl 10, sales $450,000, cert: WBENC)

5996 VELOX Integration Services, LLC
600 S Court St, Ste 322
Montgomery, AL 36104
Contact: Sherrell Love CEO
Tel: 334-233-3328
Email: sherrell@veloxintegration.com
Website: http://veloxintegration.com
Dist medical supplies & equipment, construction management. (Woman/AA, estab 2014, empl 2, sales , cert: State)

Arizona

5997 CJPS Healthcare Supplies & Equipment LLC
14201 N Hayden Rd Bldg B4
Scottsdale, AZ 85260
Contact: President
Tel: 480-939-4362
Email:
Website: http://CJPS-Healthcare.com
Dist VitalPoint remote monitoring system, enables comprehensive measurement across 9 vitals in one device. (Woman/As-Pac, estab 2009, empl 10, sales $250,000, cert: NMSDC)

5998 Magnum Medical LLC
3265 N Nevada St
Chandler, AZ 85225
Contact: Omar Hameed Mktg Dir
Tel: 800-336-9710
Email: ohameed@magnummed.com
Website: www.magnummed.com
Import & dist surgical instruments, plastic instruments & related items. (As-Ind, estab 1984, empl 9, sales $3,000,000, cert: NMSDC)

California

5999 Abell Marketing Group, Inc.
15057 Avenida De Las Flores
Chino Hills, CA 91709
Contact: James Lohan Project Mgr
Tel: 909-456-8905
Email: james@abellmarketinggroup.com
Website: www.abellmarketinggroup.com
Protective clothing & medical/industrial nitrile, vinyl & latex gloves. (Woman, estab 1998, empl 2, sales $375,000, cert: WBENC)

6000 Active Potential Inc.
7898 Ostrow St Ste G
San Diego, CA 92111
Contact: CEO
Tel: 858-292-4128
Email:
Website: www.activepotentialmedical.com
Safety devices, Arc Flash protection, Emergency & Exam room supplies, Emergency preparedness, Ergonomics, Eye protection & accessories, Fall protection, Fire protection, Safety storage, Work wear, Gloves & hand protection. (Woman/AA, estab 2006, empl 7, sales $247,300, cert: NMSDC, CPUC)

6001 Advanced ImmunoChemical, Inc.
111 W Ocean Blvd, 4th Fl
Long Beach, CA 90802
Contact: President
Tel: 562-434-4676
Email:
Website: www.advimmuno.com
Mfr laboratory reagents for In vitro diagnostics & research, Cardiac Disease, Tumor Markers, Metabolic Syndrome, Inflammation, Emerging Infectious Diseases, Biowarfare Threats, Hormones, Autoimmune Disease, Neuroscience. (Woman, estab 1986, empl 2, sales , cert: WBENC)

6002 Alcam Medical Inc.
1760 Chicago Ave, Ste L-21
Riverside, CA 92507
Contact: Cameron Stewart VP
Tel: 866-847-7187
Email: cameron@alcammedical.com
Website: www.alcammedical.com
We provide Orthotic and Prosthetic Services. We evaluate and fit for upper and lower extremity prosthetics, custom orthotics, diabetic shoes, compression garments, cranial helmets, knee braces, back braces, pediatric orthotics, mastectomy bras. (AA, estab 2006, empl 69, sales $8,100,000, cert: CPUC)

6003 Ames Medical Equipment, Inc.
      301 N Jackson Ave, Ste 7A
      San Jose, CA 95133
      Contact: patel Mike Treasurer
      Tel: 408-942-9000
      Email: mspatel101@hotmail.com
      Website: www.Alliancemedsupply.com
Dist durable medical equipment & supplies. (Woman/As-Pac, estab 2005, empl 2, sales , cert: State)

6004 Axiom Medical, Inc.
      19320 VANNESS AVENUE.
      TORRANCE,, CA 90501
      Contact: valerie ramsay Dir of operations
      Tel: 310-533-9020
      Email: valerie@axiommed.com
      Website: https://axiommed.com
Mfr silicone & PVC disposable wound drainage catheters. (Woman, estab , empl , sales , cert: State)

6005 BioMed Resources Inc.
      6646 Doolittle Ave
      Riverside, CA 92503
      Contact: Lisa Liu CEO
      Tel: 310-323-3888
      Email: lisal@bmres.com
      Website: www.bmres.com
Dist specimen containers, transfer pipettes, conical tubes, irrigation syringes, lab jackets, lab coats, isolation gowns & cover gowns. (Woman/As-Pac, estab 2002, empl 15, sales $4,300,000, cert: NMSDC)

6006 Broadline Medical, Inc.
      2100 Atlas Rd, Ste E
      Richmond, CA 94806
      Contact: Georgia W. Richardson President & CEO
      Tel: 510-662-5270
      Email: grichardson@broadline.com
      Website: www.broadline.com
Dist disposable medical apparel: headwear, footwear, labcoats & lab jackets, OR towels, lap sponges, gowns & non sterile kits. (Woman/AA, estab 1994, empl 10, sales $3,000,000, cert: NMSDC)

6007 Clariti Eyewear, Inc.
      940 Ajax Ave
      City of Industry, CA 91748
      Contact: Dominique Yonemoto President
      Tel: 800-372-6372
      Email: gene@claritieyewear.com
      Website: www.claritieyewear.com
Eyeglasses, Optical frames, Eyeglass frames, Eyewear, Sunglasses, Eyeglass cases, Cleaning cloths, Cleaning Kit. (Woman/As-Pac, estab 1993, empl 14, sales $3,219,627, cert: State, NMSDC)

6008 Clear Breath LLC
      1113 Tahoe Lane
      Palo Alto, CA 94303
      Contact: Ed Lim CEO
      Tel: 510-828-4331
      Email: sales@clear-breath.net
      Website: https://clear-breath.net
Dist PPE Supplies such as medical masks and gowns. (As-Pac, estab 2020, empl 3, sales $100,000, cert: State)

6009 Duncan & Duncan Medical, Inc.
      911 Marina Way S Unite E2
      Richmond, CA 94804
      Contact: Luta Duncan President
      Tel: 510-799-0100
      Email: glovesbylu@aol.com
      Website: http://duncanmeds.com
Medical, surgical, laboratory supplies & equipment, medical books, cleaning supplies, housekeeping supplies, apparel, gloves, incontinence, textiles, orthopedic , nutritional & feeding supplies, personal hygiene, physical therapy. (Woman/AA, estab 2011, empl 3, sales $429,000, cert: CPUC)

6010 EMS Safety Services, Inc.
      1046 Calle Recodo Ste K
      San Clemente, CA 92673
      Contact: Marian Lepore CEO
      Tel: 800-215-9555
      Email: bids@emssafety.com
      Website: www.emssafetyservices.com
Training curriculums & products: CPR, AED, First Aid & Bloodborne Pathogens. (Woman/As-Pac, estab 1993, empl 18, sales $2,700,000, cert: NMSDC, CPUC, WBENC)

6011 Flying Medical USA
      18187 Valley
      La Puente, CA 91744
      Contact: Conrad Reveles Sales Exec
      Tel: 855-227-3080
      Email: sales3@flyingmedusa.com
      Website: www.flyingmedusa.com
Mfr medical supplies: band aid, ice packs, finger splints, etc. (As-Pac, estab 2008, empl 4, sales , cert: State)

6012 Hand and Hand Medical
      822 Wakefield Dr
      Oakdale, CA 95361
      Contact: Sharon Devereaux CEO
      Tel: 209-322-2699
      Email: dwight@handandhand.com
      Website: www.handandhandmed.com
Dist surgical post-op "JP Drain" Management Systems, unique effective product, US Patent Awarded 2015. (Woman, estab 2016, empl 3, sales $750,000, cert: WBENC)

6013 HSI (Hospital Systems, Inc.)
      750 Garcia Ave
      Pittsburg, CA 94565
      Contact: Kathie Campbell VP Operations
      Tel: 925-427-7800
      Email: kcampbelll@hsiheadwalls.com
      Website: www.HSIheadwalls.com
Mfr patient headwalls, patient service columns, Isolated power panels, patient care systems & neo natal. Dist hospital accessories. (Woman, estab , empl , sales $6,210,000, cert: State, WBENC)

6014 IDEAON
      1855, Gateway Blvd Ste 170
      Concord, CA 94520
      Contact: Shankar Krishna Director
      Tel: 925-465-2175
      Email: shankar@ideaoninc.com
      Website: www.ideaoninc.com
Custom Computer Programming Services, medical supplies. (As-Ind, estab 2003, empl 5, sales $1,500,000, cert: NMSDC)

6015 Kili Summit Corporation
2110 K St
Sacramento, CA 95816
Contact: Cinde Dolphin CEO
Tel: 916-794-1653
Email: cinde@medicaldraincarrier.com
Website: https://medicaldraincarrier.com
Manage JP wound-care drains after mastectomy, cancer, cardiac and organ transplant surgeries. (Woman, estab 2015, empl 2, sales , cert: WBENC)

6016 Legend Medical Devices Inc.
16714 E Johnson Dr
City Of Industry, CA 91745
Contact: Mark Sevilla Dir of Sales
Tel: 626-350-9733
Email: msevilla@legendmd.com
Website: www.legendmd.com
Mfr & dist CPAP, anesthesia, respiratory care & infection control products. (Woman/As-Pac, estab 2006, empl 8, sales $1,500,000, cert: CPUC)

6017 Medi Max Tech
2805 E Ana St
East Rancho Dominguez, CA 90221
Contact: Natl Contracting Mgr
Tel: 716-868-6108
Email:
Website: www.medimaxtech.com
Dist electrosurgical pencils: Telescopic Smoke and Ergonomic Pencils. (Woman/As-Pac, estab 2012, empl 10, sales , cert: NMSDC, WBENC)

6018 Medical Receivables Solutions, Inc.
802 Wilmington
Fairfield, CA 94533
Contact: Aleshia Hunter President
Tel: 415-377-3775
Email: aleshia@medicalreceivables.net
Website: www.medicalreceivables.net
Account receivables and medical billing shortage, Medical Receivables Solutions Inc. (Woman/AA, estab 2002, empl 7, sales $250,000, cert: CPUC)

6019 Plus One Lab Works Inc.
2872 Walnut Ave, Ste C
Tustin, CA 92780
Contact: Jason Vi Mgr
Tel: 714-558-8009
Email: jason@plusonelab.com
Website: www.plusonelab.com
Dist disposable products for use in labs, clean rooms, hospitals, dental & medical offices. (As-Pac, estab 2010, empl 5, sales , cert: NMSDC)

6020 Small Beginnings, Inc.
17229 Lemon St Ste B2
Hesperia, CA 92345
Contact: Kelly Brockelmeyer Exec Admin
Tel: 760-949-7707
Email: kelly@small-beginnings.com
Website: www.small-beginnings.com
Mfr Neonatal Intensive Care Unit disposable products: diapers, photo-therapy masks, suction devices, pacifiers, & meconium aspirators. (Woman, estab 2001, empl 8, sales $1,071,101, cert: WBENC)

6021 Teco Diagnostics Inc.
1268 N Lakeview Ave
Anaheim, CA 92807
Contact: Lewis Cabrera Dir of Sales
Tel: 714-463-1111
Email: lewis@tecodiagnostics.com
Website: www.tecodiag.com
Mfr vitro clinical diagnostic tests and instruments. (As-Pac, estab 1987, empl 50, sales $7,000,000, cert: NMSDC)

6022 The Andwin Corp.
6636 Variel Ave
Canoga Park, CA 91303
Contact: Arnie Shedlow Sr VP sales
Tel: 818-999-2828
Email: jpalaganas@andwin.com
Website: www.andwinsci.com
Dist medical & lab supplies & product kits: boxes, labels, bar codes, instruction inserts & kit components. (Woman, estab 1950, empl 98, sales $32,000,000, cert: WBENC)

6023 Total Resources International
420 S Lemon Ave
Walnut, CA 91789
Contact: Andre Dela Victoria Sales Mgr
Tel: 909-594-1220
Email: andrev@totalresourcesintl.com
Website: www.totalresourcesintl.com
Mfr First Aid Kits & Emergency Survival Essentials. (As-Pac, estab 1990, empl 150, sales $13,000,000, cert: NMSDC)

Colorado

6024 in3corp Inc.
1750 30th St, Ste 216
Boulder, CO 80301
Contact: Patricia Gilpin Acct Coord
Tel: 303-448-1191
Email: gilpin@in3corp.com
Website: www.in3corp.com/
Our firm has a variety of capabilities to help audit supplier invoice payments. Our projects find transaction errors in order to deliver lost money to clients; but we also reinforce existing best practices, identify new optimization strategies (Hisp, estab 2000, empl 79, sales $2,200,000, cert: NMSDC)

6025 LifeHealth LLC
5951 S Middlefield Rd, Ste 102
Littleton, CO 80123
Contact: Margot Langstaff Managing Partner
Tel: 303-730-1902
Email: margot@lifehealthcorp.com
Website: www.lifehealthcorp.com
Clinical health care services & solutions. (Woman, estab 2004, empl 5, sales $870,000, cert: State, WBENC)

6026 Mountainside Medical Colorado, LLC
6165 Lookout Rd
Boulder, CO 80301
Contact: Susan Neidecker President
Tel: 303-222-1271
Email: sneidecker@mountainsidemed.com
Website: www.mountainsidemed.com
Contract manufacturing for complex, tight-tolerance medical products, Multi-axis Machining Assembly, Wire EDMCNC, Swiss type machining centers, Laser welding & Laser marking, Finishing Metal Forming. (Woman, estab 2006, empl 90, sales $12,731,416, cert: WBENC)

6027 Relius Medical LLC
615 Wooten Rd Ste 150
Colorado Springs, CO 80915
Contact: Lauralee Martin Owner
Tel: 719-725-6444
Email: lmartin@reliusmed.com
Website: http://reliusmed.com
Orthopedic Medical Device Manufacturer: Implants,
External Fixation Devices, Instrumentation. (Woman, estab
2014, empl 125, sales $1,010,907,952, cert: WBENC)

6028 The Medcom Group, Ltd.
541 East Garden Dr, Unit Q
Windsor, CO 80550
Contact: Steven Barnett
Tel: 970-674-3032
Email: novation@medcomgroup.com
Website: www.medcomgroup.com
Dist orthopedic rehabilitative equipment. (Woman, estab ,
empl , sales $2,500,000, cert: WBENC)

Connecticut

6029 Quaisar Enterprises LLC dba Health Products ForYou
82 North St
Danbury, CT 06810
Contact: Masarrat Quaisar Dir of Sales
Tel: 203-616-2850
Email: masarrat@healthproductsforyou.com
Website: www.healthproductsforyou.com
Dist medical equipment & supplies. (Woman/As-Ind, estab
2002, empl 12, sales $11,000,000, cert: State)

District of Columbia

6030 Medical Supply Systems, Inc.
3182 Bladensburg Rd NE
Washington, DC 20018
Contact: President
Tel: 202-832-5000
Email:
Website:
Dist general medical & surgical supplies & equipment,
mortuary supplies, laboratory supplies. (Woman/AA, estab
1985, empl 5, sales $1,499,998, cert: State)

Delaware

6031 AquaCast Liner LLC
364 E Main St Ste 422
Middletown, DE 19709
Contact: Mark Monahan VP
Tel: 855-938-2278
Email: markm@aquacastliner.com
Website: www.aquacast.com
Mfr waterproof cast liners for fracture care management.
(Woman, estab 2011, empl 15, sales , cert: State)

6032 Med-Tech Equipment, Inc.
2207 Concord Pike Ste 135
Wilmington, DE 19803
Contact: David Gentile VP
Tel: 800-322-2609
Email: info@buymedtech.com
Website: www.buymedtech.com
Dist, service & maintain sport medicine modalities &
training equipment: Electrotherapy Ultrasound, Stim, Laser
and Combo units, Hydrotherapy Whirlpools, Traction/
Decompression Systems, Treatment Tables, Extremity
Testing Systems. (Woman, estab 1989, empl 2, sales
$250,000, cert: State)

Florida

6033 Advanced Surgical Technologies, Inc.
901 SW Martin Downs Blvd, 200A
Palm City, FL 34990
Contact: Barbara Alfaro President
Tel: 561-801-2314
Email: balfaro@astlaser.com
Website: www.astlaser.com
Medical laser rental and related supplies. (Hisp, estab
2017, empl 10, sales $600,000, cert: NMSDC)

6034 AmCar Group, LLC
342 Pike Rd, Ste 19
West Palm Beach, FL 33411
Contact: Herbert Bernard Co-Owner
Tel: 954-557-8697
Email: amcarmedical@gmail.com
Website:
Dist disposable/consumable medical
supplies, medical equipment. (AA, estab 2013, empl 3,
sales , cert: State)

6035 American Medicals
8900 Corporate Square Court
Jacksonville, FL 32216
Contact: B G Bihani President
Tel: 904-636-9451
Email: bg.bihani@americanmedicals.com
Website: www.americanmedicals.com
Mfr & dist medical, surgical & healthcare products. (As-
Ind, estab 2001, empl 3, sales , cert: State)

6036 American Purchasing Services
10315 USA Today Way
Miramar, FL 33025
Contact: Akhil Agrawal President
Tel: 305-364-0888
Email: akhil.agrawal@american-depot.com
Website: www.american-depot.com
Dist medical supplies. (As-Ind, As-Pac, estab , empl ,
sales , cert: NMSDC)

6037 Anexa Biomedical, Inc.
40423 Air Time Ave
Zephyrhills, FL 33542
Contact: Lenny Budloo President
Tel: 813-780-7927
Email: lenny@anexabiomedical.com
Website: www.anexabiomedical.com
Mfr USP Sterile Saline and Sterile Water solutions for
moistening of wound dressings, wound debridement,
and device irrigation. (Hisp, estab 2010, empl 8, sales ,
cert: State)

6038 Bayside Medical Supply Company, Inc.
3924 W Palmetto St
Tampa, FL 33607
Contact: Reginald Nickson CEO
Tel: 813-879-2731
Email: rjnickson@netzero.net
Website: http://baysidemedicalsupply.com
Dist disposable & durable medical supplies & equip-
ment: furniture, bandages, exam room, gloves, ortho-
paedic, needles, syringes, point of care testing, infection
control, instruments, surgical supplies, respiratory,
personal care, etc. (AA, estab 1990, empl , sales
$1,100,000, cert: State)

6039   Care-Full Products
      3905 Tampa Rd, Ste 432
      Oldsmar, FL 34677
      Contact: Colleen Meloff President
      Tel: 813-602-2824
      Email: cmeloff@carefullproducts.com
      Website: www.carefullproducts.com
Mfr CareFull Catch disposable specimen cup holder.
(Woman, estab 2015, empl 1, sales , cert: NWBOC)

6040   Carter-Health Disposables LLC
      4201 Vineland Road Ste I-13-14
      Orlando, FL 32811
      Contact: Office Admin
      Tel: 407-296-6689
      Email: nancy@carterhealth.com
      Website: www.carter-health.com
Disposable medical supplies & medical devices, Pharmacy
support products & consultation, Disposable, high quality,
low-lint, non-woven gowning apparel, Lab Coats, Isolation
Gowns & Coveralls, shoe covers, hair covers. (Woman/AA,
estab , empl , sales $1,900,000, cert: NMSDC, WBENC)

6041   Customed USA, LLC
      10805 Southport Dr
      Orlando, FL 32824
      Contact: Milexis Torres Dir of Sales
      Tel: 407-850-5558
      Email: milexis.torres@prhospital.com
      Website: http://customedhealing.com
Dist hospital, medical supplies, imaging products, custom
surgical products. (Hisp, estab 2010, empl 240, sales
$1,100,000, cert: NMSDC)

6042   EncompasUnlimited, Inc.
      2219 Whitfield Park Dr
      Sarasota, FL 34243
      Contact: Marybeth Flynn VP
      Tel: 941-751-3385
      Email: marybeth@encompasunlimited.com
      Website: http://encompasunlimited.com
Dist endoscopy accessories, specimen caddies, multiple
glove dispenser boxes, endoscopy wedges & headrests.
(Woman, estab 1977, empl 4, sales $2,400,000, cert:
NWBOC)

6043   Global Sourcing, LLC
      2415 Albany Ave
      Tampa, FL 33607
      Contact: Tom Irby VP of Strategic Partnerships
      Tel: 512-293-8709
      Email: tom.irby@globalsourcingppe.com
      Website: www.globalsourcingppe.com
Dist PPE items, N95 masks, ASTM level 1,2,3 surgical
masks, face shields, surgical gowns level 1/2/3/4, nitrile
FDA 510k exam gloves, latex gloves, vinyl gloves, show
covers/boots, alcohol EPA list N wipes, hand sanitizers.
(Woman, estab 2020, empl 20, sales $25,500,000, cert:
WBENC)

6044   Healthcare Supply Solutions, Inc.
      13949 Alvarez Rd Ste 100
      Jacksonville, FL 32218
      Contact: Lara Cheek
      Tel: 904-638-5520
      Email: lcheek@hssone.com
      Website: http://hssone.com
Dist healthcare products & services. (Hisp, estab 2008,
empl 14, sales $10,000,000, cert: NMSDC)

6045   HNM Medical USA
      20855 Northeast 16th Ave, Ste C15
      Miami, FL 11111
      Contact: Yoav Anisz President
      Tel: 866-291-8498
      Email: yanisz@hnmmedical.com
      Website: www.hnmmedical.com
Dist medical equipment and supplies. (Hisp, estab , empl
, sales $7,000,000, cert: NMSDC)

6046   Kramer Laboratories, Inc.
      400 University Dr Ste 400
      Coral Gables, FL 33134
      Contact: Myrna Patterson Sales Mgr
      Tel: 800-824-4894
      Email: mpatterson@kramerlabs.com
      Website: www.kramerlabs.com
Fungi Nail Brand, Safetussin CD Cough Relief/Nasal
Decongestant Formula, Safetussin DM Cough Formula.
(Woman/Hisp, estab 1987, empl 14, sales , cert: NMSDC,
WBENC)

6047   Lipotriad LLC
      219 Via Emilia
      Palm Beach Gardens, FL 33418
      Contact: Joan McCabe CEO
      Tel: 203-561-0970
      Email: joan@lipotriad.com
      Website: www.lipotriadvitamins.com
Eye vitamins for eye health (Woman, estab 2009, empl
13, sales $2,000,000, cert: WBENC, NWBOC)

6048   Medgluv Inc
      4100 Coral Ridge Dr Ste 100
      Coral Springs, FL 33065
      Contact: Jerry Leong CEO
      Tel: 954-586-5309
      Email: jleong@medgluv.com
      Website: www.medgluv.com
Mfr & dist examination gloves. (As-Pac, estab 2001, empl
6, sales $8,000,000, cert: State, NMSDC)

6049   Medical Support International, LLC
      2626 Sawyer Terr
      Wellington, FL 33414
      Contact: Edgar Rivera CEO
      Tel: 561-337-4866
      Email: edgar.rivera@medsupportintl.com
      Website:
Dist medical, dental, veterinary, surgical & hospital
supplies & equipment. (Hisp, estab 2009, empl 2, sales ,
cert: NMSDC)

6050   Med-Lab Supply Co. Inc
      800 Waterford Way Ste 950
      Miami, FL 33126
      Contact: Lucas Diaz VP Sales
      Tel: 800-330-3183
      Email: lucas.diaz@med-lab.com
      Website: www.med-lab.com
Dist & service Siemens medical equipment. (Hisp, estab
1964, empl 79, sales $25,000,000, cert: NMSDC)

6051 Mellow Enterprises LLC
201 SW 63rd Ave
Plantation, FL 33317
Contact: Helen F Litsky President
Tel: 954-312-7175
Email: me@mellowllc.com
Website: http://voacorp.com/
mellowenterprises.net
Safety & fire related training, medical supplies. (Woman/AA, estab 2010, empl 1, sales , cert: City)

6052 Surgimed Corporation
1303 NW 78th Ave
Doral, FL 33126
Contact: Luis Arias VP
Tel: 305-594-1121
Email: larias@surgimedcorp.com
Website: www.surgimedcorp.com/
Dist endotracheal tubes, stylets, guedels, suction catheters, tracheostomy tubes, endobroncheal tubes, foley catheters, urinary collection bags, leg bags, urine meters, pediatric urine collectors, foley Catheterization trays, irrigation syringes & trays. (Hisp, estab 1981, empl 13, sales $4,000,000, cert: NMSDC)

6053 US Medical International LLC
6989 NW 82nd Ave
Miami, FL 33166
Contact: Ryan Kissane Sales/Operations Mgr
Tel: 305-468-3248
Email: ryan@usmedicalintl.com
Website: www.usmedicalintl.com
Mfr & dist disposable medical supplies. (Hisp, estab 2009, empl 3, sales , cert: State, NMSDC)

6054 ValorPoint, LLC
7827 Chase Meadows Dr E
Jacksonville, FL 32256
Contact: Markus hardy CEO
Tel: 904-321-7007
Email: mark.hardy@valorpointllc.com
Website: www.valorpointllc.com
Dist Personal Protective Equipment (PPE) for government and non-government entities. (AA, estab 2016, empl 2, sales , cert: NMSDC)

6055 VetMeds, Inc.
8950 SW 74th Court Ste 2201
Miami, FL 33156
Contact: President
Tel: 786-220-3634
Email:
Website: www.vetmedsinc.biz
Dist medical equipment, medical apparel, wound care supplies, medical furniture, exam room supplies, extrication-patient transport equipment, surgical gloves, IV therapy & laboratory supplies. (Woman/AA, estab 2012, empl 5, sales , cert: State)

Georgia

6056 American Clinics for Preventive Medicine
1343 Terrell Mill Rd Ste 100
Marietta, GA 30067
Contact: Juanita Cato Office Asst
Tel: 767-836-3477
Email: americanclinicpm@gmail.com
Website: http://acpm.net
Provide physical exams, alternative medical treatment options, nutritional infusion therapy, high dose Vitamin C infusions, primary prevention exams, alternative complimentary cancer therapies, detoxification programs. (AA, estab 1985, empl 10, sales , cert: State)

6057 Attain Med, Inc.
5825 Glenridge Dr NE Bldg 4, Ste 106
Atlanta, GA 30328
Contact: Charles Stafford VP Diversity Partnerships
Tel: 770-288-2466
Email: charles.stafford@attainmed.com
Website: www.attainmed.com
Dist pharmaceuticals. (AA, As-Ind, Hisp, estab , empl , sales $8,000,000, cert: NMSDC, 8a)

6058 Black Knight Medical, LLC
50 Hurt Plaza SE, Ste 803
Atlanta, GA 30303
Contact: Ron Thomas President
Tel: 877-767-3792
Email: ron@blackknightmedical.com
Website: www.blackknightmedical.com
Medical supply distributor servicing healthcare systems both
domestically and abroad. (AA, estab 2017, empl 4, sales $5,900,000, cert: City)

6059 Canterbury Pointe LLC
3350 Riverwood Parkway, Ste 1900
Atlanta, GA 30339
Contact: President & CEO
Tel: 770-633-2570
Email:
Website: http://cpointellc.com
Medical Supplies, Pharmacy Benefit Management, Energy Management & Insurance Services. (Woman/AA, estab 2015, empl 1, sales , cert: WBENC)

6060 DOC Development Inc
2500 Park Central Blvd Ste 30035
Decatur, GA 30094
Contact: Radcliff Quarterman COO
Tel: 678-509-1501
Email: rquarterman@doc-development.com
Website: www.doc-development.com
Medical Supplies. (AA, estab 2001, empl , sales $110,000,000, cert: 8a)

6061 MedX Diagnostic Solutions, LLC
2004 Eastview Pkwy Ste 108
Conyers, GA 30013
Contact: Gerald Patterson COO
Tel: 770-278-0199
Email: gpatterson@medxghs.com
Website: www.medxghs.com
Dist healthcare materials, supplies, furniture, diagnostic kits, biomedical equipment services & repairs. (Woman/AA, estab 2014, empl 3, sales , cert: NMSDC)

6062 Pulse Medical Inc.
      1130 Ada St, Ste B
      Blue Ridge, GA 30513
      Contact: Barbara Boyce President
      Tel: 706-632-1370
      Email: bboyce@pulsemedical.net
      Website:
Dist medical supplies. (Woman, estab 0, empl , sales , cert: WBENC)

6063 U.S. Imaging, Inc.
      2234 Bryant Place Court
      Marietta, GA 30066
      Contact: Sherman Weston President
      Tel: 404-934-9054
      Email: sweston@bellsouth.net
      Website: http://usimagingsite.com
Dist bio-medical, medical supplies & medical imaging equipment. (AA, estab , empl , sales $949,000, cert: NMSDC)

6064 Unyter Enterprises
      6065 Parkway North Dr Ste 200
      Cumming, GA 30040
      Contact: RRayfus D'Yana President
      Tel: 678-500-9568
      Email: drayfus@unyter.com
      Website: www.unyter.com
Dist pharmaceuticals, medical/surgical supplies & equipment. (AA, estab 2009, empl 10, sales , cert: City)

6065 Vanguard Safety Company LLC
      P.O. Box 608
      Savannah, GA 31402
      Contact: Howard Genser Jr. Exec VP/COO
      Tel: 912-236-1766
      Email: howardg@vanguardsafetyco.com
      Website: www.vanguardsafetyco.com
Dist occupational health & safety products. (AA, estab 1985, empl 21, sales $8,700,000, cert: NMSDC)

6066 WellSol Medical Inc.
      1261 LaVista Rd, Ste D1
      Atlanta, GA 30324
      Contact: William Moylan CFO/COO
      Tel: 855-935-5765
      Email: bill@wellsolmed.com
      Website: www.wellsolmed.com
Dist medical equipment. (Hisp, estab 2015, empl 4, sales , cert: NMSDC)

Illinois

6067 Cura Surgical Inc.
      2571 Kaneville Ct
      Geneva, IL 60134
      Contact: Lynn Uvodich Controller
      Tel: 630-232-2510
      Email: luvodich@curasurgical.com
      Website: www.curasurgical.com
Dist surgical & burn wound dressings (Hisp, estab 2006, empl 10, sales $5,261,075, cert: NMSDC)

6068 Ekla Corporation
      1707 Quincy Ave, Ste 127
      Naperville, IL 11111
      Contact: Jeff Prendergast President
      Tel: 630-258-6242
      Email: jeff@eklacorp.com
      Website: www.eklacorp.com
Medcal surgical and equipment supplies and services. (Woman/As-Ind, estab , empl , sales $7,100,000, cert: City, WBENC)

6069 Global Medical Services LLC
      707 Davis Rd, Ste 102B
      Elgin, IL 60123
      Contact: Kelvin Udogu CEO
      Tel: 224-238-3273
      Email: kudogu@gmail.com
      Website: www.globalmedsllc.com
Dist pharmaceuticals & medical equipment. (Woman/AA, estab 2009, empl 5, sales $450,000, cert: 8a)

6070 Goodhealth Medical Products
      14818 Drexel Ave
      Dolton, IL 60419
      Contact: David Wilson President
      Tel: 708-841-1700
      Email: info@goodhealthmed.com
      Website: www.goodhealthmed.com
Dist medical, dental, and surgical supplies. (AA, estab 2001, empl 15, sales $2,000,000, cert: State, NMSDC)

6071 JERO Medical Equipment & Supplies, Inc.
      4108 W Division St
      Chicago, IL 60651
      Contact: President
      Tel: 312-829-5376
      Email:
      Website: http://jeromedical.com
Mfr disposbable wearing apparels, kit assembler, 1st aid, disaster, admission. (AA, estab 1987, empl 24, sales $4,000,000, cert: City)

6072 MAC Medical Supply Co.
      525 W Monroe St Ste 2360
      Chicago, IL 60661
      Contact: Millie Maddocks CEO
      Tel: 773-650-9400
      Email: millie.maddocks@macmed.com
      Website: www.macmed.com
Dist medical & safety supplies; cleaning products. (Woman, estab 2000, empl 14, sales $44,529,940, cert: WBENC)

6073 MC Squared Medical, Inc.
      7801 Industrial Dr Ste F
      Spring Grove, IL 60081
      Contact: Mccrea, Jody President
      Tel: 815-322-2485
      Email: jodymccrea@gmail.com
      Website: www.mc-squared-group.com
Dist peripheral nerve products, Neurolac nerve tube conduit & Vivosorb nerve tube wrap to prevent adhesions. (Woman, estab 2011, empl 3, sales , cert: State)

6074 Medefil, Inc.
      250 Windy Point Dr
      Glendale Heights, IL 11111
      Contact: Praveen Aggarwal Exec VP
      Tel: 630-682-4600
      Email: contracts@medefilinc.com
      Website: www.medefilinc.com
Mfr prefilled syringes filled with saline & hepain for IV flush. (AA, As-Ind, estab , empl , sales , cert: NMSDC)

6075 MedGyn Products, Inc.
      100 W Industrial Rd
      Addison, IL 60101
      Contact: Aarathi Singh
      Tel: 630-627-4105
      Email: asingh@medgyn.com
      Website: www.medgyn.com
Dist disposables, medical devices, diagnostic equipment & surgical/procedure instruments. (As-Ind, estab 1975, empl 70, sales , cert: State)

6076 Nexus Pharmaceuticals, Inc.
      400 KNIGHTSBRIDGE PKWY
      LINCOLNSHIRE, IL 60069
      Contact: Chris Conroy Dir Natl Accouts
      Tel: 847-996-3790
      Email: cconroy@nexuspharma.net
      Website: http://nexuspharma.net
Mfr sterile generic injectable pharmaceuticals. (Woman/As-Ind, estab , empl , sales $750,000, cert: NMSDC, WBENC)

6077 Novo Surgical, Inc.
      700 Commerce Dr Ste 500
      Oak Brook, IL 60523
      Contact: Abed Moiduddin VP
      Tel: 877-860-6686
      Email: abed.moiduddin@novosurgical.com
      Website: www.novosurgical.com
Custom instrument design & mfg, premium, specialty surgical instrumentation. (As-Ind, As-Pac, estab , empl , sales , cert: NMSDC)

6078 Saris and Things Inc.
      3836 Mistflower Ln
      Naperville, IL 60564
      Contact: Shital Daftari CEO
      Tel: 630-346-6531
      Email: shital@sarisandthings.com
      Website: www.sntbiotech.com
Dist PPE and Hand Sanitizers and Covid Tests and testing supplies for labs. NIOSH N95, CDC & EAU KN95, Hand Sanitizers, Covid Tests, Swabs, VTM Kits, Cryovial Tubes, Extraction Tubes, Covid Antigen Tests. (Woman/As-Ind, estab 2011, empl 6, sales $6,573,548, cert: City, WBENC)

6079 Senegal Enterprises Medical Inc.
      3342 Bramanti Trail
      Steger, IL 60475
      Contact: MJ Senegal CEO
      Tel: 563-340-1602
      Email: mjsenegal@senegalmed.com
      Website: www.senegalmed.com
Dist medical supplies & equipment. (AA, estab 2014, empl 1, sales , cert: State)

6080 Tetra Medical Supply Corp.
      6364 W Gross Point Rd
      Niles, IL 60714
      Contact: Mike Imhoff Dir of Marketing
      Tel: 800-621-4041
      Email: mike@tetramed.com
      Website: www.tetramed.com
Mfr & dist medical supplies. (Woman, estab , empl , sales $5,500,000, cert: WBENC)

Indiana

6081 Armada Optical Services, Inc.
      701 N Weinbach Ave Ste 410
      Evansville, IN 47711
      Contact: Julia Coakley GM
      Tel: 812-476-6623
      Email: jcoakley@armadaoptical.com
      Website: www.armadaoptical.com
Safety prescription eyewear, mfr plastic, polycarbonate, trilogy & other products. (Woman, estab 1990, empl 11, sales , cert: State)

Kentucky

6082 Blu Pharmaceuticals
      301 Robey St
      Franklin, KY 42134
      Contact: Bill Luster Contract Mgr
      Tel: 270-586-6386
      Email: jfurlong@blurx.us
      Website: www.blurx.us
mfr & dist generic pharmaceuticals. (Woman/Hisp, estab 2006, empl 15, sales $39,613,667, cert: State)

6083 Marian Medical, Inc.
      319 Westport Dr
      Louisville, KY 40207
      Contact: Lisa Stewart Clinical Sales Mgr
      Tel: 502-425-6363
      Email: lisa@marianmedicalonline.com
      Website: http://marianmedicalonline.com
Neonatal products: Enteral System, Urinary Catheters, Urinary Collection Kit, Circumcision Tray, Chest Tube Kit, Exchange Transfusion Tray, Blood Administration Syringe Sets, PICC Procedure Kits. (Woman, estab , empl , sales , cert: City)

Louisiana

6084 Carousel Medical Equipment LLC
      2138 Wooddale Blvd Bldg B, Ste 13
      Baton Rouge, LA 70806
      Contact: Lizzset Gordon Owner
      Tel: 225-216-0360
      Email: carouselmedical@bellsouth.net
      Website: www.carouselmedical.com
Dist medical equipment & supplies. (Woman/AA, estab 2007, empl 2, sales , cert: 8a)

Massachusetts

6085 Genesis Medical Products, Inc.
      40 Farm Hill Rd
      Wrentham, MA 02093
      Contact: Kevin Kelliher Principal
      Tel: 877-933-5437
      Email: genesismedical@aol.com
      Website: http://iGenesisMedical.com
Dist neonatal, pediatric, labor & delivery soft goods. (Woman, estab 1996, empl 10, sales $300,000, cert: State)

6086　Shinemound Enterprise Inc.
17A Sterling Rd
North Billerica, MA 01862
Contact: Gloria Shiao VP
Tel:　978-436-9980
Email: info@shinemound.com
Website: www.shinemound.com
Mfr latex & non-latex products: disposable PVC, synthetic, vinyl & nitrile, CPE & PE gloves. (As-Pac, estab 1988, empl 6, sales , cert: State)

6087　Westnet Inc.
55 North St
Canton, MA 02021
Contact:　Gordon Thompson CEO
Tel:　781-828-7772
Email: gordon@westnetmed.com
Website: www.westnetmed.com
Dist medical/surgical supplies & equipment; life science products & industrial paper. (AA, estab 1994, empl 37, sales , cert: NMSDC)

Maryland

6088　1st Needs Medical LLC
7003 Glenn Dale Rd Ste 151
Glenn Dale, MD 20769
Contact:　Partner
Tel:　301-928-2557
Email:
Website: www.1stneedsmedical.com
Durable Medical Equipment & daily use medical supplies. (AA, estab 2014, empl 2, sales , cert: State, NMSDC)

6089　Asclepius Solutions Inc.
3510 Raymoor Rd
Kensington, MD 20895
Contact: Deven Shah VP
Tel:　301-685-3557
Email: deven.shah@asclepius.net
Website: www.asclepius.net
Clinical Trials Support Solutions & Services, Protocol Lifecycle Management, Clinical Monitoring, Clinical Data Management, Safety Reporting, Electronic Data Capture, Dictionary Management, Patient Registration. (Woman/As-Ind, estab 2003, empl 15, sales , cert: State)

6090　Lifeline Medical Services, Inc.
2955 Mercy Lane
Cheverly, MD 20785
Contact: Eze Nwoji President
Tel:　301-386-0000
Email: eze@lifelinemeds.com
Website: www.lifelinemedicalsupplies.com
Dist automatic sanitary shoe dispenser, hand held EKG monitor, ambulatory product, bathroom product, gloves, dental supplies, woundcare supplies, diagnotics equipment, medical apparels hospital beds & accessories. (AA, estab 2003, empl 4, sales $385,000, cert: State)

6091　The McConnell Group, Inc.
8400 Corporate Dr Ste 120
Landover, MD 20785
Contact: Irving McConnell CEO
Tel:　301-309-8310
Email: imcconnell@themccgroup.com
Website: www.themccgroup.com
Dist laboratory & medical supplies. (AA, estab 1996, empl 200, sales , cert: State)

6092　Universal Medical Associates, Inc.
111 Hamlet Hill Rd Ste 710
Baltimore, MD 21210
Contact: Renee Parks
Tel:　443-765-9366
Email:
reneeparks@universalmedicalassociates.com
Website: www.UniversalMedicalAssociates.com
Medical & surgical implants, osteobiologics & regenerative medicine products, Osteobiologics, Sports Medicine Allografts, Synthetic Biologics &
Regenerative Tissue products. (AA, estab 2010, empl 3, sales $621,930, cert: NMSDC)

Michigan

6093　Heritage Vision Plans, Inc.
One Woodward Ave Ste 2020
Detroit, MI 48226
Contact: Leonard T. Barnes VP, Sales & BD
Tel:　313-863-1633
Email: lbarnes@heritagevisionplans.com
Website: www.heritagevisionplans.com
Optical goods & services: eye exams, frames, lenses & contact lenses. (AA, estab 1975, empl 18, sales $11,154,350, cert: NMSDC)

6094　J and B Medical Supply Company Inc.
50496 W Pontiac Trail
Wixom, MI 48393
Contact: Julian Shaya Exec VP
Tel:　800-737-0045
Email: jshaya@jandbmedical.com
Website: http://jandbmedicalsupply.com
Dist Medical Surgical & Emergency Medical Supplies. (Woman, estab 1996, empl 500, sales $925,000, cert: WBENC)

6095　MMS Holdings Inc.
6880 Commerce Blvd
Canton, MI 48187
Contact: Prasad M. Koppolu EVP & COO
Tel:　734-245-0310
Email: pkoppolu@mmsholdings.com
Website: www.mmsholdings.com
Clinical research, regulatory submission support for the pharmaceutical, biotech and medical device industries. (Woman/As-Ind, As-Pac, estab 2005, empl 362, sales $82,294,495, cert: NMSDC)

6096　OCS Inc.
916 Fremont St
Bay City, MI 48708
Contact: Amy Swackhamer Dir of communications
Tel:　989-714-0719
Email: amy@ocsmgt.com
Website: www.ocsmgt.com
Medical & vocational management, occupational therapy consultating & cost containment services. (Woman, estab 2010, empl 12, sales $1,000,000, cert: WBENC)

6097　Revive Surgical Instrument Service & Repair, LLC
201 Streamview Ct
Canton, MI 48188
Contact:　President
Tel:　734-796-3143
Email:
Website:
www.revivesurgicalinstrumentrepair.com
Surgical instrument repair. (Woman/AA, estab 2011, empl 3, sales $243,000, cert: WBENC)

6098   TerryWorldWide, LLC
       6505 Grandville Ave
       Detroit, MI 48228
       Contact: Terry Willis CEO
       Tel: 313-974-8341
       Email: terry@terryworldwide.com
       Website: www.terryworldwide.com
Dist CanAm Medical/SiO2 Ultra Thin Liquid Glass Coatings.
(AA, estab 2010, empl 1, sales , cert: NMSDC)

6099   The Black Moon Group dba BMG Medical Supply
       6026 Kalamazoo Ave, Ste 237
       Grand Rapids, MI 49508
       Contact: Bill McCurdy CEO
       Tel: 616-275-9109
       Email: bmccurdy@theblackmoongroup.com
       Website: www.BMGmed.com
Dist Medline and McKesson Medical Supply and Equipment. (AA, estab 2015, empl 5, sales , cert: NMSDC)

6100   Veteran Medical Products, Inc.
       813 Franklin St SE
       Grand Rapids, MI 49507
       Contact: Roosevelt Tillman President
       Tel: 616-451-8486
       Email: rt@veteranmedical.com
       Website: www.veteranmedical.com
Disposable medical supplies. (AA, estab 2005, empl 2, sales
$100,000, cert: NMSDC)

Minnesota

6101   Global International LLC
       P.O. Box 240385
       Apple Valley, MN 55124
       Contact: Ambrose Kpoto Dir Strategic Partnership
       Tel: 612-404-1051
       Email: ambrose@fgmmedical.com
       Website: www.fgmmedical.com
Dist medical, dental, and pharmaceuticals. (AA, estab
2014, empl 30, sales $3,000,000, cert: NMSDC)

6102   NavasDRSTi, LLC
       1714 Basswood Court
       Carver, MN 55315
       Contact: Yog Ohneswere CEO
       Tel: 888-628-2860
       Email: yohnes@navadrsti.com
       Website: www.navadrsti.com
Electro-Surgical Units, Cardio-Vascular & Cardiology
Equipment & Instruments, Radiology, Ultrasound, Diagnos-
tic Imaging & Testing Equipment, Orthopedic Devices,
Implants & Tools, Surgical Equipment, Instruments,
Supplies & Disposables. (As-Ind, estab 2016, empl 2, sales ,
cert: State)

6103   Ulmer Pharmacal
       1614 Industry Ave W
       Park Rapids, MN 56470
       Contact: Brent Swanson CFO
       Tel: 218-732-2656
       Email: bswanson@lobanaproducts.com
       Website: www.ulmerpharmacal.com
Mfr premium cleaning & infection control products,
patient lubricating jellies & skin care products.. (Woman,
estab 2013, empl 10, sales $520,000, cert: State)

Missouri

6104   Emed Medical Company
       11551 Adie Rd
       Maryland Heights, MO 63043
       Contact: Bailey Eric President
       Tel: 314-291-3633
       Email: SJONES@EMEDMEDICAL.COM
       Website: www.emedmedical.com
Dist medical & pharmaceutical products. (AA, estab ,
empl , sales $26,000,000, cert: State, NMSDC)

6105   I.V. House, Inc.
       418 Seven Gables Ct
       Chesterfield, MO 63017
       Contact: Angela Cressey
       Tel: 314-453-9200
       Email: angela@ivhouse.com
       Website: www.ivhouse.com
Mfr & dist I.V. House Ultra Dressings & Ultra Domes, IV
site protectors for all ages. (Woman, estab , empl , sales
, cert: State)

6106   SimmCo Distribution
       4813 Lee Ave
       St. Louis, MO 63115
       Contact: Shaun Simms President
       Tel: 314-389-3630
       Email: info@simmcodistribution.com
       Website: www.simmcodistribution.com
Dist Medical Devices, Medical Supplies & Pharmaceuticals. (AA, estab 2012, empl 5, sales , cert: State, City)

North Carolina

6107   Make It Market USA
       10612 Providence Rd Ste D343
       Charlotte, NC 28277
       Contact: Kate Liddle Founder, Sr Partner
       Tel: 877-647-7639
       Email: kliddle@makeitmarketusa.com
       Website: http://makeitmarketusa.com
InjuryShield is a thermoplastic-based, self-contained
wound & splinting system that is biocompatible,
radiolucent, latex-free. (Minority, Woman, estab 2014,
empl 2, sales $115,000, cert: State)

6108   Seniors Medical Supply, Inc.
       540 W Elm St
       Graham, NC 27253
       Contact: Gavin Coble President
       Tel: 336-227-0730
       Email: seniorsmedical@bellsouth.net
       Website: http://seniorsmedicalsupply.net
Dist medical equipment: power & manual wheelchairs,
canes, commodes, walkers, lift chairs, surgical equipment & supplies, hospital beds & sheets, oxygen, wound
care products, compression therapy, ED pumps, diabetic
shoes. (Woman/AA, estab 2004, empl 6, sales $345,789,
cert: WBENC)

New Jersey

6109   Amneal Pharmaceuticals
       400 Crossing Blvd 3rd Fl
       Bridgewater, NJ 08807
       Contact: Brown Massey Dir Sales
       Tel: 908-947-3120
       Email: bmassey@amneal.com
       Website: http://amneal.com
Develop, mfg & dist generic pharmaceutical products.
(As-Ind, estab 2002, empl 4727, sales , cert: NMSDC)

6110   BLOXR Solutions LLC
P.O. Box 5148
North Branch, NJ 08876
Contact: John Buday Cstmr Service
Tel: 801-590-9880
Email: order@bloxr.com
Website: www.bloxr.com
Mfr radiation protection cream and apparel. (Woman/As-Pac, estab 2015, empl 14, sales , cert: WBENC)

6111   Case Medical Inc.
19 Empire Blvd
South Hackensack, NJ 07606
Contact: Steven Beltis Contract Mgr
Tel: 201-313-1999
Email: sbeltis@casemed.com
Website: www.casemed.com
Mfr decontamination & sterilization products. (Woman, estab , empl , sales $7,000,000, cert: State, WBENC)

6112   Cenmed Enterprises
121 Jersey Ave
New Brunswick, NJ 08901
Contact: Rizwan Chaudhry Operations
Tel: 732-447-1100
Email: rizwan@cenmed.com
Website: www.cenmed.com
Dist medical supplies, laboratory supplies, hospital supplies, surgical supplies, emt supplies, safety supplies, fire supplies. (Woman/As-Ind, estab 1992, empl 25, sales $8,400,000, cert: State, City, NMSDC, WBENC, SDB)

6113   Discovery ChemScience LLC
66 Witherspoon St, Ste 1100
Princeton, NJ 08542
Contact: Qun Sun President
Tel: 609-475-5097
Email: qsun@dischemsci.com
Website: www.dischemsci.com
Provide discovery, medicinal chemistry & custom synthesis CRO services. (As-Pac, estab 2004, empl 2, sales $2,900,000, cert: NMSDC)

6114   Earth2Earth LLC
8 Promenade Place
Voorhees, NJ 08043
Contact: Sita Rentala Owner
Tel: 856-843-1441
Email: earth2earth45@gmail.com
Website: http://earth2earthonline.com
PPE products to the Health Care Industry, as well as Biodegradable Toothbrushes to Dentists and Environmentalists. Our products are made from renewable resources that include plant fiber, bamboo, sugar cane, unbleached, and recycled items. (Woman/As-Ind, estab 2018, empl 5, sales , cert: City, WBENC)

6115   NEXT Medical Products Company, LLC
45 Columbia Rd
Branchburg, NJ 08876
Contact: John Buday Dir Customer Service
Tel: 908-722-4549
Email: jbuday@nextmedicalproducts.com
Website: www.nextmedicalproducts.com
Mfr Clear Image & LithoClear Ultrasound Gel brands, sterile & non-sterile single patient packets. (Woman/As-Pac, estab , empl , sales $5,000,000, cert: WBENC)

6116   Precision Medical Devices, Inc.
121 Jersey Ave
New Brunswick, NJ 08901
Contact: Lynn Indyk Business Develop Mgr
Tel: 732-447-2587
Email: lindyk@pmdmfg.com
Website: www.pmdinstruments.com
Mfr medical devices, instrument systems & clinical products, surgical instruments. (As-Ind, estab 2008, empl 6, sales $275,000, cert: NMSDC)

6117   Siris Pharmaceutical Services
75 North St Ste 1
Bloomsbury, NJ 08804
Contact: Andrew Voigt Business Development
Tel: 908-479-1331
Email: andrewv@sirispharma.com
Website: http://sirispharma.com
Clinical packaging, distribution, drug storage, and drug returns/destruction services. (Woman, estab 2001, empl 12, sales $672,000, cert: WBENC)

6118   United Medical Supplies Inc.
25 Craig Place
North Plainfield, NJ 07059
Contact: Raman Alaigh CEO
Tel: 908-757-0075
Email: rayalaigh@unitedmedsupplies.com
Website:
Dist synthetic, latex & nitrile exam gloves, walkers, wheelchairs, bathroom accessories, bath benches, commodes, rollators, crutches, disposable medical supplies, alternating pressure relief mattress, overlay mattress. nebulizers, oxygen tubing. (Woman/As-Pac, estab 2007, empl 4, sales , cert: State)

New Mexico

6119   R & M Government Services
650 Montana Ave, Ste A
Las Cruces, NM 88001
Contact: Sharon Guerrero VP
Tel: 575-522-0430
Email: sharon@rmgovernmentservices.com
Website: http://rmgovernmentservices.com
Abaxis- Veterinary Diagnostics, Vetscan
ACR Mechanical- Construction A-dec Dental Chairs-Handpieces, Delivery Systems, & Installation Air Liquide - Gases Airgas ï¿½Gases / Refrigerants Alcon- Surgical, pharmaceutical (Woman/Hisp, estab 2011, empl 8, sales , cert: WBENC)

Nevada

6120   PPE Catalog LLC
3540 W Sahara Ave, Ste 901
Las Vegas, NV 89102
Contact: Michael Gordon Chairman
Tel: 949-484-8806
Email: michaelgordon@ppecatalog.com
Website: https://ppecatalog.com
Dist PPE equipment and supplies, disinfectant wipes, and other disinfectant products, sanitizing products, NIOSH N95 respirators, N95 masks. (Woman, estab 2020, empl 5, sales $3,500,000, cert: WBENC)

New York

6121 Alpha Medical Distributor, Inc.
60-B Commerce Place Unit B
Hicksville, NY 11801
Contact: Jonathan Lee President
Tel: 516-681-5290
Email: alphameddis@aol.com
Website: www.MortuarySuppliesUSA.com
Dist body bags, cadaver bags, transport bags & mortuary supplies. (Woman/As-Pac, estab 2000, empl 4, sales $500,000, cert: State)

6122 BFFL Co., LLC
20 Kensington Rd
Scarsdale, NY 10583
Contact: Elizabeth Thompson CEO
Tel: 914-713-8550
Email: drelizabeth@bfflco.com
Website: http://bfflco.com
Surgical Bras, surgical vests, compression bras, comfort and recovery garments, compression wear, hospital gowns, orthopedic dressings. (Woman, estab 2011, empl 5, sales $1,549,736, cert: WBENC)

6123 Coats Resources, LLC
6147 Pannell Rd
Farmington, NY 14425
Contact: Sarah Coats Owner
Tel: 585-943-7675
Email: 2coatsmedical@gmail.com
Website:
Dist PPE products, anti fatigue mats and other healthcare related items (Woman, estab 2014, empl 1, sales , cert: WBENC)

6124 Danlee Medical Products, Inc.
6075 E Molloy Rd, Ste 5 Bldg. 5
Syracuse, NY 13211
Contact: Joni Walton Operations
Tel: 315-431-0143
Email: joni@danleemedical.com
Website: www.danleemedical.com
Mfr custom hook-up kits, boxer shorts & endoscopy shorts, disposable pouches for holter & event recording, disposable scrubs & disposable blood pressure cuff liners. (Woman, estab 1994, empl 13, sales $2,900,000, cert: State, City, WBENC)

6125 Empire Medical and Dental Supplies
320 Roebling St, Ste 330
Brooklyn, NY 11211
Contact: Esther Mayer Bids & Contracts Admin
Tel: 718-532-4112
Email: esther@empiredentalsupplies.com
Website: www.empiredentalsupplies.com
Dist dental supplies and dental equipment. (Woman, estab 2006, empl 10, sales $2,500,000, cert: State)

6126 JLGJ Trading, Inc.
65 East Bethpage Rd Ste 400
Plainview, NY 11803
Contact: Edie Berntson VP Sales
Tel: 888-222-2237
Email: edie@jlgjtrading.com
Website: www.ourcaresupplies.com
Dist medical supplies. (Woman, estab 2004, empl 4, sales , cert: NWBOC)

6127 Medi-Tech International Corp.
26 Court St, Ste 1301
Brooklyn, NY 11242
Contact: Victoria LaMantia COO
Tel: 718-272-6390
Email: vicky.lamantia@medi-techintl.com
Website: www.medi-techintl.com
Mfr wound management products. (Woman, estab 1971, empl 48, sales $4,000,000, cert: WBENC)

6128 Silarx Pharmaceuticals, Inc.
19 West St
Spring Valley, NY 10977
Contact: George Hauss RA/QA coord
Tel: 845-325-4020
Email: ghauss@silarx.com
Website: www.silarx.com
Mfr liquid generic pharmaceutical & nutritional supplements. (As-Ind, estab 1985, empl 40, sales $11,130,742, cert: NMSDC)

6129 SS Elder In-Home Care, Inc.
145-69 167th St
Jamaica, NY 11434
Contact: President
Tel: 718-949-3316
Email:
Website: www.sselderinc.com
Medical Equipment, Medical Supplies, Health Care. (AA, estab 2014, empl 3, sales , cert: City)

Ohio

6130 AMedEquip
7031 Corporate Way Ste 201
Cincinnati, OH 45459
Contact: Dir of Operations
Tel: 513-988-8550
Email:
Website: www.amedequip.com
Dist medical & lab equipment & supplies. (Woman/As-Ind, estab 2007, empl 2, sales $100,000, cert: State)

6131 C&M Medical Supply, Inc.
8600 S Wilkinson Way, Ste C
Perrysburg, OH 43551
Contact: Creston Tarrant President
Tel: 419-872-0033
Email: ctarrant@cmmedicalsupply.com
Website: www.cmmedicalsupply.com
Diagnostic & respiratory equipment & supplies, advanced woundcare, latex, vinyl & nitrile exam gloves, ultrasound & electro medical products, portable EKG, spirometry, holter, blood pressure & oximetry. (AA, estab 2005, empl 8, sales $486,000, cert: State, NMSDC)

6132 Cincinnati Sub-Zero Products, LLC
12011 Mosteller Rd
Cincinnati, OH 45241
Contact: Matt McCurdy Natl Sales Mgr
Tel: 513-772-8810
Email: mmccurdy@genthermcsz.com
Website: www.cszindustrial.com
Hyper-Hypothermia systems for use in hosptials before during and after surgery. Patient temperature controlled. (Woman, estab 1940, empl 200, sales , cert: City)

6133 Kadiri Health, LLC
714 E Monument Ave, Ste 134
Dayton, OH 45402
Contact: Christopher Cox Sr Consultant
Tel: 310-435-5455
Email: ccox@kadirihealth.com
Website: www.kadirihealth.com
Dist medical, laboratory, scientific, diagnostic, & research equipment, supplies & furniture. (AA, estab , empl , sales , cert: NMSDC)

6134 Medical Resources
8377 C Green Meadow, Ste C
Lewis Center, OH 43035
Contact: Randy Reichenbach GM
Tel: 800-860-4716
Email: randy@medicalresources.com
Website: www.MedicalResources.com
Mfr Stainless Steel Products for Healthcare Facilities: blanket warming cabinets, instrument cabinets, instrument stands, back tables, and endoscope cabinets. (Woman, estab , empl , sales $8,955,000, cert: State, NWBOC)

6135 Nnodum Pharmaceuticals Corp.
483 Northland Blvd
Cincinnati, OH 45240
Contact: Nnodum Iheme President
Tel: 513-861-2329
Email: n.iheme@nnodumpharma.com
Website: www.nnodumpharma.com
Research, development & mfg over the counter & generic pharmaceuticals: prenatal Vitamins, dialysis vitamins, topical analgesics, lotions & creams for diabetic patients. (AA, estab 1997, empl 10, sales $30,000,000, cert: State, 8a)

6136 Premium Contractor Solution LLC
2601 W Stroop Rd, Ste 500
Moraine, OH 45439
Contact: Dexiang Bao Sales Dir
Tel: 216-527-4338
Email: dbao@premiumcontractorsolution.com
Website: http://premiumcontractorsolution.com
Provide PPE, N95 mask, KN95 mask, Gowns, Thermometer, surgical mask, cotton face mask, Ventilator, gloves and etc. (Woman, estab 2014, empl 15, sales $4,134,000, cert: WBENC)

6137 Procura Select
30700-E Carter St
Solon, OH 44139
Contact: Patricia Palermo President
Tel: 440-248-1622
Email: ppalermo@procuraselect.com
Website: www.procuraselect.com
Dist medical carts, shelving, storage & organization products. (Woman, estab 2014, empl 3, sales , cert: WBENC)

6138 Pyramid Enterprise Supplies
32593 Haverhill Dr
Solon, OH 44139
Contact: Linda Colson Owner
Tel: 440-248-7008
Email: pyramid44139@yahoo.com
Website:
Pharmaceuticals, supplies, gowns, surgery sets & supplies, bedding, curtains, trays & kitchen items. (Woman/AA, estab 2000, empl , sales $869,018, cert: State)

6139 Reidy Medical Supply, Inc.
P.O. Box 713079
Cincinnati, OH 45271
Contact: Ted Stitzel President
Tel: 330-686-4485
Email: tstitzel@reidymed.com
Website: http://reidymed.com
Dist disposable medical supplies. (Woman, estab 1992, empl 26, sales $9,000,000, cert: WBENC)

6140 SGM Contracting Inc.
9485 Root Rd
North Ridgeville, OH 44039
Contact: Regina Morris Owner
Tel: 216-337-0742
Email: ginamorris@sgmcontracting.com
Website: www.sgmcontracting.com
Engineered medical support systems: cath, x-ray, surgical & exam light supports, operable walls & specialty support systems. (Woman, estab 2008, empl 3, sales $265,000, cert: City)

6141 Transworld Supply Network, LLC
6576 Rosewood Lane
Mason, OH 45040
Contact: Christopher Che CEO
Tel: 513-229-7595
Email: cche@cheinternationalgroup.com
Website: www.transworldsn.com
Global importer of healthcare disposables. (AA, estab 2018, empl , sales $10,000,000, cert: NMSDC)

Oregon

6142 Ascent Group Medical LLC
1631 NE Broadway St, Ste 308
Portland, OR 97211
Contact: Nuradin Kariye CEO
Tel: 888-386-1112
Email: nuradin@ascentgroupmedical.com
Website: www.ascentgroupmedical.com
Dist medical surgical supplies, equipment & medical staffing. (AA, estab 2011, empl 1, sales , cert: State)

6143 Panga Eco-Friendly Dental Supply
2269 SE Lindenbrook Ct
Milwaukie, OR 97222
Contact: Ingrid Adeogun Owner
Tel: 503-523-9442
Email: ingrid@wearepanga.com
Website: www.wearepanga.com
Mfr & dist eco-friendly dental products: Tongue Scraper, Bamboo Toothbrush, eco-friendly floss. (Woman/Hisp, estab 2019, empl 1, sales , cert: WBENC)

Pennsylvania

6144 Coleman Laboratories
1150 First Ave, Ste 501
King of Prussia, PA 19406
Contact: Le-Jun Yin President
Tel: 267-644-7767
Email: lejun.yin@colemanlabs.com
Website: www.colemanlabs.com
Develop & mfr IV status monitors. The LM series Fluid Level Monitor is a passive sensing device that alarms when the infusion fluid level is low. The device provides both visual and audible alarms when preset condition is met. (As-Pac, estab 2010, empl 4, sales $200,000, cert: NMSDC)

6145   Gray Physicians Supply, Inc.
       1330 Graham Ave
       Windber, PA 15963
       Contact: Bethany Gray President
       Tel: 814-254-2188
       Email: grayphysiciansupply@verizon.net
       Website: http://gpsmedicalonline.com
Dist stethoscopes, syringes, gauze, bandages, blood
pressure cuffs, exam tables, latex & latex free gloves,
sterile gloves. (Woman, estab 2012, empl 1, sales
$107,000, cert: State)

6146   Hayes
       157 S Broad St, Ste 200
       Lansdale, PA 19446
       Contact: Glenn Phillips Dir Provider Sales
       Tel: 215-855-0615
       Email: gphillips@hayesinc.com
       Website: http://hayesinc.com
Devices, procedures, drugs/biologics, laboratory equipment & genetic tests. (Woman, estab 1989, empl 60, sales
, cert: WBENC)

6147   SlateBelt Safety
       1694 Southlawn Dr
       Lancaster, PA 17603
       Contact: Robert D Williams President
       Tel: 888-642-0001
       Email: robert@slatebeltsafety.com
       Website: www.slatebeltsafety.com
Dist occupational safety prescription eyewear. (AA, estab
2006, empl 21, sales $1,000,000, cert: NMSDC)

Puerto Rico

6148   Cesar Castillo, Inc.
       361 Calle Angel Buonomo St Tres Monjitas Industrial
       Pk
       Hato Rey, PR 00917
       Contact: Luis Vazquez VP
       Tel: 787-999-1616
       Email: lvazquez@cesarcastillo.com
       Website: www.cesarcastillo.com
Dist pharmaceutical products, health & beauty care,
consumer goods, Specialty Pharmaceutical Products to
Physicians and Specialty Pharmacies. (Hisp, estab 1946,
empl 400, sales $177,000,000, cert: NMSDC)

6149   J.C. Gonzalez, Inc.
       2 St KM 178.2 Interior BO. Minillas Alto
       San German, PR 00683
       Contact: Julio C. Gonzalez Santiago CEO
       Tel: 787-892-0047
       Email: sales@jcgonzalezinc.com
       Website: www.jcgonzalezinc.com
Dist & service scientific & research equipment, laboratory
equipment & consumables, microscopes, stereoscopes,
freezers, refrigerators. (Hisp, estab 2001, empl 6, sales
$865,047, cert: NMSDC, SDB)

6150   R & G Clean Room Laboratory, Inc.
       Ave Esmeralda #53 PMB 112
       Guaynabo, PR 00969
       Contact: Ruben Gomez President
       Tel: 787-993-1781
       Email: rgomez@crlrd.com
       Website: www.cleanroomlab.com
R & G Clean Room Laboratory, Inc provides specialty
laboratory and clean room products to Biotech, Medical
Devices, Animal Research and Pharmaceutical. (Hisp,
estab 2007, empl 10, sales $700,000, cert: NMSDC)

6151   Steri-Tech Inc.
       Road 701 Km. 0.7, Salinas Ind. Park
       Salinas, PR 00725
       Contact: Juan Argüelles Managing Dir
       Tel: 787-824-4040
       Email: jarguelles@steri-tech.com
       Website: www.steri-tech.com
Dist cleanroom products & contract sterilization ser-
vices. (Hisp, estab 1986, empl 30, sales $3,020,000, cert:
NMSDC)

South Carolina

6152   Bennett Wholesale Distributors LLC
       300 Long Point Ln Ste 220-O
       Columbia, SC 29229
       Contact: Jameel Bennett Owner
       Tel: 800-650-0616
       Email: jb@bennettwholesale.com
       Website: www.bennettwholesale.com
Dist medical supplies / equipment and laboratory
services. (AA, estab 2003, empl 1, sales $250,000, cert:
NMSDC)

6153   Cambridge Marketing, Inc.
       P.O. Box 4481
       Rock Hill, SC 39732
       Contact: Carol Ballard Owner
       Tel: 803-328-3167
       Email: carolcmi@aol.com
       Website: http://cambridgemarketingcorp.com
Dist hospital products: custom sterile kits, suture
removal kits & ER kits. (Woman/Nat Ame, estab 1983,
empl 2, sales $326,813, cert: State)

6154   Carolina Diagnostic Solutions
       100 Old Cherokee Rd Ste F 301
       Lexington, SC 29072
       Contact: Amanda Clark President
       Tel: 803-360-3410
       Email: amanda@carolinadxsol.com
       Website: http://carolinadiagnosticsolutions.com/
Pulmonary diagnostic related equipment, supplies,
consultation & clinical service, body box/ plethysmogra-
phy, gas measurement (FRC lung volumes, diffusing
capacity), Spirometry equipment, handheld spirometer,
portable spirometer. (Woman, estab 2014, empl 2, sales
, cert: State)

6155   CPT Medical
       6000 Pelham Rd
       Greenville, SC 29615
       Contact: Liesman, Connie CEO
       Tel: 866-584-3713
       Email: cliesman@cptmed.com
       Website: www.cptmed.com
Mfr surgical packs, kits, trays (sterile & non sterile),
laboratory services. (Woman, estab , empl , sales , cert:
State)

6156   Pediatric Medical Solutions
       974 Harbortowne Rd
       Charleston, SC 29412
       Contact: Heather Able Owner
       Tel: 843-762-6769
       Email: theableco@aol.com
       Website: http://pediatricmedicalsolutions.com
Snuggle Wraps, Pediatric Elbow Immobilizers. (Woman,
estab 1998, empl 2, sales $155,000, cert: City)

6157   Professional Healthcare Services LLC
1007 Pendleton St
Greenville, SC 29601
Contact: Doris Haley President
Tel: 864-505-6747
Email: dhaley@phsonline.com
Website: www.phsonline.com

Alcohol & drug screening, pre employment physicals & health screening & health fairs, injury management programs & medical case management, On Site nursing care. (Woman/AA, estab 1998, empl 7, sales $259,000, cert: NMSDC)

6158   Rhino Medical Supply
649 Rosewood Dr, Ste B
Columbia, SC 29201
Contact: Elliott Haynie COO
Tel: 404-704-7961
Email: info@rhinomedicalsuppy.com
Website: www.rhinomedicalsupply.com/

Dist Personal Protective Equipment (PPE), medical devices, and disinfectants. (AA, estab 2020, empl 10, sales $8,500,000, cert: NMSDC)

Tennessee

6159   Global Industrial Components Inc.
705 S College St
Woodbury, TN 37190
Contact: David W. Vance Automtive Product Mgr
Tel: 615-563-5120
Email: dvance@gic-co.com
Website: www.gic-co.com

Dist medical kits, ER kits, roadside emergency kits, dental & medical supplies & equipment, component hardware. (Hisp, estab 1994, empl 47, sales $14,900,000, cert: NMSDC)

6160   GQSI
3777 Winchester Rd Ste 1
Memphis, TN 38118
Contact: Williette Graham President
Tel: 901-365-9566
Email: willgraham@gqsi.net
Website: http://gqsi.net

Engineering & technical services, medical devices, process & special processes equipment & validation, laser marking, CMM inspection services, product inspection, engineering support, supplier support services. (Woman/AA, estab 2005, empl 6, sales $160,000, cert: State)

6161   International Medical & Laboratory Supply, LLC
9093 Valkrie Lane
Lakeland, TN 38002
Contact: Michael Tharps VP
Tel: 901-377-0191
Email: michaeltharps@bellsouth.net
Website: www.internationalmedlab.com

Dist medical, safety, automotive, print management & laboratory supplies. (AA, estab 2004, empl 2, sales , cert: NMSDC)

6162   MRP, LLC   dba Aquabiliti & AmUSA
5209 Linbar Dr Ste 640
Nashville, TN 11111
Contact: Timir Patel CEO
Tel: 615-833-2633
Email: accounts@aquabiliti.com
Website: http://aquabiliti.com

Mfr terminally sterilized pre-filled flush syringes used for maintaining IV (intravenous) catheter patency. (AA, As-Ind, As-Pac, Hisp, estab 2005, empl 25, sales $8,016,000, cert: NMSDC)

6163   Princeton Medical Group, Inc.
1601 Championship Blvd Ste 233
Franklin, TN 37064
Contact: Terry Rust VP Marketing
Tel: 601-594-9495
Email: tcrust50@gmail.com
Website: www.princetonmedical.net

Dist surgical instruments. (Woman, estab 1991, empl 20, sales $1,400,000, cert: WBENC)

6164   The Premier Group
4600 Cromwell Ave, Ste 101
Memphis, TN 38118
Contact: JW   Gibson CEO
Tel: 901-346-9002
Email: jwgibson@gibsoncompanies.com
Website: www.gibsoncompanies.com

Dist medical supplies, laboratory & scientific equipment & related supplies. (AA, estab 1991, empl 7, sales $8,692,576, cert: NMSDC)

Texas

6165   Ace Delivery
7308 Gaines Mill Ln
Austin, TX 78745
Contact: Tammie Garcia Office Mgr
Tel: 512-326-3553
Email: viaace1@gmail.com
Website: www.acedeliveryatx.com

Dist medical products to all hospitals and supply chains. (Woman/Hisp, estab 1980, empl 7, sales $947,931, cert: City)

6166   Adair Visual, Inc.
3550 W 7th St
Fort Worth, TX 76107
Contact: Alyce Jones President
Tel: 817-377-3500
Email: melanie@adaireyewear.com
Website: http://adaireyewear.com

Protective eyewear & surgical loupes. (AA, estab 1980, empl 6, sales $1,484,023, cert: State, NMSDC)

6167   Alea Health dba Kersh Health
2600 Technology Dr, Ste 100
Plano, TX 75074
Contact: Bruce Brown VP Advanced Clinical Services
Tel: 469-241-2500
Email: program.coordinator@aleahealth.com
Website: http://kershhealth.com

Population health management, Health Risk Assessment, Diabetes Disease Management, Weight Loss, Stop Smoking, Activity Monitoring, Wellness Programs. (Nat Ame, estab 2015, empl 37, sales , cert: City)

6168 Bracane Company, Inc.
1201 W. 15th St. Ste 330
Plano, TX 75075
Contact: CEO
Tel: 888-568-4271
Email:
Website: www.bracaneco.com
Dist medical supplies: lab equipment, Iv pumps, hospital beds, lab kits and supplies. (Woman/AA, estab 2002, empl 12, sales , cert: NMSDC, WBENC)

6169 Cina Pharamceutical
15622 Silver Ridge Dr, Ste B
Houston, TX 77090
Contact: Mel Martino Office Mgr
Tel: 281-602-3492
Email: mmartino.cinapharma@gmail.com
Website:
Dist pharmaceuticals. (AA, estab 2014, empl 15, sales $2,000,000, cert: State)

6170 Dalton Medical Corp.
4259 McEwen Rd
Farmers Branch, TX 75244
Contact: Jennifer Yu COO
Tel: 469-329-5200
Email: jennifery@daltonmed.net
Website: www.daltonmedical.com
Dist bariatric wheelchairs; walking aids, rollators, forearm rollators, walkers, and U-shape moving walkers with seat; cane stand; knee walker; foot pillow; acrylic medicine organizer; DryAid incontinence supply, protective underwear. (As-Pac, estab 1993, empl 25, sales $4,500,000, cert: State, NMSDC)

6171 Double First Medical, LLC
1817 W Pioneer Dr, Ste 1024
Irving, TX 75061
Contact: Melissa Klingbeil Sylvester Managing Partner
Tel: 817-470-1772
Email: melissa.sylvester@doublefirstmedical.com
Website: http://doublefirstmedical.com
Dist medical equipment and supplies, diagnostic cardiology & patient monitoring technologies and devices, EKG, ECG, Stress testing, Holter, Patient Monitoring, Telemetry, Vital Signs monitoring, Treadmills. (Woman, estab 2018, empl 2, sales , cert: State)

6172 GTL Supply Solutions, LLC
101C N Greenville Ave, Ste 423
Allen, TX 75002
Contact: Famira Green Inside Sales Acct Mgr
Tel: 972-359-7300
Email: fgreen@gtlsolutions.com
Website: www.gtlsolutions.com
Dist medical supplies & equipment. (Woman/AA, estab 2007, empl 10, sales $2,300,000, cert: State)

6173 Instrument Specialists, Inc.
32390 Iinterstate 10 W
Boerne, TX 78006
Contact: Scott Kaanek
Tel: 800-537-1945
Email: scott@isisurgery.com
Website: www.isisurgery.com
Endoscopic repairs, operating room supplies & surgical instrument cleaners. (Woman, estab , empl , sales $322,031,300, cert: State, WBENC)

6174 Jackson & Associates, Inc.
8633 Schumacher Ln
Houston, TX 77063
Contact: Saul Szub President
Tel: 713-777-1155
Email: saul@dealmedical.com
Website: www.dealmedical.com
Dist medical, dental, surgical, pharmaceuticals, beauty, health & safety supplies & equipment. (Hisp, estab 1998, empl 6, sales $1,210,000, cert: State, City)

6175 MDD Marketing Inc.
5773 Woodway, Ste 214
Houston, TX 77057
Contact: Jennifer Hess Acct Mgr
Tel: 713-647-8240
Email: jennifer.hess@sterlingtonmedical.com
Website: www.aedtoday.com
AEDs and Manual Defibrillators. (Woman, estab 2000, empl 7, sales $2,000,000, cert: State)

6176 MJW Medical Solutions, Inc.
45 NE Loop 410, Ste 250
San Antonio, TX 78216
Contact: CEO
Tel: 210-858-8997
Email:
Website: www.mjwmedicalsolutions.com
Medical equipment & supplies. (AA, estab 2006, empl 7, sales $3,500,000, cert: State)

6177 Mpulse Healthcare, LLC
54 Sugar Creek Center Ste 300
Sugarland, TX 77478
Contact: Tyrone Dixon CEO
Tel: 281-277-4410
Email: tdixon@mpulsehealth.com
Website: www.mpulsehealth.com
Dist medical, veterinary, dental, athletic & scientific supplies, products & equipment. (AA, estab 2005, empl 2, sales $100,000, cert: State, NMSDC)

6178 MRC - Medical Research Consultants
10550 Richmond Ave Ste 310
Houston, TX 77042
Contact: Gretchen Watson CEO
Tel: 713-528-6326
Email: gwatson@mrchouston.com
Website: www.mrchouston.com
Medical litigation support services: nurse reviews, mass tort expertise, record retrieval & document management. (Woman, estab 1983, empl 268, sales $9,102,297, cert: WBENC)

6179 Prestige Ameritech LTD
7201 Iron Horse Blvd
North Richland Hills, TX 76180
Contact: Elizabeth Givens
Tel: 817-427-7200
Email: elizabeth@prestigeam.com
Website: http://prestigeameritech.com
Mfr surgcal masks & face shields. (Nat Ame, estab , empl , sales $7,000,000, cert: State)

6180　Products Unlimited, Inc.
P.O. Box 339
Justin, TX 76247
Contact: Raithel Susan Sales Mgr
Tel:　940-648-3073
Email: sraithel@products-unlimited.com
Website: www.products-unlimited.com
Dist medical, lab & safety supplies & equipment. (Woman, estab 1992, empl 7, sales $5,020,000, cert: State)

6181　VM Positioning, Inc
4235 Centergate St
San Antonio, TX 78217
Contact: Sara Weyman President
Tel:　800-247-6294
Email: info@vossmedicalproducts.com
Website: www.vossmedicalproducts.com
Manufacture & dist disposable foam patient positioning devices for the operating room, prone head positioners, cardiac leg supports, round supports. (Woman, estab 2005, empl 5, sales $409,000, cert: WBENC)

Utah

6182　Acquire Med LLC
528 N Kays Dr, Ste 1
Kaysville, UT 84037
Contact: Austin Wood Dir of Contracts
Tel:　801-973-1133
Email: sales@acquiremed.com
Website:
Sales of Urology disposables and surgical equipment rental to Hospital and Surgery center operating rooms. (Woman, estab 2013, empl 4, sales $3,325,000, cert: WBENC)

Virginia

6183　Evident, Inc.
739 Brooks Mill Rd
Union Hall, VA 24176
Contact: Michael Grimm President
Tel:　800-576-7606
Email: michael@evident.cc
Website: www.ShopEVIDENT.com
Crime scene & forensic identification products: fingerprint products, evidence supplies, DNA collection materials, identification equipment, & crime scene kits for police & law enforcement. (Woman, estab 1992, empl 15, sales , cert: State)

6184　Ipheion Development Corporation
18471 Cattail Spring Dr
Leesburg, VA 20176
Contact: Elsa Rose Hoffmann President
Tel:　240-281-1568
Email: ehoffmann@ipheion.us
Website: www.ipheion.us
Engineering optical & optomechanical devices. (Woman/Hisp, estab 2013, empl 2, sales $100,000, cert: State)

6185　JKICT, Inc.
11240 Waples Mill Rd Ste 400
Fairfax, VA 22030
Contact: Jay Kim President
Tel:　703-474-4924
Email: jeakuk@gmail.com
Website: www.jkict.net
Digital X-Ray Imaging System, High frequency X-Ray generator, Digital Radiology System, ECG Electrodes, ESU Pencils, ESU Plates, TENS/EMS Units, Cutaneous Electrodes, Robotic Assisted Gait Training System. (As-Pac, estab 2008, empl 2, sales , cert: State)

6186　M.E.Z Distributors LLC
45910 Transamerica Plaza Ste 104
Sterling, VA 20166
Contact: Adeel Shah President
Tel:　703-821-6760
Email: adeel@sterlingsurgical.com
Website: www.sterlingsurgical.com
Dist medical supplies, medical equipment & equipment maintenance/service. (As-Ind, estab , empl , sales $1,700,000, cert: State)

6187　Reliant Medical Supply
1431 Abingden Road
W. Chesterfield, VA 23236
Contact: stacey worthington Owner
Tel:　804-814-3180
Email: staceyworthington@reliantmedicalsupply.com
Website: www.reliantmedicalsupply.com
Dist medical supplies. (Woman, estab 2008, empl 2, sales , cert: State)

6188　Triton Light Medical, LLC
8412 MacAndrew Terr
Chesterfield, VA 23838
Contact:　Principal
Tel:　804-543-8137
Email:
Website: www.tritonlightmedical.com
Dist our proprietary line of instruments crafted in Tuttlingen, Germany, the global center of first-quality, surgical-grade instruments and operating room (OR) equipment. (AA, estab 2017, empl 1, sales , cert: State, NMSDC)

Washington

6189　Anesthesia Equipment Supply, Inc.
24301 Roberts Dr.
Black Diamond, WA 98010
Contact: Michelle Norrie President
Tel:　253-631-8008
Email: michelle@aesol.com
Website: www.aesol.com
Dist custom medical equipment. (Woman, estab 1967, empl 15, sales , cert: WBENC)

6190 Attunix Corporation
405 114th Ave SE Ste 110
Bellevue, WA 98004
Contact: Matt O'Donnell CEO
Tel: 206-774-3163
Email: matto@attunix.com
Website: www.attunix.com
Custom Development, Portals and Web, Cloud Integration, and Mobile Solutions, Program Management. Technology capabilities include Microsoft .Net, SQL Server, Windows Phone 7, SharePoint (Hisp, estab 2006, empl 12, sales $1,935,000, cert: State, NMSDC)

6191 Summit Imaging
15000 Woodinville Redmond Rd Bldg B, Ste 800
Woodinville, WA 98072
Contact: Jessica Curtiss Customer Outreach Coord
Tel: 866-586-3744
Email: sales@mysummitimaging.com
Website: www.mysummitimaging.com
Ultrasound transducers & parts. (As-Ind, estab 2006, empl 41, sales , cert: NMSDC)

Wisconsin

6192 Alpha Source Inc.
6619 W Calumet Rd
Milwaukee, WI 53223
Contact: Norine Carlson-Weber
Tel: 800-654-9845
Email: norine.carlson-weber@alphasource.com
Website: www.alphasource.com
Mfr medical batteries, dist medical lighting, diagnostic instruments, repair parts for medical equipment. (Woman, estab 1986, empl 40, sales $18,219,000, cert: WBENC)

6193 Fox Converting, Inc.
P.O. Box 12795
Green Bay, WI 54307
Contact: Accounting Mgr
Tel: 920-434-5272
Email:
Website: http://foxconverting.com
Sterilization Bags/Envelopes, 8" & 16" Swabs -Sterilizable, CSR Sterilizer Wraps, Hospital Bedside Disposal Bags, X-Ray Envelopes. (As-Pac, estab 1960, empl 60, sales $15,150,000, cert: State)

METAL CASTING
Non-ferrous foundries and molds. (Also see six other METAL categories). NAICS Code 33

California

6194   JDH Pacific Inc.
14821 Artesia Blvd.
La Mirada, CA 90638
Contact: David Unger Sales Mgr
Tel: 562-207-1764
Email: dunger@jdhpacific.com
Website: www.jdhpacific.com
Cast & forged components. (As-Pac, estab 1989, empl 35, sales $18,000,000, cert: NMSDC)

6195   KFM International Industries, Inc.
20277 Valley Blvd, Ste L
Walnut, CA 91789
Contact: Dennis Boribor Engineer
Tel: 626-369-9556
Email: dennis@kfmii.com
Website: www.kfmii.com
Casting: Sand Cast, Die Casting, Investment Casting & Permanent Mold Forging: Hot & Cold Formed Sheet Metal Stamping Machining: CNC,Turning & Milling Powder Metal. (Woman/As-Pac, estab 2000, empl 6, sales $2,500,000, cert: City, CPUC)

Illinois

6196   Calumet Brass Foundry, Inc.
14610 Lakeside Ave
Dolton, IL 60419
Contact: Dawn Stromberg President
Tel: 708-344-7874
Email: dawn@calumetbrassfoundry.com
Website: www.calumetbrassfoundry.com
Mfr bushings, bearings, liners & guides, bronze sand casting, foundry. (Woman/Hisp, estab , empl , sales , cert: WBENC)

Michigan

6197   Aerostar Manufacturing
28275 Northline Rd
Romulus, MI 48174
Contact: Robert Johnson VP
Tel: 734-942-8440
Email: rjohnson@aerostarmfg.com
Website: www.aerostarmfg.com
CNC machining assembly, prototyping, machine castings & forgings, sand casting. (As-Pac, estab 1970, empl 200, sales , cert: NMSDC)

6198   DEE & Associates
1665 Devonshire Dr
Troy, MI 48098
Contact: Pradeep Korgavkar Dir
Tel: 248-641-0668
Email: pkorgavkar@aol.com
Website:
Warehouse NAAMS standard products, import castings, machine castings, aluminum machined castings. (Woman/As-Ind, estab 1995, empl 2, sales $1,200,000, cert: NMSDC)

6199   GK Tech, LLC
3331 W Big Beaver Rd Ste 106
Troy, MI 48084
Contact: Kelly Choi
Tel: 248-494-1960
Email: kellychoi@gktechusa.com
Website: www.gktechllc.com
Marketing specialist, consulting, business development, forging, die-casting, stamping, spring, magnesium pulley, rubber bushing, fasteners, machining, plastic injection molding. (Woman/As-Pac, estab 2015, empl 3, sales , cert: NMSDC)

6200   Lucerne International
40 Corporate Dr
Auburn Hills, MI 48326
Contact: Karen Ryan Finance Mgr
Tel: 248-674-7210
Email: kryan@lucerneintl.com
Website: www.lucerneintl.com
Advanced metal forming components & assemblies, body structures, chassis systems & powertrain systems. Mfg aluminum & steel forgings, stampings, aluminum & zinc die castings & steel. (Woman, estab 1993, empl 58, sales , cert: WBENC)

6201   New Products Corporation
448 North Shore Dr
Benton Harbor, MI 49022
Contact: Kristy Lovejoy VP
Tel: 269-925-2161
Email: kristy.lovejoy@newproductscorp.com
Website: www.newproductscorp.com
Custom, precision, high-pressure aluminum and zinc die casting. (Woman, estab , empl 50, sales , cert: WBENC)

6202   Precision Components Manufacturing, LLC
35855 Stanley
Sterling Heights, MI 48312
Contact: Tommy Longest CEO
Tel: 586-939-8500
Email: tommy@pcmfettes.com
Website: www.pcmfettes.com
Mfr cast tooling, castings iron/aluminum, steel forging, fully machined castings & assembly, ferrous & non-ferrous products, forging, sand & die casting. (AA, estab 2009, empl 30, sales $7,010,000, cert: NMSDC)

METAL COATING
Includes plating, polishing, spray painting, metal finishing, paint stripping, de-oiling, anodizing, etc. (Also see six other METAL categories). NAICS Code 33

Arizona

6203 Best Finishing, Inc.
7670 E Broadway Blvd Ste 203
Tucson, AZ 85710
Contact: Chris Schlesinger President
Tel: 520-546-7763
Email: chris@bestfinishing.com
Website: www.bestfinishing.com
Metal finishing, polishing & buffing: aluminum castings, exhaust systems, metal moldings, body hardware, stampings, aluminum heads & blocks, magnesium components, closures. (Woman, estab 2000, empl 5, sales $985,981, cert: WBENC)

Connecticut

6204 Colonial Coatings, Inc.
66 Erna Ave
Milford, CT 06460
Contact: Russell Colon President
Tel: 203-783-9933
Email: russ@colonialcoatings.com
Website: www.colonialcoatings.com
HAE Magnesium anodize, paint sealants, plasma & high temperature coatings. (Hisp, estab 1982, empl 50, sales $8,000,000, cert: NMSDC)

Florida

6205 AmeriCoat Corporation
2935 Barneys Pumps Pl
Lakeland, FL 33812
Contact: Shrikant Desai President
Tel: 863-667-1035
Email: americoatusa@yahoo.com
Website: www.ameri-coat.com
Powder coating, fluoropolymers, metal finishing, coating, blasting, stripping. (As-Ind, estab 1995, empl 5, sales , cert: State)

Illinois

6206 Advance Coating Solutions
748 E Sunnyside Ave
Libertyville, IL 60048
Contact: Joseph Webb CEO
Tel: 847-732-1118
Email: joseph@acsco.us
Website: www.acsco.us
Epoxy coating solutions. (AA, estab 2008, empl 7, sales , cert: State, NMSDC)

Indiana

6207 Danco Anodizing
2450 Deelyn Dr
Warsaw, IN 46580
Contact: VP Operations
Tel: 574-269-5900
Email:
Website: www.danco.net
Aluminum anodizing, anodizing, stainless steel, citric & nitric passivation electropolishing . (Woman, estab 1971, empl 150, sales $15,000,000, cert: WBENC)

6208 Riepen LLC.
P.O. Box 2050
Warsaw, IN 46581
Contact: Sales Mgr
Tel: 574-269-5900
Email:
Website: www.danco.net
Titanium Anodize (Type 2 & Color), Aluminum Anodize, Electropolish, Passivation (Nitric & Citric), Laser Marking, Electroless Nickel, Chemfilm, NDT Services, Low Friction Chrome Coating & metal finishing services. (Woman, estab 1971, empl 100, sales , cert: WBENC)

Massachusetts

6209 The Falmer Associates, Inc.
96 Swampscott Road Unit 10
Salem, MA 01970
Contact: Stacy Ames President
Tel: 978-745-4000
Email: sames@falmer.com
Website: www.falmer.com
Machining, grinding & thermal spray coating svcs: metal, ceramic & carbide coatings, wear, corrosion, erosion, galling, thermal insulation or conduction, electrical insulation or conduction, anti-skid. (Woman, estab 1961, empl 4, sales $400,000, cert: WBENC)

Michigan

6210 Dhake Industries
15169 Northville Rd
Plymouth, MI 48170
Contact: Arjun Dhake VP
Tel: 734-420-0101
Email: adhake@dhakeindustries.com
Website: www.dhakeindustries.com
Mfr automotive coatings. (As-Ind, estab 1979, empl 25, sales $12,000,000, cert: NMSDC)

6211 Great Lakes Finishing, Inc.
510 W Hackley Ave
Muskegon, MI 49444
Contact: Diana Bench President
Tel: 231-733-9566
Email: dbench@greatlakesfinishinginc.com
Website: www.greatlakesfinishinginc.com
Alkaline and Chloride zinc plating. Barrel plating for small parts. Rack plating for parts up to 12' long. Two automatic lines. RoHS compliant. Chromates: bright, yellow, black and olive drab. (Woman, estab 2002, empl 12, sales $1,000,000, cert: WBENC)

6212 Jackson Tumble Finish
1801 Mitchell St
Jackson, MI 49203
Contact: Denise L. Losey President
Tel:　517-787-0368
Email: denise@jacksontumble.com
Website: www.jacksontumble.com
Zinc phosphate, fine, med, heavy grain; calcium modified fine grain phosphate, manganese phosphate, phos. and lube, black oxide, tumble and vibratory deburr, shot blast, glass bead, acid pickle, wash/degrease, and passivate, sort and packaging. (Woman, estab 1956, empl 45, sales $4,700,000, cert: WBENC)

Minnesota

6213 Coating Solutions, Inc.
13525 Fenway Blvd N
Hugo, MN 55038
Contact: Kimberly Northrop CFO
Tel:　651-762-5700
Email: knorthrop@coatingsolutions.com
Website: www.coatingsolutions.com
DuPont teflon industrial coatings. (Woman, estab 1995, empl 7, sales , cert: WBENC)

New Jersey

6214 Karnak Corporation
330 Central Ave
Clark, NJ 07066
Contact: Sarah Jane Jelin President
Tel:　800-526-4236
Email: sjjelin@karnakcorp.com
Website: www.karnakcorp.com
Protective roof coatings, reflective roof coatings, aluminum coatings, elastomeric coatings, Energy Star & LEED compliant coatings, dampproofing, waterproofing, flashing cements, primers, sealants, membranes, reinforcing fabrics. (Woman, estab 1933, empl 97, sales $60,000,000, cert: WBENC)

Ohio

6215 Cleveland Die & Mfg. Co.
20303 First Ave
Middleburg Heights, OH 44130
Contact: Marty Curry sales/engineering
Tel:　440-243-3404
Email: mcurry@clevelanddie.com
Website: www.clevelanddie.com/
Ecoat & powder coat line, automatic & single hit presses, spot & robotic welders, CNC machining. (Hisp, estab 1973, empl 300, sales $24,000,000, cert: NMSDC)

6216 Great Lakes Maintenance, Inc.
1213 Maple Ave.
Hamilton, OH 45011
Contact: Marilyn Barlow President
Tel:　513-423-0800
Email: glmbarlow@hotmail.com
Website: www.greatlakesmtce.com
Tank linings & coatings, abrasive blasting, industrial & maintenance painting, leak repair to live gas, water, sludge, fume exhaust & liquor piping, secondary containment coatings & repairs, fiberglass repairs & fabrications. (Woman/Hisp, estab 1997, empl 14, sales $14,000,000, cert: State, NMSDC, WBENC)

6217 Steelcote, Inc.
215 Eastview Dr
Brooklyn Heights, OH 44131
Contact: Mohan Kapahi President
Tel:　216-635-2585
Email: mohan_kapahi@steelcoteinc.com
Website: http://steelcoteinc.com
Anti-corrosion coatings on metal stampings & assemblies. (AA, As-Ind, estab 2002, empl 9, sales $1,000,000, cert: NMSDC)

6218 Westwood Finishing Company
5881 Wolf Creek Pike
Trotwood, OH 45426
Contact: Owner
Tel:　937-854-6608
Email:
Website: http://westfinish.com
Apply all types of paint material: wet coating, epoxy, urethane, enamels and copper coatings (EMI and RFI shielding. (Woman, estab 1995, empl 11, sales $530,864, cert: WBENC)

South Carolina

6219 JBE, Inc.
512 Hartland Dr
Hartsville, SC 29551
Contact: John Miller Dir Business Devel
Tel:　843-332-0589
Email: johnmiller@jbeinc.net
Website: www.jbeinc.net
Metal finishing; preplate finishing; abrasive blasting, manual & auto buffing, plating needs, chrome, decorative & hard, brite & electroless, silver & tin. Pre-eng bldgs; structure steel & metal fab. Sub-assembly for auto field. (AA, estab 1982, empl 40, sales $348,000,000, cert: NMSDC)

Tennessee

6220 Y&W Technologies LLC
2883 Director Cove
Memphis, TN 38131
Contact: Willis Yates President
Tel:　901-396-3380
Email: wyates@ywtech.com
Website: www.ywtech.com
Chrome plating, titanium anodizing, metal finishing, electroplating, laser marking, critic & nitric passivation. (AA, estab 2001, empl 20, sales $1,200,000, cert: NMSDC)

Texas

6221 Cimcon Finishing, LLC
2314 Executive Dr
Garland, TX 75041
Contact: Mike Gilbert VP Sales
Tel:　972-840-0934
Email: mike@cimconfinishing.com
Website: www.cimconfinishing.com
Electroplate: hard anodize, anodize, chemfilm, electroless nickel, nickel, tin, zinc, powder coat. (AA, estab 1994, empl 48, sales $3,200,000, cert: NMSDC)

6222 Texas Finishing Company
      P.O. Box 59445
      Dallas, TX 75229
      Contact: Carolyn Beard President
      Tel: 972-416-2961
      Email: cbeard@texasfinishing.com
      Website: http://texasfinishing.com
Paint application & custom metal fabrication. (Woman,
estab 1982, empl 45, sales , cert: State, WBENC)

Washington

6223 Dunkin & Bush, Inc.
      P.O. Box 97080
      Kirkland, WA 98083
      Contact: Deidre Dunkin President
      Tel: 425-885-7064
      Email: ddunkin@dunkinandbush.com
      Website: www.dunkinandbush.com
Industrial painting, scaffolding, insulation, rigging, containment, lead abatement, shop coating aplication, concrete
restoration, plural applied tank linings, abrasive blasting,
specialty blasting, water jetting, high heat coating applications. (Woman, estab 2008, empl 300, sales , cert: WBENC)

METAL FABRICATION
Includes tanks and tank liners, steel containers, aircraft framework parts, electronic chassis, work stands, ornamental ironwork, fences, sheet metal components, etc. (Also see six other METAL categories). NAICS Code 33

Alaska

6224 Katmai Support Services, LLC
701 E Tudor Rd, Ste 215
Anchorage, AK 99503
Contact: Katherine Tweidt Business Dev Mgr
Tel: 907-333-7000
Email: eric@anc8a.com
Website:
Mfr, overhaul, repair & modification of advanced composites & bonded honeycomb structures for numerous space & airframe applications in new generations of aircraft and space vehicles. (Nat Ame, estab 2003, empl , sales $521,411, cert: State)

Alabama

6225 Majestic Solutions, Inc.
241 Production Ave
Madison, AL 35758
Contact: Grace Lo President
Tel: 256-772-3232
Email: grace@majesticsolutionsinc.net
Website: www.majesticsolutionsinc.net
Mfr institutional metal furniture & security products: lockers, bunk beds, electronic enclosures, dayroom tables, benches, access panel, shelves, storage cabinets, railings, stairs, wire mesh partition/fence, tubings. (Woman/As-Pac, estab 2004, empl 10, sales $1,000,000, cert: State, City, SDB)

Arizona

6226 K&R Holdings, Inc.
2322 W Detroit Pl
Chandler, AZ 85224
Contact: Wayne Armoogam President
Tel: 480-236-2682
Email: warmoogam@lumawaresafety.com
Website: www.lumawaresafety.com
Supply and install photoluminescent egress systems for facilities. (As-Ind, estab 2007, empl 5, sales $100,000, cert: NMSDC)

6227 Kirin Manufacturing
3300 E. 36th St
Tucson, AZ 85713
Contact: President
Tel: 602-319-4239
Email:
Website: www.kirinmfg.com
Prototype manufacturing equipment & special equipment for various aerospace OEM's. Form, shape, mill, weld & finish a multitude of materials into an infinite number of fabrications. (Hisp, estab 2011, empl 30, sales $5,178,000, cert: NMSDC)

6228 PVB Fabrications, Inc.
2311 N 14th Ave
Tucson, AZ 85705
Contact: Pete Van Bogaert President
Tel: 520-623-3529
Email: pete@pvbfabs.com
Website: www.pvbfabs.com
Metal fabrication, waterjet cutting & CNC plasma cutting capabilities. (Hisp, estab 2003, empl 39, sales $5,100,000, cert: 8a)

6229 Vics Welding Company, LLC
8376 N El Mirage Rd Bldg 3
El Mirage, AZ 85335
Contact: Victor Valencia President
Tel: 623-925-5696
Email: vic@vicswelding.com
Website: www.vicswelding.com
Metal fabrication, field welding, structural, piping, ASME pressure vessel repair or manufacturing, aerospace welding. (Woman/Hisp, estab 1996, empl 6, sales $970,000, cert: City)

California

6230 A-1 Truck and Equipment, Inc.
1588 Los Angeles Ave
Ventura, CA 93004
Contact: Dan Poole President
Tel: 805-659-1817
Email: dan@a1truck.com
Website: http://a1truck.com
Rotating equipment repair, body repair, truck, trailers & equipment blasting & paint repairs, metal fabrication & welding. (Hisp, estab 2008, empl 30, sales $2,200,000, cert: NMSDC)

6231 Bueno Enterprises
25589 Seaboard Ln
Hayward, CA 94545
Contact: Lydia Bueno Sec/Treas
Tel: 510-782-2225
Email: lydia@metalspecialists.com
Website: www.metalspecialists.com
Precision sheet metal, laser cutting, machining & powder coat painting, fabricate metal parts. (Hisp, estab 1988, empl 10, sales , cert: CPUC)

6232 Columbia Sanitary Products, Inc.
1622 Browning
Irvine, CA 92606
Contact: Paul Escalera
Tel: 847-559-6132
Email: p.escalera@columbiasinks.com
Website: www.columbiasinks.com
Mfr stainless steel products: sinks, wash stations, sink accessories, faucets, heavy-duty forks, shovels, scoops, valves, knife sterilizers & trays. (Woman, estab 1949, empl 8, sales , cert: State)

6233 CX Enterprise Inc.
14408 Iseli Rd
Santa Fe Springs, CA 90670
Contact: Steve Chin Mgr
Tel: 562-407-1088
Email: stevechin@cxenterprise.com
Website: www.cxenterprise.com
Steel strapping. (Woman/As-Pac, estab 1991, empl 5, sales $1,771,000, cert: CPUC)

6234 International Rite-Way Products
1725 S Campus Ave
Ontario, CA 91761
Contact: Ravi Joshi President
Tel: 909-985-8300
Email: ravi@intlrwp.com
Website: www.intlrwp.com
Precision aerospace sheet metal mfg: roll forming, hydro-
forming, extrusion & skin stretch forming of aerospace
components (ribs, spars, brackets, formers, etc.). Complete
program management capabilities. (As-Ind, estab 1994,
empl 10, sales $1,250,000, cert: 8a)

6235 Pacific HVAC Depot Corporation
3029 Teagarden St
San Leandro, CA 94577
Contact: Phyllis La Voy CEO
Tel: 510-346-6500
Email: pacifichvacdepot@aol.com
Website: www.pacifichvacdepot.com
Dist hardcast duct sealants, coils & condensers, sheet
metal products, fittings & heat ducts. (Woman/Hisp, estab
2000, empl 6, sales $2,300,000, cert: WBENC)

6236 Scott Engineering, Inc.
5051 Edison Ave
Chino, CA 91710
Contact: CFO/COO
Tel: 909-594-9637
Email:
Website: www.scott-eng.com
Mfr medium voltage custom fabricated mild steel, stainless
steel, & aluminum electrical cabinets & metal fabricated
products. (Hisp, estab 1967, empl 75, sales $14,990,887,
cert: CPUC)

6237 Tanfel
1945 Camino Vida Roble, Ste J
Carlsbad, CA 92008
Contact: Greg Lange Owner
Tel: 760-720-9632
Email: glange@tanfel.com
Website: www.tanfel.com
Custom metal parts: stamping, extrusion, casting, metal
injection molding, machining, turning, prototype to large
production with warehousing capabilities. (Hisp, estab
2008, empl 5, sales , cert: NMSDC)

6238 THISAI LLC
1834 Blazewood St
Simi Valley, CA 93063
Contact: Ramalingam Subramaniam Owner
Tel: 747-206-3886
Email: ram@thisaillc.com
Website: www.thisaillc.com
Electrical products, cables, switches, wire, lighting fixtures,
metal products, aluminum, sheet metal, laser cut, bent &
fabricated. (As-Ind, As-Pac, estab 2015, empl 2, sales , cert:
State)

6239 West Coast Form Grinding
2548 S Fairview St
Santa Ana, CA 92704
Contact: Adrian Calderon President
Tel: 714-540-5621
Email: adrian@precisioncorepins.com
Website: www.precisioncorepins.com
Mfr mold components, core pins, sleeves, ejector pins,
luer taper pins. (Hisp, estab 2005, empl 10, sales
$1,222,670, cert: NMSDC)

Colorado

6240 Excalibur Machine & Sheet Metal
208 W Buchanan St, Unit C
Colorado Springs, CO 80907
Contact: Douglas McDaniel Plant Mgr
Tel: 719-520-5404
Email: doug@excaliburmfg.com
Website: www.excaliburmfg.com/
Precision machining & sheet metal fabrication, welding,
assembly, powder coating. (Hisp, estab 1989, empl 25,
sales $2,600,000, cert: NMSDC)

Connecticut

6241 Turbo America Technology, LLC
1400 Old North Colony Rd
Meriden, CT 06450
Contact: Liliane Yebarth
Tel: 860-970-8777
Email: liliane@turboamericatech.com
Website: www.turboamericatech.com
Mfr & repair Industrial Gas Turbine components. (Hisp,
estab 2014, empl 5, sales $341,000, cert: NMSDC)

Delaware

6242 M. Davis & Sons, Inc.
19 Germay Dr
Wilmington, DE 19804
Contact: Margaret Del Fabbro Mgr of Business
Development
Tel: 952-742-4096
Email: peggy.delfabbro@mdavisinc.com
Website: www.mdavisinc.com
Metal fabrication: welding, piping, mechancial installa-
tions, sheetmetal, structural steel, tank fabrication &
control panels. (Woman, estab , empl 480, sales
$80,000,000, cert: WBENC)

Florida

6243 Blue Water Dynamics LLC DBA Dougherty Manu-
facturing
301 S Old County Rd
Edgewater, FL 32132
Contact: Davey Carroll Sales Dir
Tel: 386-316-5939
Email: dcarroll@dougherty-mfg.com
Website: http://doughertymanufacturing.com
Fabricate metals (aluminum, steel & stainless steel) &
composites/FRP, engineering, design, tooling,
prototyping & manufacturing. (Woman, estab 2010,
empl 46, sales $2,500,000, cert: State, WBENC)

6244 Coastal Steel Inc.
870 Cidco Rd
Cocoa, FL 32926
Contact: Dale Coxwell
Tel: 321-632-8228
Email: dcoxwell@coastalsteelmfg.com
Website: www.coastalsteel.com
Complex & Iconic Structures (AISC Fabrication & Erec-
tion), Ride & Show (AISC Fabrication & Installation),
Machining (Large Capacity 5 Axis Vertical & Horiz), CMM
(Zeiss Contra G2 & FERO). (Nat Ame, estab 1976, empl
90, sales $14,000,000, cert: State, NMSDC)

6245 Cool Tactics LLC
      910 S 8th St, Ste 302
      Fernandina Beach, FL 32034
      Contact: Dana Brodsky President
      Tel: 904-420-0070
      Email: contact@cooltactics.com
      Website: https://cooltactics.com
Installs Insulated Metal Panels (IMPs), underfloor insulation systems, and specialty doors for cold storage and food
processing facilities, refrigerated warehouses and distribution. (Woman, estab 2019, empl 7, sales , cert: WBENC)

Georgia

6246 Harbor Enterprises, LLC
      1207 Sunset Dr
      Thomasville, GA 31792
      Contact: Brandy Spradlin CEO
      Tel: 229-226-0911
      Email: sba@harborenterprisesllc.com
      Website: www.survive-a-storm.com
Wood & metal fabrication, mfr solid steel above ground
safe rooms & underground storm shelters. (Nat Ame,
estab 2009, empl 25, sales $5,500,000, cert: NMSDC, 8a)

6247 The Good Lord's Mobile Welding Service
      3380 Thornbridge Dr
      Powder Springs, GA 30127
      Contact: Carl Lomax Owner
      Tel: 661-302-6128
      Email: carl_lomax@yahoo.com
      Website:
Onsite Welding and Metal Fabrication. Metal Repair,
Construction, Commercial construction Structural and
Installation. (AA, estab 2017, empl 1, sales , cert: State)

Iowa

6248 Air Control, Inc.
      80 14th Ave N
      Clinton, IA 52732
      Contact: Mary Connell President & CEO
      Tel: 563-243-7228
      Email: marypat@acifabricators.com
      Website: www.acifabricators.com
HVAC contracting, specialty steel fabrication, tank fabrica-
tion. (Woman, estab 1956, empl 45, sales $8,000,000, cert:
WBENC, 8a)

6249 EIP Manufacturing, LLC
      2677 - 221st St
      Earlville, IA 52041
      Contact: Kathy Krapfl VP Sales/Mktg
      Tel: 800-942-2226
      Email: kkrapfl@eipmfg.com
      Website: www.eipmfg.com
Steel fabricated components, structural steel, rebar.
(Woman, estab 1975, empl 45, sales $7,700,000, cert:
State)

Idaho

6250 Burly Products, Inc.
      3999 St. Joe Ave
      Post Falls, ID 83854
      Contact: Stephani Morris Admin Asst
      Tel: 208-262-9531
      Email: stephani@burlyproducts.com
      Website: www.burlyproducts.com
Design & mfr steel & aluminum products. (Nat Ame, estab
2006, empl 18, sales , cert: State)

Illinois

6251 American Chrome Chicago Company, Inc.
      518 W Crossroads Pkwy
      Bolingbrook, IL 60440
      Contact: Linda Hou President
      Tel: 630-685-2200
      Email: linda.hou@americanchrome.com
      Website: www.americanchrome.com
Dist chrome, stainless steel & PC/ABS chrome products,
mirrors, exhaust products, clam shells for catalytic
converters, shock absorbers & components, rubber
products / bushings, u-joints, grease caps, air tubes,
clutch control rods. (Woman/As-Pac, estab 1983, empl
26, sales $11,695,000, cert: NMSDC, WBENC)

6252 Combined Metals of Chicago LLC
      2401 W Grant Ave
      Bellwood, IL 60104
      Contact: John Dicello Dirminority dev
      Tel: 708-547-8800
      Email: johnd@combmet.com
      Website: www.combmet.com
Stainless steel: flat rolled stainless steel strip, sheet &
foil. (As-Pac, estab 1975, empl 279, sales $ 0, cert:
NMSDC)

6253 KSO Metalfab, Inc.
      250 Roma Jean Pkwy
      Streamwood, IL 60107
      Contact: Dora Kuzelka President
      Tel: 630-372-1200
      Email: dkuzelka@kso.com
      Website: www.kso.com
Precision sheet metal fab: short to large runs. (Woman,
estab 1973, empl 33, sales $3,700,000, cert: State)

6254 Patel International
      30 N River Rd Ste 102
      Des Plaines, IL 60016
      Contact: Steve Gordon Sales Rep
      Tel: 847-795-3006
      Email: sgordon@patelintl.com
      Website: www.sejasmi.com
Injection molding, aluminum die casting. (As-Ind, estab
2005, empl 65, sales $8,000,000, cert: NMSDC)

6255 Rockford Specialties Company
      5601 Industrial Ave
      Rockford, IL 61111
      Contact: Lisa Stankey President
      Tel: 815-877-6000
      Email: lisas@rswire.com
      Website: http://rockfordspecialties.com
Mfr wire, tube & sheet metal custom displays & components, counter racks, free standing floor displays, wire
dividers & aisle extenders, plating & powder painting,
laser cutting, forming & welding, MIG, TIG, resistance &
robotic welding. (Woman, estab 1979, empl 45, sales
$10,780,000, cert: WBENC)

6256 W.E.B. Production & Fabricating, Inc.
      448 N Artesian Ave
      Chicago, IL 60612
      Contact: Maureen Kendziera President
      Tel: 312-733-6800
      Email:
      maureenk@webproductionandfabricating.com
      Website: www.webproductionandfabricating.com
Welding, shearing, bending, punching, stamping, &
drilling, MIG & TIG welding, aluminum, stainless steel,
carbon steel, handrails, guardrails & metal stair frames.
(Woman, estab 1993, empl 24, sales $3,068,370, cert:
State)

6257 Young Technology Inc.
900 W. Fullerton Ave.
Addison, IL 60101
Contact: Young Sohn President
Tel: 630-690-4320
Email: youngsohn@ytinc.com
Website: www.ytinc.com
Mfr molded rubber, plastic & forged steel: shifter knobs, bezels, decorative molding & cable components, leather wrapped & chrome plated. (As-Pac, estab 1985, empl 350, sales $6,000,000, cert: NMSDC)

Indiana

6258 Circle City Rebar, LLC
4002 Industrial Blvd
Indianapolis, IN 46254
Contact: Heidi Russo Controller
Tel: 317-917-8566
Email: hrusso@circlecityrebar.com
Website: http://circlecityrebar.com
Concrete reinforcing steel bars (rebar) in all sizes; plain and epoxy coated. (AA, estab 2005, empl 14, sales $7,541,942, cert: NMSDC)

6259 Diversified Quality Services of Indiana, LLC
1315 W 18th St
Anderson, IN 46016
Contact: Sharon Montgomery CEO
Tel: 765-644-7712
Email: sharon.montgomery@dqsicorp.com
Website: www.dqsicorp.com
Design, prototyping, production, modification & repair steel racks, containers & dunnage. (AA, estab 2003, empl 123, sales $5,000,000, cert: NMSDC)

6260 Eagle Magnetic Company Inc.
7417 Crawfordsville Rd
Indianapolis, IN 46214
Contact: Ron Jaggers VP Inside Sales
Tel: 317-297-1030
Email: rjaggers@eaglemagnetic.com
Website: www.eaglemagnetic.com
Magnetic shielding, precision sheet metal fabrication, precision machining. (Woman, estab 1970, empl 39, sales $3,275,000, cert: State)

6261 Electric Metal Fab, Inc.
4889 Helmsburg Rd
Nashville, IN 47448
Contact: Mandy Chittum President
Tel: 812-988-9353
Email: mandy@electricmetalfab.com
Website: www.electricmetalfab.com
Mfr Stainless Steel Equipment & Products for the Pharmaceutical & Food Industries, turn-key conveyor systems for production lines, specialty products, etc. Cabinets, Carts, Tables, Racks, Platforms, Lab Furnishings, etc. (Woman, estab 1993, empl 16, sales $1,177,089, cert: WBENC)

6262 Indiana Bridge-Midwest Steel, Inc.
1810 S Macedonia Ave
Muncie, IN 47307
Contact: Sheryl Bronnenberg Office Mgr
Tel: 765-288-1985
Email: sheryl@indianabridge.net
Website: www.indianabridge.net/
Fabricate structural steel & rack structures, design build & erection services. (As-Pac, estab 2001, empl 35, sales $26,790,376, cert: NMSDC)

6263 Irons Metal Processing LLC
1605 Adler Cir Ste I
Portage, IN 46368
Contact: Earmon Irons CEO
Tel: 219-764-9999
Email: earmon@ironsmetalprocessing.com
Website: www.ironsmetalprocessing.com
Processed metal products. (AA, estab 2007, empl 3, sales , cert: NMSDC)

6264 Lacay Fabrication and Mfg Inc.
52941 Glenview Dr
Elkhart, IN 46514
Contact: Ann Filley President
Tel: 574-288-4678
Email: ann@lacayfab.com
Website: www.lacayfab.com
Mfr material handling racks, Baskets, Industrial & Production Welding, Machining, Robotic Welding, Stamping, Custom Fabrication, Prototyping. (Woman, estab 1975, empl 70, sales , cert: WBENC)

6265 Royalty Investments, LLC
2476 E US Hwy 50
Seymour, IN 47274
Contact: Marshall Royalty Member
Tel: 812-358-3534
Email: mroyalty@cranehillmachine.com
Website: www.cranehillmachine.com
Machining, fabricating & assembly: steel, aluminum & plastic components. Design, engineering & coating applications. (Woman, estab 1989, empl 30, sales $3,714,618, cert: State, WBENC)

6266 The Phillips Company, Inc.
6330 East 100 South
Columbus, IN 47201
Contact: Valerie Phillips CEO
Tel: 812-378-3797
Email: valeriephillips@thephillipscompany.com
Website: www.thephillipscompany.com
Cast iron & aluminum parts: pulleys, lube pumps, oil coolers, wire harnesses, water pumps, blocks, heads, gear covers. (Woman/AA, estab 1986, empl 47, sales $2,800,000, cert: NMSDC)

Kansas

6267 American Energy Products, Inc.
1105 Industrial St
Lansing, KS 66043
Contact: Gail Watson President
Tel: 913-351-3388
Email: administrator@americanenergyinc.com
Website: www.americanenergyinc.com
Mfr metal products: corrugated seal plate, seal skirting, dip seal plate, drip screen, wire cloth, drip lips, wareplate, scrubber modules, coal piping, pyrite hoppers, ducting work, seal trough, water trough, telescopic coal chutes. (Woman, estab 2000, empl 3, sales $1,200,000, cert: WBENC)

6268 PTMW, Inc.
5040 NW US Hwy 24
Topeka, KS 66618
Contact: Ashley Bettis CEO
Tel: 785-232-7792
Email: abettis@ptmw.com
Website: www.ptmw.com
OEM metal fabrication & assembly: metal parts, enclo-
sures & cases, assembly & powdercoating. (Woman, estab
1983, empl 220, sales $57,000,000, cert: CPUC, WBENC)

Louisiana

6269 JRE LLC dba Ascension Roofing and Sheet Metal
2140 S Philippe Ave
Gonzales, LA 70737
Contact: Rebecca Evans President
Tel: 225-647-3576
Email: rebevans@ascensionrsm.com
Website: www.ascensionrsm.com
Metal fabrication: stainless steel, carbon steel, galvanized
metal & specialty alloys. (Woman, estab 1954, empl 31,
sales $2,260,000, cert: WBENC)

6270 New Orleans Copper, Inc.
827 Tchoupitoulas St
New Orleans, LA 70130
Contact: President
Tel: 504-525-7426
Email:
Website: www.neworleanscopperinc.com
Pipe & tube bending services. (Woman, estab 1956, empl
6, sales $ 0, cert: WBENC)

Massachusetts

6271 Heat Exchanger Products Corp.
55 Industrial Park Rd
Hingham, MA 02043
Contact: Tracy Hennigan Bonnyman President
Tel: 781-749-0220
Email: hepco@heatexchangerproducts.com
Website: www.HeatExchangerProducts.com
Mfr tube plugs for condensers, heat exchangers, boilers in
sizes 5/8" up to 1 1/4" in materials; Brass, 316 and 314
Stainless Steel, Titanium and Ultem & Non-Metallic High
Performance Polymer plug. (Woman, estab 1985, empl 5,
sales $ 0, cert: WBENC)

6272 Precision Engineering Inc
29 Industrial Dr
Uxbridge, MA 01569
Contact: Liora Stone President
Tel: 508-278-5700
Email: lstone@precisionengineering.com
Website: www.precisionengineering.com/
Laser cutting, punching, forming, powder coating (with 5-
stage prewash), AWS-certified welding, spot welding,
hardware insertion, finishing (graining/deburring),
assembly, kitting, labeling, part marking, local to global
shipping. (Woman, estab 1988, empl 32, sales $4,549,240,
cert: State, WBENC)

6273 Wrobel Engineering Co., Inc.
154 Bodwell St
Avon, MA 02322
Contact: Michael Long General/QA Mgr.
Tel: 508-586-8338
Email: mlong@wrobeleng.com
Website: www.wrobeleng.com
Mfr precision sheet metal fabricated parts per customer
specs, precision machining, milling & turning, metal
stamping, long & short runs, tool & die making, assem-
bly mechanical & electrical, welding all materials.
(Woman, estab 1976, empl 86, sales $14,800,000, cert:
State, City)

Maryland

6274 Waltons Welding & Fabrication, Inc.
155 Prospect Dr
Huntingtown, MD 20639
Contact: Fay Walton President
Tel: 301-855-2944
Email: metalfab@waltonswelding.net
Website: http://waltonswelding.com
Metal fabrication: elctrode welding, mig welding, tig
welding, aluminum welding, stainless steel welding,
tourch cutting, saw cutting, plasma cutting, shear
cutting, drilling, rolling, bending, sanding, grinding,
tapping & punching. (Woman, estab 2000, empl 5, sales
$154,007, cert: State)

Michigan

6275 Airodyne Industries, Inc.
95 E 10 Mile Rd
Madison Heights, MI 48071
Contact: Celeste Herpel President
Tel: 248-548-3336
Email: caherpel@airodyne.com
Website: www.airodyne.com
Mfr & dist aerodynamic & fuel-saving devices. (Woman,
estab 2004, empl 3, sales $1,265,000, cert: WBENC)

6276 Anderson Express, Inc.
580 W Sherman Blvd
Muskegon Heights, MI 49444
Contact: Angel Ball HR Mgr
Tel: 231-733-6001
Email: aball@andersonexpressinc.com
Website: www.andersonexpressinc.com
Rapid tooling & tooling prototypes for small & medium
projects. (Woman, estab 2011, empl 17, sales $ 0, cert:
WBENC)

6277 Clips & Clamps Industries
15050 Keel St
Plymouth, MI 48170
Contact: Jeff Aznavorian President
Tel: 734-455-0880
Email: jaznavorian@clipsclamps.com
Website: www.clipsclamps.com
Metal forming, progressive dies, four slide, CNC wire
forming, tool building, MIG & TIG welding, tapping,
riveting, automated assemblies, prototyping & produc-
tion volumes, engineering services, design services, sales
support. (Woman, estab 1954, empl 62, sales $ 0, cert:
WBENC)

6278 Cortar Laser and Fab. LLC
12828 Emerson Dr
Brighton, MI 48116
Contact: Livia Walker Managing Member
Tel: 248-446-1110
Email: lwalker@cortarlaser.com
Website:
Dist precision laser cut blanks & formed sheet metal parts. (Woman/Hisp, estab 2007, empl 4, sales , cert: WBENC)

6279 Dawson Mfg Co. - Benton Harbor Division
1042 N Crystal Ave
Benton Harbor, MI 49022
Contact: Neil Trivedi VP
Tel: 269-925-0100
Email: neil.trivedi@vibracoustic.com.com
Website: http://dawsonmfg.com
Mfr body mounts, engine mounts, strut mounts, link assemblies & bushings, dist anti-vibration components, rubber injection molding. (As-Pac, estab 1988, empl 90, sales $36,000,000, cert: NMSDC)

6280 DGH Enterprises, Inc. dba K-O Products Co.
1225 Milton St
Benton Harbor, MI 49022
Contact: Barbara Herrold CEO
Tel: 269-925-0657
Email: barbaraherrold@koproducts.com
Website: www.koproducts.com
Metal stampings, welded & fabricated assemblies, electrical & mechanical assemblies, metal hardware, metal truck parts & assemblies, metal stamped components for auto, appliances, off-road equipment, metal welding, mig welding, spot welding. (Woman, estab 1938, empl 28, sales $5,700,000, cert: WBENC)

6281 Gill Industries Inc.
5271 Plainfield Ave
Grand Rapids, MI 49525
Contact: Regina Wilk Sales Acct Mgr
Tel: 616-559-2700
Email: rwilk@gill-industries.com
Website: www.gill-industries.com/
Stamped weldments & structural assemblies, seat, chassis, body & powertrain structural assemblies, folding head restraint & seat mechanisms. (Woman, estab 1964, empl 1923, sales $340,000,000, cert: WBENC)

6282 Globe Tech LLC.
101 Industrial Dr
Plymouth, MI 48170
Contact: Amanda Menchinger President
Tel: 734-656-2200
Email: mmenchinger@globe-tech.biz
Website: www.globe-tech.biz
Machining, fabrication & welding, metal stamping. (Woman, estab 2009, empl 72, sales , cert: WBENC)

6283 Harbin Steel
440 Burroughs St, Ste 133
Detroit, MI 48202
Contact: Anthony Harbin President
Tel: 248-974-5793
Email: anthony@harbinsteel.com
Website: www.harbinsteel.com
Miscellaneous/structural steel fabrication & installation. (AA, estab 2016, empl 1, sales , cert: NMSDC)

6284 HDN F&A, Inc. dba F&A Fabricating
104 Arbor St
Battle Creek, MI 49015
Contact: Hiep Nguyen President
Tel: 269-965-3268
Email: hiep.nguyen@fa-fabricating.com
Website: www.fa-fabricating.com
Custom sheet metal fabrication, food grade stainless steel, dist sheet metal, tubing. (As-Pac, estab 1956, empl 25, sales $3,000,000, cert: NMSDC)

6285 I F Metalworks
14009 Achyl
Warren, MI 48313
Contact: Karen Arondoski President
Tel: 586-776-8311
Email: karen@ifmetalworks.com
Website: www.ifmetalworks.com
Welding, fabrication, design, weldments, assemblies, prototype, short & long run, decorative, railings, staircases, ballisters, custom furniture, artistic works, architectural, trailers, foodservice production equipment, racks & repair. (Woman, estab 2002, empl 10, sales $425,000, cert: WBENC)

6286 International Specialty Tube
6600 Mt. Elliott
Detroit, MI 48124
Contact: Jason VanDeVen Sales Mgr
Tel: 313-841-6900
Email: quality@istube.com
Website: www.istube.com
Mfr stainless steel tubing for automotive exhaust. (AA, estab 0, empl , sales $29,000,000, cert: NMSDC)

6287 JLC Group LLC
287 Executive Dr
Troy, MI 48083
Contact: William Chen Dir Ph.D.
Tel: 248-792-3281
Email: wchen@jlcgroupllc.com
Website: www.jlcgroupllc.com
Dist casting parts, forging parts & machine finished parts, plastic injected molds & plastic parts. (Woman/As-Pac, estab 2010, empl 5, sales , cert: WBENC)

6288 Jorgensen Steel Machining & Fabrication
101 Spires Pkwy
Tekonsha, MI 49092
Contact: Matt Jorgensen President
Tel: 517-767-4600
Email: mjorgensen@jorgensen-usa.com
Website: www.jorgensen-usa.com
Design & manufacture contract machinery & contour formed products for the aviation, space & defense industries. (Nat Ame, estab 2001, empl 26, sales $6,334,000, cert: State, NMSDC)

6289 Midbrook Industrial Washers Inc.
2080 Brooklyn Rd
Jackson, MI 49204
Contact: Rodney Sims govt & diversity sales
Tel: 517-787-3481
Email: rsims@midbrookindustrial.com
Website: www.midbrookindustrial.com
Custom sheet metal fabrication. (Woman/AA, As-Pac, estab 2012, empl 70, sales $ 0, cert: WBENC)

6290 Mintech LLC
      P.O. Box 428
      Niles, MI 49120
      Contact: Minnie Warren President
      Tel: 269-683-4551
      Email: minnie@mintechllc.com
      Website: www.mintechllc.com
Metal fabrication, stamping, light assembly, sort,
vibratory deburring, rollforming. (Woman, estab 0, empl ,
sales $ 0, cert: WBENC)

6291 MRD Aerospace, LLC
      23565 Schoenherr Rd
      Warren, MI 48089
      Contact: Michele Dew Managing Member
      Tel: 586-443-5350
      Email: r7mdew@aol.com
      Website: www.mrdaerospace.com
Prototype machining, milling, turning, jig grinding, ID/OD
grinding, surface grinding, honing & lapping, hydraulic
cylinder blocks, drive shafts, rotors, housings, broaching ID
splines, valve plates, pistons, sleeved cylinder blocks, etc.
(Woman, estab 2011, empl 9, sales $440,311, cert:
WBENC)

6292 Northern Wings Repair, Inc.
      6679 County Rd 392
      Newberry, MI 49868
      Contact: David Goudreau President
      Tel: 906-477-6176
      Email: dave@nwrepair.com
      Website: www.nwrepair.com
Mfr, repair & dist commercial & military aircraft parts,
material & services. (Nat Ame, estab 2001, empl 20, sales
$11,650,000, cert: State)

6293 Rochester Tube Products, Ltd.
      51366 Fischer Park Dr
      Shelby Township, MI 48316
      Contact: Jennie Preston Dir of Mktg
      Tel: 586-726-4816
      Email: jennie@rochestertube.com
      Website: www.rochestertube.com
Fabricate steel parts; specifically tube. (Woman, estab
1973, empl 25, sales $ 0, cert: WBENC)

6294 Rose-A-Lee Technologies, Inc
      7448 19 Mile Rd
      Sterling Heights, MI 48314
      Contact: Julie Wood Dir Business Dev
      Tel: 586-799-4555
      Email: jwood@rosealeetechnologies.com
      Website: www.rosealeetechnologies.com
CAD design (surface and solid modeling), stamping,
assembly/kitting, tube bending, welding (mig, tig, stud
arc), etc. (Woman, estab 2013, empl 2, sales , cert:
WBENC)

6295 Santanna Tool &Design LLC
      25880 Commerce Dr
      Madison Heights, MI 48071
      Contact: Jamilce & Newton President & CEO
      Tel: 248-541-3500
      Email: jsnewton@santannatool.com
      Website: www.santannatool.com
Design & mfr conveyors, tooling & welding. (Woman/Hisp,
estab , empl , sales $1,376,927,385, cert: NMSDC, WBENC)

6296 The Ideal Group
      2525 Clark St
      Detroit, MI 48209
      Contact: Linzie Venegas Sales
      Tel: 313-842-7290
      Email: linzie@idealshield.com
      Website: www.weareideal.com
Architectural & engineering svcs; general contracting &
construction mgmt, rigging. Mfr, dist, fabricate & erect
structural & misc steel. Patent for "Ideal Shield"
Protective Guard Rail System. (Hisp, estab 1979, empl
120, sales $ 0, cert: NMSDC)

6297 Thompson Marketing, LLC
      15890 Sturgeon CT
      Roseville, MI 48066
      Contact: Derek Thompson President
      Tel: 248-761-6802
      Email: derek@tmsglobalservices.com
      Website: www.tmsglobalservices.com
Mfr shipping racks & fixtures. (AA, estab 1999, empl 7,
sales $370,000, cert: NMSDC)

Minnesota

6298 JML Fabrication, LLC
      21054 Chippendale Ct
      Farmington, MN 55024
      Contact: Margo Lackore President
      Tel: 612-444-3025
      Email: margo@jmlfabrication.com
      Website: www.jmlfabrication.com
Aluminum welding, Aluminum Fabrication, Stainless
steel welding, Stainless steel fabrication, Steel welding,
Steel fabrication, Certified Welding, Bending, Shearing.
MIG/TIG welding, Flux core welding, large structural
steel fabrication. (Woman/As-Pac, estab 2004, empl 7,
sales $2,400,000, cert: WBENC)

6299 Jones Metal Inc.
      3201 3rd Ave
      Mankato, MN 56001
      Contact: John Clifford Natl Business Devel
      Tel: 507-625-4436
      Email: jclifford@jonesmetalinc.com
      Website: www.jonesmetalinc.com
Metal fabrication, laser technology, water jet, saw,
punch presses, press brakes, rollers & machining
capabilities. (Woman, estab 1942, empl 100, sales
$12,000,000, cert: WBENC)

6300 Wyoming Machine, Inc.
      30680 Forest Blvd
      Stacy, MN 55079
      Contact: Lori Tapani President
      Tel: 651-462-4156
      Email: ltapani@wyomingmachine.com
      Website: www.wyomingmachine.com
Precision metal fabrication: aser cutting, CNC punching,
forming & welding. (Woman, estab 1974, empl 65, sales
$ 0, cert: WBENC)

Missouri

6301 Sinclair Industries, Inc.
      1317 Kentucky Ave
      St. Louis, MO 63110
      Contact: Jagdish Hinduja President
      Tel: 314-535-6335
      Email: sinclair.inc@sbcglobal.net
      Website: www.snclr.com
Metal fabrication. (As-Ind, estab 1978, empl 9, sales
$1,200,000, cert: City)

Montana

6302 Montana Hydraulics, LLC
888 Florence St
Helena, MT 59601
Contact: Jay Krause Natl Contracts Mgr
Tel: 814-592-5412
Email: mthyd@ironfurnace.com
Website: www.montanahydraulics.com
Mfr industrial metal, compaction attachments for heavy equipment (roller compaction buckets & wheels, vibratory compaction buckets), bedding boxes & doweling machines, CNC machining, turning & lathe, manual machining, custom fabrication. (Woman, estab 1998, empl 47, sales $6,027,445, cert: State)

North Carolina

6303 QMF Metal & Electronic Solutions, Inc.
324 Berry Garden Rd
Kernersville, NC 27284
Contact: Raymond Polomski Sales Assoc
Tel: 336-992-6501
Email: rpolomski@qmf-usa.com
Website: www.qmf-usa.com
Custom sheet metal fabrication, punching, forming, welding, robotic welding, machining, hardware installation, wet and powder coat painting, silk screening, mechanical & electronic assembly. (Woman, estab 1978, empl 75, sales $7,000,000, cert: WBENC)

New Jersey

6304 Central Metals, Inc.
1054 S 2nd St
Camden, NJ 08103
Contact: Susan Vilotti President
Tel: 856-963-5844
Email: vilotti@aol.com
Website: www.centralmetals.com
Steel fabrication, structural steel, miscellaneous metals, ornamental metals, railings, stairs & iron. (Woman, estab 1981, empl 57, sales $29,770,000, cert: WBENC, NWBOC)

6305 Holtec International
1 Holtec Blvd
Camden, NJ 08104
Contact: Jordan Landis Sales/Mktg Mgr
Tel: 856-797-0900
Email: j.landis@holte.com
Website: www.holtecinternational.com
Design & mfr storage systems for wet & dry spent nuclear fuel, takes, vessels, hoists, cranes. (As-Ind, estab , empl , sales $99,000,000, cert: NMSDC)

New York

6306 ASP Industries
9 Evelyn St
Rochester, NY 14606
Contact: Robert Uerkvitz Acct Exec
Tel: 585-254-9130
Email: robert@aspindustries.com
Website: www.aspindustries.com
Sheet metal fabrication, laser, welding, machine. (Woman, estab 1980, empl 25, sales $205,000, cert: State)

6307 Bailey Manufacturing Co., LLC
10987 Bennett State Rd
Forestville, NY 14062
Contact: John Hines President
Tel: 716-965-2731
Email: bailey03@netsync.net
Website: www.baileymfgcollc.com
Metal Stamping, Sheet Metal Fabrication, Welding, Multi-Part Assemblies, Zinc Plating, Rust Proofing, Quality Inspection, E-Coat Painting. (AA, estab 2002, empl 100, sales $8,500,000, cert: NMSDC)

6308 Technical Welding Fabricators LLC
27 Thatcher St
Albany, NY 12207
Contact: Carole Boyer Owner
Tel: 518-463-2229
Email: caroleboyer@aol.com
Website: http://technicalweldingfabricators.com
Metals & structural steel, railings, columns, beams, repairs. (Woman, estab 2006, empl 5, sales $1,600,000, cert: State)

Ohio

6309 Armor Metal Group
4600 Mason-Montgomery Rd
Mason, OH 45040
Contact: John Ravana Inside sales
Tel: 800-543-7417
Email: jravana@witt.com
Website: www.witt.com
Fabrication, burn, grind, machining, lathe, blanchard, surface, roll, laser, form, weld, paint, blast. (Woman, estab 1950, empl 250, sales $51,000,000, cert: WBENC)

6310 Aster Industries
275-299 N Arlington St
Akron, OH 44305
Contact: Kaitlyn Oplinger Admin Asst
Tel: 330-762-7965
Email: kmoplinger@asterind.com
Website: www.asterind.com
Custom millwork manufacturing, commercial booth seating, interior design, stainless steel fabrication, and full construction management. (Woman, estab 1990, empl 25, sales $6,000,000, cert: WBENC)

6311 Extol of Ohio, Inc.
208 Republic St
Norwalk, OH 44857
Contact: Andrea Buggele Inside Sales
Tel: 419-668-2072
Email: andrea@extolohio.com
Website: www.extolohio.com
Fabricate & dist thermally efficient, non-wicking rigid pipe insulation products & accessories. (Woman, estab 1985, empl 50, sales $22,919,925, cert: WBENC)

6312 Fabrication Group LLC
3453 W 140th St
Cleveland, OH 44111
Contact: Patricia Setlock President
Tel: 216-251-1125
Email: patty@fabricationgroup.com
Website: www.fabricationgroup.com
Metal fabrications, welded assemblies, guardrails, handrails, bollards, stair railings, cutting, shearing, roll forming, punch presses, sheet metal fabrication equipment. (Woman, estab 2008, empl 10, sales $433,345, cert: WBENC)

6313   Ferragon Corporation
11103 Memphis Ave
Cleveland, OH 44144
Contact: Luis J. Gonzalez Mgr
Tel: 216-671-6161
Email: lgonzalez@ferrousmetalprocessing.com
Website: www.ferrousmetalprocessing.com
Hot roll steel toll processing: pickle, slit, level, shear, decamber & warehousing. (Hisp, estab 1983, empl 144, sales $16,200,000, cert: NMSDC)

6314   GOJO Industries, Inc.
1 Gojo Plaza
Akron, OH 44311
Contact: Ann Bemer Sr Pricing Mgr
Tel: 330-255-6731
Email: bemera@gojo.com
Website: www.gojo.com
Miscellaneous Fabricated Metal Product Manufacturing. (Woman, estab 1946, empl 3500, sales $ 0, cert: WBENC)

6315   Journey Steel, Inc.
7655 Production Dr
Cincinnati, OH 45237
Contact: Barbara Smith President
Tel: 513-731-2930
Email: bsmith@journeysteel.com
Website: www.journeysteel.com/
Remodeling & Expanding: retrofit piping, staircases, overhead walkways. Structural & Mechanical Erector: mechanical devices & assorted equipment supported & erected. (Woman/AA, estab 2009, empl 4, sales $3,900,000, cert: State, NMSDC, WBENC)

6316   KeYAH International Trading, LLC
4655 Urbana Rd
Springfield, OH 45502
Contact: Ramon Vasquez VP
Tel: 937-399-3140
Email: rvasquez@keyahint.com
Website: www.keyahint.com
Die cut, RF weld/sonic weld, automotive interior trim components, sub-assemblies. (Woman/Nat Ame, estab 2000, empl 85, sales $2,000,000, cert: WBENC)

6317   Magni-Power Company
5511 Lincoln Way E
Wooster, OH 44691
Contact: Kim Coblentz New Business Devel
Tel: 330-264-3637
Email: kcoblentz@magnipower.com
Website: www.magnipower.com
Metal fabrication & stamping: process steel, aluminum, stainless steel, CNC punching, forming, laser cutting, robotic welding, in-house powder coating & assembly. (As-Ind, estab 1948, empl 230, sales $27,000,000, cert: NMSDC)

6318   Main Metal Products, Inc.
8800 US Highway 68 N
West Liberty, OH 43357
Contact: Cynthia Haddix Owner
Tel: 937-465-9353
Email: mmp@loganrec.com
Website:
Welding & fabricating, custom fixturing, custom prototyping, automotive rack mfg, rack designs & modifications, material handling products, custom machine guarding, mig & tig welding. (Woman, estab 1995, empl 17, sales $1,250,000, cert: WBENC)

6319   MCM Industries Co., Inc.
25825 Science Park Dr Ste 260
Beachwood, OH 44122
Contact: Gloria Reljanovic Owner
Tel: 216-292-4708
Email: greljanovic@mcmindustries.com
Website: www.mcmindustries.com
Mfr, dist & import finished steel & plastic parts: precision & bicycle chains, non-metal chains, steel ball bearings. (Woman/Hisp, estab 1986, empl 50, sales $ 0, cert: NMSDC)

6320   Middletown Tube Works, Inc.
2201 Trine St
Middletown, OH 45044
Contact: Angela Phillips CEO
Tel: 513-727-0080
Email: aphillips@middletowntube.com
Website: www.middletowntube.com
Mfr as-welded steel tubes for Automotive, Appliance, HVAC and Packaging industries. (Woman, estab 0, empl , sales $ 0, cert: WBENC)

6321   Mid-West Materials, Inc.
3687 Shepard Rd
Perry, OH 44081
Contact: Scott Dennis Sales Rep
Tel: 440-259-5200
Email: scott.dennis@midwestmaterials.com
Website: www.midwestmaterials.com
Flat rolled steel service center, hot rolled, hot rolled, pickled & oiled & coated steel in commercial quality, high strength-low alloy & low through high carbon chemistries. (Woman, estab 1952, empl 50, sales $50,000,000, cert: State)

6322   Morrison Metalweld Process Corporation
3685 Stutz Dr, Ste 102
Canfield, OH 44406
Contact: Robin Eisenbrei CEO
Tel: 330-702-5188
Email: robin@morrisonmetalweld.com
Website: www.morrisonmetalweld.com
Railroad track & crane rail welding services & products. (Woman, estab 1929, empl 9, sales $ 0, cert: WBENC)

6323   Salinas Inudstries
1010 N Forth St
Miamisburg, OH 45342
Contact: Robert Salinas President
Tel: 937-866-0886
Email: salinas@infinet.com
Website:
Mfr sound deadners & insulators for automotive use, die cut & assemble finished goods. (Hisp, estab 2000, empl 10, sales $754,217, cert: NMSDC)

6324   Shelby Welded Tube
5578 State Route 61 North
Shelby, OH 44875
Contact: Kelly Kleman Sales
Tel: 419-347-1720
Email: kkleman@shelbytube.com
Website: www.shelbytube.com
Dist welded steel tubes. (Woman, estab 1967, empl 81, sales $22,000,000, cert: WBENC)

6325 Thieman Quality Metal Fab, Inc.
      05140 Dicke Rd
      New Bremen, OH 45869
      Contact: Ben Wissman Sales Mgr
      Tel: 419-629-2612
      Email: bwissman@thieman.com
      Website: www.thieman.com
Engineering: AutoCAD, 2000i, Solid Edge & Metamation
CAD/CAM Software, Welding:
MIG, TIG, Robotic & Spot welding, Fabrication:
Sawing, Machining, Drilling, Hy Def Plasma, Turret Punch,
Lasers, Press Break. (Woman, estab 1951, empl 90, sales
$16,200,000, cert: NWBOC)

6326 Tylok International, Inc.
      1061 E 260th St
      Euclid, OH 44132
      Contact: Michael Palinkas VP Sales
      Tel: 216-261-7310
      Email: mpalinkas@tylok.com
      Website: www.tylok.com
Mfr stainless steel, brass & steel tube fittings, pipe & weld
fittings, ball valves, needle valves, manifolds & double
block & bleed valves. (Woman, estab 1955, empl 75, sales
$8,600,000, cert: WBENC)

Oregon

6327 Ebony Iron Works, Inc.
      2401 NW 22nd Ave
      Portland, OR 97210
      Contact: Edward Holmes President
      Tel: 503-224-3038
      Email: ebonyiron@aol.com
      Website:
Structural steel fabrication. (AA, estab 1993, empl 25, sales
$ 0, cert: State)

6328 General Sheet Metal Works, Inc.
      P.O. Box 1490
      Clackamas, OR 97015
      Contact: Carol Duncan President
      Tel: 503-650-0405
      Email: carol@gsmw.com
      Website: www.gsmw.com
Sheet metal fabrication, installation, design & support.
(Woman, estab 1932, empl 40, sales $7,620,093, cert:
WBENC)

Pennsylvania

6329 American Roll Suppliers, Inc.
      186 Compass Rd
      Parkesburg, PA 19365
      Contact: Karen Neuhauser President
      Tel: 610-857-2988
      Email: kneuhauser@peoplepc.com
      Website:
Metal fabrication & machining. (Woman, estab 0, empl ,
sales $ 0, cert: WBENC)

6330 Cromedy Construction Corporation
      5702 Newtown Ave
      Philadelphia, PA 19120
      Contact: Bill Cromedy President
      Tel: 215-437-7606
      Email: bcromedy@cromedyconstruction.com
      Website: www.cromedyconstruction.com
HVAC, Sheetmetal (AA, estab 2004, empl 15, sales
$14,000,000, cert: State, NMSDC, 8a)

6331 Flexospan Steel Buildings, Inc.
      P.O. Box 515
      Sandy Lake, PA 16145
      Contact: Karla Black Exec Asst
      Tel: 724-376-7221
      Email: karla@flexospan.com
      Website: www.flexospan.com
Mfr metal roofing and siding panels, matching trims,
decking, structural components, custom engineered
metal buildings, as well as complete self storage
building packages. (Woman, estab 1969, empl 44, sales
$10,872,000, cert: WBENC)

6332 General Carbide Corporation
      1151 Garden St
      Greensburg, PA 15601
      Contact: Carrie Gartland Admin Exec
      Tel: 800-245-2465
      Email: sales@generalcarbide.com
      Website: www.generalcarbide.com
Mfr tungsten carbide preforms & blanks used in wear
resistant, cutting & metal forming operations. (Woman,
estab 0, empl , sales $ 0, cert: WBENC)

Puerto Rico

6333 RAC Enterprises, Inc.
      Road 1, KM 24.8
      Caguas, PR 00726
      Contact: Vivian Carballo President
      Tel: 787-789-9338
      Email: rac@racsteeldrums.com
      Website: www.racsteeldrums.com
Mfr steel drums, dist plastic, steel & stainless containers, sorbent products, secondary containment: spill
pallets, drain seals. Stormwater management products,
PPE & material handling, monitors. (Hisp, estab 1995,
empl 15, sales $2,300,000, cert: NMSDC)

South Carolina

6334 E=MC4I Inc.
      3216 Industry Dr Ste C
      North Charleston, SC 29418
      Contact: Jennifer Gomez President
      Tel: 843-225-4091
      Email: jennifer@emc4i.com
      Website: www.emc4i.com
Metal fabricating: fencing & machine gun mounts,
communication assemblies & military parts. (Woman/
Hisp, estab 1997, empl 30, sales $1,000,000, cert: 8a)

6335 J.I.T. Manufacturing, Inc.
      428 Oglesby Lane
      Cowpens, SC 29330
      Contact: Dan Hunter Production / Sales Mgr.
      Tel: 864-463-0581
      Email: dan@jitmanufacturing.com
      Website: http://jitmfg.net
Laser cutting, welding, forming, CNC punching, CNC
machines, fabrication, sheetmetal, powdercoating,
pressbrakes, modifications, spot welding, control boxes,
mounting plates, brackets, CAD programing, Cad design.
(Woman, estab 1992, empl 22, sales $2,910,792, cert:
City, WBENC)

6336 Lamar's Fabrication, Inc.
      210 Ashley Circle
      North Augusta, SC 29841
      Contact: Michael Lamar CEO
      Tel: 706-513-1992
      Email: michael.lfab@gmail.com
      Website: www.LamarsFabrication.com
Process Pipe, Structural Steel, Carbon steel, Stainless steel,
Chromemoly, Inconel, Hastelloy, GTAW, SMAW, FCAW, CNC
Plasma cutting, C.A.D. Detailing and Design, 3D Modeling.
(AA, estab 2008, empl 2, sales , cert: State, City, NMSDC)

Texas

6337 A & A Aero Structures Inc.
      800 Schneider Bldg M
      Cibolo, TX 78108
      Contact: Ronald D Atkins Owner
      Tel: 210-566-3660
      Email: ron@aaaerostructures.com
      Website: http://aaaerostructures.com
Fabricate, assemble & mfr aircraft parts & components.
(AA, estab 2007, empl 4, sales , cert: State)

6338 Advanced Turbine Solutions LLC
      15653 N Brentwood
      Channelview, TX 77530
      Contact: Tim Donohue International Sales Mgr
      Tel: 314-494-1900
      Email: donohuet@atshouston.com
      Website: www.ATSHouston.com
Fabrication, piping, structural & skids, welding, carbon
steel to exotic metals. (As-Pac, Hisp, estab 2010, empl 12,
sales $2,850,000, cert: NMSDC)

6339 GABS LLC
      1011 Regal Row
      Dallas, TX 75247
      Contact: Dot Haymann CEO
      Tel: 972-354-6512
      Email: dhaymann@guard-all.com
      Website: www.guard-all.com
Engineer, design & manufacture steel framed, tension
fabric buildings for a multitude of applications. (Woman,
estab 2011, empl 45, sales $4,990,000, cert: State, WBENC)

6340 GST Manufacturing, Ltd.
      4201 Janada St
      Haltom City, TX 76117
      Contact: Sharrian Lamberth Owner
      Tel: 817-520-2320
      Email: info@gstmanufacturing.com
      Website: www.gstmanufacturing.com
Metal fabrication, in plant maintenance. (Woman, estab
2000, empl 250, sales $50,800,000, cert: State)

6341 Harris Composites, Inc.
      600 Holmes Dr
      Granbury, TX 76048
      Contact: Debra Harris CEO
      Tel: 817-279-9546
      Email: hci@itexas.net
      Website: www.harriscomposites.com
Mfr & produce all size composite parts. (Woman, estab
2000, empl 25, sales $3,500,000, cert: State, WBENC)

6342 Llano River Fence Company, LLC
      11418 Lake June Rd
      Balch Springs, TX 75180
      Contact: Ashanti Smith President
      Tel: 972-286-4316
      Email: asmith@llanoriverfence.com
      Website: www.llanoriverfence.com
Custom iron products: gates, iron doors, handrails, &
puppy panels, fencing, automatic gates installation &
automatic gate operator maintenance. (Woman/AA,
estab 2006, empl 13, sales $1,250,000, cert: State)

6343 Magni-Fab Southwest Company
      P.O. Box 578
      Howe, TX 75459
      Contact: Wayne Swineford Dir of Sales
      Tel: 903-532-5533
      Email: wswineford@mfsw.net
      Website: www.magnifab.com
Sheet metal fabrication, shearing, CNC punching, laser
cutting, stamping, forming, sawing, spot welding, arc
welding, robotic welding, powder coating. (As-Pac,
estab 1971, empl 105, sales $10,350,000, cert: NMSDC)

6344 MagRabbit-Alamo Iron Works, LLC
      P.O. Box 2341
      San Antonio, TX 78298
      Contact: Wayne Dennis Diversity Coord
      Tel: 210-704-8520
      Email: wdennis@aiwnet.com
      Website: www.magrabbit-aiw.com
Dist industrial supplies, steel service & fabrication, hand
& power tools, equipment repair & installation, logistics,
transportation & freight forwarding. (As-Pac, estab
2004, empl 150, sales $1,573,543, cert: NMSDC)

6345 Quality Fabrication & Design
      955 Freeport Pkwy Ste 400
      Coppell, TX 75019
      Contact: Alex Pier President
      Tel: 972-304-3266
      Email: alexpier@quality-fabrication.com
      Website: www.quality-fabrication.com
Mfr custom stainless steel & mild steel equipment:
conveyors, drags, belts & bucket, structural steel
platforms, waterjet cutting & complete food processing
lines. (Hisp, estab 1987, empl 65, sales $6,000,000, cert:
State, NMSDC)

6346 Texas Finishing Company
      P.O. Box 59445
      Dallas, TX 75229
      Contact: Carolyn Beard President
      Tel: 972-416-2961
      Email: cbeard@texasfinishing.com
      Website: http://texasfinishing.com
Paint application & custom metal fabrication. (Woman,
estab 1982, empl 45, sales , cert: State, WBENC)

Viriginia

6347 Metal Tech Inc.
2629 Richard Ave NE
Roanoke, VA 24012
Contact: Natasha Crowder project estimator
Tel: 540-798-4193
Email: metaltech@cox.net
Website: www.metaltechincorporated.com
Custom metal fabrication: sandblasting, punching, machine cutting, CNC plasma cutting, water jet cutting, pipe bending, ornamental bender machine, surface preparation & coating. (Woman, estab 1996, empl 2, sales $150,000, cert: State)

6348 Shickel Corporation
115 Dry River Rd
Bridgewater, VA 22812
Contact: Don Crawford Sales Mgr
Tel: 540-828-2536
Email: donc@shickel.com
Website: www.shickel.com
Custom metal fabricating, engineering, design, project management, welding, fabrication, precision machining, finishing & installation services. (Woman, estab 1938, empl 80, sales $11,200,000, cert: State)

6349 Valley Industrial Piping, Inc.
P.O. Box 1751
Waynesboro, VA 22980
Contact: Michelle Carter President & CEO
Tel: 540-942-4469
Email: michelle@valleypipes.com
Website: www.valleypipes.com
Industrial maintenance, fabricate & install process skid systems, pressure vessels, tank installation & repair, structural steel, carbon & stainless steel platforms, mezzanines, ladders & stairways, piping, in-line instrumentation & equipment installation (Woman, estab 2004, empl 10, sales $984,906, cert: State, WBENC)

Vermont

6350 Vermont Precision Tools, Inc.
10 Precision Ln
Swanton, VT 05488
Contact: Monica Greene President
Tel: 802-868-4246
Email: mgreene@vermontprecisiontools.com
Website: http://vermontprecisiontools.com
Mfr high quality precision ground medical burr blanks for the OEM medical industry. (Woman, estab 1968, empl 190, sales $32,527,681, cert: WBENC)

Washington

6351 JIT Manufacturing
19510 144th Ave NE, Ste E 7
Woodinville, WA 98072
Contact: Duane Parrish Sales Mgr
Tel: 425-487-0672
Email: duanep@jit-mfg.com
Website: www.jit-mfg.com
Aerospace Sheet Metal Manufacturing, complete parts, Punching, Laser, Bending, Forming, Hardware & Assembly, Finish, Chem Treat, Paint, Primer. (Woman, estab 1985, empl 60, sales $ 0, cert: State)

Wisconsin

6352 Church Metal Spinning Company
5050 N 124th St
Milwaukee, WI 53225
Contact: Brenda Birno President
Tel: 414-461-6460
Email: markv@churchmetal.com
Website: http://churchmetal.com
Metal fabrications including metal stampings, metal spun, laser cut, press brake parts. Also, complete assembly and welding of multi-part components. (Woman, estab 1944, empl 30, sales $6,600,000, cert: State)

6353 Creative CNC LLC
712 Rose Dr
Hartland, WI 53029
Contact: Janet Murphy President
Tel: 262-347-3939
Email: jmurphy@creativecnc.net
Website: www.creativecnc.net
Mfr metal parts: aerospace, medical, automotive, turbomachinery, etc. (Woman, estab 2010, empl 3, sales , cert: WBENC)

6354 Metal-Era, Inc.
1600 Airport Rd
Waukesha, WI 53188
Contact: Jody Delie Channel Marketing Mgr
Tel: 800-373-9156
Email: info@metalera.com
Website: www.metalera.com/Home.aspx
Mfr perimeter edge metal for the low sloped commercial roofing industry. (Hisp, estab 1980, empl 148, sales $36,700,000, cert: State, NMSDC)

6355 Ridgway LLC dba The Price Erecting Co.
10910 W Lapham St
Milwaukee, WI 53214
Contact: Fred Quilling Estimator
Tel: 414-778-0300
Email: fquilling@priceerecting.com
Website: www.priceerecting.com
Equipment installation & removal, steel erection, fabrication & machining. (Minority, estab 1915, empl 40, sales $9,000,000, cert: State)

6356 Safeway Sling USA, Inc.
6209 Industrial Ct
Greendale, WI 53129
Contact: Susan Szymczak President
Tel: 414-421-7303
Email: sales@safewaysling.com
Website: www.safewaysling.com
Mfr nylon & polyester web lifting slings, polyester round slings, alloy chain slings, wire rope slings, metal mesh slings & tie down assemblies. (Woman, estab 1980, empl 36, sales $6,800,000, cert: WBENC)

> ## METAL STAMPING
> Services include forming, welding, tapping, tooling, tube fabrication and bending, etc. (Also see six other METAL categories). NAICS Code 33

California

6357 Proformance Manufacturing, Inc.
     1922 Elise Circle
     Corona, CA 92879
     Contact: Tim Borth Technical Sales Mgr
     Tel: 951-279-1230
     Email: tborth@proformancemfg.com
     Website: www.proformancemfg.com
Precision metal stampings, deep draw parts & machined components & parts. Components formed from flat sheet stock are produced in mechanical & hydraulic presses. (Hisp, estab 1987, empl 21, sales $2,200,000, cert: NMSDC)

6358 Tanfel
     1945 Camino Vida Roble, Ste J
     Carlsbad, CA 92008
     Contact: Greg Lange Owner
     Tel: 760-720-9632
     Email: glange@tanfel.com
     Website: www.tanfel.com
Custom metal parts: stamping, extrusion, casting, metal injection molding, machining, turning, prototype to large production with warehousing capabilities. (Hisp, estab 2008, empl 5, sales , cert: NMSDC)

Connecticut

6359 Hylie Products, Inc.
     669 Straits Tpke
     Watertown, CT 06795
     Contact: Bill Thompson CEO
     Tel: 860-274-5447
     Email: donna@hylie.com
     Website: www.hylie.com
Mfr high-volume, customer-specific, high-precision, quality-critical, metal stampings & progressively drawn eyelets, four-slide stamped & formed parts. (Woman, estab 1963, empl 17, sales $2,500,000, cert: WBENC)

6360 WCES, Inc.
     225 S Leonard St
     Waterbury, CT 06708
     Contact:
     Tel: 203-573-1325
     Email:
     Website: www.waterburycontract.com
Deep drawn eyelets & metal stampings, die design & manufacture, long run production, assembly, finishing & plating. (Woman, estab , empl , sales , cert: WBENC)

Georgia

6361 Dixien LLC
     5286 Circle Dr
     Lake City, GA 30260
     Contact: Alex Garcia VP Marketing
     Tel: 404-366-7427
     Email: agarcia@dixien.com
     Website: www.dixien.com
Stamping 100 ton to 1000 ton, welded sub-assemblies, tooling, plastic injection molding, blow molding & vaccum forming. (Hisp, estab 1961, empl 400, sales $25,000,000, cert: NMSDC)

Illinois

6362 Altak Inc.
     250 Covington Dr
     Bloomingdale, IL 60108
     Contact: Steve Janas Sales Mgr
     Tel: 630-622-0300
     Email: rtakayama@arktechno.com
     Website: www.altakinc.com
Wire Harness manufacturing, Switch Assembly manufacturing, Spring manufacturing, Stampings - 30 to 800 ton, Wire Forms, IATF 16949 and ISO 9001 certified. (As-Pac, estab 1980, empl 400, sales $37,000,000, cert: NMSDC)

6363 Flex-N-Gate Corp.
     5663 E 9 Mile Rd
     Urbana, IL 61802
     Contact: Teresa DeStefanis Acct Mgr
     Tel: 586-759-8613
     Email: tdestefanis@flexngate-mi.com
     Website: www.flex-n-gate.com
Automotive stampings, injection moldings, functional/ mechanical assemblies for OEMs, chrome plating & painting parts . (As-Ind, estab 1978, empl 9200, sales , cert: State)

6364 North Star Stamping & Tool, Inc.
     1264 Industrial Dr
     Lake in the Hills, IL 60156
     Contact: Catherine O'Brien
     Tel: 847-658-9400
     Email: nstar9400@aol.com
     Website: www.northstarstampingandtool.com
Metal stamping & assembly: 32 ton press to 200 ton press. (Woman, estab 1993, empl 9, sales , cert: WBENC)

6365 Reliable Machine Company
     1327 10th Ave
     Rockford, IL 61104
     Contact: Gloria Pernacciaro CEO
     Tel: 815-968-8803
     Email: gloriap@reliablemachine.com
     Website: www.reliablemachine.com
Metal Stampings, Part Production Capabilities: Deep draw up to 5 inches, Flat stampings, Stampings with multiple geometric forms, Secondary operations (piercing, staking, trimming and forming). (Woman, estab 1921, empl 40, sales $8,000,000, cert: WBENC)

Indiana

6366 Lacay Fabrication and Mfg Inc.
      52941 Glenview Dr
      Elkhart, IN 46514
      Contact: Ann Filley President
      Tel: 574-288-4678
      Email: ann@lacayfab.com
      Website: www.lacayfab.com
Mfr material handling racks, Baskets, Industrial & Production Welding, Machining, Robotic Welding, Stamping,
Custom Fabrication, Prototyping. (Woman, estab 1975,
empl 70, sales , cert: WBENC)

Massachusetts

6367 Springfield Spring
      311 Shaker Rd
      Longmeadow, MA 01028
      Contact: Norman Rodriques President
      Tel: 413-525-6837
      Email: pat@springfieldspring.com
      Website: www.springfieldspring.com
Mfr precision engineered compression springs, torsion
springs, extension springs, wire forms, fourslide-produced
stampings, assemblies. (Hisp, estab 1942, empl 39, sales
$7,200,000, cert: NMSDC)

Michigan

6368 Apex Spring & Stamping
      11420 First Ave
      Grand Rapids, MI 49534
      Contact: Doug Furness Sales/Eng Mgr
      Tel: 616-453-5463
      Email: djf@apexspring.com
      Website: www.apexspring.com
4 slide & vertislide, CNC winders, stamping presse to 110
ton & various assembly equipment, in-house tool room,
proto-type capability. (As-Pac, estab 1977, empl 40, sales
$12,000,000, cert: NMSDC)

6369 Atlas Tool Inc.
      29880 Groesbeck Hwy
      Roseville, MI 48066
      Contact: Douglas Flanagan Business Develop Mgr
      Tel: 586-778-3570
      Email: doug@atlastool.com
      Website: www.atlastool.com
Stamping dies, service parts production, prototype parts,
machining, engineering, die repair. (Woman, estab 1962,
empl 200, sales , cert: WBENC)

6370 Delaco Steel Corporation
      8111 Tireman, Ste 1
      Dearborn, MI 48126
      Contact: Michael Roualet VP of Quality
      Tel: 313-491-1200
      Email: mike.roualet@delacosteel.com
      Website: www.delacosteel.com
Dist & process steel & aluminum. Blanking, warehousing,
slitting, stampings, etc. (Woman/Hisp, estab 1974, empl
650, sales , cert: NMSDC, WBENC)

6371 DGH Enterprises, Inc. dba K-O Products Co.
      1225 Milton St
      Benton Harbor, MI 49022
      Contact: Barbara Herrold CEO
      Tel: 269-925-0657
      Email: barbaraherrold@koproducts.com
      Website: www.koproducts.com
Metal stampings, welded & fabricated assemblies,
electrical & mechanical assemblies, metal hardware,
metal truck parts & assemblies, metal stamped components for auto, appliances, off-road equipment, metal
welding, mig welding, spot welding. (Woman, estab
1938, empl 28, sales $5,700,000, cert: WBENC)

6372 Die Cad Group
      3258 Clear Vista Court NE
      Grand Rapids, MI 49525
      Contact: Bobbie Blanton President
      Tel: 616-365-2454
      Email: bobbie@diecadgroup.com
      Website: www.diecadgroup.com
Product & process simulation, tool & die design, mold
design, special purpose machine design, transfer press
simulation, die details sourcing, metal stamping die
design, metal stamping process development, stamped
parts formation. (Woman, estab 1995, empl 41, sales
$8,150,746, cert: WBENC)

6373 GK Tech, LLC
      3331 W Big Beaver Rd Ste 106
      Troy, MI 48084
      Contact: Kelly Choi
      Tel: 248-494-1960
      Email: kellychoi@gktechusa.com
      Website: www.gktechllc.com
Marketing specialist, consulting, business development,
forging, die-casting, stamping, spring, magnesium pulley,
rubber bushing, fasteners, machining, plastic injection
molding. (Woman/As-Pac, estab 2015, empl 3, sales ,
cert: NMSDC)

6374 Globe Tech LLC.
      101 Industrial Dr
      Plymouth, MI 48170
      Contact: Amanda Menchinger President
      Tel: 734-656-2200
      Email: mmenchinger@globe-tech.biz
      Website: www.globe-tech.biz
Machining, fabrication & welding, metal stamping.
(Woman, estab 2009, empl 72, sales , cert: WBENC)

6375 Lapeer Metal Stamping Companies, Inc.
      930 S Saginaw St
      Lapeer, MI 48446
      Contact: Joe Wierbicki VP sales/program mgmt
      Tel: 810-664-8588
      Email: jwierbicki@lapeermetal.com
      Website: www.lapeermetal.com
Mfr metal stampings & assemblies: seat frame assemblies, dash panels assemblies, heat shields, fuel tank
straps, pedals, brake, clutch, latches & hinges,
crossmembers, air bag components & structural body
components. (Hisp, estab 1960, empl 500, sales
$101,781,836, cert: NMSDC)

6376   Lucerne International
40 Corporate Dr
Auburn Hills, MI 48326
Contact: Karen Ryan Finance Mgr
Tel: 248-674-7210
Email: kryan@lucerneintl.com
Website: www.lucerneintl.com
Advanced metal forming components & assemblies, body structures, chassis systems & powertrain systems. Mfg aluminum & steel forgings, stampings, aluminum & zinc die castings & steel. (Woman, estab 1993, empl 58, sales , cert: WBENC)

6377   McKechnie Vehicle Components
27087 Gratiot Ave, 2 Fl
Roseville, MI 48066
Contact: Linda Torakis President
Tel: 586-491-2622
Email: ltorakis@mvcusa.com
Website: www.mvcusa.com
Mfr decorative trim products: nickel chrome plating on plastic and stainless surfaces, plastic injection molding, metal stamping, base and clear coat painting and assembly. (Woman, estab 0, empl , sales , cert: WBENC)

6378   Mico Industries, Inc.
2929 32nd St SE
Kentwood, MI 49512
Contact: Tracy DeKlein VP Technical Sales
Tel: 616-245-6426
Email: tdeklein@micoind.com
Website: www.micoindustries.com
Mfr metal stampings, welding, assemblies. (Hisp, estab 1983, empl 75, sales $12,000,000, cert: NMSDC)

6379   Motor City Stamping
47783 N Gratiot Ave
Chesterfield Twp, MI 48051
Contact: Paul Lachowicz controller
Tel: 586-949-8420
Email: plachowicz@mcstamp.com
Website: www.mcstamp.com
Medium stampings & multi-welded assemblies. (Minority/Woman, estab 1969, empl 350, sales $48,000,000, cert: WBENC)

6380   Proos Manufacturing, Inc.
1037 Michigan St NE
Grand Rapids, MI 49503
Contact: Amy Engelsman CEO
Tel: 616-454-5622
Email: aengelsman@proos.com
Website: www.proos.com
Metal stampings & assemblies. (Woman, estab 1919, empl , sales , cert: WBENC)

6381   PTM Corporation
6560 Bethuy
Fair Haven, MI 48023
Contact: Nicole Robinson Sales
Tel: 248-670-2650
Email: nrobinson@ptmcorporation.com
Website: http://ptmcorporation.com
Metal stamping, production up to 600 ton, prototype/low volume up to 1000 ton, tool design & build, laser, EDM, CNC, welding & assemblies. (Woman, estab 1972, empl 196, sales $60,000,000, cert: WBENC)

6382   Quasar Industries, Inc.
1911 Northfield Dr
Rochester Hills, MI 48309
Contact: Shane Majesky Qualtiy/Safety Mgr
Tel: 248-852-0300
Email: quality@quasar.com
Website: www.quasar.com
Prototypes, hydroforming, tube processing, deep draw & exotic metal stampings, laser cutting & welding, robotic welding, assemblies, fixture design & mfg, inspection, short run production, CNC machining, wire EDM & waterjet cutting. (Woman, estab 1967, empl 79, sales $13,000,000, cert: State)

6383   Rose-A-Lee Technologies, Inc
7448 19 Mile Rd
Sterling Heights, MI 48314
Contact: Julie Wood Dir Business Dev
Tel: 586-799-4555
Email: jwood@rosealeetechnologies.com
Website: www.rosealeetechnologies.com
CAD design (surface and solid modeling), stamping, assembly/kitting, tube bending, welding (mig, tig, stud arc), etc. (Woman, estab 2013, empl 2, sales , cert: WBENC)

6384   Roth-Williams Industries Inc. dba Lunar Industries
34335 Groesbeck Hwy
Clinton Township, MI 48035
Contact: Patricia Williams President
Tel: 586-792-0090
Email: pat@lunarind.com
Website: www.lunarind.com
Design & mfr custom tooling, fixtures, gages, stamping dies, prototype parts & stamped metal parts. (Woman, estab 1966, empl 9, sales $1,224,083, cert: NWBOC)

6385   Sequoia Tool
44831 N Groesbeck Hwy
Clinton Township, MI 48036
Contact: James Coates Acct Mgr
Tel: 586-463-4400
Email: bcoates@sequoiatool.net
Website: www.sequoiatool.net
Mfr prototype sheet metal stampings & assemblies, low volume production and short run svcs. (Nat Ame, estab 1988, empl 65, sales $10,000,000, cert: NMSDC)

Minnesota

6386   Bokers Inc.
3104 Snelling Ave
Minneapolis, MN 55406
Contact: Linda Demma CFO
Tel: 800-448-7492
Email: ldemma@bokers.com
Website: www.bokers.com
Mfr precision metallic & non-metallic stampings & washers. (Woman/AA, estab 1919, empl 110, sales , cert: WBENC)

6387   Top Tool Company
       3100 84th Lane Northeast
       Blaine, MN 55449
       Contact: Duane Kari Sales Mgr
       Tel: 763-786-0030
       Email: dakari@toptool.com
       Website: www.toptool.com
Dies, precision metal stampings & wire EDM, exotic &
precious metals, platinum, iridium, titanium, MP35N,
copper alloys, phos bronze, gold & silver plating. (Woman,
estab 1966, empl 30, sales $4,427,000, cert: State)

Missouri

6388   Thiel Tool & Engineering Co., Inc.
       4622 Bulwer Ave
       St. Louis, MO 63147
       Contact: Gary Shamel Sales Mgr
       Tel: 314-241-6121
       Email: gshamel@thieltool.com
       Website: www.thieltool.com
Automotive stampings & sub-assemblies. (Woman, estab
1945, empl 42, sales $10,000,000, cert: WBENC)

New York

6389   Bailey Manufacturing Co., LLC
       10987 Bennett State Rd
       Forestville, NY 14062
       Contact: John Hines President
       Tel: 716-965-2731
       Email: bailey03@netsync.net
       Website: www.baileymfgcollc.com
Metal Stamping, Sheet Metal Fabrication, Welding, Multi-
Part Assemblies, Zinc Plating, Rust Proofing, Quality
Inspection, E-Coat Painting. (AA, estab 2002, empl 100,
sales $8,500,000, cert: NMSDC)

6390   Cannon Industries, Inc.
       525 Lee Rd
       Rochester, NY 14606
       Contact: Reggie Cannon President
       Tel: 585-254-8080
       Email: rcannon@cannonind.com
       Website: www.cannonind.com
Sheet metal fabrication, welding fabrication, laser &
plasma cutting, metal stamping, CNC machining & turning,
mechanical assembly, spot welding. (AA, estab 1979, empl
104, sales $16,000,000, cert: NMSDC)

Ohio

6391   Die-Mension Corporation
       3020 Nationwide Pkwy
       Brunswick, OH 44212
       Contact: Karen Thompson President
       Tel: 330-273-5872
       Email: karen@diemension.com
       Website: www.diemension.com
Mfr & design precision progressive die & metal stampings.
(Woman, estab 1985, empl 8, sales $1,500,000, cert:
WBENC)

6392   GB Manufacturing Company
       100 Adams St
       Delta, OH 43515
       Contact: Teresa Elling Sales
       Tel: 419-822-5323
       Email: apetree@gbmfg.com
       Website: www.gbmfg.com
Stamping, laser blanking, fabrication & assembly, tool
making, robotic & hand welding, spot welding, press
braking, productin machining, prototyping. (As-Pac,
Hisp, estab 1975, empl 85, sales $24,500,000, cert:
NMSDC)

6393   Green Rock Lighting, LLC
       3175 W 33rd St
       Cleveland, OH 44109
       Contact: Tina Haddad CEO
       Tel: 216-651-6446
       Email: thaddad@greenrocklighting.com
       Website: www.greenrocklighting.com
Laser cutting, wire bending & forming, press brake,
spinning, stamping, mig, tig & stick welding, spot
welding, machining, destructive & non-destructive
testing, packaging & assembly. (Woman, estab 2011,
empl , sales $150,000, cert: State, WBENC)

6394   Hamlin Acquisition, LLC dba Hamlin Steel Prod-
       ucts
       2741 Wingate Ave
       Akron, OH 44314
       Contact: Lal Tekchandani President
       Tel: 330-753-7791
       Email: jkunczt@hnmetalstamping.com
       Website: www.hamlinsteel.com
Small to medium size metal stampings, assembly &
robotic welding capabilities. (As-Ind, estab 1953, empl
95, sales $15,000,000, cert: NMSDC)

6395   Hamlin Newco, LLC
       2741 Wingate Ave
       Akron, OH 44314
       Contact: Rick Sadd Sales Mgr
       Tel: 216-924-5449
       Email: ricksadd@gmail.com
       Website: www.hnmetalstamping.com/
Metal stampings & welded assemblies with presses up
to 800 tons for the automotive industry. (As-Pac, estab
1945, empl 105, sales $16,000,000, cert: NMSDC)

6396   Magni-Power Company
       5511 Lincoln Way E
       Wooster, OH 44691
       Contact: Kim Coblentz New Business Devel
       Tel: 330-264-3637
       Email: kcoblentz@magnipower.com
       Website: www.magnipower.com
Metal fabrication & stamping: process steel, aluminum,
stainless steel, CNC punching, forming, laser cutting,
robotic welding, in-house powder coating & assembly.
(As-Ind, estab 1948, empl 230, sales $27,000,000, cert:
NMSDC)

6397 Mohr Stamping, Inc.
      22038 Fairgrounds Rd
      Wellington, OH 44090
      Contact: Amber Mohrman CEO
      Tel: 440-647-4316
      Email: sales@mohrstamping.com
      Website: www.mohrstamping.com
Metal Stampings, Die design and Build, Assembly.
(Woman, estab 1967, empl 25, sales $4,000,000, cert:
WBENC)

6398 Tech-Matic Industries, Inc.
      17941 Englewood Dr
      Middleburg Heights, OH 44130
      Contact: Kathleen Byrnes President
      Tel: 440-826-3191
      Email: kbyrnes@tc-tm.com
      Website: www.tc-tm.com
Metal stamping for automotive industry. (Woman, estab
1985, empl 9, sales $4,000,000, cert: WBENC)

6399 Wrena, LLC dba Angstrom-USA, LLC
      265 Lightner Rd
      Tipp City, OH 45371
      Contact: Nagesh Palakurthi CEO
      Tel: 937-667-4403
      Email: pyenger@wrenallc.com
      Website: http://angstrom-usa.com
Stampings, tubular products, machining, welding, robotic
welding, steel forgings (Warm & Cold), aluminum forgings,
assemblies, plastic injection molding, needle bearings,
starter assemblies (As-Pac, estab 2011, empl 46, sales ,
cert: NMSDC)

6400 Zip Tool & Die Inc.
      12200 Sprecher Ave
      Cleveland, OH 44135
      Contact: Victor De Leaon CEO
      Tel: 216-267-1117
      Email: vdeleon@tritonduro.com
      Website: www.ziptool.com
Engineering, Prototyping, Metal Forming, Metal Stamping
& Tool & Die solutions. (Hisp, estab 1968, empl 10, sales
$650,000, cert: NMSDC)

Pennsylvania

6401 Spalding Automotive, Inc.
      1011 Cedar Ave
      Croydon, PA 19021
      Contact: Vincent Florio Business Development
      Tel: 215-826-4061
      Email: vflorio@spaldingautomotive.com
      Website: www.spaldingautomotive.com
Metal stampings, roll form components, welding, mechanical assemblies & design & build tooling. (Hisp, estab
1987, empl 75, sales $18,518,000, cert: NMSDC)

6402 Tottser Tool and Manufacturing
      1630 Republic Rd
      Huntingdon Valley, PA 19006
      Contact: Linda Macht President
      Tel: 215-357-7600
      Email: lmacht@tottser.com
      Website: www.tottser.com
Metal stampings, tool & die. (Woman, estab 0, empl , sales
, cert: WBENC)

Wisconsin

6403 Church Metal Spinning Company
      5050 N 124th St
      Milwaukee, WI 53225
      Contact: Brenda Birno President
      Tel: 414-461-6460
      Email: markv@churchmetal.com
      Website: http://churchmetal.com
Metal fabrications including metal stampings, metal
spun, laser cut, press brake parts. Also, complete
assembly and welding of multi-part components.
(Woman, estab 1944, empl 30, sales $6,600,000, cert:
State)

6404 Universal Die & Stampings
      735 15th St
      Prairie du Sac, WI 53555
      Contact: Karl Andersson Sales Mgr
      Tel: 608-643-2477
      Email: kanders@unidie.com
      Website: www.unidie.com
Precision, high volume metal stamping, full tooling.
(Woman, estab 1967, empl 32, sales $6,000,000, cert:
City)

METAL, GENERAL MACHINING
Job shops, prototypes, short and long run production work. Tool and dies, jigs and fixtures, electromechanical assemblies, etc. (Also see six other METAL categories). NAICS Code 33

Alaska

6405 Superior Machine & Welding Inc.
1745 Ship Ave
Anchorage, AK 99501
Contact: President
Tel: 907-277-3538
Email:
Website: www.superiormachine.net
Machine & welding. (Woman, estab 1950, empl 10, sales , cert: WBENC)

Alabama

6406 Theonics Inc.
12525 Memorial Pkwy SW
Huntsville, AL 35803
Contact: Shelley Coxwell President
Tel: 256-885-3500
Email: shelley.coxwell@theonicsinc.com
Website: www.theonicsinc.com
Precision machining, CMM inspection & assembly of complex hardware. (Woman, estab 2012, empl 31, sales $1,300,000, cert: WBENC)

Arizona

6407 Conway Machine, Inc.
192 Commerce Rd
Conway, AR 72032
Contact: Anthony Davis President
Tel: 501-327-1311
Email: tonyd@conwaymachine.com
Website: www.ConwayMachine.com
Precision milling & turning machining. (Woman, estab 1970, empl 25, sales $2,400,000, cert: WBENC)

6408 J.B.'s Precision Industries
2320 W Parkside Lane
Phoenix, AZ 85027
Contact: Steve Hoffner GM
Tel: 623-581-9088
Email: steve@jbsprecision.com
Website: www.jbsprecision.com
CNC machining, 4 mills, 3 lathes & multiple manual machines. (Woman, estab 1966, empl 11, sales $1,400,000, cert: State)

6409 State Technology & Manufacturing
2555 E University Dr
Phoenix, AZ 85034
Contact: Ruben Cadena CEO
Tel: 602-275-0990
Email: ruben@azsip.com
Website: www.azsip.com
Machinng, mill, lathe, CNC, welding, fabricating, dist steel, copper, brass, bronze, stainless steel, aluminum. (Hisp, estab 2003, empl 21, sales $3,000,000, cert: State, City, NMSDC)

California

6410 3D Machine Company, Inc.
4790 E Wesley Dr
Anaheim, CA 92807
Contact: Maria Falcusan President
Tel: 714-777-8985
Email: costel@3dmachineco.com
Website: www.3dmachineco.com
CNC machining, 5-axis CNC capability, CAD/CAM software, precision-machined parts & assemblies. (Woman, estab 1996, empl 35, sales , cert: CPUC)

6411 A Better Affect, Inc. dba ABACORP CNC
9165 Independence Ave
Chatsworth, CA 91311
Contact: Kim Frankel President
Tel: 818-771-7671
Email: kim@abacorpcnc.com
Website: www.abacorpcnc.com
CNC machining services. (Woman, estab 1998, empl 38, sales $3,349,575, cert: State)

6412 ACC Precision, Inc.
321 Hearst Dr
Oxnard, CA 93030
Contact: Arturo Alfaro GM
Tel: 805-278-9801
Email: aalfaro@accprecision.com
Website: www.accprecision.com
Precision manufacturing & assembly: CNC Turning, CNC Milling, DNC Software Tooling & measuring machines. (Hisp, estab 1998, empl 22, sales $1,867,833, cert: 8a)

6413 Acutek US
1488 E Valencia Dr
Fullerton, CA 92831
Contact: Charley Yoo Owner
Tel: 714-278-0912
Email: cyoo@acutekus.com
Website: www.acutekus.com
CNC milling, turning: aluminum, steel, titanium, copper, brass. 3 & 4 axis programming tooling fixtures, electronic file transfer. (As-Pac, estab 2003, empl 60, sales $10,700,000, cert: CPUC)

6414 Aranda Tooling, Inc.
15301 Springdale St
Huntington Beach, CA 92649
Contact: Gerrard Connolly GM
Tel: 714-379-6565
Email: gerrard.connolly@arandatooling.com
Website: www.arandatooling.com
Medium to high production metal stamping, assembly, robotic welding, tooling, EDM, prototypes. (Hisp, estab 1975, empl 125, sales , cert: NMSDC)

6415 Azachorok Contract Services LLC
320 Grand Cypress Ave Ste 502
Palmdale, CA 93551
Contact: Gene Souza Mgr
Tel: 661-951-6566
Email: gsouza@azachorok.com
Website: www.azcsllc.com
Precision CNC machining & turnining, aircraft structures, machined housings, castings, aluminum, steel, titanium, copper, brass etc. (Nat Ame, estab 1998, empl 12, sales $550,000, cert: 8a, SDB)

6416   Bay Tank and Boiler Works
       825 W 14th St
       Eureka, CA 95501
       Contact: Amandy Massey Office Mgr
       Tel: 707-443-0934
       Email: info@btmetals.com
       Website: http://baytankandboilerworks.com
Carbon Steel Products Stainless Steel Products Aluminum
Products Rebar Industrial Fasteners (Stock and Custom)
We specialize in Made in the USA Certified Welding
Drilling, Milling, Plasma Cutting, Oxy Fuel Cutting, laser
Forming, Press (Woman, estab 1956, empl 7, sales
$500,000, cert: CPUC)

6417   Bishop-Wisecarver Corporation
       2104 Martin Way
       Pittsburg, CA 94565
       Contact: Barbara Williams Supplier Diversity
       Administrator
       Tel: 888-580-8272
       Email: bwilliams@bwc.com
       Website: www.bwc.com
Mfr linear & rotary motion components, custom engineering services, bearings, vee guide wheels, linear guides,
linear actuator, custom machine shop, XYZ systems, gantry,
rotary tables, custom assembly, linear slides, linear
bearing, dualvee. (Woman, estab 1950, empl 64, sales
$21,000,000, cert: WBENC)

6418   California Machine Specialties
       12282 Colony Ave
       Chino, CA 91710
       Contact: Anand Jagani Owner
       Tel: 909-464-0405
       Email: anand@calmachine.com
       Website: www.calmachine.com
Precision machining, CNC milling, 4 axis milling, CNC
turning, machining of castings & forgings, bar & plate
stocks, mechanical assemblies, brazed assemblies, hardware installation, bushing & bearing installation, adhesive
bonding. (As-Ind, estab 1977, empl 19, sales $1,500,000,
cert: State)

6419   Dinucci Corporation
       1057 Shary Cir
       Concord, CA 94518
       Contact: Gabriela Dinucci COO
       Tel: 925-798-3946
       Email: gabriela@dinuccicorp.com
       Website: www.dinuccicorp.com
Machine shop; computerized mfg & precision prototypes.
(Woman/Hisp, estab 1978, empl 25, sales $4,227,662, cert:
NMSDC)

6420   Fabtronics, Inc.
       5026 Calmview Ave
       Baldwin Park, CA 91706
       Contact: David K. Thompson VP of Operations
       Tel: 626-962-3293
       Email: contact@fabtronics.com
       Website: www.fabtronics.com
Precision sheet metal mfg, CNC turret punching, spot
welding, enclosures, tubular frame weldments, skins &
chassis. (Hisp, estab 1976, empl 14, sales $3,500,000, cert:
NMSDC)

6421   G.B.F. Enterprises, Inc.
       2709 S Halladay St
       Santa Ana, CA 92705
       Contact: Keith Garrison VP
       Tel: 714-979-7131
       Email: keith@gbfenterprises.com
       Website: www.gbfenterprises.com
Mfr precision lathe & mill parts per customer specifications. (Woman, estab 1976, empl 24, sales $2,194,551,
cert: State)

6422   Hunter Hawk, Inc.
       1842 Taft St
       Concord, CA 94521
       Contact: Sandy Hunter President
       Tel: 925-798-4950
       Email: sandy@hunterhawk.com
       Website: www.hunterhawk.com
Precision mechanical components, fabrication, reverse
engineering, documentation, critical inventory &
equipment boxes. (Woman, estab 1994, empl 4, sales
$1,886,100, cert: State, CPUC, WBENC)

6423   Infinity Precision Inc.
       6919 Eton Ave
       Canoga Park, CA 91303
       Contact: President
       Tel: 818-447-3008
       Email:
       Website: www.ipinc-usa.com
Hydroforming, Machined parts per print, CAD/CAM/
CNC Machining, 5-Axiss Water Jet Cutting, Honing, Sheet
Metal Fabrication (Woman, estab 1996, empl 19, sales
$2,338,000, cert: WBENC)

6424   Ingels Engineering Inc.
       1828 Evergreen St
       Duarte, CA 91010
       Contact: Enilde Ingels VP
       Tel: 626-256-1967
       Email: eeemachineshop@earthlink.net
       Website: www.ingelsengineeringservices.com
Machining & engineering consulting services, specialized
medical devices, prototype works, short run productions
in Stainless Steel, Aluminum, Delrin, Brass, Copper or
plastics. (Woman/Hisp, estab 1997, empl 7, sales
$230,000, cert: State, City)

6425   International Rite-Way Products
       1725 S Campus Ave
       Ontario, CA 91761
       Contact: Ravi Joshi President
       Tel: 909-985-8300
       Email: ravi@intlrwp.com
       Website: www.intlrwp.com
Precision aerospace sheet metal mfg: roll forming,
hydroforming, extrusion & skin stretch forming of
aerospace components (ribs, spars, brackets, formers,
etc.). Complete program management capabilities. (As-
Ind, estab 1994, empl 10, sales $1,250,000, cert: 8a)

6426   JB Manufacturing
       2814 Aiello Dr Ste D
       San Jose, CA 95111
       Contact: Jim Ogawa GM
       Tel: 408-281-9994
       Email: jim@jb-mfg.com
       Website: www.jb-mfg.com
CNC milling & turning, 5 CNC vertical mills & 1 CNC
lathe. (As-Pac, estab 1985, empl 4, sales $325,000, cert:
NMSDC)

6427   KFM International Industries, Inc.
       20277 Valley Blvd, Ste L
       Walnut, CA 91789
       Contact: Dennis Boribor Engineer
       Tel: 626-369-9556
       Email: dennis@kfmii.com
       Website: www.kfmii.com
Casting: Sand Cast, Die Casting, Investment Casting &
Permanent Mold Forging: Hot & Cold Formed Sheet Metal
Stamping Machining: CNC,Turning & Milling Powder Metal.
(Woman/As-Pac, estab 2000, empl 6, sales $2,500,000,
cert: City, CPUC)

6428   Kimberly Machine Inc.
       12822 Joy St
       Garden Grove, CA 92840
       Contact: Matias Clark GM
       Tel: 714-539-0151
       Email: matias@kimberlymachine.com
       Website: www.kimberlymachine.com
Mfr precision machined parts, Precision CNC machining &
Assembly Prototype to production- Simple to Complex 2D
to 3D. (As-Pac, estab 1975, empl 24, sales $4,233,384, cert:
State)

6429   LT CNC Machining, Inc.
       7945 Silverton Ave, Ste 1103
       San Diego, CA 92126
       Contact: Liem Phan President
       Tel: 858-586-7705
       Email: liem@ltmachininginc.com
       Website: www.ltmachininginc.com
CNC milling & machining. (Woman/As-Pac, estab 2006,
empl 7, sales $800,000, cert: State)

6430   M&L Precision Machining
       18655 Madrone Pkwy
       Morgan Hill, CA 95037
       Contact: Mike Sullivan Business Specialist
       Tel: 408-436-3955
       Email: mikes@mlprecision.com
       Website: www.mlprecision.com
Precision machining done with over 55 mills and multiple
lathes. (Woman, estab 1971, empl 110, sales $18,000,000,
cert: WBENC)

6431   Machining Solutions Inc.
       22122 S Vermont Ste F
       Torrance, CA 90502
       Contact: Edward Dennis President
       Tel: 310-787-1790
       Email: edward.dennis@machining-sol.com
       Website: www.machining-sol.com
Machining: stainless steel, titanium, Inconel & other high
temperature grades. (AA, estab 1998, empl 6, sales
$750,000, cert: State)

6432   Mirofine Company
       1940 W 144th St
       Gardenia, CA 90249
       Contact: Wayne Perez President
       Tel: 310-327-2622
       Email: mirofine@mirofine.com
       Website: www.mirofine.com
CNC precision turning & milling. (Hisp, estab 1970, empl 6,
sales , cert: State)

6433   Nichols Manufacturing, Inc.
       913 Hanson Ct
       Milpitas, CA 95035
       Contact: Maria Nichols President
       Tel: 408-945-0911
       Email: lnichols@nicholsmfg.com
       Website: www.nicholsmfg.com
Machined parts & fasteners, CNC mills, conventional
mills & lathes. (Woman/Hisp, estab 1978, empl 17, sales
$1,800,000, cert: State)

6434   Qualitask, Inc.
       2840 E Gretta Lane
       Anaheim, CA 92806
       Contact: Som Suntharaphat President
       Tel: 714-237-0900
       Email: soms@qualitask.net
       Website: www.qualitask.com
CNC Milling & Turning, Research & Development,
Prototype & Production Machining, Jigs & Fixtures,
steel, stainless steel, titanium, aluminum, plastics. (As-
Pac, estab 1992, empl 30, sales $1,187,381, cert:
NMSDC)

6435   Spec-Metal Inc.
       P.O. Box 660536
       Arcadia, CA 91066
       Contact: Evelyn Chen
       Tel: 626-301-7969
       Email: evelync@spec-metal.com
       Website: www.Spec-Metal.com
Machine metal precision machined parts: aluminum,
brass, copper, carbon steel & stainless steel. Engineering design, product development, manufacturing,
logistics & customer service. (Woman/As-Pac, estab
2008, empl 4, sales $2,600,000, cert: NMSDC)

6436   UDASH Corp.
       200 N Ashdale Ave
       Los Angeles, CA 90049
       Contact: George Melamed tech sales
       Tel: 310-472-2798
       Email: udash26@hotmail.com
       Website: www.udash.com
CNC milling, turning & 5-axis machining. (Woman/As-
Ind, estab 1981, empl 6, sales , cert: State)

Colorado

6437   Custom Machining Corporation
       2090 W College Ave
       Englewood, CO 80110
       Contact: Terri Yount-Ross
       Tel: 303-762-0333
       Email: terri.ross@cmc1.net
       Website:
Can lining machining. (Woman, estab 0, empl , sales ,
cert: WBENC)

6438   Excalibur Machine & Sheet Metal
       208 W Buchanan St, Unit C
       Colorado Springs, CO 80907
       Contact: Douglas McDaniel Plant Mgr
       Tel: 719-520-5404
       Email: doug@excaliburmfg.com
       Website: www.excaliburmfg.com/
Precision machining & sheet metal fabrication, welding,
assembly, powder coating. (Hisp, estab 1989, empl 25,
sales $2,600,000, cert: NMSDC)

6439 Mountainside Medical Colorado, LLC
6165 Lookout Rd
Boulder, CO 80301
Contact: Susan Neidecker President
Tel: 303-222-1271
Email: sneidecker@mountainsidemed.com
Website: www.mountainsidemed.com
Contract manufacturing for complex, tight-tolerance medical products, Multi-axis Machining Assembly, Wire EDMCNC, Swiss type machining centers, Laser welding & Laser marking, Finishing Metal Forming. (Woman, estab 2006, empl 90, sales $12,731,416, cert: WBENC)

Florida

6440 Custom Manufacturing & Engineering, Inc.
3690 70th Ave North
Pinellas Park, FL 33781
Contact: Fred Munro VP
Tel: 727-547-9799
Email: fmunro@custom-mfg-eng.com
Website: www.custom-mfg-eng.com
Subassemblies, turn-key, integrated test systems & process equip. (Woman, estab 1997, empl 40, sales $10,300,000, cert: WBENC)

6441 KN Machine & Tool, Inc.
3125 Jupiter Park Circle Ste 4
Jupiter, FL 33458
Contact: Ron Passino Operations Mgr
Tel: 561-748-3035
Email: ron@knmachine.com
Website: www.knmachine.com
High Speed Machining on Milling machines capable of handling parts up 40"x20"x20".
Turning w/ Live Tooling up to 2-5/8" Bar Capacity and up to 12" O.D. Turning. (As-Pac, estab 2000, empl 10, sales $1,300,000, cert: State)

6442 Mashack & Associates, Inc.
503 Tuscanny St
Brandon, FL 33511
Contact: Brenda Rhym President
Tel: 813-662-7353
Email: bdrhym@verizon.net
Website:
CNC machining & printed circuit board assembly. (Woman/AA, estab 1998, empl 2, sales $105,000, cert: 8a)

6443 Skill-Metric Machine and Tool, Inc.
1424 Gwenzell Ave
Delray Beach, FL 33444
Contact: Anthony Kresty COO
Tel: 561-454-8895
Email: akresty@skill-metric.com
Website: www.skill-metric.com
Jet engine tooling, ground support equipment, munitions handling equipment, airframe components, precision machined parts. (Woman/AA, As-Ind, As-Pac, Hisp, estab 1978, empl 30, sales $4,600,000, cert: State)

6444 Velezco Inc.
4401 112th Terrace N, Unit F
Clearwater, FL 33762
Contact: Travis Smith Office Mgr
Tel: 727-571-1026
Email: travis@velezco.com
Website: www.velezco.com
CNC & manual machining. (Hisp, estab 2002, empl 6, sales $344,642, cert: State)

Georgia

6445 Omni Machine Works, Inc.
30-A Chamisa Rd
Covington, GA 30016
Contact: Claudia Engelbracht President
Tel: 404-861-9035
Email: claudia@omnimachineworks.com
Website: www.omnimachineworks.com
Full service machine shope, custom machine manufacturer & engineering/design resource. (Woman, estab 0, empl , sales , cert: WBENC)

Iowa

6446 Indoshell Precision Technologies, LLC
435 Precision Pkwy
Story City, IA 50248
Contact: Ramki Ramakrishan Owner
Tel: 713-992-6666
Email: paul.diggins@isptglobal.com
Website: www.isptglobal.com
Precision machine aluminum and steel, CNC Turning Centers and Swiss Turning Centers; Multi axis CNC HMC and VMC Machining Centers with pallet changers; as well as lapping, honing and grinding work centers. (As-Ind, estab 2009, empl 75, sales $12,000,000, cert: NMSDC)

Illinois

6447 ADC LP
1720 Wolf Rd
Wheeling, IL 60090
Contact: Patrick Tang President
Tel: 847-541-3030
Email: ptang@adclp.com
Website: www.adclp.com
High pressure aluminum die casting, CNC machining, automated assembly. (As-Pac, estab 1991, empl 243, sales $35,000,000, cert: NMSDC)

6448 Craftsman Custom Metals, LLC
3838 N River Rd
Schiller Park, IL 60176
Contact: William Johnson Business Develop Mgr
Tel: 847-655-0040
Email: wjohnson@ccm.com
Website: www.ccm.com
Custom chassis & enclosures, cabinets, brackets, structural components, OEM's & EMS's, prototype development, precision milling, metal stamping, testing, weilding, engineering support, mechanical & electro-mechanical assembly. (Hisp, estab 1953, empl 65, sales $10,000,000, cert: NMSDC)

6449 Edmik Inc.
3850 Grove Ave
Gurnee, IL 60031
Contact: Heidi Knill VP
Tel: 847-263-0460
Email: edmik@edmik1.com
Website: www.edmik1.com/
Production, custom tooling, machinery & engineering, CAD/CAM, contract & production assembly, industrial appliances, machining & tooling services. (Woman/Hisp, estab 1957, empl 32, sales $3,200,000, cert: NMSDC)

6450 KDL Machining, Inc.
1917 S 2nd St
Pekin, IL 61554
Contact: Deborah Lutz President
Tel: 309-477-3036
Email: kdl@grics.net
Website:
Portable machining, turning, welding, boring, milling, pump repair, piercing & forming, die fabrication & repair, large shafting, mold building & repair, production, grinding, vertical machining production work, industrial repair work. (Woman, estab 1998, empl 12, sales $827,551, cert: NWBOC)

6451 KrisDee & Associates, Inc.
755 Schneider Dr
South Elgin, IL 60177
Contact: Hermann VP
Tel: 847-608-8300
Email: gregg.m@krisdee.com
Website: www.krisdee.com
Precision machining of non ferrous prismatic components. (Nat Ame, estab 1983, empl 65, sales $14,000,000, cert: NMSDC)

6452 Lakeview Precision Machining, Inc.
751 Schneider Dr
South Elgin, IL 60177
Contact: President
Tel: 847-742-7170
Email:
Website: www.lakeviewprecision.com
CNC precision machining. (Woman, estab 2006, empl 15, sales $1,600,000, cert: WBENC)

6453 Machined Products Co.
2121 Landmeier Rd
Elk Grove Village, IL 60007
Contact: Mohammed Qureshi President
Tel: 847-718-1300
Email: mirna@machinedproducts.com
Website: www.machinedproducts.com
Machine iron, steel & aluminum. (As-Ind, estab 1958, empl 100, sales , cert: NMSDC)

6454 Microtech Machine Company, Inc.
222 Camp McDonald Rd
Wheeling, IL 60090
Contact: Elizabeth A. Iwanicki CEO
Tel: 847-870-0707
Email: microcamp@aol.com
Website: www.microtech-machine.com
Engineering services & precision machined prototype & production components, precision machining, machine design & building, assembly & welding. (Woman, estab 1984, empl 22, sales $4,000,000, cert: NWBOC)

6455 Monnex Precision Inc.
476 Diens Dr
Wheeling, IL 60090
Contact: James E. Wallace Sr. President
Tel: 847-478-1800
Email: jwallace@monnex.net
Website:
Metals, die casting, stampings & fasteners. (AA, As-Pac, estab 1985, empl 620, sales $5,000,000, cert: NMSDC)

6456 Multitech Industries, Inc.
350 Village Dr
Carol Stream, IL 60188
Contact: Nick S. Anastopoulos Business Dev Mgr
Tel: 630-784-9200
Email: nick@multitechind.com
Website: www.multitechind.com
Wire forms, castings, forgings, stampings, machining, cold-heading. (As-Ind, estab 1993, empl 60, sales $100,000,000, cert: NMSDC)

6457 Pioneer Service Inc.
542 W Factory Rd
Addison, IL 60101
Contact: Beth Swanson VP Sales/Mktg
Tel: 630-628-0249
Email: bswanson@pioneerserviceinc.com
Website: www.pioneerserviceinc.com/
Contract mfr screw machine products & centerless grinding services: shafts, axles, bolts, bushings, dowels, pins, rods, spacers, valve stems, deburring, drilling, flatting, grinding, knurling, slotting, tapping, threading, heat treating. (Woman, estab 1990, empl 40, sales $5,000,000, cert: CPUC, WBENC)

6458 Precise Products Inc.
3286 Talbot Ave
Warrenville, IL 60555
Contact: Ernest Tucker CEO
Tel: 630-393-9698
Email: preciseproducts@ameritech.net
Website:
Automatic screw & CNC machined parts. (AA, estab 1966, empl 30, sales $3,000,000, cert: NMSDC)

6459 Tuson Corporation
475 Bunker Court
Vernon Hills, IL 60061
Contact: Michael Jin Sales Mgr
Tel: 847-816-8800
Email: michael-jin@tuson.com
Website: www.tuson.com
Precision CNC machining, powdered metal, forging, casting, gear, hydraulic relief valve assembly, pump, motor & cylinder components, electric motor. (As-Pac, estab 1987, empl 200, sales $29,000,000, cert: NMSDC)

Indiana

6460 A&A Custom Automation, Inc.
2125 Bergdolt Rd
Evansville, IN 47711
Contact: Bill Frey Sales Rep
Tel: 812-464-3650
Email: bfrey@aacustomautomation.com
Website: http://AAcustomautomation.com
Precision CNC machining, steel fabrication, design, mfg & rebuild automated equipment, mechanical & electrical engineering, (Woman, estab 1989, empl 55, sales , cert: NWBOC)

6461 Accutech Mold & Machine, Inc.
2817 Goshen Rd
Fort Wayne, IN 46808
Contact: Darrin Geiger VP
Tel: 260-471-6102
Email: dgeiger@accutechmoldinc.com
Website: http://accutechmoldinc.com
Plastic injection molding, Insert plastic injection molder of cables/connectors, rapid prototype tooling builder/ injection molding, production machining of brass, aluminum & metals, prototype machining of brass, aluminum & metals. (Woman, estab 1996, empl 70, sales $3,000,000, cert: WBENC)

6462 AMG Engineering & Machining, Inc.
4030 Guion Ln
Indianapolis, IN 46268
Contact: Chris Chadd Business Development
Tel: 317-329-4000
Email: cchadd@amgindy.com
Website: www.amgindy.com
Mfr & design machined components, fluid controls & connectors, adapters, fittings, plugs, check valves, gas regulators & pressure relief valves. (AA, estab 1989, empl 46, sales , cert: NMSDC)

6463 Brinly-Hardy Company
3230 Industrial Pkwy
Jeffersonville, IN 47130
Contact: Scott Whitehouse Sales Mgr
Tel: 812-218-7219
Email: swhitehouse@brinly.com
Website: www.brinly.com
Bending & forming, welding, powder painting, assembly & packaging. (Woman, estab , empl 150, sales $28,000,001, cert: WBENC)

6464 Exacto, Inc. of South Bend
1137 S Lafayette Blvd
South Bend, IN 46601
Contact: Barbara Jordan CEO
Tel: 574-288-4716
Email: bjordan@exacto-inc.com
Website: www.exacto-inc.com
CNC turning, CNC milling, OD/ID grinding, lapping & honing (Woman, estab 1970, empl 52, sales $4,000,000, cert: WBENC)

6465 Mercer Machine
1421 S Holt Rd
Indianapolis, IN 46241
Contact: Joe Robinson VP Sales
Tel: 317-441-0877
Email: jrobinson@mercermachine.net
Website: www.mercermachine.net
CNN machining. (Woman, estab 1954, empl 20, sales $2,000,000, cert: WBENC)

6466 Precision Cadcam, Inc.
8446 Brookville Rd
Indianapolis, IN 46239
Contact: Darryl Williams President
Tel: 317-353-8058
Email: precisioncadcam@sbcglobal.net
Website: http://pccinc.org
Precision maching and molding, tool & dies. (AA, estab 2004, empl 2, sales $170,000, cert: NMSDC)

6467 Royalty Investments, LLC
2476 E US Hwy 50
Seymour, IN 47274
Contact: Marshall Royalty Member
Tel: 812-358-3534
Email: mroyalty@cranehillmachine.com
Website: www.cranehillmachine.com
Machining, fabricating & assembly: steel, aluminum & plastic components. Design, engineering & coating applications. (Woman, estab 1989, empl 30, sales $3,714,618, cert: State, WBENC)

6468 Sceptre Mechanical Inc.
93 E County Rd, Ste 200 N
Rockport, IN 47635
Contact: Joe Hagan GM
Tel: 812-649-9820
Email: Joe.Hagan@SceptreMech.com
Website: www.sceptremech.com
Industrial maintenance & machining services, dist & repair industrial tools. (Woman/Nat Ame, estab 1991, empl 45, sales , cert: State, WBENC)

Louisiana

6469 P&R Accessories, LLC
15396 Hwy 90
Paradis, LA 70080
Contact: Philip Strother Owner
Tel: 985-758-5558
Email: philip@acu-jet.com
Website: http://pandraccessories.com
Mfr & construction: naval ship computer simulation, injected molded plastics, lasercutting, waterjet machining, EDM machining, circuit board printing, pulsed laser deposition mfg of composites & superconductors. (Nat Ame, estab 2002, empl 4, sales $490,566, cert: 8a)

6470 Vast Industries
108 Venus St Ste 200
Morgan City, LA 70380
Contact: Yvette Archuleta-Tudury Owner
Tel: 985-312-1592
Email: yvette@vast-ind.com
Website: www.Vast-Ind.com
Wire EDM & precision machined parts manufacturing, custom product design, reverse engineering & aluminum & steel fabrication. (Woman/Nat Ame, Hisp, estab 2007, empl 7, sales $600,000, cert: NMSDC, WBENC, 8a)

Massachusetts

6471 Boulevard Machine & Gear
326 Lockhouse Road
Westfield, MA 01085
Contact: Susan Kasa President
Tel: 413-788-6466
Email: tanya@boulevardmachine.com
Website: http://boulevardmachine.com/
Mfr aerospace, defense, paper & commercial parts, precision machining, CNC turning, lathe & milling, manual lathes & millers, grinding, splines, rack cutting, turning, honing, stamping & assembly. (Woman, estab 1954, empl 22, sales , cert: WBENC)

6472   Fitz Machine Inc.
4 Railroad Ave
Wakefield, MA 01880
Contact: Kathleen Fitzgerald President
Tel: 781-245-5966
Email: kathleen@fitzmachine.com
Website: www.fitzmachine.com
Precision CNC machined components, multi axis capabilities, prototype & production machining, long & short production runs, in-house tooling design. (Woman, estab 1994, empl 15, sales $1,300,000, cert: WBENC)

6473   M&K Engineering
66 Concord St
North Reading, MA 01864
Contact: Gene Ungvarsky Business Dev Mgr
Tel: 978-276-1973
Email: gene@mkeng.com
Website: www.mkeng.com
Precision machining: CNC & swiss screw CNC. (Minority, Woman, estab 1990, empl 28, sales $4,464,492, cert: NMSDC)

6474   PremaTech Advanced Ceramics
2 Coppage Dr
Worcester, MA 01603
Contact: Thomas Shearer Dir Business Dev
Tel: 508-791-9549
Email: info@prematechac.com
Website: www.PremaTechAC.com
Fabricate technical ceramics, sapphire, composite & exotic materials, machining & grinding, ceramic components, refractories, cordierite, kiln furniture, porous metal parts, stainless steel, bronze & titanium filters, zinc, zinc selenide. (Woman, estab 1980, empl 35, sales $3,525,000, cert: WBENC)

6475   Wrobel Engineering Co., Inc.
154 Bodwell St
Avon, MA 02322
Contact: Michael Long General/QA Mgr.
Tel: 508-586-8338
Email: mlong@wrobeleng.com
Website: www.wrobeleng.com
Mfr precision sheet metal fabricated parts per customer specs, precision machining, milling & turning, metal stamping, long & short runs, tool & die making, assembly mechanical & electrical, welding all materials. (Woman, estab 1976, empl 86, sales $14,800,000, cert: State, City)

Maryland

6476   FlexFit Hose LLC
7948 E. Baltimore St.
Baltimore, MD 21224
Contact: Arjun Radhakrishnan Managing Partner
Tel: 410-327-0758
Email: sales@flexfithose.com
Website: www.ffhose.com
CNC Swiss machining, MNT, Female NPT, Female JIC, Tube Adaptors, Tri-Clamps, Mini Tri-Clamps. (AA, estab 2008, empl 4, sales $1,400,000, cert: NMSDC, SDB)

6477   Ray Machine Inc.
12 Lynbrook Rd
Baltimore, MD 21220
Contact: Dan Solomon GM
Tel: 410-686-6955
Email: dsolomon@rayamch.com
Website: www.raymachine.com
CNC & conventional machining; precision sheet metal fab, welding, mechanical & elec assembly, etc. (As-Ind, estab 1950, empl 42, sales $4,711,000, cert: NMSDC)

Michigan

6478   2K Tool LLC
3025 Madison Ave SE
Wyoming, MI 49548
Contact: Kevin Smith Engineering Mgr
Tel: 616-452-4927
Email: kevin@2ktool.com
Website: www.2ktool.com
Moldmaker, machining, tooling, plastic injection molds, compression tooling, composite machining, casting machining, small part Injection molding. (Woman, estab 2004, empl 19, sales $2,269,151, cert: WBENC)

6479   Accu-Shape Die Cutting, Inc.
4050 Market Place Dr
Flint, MI 48507
Contact: Joe Brooks New Business Devel
Tel: 810-230-2445
Email: joebrooks@accushape.com
Website: www.accushape.com
Large parts a specialty up to 84" x 75" in size with kiss cutting capability from larger roll stock. Lamination of pressure sensitive adhesives up to 54" wide. Slitting and Sheeting of rolled goods up to 85" wide. (AA, estab 1998, empl 36, sales $3,200,000, cert: NMSDC)

6480   Action Tool & Machine Inc.
5976 Ford Ct
Brighton, MI 48116
Contact: Doug Lademan Dir minority bus dev
Tel: 810-229-6300
Email: actiontool@actiontoolmachine.com
Website: www.actiontoolmachine.com
Machining & assembly svcs: build-to-print, part-to-print reverse engineering svcs. (As-Pac, estab 1993, empl 30, sales $3,700,000, cert: NMSDC)

6481   Aerostar Manufacturing
28275 Northline Rd
Romulus, MI 48174
Contact: Robert Johnson VP
Tel: 734-942-8440
Email: rjohnson@aerostarmfg.com
Website: www.aerostarmfg.com
CNC machining assembly, prototyping, machine castings & forgings, sand casting. (As-Pac, estab 1970, empl 200, sales , cert: NMSDC)

6482   ALBAH Manufacturing Technologies Corp.
1985 Ring Rd
Troy, MI 48083
Contact: Kofi Adomako VP
Tel: 519-972-7222
Email: kadomako@albah.com
Website: www.albah.com
Automation & robotics, machine load/unload, material handling, assembly, dispensing, palletizing & material removal. (Woman/AA, estab 1992, empl 27, sales $5,000,000, cert: NMSDC)

6483   Alphi Manufacturing, LLC
       576 Beck St
       Jonesville, MI 49250
       Contact: Ed Carter Dir Diversity Devel
       Tel: 517-849-9945
       Email: ecarter@crownegroupllc.com
       Website: http://alphimfg.com/
Fabrication (bending, piercing, end forming, miter cutting,
welding) of ferrous and non-ferrous tubalur products.
Fabricated exhaust components, Fabricated structural
components. (Nat Ame, estab 1959, empl 125, sales
$19,939,913, cert: NMSDC)

6484   Aluminum Blanking Company, Inc
       360 W Sheffield
       Pontiac, MI 48340
       Contact: Michael Rutkowski VP Finance & Admin
       Tel: 248-338-4422
       Email: mrutkowski@albl.com
       Website: www.albl.com
Leveling, Blanking, lubing, edge-trimming and slitting of
Aluminum, Stainless and other surface sensitive materials.
(Woman, estab 1979, empl 120, sales $9,864,397, cert:
WBENC)

6485   Axly Tool & Bushing
       700 E Soper Rd
       Bad Axe, MI 48413
       Contact: Mark Tomlinson Project Leader
       Tel: 989-269-9702
       Email: mtomlinson@geminigroup.net
       Website: www.geminigroup.net
CNC machining, contract machining. (Woman, estab 1970,
empl 70, sales $25,000,000, cert: WBENC)

6486   Aztec Manufacturing Corporation
       15378 Oakwood Dr
       Romulus, MI 48174
       Contact: Richard Johnson President
       Tel: 734-942-7433
       Email: rjohnson@aztecmfgcorp.com
       Website: www.aztecmfgcorp.com
Machined aluminum, ductile iron castings & forgings.
(Hisp, estab 1983, empl 55, sales $25,000,000, cert:
NMSDC)

6487   Casemer Tool
       2765 Metamora Rd
       Oxford, MI 48371
       Contact: Ray Wrubel Sales
       Tel: 248-860-3689
       Email: Ray@casemer.com
       Website: http://casemer.com
CNC machining, large diameter turning 32" x 120 ", bridge
Mill 59" x 119" (Woman, estab 1979, empl 85, sales
$15,000,000, cert: WBENC)

6488   CKS Precision Machining
       700 E Soper Rd
       Bad Axe, MI 48413
       Contact: Frank Gerbig Dir of Sales
       Tel: 989-269-9702
       Email: fgerbig@geminigroup.net
       Website: www.ckstool.com
CNC machining: lathe, mill, grind & heat treating. (Woman,
estab 1979, empl 100, sales $15,709,000, cert: WBENC)

6489   Clips & Clamps Industries
       15050 Keel St
       Plymouth, MI 48170
       Contact: Jeff Aznavorian President
       Tel: 734-455-0880
       Email: jaznavorian@clipsclamps.com
       Website: www.clipsclamps.com
Metal forming, progressive dies, four slide, CNC wire
forming, tool building, MIG & TIG welding, tapping,
riveting, automated assemblies, prototyping & production volumes, engineering services, design services, sales
support. (Woman, estab 1954, empl 62, sales , cert:
WBENC)

6490   CNC Products Inc.
       2126 S 11th St
       Niles, MI 49120
       Contact: President
       Tel: 269-684-5500
       Email:
       Website: http://cncproductsinc.com/
CNC machining. (Woman, estab 2019, empl 18, sales
$2,500,000, cert: WBENC)

6491   Costello Enterprises, LLC
       56358 Precision Dr
       Chesterfield Township, MI 48051
       Contact: Tom Orban VP
       Tel: 586-615-6307
       Email: torban@costelloenterprises.com
       Website: www.costelloenterprises.com
CNC machining & dimensional inspection services. (Hisp,
estab 2000, empl 25, sales , cert: NMSDC)

6492   Costello Machine LLC
       56358 Precision Dr
       Chesterfield, MI 48051
       Contact: Frank Keena Operations Mgr
       Tel: 586-749-0136
       Email: fkeena@costellomachine.com
       Website: www.costellomachine.com
Precision machining, boring mill & assemblies. (Hisp,
estab 2000, empl 25, sales $3,500,000, cert: NMSDC)

6493   Dalany Metal Products Inc.
       4450 13th St
       Wyandotte, MI 48192
       Contact: Al Yglesias President
       Tel: 734-282-6666
       Email: al.yglesias@dalany.com
       Website: www.dalany.com
Machine formed metal parts: cold heading, rod heading,
wire forming, stampers & screw machine, grooves,
reamed holes, cross holes, plating. (Hisp, estab 2004,
empl 9, sales $525,000, cert: NMSDC)

6494   Dienamic Tool Corporation
       4541 Patterson Ave SE
       Kentwood, MI 49512
       Contact: Rogelio (Roger) Ramirez President
       Tel: 616-954-7882
       Email: rramirez@dienamictoolcorp.com
       Website: www.dienamictoolcorp.com
Die Build, Reverse Engineering, CNC Machining, Fixture
Build. (Hisp, estab 1998, empl 16, sales $1,856,444, cert:
NMSDC)

6495 Dowding Industries
503 Marilin
Eaton Rapids, MI 48827
Contact: Roger Cope VP Sales
Tel: 517-663-5455
Email: roger@willowhill.net
Website: http://dowdingindustries.com
CNC machining, milling & boring. (Woman, estab 1965, empl , sales $300,000, cert: WBENC)

6496 GK Tech, LLC
3331 W Big Beaver Rd Ste 106
Troy, MI 48084
Contact: Kelly Choi
Tel: 248-494-1960
Email: kellychoi@gktechusa.com
Website: www.gktechllc.com
Marketing specialist, consulting, business development, forging, die-casting, stamping, spring, magnesium pulley, rubber bushing, fasteners, machining, plastic injection molding. (Woman/As-Pac, estab 2015, empl 3, sales , cert: NMSDC)

6497 Jolico/J-B Tool, Inc.
4325 22 Mile Rd
Utica, MI 48317
Contact: Patricia Wieland President
Tel: 586-739-5555
Email: pwieland@jolico.com
Website: www.jolico.com
CNC turning, vertical, multipallet machining, welding, suface, wet & blanchard grinding. (Woman, estab 1963, empl 38, sales , cert: WBENC)

6498 KJL Industries, Inc.
44057 Phoenix Dr
Sterling Heights, MI 48314
Contact: Kristin Wikol President
Tel: 586-803-1818
Email: kwikol@kjlindustries.com
Website: www.kjlindustries.com
Precision machining, tight tolerance, complex parts. (Woman, estab 1984, empl 15, sales $2,000,000, cert: WBENC)

6499 Maya Jig Grinding & Gage Co.
20770 Parker Rd
Farmington Hills, MI 48336
Contact: Jeff Beier VP
Tel: 248-471-0802
Email: jbeier@mayagage.com
Website: www.MayaGage.com
Automatic gages, variable gages, functional gages, hand gages, masters, fixtures & tooling. (Woman, estab 1976, empl 20, sales $3,000,000, cert: WBENC)

6500 MRD Aerospace, LLC
23565 Schoenherr Rd
Warren, MI 48089
Contact: Michele Dew Managing Member
Tel: 586-443-5350
Email: r7mdew@aol.com
Website: www.mrdaerospace.com
Prototype machining, milling, turning, jig grinding, ID/OD grinding, surface grinding, honing & lapping, hydraulic cylinder blocks, drive shafts, rotors, housings, broaching ID splines, valve plates, pistons, sleeved cylinder blocks, etc. (Woman, estab 2011, empl 9, sales $440,311, cert: WBENC)

6501 Pioneer Machine & Tech
1167 East 10 Mile Rd
Madison Heights, MI 48071
Contact: Jeffery Harris President
Tel: 248-546-4451
Email: jharris@pioneermachinetech.com
Website: www.pioneermachinetech.com
Machining: custom & precision machining, fabrication, grinding & repair of components & fixtures. (AA, estab 1998, empl 15, sales $1,500,000, cert: NMSDC)

6502 Precision Components Manufacturing, LLC
35855 Stanley
Sterling Heights, MI 48312
Contact: Tommy Longest CEO
Tel: 586-939-8500
Email: tommy@pcmfettes.com
Website: www.pcmfettes.com
Mfr cast tooling, castings iron/aluminum, steel forging, fully machined castings & assembly, ferrous & non-ferrous products, forging, sand & die casting. (AA, estab 2009, empl 30, sales $7,010,000, cert: NMSDC)

6503 ProMax Engineering, LLC
7522 Baron Dr
Canton, MI 48187
Contact: Jeff Hampton Dir Sales/Marketing
Tel: 734-468-0146
Email: jeff@betasales.com
Website:
Machining: castings, forgings, powder metal & cold formed steel. (As-Pac, estab 1999, empl 75, sales $15,000,000, cert: NMSDC)

6504 Quasar Industries, Inc.
1911 Northfield Dr
Rochester Hills, MI 48309
Contact: Shane Majesky Qualtiy/Safety Mgr
Tel: 248-852-0300
Email: quality@quasar.com
Website: www.quasar.com
Prototypes, hydroforming, tube processing, deep draw & exotic metal stampings, laser cutting & welding, robotic welding, assemblies, fixture design & mfg, inspection, short run production, CNC machining, wire EDM & waterjet cutting. (Woman, estab 1967, empl 79, sales $13,000,000, cert: State)

6505 Robinson Industries, Inc.
3051 W Curtis Rd
Coleman, MI 48618
Contact: Marvin Ries Sales
Tel: 989-465-6111
Email: mries@robinsonind.com
Website: www.robinsonind.com
Custom design & mfg, vacuum forming, injection molding, extrusion, tool & die shop. (Woman, estab 1950, empl 200, sales $28,348,370, cert: WBENC)

6506 Sequoia Tool
44831 N Groesbeck Hwy
Clinton Township, MI 48036
Contact: James Coates Acct Mgr
Tel: 586-463-4400
Email: bcoates@sequoiatool.net
Website: www.sequoiatool.net
Mfr prototype sheet metal stampings & assemblies, low volume production and short run svcs. (Nat Ame, estab 1988, empl 65, sales $10,000,000, cert: NMSDC)

6507 Set Enterprises, Inc.
38600 Van Dyke Ave Ste 325
Sterling Heights, MI 48093
Contact: Antoinette Turner Mgr Corp Communication
Tel: 586-573-3600
Email: aturner@setenterprises.com
Website: www.setenterprises.com
Metal processing services, blanking, slitting & warehousing of metal products. (AA, estab 0, empl 310, sales , cert: NMSDC)

6508 Steadfast Engineered Products, LLC
775 Woodlawn Ave
Grand Haven, MI 49417
Contact: Jay Cutie Managing Partner
Tel: 616-846-4747
Email: jcutie@steadfastep.com
Website: www.steadfastep.com
Screw machine products, turned parts. (AA, Hisp, estab 1986, empl 12, sales $6,000,000, cert: NMSDC)

6509 Sure Solutions LLC
5385 Perry Dr
Waterford, MI 48329
Contact: Art Huge Sales
Tel: 248-674-7210
Email: info@suresolutionsmbe.com
Website: www.suresolutionsmbe.com/
Stampings, plating, coatings, roll forming, machining, castings, forgings, assembly, packaging, warehousing & distribution, containment. (Woman/As-Ind, estab 1990, empl 25, sales $8,250,000, cert: WBENC)

6510 Systrand Manufacturing Corporation
19050 Allen Rd
Brownstown, MI 48329
Contact: Jim Meadows Dir of Finance
Tel: 734-479-8100
Email: jim.meadows@systrand.com
Website: www.systrand.com
High volume production machining: cast iron, aluminum, steel & powdered metal components. (Woman/Nat Ame, estab 1982, empl 200, sales $65,000,000, cert: NMSDC, WBENC)

6511 T&D Machine, Inc.
2485 E Monroe Rd
Tecumseh, MI 49286
Contact: Debra Fowle President
Tel: 517-423-0778
Email: tdmachine@lni.net
Website: http://tdmachineinc.net
Precision machined products: steel, aluminum, brass & plastic parts, hand tools, scribers, torque, screwdriver, pliers, mirrors, telescoping tools, magnet hand tools, spark plug pliers. (Woman/Hisp, estab 1985, empl 3, sales $200,000, cert: State)

6512 Triple Tool, LLC
40715 Brentwood
Sterling Heights, MI 48310
Contact: Ursula Czachor Owner
Tel: 586-795-1785
Email: tripletool@yahoo.com
Website:
Precision machining and fabrication to the automotive, aerospace, robotics, and medical industries. (Woman, estab 2009, empl 15, sales $1,500,000, cert: State)

6513 Trutron Corporation
274 Executive Dr
Troy, MI 48083
Contact: Lisa Kingsley President
Tel: 248-583-9166
Email: lkingsley@trutron.com
Website: www.trutron.com
Precision machining, CNC turning, milling, grinding: pressure plates, valve plates, wafer plates, cam rings, rotors, housings, manifolds, radial rings, levers, sleeves, actuator pistons, tooling & gauging. (Woman, estab 1967, empl 26, sales $5,239,911, cert: WBENC)

6514 United Manufacturing Network Inc.
12 Lincoln St
Mt. Clemens, MI 48043
Contact: Cathy DeNardo President
Tel: 586-468-7443
Email: cathydenardo@comcast.net
Website: www.unitedmanufacturingnetwork.com
Design & build fixtures & gages, tool & dies injection molds, molded parts & rapid prototype CNC machining, turning, milling & boring mill OD, ID, surface & centerless grinding, precision jig grinding & wire EDM. (Woman, estab 2004, empl 3, sales $104,202, cert: WBENC)

6515 West Michigan Flocking
78277 County Rd378
Covert, MI 49043
Contact: Garrett Fox VP Sales
Tel: 269-639-1634
Email: gfox@wmflocking.com
Website: www.wmflocking.com
Object flocking, injection molding, in-line attachment assembly, sub assembly & sonic welding. (AA, estab 1978, empl 50, sales $4,500,000, cert: NMSDC)

6516 Witco Inc.
6401 Bricker Rd
Avoca, MI 48006
Contact: Tom Kean Sales Engineer
Tel: 810-387-4231
Email: tomk@witcoinc.com
Website: www.witcoinc.com
CNC precision machine parts: milling, turning, grinding, gear shaping & assembly. (Woman, estab 1977, empl 60, sales $7,000,000, cert: WBENC)

6517 Zoatex
25580 Brest Road
Taylor, MI 48180
Contact: Hamid Servati Partner
Tel: 734-697-5555
Email: hservati@zoatex.com
Website: www.zoatex.com
Manufacturing & machining, powertrain devel, emissions, durability testing, project mgmt, prototyping. (AA, estab 2002, empl 20, sales $12,000,000, cert: NMSDC)

Minnesota

6518 Columbia Precision Machine Corp.
      2970 Lexington Ave S
      Eagan, MN 55121
      Contact: Nancy Cruise VP
      Tel: 952-890-1003
      Email: info@columbiapmc.com
      Website: www.columbiapmc.com
Precision machine shop: milling, turning, light assembly,
prototype, small batch, production qtys. MIL-I-45208A.
(AA, estab 1983, empl 26, sales $3,773,000, cert: State)

6519 Lake Country Machining
      P.O. Box 127
      Two Harbors, MN 55616
      Contact: Clara Mikkelsen CEO
      Tel: 218-834-7033
      Email: clara@lakecountrymachining.net
      Website: www.lakecountrymachining.net
Precision machining: aluminum, stainless steel & non-
ferrous machining. (Woman, estab 2001, empl 5, sales ,
cert: State)

6520 Mack Engineering Corporation
      3215 E 26th St
      Minneapolis, MN 55406
      Contact: Jennifer Salisbury President
      Tel: 612-721-2471
      Email: info@mackengineering.com
      Website: www.mackengineering.com
Mfr precision-machined components utilizing a dock to
stock quality system. (Woman, estab 1943, empl 30, sales ,
cert: WBENC)

6521 Metal Craft Machine & Engineering, Inc.
      13760 Businesss Center Dr
      Elk River, MN 55330
      Contact: Trisha Mowry CEO
      Tel: 763-441-1855
      Email: trisha@metal-craft.com
      Website: www.metal-craft.com
Contract manufacturing & engineering design: CNC milling
& turning, multi-tasking machining, 7-axis CNC grinding,
wire EDM, swiss gundrilling, laser & GTAW (Tig.), welding
blasting, deburring, & finishing. (Woman, estab 1978, empl
185, sales , cert: WBENC)

6522 Miller Machine Company
      14105 Commerce Dr
      Becker, MN 55308
      Contact: Cynthia Wahl President
      Tel: 763-263-0091
      Email: cyndiw@millermachinecompany.com
      Website: www.millermachinecompany.com
CNC mills & lathes, brown & sharpe screw machines,
automatice saws, bridgeports, hardinges. (Woman, estab
1944, empl 15, sales $1,764,305, cert: WBENC)

6523 Modern Manufacturing & Engineering, Inc.
      9380 Winnetka Ave N
      Brooklyn Park, MN 55445
      Contact: Nancy Lien Berndt President
      Tel: 612-781-3347
      Email: nancyl@mmeincmn.com
      Website: www.mmeincmn.com
Precision custom machining, milling, turning, grinding,
assembly, plating, painting. (As-Pac, estab 1958, empl 156,
sales , cert: NMSDC)

6524 Northern U & S, Inc. dba Quali-Mac, Inc.
      9208 James Ave S, Ste 11
      Bloomington, MN 55431
      Contact: Shawn Thai President
      Tel: 952-881-6677
      Email: shawnt@qualimac-inc.com
      Website: www.qualimac-inc.com
Precision, CNC machining, metal/plastic machining,
turning, vertical milling, protoype, production machining. (As-Pac, estab 1974, empl 7, sales $400,000, cert:
NMSDC)

6525 Riverside Manufacturing, Inc.
      14280 Sunfish Lake Blvd NW
      Ramsey, MN 55303
      Contact: Mic Wieshaar President
      Tel: 763-274-2193
      Email: riversidemnf@earthlink.net
      Website: www.riversidemnf.com
CNC machining, complex horizontal machining. (Nat
Ame, estab 1997, empl 15, sales $3,450,000, cert:
NMSDC)

Montana

6526 Montana Hydraulics, LLC
      888 Florence St
      Helena, MT 59601
      Contact: Jay Krause Natl Contracts Mgr
      Tel: 814-592-5412
      Email: mthyd@ironfurnace.com
      Website: www.montanahydraulics.com
Mfr industrial metal, compaction attachments for heavy
equipment (roller compaction buckets & wheels,
vibratory compaction buckets), bedding boxes &
doweling machines, CNC machining, turning & lathe,
manual machining, custom fabrication. (Woman, estab
1998, empl 47, sales $6,027,445, cert: State)

North Carolina

6527 C & J Machine Company Inc.
      3519 Philadelphia Ch Rd
      Dallas, NC 28034
      Contact: Amy Hunt President
      Tel: 704-922-5913
      Email: cjmachinecompany@gmail.com
      Website:
Mfr machine parts & fixtures, tool & dies, CRS, HRS, tool
steel, plastics, copper, bronze, stainless steel. (Woman,
estab 1976, empl 4, sales $350,000, cert: State)

New Hampshire

6528 Maclean Precision Machine
      1928 Village Rd
      Madison, NH 03849
      Contact: Deborah Folsom President
      Tel: 603-367-9011
      Email: d.folsom@macleanprecision.com
      Website: www.macleanprecision.com
Precision machining, tight tolerance parts, Titanium,
Inconel, Stainless Steel, Aluminum, Castings, Bar Stock &
Plate. (Woman, estab 1977, empl 33, sales $3,800,000,
cert: NWBOC)

New Jersey

6529   Arlington Machine & Tool
       90 New Dutch Ln
       Fairfield, NJ 07004
       Contact: Susan Blanck President & CEO
       Tel: 973-276-1377
       Email: sblanck@arlingtonmachine.com
       Website: www.arlingtonmachine.com
CNC machining & turning, manufacturing, assemblies &
systems. (Woman, estab 1963, empl 100, sales
$16,000,000, cert: State, WBENC)

6530   Computa-Base Machining
       411 N Grove St
       Berlin, NJ 08009
       Contact: Agustin Rosado President
       Tel: 856-767-3509
       Email: cbmpresident@computabase.com
       Website: www.computabase.com
Close tolerance, special metals, nickel, inconell, kamenell,
etc. (Hisp, estab 1981, empl 20, sales $1,000,000, cert:
NMSDC, SDB)

6531   Kaizen Technologies Inc.
       1 Lincoln Hwy, Ste 10
       Edison, NJ 08820
       Contact: Prakash Bahumanyam VP
       Tel: 732-452-9555
       Email: prakashb@kaizentek.com
       Website: www.kaizentek.com
Precision machining, tooling, jigs & fixtures. (As-Ind, estab
1995, empl 150, sales $11,000,000, cert: State)

6532   Progressive Machinery Inc.
       19 E Centre St
       Nutley, NJ 07110
       Contact: VP - Finance
       Tel: 833-776-6224
       Email:
       Website: http://pro-machinery.com
CNC milling and turning, grinding, welding, die & mold
fabrication, multi-slide forming & assembly on Bihler
machines & CMM inspections, molding, stamping
forming, punching, cutting, welding, tapping, inserting,
assembling, and sheet metal fabrication. (Woman, estab
2009, empl 10, sales $1,500,000, cert: State, WBENC)

New Mexico

6533   Las Cruces Machine, Mfg. & Engineering
       6000 S Main, Ste B
       Mesilla Park, NM 88047
       Contact: Rod Mitchell President
       Tel: 575-526-1411
       Email: rmitchell@lascrucesmachine.com
       Website: www.lascrucesmachine.com
CNC precision machining capabilities. (Woman, estab
1975, empl 40, sales $3,907,000, cert: WBENC)

New York

6534   Cannon Industries, Inc.
       525 Lee Rd
       Rochester, NY 14606
       Contact: Reggie Cannon President
       Tel: 585-254-8080
       Email: rcannon@cannonind.com
       Website: www.cannonind.com
Sheet metal fabrication, welding fabrication, laser &
plasma cutting, metal stamping, CNC machining &
turning, mechanical assembly, spot welding. (AA, estab
1979, empl 104, sales $16,000,000, cert: NMSDC)

6535   Greno Industries Inc.
       P.O. Box 542
       Schenectady, NY 12301
       Contact: Joe Vainauskas VP Operations
       Tel: 518-393-4195
       Email: jvainauskas@greno.com
       Website: www.greno.com
Contract OEM machining, milling & turning services,
CAD/CAM capabilities, modern equipment. (Woman,
estab 1961, empl 65, sales $15,500,000, cert: WBENC)

6536   Ingleside Machine Company, Inc.
       1120 Hook Rd
       Farmington, NY 14425
       Contact: Gary Veomett
       Tel: 585-924-3046
       Email: office@inglesidemachine.com
       Website: http://Inglesidemachine.com
CNC milling, turning, sheet metal fabrication, welding,
finishing & assembly. (Woman, estab 1974, empl 85,
sales , cert: State)

Ohio

6537   Action Precision Products Inc.
       100 E North Ave Box 188
       Pioneer, OH 43554
       Contact: Linda Heisler President
       Tel: 419-737-2348
       Email: linda@actionprecision.com
       Website: www.actionprecision.com
Machining: low volume, high tolerance blue print items,
steel, brass, bronze & plastics, CNC turning, milling &
grinding operations. (Woman, estab 1972, empl 10, sales
$1,020,000, cert: WBENC)

6538   Chippewa Industries, Inc. dba, Seaport Mold &
       Casting
       1309 West Bancroft St
       Toledo, OH 43606
       Contact: Jeff St. Louis President
       Tel: 419-243-1422
       Email: jstlouis@chippewaindustries.com
       Website: www.chippewaindustries.com
CNC Machining, vertical and horizontal 3 Axis, 4 Axis and
5 Axis CNC machining capabilities. We provide Billet,
Sand Castings, Metal Castings, Aluminum Castings,
Investment Castings, Plaster Casting, Die Casting,
Prototype, and Short to Medium Production. (Nat Ame,
estab 2015, empl 25, sales $6,000,000, cert: NMSDC)

6539 Cleveland Die & Mfg. Co.
20303 First Ave
Middleburg Heights, OH 44130
Contact: Marty Curry sales/engineering
Tel: 440-243-3404
Email: mcurry@clevelanddie.com
Website: www.clevelanddie.com/
Ecoat & powder coat line, automatic & single hit presses, spot & robotic welders, CNC machining. (Hisp, estab 1973, empl 300, sales $24,000,000, cert: NMSDC)

6540 EnKon, LLC dba Broadway
6344 Webster St
Dayton, OH 45414
Contact: Jodi Walters Member
Tel: 937-890-2221
Email: jodi.walters@enkonllc.com
Website: www.broadwaymold.com
Injection molds, components, mold repairs, Precision Fabrication,
CNC Machining, welding, turning, Electrode manufacturing, EDM'ING, Wire EDM, Polish, Milling, OD, ID, and surface grinding, Design. (Woman, estab 1955, empl 12, sales , cert: WBENC)

6541 GB Manufacturing Company
100 Adams St
Delta, OH 43515
Contact: Teresa Elling Sales
Tel: 419-822-5323
Email: apetree@gbmfg.com
Website: www.gbmfg.com
Stamping, laser blanking, fabrication & assembly, tool making, robotic & hand welding, spot welding, press braking, productin machining, prototyping. (As-Pac, Hisp, estab 1975, empl 85, sales $24,500,000, cert: NMSDC)

6542 Green Rock Lighting, LLC
3175 W 33rd St
Cleveland, OH 44109
Contact: Tina Haddad CEO
Tel: 216-651-6446
Email: thaddad@greenrocklighting.com
Website: www.greenrocklighting.com
Laser cutting, wire bending & forming, press brake, spinning, stamping, mig, tig & stick welding, spot welding, machining, destructive & non-destructive testing, packaging & assembly. (Woman, estab 2011, empl , sales $150,000, cert: State, WBENC)

6543 Industrial Machining and Design Services, Inc.
2007 South Ave
Youngstown, OH 44502
Contact: Robert Hill Jr. CEO
Tel: 330-747-4637
Email: rahilljr@imds-ohio.com
Website: www.imds-ohio.com
Precision machining, CNC, high tolerance machining: forgings, castings, bearings, land vehicles, brakes, calipers, rotor castings, etc. (AA, estab 1991, empl 10, sales $1,050,000, cert: State)

6544 Kaskell Manufacturing, Inc.
240 Hiawatha Trail
Springboro, OH 45066
Contact: Brian Harris VP
Tel: 937-704-9700
Email: bharris@kaskellmfg.com
Website: www.kaskellmfg.com
CNC machining, milling & turning. (Woman, estab 2000, empl 12, sales $1,250,000, cert: WBENC)

6545 Lewis Unlimited, Inc.
165 Jackson Dr
Cleveland, OH 44022
Contact: Joseph Lewis, Jr. President
Tel: 216-514-8282
Email: jlewis@lewisunlimited.com
Website: www.lewisunlimited.com
CNC precision machined components, multi axis machining centers, single & multi-spindle screw products, CNC Swiss machined components. (AA, estab 1991, empl 10, sales $6,043,537, cert: State, NMSDC)

6546 Magni-Power Company
5511 Lincoln Way E
Wooster, OH 44691
Contact: Kim Coblentz New Business Devel
Tel: 330-264-3637
Email: kcoblentz@magnipower.com
Website: www.magnipower.com
Metal fabrication & stamping: process steel, aluminum, stainless steel, CNC punching, forming, laser cutting, robotic welding, in-house powder coating & assembly. (As-Ind, estab 1948, empl 230, sales $27,000,000, cert: NMSDC)

6547 Mantych Metalworking, Inc.
3175 Plainfield Rd
Dayton, OH 45432
Contact: Bill Sewell Sales
Tel: 937-258-1373
Email: bill@mantych.net
Website: http://mantych.net
Precision CNC machining & sheet metal fabrication. (Woman, estab 1971, empl 34, sales $8,000,000, cert: WBENC)

6548 Ohio Transitional Machine & Tool Inc.
3940 Castener St
Toledo, OH 43612
Contact: Marten Whalen President
Tel: 419-476-0820
Email: ohiotransitional@hotmail.com
Website: www.ohiotransitional.com
CNC milling & turning, wire EDM, boringmill, general machining, blanchard grinding, 3D machining, jigs & fixtures, prototypes, R&D, welding, painting & assembly. (Nat Ame, estab 1985, empl 10, sales $800,000, cert: NMSDC)

6549 Schnipke Engraving Co. Inc.
14223 Rd24
Ottoville, OH 45876
Contact: CEO
Tel: 419-453-3376
Email:
Website: www.schnipkeengraving.com
Precision injection molding, tool design & build, precision assembly, insert molding, overmolding. (Woman, estab 1962, empl 350, sales $33,592,463, cert: WBENC)

6550   Vantage Agora
23811 Chagrin Blvd Ste 244
Beachwood, OH 44122
Contact: Sudhir Achar President
Tel: 888-246-7211
Email: sudhir@vantageagora.com
Website: www.vantageagora.com
Mfr turned parts, machining, hot & cold forging, printing, precision parts. (As-Ind, estab 2004, empl 19, sales $3,697,558, cert: NMSDC)

6551   Wrena, LLC dba Angstrom-USA, LLC
265 Lightner Rd
Tipp City, OH 45371
Contact: Nagesh Palakurthi CEO
Tel: 937-667-4403
Email: pyenger@wrenallc.com
Website: http://angstrom-usa.com
Stampings, tubular products, machining, welding, robotic welding, steel forgings (Warm & Cold), aluminum forgings, assemblies, plastic injection molding, needle bearings, starter assemblies (As-Pac, estab 2011, empl 46, sales , cert: NMSDC)

Oregon

6552   Browns Machine
90500B Hwy 99N
Eugene, OR 97402
Contact: Kevin Brown President
Tel: 541-344-1466
Email: kevin@brownsmachine.com
Website: www.brownsmachine.com
Custom machining, first article inspections, material certifications. (Nat Ame, estab 2003, empl 31, sales , cert: State)

6553   Hy Speed Machining, Inc.
353 California Ave
Grants Pass, OR 97526
Contact: Rachel Chamberland HR Mgr
Tel: 541-476-0769
Email: rachelc@hyspeedmachining.com
Website: http://hyspeedmachining.com
Machine shop specializing in machined parts; all materials; close tolerance, high volume. (Woman/Hisp, estab 1984, empl 19, sales $3,049,034, cert: State)

Pennsylvania

6554   Acutec Precision Aerospace Inc.
13555 Broadway
Meadville, PA 16335
Contact: Rich Shaffer Sr Acct Mgr
Tel:
Email: rshaffer@acutecprecision.com
Website: www.acutecprecision.com
Milling, turning, grinding, honing, lapping, EDM & light assembly of aluminum, titanium, stainless steel, inconel, hastalloy, hastx, plastics. (Woman, estab 1988, empl 385, sales $100,000,000, cert: WBENC)

6555   Agape Precision Manufacturing, LLC
320 Circle of Progress Dr Ste 108
Pottstown, PA 19464
Contact: Dana Wolfe President
Tel: 484-824-3134
Email: dana.wolfe@agapeprecision.com
Website: www.agapeprecision.com
Machining, fabrication, bending, assemblies, hardware, some special processes, brackets, prototyping, metals, delron, plastics, aerospace manufacturing. (Woman, estab 2006, empl 11, sales $1,100,000, cert: State)

6556   American Roll Suppliers, Inc.
186 Compass Rd
Parkesburg, PA 19365
Contact: Karen Neuhauser President
Tel: 610-857-2988
Email: kneuhauser@peoplepc.com
Website:
Metal fabrication & machining. (Woman, estab 0, empl , sales , cert: WBENC)

6557   Amity Industries
491 Old Swede Rd
Douglassville, PA 19518
Contact: Monica Lubinsky CEO
Tel: 610-385-6075
Email: mlubins@amityindustries.com
Website: www.amityindustries.com
Custom fabrication, machining & assembly. (Nat Ame, estab 1973, empl 45, sales $10,000,000, cert: NMSDC)

6558   Atlas Machining & Welding, Inc.
777 Smith Lane
Northampton, PA 18067
Contact: Andrew Weiss Project Mgr
Tel: 610-262-1374
Email: info@atlasmw.com
Website: www.atlasmw.com
CNC machine & steel fabrication, vertical & horizontal boring mills, vertical machine centers, lathes & turning. (Woman, estab 1981, empl 65, sales $13,000,000, cert: NWBOC)

6559   C.A. Spalding, Co.
1011 Cedar Ave
Croydon, PA 19021
Contact: Javier Kuehnle CEO
Tel: 215-850-5777
Email: nteubert@spaldingautomotive.com
Website: www.caspalding.com
High-precision forming, laser cutting & bracket machining. (Hisp, estab 1938, empl 30, sales $18,231,344, cert: NMSDC)

6560   D & R Machine Co.
1330 Industrial Hwy
Southampton, PA 18966
Contact: Nelson Redante Mgr, Business Dev
Tel: 215-526-2080
Email: nelsonredante@drmachine.com
Website: www.drmachine.com
Mfr precision machine parts to cstmr specs. (Hisp, estab 1971, empl 38, sales , cert: NMSDC)

Puerto Rico

6561 SQS, Inc. (Successful Quality Systems)
Palmas Industrial Park Road 869 KM. 2.0 Street 4
Catano, PR 00962
Contact: Wilda Aguirre President
Tel: 787-275-2424
Email: wildaaguirre@sqswarehouse.com
Website: www.sqswarehouse.com
Specialized Storage and Inventory Management Services of materials and products for the pharmaceutical, medical devices, biotech and consumer industries as well as to the safe-guarding of documents (Woman/Hisp, estab 2003, empl 8, sales $2,500,000, cert: NMSDC)

Rhode Island

6562 East Bay Manufacturing
400 Franklin St
Bristol, RI 02809
Contact: Randy Medina GM
Tel: 401-254-2960
Email: randy@eastbaymfg.com
Website: www.eastbaymfg.com
CNC machining & fabrication resources. (Hisp, estab 1985, empl 14, sales , cert: State)

South Carolina

6563 Bunty, LLC
444 Fairforest Way
Greenville, SC 29607
Contact: Rajeev Jindal President
Tel: 864-567-0498
Email: rajeev@buntyllc.com
Website: www.buntyllc.com
Precision machined components, assemblies, metal fabrication, jigs & fixtures, forgings, castings, dies, re-engineered OEM parts, CNC milling, CNC turning. (As-Pac, estab 2000, empl 10, sales $1,600,000, cert: NMSDC)

6564 J.I.T. Manufacturing, Inc.
428 Oglesby Lane
Cowpens, SC 29330
Contact: Dan Hunter Production / Sales Mgr.
Tel: 864-463-0581
Email: dan@jitmanufacturing.com
Website: http://jitmfg.net
Laser cutting, welding, forming, CNC punching, CNC machines, fabrication, sheetmetal, powdercoating, pressbrakes, modifications, spot welding, control boxes, mounting plates, brackets, CAD programing, Cad design. (Woman, estab 1992, empl 22, sales $2,910,792, cert: City, WBENC)

6565 Secondary Solutions, Inc.
101 Northeast Dr
Spartanburg, SC 29303
Contact: Mark Mahaffey Sales
Tel: 864-494-5337
Email: markmahaffey@secondarysolutionsinc.net
Website: www.ssiservesyou.net
Machining, fabrication, drilling, tapping, grinding, warehousing, assembly, boring, wire marking, wire harness assembly, 3rd party inspection services, buffing, polishing, packaging. (Woman, estab 1997, empl 10, sales $550,000, cert: WBENC)

Tennessee

6566 Gonzalez Group LLC
237 Kraft St
Clarksville, TN 37040
Contact: Felix Gonzalez CEO
Tel: 517-542-2928
Email: fg@gonzalezmfg.com
Website: www.gonzalezmfg.com
Mfr precision turned machined parts. (Hisp, estab 1974, empl 135, sales $14,000,000, cert: NMSDC)

Texas

6567 365 Machine Inc.
27890 Commercial Park Lane
Tomball, TX 77375
Contact: Billy Helveston VP Sales/Mktg
Tel: 281-378-7811
Email: billy@365-machine.com
Website: www.365-machine.com
Precision CNC machining, 4 CNC lathes, 5 CNC mills, horizontal mill. (Woman, estab 2013, empl 13, sales $1,200,000, cert: State, WBENC)

6568 Aero CNC, Inc.
960 S Burleson Blvd
Burleson, TX 76028
Contact: Chris Layne GM
Tel: 817-295-0184
Email: clayne@aerocnc.com
Website: www.aerocnc.com
Aerospace machined parts, exotic metals & swarf contour machining. (Woman/Nat Ame, estab 1981, empl 30, sales $4,250,000, cert: State)

6569 Best Sheet Metal Solutions
923 KCK Way, Ste A
Cedar Hill, TX 75104
Contact: Jacob Bell Owner
Tel: 214-384-1951
Email: jacob@bestsheetmetalsolutions.com
Website: www.bestsheetmetalsolutions.com
Close Tolerance CNC Machining, CNC Vertical Machining Center & Haas CNC Horitzonal Turning Center (Lathe), Machine Heat Sinks, Buss bar, Surfacing, Profiling, Casting Molds, (AA, estab 2008, empl 3, sales $150,000, cert: NMSDC)

6570 Buks Tool Company, Inc.
6410-X Langfield Rd
Houston, TX 77092
Contact: Danielle Buks President
Tel: 713-974-5187
Email: danielle@bukstool.com
Website: www.bukstool.com
CNC Machining, Conventional machining, coordinate measuring machine, welding, grinding, boring, jig bore, tooling, design, EDM, sawing, hydrostatic pressure testing, high pressure pumps, components & assemblies. (Woman, estab 1978, empl 22, sales , cert: WBENC)

6571 Clay Precision, Ltd.
1102 FM 1417 NE
Sherman, TX 75090
Contact: President
Tel: 903-891-9022
Email:
Website: www.clayprecision.com
Milling, turning, 4th axis capabilities, fixturing, plastic weldment, assemblies, heat treating, grinding, dock-to-stock quality, fabrication of custom metal and plastic machined parts and assemblies, prototypes, exotic metals, exotic plastics. (Woman, estab 1996, empl 11, sales $1,293,930, cert: State, WBENC)

6572 Coastal Machine & Mechanical, LLC
14004 S Hwy 288B
Angleton, TX 77515
Contact: Mike Adams GM
Tel: 979-848-8900
Email: madams@coastalmandm.com
Website: www.coastalmandm.com
Custom machining & fabrication, millwright & welding services, maintenance services & balancing, rebuild pumps, gearboxes, ASME "R" stamp certificate. (Hisp, estab 2010, empl 28, sales , cert: State)

6573 Cutting Source Precision, Inc.
14011 Fm 529 Bldg B
Houston, TX 77065
Contact: Larry Boyd Dir govt sales
Tel: 281-859-2900
Email: info@cspmachine.com
Website: www.cspmachine.com
Machining, CNC milling & turning, waterjet saw cutting, carbon, aluminum, stainless, Monel, Inconel, Ferrilum, Titanium, Delrin, & Duplex. (Woman, estab 2000, empl 20, sales $1,900,000, cert: WBENC, NWBOC)

6574 Gretna Machine Shop, Inc.
3450 Lang Rd
Houston, TX 77092
Contact: Aerospace Div. Mgr.
Tel: 713-690-7328
Email:
Website: www.gretnamachine.com
CNC turning machines, CAD/CAM software programming, Sawing, Marking, Deburring services, Real-time order tracking, Worldwide Packaging & Delivery. (Woman/Hisp, estab 1980, empl 85, sales , cert: WBENC)

6575 Guzman Manufacturing, Inc.
4206 Industrial St
Rowlett, TX 75088
Contact: Annabell Acuna Office Mgr
Tel: 972-475-3003
Email: info@gzmfg.com
Website: www.gzmfg.com
Machine shop: precision sheet metal, spot welding, CNC, etc. (Hisp, estab 1975, empl 15, sales , cert: State)

6576 Mentco Inc.
15926 University Oak
San Antonio, TX 78249
Contact: Matt Weber SR. Mgr
Tel: 210-494-3100
Email: matt.weber@mentco.com
Website: www.mentcoinc.com
Mfr high precision, tight tolerance machined parts from bar stock, castings or forgings. Stainless Steel, (all grades), Inconel, Monel, Hastelloy, 15-5PH, 17-4PH, Titanium, Aluminum, Copper, Brass, Bronze. (As-Ind, estab 2006, empl 55, sales , cert: State, NMSDC)

6577 QMF Steel, Inc.
3846 IH-30 East
Campbell, TX 75422
Contact: President
Tel: 903-455-3618
Email:
Website: www.qmfsteel.com
CNC plate saw precision cutting, CNC plasma cutting, CNC machining, CNC lathe/turning, bundle cutting, threading, polishing: aluminum, stainless, hot roll, cold roll, alloy, magnesium, brass, copper & other metal products. (Woman, estab 1994, empl 49, sales $15,000,000, cert: State, WBENC)

6578 Spring International
23594 Dogwood Trail Dr Ste A
Hockley, TX 77447
Contact: President
Tel: 281-966-5109
Email:
Website: www.springintl.net
Machining, turn key, assembly, coat. etc. (Woman/AA, estab 2014, empl 5, sales $500,000, cert: State)

6579 Standard Industrial Products Company
12610 Galveston Rd
Webster, TX 77059
Contact: Walter Gomez Dir Operation & Mktg
Tel: 281-480-8711
Email: wgomez@sipco-mls.com
Website: www.sipco-mls.com
Engineering, Electro - Mechanical Design, Validation & System Integration, CNC Milling, CNC Turning, Sawing, Mechanical System assembly & integration, Gearing - Design, Sourcing, Assembly & System Integration. (Hisp, estab 1984, empl 15, sales $2,099,000, cert: NMSDC)

6580 Systems Integration, Inc.
7316 Business Pl
Arlington, TX 76001
Contact: Rhonda Smith Acct Mgr
Tel: 817-468-1494
Email: rsmith@sitexas.com
Website: www.sitexas.com
Engineering & Design, Reverse Engineering, Fabrication, Installation, Structural & Civil, Manufacturing, Machinery, Mechanical, CNC Machining, Electrical & Controls, Test Structures, Tooling. (Hisp, estab 1992, empl 20, sales $4,000,000, cert: State)

6581 VLJ Inc. dba Smith Tool & Mfg.
116 Regency Dr
Wylie, TX 75098
Contact: Kevin Hefley Sales Mgr
Tel: 972-442-4673
Email: smithtoolsales@airmail.net
Website: www.smithtoolmfg.com
Precision sheet metal mfg, stamping, tool & die, laser cutting, spinning, maching, turning. (Woman, estab 2001, empl 35, sales $570,000, cert: State)

Virginia

6582 High-Tech Machine Mfg, Inc.
11010 Trade Rd
North Chesterfield, VA 23236
Contact: President
Tel: 804-794-8640
Email: sales@hightechmachineinc.com
Website: www.high-techmachine.com
Production machining, swiss screw machine, CNC milling & turning, stock & release program. (Woman, estab 1984, empl 10, sales $1,100,000, cert: State, WBENC)

6583 HUB Pattern Corporation
2113 Salem Ave SW
Roanoke, VA 24016
Contact: Hubert Humphrey CEO
Tel: 540-342-3505
Email: hub@hubcorp.net
Website: www.hubcorp.net
Custom manufacturing CNC Machine Shop specializing in true 5-Axis complex programming and machining, concentrating on projects with complex surfaces and multi-sided machining requirements, molds, parts, tools and dies. (AA, estab 1966, empl 17, sales $5,500,000, cert: NMSDC)

6584 Metal Tech Inc.
2629 Richard Ave NE
Roanoke, VA 24012
Contact: Natasha Crowder project estimator
Tel: 540-798-4193
Email: metaltech@cox.net
Website: www.metaltechincorporated.com
Custom metal fabrication: sandblasting, punching, machine cutting, CNC plasma cutting, water jet cutting, pipe bending, ornamental bender machine, surface preparation & coating. (Woman, estab 1996, empl 2, sales $150,000, cert: State)

Washington

6585 Premier Manufacturing
1711 N Madison
Liberty Lake, WA 99019
Contact: Britt La Chance Sales Dir
Tel: 509-993-6800
Email: britt@premier-manufacturing.com
Website: http://premier-manufacturing.net
Mfr precision sheet metal products. (Woman, estab 2001, empl 100, sales $8,486,433, cert: WBENC)

Wisconsin

6586 American Metal Technologies LLC
8213 Durand Ave
Sturtevant, WI 53177
Contact: San Santharam President
Tel: 262-633-1756
Email: san@amermetals.com
Website: www.amermetals.com
Precision CNC machining & assembly: ferrous & non-ferrous components, fluid retention components, FEAD brackets & vibration dampening products. (As-Pac, estab 2000, empl 142, sales $25,500,000, cert: NMSDC)

6587 Bothe Associates Inc.
6901-46th St
Kenosha, WI 53144
Contact: Laura Bothe VP
Tel: 262-656-1860
Email: lbothe@bothe.com
Website: www.bothe.com
Machine shop & assembly: prototype, short & long run metal & plastic parts, high tolerance, tooling lathes, mills. (Woman, estab 1950, empl 45, sales $6,464,000, cert: WBENC)

6588 Cardinal Components, Inc.
N59W13500 Manhardt Dr
Menomonee Falls, WI 53051
Contact: Leann Kurey President
Tel: 262-437-1510
Email: nelsonm@cardinalcomponents.com
Website: www.cardinalcomponents.com
Dist Metal Components: Rivet-Nut Fasteners; Precision Machining: CNC Turning and Milling; Metal Fabrication: Brake Press, Laser, Stamping and Welding-Spot; Wire Forming and Springs. (Woman, estab 1983, empl 17, sales $7,000,100, cert: CPUC)

6589 eTek Tool and Manufacturing LLC
N37 W5677 Hamilton Rd
Cedarburg, WI 53012
Contact: Christopher Ernster Partner
Tel: 262-377-4150
Email: chris@etektool.com
Website: www.eTekTool.com
CNC machining, fabrication & tooling. (Woman, estab 2011, empl 2, sales , cert: State)

6590 Mantz Automation
1630 Innovation Way
Hartford, WI 53027
Contact: Gary Sonnenburg Sales Rep
Tel: 262-224-7528
Email: tnewman@mantzautomation.com
Website: www.mantzautomation.com
Machining components: alloys, design & build tooling, gages, fitures, CNC machinery, 5 axis machinng centers with large envelope of 60" x 120" x 48". (Woman/Hisp, estab 1986, empl 105, sales $22,300,000, cert: State)

6591 R.J. Zeman Tool & Mfg. Co., Inc.
W228 N575 Westmound Dr
Waukesha, WI 53186
Contact: Spencer Schreindl President
Tel: 262-549-4400
Email: sschreindl@zemantool.com
Website:
Machining, design, mfr & inspect fixtures, special machines, gages, die cast dies, plastic injection molds, permanent molds, core boxes, patterns for sand casting & short and long-run production parts. (Woman, estab 1966, empl 48, sales $9,600,000, cert: WBENC)

6592 Stanek Tool Corporation
2500 S Calhoun Rd
New Berlin, WI 53151
Contact: Paul Bartkowiak VP - Workholding
Tel: 262-786-0120
Email: pbartkowiak@stanektool.com
Website: www.stanektool.com
Design & build machining fixtures, plastic molds, & precision machined parts & assemblies. (Woman, estab 1924, empl 50, sales $10,000,000, cert: WBENC)

METAL RAW STOCK
Includes distributors of metal sheets, plates, rods, pipe, etc. Many can provide cutting and other metal processing services. (Also see six other METAL categories). NAICS Code 33

Arizona

6593   HiTemp Management Consulting, Inc.
4650 S Coach Dr Ste 120
Tucson, AZ 85714
Contact: Carlos Ruiz CEO
Tel: 520-807-6157
Email: carlos@htmetals.com
Website: http://htmetals.com
Raw Material Distribution, Aluminum, Stainless Steel, Specialty Steels, Brass, Bronze, Superalloys, Titanium, Abrasive waterjet cutting,
Cut to length band saw cutting. (Hisp, estab 2003, empl 6, sales $1,440,000, cert: 8a)

Arizona

6594   K&R Holdings, Inc.
2322 W Detroit Pl
Chandler, AZ 85224
Contact: Wayne Armoogam President
Tel: 480-236-2682
Email: warmoogam@lumawaresafety.com
Website: www.lumawaresafety.com
Supply and install photoluminescent egress systems for facilities. Our technologies for egress requires no electricity, external power source or batteries to provide the illumination required for safe movement of employees (As-Ind, estab 2007, empl 5, sales $100,000, cert: NMSDC)

California

6595   California Metal & Supply Inc.
10230 Freeman Ave
Santa Fe Springs, CA 90670
Contact: Kenneth Minkyu Lee President
Tel: 800-707-6061
Email: klee@californiametal.com
Website: www.CaliforniaMetal.com
Titanium, Inconel, Aluminum, Stainless, Magnesium Sheet, Plate, Bar, Tube & Tubing, Pipe, Tubing: Stainless, Carbon Steel, Aluminum, Brass, Valves. (As-Pac, estab 1984, empl 12, sales $60,000,000, cert: NMSDC)

6596   Carnegie Metals Inc.
2700 Rose Ave, Ste J
Long Beach, CA 90755
Contact: Carl Grigsby President
Tel: 562-989-6431
Email: carl@carnegiemetals.com
Website: www.carnegiemetals.com
Scrap & surplus metals, ferrous & non-ferrous scrap, aluminum & titanium, clean, strip, sort, separate & process metals. (AA, estab 1993, empl 2, sales , cert: State)

6597   Global Steel Alliance Corp.
14241 E Firestone Blvd, Ste 400
La Mirada, CA 90638
Contact: Keith Shiozaki President
Tel: 562-293-4086
Email: keith@steel-alliance.net
Website: www.steel-alliance.net
Dist carbon steel pipe. (As-Pac, estab 2008, empl , sales $2,779,880, cert: NMSDC)

6598   International Metal Source
17605 Fabrica Way Ste E & F
Cerritos, CA 90703
Contact: Jaymee Del Rosario CEO
Tel: 714-676-5669
Email: jaymee@imetalsource.com
Website: www.imetalsource.com
Dist Aluminum, Nickel, Titanium, Stainless Steel, High-Temperature & Specialty Steels, Ferrous, Non-Ferrous & Non-Metallic Raw Material in Sheet, Plate, Rod, Bar, Extrusions, Tubes & Formed Shapes. (Woman/As-Pac, estab 2009, empl 10, sales $889,000, cert: CPUC, SDB)

6599   Southern California Metals, Inc.
9900 Bell Ranch Dr
Santa Fe Springs, CA 90670
Contact: Alisa Thorpe President
Tel: 562-941-1616
Email: alisa@socalmetals.com
Website: www.socalmetals.com
Dist alloys, steels, stainless steels, titanium, nickel based alloys, aluminum & copper alloys in plate, sheet, bar, extrusion, forgings & castings, plastic lexan sheets, aviation rivets, nuts, fasteners, screws & seat tracks. (Woman, estab 1995, empl 15, sales $4,001,000, cert: State, CPUC)

Florida

6600 Aluminum Distributing, Inc. dba ADI Metal
2930 SW Second Ave
Fort Lauderdale, FL 33315
Contact: Betsy McGee President
Tel: 954-523-6474
Email: betsy@adimetal.com
Website: www.adimetal.com
Dist aluminum for the marine and industrial markets. (Woman, estab 1958, empl 16, sales $5,300,000, cert: State, WBENC)

6601 ASM Aerospace Specifications Metals, Inc.
2501 NW 34th Place, B28
Pompano Beach, FL 33069
Contact: Douglas Bridges VP
Tel: 954-977-0666
Email: dbridges@aerospacemetals.com
Website: www.aerospacemetals.com
Dist raw materials: aircraft quality metals, sheet, plate, rod, wire, bar, tubing & extruded shapes. (Woman/Hisp, estab 2001, empl 14, sales $7,000,000, cert: NMSDC)

6602 Manzi Metals, Inc.
15293 Flight Path Dr
Brooksville, FL 34604
Contact: Dorsey Peterson Small Business Specialist
Tel: 352-277-5852
Email: dpeterson@manzimetals.com
Website: www.manzimetals.com
Dist aerospace & commercial metals: aluminum, stainless, alloy steel, copper, brass, titanium, high temps in sheet, plate, bar, rod, hex, tube, etc. forgings, castings, ingots, billets. (Woman/AA, estab 1993, empl 10, sales $3,600,000, cert: State, City, NMSDC, SDB)

Illinois

6603 Elgiloy Specialty Metals
1565 Fleetwood Dr
Elgin, IL 60123
Contact: Margaret Wilson Wire Sales Rep
Tel: 847-695-1900
Email: margaretw@elgiloy.com
Website: www.elgiloy.com
Strip, wire, rod & bar specialty alloys; various gauges/diameters and widths. Strip: rolling, slitting, annealing. Wire/bar/rod: drawing, annealing. In-house lab. (As-Pac, estab 1975, empl 75, sales , cert: NMSDC)

6604 HL Metals, LLC
910 Spruce St
Winnetka, IL 60093
Contact: Hui Lin Lim President
Tel: 312-590-3360
Email: hlim@hlmetalsllc.com
Website: www.hlmetalsllc.com
Dist P1020 aluminum sows/aluminum sheet ingot. (Woman/As-Pac, estab 2007, empl , sales $55,000,000, cert: CPUC, NWBOC)

6605 Michlin Metals Inc.
3100 Dundee Rd, Ste 710
Northbrook, IL 60062
Contact: President
Tel: 847-272-3240
Email: skus1@sbcglobal.net
Website: www.michlinmetals.com
Dist stainless steel, aerospace alloys, general alloys, steel, aluminum, brass, monel, inconel, exotics, specialty steels & bronze, heat treating, grinding & cut to size material. (Woman, estab 1984, empl 15, sales , cert: State)

6606 Nak-Man Corporation
5677 W Howard
Niles, IL 60714
Contact: Perry Nakachi President
Tel: 847-673-7377
Email: nakmancorp@aol.com
Website:
Dist carbon steel, stainless steel, structural steel, aluminum, copper, brass, bronze, plastics, machined & fabricated parts. (As-Pac, estab 1989, empl 12, sales $4,796,534, cert: City, NMSDC)

6607 National Material Company, L.L.C.
1965 Pratt Blvd
Elk Grove Village, IL 60007
Contact: Jim Osborne Dir Minority Development
Tel: 847-806-4742
Email: josborne@nmlp.com
Website: www.nmlp.com
Steel service & processing. (As-Pac, estab 1999, empl 299, sales $370,000,000, cert: NMSDC)

6608 North States Steel Corp.
12255 Highway 173
Hebron, IL 60034
Contact: Sandra Myers President
Tel: 815-648-1500
Email: smyers@northstatessteel.com
Website: www.northstatessteel.com
Hot rolled, cold rolled, aluminum stainless steel sheets. (Woman, estab 1971, empl 25, sales $14,000,000, cert: State, WBENC, SDB)

6609   S & S International,Inc.
       457 St. Paul Blvd
       Carol Stream, IL 60188
       Contact: Rich Isom Sr Acct Exec
       Tel: 708-805-5701
       Email: icemanandfamily1@msn.com
       Website: www.ssistainless.com
Dist stainless steel: sheet, plate, strip, coil, bars, structural
shapes, square & rectangular tubing, pipe & fittings,
aluminum sheet, strip & coil. (As-Ind, As-Pac, estab 1991,
empl 105, sales $30,000,000, cert: NMSDC)

Indiana

6610   Advanced Metal Services, LLC
       2324 Longleaf Dr
       Fort Wayne, IN 46804
       Contact: Jason L. Redden, Jr. Exec VP
       Tel: 260-625-5046
       Email: slyred01@aol.com
       Website:
Metal recycling; dist flat rolled steel (Hisp, estab 1999,
empl 2, sales , cert: NMSDC)

6611   Circle City Rebar, LLC
       4002 Industrial Blvd
       Indianapolis, IN 46254
       Contact: Heidi Russo Controller
       Tel: 317-917-8566
       Email: hrusso@circlecityrebar.com
       Website: http://circlecityrebar.com
Supplier and Fabricator of concrete reinforcing steel bars
(rebar) in all sizes; plain and epoxy coated. (AA, estab
2005, empl 14, sales $7,541,942, cert: NMSDC)

6612   Eagle Steel Products, Inc.
       5150 Loop Rd
       Jeffersonville, IN 47130
       Contact: Gary Shumate GM Sales
       Tel: 812-282-7090
       Email: gshumate@eaglesteelproducts.com
       Website: www.eaglesteelproducts.com
Mfr strip steel; flat rolled products, blanking; covered
barge & rail loading & unloading svcs, warehousing, etc.
(Woman/As-Pac, estab 1982, empl 83, sales $32,000,000,
cert: NMSDC)

Michigan

6613   Delaco Steel Corporation
       8111 Tireman, Ste 1
       Dearborn, MI 48126
       Contact: Michael Roualet VP of Quality
       Tel: 313-491-1200
       Email: mike.roualet@delacosteel.com
       Website: www.delacosteel.com
Dist & process steel & aluminum. Blanking, warehousing,
slitting, stampings, etc. (Woman/Hisp, estab 1974, empl
650, sales , cert: NMSDC, WBENC)

6614   Ferrous Processing & Trading
       2920 Scotten
       Detroit, MI 48210
       Contact: Kristy Boismier President
       Tel: 313-567-9710
       Email: kristy.boismier@fptscrap.com
       Website: www.fptscrap.com
Process, distribute & recycle scrap metals. (AA, estab 0,
empl , sales , cert: NMSDC)

6615   H&H Metal Source
       1909 Turner Ave NW
       Grand Rapids, MI 49504
       Contact: JR Hartman Operations Mgr
       Tel: 616-364-0113
       Email: jr@hhmetalsource.com
       Website: http://hhmetalsource.com
Flat rolled steel in coil or blanks. (Woman, estab 1992,
empl 30, sales $38,000,000, cert: WBENC)

6616   Instramed
       3071 Commerce Dr. Ste C
       Ft. Gratiot, MI 48059
       Contact: Cori Bonkoske Office Mgr
       Tel: 800-451-5840
       Email: allinfo@instramedinc.com
       Website: www.instramedinc.com
Scrap metal & recyclable materials, ferrous & non-
ferrous scrap metal. (Woman, estab 1987, empl , sales ,
cert: NWBOC)

6617   National Material Co.
       1505 N Dixie Dr, Ste 2
       Monroe, MI 48162
       Contact: John Allen Sales Rep
       Tel: 734-384-9720
       Email: jballen53@msn.com
       Website: www.nmcmonroe.com
Steel coil, sheet, blank, painted steel, galvanized,
aluminum,stainless HSLA, CS, DS. (As-Pac, estab 0, empl
0, sales $750,000,000, cert: NMSDC)

6618   Scion Steel
       21555 Mullin Ave
       Warren, MI 48089
       Contact: Micky Tschirhart VP
       Tel: 800-288-2127
       Email: mtschirhart@scionsteel.com
       Website: www.scionsteel.com
Full line steel service center - processed & fabricated to
order. (Hisp, estab 1984, empl 51, sales , cert: NMSDC)

6619   Torch Steel Sales LLC
18501 Krause St
Riverview, MI 48193
Contact: Cristina Simone Owner
Tel: 734-783-2018
Email: csimone@torchsteelsales.com
Website: www.torchsteelsales.com
Steel service center: slitting, blanking, shearing, & slearing of non-ferrous flat rolled steel products, Hot Rolled, Cold Rolled, Hot Dipped Galvanized, Electro Galvanized, Galvanneal, & Aluminized. (Woman, estab 2013, empl 2, sales $700,600, cert: WBENC)

North Carolina

6620   Accro-Met, Inc.
3406 Westwood Industrial Dr
Monroe, NC 28110
Contact: Andrea Doolittle Sales
Tel: 704-283-2111
Email: alm@accromet.com
Website: www.accromet.com
Dist metal: stainless, nickel, aluminum, copper, brass, bronze, sheet, plate, bar, shapes. (Woman, estab 1988, empl 15, sales $6,000,000, cert: WBENC)

New Jersey

6621   L-E-M Plastics& Supply Inc.
255 Highland Cross
Rutherford, NJ 07070
Contact: Ellen Pietrowitz-Phillips President
Tel: 201-933-9150
Email: ellenp@l-e-mplastics.com
Website: www.l-e-mplastics.com
Fabricate & dist raw material plastic & rubber, Sheet, rod, tubing & film cut to size. Machining of all plastic, build to print. Steel rule die punching of thin plastic & rubber. (Woman, estab 1974, empl 12, sales $1,200,000, cert: WBENC)

New York

6622   O.S.S. Metals Inc.
14939 Guy R Brewer Blvd
Jamaica, NY 11434
Contact: Sattesh Singh CEO
Tel: 718-553-2054
Email: sattesh@ossmetals.com
Website: www.ossmetals.com
Provide raw material: Aluminum, Stainless Steel, Titanium, Carbon Steel & specialty alloys. (As-Ind, estab 2012, empl 3, sales $750,000, cert: State)

Ohio

6623   CT Metal Source
9551 St Christine Ct
Sylvania, OH 43560
Contact: Chad Crooks President
Tel: 419-779-6172
Email: ccrooks@ctmetalsource.com
Website: www.ctmetalsource.com
Dist metal castings, rail car parts, vent registers & steel coils. (Hisp, estab 2005, empl 5, sales $7,000,000, cert: NMSDC)

6624   Ferrolux Metals Co. of Ohio, LLC
8055A Highland Pointe Pkwy
Macedonia, OH 44056
Contact: Mark Nester GM
Tel: 330-468-1008
Email: mnester@ferrolux.com
Website: www.ferrolux.com
Dist flat rolled processed steel, Cold rolled, Coated, Slitting & Inspection, Storage, Transportation. (Hisp, estab 2004, empl 22, sales , cert: NMSDC)

6625   MasterSource Co., Inc.
1208 Massillon Rd Ste 2
Akron, OH 44306
Contact: Tracy Skinner Cstmr Service
Tel: 800-968-1718
Email: tracy@mastersourceco.com
Website: www.mastersourceco.com
Aluminum, brass, bronze, copper, alloy & carbon steel, nylon, stainless, tool steel: bar, rod, plate, sheet, tube, foil, wire, structural shapes, bushings. (Woman/As-Pac, estab 1992, empl 4, sales $1,090,000, cert: State)

6626   Mid-West Materials, Inc.
3687 Shepard Rd
Perry, OH 44081
Contact: Scott Dennis Sales Rep
Tel: 440-259-5200
Email: scott.dennis@midwestmaterials.com
Website: www.midwestmaterials.com
Flat rolled steel service center, hot rolled, hot rolled, pickled & oiled & coated steel in commercial quality, high strength-low alloy & low through high carbon chemistries. (Woman, estab 1952, empl 50, sales $50,000,000, cert: State)

6627   Nu Tek Steel, LLC
       6180 American Road
       Toledo, OH 43612
       Contact: Sarah Bates President & CEO
       Tel: 419-724-0891
       Email: sarah.bates@ntsteel.net
       Website: www.ntsteel.net
Steel services: slitting, pickling, blanking, leveling, special
bar quality, construction & medical. (Woman/AA, estab
2000, empl 10, sales $4,300,000, cert: State, WBENC)

6628   Slice Of Stainless Inc.
       1015 Seabrook Way
       Cincinnati, OH 45245
       Contact: Jim Schneible Sales Mgr
       Tel: 513-943-1290
       Email: jim@sliceofstainless.com
       Website: www.sliceofstainless.com
Dist stainless steal & high nickel alloys sheet & plate.
(Woman, estab 1992, empl 20, sales $7,100,000, cert:
WBENC)

Texas

6629   Texas Specialty Metals, Inc.
       4989 FM 1461
       McKinney, TX 75071
       Contact: Andy Dimock Mgr
       Tel: 972-347-5557
       Email: andy@txspec.com
       Website: www.texasspecialtymetals.com
Stainless steel, aluminum & steel, titanium, nickel, invar,
vespel & alloys. (Woman/Nat Ame, estab 1998, empl 3,
sales $250,000, cert: State)

Virginia

6630   United Scrap Metal
       2900 Terminal Ave
       Richmond, VA 23234
       Contact: Owen Tomlinson Recycling Consultant
       Tel: 434-430-1039
       Email: otomlinson@unitedscrap.com
       Website: www.unitedscrap.com
Metal recycling. (Woman, estab 1978, empl 170, sales ,
cert: WBENC)

METAL, WIRE PRODUCTS
See six other METAL categories. NAICS Code 33

California

6631 Calmont Wire & Cable
420 E Alton Ave
Santa Ana, CA 92707
Contact: Barbara Monteleone CEO
Tel: 714-549-0336
Email: bobbem@calmont.com
Website: www.calmont.com
Custom mfr precision wire & cable, including high-flex &
high-temp Silicone & FEP. (Woman, estab 1958, empl 32,
sales , cert: State)

6632 Top-Shelf Fixtures
5263 Schaefer Ave
Chino, CA 91710
Contact: Michelle Burguan controller
Tel: 909-627-7423
Email: sprochnow@topshelffixtures.com
Website: www.topshelffixtures.com
Wire fabrication: sheet metal & structural steel for
gondola shelving. (Hisp, estab 2002, empl 123, sales
$8,500,000, cert: NMSDC)

Georgia

6633 Healthier & Happier, Inc.
1853 Whitehall Forest Ct.
Atlanta, GA 30316
Contact: Jing Carter-Lu President
Tel: 678-900-6617
Email: jing.carter-lu@healthier-happier.com
Website: www.healthier-happier.com
Dist wire rope, steel rope, carbon spring steel wire, bead
wire, hose wire, plastic coated wire rope, PC stranded
wire, bunched wire, galvanized stranded wire & zinc-plated
steel wire. (Woman/As-Pac, estab 2003, empl 2, sales
$120,000, cert: City)

Illinois

6634 Altak Inc.
250 Covington Dr
Bloomingdale, IL 60108
Contact: Steve Janas Sales Mgr
Tel: 630-622-0300
Email: rtakayama@arktechno.com
Website: www.altakinc.com
Wire Harness manufacturing, Switch Assembly manufac-
turing, Spring manufacturing, Stampings - 30 to 800 ton,
Wire Forms, IATF 16949 and ISO 9001 certified. (As-Pac,
estab 1980, empl 400, sales $37,000,000, cert: NMSDC)

6635 Solar Spring & Wire Forms
345 Criss Circle
Elk Grove Village, IL 60007
Contact: Aida Carrera Dir of Global Sales
Tel: 847-437-7838
Email: acarrera@solarspring.com
Website: www.solarspring.com
Mfr springs, wire forms & stampings. (Hisp, estab 1979,
empl 110, sales $11,100,000, cert: NMSDC)

Louisiana

6636 Vast Industries
108 Venus St Ste 200
Morgan City, LA 70380
Contact: Yvette Archuleta-Tudury Owner
Tel: 985-312-1592
Email: yvette@vast-ind.com
Website: www.Vast-Ind.com
Wire EDM & precision machined parts manufacturing,
custom product design, reverse engineering & aluminum
& steel fabrication. (Woman/Nat Ame, Hisp, estab 2007,
empl 7, sales $600,000, cert: NMSDC, WBENC, 8a)

Massachusetts

6637 Springfield Spring
311 Shaker Rd
Longmeadow, MA 01028
Contact: Norman Rodriques President
Tel: 413-525-6837
Email: pat@springfieldspring.com
Website: www.springfieldspring.com
Mfr precision engineered compression springs, torsion
springs, extension springs, wire forms, fourslide-
produced stampings, assemblies. (Hisp, estab 1942,
empl 39, sales $7,200,000, cert: NMSDC)

Ohio

6638 MCM Ind. Co., Inc.
7800 Finney Ave
Cleveland, OH 44105
Contact: Abby Werner VP
Tel: 216-641-6300
Email: awerner@northcoastspring.com
Website: www.mcmindustries.com
Wire & spring forming. (AA, Hisp, estab 1980, empl 25,
sales , cert: NMSDC)

6639 Mid West Fabricating
      313 N Johns St
      Amanda, OH 43102
      Contact: Dave Gallimore Business Development
      Tel: 740-969-4411
      Email: dgallimore@midwestfab.com
      Website: www.midwestfab.com
Cold formed rod & wire products, fasteners, CNC
wireforming, cold forming. (Woman, estab 1945, empl
200, sales $32,000,000, cert: WBENC)

Oklahoma

6640 Ebsco Spring Company, Inc.
      4949 S 83rd Ave E
      Tulsa, OK 74145
      Contact: Todd Pfeifer Sales
      Tel: 918-628-1680
      Email: toddp@ebscospring.com
      Website: www.ebscospring.com
Mfr & engineer custom, high quality compression, extension & torsion springs. (Woman, estab 1940, empl 75, sales
$6,500,000, cert: WBENC)

Pennsylvania

6641 LEM Products, Inc.
      147 Keystone Dr
      Montgomeryville, PA 18936
      Contact: Nicole Adamczyk Sales
      Tel: 800-220-2400
      Email: nadamczyk@lemproductsinc.com
      Website: www.lemproductsinc.com
Mfr wire identification safety products: wire marker cards
& books, voltage markers, transformer marking, hand
writeable cable markers, laser coded bar codes, lockout
tags, roll
dispensers, heat shrinkables, etc. (Woman, estab 1967,
empl 38, sales $5,500,000, cert: CPUC, WBENC)

6642 R.A.W. Consulting, LLC
      126 Mervis Dr
      Beaver Falls, PA 15010
      Contact: Robert Washington President
      Tel: 724-384-1559
      Email: rawconsultantsllc@gmail.com
      Website: http://R-A-W-LLC.com
Distribution & warehousing of Stainless & alloy tubing,
Cold rolled wire, Metal grating, Deformed wire. (AA, estab
2013, empl 3, sales $309,996, cert: State, NMSDC)

Texas

6643 M3 Associates, Inc.
      P.O. Box 224075
      Dallas, TX 75222
      Contact: Yvonne Newhouse President
      Tel: 214-339-2117
      Email: yvonne@m3associatesinc.com
      Website: www.m3associatesinc.com
Distributor of wire, cable, tubing, sleeving, solder
sleeves, heat shrink molded, shapes, boots (Woman/AA,
estab 1988, empl 5, sales , cert: State)

Virginia

6644 Jo Kell, Inc.
      1716 Lambert Ct
      Chesapeake, VA 23320
      Contact: Patricia Galiney Sales
      Tel: 904-260-8420
      Email: customerservice@jokell.com
      Website: www.jokell.com
Dist electrical apparatus & equipment, wiring supplies &
related equipment. (Woman, estab 1977, empl 50, sales
$30,383,075, cert: WBENC)

OFFICE SUPPLIES
Manufacturers and distributors of office supplies and equipment: rubber stamps, writing implements, binders and portfolios, business forms, calculators, envelopes, tape, ink, office machines and furniture, paper and maintenance products, paper recycling, paper conversion, toner cartridges, printers, etc. NAICS Code 42

Alabama

6645   E.S. Robbins Corp.
2802 E Avalon Ave
Muscle Shoals, AL 35661
Contact: Bonnie Donato Channel Marketing Mgr
Tel: 256-248-2494
Email: badonato@esrobbins.com
Website: www.esrchairmats.com
Dist office products & furnishings. Mfr polymer products. (Woman, estab 1967, empl 187, sales , cert: WBENC)

Arkansas

6646   Burris Inc.
113 S Arkansas Ave
Russellville, AR 72801
Contact: President
Tel: 479-968-4888
Email:
Website: www.burrisinc.com
Office supplies & office furniture, panel systems, custom millwork, office layout & design. (Woman, estab 1953, empl 15, sales $3,374,600, cert: WBENC)

6647   Goddess Products, Inc.
6142 Getty Dr
North Little Rock, AR 72117
Contact: Andrew Sigeti Acct Mgr
Tel: 501-372-4002
Email: asigeti@ussco.com
Website: www.goddessproductsinc.com
Dist office products, office equipment, office furniture, computer peripherals, janitorial supplies & safety equipment. (Woman/AA, estab 2006, empl 5, sales $375,000, cert: WBENC)

California

6648   American Textile Systems, Inc. DBA American Paper
13151 Midway Place
Cerritos, CA 90703
Contact: Mike Khan VP Corporate Markets
Tel: 562-229-0036
Email: mike@amtexsys.com
Website: http://amtexsys.com
Healthcare & hospitality related textile & paper products. (As-Ind, estab 1993, empl 25, sales $20,000,000, cert: State)

6649   Big Red Print Solutions, LLC
2100 Sawtelle Blvd Ste 201
Los Angeles, CA 90025
Contact: Rudy Wrabel Director
Tel: 213-985-7201
Email: rudy@bigredink.com
Website: www.bigredink.com
Dist office equipment, supplies & technology products. (Minority/Woman, estab 2010, empl 7, sales $1,100,000, cert: NMSDC, CPUC)

6650   DD Office Products, Inc
5025 Hampton St
Los Angeles, CA 90058
Contact: John Kim GSA Contract Administrator
Tel: 323-973-4569
Email: johnk@libertypp.com
Website: www.libertypp.com
Dist office paper. (As-Ind, estab 2001, empl 14, sales $36,617,778, cert: NMSDC)

6651   Garza Industries
1870 N Glassell St
Orange, CA 92865
Contact: James Garza
Tel: 714-769-2777
Email: james@garzaindustries.com
Website: www.garzaindustries.com
Dist office supplies: copy paper, laser toner cartridges, fax & copier supplies, furniture, direct mail svcs, commercial printing, corporate apparel, promotional items. (Woman/Hisp, estab 1991, empl 35, sales , cert: CPUC)

6652   Kleenslate Concepts, LP
14997 Camage Ave, Unit B
Sonora, CA 94370
Contact: Julia Rhodes CEO
Tel: 209-588-0375
Email: julia@kleenslate.com
Website: www.kleenslate.com
Dist attachable white board markers erasers, white board products (Woman/As-Pac, Hisp, estab 2001, empl 12, sales , cert: WBENC)

6653   New Century Technologies Inc.
4290 Kendall St
San Diego, CA 92109
Contact: Peter Steiner COO
Tel: 800-457-4313
Email: peter@nctsolution.com
Website: www.nctsolution.com
Toner cartridges, office supplies/products, office equipment, office furniture, janitorial supplies, breakroom supplies, industrial supplies/products, hard drive, memory, IT products that offers hardware, software, related services. (Woman/As-Pac, estab 2006, empl 3, sales $1,391,800, cert: 8a)

6654   Z Venture Capital Frontiers, Inc.
1625 W Vernon Ave
Los Angeles, CA 90062
Contact: Karim Zaman President
Tel: 323-596-4690
Email: karim@thezamangroup.com
Website: www.thezamangroup.com
Dist office supplies, inkjet, laser, toner cartridge, thermal fax ribbon. (AA, estab 1997, empl 2, sales $1,300,000, cert: State, City, CPUC)

Colorado

6655   CADDO Design Inc. dba CADDO Solutions
2760 W 5th Ave
Denver, CO 80204
Contact: Donald Kelin CEO
Tel: 303-534-3252
Email: dkelin@caddosolutions.com
Website: www.caddosolutions.com
Dist office products, office furniture, coffee & refreshments, ad specialty items, printing, print management. (Nat Ame, estab 1990, empl 45, sales $5,000,000, cert: State)

6656   Eon Office
       60 Tejon St
       Denver, CO 80223
       Contact: Jeniffer Beam VP Sales
       Tel: 720-570-5400
       Email: jbeam@eonoffice.com
       Website: www.eonoffice.com
Office Supplies, Furniture and Design, Printing, Breakroom, Janitorial (Woman, estab 2001, empl 86, sales , cert: WBENC)

6657   Faison Office Products, Inc
       12508 E Briarwood Ave Ste 1A
       Centennial, CO 80012
       Contact: Bonnie Key Exec Coordinator
       Tel: 303-340-3672
       Email: bkey@faisonopc.com
       Website: www.faisonopc.com
Dist office supplies & furniture; word processing & data processing supplies & furniture. (AA, estab 1981, empl 55, sales $45,000,000, cert: NMSDC)

District of Columbia

6658   The Hamilton Group
       4406 Gault Place NE
       Washington, DC 20019
       Contact: Kaari Hamilton President
       Tel: 202-689-4304
       Email: kayhhpbp@verizon.net
       Website: www.thehamiltongroupllc.net
Dist office supplies, advertisement & promotional products, office equipment & clothing wearables. (Woman/AA, estab 2007, empl , sales $731,000, cert: City, NMSDC, WBENC)

Florida

6659   Apex Office Products, Inc.
       5209 N Howard Ave
       Tampa, FL 33603
       Contact: Aurelio Llorente, Jr President
       Tel: 800-227-1563
       Email: allorentejr@apexop.com
       Website: www.apexofficeproducts.com
Dist office supplies & furniture, data supplies & furniture, paper products, rubber stamps. (Woman/Hisp, estab 1981, empl 55, sales , cert: State, NMSDC)

6660   J&E Office Supplies, Inc.
       7911 NW 72nd Ave, Unit 110A
       Medley, FL 33166
       Contact: Jaime Hernandez Owner
       Tel: 305-887-7339
       Email: jeoffice@mindspring.com
       Website: www.biggestbook.com/index.faces
Office supplies & office furniture. (Hisp, estab 1985, empl 4, sales $2,500,000, cert: State)

6661   Konie Cups International, Inc.
       9001 NW 105th Way
       Medley, FL 33178
       Contact: Fiorella Roversi Sales Analyst
       Tel: 786-337-7967
       Email: fiorellaroversi@koniecups.com
       Website: www.koniecups.com
Mfr paper cone cups & funnels. (Hisp, estab 1991, empl 56, sales $9,223,670, cert: NMSDC)

6662   Mammoth Office Products, LLC
       7351 Southampton Terr
       Boynton Beach, FL 33436
       Contact: Managing Member
       Tel: 561-251-8662
       Email:
       Website: http://mammothofficeproducts.com
Office products & supplies. (Woman, estab 2012, empl 1, sales $200,000, cert: WBENC)

6663   MarkMaster, Inc.
       11111 N 46th St
       Tampa, FL 33617
       Contact: Deborah Jordan Sales Rep
       Tel: 813-988-6000
       Email: sales@markmasterinc.com
       Website: www.markmasterinc.com
Mfr rubber stamps, engraved & screened signage & badges; industrial marking equip. (Hisp, estab 1933, empl 65, sales $8,700,993, cert: NMSDC)

6664   Source One Distributors, Inc.
       3125 Fortune Way, Ste 1
       Wellington, FL 33414
       Contact: Mark Llano CEO
       Tel: 561-296-0520
       Email: mllano@buysourceone.com
       Website: www.buysourceone.com
Dist office products & furniture, safety & janitorial products, light sticks, snap light, cyalume, camo face paint. (Hisp, estab 2003, empl 5, sales $1,800,000, cert: State)

Georgia

6665   ABC Laser USA, Inc.
       6000 G Unity Dr
       Norcross, GA 30092
       Contact: Kammie Lee Acct Mgr
       Tel: 770-448-5867
       Email: kmichell@abclaserusa.com
       Website: www.abclaserusa.com
Office Supplies, Ink, Toner, Furniture, Paper, Disc, Printers, Faxes, Pens, Pencils, Maintenance, Service, Janitorial Supplies, Cleaners, Toilet Paper, Paper Towels, Recycle Toner, Hewlett Packard, Lexmark, Dell, Canon. (Woman/As-Pac, estab 1996, empl 6, sales , cert: City)

6666   Freeman Forms & Supplies dba MySupplies
       800 Doug Davis Dr
       Atlanta, GA 30354
       Contact: Nancy Freeman Balkcom President
       Tel: 404-768-2387
       Email: nancy@mysupplies.com
       Website: www.mysupplies.com
Dist office product & furniture. (Woman, estab 1970, empl 22, sales $6,000,000, cert: State)

6667   Peachtree Supplies, Inc.
       233 Peachtree St NE, Ste 1265
       Atlanta, GA 30303
       Contact: Al Graham President
       Tel: 404-963-2410
       Email: agraham@peachtreesupplies.com
       Website: www.peachtreesupplies.com
Office supplies, furniture, ink & toner, paper, cleaning supplies, technology. (Woman/AA, estab 2009, empl 10, sales $1,350,000, cert: NMSDC)

6668　Sierra International LLC
9308 Industrial Dr
Covington, GA 30014
Contact: Darryl Jackson Dir outside sales
Tel:　770-786-5301
Email: dmjackson@sierrainternationalllc.com
Website: www.sierrainternationalllc.com
Mfr paper cups & paper plates. Dist foam/plastic, utensils, tissue, paper towels & other foodservice disposable items. (AA, estab 2007, empl 5, sales , cert: State)

6669　South Coast Paper LLC
2300 Windy Ridge Pkwy, Ste 830
Atlanta, GA 30339
Contact: LaJoia Broughton Supplier Diversity
Tel:　770-933-3411
Email: supplierdiversity@southcoastpaper.com
Website: www.southcoastpaper.com
Mfr & convert uncoated, coated, photographic & digital paper grades, cut, wrap, package, palletize & ship product. (AA, estab 2000, empl 49, sales $18,000,000, cert: NMSDC)

Iowa

6670　American Diversity Business Solutions
9834 Hickory Dr
Urbandale, IA 50322
Contact: Joe Riggsbee Sr Acct Exec
Tel:　515-276-1232
Email: jriggsbee@americanmin.com
Website: www.americandiv.com
Dist custom business forms, office supplies, & promotional items. (Woman, estab 1992, empl 15, sales $23,941,250, cert: WBENC)

6671　Bailey Office Equipment, Inc.
123 E 2nd St
Ottumwa, IA 52501
Contact: Linda Gardner President
Tel:　800-728-0407
Email: linda@baileyoffice.com
Website: www.baileyoffice.com
Dist office supplies, business machines, office furniture, cleaning supplies, safety equipment & breakroom essentials. (Woman, estab 1925, empl 10, sales $2,798,000, cert: WBENC)

Illinois

6672　Bren Products
437 E 103rd St
Chicago, IL 60628
Contact: Rochelle Gary Comptroller
Tel:　773-568-9900
Email: brenprod@sbcglobal.net
Website:
Dist office machines & supplies, office furniture, custom printing, file folders & envelopes, recycling containers & supplies. (AA, estab 1994, empl 3, sales $5,600,000, cert: NMSDC)

6673　Chicago Green Office Company dba National Office Works, Inc.
7930 S Madison St
Burr Ridge, IL 60527
Contact: Joanna Davidson President
Tel:　312-455-9343
Email: joanna.davidson@nationalofficeworks.com
Website: www.nationalofficeworks.com
Dist office supplies. (Woman, estab , empl , sales $750,000, cert: State, WBENC)

6674　Gorilla Paper Inc.
1125 Lunt Ave
Elk Grove Village, IL 60007
Contact: Su Chang Lim President
Tel:　773-789-8113
Email: suchang@gorillapaper.com
Website: www.gorillapaper.com
POS Thermal Paper rolls, carbonless paper rolls, & related Ink Ribbons. (As-Pac, estab 2009, empl , sales $18,598,936, cert: NMSDC)

6675　Logsdon Office Supply
111 S Fairbank
Addison, IL 60101
Contact: Jack Dern VP
Tel:　847-593-8282
Email: jdern@logsdonofficesupply.com
Website: www.logsdonofficesupply.com
Dist office supplies. (AA, estab 1966, empl 25, sales $7,000,000, cert: City, NMSDC)

6676　Montenegro Paper, Ltd.
25 E Main St. #205
Roselle, IL 60172
Contact: Ed Enciso President
Tel:　630-894-0350
Email: mbe@montenegro-inc.com
Website: www.montenegropaper.com
Dist commercial printing paper & packaging supplies. (Hisp, estab 1996, empl 6, sales $23,173,000, cert: State, City, NMSDC)

6677　Norwood Paper
7001 W 60th St
Chicago, IL 60674
Contact: Laura Martin Natl Sales Mgr
Tel:　773-788-1508
Email: laura@norwoodpaper.com
Website: www.norwoodpaper.com
Dist non-box related packaging chipboard, skid liners, dust covers, interleavers, divider sheets, pallet liners, pallet pads. (Woman, estab 1972, empl , sales $8,000,000, cert: WBENC)

6678　Pointe International
234 Oakwood Road
Lake Zurich, IL 60047
Contact: Sheila Liao President
Tel:　847-550-7001
Email: sheila.liao@pointecompany.com
Website: www.pointecompany.com
Mfr & dist wooden case pencils, mechanic pencils, desk stapler, office supplies & promotional items. (Woman/As-Pac, estab 1997, empl 12, sales $1,800,000, cert: NMSDC, WBENC)

6679　Taylor Made Business Solutions LLC
318 W. Adams St 16th Fl
Chicago, IL 60606
Contact: Evonne Taylor CEO
Tel:　312-803-5635
Email: etaylor@tmbsllc.com
Website: http://TMBSLLC.com
Dist general office supplies, office furniture, break room & janitorial supplies. (Woman/AA, estab 2011, empl 3, sales $2,762,000, cert: State, NMSDC)

6680   Working Hands, Inc.
39W254 Sheldon Ct
Geneva, IL 60134
Contact: Maureen Vedder President
Tel: 630-270-1097
Email: maureen@workinghandsinc.com
Website: www.workinghandsinc.com
GBC equipment & supplies, copier tabs, laminating rolls & pouches, clear presentation covers, black composition back covers prepunched, binding coils, 3 ring clear view binders, plain or mylar docucopy copier tabs. (Woman, estab 2003, empl 2, sales $250,000, cert: NWBOC)

Indiana

6681   Kramer & Leonard, Inc.
312 Roberts Rd
Chesterton, IN 46304
Contact: Mary Fox President
Tel: 219-926-1171
Email: mfox@kramerleonard.com
Website: www.kramerleonard.com
Office products, office supplies, computer supplies, office furniture, commercial interior design services, copier sales, copier service. (Woman, estab 0, empl , sales , cert: State, WBENC)

6682   OfficeWorks Services LLC
12000 Exit Five Pkwy
Fishers, IN 46037
Contact: Joyce Posson VP Admin
Tel: 317-577-3519
Email: jposson@officeworks.net
Website: www.officeworks.net
Dist office furniture & material handling equip. (Hisp, estab 1984, empl 60, sales $43,000,000, cert: State, NMSDC)

6683   Rite Quality Office Supplies, Inc.
710 N Washington St
Kokomo, IN 46901
Contact: Douglas Vaughn President
Tel: 765-459-4788
Email: riteq@netusa1.net
Website: www.ritequality.com
Dist office & janitorial supplies & office furniture. (AA, estab 1989, empl 10, sales , cert: State, NMSDC)

Kansas

6684   Supplies Express LLC
626 S 10th St
Manhattan, KS 66502
Contact: Enrique Garibay Managing Partner
Tel: 785-341-2123
Email: suppliesexpressllc@gmail.com
Website: www.suppliesexpress.us
Mfr the world's only water-resistant paper drinking straws, import water-resistant paper grocery bags. (Hisp, estab 2017, empl 4, sales , cert: State)

Massachusetts

6685   Alpha Identification, Inc.
7 Spanish River Rd
Grafton, MA 01519
Contact: Frank Ng Treasurer
Tel: 508-839-6144
Email: alphaidinc@gmail.com
Website: www.alphaidinc.com
Dist photo ID equip & supplies for employee & student ID badges: Polaroid films, cameras, laminators, die-cutters, etc. (Woman/As-Pac, estab 1987, empl 2, sales $918,810, cert: State, City, CPUC)

6686   New England Office Supply
135 Lundquist Dr
Braintree, MA 02184
Contact: Peter Tracy Operations Dir
Tel: 866-636-7872
Email: petert@neosusa.com
Website: www.neosusa.com
Dist office computer supplies & furniture. (Woman/As-Ind, estab 1993, empl 75, sales , cert: State)

Maryland

6687   Rudolph's Office & Computer Supply, Inc.
5020 Campbell Blvd Ste C
Baltimore, MD 21014
Contact: Henry Dow VP Sales
Tel: 410-931-4150
Email: henry@rudolphsupply.com
Website: www.rudolphsupply.com
Dist office, computer & janitorial supplies, custom stamps, office furniture, space planning. (Woman, estab 1980, empl 60, sales $1,600,000, cert: State)

6688   Sue-Ann's Office Supply, Inc.
4147 Hayward Ave
Baltimore, MD 21215
Contact: Beverly Williams CEO
Tel: 410-664-6226
Email: bwms@sueannsofficesupply.com
Website: www.sueannsofficesupply.com
Dist office products; office furniture; workstations; computer products. (Woman/AA, estab 1986, empl 5, sales $1,503,484, cert: State, City)

Michigan

6689   AVE Solutions
1155 Brewery Park Blvd., #350
Detroit, MI 48207
Contact: Carol Kirkland Exec VP
Tel:
Email: carol@avesolutions.net
Website: www.avesolutions.net
Dist office supplies, office furniture, office equipment, audio visual equipment, computer equipment & supplies, printer equipment & supplies, paper, janitorial supplies, first aid supplies. (Woman/AA, estab 1990, empl 6, sales , cert: NMSDC, WBENC)

6690   Caracal Apparel and Products Corp.
805 Trinway Rd
Troy, MI 48085
Contact: Rebecca Miller Dir Sales/Marketing
Tel: 877-898-2847
Email: rmiller@caracalcorp.com
Website:
Paper (roll, cut, coated, uncoated), Print Management, office supplies, PPE (to include disposable and cloth 3-ply customizable masks, hand sanitizer, disinfectant spray, wipes, air filters), surgical apparel. (AA, estab 2004, empl 42, sales $60,000,000, cert: NMSDC)

6691   Hercules & Hercules, Inc.
19055 W Davison
Detroit, MI 48223
Contact: Belinda Jefferson President
Tel: 313-933-6669
Email: bjefferson@herculesandherculesinc.com
Website: www.herculesandherculesinc.com
Dist maintenance supplies & equip, office supplies & equip, office furniture. (AA, estab , empl , sales $7,000,000, cert: NMSDC)

6692 Kamar Office Express
      1280 E Big Beaver Rd
      Troy, MI 48083
      Contact: Kevin Monreal
      Tel: 866-996-8952
      Email: kevinm@oexusa.com
      Website: www.kamaroe.com
Dist office supplies & furniture. (AA, estab 2005, empl 15, sales , cert: NMSDC)

6693 KamarOE
      1280 E Big Beaver Ste A
      Troy, MI 48083
      Contact: Devin Durrell
      Tel: 866-996-8952
      Email: devind@kamaroe.com
      Website: www.kamaroe.com
Dist office supplies. (AA, estab 2005, empl 10, sales , cert: NMSDC)

6694 More Computer Supplies
      14132 10 Mile Rd
      Warren, MI 48089
      Contact: Steve Llorens Dir
      Tel: 586-771-4030
      Email: moresupplies@aol.com
      Website: http://more-office.biz
Office supplies, printer supplies, bar code labels, furniture, printers, fax machines and supplies. (As-Ind, estab 2001, empl 9, sales $9,800,000, cert: NMSDC)

6695 Nationwide Envelope Specialists, Inc.
      1259 Doris Rd
      Auburn Hills, MI 48326
      Contact: David Dzuris Sales
      Tel: 248-373-0111
      Email: sales@nespn.com
      Website: www.nespn.com
Printed & plain envelopes: special sizes & windows; commercial, booklet & open-end. (Hisp, estab 1990, empl 16, sales $5,200,000, cert: NMSDC)

6696 Paperworks, Inc.
      15477 Woodrow Wilson St
      Detroit, MI 48238
      Contact: Katrece Business Unit Mgr
      Tel: 800-243-1424
      Email: customerservice@pwi-inc.com
      Website: www.dchem.com
Dist paper & paper related products & office supplies. (AA, estab 1981, empl 23, sales $26,000,000, cert: NMSDC)

6697 Remco Storage Systems, Inc.
      2328 Livernois Road Ste 1070
      Troy, MI 48083
      Contact: Donna Tamburo-Wilson President & CEO
      Tel: 248-362-0500
      Email: donna@remcoequipment.com
      Website: www.remcoequipment.com
Storage & retrieval systems: vertical lifts & carousels, electric lateral filing systems, movable shelving, rotary files, cabinets, records mgmt systems, color coded labels, custom filing systems, folders & indexes. (Woman, estab 1976, empl 7, sales $2,000,000, cert: WBENC)

6698 RM International Resource Group. Ltd.
      22759 Heslip Dr
      Novi, MI 48375
      Contact: Reuben Levy President
      Tel: 877-637-6468
      Email: rlevy@rmintrg.com
      Website: www.rmintrg.com
Dist office supplies & furniture. (AA, estab 1998, empl , sales $800,000, cert: NMSDC)

6699 Rubber Stamps Unlimited, Inc.
      334 S Harvey St
      Plymouth, MI 48170
      Contact: Maryellen Lewandowski President
      Tel: 888-451-7300
      Email: mlew@thestampmaker.com
      Website: www.thestampmaker.com
Custom rubber stamps, self inking stamps, date stamps, seals, embossers & signs in one day. (Woman, estab 1993, empl 12, sales $3,306,000, cert: WBENC)

6700 Swift Computer Supply, Inc.
      37676 Enterprise Court
      Farmington Hills, MI 48331
      Contact: Henry Swift President
      Tel: 248-489-9250
      Email: meberle@smartofficedeals.com
      Website: www.shopSOSnow.com
Office supplies, furniture, printing, promotional items, janitorial & break room supplies. (AA, estab 1985, empl , sales $467,200, cert: NMSDC)

6701 Workplace Integrators
      30700 Telegraph, Ste 4800
      Bingham Farms, MI 48025
      Contact: Joe Eatman President
      Tel: 248-430-2345
      Email: jeatman@wp-int.com
      Website: www.wp-int.com
Dist office supplies: paper, writing instruments, folders, technology products, fastners, etc. (AA, estab 1938, empl , sales $50,000,000, cert: NMSDC)

Minnesota

6702 Crown Marking, Inc.
      4270 Dahlberg Dr
      Golden Valley, MN 55422
      Contact: Gregg Prest Treasurer
      Tel: 763-543-8243
      Email: gprest@crownmarking.com
      Website: www.crownmarking.com
Mfr & dist rubber & photopolymer stamps, daters, embossers & related stamping supplies. (Woman, estab 1928, empl 9, sales $5,000,000, cert: WBENC)

6703 ecoThynk
      607 Dayton Ave
      Saint Paul, MN 55012
      Contact: Gale Ward President
      Tel: 612-605-4885
      Email: gale@ecoenvelopes.com
      Website: www.ecothynk.com
Mfr reusable envelopes. (Woman, estab 2002, empl 5, sales $210,000, cert: WBENC)

6704 Innovative Office Solutions, LLC
      151 E Cliff Rd
      Burnsville, MN 55337
      Contact: Kathy Hovde Sr Acct Exec, Sales & Diversity
      Tel: 952-808-9900
      Email: khovde@innovativeos.com
      Website: www.innovativeos.com
Dist office, school, janitorial supplies & furniture. (Woman, estab 2001, empl 213, sales $100,000,000, cert: WBENC)

6705 Smead Manufacturing Company
600 Smead Blvd
Hastings, MN 55033
Contact: Michelle Hanson
Tel: 651-437-4111
Email: michelle.hanson@smead.com
Website: www.smead.com
Mfr & dist office filling supplies, systems & record mgmt software. (Woman, estab 1906, empl 2800, sales $225,000,000, cert: WBENC)

Missouri

6706 Missouri Office Systems & Supplies, Inc.
941 W 141st Terrace Ste B
Kansas City, MO 64145
Contact: Virgie Dillard President
Tel: 816-761-5152
Email: vld@8asupplier.com
Website: www.8asupplier.com
Dist office supplies, furniture, ethernet, media, printers, software, hardware, ribbons, fax, scanners, computers, routers, hubs, toners, servers. (Woman/AA, estab 1993, empl 9, sales $8,775,113, cert: State, City, NMSDC)

6707 Offices Unlimited Inc.
2127 William St
Cape Girardeau, MO 63703
Contact: Celeste "Sally" LeGrand Owner
Tel: 573-332-0202
Email: sally@officesunlimited.com
Website: www.officesunlimited.com
Office supplies, stationary, office furniture, office partitions, panel systems, office equipment, copiers, faxes, toners, medical supplies, break room furniture, break room foods, janitorial products. (Woman, estab 2001, empl 6, sales $2,000,000, cert: State)

Montana

6708 e Office Supply
117 N 24th Ave
Bozeman, MT 59718
Contact: Louis Bowker Owner
Tel: 888-603-0274
Email: bowker@eofficesupply.biz
Website: www.eofficesupply.biz
Dist office products, computer supplies & equipment. (Nat Ame, estab 2003, empl 1, sales , cert: State)

North Carolina

6709 American Product Distributors, Inc.
8350 Arrowridge Blvd
Charlotte, NC 28273
Contact: Ray Kennedy CEO
Tel: 704-522-9411
Email: registration@americanproduct.com
Website: www.americanproduct.com
Dist office imaging supplies, remanufactured toner cartridges, cut sheet paper, wide format paper, rolled paper & ribbons, business & manufacturing labels. (AA, estab 1992, empl 50, sales $40,000,000, cert: NMSDC)

6710 Kennedy Office Supply Inc.
4211-A Atlantic Ave
Raleigh, NC 27604
Contact: Linda McCotter Accounting Mgr
Tel: 919-878-5400
Email: lmccotter@kennedyoffice.com
Website: www.kennedyofficesupply.com
Dist office supplies, breakroom products, technology & janitorial supplies. (Woman, estab 1960, empl 50, sales $13,200,000, cert: State)

6711 New Generation Product, Inc.
5736 North Tryon St Ste 223B
Charlotte, NC 28213
Contact: Donald Black President
Tel: 704-596-5327
Email: don.black@newgenproduct.com
Website: www.NewGenProduct.com
Provide biomass papers made from recycled agricultural fibers. (AA, estab 2010, empl 1, sales , cert: State, CPUC)

New Hampshire

6712 Gorham Paper and Tissue LLC
72 Cascade Flats
Gorham, NH 03581
Contact: Wayne Johnson Sales
Tel: 603-342-2000
Email: wayne.johnson@gorhampt.com
Website: www.gorhampt.com
Mfr specialty paper, tissue & towel papers, baking (baking cups, release papers) or food applications like tray liners, food bags & pouches that require grease resistance or wets strength. (Woman, estab 2011, empl 200, sales , cert: WBENC)

New Jersey

6713 Corporate Diversity Solutions
615 Franklin Turnpike Ste 5
Ridgewood, NJ 07450
Contact: Stacey Scarpa President
Tel: 201-444-1506
Email: stscarpa@corporatediversitysolutions.com
Website: www.corporatediversitysolutions.com
Dist stationery & office supplies. (Woman, estab 2009, empl 7, sales $4,300,000, cert: WBENC)

6714 CSS Building Services Inc.
12 Stults Rd, Ste 132
Dayton, NJ 08810
Contact: Vic Tartara Sales
Tel: 732-246-0554
Email: lcoury@cssbuildingservices.com
Website: www.cssofficesupply.com
Dist office supplies. (Woman/Hisp, estab 2004, empl 25, sales , cert: WBENC)

6715 The Fisher Group
P.O. Box 1653
Dover, NJ 07802
Contact: Irving Fisher Managing Partner
Tel: 973-442-3000
Email: irving@fisherpaper.net
Website: www.fisherpaper.net
Dist paper. (AA, estab 2000, empl 4, sales $3,556,001, cert: NMSDC)

New Mexico

6716 Desert Paper & Envelope Company, Inc.
2700 Girard Blvd NE
Albuquerque, NM 87107
Contact: VP Finance
Tel: 800-228-2298
Email:
Website: www.desertpaper.com
Mfr & print envelopes. (Woman/Hisp, estab 1973, empl 40, sales $5,435,600, cert: NMSDC, WBENC)

6717 Midway Office Supply Inc.
      5900 Midway Park Blvd NE
      Albuquerque, NM 87109
      Contact: Mike Sei President
      Tel: 505-345-3414
      Email: mikesei@midwayos.com
      Website: www.midwayos.com
Dist office supplies. (As-Pac, Hisp, estab 1980, empl 10, sales $9,000,000, cert: NMSDC)

6718 Roses Southwest Paper, Inc.
      1701 2nd St SW
      Albuquerque, NM 87102
      Contact: James Hinkle NSM
      Tel: 734-968-8103
      Email: jmhinkle@aol.com
      Website: www.rosessouthwest.com
Mfr sanitary paper products: hard roll towels, multi fold towels, jumbo roll toilet tissue, standard roll toilet tissue, facial tissue, seat covers, dispenser napkins, dinner napkins, cocktail napkins, kitchen roll towels. (Hisp, estab 1984, empl 215, sales $58,980,000, cert: NMSDC)

6719 Stride, Inc.
      1021 Carlisle Blvd SE
      Albuquerque, NM 87106
      Contact: Kerry Bertram President & CEO
      Tel: 505-232-3201
      Email: kerry@strideinc.com
      Website: www.strideinc.com
Mfr & dist writing instruments, binders & office products: pens & markers for wood finishes, parts marking, black light, crafts, photographic, cosmetics, cleaning devices & voter marking pens. (Woman, estab 1988, empl 11, sales $7,000,000, cert: State, WBENC)

New York

6720 Asian & Hispanic Trading & Consulting Inc.
      37 West 39th St Ste 503
      New York, NY 10018
      Contact: Suzanne Cohon Business Dev Mgr
      Tel: 212-252-8988
      Email: suzanne@asc-to.com
      Website: www.aandhtc.com
Dist office supplies, furniture, computer equipment, and promotional products. (Woman/As-Pac, estab 2016, empl 3, sales $295,000, cert: State, City)

6721 Ebony Office Products, Inc.
      10-17 44th Ave
      Long Island City, NY 11101
      Contact: Michael Ukhueduan Dir Business Dev
      Tel: 718-706-8200
      Email: info@ebonyproducts.com
      Website: www.ebonyproducts.com
Dist office supplies, office furniture, computer supplies, printing services. (AA, estab 1982, empl 10, sales $1,500,000, cert: State, City)

6722 Impact Enterprises, Inc.
      11 Horse Hill Lane
      Warwick, NY 10990
      Contact: Ralph Salisbury Sr. VP
      Tel: 845-988-1900
      Email: rsalisbury@impactenterprises.com
      Website: www.impactenterprises.com
Mfr custom binder covers, award covers, presentation folders, portfolio covers, sales kits & other custom covers. (Woman, estab 1987, empl 8, sales $2,500,000, cert: WBENC)

6723 Mrs. Paper
      31 West 34th St, Ste 8044
      New York, NY 10001
      Contact: Marion Hindenburg President
      Tel: 212-532-7777
      Email: marion@mrspaper.com
      Website: www.mrspaper.com
Dist copy & computer paper, janitorial/sanitary supplies & advertising specialties. (Woman, estab 1982, empl 3, sales $4,082,000, cert: City, WBENC)

6724 Proftech LLC
      200 Clearbrook Rd
      Elmsford, NY 10523
      Contact: Jose Montiel President
      Tel: 800-937-8354
      Email: jmontiel@proftech.com
      Website: www.PROFTECH.COM
Dist office supplies; computer supplies; packaging supplies; drafting & art supplies; furniture; janitorial supplies; remanufactured toner cartridges. (Hisp, estab 1998, empl 55, sales , cert: State, City, NMSDC)

6725 Royal Automation Supplies
      1982 Crotona Pkwy
      Bronx, NY 10460
      Contact: David Changar VP
      Tel: 718-842-5900
      Email: royalautomation@aol.com
      Website: www.royalautomation.com
Dist paper & office supplies. (As-Ind, estab 1954, empl 5, sales $1,200,000, cert: City, NMSDC)

6726 S & B Computer & Office Products Inc.
      17 Wood Road Ste 700
      Round Lake, NY 12151
      Contact: Brittany Woods-Holmes President
      Tel: 518-877-9500
      Email: info@royalflashphotobooths.com
      Website: www.sbcomputers-office.com
Dist office & computer supplies, office furniture & promotional products. (Woman/As-Ind, estab 1989, empl 9, sales $5,695,685, cert: State)

Ohio

6727 BoLinds Solutions Services, Inc.
      850 Euclid Ave, Ste 1314
      Cleveland, OH 44114
      Contact: Sales
      Tel: 216-479-0290
      Email: service@bolinds.com
      Website: www.bolinds.com
Dist office products, office furniture, remanufactured & compatible toner cartridges, fax machines & office equipment repair. (Woman/AA, estab 1990, empl 6, sales , cert: State, NMSDC)

6728 Office Partners, LLC
      826 E Edgerton
      Bryan, OH 43506
      Contact: Cookie Lehman President
      Tel: 419-636-7260
      Email: cookie1@bright.net
      Website: www.officepartnersonline.com
Office products. (Hisp, estab 2002, empl 3, sales , cert: NMSDC)

6729 Quality Ribbons and Supplies Co.
2769 Commercial Rd
Cleveland, OH 44113
Contact: Jacqueline Litz Owner
Tel: 216-579-6200
Email: jackielitz@qr-s.com
Website: www.qr-s.com
Dist office, computer & janitorial supplies & small equip.
(Woman, estab 1982, empl 5, sales , cert: City)

6730 SeaGate Office Products, Inc.
1044 Hamilton Dr
Holland, OH 43528
Contact: Connie Leonardi President
Tel: 419-861-6161
Email: cleonardi@seagateop.com
Website: www.seagteop.com
Dist office supplies: copy & writing paper, pens, post it
notes, toner cartridges, ink, stamps, computer supplies,
promotional items, mugs, golf balls and, pens, uniforms,
desk accessories, binder clips, pencils, staples, tape &
dispensers. (Woman, estab 1985, empl 14, sales
$5,300,000, cert: WBENC)

6731 Signal Office Supply, Inc.
415 W Benson St
Cincinnati, OH 45215
Contact: Matt Thiergartner VP contract sales
Tel: 513-821-2280
Email: matt@signaloffice.com
Website: www.signaloffice.com
Dist office products, furniture, computers, etc. (Woman,
estab 1958, empl 1, sales , cert: State)

6732 The Millcraft Paper Company
6800 Grant Ave
Cleveland, OH 44105
Contact: Lisa Rogala Corp Business Develop Mgr
Tel: 216-441-5500
Email: rogalal@millcraft.com
Website: www.millcraft.com
Paper converting, mfr envelopes, printing, inventory
management. (Woman, estab 1920, empl 225, sales
$139,988,865, cert: WBENC)

6733 World Pac Paper, LLC
1821 Summit Rd, Ste 317
Cincinnati, OH 45237
Contact: Edgar Smith CEO
Tel: 513-779-9595
Email: elsmith@worldpacpaperllc.com
Website: www.worldpacpaperllc.com
Dist printing & packaging papers. (AA, estab 2004, empl
22, sales $3,563,898, cert: NMSDC)

Oklahoma

6734 Miami Business Services, Inc.
28 N Main
Miami, OK 74354
Contact: Gary Shelton Econ Dev Mgr
Tel: 918-541-2195
Email: gshelton@mn-e.com
Website: http://mbs.mn-e.com
Dist office products, remanufactured & compatible
imaging products. (Nat Ame, estab 1987, empl 5, sales
$263,158, cert: State)

Pennsylvania

6735 Alpha Office Supplies, Inc.
4950 Parkside Ave Ste 500
Philadelphia, PA 19131
Contact: Chester Riddick CEO
Tel: 215-226-2690
Email: chet.riddick@alphaos.com
Website: www.alphaos.com
Dist office furniture & supplies, paper, computers &
accessories; desktop delivery, installation, space plan-
ning & project mgmt. (AA, estab 1985, empl 29, sales
$26,000,000, cert: NMSDC)

6736 Max International
2360 Dairy Rd
Lancaster, PA 17603
Contact: Tiffanie Shaud Mktg Mgr
Tel: 800-233-0222
Email: tjs@maxintl.com
Website: www.maxintl.com
Roll paper converting: standard & special sizes,
slittering, 4-color printing. (Woman, estab 1992, empl
22, sales $7,500,000, cert: WBENC)

6737 SUPRA Office Solutions, Inc.
5070 PArkside Ave Ste 3200
Philadelphia, PA 19131
Contact: COO
Tel: 855-777-8772
Email: ken.carter@supraos.com
Website: www.supraos.com
Office supplies, office furniture, janitorial & break-room,
paper & paper products, technology items, medical &
chemical supplies. (AA, estab 2011, empl 16, sales
$19,000,000, cert: State, NMSDC)

6738 Telrose Corporation
3801 Ridge Ave
Philadelphia, PA 19132
Contact: CEO
Tel: 215-229-0500
Email:
Website: www.telrosecorp.com
Dist office supplies, equipment & furniture. (AA, estab
1995, empl 19, sales $8,000,000, cert: City, NMSDC)

South Carolina

6739 Ebony Holding
1204 Lexington Ave Unit 1, A-2
Irmo, SC 29063
Contact: Pam Heirs Acct Exec
Tel: 803-798-7777
Email: pamh@jmgrace.com
Website: www.jmgrace.com
Office Supplies, Office Furniture, Business Machines,
Printing, Promotional Items, Embroidered Apparel,
Janitorial Supplies, Breakroom Items, Safety Equipment.
(Woman/AA, estab 2013, empl 7, sales $590,692, cert:
State)

Tennessee

6740 DevMar Products, LLC
1865 Air Lane Dr, Ste 2
Nashville, TN 37210
Contact: Sharon W. Reynolds CEO
Tel: 615-232-7040
Email: sharaon@devmarproducts.com
Website: www.devmarproducts.com
Janitorial supplies; chemicals; personal paper; MRO;
biohazard spillkits, office supplies. (Woman/AA, estab
2007, empl 5, sales $1,000,000, cert: NMSDC, WBENC)

6741 Guy Brown, LLC
      7111 Commerce Way
      Brentwood, TN 37027
      Contact: Lauren Dooros Sales & Marketing Mgr
      Tel: 615-777-1500
      Email: lauren.dooros@guybrown.com
      Website: www.guybrown.com
Mfr recycled laser toner cartridges & office products. (Woman/AA, As-Pac, Hisp, estab 1997, empl 76, sales $204,877,006, cert: NMSDC, WBENC)

Texas

6742 2M Business Products
      2630 Nova Dr
      Dallas, TX 75229
      Contact: Ali Mamdani GM
      Tel: 972-484-0000
      Email: ali@2mbp.com
      Website: www.2mbp.com
Dist office supplies, computer supplies, office furniture, new & remanufactured toner cartridges. rubber stamps, printing. (As-Ind, estab 1980, empl 8, sales $2,000,000, cert: NMSDC)

6743 Dallas Paper & Packaging
      880 Gerault Rd
      Flower Mound, TX 75028
      Contact: Nemosthenes Baker Owner
      Tel: 817-422-3089
      Email: nemo@dallaspaperpackaging.com
      Website: www.dallaspaperpackaging.com
Dist toner & ink cartridges, trash bags, food gloves, white T-shirts, grey sweat pants, shirts, drinking water carts, janitorial supplies, ribbons, first aid kits, popcorn, hazard & medical supplies. (AA, estab 1984, empl 2, sales $745,963, cert: State, NMSDC)

6744 EIS Office Solutions, Inc.
      5803 Sovereign Dr, Ste 214
      Houston, TX 77036
      Contact: Judy Lanum Acct Exec
      Tel: 713-484-7300
      Email: judy.lanum@secor.cc
      Website: www.eisoffice.net
Dist OEM & Compatible printer ink & toner cartridges, office supplies. (As-Pac, estab 2004, empl 11, sales $1,700,000, cert: State)

6745 General Office Plus
      1020 W 8th Ave
      Amarillo, TX 79101
      Contact: Loretta Redmon President
      Tel: 806-373-2877
      Email: lredmon@generalofficeplus.com
      Website: www.general-officesupply.com
Dist office supplies, machines, furniture. (Woman, estab 1948, empl 15, sales $1,803,887, cert: State)

6746 Hogan Paper Co.
      6904 Hillcroft Dr
      Austin, TX 78724
      Contact: Alfred Hogan Owner
      Tel: 512-926-6134
      Email: ahogan3@austin.rr.com
      Website:
Dist toilet tissue, paper towels, plastic trashliners, & copier paper. (AA, estab 1983, empl , sales $24,779,577, cert: State)

6747 J R Rodriguez International Corporation
      4541 Leston St
      Dallas, TX 75247
      Contact: Jim Lohr Natl Sales Mgr
      Tel: 214-905-5086
      Email: jim@interconpaper.com
      Website: www.interconpaper.com
Printing paper in rolls & sheets: offset, gloss, matte/dull, board, Hi-Brite, groundwood coated, newsprint, digital sizes, cut size xerographic, slitting & rewinding. (Hisp, estab 1998, empl 61, sales $25,100,000, cert: NMSDC)

6748 Lee Office Solutions
      202 Travis ST, Ste 205
      Houston, TX 77002
      Contact: Cathleen Nguyen Exec Asst
      Tel: 713-227-1010
      Email: cathleen@leeofficesolutions.com
      Website: www.leeofficesolutions.com
Dist office supplies & products, electronics, furniture, paper, facilities mgmt & system design. (As-Pac, estab 1970, empl 5, sales $308,647, cert: NMSDC)

6749 Longhorn Office Products, Inc.
      2210 Denton Dr. Ste. 109
      Austin, TX 78758
      Contact: Marcia Winkler CEO
      Tel: 512-672-4567
      Email: mswinkler@longhornop.com
      Website: www.longhornop.com
Dist office products & furniture. (Woman, estab 1999, empl 13, sales $2,386,005, cert: State, City, WBENC)

6750 P.D. Morrison Enterprises, Inc.
      1120 Toro Grande Blvd Bldg 2, Ste 208
      Cedar Park, TX 78613
      Contact: P.D. Morrison CEO
      Tel: 512-879-3070
      Email: pd@pdme.com
      Website: www.pdme.com
Dist office & computer supplies, office furniture. (AA, estab 1994, empl 10, sales , cert: NMSDC)

6751 Pearle, Inc.
      3660 Richmond Ave Ste 370
      Houston, TX 77046
      Contact: Erskine Black Jr. President
      Tel: 832-304-9571
      Email: eblack@pearle-inc.com
      Website: www.pearle-inc.com
Dist disposable paper goods. (AA, estab 2013, empl 1, sales , cert: State, City, NMSDC)

6752 R.W. Gonzalez Office Products, Inc.
      600 Congress Ave 14th Fl
      Austin, TX 78701
      Contact: Pamela Gonzalez VP
      Tel: 512-717-6623
      Email: diversity@gonzalezop.com
      Website: MBEpartners.com
Dist office products. (Hisp, estab 2002, empl 7, sales , cert: State, NMSDC)

6753 Reliant Business Products, Inc
      10641 Haddington Dr, Ste 100
      Houston, TX 77043
      Contact: Steven Woodall V.P. of Sales & I.T.
      Tel: 713-980-7140
      Email: stevenw@rbp.com
      Website: www.rbp.com
Office Products, Office Supplies, Industrial Supplies, HS&E, MRO, Office Furniture, Coffee Service, Break Room Supplies, Printing. (Nat Ame, estab 1984, empl 17, sales $7,000,000, cert: State, NMSDC)

6754 Summus Industries, Inc.
      245 Commerce Green Blvd Ste 155
      Sugar Land, TX 77478
      Contact: Rodney Craig CEO
      Tel: 281-640-1765
      Email: rcraig@summusindustries.com
      Website: www.summusindustries.com
Dist office supplies. (AA, estab 1997, empl 21, sales
$21,000,000, cert: State, City, NMSDC)

6755 Tejas Office Products, Inc.
      1225 W 20th St
      Houston, TX 77008
      Contact: Stephen M. Fraga President
      Tel: 713-864-6004
      Email: stephenf@tejasoffice.com
      Website: www.tejasoffice.com
Dist office products. (Hisp, estab 1962, empl 50, sales ,
cert: NMSDC)

6756 Today's Business Solutions
      1919 Lubbock St.
      Houston, TX 77007
      Contact: Priscilla Luna VP
      Tel: 713-861-8508
      Email: priscilla@tbstx.com
      Website: www.tbstx.com
Dist office supplies. (Hisp, estab 2003, empl 13, sales
$31,582,773, cert: State, City, NMSDC)

Virginia

6757 Access Office Products
      6 W Cary St
      Richmond, VA 23220
      Contact: AJ Scott President & CEO
      Tel: 804-767-7211
      Email: aj@accessofficeproducts.com
      Website: www.accessofficeproducts.com
Dist office supplies, technology & furniture. (AA, estab
2009, empl 2, sales $119,231, cert: State, NMSDC)

6758 Ball Office Products, LLC
      2218 Tomlyn St
      Richmond, VA 23230
      Contact: Managing Member
      Tel: 804-204-1774
      Email:
      Website: www.ballop.com
Dist business furniture & office supplies. (Woman, estab
2000, empl 17, sales $7,050,591, cert: State, WBENC)

6759 Corporate Office Solutions, LLC
      4094 Majestic Ln, Ste 33
      Fairfax, VA 22033
      Contact: Katrina Funkhouser President
      Tel: 703-352-2029
      Email: kf@cosdirect.com
      Website: www.cosdirect.com
Dist computer products, office equipment & supplies,
printer service, computer repair, networking & office
furniture. (Woman/As-Ind, estab 1996, empl 8, sales
$2,386,109, cert: State)

6760 Envelopes Only Plus, Inc.
      133 Roxbury Industrial Ctr
      Charles City, VA 23030
      Contact: Stuart Peyton GM
      Tel: 804-966-5479
      Email: stuart@envelopesonly.com
      Website: www.envelopesonly.com
Dist envelopes: commercial, coin, catalog, booklet.
(Woman/AA, Nat Ame, As-Pac, Hisp, estab 1984, empl
32, sales $4,625,000, cert: State)

6761 Snap Office Supplies, LLC
      9710 Farrar Court Ste M
      Richmond, VA 23236
      Contact: Andy Todd VP Sales
      Tel: 804-794-9387
      Email: andy@snapsupplies.com
      Website: www.snapsupplies.com
Dist Office & Point-of-Sale supplies. (Woman, estab
1980, empl 7, sales $1,500,000, cert: State)

6762 TSRC, Inc.
      P.O. Box 1810
      Ashland, VA 23005
      Contact: David Johnson Acct Mgr
      Tel: 804-412-1200
      Email: djohnson@thesupplyroom.com
      Website: www.thesupplyroom.com
Dist office supplies & furniture. (Woman, estab 1986,
empl 187, sales $45,000,000, cert: State)

Wisconsin

6763 H.Derksen & Sons Co., Inc.
      250 Industrial Dr
      Omro, WI 50310
      Contact: Mike Willeford VP
      Tel: 920-685-4000
      Email: mike@hderksen.com
      Website: www.hderksen.com
Pressure sensitive labels, wide format digital printing,
business forms, computer paper, paper & packaging
products, mobility solutions, bar code label printers, bar
coding software. (Nat Ame, estab , empl 11, sales
$8,000,000, cert: NMSDC)

PACKAGING & PACKING SERVICES & SUPPLIES

Contract packaging and crating, shrink or blister packaging and bagging. Manufacturers and distributors of foam packaging, rope and twine, bottles, shrink wrap, corrugated cardboard boxes or bags of various materials such as paper, plastic, etc. NAICS Code 32

Alabama

6764　ARD Logistics, LLC
　　　10098 Brose Dr
　　　Vance, AL 35490
　　　Contact: Courtney Waters Sales & Marketing Rep
　　　Tel:　205-393-5207
　　　Email: cwaters@ardlogistics.com
　　　Website: www.ardlogistics.com
Distribution operations: sequencing, sub-assembly, warehousing, inventory mgmt, shipping & receiving materials handling maintenance, packaging & repackaging, transportation mgmt, transportation svcs. (AA, estab 1998, empl 900, sales $68,717,549, cert: NMSDC)

6765　Containers Plus, Inc.
　　　3068 Alabama Hwy 53
　　　Huntsville, AL 35806
　　　Contact: Ajesh Khanijow Business Dev Mgr
　　　Tel:　256-746-8002
　　　Email: akhanijow@containersplususa.com
　　　Website: www.containersplususa.com
Wooden crates, pallets, cardboard boxes, heat shrink, milspec packaging, packaging, RFID, UID, Mil-std-129, mil-std-2073, warehousing, logistics, hazmat packaging. (As-Pac, estab 2014, empl 5, sales $180,000, cert: NMSDC)

6766　Prystup Packaging Products
　　　430 North Industrial PArk Dr
　　　Livingston, AL 35470
　　　Contact: Corey Hayden Technical Sales Engineer
　　　Tel:　205-499-9397
　　　Email: chayden@prystup.com
　　　Website: www.prystup.com
Mfr folding paper cartons: food, consumer goods & electronics. (Woman/Nat Ame, estab 1980, empl 160, sales $38,000,000, cert: WBENC)

6767　The Trinity Design Group, LLC
　　　1107 Dowzer Ave
　　　Pell City, AL 35125
　　　Contact: Fernando Valentin CEO
　　　Tel:　205-338-6888
　　　Email: fvalentin@thetrinitydesigngroup.com
　　　Website: www.thetrinitydesigngroup.com
Design, mfr & copack packaging, corrugated, paper, plastics, point of purchase & promotional materials. (AA, Hisp, estab 2004, empl 15, sales $2,028,500, cert: NMSDC)

Arkansas

6768　Sigma Supply North America
　　　824 Mid America Blvd
　　　Hot Springs, AR 71913
　　　Contact: Brooke Griffin Natl Acct Mgr
　　　Tel:　501-760-1151
　　　Email: supplierdiversity@sigmasupply.com
　　　Website: www.sigmasupply.com
Packaging solutions, turnkey solution for warehouse equipment, bulk storage, individual shipment packaging, labeling & inventory control. (Woman, estab 2003, empl 210, sales $289,500,000, cert: WBENC, NWBOC)

Arizona

6769　All-Pac Distributng LLC
　　　4859 E Gleneagle Dr
　　　Chandler, AZ 85249
　　　Contact: Adam Snow Sales Mgr
　　　Tel:　480-861-0842
　　　Email: asnow@allpaconline.com
　　　Website: www.allpaconline.com
Mfr & dist returnable plastic packaging, injection molding, compression molding. (Woman, estab 2001, empl 3, sales $1,150,000, cert: NWBOC)

6770　La Fiesta Label & Packaging Systems
　　　6162 W Detroit St
　　　Chandler, AZ 85226
　　　Contact: Kirk Valadez VP Operations
　　　Tel:　480-785-3900
　　　Email: kvaladez@lafiestalabel.com
　　　Website: www.lafiestalabel.com
Mfr shrink sleeves, unsupported film pouches & packets, pressure sensitive labels, fold out coupons, cartons, static cling, consecutive number, UV & laminate coating. (Hisp, estab 1985, empl 20, sales , cert: NMSDC)

California

6771　ACME Bag Inc Dba The Bulk Bag Company
　　　14730 Northam St, La Mirada, CA,
　　　La Mirada, CA 90638
　　　Contact: John Willoughby Natl Sales Director
　　　Tel:　866-517-4699
　　　Email: john@thebulkbagcompany.com
　　　Website: www.thebulkbagcompany.com
Soilsaver Rolls, SOD Staples, Construction Fabrics, Landscaping Fabrics & Tarps, Agriculture Packaging, FIBC Bags & Woven Polypropyline Bags, Sand Bags- Burlap & WPP, Treated Burlap Sqares, Silt Fences, Truncated Wire Baskets. (As-Pac, estab 1975, empl 24, sales $20,000,000, cert: NMSDC)

6772　ALOM Technologies Corporation
　　　48105 Warm Springs Blvd
　　　Fremont, CA 94539
　　　Contact: Lisa Dolan VP Supply Chain Strategy
　　　Tel:　510-360-3600
　　　Email: customerservice@alom.com
　　　Website: www.alom.com
Fulfillment, assembly, contract packaging, video & audio tape duplication, CD & DVD duplication (Woman, estab 1997, empl 225, sales $83,859,000, cert: WBENC)

6773　American Supply
　　　P.O. Box 2322
　　　Chino, CA 91710
　　　Contact: Vonn Castillo Business Develop Mgr
　　　Tel:　949-216-0468
　　　Email: vcastillo@myamericansupply.com
　　　Website: www.myamericansupply.com
Mfr & customize bags & covers, janitorial, housekeeping, promotional & OEM products. Mfr replacement cart bags, laundry bags, caddy bags, laundry truck liners, hair dryer bags, etc. (Woman/As-Pac, estab 2013, empl 5, sales $300,000, cert: CPUC)

6774 Atlantis Paper & Packaging
  13405 Benson Ave
  Chino, CA 91710
  Contact: James Montano Sales Rep
  Tel: 909-591-1809
  Email: james@atlantispkg.com
  Website: www.atlantispkg.com
Dist packaging products & machinery, corrugated boxes, stretch wrap, poly bags, ice pages, tape, cold storage, pallets, etc. (Hisp, estab 1984, empl 15, sales $15,000,000, cert: NMSDC)

6775 Corporate Packaging, Inc.
  1555 S Archibald Ave
  Ontario, CA 91761
  Contact: Craig Johnson VP
  Tel: 909-390-1112
  Email: craig@corporatepackaginginc.com
  Website: www.corporatepackaginginc.com
Contract packaging & promotional packaging services. (Woman, estab 1989, empl 50, sales $2,000,000, cert: State)

6776 Future Commodities Int'l Inc.
  10676 Fulton Ct
  Rancho Cucamonga, CA 91730
  Contact: Matthew Lim VP Operations
  Tel: 909-987-4258
  Email: mlim@bestpack.com
  Website: www.bestpack.com
Mfr & import carton sealing equipment, carton sealing tape. (As-Pac, estab 1984, empl 14, sales $10,200,000, cert: NMSDC)

6777 Industrial Container Corporation
  2015 Acacia Court
  Compton, CA 90220
  Contact: Josh Rodgers Operations
  Tel: 310-763-3550
  Email: sales@industrialcontainer.com
  Website: www.industrialcontainer.com
Packaging design services & protective packaging, Customer Design/CAD Documentation, Prototyping, Performance Certification, Manufacturing Responsibility, Total Quality control, Supply Chain Management, Maquiladora/JIT & warehousing. (Hisp, estab 1971, empl 35, sales , cert: NMSDC)

6778 MikaPak Inc.
  P.O. Box 4276
  Walnut Creek, CA 94596
  Contact: Helen Ma President
  Tel: 800-579-0880
  Email: helen@mikapak.com
  Website: www.mikapak.com
Sustainable, compostable products from plate wares, utensils, drink cups, food containers to packaging labels using renewable plant base raw materials. (Woman/As-Pac, estab 1995, empl 1, sales $279,000, cert: NMSDC)

6779 PKG Packaging
  311 Hearst Dr
  Oxnard, CA 93030
  Contact: Carlos Rodriguez Cstmr Service
  Tel: 805-278-6648
  Email: c.rodriguez@pkgpackaging.com
  Website: www.pkgpackaging.com
Design, mfr & dist packaging material. (Woman/Hisp, estab 1987, empl 10, sales $3,805,000, cert: NMSDC, WBENC)

6780 Premier Packaging/Assembly div of Haringa Inc.
  14422 Best Ave
  Santa Fe Springs, CA 90670
  Contact: Vicki Haringa CEO
  Tel: 562-802-2765
  Email: vharinga@premierpkg.com
  Website: www.premierpkg.com
Packaging services. (Woman, estab 1987, empl 6, sales $13,882,899, cert: WBENC)

6781 Uniq Seal, LLC
  5753-G Santa Ana Canyon Rd
  Anaheim, CA 92807
  Contact: Jacek Zdzienicki VP Sales
  Tel: 714-299-5899
  Email: jacek@nafm.com
  Website: www.nafm.com
Contract sleeving & shrink labeling, multi-pack assemblies, shrink overwrap, tray assembly, re-packing & special assemblies, casing & cartoning, displays assembly, packaging R&D, fulfillment. (Woman/As-Pac, estab 1993, empl 7, sales $3,500,000, cert: NMSDC)

Colorado

6782 Craters and Freighters
  331 Corporate Circle, Ste J
  Golden, CO 80401
  Contact: Chad Brockmeyer Natl Sales Mgr
  Tel: 720-287-7805
  Email: chad@cratersandfreighters.com
  Website: www.cratersandfreighters.com
Custom wood crating, plastic hard cases and freight services. (Woman, estab 1990, empl 12, sales $55,000,000, cert: WBENC)

6783 Die Cut Technologies/Denver Gasket
  10943 Leroy Dr
  Northglenn, CO 80233
  Contact: Evelyn Meyers CEO
  Tel: 303-452-4600
  Email: evelyn@diecuttech.com
  Website: www.diecuttech.com
Mfr gaskets, die cut parts & converted non-metallic materials. Also dist sponge, foam tapes rubber, bridge bearing pads, expansion joints, impact attenuators & adhesives, contract assembly & packaging svcs. (Hisp, estab 1961, empl 20, sales $2,524,000, cert: NMSDC, SDB)

6784 Rocky Mountain Pioneer, LLC
  13802 E 33rd Pl, Unit B
  Aurora, CO 80011
  Contact: Diane Hamilton Acct Mgr
  Tel: 303-371-6070
  Email: diane@pioneerdenver.com
  Website: www.hpcorporategroup.com
Custom & stock packaging materials: corrugated boxes, folding carton, bubble, foam protective packaging, shrink & stretch films, banding & tapes, fulfillment services. (Woman, estab 2004, empl 9, sales $5,000,000, cert: WBENC)

6785 Summit Container Corporation
      901Synthes Ave
      Monument, CO 80132
      Contact: Adam Walker CEO
      Tel: 719-481-8400
      Email: awalker@summitcontainer.com
      Website: www.summitcontainer.com
Packaging solutions, custom packaging, warehousing,
distribution, assembly & kitting, (AA, estab 1989, empl
200, sales , cert: NMSDC)

6786 Universal Packaging
      11440 E 56th Ave
      Denver, CO 80239
      Contact: Karen Millwater VP
      Tel: 303-373-2523
      Email: kmillwater@upc-solutions.com
      Website: www.upc-solutions.com
Dist industrial packaging supplies: bubble, foam, tape,
stretch, shrink wrap, banding, bags, cable ties, boxes,
styrofoam, rolled corrugated, mailing tubes, etc. (Woman,
estab 1980, empl 13, sales $8,000,000, cert: City)

Connecticut

6787 Eastern Bag & Paper Company, Inc.
      200 Research Dr
      Milford, CT 06460
      Contact: Meredith Reuben CEO
      Tel: 203-878-1814
      Email: mreuben@ebpsupply.com
      Website: www.ebpsupply.com
Dist paper, packaging & allied products. (Woman, estab
1918, empl 270, sales $196,987,948, cert: WBENC)

6788 Flexo Converters USA, Inc.
      1200 Northrop Rd
      Meriden, CT 06450
      Contact: Emily Gerrard Mktg/Sales Mgr
      Tel: 203-639-7070
      Email: egerrard@flexobags.com
      Website: www.flexobags.com
Mfr twisted handle paper shopping & merchandise bags.
(As-Ind, As-Pac, estab 1994, empl 51, sales $15,000,000,
cert: NMSDC)

6789 New England Packaging Co. LLC
      119 Sherman Ct
      Fairfield, CT 06824
      Contact: Mark Hyman President
      Tel: 203-256-2350
      Email: mark@zero-contact.com
      Website: www.zero-contact.com
Dist corrugated & paper products. (Hisp, estab 1997, empl
6, sales $200,000, cert: NMSDC)

6790 Penmar Industries, Inc.
      35 Ontario St
      Stratford, CT 06615
      Contact: Ed Rodriguez President
      Tel: 203-853-4868
      Email: eddy@penmar-industries.com
      Website: www.penmar-industries.com
Mfr & convert custom labels & tapes, dist packaging
materials, carton sealing tapes, cartons & shipping room
supplies. (Hisp, estab 1964, empl 15, sales $2,900,000,
cert: NMSDC)

Florida

6791 3 Points Packaging LLC
      3505 NW 123rd St
      Miami, FL 33167
      Contact: Noel Bosh President
      Tel: 305-624-8343
      Email: info@3pointspackaging.com
      Website: www.3PointsPackaging.com
Packaging & janitorial products. (AA, estab 2011, empl 2,
sales $660,000, cert: NMSDC)

6792 All American Containers, Inc
      9330 NW 110th Ave
      Miami, FL 33178
      Contact: Richard Cabrera VP Int'l Division
      Tel: 305-913-0624
      Email: richardc@americancontainers.com
      Website: www.americancontainers.com
Dist packaging supplies. (Woman/Hisp, estab 1991, empl
284, sales , cert: NMSDC)

6793 Diverse Solution and Supplies
      7305 Lismore Ct.
      Orlando, FL 32835
      Contact: Carolyn Griffin President
      Tel: 407-256-2653
      Email: carolyn.griffin@div-erse.com
      Website: www.div-erse.com
Dist packaging & facility supplies: stretch wrap, corrugated, tapes, cushioning, bundling material, void fill,
floor cleaning equipment, mats, bags, etc. (Woman,
estab 2013, empl 2, sales $279,000, cert: WBENC)

6794 FlexSol Packaging Corp.
      1531 NW 12th Ave
      Pompano Beach, FL 33069
      Contact: Bonni O'Connell Dir Sales/Marketing
      Tel: 800-325-7740
      Email: bonnio@flexsolpackaging.com
      Website: www.flexsolpackaging.com
Mfr flexible packaging & value-added plastic films,
custom bags & film, shrink & hood films, performance &
barrier films & can liners. (As-Pac, estab 2009, empl 425,
sales , cert: NMSDC)

6795 National Packaging, LLC
      6346-65 Lantana Rd, Ste 126
      Lake Worth, FL 33463
      Contact: Kerry Lowe Mgr
      Tel: 561-968-4420
      Email: klowe@nationalpack.net
      Website: www.nationalpack.net
Flexible packaging, Bag films. (Woman/AA, estab 2006,
empl 2, sales , cert: NMSDC)

Georgia

6796 Alliance Packaging Group, Inc.
      940 Sherwin Pkwy, Ste 100
      Buford, GA 30517
      Contact: Michelle Calvert CEO
      Tel: 770-309-1012
      Email: mcalvert@alliancepkggroup.com
      Website: http://alliancepkggroup.com
Packaging, janitorial & shipping supplies. (Woman, estab
2007, empl 5, sales $2,733,290, cert: WBENC)

6797 Containers Unlimited, Inc.
      400 Claridge Trace
      Atlanta, GA 30331
      Contact: C. Eric Jones President
      Tel: 714-734-8608
      Email: chuck@containersunlimited.net
      Website: www.containersunlimited.net
Diat stock & custom boxes & packaging materials. (AA,
estab 1999, empl 4, sales , cert: State)

6798 E. Smith Box, Inc.
      1875 Rockdale Industrial Blvd
      Conyers, GA 30012
      Contact: Jaquacer Middlebrooks President
      Tel: 770-388-7787
      Email: sales@esmithbox.com
      Website: www.esmithbox.com
Mfr corrugated boxes. (AA, estab 1987, empl 35, sales
$1,300,000, cert: NMSDC)

6799 FilmLOC Inc.
      4190 Thurmon Tanner Pkwy
      Flowery Branch, GA 30542
      Contact: Shirl Handly President
      Tel: 404-892-8778
      Email: shirl@filmloc.com
      Website: www.filmloc.com
Mfr Intelli-Placï¿½ placards for labeling & re-labeling
reusable containers, totes & pallets, shelves, equipment,
racking, manufactured goods in process, shipping crates.
(Woman, estab 2002, empl 5, sales $749,359, cert:
WBENC)

6800 Meristem Packaging Company LLC
      5090 Old Ellis Point
      Roswell, GA 30076
      Contact: Paige Mesaros Supply Chain Mgr
      Tel: 770-998-7120
      Email: pmesaros@meristempkg.com
      Website: http://meristempkg.com
Packaging, folding cartons/boxes, plastic bags & styrofoam
coolers. (AA, Hisp, estab 2009, empl 5, sales $7,444,000,
cert: NMSDC)

6801 Palmetto Industries International, Inc.
      6001 Horizon West Pkwy
      Grovetown, GA 30813
      Contact: Purvis King VP
      Tel: 706-737-7995
      Email: customerservice@palmetto-industries.com
      Website: www.palmetto-industries.com
Mfr & dist polymer & paper packaging products. (As-Ind,
As-Pac, estab , empl , sales $20,000,000, cert: NMSDC)

6802 SquarePac LTD
      7115 Oak Ridge Parkway Ste 110
      Austell, GA 30168
      Contact: Walter Griggs CFO
      Tel: 770-617-5688
      Email: admin@squarepac.us
      Website: www.squarepac.us
Returnable packaging & material handling solutions, eco-
friendly containers & packaging, totes, pallets & metal
racks. (AA, estab 2013, empl 8, sales , cert: NMSDC, SDB)

Illinois

6803 Action Bag Company
      1001 Entry Dr.
      Bensenville, IL 60640
      Contact: Martha Quintero
      Tel: 866-349-8853
      Email: mquintero@actionbag.com
      Website: www.actionhealth.com
Printed bags, bags, retail packaging products, printed
promotional products, promotional items, packaging
supplies, labels, tissue paper, gift cards, specialty
packaging, custom bags, custom printed items, rush
orders, in-stock products. (Woman, estab , empl , sales ,
cert: City, WBENC)

6804 Alta Packaging, Inc.
      150 Chaddick Dr
      Wheeling, IL 60090
      Contact: Jill Zienkiewicz
      Tel: 847-215-2582
      Email: jillz@altapackaging.com
      Website: www.altapackaging.com
Dist industrial packaging supplies. (Woman, estab 1995,
empl 10, sales $5,276,581, cert: WBENC)

6805 BAF Packaging, LLC
      1053 E. 95th St.
      Chicago, IL 60619
      Contact: Valerie Matthews President
      Tel: 888-225-8221
      Email: vam@bafpack-rite.com
      Website: http://bafpack-rite.com
Contract Packaging, shrink wrap packaging, Light
industrial assembly, Fulfillment, Distribution warehouse
capabilities. (Woman/AA, estab 2013, empl 3, sales
$350,000, cert: NMSDC)

6806 Cano Container Corporation
      3920 Enterprise Court
      Aurora, IL 60504
      Contact: Juventino Cano President
      Tel: 630-585-7500
      Email: juventino@canocontainer.com
      Website: www.canocontainer.com
Mfr corrugated shipping containers. (Hisp, estab 1986,
empl , sales $20,000,000, cert: NMSDC)

6807 Carter Paper & Packaging, Inc.
      3400 SW Washington St
      Peoria, IL 61607
      Contact: Mike Krost Sales
      Tel: 309-637-7711
      Email: mike@carterpaper.com
      Website: www.erpaper.com
Dist paper & plastic packaging, bags, towels, wipers,
tissue, VCI paper, loose fill, foam, tape, adhesives &
specialty items. (Woman, estab 1957, empl 18, sales ,
cert: WBENC)

6808 Commercial Bag Company
      1 Paper Chase
      Normal, IL 61761
      Contact: Rachel Bowling
      Tel: 309-862-0144
      Email: rbowling@commercialpackaging.com
      Website: www.commercialpackaging.com
Flexible Packaging, stand up pouches, Bulk Bags/Totes,
Woven Poly Bags, Multiwall Bags. (Woman, estab , empl
, sales $95,000,000, cert: WBENC)

6809 Cross Packaging Supply, Inc.
      968 Dundee Ave Ste B
      Elgin, IL 60120
      Contact: AJ Loredo President
      Tel: 847-780-7225
      Email: aloredo@crosspackaging.com
      Website: http://crosspackaging.com
Packaging supplies (boxes, paper, tape, stretch film, bubble
wrap, poly bags, bubble mailers, mailers, labels, can liners,
etc). (Hisp, estab 2013, empl 2, sales $500,000, cert:
NMSDC)

6810 Dynamic Packaging
      1248 W Jackson Blvd, Ste 2E
      Chicago, IL 60607
      Contact: Elson Seale President
      Tel: 312-374-4445
      Email: elson@dynam-pak.com
      Website: www.dynam-pak.com
Dist industrial & janitorial supplies: corrugated boxes, tape,
stretch-film, shrink-film, poly-bags, bubble wrap. (Woman/
AA, estab 2014, empl 5, sales $250,000, cert: NMSDC)

6811 H&H Sorting Services
      1021 St. Charles St
      Elgin, IL 60120
      Contact: Jeanne Hintz President
      Tel: 847-741-8479
      Email: jeanne@hhsort.com
      Website: www.hhsort.com
Sorting & inspection, assembly, packaging, labeling of
fasteners & molded plastics & other pre-manufactured
parts. (Woman, estab 1989, empl 48, sales $1,737,436,
cert: WBENC)

6812 Magenta LLC
      15160 New Ave
      Lockport, IL 60441
      Contact: Stephanie Smith Business Develop Exec
      Tel: 630-737-9606
      Email: ssmith@magentallc.com
      Website: www.magentallc.com
Design, development & mfr injection molded components-
primarily packaging— closures and containers. (Woman,
estab 1969, empl 81, sales $14,900,000, cert: WBENC)

6813 Midwest Mailing & Shipping Systems Inc.
      3006 Gill St, Ste A
      Bloomington, IL 61704
      Contact: Dave Rappa VP Sales
      Tel: 309-661-1144
      Email: dave@midwestmailing.com
      Website: www.midwestmailing.com
Dist mailing systems, folder inserters, letter openers,
inbound letter & parcel tracking systems, shipping systems, addressing systems, CASS/PAVE certified software,
electronic scales, shredders, pressure sealers, bursters,
collators, etc. (Woman, estab 1988, empl 9, sales
$1,650,000, cert: WBENC)

6814 Morris Packaging
      211 N Williamsburg Dr, Ste A
      Bloomington, IL 61701
      Contact: Penny Steinwagner Sales/Mktg Mgr
      Tel: 309-663-9100
      Email: psteinwagner@morrispkg.com
      Website: www.morrispkg.com
Flexible packaging manufacturer. (Nat Ame, estab 2004,
empl 263, sales $100,000,000, cert: NMSDC)

6815 Numeridex, Inc.
      632 Wheeling Rd
      Wheeling, IL 60090
      Contact: Alberto Hoyos President
      Tel: 847-541-8840
      Email: debbie@numeridex.com
      Website: www.numeridex.com
Dist labeling & bar code products: thermal transfer
printers, labels, ribbons, scanners, packaging & shipping
supplies, corrugated cartons, stretch film, carton sealing
tape. (Hisp, estab 1967, empl 10, sales $2,370,000, cert:
NMSDC)

6816 Planned Packaging of Illinois Corp.
      19558 S Harlem Ave Ste 5
      Frankfort, IL 60423
      Contact: Jack Callham Exec VP
      Tel: 815-277-5270
      Email: tiffany@ppoic.com
      Website: www.ppoic.com
Dist industrial packaging supplies: corrugated boxes,
film, foams, pallets, etc. (AA, estab 2001, empl 30, sales
$270,218, cert: NMSDC)

6817 Poly-Pak and Ship, Inc.
      2021 Illini Ave
      Vandalia, IL 62471
      Contact: JoAnn Boggs President
      Tel: 618-283-2397
      Email: joannboggs@polypakusa.com
      Website: www.polypakusa.com
Warehousing, packaging, labeling, addressing, mailing,
distribution printed matter, direct mail svcs.
 (Woman, estab 1985, empl 85, sales $2,658,671, cert:
State, City, WBENC)

6818 Primary Resources Inc.
      405 Busse Road
      Elk Grove Village, IL 60007
      Contact: Enza Fragassi President
      Tel: 847-808-7684
      Email: enza@primarypkg.com
      Website: www.primaryresources.net
Corrugated packaging, fibre board slip sheets, folding
cartons, corrugated, chip partitions, flexible films,
barrier bags, pouches, bundling, film products, shrink,
stretch, polyethylene, labels, tamper evident products,
bio-degradable materials. (Woman/Hisp, estab 2001,
empl 10, sales , cert: NMSDC)

6819 Scout Sourcing, Inc.
      2340 South River Road Ste 309
      Des Plaines, IL 60018
      Contact: Anne Cowherd President
      Tel: 917-428-8184
      Email: acowherd@scoutsourcinginc.com
      Website: www.scoutsourcinginc.com
Dist paper & packaging. (Woman, estab 2006, empl ,
sales $95,000,000, cert: WBENC)

6820 Service Packaging Design, Inc.
      6238 Lincoln Ave
      Morton Grove, IL 60053
      Contact: Norman Croft President
      Tel: 847-966-6556
      Email: ncroft@servicepackaging.com
      Website: www.servicepackaging.com
Mfr & dist corrugated boxes, wood products, tags &
labels, gum & poly tape, stretch wrap. (AA, estab 1982,
empl 7, sales $1,250,000, cert: NMSDC)

6821 Skyline Container Corporation
      9755 W 143rd St
      Orland Park, IL 60462
      Contact: Dawn Souliotis President & CEO
      Tel: 708-460-7965
      Email: dawn@skyline99.com
      Website: www.skyline99.com
Dist corrugated boxes. (Woman, estab 1990, empl 5, sales
$1,697,049, cert: City, WBENC)

6822 TransWorld Plastic Films, Inc.
      150 N 15th St
      Rochelle, IL 61068
      Contact: Rodolfo Hernandez Business Dev
      Tel: 815-561-7117
      Email: rhernandez@transworldplasticfilms.com
      Website: www.transworldplasticfilms.com
Polyethylene film for the automotive, tire & rubber
industries used in the manufacturing & packaging process.
(Woman/Hisp, estab 2007, empl 31, sales , cert: NMSDC,
WBENC)

6823 Trinity Graphic & Packaging Solutions, LLC
      28W031 Greenview Ave
      Warrenville, IL 60555
      Contact: Hardy Leonard President
      Tel: 630-393-7550
      Email: len.hardy@trinitygraphic.net
      Website: www.trinitygraphic.net
Dist thermal transfer ribbons, thermal transfer printers,
thermal transfer print heads, printed labels, warehouse
labels, promotional labels. (Woman/AA, Nat Ame, estab
2001, empl 1, sales , cert: State)

Indiana

6824 AIM Solutions, Inc.
      P.O. Box 340
      McCordsville, IN 46055
      Contact: John Laakso Director
      Tel: 239-316-0004
      Email: john.laakso@aimsolutionsinc.net
      Website: www.aimsolutionsinc.net
Packaging & shipping supplies, pallets, boxes, film, bubble
sheet stock, package automation engineering, foam,
packaging equipment, plastic trays, labeling products &
equipment, tape. (As-Pac, estab 2006, empl 7, sales
$1,500,000, cert: State)

6825 Brown Tape Products Company
      8909 Sargent Rd
      Indianapolis, IN 46256
      Contact: Janice Brown President
      Tel: 866-276-9682
      Email: janbrown@browntapeproducts.com
      Website: www.browntapeproducts.com
Adhesive tape, cardboard boxes, mailers, steel banding,
plastic banding, banding tools, stretch film, bubble pack,
foam packaging, tape dispensers, newsprint, nylon cable
ties, rolled corrugated, packing slip envelopes, plastic bags.
(Woman, estab 1984, empl 5, sales $1,000,000, cert: City)

6826 Morales Group, Inc.
      5628 W 74th St
      Indianapolis, IN 46278
      Contact: Seth Morales Sales Mgr
      Tel: 317-334-0950
      Email: smorales@moralesgroup.net
      Website: www.moralesgroup.net
Assembly, packaging & warehousing services, Point of
Purchase display assembly, Kitting, Literature collation,
insertion, Sort/rework. (Hisp, estab 2003, empl 28, sales
$14,900,000, cert: NMSDC)

6827 MSW (Mahomed Sales & Warehousing, LLC)
      8258 Zionsville Rd
      Indianapolis, IN 46268
      Contact: Keith Kanipe Sr VP
      Tel: 317-472-5800
      Email: kkanipe@whse.com
      Website: www.whse.com
Assembly, Sub-assembly Packaging, Kitting, Warehousing, Supply Chain Mgmt & Sorting services. (As-Ind,
estab 1996, empl 110, sales $87,000,000, cert: NMSDC)

6828 Premier Business Solutions
      3202 N Kenmore
      South Bend, IN 46628
      Contact: President
      Tel: 574-232-8840
      Email:
      Website: www.premierbus.com
Fulfillment & marketing services: product & literature
fulfillment, rebate & free offer processing, network
programs, lead mgmt programs, pick pack, warehousing
& inventory management.
We help our clients execute all facets of their marketing
plan. (Woman, estab 2001, empl 15, sales , cert:
WBENC)

6829 The Servants, Inc.
      3145 Lottes Dr
      Jasper, IN 47546
      Contact: Jerome Balbach controller
      Tel: 812-634-2201
      Email: jerome@servants.com
      Website: www.servants.com
Corrugated packaging & packaging accessories.
(Woman/AA, estab 1973, empl 55, sales $10,000,000,
cert: NWBOC)

6830 Vesta Ingredients, Inc.
      5767 Thunderbird Rd
      Indianapolis, IN 46236
      Contact: Richard Pinner Client Relationship Mgr
      Tel: 317-397-9004
      Email: richard@vestaingredients.com
      Website: www.vestaingredients.com
Contract manufacturing & packaging. (As-Pac, estab
1997, empl 20, sales $10,000,010, cert: NMSDC)

Kansas

6831 Pitt Plastics, Inc. dba IBS Solutions
      P.O. Box 356
      Pittsburg, KS 66762
      Contact: Randy Orscheln VP of Sales, Strategic
      Accts
      Tel: 800-835-0366
      Email: randyo@pittplastics.com
      Website: www.pittplastics.com
Dist bags: can liners & poly bags, rolls or flat pack. (Nat
Ame, estab 1971, empl 450, sales , cert: NMSDC)

Kentucky

6832 Chavira Packaging Products, Inc.
701-4 Dishman
Bowling Green, KY 42104
Contact: Dawn Dodd President
Tel: 877-823-1316
Email: chavirapackaging@bellsouth.net
Website:
Dist shipping & packaging material: wood pallets, crates, dunnage & industrial lumber. (Hisp, estab , empl , sales , cert: NMSDC)

6833 CSS Distribution Group, Inc.
3600 Chamberlain Ln Ste 216
Louisville, KY 40241
Contact: Sandy Allemang CEO
Tel: 502-423-1011
Email: sandya@customersourcingsolutions.com
Website: www.customersourcingsolutions.com
Dist packaging tape, edge protector, pallets, packaging & automation equipment, forklift software tracking program. (Woman, estab 2006, empl 12, sales $2,200,000, cert: WBENC)

6834 Kyana Packaging & Industrial Supply, Inc.
2501 Ampere Dr
Louisville, KY 40291
Contact: Kimberly Osborne CEO
Tel: 502-992-3333
Email: kim@kyanaind.com
Website: www.kyanaind.com
Dist packaging & shipping supplies: boxes, tape, stretch wrap, bubble wrap, strapping, adhesives, air pillow machines, stretch wrappers, strapping machines, automatic tape machines, shrink wrap equipment & film, poly bags, plastic films. (Woman, estab 1976, empl 37, sales $9,737,350, cert: WBENC)

6835 P3 Protective Packaging Products
P.O. Box 3583
Louisville, KY 40201
Contact: Anne Sizemore VP
Tel: 502-357-6872
Email: annes@p3products.com
Website: http://p3products.com
Expendable/Returnable Packaging & design. Retail package supplier/distributor. (Woman, estab 2001, empl 22, sales $7,000,000, cert: WBENC)

Louisiana

6836 IPC Louisiana LLC
2015 Chanute Dr
Alexandria, LA 71303
Contact: Mark Vassar VP Sales/Mktg
Tel: 318-473-0400
Email: mark.vassar@ipcboxes.com
Website: www.ipcboxes.com
Mfr corrugated packaging, brown box & multicolor packaging, POP's. (AA, estab 2004, empl 30, sales $17,000,000, cert: NMSDC)

Massachusetts

6837 Lancaster Packaging, Inc.
560 Main St, Ste 2
Hudson, MA 01749
Contact: Marianne Lancaster President
Tel: 978-562-0100
Email: mlancaster@lancasterpackaging.com
Website: www.lancasterpackaging.com
Dist bank tamper evident bags, file storage boxes, corrugated materials, stretch wrap, shipping supplies. (Woman/AA, estab 1989, empl 10, sales $12,180,000, cert: NMSDC, WBENC)

Maryland

6838 projectWorks, LLC
6900 English Muffin Way, Ste E
Frederick, MD 21703
Contact: Michelle Stephens CEO
Tel: 301-682-4800
Email: michelle@projectworks.com
Website: www.projectworks.com
Fulfillment & marketing support svcs: warehouse & distribution, assembly & order fulfillment, printing & direct mail, eCommerce & inventory mgmt, advertising specialties & premiums. (Hisp, estab 1998, empl 7, sales $808,117, cert: State)

6839 Vac Pac, Inc.
150 W Ostend St, Ste 160
Baltimore, MD 21230
Contact: Hessa Tary CEO
Tel: 410-685-5181
Email: hessa.tary@vacpacinc.com
Website: www.vacpacinc.com
Print & convert flexible packaging, poly, polyprop, polyester, cellophane, nylon
high temeprature. (Woman, estab 1949, empl 25, sales $4,000,000, cert: WBENC)

Michigan

6840 Aldez Containers, LLC
4260 Van Dyke, Ste 109
Almont, MI 48003
Contact: Diane Pattison VP
Tel: 586-243-0596
Email: dpattison@aldezcontainers.com
Website: http://aldezcontainers.com
Mfr corrugated packaging & dunnage, service parts packaging. (Woman/Hisp, estab 1998, empl 78, sales $10,000,000, cert: NMSDC)

6841 Bay Corrugated Container, Inc.
1655 W 7th St
Monroe, MI 48161
Contact: Judy Thoma Exec Admin
Tel: 734-243-5400
Email: jthoma@baycorr.com
Website: www.baycorr.com
Mfr corrugated boxes/folding cartons, corrugated pallets, corrugated interior packaging materials, stretchwrap, chipboard, board coatings, linerboard/fine paper, stickers, labels, etc. (Woman/Hisp, estab 1964, empl 250, sales $65,027,000, cert: NMSDC, WBENC)

6842 Contract Source & Assembly Inc.
       5230 33rd St SE
       Grand Rapids, MI 49512
       Contact: Bryce Cooper
       Tel: 616-897-2185
       Email: bryce@contractmi.com
       Website: www.contractmi.com
Light Manufacturing & Contract Assembly, Contract
Packaging & Inventory Management, Supply Chain
Management, Inspection & Re-work. (As-Pac, estab 2001,
empl 13, sales $18,000,000, cert: NMSDC)

6843 Diversity Products
       32031 Howard St
       Madison Heights, MI 48071
       Contact: Darlene Fleser Operations Dir
       Tel: 248-585-1200
       Email: dfleser@diversityproducts.com
       Website: www.diversityproducts.com
Packaging engineering support, cost reduction, vendor
consolidation, packaging program mgmt, returnable
container repair, cleaning & tracking, inventory management. (Woman/AA, estab 1998, empl 35, sales $9,000,000,
cert: NMSDC)

6844 Galaxy Forest Products LLC
       1655 W 7th St
       Monroe, MI 48161
       Contact: Judy Thoma Exec Admin
       Tel: 734-243-5400
       Email: jthoma@galaxyforestproducts.com
       Website: www.galaxytforestproducts.com
Packaging materials, pulp, microflute, consumer boxes,
corrugated containers, slip sheets, folding cartons, corner/
angle protectors, dunnage packaging. (Woman/Hisp, estab
2005, empl , sales $2,058,358, cert: State, NMSDC)

6845 Genesee Packaging, Inc (The Genesee Group)
       2010 N. Dort Hwy, P.O. Box 7716
       Flint, MI 48506
       Contact: Ken Miller Sales Mgr
       Tel: 248-514-1883
       Email: kmiller@genpackaging.com
       Website: www.genpackaging.com
Packaging supplies & services. (Woman, estab 1979, empl
125, sales $190,000,000, cert: WBENC)

6846 Harbor Foam, Inc.
       2950 Prairie St SW, Ste 300
       Grandville, MI 49418
       Contact: Laura Kuperus Owner
       Tel: 616-855-8150
       Email: harborfoam@hotmail.com
       Website:
Dist polystyrene foam, white ridgid foam used for packaging & insulation. (Woman, estab 2007, empl 8, sales
$500,000, cert: WBENC)

6847 Integrated Packaging Company
       6400 Harper Ave
       Detroit, MI 48211
       Contact: Jeffrey Laney strategic accts Mgr
       Tel: 612-802-1736
       Email: jeff.laney@ipcboxes.com
       Website: www.ipcboxes.com
Packaging solutions, packaging & displays, Design, Concept
& Development. (AA, estab 1992, empl , sales
$20,000,000, cert: NMSDC)

6848 James Group International
       4335 W Fort St
       Detroit, MI 48209
       Contact: Lorron James Sales Mgr
       Tel: 313-842-4543
       Email: lorron.james@jamesgroupintl.com
       Website: www.jamesgroupintl.com
Logistics, sequencing, warehousing & distribution,
deconsidation, re-packing, sub-assembly, inventory
management. (AA, estab 1971, empl 171, sales
$30,000,000, cert: NMSDC)

6849 Macomb Wholesale Supply Corp.
       17730 E 14 Mile Rd
       Fraser, MI 48026
       Contact: Catherine David President
       Tel:
       Email: online@macombwholesale.com
       Website: www.macombwholesale.com
Dist Packaging, Safety, Janitorial & Facility Maintenance
Supplies, corrugated, poly bags, tape, paper, chemical,
packaging, gloves, safety & facility cleaning supplies.
(Woman, estab 1988, empl 10, sales $2,500,000, cert:
WBENC)

6850 Packaging Integration, LLC
       13235 Avalon Ct
       Brighton, MI 48116
       Contact: Scott Bradford President
       Tel: 248-437-1900
       Email: scott.bradford@packagingintegration.com
       Website: www.packagingintegration.com
Dist packaging materials. (Hisp, estab 2005, empl 5, sales
$5,000,000, cert: NMSDC)

6851 Patriot Packaging Solutions and Consulting
       269 Walker St, Ste 522
       Detroit, MI 48207
       Contact: Jay Jackson VP
       Tel: 313-580-1538
       Email: jay.jackson@patriotgm1.com
       Website:
       www.patriotpackagingsolutionsconsuting.com
Packaging services: corrugated box, bulk boxes, displays,
single face, bubble wrap, stretch wrap, trays, sheets,
tape & labels. (AA, estab 2011, empl 4, sales $500,250,
cert: NMSDC)

6852 Peach State Packaging Solutions
       8803 Cairn Hwy
       Elk Rapids, MI 49629
       Contact: Lisa McCririe President
       Tel: 819-599-2594
       Email:
       lmccririe@peachstatepackagingsolutions.com
       Website:
       www.peachstatepackagingsolutions.com
Dist packaging supplies. (Woman, estab 2006, empl ,
sales $800,000, cert: WBENC)

6853 Pro-Pak Products, Ltd.
       17580 Helro Dr
       Fraser, MI 48026
       Contact: Nancy Stachnik President
       Tel: 586-415-1500
       Email: propakltd@aol.com
       Website: www.propakproductsltd.com
Packaging supplies & services. (Woman, estab 1993,
empl 5, sales , cert: NWBOC)

6854 Quixerve Corporation
      341 N Helmer Rd
      Springfield, MI 49037
      Contact: Linda Gillett President
      Tel: 269-441-0700
      Email: lgillett@quixerve.com
      Website: www.quixerve.com
Printing, Labeling, Packaging, Fulfillment, Warehousing,
Inventory Control, Distribution. (Woman, estab 2003, empl
3, sales $225,000, cert: WBENC)

6855 Ryan Industries, Inc.
      30369 Beck Rd
      Wixom, MI 48382
      Contact: Brenda Ryan President
      Tel: 248-926-5254
      Email: bryan@ryanind.net
      Website: www.ryanind.net
Warehousing, packaging, light assembly, kitting, distribution, rework. (Woman/AA, estab 1995, empl 10, sales ,
cert: NMSDC, WBENC)

6856 Sibley Laboratories LLC
      8816 Charbane St
      White Lake, MI 48386
      Contact: Kathleen Sibley Managing Partner
      Tel: 248-363-3972
      Email: ksibley@sibleylabs.com
      Website: www.sibleylabs.com
Dist ergonomically safe trash collection receptacles & trash
bags. (Woman, estab 2001, empl 3, sales , cert: WBENC)

6857 Stewart Industries, LLC
      150 McQuiston Dr
      Battle Creek, MI 49037
      Contact: Matt Amos Business Dev Mgr
      Tel: 269-998-0608
      Email: mamos@stewartindustriesusa.com
      Website: www.stewartindustriesusa.com
Third party inspection, sorting, rework, light assembly,
packaging. (AA, estab 2000, empl 60, sales $37,615,000,
cert: NMSDC)

6858 Tabb Packaging Solutions
      41605 Ann Arbor Rd Ste 2
      Plymouth, MI 48170
      Contact: Julie Kavulich Business Dev Mgr
      Tel: 734-254-0251
      Email: jkavulich@tabbpackaging.com
      Website: www.tabbpackaging.com
Post Consumer Recycled Materials, HDPE & PET, Primary
Processing Operations, Market Color Concentrates &
Additives, Packaging Materials & Label Substrate (IML),
Virgin & PCR Pre-blend Resins. (Woman, estab 2007, empl
7, sales , cert: WBENC)

6859 Valmec Inc.
      1274 S Holly Rd
      Fenton, MI 48430
      Contact: Krystn Tatus CEO
      Tel: 810-629-8750
      Email: valmec@comcast.net
      Website: http://valmecinc.com
Material handling & packaging, conveyors, returnable
packaging, installation, tear-outs & complete system
integration. (Woman, estab 1971, empl 5, sales
$1,344,664, cert: WBENC)

6860 Venchurs, Inc.
      800 Liberty St
      Adrian, MI 49221
      Contact: Erica Wilt Program Mgr
      Tel: 517-264-4392
      Email: esellers@venchurs.com
      Website: www.venchurs.com
Custom package design & flexible packaging solutions.
Global Sourcing, Supply Chain Management, Inventory
Management, Packaging, Warehousing & Distribution.
(Hisp, estab 1973, empl 86, sales , cert: NMSDC)

6861 Whisper Creative Products, Inc.
      1585 Wells Rd
      Dundee, MI 48131
      Contact: Dolores Rodriguez CEO
      Tel: 734-529-2734
      Email: whisper@cass.net
      Website:
Packaging supplies, expendable & returnable packaging.
(Woman/Hisp, estab 1997, empl 10, sales $300,000,
cert: NMSDC, WBENC)

6862 World Corrugated Container
      P.O. Box 840
      Albion, MI 49224
      Contact: Tara Saumier Human Resources
      Tel: 517-629-9400
      Email: tsaumier@worldcorrugated.com
      Website: www.worldcorrugated.com
Mfr & dist corrugated containers. (Woman/Hisp, estab
1991, empl 40, sales $7,900,000, cert: WBENC)

Minnesota

6863 Independent Packing Services, Inc.
      7600 32nd Ave N
      Crystal, MN 55427
      Contact: Joseph Wallace President
      Tel: 763-425-7155
      Email: jwallace@ipsipack.com
      Website: www.ipsipack.com
Mfr industrial crating for domestic & export shipments;
electronics & fragile artwork. (AA, estab 1976, empl 60,
sales , cert: NMSDC)

6864 Polybest, Inc.
      2962 Cleveland Ave N
      Roseville, MN 55113
      Contact: Zongzhao Li President
      Tel: 651-633-1688
      Email: johnli@polybestinc.com
      Website: www.polybestinc.com
Mfr packaging materials such as all kinds of plastic and
compostable bags, hazard trash bags, disposal bags,
trash canliners, wrapping film, etc. (As-Pac, estab 2006,
empl 4, sales $1,234,157, cert: NMSDC)

6865 Promotion Management Center, Inc.
      31205 Falcon Ave
      Stacy, MN 55079
      Contact: Tom Diffley Business Development
      Tel: 651-321-8734
      Email: tdiffley@pmci.com
      Website: www.pmci.com
Fulfillment, direct mail, sweepstakes, packaging.
(Woman, estab 1983, empl 40, sales $3,000,000, cert:
WBENC)

6866 SeaChange Print Innovations
14505 27th Ave N
Plymouth, MN 55447
Contact: Nancy Servais Business Development
Tel: 763-586-3700
Email: nancy.servais@seachangem.com
Website: www.seachangemn.com
Folding carton & marketing print production, Folding Carton Packaging, Marketing Printing, Commercial Printing, Direct Mail Printing, Digital Printing. (Woman, estab 2014, empl 90, sales $13,100,000, cert: WBENC)

6867 TJ's Packaging Inc
19950 177th St NW
Big Lake, MN 55309
Contact: Kristy Murray COO
Tel: 763-241-2022
Email: jfarrington@tjpackaging.com
Website: www.tjpackaging.com
Packaging supplies & automated packaging equipment. (Woman, estab 1998, empl 4, sales $1,862,202, cert: WBENC)

Missouri

6868 Bennett Packaging of Kansas City, Inc.
220 NW Space Center Cir
Lee's Summit, MO 64064
Contact: Traci Strickert Dir of Marketing
Tel: 816-379-5001
Email: traci.strickert@bpkc.com
Website: www.BennettKC.com
Design & mfr corrugated boxes, point-of-purchase displays, co-packing, fulfillment, warehousing & distribution. (Woman, estab 1987, empl 240, sales $65,153,256, cert: WBENC)

6869 Crossroads USA
14004 Century Lane
Grandview, MO 64030
Contact: Jason Begnaud Dir of Sales
Tel: 816-767-8008
Email: service@bestwaylogistics.com
Website: http://bestwaylogistics.com/
Single source packaging & shipping solutions nationwide. (Woman, estab 2000, empl 14, sales $5,050,000, cert: WBENC)

6870 Engineered Packaging Systems, Inc.
16141 Westwoods Business Park
Ellisville, MO 63021
Contact: Debra Debra Runtzel-Young CEO
Tel: 636-227-8600
Email: info@packeps.com
Website: http://packeps.com
Full service packaging machinery and packaging materials or consumables, CAD layout drawings, installation, service, shrink film, stretch film, tapes, adhesives, cartons, custom printed bags, powder filling, liquid filling, labeling machines and labels. (Woman, estab 2004, empl 11, sales $9,000,000, cert: WBENC)

6871 Swan Packaging Inc.
P.O. Box 1558
St. Louis, MO 63026
Contact: President
Tel: 314-771-9777
Email:
Website: www.swanpackaginginc.com
Dist shrink sleeves, lidding films, printed rollstock & pouches, rotogravure & flexographic printing, multilayer films, extrusion & off-line lamination, films, paper & foil. (Woman, estab 1999, empl 6, sales $3,519,000, cert: WBENC)

Mississippi

6872 Innpack LLC
10511 High Point Rd
Olive Branch, MS 38654
Contact: Jin Ahn CFO
Tel: 901-949-4977
Email: jahn@innpack.com
Website: www.innpack.com
Mfr & dist packaging solutions: burlap, cotton, PP woven, laminated & FBIC bags. (As-Pac, estab 1997, empl 20, sales $9,000,000, cert: NMSDC)

North Carolina

6873 AAKCo. Packaging
256 Highgate Circle
Wake Forest, NC 27587
Contact: Danielle Kerner CEO
Tel: 919-609-7486
Email: aakcopackaging@outlook.com
Website:
Packaging for pharmaceutical products. (Woman, estab 2015, empl 1, sales , cert: WBENC)

6874 Carolina Industrial Resources, Inc
4303 Oak Level Rd
Rocky Mount, NC 27803
Contact: Margaret Hoyle President
Tel: 800-849-1819
Email: tphoyle@cir-poly.com
Website: www.cir-poly.com
Dist polyethylene plastic packaging products. (Woman, estab 1986, empl 359, sales $155,000,000, cert: WBENC)

6875 PolySi Technologies, Inc.
5108 Rex McLeod Dr
Sanford, NC 27330
Contact: Lynn Richardson Operations Mgr
Tel: 919-775-4989
Email: lynn@polysi.com
Website: www.polysi.com
Mfr silicone, synthetic greases & silicone fluids, industrial packaging, retail packaging, contract filling & custom packaging. (Woman, estab 1995, empl 25, sales $7,000,000, cert: WBENC)

6876 SLR Designs, LLC
11220 Elm Lane, Ste 200
Charlotte, NC 28277
Contact: Linda Tilley Managing Member
Tel: 704-546-8448
Email: linda@slrdesignsllc.com
Website: www.slrdesignsllc.com
Design & dist customer packaging, PVC, mPE & phthalate free materials. (Woman, estab 2011, empl 4, sales $3,247,681, cert: WBENC)

6877 Southern Film Extruders, Inc.
2319 English Rd
High Point, NC 27265
Contact: John Barnes VP Finance
Tel: 800-334-6101
Email: sales@southernfilm.com
Website: www.southernfilm.com
Extrudes polyethylene packaging films using LDPE,
LLDPE,HDPE and Metallocene resins for various packaging
applications, shrink film, film for bags, laminations etc.
(Hisp, estab 1965, empl 150, sales $65,000,000, cert:
NMSDC)

Nebraska

6878 Frontier Bag Company, Inc
2520 Grant St
Omaha, NE 68111
Contact: Rendell Gines Reg Sales Mgr
Tel: 402-342-0992
Email: jplee@frontierbagco.com
Website: www.frontierbagco.com
Dist plastic bags & packaging, film wrap & shrink wrap.
(Woman/AA, estab 1946, empl 15, sales $1,430,000, cert:
WBENC)

New Jersey

6879 Accurate Box Company
86 Fifth Ave
Paterson, NJ 07524
Contact: Samara Schlossman Sales/Mktg Mgr
Tel:
Email: sschlossman@accuratebox.com
Website: www.accuratebox.com
Litholaminated E, B & F flute packaging & displays.
(Woman, estab 1944, empl 315, sales $120,000,000, cert:
WBENC)

6880 Alpha Industries Inc. dba Sigma Stretch Film
Page and Schuyler
Lyndhurst, NJ 07071
Contact: John Buchan Mgr strategic accts
Tel: 214-799-3975
Email: johnbuchan@sigmaplastics.com
Website: www.sigmaplastics.com
Mfr custom barrier & sealant mono & co-ex blown films
for dry,frozen, refrigerated & liquid food applications..
(As-Pac, estab 1997, empl 70, sales $57,500,000, cert:
NMSDC)

6881 Creative Packaging Solutions Corporation
5 W First St
Keyport, NJ 07735
Contact: President
Tel: 732-335-3700
Email:
Website: www.packaging-usa.com
Dist packaging containers, parts & components: bottles,
jars, flexible tubes, rigid tubes aand canister, caps, spray-
ers, lotion pumps, folding boxes, rigid gift set up boxes,
ribbons, thermoformed blisters and trays. (Woman, estab
2003, empl 2, sales $176,677, cert: State, WBENC)

6882 G&T Trading International
128 Circle Ave
Clifton, NJ 07011
Contact: George Chen President
Tel: 973-340-8003
Email: philipgttic@gmail.com
Website: http://gttic.com
Dist stretch film, wooden pallets, chipboard, stretch film
equip, annual equipment audits, shrink film, shrink wrap
& bundling equip, carton sealing & bagging equip,
supporting films & tapes. (As-Pac, estab 1977, empl 6,
sales $23,987,513, cert: State, NMSDC)

6883 Glopak Corporation
132 Case Dr
South Plainfield, NJ 07080
Contact: Elyne Williams Sales Dir
Tel: 908-753-8735
Email: glopakinc@aol.com
Website: www.glopakcorp.com
Dist plastic bags & liners. (Woman/AA, estab 1966, empl
33, sales , cert: NMSDC)

6884 Pro Pack Inc.
500 W Main St
Wyckoff, NJ 07481
Contact: Peter Quercia CEO
Tel: 201-337-1001
Email: peter@shrinkfilm.com
Website: www.shrinkfilm.com
Packaging materials, form, fill & seal systems, doy-pack
systems, metal detectors & check
weighers, labeling systems, clip & twist systems, shrink
wrappers, carton sealers, stretch wrappers, strapping
machines, conveyors, band sealers, filling systems.
(Woman, estab 1976, empl 10, sales $4,000,000, cert:
WBENC)

6885 Products Distribution, Inc.
7 Santa Fe Way Ste 701
Cranbury, NJ 08512
Contact: Dawn Dunbar President
Tel: 609-655-1341
Email: requests@productsdistribution.com
Website: www.productsdistribution.com
Warehousing, distribution, fulfillment, assembly, kitting,
pick pack, container unloading, palletizing, ingredient
storage, bulk storage, EDI, custom assembly, display
assembly, GWP assembly, rack storage, raw material
storage. (Woman, estab 1979, empl 7, sales $1,119,000,
cert: WBENC)

6886 Quality Packaging Specialists International, LLC
2030 US 130 N
Florence, NJ 08518
Contact: Jeff Lemke Sales Exec
Tel: 609-273-6364
Email: jlemke@qpsiusa.com
Website: www.qpsiusa.com
Packaging & fulfillment, merchandising displays, con-
tract packaging, logistics & distribution services. (AA,
estab 1972, empl 1500, sales $300,000,000, cert:
NMSDC)

6887   RKS Plastics Inc.
       100 Jersey Ave
       New Brunswick, NJ 08903
       Contact: Sudhir Shah President
       Tel: 800-635-9959
       Email: srshah@rksplastics.com
       Website: www.rksplastics.com
Dist polyethylene & polyproylene bags, drum/box liners,
sheeting & tubing, zipper lock bags, anti-static bags,
printed bags, wicket/staple pack, stretch wrap & tapes.
In addition, we also offer design services. (AA, As-Pac,
estab 1993, empl 7, sales $4,223,000, cert: NMSDC)

6888   SunFlex Packagers Inc.
       2 Commerce Dr
       Cranford, NJ 07016
       Contact: Manny Patel CEO
       Tel: 908-709-1500
       Email: mannypatel@sunflexpackagers.com
       Website: www.sunflexpackagers.com
Convert & dist flexible packaging material: roll form, bags
& specialty pouches. (As-Ind, estab 2002, empl 15, sales
$5,900,000, cert: NMSDC)

6889   West Pack Industries, LLC.
       2225 E Greg St, Ste 107
       Sparks, NV 89431
       Contact: James Alford GM
       Tel: 775-351-3345
       Email: james@westpackcopack.com
       Website: www.westpackcopack.com/
Flexible packaging, contract packaging, dry product filling,
mixing, blending. Stand up pouch filling, Vertical Form Fill
Seal filling, volume metric filling, scale filling. Snack Foods,
candy, confectionery, powdered beverages. (Nat Ame,
estab 2003, empl 44, sales $1,850,000, cert: NMSDC)

New York

6890   Aluf Plastics div. of API Industries, Inc.
       2 Glenshaw St
       Orangeburg, NY 10962
       Contact: Tom Cross VP of Retail Sales
       Tel: 845-365-2200
       Email: tom.c@alufplastics.com
       Website: www.alufplastics.com
Mfr plastic bags. (Woman, estab 1977, empl 314, sales ,
cert: WBENC)

6891   Berry Industrial Group, Inc.
       30 Main St
       Nyack, NY 10960
       Contact: Debra Berry CEO
       Tel: 845-353-8338
       Email: debra.berry@berryindustrial.com
       Website: www.berryindustrial.com
Mfr, recycle & dist industrial shipping pallets. (Woman,
estab 1984, empl 7, sales $22,636,656, cert: WBENC)

6892   Bluepack
       215 John Glenn Dr
       Amherst, NY 14228
       Contact: Helen Ma President
       Tel: 716-923-0032
       Email: hma@bluepackinc.com
       Website: www.bluepackinc.com
Mfr printed & unprinted shrink labels, neck bands & safety
seals. We have 8 color flexo and rotogravure presses.
(Woman/As-Pac, estab 1999, empl 65, sales $10,000,000,
cert: NMSDC)

6893   Diamond Packaging
       111 Commerce Dr
       Rochester, NY 14623
       Contact: Dennis Bacchetta Dir of Marketing
       Tel: 585-334-8030
       Email: sales@diamondpkg.com
       Website: www.diamondpackaging.com
Contract mfg & packaging services: automatic cartoning,
bagging bar coding, blister sealing, EAS source tagging,
flexible packaging, form, fill & seal, fulfillment, labeling,
POP displays, product assembly, RF sealing, shrink
wrapping & skin packaging. (Woman/AA, estab 1911,
empl 262, sales $64,200,000, cert: WBENC)

6894   Eltrex Industries, Inc.
       65 Sullivan St
       Rochester, NY 14605
       Contact: Avis Williams Business Dev Mgr
       Tel: 585-454-6100
       Email: avis.williams@eltrex.com
       Website: www.eltrex.com
Mechanical & electromechanical assemblies,
remanufacturing, kitting & logistics services: material
purchasing & consignment, packaging & distribution,
warehousing. (AA, estab 1968, empl 200, sales
$18,000,000, cert: State)

6895   F.M. Howell & Company
       79 Pennsylvania Ave
       Elmira, NY 14904
       Contact: Business Dev Mgr
       Tel: 908-303-0013
       Email:
       Website: www.howellpkg.com
Mfr printed folding cartons and thermo-formed plastic
components internally. (Woman, estab , empl 190, sales
, cert: WBENC)

6896   Global Packaging Solutions LLC
       70 E Sunrise Hwy Ste 611
       Valley Stream, NY 11581
       Contact: Mitchell Sloane Managing Dir
       Tel: 516-256-7416
       Email: msloane@glopackllc.com
       Website: www.glopackllc.com
Bags, plastic bags, reusable bags, trash liners, shopping
bags. (AA, estab 2011, empl 5, sales $3,500,000, cert:
State)

6897   Golden Group International, Ltd.
       305 Quaker Rd
       Patterson, NY 12563
       Contact: President
       Tel: 845-440-5220
       Email:
       Website: www.GoldenGroupInternational.com
Mfr & dist bags, dispensers, receptacles and cabinets.
(Woman, estab 2009, empl 8, sales , cert: WBENC)

6898   Ongweoweh Corp
       5 Barr Road
       Ithaca, NY 14850
       Contact: Brett Bucktooth Supplier Diversity Mgr
       Tel: 607-266-7070
       Email: supplierdiversity@ongweoweh.com
       Website: www.ongweoweh.com
Mfr & dist wooden pallets & specialty containers. (Nat
Ame, estab 1978, empl 96, sales $252,000,000, cert:
NMSDC)

6899   Prism Packaging
      70 E Sunrise Hwy, Ste 611
      Valley Stream, NY 11581
      Contact: Randi Norfleet Exec Director
      Tel:
      Email: rnorfleet@witlogistics.com
      Website: www.walkerscm.com
Print, packaging & logistics solutions. (AA, estab 2015, empl 1, sales , cert: NMSDC)

6900   Star Poly Bag Inc.
      200 Liberty Ave.
      Brooklyn, NY 11207
      Contact: Rachel Posen President
      Tel: 718-384-3130
      Email: rachel@starpoly.com
      Website: www.starpoly.com
Mfr poly bags. (Woman, estab 1961, empl 15, sales $3,550,000, cert: State, City, WBENC)

6901   The Standard Group
      1010 Northern Blvd Ste 236
      Great Neck, NY 11021
      Contact: James Gregory Acct Exec
      Tel: 718-310-5512
      Email: jamesg@thestandardgroup.com
      Website: www.thestandardgroup.com
Folding carton, specialty printed packaging & paperboard converter. (Hisp, estab 1932, empl 130, sales $35,000,000, cert: NMSDC)

6902   Universal Packaging Systems
      6080 Jericho Turnpike
      Commack, NY 11725
      Contact: David Boone Natl Acct Mgr
      Tel: 404-554-0770
      Email: dboone@paklab.com
      Website: http://paklab.com
Contract manufacturing & flexible film, extended gamut flexographic printing of roll stock & pouches with gussets & fitments. (AA, estab 1987, empl 600, sales $116,400,000, cert: NMSDC)

6903   Walker International Transportation, LLC.
      70 E Sunrise Hwy Ste 611
      Valley Stream, NY 11581
      Contact: Maria Hill Dir of Sales
      Tel: 516-568-2080
      Email: mhill@walkerscm.com
      Website: www.walkerscm.com
Assembly & contract packaging services. (AA, estab 1989, empl 700, sales $112,000,000, cert: NMSDC)

Ohio

6904   Accel inc.
      9000 Smith's Mill Road
      New Albany, OH 43054
      Contact: Chairwoman
      Tel: 614-656-1100
      Email:
      Website: www.accel-inc.com
Contract packaging & fulfillment svcs: design, sourcing, assembly, shrink-wrapping, warehousing, dist & e-fulfillment svcs. (Woman, estab 1995, empl 375, sales $25,890,000, cert: WBENC)

6905   Allied Shipping and Packaging Supplies
      3681 Vance Road
      Moraine, OH 45439
      Contact: Shelly Heller President
      Tel: 937-222-7422
      Email: sheller@asapi.com
      Website: www.asapi.com
Dist packaging supplies: special size boxes, printed boxes, printed tape, special inserts or cell partitions, printed poly bags or special size poly bags. (Woman, estab 1982, empl 12, sales $4,034,225, cert: WBENC)

6906   Arrowhead Packaging Services
      P.O. Box 1284
      Perrysburg, OH 43551
      Contact: Brian Deiger VP Sales
      Tel: 419-344-7373
      Email: brian@apackserv.com
      Website: www.apackserv.com
Packaging & packaging services, fulfillment operations, sequencing, storage & logistics. (AA, estab 2010, empl 2, sales $120,000, cert: NMSDC)

6907   Bickley Innovations, LLC
      607 Redna Terr, Ste 700
      Cincinnati, OH 45215
      Contact: Kendra Alexander President
      Tel: 513-655-6074
      Email: information@bickleyllc.com
      Website: www.bickleyllc.com
Dist packaging & industrial supplies. (Woman/AA, estab 2015, empl 1, sales , cert: NMSDC, WBENC)

6908   Custom Paper Tubes
      15900 Industrial Pkwy
      Cleveland, OH 44135
      Contact: Emily Miller Marketing Mgr
      Tel: 216-362-2964
      Email: emiller@custompapertubes.com
      Website: www.custompapertubes.com
Produce sustainable, recyclable & biodegradable packaging for all types of products. (Woman/AA, Hisp, estab 1964, empl 25, sales $5,500,000, cert: WBENC, SDB)

6909   Forest City Companies, Inc.
      3607 W 56th St
      Cleveland, OH 44102
      Contact: Anthony Galang
      Tel: 216-634-9000
      Email: tgalang@forestcityco.com
      Website: www.forestcityco.com
Military packaging service & supplies, laser marking services, wood boxes, export packing & crating, hazmat packaging service & supplies, induatrial sewing, bellows, insulated blankets. (Minority, estab 1993, empl 14, sales $3,600,000, cert: NMSDC)

6910   Joshen Paper and Packaging
      5800 Grant Ave
      Cuyahoga Heights, OH 44105
      Contact: Anthony Salyers
      Tel: 216-441-5600
      Email: greiser@joshen.com
      Website: www.joshen.com
Dist packaging supplies, bags, office supplies, custom printing, sanitation, chemicals & floor care programs. (Woman, estab 1988, empl 152, sales $180,500,000, cert: NWBOC)

6911 LEFCO Worthington, LLC
18451 Euclid Ave
Cleveland, OH 44112
Contact: Larry Fulton President
Tel: 216-432-4422
Email: larry.fulton@lefcoworthington.com
Website: www.LEFCOWorthington.com
Dist wooden crates, OSB Boxes, custom pallets, sub-assembly & packaging services. (AA, estab 2003, empl 30, sales $3,600,000, cert: State, NMSDC)

6912 TrueChoicePack Corp.
9565 Cincinnati Columbus Road
Cincinnati, OH 45069
Contact: Rakesh Rathore COO
Tel: 513-759-5540
Email: info@truechoicepack.com
Website: www.truechoicepack.com
Mfr environmentally friendly green packaging products, biodegradable & compostable food service packaging & disposable products. (Woman/AA, As-Ind, estab 2008, empl 10, sales $50,560,000, cert: NMSDC, WBENC)

Oregon

6913 Standard Bag Manufacturing Company
1800 SW Merlo Dr
Beaverton, OR 97003
Contact: Rita Fung Controller
Tel: 503-616-7307
Email: rfung@standardbag.com
Website: www.standardbag.com
Mfr bags: sewn open mouth, pinch bottom open mouth & pinch block bottom bags. (As-Pac, estab 1985, empl 140, sales , cert: NMSDC)

6914 Yoshida Foods International
8440 NE Alderwood Rd, Ste A
Portland, OR 97220
Contact: Junki Yoshida Sales Mgr
Tel: 503-872-8450
Email: junki.yoshida@yoshida.com
Website: www.yoshidafoodsinternational.com
Liquid hot-fill bottling, industrial packaging, portion packaging. (As-Pac, estab 1982, empl 241, sales , cert: NMSDC)

Pennsylvania

6915 Alpine Packaging Inc.
4000 Crooked Run Rd
North Versailles, PA 15137
Contact: Jan Lehigh President
Tel: 412-664-4000
Email: jlehigh@alpinepackaging.com
Website: www.alpinepackaging.com
Packaging supplies & services. (Woman, estab 1972, empl 38, sales $14,180,198, cert: WBENC)

6916 Carlisle Packaging Company, Inc.
750 Claremont Rd
Carlisle, PA 17013
Contact: Ed Schimmel CEO
Tel: 717-249-2444
Email: eschimmel@carlislecontainer.net
Website: www.carlislecontainer.net
Mfr corrugated packaging & displays. (Woman, estab 1965, empl 40, sales $7,173,000, cert: State, WBENC)

6917 Kalstar Enterprises, LLC
P.O. Box 931
Scranton, PA 18501
Contact: Adam Zaranski Dir Client Solutions
Tel: 973-553-5370
Email: adam.zaranski@kalstar.com
Website: www.kalstar.com
Packaging, kitting other labor services to manufacturing companies. (Woman, estab 2004, empl 206, sales $33,600,000, cert: WBENC)

6918 S&G Corrugated Packaging
195 Slocum St
Swoyersville, PA 18704
Contact: Earl Sampson CEO
Tel: 570-287-1718
Email: sgcorrugated@verizon.net
Website: www.s-gcorrugatedpackaging.com
Mfr corrugated cartons & corrugated sheets: assembled partitions, corrugated trays, half slotted cartons, one & five panel folders, scored sheets, coated pads, telescoping cartons, die cutting items, slip sheets, packaging tapes. (AA, estab 2007, empl 10, sales , cert: NMSDC)

6919 Secure Applications, LLC
419 West Market St Ste C
Bethlehem, PA 18018
Contact: Gina Uzzolino President
Tel: 732-874-0954
Email: guzzolino@secureapplications.net
Website: www.secureapplications.net
Packaging materials for Product Security, Tamper Evident, Non-Tamper Evident tapes & labels, security bags, stretch film & Temperature Monitoring Systems for cold chain applications as well as security containers & seals. (Woman, estab 2011, empl 2, sales $110,000, cert: State, CPUC)

6920 Union Packaging, LLC
6250 Baltimore Ave
Yeadon, PA 19050
Contact: Michael K. Pearson President & CEO
Tel: 610-622-7001
Email: mpearson@unionpkg.com
Website: www.unionpkg.com
Mfr folding cartons, paperboard printing & converting. (AA, estab 1999, empl 82, sales $9,287,115, cert: NMSDC)

6921 Wexler Packaging Products, Inc.
777-M Schwab Rd
Hatfield, PA 19440
Contact: Tara Utain VP Sales
Tel: 800-878-3878
Email: tara@wexlerpackaging.com
Website: www.wexlerpackaging.com
Packaging products. (Woman, estab 1997, empl 20, sales , cert: WBENC)

Puerto Rico

6922 3A Press
P.O. Box 47
Lajas, PR 00667
Contact: Marie Rosado President
Tel: 787-899-0110
Email: mrosado@3apress.com
Website: www.3apress.com
Mfr & print pharmaceutical, commercial & folding cartons, inserts, stitched & perfect bound booklets/magazines, printed literature. (Hisp, estab 1996, empl 126, sales $11,200,000, cert: NMSDC)

6923 Flexible Packaging Company, Inc.
      KM 5 1 BO Guaragua RR 176 Bayamon Gardens
      Station
      Bayamon, PR 00959
      Contact: Esteban Serrano Sales Mgr
      Tel: 787-622-7225
      Email: eserrano@flepak.com
      Website: www.flepak.com
Flexible packaging solutions. (Hisp, estab 1976, empl 170,
sales , cert: NMSDC)

6924 Inter-Strap Packaging Systems
      P.O. Box 12367
      San Juan, PR 00914
      Contact: Antonio Fernández GM
      Tel: 787-771-5230
      Email: afernandez@inter-strap.com
      Website: www.inter-strap.com
Dist packaging equipment & materials. (Woman/Hisp,
estab 1991, empl 18, sales $6,317,564, cert: NMSDC)

6925 Johnny Rullan & Co.,
      Road # 1 Km. 20.9 RR-3 Box 3710 RR-3 Box 3710
      San Juan, PR 00926
      Contact: Julio Pizarro Accountant Clerk
      Tel: 787-789-3050
      Email: accountsreceivable@johnnyrullan.com
      Website: www.johnnyrullan.com
Packaging equipment sales & service. (Hisp, estab 1970,
empl 25, sales , cert: NMSDC)

Rhode Island

6926 Banneker Industries, Inc.
      582 Great Rd, Ste 101
      North Smithfield, RI 02896
      Contact: Joe Cefalo Sales & Marketing Mgr
      Tel: 603-819-6966
      Email: marketing@banneker.com
      Website: www.banneker.com
Supply chain management services: e-business services,
assembly & packaging, bar coding, dist packaging materials, third party logistics (3PL), warehousing, material flow
& inventory management. (Woman/AA, estab 1991, empl
72, sales $10,072,400, cert: NMSDC, WBENC)

South Carolina

6927 Alpha Pack LLC
      P.O. Box 30266
      Charleston, SC 29417
      Contact: Carver Wright Jr. Owner
      Tel: 843-737-3931
      Email: wright.pkg@alphapackllc.com
      Website: www.alphapackllc.com
Flexible packaging,polybags, shrink bags, printed bags,
tubing, vci bags, sheeting & can liners. (AA, estab 2012,
empl 2, sales , cert: NMSDC)

6928 Milagro Packaging LLC
      60 Fairview Church Rd
      Spartanburg, SC 29306
      Contact: Jill McCurry President
      Tel: 864-578-0085
      Email: jillm@concept-pkg.com
      Website: www.milagro-pkg.com
Mfr corrugated & solid fiber boxes, polystyrene foam
products & urethane foam products. (Hisp, estab 2001,
empl 425, sales $94,873,435, cert: NMSDC)

6929 Progressive Packaging
      1224 Old Stage Rd
      Greenville, SC 29681
      Contact: Mark Hutcherson Sales Exec
      Tel: 864-271-8106
      Email: hutcherson64@gmail.com
      Website: www.progpack.com
Corrugated packaging, boxes, sheet plant, assembly.
(Woman, estab 1996, empl 55, sales $19,000,000, cert:
WBENC)

6930 Solution Packaging LLC
      2131 Woodruff Rd, Ste 196
      Greenville, SC 29607
      Contact: Joe Nichol VP Sales
      Tel: 864-313-9595
      Email: joe@solutionplastics.net
      Website: www.solutionplastics.net
Mfr & dist polyethylene based end product & solutions,
packaging, poly film, etc. (Woman/Hisp, estab 2013,
empl 2, sales , cert: WBENC)

6931 WDS, Inc.
      1414 Village Harbor Dr
      Lake Wylie, SC 29710
      Contact: Jennfer Maier CEO
      Tel: 803-619-0301
      Email: jennifer.maier@womends.com
      Website: www.womends.com
Dist industrial supplies: paper products, chipboard, films
& plastics. (Woman, estab 2007, empl 180, sales
$186,000,000, cert: WBENC)

Tennessee

6932 DSI Warehouse Inc
      1315 Farmville Rd
      Memphis, TN 38122
      Contact: Debbie Martin President
      Tel: 901-345-6608
      Email: debbiemartin@dsiwarehouse.com
      Website: www.dsiwarehouseandstorage.com
Warehousing & Storage, Packing & Crating, Packaging &
Labeling, Kitting Pack Services, Storage & Handling
Equipment & Supplies, Distribution Fulfillment.
(Woman/AA, estab 2013, empl 20, sales $1,455,421,
cert: NMSDC, WBENC)

6933 Johnson Bryce, Inc.
      5405 Hickory Hill
      Memphis, TN 38141
      Contact: Ron Purifoy CEO
      Tel: 901-942-6522
      Email: rpurifoy@johnsonbryce.com
      Website: www.johnsonbryce.com
Mfr flexible packaging. (AA, estab 1991, empl 25, sales
$27,500,000, cert: NMSDC)

6934 OTB Container, LLC
      1380 Poplar Ave
      Memphis, TN 38104
      Contact: Daniel Coates President
      Tel: 901-270-5407
      Email: daniel@otbcontainer.com
      Website: www.otbcontainer.com
Supplies corrugated shipping boxes. (AA, estab 2015,
empl 5, sales $589,000, cert: NMSDC)

6935   Puffy Stuff
       9 Music Square S, Ste 376
       Nashville, TN 37203
       Contact:
       Tel: 877-833-9872
       Email: info@puffystufftn.com
       Website: www.puffystufftn.com
Mfr 100% biodegradable packing peanuts. (Woman, estab
2000, empl , sales $100,000, cert: State)

6936   RD Plastics
       P.O. Box 111300
       Nashville, TN 37222
       Contact: Jeffrey D. Loveless VP Natl Accts
       Tel: 615-781-0007
       Email: jeffl@rdplastics.com
       Website: www.rdplastics.com
Bags: biohazard ziplock, clear ziplock, adhesive closure,
specimen transport, open end, security seals, pill crushers,
personal belonging. (Woman, estab , empl , sales
$16,502,500, cert: WBENC)

6937   Remar Inc
       6200 E Division St
       Lebanon, TN 37090
       Contact: Lee Whittaker President & CEO
       Tel: 720-601-4785
       Email: lwhittaker@remarinc.com
       Website: www.remarinc.com
Dist blister packaging, fin seal wrap, shrink wrap, inventory
mgmt, point of purchase displays, media replication, direct
mail services, turn key or component projects. (Hisp, estab
, empl 150, sales , cert: State, NMSDC)

6938   TSS Industrial Packaging, LLC
       P.O. Box 3181
       Jackson, TN 38303
       Contact: Michelle Boyd CEO
       Tel: 888-424-1946
       Email: mboyd@tssip.com
       Website: www.tssip.com
Dist industrial packaging materials: industrial sewing
thread & yarn for closing bags, crepe paper sewing tape,
pull tape, twine, slip sheets, pallet covers, stretch film &
stretch wrap. (Woman, estab 2006, empl 4, sales
$3,803,124, cert: State, WBENC)

6939   Worldwide Label & Packaging LLC
       158 Madison Ave Ste 101
       Memphis, TN 38103
       Contact: Anthony Norris President
       Tel: 901-454-9290
       Email: anorris@worldwidebg.com
       Website: www.worldwidebg.com
Mfr printed packaging: pressure sensitive labels, flexible
packaging & continuous roll forms. (AA, estab 2000, empl
20, sales $4,817,859, cert: NMSDC)

Texas

6940   Accredo Packaging, Inc.
       12682 Cardinal Meadow Dr
       Sugar Land, TX 77478
       Contact: Malcolm Cohn Dir of Sustainability
       Tel: 713-580-4872
       Email: mcohn@accredopkg.com
       Website: www.accredopackaging.com
Dist biopolymer resins. (As-Pac, estab 2007, empl 350,
sales $305,000,000, cert: State, NMSDC)

6941   Age Industries, Ltd.
       3601 County Rd, Ste 316C
       Cleburne, TX 76031
       Contact: Max Walls VP Packaging Division
       Tel: 281-799-0935
       Email: max@ageindustries.com
       Website: www.ageindustries.com
Mfr & dist packaging products. (Woman, estab 1974,
empl 247, sales $72,000,000, cert: WBENC)

6942   Argent Associates, Inc.
       2800 E Plano Pkwy Ste 400
       Plano, TX 75074
       Contact: Betty Manetta VP Supply Chain
       Tel: 732-512-9009
       Email: bmanetta@argentassociates.com
       Website: www.argentassociates.com
Inventory mgmt, warehousing, dist, logistics, packaging,
installation & commercial construction. (Woman/Hisp,
estab 1998, empl 65, sales $181,676,013, cert: NMSDC,
WBENC)

6943   B.A.G. Corp.
       1155 Kas Dr. Ste 170
       Richardson, TX 75081
       Contact: Sherlene A Wegner Marketing Asst
       Tel: 214-340-7060
       Email: sherlene@bagcorp.com
       Website: www.bagcorp.com
Bulk handling & supply chain solutions. (Woman, estab
1969, empl 100, sales $70,000,000, cert: WBENC)

6944   Castle Business Solutions, LLC
       2777 North Stemmons Frwy Ste 1242
       Dallas, TX 75207
       Contact: Sharon King CEO
       Tel: 214-599-2880
       Email: sharon@castlebusinesssolutions.net
       Website: http://castlebusinesssolutions.com/
Directory & mailing list publishing, direct mail advertising, packaging & labeling services, warehousing &
storage, custom computer programming services, data
processing, hosting & related services. (Woman/AA,
estab 2010, empl 3, sales $615,880, cert: State, NMSDC)

6945   CCA Distributions
       12832 Tierra Karla Dr
       El Paso, TX 79938
       Contact: Carlos Camarena Owner
       Tel: 915-239-1870
       Email: carlos@ccadistributions.com
       Website: http://ccadistributions.com
Dist Packaging Material: Stretch Film, Kraft Paper, Tape,
Poly Strapping, Metal Strapping, Boxes, Kraft Paper
Tubes, Chipboard. Poly Sheeting, Poly Bags, and more.
(Woman/Hisp, estab 2007, empl 2, sales , cert: State,
NMSDC)

6946   Diamond Display Group Partners, Inc.
       2637 Summit Ave Ste 303
       Plano, TX 75074
       Contact: Glenn Towery Business Develop Mgr
       Tel: 972-636-0781
       Email: glenn@ddg-corp.com
       Website: www.diamonddisplaygroup.com
Corrugated & permanent displays & packaging, shipper
style corrugated displays & POS signage, styrene,
foamboard, vinyl, acrylic and metal. (Woman, estab
2003, empl 5, sales , cert: State, WBENC)

6947　Formers International, Inc.
3533 Preston Ave
Pasadena, TX 77505
Contact: Corina Carmona Business Dev Mgr
Tel:　281-998-9570
Email: corina@formers.com
Website: www.formers.com
Mfr bag forming assemblies: vertical form, fill & seal packaging machines. (Hisp, estab 1975, empl 39, sales , cert: City)

6948　Guardian Packaging Industries, LP
3615 Security St
Garland, TX 75042
Contact:　President
Tel:　214-349-1500
Email:
Website: www.guardianpackaging.com
Design & manufacture protective packaging, Polyure-thanes, Polyethylene's, Expanded Polystyrene, Rigid Urethanes and all Military Spec Foams, corrugated box shop. (Woman, estab 2005, empl 35, sales $3,900,000, cert: State, WBENC)

6949　International Print & Packaging, Inc.
951 Hwy 183 N.
Liberty Hill, TX 78642
Contact: Shelly Armstrong Digital Solutions Special-ist
Tel:　512-515-6333
Email: shelly@dle-corp.com
Website: www.ipp-corp.com
Mfr flexible packaging: labels, stickers, decals, shrink film, printed film, lidding materials, POP products, displays, table tents, shelf strips, hang tags, folding cartons, self sufficient manufacturing, inhouse graphics design depart-ment. (Woman, estab 1996, empl 90, sales , cert: State)

6950　Komplete Group, Inc.
202 N Great Southwest Pkwy
Grand Prairie, TX 75050
Contact: Tariq Usmani Diversity Coord
Tel:　214-252-8102
Email: tusmani@kpak.com
Website: www.kpak.com
Food copackaging, packaging equipment & supplies, thermoforming, commercial printing. (As-Pac, estab 1995, empl 150, sales $781,401, cert: State, NMSDC)

6951　New Century Packaging Systems, LLC
401 N Carrol Ave, Ste 124
Southlake, TX 76092
Contact: Vanessa Brown GM
Tel:　972-725-0311
Email: vbrown@newcenturypkg.net
Website: www.newcenturypkg.net
Dist packaging materials & packaging equipment. (AA, estab 1972, empl 4, sales $1,900,000, cert: NMSDC)

6952　Southwest Packaging Solutions, LLC
2472 Southwell Rd
Dallas, TX 75229
Contact: Edgar Sotelo President
Tel:　903-440-3628
Email: edgar@southwestpackaging.net
Website: www.southwestpackaging.net
Contract packaging services, printed registered film packaging services, warehousing, display building, bundling, reverse logistics, blister pack, skin pack, mfg consulting for improved efficiencies. (Hisp, estab 2009, empl 30, sales $1,800,000, cert: NMSDC)

6953　Starpak Ltd.
9690 W Wingfoot Rd
Houston, TX 77041
Contact: Catherine Beers Cstmr Service
Tel:　713-329-9183
Email: cbeers@starpakltd.com
Website: www.starpakltd.com
Converter and printer of flexible films for packaging of Food and Beverage products (Hisp, estab 2003, empl 350, sales $106,196,322, cert: NMSDC)

6954　Superbag USA Corp.
9291 Baythorne Dr
Houston, TX 77041
Contact: Woody Hunt VP Sales
Tel:　713-462-1173
Email: whunt@superbag.com
Website: www.superbag.com
Dist high density polyethylene grocery, retail bags & woven polypropylene bags. (Hisp, estab 1999, empl 250, sales $149,000,000, cert: State, NMSDC)

6955　TCP Universal
3536 Hwy 6 South, Ste 118
Sugarland, TX 77478
Contact: Pep Ly President
Tel:　281-966-8208
Email: pep.ly@tcpuniversal.com
Website: www.tcpuniversal.com
Can Liners, Biohazard Bags, Composite Bags, Ice Bags, Poly Bags, Produce Bags. (Woman/As-Pac, estab 2015, empl 3, sales , cert: State, City)

Wisconsin

6956　A&M Integrated Packaging
1645 Bergstrom Rd
Neenah, WI 54956
Contact: Terry Spielbauer Sales Mgr
Tel:　920-751-1043
Email: terry.spielbauer@menasha.com
Website:
Packaging: cartons, shrink wrap, liquid & dry filling, pouching, assembly, form, fill & seal, stuffing, bagging, repacking, labeling, blister & skin packaging, point-of-purchase displays, promotional mass mailing, e-com-merce fulfillment, etc. (Woman/AA, estab 1968, empl 10, sales , cert: NMSDC)

6957   Chryspac - Quality Custom Solutions
       130 W Edgerton Ave Ste 130
       Milwaukee, WI 53207
       Contact: Warren Scurlock Business Develop Mgr
       Tel: 414-372-0541
       Email: sales@chryspac.com
       Website: www.chryspac.com
Packaging & assembly: quality inspection, containment
sorting, assembling, re-work, reclamation, shrink wrapping
& labeling. (AA, estab 2000, empl 50, sales $816,456, cert:
NMSDC)

6958   Pac Basic
       S10744 State Rd93
       Eleva, WI 54738
       Contact: Mindy Pedersen President
       Tel: 715-552-1722
       Email: mpedersen@pacbasic.com
       Website: www.pacbasic.com
Packaging, corrugated, molded pulp & other various
protective materials. (Woman, estab 2007, empl 4, sales
$1,978,000, cert: WBENC)

6959   Packaging Specialties Inc.
       W130 N10751 Washington Dr
       Germantown, WI 53022
       Contact: Hugh Ahn President & CEO
       Tel: 262-512-1261
       Email: hahn@packaging-specialties.com
       Website: www.packaging-specialties.com
Dist packaging systems & materials. (As-Pac, estab 1973,
empl 30, sales , cert: NMSDC)

6960   TechniSource Services Group
       1025 S Moorland Rd 2057
       Brookfield, WI 53005
       Contact: Elizabeth Tran President
       Tel: 800-864-2317
       Email: james@technisourcegroup.com
       Website: www.technisourcegroup.com
Dist packaging products & services: stretch films, shrink
film, poly films, carton sealers, erectors, stretch wrappers,
tapes & adhesives, corrugated & fiber boxes. (Woman/As-
Pac, estab 1994, empl 50, sales $25,000,000, cert: NMSDC)

6961   Twin River LLC
       2721 Harvey St
       Hudson, WI 54016
       Contact: Kathy Enerson President
       Tel: 715-381-3067
       Email: kathyb@twinriverllc.com
       Website: www.twinriverllc.com
Packaging, fulfillment, high-speed shrink wrapping, blister
pack, clamshells, poly & paper banding, labeling,
barcoding, kitting, assembly, distribution, warehousing,
POP displays, quality inspections & mailings. (Woman,
estab 2009, empl 8, sales $357,450, cert: WBENC)

PHOTOGRAPHY, MOTION & STILL
Commercial photographers. Includes aerial photography, topographic mapping, film processors, photo labs, corporate and professional photography. NAICS Code 54

California

6962   Number 3 Inc.
108 W 2nd St, Ste 706
Los Angeles, CA 90012
Contact: Kal Yee
Tel: 323-646-8764
Email: kal@kalyee.com
Website: www.kalyee.com
Photography & videography. (As-Pac, estab 2000, empl 2, sales $100,000, cert: CPUC)

Florida

6963   APImaging, Inc.
19 SW 6th St
Miami, FL 33130
Contact: Diana Herrera VP Sales
Tel: 305-373-4774
Email: dianah@apimaging.com
Website: www.apimaging.com
Photo imaging & photo finishing services, commercial printing, studio photography, self adhesive signs & graphics, directional signs, posters, point of purchase signs, graphic displays, graphic design, trade shows & exhibits. (Woman/Hisp, estab 2013, empl 22, sales , cert: WBENC)

6964   Kerrick Williams Photography LLC
811 Hickory Glen Dr
Seffner, FL 33584
Contact: Kerrick Williams Owner
Tel: 813-571-3768
Email: kerrick@kerrickwilliams.com
Website: http://KerrickWilliams.com
Corporate Photography, Video Production: special event coverage, advertising, marketing archival. Onsite printing, Executive portraits, Head Shots, group functions. (AA, estab 1992, empl 1, sales , cert: State, City, NMSDC)

Illinois

6965   McLaren Photographic LLC
1482 Armstrong Court
Elk Grove Village, IL 60007
Contact: Fiona McLaren Owner
Tel: 847-668-8615
Email: fmclaren@mclarenphotographic.com
Website: www.mclarenphotographic.com
HD video, time-lapse, commercial photography, gigapanography & virtual mobile tours, commercial photographic services with portable studios & editing capabilities. (Woman, estab 2009, empl 1, sales , cert: WBENC)

6966   Powell Photography, Inc.
531 S Plymouth Court, Ste 101
Chicago, IL 60605
Contact: Victor Powell President
Tel: 312-922-6366
Email: vpowell@powellphotography.com
Website: www.powellphotography.com
Photography, photography services, digital imaging & retouching, photo composition, video, multi-media & graphics pre-production. (AA, estab 1976, empl 3, sales $440,000, cert: State, NMSDC)

6967   Yates Enterprises
213 N Stetson Ave
Chicago, IL 60601
Contact: Owen Donnelly VP Operations
Tel: 419-308-9938
Email: owen@yatesprotect.com
Website: www.yatesprotect.com
Photography & graphic design services. (AA, estab 2013, empl 10, sales $2,000,000, cert: NMSDC)

Massachusetts

6968   Melvin's Photo
34 Frank st
Watertown, MA 02472
Contact: Melvin Guante Owner
Tel: 617-942-3432
Email: melvin@melvinsphoto.com
Website: www.Melvinsphoto.com
Portrait photographic studios, still or video photography, business portrait, commercial, real estate & corporate event. (AA, Hisp, estab 2001, empl 1, sales , cert: State)

Michigan

6969   Stage 3 Productions
1532 N. Opdyke Rd Ste 700
Auburn Hills, MI 48326
Contact: Andre LaRoche President
Tel: 248-955-1250
Email: andre@stage3.com
Website: www.stage3.com
Commercial, advertising photography, digital imaging, illustration, graphic design, stage rental. (AA, estab 1984, empl 8, sales , cert: NMSDC)

Minnesota

6970   Code Creative Services
6001 Code Ave
Edina, MN 55436
Contact: Erin Schwind Owner
Tel: 952-922-8348
Email: erin@codecreativeservices.com
Website: www.codecreativeservices.com
Photography production, Estimating, Crew Sourcing, Location Scouting, Casting, Talent Negotiations, Budget Management, Catering, Travel Arrangements, Props, Permits & Insurance & Billing. (Woman, estab 2012, empl 1, sales $120,262, cert: WBENC)

Nevada

6971 Infinity Enterprises, Inc.
3347 S Highland Dr, Ste 304
Las Vegas, NV 89109
Contact: Audrey Dempsey President
Tel: 702-837-1128
Email: audrey@infinity-photo.com
Website: http://infinity-photo.com
Photography & graphic design: conventions & special events, food, corporate headshots, products & architecture, private sittings, weddings & retouching, web & print design, company branding, logo design & marketing, video editing. (Woman, estab 1993, empl 5, sales $532,467, cert: WBENC)

6972 Square Shooting
1800 Industrial Rd, Ste 103
Las Vegas, NV 89102
Contact: Jennifer Burkart Managing Partner
Tel: 702-721-9893
Email: jennifer@squareshooting.com
Website: www.squareshooting.com
Commercial photography, professional photographer, executive portrait photography, architecture, interior design, editorial, food & cocktail photography, advertising, fashion, lifestyle, resort, product, photography studio. Established in 2013, Square (Woman, estab 2013, empl 2, sales , cert: WBENC)

New York

6973 5th Avenue Digital
231W 29th St, Ste 1006
New York, NY 10001
Contact: Caitlin Elby Corporate Sales Assoc
Tel: 212-741-6427
Email: caitlin@5thavenuedigital.com
Website: www.5thavenuedigital.com
Corporate photography: promotional & marketing events, meetings & conventions, galas & award ceremonies, headshots, group photos & product shots. (Woman, estab 2008, empl 5, sales $2,560,552, cert: WBENC)

6974 Adrienne Nicole Productions, LLC
14 Dekalb Ave 3rd Fl
Brooklyn, NY 11201
Contact: Adrienne Nicole Exec Producer
Tel: 646-599-4911
Email: info@producedbyanp.com
Website: www.producedbyanp.com
Videography, aerial video, drone video photography, drone photography, progress photos, story development, pre-production, post-production, motion graphics and animation, casting, photography, progress photos. (Woman/AA, estab 2011, empl , sales $986,000, cert: State, City, NMSDC)

6975 E. Lee White Photography, LLC
116 Duane St, 3rd F
New York, NY 10007
Contact: E. Lee White President
Tel: 917-584-8000
Email: lee@leewhite.com
Website: www.leewhite.com
Advertising photography, executive portraits. (AA, estab 2004, empl 1, sales , cert: NMSDC)

6976 SPA Digital Images, Ltd.
54 W 39th St, 16th fl
New York, NY 10018
Contact: Kelly Murphy President
Tel: 917-420-0940
Email: janine@spadigital.com
Website: www.spadigital.com
Commercial digital photography & digital retouching services. (Woman, estab 1994, empl 15, sales $5,165,450, cert: WBENC)

Ohio

6977 The Couple Creative Imagery & Design, LLC
9912 Atena Rd Ste 2
Cleveland, OH 44105
Contact: Theresa Highbaugh Co-Owner
Tel: 216-271-0654
Email: thecouple@roadrunner.com
Website:
Photography & graphic design services. (AA, estab 2009, empl 2, sales , cert: City)

Washington

6978 Mike Nakamura Photography LLC
7414 337th Place SE
Fall City, WA 98024
Contact: Mike Nakamura Owner
Tel: 425-260-4033
Email: mike@mikenakamuraphotography.com
Website: www.mikenakamuraphotography.com/
Headshots, event & lifestyle photography, aerial & commercial photography. (As-Pac, estab 2013, empl 1, sales $110,000, cert: NMSDC)

PLASTIC PRODUCTS
Manufacturers and distributors of plexiglass, plastic, rubber and fiberglass products. Products range from supplies to aircraft and automobile parts, housewares and apparel accessories. NAICS Code 42

Arizona

6979 4front Tooling LLC dba 4front Manufacturing
3820 E Watkins St
Phoenix, AZ 85034
Contact: Joseph Baiz Owner
Tel: 480-966-1088
Email: joebaiz@4frontmfg.com
Website: www.4frontmfg.com
Plastic injection mold making, molding prototype & production, stampings, assembly & decorating. (Hisp, estab 2008, empl 20, sales $2,595,172, cert: NMSDC)

6980 All-Pac Distributng LLC
4859 E Gleneagle Dr
Chandler, AZ 85249
Contact: Adam Snow Sales Mgr
Tel: 480-861-0842
Email: asnow@allpaconline.com
Website: www.allpaconline.com
Mfr & dist returnable plastic packaging, injection molding, compression molding. (Woman, estab 2001, empl 3, sales $1,150,000, cert: NWBOC)

California

6981 Benchmark Displays LLC
75-145 St. Charles Place Ste 5
Palm Desert, CA 92211
Contact: Bonnie Miller VP Sales
Tel: 760-775-2424
Email: bonnie@benchmarkdisplays.com
Website: www.benchmarkdisplays.com
Mfr soft & hard vinyl store merchandising products, acrylic pos displays & fixtures, stock & custom molded & fabri-cated plastic literature holders. (Woman, estab 2009, empl 3, sales $349,750, cert: WBENC)

6982 Fairway Injection Molding Systems, Inc.
20109 Paseo Del Prado
Walnut, CA 91789
Contact: David Cockrell VP - General Mgr
Tel: 909-595-2201
Email: dcockrell@fairwaymolds.com
Website: www.fairwaymolds.com
Plastic injection molding. (As-Pac, estab 2006, empl 72, sales , cert: NMSDC)

6983 L.W. Reinhold Plastics
8763 Crocker St
Los Angeles, CA 90003
Contact: Everett Woolum Engineering Mgr
Tel: 562-862-2714
Email: brenda@rpiplastics.com
Website: www.rpiplastics.com
Injection molded thermosets & thermoplastics, compression molded thermosets & transfer molded thermoset, prototyping, machining. (Woman/Hisp, estab 1943, empl 26, sales $1,800,000, cert: NMSDC)

6984 Plastek Cards, Inc.
24412 S Main St Ste 104
Carson, CA 90745
Contact: Mark Robinson Dir of Marketing
Tel: 888-762-2737
Email: mark.robinson@plastekcards.com
Website: www.plastekcards.com
Blank, white PVC plastic cards with & without a magnetic strip, high coercivity Hi-Co or low coercivity Lo-Co. (As-Pac, estab 2004, empl 51, sales , cert: NMSDC)

6985 Plastikon Industries, Inc.
688 Sandoval Way
Hayward, CA 94544
Contact: Ron Yerrick Sales Specialist
Tel: 989-525-3310
Email: ryerrick@plastikon.com
Website: www.plastikon.com
Custom injection molding of thermal plastic products & packaging. (Nat Ame, estab 1984, empl 100, sales $38,000,000, cert: NMSDC)

6986 Weldon Works, Inc.
1650 Mabury Rd
San Jose, CA 95133
Contact: Jennifer Easom CEO
Tel: 408-251-1161
Email: jenn@weldonworks.com
Website: www.weldonworks.com
Plastic Fabrication & Signage, Interior & Exterior Signs, ADA Signage, Lobby Signs, Window Graphics & Lettering, Menu Boards, Isle Signage, Banner, Stencils, Reflective Road Work/ Parking Signs, Full Color Digital Printing. (Woman, estab 1982, empl 3, sales $100,000, cert: State)

6987 Wright Engineered Plastics, Inc.
3663 N Laughlin Road Ste 201
Santa Rosa, CA 95403
Contact: Mike Nellis VP Marketing
Tel: 707-575-1218
Email: mnellis@wepmolding.com
Website: www.wepmolding.com
Plastic injection molding & contract manufacturing. (Woman, estab 1970, empl 48, sales $5,040,000, cert: CPUC)

6988 Yamada Enterprises Inc.
14070 Montfort Ct
San Diego, CA 92128
Contact: Hidehiko Yamada President
Tel: 858-248-1928
Email: hyamada@ugoplastics.com
Website: www.ugoplastics.com
Outsourcing plastic parts manufacturing. Plastic injection machine sales. Packaging machine sales. SMT surface mount technology machines sales. Consultation production machines. Capital equipment consultant. Cartner, Caser, palletizer. Conveyors. (As-Pac, estab 2013, empl 2, sales $300,000, cert: NMSDC)

Florida

6989 American Tool and Mold LLC
1700 Sunshine Dr
Clearwater, FL 33765
Contact: Phil Gaitan Dir of Sales
Tel: 727-447-7377
Email: pgaitan@a-t-m.com
Website: www.atmmolding.com
Design & construct complex, precision, multi-cavity plastic injection molding, thin-wall, stack, hot runner, unscrewing & two-shot molds built with the latest methods & technologies available. (Woman, estab 1992, empl 220, sales , cert: WBENC)

6990 JTF Ventures, LLC
7545 W 2 Ct
Hialeah, FL 33014
Contact: Tania Garza President
Tel: 305-556-5156
Email: tania.garza@advak.com
Website: www.advak.com
Full service thermoform manufacturing company specializing in heavy guage polymer manipulation. (Woman/Hisp, estab 2006, empl 11, sales $1,200,000, cert: State)

6991 Plastec USA Inc.
7752 NW 74th Ave
Miami, FL 33166
Contact: Julio Mejia Dir of Sales
Tel: 513-708-9091
Email: julio.mejia@mejiatechnologies.com
Website: www.plastecusa.com
Dist plastics processing machinery, ancillary equipment, spare parts & MRO services, chemicals & plastic goods. (Hisp, estab 1985, empl 23, sales $20,000,000, cert: NMSDC)

6992 Precision Tool and Mold, Inc.
12050 44th St N
Clearwater, FL 33762
Contact: Sherry Mowery President
Tel: 727-573-4441
Email: sherry@precisiontoolmoldinc.com
Website: http://precisiontoolmoldinc.com
Design build & run plastic injection molded parts. Small to medium sized molds. Assembly work, pad printing, over molding & insert molding. (Woman, estab 1981, empl 30, sales $2,665,365, cert: WBENC)

Georgia

6993 Citation Plastics, LLC
5828 Riverstone Circle
Atlanta, GA 30339
Contact: Gregory Collingwood President
Tel: 248-798-7705
Email: gregcollingwood@citationplastics.com
Website: www.citationplastics.com
Dist Plastic Resins: High Density Polyethylene (HDPE)- Polypropylene (PP)- Talc & Glassed Filled Polypropylene- Glass Filled Nylon 6 & 66 (AA, estab 1998, empl 7, sales $189,000, cert: NMSDC)

6994 Dixien LLC
5286 Circle Dr
Lake City, GA 30260
Contact: Alex Garcia VP Marketing
Tel: 404-366-7427
Email: agarcia@dixien.com
Website: www.dixien.com
Stamping 100 ton to 1000 ton, welded sub-assemblies, tooling, plastic injection molding, blow molding & vaccum forming. (Hisp, estab 1961, empl 400, sales $25,000,000, cert: NMSDC)

6995 Joyce Fabrication LLC dba Custom Plastics and More
2625 Jason Industrial Pkwy #700
Winston, GA 30187
Contact: Gail Moore President
Tel: 770-577-0661
Email: gailmoore@customplasticsandmore.com
Website: www.customplasticsandmore.com
Rigid plastic fabrication, hand cut sheet plastic; die stamped parts, CNC or hand routed plastic. (Woman, estab 2004, empl 4, sales $318,365, cert: WBENC)

6996 Marglen Industries
1748 Ward Mountain Rd
Rome, GA 30161
Contact: Ben McElrath President
Tel: 706-295-5621
Email: bmcelrath@marglen.us
Website: www.marglen.us
Recycle PET plastic containers, convert recycled PET water & soda bottles into cleaned washed flake, then convert the clean washed flake into a FDA approved, high IV, melt filtered pellet that can be used to make new bottles. (Woman, estab 1971, empl 150, sales $62,513,555, cert: WBENC)

6997 Standridge Color Corp.
1196 E Hightower Trail
Social Circle, GA 30025
Contact: Sherry Waters President
Tel: 770-464-3362
Email: swaters@standridgecolor.com
Website: www.standridgecolor.com
Mfr pellitized plastic pellets and color concentrates for the plastics industry. (Woman, estab 0, empl 1, sales , cert: WBENC)

6998 United Seal & Rubber Co. Inc.
7025 C Amwiler Industrial Dr
Atlanta, GA 30360
Contact: Kathy Alonso VP/General Mgr
Tel: 770-729-8880
Email: kalonso@unitedseal.com
Website: www.unitedseal.com
Mfr seals, gaskets, custom molded rubber parts, EMI Shielding products, lathe cut seals, extrusions, rubber to metal bonded parts, spliced & vulcanized parts. (Hisp, estab 1974, empl 28, sales $8,000,000, cert: SDB)

Iowa

6999 Engineered Plastic Components Inc.
1408 Zimmerman Dr S
Grinnell, IA 50112
Contact: Jeremy Barger Sales
Tel: 641-236-3100
Email: jbarger@epcmfg.com
Website: www.epcmfg.com
Mfr wire harness cover caps, injection molding. (As-Ind, estab 1998, empl 500, sales $200,000,000, cert: NMSDC)

Illinois

7000 Amtec Molded Products, Inc.
1355 Holmes RdUnit A
Elgin, IL 60123
Contact: Adithya Jayakar Sales Mgr
Tel: 815-226-0187
Email: adithyaj@amtecmolded.com
Website: www.amtecmolded.com
Plastic injection molding, insert molding, pad printing & sub-assemblies. (As-Ind, estab 1998, empl 35, sales $3,862,500, cert: NMSDC)

7001 Best Foam Fabricators, Inc.
9633 S Cottage Grove
Chicago, IL 60628
Contact: Aqui Hasty Mktg
Tel: 773-721-1006
Email: aqui@bff.com
Website: www.bff.com
Mfr thermoforming, high speed die cutting, heat sealing, CNC machining & injection molding. (Woman/AA, estab 1981, empl 60, sales $14,750,000, cert: NMSDC)

7002 E James & Co.
6000 S Oak Park Ave
Chicago, IL 60638
Contact: Mike Romano
Tel: 773-788-1881
Email: mike.romano@ejames.com
Website: www.ejames.com
Mfr & dist rubber & plastic products: V belts, rubber hose, plastic hose & hose assemblies. (Hisp, estab 1955, empl 14, sales $2,200,000, cert: NMSDC)

7003 Ebco
1330 Holmes Rd
Elgin, IL 60123
Contact: Bill Bernardo Sales
Tel: 847-531-9500
Email: bbernardo@ebcoinc.com
Website: www.ebcoinc.com
Rubber products: molded, extruded, rubber bonded, metal vibration isolators & plastic extrusions. (Hisp, estab 1951, empl 48, sales $20,000,000, cert: NMSDC)

7004 First American Plastics Molding Enterprise
810 Progressive Ln
South Beloit, IL 61080
Contact: Steven McGaw Sales Engineer
Tel: 815-624-8538
Email: info@firstamericanplastic.com
Website: www.firstamericanplastic.com
Custom plastic injection molding. (Nat Ame, estab 1993, empl 130, sales $12,000,000, cert: NMSDC)

7005 HST Materials, Inc.
1631 Brummel Ave
Elk Grove Village, IL 60007
Contact: Kathryn Miller President
Tel: 847-640-1803
Email: kmiller@hstmaterials.com
Website: www.hstmaterials.com
Custom die-cutting & fabrication of non-metallics, including sponge & dense rubber, plastic, films & tapes used as gaskets & sealing devices. (Woman, estab 1987, empl 20, sales $4,428,617, cert: WBENC)

7006 LSL Industries, Inc.
5535 N Wolcott Ave
Chicago, IL 60640
Contact: Jerry Czaja
Tel: 773-878-1100
Email: jerry.czaja@lslhealthcare.com
Website: www.lslhealthcare.com
Mfg plastics & procedural kit assembly & packaging. (As-Ind, estab , empl , sales , cert: NMSDC)

7007 Magenta LLC
15160 New Ave
Lockport, IL 60441
Contact: Stephanie Smith Business Develop Exec
Tel: 630-737-9606
Email: ssmith@magentallc.com
Website: www.magentallc.com
Design, development & mfr injection molded components-primarily packaging— closures and containers. (Woman, estab 1969, empl 81, sales $14,900,000, cert: WBENC)

7008 Midwest Insert Composite Molding & Assembly Corp.
3940 Industrial Ave
Rolling Meadows, IL 60008
Contact: Chirag Patel President
Tel: 847-818-8444
Email: chirag.pate@micmolding.com
Website: www.micmolding.com
Mfr plastic injection molded products. (Minority, estab 2015, empl 23, sales $2,526,000, cert: NMSDC)

7009 Shamrock Plastics, Inc.
P.O. Box 3530
Peoria, IL 61612
Contact: Cstmr Service
Tel: 309-243-7723
Email:
Website: www.shamrockplastics.net
Mfr custom, vacuum & pressure formed plastic parts. (Woman, estab 1968, empl 25, sales $4,000,000, cert: State)

7010 Thermal-Tech Systems, Inc.
750 W Hawthorne Lane
West Chicago, IL 60185
Contact: Joe Majchrowski Sales
Tel: 630-639-5115
Email: jm@thermal-tech.com
Website: http://thermal-tech.com
Dist plastic injection molders, service and repair of manifolds. (Woman, estab 1986, empl 10, sales $2,500,000, cert: WBENC)

7011 TransWorld Plastic Films, Inc.
150 N 15th St
Rochelle, IL 61068
Contact: Rodolfo Hernandez Business Development
Tel: 815-561-7117
Email: rhernandez@transworldplasticfilms.com
Website: www.transworldplasticfilms.com
Polyethylene film for the automotive, tire & rubber industries used in the manufacturing & packaging process. (Woman/Hisp, estab 2007, empl 31, sales , cert: NMSDC, WBENC)

7012 Young Technology Inc.
900 W. Fullerton Ave.
Addison, IL 60101
Contact: Young Sohn President
Tel: 630-690-4320
Email: youngsohn@ytinc.com
Website: www.ytinc.com
Mfr molded rubber, plastic & forged steel: shifter knobs, bezels, decorative molding & cable components, leather wrapped & chrome plated. (As-Pac, estab 1985, empl 350, sales $6,000,000, cert: NMSDC)

Indiana

7013 A. H. Furnico, Inc.
6425 English Ave. Unit 1A
Indianapolis, IN 46278
Contact: Benjamin Liu President
Tel: 317-802-9363
Email: ben.liu@ahfurnico.com
Website: www.ahfurnico.com
Polystyrene extruded mouldings with PVC veneers. (As-Pac, estab 1999, empl 5, sales $3,880,000, cert: NMSDC)

7014 Accutech Mold & Machine, Inc.
2817 Goshen Rd
Fort Wayne, IN 46808
Contact: Darrin Geiger VP
Tel: 260-471-6102
Email: dgeiger@accutechmoldinc.com
Website: http://accutechmoldinc.com
Plastic injection molding, Insert plastic injection molder of cables/connectors, rapid prototype tooling builder/ injection molding, production machining of brass, aluminum & metals, prototype machining of brass, aluminum & metals. (Woman, estab 1996, empl 70, sales $3,000,000, cert: WBENC)

7015 Calico Precision Molding, LLC
1211 Progress Rd
Fort Wayne, IN 46808
Contact: Nancy Rivera Sales Rep
Tel: 260-484-4500
Email: nancyr@calicopm.com
Website: www.calicopm.com/
Custom plastic injection molding. (AA, estab 2001, empl 28, sales , cert: NMSDC)

7016 Hi-Tech Foam Products, LLC
One Technology Way
Indianapolis, IN 46268
Contact: John Metaxas VP
Tel: 317-615-1515
Email: jmetaxas@hitechfoam.com
Website: www.hitechfoam.com
Convert, design, package, mold, form, cut & route foam rubber. Laminating foam to foam, foam to corrugated, foam to plastic. Protective, cushioning, acoustical, thermal, polyethylene, polyurethane, crosslink, EVA, EDPM rubber. (AA, estab , empl 35, sales $6,000,000, cert: NMSDC)

7017 Lorentson Manufacturing Co., Inc.
P.O. Box 932
Kokomo, IN 46903
Contact: John Routt VP / COO
Tel: 765-452-4425
Email: jroutt@lorentson.com
Website: www.lorentson.com
Design & build plastic injection molds, injection molding machines. (Woman, estab 1949, empl 100, sales $16,000,000, cert: WBENC)

7018 Tomken Plastic Technologies, Inc.
4601 N Superior Dr.
Muncie, IN 47303
Contact: Kevin Undem Sales/Engineering
Tel: 765-284-2472
Email: kevinu@tomkenplastics.com
Website: www.tomkenplastics.com
Precision plastic injection molding, tooling, & injection molding. (Woman, estab 1960, empl 40, sales $6,000,000, cert: WBENC)

7019 Vidal Plastics, LLC
318 Main St Ste 207
Evansville, IN 47708
Contact: Alfonso Vidal President
Tel: 812-431-8075
Email: alfonso@vidalplastics.com
Website: www.vidalplastics.com
Dist resins, from prime raw materials to recycled compounds. (Minority, estab 2009, empl 2, sales , cert: NMSDC)

Louisiana

7020 Noble Plastics Inc.
318 Burleigh Lane
Grand Coteau, LA 70541
Contact: Sandy Rowell Inside sales
Tel: 337-662-5374
Email: sandy@nobleplastics.com
Website: www.nobleplastics.com
SPE, MAPP, ASME, Product design, Contract manufacturing, Scientific molding, Inspection, Assembly & fulfillment, Automation systems. (Woman, estab 2000, empl 30, sales $4,900,000, cert: WBENC)

Massachusetts

7021 Polyneer, Inc.
259D Samuel Barnet Blvd
New Bedford, MA 02745
Contact: Nancy DeOliveira Cstmr Service
Tel:　508-998-5225
Email: ndeoliveira@polyneer.com
Website: www.polyneer.com
Design & mfg polymeric products. (Hisp, estab 2001, empl 39, sales $2,600,000, cert: NMSDC)

7022 TPE Solutions, Inc.
3 Patterson Rd
Shirley, MA 01464
Contact: Jonas Angus President
Tel:　978-425-3033
Email: jonas.angus@tpesinc.com
Website: www.tpesinc.com
Design, mfr & dist Thermoplastic elastomers (TPEs). (AA, estab 2004, empl 5, sales $3,000,000, cert: NMSDC)

Michigan

7023 Accu-Mold, LLC
7622 S Sprinkle Rd
Portage, MI 49002
Contact: Dave Felicijan President
Tel:　269-323-0388
Email: davidf@accu-moldinc.com
Website: www.accum-moldinc.com
Overmold & two shot mold, hybrid metal/plastic parts, high & low pressure plastic injection molds, machined plastic or metal parts, SLA plastic parts, metal-to-plastic conversions. (Nat Ame, estab 1977, empl 15, sales $4,118,893, cert: NMSDC)

7024 Agape Plastics, Inc.
11474 1st Ave NW
Grand Rapids, MI 49534
Contact: Jeff Powers Sales Admin
Tel:　616-735-4091
Email: jpowers@agapeplastics.com
Website: www.agapeplastics.com
Plastic Injection molder serving the automotive and furniture industries. (Woman, estab 1975, empl 150, sales , cert: WBENC)

7025 Ammex Plastics
725 Ternes Dr
Monroe, MI 48162
Contact: David Ayala President
Tel:　734-241-9622
Email: dfaammex@provide.net
Website:
Mfr & design plastic injection molded parts. (Hisp, estab 1999, empl 17, sales $3,300,000, cert: NMSDC)

7026 Argent International
41016 Concept Dr
Plymouth, MI 48170
Contact: Tomas Flores Sales Mgr
Tel:　734-582-9800
Email: tflores@argent-international.com
Website: www.argent-international.com
Die cut foam, felt, fabric adhesive. (Woman, estab 1976, empl 120, sales , cert: WBENC)

7027 Atlantic Precision Products
51234 Filomena Dr
Shelby Twp, MI 48315
Contact: Rob Pryomski GM
Tel:　586-532-9420
Email: rpryomski@atlanticpp.com
Website:
Custom injection molding, functional/decorative plastics, insert molding, welding, sonic, vibration, heatstaking, assembly. Fully certified CMM Lab with color approval capabilities. (Woman/Hisp, estab 2004, empl 26, sales $5,200,000, cert: NMSDC)

7028 CG Plastics, Inc.
5349 Rusche Dr NW
Comstock Park, MI 49321
Contact: Jane Bulkowski-Bouwman President
Tel:　616-785-1900
Email: jane.bouwman@cgplastics.com
Website: www.cgplastics.com
Tryout, sampling and production plastic injection molding. Capabilities for design and manufacturing of plastic injection molds and custom molding. Gauge & Fixture, Automation, 6-axis robots, Large 5-axis CNC machining. (Woman, estab 0, empl , sales , cert: WBENC)

7029 Colonial Plastics, Inc
51734 Filomena Dr
Shelby Township, MI 48315
Contact: Michele Simo
Tel:　586-991-5150
Email: mms@colgrp.com
Website: www.colgrp.com
Injection molds, compression molds, blow molds, vacuum molds, prototype molds, hybrid molds, bridge molds, production molds, machining, assemblies, tryouts, product developement, product design & sorting. (Woman, estab 1988, empl 110, sales $8,200,000, cert: WBENC)

7030 Concordant Healthcare Solutions, Inc.
200 E. Big Beaver
Troy, MI 48083
Contact: James P Young CEO
Tel:　248-321-3899
Email: jyoung@concordanthealth.com
Website: www.concordanthealth.com
NCQA Certified in Patient Centered Medical Home Recognition for PCPs and Specialists. Staff training in cultural competency and communication skills. Improve hospital HCAHPS total performance scores. (AA, estab 2009, empl 8, sales , cert: NMSDC)

7031 Diversified Engineering & Plastics
1801 Wildwood Ave
Jackson, MI 49202
Contact: Anita Quillen President & CEO
Tel:　517-789-8118
Email: aquillen@deplastics.com
Website: http://wwww.deplastics.com
Plastic Injection Molding, Design/Engineering Services, Plastic Part Assembly. (Woman/Hisp, estab 2010, empl 130, sales $14,497,480, cert: NMSDC)

7032   DN Plastics
       1415 Steele Ave SW
       Grand Rapids, MI 49507
       Contact: Raj Agrawal President
       Tel: 616-942-6060
       Email: raj@dnplasticscorp.com
       Website: www.dnplasticscorp.com
Polymer compounding for custom & toll manufacturing,
Thermoplastic Elastomers (TPE), Thermoplastic Olefins
(TPO) & filled Polypropylene compounds. (As-Ind, estab 0,
empl 1, sales , cert: NMSDC)

7033   Eagle Fasteners
       185 Park Dr
       Troy, MI 48083
       Contact: Theresa C. Srock President
       Tel: 248-373-1441
       Email: tsrock@eaglefasteners.com
       Website: www.eaglefasteners.com
Custom injection molded plastic parts, design & fabricate
tooling. (Woman, estab 1976, empl 9, sales , cert: WBENC)

7034   Elite Mold & Engineering
       51548 Filomena Dr
       Shelby Township, MI 48315
       Contact: Daniel Mandeville Sales Engineer
       Tel: 586-314-4000
       Email: dj@teameliteonline.com
       Website: www.teameliteonline.com
Dist close tolerance plastic parts for the automotive,
consumer product, electronic & medical device industries.
(Nat Ame, estab 1982, empl 34, sales $3,576,887, cert:
NMSDC)

7035   Engineered Plastic Products
       699 James L. Hart Pkwy
       Ypsilanti, MI 48197
       Contact: Aschandria Fisher Business Mgr
       Tel: 734-483-2500
       Email: afisher@eppmfg.com
       Website: www.eppmfg.com
Injection molded plastic assembly & sequencing. (AA,
estab 1987, empl 500, sales $50,000,000, cert: NMSDC)

7036   Gemini Plastics, Inc.
       4385 Garfield St
       Ubly, MI 48475
       Contact: Melanie Cappello Mgr, new business devel
       Tel: 248-435-7271
       Email: melaniecappello@geminigroup.net
       Website: www.geminigroup.net
Mfr engineered plastic extrusion products: transportation,
medical, lawn & garden, consumer, & appliance. (Woman,
estab 1972, empl 110, sales $60,000,000, cert: WBENC)

7037   Intex Technologies LLC
       3133 Highland Blvd
       Hudsonville, MI 49426
       Contact: Randi Sniegowski Sales
       Tel: 616-662-0276
       Email: randi.sniegowski@intextech.net
       Website: www.intextech.net
Mfr integral skin flexible foam automotive interior parts:
arm rests, center console, console door, sun visor, steering
wheel, soft-touch points on door handles, cup holders,
seals, jounce bumpers & insulation components. (Hisp,
estab 2008, empl 50, sales $14,800,000, cert: NMSDC)

7038   Jenerxx Inc.
       307 West Sixth St Ste 209
       Royal Oak, MI 48067
       Contact: Paul Chaplin Acct Mgr
       Tel: 810-225-1600
       Email: paul@jenerxx.com
       Website: www.jenerxx.com
Dist injection grade resins ranging from engineered
plastics to commodities. (Woman, estab 2000, empl 5,
sales $760,000, cert: WBENC)

7039   JLC Group LLC
       287 Executive Dr
       Troy, MI 48083
       Contact: William Chen Dir Ph.D.
       Tel: 248-792-3281
       Email: wchen@jlcgroupllc.com
       Website: www.jlcgroupllc.com
Dist casting parts, forging parts & machine finished
parts, plastic injected molds & plastic parts. (Woman/As-
Pac, estab 2010, empl 5, sales , cert: WBENC)

7040   Latin American Industries, LLC
       1036 Ken-O-Sha Industrial Dr SE
       Grand Rapids, MI 49508
       Contact: Scott Bigger GM
       Tel: 616-301-1878
       Email: sbigger@laiinc.net
       Website: www.laiinc.net
Plastic injection molding & assembly, molding machines.
(Woman/Hisp, estab 2000, empl 10, sales $1,000,000,
cert: NMSDC)

7041   Molding Concepts, Inc.
       6700 Sims St
       Sterling Heights, MI 48313
       Contact: Norman Fouts President
       Tel: 586-264-6990
       Email: slfouts@moldingconcepts.com
       Website: www.moldingconcepts.com
Plastic injection molds, plastic injection parts, plastic
parts, CNC machining, 3D printing, Additive manufactur-
ing, Prototype, Short run, Production, High heat resin.
(Woman, estab 1987, empl 9, sales $800,000, cert:
WBENC)

7042   Polymerica Limited Co. LLC
       26909 Woodard Ave
       Huntington Woods, MI 48070
       Contact: Marilyn M. Kunz President
       Tel: 248-542-2000
       Email: mkunz@globalent.org
       Website:
Mfr plastics, automotive extruded plastic parts, co-
extrusions, flocking, steel inserts, extruded sheet plastic.
(Woman, estab 0, empl , sales , cert: WBENC)

7043   Premier Plastic Resins, Inc.
       3079 S Baldwin Rd
       Orion, MI 48359
       Contact: Michelle Cloutier Sales Engineer
       Tel:
       Email: mcloutier@premierplasticresins.com
       Website: www.premierplasticresins.com
Dist thermoplastic resins for injection molding. ABS,
Nylon, Polycarbonate, PBT, Acetal. Automotive approved grades. Prime branded materials available, such
as DuPont, Sabic, Covestro, etc. (Woman, estab 2007,
empl 5, sales $1,200,000, cert: WBENC)

7044   Primera Plastics
       3424 Production Court
       Zeeland, MI 49464
       Contact: Noel Cuellar President
       Tel: 616-748-6248
       Email: noelc@primera-inc.com
       Website: www.primera-inc.com
Plastic injection molding & assembly. (Hisp, estab 1994,
empl 140, sales , cert: NMSDC)

7045   Quality Assured Plastics, Inc.
       1200 Crandall Pkwy
       Lawrence, MI 49064
       Contact: Annette Crandall President
       Tel: 269-674-3888
       Email: acrandall@qapinc.com
       Website: www.qapinc.com
Custom injection molding, insert/overmolding, & assembly
capabilities, molding commodity & engineering resins,
Nylon, TPE, ABS, PEEK, Valox, Polystyrene, HDPE, TPO &
Polypropylene. (Woman, estab 1986, empl 60, sales
$5,200,000, cert: WBENC)

7046   Sejasmi Industries, Inc.
       6100 Bethuy
       Fair Haven, MI 48023
       Contact: Nichole Roemer Production Control
       Tel: 586-725-5300
       Email: nicholer@us.sejasmi.com
       Website: www.us.sejasmi.com
Contract manufacturer of plastic injection molded parts &
light assemblies. (As-Ind, estab 2007, empl 50, sales , cert:
NMSDC)

7047   Sur-Flo Plastics & Engineering, Inc.
       24358 Groesbeck Hwy
       Warren, MI 48089
       Contact: Jean Douglass IT Security Mgr
       Tel: 586-859-6050
       Email: jdouglass@sur-flo.com
       Website: www.sur-flo.com
Custom injection molded component or assembly: Plastic
Injection Molding, Engineering, Program Management,
Assembly, Quality. (Minority, estab 1977, empl 207, sales ,
cert: NMSDC)

7048   Western Diversified Plastics LLC
       53150 N Main St
       Mattawan, MI 49071
       Contact: George Kawwas Dir of Business Dev
       Tel: 269-668-3377
       Email: george.kawwas@westerndp.com
       Website: www.westerndp.com
Mfr close tolerance injection & insert molded electro-
mechanical components, engineering grade plastic resin.
(AA, estab 2005, empl 75, sales , cert: NMSDC)

7049   Williamston Products, Inc.
       845 Progress Ct
       Williamston, MI 48895
       Contact: Nigam Tripathi President
       Tel: 517-655-2131
       Email: nigam@wpius.com
       Website: www.wpius.com
Blow mold, injection mold, foaming, hand wrapping,
cutting, trim, sewing, lamination, prototyping, assembly.
(As-Ind, estab 2006, empl 450, sales $42,000,000, cert:
NMSDC)

Minnesota

7050   Classic Acrylics Inc.
       11040 Industrial Circle NW
       Elk River, MN 55330
       Contact: Kathy Berg Sales Exec
       Tel: 763-241-5221
       Email: kberg@classicacrylics.com
       Website: www.classicacrylics.com
Plastic fabrication: POP & POS displays, acrylic cereal
boxes, literature & brochure holders, advertising &
specialty items, sign holders, screened acrylic signs,
display cases, food service bins, LED lighting. (Hisp, estab
1998, empl 22, sales $3,754,000, cert: NMSDC)

7051   Steinwall
       1759 116th Ave
       Coon Rapids, MN 55448
       Contact: Jake Northrup Sales Engineer
       Tel: 800-229-9199
       Email: jnorthrup@steinwall.com
       Website: http://steinwall.com
Custom thermoplastic injection molding, full service
plastics manufacturing, 30 ton to 1750 ton injection
press size capabilities, 2-shot molding, production
automation, engineering, tooling, injection molding,
quality and inspection. (Minority, Woman, estab 1965,
empl 120, sales $20,000,000, cert: State)

7052   Thermotech, Inc.
       1302 S 5th St
       Hopkins, MN 55343
       Contact: Andrea Hinrichs
       Tel: 734-634-1816
       Email: andrea.hinrichs@thermotech.com
       Website: www.thermotech.com
Mfr precision plastic parts, thermoplastic molding,
thermoset molding, insert molding, two-shot molding,
micromolding & assembly. (As-Ind, estab 1949, empl
522, sales $83,000,000, cert: NMSDC)

7053   TMI Coatings, Inc.
       3291 Terminal Dr
       St. Paul, MN 55121
       Contact: Tracy Gliori President
       Tel: 651-452-6100
       Email: tmi@tmicoatings.com
       Website: www.tmicoatings.com
Protective coatings & linings, spray on urethane foam
insulation, chemical resistant floor coverings & containment dike linings. (Woman, estab 1985, empl 75, sales
$12,162,000, cert: WBENC)

North Carolina

7054   Central Carolina Products
       250 W Old Glencoe Rd
       Burlington, NC 27217
       Contact: Jason Greenhill President
       Tel: 336-226-0005
       Email: jgreenhill@isotechintl.com
       Website: www.centralcarolinaproducts.com
Plastic injection molding: assembly & finishing capabilities. (Hisp, estab 1993, empl 72, sales , cert: NMSDC)

7055   Core Technology Molding Corp
       4300 Piedmont Pkwy
       Greensboro, NC 27410
       Contact: Geoff Foster CEO
       Tel: 336-708-2673
       Email: geoff.foster@coretechnologycorp.com
       Website: http://coretechnologycorp.com
Plastic injection molded parts. (AA, estab 2006, empl 14,
sales $4,000,000, cert: NMSDC)

7056   Core Technology Molding Corp.
       2911 E. Gate City Blvd
       Greensboro, NC 27410
       Contact: Brandon Frederick Mfg Engineer
       Tel: 919-273-3408
       Email: brandon.frederick@coretechnologycorp.com
       Website: http://coretechnologycorp.com
Product concept & design services, CAD part & mold
design, Mold Flow analysis, Prototyping, raw material
selection & testing, New all-electric injection molding
machines ranging from 200 ton to 400 ton. (AA, estab
2007, empl 25, sales $10,000,000, cert: NMSDC)

7057   Raleigh-Durham Rubber & Gasket Co., Inc.
       P.O. Box 90397
       Raleigh, NC 27675
       Contact: Judy Hooks President
       Tel: 919-781-6817
       Email: judyh@raleighdurhamrubber.com
       Website: www.raleighdurhamrubber.com
Mfr & dist rubber gaskets. (Woman, estab , empl , sales ,
cert: WBENC)

7058   RubberMill, Inc.
       9897 Old Liberty Rd
       Liberty, NC 27298
       Contact: Shawn Baldwin Sales Mgr
       Tel: 704-458-2653
       Email: sbaldwin@rubbermill.com
       Website: http://rubbermill.com
OEM custom parts manufactured from solid and sponge
rubber, foams, and nonwovens. Gaskets and Seals, Custom
Molded Parts, Acoustical Insulation Parts, Urethane
Products, Balls, Lab Stoppers, Cleanout Balls. (Woman,
estab 1987, empl 56, sales $11,000,000, cert: WBENC)

7059   Sky Leap LLC
       P.O. Box 16368
       Chapel Hill, NC 27516
       Contact: Lili Engelhardt CEO
       Tel: 919-338-2580
       Email: office@skyleapllc.com
       Website: www.skyleapllc.com
Mfr & design injected molded tool organizers for tools:
wrenches, screw drivers, pliers, and sockets. (Woman/As-
Pac, estab 2013, empl 2, sales $425,000, cert: NMSDC)

Nebraska

7060   Lenco, Inc.
       10240 Deer Park Rd
       Waverly, NE 68462
       Contact: Clarke McGuire VP
       Tel: 402-786-2000
       Email: cmcguire@pmc-group.com
       Website: www.lencopmc.com
Dist defect-free molded & assembled products, injection
molding. (As-Ind, estab 1963, empl 160, sales , cert: State,
NMSDC)

New Jersey

7061   L-E-M Plastics& Supply Inc.
       255 Highland Cross
       Rutherford, NJ 07070
       Contact: Ellen Pietrowitz-Phillips President
       Tel: 201-933-9150
       Email: ellenp@l-e-mplastics.com
       Website: www.l-e-mplastics.com
Fabriate & dist raw material plastic & rubber, Sheet,
rod, tubing & film cut to size. Machining of all plastic,
build to print. Steel rule die punching of thin plastic &
rubber. (Woman, estab 1974, empl 12, sales $1,200,000,
cert: WBENC)

7062   Sigma Extruding Corp. DBA Sigma Stretch Film
       808 Page Ave, Bldg 8 Bldg 8
       Lyndhurst, NJ 07071
       Contact: Maria Samuelson
       Tel: 201-507-9100
       Email: maria.samuelson@sigmaplastics.com
       Website: www.sigmastretchfilm.com
Mfr plastics. (As-Pac, estab 1988, empl 354, sales
$396,000,000, cert: NMSDC)

7063   SYSMIND LLC
       38 Washington Rd
       Princeton Junction, NJ 08550
       Contact: Business Devel Specialist
       Tel: 609-897-9670
       Email:
       Website: www.sysmind.com
Fabricate plastic components & fasteners for computer,
aerospace, electronic, instrumentation, etc. applications.
Prototype to production. Also stock molded nylon
fasteners. (Woman/As-Ind, estab 1999, empl 456, sales
$45,000,000, cert: NMSDC, WBENC)

New York

7064   Extreme Molding LLC
       25 Gibson St
       Watervliet, NY 12189
       Contact: Joanne Moon Managing Partner
       Tel: 518-266-6261
       Email: joanne@extrememolding.com
       Website: www.extrememolding.com
Injection molding: silicone, TPE, floropolymers, teflon,
polycarbonate, polypropelene, Ultem, CAD design,
material selection assistance, rapid prototyping,
overmolding, compression molding, packaging. (Woman,
estab 2002, empl 20, sales $1,000,000, cert: State)

7065   Mechanical Rubber Products Company, Inc.
       77 Forester Ave, Ste 1
       Warwick, NY 10990
       Contact: Cedric Glasper President & CEO
       Tel: 845-986-2271
       Email: alisa.sherow@mechanicalrubber.com
       Website: www.mechanicalrubber.com
Mfr elastomeric (rubber) products. (AA, estab 1995,
empl 21, sales $945,000, cert: NMSDC)

Ohio

7066 Advanced Engineering Solutions Incorporated
250 Advanced Dr
Springboro, OH 45066
Contact: Scott Paulson Business Dev Mgr
Tel: 937-743-6900
Email: spaulson@aesi-usa.com
Website: www.advancedinternational.com
Tooling, CNC, punch press, subassembly, automated equipment, injection molded plastics. (Woman/As-Pac, estab 1995, empl 35, sales $2,250,000, cert: NMSDC)

7067 Axium Plastics LLC
9005 Smiths Mill Rd N
Johnstown, OH 43031
Contact: Tammy Hoffman Business Dev Mgr
Tel: 678-464-2259
Email: thoffman@axiumplastics.com
Website: www.axiumplastics.com
Extrusion Blow Molding, Injection Stretch Blow Molding, Injection Molding, Modeling, Design, Silk Screening, Pressure Sensitive Labeling (As-Ind, estab 2010, empl 250, sales $102,000,000, cert: NMSDC)

7068 Composite Technologies LLC
401 N Keowee St
Dayton, OH 45404
Contact: Karen Pierce Sales & Marketing Mgr
Tel: 937-228-2880
Email: kpierce@ctcplastics.com
Website: www.ctcplastics.com
Mfr plastic pallets made from 100% recycled plastic, compression & injection molding, of plastic parts made from recycled & virgin materials. (As-Pac, estab 1994, empl 150, sales $27,000,000, cert: NMSDC)

7069 Cox Financial Corporation
105 E Fourth St
Cincinnati, OH 45202
Contact: Ethan Cox CEO
Tel: 513-621-1771
Email: ethancox@coxfinco.com
Website: www.coxfinco.com
Long Term & Short Term Disability Plans - Cox Financial provides plans that are customized to fit your organizations needs offered at premium discounts. (AA, estab 1972, empl 12, sales $1,436,689, cert: NMSDC)

7070 EnKon, LLC dba Broadway
6344 Webster St
Dayton, OH 45414
Contact: Jodi Walters Member
Tel: 937-890-2221
Email: jodi.walters@enkonllc.com
Website: www.broadwaymold.com
Injection molds, components, mold repairs, Precision Fabrication,
CNC Machining, welding, turning, Electrode manufacturing, EDM'ING, Wire EDM, Polish, Milling, OD, ID, and surface grinding, Design. (Woman, estab 1955, empl 12, sales , cert: WBENC)

7071 Ernie Green Industries
2030 Dividend Dr
Columbus, OH 43228
Contact: Bill Dunlevy VP, Sales & Marketing
Tel: 614-949-1714
Email: bdunlevy@egindustries.com
Website: http://egi.net/
Plastic injection molding, paint, pad print, silk screen, hot stamp, graphic emblems, sonic welding, chrome plating, assembly, bar code labeling, shrink wrap & kit/unitized packaging. (AA, estab 1987, empl 450, sales $28,000,000, cert: NMSDC)

7072 HESS Advanced Technology, Inc.
P.O. Box 17669
Dayton, OH 45417
Contact: Frederick Edmonds CEO
Tel: 937-268-4377
Email: fred.edmonds@gmail.com
Website: www.plastikleen.net
Mfr protective coatings: surveillance cameras, lens/domes, PC's, laptops, PDA's, plasma screens & anti-microbial skin protector. (AA, estab , empl , sales $825,000, cert: NMSDC)

7073 Industry Products Company
500 Statler Rd
Piqua, OH 45356
Contact: Aaron Blakely Sales Specialist
Tel: 937-778-0585
Email: ablakely@industryproductsco.com
Website: www.industryproductsco.com
Mfr precision die-cut & formed products, gasket & sealing products, rubber-coated steel & alloys, compressed fiber, cork, neoprene, phenolic, nylon, Mylar, felts, PE, PP, rubber, etc. (Woman, estab 1966, empl 450, sales $80,000,000, cert: WBENC)

7074 Jensar Manufacturing LLC
1230 Expressway South Dr
Toledo, OH 43608
Contact: Luis Villaflor President
Tel: 419-727-8320
Email: jensar@sbcglobal.net
Website:
Mfr plastic injection molded products. (As-Pac, estab 1996, empl 4, sales $1,228,000, cert: NMSDC)

7075 MVP Plastics, Inc.
15005 Enterprise Way
Middlefield, OH 44062
Contact: Darrell McNair President
Tel: 440-834-1790
Email: darrellm@mvpplastics.com
Website: http://mvpplastics.com
Custom injection molding, decorating & assembly of plastics components. (AA, estab 2009, empl 30, sales $20,000,000, cert: NMSDC)

7076 PMC SMART Solutions LLC
9825 Kenwood Rd Ste 302
Cincinnati, OH 45242
Contact: Lisa Jennings CEO
Tel: 513-557-5222
Email: ljennings@pmcsmartsolutions.com
Website: http://pmcsmartsolutions.com
Development engineering, contract manufacturing & injection molding services for medical device, transportation & commercial electronics markets. (Woman, estab 1929, empl 200, sales $33,000,000, cert: WBENC)

7077   Polymer Technologies
       1835 James Pkwy
       Heath, OH 43056
       Contact: Sharad Thakkar President
       Tel: 740-929-5500
       Email: sharad@polymertechnologiesinc.com
       Website: www.polymertechnologiesinc.com
Provide reprocessed & wide spec resins, form, film.
powder, parts & return back in certified pellet form. (As-
Ind, estab 2002, empl 38, sales $7,000,000, cert: NMSDC)

7078   Shirley K's Storage Trays LLC
       P.O. Box 2519
       Zanesville, OH 43702
       Contact: Devin Hall Sales & Marketing Coord
       Tel: 740-868-8140
       Email: devin.hall@shirleyks.com
       Website: www.shirleyks.com
Mfr storage products, high-impact polystyrene or high-
density polyethylene; labeling tags, casters, locking lids &
imprinting. (Woman, estab 2013, empl 8, sales $1,410,400,
cert: WBENC)

7079   Tom Smith Industries, Inc.
       500 Smith Dr
       Clayton, OH 45315
       Contact: James Pugh Sales Mgr
       Tel: 937-832-1555
       Email: jpugh@tomsmithindustries.com
       Website: www.tomsmithindustries.com
Design & build plastic injection molds. Custom injection
molding of thermoplastics; assemble computer components. (Woman/Nat Ame, estab 1980, empl 125, sales
$25,367,000, cert: WBENC)

7080   Triple Diamond Plastics, Inc.
       405 N Pleasantview Dr
       Liberty Center, OH 43532
       Contact: Josh Purdy VP
       Tel: 941-484-7750
       Email: josh.purdy@tdplastics.com
       Website: www.tdplastics.com
Mfr structural foam, multiple plastic pallets & collapsible
bins, large plastic contract products. (Woman, estab 2005,
empl 35, sales $3,500,000, cert: WBENC)

Oklahoma

7081   DA/PRO Rubber Inc.
       601 N Poplar Ave
       Broken Arrow, OK 74012
       Contact: Gretchen Brauninger CEO
       Tel: 918-258-9386
       Email: gbrauninger@daprorubber.com
       Website: www.daprorubber.com
High quality rubber, TPE & plastic custom components,
diaphragms, seals, connectors, custom molded shapes,
rubber-to-metal parts & molded to precision tolerances.
(Woman, estab 1961, empl 320, sales , cert: WBENC)

Oregon

7082   Griffith Rubber Mills
       2625 NW Industrial
       Portland, OR 97296
       Contact: Rick McClain Corporate Quality Mgr
       Tel: 503-226-6971
       Email: rickm@griffithrubber.com
       Website: http://griffithrubber.com
Custom rubber products (Woman, estab 1911, empl
250, sales , cert: NWBOC)

7083   Warm Springs Composite Products
       Highway 26, Bldg 8
       Warm Springs, OR 97761
       Contact: Charles Currier CFO
       Tel: 541-553-1143
       Email: curriercw@bendnet.com
       Website: www.wscp.com
Composite panel mfg & product devel: thermal setting,
thermal plastic, radio frequncy & cold pressing processes, ballistic & non-ballistic fabrics laminiation, s-
glass, e-glass, spectra, dynema, kevlar. (Nat Ame, estab
1994, empl 50, sales $6,200,000, cert: 8a)

Pennsylvania

7084   Pittsburgh Plastics Manufacturing
       140 Kriess Rd
       Butler, PA 16001
       Contact: Emily Crawford Acct Mgr
       Tel: 724-789-9300
       Email: ecrawford@pittsburghplastics.com
       Website: www.pittsburghplastics.com
Polyurethanes, TPEs, Silicones, Hydrogels & Foams.
(Woman, estab 1977, empl 100, sales , cert: WBENC)

7085   PMC-Polymer Products Company, Inc.
       100 Station Ave
       Stockertown, PA 18083
       Contact: Don Barber Business Mgr
       Tel: 610-759-3690
       Email: donbarber@pmc-group.com
       Website: www.polymerproductscompany.com/
       index.htm
Design & develop additive masterbatches & ignition
resistant thermoplastic compounds. (As-Ind, estab 1965,
empl 75, sales $25,500,000, cert: NMSDC)

7086   Precise Plastics, Inc.
       7700 Middle Rd
       Fairview, PA 16415
       Contact: Charlotte Farrell President
       Tel: 814-474-5504
       Email: char.farrell@ppi-erie.com
       Website: www.ppi-erie.com
Injection molding manufacturer. Non Clean room
medical. Design - Build and Run Capability. (Woman,
estab 1969, empl 15, sales $2,498,070, cert: State)

Puerto Rico

7087   Vassallo International
       1000 St 506
       Cotolaurel, PR 00780
       Contact: Rafael Vassallo CEO
       Tel: 787-848-1515
       Email: faelo@vassalloindustries.com
       Website: http://vassallointernational.com
Lines of PVC & plastics, Water Tanks. (Woman/Hisp,
estab 1962, empl 90, sales $15,000,000, cert: NMSDC)

South Carolina

7088 Milagro Packaging LLC
60 Fairview Church Rd
Spartanburg, SC 29306
Contact: Jill McCurry President
Tel: 864-578-0085
Email: jillm@concept-pkg.com
Website: www.milagro-pkg.com
Mfr corrugated & solid fiber boxes, polystyrene foam products & urethane foam products. (Hisp, estab 2001, empl 425, sales $94,873,435, cert: NMSDC)

Tennessee

7089 Innovative Plastics
2900 Old Franklin Rd
Antioch, TN 37013
Contact: Tom Florence Sales
Tel: 404-402-8062
Email: tomf4plastics@aol.com
Website: www.innovative-plastics.com
Custom thermoform & RF contract packaging: PVC, PETG, Styrene, Barex & HDPE. (Woman, estab 1985, empl 350, sales , cert: NWBOC)

Texas

7090 Belco Manufacturing Company, Inc.
2303 Taylor's Valley Rd
Belton, TX 76513
Contact: Steve Macy President
Tel: 254-933-9000
Email: sales@belco-mfg.com
Website: http://belco-mfg.com
Industrial fiberglass reinforced plastics products. (Woman, estab 0, empl , sales , cert: WBENC)

7091 CamLow, LLC
105 S Friendswood Dr, Ste B
Friendswood, TX 77546
Contact: Karen Wiest President
Tel: 281-474-2613
Email: kawiest@camlow.com
Website: www.camlow.com
Polyurethane spray foam insulation, closed cell spray foam, open cell spray foam, roof spray foam insulation, hurricane protection, hurricane panels, storm panels, storm shutters, roll down shutters, accordian shutters, stainless steel screens. (Woman, estab 2005, empl 4, sales $317,000, cert: State, City)

7092 Chemplast, Inc.
1002 Texas Pkwy, Ste A
Stafford, TX 77477
Contact: Jubin Alexander Business Dev Mgr
Tel: 281-208-2585
Email: jubin@chemplastinc.com
Website: www.chemplastinc.com
Plastic Injection Molding with high performance Engineering Grade Plastics, Compression Molding, Thermoforming, Parts Assembly. (As-Ind, estab 2000, empl 47, sales $15,000,000, cert: NMSDC, CPUC)

7093 Clay Precision, Ltd.
1102 FM 1417 NE
Sherman, TX 75090
Contact: President
Tel: 903-891-9022
Email:
Website: www.clayprecision.com
Milling, turning, 4th axis capabilities, fixturing, plastic weldment, assemblies, heat treating, grinding, dock-to-stock quality, fabrication of custom metal and plastic machined parts and assemblies, prototypes, exotic metals, exotic plastics. (Woman, estab 1996, empl 11, sales $1,293,930, cert: State, WBENC)

7094 Idea Planet, LP
6001 Summerside Dr Ste 204
Dallas, TX 75252
Contact: Michael Flecker President
Tel: 972-380-9867
Email: mflecker@ideaplanetinc.com
Website: www.ideaplanetinc.com
Plastic injected molding, resin, metal & glass manufacturing. (Woman, estab 1999, empl 18, sales $19,000,000, cert: WBENC)

7095 King's Eco Plastics, LLC
4001 W Military Hwy
McAllen, TX 78503
Contact: Owen Stewart President
Tel: 956-631-1115
Email: ostewart@kingsecoplastics.com
Website: www.kingsecoplastics.com
Custom-molded plastics, product assembly & finishing services. (Woman/AA, As-Pac, estab 1986, empl 75, sales $8,109,000, cert: NMSDC, WBENC)

7096 Mexican Technologies Co
8650 Yermoland Dr
El Paso, TX 79907
Contact: Alfredo Baca Sales Mgr
Tel: 915-595-2285
Email: abaca@uniqueproductsinc.com
Website: www.uniqueproductsinc.com
Die cutting, converting, lamination, plastic fabrication, extrusion & coextrusion, slitting, sewing. (Hisp, estab 2002, empl 20, sales , cert: State)

7097 Nicor Inc.
100 Commons Rd, Ste 7-355
Dripping Springs, TX 78620
Contact: Jeff Cook VP Sales/Mktg
Tel: 707-484-0835
Email: jeffacook@nicorinc.net
Website: www.nicorinc.net
Custom injection molding, polymer replacement meter pit lids that are traffic rated. (Woman, estab 1988, empl 5, sales $2,000,000, cert: State)

7098 Precision Mold & Tool Group
315 N Park Dr
San Antonio, TX 78216
Contact: Domingo Auces Dir of Marketing
Tel: 210-525-0094
Email: dhauces@pmtool.com
Website: www.precision-group.com
Injection molding & mold making. (Woman, estab 1985, empl 36, sales $6,505,000, cert: WBENC)

7099 Premier Polymers LLC
16800 Imperial Valley, Ste 200
Houston, TX 77060
Contact: Melwani Kwan Supply Chain Mgr
Tel: 281-902-0909
Email: mkwan@premierpolymers.com
Website: www.premierpolymers.com
Dist Plastic Resin. (As-Pac, estab 2009, empl 22, sales ,
cert: State, NMSDC)

7100 Rhino Contractors
26163 Altas Palmas Rd
Harlingen, TX 78552
Contact: Brandon Russell Director
Tel: 956-535-3699
Email: brandon@rhino-rgv.com
Website: www.rhino-plastics.com
Mfr ABS plastic substrate made out of 100% post con-
sumer e-waste (electronic) plastics. (Woman, estab 2003,
empl 8, sales $1,600,000, cert: 8a)

Utah

7101 Kaddas Enterprises, Inc.
255 N. Apollo Rd. Ste 500
Salt Lake City, UT 84116
Contact: Patrick Scott Dir of Sales
Tel: 801-972-5400
Email: patricks@kaddas.com
Website: www.kaddas.com
Custom Thermoforming, Pressure Forming, Hand Fabrica-
tion, 5-Axis CNC Router, Master CAM, Solid Works Model-
ing, 3-Axis CNC Router, vacuum formed or hand fabricated
polymer solutions. (Woman, estab 1966, empl 28, sales
$4,296,559, cert: CPUC, WBENC)

Virginia

7102 Dynaric Inc.
5740 Bayside Rd
Virginia Beach, VA 23455
Contact: Kenny Samdahl Cstmr Service
Tel: 757-363-5851
Email: kens@dynaric.com
Website: www.dynaric.com
Mfr plastic strapping & strapping systems. (Hisp, estab
1973, empl 150, sales $122,000,000, cert: NMSDC)

7103 Polyfab Display Company
14892 Persistence Dr
Woodbridge, VA 22191
Contact: Al Parker Owner
Tel: 703-497-4577
Email: al@polyfab-display.com
Website: www.polyfab-display.com
Mfr & dist acrylic fabricated products: point-of-purchase
displays (countertop, wall-mount, slatwall and free-
standing), fixtures, signage, protective covers & medical
device holders. (AA, estab 1987, empl 15, sales
$1,189,000, cert: State, NMSDC)

Wisconsin

7104 Custom Service Plastics, Inc.
1101 S Wells St
Lake Geneva, WI 53147
Contact: Minoo Seifoddini President
Tel: 262-248-9557
Email: john@csplastics.com
Website: www.csplastics.com
Plastics injection molding: autotmotive & non
automaotive parts & assemblies. (Woman/As-Pac, estab
0, empl 160, sales $12,000,000, cert: WBENC)

7105 Molded Dimensions, Inc.
701 Sunset Rd
Port Washington, WI 53074
Contact: Sue Bialzik Cstmr Service
Tel: 262-284-9455
Email: sue@moldeddimensions.com
Website: www.moldeddimensions.com
Rubber & polyurethane custom molded components.
(Woman, estab 1952, empl 70, sales $12,500,000, cert:
WBENC)

7106 Shell Plastics LLC
1010 Valley Rd
Plymouth, WI 53073
Contact: Mary Beth Dellger President
Tel: 920-893-6281
Email: marybeth@shellplastics.com
Website: www.shellplastics.com
Job Shop, Plastic Fabrication, Screen Printing, Vacuum
Forming, CNC routing, Heat Bending, Cold Bending,
Flame Polishing, Solvent Bonding, Laminating, Spray
Painting, Die Cutting, Buffing, Drape Forming, Assembly,
Packaging, Fulfillment. (Woman, estab 1953, empl 15,
sales $2,924,884, cert: State)

7107 SMC Ltd.
330 SMC Dr
Somerset, WI 54025
Contact: Eugene Puckhaber Corporate Controller
Tel: 978-422-6800
Email: eugene.puckhaber@smcltd.com
Website: www.smcltd.com
Contract manufacturing & molding services, design,
engineering, thermoplastic molding including insert &
two-shot, micro molding. (As-Ind, estab 1989, empl 700,
sales , cert: State, NMSDC)

7108 TJM Innovations, LLC
5519 W Woolworth Ave
Milwaukee, WI 53218
Contact: Sean OBrien Dir Marketing/Ecommerce
Tel: 414-446-8778
Email: sean@tjminnovations.com
Website: http://tjminnovations.com
Designs, engineers, manufactures and distributes foam
fabrication, batch mixing and heat-treating products and
services. (Woman, estab 2007, empl 20, sales , cert:
WBENC)

Alabama

7109 Advanced Label Worx
1006 Larsen Dr
Oak Ridge, AL 37830
Contact: Lana Sellers President
Tel: 865-966-8711
Email: lsellers@advancedlabelworx.com
Website: www.advancedlabelworx.com
Flexographic pressure-sensitive labels, specialty converting, die-cut components, digital imprinting. (Woman, estab 1968, empl 120, sales , cert: WBENC)

Arizona

7110 Sapphire Printing Group, Inc.
3800 N. 38th Ave
Phoenix, AZ 85019
Contact: Kenn Gary Dir of Sales
Tel: 714-941-9534
Email: kenng@sapphireprinting.com
Website: www.sapphireprinting.com
Commercial web printing, mailing & fulfillment services. (Woman, estab 2004, empl 115, sales $22,000,000, cert: CPUC)

7111 Squala LLC
2909 E Broadway
Phoenix, AZ 85040
Contact: Angela Lawrence Dir natl sales
Tel: 602-547-7020
Email: alawrence@sherrimayco.com
Website: www.sherrimayco.com
Brand development, graphic design, copy writing, direct marketing integrated campaigns, websites, mobile, data analytics & public relations, web, sheetfed, digital variable, large format, flexo, retail packaging & folding cartons. (Woman, estab 2010, empl 10, sales $3,550,646, cert: State)

California

7112 Acme Press Inc., dba California Lithographers
2312 Stanwell Dr
Concord, CA 94520
Contact: VP
Tel: 925-682-1111
Email:
Website: http://Calitho.com
Commercial printing, digital printing, fulfillment, mailing, packaging. (Woman, estab 1976, empl 75, sales $11,530,090, cert: WBENC)

7113 Clear Image Printing, Inc.
12744 San Fernando Road Bldg #2
Sylmar, CA 91342
Contact: Gene Byrne Dir mktg/sales
Tel: 818-630-7670
Email: eugene@clearimageprinting.com
Website: www.clearimageprinting.com
Offset sheet fed & digital printing, Brochures, Catalogues, Direct mail campaigns, Special Packaging, Books, Foil stamping, Die-cutting, Posters, Large Format Banners, Graphic Design, Modern-Media. (As-Pac, estab 2008, empl 45, sales $5,005,000, cert: CPUC)

7114 Digital Mania, Inc.
455 Market St Ste 180
San Francisco, CA 94105
Contact: Darius Meykadeh CEO
Tel: 415-896-0500
Email: copymat@copymatsf.com
Website: http://copymat1.com
Indoor & outdoor signs, brochures, booklets, RFPs, oversized prints, desktop publishing & design, mailing services, newsletters, name tents, name badges, conference materials, etc. (As-Ind, estab 1994, empl 20, sales $4,000,000, cert: City)

7115 Digital Services Enterprises
40 Tesla, Ste B
Irvine, CA 92618
Contact: Sales Mgr
Tel: 949-387-6200
Email:
Website: www.sirspeedyprinter.com
Offset printing, digital printing, color copies, photocopying, promotional products, Signs, banners, posters, floor graphics, direct mail, fulfillment, high speedy copies, training manuals, human resource manuals, direct marketing. (Woman, estab 1974, empl 17, sales $2,757,000, cert: CPUC)

7116 Dulco Printing
740 E Belmont Ave
Fresno, CA 93701
Contact: Kipp Weber President
Tel: 559-266-8245
Email: info@dulcoprinting.com
Website: www.dulcoprinting.com
Commercial printing, collating & binding: books, manuals & full color promotional material. (Woman, estab 2002, empl 4, sales , cert: State)

7117 Essence Printing
151 Mitchell Ave
South San Francisco, CA 94080
Contact: Bau-Lin Yueh President
Tel: 650-952-5072
Email: baulin@essenceprinting.com
Website: www.essenceprinting.com
Printing: marketing material, brochures, datasheets, newsletters, tradeshow posters, business cards, letterheads, etc. (As-Pac, estab 1976, empl 60, sales , cert: CPUC)

7118 Financial Statement Services, Inc.
3300 S Fairview St
Santa Ana, CA 92704
Contact: Business Development
Tel: 714-436-3300
Email:
Website: www.fssi-ca.com
Printing, mailing & electronic invoices, statements, bills & marketing communications. (Woman, estab 1980, empl 187, sales $5,000,000, cert: WBENC)

7119 Fong & Fong Printers and Lithographers
3009 65th St
Sacramento, CA 95820
Contact: Karen Cotton Controller
Tel: 916-739-1313
Email: kcotton@fongprinters.com
Website: www.fongprinters.com
Commercial printing services: sales literature, brochures, folders, packaging, annual reports, data sheets, direct mail & posters. (Woman/As-Pac, estab 1962, empl 51, sales $12,000,000, cert: CPUC)

7120 Fruitridge Printing and Lithograph
3258 Stockton Blvd
Sacramento, CA 95820
Contact: Karen Young VP
Tel: 916-452-9213
Email: karen@fruitridge.com
Website: www.fruitridge.com
Commercial offset and digital printing, in house bindery & mailing capabilities. (Woman, estab 1970, empl 35, sales $5,100,000, cert: CPUC)

7121 Gibraltar Graphics
5075 Brooks St
Montclair, CA 91763
Contact: Hector Rosado Sales Mgr
Tel: 909-624-6171
Email: hectorr@gPrint4u.com
Website: www.gPrint4u.com
Printing, inhouse bindery, heatset web presses, pick up and delivery, brochures, envelopes, laser forms, newsletters, booklets, scratch pads, laser forms, (Hisp, estab 1989, empl 18, sales $410,000, cert: CPUC)

7122 Image Quest Plus, LLC
215 No Marengo Ave. Third Floor
Pasadena, CA 91101
Contact: Margaret Floyd Member
Tel: 626-744-1333
Email: margaret@iqcopy.com
Website: www.iqcopy.com
Photocopy services: document reproduction, scanning & imaging, color copies, wideformat printing, binding, off-site document reproduction. (Woman/AA, estab 1998, empl 5, sales $661,441, cert: NMSDC, CPUC)

7123 Impact Printing
23278 Bernhardt St
Hayward, CA 94545
Contact: Sarah Elder VP Sales
Tel: 510-783-7977
Email: impactprint@impactprint.com
Website: www.impactprint.com
Digital & offset printing, full bindery, graphics. (Minority/Woman, estab 1985, empl 25, sales $2,500,000, cert: CPUC)

7124 Ink Link, Incorporated
351 Oak Place, Ste J
Brea, CA 92821
Contact: Linda Brooking CEO
Tel: 714-256-9700
Email: linda@myinklink.com
Website: www.myinklink.com
Commercial printing: banners, signs, displays, floor graphics. (Woman, estab 2003, empl 4, sales $850,000, cert: State, CPUC, WBENC)

7125 International Diversified Marketing, Inc.
18277 Pasadena St., Ste B102
Lake Elsinore, CA 92530
Contact: Jan Northcutt President
Tel: 714-550-4971
Email: jn@comfortfirst.us
Website: www.ComfortFirstProducts.com
Comfort First Filtered Diffuser™If you want to go GREEN and save energy, improve employee comfort and health, all while improving indoor air quality, this diffuser is the solution you've been looking for. (Woman, estab 2003, empl 3, sales $458,000, cert: WBENC)

7126 Lester Lithograph Inc. (dba Castle Press)
1128 N Gilbert St
Anaheim, CA 92801
Contact: Larry Lester
Tel: 714-491-3981
Email: amy@castlepress.com
Website: www.castlepress.com
Commercial printing. (Woman, estab 1980, empl 45, sales $5,500,000, cert: CPUC, WBENC)

7127 Metropolitan West, Inc.
11901 Santa Monica Blvd, Ste 350
Los Angeles, CA 90025
Contact: Kelly Taylor President
Tel: 310-829-5701
Email: nikki@metwest.com
Website: www.metwest.com
Dist film products: solar, safety, anti-graffiti, designer, custom & digital film. (Woman, estab 1992, empl 5, sales $1,200,000, cert: WBENC)

7128 PGI Pacific Graphics International
14938 Nelson Ave
City of Industry, CA 91744
Contact: Rick Wasson President
Tel: 626-336-7707
Email: rwasson@pacgraphics.com
Website: www.pacgraphics.com
Printing & graphics, business forms, etc. (Woman/Hisp, estab 1989, empl 20, sales $3,511,247, cert: NMSDC, CPUC, SDB)

7129 Photomation
2551 W La Palma Ave
Anaheim, CA 92801
Contact: Francisco Flores Production Mgr/Sales
Tel: 714-236-2121
Email: fflores@photomation.com
Website: www.photomation.com
Digital Graphics, Trade show, Digital Imaging, Photographics prints, Banners, POP displays, Standees, Wallcovering, Large wall Murals, Lobby art, Custom framing, Awards and recognition, office décor. (Woman, estab 1955, empl 21, sales , cert: State, CPUC, WBENC)

7130 Precise Panel Engraving CO, Inc.
12881 Western Ave, Unit B
Garden Grove, CA 92841
Contact: Joan VonKarvaly President
Tel: 714-898-6510
Email: precisepanel@verizon.net
Website: www.government-vendor.us/precisepanel
Industrial engraving: signs, labels, nameplates, control panels; sheet metal fab; metal & plastic panel machining; mylar & metal marking. (Woman, estab 1978, empl 7, sales $255,000, cert: State)

7131 Summit Graphics Inc.
      11354 Burbank Blvd, Ste A
      North Hollywood, CA 91601
      Contact: Jorge Ververa VP Marketing
      Tel: 818-753-5075
      Email: jorge@summit-graphics.net
      Website: www.summit-graphics.net
Medium to large runs in offset, digital & large format
printing: mailers, inkjet address, brochures, catalogues,
booklets, bindery, die-cutting, packaging, coallating, hand
fulfillment. (Hisp, estab 2001, empl 4, sales $1,436,504,
cert: State, NMSDC)

7132 Transworld Printing Services, Inc.
      2857 Transworld Dr
      Stockton, CA 95206
      Contact: Daphyne Brown CEO
      Tel: 209-982-1511
      Email: daphyne@tpslabels.com
      Website: www.tpslabels.com
Flexographic & digital label manufacturer. (Woman/AA,
estab 1996, empl 15, sales $2,065,000, cert: NMSDC,
NWBOC)

Colorado

7133 DT Investments Inc. dba Beacon Printing Inc.
      2161 S Platte River Dr
      Denver, CO 80223
      Contact: Terri Witt CEO
      Tel: 303-922-4384
      Email: beacon.sales@qwestoffice.net
      Website: http://beaconprintingdenver.com
Printing services, large format sheetfed, digital, full color,
PMS color, pocket folders, post cards, letterhead, envelopes, posters, booklets, annual reports, brochures, forms,
rack cards, pamphlets, catalogs, tabs, loose leaf, inserts.
(Woman/Nat Ame, estab 1995, empl 10, sales $1,200,000,
cert: City)

7134 Mar-Tek Industries, Inc.
      3545 S Platte River Dr, Ste G
      Englewood, CO 80110
      Contact: Irene Smith President
      Tel: 303-789-4067
      Email: irene@mar-tekind.com
      Website: www.mar-tekind.com
Mfr & dist screen printed & digital graphic labels, decals,
overlays. (Woman, estab 1987, empl 45, sales $4,500,000,
cert: WBENC)

Connecticut

7135 Enhance a Colour Corp.
      43b Beaver Brook Road
      Danbury, CT 06810
      Contact: Lenore Nespoli Sales Mgr
      Tel: 203-748-5111
      Email: lnespoli@eacgs.com
      Website: www.eacgs.com
Large format digitally printed graphics, printing dyesub
fabrics & carpets up to 16' wide, UV printing, full color &
white ink direct to rigid and flexible substrates, pressure
sensitive, regular & mesh substrates. (Woman, estab 1988,
empl 32, sales $4,014,058, cert: WBENC)

7136 Turnstone Inc. dba Alphagraphics
      915 Main St
      Hartford, CT 06103
      Contact: VP Sales
      Tel: 860-247-3766
      Email:
      Website: www.hartford.alphagraphics.com
Brochures, Reports, Training books, Posters, Reports,
mailings. Forms, labels, Flyers, Design Services. Fulfillment, Signs & banners, marketing material. (Woman,
estab 1989, empl 23, sales $3,100,000, cert: WBENC)

Florida

7137 Alpha Press, Inc.
      3804 N John Young Pkwy, Ste 2
      Orlando, FL 32804
      Contact: GM
      Tel: 407-299-2121
      Email:
      Website: www.alphapressfl.com
Four color press: brochures, business cards, envelopes,
pamplets, magazines & publications. (Woman/Hisp,
estab 1996, empl 5, sales $870,000, cert: City)

7138 APImaging, Inc.
      19 SW 6th St
      Miami, FL 33130
      Contact: Diana Herrera VP Sales
      Tel: 305-373-4774
      Email: dianah@apimaging.com
      Website: www.apimaging.com
Photo imaging & photo finishing services, commercial
printing, studio photography, self adhesive signs &
graphics, directional signs, posters, point of purchase
signs, graphic displays, graphic design, trade shows &
exhibits. (Woman/Hisp, estab 2013, empl 22, sales , cert:
WBENC)

7139 Bellak Color
      P.O. Box 227656
      Miami, FL 33222
      Contact: Manny Fernandez VP
      Tel: 305-854-8525
      Email: manny@bellak.com
      Website: www.bellak.com
Commerical sheet-fed printing - print publications,
magazines, brochures, rack brochures, catalogs, stationery packages, POS pieces, postcards, pamplets, invitations, folders. (Hisp, estab 1960, empl 47, sales
$6,500,000, cert: NMSDC)

7140 Colonial Press International, Inc.
      3690 NW 50th St
      Miami, FL 33142
      Contact: Jeff Statler EVP Corporate Sales
      Tel: 540-347-1402
      Email: jstatler@colonialpress.com
      Website: www.colonialpressintl.com
Printing svcs: web & sheet fed, 4-6 color, brochures,
rack cards, magazines, etc. (Hisp, estab 1952, empl 221,
sales $31,000,000, cert: NMSDC)

7141 Innovative Printing & Graphics
      310 S Federal Hwy
      Boynton Beach, FL 33435
      Contact: Amy Bernard Sales Assoc
      Tel: 561-742-2977
      Email: info@ipgprinting.com
      Website: www.ipgprinting.com
Commercial printing: full color, magazines, NCR forms,
pocket folders, postcard mailers, letterhead, invitations,
etc. (Woman, estab 2006, empl 9, sales $250,000, cert:
City)

7142 Lawton Printers, Inc.
      649 Triumph Court
      Orlando, FL 32804
      Contact: Kimberly Lawton Koon President
      Tel: 407-260-0400
      Email: kimberly@lawtonprinters.com
      Website: www.LawtonPrinters.com
Printing ; offset, digital & wide-format printing equipment.
(Woman, estab , empl 27, sales $3,600,000, cert: State,
WBENC)

7143 NIS Print
      1809 S Division Ave
      Orlando, FL 32805
      Contact: President
      Tel: 407-423-7575
      Email:
      Website: www.nisprint.com
Specialty Binding, Employee Handbooks, Training Manuals,
Sales Presentations, Specialty Boxes, Custom Index Tabs,
Guestroom Compendiums, Custom Index Tabs, Commer-
cial Printing. (Woman, estab 1986, empl 17, sales , cert:
WBENC)

7144 Quadco Printing & Signs
      8953 NW 23rd St
      Doral, FL 33172
      Contact: Jorge Quadreny President
      Tel: 305-519-1234
      Email: jorge@quadcoonline.com
      Website: http://quadcoonline.com
Full color printing services, advertising specialties, promo-
tional items, trade show & retractable banner stands.
(Hisp, estab 1982, empl 8, sales $140,000,000, cert: State)

7145 Sol Davis Printing, Inc.
      5205 N Lois Ave
      Tampa, FL 33614
      Contact: Solomon E. Davis President
      Tel: 813-353-3609
      Email: soldavis.print@verizon.net
      Website: www.soldavisprinting.com
Offset printing: 1, 2, 3 & 4 color process, graphic design,
typesetting & bindery services. (Woman/AA, estab 1999,
empl 9, sales , cert: State, City, NMSDC)

7146 Solo Printing, LLC
      7860 NW 66th St
      Miami, FL 33166
      Contact: Lorenzo Cosio Sr. Acct Exec
      Tel: 305-594-8699
      Email: lorenzo@soloprinting.com
      Website: www.soloprinting.com
Commercial printing, binding & fullfillment. (Hisp, estab
1985, empl 180, sales $49,000,000, cert: NMSDC)

7147 Vista Color Corporation
      1401 NW 78th Ave
      Miami, FL 33126
      Contact: Catherine Finnemore Sr Acct Exec
      Tel: 305-635-2000
      Email: cfinnemore@vistacolor.com
      Website: www.vistacolor.com
Pre-press & printing svcs. (Hisp, estab 1968, empl 120,
sales $22,000,000, cert: NMSDC)

Georgia

7148 American Reprographics Corporation
      7800 Jett Ferry Rd
      Atlanta, GA 30350
      Contact: Mindy Godwin President
      Tel: 770-394-2465
      Email: mindy@arcinatlanta.com
      Website: http://arcinatlanta.com
Full service printing: business cards, letterhead, envelopes, check stock, brochures, mailings, graphic design
services. (Woman, estab 1978, empl 3, sales , cert:
WBENC)

7149 Barcode Warehouse
      101 Smoke Hill Lane Ste 130
      Woodstock, GA 30188
      Contact: Margie Benton VP Sales Operations
      Tel:
      Email: mbenton@barcodewarehouse.biz
      Website: www.barcodewarehouse.biz
Mfr labels & tags, full color product branding labels,
blank labels & tags for variable data printing. (Woman,
estab 2004, empl 18, sales $4,225,778, cert: WBENC)

7150 Basiqa, LLC
      1555 Oakbrook Dr Ste 135
      Norcross, GA 30093
      Contact: Winston Dzose VP Digital Marketing
      Tel: 678-824-6460
      Email: winston@basiqa.com
      Website: www.basiqa.com
Direct mail, advertising, material preparation services
for mailing or other direct distribution, digital printing.
(AA, estab 2009, empl 16, sales $3,000,000, cert:
NMSDC)

7151 Dixie Graphics
      2074 E Park Dr NE
      Conyers, GA 30013
      Contact: Denise Hindle COE
      Tel: 770-972-2354
      Email: dhindle@dixiegraphicsinc.com
      Website: www.dixiegraphicsinc.com
Commercial offset printing & large format, graphics
design & full mail room capabilities. (Woman, estab
1980, empl 14, sales $2,012,337, cert: WBENC)

7152 Fuentes Enterprises Inc. dba Interprint, Inc.
      2605 Park Central Blvd
      Decatur, GA 30035
      Contact: Monica Maldonado CEO
      Tel: 770-987-7400
      Email: mmaldonado@ok2print.com
      Website: http://ok2print.com
Commercial printing, graphic design, posters, billboards,
marketing collateral materials, annual reports, ads, etc.
(Woman/Hisp, estab 1984, empl 20, sales $1,990,000,
cert: NMSDC, WBENC)

7153 Initio Partners LLC
      300 Colonial Center Pkwy, Ste 100
      Roswell, GA 30076
      Contact: Jeffrey Johnson COO
      Tel: 678-353-3233
      Email: jjohnson@initiopartners.com
      Website: http://initiopartners.com
Large format digital printing: banners, posters, signs,
trade show displays & banner stands, vehicle wraps,
vinyl lettering, wall, window & floor graphics, stickers &
decals. (Hisp, estab 2010, empl 2, sales $6,000,000, cert:
State)

7154 LittKare, LLC
      200 Cobb Pkwy N Ste 130
      Marietta, GA 30062
      Contact: Littie Brown President
      Tel: 770-693-1767
      Email: lbrown@speedpro.com
      Website: www.speedpromarietta.com
Large format digital printing: banners, posters, signs, trade show displays & banner stands, vehicle wraps, vinyl lettering, wall, window & floor graphics, stickers & decals. (Woman/AA, estab 2010, empl 2, sales $373,880, cert: NMSDC, WBENC)

7155 Matoaka Enterprises, LLC
      2455 Bridlewood Dr
      Smyrna, GA 30080
      Contact: Julie Custalow Owner
      Tel: 404-932-6825
      Email: julie@matoaka.com
      Website: www.matoaka-ent.com
Large format graphics, banners, signs, window clings, vehicle wraps, LEED certified wall paper, custom printed litho & digital printing, custom printed promotional items, apparel. (Woman/Nat Ame, estab 2010, empl 1, sales $181,611, cert: NMSDC)

7156 NorthStar Print, LLC
      6050 Peachtree Pkwy Ste 240359
      Norcross, GA 30092
      Contact: Jacki Suckow President
      Tel: 770-490-6251
      Email: jacki@northstarprint.net
      Website: www.northstarprint.net
Print & promotional products, marketing materials, traditional business forms, POP items, promotional items & just-in-time digital printing, distribution & kitting services. (Woman, estab 1991, empl 8, sales $3,000,000, cert: NWBOC)

7157 PrinTech Label Corporation
      2550 Collins Springs Dr
      Smyrna, GA 30080
      Contact: Kelly Weaver CFO
      Tel: 404-792-1133
      Email: kelly@printechlabel.com
      Website: www.printechlabel.com
Pressure senstive labels, custom printed tags, 4 color process, 6 color capability, hot stamp labels, cold foil labels, UL registered label vendor, IRC's, IRC, redeemable coupons, silver coupon, thermal transfer blanks, direct thermal blanks. (Woman/Nat Ame, estab 1993, empl 14, sales $1,701,002, cert: WBENC)

7158 Printing and Marketing Services, Inc.
      1500 Southland Circle, Ste A
      Atlanta, GA 30318
      Contact: BRIAN MCDANIEL Sr Acct Mgr
      Tel: 404-724-9080
      Email: bmcdaniel@alphagraphics.com
      Website: www.us756.alphagraphics.com
Printing: digital color, digital black & white, offset printing, envelopes, stationery, large format signs & banners. (AA, estab 2015, empl 13, sales $1,695,647, cert: NMSDC)

7159 The Printing People, Inc.
      3427 Oakcliff Rd. Ste 112
      Doraville, GA 30340
      Contact: Misael Millan VP
      Tel: 770-452-7561
      Email: misa@printingpeople.com
      Website: www.printingpeople.com
Commercial offset & digital printing: brochures, postcards, catalogs, posters, folders, manuals & stationery. (Hisp, estab 1980, empl 13, sales $1,400,000, cert: NMSDC)

Iowa

7160 Promotion Support Services, Inc.
      1320 W Kimberly Rd
      Davenport, IA 52806
      Contact: Terance VanWinkle Director
      Tel: 563-362-6002
      Email: tvanwinkle@pss-inc.net
      Website: http://pss-inc.net
Offset printing, Digital printing (static & variable), Commercial printing, Transactional print & mail services, Transcription Services, Data capture, Medical Transcription, Outbound call center, warehousing, Fulfillment, Kitting. (Woman, estab 1989, empl 56, sales $5,600,000, cert: WBENC)

Illinois

7161 AmeriPrint Corporation
      1401 W Diggins St
      Harvard, IL 60098
      Contact: Taylor Schulty Marking & Sales Dir
      Tel: 800-366-8573
      Email: taylors@ameriprint.com
      Website: www.ameriprint.com
Continuous forms & checks, snap sets, laser cut-sheets, booked & padded sets, integral card forms & labels, decals, re-positionable labels, key tags, magnets, thermal labels, barcoding, jumbo numbering & rolls. (Woman, estab 1990, empl 63, sales $8,603,265, cert: NWBOC)

7162 Clyde Printing Company
      3520 S Morgan
      Chicago, IL 60609
      Contact: Colleen Woulfe President
      Tel: 773-847-5900
      Email: clydeprint@sbcglobal.net
      Website: www.clydeprinting.com
Sheet fed commercial printing, conventional & digital printing, fullfillment & mailing. (Woman, estab 1942, empl 10, sales $792,852, cert: WBENC)

7163 ComGraphics Inc.
      329 W 18th St, 10 Fl
      Chicago, IL 60616
      Contact: Lydia Erickson CFO
      Tel: 312-226-0900
      Email: lydiae@cgichicago.com
      Website: www.cgichicago.com
Digital printing svcs, folding & inserting operations, internet hosting, statement processing, web statement, laser svcs, invoicing, marketing & fulfillment, data archiving, scanning svcs, direct mail. (Woman, estab 1980, empl 55, sales , cert: WBENC)

7164 Consolidated Printing Company
      5942 N Northwest Hwy
      Chicago, IL 60631
      Contact: Marilyn Jones President
      Tel: 773-631-2800
      Email: marilyn@consolidatedprinting.net
      Website: www.consolidatedprinting.net
Commercial printing includes: design, computer to plate, color digital, offset short & long run: advertising materials, annual reports, banners, brochures, booklets, buttons, business cards, conference materials, digital printing, door hangers. (Woman, estab 1973, empl 15, sales , cert: WBENC)

7165   D&D Business Inc. dba DDI Printing
       7830 Quincy St
       Willowbrook, IL 60527
       Contact: Darmi Parikh CEO
       Tel: 630-734-1455
       Email: darmi@ddimage.com
       Website: www.ddimage.com
Graphic design, Commercial colored printing, digital
printing, full bindery & fullfillment. (Woman/As-Pac, estab
1994, empl 5, sales $560,000, cert: State, City, NMSDC)

7166   Envelopes Only, Inc.
       2000 Park Ave
       Streamwood, IL 60107
       Contact: Acct Mgr
       Tel: 630-213-2563
       Email:
       Website: http://envelopesonly.net
Printing envelopes & letterheads. (Woman, estab 1983,
empl 24, sales $7,287,492, cert: State, WBENC)

7167   Krick Enterprises, Inc.
       1548 Ogden Ave
       Downers Grove, IL 60515
       Contact: Pres Sales & Marketing
       Tel: 630-515-1085
       Email:
       Website: http://signsnowdownersgrove.com
Graphic Design & Layout, commercial & digital printing.
Signs & Posters, Brochures, Business Cards, Training
Manuals & materials, Promotional items. (Woman/As-Pac,
estab 1991, empl 7, sales $600,000, cert: State, NMSDC)

7168   LabelQuest Inc.
       493 W. Fullerton Ave.
       Elmhurst, IL 60126
       Contact: Patricia Vandenberg President
       Tel: 630-833-9400
       Email: labelquest@sbcglobal.net
       Website:
Custom printing & print management: offset, flexo, screen
& digital printing, safe storage & fulfillment capabilities.
(Woman, estab 1996, empl 4, sales $1,646,670, cert:
WBENC)

7169   M & R Graphics
       2401 Bond St
       University Park, IL 60466
       Contact: Keith Reimel VP
       Tel: 708-534-6621
       Email: kreimel@mrgraphics.biz
       Website: www.mrgraphics.biz
Mfr pressure sensitive labels & flexographic printing.
(Woman/AA, estab 1989, empl 17, sales , cert: NMSDC)

7170   Master Marketing International
       280 Gerzverske Lane
       Carol Stream, IL 60188
       Contact: Rene Asselmeier Sr. Sales Exec
       Tel: 630-653-5525
       Email: rasselmeier@magnetstreet.com
       Website: www.magnetstreet.com
Magnet printing, high-end stationary products, digital
printer and mail house. (Woman, estab 1990, empl 66,
sales $10,800,000, cert: WBENC)

7171   Motr Grafx, LLC
       7430 N Lehigh
       Niles, IL 60714
       Contact: Lissette Herin VP
       Tel: 847-529-7454
       Email: Lherin@motrgx.com
       Website: www.motrgrafx.com
Print/media production, design, print, finishing, fulfillment & distribution, digital, sheet fed, large format, web
printing, screen printing, direct mail, POP/packaging
services. (Woman/Hisp, estab 2011, empl 10, sales
$2,980,000, cert: City, NMSDC, WBENC)

7172   Printing Master Services
       6370 W Emerald Pkwy
       Monee, IL 60449
       Contact: Gary De La Fuente President
       Tel: 708-534-8535
       Email: gary@printingmasterservices.com
       Website: www.printingmasterservices.com
Commercial sheetfed printing: books, brochures,
posters, displays, manuals, banners, window displays,
coupons, adslicks, digital printing & proofing, cd duplication & website design. (Hisp, estab 1978, empl 13, sales
$2,050,000, cert: State)

7173   Richards Graphic Communications, Inc.
       2700 Van Buren St
       Bellwood, IL 60104
       Contact: Mary Lawrence President
       Tel: 708-731-2103
       Email: maryl@rgcnet.com
       Website: www.rgcnet.com
Printing & communications, creative concept development, language translations, digital imaging, printing,
finishing & mailing. (Woman, estab 1925, empl 23, sales
$4,400,000, cert: State, WBENC)

7174   Shree Ganesha, Inc.
       311 S Wacker Dr
       Chicago, IL 60606
       Contact: Tina Kuvadia Production Mgr
       Tel: 312-408-1080
       Email: printxpress@printx-press.com
       Website: http://printx-press.com
Offset printing, copying, binding, large format, digital
printing & graphic designing capabilities. (Woman/As-
Pac, estab 2008, empl 9, sales , cert: City)

7175   Signcraft Screenprint, Inc.
       100 AJ Harle Dr
       Galena, IL 61036
       Contact: Sandy Redington President
       Tel: 815-777-3030
       Email: sandy@signcraftinc.com
       Website: www.signcraftinc.com
Custom screen printing, mfr pressure sensitive decals,
signs & anti-skid plates. (Woman, estab 1947, empl 133,
sales $11,500,000, cert: State)

7176   Sunrise Hitek Service, Inc.
       5915 N Northwest Hwy
       Chicago, IL 60631
       Contact: Mark Finch VP
       Tel: 773-792-8880
       Email: mfinch@sunrisedigital.us
       Website: www.sunrisehitek.com
Large format printing; displays, exhibit boards, POP
displays, signs, floor graphics, etc. (As-Pac, estab 1987,
empl 15, sales $3,700,000, cert: State, NMSDC)

7177   THM Creative, Inc. dba Advanced Imaging Inc.
1944 University Lane
Lisle, IL 60532
Contact: Tim Donnell Sales
Tel: 630-969-1300
Email: tim@aiprolab.com
Website: www.aiprolab.com
Digital Color Lab, Photographic Printing & Processing, Enlargements to 30x40, Inkjet/Giglee Printing, Online Order Fulfillment. (Minority/Woman, estab 1994, empl 6, sales , cert: NMSDC)

7178   Wyka LLC d/b/a Edison Graphics
1515 S Mt. Prospect Rd
Des Plaines, IL 60018
Contact: Larae J. Breitenstein CEO
Tel: 847-298-0740
Email: larae@edison-graphics.com
Website: www.edison-graphics.com
Printing svcs: 6 colors & coater sheet fed printing, in-house finishing, cutters, MBO folders, stitcher, digital printing & wide format printing. (Woman, estab 1998, empl 14, sales $3,215,000, cert: WBENC)

Indiana

7179   Fineline Printing Group
8081 Zionsville Rd
Indianapolis, IN 46268
Contact: Richard Miller President
Tel: 317-802-1964
Email: richardm@finelineprintinggroup.com
Website: http://FinelinePrintingGroup.com
Commercial sheetfed printing, inhouse bindery, mailing svcs, prepress svcs: scanning, design, ctp & high end color corrections. (Woman/Hisp, estab 1981, empl 59, sales $11,500,000, cert: State, NMSDC)

7180   International Label Mfg.
1925 S 13th St
Terre Haute, IN 47802
Contact: Lisa Gonzales VP
Tel: 800-525-8469
Email: lisagonzales@internationallabelmfg.com
Website: www.internationallabelmfg.com
Custom label mfr & commercial printer. (Woman, estab 1972, empl 18, sales $2,900,000, cert: State, WBENC)

7181   Miles Printing Corporation
4923 W 78th St
Indianapolis, IN 46268
Contact: Exec VP & Owner
Tel: 317-870-6145
Email:
Website: www.milesprinting.com
Commercial printing, offering digital, multi-color UV sheet-fed, large format printing, complete bindery, mailing & fulfillment capabilities. (Woman, estab 2006, empl 38, sales $13,600,000, cert: State, WBENC)

7182   Nicholson Printing Inc.
209 Eastern Blvd
Jeffersonville, IN 47130
Contact: Chris Nicholson VP
Tel: 812-283-1200
Email: chris@nicholsonprinting.com
Website: www.nicholsonprinting.com
Commercial & quick printing, graphic design, full-color printing, disk to print, digital color, digital black & white, copying, letterheads, envelopes, business cards, memos, business forms, carbonless forms, time cards, folders, books. (Woman, estab 1979, empl 12, sales $1,118,000, cert: State)

7183   Offset House Printing, Inc.
9374 Castlegate Dr
Indianapolis, IN 46256
Contact: Jay Williamson Acct Mgr
Tel: 317-849-5155
Email: jwilliamson@offsethouse.biz
Website: www.offsethouseinc.com
Commercial printing, graphic design & direct mail capabilities. (Woman, estab 1964, empl 13, sales , cert: State)

7184   Printing Inc of Louisville Kentucky
1600 Dutch Lane Ste A
Jeffersonville, IN 47130
Contact: Kelly Abney Mgr business devel
Tel: 502-368-6555
Email: wbe@prettyincredible.com
Website: http://prettyincredible.com
Print, fulfillment, distribution, marketing consulting, project management, direct mail with management of distributions, inventory & fulfillment of literature, bindery & kit packing. (Woman, estab 1971, empl 19, sales $3,000,000, cert: State)

7185   Thomas E. Slade, Inc.
6220 Vogel Road
Evansville, IN 47715
Contact: Lisa Slade President
Tel: 812-437-5233
Email: tom@sladeprint.com
Website: www.sladeprint.com
Printing, graphic design, website design, wide format posters & banners, mailing, promotional products, letterhead, envelopes, business cards, labels, tags, inserts, marketing services, augmented reality, QR codes for tracking, signs. (Woman, estab 1993, empl 17, sales $2,500,000, cert: State)

7186   Town & Country Printing
1001 E Summit St
Crown Point, IN 46307
Contact: Debera Hinchy President & CEO
Tel: 219-924-0441
Email: dhinchy@tandcii.com
Website: www.townandcountryprinting.com
Commercial printing - offset & digital. Traditional, large/grand format printing. Full color business cards, stationery, notepads, banners, indoor and outdoor signage, brochures, booklets, wall and floor graphics, decals (window, wall, floor). (Woman, estab 1970, empl 18, sales $1,800,000, cert: WBENC)

7187   UN Communications Group, Inc.
1429 Chase Court
Carmel, IN 46032
Contact: Denise Purvis President
Tel: 317-218-8262
Email: dpurvis@uncommgroup.com
Website: www.uncommgroup.com
Commercial, digital & wide format print services, mailing services, brochures, catalogs & annual reports, banners, vehicle wraps & tradeshow signage. (Woman, estab 1975, empl 32, sales $4,500,000, cert: State, City, WBENC)

7188   Valley Screen Process Company, Inc.
58740 Executive Dr
Mishawaka, IN 46544
Contact: Karen Barnett CEO
Tel: 574-256-0901
Email: karenb@valleyscreen.com
Website: www.valleyscreen.com
Commercial screen & digital printing. (Woman, estab 1967, empl 50, sales $7,445,882, cert: WBENC)

Kansas

7189 Total Print Solutions, Inc.
3220 W 121st Terr
Leawood, KS 66209
Contact: Constance Kingsley President
Tel: 913-481-7393
Email: ckingsley@tpsmidwest.com
Website: http://tpsmidwest.com
Commercial printing, pharma labels, digital print, magazine type publications, business forms, direct mail, warehousing & distribution. (Woman/Hisp, estab 2000, empl 2, sales $800,000, cert: State, NMSDC)

Kentucky

7190 EDJ Inc.
8158 Mall Rd
Florence, KY 41042
Contact: Maureen Schuler President
Tel: 859-525-1199
Email: maureen.schuler@fastsigns.com
Website: www.fastsigns.com/226
Banners, posters, foam boards, decals,
site signs, dimensional logos, coroplast signs, now hiring signs, production boards,
& tradeshow products and graphics. (Woman, estab 1995, empl 5, sales $856,000, cert: WBENC)

7191 Multi-Craft Litho, Inc.
131 E Sixth St
Newport, KY 41072
Contact: Debbie Simpson President
Tel: 859-655-8863
Email: dsimpson@multi-craft.com
Website: www.multi-craft.com
Commercial printing: pocket folders, annual reports, posters, brochures, sell sheets, packaging, etc. (Woman, estab 1955, empl 50, sales $9,500,000, cert: WBENC)

Louisiana

7192 Advanced Graphic Engraving, LLC
3105 Melancon Rd
Broussard, LA 70518
Contact: Monica Duplantis Mgr
Tel: 337-364-1991
Email: monica@tagsfast.com
Website: www.tagsfast.com
Industrial Engraving: Safety Signage, Architectural signage, Vinyl signs & decals, Master/Well Control Panels, Sub Sea Well Control Panels, Flow Schematics, Data Tags, Operating Instruction Tags, Dual Language Tags, Angle Indicators, Crane Hand Signals. (Woman, estab 1997, empl 21, sales $2,000,000, cert: WBENC)

Massachusetts

7193 Adam Graphic Corporation
16 Mason Ave Unit 4
North Attleboro, MA 02760
Contact: Nancy Ruo President
Tel: 508-699-2089
Email: nancy@adamgraphic.com
Website: www.adamgraphic.com
Printing, print management, forms, envelopes, marketing brochures, folders, binders, ID cards, labels, commerical print, digital print, signage, mailings, fulfillment, kitting, warehousing, on-line ordering, promotional products. (Woman, estab 1985, empl 5, sales $1,193,045, cert: State, WBENC)

7194 CSW Inc.
45 Tyburski Rd
Ludlow, MA 01056
Contact: Scott Ellison VP Sales
Tel: 800-800-9522
Email: scotte@cswgraphics.com
Website: www.cswgraphics.com
Packaging pre press, design, flexo plates, cutting dies. (Woman, estab 1936, empl 150, sales $16,160,013, cert: State, WBENC)

7195 Gangi Printing, Inc.
17 Kensington Ave
Somerville, MA 02145
Contact: Stephen Gangi Sales
Tel: 617-776-6071
Email: steve@gangiprinting.com
Website: www.gangiprinting.com
Promotional printing & book binding services, printed apparel, trade show displays & direct mail pieces. (Woman, estab 1972, empl 9, sales $1,200,000, cert: State)

7196 Print & More Associates
143 North St
Mattapoisett, MA 02739
Contact: Fred Ford Sales Rep
Tel: 617-899-3664
Email: frford@p-massociates.com
Website: www.p-massociates.com
Commercial printing, stationary, brochures, catalogs, window displays, POP, floor mats & banners. (AA, estab 2005, empl 6, sales $1,000,000, cert: NMSDC)

7197 Pyramid Printing and Advertising Inc
58 Mathewson Dr
Weymouth, MA 02189
Contact: Bill Scheufele Sales Rep
Tel: 781-337-7609
Email: bill@pyramidprinting.net
Website: www.pyramidprinting.net
Multicolor offset & digital graphics. (Woman, estab 1978, empl 14, sales $1,400,000, cert: State)

7198 Schmidt Printing, Inc.
237 Chandler St
Worcester, MA 01609
Contact: Ariel Schmidt Dir Sales/Marketing
Tel: 508-752-7600
Email: ariel@schmidtprinting.ink
Website: www.schmidtprinting.ink
Eight Color Offset Printing, HP Indigo Printing, Variable Data Printing, Stochastic Screening, Online Remote Proofing, In-House Mailing Services, Full Service Bindery & Fulfillment. (Hisp, estab 2011, empl 2, sales , cert: NMSDC)

7199 Shafiis' Inc.
P.O. Box 215
East Longmeadow, MA 01028
Contact: Jennifer Shafii CEO
Tel: 413-224-2100
Email: jennifer@tigerpress.com
Website: www.tigerpress.com
Custom printing, digital prepress, packaging & bindery services. (Woman, estab 1985, empl 70, sales $8,800,000, cert: State)

7200 Spotlight Graphics, Inc.
      9-B Whalley Way
      Southwick, MA 01077
      Contact: Diane Demarco Sales
      Tel: 413-998-3232
      Email: info@SpotlightGraphicsInc.com
      Website: www.SpotlightGraphicsInc.com
Large format printing. (Woman, estab 2013, empl 5, sales
$165,000, cert: State, WBENC)

7201 Standard Modern Company, Inc.
      186 Duchaine Blvd.
      New Bedford, MA 02745
      Contact:
      Tel: 508-586-4300
      Email:
      Website: www.standardmodern.com
Commercial printing. (Woman, estab 1974, empl 44, sales
$7,596,467, cert: State, WBENC)

7202 Starburst Printing & Graphics
      300 Hopping Brook Rd
      Holliston, MA 01764
      Contact: Jason Grondin VP
      Tel: 800-244-8396
      Email: jgrondin@starburstprinting.com
      Website: www.starburstprinting.com
Printing svcs: prepress, digital & offset & post press
services. (Hisp, estab 1988, empl 22, sales $2,600,000,
cert: State, NMSDC)

7203 Summit Press Inc.
      63 Sixth St
      Chelsea, MA 02150
      Contact: Lenore DelVecchio President
      Tel: 617-889-3991
      Email: lsava@summitpress.com
      Website: www.summitpress.com
Printing services: 2-6 color sheetfed. (Woman, estab 1961,
empl 22, sales $2,910,000, cert: State)

7204 The Matlet Group
      30 Industrial Way
      Wilmington, MA 01887
      Contact: Sheldon Ross Dir of Natl Accts
      Tel: 401-834-3007
      Email: sross@thematletgroup.com
      Website: www.thematletgroup.com
Printing & graphic services. (As-Pac, estab 2005, empl 408,
sales $99,498,000, cert: NMSDC)

Maryland

7205 Alpha Graphics, Inc.
      1750 Union Ave, Unit B
      Baltimore, MD 21211
      Contact: Christine Walsh President
      Tel: 410-727-1400
      Email: cwalsh@alphagrap.com
      Website: www.alpha-graphics.net
Large format printing: banners & signs, posters, mounting,
laminating, framing, graphic design, menu boards, adhesive vinyl, cut vinyl, trade show display (Woman, estab
1972, empl 7, sales $853,948, cert: State, City, WBENC)

7206 Art & Negative Graphics, Inc.
      4621 Boston Way Ste C
      Lanham, MD 20706
      Contact: Strategic Acct Exec
      Tel: 301-459-8911
      Email:
      Website: www.artneg.com
Prepress, digital & offset printing; full bindery; mailing
services; storage and fulfillment. (Woman, estab 1981,
empl 42, sales $6,425,530, cert: State, WBENC)

7207 Black Classic Press
      3921 Vero Rd Ste F
      Halethorpe, MD 21227
      Contact: Print Mgr
      Tel: 410-242-6954
      Email:
      Website: www.bcpdigital.com
Printing svcs: ultra short-run book & document printing,
digital. (AA, estab 1978, empl 9, sales $1,500,000, cert:
State)

7208 Britt's Industries Inc.
      40 Hudson St Ste 112
      Annapolis, MD 21401
      Contact: President
      Tel: 410-266-8100
      Email:
      Website: www.wosbprinting.com
Commercial printing, offset, digital, prepress, graphic
design, business cards, envelopes, letterhead, brochures,
pamphlets. (Woman/As-Pac, estab 1976, empl 17, sales
$784,035, cert: WBENC, 8a)

7209 IVY Services, LLC
      P.O. Box 20092
      Baltimore, MD 21284
      Contact: Tammy Boccia VP
      Tel: 410-235-1489
      Email: tboccia@ivy-services.com
      Website: www.ivy-services.com
Offset printing: letterhead, envelopes, business cards,
brochures, flyers, string & button, metal clasp, latex,
peel & seal, tear strip & shrink wrapping. (Woman, estab
2004, empl 2, sales $5,511,950, cert: State, WBENC)

7210 Strouse
      1211 Independence Way
      Westminster, MD 21157
      Contact: Scott Chambers Business Develop Mgr
      Tel: 410-848-1611
      Email: dchambers@strouse.com
      Website: www.strouse.com
Rotary die-cutting, slitting, 6 color printing, laminations.
(Woman, estab 1986, empl 70, sales $18,500,000, cert:
WBENC)

Michigan

7211 Graphic Resource Group
      528 Robbins Dr
      Troy, MI 48083
      Contact: Allen Pyc President
      Tel: 248-588-6100
      Email: apyc@graphicresource.com
      Website: www.graphicresource.com
Large format digital & screen printing, offset printing on
plastics, promotional products. (Woman, estab 1990,
empl 20, sales , cert: WBENC)

7212 Graywolf Printing
      757 S Eton St
      Birmingham, MI 48009
      Contact: Max Grayvold President
      Tel: 248-540-5930
      Email: graywolf@ameritech.net
      Website: www.graywolfprinting.com/
Printing services. (Nat Ame, estab 0, empl 0, sales
$772,368, cert: NMSDC)

7213 Hatteras Printing, Inc.
      12801 Prospect St
      Dearborn, MI 48126
      Contact: Rebecca McFarlane VP
      Tel: 313-624-3300
      Email: bmcfarlane@4hatteras.com
      Website: www.4hatteras.com
Commercial printing. (Woman, estab 1977, empl 70, sales ,
cert: WBENC)

7214 Imax Company Inc.
      22326 Woodward Ave
      Ferndale, MI 48220
      Contact: Jay Williams President
      Tel: 248-629-9680
      Email: jay@imaxprinting.com
      Website: www.imaxprinting.com
Commercial printing, offset full color printing, multi page
booklets, manuals, business cards, brochures, sales sheets,
envelopes, posters, postcards, flyers, rack cards, special
shapes (die cutting). (AA, estab 2009, empl 5, sales
$879,852, cert: NMSDC)

7215 Impact Label Corp.
      3434 S Burdick St
      Kalamazoo, MI 49001
      Contact: Jill Jones Acct Mgr
      Tel: 269-381-4280
      Email: jillj@impactlabel.com
      Website: www.impactlabel.com
Labels, domed labels,tamper evident labels, nameplates,
tags, polycarbonate overlays, control panel overlays,
warning labels, product identification, serial numbers,
security tags, inventory tags, asset labels, ingredient
labels. (Woman, estab 1964, empl 50, sales , cert: WBENC)

7216 Kargilis Business Solutions, LLC
      212 Shagbark Dr.
      Rochester Hills, MI 48309
      Contact: Marilyn Kargilis President
      Tel: 248-477-1145
      Email: kargilisbiz@sbcglobal.net
      Website:
Printing services: business forms, direct mail programs,
commercial printing, labels, manuals, kit assembly,
warehousing, document management & promotional
products. (Woman, estab 0, empl , sales , cert: WBENC)

7217 Kimprint, Inc. dba Progressive Printing
      1326 Goldsmith
      Plymouth, MI 48170
      Contact: Bruce Price VP
      Tel: 734-459-2960
      Email: sales@progressiveprint.com
      Website: www.progressiveprint.com
Full color printing: flyers, brochures, postcards, directmail,
stock & color consulting. (Woman, estab 1989, empl 20,
sales $2,300,000, cert: WBENC)

7218 New Echelon
      280 S Southbound Gratiot Ave
      Mt. Clemens, MI 48043
      Contact: Michael Arnold President
      Tel: 586-307-8001
      Email: mcarnold@newechelon.com
      Website: www.newechelon.com
Printing, bindery, big color output services. (AA, estab
1996, empl 8, sales , cert: NMSDC)

7219 Stylerite Label Corporation
      2140 Avon Industrial Dr
      Rochester Hills, MI 48309
      Contact: Danielle J. Kay Sales Exec
      Tel: 419-367-3772
      Email: dkay@styleritelabel.com
      Website: www.styleritelabel.com
Mfr Tags & Forms, short to long runs, 4 color process up
to 8 colors, rolls, sheets, singles, fan-folded, continuous,
printing on adhesive side of labels, lamination, UV
varnish. (Woman, estab 1989, empl 25, sales
$6,200,000, cert: WBENC)

7220 The MardonGroup LLC
      701 Woodward Heights Ste 128
      Ferndale, MI 48220
      Contact: Shawn Torrence VP Business Dev
      Tel: 248-336-3376
      Email: s.torrence@mardongroup.com
      Website: www.mardongroup.com
Sheet-Fed Printing, Digital Printing, Design, Creative,
Layout, Desktop Publishing, Binding, Envelopes, Mail list
Processing, List Rental/Purchase, Offline Finishing,
Digital/Mobile marketing. (AA, estab 2005, empl 15,
sales , cert: NMSDC)

Minnesota

7221 Booth Publications Ink
      1217 Seminole Ave
      West St Paul, MN 55118
      Contact: Jason Booth CEO
      Tel: 651-338-8140
      Email: jason@boothpublications.com
      Website: http://boothpublications.com
Print services: off-set (web & sheet fed), digital, large
format & plastic card printing. (Nat Ame, estab 1999,
empl 6, sales $3,000,000, cert: NMSDC)

7222 Bywater Business Solutions LLC
      800 Washington Ave SE Ste 203
      Minneapolis, MN 55414
      Contact: Christopher Ferguson CEO
      Tel: 763-244-1090
      Email: chris@bywater.co
      Website: http://bywater.co
Printing: envelopes, labels, letterhead, notecards,
folders, business forms, booklets, checks, business
cards, direct mail, signs, annual reports, post-it notes.
(Hisp, estab 2009, empl 3, sales $185,000, cert: State)

7223 Char-Dell Sign Co.
      1017 109th Ave NE
      Blaine, MN 55434
      Contact: Charlette Grandell VP
      Tel: 763-784-8252
      Email: ken.grandell@fastsigns.com
      Website: http://fastsigns.com/337
Wide Format Digital Printing, Banners, Banner Stands,
Trade Show Booths, Trade Show Graphics,ADA & OSHA
Compliant, Safety & Identification Materials, Presenta-
tion Materials, Posters, Name Tags, Large & Small
Vehicle. (Woman, estab 1998, empl 4, sales $400,000,
cert: City)

7224 Cimarron Graphics
15400 28th Ave N
Plymouth, MN 55447
Contact: Barbara Schulz CEO
Tel: 952-697-3400
Email: barb@cimgraphics.com
Website: www.cimgraphics.com
Commercial sheet fed & digital printing: postcards, catalogs, business forms, calendars, tabs, magnets, greeting cards, envelopes, labels, annual reports, flyers, header cards, inserts, pocket folders. (Woman, estab 2004, empl 15, sales $1,598,609, cert: State)

7225 Clear Lake Press, Inc.
300 16th Ave SE
Waseca, MN 56093
Contact: Phyllis Beschnett CEO
Tel: 507-835-4430
Email: pbeschnett@clearlakepress.com
Website: www.clearlakepress.com
Marketing & printing solutions, sheet-fed, digital & variable, fulfillment, design services, collateral dev & direct marketing, outdoor advertising & customized apparel services. (Woman, estab 1988, empl 34, sales $4,099,574, cert: WBENC)

7226 Dan Dolan Printing
2301 E Hennepin Ave
Minneapolis, MN 55413
Contact: Jeanne Dolan CEO
Tel: 612-379-2311
Email: jeannedolan@dolanprinting.com
Website: www.dolanprinting.com
Printing & marketing services: offset/lithographic printing, digital printing, large format printing, signage, banners, publications, business cards, textile printing, light boxes, trade show displays, pamphlet, letterhead, stationary, printed packaging. (Woman, estab 1985, empl 28, sales $6,434,227, cert: WBENC)

7227 Docunet Corporation
2435 Xenium Ln N
Plymouth, MN 55441
Contact: Wendy Morical President
Tel: 800-936-2863
Email: wnm@docunetworks.com
Website: www.docunetworks.com
Digital printing: black & white, color, database management, direct mail & fulfillment. (Woman, estab 1991, empl 12, sales $1,790,000, cert: WBENC)

7228 Highlight Printing Inc.
3839 Washington Ave N
Minneapolis, MN 55412
Contact: Lisa Bickford President
Tel: 612-522-7600
Email: lisab@highlightprinting.com
Website: www.highlightprinting.com
Offset & digital 1-4 color printing, high-impact high-touch projects, thermography, design, direct mail, warehousing, kitting, niche fulfillment, distribution, work-flow system, saddle stitching, wire-o binding, binding. (Woman, estab , empl , sales $1,205,000, cert: WBENC)

7229 Ideal Printers
645 Olive St
Saint Paul, MN 55130
Contact: Emily Stevenson Acct Rep
Tel: 651-855-1064
Email: emily.stevenson@idealprint.com
Website: www.idealprint.com
Commercial sheetfed printing: 1-6 color & aqueous coating, brochures, newsletters, annual reports, posters, catalogs, packaging, stationary products. (Woman, estab 1979, empl 85, sales $12,625,028, cert: WBENC)

7230 IntegriPrint, Inc.
309 12th Ave S
Buffalo, MN 55313
Contact: Jacqueline Wurm Owner
Tel: 763-682-3750
Email: jackie@integriprint.com
Website: www.integriprint.com
Printing, graphic design & mailing services. (Woman, estab 1994, empl 5, sales $590,338, cert: WBENC)

7231 Lightning Printing dba Wallace Carlson Co.
10825 Greenbrier Rd
Minnetonka, MN 55305
Contact: Ann Turbeville CEO
Tel: 952-277-1210
Email: ann@wc-print.com
Website: www.wc-print.com
Printing svcs: 1-6color offset, sheetfed, aqueous coating, full color & B/W digital printing, mailing & fullfillment services. (Woman, estab 1984, empl 47, sales $9,128,000, cert: WBENC)

7232 Northstar Imaging Services, Inc.
1325 Eagandale Court Ste 130
Eagan, MN 55121
Contact: Martha Smyre CEO
Tel: 651-686-0477
Email: planroom@northstarimaging.com
Website: www.northstarimaging.com
Reprographic services, large & small format copying, plotting, scanning, color imagery & document management. (Woman, estab 1997, empl 5, sales $6,500,000, cert: State, City)

7233 SeaChange Print Innovations
14505 27th Ave N
Plymouth, MN 55447
Contact: Nancy Servais Business Development
Tel: 763-586-3700
Email: nancy.servais@seachangem.com
Website: www.seachangemn.com
Folding carton & marketing print production, Folding Carton Packaging, Marketing Printing, Commercial Printing, Direct Mail Printing, Digital Printing. (Woman, estab 2014, empl 90, sales $13,100,000, cert: WBENC)

7234 Team One Printing, Inc.
635 Ninth St SE, Ste 180
Minneapolis, MN 55414
Contact: Grace Wong President
Tel: 612-481-5907
Email: grace@teamoneprinting.com
Website: www.teamoneprinting.com
Commercial print & display graphics: brochures, newsletters, manuals, directories, catalogs, labels, direct mail pieces, portable trade show displays, banner stands, wall murals, vehicle graphics, sign & banner graphics, large format posters. (Woman/As-Pac, estab 2006, empl 3, sales , cert: NMSDC)

Missouri

7235 Brown Printing, Inc.
411 Madison St
Jefferson City, MO 65101
Contact: Darla Porter President
Tel: 573-636-8012
Email: dporter@brownprint.com
Website: www.modernlitho.com
Commercial printing, digital printing, mailing & fulfillment services, warehousing. (Woman, estab 1982, empl 36, sales $4,224,724, cert: State)

7236 Complete Solutions LLC
2233 N Village
St. Charles, MO 63303
Contact: Donna Gastreich Owner
Tel: 314-640-6633
Email: dgastreich@complete-solutionsllc.com
Website: www.complete-solutionsllc.com
Printing svcs: letterhead, business cards, envelopes, invoices, BOL, labels, tags, folders, binders, index tabs, brochures, catalogs & checks, direct mail services, promotional products & advertising specialty items. (Woman, estab 2008, empl 1, sales , cert: State, City)

7237 Isringhaus Printing LLC
11012 Lin Valle Dr, Ste D
Affton, MO 63123
Contact: Patricia Isringhaus Owner
Tel: 314-416-9955
Email: patti@isringhausprinting.com
Website: www.isringhausprinting.com
Commercial printing services. (Woman, estab 2002, empl 6, sales $600,000, cert: State, WBENC)

7238 Modern Litho-Print Co.
6009 Stertzer Rd
Jefferson City, MO 65101
Contact: Debra Patterson customer consultant
Tel: 573-635-6119
Email: debra@modernlitho.com
Website: www.modernlitho.com
Printing: annual reports, newsletters, books, magazines, promotional materials, labels, etc. (Woman, estab 1937, empl 88, sales $14,500,000, cert: State)

7239 PrintCOR Solutions
826 Heatherhaven Dr
Ballwin, MO 63011
Contact: Kelly Kohn Owner
Tel: 636-891-9900
Email: customerservice@printcorsolutions.com
Website: www.printcorsolutions.com
Labels/tags: blank stock labels, barcode pre-printed product labels, consecutively numbered barcode labels, thermal ribbons, integrated labels, piggy back labels, full color labels, die cut labels & custom labels. (Woman, estab 2006, empl 2, sales $1,500,000, cert: State)

7240 PrintFlex Graphics
2201 January Ave
St. Louis, MO 63110
Contact: Elizabeth Pecha-Poelker CEO
Tel: 800-406-7093
Email: eap@print-flex.com
Website: printflexgraphics.com
Promotional printing: instant redeemable coupons, dry release, folded & placed booklets, USDA & FDA direct food contact printing. (Woman, estab 1995, empl 35, sales $6,128,000, cert: State, NWBOC)

Mississippi

7241 Ranger Distributing, Inc dba Ranger Label
286 Commerce Park Dr
Ridgeland, MS 39157
Contact: Bob Anger VP
Tel: 601-898-1380
Email: banger@rangerlabel.com
Website: www.rangerlabel.com
Prime 8 color pressure sensitive labels, blank thermal labels, complete color process controls. (Woman, estab 1979, empl 14, sales $3,000,000, cert: WBENC)

North Carolina

7242 DocuSource of North Carolina
2800 Slater Rd
Morrisville, NC 27560
Contact: Michael Chorba President
Tel: 919-459-5909
Email: mchorba@docusourceofnc.com
Website: www.docusourceofnc.com
Commercial digital printing, bindery, fulfillment & distribution services. (Woman, estab 2002, empl 46, sales $8,000,000, cert: State)

7243 Labels, Tags & Inserts, Inc.
2302 Air Park Dr
Burlington, NC 27215
Contact: Rhonda Baker President
Tel: 336-227-8485
Email: rhondab@lti-us.com
Website: www.labelstagsandinserts.com
Flexographic printing services: pressure sensitive labels, shrink film sleeves, vinyl labels, scratch off labels, tamper-evident labels, clear labels, hot foil labels, embossed labels, holographic labels. (Woman, estab 1995, empl 27, sales $7,000,000, cert: WBENC)

7244 PharmaPress, Inc.
3360 Old Lexington Rd
Winston-Salem, NC 27107
Contact: Terri Roth President & CEO
Tel: 973-376-6625
Email: pharmapress@gmail.com
Website: www.pharmapressinc.com
Mfr inserts, outserts, booklets, pamphlets, cards and pads. (Woman, estab 2004, empl 164, sales $2,400,000, cert: State)

7245 Progressive Business Solutions, Inc.
508 New Hope Rd
Raleigh, NC 27610
Contact: Tim Catlett President
Tel: 919-255-6500
Email: tcatlett@progform.com
Website: www.progform.com
Commercial printing, business forms, promotional products, web ordering capabilities, office supplies, forms mgmt & warehouse dist. (AA, estab 1988, empl 27, sales $6,000,000, cert: NMSDC)

7246 Southern Print & Imaging, Inc.
9311-D Monroe Rd
Charlotte, NC 28270
Contact: Barbara Jones President
Tel: 704-708-5818
Email: barbara@allegracharlotte.com
Website: www.allegracharlotte.com
Offset & digital printing, mail services, list sourcing, direct mail, brochures, flyers, newsletters, postcards, booklets & promotional products. (Woman, estab 2004, empl 4, sales $411,000, cert: City)

New Jersey

7247 4 Banner Inc. (DBA Alchemy Printing)
125 5th Ave
Paterson, NJ 07524
Contact: Brett Haikins Production Coordinator
Tel: 973-341-1311
Email: jobs@4banner.com
Website: www.4banner.com
Large format printing: vinyl banners, mesh banners, dye sublimation fabric banners, trade show displays, banner stands, flatbed UV printing. (As-Pac, estab 2010, empl 6, sales $550,000, cert: NMSDC)

7248 A+ Letter Service
200 Syracuse Ct
Lakewood, NJ 08701
Contact: Elizabeth Fricke sales support specialist
Tel: 732-905-2010
Email: aplus@aplusletter.com
Website: www.aplusletter.com
Print mailing inserts, postcards, brochures, marketing fulfillment, four-color digital printing, mailing services. (Woman, estab 1986, empl 75, sales $5,000,000, cert: State)

7249 AJ Images.com
259 E First Ave
Roselle, NJ 07203
Contact: Lisa Greebel
Tel: 908-241-6900
Email: lisa@ajimages.com
Website: www.ajimages.com
Commercial printing: brochures, newsletters, annual reports, magazines, technical pieces, posters, postcards, bill stuffers, direct mail, price lists & catalogs. (Woman, estab 1967, empl 23, sales $4,500,000, cert: State)

7250 American Plus Printers, Inc.
2604 Atlantic Ave Ste 300
Wall, NJ 07719
Contact: President & CEO
Tel: 732-528-2170
Email:
Website: www.americanplusprinters.com
Commercial printing, six color printing, digital page processing, photo retouching, color proofing & digital plate-making. (Woman, estab 2002, empl 10, sales $1,150,000, cert: State)

7251 Arna Marketing
60 Readington Road
Branchburg, NJ 08876
Contact: Jakob Hegna Sales Rep
Tel: 908-231-1100
Email: jhegna@arnamarketing.com
Website: www.arnamarketing.com
Digital printing: mailings, brochures, flyers, booklets, envelopes, letterhead, business cards, newsletters, coupons, etc. (Woman, estab 2005, empl 80, sales $40,000,000, cert: WBENC)

7252 Capital Printing Corporation
420 South Ave
Middlesex, NJ 08846
Contact: Brett Russo
Tel: 732-560-1515
Email: brettr@capitalprintingcorp.com
Website: http://capitalprintingcorp.com
Printing services, die cutting & binding, automated in-line gluing & inserting, warehouse & mailing abilities. (Woman, estab 1983, empl 85, sales $15,100,000, cert: WBENC)

7253 CCG Marketing Services
14 Henderson Dr
West Caldwell, NJ 07006
Contact: Steve Stern Sr Acct Exec
Tel: 973-808-0009
Email: sstern@corpcomm.com
Website: www.ccgms.com
Printing, offset, digital with variable data, web 1:1 Marketing with Variable Data, Digital Print Technology, Sales Collateral & Promotional Materials, Sales Force Support, Order Fulfillment. (Woman, estab , empl , sales $20,000,000, cert: WBENC)

7254 CRW Graphics
9100 Pennsauken Hwy
Pennsauken, NJ 08110
Contact: Kathleen Chinnici Acct Director
Tel: 800-820-3000
Email: kchinnici@crwgraphics.com
Website: www.crwgraphics.com
Digital & critical color prepress services & printing: 1 to 6 colors, bindery, fulfillment & mailing services. (Woman, estab 1993, empl 90, sales $15,500,000, cert: WBENC)

7255 Federal Business Products Inc.
150 Clove Road, 5th Floor 5th Fl
Little Falls, NJ 07424
Contact: Angela Stubbs President
Tel: 973-272-7066
Email: astubbs@feddirect.com
Website: http://feddirect.com
Print, direct mail data & fulfillment services: data processing, sheet digital print, continuous form printing to 10 colors, continuous form laser (simplex, duplex, MICR) & inkjet personalization, bindery, fulfillment lettershop mailing services. (Woman, estab , empl , sales $15,663,435, cert: WBENC)

7256 FrontEnd Graphics Inc.
1951 Old Cuthbert Road, Ste 414
Cherry Hill, NJ 08034
Contact: Elizabeth Maul President
Tel: 856-547-1600
Email: bettymaul@frontendgraphics.com
Website: www.frontendgraphics.com
Layout, design, database mgmt, large project mgmt, digital photography, large output, direct to plate & press, finishing, distribution, kitting, mailing. Sheet fed, web, envelopes, label, manual, technical illustration, book publishing. (Woman, estab 1983, empl 13, sales $1,300,000, cert: WBENC)

7257 HighRoad Press, LLC
220 Anderson Ave
Moonachie, NJ 07074
Contact: Hallie Satz CEO
Tel: 201-708-6900
Email: hallie@highroadpress.com
Website: www.highroadpress.com
Printing: web & sheet fed, offset sheet fed printing, offset half web didde press, coldset web & offset full web, packaging. (Woman, estab 2004, empl 45, sales $10,000,000, cert: State, WBENC)

7258 Industrial Labeling Systems, Inc.
50 Kulick Rd
Fairfield, NJ 07004
Contact: Keith Meyer Reg Sales Mgr
Tel: 973-882-9688
Email: kmeyer@e-ilsi.com
Website: www.e-ilsi.com
Mfr & dist pressure-sensitive labels, prime labels, mailing labels, product ID labels, direct thermal labels, supermarket thermal scale labels, coupons, bar codes, tub labels, retail shelf marketing labels. (As-Pac, estab 1997, empl 23, sales $3,500,000, cert: State)

7259 Mahin Impressions, Inc. DBA Kirkwood Mahin
600 Meadowlands Parkway
Secaucus, NJ 07094
Contact: Sharon Mahin President & CEO
Tel: 201-870-6300
Email: smahin@kirkwood-mahin.com
Website: www.kirkwood-mahin.com/
Offset & digital printing, digital & xerograhpy services, large format, finishing, binding, fullfillment & mailing. (Woman, estab 1983, empl 250, sales $20,000,000, cert: WBENC, SDB)

7260 Mountain Printing Company Inc.
P.O. Box 608
Berlin, NJ 08009
Contact: Mark DiClementi Dir of Operations
Tel: 856-767-7600
Email: mark@mountainprinting.com
Website: www.mountainprinting.com
Commerical, packaging & digial printing services: bindery, pre-press, press, bindery, coatings, die cutting, foil stamping, embossing, box mfg & mailing capabilities. (Woman, estab 1962, empl 25, sales $2,499,116, cert: State)

7261 Nextwave Web LLC
229 Marshall St
Paterson, NJ 07503
Contact: Alia Suqi Owner
Tel: 973-742-4339
Email: alia@nextwaveweb.com
Website: www.nextwaveweb.com
Commercial offset & digital printing: print packaging/prototyping posters, banners, displays, customized shaped posters, books, booklets, magazines, catalogs, manuals, newsletters, flyers, brochures. (Woman, estab 2003, empl 8, sales $1,700,000, cert: State, WBENC)

7262 P/EK Press
7 Essex Rd
Scotch Plains, NJ 07076
Contact: Ann Kahn Owner
Tel: 908-305-1960
Email: annelizabethkahn@gmail.com
Website: http://pekpress.com
Commercial printing & graphic design: NCR forms, Brochures, Stationery, Posters, Direct Mail, Letterhead, Envelopes, Business Cards, Postcards, Note Cards, Presentation Folders, Pads. (Woman, estab 1989, empl 1, sales $126,000, cert: State)

7263 Positive Publications LLC
65 Madison Ave Ste 510
Morristown, NJ 07960
Contact: Susan Poeton COO
Tel: 973-218-0310
Email: spoeton@positivepublications.us
Website: www.positivepublications.us
Publishing, magazines, guides, pamphlets, periodicals, reprints, newsletters &
e-newsletters. (Woman, estab 1998, empl 8, sales $827,880, cert: State)

7264 Primary Colors Graphics Inc.
629 Grove St 7th Fl
Jersey City, NJ 07310
Contact: Cecilia Chin Controller
Tel: 201-526-9300
Email: cecilia@primarycolorsgraphics.com
Website: www.primarycolorsgraphics.com
Commercial Offset Printing, Lithographic Printing, business cards, posters, finishing, trimming, die-cut, score, foil stamping, embossing. (As-Pac, estab 2012, empl 12, sales $1,303,673, cert: State)

7265 Riegal Printing Inc.
One Graphics Dr
Ewing, NJ 08628
Contact: Brian Haley Acct Exec
Tel: 609-771-0555
Email: brian.haley@riegelcg.com
Website: www.riegelprintinginc.com
Digital pre-press services, conventional multi-color printing capabilities, digital print on demand, bindery & finishing, foil stamping, embossing, debossing & diecutting. (Woman, estab 1935, empl 75, sales $28,000,000, cert: WBENC)

7266 RJ Graphics, Inc.
206 Crown Point Rd
West Deptford, NJ 08086
Contact: John Iannelli Director
Tel: 856-848-1986
Email: jiannelli@rjgraphicsprinting.com
Website: www.rjgraphicsprinting.com
Commercial sheet-fed printing, digital printing, fulfillment, direct mail & web creative services. (Woman, estab 1979, empl 22, sales $3,300,000, cert: WBENC)

7267 Sheroy Printing
220 Entin Rd
Clifton, NJ 07014
Contact: Robert Sternau Dir New Business Devel
Tel: 973-242-4040
Email: roberts@onesourcenj.com
Website: www.onesourcenj.com
Graphic communications, marketing collateral, annual reports, catalogs, presentation kits, packaging, wide format point-of-purchase materials, direct mail & publications. (Woman, estab 1984, empl 65, sales $2,000,000, cert: State)

7268 Wheal-Grace Corporation
300 Ralph St
Belleville, NJ 07109
Contact: Emil Salvini Dir of Marketing
Tel: 973-450-8100
Email: salvini@wheal-grace.com
Website: www.wheal-grace.com
Printing: corporate literature, product information, news magazines, business cards, letterheads, portfolios, posters. (Woman, estab 1946, empl 16, sales $11,301,000, cert: State)

New Mexico

7269 Captiva Group
3838 Bogan Ave NE
Albuquerque, NM 87109
Contact: Jane Fernandez VP Business Dev
Tel: 505-872-2200
Email: jfernandez@thecaptivagroup.com
Website: www.thecaptivagroup.com
Four color offset commercial printing; newsletters, business forms, envelopes, posters, books, etc. (Hisp, estab 1981, empl 100, sales $22,000,000, cert: NMSDC)

7270 R.W. Chavez, Inc.
1361 Flight Way SE
Albuquerque, NM 87106
Contact: Nate Tapia Sales
Tel: 505-264-2453
Email: nate@stixon.com
Website: www.stixon.com
Commercial flexographic printing & mfr labels, pressure sensitive labels. (Woman/Hisp, estab 1985, empl 15, sales $2,800,000, cert: NWBOC)

Nevada

7271 Haig's Quality Printing
6360 Sunset Corporate Dr
Las Vegas, NV 89120
Contact: Garo Atamian VP
Tel: 702-966-1000
Email: gatamian@haigsprinting.com
Website: http://haigsprinting.com
Commercial print and mail shop, off-set and digital. (Woman, estab 1996, empl 25, sales $3,500,000, cert: WBENC)

New York

7272 Ampie Enterprises, Inc.
100 College Ave Ste 130
Rochester, NY 14607
Contact: Tina Paradiso President
Tel: 585-482-4400
Email: tinap@imprintablesolutions.com
Website: http://imprintablesolutions.com
Envelopes, forms, carbonless sheets, reports, brochures & informational collateral. (Woman, estab 2013, empl 8, sales $1,500,000, cert: State)

7273 Bell Imaging Inc.
2055 Cruger Ave, Ste 5E
Bronx County, NY 10462
Contact: Megan Blackburn Sales Mgr
Tel: 862-262-6128
Email: mblackburn@bellimagingonline.com
Website: www.bellimagingonline.com
Printing services,1 to 6 color, commercial & direct mail, bindery, pre-press, fullfilment. (AA, estab 2004, empl 8, sales , cert: NMSDC)

7274 Brigar XPress Solutions Inc, dba Digital XPress
5 Sand Creek Rd
Albany, NY 12205
Contact: Tracy Terry VP Sales
Tel: 518-437-5349
Email: tracy@dxp1.com
Website: www.dxp1.com
Print and mail services, offset, digital, and large format printing. (Minority, Woman, estab 1988, empl 72, sales $9,435,127, cert: State)

7275 Classic Labels Inc.
217 River Ave
Patchogue, NY 11772
Contact: Steven Ayala President
Tel: 718-463-0256
Email: sayala@classiclabels.com
Website: www.classiclabels.com
Specialty pressure sensitive labels. (Hisp, estab 1979, empl 100, sales , cert: NMSDC)

7276 Dakota Print and Premiums LLC
150 Barton Road
White Plains, NY 10605
Contact: Stuart Standard President
Tel: 914-831-9101
Email: stuart@fuseprinting.com
Website: www.fuseprinting.com
Promotional products, commercial printing, wide format & transit advertising, vehicle wraps, directories, transit & marketing tools provider, screen printing, banners, posters, postcards, journals, award items, etc. (Woman/AA, estab 2004, empl 3, sales $606,000, cert: State, City, NMSDC)

7277 Fred Weidner & Daughter Printers
15 Maiden Ln, Ste 1601
New York, NY 10038
Contact: Cynthia Weidner President
Tel: 212-964-8676
Email: cynthia@fwdprinters.com
Website: www.fwdprinters.com
Printing services. (Woman, estab , empl 6, sales , cert: State)

7278 Fulcrum Group
135 W 41st St
New York, NY 10036
Contact: Partner
Tel: 203-909-6362
Email:
Website: www.fulcrumgrp.com
Incentive Programs, Apparel, Promotional Merchandise, Printing & Creative Services, Large Format & Signage, Event Production, E-commerce& Fulfillment, Print Media. (Woman, estab 2010, empl 7, sales $1,200,000, cert: WBENC)

7279 Graphic Arts Inc.
11 Bertel Ave
Mount Vernon, NY 10550
Contact: Wayne Purveille
Tel: 914-663-8395
Email: wp@graphicartsinc.net
Website: www.graphicartsinc.net
Design & print brochures, newsletters, pamphlets, pocket folders, annual reports, sheets catalog mailing inserts, etc. (Woman/AA, estab 1994, empl 9, sales , cert: State, City, NMSDC)

7280 Minority Graphics Inc.
4202 Third Ave
Brooklyn, NY 11232
Contact: President
Tel: 212-255-4355
Email: alec@minoritygraphics.com
Website: www.minoritygraphics.com
Offset & digital printing, fulfillment. (Woman/AA, estab 2004, empl 3, sales $190,000, cert: City, NMSDC)

7281 New York Image Studio LLC
68 Jay St Ste 810
Brooklyn, NY 11201
Contact: Carole Fakler Owner
Tel: 212-400-8889
Email: carole@nyimagestudio.com
Website: www.nyimagestudio.com
Post Production, PrePress, Image Editing, Photo Re-touching, Digital Printing, Large format printing, CGI, Design. (Woman, estab 2011, empl 5, sales $450,000, cert: State)

7282 No Other Impressions, Inc.
27 Tower Dr
Rochester, NY 14623
Contact: Elaine McCarthy CEO
Tel: 585-436-8500
Email: elaine@nootherimpressions.com
Website: www.nootherimpressions.com
Commercial color printing & fullfillment, digital & offset printing process. Complete in house bindery & fullfillment services. (Woman, estab 1990, empl 15, sales $1,800,000, cert: WBENC)

7283 North American D.F., Inc.
280 Watchogue Rd
Staten Island, NY 10314
Contact: DEBBIE AYALA President
Tel: 718-698-2500
Email: debbie@northamericandf.com
Website: www.northamericandf.com
Commercial printing: eight color, web & sheet fed, business forms, brochures, booklets, business stationary, folders, direct mailers, posters labels. (Woman, estab 1992, empl 10, sales $3,000,000, cert: State, City, WBENC)

7284 Panther Graphics Inc.
465 Central Ave
Rochester, NY 14605
Contact: Henry Ehindero Sales Mgr
Tel: 585-546-7163
Email: henry@panthergraphics.net
Website: www.panthergraphics.net
Commercial printing: brochures, coupons, marketing & promotional materials, large format printing, folding cartons, kit packing & distribution. (AA, estab 1993, empl 25, sales $1,035,000, cert: City)

Ohio

7285 Associated Visual Communications, Inc.
200 Cherry Ave NE
Canton, OH 44702
Contact: Raymond J Gonzalez President
Tel: 330-452-4449
Email: rgonzalez@avcprint.com
Website: www.avcprint.com
Printing services: screen, digital & offset. (Hisp, estab 1979, empl 32, sales $2,814,501, cert: NMSDC)

7286 Bridge Media, LLC
1457 E 252nd St Ste 100
Euclid, OH 44117
Contact: Craig Brooks, Sr. President
Tel: 216-526-3044
Email: craig@bridge-ohio.com
Website: www.bridge-ohio.com
Printing: professional business cards, brochures & promotional materials, annual reports & glossy publications. (AA, estab 2008, empl 4, sales , cert: State)

7287 Cannell Graphics
5787 Linworth Rd
Worthington, OH 43085
Contact: Phil Ferguson CEO
Tel: 614-330-9110
Email: pferguson@cannellgraphics.biz
Website: www.cannellgraphics.biz
Large & small digital, screen, offset format, mounting & laminating, scanning, document management, litigation support, copier services. (Woman/AA, estab 1964, empl 7, sales , cert: State, NMSDC)

7288 Commodity Management Services CMS
7233 Freedom Ave. NW
North Canton, OH 44720
Contact: Curt Keels Business Develop Exec
Tel: 614-207-2707
Email: ckeels@cmsprintsolutions.com
Website: www.cmsprintsolutions.com
Printing: business forms, print mgmt, print solutions, labels. (AA, estab 1999, empl 525, sales $72,893,797, cert: NMSDC)

7289 Copy King, Inc.
3333 Chester Ave
Cleveland, OH 44114
Contact: Peg Walsh President
Tel: 216-861-3377
Email: peg@copy-king.com
Website: www.copy-king.com
Digital & offset press printing, binding, in house graphic design services, digital color printing, posters & large format printing, business cards. (Woman, estab 1995, empl 21, sales , cert: City)

7290 Corporate Document Solutions, Inc.
11120 Ashburn Rd
Cincinnati, OH 45240
Contact: Mary Percy President
Tel: 513-595-8200
Email: mpercy@cdsprint.com
Website: www.cdsPRINT.com
Design & pre-press services, layout compatibility, graphic file resolution, press imaging sizes & preferred file submission methods, black & white printing. (Woman, estab 1992, empl 18, sales $2,000,000, cert: WBENC)

7291 D Johnson Enterprises
912 Thayer Dr
Columbus, OH 43230
Contact: President
Tel: 614-440-7559
Email:
Website: www.djohnson-ent.com
Printing & imprinting services: digital 1-6 color & full color, news & media, scanning, digitizing, bulk mailing, books, charts, maps, brochures, menus, programs, wide angle custom formats, ad inserts, fliers, folders, envelopes. (AA, estab 1982, empl 8, sales $250,000, cert: NMSDC)

7292 Dana Graphics, Inc.
P.O. Box 42219
Cincinnati, OH 45242
Contact: Mgr, cstmr service
Tel: 513-351-4400
Email:
Website: www.danalink.com
Graphic design, commercial & digital printing. (Woman, estab 1980, empl 8, sales $387,000, cert: WBENC)

7293 Dancor Inc.
2155 Dublin Rd
Columbus, OH 43228
Contact: Michael Michalski Controller
Tel: 614-737-3221
Email: mmichalski@dancorinc.com
Website:
Commercial printing. (Woman, estab 0, empl , sales $8,041,000, cert: WBENC)

7294 DINATCO Inc.
814 Morrison Rd
Gahanna, OH 43230
Contact: Tony Segarra President
Tel: 614-367-1910
Email: tony-segarra@crossbowsystems.net
Website: www.crossbowsystems.net
Design and Installation Services, Technology Infrastructure Engineering, and Media Services. Our core competency is voice and data structural cable infrastructure design and installation. (Hisp, estab 2009, empl 8, sales , cert: State)

7295 Hooven-Dayton Corporation
511 Byers Rd
Miamisburg, OH 45342
Contact: Evan Arrindell VP Sales & Marketing
Tel: 937-233-4473
Email: diversesupplier1@hoovendayton.com
Website: www.hoovendayton.com
print & convert pressure sensitive labels, coupons & custom specific solutions. (AA, estab 1935, empl 101, sales $24,899,000, cert: NMSDC)

7296 IC3D
      1697 Westbelt Dr
      Columbus, OH 43228
      Contact: Michael Cao CEO
      Tel: 614-260-5631
      Email: michael@ic3dprinters.com
      Website: www.ic3dprinters.com/
3D printing services, prototyping & low volume manufacturing. (As-Pac, estab 2012, empl 10, sales $500,000, cert: NMSDC)

7297 Identification Systems, Inc. dba Identity Systems,
      1324 Stimmel Road
      Columbus, OH 43223
      Contact: DeeDee Warden Acct Exec
      Tel: 614-448-1741
      Email: dwarden@identitysystemsinc.com
      Website: www.identitysystemsinc.com
Commercial screen printing: vinyl, styrene, ABS & engraveable stock. Mfr name badges, signage, architectural signage, signage systems inserts, accordion/ spiral signs, engraved signs, nameplates, equipment tags, decals, plaques. (Woman, estab 1986, empl 34, sales $3,626,392, cert: WBENC)

7298 JSCS Group, Inc. dba Market Direct
      3478 Hauck Road, Ste C
      Cincinnati, OH 45241
      Contact: Stephanie Harmon President
      Tel: 513-563-4900
      Email: stephanie@marketdirectinc.com
      Website: www.marketdirectinc.com
Printing: offset & digital on-demand, direct marketing, direct mailing & fulfillment, mailing, target list development & management, graphic design. (AA, estab 2004, empl 5, sales $130,000, cert: NMSDC)

7299 Link to Success dba HARKNESServices
      947 E Johnstown Rd, Ste 127
      Gahanna, OH 43230
      Contact: Tara Harkness President
      Tel: 888-959-4203
      Email: tharkness@harknessservices.com
      Website: www.harknesservices.com
Printing services. (Woman/AA, estab 2011, empl 8, sales $41,222,200, cert: State, NMSDC)

7300 RPI Color Service, Inc.
      1950 Radcliff Dr
      Cincinnati, OH 45204
      Contact: Karen Rellar EVP Mktg/Communications
      Tel: 513-471-4040
      Email: karen.rellar@rpigraphic.com
      Website: www.rpigraphic.com
Off-set & digital printing, large & small format printing, die cutting, bindery & finishing, on demand printing, signage, packaging, sales samples, prototyping, displays, mailing services, point of sale materials, web-based tools. (Woman, estab 1969, empl 50, sales $8,500,000, cert: WBENC)

7301 Swimmer Printing dba Alphagraphics
      1701 E 12th St
      Cleveland, OH 44114
      Contact: Judith Swimmer President
      Tel: 216-623-1005
      Email: us320@alphagraphics.com
      Website: www.us320.alphagraphics.com
One to four color offset printing, B&W & color copy services, Mailing services, Digital archiving, Poster & banner printing, Prepress & design services, Finishing & bindery services. (Woman, estab 1991, empl 9, sales $1,400,000, cert: City)

7302 Ten 10 Design LLC
      119 Main St
      Chardon, OH 44024
      Contact: Joe Zulandt VP New Business Development
      Tel: 440-286-4367
      Email: joe@ten10design.com
      Website: www.ten10design.com
Printing (offset and digital), promotional items, ad specialties, mailing services, labels & decals, graphic design, web design. (Woman/AA, estab 2009, empl 6, sales $3,093,663, cert: State, NMSDC, WBENC)

7303 Three Leaf Productions, Inc.
      261 West Johnstown Road Ste 200
      Gahanna, OH 43230
      Contact: Ron Stokes President & CEO
      Tel: 614-626-4941
      Email: rstokes@three-leaf.com
      Website: www.three-leaf.com
Commercial & large digital format printing: retail packaging, point of purchase displays, banners & signs, fulfillment services, pick & pack, kitting, promotional premiums. (AA, estab 1995, empl 15, sales $10,271,000, cert: State, NMSDC)

Oklahoma

7304 OakTree Software, Inc.
      1437 S Boulder Ave, Ste 300
      Tulsa, OK 74119
      Contact: Tony Floyd Business Development
      Tel: 918-584-7900
      Email: tony.floyd@oaktreesoftware.com
      Website: http://oaktreesoftware.com
IT Consulting, training and services (Woman, estab 1995, empl 100, sales $10,000,000, cert: WBENC)

7305 Professional Image
      12437 E 60th St
      Tulsa, OK 74146
      Contact: President
      Tel: 918-461-0609
      Email:
      Website: www.pi-pkg.com
Printing svcs: full color, digital prepress, custom graphic design, digital die templates, foil stamping, aqueous & UV coating, lamination, embossing, color mgmt. (Woman, estab 1984, empl 43, sales , cert: WBENC)

Oregon

7306 Industrial Safety Solutions Corporation
      14791 SE 82nd Dr
      Clackamas, OR 97015
      Contact: Rhonda Evans President
      Tel: 503-303-5958
      Email: revans@industrialsafetysolution.com
      Website: www.industrialsafetysolution.com
Industrial labeling systems, in-house pipe marking, 5S, Kaizen & general directional labeling. (Woman/As-Pac, estab 2004, empl 6, sales $854,257, cert: State)

7307 PrintSync, Inc.
      6775 SW 111th Ave, Ste 10
      Beaverton, OR 97008
      Contact: President
      Tel: 503-520-2000
      Email:
      Website: www.printsync.com
Printing & copying, direct mail & fulfillment. (Woman, estab 1991, empl 10, sales $2,048,000, cert: WBENC)

Pennsylvania

7308 Brenneman Printing, Inc.
1909 Olde Homestead Lane
Lancaster, PA 17601
Contact: Dir Sales & Marketing
Tel: 717-299-2847
Email: ed.nevling@brennemaninc.com
Website: www.brennemaninc.com
Commercial printing: offset printing 1-5 colors, thermography, digital printing, variable data printing, inkjet addressing, mailing services, inserting, database management, online ordering storefronts, mail list acquisition, custom distribution services. (Woman, estab 1969, empl 30, sales , cert: State, WBENC)

7309 Chaucer Press, Inc.
535 Stewart Rd
Wilkes-Barre, PA 18706
Contact: Patricia Frances CEO
Tel: 570-825-2005
Email: pfrances@chaucerpress.com
Website: www.chaucerpress.com
Printed packaging & on-pack promotional materials: pressure-sensitive, cut & extended content labels, folding cartons, inserts, on-serts, blister cards, sleeves, foilstamping, embossing, screen printing, structural design. (Woman, estab 1965, empl 52, sales $15,000,000, cert: WBENC)

7310 Diamond Graphics Inc.
456 Acorn Lane
Downingtown, PA 19335
Contact: Barbara Martin Owner
Tel: 610-269-7010
Email: barb@diamondgraphicsprint.com
Website: www.diamondgraphicsprint.com
Commercial Printing, Direct Mail, Web Offset, Brochures, Pharmaceutical inserts, Letters, Flyers, Circulars, Instruction Manuals, Note Pads, Inserts, Reply Cards, Order Cards. (Woman, estab 1999, empl 40, sales $6,500,000, cert: WBENC)

7311 Graphic Arts, Incorporated
2867 East Alleghany Ave
Philadelphia, PA 19134
Contact: Fred Binder Acct Exec
Tel: 215-382-5500
Email: fbinder@galitho.com
Website: www.galitho.com
Full color sheet fed printing: finish, fulfill & mail. (Woman, estab 1928, empl 100, sales $6,135,881, cert: City, WBENC)

7312 Imprints Unlimited Inc.
5070 Parkside Ave, Ste 3500B
Philadelphia, PA 19131
Contact: Andrew D. Magnus CEO
Tel: 215-879-9484
Email: andrew@imprints-unlimited.com
Website: www.imprints-unlimited.com
Commercial printing. (AA, estab 1985, empl 6, sales $620,553, cert: State)

7313 Innovation Marketing Communications LLC
232 Conestoga Rd
Wayne, PA 19154
Contact: George Slater Major Accts Mgr
Tel: 215-802-2885
Email: gslater@phoenixlitho.com
Website: http://innomc.com
Creative, offset & digital printing, wide format, physical & virtual events, warehousing & web-to-print solutions. (As-Pac, estab 1973, empl 92, sales $20,500,000, cert: NMSDC)

7314 Lizzie Bullets LLC dba KDC
2100 Babcock Blvd.
Pittsburgh, PA 15209
Contact: Kristine King CEO
Tel: 412-446-2784
Email: kking@printpgh.com
Website: www.printpgh.com
Print and communication: digital printing, conventional/commercial offset printing & wide format signage & banners, design, data archiving, direct mail, variable data and web-to-print services. (Woman, estab 2005, empl 22, sales $2,650,000, cert: WBENC)

7315 Migu Press Inc.
260 Ivyland Rd
Warminster, PA 18974
Contact: Ken Bucker New Business Devel
Tel: 215-957-9763
Email: kenb@migu4u.com
Website: migu4u.com
Commercial printing. (Woman, estab 1988, empl 28, sales , cert: State, WBENC)

7316 Movad
801 Bristol Pike
Bensalem, PA 19020
Contact: Terri Gasbarra Business Development
Tel: 215-638-2679
Email: bhanf@gostrata.com
Website: www.movadcorp.com
Digital & offset printing, mailing services, bindery & finishing, fulfillment, variable data printing, database services, graphic design & pre-press, online ordering & proofing. (Woman, estab 1986, empl 11, sales $1,500,000, cert: WBENC)

7317 PAP Technologies, Inc.
1813 Colonial Village Ln
Lancaster, PA 17601
Contact: Michael Robinson President
Tel: 717-399-3333
Email: mrobinson@paptech.net
Website: www.paptech.net
Printing, warehousing, distribution, fulfillment & machine automation, electrical control panels. (AA, estab 1988, empl 54, sales , cert: State, NMSDC)

7318 Standard Offset Printing Co., Inc.
433 Pearl St
Reading, PA 19603
Contact: Hobart Clark Rep
Tel: 610-375-6174
Email: hclark@standardgroup.com
Website: http://standardgroup.com
Printing: 6 color offset printing, digital black & white, digital full color, aqueous coating, film lamination, UV coatings, online storefront ordering
trim, fold, stitch, die cutting, coil binding
hand assembly, flexible laminated magnets. (Woman, estab , empl 160, sales $25,000,000, cert: State)

7319 TMMPROMOS.COM dba The Artifactori
140 Christopher Ln, Ste 101
Harleysville, PA 19438
Contact: Victoria Magagna President
Tel: 215-513-1693
Email: tori@theartifactori.com
Website: www.theartifactori.com
Commercial Printing, Large-Format Printing, Direct mail, Fulfillment, Warehousing, and Custom Distribution, Branded Promotional Products, and Custom Apparel. (Woman, estab 2014, empl 3, sales $617,000, cert: WBENC)

7320   Triangle Press Inc.
       6720 Allentown Blvd
       Harrisburg, PA 17112
       Contact: Tammy Shelley VP
       Tel: 717-541-9315
       Email: tammy@trianglepress.net
       Website: www.trianglepress.net
Graphic design, wide format printing, digital printing,
variable data, 5-color offset printing, fulfillment &
delivery. (Woman, estab 1970, empl 21, sales
$3,175,100, cert: WBENC)

7321   Unity Printing Co., Inc.
       5848 State Route 981
       Latrobe, PA 15650
       Contact: Lori Askins President
       Tel: 724-537-5800
       Email: lori@unipakcorp.net
       Website: www.UnityPrinting.com
Digital Printing, Offset Printing, Direct Mail, services,
Variable Data Services, Warehousing. (Woman, estab
1979, empl 40, sales $3,660,000, cert: WBENC)

7322   Universal Printing Company LLC
       1205 O'Neill Hwy
       Dunmore, PA 18512
       Contact: Margaret McGrath CEO
       Tel: 570-342-1243
       Email: mah@universalprintingcompany.com
       Website: www.universalprintingcompany.com
Commercial printing, fulfillment, 4, 8 & 10 color presses
with roll-to-sheet capabilities. (Woman, estab 1995,
empl 150, sales $32,396,000, cert: WBENC)

Peurto Rico

7323   3A Press
       P.O. Box 47
       Lajas, PR 00667
       Contact: Marie Rosado President
       Tel: 787-899-0110
       Email: mrosado@3apress.com
       Website: www.3apress.com
Mfr & print pharmaceutical, commercial & folding
cartons, inserts, stitched & perfect bound booklets/
magazines, printed literature. (Hisp, estab 1996, empl
126, sales $11,200,000, cert: NMSDC)

7324   Pardo and Company, LLC
       P.O. Box 190639
       San Juan, PR 00919
       Contact: Isabel Pardo President
       Tel:
       Email: isabel.pardo@pardoandcompany.com
       Website: www.pardoandcompany.com
Pardo and Company (ï¿½Pardoï¿½) is an enterprise that
has a close relationship with Bio-Nuclear of Puerto Rico,
Inc. We not only purchase and resell products from
then, but we share facilities (given our lease agreement)
(Woman/Hisp, estab 2013, empl 1, sales , cert: NMSDC)

South Carolina

7325   National Beverage Screen Printers, Inc
       12000 Main St
       Williston, SC 29853
       Contact: Janet Roberson President
       Tel: 803-266-5272
       Email: jroberson@nbsinc.net
       Website: www.nbsinc.net
Screen printing, digital printing, plastic injection & metal
fabrication. (Woman, estab 1984, empl 38, sales
$7,000,000, cert: WBENC)

7326   Print Solutions Inc.
       1273 Bowater Rd
       Rock Hill, SC 29732
       Contact: Wyman Wilson Acct Rep
       Tel: 803-366-1510
       Email: wyman.wilson@printsolutions.org
       Website: www.printsolutions.org
Thermal Products, Printheads, Ribbons, Labels & Tags,
Continuous Labels & Tags Laser Labels & Tags Custom,
Stock Labels & Tags. (Woman, estab 2001, empl 3, sales
$325,000, cert: State)

Tennessee

7327   A-1 Printing Services
       810 E Brooks Rd
       Memphis, TN 38116
       Contact: Frazer Windless President
       Tel: 901-396-2023
       Email: fwindless@a1printingsvc.com
       Website: www.a1printingsvc.com
Commercial sheet-fed printing. (AA, estab 1988, empl
12, sales $1,179,800, cert: NMSDC)

7328   Broadwater & Associates Group, Inc.
       315 Tenth Ave N, Ste 93
       Nashville, TN 37203
       Contact: Al Jenkins Solutions Consultant
       Tel: 615-256-6707
       Email: al.jenkins@broadwaterprint.com
       Website: www.broadwaterprint.com
Commercial printing, promotional products. (AA, estab
2001, empl 5, sales $353,000, cert: State)

7329   Graphic Label Solutions
       2407 Pulaski Hwy
       Columbia, TN 38401
       Contact: Bob Offord VP
       Tel: 931-490-0019
       Email: bob.offord@abrandcompany.com
       Website: https://graphiclabelsolutions.com/
Labels, decals, overlays, nameplates, membrane
switches, RFID, EAS. (Woman, estab 2002, empl 5, sales
$5,000,000, cert: State, WBENC)

7330   Resource Regeneration LLC dba S3 Asset Manage-
       ment
       1309 Elm Hill Pike
       Nashville, TN 37210
       Contact: Rod McDaniel CEO
       Tel: 615-873-4466
       Email: rmcdaniel@s3rs.com
       Website: www.s3rs.com
Printing services. (AA, estab 2006, empl 20, sales
$500,000, cert: NMSDC)

7331   Tec-Print, LLC
       4600 Cromwell Ave, Ste 101
       Memphis, TN 38118
       Contact: Lynn Higgs Business Develop
       Tel: 865-471-1846
       Email: lhiggs@nashua.com
       Website: www.tec-print.com
Printing: labels, tickets, cash register receipts, brochures,
pamphlets, forms, digital off-set or roll fed web, etc. (AA,
estab 2004, empl 23, sales $896,000, cert: NMSDC)

7332 Women in Printing, LLC
2285 Hwy 47 N
White Bluff, TN 37187
Contact: Teri Doochin President
Tel: 615-797-9811
Email: tdoochin@womeninprinting.com
Website: www.womeninprinting.com
Flexographic & offset printing, films & laminated structures, labels, coupons, blister-board, offset and rotary printing, finished pouches & bags. (Woman, estab 2004, empl 15, sales $2,500,000, cert: WBENC)

7333 Worldwide Business Group
158 Madison Ave, Ste 101
Memphis, TN 38103
Contact: Reg Sales Mgr
Tel: 901-454-9290
Email:
Website: http://worldwidebg.com
Printed product labels: pressure sensitive, reseal & extended content, bill paper forms, jumbo roll forms & Information for Use inserts. (AA, estab 2000, empl 26, sales $5,000,000, cert: NMSDC)

Texas

7334 AC Printing LLC
3400-1 S Raider Dr
Euless, TX 76040
Contact: Robert Bolt Sales
Tel: 817-267-8990
Email: acpsales@acprinting.com
Website: www.acprinting.com
Commercial printing. (As-Ind, estab 1989, empl 40, sales $7,790,014, cert: State, NMSDC, SDB)

7335 Advanced Business Graphics, Inc.
680 S Royal Lane, Ste 200
Coppell, TX 75019
Contact: Sales
Tel: 972-471-3740
Email: abgi@abgi.com
Website: www.abgi.com
Printed products-business forms, checks, labels, commercial printing, promotional items, packaging, printer supplies, stationery items, presentation materials, office supplies. (Woman, estab 1995, empl 8, sales $5,884,880, cert: State, WBENC)

7336 Alliance of Diversity Printers, LLC
15950 Dallas Parkway Ste 400
Dallas, TX 75248
Contact: Terri Quinton CEO
Tel: 214-856-8368
Email: terri@adp-llc.com
Website: www.adp-llc.com
Print management solution. (Woman/AA, As-Pac, Hisp, estab 2008, empl 12, sales $12,700,000, cert: State, NMSDC, WBENC)

7337 Bayside Printing Co, Inc
160 Lockhaven Dr
Houston, TX 77073
Contact: David Solis VP Business Dev
Tel: 281-209-9500
Email: david@baysideprinting.com
Website: www.baysideprinting.com
Commercial multi-color printing: prepress, multiple sheet fed presses, 6 color, coaters, in-house bindery, die cutting & assembly, mailing & fulfillment. (Woman/Hisp, estab 1973, empl 30, sales $7,000,000, cert: NMSDC, WBENC)

7338 Best Press Inc.
4201 Airborn Dr
Addison, TX 75001
Contact: Bobby Yocum Marketing/Business Develop
Tel: 972-930-1000
Email: admin@bestpress.com
Website: www.bestpress.com
Commercial printing. (Woman, estab 1993, empl 100, sales $13,200,000, cert: State, WBENC)

7339 Creative Menus & Folders, LLC dba Texas Covers
409 Old Hwy 80
Olden, TX 76466
Contact: Renee Forguson Asst Production Mgr
Tel: 254-653-2775
Email: reneeforguson@texascovers.com
Website: http://texascovers.com
Presentation/Executive Binders, folders, business cards, printing (screen, digital, offset, foil stamp, deboss, specialty color cast printing, plastic ID badge holders, ID badges, name tags, souvenir printing, banners, signage, laminating, caps. (As-Pac, estab 2015, empl , sales $135,353, cert: NMSDC)

7340 Digi-Color, LP
4414 Hollister
Houston, TX 77040
Contact: Barkla Tully Managing Partner
Tel: 713-934-9800
Email: barkla@digi-color.com
Website: www.digi-color.com
Digital printing; climate-controlled warehousing & fulfillment, mailing, on-line inventory management - ordering & reporting, on-demand 4 color & black/white digital printing, document management services, binding & finishing, packaging, kitting. (Woman, estab 2004, empl 20, sales $4,525,142, cert: State, WBENC)

7341 Dragonfly Group
1015 Amesbury Dr
Murphy, TX 75094
Contact: Laura McClain President
Tel: 972-742-2215
Email: laura@thedragonflygroup.net
Website: www.thedragonflygroup.net
Print production & creative design: litho, UV, web, silkscreen, digital & flexo printing, full bindery, finishing, diecutting, assembly, kitting & fulfillment. (Woman/Nat Ame, estab 2004, empl , sales $1,163,510, cert: WBENC)

7342 Dream Big Media Solutions dba Alphagraphics 114
7801 Mesquite Bend Dr
Irving, TX 75063
Contact: Sam Reed Owner
Tel: 972-570-0868
Email: us114@alphagraphics.com
Website: www.us114.alphagraphics.com
Printing, graphic design, marketing, and signage, envelopes, brochures, blueprints, business cards, digital printing, letterhead, forms, postcards, stationery, banners, signs, wall graphics. (AA, estab 1984, empl 5, sales $1,047,076, cert: State, NMSDC)

7343   Dynamic Color Graphics
P.O. Box 161758
Fort Worth, TX 76161
Contact: Kathy Bowers President
Tel: 817-520-6631
Email: kathy@dynamiccolorgraphics.com
Website: www.dynamiccolorgraphics.com
Printing: large format digital printing, banners, posters, trade show graphics, booths, vehicle graphics, floor graphics, murals, fine art reproduction, digital photo lab. (Woman, estab 2000, empl 19, sales $9,403,342, cert: State)

7344   Exalt Printing Solutions
1875 Monetary Lane
Carrollton, TX 75006
Contact: Lisa Marta CEO
Tel: 972-245-3858
Email: lisa@exaltprinting.com
Website: www.exaltprinting.com
Printing, promotional & office products, forms, labels, brochures, checks, direct mail. (Woman, estab , empl , sales $8,150,000, cert: State, WBENC)

7345   FBC Enterprises, Inc.
5110 Rondo Dr
Fort Worth, TX 76106
Contact: Teresa McClain Sales Rep
Tel: 817-740-1951
Email: tmcclain@customgs.com
Website: www.customgs.com
Commercial printing, web & sheetfed, bindery svcs: direct mail, booklets, catalogs, posters, pocket folders, door hangers & brochures, hand assembly, kitting, custom distribution & fulfillment. (Woman, estab 1990, empl 45, sales $4,500,000, cert: WBENC)

7346   Global Bridge Infotech Inc.
5525 N Macarthur Blvd, Ste 670
Irving, TX 75038
Contact: Vishnu Sethuraman Swarna Dir Business Dev
Tel: 972-550-9400
Email: vishnu@gbitinc.com
Website: www.gbitinc.com
Commercial, full-color web offset printing, sheet-fed, digital design & print. (As-Ind, estab 2006, empl 97, sales $9,000,000, cert: State, NMSDC)

7347   ISSGR, Inc. dba ImageSet
6611 Portwest Dr Ste 190
Houston, TX 77024
Contact: President
Tel: 713-869-7700
Email:
Website: www.imageset.com
Digital printing, large format graphics, premedia & graphic design. (Woman, estab 1985, empl 31, sales $4,325,248, cert: WBENC)

7348   Label Systems, Inc.
4111 Lindberg Dr
Addison, TX 75001
Contact: Amy Van Brunt President
Tel: 972-387-4512
Email: amy@labelsystemsinc.com
Website: www.labelsystemsinc.com
Mfr custom labels, flexography, hot stamping & silkscreening, promotional products & incentive programs (Woman, estab 1994, empl 10, sales $350,000, cert: State, WBENC)

7349   Marfield Corporate Stationery
1225 E Crosby Rd Ste B-1
Carrollton, TX 75006
Contact: Andrea Rowe SVP-Sales
Tel: 877-245-9122
Email: accounting@marfield.com
Website: www.marfield.com
Printing, engraving, embossing, foil stamping: business cards, letterheads & envelopes. (Woman, estab 1968, empl 17, sales $2,100,000, cert: State, WBENC)

7350   Nicholas Earth Printing, LLC
7021 Portwest Dr. Ste 100
Houston, TX 77024
Contact: Marvin (Bob) Nicholas President & CEO
Tel: 713-880-0195
Email: bnicholas@nicholasearth.com
Website: www.nicholasearth.com
Sheetfed printing, UV & aqueous coating, web printing & inline, digital prepress & computer to plate, digital archiving, bindery, fulfillment, outdoor advertising. (Woman/AA, estab 2003, empl 18, sales , cert: State)

7351   Nieman Printing
10615 Newkirk St
Dallas, TX 75220
Contact: James Quinonez Acct Rep
Tel: 214-458-8011
Email: jq@niemanprinting.com
Website: www.niemanprinting.com
Digital pritning: short runs, small press, large press up to 12 colors with UV or AQ on paper or plastic. (Woman, estab 1984, empl 160, sales $22,000,000, cert: State, WBENC)

7352   Parker Business Forms, Inc.
7395 Frint Dr
Beaumont, TX 77705
Contact: Heather Camp VP
Tel: 409-842-5251
Email: heather@parkerbf.com
Website: www.parkerbf.com
Commercial & industrial printing: letterheads, envelopes, thank you cards, note cards, Christmas Cards, carbonless forms - invoices, purchase orders, shipping manifest, etc., full color(shortand long run). (Woman, estab 0, empl 20, sales $6,000,000, cert: WBENC)

7353   Peacock Press LLC
538 Shepherd
Garland, TX 75042
Contact: Ru Patel COO
Tel: 972-272-7764
Email: ru@peacockpress.net
Website: http://peacockpress.net
Digital printing, offset printing, complete finishing capabilities. (As-Ind, estab 2003, empl 15, sales $2,500,000, cert: State, NMSDC)

Virginia

7354   BBR Print Inc.
807 Oliver Hill Way
Richmond, VA 23219
Contact: Brooke Rhodes Cstmr Service
Tel: 804-901-2535
Email: brooke@jamesriverpress.com
Website: www.jamesriverpress.com
Printing services: in-house art dept, offset press & copy svcs, bindery. (Woman, estab 1997, empl 15, sales $1,143,000, cert: State)

7355 Grubb Printing & Stamp Co.
3303 Airline Blvd, Ste 1G
Portsmouth, VA 23701
Contact: Darla Alexander Sales Rep
Tel: 757-465-7855
Email: darla@grubbprint.com
Website: www.grubbprint.com
Commercial printing. (Woman, estab , empl 16, sales
$17,002,000, cert: State)

7356 JoMoCo Studio LLC
8416 Staples Mill Rd
Richmond, VA 23228
Contact: Joe Coleman Mgr
Tel: 804-262-3555
Email: engraving@jomocostudio.com
Website: www.jomocostudio.com
Engraving: stainless steel, brass, aluminum & plastic signs,
nameplates, name badges, labels, legends, tags, awards &
plaques, vinyl signs, braille signs, acrylic awards & laser
engraved metals & glass. (Woman, estab 1985, empl 3,
sales $523,155, cert: State)

7357 Premier Reprographics, Inc.
4701-A Eisenhower Ave
Alexandria, VA 22304
Contact: Vickie Banks CEO
Tel: 703-370-6612
Email: vickie@premierrepro.com
Website: www.premierrepro.com
Digital printing, copying, binding, scanning, posters,
manuals, newsletters, booklets, reports, proposals,
marketing collateral, presentations, laminating,
blueprinting, drymounting, large & small format color.
(Woman/AA, estab 1993, empl 10, sales $1,000,000, cert:
State)

Washington

7358 Angel Screen Printing, Inc.
8459 S 208th St, Bldg N
Kent, WA 98031
Contact: Rex Korrell Mktg Mgr
Tel: 206-755-7737
Email: rex@angelscreenprinting.net
Website: http://angelscreenprinting.net
Screen printing and Embroidery services. (Woman/As-Pac,
estab 2004, empl 8, sales $672,896, cert: State, NMSDC)

7359 EE Printing. LLC
8258 S 192nd St
Kent, WA 98032
Contact: Tory Nguyen
Tel: 425-656-1250
Email: tory@eeprinting.com
Website: www.eeprinting.com
From one color to full color, offset to digital, business
forms, business cards, stationary, bulk volume envelopes,
signs, posters, manuals, books, NCR forms, flyer, bro-
chures. (Woman/As-Pac, estab 2007, empl 3, sales
$190,752, cert: State, NMSDC)

7360 Risque Inc.
1122 N State St
Bellingham, WA 98225
Contact: Nadeem Israr President
Tel: 360-738-1280
Email: nadeem@copysource.com
Website: www.copysource.com
Printing services: digital printing, poster printing, offset
printing, copying, publishing, etc. (Woman/As-Ind, As-
Pac, estab 1990, empl 15, sales $1,200,000, cert: State)

Wisconsin

7361 Crossmark Graphics, Inc.
16100 W Overland Dr
New Berlin, WI 53151
Contact: Tammy Rechner President
Tel: 262-821-1343
Email: trechner@crossmarkgraphicsinc.com
Website: www.crossmarkgraphicsinc.com
Print communication, litho, UV printing, lenticular, POS,
digital, PURLs, fulfillment/kit packing & web-to-print.
(Woman, estab 1987, empl 48, sales $12,703,065, cert:
WBENC)

7362 Flex Pre-Press, Inc.
6812 S 112th St
Franklin, WI 53132
Contact: Burt Tabora President
Tel: 414-427-8833
Email: btabora@flexprepress.com
Website: www.flexprepress.com
Photopolymer printing plates, DuPont WaterProofs,
color keys, film negatives, analog & digital proofing,
high-end color separations, photo retouching, package
design, file management & printing, digital plates. (Hisp,
estab 1995, empl 15, sales $1,100,000, cert: State,
NMSDC)

7363 H.Derksen & Sons Co., Inc.
250 Industrial Dr
Omro, WI 50310
Contact: Mike Willeford VP
Tel: 920-685-4000
Email: mike@hderksen.com
Website: www.hderksen.com
Pressure sensitive labels, wide format digital printing,
business forms, computer paper, paper & packaging
products, mobility solutions, bar code label printers, bar
coding software. (Nat Ame, estab , empl 11, sales
$8,000,000, cert: NMSDC)

7364 Industrial Graphics Inc.
304 Industrial Dr
Fredonia, WI 53021
Contact: Teri Swenson Acct Mgr
Tel: 262-692-2424
Email: tswenson@igc-image.com
Website: www.industrialgraphics.com
Digital Printing, Screen Printing, Creative Services, Cad
Cut Lettering, Fleet Wrapping, Advertising, Point of
Purchase Displays, Priting on Metals, Prototyping, High
Volume Sourcing, Architectural Decorating, Wall Paper
Printing, Ceiling Tile Printing. (Woman, estab 1969, empl
20, sales $2,750,000, cert: State)

7365   Kubin-Nicholson Corporation
       8440 N 87th St
       Milwaukee, WI 53224
       Contact: Margaret Rees CEO
       Tel: 414-586-4300
       Email: rees.p@kubin.com
       Website: www.kubin.com
Commerical printed products: billboards, banners, transit posters, in store signs, floor graphics, wall scapes, vehicle wraps, building wraps, POP displays. (Woman, estab 1935, empl 63, sales $16,000,000, cert: State)

7366   Promo Print Solutions Inc.
       420 S Koeller St, Ste 208
       Oshkosh, WI 54902
       Contact: Paula Condor President
       Tel: 920-233-7900
       Email: paula.condor@promoprintsolutions.com
       Website: www.promoprintsolutions.com
print collateral: in-store promotions, sales promotions, commerical printing, giveaways & sampling. (Woman, estab 2000, empl 4, sales $2,087,395, cert: WBENC)

7367   Red Oak Label, LLC
       2923 S 160th St
       New Berlin, WI 53151
       Contact: President
       Tel: 262-780-9797
       Email:
       Website: www.redoaklabel.com
Pressure sensitive flexographic labels & tags. (Woman, estab 1997, empl 6, sales $510,900, cert: WBENC)

PROFESSIONAL SERVICES: Financial
Provide various financial consulting services: auditing/tax, 401K, pension and employee benefits, risk and injury management insurance, asset management and investment advice, money management, collection services, certified public accounting firms, etc. NAICS Code 54

Alabama

7368　Optimum Financial Corporation
　　　1300 Meridian St Ste 12
　　　Huntsville, AL 35801
　　　Contact: Thomas Parker Dir Business Dev
　　　Tel:　256-539-3994
　　　Email: tparker@optimumcorp.com
　　　Website: www.optimumcorp.com
Administrative & financial support services, revenue cycle, management consulting, asset managment, budgeting, const analysis, data entry, debt collection and records management. (AA, estab 1995, empl 20, sales $1,000,000, cert: NMSDC)

California

7369　Advertising Audit Services International, LLC
　　　32663 Red Maple St Suit 100
　　　Union City, CA 94587
　　　Contact: Pankaj Sewal Chief Auditing Officer
　　　Tel:　415-828-0779
　　　Email: psewal@adauditservintl.com
　　　Website: www.adauditservintl.com
Contract compliance audits & analysis: vendor compliance, financial accounting accuracy & advertiser best practices. (As-Ind, As-Pac, estab 2005, empl 5, sales $3,000,000, cert: NMSDC)

7370　Amerivet Securities, Inc.
　　　26550 Silverado Court
　　　Moreno Valley, CA 92555
　　　Contact: Steven Kay President
　　　Tel:　888-960-0644
　　　Email: skay@amerivetsecurities.com
　　　Website: www.amerivetsecurities.com
Securities business, commodities business & registered investment advisory business. (AA, estab 1993, empl 20, sales $862,000, cert: CPUC)

7371　Blaylock Van, LLC
　　　350 Frank H Ogawa Plaza
　　　Oakland, CA 94612
　　　Contact: Tarrell Gamble VP
　　　Tel:　510-208-6100
　　　Email: tgamble@brv-llc.com
　　　Website: www.brv-llc.com
Investment banking & financial services: corporate debt & equity underwriting, equity research, share repurchase, pension sales & trading & municipal finance. (AA, estab 1991, empl 48, sales , cert: State, NMSDC)

7372　Coast to Coast Financial Solutions Inc.
　　　101 Hodencamp Rd Ste 120
　　　Thousand Oaks, CA 91360
　　　Contact: John Mastro Director
　　　Tel:　888-877-4700
　　　Email: jmastro@c2cfsi.com
　　　Website: www.c2cfsi.com
Debt collection services. (AA, estab 2002, empl 14, sales $1,412,059, cert: NMSDC)

7373　Consumer Financial Service Corporation
　　　1500 Park Ave Ste 116
　　　Emeryville, CA 94608
　　　Contact: Loy Sheflott President
　　　Tel:　510-596-4100
　　　Email: lsheflott@consumerfinancial.com
　　　Website: www.consumerfinancial.com
Financial services. (Woman, estab 1994, empl 30, sales $1,100,000, cert: WBENC)

7374　Corporate Tax Incentives
　　　P.O. Box 2770
　　　Rancho Cordova, CA 95670
　　　Contact: Shawn Battle Controller/HR Mgr
　　　Tel:　916-366-0144
　　　Email: ebarajas@ctillc.com
　　　Website: www.ctillc.com
State and federal tax incentives, provide complete business incentives consulting services. (AA, As-Pac, estab 2008, empl 44, sales $10,542,392, cert: NMSDC)

7375　Garnier Group and Associates
　　　10679 Westview Parkway, 2nd Fl.
　　　San Diego, CA 92126
　　　Contact: Winslow Garnier President
　　　Tel:　858-530-2468
　　　Email: winslow@garniergroup.com
　　　Website: www.garniergroup.com
Equipment finance leasing, appraisal services, computer leasing, analytical lab instrumentation leasing. (AA, estab 2003, empl 19, sales $7,023,000, cert: NMSDC, CPUC, 8a)

7376　Jules & Associates, Inc.
　　　515 S Figeroa St, Ste 1950
　　　Los Angeles, CA 90071
　　　Contact: Vincent Alexander Sr Acct Exec
　　　Tel:　213-362-5600
　　　Email: vincea@julesandassociates.com
　　　Website: www.julesandassociates.com
Equipment finance corporate acquisitions. (Hisp, estab 1989, empl 31, sales $　0, cert: CPUC)

7377　LNL Solutions LLC
　　　423 W Adams Ave
　　　Alhambra, CA 91801
　　　Contact: Philip Li Dir of Finance
　　　Tel:　424-256-5894
　　　Email: info@lnl-solutions.com
　　　Website: www.lnl-solutions.com
Middle market & boutique accounting & financial services. (As-Pac, Hisp, estab 2013, empl 2, sales , cert: State, City, NMSDC)

7378　Pacific Rim Capital, Inc.
　　　525 Technology Dr Ste 400
　　　Irvine, CA 92618
　　　Contact: Tom Budnick VP Sales
　　　Tel:　949-389-0800
　　　Email: sales@pacrimcap.com
　　　Website: www.pacificrimcapital.com
Lease financing: materials handling & IT equip, also dist new & reconditioned IT hardware. (AA, estab 1990, empl 73, sales $43,071,762, cert: NMSDC)

7379 Receivables Solutions, Inc.
      2910 Inland Empire Blvd Ste 100
      Ontario, CA 91764
      Contact: Regina Cameron
      Tel: 909-360-8140
      Email: rcameron@rsinc.us
      Website: www.rsinc.us
National accounts receivable management (ARM), 1st
party collections (pre-charge off), 3rd party collections &
billing. (Woman/AA, estab 2015, empl 2, sales , cert: CPUC)

7380 Sequoia Financial Services
      28632 Roadside Dr Ste 110
      Agoura Hills, CA 91301
      Contact: Roy C. duPlessis CEO
      Tel: 818-409-6000
      Email: secon@sequoiafinancial.com
      Website: www.sequoiafinancial.com
Collection services. (Woman/AA, estab 1991, empl 73,
sales $3,000,000, cert: CPUC, WBENC)

7381 Southern California Leasing Inc.
      180 E Main, Ste 204
      Tustin, CA 92780
      Contact: Barbara Griffith President
      Tel: 714-573-9804
      Email: bgriffith@socalleasing.com
      Website: http://socalleasing.com
Equipment leasing & financing. (Woman, estab 1992, empl
7, sales $1,200,000, cert: WBENC)

7382 Strategic Partners Consultants
      8889 W Olympic Blvd, Ste 1000
      Beverly Hills, CA 90211
      Contact: Brenda West CEO
      Tel: 310-870-7055
      Email:
      brenda.west@strategicpartnersconsultants.com
      Website: http://strategicpartnersconsultants.com/
      page/168/1
Consulting & outsourcing, Bank Regulatory Compliance
issues, Internal Audit functions & Risk Assessment activities. (Woman, estab 2014, empl 3, sales , cert: WBENC)

7383 The Gilson Group, LLC
      2967 Michelson Dr Ste G102
      Irvine, CA 92612
      Contact: Catherine Doll CEO
      Tel: 949-830-3499
      Email: catherine@thegilsongroup.com
      Website: http://TheGilsonGroup.com
Accounting, mergers, financial analysis, due diligence,
internal controls, general ledger, forecasting, cash flow,
process improvement, Quickbooks, SOX, SEC, cost accounting, financial reporting, internal audit, risk management,
GAAP. (Woman, estab 2006, empl 20, sales $502,000, cert:
WBENC)

7384 The Zamzow Group, Inc.
      264 S La Cienega Blvd, Ste 1120
      Beverly Hills, CA 90211
      Contact: Brenda Zamzow President
      Tel: 310-551-3000
      Email: wbe@thezamzowgroup.com
      Website: www.thezamzowgroup.com
Accounting services. (Woman, estab 2003, empl 20, sales
$1,600,000, cert: State, City)

7385 Venpalia LLC
      1331 N Cuyamaca St, Ste G
      El Cajon, CA 92020
      Contact: Liza Amog Principal
      Tel: 619-788-3781
      Email: liza@venpalia.com
      Website: www.venpalia.com
Finance, risk management. (Woman/As-Pac, estab 2010,
empl 1, sales $150,000, cert: NMSDC, CPUC)

Colorado

7386 Aspen Capital Company, Inc.
      530 North Jefferson Ave Unit A
      Loveland, CO 80537
      Contact: Peggy Tomcheck
      Tel: 303-716-2898
      Email: plapp@aspencapitalcompany.com
      Website: www.aspencapitalcompany.com
Custom asset tracking & invoicing solutions, educational
laptop program lease structures, unique iPad refresh
programs, consignment solutions, electronic invoicing &
billing processes, web based equipment stores. (Woman,
estab 2001, empl 8, sales $10,385,908, cert: WBENC)

Connecticut

7387 Airlink Ground Transportation, LLC
      39 Old Ridgebury Rd D1-243
      Danbury, CT 06810
      Contact: Atif Jilani Member
      Tel: 203-297-6060
      Email: atif@airlinklimo.com
      Website: http://airlinklimo.com
Black Car Service to/from CT,NY,NJ airports (As-Ind,
estab 2011, empl 3, sales $185,320, cert: NMSDC)

7388 Argus Investors' Counsel, Inc.
      1266 E Main St 4th Fl
      Stamford, CT 06902
      Contact: Sharon Wagoner President
      Tel: 203-316-9000
      Email: clesko@argusinvest.com
      Website: www.argusinvest.com
Manage portfolios: pensions, endowments & founda-
tions. (Woman, estab 1960, empl 6, sales $ 0, cert:
WBENC)

7389 Soundview Capital Solutions
      116 Washington Ave
      North Haven, CT 06473
      Contact: John Abella CEO
      Tel: 203-821-7830
      Email:
      johnabella@soundviewcapitalsolutions.com
      Website: www.soundviewcapitalsolutions.com
Third-party leasing specializing in technology financing.
(Hisp, estab 2009, empl 3, sales $100,000, cert: NMSDC)

District of Columbia

7390 McKissack & McKissack of Washington, Inc.
      901 K St, NW 6th Fl
      Washington, DC 20001
      Contact: Pamela Prue Marketing & Proposal Mgr
      Tel: 202-347-1446
      Email: registrations@mckinc.com
      Website: www.mckinc.com
Budget preparation, scheduling, programming, scope
preparation, financial consulting. (Woman/AA, estab
1990, empl 130, sales $24,010,225, cert: State, City,
NMSDC, WBENC)

Delaware

7391 Faw Casson
160 Greentree Dr, Ste 203
Dover, DE 19904
Contact: Tammy Ordway Dir of ES
Tel: 302-674-4305
Email: tjo@fawcasson.com
Website: www.fawcasson.com
Employee benefit plan audits, business valuations, fraud services, EBP audits, agreed-upon procedures, internal audit staffing & tax services. (Woman, estab 1944, empl 39, sales $6,460,702, cert: WBENC)

Florida

7392 AMI Risk Consultants
1336 SW 146th Court
Miami, FL 33184
Contact: Actuary Analyst /Admin
Tel: 305-173-1589
Email: cingo@comcast.net
Website: www.amirisk.com
Property/casualty actuarial & risk management consulting. (As-Pac, estab 1992, empl 7, sales , cert: NMSDC)

7393 Carter-Health LLC
4201 Vineland Road Ste I-13-14
Orlando, FL 32811
Contact: Rodney Carter President
Tel: 407-296-6689
Email: rodney@carterhealth.com
Website: www.carter-health.com
Healthcare facilities in meeting the stringent requirements of (AA, estab 2007, empl 5, sales $2,500,000, cert: NMSDC)

7394 Commonwealth Capital Corp
4532 US Hwy 19 N Ste 200
New Port Richey, FL 34652
Contact: Kim Springsteen-Abbott Business Dev
Tel: 800-249-3700
Email: kspringsteen@ccclease.com
Website: www.ccclease.com
Equipment leasing: IT, telecom & medical equipment. (Woman, estab 1978, empl 45, sales $10,000,000, cert: WBENC)

7395 Empower Benefits Inc. dba Corestream
3606 Enterprise Ave, Ste 304
Naples, FL 34104
Contact: President
Tel: 917-686-5886
Email:
Website: www.corestream.com
Provides consolidated payroll deduction, voluntary benefits portals, employee discount shopping portals, group auto insurance real time comparative quoting, online enrollment and voluntary benefits brokerage. (As-Ind, estab 2006, empl 30, sales , cert: NMSDC)

7396 Enfusion, Inc.
2429 Grand Teton Circle
Winter Park, FL 32792
Contact: Anita White CEO
Tel: 407-802-0006
Email: anita@enfusionfinance.com
Website: www.enfusionfinance.com
Financial intelligence consulting, expense & cost management. (Woman/AA, estab 2007, empl 1, sales , cert: WBENC)

7397 Hanks Hanks and Associates LLC
213 S Dillard St Ste 120 B
Winter Garden, FL 34787
Contact: Phadra Hanks CEO
Tel: 301-653-5134
Email: phanks@hhallcmd.com
Website: http://hhallcmd.com
Financial management & accounting, program management, management consulting & smart business solutions. (Woman/AA, estab 2002, empl 45, sales $4,000,000, cert: State)

7398 Risk & Re-Insurance Solutions Corporation
1500 San Remo Ave Ste 247B
Coral Gables, FL 33146
Contact: Steven Pacholick VP
Tel: 770-437-8880
Email: spacholick@rrisc.com
Website: www.rrisc.com
Risk management, advisory & risk financing needs to corporate & governmental clients. (Hisp, estab 2001, empl 10, sales $2,550,000, cert: NMSDC)

Georgia

7399 Accountant In A Minute
1781 Chadds Lake Dr
Marietta, GA 30068
Contact: Alison Nicholson President
Tel: 404-804-5778
Email: alison.nicholson@aimaccountingservices.com
Website: www.aimaccountingservices.com
Accounting Services: Reconciliations Statement reconciliations & Expenses Bank reconciliations, Recording transactions Financial Statement preparation & tutorials Month, Quarter close support, Audit support (Failing Audits) System Migration. (Woman, estab 2017, empl 2, sales $100,000, cert: NWBOC)

7400 Corporate Reports, Inc.
3610 Piedmont Rd NE Ste 200
Atlanta, GA 30305
Contact: Angela King Controller
Tel: 404-233-2230
Email: angela.king@corporatereport.com
Website: www.corporatereport.com
Annual (financial) & sustainability/corporate responsibility/citizenship reporting. (Woman, estab , empl , sales $3,500,000, cert: WBENC)

7401 Infinite Financial Concepts, LLC
P.O. Box 953
Stone Mountain, GA 30086
Contact: Amin Hassan President
Tel: 678-933-5304
Email: amin@ifc326.com
Website: www.ifc326.com
Accounting & financial reporting. (AA, estab 2011, empl 1, sales , cert: City)

7402 Lewis Business Services, Inc.
43 Forsyth St
Atlanta, GA 30303
Contact: Alberteen Lewis
Tel: 404-521-3634
Email: lbstax@bellsouth.net
Website:
Accounting, budgeting, auditing, financial advisory, tax representation & tax return preparation, collections & group entertainment. (Woman/AA, estab 1998, empl 4, sales $ 0, cert: State)

7403   Resurgens Risk Management, Inc.
1201 Peachtree St NE
Atlanta, GA 30361
Contact: Clifton McKnight, Sr. Asst VP
Tel: 678-298-5119
Email: cmcknight@rrmgt.com
Website: www.rrmgt.com
Human resources consulting services, financial products, employee benefits, commercial property & liability insurance & consultative services. (AA, estab 1987, empl 33, sales $3,000,000, cert: NMSDC)

7404   RiverStone Associates, LLC
750 Olde Clubs Dr
Alpharetta, GA 30022
Contact: Monty Brinkley President
Tel: 770-656-7820
Email: mbrinkley@riverstone-us.com
Website: www.riverstone-us.com
Professional svcs: internal audit, accounting, IT security, process improvement & risk management solutions. (AA, estab 2007, empl 2, sales , cert: State)

7405   VAAS Professionals, LLC
325 Edgewood Ave Ste 600
Atlanta, GA 30312
Contact: Steve Julal Owner
Tel: 404-223-1058
Email: steve.julal@vaasprofessionals.com
Website: www.vaasprofessionals.com
Accounting & finance services, audits, payroll solutions, capital & treasury management, reviews, computer & technology assessments, financial reporting, due diligence & human capital management. (AA, estab 2005, empl 4, sales , cert: 8a)

Illinois

7406   A3B, LLC
100 S Saunders Rd, Ste 150
Lake Forest, IL 60045
Contact: Betsey Robinson President & CEO
Tel: 847-574-7227
Email: betsey@a3bllc.com
Website: http://a3bllc.com
Accounting & Finance Consulting Services, business process improvements resulting in cost savings, financial accounting reporting & analysis, financial transformation of shared services centers, management of change. (Woman/AA, estab 2013, empl 3, sales , cert: NMSDC, WBENC)

7407   Adelfia LLC
400 E Randolph Str Ste 705
Chicago, IL 60601
Contact: Stella Marie Santos
Tel: 312-240-9500
Email: sbsantos@adelfiacpas.com
Website: www.adelfiacpas.com
Assurance & advisory services: financial audit, compliance examination, internal audit, agreed-upon procedures, tax services, tax preparation, payroll tax returns, tax notices/audit assistance, tax planning, accounting services. (Woman/As-Pac, Hisp, estab 2011, empl 30, sales $541,996, cert: State, City, NMSDC)

7408   Ariel Investments
200 E Randolph St Ste 2900
Chicago, IL 60601
Contact: Gary L. Rozier Sr VP
Tel: 312-726-0140
Email: grozier@arielinvestments.com
Website: www.arielinvestments.com
Financial management services. (AA, estab 1983, empl 88, sales $54,074,660, cert: NMSDC)

7409   B3 Consulting Inc.
1025 N Riverwalk St
Chicago, IL 60610
Contact: CEO
Tel: 312-722-9420
Email:
Website: www.b3consultinginc.com
Risk Advisory Services: Entity Wide, Risk Assessments, Internal Audit, Sarbanes Oxley, Third Party Validation, Business Process Architecture, Compliance Services, Contract Compliance, Regulatory/Other Compliance. (Woman, estab 2016, empl 1, sales , cert: City, WBENC)

7410   Benford Brown & Associates LLC
8334 S Stony Island Ave
Chicago, IL 60617
Contact: Kim Ellen Partner
Tel: 773-731-1300
Email: kellen@benfordbrown.com
Website: www.benfordbrown.com
Auditing, accounting, tax & small business consulting services. (Woman/AA, estab 1996, empl 7, sales $1,005,155, cert: State, NMSDC, WBENC)

7411   Cabrera Capital Markets, LLC
10 S LaSalle St Ste 1050
Chicago, IL 60603
Contact: William Feeley Managing Dir
Tel: 312-236-8888
Email: mfeeley@cabreracapital.com
Website: www.cabreracapital.com
Investment banking services, domestic & international equity brokerage, taxable fixed income brokerage, mergers & acquisitions. (Hisp, estab 2001, empl 74, sales $25,109,305, cert: State, NMSDC)

7412   Davenport Capital Management
312 N Clark St Ste 500
Chicago, IL 60654
Contact: Thomas Davenport Managing Partner
Tel: 312-445-6406
Email: thomas@davenportcap.com
Website: www.davenportcap.com
Merchant banking, strategic advisory & investments. (AA, estab 2014, empl 4, sales $800,000, cert: NMSDC)

7413   E.C. Ortiz & Co., LLP
333 S Des Plaines St, Ste 2-N
Chicago, IL 60661
Contact: Edilberto C. Ortiz Managing Partner
Tel: 312-876-1900
Email: ecortiz@ecortiz.com
Website: www.ecortiz.com
Auditing, accounting, consulting, taxation, employee benefit plan audits, management services & financial advice. (As-Pac, estab 1974, empl 65, sales $3,968,725, cert: State, City, NMSDC)

7414   Global Capital, Ltd.
       205 W. Wacker Dr. Ste 730
       Chicago, IL 60606
       Contact: Terri McNally President & CEO
       Tel: 312-846-6918
       Email: brian@globelease.com
       Website: www.globalcapitalltd.com
Equipment leasing & financing: aircraft, rails, trailers, vehicles, computers, manufacturing & construction equipment. (Woman, estab 1999, empl 7, sales $34,465,113, cert: WBENC)

7415   Holland Capital Management LLC
       303 West Madison Ste 700
       Chicago, IL 60606
       Contact: Valerie King Dir of Marketing
       Tel: 312-553-4830
       Email: vking@hollandcap.com
       Website: www.hollandcap.com
Equity & fixed income institutional management. (Woman/AA, As-Ind, estab 1991, empl 22, sales $6,966,000, cert: State, NMSDC)

7416   Loop Capital Markets
       111 W Jackson Blvd Ste 1901
       Chicago, IL 60604
       Contact: Sidney Dillard Partner
       Tel: 312-356-5008
       Email: nancy.ziagos@loopcapital.com
       Website: www.loopcapital.com
Corporate debt & issuances, sub notes, floating rate notes, bonds, securities, credit cards, equity, common stock, variable rate debt, etc. (AA, estab 1997, empl 150, sales , cert: NMSDC)

7417   Sierra Forensic Group
       30 S Wacker Dr Ste 2200
       Chicago, IL 60606
       Contact: Adrian Sierra CEO
       Tel: 312-674-7100
       Email: adrian.sierra@sfg-global.com
       Website: www.sfg-global.com
Forensic accounting & investigative services. (Hisp, estab 2005, empl 8, sales $327,688, cert: NMSDC)

Indiana

7418   Engaging Solutions, LLC
       3965 N Meridian St Ste 1B
       Indianapolis, IN 46208
       Contact: Debbie Wilson Managing Principal
       Tel: 317-283-8300
       Email: debbie@engagingsolutions.net
       Website: www.engagingsolutions.net
Fiscal Management & Accountability, Financial Compliance Audits, Program Audits, Financial Reviews, Compilations, Agreed Upon Procedures, Internal Controls Reviews, Tax Preparation, Ta Audit Representation. (Woman/AA, estab 2005, empl 26, sales $2,009,000, cert: State)

7419   Moore Accounting, LLC
       9465 Counselors Row, Ste 200
       Indianapolis, IN 46240
       Contact: April Moore Owner
       Tel: 317-504-0296
       Email: afreeman@mooreacctg.com
       Website: www.mooreacctg.com
Accounting, bookkeeping, Tax, Payroll, Tier 2 Audit Services, Davis Bacon & Related Acts, Long-Term Care, Mental Health, Transportation, A133, Echos, Housing Authority, Section 8, Tax Credit Housing, Public Housing. (Woman/AA, estab 2010, empl 3, sales , cert: State, City, WBENC)

7420   Putnam Industries Inc.
       4582 NW Plaza W Dr# 100
       Zionsville, IN 46077
       Contact: Jim Pickens President
       Tel: 317-275-3153
       Email: jpickens@putnamindustriesinc.com
       Website: www.putnamindustriesinc.com
Equipment leasing & finance: computers, software, hardware, copiers, office furniture, fleet vehlices, medical equipment, trucks, buses, lighting, HVAC systems, bulldozers, forklifts, heavy machinery, telephone systems, alarm systems. (AA, estab 2007, empl 5, sales $3,836,816, cert: NMSDC)

7421   Solace Risk Management
       9247 N Meridian St Ste 221
       Indianapolis, IN 46260
       Contact: Charles Moorer President & CEO
       Tel: 317-423-3947
       Email: charles.moorer@srm-cs.com
       Website: www.srm-cs.com
Designs comprehensive fully insured & self-insured risk financing & risk management programs. (AA, estab 2011, empl 3, sales , cert: State, NMSDC)

7422   Thomas & Reed, LLC
       148 E. Market St Ste 300
       Indianapolis, IN 46204
       Contact: Stephen A Reed
       Tel: 317-955-6933
       Email: tclemons@trllc-cpa.com
       Website: www.trlllc-cpa.com
Certified public accounting: auditing, reviews, compilations, controllership, bookkeeping, financial software system installation & training, payroll, staff outsourcing, rate analysis, Davis Bacon Compliance, contract compliance. (Woman/AA, estab 2004, empl 3, sales $267,340, cert: City)

Massachusetts

7423   Spafford Leasing Associates, Inc.
       1350 Main St Ste 318
       Springfield, MA 01103
       Contact: CEO
       Tel: 413-526-0975
       Email:
       Website: www.spafford.com
Equipment leasing, computer systems, hospital equipment, copiers, telephone systems, computer software, manufacturing equipment, for lease terms ranging from 3-7 years. (Woman, estab 1989, empl 2, sales $500,000, cert: WBENC)

7424 The Locator Services Group Ltd.
      280 Summer St Ste 400
      Boston, MA 02210
      Contact: President
      Tel: 617-859-0600
      Email:
      Website: www.tlsgltd.com
Asset & unclaimed funds identification & recovery
program. (Woman, estab 1994, empl 23, sales
$34,948,343, cert: WBENC)

Maryland

7425 AdNet/AccountNet, Inc.
      757 Frederick Rd Ste 102
      Catonsville, MD 21228
      Contact: Betsy Cerulo CEO
      Tel: 410-715-4040
      Email: bcerulo@adnetp3.com
      Website: www.adnetp3.com
Accounting/Financial, Information Tecnology, Human
Resources and Administrative staffing. (Woman, estab
1990, empl 23, sales $2,000,000, cert: State, WBENC)

7426 Beasley Financial Group LLC
      4815 Coyle Rd, Ste 103
      Owings Mills, MD 21117
      Contact: Marcus Beasley CEO
      Tel: 877-265-1264
      Email: mbeasley@beasleyfinancialgroup.com
      Website: www.beasleyfinancialgroup.com
Financial advisory, brokerage & consulting: 401(k) retirement plans, life, health, dental, disability & long term care
insurance benefit plans. (Woman/AA, estab 2005, empl 3,
sales , cert: State)

7427 Beyond The Bottom Line, Inc.
      1300 Mercantile Lane Ste 139-MM
      Largo, MD 20774
      Contact: Corinda Davis President
      Tel: 301-322-4083
      Email: bblinc@beyondbottomline.com
      Website: www.beyondbottomline.com
Budget formulation, execution & monitoring processes,
data mining to compile raw data to help clients recognize
significant facts, relationships, trends, patterns, exceptions
& anomalies. (Woman/AA, estab 2003, empl 16, sales
$1,202,364, cert: State)

7428 DeAnder Associates LLC
      7233 Hanover Pkwy, Ste D
      Greenbelt, MD 20770
      Contact: Edward Prater business devel spec
      Tel: 301-262-0111
      Email: eprater@deander.com
      Website: www.deander.com
Financial mgmt consulting: finance & accounting, contract
closeout & admin, grants mgmt, compliance assistance &
accounting system review and implementation. (Woman/
AA, estab 1997, empl 35, sales $2,966,827, cert: State)

7429 EurekaFacts, LLC
      51 Monroe St, PE-10
      Rockville, MD 20850
      Contact: Jorge Restrepo Dir Business Devel
      Tel: 240-403-1646
      Email: certifications@eurekafacts.com
      Website: www.eurekafacts.com
Research design, rigorous data collection, & advanced
analytic & statistical services. (Hisp, estab 2003, empl 23,
sales $4,281,146, cert: NMSDC)

7430 Gonzalez, Hawkins & Johnson LLC
      P.O. Box 2705
      Upper Marlboro, MD 20772
      Contact: Alejandro Gonzalez Partner
      Tel: 240-865-6052
      Email: agonzalez@ghjaccounting.com
      Website: www.ghjaccounting.com
Federal Financial Consulting. (Woman/AA, Hisp, estab
2008, empl 3, sales , cert: State, 8a)

7431 IMB Development Corporation, LLC
      7201 Wisconsin Ave., Ste 440
      Bethesda, MD 20814
      Contact: Tarrus Richardson CEO
      Tel: 240-507-1660
      Email: trichardson@imbdc.com
      Website: www.imbdc.com
Enterprise risk management & insurance solutions,
supplier diversity strategy & capacity building, M&A
advisory & direct private equity investing. (AA, estab
2010, empl 6, sales $2,012,892, cert: State, NMSDC)

7432 Intelligent Fiscal Optimal Solutions
      10632 Little Patuxent Pkwy Ste 306
      Columbia, MD 21044
      Contact: Brian Schwartz Corp Business Dev Mgr
      Tel: 301-837-9735
      Email: inquiry@ifoscorp.com
      Website: www.ifoscorp.com
Accounting, GAAP, GAGAS, Budget, Payroll, Cost Ac-
counting, Grants Admin, Grants Onsite/Desk Reviews,
Audit Readiness & Remediation, Reconciliations, Year-
End Closing, e-Travel, Travel Program & Travel Card
Admin, Acquisition SME, Contract Audits. (Woman/AA,
estab 2009, empl 30, sales , cert: 8a)

7433 New Century Advisors, LLC
      2 Wisconsin Circle, Ste 940
      Chevy Chase, MD 20815
      Contact: Ellen Safir President
      Tel: 240-395-0550
      Email: esafir@ncallc.com
      Website: www.newcenturyadvisors.com
Investment Management Services. (Woman, estab 2002,
empl 14, sales $4,695,000, cert: WBENC)

7434 Premier Group Services Inc.
      4200 Forbes Blvd Ste 208
      Lanham, MD 20706
      Contact: Joye Smith
      Tel: 301-577-6444
      Email: jsmith@pgservicesinc.com
      Website: www.pgservicesinc.com
CPA & management: audits, fraud, waste & abuse
support, government contracting consulting & audits,
temporary accounting staff, attestation services, business consulting, budgeting, taxes & payroll, financial
forecasting & projections. (Woman/AA, estab 2005,
empl 5, sales $139,000, cert: State, NMSDC, 8a)

7435 SB & Company, LLC.
      200 International Cir, Ste 5500
      Hunt Valley, MD 21030
      Contact: Stacy Wenzl Principal of Practice Dev
      Tel: 410-584-9302
      Email: swenzl@sbandcompany.com
      Website: www.sbandcompany.com
Accounting services. (Woman/AA, estab 2005, empl 95,
sales $14,050,000, cert: State, NMSDC)

7436 The CTS Group, LLC
13407 Tamarack Rd
Silver Spring, MD 20904
Contact: Calvin L. Scott, Jr. Managing Member
Tel: 301-801-1193
Email: cscott@ctsgroupllc.com
Website: http://ctsgroupllc.com
Comprehensive accounting & advisory business services, account maintenance, financial management, budget development & analysis, interim outsourcing, transaction analysis, transaction processing, data analysis & summarization. (AA, estab 2007, empl 1, sales $175,000, cert: State, 8a)

7437 TSC Enterprise
5211 Auth Rd Ste 100
Suitland, MD 20746
Contact: Salome Tinker Managing Partner
Tel:
Email: sjtinker@tsccpas.com
Website: http://TSCcpas.com
Certified public accounting, FIAR, audit readiness, tax, financial transition, compliance, assurance, management consulting, A133, yellow book, cost recovery, performance reviews, financial system implementation, financial support & staffing. (Woman/AA, estab 2001, empl 6, sales $250,000, cert: WBENC)

Michigan

7438 Baron Wealth Management
3150 Livernois Rd, Ste 250
Troy, MI 48083
Contact: Operations Mgr
Tel: 248-251-0161
Email:
Website: www.baron-wealth.com
Comprehensive wealth management services, income tax, retirement, cash flow, estate, investment, compensation, benefits & insurance planning. (Woman, estab 2010, empl 6, sales $ 0, cert: WBENC)

7439 Centennial Securities Advisory Services
515 Ship St, Ste 211
Saint Joseph, MI 49085
Contact: Jim Roberts President
Tel: 269-982-4188
Email: jim@jrcent.com
Website: www.jrcent.com
Registered Investment Advisory firm, wealth management, investments, investing, 401k, IRA, pension, foundation, financial advisor. (Nat Ame, Hisp, estab 2014, empl 3, sales $300,000, cert: NMSDC)

7440 Chippewa Capital LLC
3190 Tri Park Dr
Grand Blanc, MI 48439
Contact: Thomas Barrett VP
Tel: 810-579-0579
Email: thomas.barrett@macarthurcorp.com
Website: www.chippewacapital.com
Equipment leasing, painting,trucking, warehousing & distribution. (Nat Ame, estab 2000, empl 35, sales $2,000,000, cert: NMSDC)

7441 EVO Accounting & Financial Services
16200 W Seven Mile Rd
Detroit, MI 48235
Contact: Vencie Jackson President
Tel: 313-835-3900
Email: vjackson@evoaccounting.com
Website: www.evoaccounting.com
Accounting & financial services, tax & payroll. (AA, estab 1970, empl 15, sales $748,478, cert: State)

7442 First Independence Bank
44 Michigan Ave
Detroit, MI 48226
Contact: Rhonda Pugh Branch Admin
Tel: 313-256-8400
Email: rhondapugh@firstindependence.com
Website: www.firstindependence.com
Banking services. (AA, estab 1970, empl 62, sales $13,737,000, cert: NMSDC)

7443 Gonzales Financial Consulting, LLC
4707 Charest
Waterford, MI 48327
Contact: Rogelio Gonzales Managing Member
Tel: 810-706-1687
Email: roy@gonzalesfc.com
Website: www.gonzalesfc.com
Retirement plan consulting services, insurance coverage review, broker management & risk management support services, commercial liability, property, general liability, worker's compensation. (Hisp, estab 2015, empl 4, sales , cert: NMSDC)

7444 KCM Technical Inc.
850 Stephenson Hwy, Ste 603
Troy, MI 48083
Contact: Pamela Williford President
Tel: 877-996-3749
Email: cjohnson@kcmtech.net
Website: www.kcmtech.net
Offers Payroll, Accounting & Help Supply Services. (AA, estab 2005, empl 350, sales , cert: NMSDC)

7445 L J Ross Associates, Inc.
4 Universal Way
Jackson, MI 49204
Contact: Kaylyn Todd Marketing & Business Development Mgr
Tel: 517-544-9100
Email: kaylyn@ljross.com
Website: www.ljross.com
Debt collection: consumer & commercial debts. (Woman, estab 1992, empl 60, sales $8,012,319, cert: WBENC)

7446 Lakefront Capital, LLC
28175 Haggerty Rd
Novi, MI 48377
Contact: Sandy Fuchs Dir Ops & Client Service
Tel: 248-994-9001
Email: sandy.fuchs@lakefrontts.com
Website: www.lakefrontts.com
Lease financing & portfolio management. (As-Pac, estab 2002, empl 8, sales $10,000,000, cert: NMSDC)

7447   Martin, Arrington, & Desai, & Meyers P.C., CPA
30200 Telegraph Rd, Ste 444
Bingham Farms, MI 48025
Contact: Bettye Arrington Managing Dir
Tel: 248-645-5370
Email: bvam49@sbcglobal.net
Website: www.madmcpa.com
Audit, accounting, agreed upon procedures, due diligence, revenue recovery, tax consulting, information technology, survey & evaluation research, professional recruitment. (AA, estab 1975, empl 16, sales $1,300,000, cert: State)

7448   Minority Alliance Capital, LLC
6960 Orchard Lake Rd Ste 306
West Bloomfield, MI 48322
Contact: Tim McCormick VP - Sales
Tel: 248-236-5182
Email: mccormick.t@mac-leasing.com
Website: www.mac-leasing.com
Equipment leasing: computer & software, office furniture & fixtures, production & process control. (AA, estab 1999, empl 14, sales $248,000,000, cert: NMSDC)

7449   Optimal Leasing LLC
4301 Orchard Lake Rd, Ste 180-173
West Bloomfield, MI 48323
Contact: Larry Robinson CEO
Tel: 248-738-2699
Email: larry@optimaleasingcompany.com
Website: www.optimalleasingcompany.com
Third party lease financing of capital equipment. (AA, estab 1996, empl 50, sales , cert: NMSDC)

7450   Renaissance Capital Alliance
5440 Corporate Dr, Ste 275
Troy, MI 48098
Contact: Kyle Bell Natl Acct Mgr
Tel: 248-821-1811
Email: kylebell@rcalliance.com
Website: www.rcalliance.com
Equipment leasing: materials handling, lift trucks, transportation & warehousing equipment; fleet mgmt services. (AA, estab 2001, empl 13, sales $50,000,000, cert: NMSDC, CPUC)

Minnesota

7451   Amare & Associates LLC dba ABA Tax Accounting
10670 Hawthorn Trail
St. Paul, MN 55129
Contact: Amare Berhie CEO
Tel: 866-936-0430
Email: amare@abataxaccounting.com
Website: www.abataxaccounting.com
Finance & accounting outsourcing svcs: transaction processing & staffing services. (AA, estab 1989, empl 2, sales , cert: State, City, NMSDC)

7452   Certes Financial Pros, Inc.
5775 Wayzata Blvd, Ste 550
St. Louis Park, MN 55416
Contact: Sally Mainquist President
Tel: 952-345-4141
Email: getalife@certespros.com
Website: www.certespros.com
Provide high-end financial professionals on an interim & project basis. (Woman, estab 1994, empl 170, sales $12,000,000, cert: State)

7453   Diversified Adjustment Service, Inc.
600 Coon Rapids Blvd
Coon Rapids, MN 55433
Contact: Michelle Wendell Admin Asst
Tel: 763-783-2334
Email: diversity@diversifiedadjustment.com
Website: www.diversifiedadjustment.com
Managed collection svcs: accounts recievable mgmt & credit reporting, debt collection, pre-collect & skip-tracing svcs. (Woman, estab 1981, empl 60, sales $14,400,000, cert: CPUC, WBENC)

Missouri

7454   Colt Safety, Inc.
8300 Manchester Rd
St. Louis, MO 63144
Contact: Christine Bierman CEO
Tel: 314-961-4414
Email: christine@coltsafety.com
Website: www.coltsafety.com
Inventory management, electronic payment, EDI capable, histories & usages, tracking. (Woman, estab 1980, empl 11, sales $9,192,080, cert: State)

North Carolina

7455   Calloway & Associates, Inc.
5920 S Miami Blvd, Ste 202
Morrisville, NC 27560
Contact: VP Operations
Tel: 919-433-0245
Email:
Website: www.calloway-assoc.com
Financial accounting, management & technical consulting. (AA, estab 1985, empl 12, sales $1,000,000, cert: State)

7456   Falcon Square Capital, LLC
4000 Westchase Blvd
Raleigh, NC 27607
Contact: Melissa Pendergrass CEO
Tel: 919-825-1534
Email: mpendergrass@falconsquarecapital.com
Website: www.falconsquarecapital.com
Trading, research, portfolio construction, transition management, client commission arrangements & other institutional brokerage services. (Woman, estab 2013, empl 16, sales $1,711,975, cert: WBENC)

7457   Innovation Partners LLC
5950 Fairview Road, Ste 806
Charlotte, NC 28210
Contact: Anthony Lawrence Principal
Tel: 704-708-5461
Email: alawrence@innovationpartnersllc.com
Website: www.innovationpartnersllc.com
Deferred compensation plans, retirement planning, actuarial, pension funds, investment banking, reinsurance, securities portfolio management, risk management, asset portfoilo management, underwriting services. (Woman/AA, estab 2007, empl 20, sales $1,500,000, cert: NMSDC, WBENC)

7458   Red Bridge Consulting Group
       10700 Sikes Place, Ste 305
       Charlotte, NC 28277
       Contact: Judith Mackesy Owner
       Tel: 704-375-2040
       Email: jmackesy@redbridgecg.com
       Website: www.redbridgecg.com
Recruiting, Consulting and Staffing Services, permanent
placement, project-based consulting, temporary contract,
and contract-to-hire services. (Woman, estab 2009, empl
12, sales $ 0, cert: WBENC)

7459   Tryon Clear View Group, LLC
       816 W Mills St Ste B
       Columbus, NC 28722
       Contact: Mary Thompson Exec VP
       Tel: 828-859-6545
       Email: mthompson@oneclearview.com
       Website: www.oneclearview.com
Detect & recover overpayments to vendors, improved
financial & operational practices & procedures. (Woman,
estab , empl 13, sales $2,200,000, cert: WBENC)

New Jersey

7460   Allen, Maxwell & Silver, Inc.
       17-17 Route 208 N Ste 340
       Fair Lawn, NJ 07401
       Contact: Lisa Freidman CEO
       Tel: 201-871-0044
       Email: lisa@amscollections.com
       Website: www.amscollections.com
Commercial collections. (Woman, estab 1992, empl 38,
sales $2,650,000, cert: WBENC)

7461   Ateeca Inc.
       107 B1 Corporate Blvd,
       South Plainfield, NJ 07080
       Contact: Adam Lee Sr Business Development
       Tel: 908-427-5591
       Email: gdavis@ateeca.com
       Website: https://ateeca.com/
Payroll services. (Woman/As-Pac, estab 2005, empl 180,
sales $6,830,000, cert: NMSDC, WBENC)

7462   Broad Street Capital Markets LLC
       494 Broad St Ste 206
       Newark, NJ 07102
       Contact: Andrew Adderly CEO
       Tel: 862-367-9930
       Email: mdejesus@broadscm.com
       Website: www.broadscm.com
Investment Banking & Securities Dealing, Investment
Advice, Administrative Management & General Management Consulting. (AA, Hisp, estab 2000, empl 8, sales $
0, cert: State, NMSDC)

7463   Business Processes Redefined, LLC
       155 Passaic Ave, Ste 470
       Fairfield, NJ 07004
       Contact: President
       Tel: 800-470-6622
       Email:
       Website: www.bprllc.com
Collection services. (Woman, estab 2007, empl 12, sales
$500,000, cert: WBENC)

7464   C & M Associates, Inc.
       119 Dean St
       Harrington Park, NJ 07640
       Contact: Daniel Greene President
       Tel: 201-637-6217
       Email: dnlcminc@aol.com
       Website:
General construction; Office Renovations; Interior
Finishes; HVAC; Cogeneration; Fire Prevention; Engineer-
ing & Design (AA, estab 1989, empl 2, sales , cert: State,
City, NMSDC)

7465   Enhanced Due Diligence Advisory, Inc.
       910 Garden St
       Hoboken, NJ 07030
       Contact: Wayne Chau
       Tel: 973-727-7248
       Email: wchau@eddadvisory.com
       Website: www.eddadvisory.com
Risk assessment of domestic/international assets,
compliance, audit & logistics strategy. (As-Pac, estab
2015, empl 3, sales , cert: State, NMSDC)

7466   Runnymede Capital Management, Inc.
       10 Wilrich Glen Rd
       Morristown, NJ 07960
       Contact: Andrew Wang Sr VP
       Tel: 973-267-6886
       Email: awang@runnymede.com
       Website: http://runnymede.com
Manages investment portfolios of institutions (Taft-
Hartley, captive insurance, public pension fund, corporate, non-profit) & high-net-worth individuals. (As-Pac,
estab 1993, empl 8, sales $1,500,000, cert: NMSDC)

New York

7467   All Occasions Concierge, LLC
       1333A North Ave, Ste 149
       New Rochelle, NY 10804
       Contact: Sterling Jasper CEO
       Tel: 914-481-8312
       Email: sterling.jasper@alloccasionsconcierge.com
       Website: www.alloccasionsconcierge.com
With over fifteen years in the hospitality business, we
provide professional concierge services for busy
lifestyles.We specialize in catering to the needs of C-level
professionals.Our corporate programs offer companies
and luxury office buildings on-site (AA, estab 2006, empl
4, sales , cert: NMSDC)

7468   BCA Watson Rice LLP
       5 Penn Plaza, 15th Fl
       New York, NY 10001
       Contact: Bennie Hadnott Managing Partner
       Tel: 212-447-7300
       Email: blhadnott@bcawatsonrice.com
       Website: www.bcawatsonrice.com
Financial auditing services, retirement plan audits,
forensic accounting services, internal control services &
tax compliance services. (AA, As-Pac, estab 1982, empl
299, sales $4,597,538, cert: State)

7469   C.L. King & Associates, Inc.
410 Park Ave
New York, NY 10022
Contact: Jason Freed Sales
Tel: 212-364-1834
Email: jcf@clking.com
Website: www.clking.com
Investment banking services, stock (equity) underwriting, bond (fixed income/debt) underwriting, mergers & acquisitions advisory, securities sales, trading & distribution, stock buybacks & pension fund asset mgmt. (Woman, estab 1972, empl 125, sales $45,242,635, cert: WBENC)

7470   CastleOak Securities, L.P.
110 E 59th St, 2nd Fl
New York, NY 10022
Contact: Philip Ippolito CFO
Tel: 646-521-6700
Email: ochukwu@castleoaklp.com
Website: www.castleoaklp.com
Primary & secondary sales & trading of fixed income, equity, municipal & money market securities. (AA, estab , empl , sales $23,087,000, cert: NMSDC)

7471   CAVU Securities, LLC.
800 Third Ave, Fl 10
New York, NY 10022
Contact: Jose Reyes President
Tel: 212-916-3840
Email: jreyes@cavusecurities.com
Website: www.cavusecurities.com
Full service brokerage, investment banking & funds distribution. (AA, estab 2013, empl 12, sales $1,500,000, cert: NMSDC)

7472   Corporate Leasing Associates, Inc.
21 Morris Ave
Rockville Center, NY 11570
Contact: Mitch Gelnick Diversity Sales
Tel: 212-732-5571
Email: mitch@corplease.com
Website: www.corplease.com
Operating lease structures, lease purchase, sale & lease-back, step down & step up payments, balloon payments, single investor leases, etc. (Woman, estab 1982, empl 6, sales $4,654,218, cert: State, CPUC, WBENC)

7473   DACK Consulting Solutions
2 William St Ste 202
White Plains, NY 10601
Contact: Aleksandra Chancy CEO
Tel: 914-686-7102
Email: ggayle@dackconsulting.com
Website: www.dackconsulting.com
Cost consulting, estimating, scheduling & project management services. (Woman/AA, estab 1997, empl 24, sales $1,000,000, cert: State, City)

7474   Delta Risk Capital Group LLC
860 Fifth Ave (2L)
New York, NY 10065
Contact: Shanker Merchant Principal
Tel: 212-961-6825
Email: shanker.merchant@deltariskcapital.com
Website: www.DeltaRiskCapital.com
Model Validation Services pursuant to FHFA Requirements and Dodd-Frank Financial Regulations, Valuation on Securities, Valuation of Residential and Commercial Mortgages, Mortgage and Asset backed securities, Investment Banking, Capital Raising. (As-Pac, estab , empl , sales , cert: NMSDC)

7475   Divine Capital Markets
39 Broadway, 36 Fl
New York, NY 10006
Contact: Sales
Tel: 212-344-5867
Email:
Website: www.divinecapital.com
Investment banking, underwriting & distributions, research, corporate share repurchase programs, proprietary VWAP trading, municipal & corporate bonds, international equities. (Woman, estab 1997, empl 12, sales $13,900,000, cert: WBENC)

7476   EXIGIS LLC
589 8th Ave Fl 8
New York, NY 10018
Contact: Armand Alvarez CEO
Tel: 800-928-1963
Email: sales@exigis.com
Website: www.exigis.com
Risk management services, risk, insurance & business process automation technology. (Hisp, estab 2002, empl 35, sales $1,550,000, cert: NMSDC)

7477   Flash Exterminating, Inc.
164 Maujer St
Brooklyn, NY 11206
Contact: James Swint President
Tel: 347-748-8023
Email: flashexterminating@gmail.com
Website: www.flashexterminating.com
Flash stands for pest elimination. (AA, estab 2009, empl 3, sales $197,000, cert: City, NMSDC)

7478   KBL, LLP Certified Public Accountants & Advisors
110 Wall St, 11th Fl
New York, NY 10005
Contact: Richard Levychin Partner
Tel: 212-785-9700
Email: rlevychin@kbl.com
Website: www.kbl.com
Audit & assurance, agreed-upon procedures, compilation & review procedures, business process outsourcing, risk management & advisory services, cross border international practices, small business services, tax compliance. (AA, estab 1994, empl 50, sales $5,000,000, cert: NMSDC)

7479   Lebenthal Holdings, LLC
521 Fifth Ave Fl 15
New York, NY 10175
Contact: Steven Willis Sr managing dir
Tel: 877-425-6006
Email: swillis@lebenthal.com
Website: www.lebenthalcapitalmarkets.com
Underwrites securities, equity & corporate debt underwriting. (Woman, estab 2007, empl 38, sales $13,179,068, cert: WBENC)

7480   Masterpiece Accounting Services LLC
2 Hamilton Ave Ste 206
New Rochelle, NY 10801
Contact: Ibanessa Hogan Principal
Tel: 914-661-2798
Email: i.hogan@masterpieceaccounting.com
Website: www.masterpieceaccounting.com
Accounting & bookkeeping services, tax preparation & QuickBooks consulting. (Woman/Hisp, estab 2010, empl 1, sales , cert: State, WBENC)

7481 Mitchell & Titus LLP
80 Pine St, 32nd Floor
New York, NY 10005
Contact: Irene Davis CFO
Tel: 312-325-7422
Email: IDavis@MitchellTitus.com
Website: www.mitchelltitus.com
Certified public accounting & mgmt consulting. (AA, estab 1974, empl 97, sales $17,000,000, cert: State, NMSDC)

7482 Samuel A. Ramirez & Company, Inc.
61 Broadway 29th Fl
New York, NY 10006
Contact: Lawrence Goldman Managing Dir
Tel: 212-248-1214
Email: larry.goldman@ramirezco.com
Website: www.ramirezco.com
Investment banking & capital markets, distribution, brokerage, corporate share repurchase & research services. (Hisp, estab , empl 150, sales $72,950,961, cert: State, City, NMSDC)

7483 SWS Capital Management, LLC
100 Wall St, 18th Floor
New York, NY 10005
Contact: Lorna Maye Admin Mgr / Compliance Associate
Tel: 212-461-6500
Email: lmaye@swscapitalmanagement.com
Website: siebertwilliams.com/sales-trading/asset_management
Investment svcs: cash management & short-term fixed income investment strategies. (AA, estab 2002, empl 9, sales $291,000, cert: State, City, NMSDC)

7484 Tigress Financial Partners LLC
114 W 47th St
New York, NY 10036
Contact: George Orr
Tel: 212-430-8700
Email: gorr@tigressfp.com
Website: www.tigressfp.com
Financial services: rtesearch, trade execution, asset management, corporate advisory & investment banking. (Woman, estab 2010, empl , sales $100,000, cert: State, City, WBENC)

7485 Topeka Capital Markets Inc.
40 Wall St, Ste 1702
New York, NY 10005
Contact: Sylvester McClearn COO
Tel: 212-709-5706
Email: sm@topekacapitalmarkets.com
Website: www.topekacapitalmarkets.com
Agency-only trading domestic & international equities, traders, sales traders & research analysts. (AA, estab 2010, empl 28, sales , cert: City, NMSDC)

7486 Torres Llompart, Sanchez Ruiz LLP
Bowling Green Station
New York, NY 10274
Contact: Frank Sanchez-Ruiz Partner
Tel: 646-214-1064
Email: fsanchez@tlsr.com
Website: www.tlsr.com
Certified public accountants & business consulting: accounting, auditing, tax & corporate advisory, operational studies, management advisory, risk management, marketing consulting, franchising services, international commerce. (Hisp, estab 1989, empl 35, sales $2,410,000, cert: City, NMSDC)

7487 VJN Associates. LLC
39-38 Bell Blvd, Ste 202
Bayside, NY 11361
Contact: Victor Chin Operations Mgr
Tel: 718-279-1600
Email: victorc@vjnassociates.com
Website: www.vjnassociates.com
Assurance, accounting, book keeping, audits both financial & compliance. (Woman/As-Pac, estab 2012, empl 10, sales $169,000, cert: City, NMSDC)

Ohio

7488 Kaiser Consulting, LLC
818 Riverbend Ave
Powell, OH 43065
Contact: Lori Kaiser CEO
Tel: 614-300-1088
Email: lkaiser@kaiserconsulting.com
Website: www.kaiserconsulting.com
Financial & accounting consulting. (Woman, estab 1994, empl 63, sales $4,440,000, cert: WBENC)

7489 Kanu Asset Managment, LLC
4015 Executive Park Dr Ste 402
Cincinnati, OH 45241
Contact: Enyi Kanu CEO
Tel: 513-769-2700
Email: ktrent@kanuinvestments.com
Website: www.kanuasset.com
Registered Investment Advisory Firm (RIA) - Investments, Wealth Management, Financial Planning, Insurance, Portfolio Management, Institutional Consulting & Advisory Services. (AA, estab 1996, empl 5, sales , cert: NMSDC)

7490 McCarthy, Burgess & Wolff
26000 Cannon Rd
Cleveland, OH 44146
Contact: Paul Joseph Dir Business Devel
Tel: 440-735-5100
Email: paul.joseph@mbandw.com
Website: www.mbandw.com
Commercial collections & receivables. (Woman, estab 2000, empl 203, sales $17,200,000, cert: WBENC)

7491 Parms & Company, LLC
585 S Front St Ste 220
Columbus, OH 43215
Contact: John Parms
Tel: 614-224-3078
Email: jparms@parms.com
Website: www.parms.com
Auditing, accounting, agreed-upon procedures, forensic accounting, consulting & tax-related services. (AA, estab 1983, empl 14, sales $1,335,851, cert: State, NMSDC)

7492 Richardson and Associates, LLC
427 Appaloosa Ct
Cincinnati, OH 45231
Contact: Sherri Richardson Owner
Tel: 513-772-8348
Email: sherri@richardsonandassociates.com
Website: www.richardsonandassociates.com
Accounting services, audits, writing policies & procedures. (Woman/AA, estab 2007, empl 12, sales $300,000, cert: State, NMSDC, WBENC)

7493 The Pension & Retirement Group LLC
5900 Roche Dr Ste 435
Columbus, OH 43229
Contact: Curtis Clark Managing Partner
Tel: 800-385-5304
Email: cclark@thepensionandretirementgroup.com
Website: www.thepensionandretirementgroup.com
Financial Wellness, Retirement Planning, Insurance, Investments, 401(k) & 403(b) Plan Management, Retirement Income Planning, Supplement Benefits, Securities, Mutual Funds, IRA's. (AA, estab 2005, empl 3, sales $500,000, cert: NMSDC)

Oklahoma

7494 First Financial Network, Inc.
9211 Lake Hefner Pkwy, Ste 200
Oklahoma City, OK 73120
Contact: John A. Morris President
Tel: 405-748-4100
Email: jmorris@ffncorp.com
Website: www.ffncorp.com/
Provides the financial community with turnkey solutions to loan disposition. (Woman, estab 0, empl , sales $ 0, cert: WBENC)

Pennsylvania

7495 Caterpillar to Butterfly, LLC
12575 Chilton Rd
Philadelphia, PA 19154
Contact: Davida Godett CEO
Tel: 215-632-2575
Email: godett@caterpillartobutterfly.net
Website: www.caterpillartobutterfly.net
Caterpillar to Butterfly, LLC is dedicated to having individuals fly so you can see the color on their wings. With partnership and dedication transforming from a caterpillar to a butterfly is seamless. We believe that as you go through (Woman/AA, estab 2013, empl 1, sales , cert: NMSDC)

7496 Exude, LLC
325 Chestnut St Ste 1000
Philadelphia, PA 19106
Contact: President
Tel: 215-875-8730
Email:
Website: www.exudeinc.com
Employee Benefits, Human Resources & Risk Management Consulting. (AA, estab 2013, empl 2, sales $293,231, cert: State, NMSDC)

7497 Milligan & Company LLC
105 N 22nd St, 2nd Fl
Philadelphia, PA 19103
Contact: Angela Giunta Dir of Marketing
Tel: 215-496-9100
Email: agiunta@milligancpa.com
Website: www.milligancpa.com
Consulting & certified public accounting. (AA, estab 1985, empl 45, sales $6,400,000, cert: State)

Peurto Rico

7498 Alvarado Tax & Business Advisors LLC
P.O. Box 195598
San Juan, PR 00918
Contact: Miguel Rodriguez Admin
Tel: 787-620-7744
Email: mrodriguez@alvatax.com
Website: www.alvatax.com
Tax & business consulting, outsourcing, business operations, government compliance resolution issues, financial management, business, development, business continuation & succession, business governance. (Hisp, estab 2002, empl 32, sales $5,506,828, cert: NMSDC)

Rhode Island

7499 Axiom Actuarial Consulting
26 Knapton St
Barrington, RI 02806
Contact: Carlos Fuentes President
Tel: 860-550-0740
Email: carlos-fuentes@axiom-actuarial.com
Website: http://axiom-actuarial.com
Actuarial consulting: dental & vision coverages, pension, life insurance, employee benefits, special risk insurance, reinsurance, investment, finance & strategy. (Hisp, estab 2008, empl 4, sales , cert: 8a)

Texas

7500 Akisha Networks, Inc.
5868 A-1 Westheimer Rd, Ste 224
Houston, TX 77057
Contact: Ronald Smith VP
Tel: 713-840-7424
Email: info@akisha.net
Website: www.akisha.net
Akisha Networks Inc (ANI) is a full service Digital Systems Integrator that designs, builds and manages IP convergence solutions for today's intelligent commercial buildings. (AA, estab 2001, empl 8, sales $395,776, cert: NMSDC)

7501 Bley Investment Group
4200 S Hulen, Ste 519
Fort Worth, TX 76109
Contact: Laura Bley President
Tel: 817-732-2442
Email: laurab@bleyinvestments.com
Website: www.bleyinvestments.com
Financial services. (Woman, estab 1990, empl 7, sales $565,000, cert: State, WBENC)

7502 Capital Institutional Services, Inc.
1700 Pacific Ave, Ste 1100
Dallas, TX 75201
Contact: Dir of Business Development
Tel: 214-978-4767
Email:
Website: www.capis.com
Global execution services & commission management solutions. (Woman, estab 1977, empl 74, sales $49,957,374, cert: State, WBENC)

7503   Davis & Davis Professional Services Firm LLC
        12300 Ford Rd, Ste 290
        Dallas, TX 75234
        Contact: Chanel Davis Partner
        Tel: 972-488-5000
        Email: chanel.davis@davisanddavisllc.com
        Website: www.DavisandDavisLLC.com
Sales tax consultants, state tax audit consulting & audit defense. (Woman/AA, estab , empl , sales $1,376,000, cert: NMSDC, WBENC)

7504   DWG CPA PLLC
        5100 Westheimer, Ste 200
        Houston, TX 77056
        Contact: Darrell Groves Managing Dir
        Tel: 281-201-8348
        Email: info@dwgcpatx.com
        Website: www.dwgcpatx.com
Tax, accounting, auditing & financial management. (AA, estab 2005, empl 2, sales , cert: State, NMSDC)

7505   Galosi LLC
        16800 Dallas Pkwy, Ste 210
        Dallas, TX 75248
        Contact: J. Wayne Trimmer EVP
        Tel: 972-267-9907
        Email: wayne.trimmer@galosi.com
        Website: http://galosi.com
Cost of Money, Audit Discounts, Credit Memo Errors, Defective or Spoiled Goods Audit, Duplicate Payments, Errors Involving Returns. (Hisp, estab 2001, empl 27, sales $2,100,000, cert: State, NMSDC)

7506   Goldman, Imani & Goldberg, Inc.
        9894 Bissonnet St Ste 900
        Houston, TX 77036
        Contact: Karl Miller Dir of Marketing & Client Development
        Tel: 713-395-5120
        Email: kmiller@giginconline.com
        Website: www.giginconline.com
Collection programs, accounts receivable management, third party recovery. (AA, estab 2003, empl 26, sales $2,800,000, cert: NMSDC, 8a)

7507   Harris & Dickey, LLC.
        4127 Wycliff Ave
        Dallas, TX 75219
        Contact: Kelly Harris Partner
        Tel: 972-672-7597
        Email: kelly.harris@harris-dickey.com
        Website: www.harris-dickey.com
Accounting, finance, tax, internal audit, technology risk & special project assistance. (Woman, estab 2010, empl 12, sales $1,662,658, cert: State, City, WBENC)

7508   JN3 Global Enterprises LLC
        6034 W Courtyard Dr Ste 150
        Austin, TX 78730
        Contact: James Nowlin CEO
        Tel: 512-501-1155
        Email: jnowlin@excelglobalpartners.com
        Website: www.ExcelGlobalPartners.com
Corporate financial strategy & implementation. (AA, estab 2007, empl 10, sales $1,500,000, cert: State, NMSDC)

7509   Kipling Jones & Co., Ltd.
        1200 Smith St Ste 1600
        Houston, TX 77002
        Contact: Robbi Jones President
        Tel: 713-353-4688
        Email: rjones@kiplingjones.com
        Website: http://kiplingjones.com
Investment banking, financial advisory, bond underwriting & guidance. (Woman/AA, estab 2008, empl 7, sales $500,000, cert: State, City)

7510   McConnell & Jones LLP
        4828 Loop Central Dr, Ste 1000
        Houston, TX 77081
        Contact: Lori Jamail Marketing Dir
        Tel: 713-968-1600
        Email: info@mjlm.com
        Website: http://mcconnelljones.com
Financial statement audits, benefit plan audits, tax returns, compilations, accounting & bookkeeping services, SEC compliance services & single audits. (AA, estab , empl , sales $14,048,077, cert: NMSDC)

7511   Pharos Financial Services L.P.
        300 Crescent Ct, Ste 1380
        Dallas, TX 75201
        Contact: Vincent Mullins Natl Sales Mgr
        Tel: 214-855-0194
        Email: vmullins@pharosfinancial.com
        Website: www.pharosfunds.com
Financial loan & lease products. (AA, estab 2002, empl 12, sales , cert: State)

7512   PMB Precision Medical Billing Inc.
        8203 Willow Place Dr S Ste 230
        Houston, TX 77070
        Contact: Petria McKelvey CEO
        Tel: 713-672-7211
        Email: petria@precisionmedicalbilling.com
        Website: www.precisionmedicalbilling.com
Revenue recovery & collections services. (Woman/AA, estab 1995, empl 13, sales $1,611,635, cert: State, WBENC)

7513   PRO Consulting Services, Inc.
        500 Lovett Blvd Ste 250
        Houston, TX 77006
        Contact: Victor Juarez CEO
        Tel: 713-523-1800
        Email: vjuarez@proconsrv.com
        Website: www.proconsrv.com
Accounts receivables management services, commercial collections. (Hisp, estab 1992, empl 90, sales $4,500,000, cert: NMSDC)

7514   Real Time Resolutions, Inc.
        1349 Empire Central Dr Ste 150
        Dallas, TX 75247
        Contact: Mark Hutto SVP - Business Devel
        Tel: 214-599-6557
        Email: client.services@rtresolutions.com
        Website: http://realtimeresolutions.com
Financial services & asset recovery: auto, credit card, mortgages, direct demand accounts, student loans, installment loans & commercial loans. (Woman, estab 2000, empl 320, sales , cert: WBENC)

Utah

7515   Merrimak Capital Company LLC
823 Norfolk Ave
Park City, UT 84060
Contact: Monica Fleury VP Operations
Tel: 415-475-4100
Email: sales@merrimak.com
Website: www.merrimak.com
Financing solutions: operating leases, capital leases, lease lines, sale leasebacks & technology refresh leases. (Woman, estab 1991, empl 42, sales $150,655,616, cert: CPUC, WBENC)

Virginia

7516   Gemini Financial Strategists LLC
10 Naples Rd
Stafford, VA 22554
Contact: Jeremy Williams Managing Partner
Tel: 202-631-1430
Email: jeremy_williams@gmfis.com
Website: www.gmfis.com
Financial management & analysis, retirement plan implementation/ administration, employee retirement planning benefits. (AA, estab 2008, empl 6, sales $230,000, cert: State)

7517   Integrated Finance and Accounting Solutions, LLC
4310 Prince William Pkwy, Ste 405
Woodbridge, VA 22192
Contact: Tracy Jones Business Dev Mgr
Tel: 314-267-5847
Email: tjones@ifaasolutions.com
Website: http://ifaasolutions.com
Business Re-engineering, Process Improvement, Financial Data Analysis, Internal Control Monitoring, Program, Planning, Budget and Execution. Our Integrated Logistics Support includes supply support, technical data, design administration (Woman/AA, estab 2007, empl 29, sales $1,000,000, cert: 8a)

7518   Kodiak Finance LLC
8000 Towers Crescent Dr Ste 1350
Vienna, VA 22182
Contact: Marcy Dilworth President
Tel: 703-266-9199
Email: mdilworth@kodiakfinance.com
Website: www.kodiakfinance.com
Computer leasing & sales, asset management. (Woman/Nat Ame, estab 2004, empl 10, sales $560,357, cert: NMSDC, WBENC)

7519   RER Solutions Inc.
950 Herndon Pkwy, Ste 200
Herndon, VA 20170
Contact: Errin Green CEO
Tel: 703-742-6789
Email: errin.green@rer-solutions.com
Website: www.rer-solutions.com
Comprehensive business, real estate & financial mgmt. services, asset sale support, due diligence, portfolio management systems, technical & admin support personnel, financial modeling, document & records management, risk management. (Woman/AA, estab 1989, empl 27, sales $2,633,597, cert: State, 8a)

7520   Technology Ventures
7930 Jones Branch Dr Ste 310
McLean, VA 22102
Contact: John Earl Dir Business Dev
Tel: 703-917-1650
Email: jearl@tventures.net
Website: www.tventures.net
IT & Financial Staffing, Government & Consulting Services, Financial Services, Healthcare Communications, Consumer & Retail. (As-Ind, estab 1998, empl 150, sales , cert: State)

Washington

7521   Adekoya Business Consulting LLC
33021 Hoyt Rd SW
Federal Way, WA 98023
Contact: Andre Adekoya CEO
Tel: 206-817-9775
Email: andrew@adekoyabc.com
Website: www.adekoyabc.com
Business solutions, strategic financial planning & analysis, audits, market (digital) competitive analytics & revenue growth opportunities identification, resource planning, process re-engineering & system implementation. (AA, estab 2013, empl 5, sales $425,000, cert: State)

Wisconsin

7522   One Accord, LLC
P.O. Box 241763
Milwaukee, WI 53224
Contact: Shanna Reid President
Tel: 414-855-6342
Email: smreid@oneaccord.biz
Website: www.oneaccord.biz
Risk management & reinsurance brokerage. (Woman/AA, estab 2002, empl 3, sales , cert: State, City)

PROFESSIONAL SERVICES: Human Resources
Provide training and seminars on a variety of human resources topics: diversity, supplier diversity programs, team building, customer relations, staff development, wellness programs, policy and procedure manuals, coaching, etc. NAICS Code 54

Alabama

7523 C. Edward Lewis & Associates
3415 Buckboard Rd
Montgomery, AL 36116
Contact: Charles Lewis President
Tel: 334-272-3365
Email: charleslewis@celewisohs.com
Website: www.celewisohs.com
EEO & human resources training & consulting. (AA, estab 2004, empl 2, sales , cert: NMSDC)

7524 EAP Lifestyle Management, LLC
805 Daphne Ave Ste B
Daphne, AL 36526
Contact: Owner
Tel: 800-788-2077
Email:
Website: www.eaplifestyle.com
Employee assistance program & work/life svcs, substance abuse professional svcs, workplace training & presentation, continuing education, critical incident stress svcs. (Woman, estab 1998, empl 12, sales $299,719, cert: WBENC)

Arizona

7525 HR Wise, LLC
8399 E Indian School Rd Ste 101
Scottsdale, AZ 85251
Contact: Gregory O'Keefe CEO
Tel: 480-626-2109
Email: gokeefe@hrwisellc.com
Website: www.hrwisellc.com
Davis Bacon-Act Certified Payroll, Payroll Services, Human Resource Management, Talent Management, Benefits Administration, Time and Attendance, Human Capital Management, HR Business Process Outsourcing (HRBPO). (Hisp, estab 2008, empl 6, sales $290,000, cert: NMSDC, 8a)

California

7526 ClearPath Management Group, Inc
165 N Maple Ave #1930 Ste 102
Manteca, CA 95336
Contact: ClearPath WM Corporate Services Mgr
Tel: 209-239-8700
Email: wbe@clearpathwm.com
Website: www.clearpathwm.com
Contractor payroll, employer of record service, Contingent workforce management, business process outsourcing, Independent contractor compliance. (Woman, estab 2010, empl 16, sales $49,491,482, cert: WBENC)

7527 E. L. Goldberg & Associates
950 Siskiyou Dr
Menlo Park, CA 94025
Contact: Edie Goldberg CEO
Tel: 650-854-0854
Email: edie@elgoldberg.com
Website: http://elgoldberg.com
Human Resources Management Consulting, Talent Management, Performance Management, Career Management, Succession Planning, Selection, Leadership Development, Competency Modeling, Benchmarking, HR Strategic Planning. (Woman, estab 2001, empl 1, sales $300,000, cert: CPUC)

7528 Employers Choice Online Inc.
9845 Painter Ave. Ste B
Whittier, CA 90605
Contact: Jesus Ariel Lopez Procurement Contracts Mgr
Tel: 562-319-0413
Email: bids@ecoinc.us
Website: www.employerschoicescreening.com
Employment background checks, drug testing, physical exams & Form 1-9 services. (Hisp, estab 2011, empl 20, sales $2,034,818, cert: NMSDC, CPUC, 8a, SDB)

7529 Executive Office Services
P.O. Box 6621
Oakland, CA 94603
Contact: Detria Mixon HR consultant
Tel: 510-830-9721
Email: dmixon@exeservice.biz
Website:
Human resources business consulting services, Sales & Business Development
Finance /Accounting Healthcare / Human & Social Services Engineering & IT Technology (Woman/AA, estab 2008, empl 1, sales , cert: NMSDC, CPUC)

7530 HR Allen Consulting Services
6065 Sundale Way Ste 98
Fair Oaks, CA 95628
Contact: Michael Allen President
Tel: 916-370-7849
Email: mallen@hrallenconsulting.com
Website: http://hrallencs.com
Human resource consulting & outsourcing. (AA, Hisp, estab 2005, empl , sales $100,000, cert: State)

7531 Los Remedios
2377 S Sabre Ave
Fresno, CA 93727
Contact: Patricia Alvarado Owner
Tel: 619-813-6445
Email: pa@remedysupportservices.com
Website:
Management & human resources consulting. (Woman/ Hisp, estab 1995, empl 1, sales , cert: State)

7532 Translating Services, Inc.
1516 S Bundy Dr Ste 311
Los Angeles, CA 90025
Contact: Lisa Lazar President
Tel: 310-453-3302
Email: languages@lazar.com
Website: www.lazar.com
Translation, interpreting. (Woman, estab 1999, empl 8, sales $ 0, cert: WBENC)

Colorado

7533 Champion Business Services
2668 Dexter St
Denver, CO 80207
Contact: President
Tel: 303-873-9147
Email:
Website: www.championbusiness.com
Clerical support svcs, help supply svcs, Ccmputer pogramming, data entry processing & preparation, business svcs, clerical skills training, facilities management support svcs. (Woman/AA, estab 1986, empl 3, sales , cert: WBENC)

7534 Employee Development Systems, Inc.
7300 S Alton Way Ste 5J
Centennial, CO 80112
Contact: Sherman Updegraff Managing Dir
Tel: 800-282-3374
Email: sherm@edsiusa.com
Website: www.employeedevelopmentsystems.com
Personal training: self-confidence, understanding behavioral styles, communication skills, listening skills, self-motivation & personal accountability. (Woman, estab , empl , sales $ 0, cert: NWBOC)

7535 FirstIdea, Inc.
19029 E Plaza Dr, Ste 200
Parker, CO 80134
Contact: Annette Alvarez President
Tel: 303-840-3346
Email: info@firstidea.org
Website: https://firstidea.org
Human Resources consulting and recruitment services. (Woman/Hisp, estab 1989, empl 9, sales $600,000, cert: NMSDC, WBENC)

Florida

7536 HRSS Consulting Group
125 E Merritt Island Cswy Ste 107 #246
Merritt Island, FL 32952
Contact: Karen Gregory President & CEO
Tel: 321-576-1314
Email: kgregory@hrssconsultinggroup.com
Website: www.hrssconsultinggroup.com
Organizational development and talent management. (Woman/AA, As-Pac, Hisp, estab 2012, empl 6, sales $230,000, cert: State, WBENC)

7537 Midwest Background Inc.
200 Central Ave, Ste 820
St Petersburg, FL 33701
Contact: Syan Kazi Dir of Business Devel
Tel: 727-592-8275
Email: media@mbiworldwide.com
Website: www.mbiworldwide.com
Background screening & hiring solutions. (Woman, estab 1998, empl 27, sales $2,700,000, cert: NWBOC)

7538 Moten Tate, Inc.
301 E. Pine St Ste 250
Orlando, FL 32801
Contact: Kenneth Moten CEO
Tel: 407-843-3277
Email: kmoten@motentate.com
Website: www.motentate.com
Human resource management: staffing, HR project mgmt, reward strategies, employee development & HR outsourcing. (AA, estab 1997, empl 100, sales $3,400,000, cert: State, NMSDC)

7539 Sobriety On the Sea / Danette Arthur MD PA
4302 Hollywood Blvd
Hollywood, FL 33021
Contact: Danette Arthur MD President
Tel: 954-923-7333
Email: sos@doctorsos.org
Website: www.DrArthur.org
Pre-employment & random drug testing services. (Woman/AA, estab 2001, empl 4, sales $140,000, cert: State)

7540 Suncoast Compliance Services, LLC
16765 Fishhawk Dr, Ste 325
Lithia, FL 33547
Contact: Vincent McGrew President
Tel: 813-653-4559
Email: vroy.mcgrew@usamdt.com
Website: http://usamdt.com/westcentralflorida
Pre-employment background screening, drug-free workplace policy development & implementation, on-site drug & alcohol testing, Employer Assistance Program referral, supervisor training for DOT & non-DOT employees. (AA, estab 2012, empl 1, sales , cert: State, NMSDC)

7541 The Management Edge, Inc.
12360 66th St, Ste S
Largo, FL 33773
Contact: Patty Dunn Dir ops/finance
Tel: 727-588-9481
Email: patty.dunn@mgtedge.com
Website: www.themanagementedge.com
Organization dev, team building & partnering, executive & staff dev, training & coaching, conflict resolution, consensus building. (Woman, estab 1986, empl 18, sales $908,000, cert: State, WBENC)

Georgia

7542 Assessment Plus, Inc.
2180 Satellite Blvd Ste 400
Duluth, GA 30097
Contact: Brielle Fetrow Project Coord
Tel: 770-925-3990
Email: brielle.fetrow@assessmentplus.com
Website: www.assessmentplus.com
Employee opinion surveys, customers satisfaction surveys, leadership development, 360-degree feedback assessments, executive & leadership coaching, exit interviews & team assessments. (Woman, estab 1984, empl 14, sales $650,000, cert: WBENC)

7543 Career Connection, Inc.
1170 Peachtree St Ste 1200
Atlanta, GA 30309
Contact: Cody Stowers
Tel: 404-814-5282
Email: cstowers@ccicareers.com
Website: www.ccicareers.com
Staff augmentation, workforce solutions, permanent placement, recruitment, personnel management, HR services, administrative management, call center, customer support, IT support, Information technology, facilities management. (Woman, estab 1986, empl 1000, sales $40,000,000, cert: WBENC)

7544   CyQuest Business Solutions, Inc.
       3645 Market Place Blvd Ste 130
       East Point, GA 30344
       Contact: DeVan Brown CEO
       Tel: 404-761-6699
       Email: devan@cyquesthr.com
       Website: www.cyquesthr.com
HR outsourcing solutions: compensation, employee
benefits, retirement plans, HRIS systems, payroll processing, employee recruitment & retention. (AA, estab 2004,
empl 8, sales $107,500, cert: State, NMSDC)

7545   eVerifile.com Inc.
       900 Circle 75 Pkwy Ste 1550
       Atlanta, GA 30339
       Contact: Jennifer Brown VP Business Dev
       Tel: 404-585-4487
       Email: jennifer.brown@everifile.com
       Website: http://everifile.com
Criminal background investigations, action notification
and/or information analytics & grading, US Government
watch searches, certificate & license verification, motor
vehicle reports, employment & reference verification. (AA,
estab , empl , sales $12,000,000, cert: NMSDC)

7546   McPherson, Berry & Associates, Inc.
       4158 S River Ln Ste 110
       Ellenwood, GA 30294
       Contact: LaSonya Berry CEO
       Tel: 800-325-5269
       Email: lasonya@mcphersonberryassoc.com
       Website: www.mcphersonberry.com
Human Rrsource training, consulting & team building
event planning. (Woman/AA, estab 2000, empl 3, sales
$250,000, cert: NMSDC, WBENC)

7547   Springboard Benefits, LLC
       695 Pylant St NE Ste 232
       Atlanta, GA 30306
       Contact: Amy Parkman CEO
       Tel: 205-790-1060
       Email: aparkman@springboardbenefits.com
       Website: www.springboardbenefits.com
Project management & consulting, employee on-boarding
& off-boarding, hire to retire, new hires, open enrollment,
ACA, variable hour tracking, medicare exchange & early
termination exchanges. (Woman, estab 2014, empl 6, sales
$250,000, cert: WBENC)

7548   Steelbridge Solutions, Inc
       2451 Cumberland Pkwy Ste 3228
       Atlanta, GA 30339
       Contact: Susan Richards President
       Tel: 404-259-0865
       Email: susan.richards@steelbridgesolutions.com
       Website: www.SteelBridgeSolutions.com
Human Capital Consulting, Human Resource Consulting,
Business Transformation Consulting, Change Management
Consulting, Human resource Information System Consult-
ing, HR Transformation, HR Strategy, HR Technology.
(Woman, estab 2013, empl , sales $900,000, cert: WBENC)

Illinois

7549   JRA Consulting Services, Inc.
       10225 W Higgins Rd
       Rosemont, IL 60018
       Contact: Ross Wolfson Talent Acquisition Mgr
       Tel: 847-430-3682
       Email: rwolfson@hrcontracting.com
       Website: www.hrcontracting.com
Human resources staffing, permanent & contract
positions. (Woman, estab 1997, empl 4, sales
$2,000,000, cert: NWBOC)

7550   Ossanna Corporation
       48 Hawthorne Lane
       Barrington Hills, IL 60010
       Contact: Mariaelena Estrada Office/Contracts Mgr
       Tel: 847-255-2800
       Email: mestrada@ossanna.com
       Website: www.ossanna.com
Human resource professionals: consulting, option-to-
hire & permanent basis. (Woman, estab 1988, empl 16,
sales $3,313,000, cert: State, WBENC)

Indiana

7551   HR Alternative Consulting, Inc.
       10641 Medinah Dr
       Indianapolis, IN 46234
       Contact: Ann Fisher President
       Tel: 317-852-3590
       Email: afisher@hralternativeconsulting.com
       Website: www.hralternativeconsulting.com
Customized human resources services. (Woman, estab
2003, empl 2, sales , cert: State, City)

7552   Work-Comp Management Services
       760 Park East Blvd #5
       Lafayette, IN 47905
       Contact: Julie Ott, RN, BSN, COHN-S/CM Owner
       Tel: 765-447-7473
       Email: jott@workcompms.com
       Website: www.workcompms.net
On-site occupational health services, work comp case
management, pre-employment random drug screening,
certified collections. (Woman, estab 1996, empl 55,
sales $3,600,000, cert: WBENC)

Louisiana

7553   Debra Gould & Associates, Inc.
       P.O. Box 871211
       New Orleans, LA 70187
       Contact: Debra Gould President & CEO
       Tel: 504-244-6576
       Email: djgould@gouldassoc.com
       Website: www.gouldassoc.com
Diversity, change management, team building, leader-
ship, project management, Six Sigma & communication.
(Woman/AA, estab 1996, empl 2, sales , cert: WBENC)

Maryland

7554   AEIO, LLC
       1250 Connecticut Ave, NW Ste 200
       Washington, MD 20036
       Contact: CEO
       Tel: 202-251-3545
       Email:
       Website: www.aeioonline.com
Human resource management, staff augmentation,
conference management services. (Woman/AA, estab
2001, empl 20, sales $700,000, cert: State)

7555   Full Disclosure
       2 Industrial Park Dr Ste B
       Waldorf, MD 20602
       Contact: Felicia Denman President
       Tel: 877-214-4717
       Email: fdenman@full-disclosure.org
       Website: www.full-disclosure.org
Preemployment screening, background checks, criminal
records, employment verification, education verification,
terrorist watch list, reference check, civil records, professional license verification. (Woman/AA, estab 2006, empl
1, sales , cert: State)

7556   HR Anew, Inc.
       6350 Stevens Forest Rd Ste 250
       Columbia, MD 21046
       Contact: Melanie Freeman President & CEO
       Tel: 410-381-5220
       Email: mfreeman@hranew.com
       Website: www.hranew.com
Human resource management & consulting, training &
professional development, management & employee
coaching, recruitment & hiring, executive search, staff
augmentation, event & conference planning , employee
relations. (Woman/AA, estab 1999, empl 17, sales
$2,200,000, cert: State)

7557   The HR Source
       8181 Professional Place Ste 120
       Landover, MD 20785
       Contact: Patricia Hall Jaynes CEO
       Tel: 301-459-3133
       Email: pathj@thehrsource.com
       Website: www.thehrsource.com
Human resources staffing & consulting services, interim/
temporary & permanent staffing services, outplacement &
payroll services, administrative interim/temporary &
permanent staffing services. (Woman/AA, estab 1994,
empl 5, sales $2,894,265, cert: State, NMSDC, WBENC)

Michigan

7558   Aha! Leadership LLC
       49425 Deer Run
       Northville, MI 48167
       Contact: Robyn Marcotte President
       Tel: 248-882-2354
       Email: robyn.marcotte@ahaleadership.com
       Website: www.ahaleadership.com
Leadership Training & Development, Human Resources
Consulting Services; Customer Service Training & Develop-
ment. (Woman, estab 0, empl , sales $ 0, cert: WBENC)

7559   Ashlor Management Corporation
       3710 Davison Rd
       Flint, MI 48506
       Contact: Charles Kuta President
       Tel: 810-275-0690
       Email: charles@ashlorstaffing.com
       Website: www.ashlorstaffing.com
Human resources, staffing, payroll & complete benefit
administration. (Hisp, estab 2015, empl 5, sales , cert:
NMSDC)

7560   The Orsus Group, Inc.
       3155 W Big Beaver Rd Ste 216
       Troy, MI 48084
       Contact: Brandon Meagher Business Develop Mgr
       Tel: 248-530-3685
       Email: bmeagher@theorsusgroup.com
       Website: www.theorsusgroup.com
Employment screening: criminal checks, sex offender
registry, employment & education verification, motor
vehicle records, credit checks, sanctions checks, drug
screening, prohibited parties. (AA, estab 2007, empl 22,
sales $900,000, cert: NMSDC)

Minnesota

7561   Inclusion, Inc.
       126 N 3rd St Ste 412
       Minneapolis, MN 55401
       Contact: Shirley Engelmeier CEO
       Tel: 612-339-2202
       Email: shirley@inclusion-inc.com
       Website: www.inclusion-inc.com
Diversity & inclusion strategies: web based survey,
diversity & inclusion assesment, customized skills based
training, changing business behaviors, micro-inequities
& on-the-job application. (Woman, estab 2001, empl 21,
sales , cert: WBENC)

Missouri

7562   Hicks-Carter-Hicks, LLC
       12747 Olive Blvd, Ste 300
       St. Louis, MO 63141
       Contact: Gloria Carter-Hicks CEO
       Tel: 314-260-7587
       Email: info@h-c-h.com
       Website: www.h-c-h.com
Performance improvement consulting: mgmt & human
resources, performance coaching, training & dev,
facilitation, keynote presentations. (Woman/AA, estab
1999, empl 3, sales $ 0, cert: NMSDC, WBENC)

New Jersey

7563   Diversified Consulting Consortium, LLC
       5 Tenalfy Rd, Ste 404
       Englewood, NJ 07631
       Contact: Antonette Alonso
       Tel: 908-669-4633
       talonso@diversifiedconsultingconsortium.com
       www.diversifiedconsultingconsortium.com
Human resources management consulting, training,
investigations, diversity management, affirmative action,
employee coaching & counseling, labor relations.
(Woman/AA, Hisp, estab 2012, empl 6, sales , cert:
NMSDC)

7564 Fintech Consulting LLC DBA ApTask
  120 Wood Ave South, Ste 300
  Iselin, NJ 08830
  Contact: Taj Haslani Founder
  Tel: 212-256-9131
  Email: joshua@aptask.com
  Website: www.aptask.com
Staffing, workforce solutions, strategic outsourcing. (As-Ind, estab 2010, empl 367, sales $32,000,000, cert: NMSDC)

7565 SHIFT Employment Law Training, LLC
  26 Main St, Ste 301
  Chatham, NJ 07928
  Contact: Regina Feeney Dir of Operations
  Tel: 800-790-5030
  Email: regina@shiftelt.com
  Website: www.shiftelt.com
Online HR Compliance Training courses. (Woman, estab 2015, empl 14, sales $1,788,000, cert: WBENC)

7566 Strategic Benefit Solutions
  106 Madison Ave
  Atlantic City, NJ 08401
  Contact: Le Phan CEO
  Tel: 609-957-5309
  Email: lphan@sbscompanies.com
  Website: www.sbscompanies.com
Strategic Benefit Solutions is a full service consulting firm for voluntary worksite benefit solutions with a proven track record of delivering successful benefit solutions that deliver the results you and your employees require. (Woman/As-Pac, estab 2011, empl 6, sales $500,000, cert: NMSDC)

New York

7567 Can-Am Consultants Inc.
  208 Mill St
  Rochester, NY 14614
  Contact: Cathryn Bell CEO
  Tel: 585-777-4040
  Email: carrie.bell@can-amconsultants.com
  Website: www.can-amconsultants.com
Recruitment & Payroll, Recruitment, Staffing & Payroll of Engineering, Technical & IT Personnel. (Woman, estab 2003, empl 150, sales $19,494,834, cert: State)

7568 Corporate Screening Consulting, LLC
  4201 N Buffalo Rd Ste 10
  Orchard Park, NY 14127
  Contact: Maria DiPirro President
  Tel: 716-583-4629
  Email: mdipirro@corpscreen.com
  Website: www.corpscreen.com
Risk management advisory services, Risk Avoidance consulting, litigation support, corporate compliance, due diligence, fraud analysis, background investigations & loss prevention program design. (Woman, estab 2007, empl 3, sales $250,000, cert: State)

7569 Crown Consulting Services Company
  P.O. Box 292
  Buffalo, NY 14207
  Contact: Anthony Fitzgerald CEO
  Tel: 800-868-1323
  Email: afitzgerald@cpmsllc.com
  Website: www.cpmsllc.com
Human resource ,anagement consulting, training, programs & policy development, executive coaching, seminars & workshops. (AA, estab 2000, empl 2, sales , cert: State)

Ohio

7570 Global to Local Language Solutions, LLC
  1776 Mentor Ave Ste 319
  Cincinnati, OH 42512
  Contact: Grace Bosworth President
  Tel: 513-526-5011
  Email: grace@g2local.com
  Website: www.g2local.com
Interpreting/translation services, interpreter training & language training. (Woman, estab 2009, empl 3, sales , cert: State, WBENC)

7571 Strategic Performance Systems, LLC
  2206 Highland Ave
  Cincinnati, OH 45219
  Contact: Deborah Heater CEO
  Tel: 513-602-6200
  Email: debheater@strategicperformancesystems.com
  Website: www.strategicperformancesystems.com
Employee Development: management, leadership, compliance & risk reduction strategies, Human Resources Best Practices: effective human resources functions, Diversity Climate Assessments. (Woman/AA, estab 2013, empl 1, sales $130,000, cert: State)

7572 Stryker Green, LLC
  1240 Sharonbrook Dr
  Twinsburg, OH 44087
  Contact: Sandy Moore CEO
  Tel: 330-963-9985
  Email: sjohnson@strykergreen.com
  Website: www.strykergreen.com
Human Resource Solutions consulting & managed services. (Woman/AA, estab 2012, empl 2, sales , cert: NMSDC)

Pennsylvania

7573 Advance Sourcing Concepts, LLC
  3000 McKnight East Dr Ste 201
  Pittsburgh, PA 15237
  Contact: Judith Bernhard President
  Tel: 412-415-5081
  Email: jbernhard@ascpeople.com
  Website: www.ascpeople.com
Human Resources contract & sourcing. (Woman, estab 2005, empl 4, sales $1,200,000, cert: State, WBENC)

7574 American Personnel Managers & Consultants, Inc.
  3607 Rosemont Ave, Ste 101
  Camp Hill, PA 17011
  Contact: Pat Gingrich CEO
  Tel: 717-465-5637
  Email: patg@apmci.com
  Website: www.amerijob.com
Staffing, Human Resource Management, Consulting, Testing & Training, Procurement, Information Technology Staffing, Project Management. (Woman, estab 1998, empl 45, sales $3,000,000, cert: State)

7575 BRODY Professional Development
  115 West Ave Ste 114
  Jenkintown, PA 19046
  Contact: Laura Gabor Accounting Dept
  Tel: 215-886-1688
  Email: laura@BrodyPro.com
  Website: www.BrodyPro.com
Training & coaching. (Woman, estab 1983, empl 15, sales $2,520,316, cert: WBENC)

7576 Career Concepts, Inc.
      Arborcrest 2, 721 Arbor Way
      Blue Bell, PA 19422
      Contact: Sharon Imperiale CEO
      Tel: 610-941-4455
      Email: simperiale@cciconsulting.com
      Website: www.cciconsulting.com
Management consulting, human resources,
outplacement/career transition, recruiting, managerial &
executive coaching, leadership development, training.
(Woman, estab 1988, empl 40, sales $7,000,000, cert:
State, WBENC)

7577 FCF Schmidt Public Relations
      600 W Germantown Pike, Ste 380
      Plymouth Meeting, PA 19462
      Contact: Maribeth Schmidt President
      Tel: 610-941-0395
      Email: mschmidt@fcfschmidtpr.com
      Website: www.fcfschmidtpr.com
Strategic, integrated business-to-business & consumer
public relations programs: technical writing, media
relations, special events management, public service.
(Woman, estab 1989, empl 43, sales $8,700,000, cert:
WBENC)

7578 The Bradley Partnerships, Inc.
      207 Malbec Lane Ste 100
      Wexford, PA 15090
      Contact: Lois Bradley President
      Tel: 724-779-8170
      Email: lois@bradleypartnerships.com
      Website: http://bradleypartnerships.com
Organizational & human resource consulting services.
(Woman, estab 2002, empl 6, sales $325,000, cert: State,
City, WBENC, 8a)

Peurto Rico

7579 Smart Option Search
      P.O. Box 194088
      San Juan, PR 00917
      Contact: Melissa Concepcion Esterrich President
      Tel: 787-767-2373
      Email: mconcepcion@smartoptionsearch.com
      Website: www.smartoptionsearch.com
Recruiting and Human Resources Consulting. (Woman/
Hisp, estab 2000, empl 10, sales $398,000, cert: NMSDC)

Texas

7580 24/7 Background Checks LLC
      11520 N Central Expressway Ste 230
      Dallas, TX 75243
      Contact: Jones Ajatuaewo President
      Tel: 214-206-3565
      Email: jones@criminal411.com
      Website: www.criminal411.com
Pre employment screening services: driving records,
education & employment verification. (Woman/AA, estab
2004, empl 25, sales $600,000, cert: State, NMSDC)

7581 AGResearch International, LLC
      P.O. Box 460
      McKinney, TX 75070
      Contact: Patti T. Mayer President
      Tel: 214-842-4540
      Email: patti.mayer@agresearch.info
      Website: www.agresearch.info
Human capital services, benchmarking studies. (Woman,
estab 2002, empl 15, sales $1,450,278, cert: State,
WBENC)

7582 Aspire HR, Inc.
      5151 Belt Line Rd Ste 1125
      Dallas, TX 75254
      Contact: Managing Partner
      Tel: 972-372-2815
      Email:
      Website: http://aspirehr.com
HR services for SAP ERP HCM solutions, implementations, upgrades & support, payroll, HR renewal, data
conversions & migrations. (Woman, estab 1998, empl
50, sales , cert: WBENC)

7583 Bashen Corporation
      2603 Augusta Dr, Ste 200
      Houston, TX 77057
      Contact: Janet Bashen CEO
      Tel: 800-994-1554
      Email: sales@bashencorp.com
      Website: www.bashencorp.com
HR consulting services: EEO compliance administration,
EEO investigations/ position statements & investigative
reports, workplace training, affirmative action planning,
diversity strategies, risk management. (Woman/AA,
estab 2013, empl 20, sales $1,578,181, cert: NMSDC,
WBENC)

7584 Brook Consultants Inc.
      2500 N Dallas Pkwy Ste 180
      Plano, TX 75093
      Contact: Matt Jones VP Sales
      Tel: 972-473-8918
      Email: sales@brookvms.com
      Website: http://brookvms.com
Human Resource Management services, Contractor
onboarding, competence evaluation, E-Verify & background checks. (Woman, estab 2006, empl 125, sales
$60,000,000, cert: WBENC)

7585 Cruvel Data Analytics
      6315 Liberty ct
      Frisco, TX 75035
      Contact: Jose Owner
      Tel: 214-250-8937
      Email: jvel2572@gmail.com
      Website: www.cruvel.com
Translation & interpretation services. (Hisp, estab 2018,
empl 6, sales , cert: City)

7586 G&A Partners
      4801 Woodway Ste 210
      Houston, TX 77056
      Contact: David Vasquez VP
      Tel: 713-784-1181
      Email: dvasquez@gnapartners.com
      Website: www.gnapartners.com
Professional Employer Organization (PEO) & Human
Resources Outsourcing & Consulting. (Hisp, estab 1995,
empl 175, sales $131,230,000, cert: State)

7587 Human Capital International, LLC dba Integrated
Human Capital
7300 Viscount Blvd Ste 103
El Paso, TX 79925
Contact: Rosa Santana CEO
Tel: 915-781-2665
Email: rosa.santana@ihcus.com
Website: www.ihcus.com
HR consulting, temporary staffing, professional & executive placement, payroll svcs, skill testing, vendor mgmt, on-site staff mgmt. (Woman/Hisp, estab 2002, empl 34, sales $16,171,166, cert: State, NMSDC, WBENC)

7588 InGenesis, Inc.
10231 Kotzebue St
San Antonio, TX 78217
Contact: Dr. Veronica Edwards CEO
Tel: 210-366-0033
Email: commercial@ingenesis.com
Website: www.ingenesis.com
Workforce solutions: direct placement, direct hire, executive search, temporary staffing, contingent staffing, managed vendor, recruitment process outsourcing, managed services programs & locum tenens. (Woman/Hisp, estab , empl , sales $174,785,000, cert: NMSDC, WBENC)

7589 KAS Consulting Group
3625 North Hall Ste 610
Dallas, TX 75219
Contact: Keith Scott CEO
Tel: 214-528-3326
Email: keith@kasconsulting.com
Website: www.kasconsulting.com
Human resources consulting, direct staffing & placement svcs, outplacement svcs, performance mgmt & appraisals, leadership & performance coaching. (AA, estab 2002, empl 3, sales $1,000,000, cert: State)

Virginia

7590 Helios HR LLC
1925 Isaac Newton Sq E Ste 200
Reston, VA 20190
Contact: VP Finance
Tel: 703-860-3882
Email: ekrause@helioshr.com
Website: www.helioshr.com
HR Effectiveness & Compliance Analysis, Employee Assimilation & Onboarding, Employee Regulation Requirements, Policy Maintenance, Employee Relations & Retention, Maintain & Implement Employee Performance Management. (Woman, estab 2001, empl 20, sales $3,670,154, cert: State, WBENC)

7591 RKL Resources
6933 Commons Plaza Ste 245
Chesterfield, VA 23831
Contact: Tawanda Johnson Owner
Tel: 804-638-5991
Email: tjohnson@rklresources.com
Website: www.rklresources.com
Human resources solutions: recruitment, training, organizational development, employee relations & audits. (Woman/AA, estab 2013, empl 2, sales $552,167, cert: State)

West Virginia

7592 Edwards Management Consultants, Inc.
110 S. George St Ste 1
Charles Town, WV 25414
Contact: Christine Edwards President
Tel: 703-349-1412
Email: christinec@edwardsemc.com
Website: www.edwardsemc.com
HR Advisor/Consulting Services, HR Support Services, Recruitment - Short/Long Term Entry Level/Mid to Senior Level Candidates Managenment and Performance Management. (Woman/AA, estab 2005, empl 5, sales , cert: NMSDC)

PROFESSIONAL SERVICES: Management Consulting

Provide general management consulting services: survey research, economic forecasting, transportation studies, facilities and program management, strategic planning, training and development. NAICS Code 54

Alaska

7593 Teya Technologies, LLC
      101 E 9th Ave, Ste 9B
      Anchorage, AK 99501
      Contact: Ronald Perry CEO
      Tel: 907-339-4901
      Email: ron.perry@teyatech.com
      Website: www.teyatech.com
Construction, demolition, project management, custodial and janitorial services, administrative services, product manufacturing, housing maintenance, and conference and event planning/management. (Nat Ame, estab 2005, empl 46, sales $14,422,189, cert: NMSDC)

Alabama

7594 MJLM Engineering & Technical Services
      4825 University Square Ste 14
      Huntsville, AL 35816
      Contact: Allison M Rhen Dir Business Devel
      Tel: 256-890-1855
      Email: arhen@mjlm.com
      Website: www.mjlmengineering.com
Management consulting, auditing & assurance, tax & technology consulting, performance improvement, management performance reviews, human resources risk assessment, cost analysis of core processes. (AA, estab 2003, empl 100, sales $16,963,661, cert: State)

7595 Paragon Management Group
      P.O. Box 687
      Cottondale, AL 35453
      Contact: Ty Jones President
      Tel: 205-409-2948
      Email: tjones@paragon-mgmt.com
      Website: www.paragon-mgmt.com
Management consulting, supply chain management strategy, operations, technology & organization solutions. (Woman/AA, estab 2006, empl 5, sales $180,000, cert: NMSDC)

7596 PROJECTXYZ, Inc.
      1500 Perimeter Pkwy Ste 126
      Huntsville, AL 35806
      Contact: Larry Lewis
      Tel: 256-721-9001
      Email: larry.lewis@projectxyz.com
      Website: www.projectxyz.com
Healthcare consulting, project management, information technology, engineering & prototype/fabrication services. (Woman/AA, estab 2005, empl 30, sales $900,000, cert: State)

7597 Terrell & Associates, LLC
      2210 S Tallassee Dr
      Tallassee, AL 36078
      Contact: Shandra Terrell President
      Tel: 334-283-5156
      Email: sterrell@terrellassociates.net
      Website: www.terrellassociates.net
Training: diversity, difficult people, teamwork, customer service, speaking engagements, research & evaluation, etc. (Woman/AA, estab 2001, empl 1, sales , cert: NWBOC)

Arizona

7598 Banda Group International, LLC
      1799 E Queen Creek Rd Ste 1
      Chandler, AZ 85286
      Contact: Elisonia Valle Mktg & Communications
      Tel: 480-636-8734
      Email: elisoniav@bandagroupintl.com
      Website: www.bandagroupintl.com
Safety management, risk management, project management, training & associated engineering disciplines. (Hisp, estab 2003, empl 88, sales $9,049,000, cert: NMSDC, SDB)

7599 BLeadersEdge LLC
      721 N 106th St
      Mesa, AZ 85207
      Contact: Michael Nadeau President
      Tel: 480-269-7438
      Email: mike@bleadersedge.com
      Website: www.bleadersedge.com
Providing organizations with expanded personal, team, and organizational leadership development growth (ERG's, BRG's, AG's, PM's), increased team engagement, and continued leadership development. (Nat Ame, estab 2019, empl 1, sales , cert: NMSDC)

7600 TAX ROOF, LLC dba JT Project Management Office
      1 E Washington St Ste 500
      Phoenix, AZ 85004
      Contact: Dionne Joseph Thomas President
      Tel: 623-374-6455
      Email: admin@taxroof.com
      Website: www.jtprojectmanagementoffice.com
Program/Project Management & Implementation, Initiation; Planning; Execution; Monitoring & Control; Closing. (Woman/AA, estab 2011, empl 2, sales , cert: State, City, WBENC)

California

7601 Being Present Inc
      8601 Sunland Blvd, Ste 53
      Sun Valley, CA 91352
      Contact: Sonya Shelton CEO
      Tel: 818-473-5323
      Email: sonya@executiveleader.com
      Website: www.ExecutiveLeader.com
Management consulting & executive coaching services. (Woman/Hisp, estab 2006, empl 4, sales $970,003, cert: NMSDC, WBENC)

7602   causeIMPACTS
5301 W 119th Pl
Inglewood, CA 90304
Contact: Principal
Tel: 714-390-6301
Email:
Website: www.causeimpacts.com
Social impact strategy consulting. (Woman, estab 2015, empl 2, sales $500,000, cert: WBENC)

7603   Celerity Consulting Group, Inc.
2 Gough St, Ste 300
San Francisco, CA 94103
Contact: Yinna Wong CEO
Tel: 415-986-8850
Email: ywong@consultcelerity.com
Website: www.consultcelerity.com
Litigation & business consulting: strategic planning, quality control processes. (Woman, estab 2001, empl 98, sales $16,604,529, cert: CPUC)

7604   Cervantes-Delgado, Inc.
471 W Lambert Rd, Ste 100
Brea, CA 92821
Contact: Rick Gross President
Tel: 714-990-3940
Email: rsg@cervantes-delgado.com
Website: www.cervantes-delgado.com
Management consulting. (Hisp, estab 2001, empl 3, sales $ 0, cert: CPUC)

7605   Dilan Consulting Group
55 New Montgomery, Ste 518
San Francisco, CA 94105
Contact: Eugene Dilan CEO
Tel: 415-937-0621
Email: office@dilanconsulting.com
Website: www.dilanconsulting.com
Organizational Development & Change. (Hisp, estab , empl , sales , cert: NMSDC)

7606   Elia Erickson, LLC
11620 Wilshire Blvd. 9th Fl
Los Angeles, CA 90025
Contact: CEO
Tel: 310-479-0217
Email:
Website: https://expertmediatraining.com
Media training, presentation training, public speaking training, communication consulting, business coaching, publicity training. (Woman, estab 1999, empl 1, sales $128,741, cert: State, City, CPUC)

7607   Emerson Human Capital Consulting, Inc.
2199 Harbor Bay Pkwy
Alameda, CA 94502
Contact: CEO
Tel: 510-545-4435
Email:
Website: www.emersonhc.com
Training, diversity training & workshops, change management, organizational design, communications, intercultural svcs, process design, IT implementation, user acceptance. (Woman, estab 2001, empl 35, sales $7,459,817, cert: WBENC)

7608   Fostering Executive Leadership, Inc.
4790 Irvine Blvd, Ste 105-432
Irvine, CA 92620
Contact: Dr. Tammy Wong CEO
Tel: 949-651-6250
Email: tammy@fosteringexecutiveleadership.com
Website: www.FosteringExecutiveLeadership.com
Executive coaching, building leadership, team performance, communication, accountability & strategy. (Woman, estab 2006, empl 300, sales $1,500,000, cert: CPUC, WBENC)

7609   ICE Safety Solutions Inc.
47703 Fremont Blvd
Fremont, CA 94538
Contact: Pamela ISom CEO
Tel: 877-743-8423
Email: accounting@getice.com
Website: www.getice.com
Safety training: CPR, first aid, ERT, AED, forklift, Fire safety, fire extinguisher training, safety consulting & curriculum dev. (Woman/AA, Hisp, estab , empl , sales $1,800,000, cert: NMSDC, CPUC, WBENC)

7610   Imani Lee, Inc.
11297 Senda Luna Llena Bldg. B
San Diego, CA 92130
Contact: Lee Martin CEO
Tel: 858-523-9733
Email: translations@imanilee.com
Website: http://imanilee.com
Translation & Localization, Transcription, Transcreation, Interpreting, International Social Media Management, Consulting Services, Language & Culture training, Subtitling & Voiceover, Educational Curriculum Development. (AA, estab 2002, empl 10, sales $1,526,000, cert: NMSDC, CPUC)

7611   Julianna Hynes & Associates
1638 Freed Circle
Pittsburg, CA 94565
Contact: Julianna Hynes Principal
Tel: 925-207-1578
Email: julianna@juliannahynes.com
Website: www.juliannahynes.com
Executive coaching & leadership development services. (Woman/AA, estab 2003, empl 1, sales $139,599, cert: WBENC)

7612   K'ontinuous Technologies, Inc.
1304 W 2nd St, Ste 346
Los Angeles, CA 90026
Contact: Steve Buchanan President
Tel: 213-334-3951
Email: sbuchanan@kontinuoustech.com
Website: www.kontinuoustech.com
Program Management Oversight, Program/Project Definition & Direction, Program/Project Tracking & Documentation, Technical Resource Allocation, Client/Vendor Relations, Change Management, Risk Management. (AA, Hisp, estab 2015, empl 1, sales , cert: State)

7613 LKG-CMC, Inc.
707 Wilshire Blvd, Ste 3600
Los Angeles, CA 90017
Contact: VP
Tel: 213-892-0789
Email:
Website: www.lkgcmc.com
Project controls & configuration mgmt consulting: document control, cost control & estimating, scheduling & business continuity planning. (Woman, estab 1987, empl 70, sales $ 0, cert: CPUC)

7614 Los Remedios
2377 S Sabre Ave
Fresno, CA 93727
Contact: Patricia Alvarado Owner
Tel: 619-813-6445
Email: pa@remedysupportservices.com
Website:
Management & human resources consulting. (Woman/ Hisp, estab 1995, empl 1, sales , cert: State)

7615 Nesso Strategies
4142 Adams Ave #103-256
San Diego, CA 92116
Contact: Judy Hissong President
Tel: 619-546-7885
Email: judy@nessostrategies.com
Website: www.NessoStrategies.com
Speaking, training, consulting & facilitation, communication & conflict management, leadership development, accountability, diversity & inclusion. (Woman, estab 2009, empl 3, sales $240,000, cert: City, CPUC)

7616 Osceola Consulting llc
One Blackfield Dr, Ste 410
Tiburon, CA 94920
Contact: Neda Najibi VP business operations
Tel: 800-986-1960
Email: nnajibi@osceolac.com
Website: www.osceolac.com
Management consulting, business process consulting, information technology procurement, & computer & data processing services. (Nat Ame, estab 2006, empl 27, sales $6,103,929, cert: NMSDC, CPUC)

7617 ROI Communication Inc.
5274 Scotts Valley Dr Ste 207
Scotts Valley, CA 95066
Contact: Tricia Deeter VP of Finance
Tel: 831-430-0170
Email: accounting@roico.com
Website: www.roico.com/index.html
Strategy & planning, leader & manager communication, measurement, benchmarking & analysis, employee experience, change communication, creative & visual design, sales communication, communication architecture. (Woman, estab 2001, empl 73, sales $ 0, cert: WBENC)

7618 SCMSP (dba) of Spotswood Consulting
92 Corporate Park Ste 812
Irvine, CA 92606
Contact: Derek Spotswood President
Tel: 800-716-2360
Email: derek@scmsp.com
Website: http://scmsp.com
Management consulting, business & technology solutions. (AA, estab 2006, empl 20, sales $2,200,000, cert: NMSDC, 8a)

7619 Wentworth Consulting Group, LLC
4616 Dolores Ave
Oakland, CA 94602
Contact: Audrey Waidelich Business Mgr
Tel: 510-482-6278
Email: info@wentworthconsulting.com
Website: www.wentworthconsulting.com
Training, leadership development, organization development, executive coaching, instructional design, workplace mediation & meeting facilitation. (Woman, estab 2011, empl , sales $890,200, cert: CPUC, WBENC)

Colorado

7620 LFL International Inc.
4 W Dry Creek Circle Ste 100
Littleton, CO 80120
Contact: Loretta Lovell CEO
Tel: 303-791-8405
Email: lflinc@aol.com
Website: www.LFLINC.com
Professional, administrative & anagement support services: program/, project & construction management services. (Woman/AA, estab 1990, empl 1300, sales $3,150,000, cert: City, NMSDC)

7621 Merrill Consulting Associates
10561 Wintersweet Ct
Parker, CO 80134
Contact: Dr. Herbert Merrill II CEO
Tel: 303-805-8245
Email: hmerrill@merrillca.com
Website: http://merrillca.com
Organizational change & transformation. (AA, estab 2004, empl 8, sales , cert: State)

7622 Sanchez, Tennis & Associates, LLC
470 Fountaintree Ln
Boulder, CO 80304
Contact: Anita Sanchez Director
Tel: 303-449-5921
Email: anita@sancheztennis.com
Website: www.SanchezTennis.com
Organizational development consulting. (Woman/Hisp, estab 1976, empl 2, sales $230,000, cert: NMSDC)

Connecticut

7623 Daniel Penn Associates, LLC
151 New Park Ave, Ste 106
Hartford, CT 06106
Contact: Tony Rodriguez President
Tel: 860-232-8577
Email: info@danielpenn.com
Website: www.danielpenn.com
Mgmt consutling firm, consulting svcs, productivity improvement, supply chain optimization, lean mfg, maintenance mgmt, supplier diversity, mfr systems improvement. (Hisp, estab 1978, empl 11, sales $ 0, cert: State, NMSDC)

7624 Framework LLC
1 Atlantic St, Ste 405
Stamford, CT 06901
Contact: Cecile Girard COO
Tel: 203-563-0644
Email: cgirard@framework-llc.com
Website: www.framework-llc.com
Develop & integrate sustainable business strategy & practices & communicate performance to stakeholders. (Woman, estab 2003, empl 6, sales , cert: WBENC)

7625 HOPET Engineering Services LLC
      151 New Park Ave
      Hartford, CT 06106
      Contact: Rosa Valenzuela President
      Tel: 860-251-9587
      Email: rosa@hopetengineeringservices.com
      Website: http://hopetengineeringservices.com
Project management & engineering, government &
commercial contracts project management, supply chain,
value stream mapping, sourcing strategies, earned value
management systems, risk mitigation plans & root cause
analysis. (Woman/Hisp, estab 2013, empl 1, sales , cert:
State)

7626 N-Touch Strategies, LLC
      263 Tresser Blvd, 9 Fl
      Stamford, CT 06901
      Contact: Natasha Williams Managing Partner
      Tel: 855-686-8247
      Email: nwilliams@ntouchstrategies.com
      Website: www.ntouchstrategies.com
Strategic management, Initiate & Accelerate growth,
Improve organizational efficiency, Leadership Development. (Woman/AA, estab 2010, empl 17, sales $2,250,000,
cert: NMSDC, WBENC, 8a)

District of Columbia

7627 H Rizvi Consulting Inc.
      1345 S Capitol St SW 807
      Washington, DC 20003
      Contact: Hamid Rizvi President
      Tel: 832-640-7374
      Email: hamid.rizvi@hrizviconsulting.com
      Website: www.hrizviconsulting.com
Consulting, Administrative, and Training Services. (As-Ind,
estab 2017, empl 0, sales $ 0, cert: NMSDC)

7628 MPF Federal
      1050 17th St, NW Ste 600
      Washington, DC 20036
      Contact: Anna Gilmore-Hall Director
      Tel: 202-776-0655
      Email: info@mpffederal.com
      Website: http://mpffederal.com
Program & Project Management, Innovative Technology
Services & Comprehensive Management Consulting.
(Woman/AA, estab 2012, empl 43, sales $2,955,000, cert:
8a)

Delaware

7629 DecisivEdge LLC
      131 Continental Dr Ste 409
      Newark, DE 19713
      Contact: Michele Frayler
      Tel: 302-299-1570
      Email: michele.frayler@decisivedge.com
      Website: www.decisivedge.com
Business consulting & technology services, business
architecture & performance, business analytics, data
warehouse strategy, design, development & governance,
marketing analytics development. (As-Ind, estab 2007,
empl 41, sales $4,739,862, cert: NMSDC)

Florida

7630 Advaion LLC
      1560 Sawgrass Corporate Pkwy 4th Fl
      Sunrise, FL 33323
      Contact: Pavan Satyaketu Operations Mgr
      Tel: 954-331-7969
      Email: bhuvan@advaion.com
      Website: www.advaion.com
Transaction & risk solutions, acquisition integration svcs,
risk assessment, Sarbanes-Oxley section svcs, process &
control documentation, entity level controls review,
corporate governance. (Woman/As-Pac, estab 2003,
empl 10, sales $1,900,000, cert: NMSDC)

7631 Aikerson Consulting Group
      51 SW 11th St
      Miami, FL 33130
      Contact: LaShanya Aikerson CEO
      Tel: 678-522-1545
      Email: lashanya@aikersonconsulting.com
      Website: www.AikersonConsulting.com
Training, speaking, coaching, talent development, and
meeting facilitation services. (Woman/AA, estab 2004,
empl 1, sales $165,709, cert: NMSDC, WBENC)

7632 American Sign Language Services Corporation
      3700 Commerce Blvd Ste 216
      Kissimmee, FL 34741
      Contact: Julian Ignatowski CFO
      Tel: 407-518-7900
      Email: gabrielle@aslservices.com
      Website: www.aslservices.com
Interpretation services, sign language, onsite interpreting, Video Relay Services (VRS) & Video Remote Interpreting (VRI). (Woman/Hisp, estab 1997, empl 125, sales
$8,750,000, cert: State, NMSDC)

7633 Argos Global Partner Services, LLC
      240 Crandon Blvd. Ste 201
      Key Biscayne, FL 33149
      Contact: Luciana Ciuchini CEO
      Tel: 305-365-1096
      Email: lciuchini@argosus.com
      Website: www.argosgps.com
Supply chain solutions, sourcing, consolidation, import,
export, purchasing, quality control, logistics and warehousing. (Woman/Hisp, estab 2005, empl 15, sales
$20,120,630, cert: NMSDC, WBENC)

7634 Blue Isis LLC
      525 Caribbean Dr E
      Summerland Key, FL 33042
      Contact: Dawn Mahan CEO
      Tel: 717-412-1900
      Email: dmahan@blueisisllc.com
      Website: www.blueisisllc.com
Project management consulting & talent development
services, management consulting services, program
management, portfolio management, governance,
budgeting, forecasting, strategic planning, resource
management. (Woman/Hisp, estab 2009, empl 10, sales
$1,000,000, cert: State)

7635 Caraballo Consulting & Associates, LLC
11312 NW 65 St
Doral, FL 33178
Contact: Lourdes Cordeiro Dir New Business Devel
Tel: 305-204-2493
Email: lourdes@caraballoconsulting.com
Website: www.caraballoconsulting.com
Regulatory Compliance & Submissions, Clinical, Quality
Assurance, Manufacturing, Project Management, Black
Belt, Lean Manufacturing, Engineering & Specialized
Engineering. (Woman/Hisp, estab 2015, empl 10, sales ,
cert: NMSDC)

7636 CMA Enterprise Incorporated
207 Laurel Oak Lane Ste B
Davie, FL 33325
Contact: Gail Birks Williams President & CEO
Tel: 954-476-3525
Email: cma@cma-ent.com
Website: www.cma-ent.com
Management consulting, business process re-engineering,
supplier/corporate diversity initiatives, employee relations,
training. (Woman/AA, estab 1990, empl 2, sales $ 0, cert:
State, WBENC)

7637 Corporate Fitness Works, Inc.
1200 16th St. N
St. Petersburg, FL 33705
Contact: Ken Viglio Sr. Dir of Business Development
Tel: 727-522-2900
Email: bloube@corporatefitnessworks.com
Website: www.corporatefitnessworks.com
Manage customized fitness centers & wellness programs,
feasibility studies, facility layout & design, equipment
recommendations. (Woman/As-Pac, estab , empl 452,
sales $11,213,388, cert: NMSDC, WBENC)

7638 Global Gateway Solutions Inc.
8201 Peters Rd Ste 1000
Plantation, FL 33324
Contact: Jacqueline Sutherland CEO
Tel: 877-447-4627
Email: asutherland@callggs.com
Website: http://callggs.com
Outsourced contact center solutions, customer service,
sales, and collections. (Woman/AA, estab 2007, empl 450,
sales $14,113,423, cert: NMSDC, WBENC)

7639 Government Business Solutions
12905 SW 132nd St, Ste 4
Miami, FL 33186
Contact: Lourdes Martin-Rosa President
Tel: 786-293-1601
Email: lourdes@govbizsolutions.com
Website: www.govbizsolutions.com
Educate small businesses on procuring federal, state &
local government contracts. (Woman/Hisp, estab 2002,
empl 6, sales $125,000, cert: State, WBENC, 8a)

7640 GreenPath Energy Solutions
3218 E Colonial Dr Ste G
Orlando, FL 32803
Contact: Samuel Graham CEO
Tel: 321-948-3623
Email: sgraham@greenpathes.com
Website: www.greenpathenergysolutions.com
Energy monitoring, energy auditing, retro-commissioning,
web-based energy dashboard management software. (AA,
estab 2006, empl 3, sales $175,000, cert: State, City,
NMSDC)

7641 Impresiv Health
145 Bellagio Way
Sanford, FL 32771
Contact: Marcus Fontaine President
Tel: 305-407-0218
Email: mfontaine@impresivhealth.com
Website: www.impresivhealth.com
Accreditation Readiness, Care Management, Program
Development, Regulatory Compliance Readiness, Clinical
& Non-Clinical Managed, Care Training, System Rede-
sign, Process & Workflow Improvement. (AA, estab
2015, empl 17, sales $2,500,000, cert: State)

7642 Maria R Pearson Inc dba Own Your World
101 Del Sol Circle
Tequesta, FL 33469
Contact: Maria Pearson President
Tel: 772-287-5833
Email: mariapearson@ownyourworld.net
Website: www.OwnYourWorld.net
Training & management consulting: communication,
presentation skills, leadership effectiveness, time mgmt,
process & system improvement. (Woman/Hisp, estab
1993, empl 1, sales , cert: State)

7643 Premier Remodeling Services, Inc.
5703 Red Bug Lake Rd, Ste 328
Winter Springs, FL 32708
Contact: Geoff Gilpin
Tel: 407-489-8510
Email: ggilpin@premiergroupadvisors.com
Website: http://premiergroupadvisors.com
Policy, Planning & Program Support, Information
Management, Human Capital Optimization, Education &
Training, Infrastructure Management, Sustainability
Planning, Engineering & Technical Assistance, Supplier
Management. (AA, estab 2006, empl 8, sales
$1,500,000, cert: NMSDC, 8a)

7644 Program Evaluation Services Inc.
5521 Oak Hollow Dr
Titusville, FL 32780
Contact: Gina Beckles CEO
Tel: 321-243-4809
Email: ginabeckles@cfl.rr.com
Website: www.programevaluationservices.com
Program evaluation & performance measurement,
analytical & administrative services. (Woman/AA, estab
2006, empl 2, sales , cert: NMSDC)

7645 Trustee Capital LLC
100 S Ashley Dr, Ste 600
Apollo Beach, FL 33572
Contact: Andre Fair CEO
Tel: 813-397-3648
Email: info@trusteecap.com
Website: www.trusteecap.com
Business valuations and custom analytics solutions. (AA,
estab 2017, empl 2, sales , cert: NMSDC)

7646 Wightman & Associates LLC
720 W Montrose St
Clermont, FL 34711
Contact: Louis Dommer III CFO
Tel: 757-574-4386
Email: ldommer@wightman-associates.com
Website: www.Wightman-Associates.com
Training & organizational development products &
services. (Woman, estab 2011, empl 12, sales $836,000,
cert: State)

Georgia

7647   Asil White Enterprises, Inc.
642 Concord Lake Circle Se
Smyrna, GA 30082
Contact: Lisa L White President
Tel: 404-786-8931
Email: lw@thinkaweinc.com
Website: www.thinkaweinc.com
Instructional design, training materials, professional &
mgmt dev training, coaching, time mgmt , organizational
dev, performance improvement, project mgmt. (Woman/
AA, estab 2004, empl 1, sales , cert: State)

7648   BDM2
235 Peachtree St, Ste 400
Atlanta, GA 30303
Contact: Missy Pitcher CEO
Tel: 404-301-5879
Email: missy.pitcher@bdmsquared.com
Website: www.bdmsquared.com
BDM Squared is a premier professional services
consultancy providing our clients with Project Delivery;
PMO Creation and Management; and Project Planning for
Rapid Ignition Project Startup and Launching. (AA, estab
2016, empl 8, sales $284,000, cert: NMSDC)

7649   Bellwether Services
950 Eagles Landing Pkwy, Ste 123
Stockbridge, GA 30281
Contact: John Wilkerson Exec Dir
Tel: 404-386-2437
Email: sales@bellwether-services.com
Website: www.bellwether-services.com
Supplier audit, cost reduction, order fulfillment, process
mapping, Six Sigma projects, inventory mgmt, total quality
mgmt, business process engineering, supply chain rate
negotiations, logistics modeling & optimization. (AA, estab
2004, empl 4, sales $102,000, cert: State)

7650   Full Circle Events
6070 Black Water Trail
Atlanta, GA 30328
Contact: Sally Silverman Owner
Tel: 404-236-0440
Email: sally.fullcircle@comcast.net
Website: www.fullcircleeventsinc.com
Event, meeting & conference planning. (Woman, estab
2002, empl 5, sales $416,897, cert: WBENC)

7651   Horizon Leadership, Inc.
3295 River Exchange Dr Ste 560
Norcross, GA 30092
Contact: Cindy Larkin President
Tel: 770-552-5511
Email: clarkin@horizonleadership.com
Website: http://horizonleadership.com
Facilitation, presentation & influencing skills,
teambuilding, change management, coaching skills, etc.
(Woman, estab 2002, empl 4, sales $2,300,000, cert:
WBENC)

7652   J.O. Rodgers and Associates, Inc.
4 Hunt Valley Dr
Lithonia, GA 30058
Contact: James Rodgers President
Tel: 770-482-9452
Email: jora@thediversitycoach.com
Website: www.thediversitycoach.com
Management consulting, coaching, executive education,
culture scans, vision formulation, valuing differences
workshop, diversity council installation, & Six Sigma.
(AA, estab 1987, empl 3, sales $206,000, cert: State)

7653   LBJR Consulting LLC
2942 Darlington Run
Duluth, GA 30097
Contact: Lavoska Barton President
Tel: 678-662-9159
Email: lbarton@lbjrconsulting.com
Website: www.lbjrconsulting.com
Project Management & Planning, Cost management &
Control, Budget prioritization & Management, Vendor
Management & Control, Financial / Variance Analysis of
projects, Process Management, Six Sigma Black Belt.
(AA, estab 2005, empl 4, sales , cert: State)

7654   LEAP Leadership
1011 Carriage Lane SE
Smyrna, GA 30082
Contact: Kim Radford Partner
Tel: 404-414-8624
Email: kr@leaplead.com
Website: http://leaplead.com
Leadership education, executive coaching & organiza-
tional development services. (Woman/AA, estab 2009,
empl 3, sales $590,405, cert: NMSDC)

7655   Peerless Performance, LLC
9040 Roswell Road Ste 460
Atlanta, GA 30350
Contact: LeeAnne Canecchio Acct Director
Tel: 404-551-5181
Email:
leeannecanecchio@peerlessperformance.net
Website: www.peerlessperformance.net
Performance Improvement, Culture Engineering Agency.
(Woman, estab 2017, empl 8, sales $550,000, cert:
WBENC)

7656   Renaissance Management Solutions, LLC
6555 Sugarloaf Pkwy Ste 307
Duluth, GA 30097
Contact: Russell Julian CEO
Tel: 404-484-4116
Email: russell@ren-mgt.com
Website: www.ren-mgt.com
Training services & systems: front-end training analysis,
training systems design & curriculum development to
delivery, logistics & evaluation. (AA, estab 2005, empl 3,
sales $420,000, cert: 8a)

7657   The Cadence Group, Inc.
1095 Zonolite Rd Ste 105
Atlanta, GA 30306
Contact:
Tel: 404-874-0544
Email:
Website: www.cadence-group.com
Information management: acquire, organize & dissemi-
nate information. (Woman, estab 1988, empl 46, sales
$2,890,048, cert: WBENC)

7658   The Intuition Consulting Firm, LLC.
3017 Bolling Way NE Office 257A
Atlanta, GA 30305
Contact: Roy Broderick Jr President & CEO
Tel: 404-487-9587
Email: roy@authentiqueagency.com
Website: www.authentiqueagency.com
Multicultural integration and programming. (AA, estab 2016, empl 10, sales $933,568, cert: NMSDC)

7659   Translation Station, Inc.
3460 Chamblee Dunwoody Way
Chamblee, GA 30341
Contact: Lindsey Cambardella CEO
Tel: 770-234-9387
Email: lindsey@translationstation.com
Website: www.translationstation.com
Foreign language translation: technical, legal, medical documents, benefits, software localization, website translation, interpretation for meetings, conferences, courts, depositions, conflict resolution, etc. (Woman, estab 1998, empl 5, sales $703,000, cert: WBENC)

7660   Tricia Browning Design Group
102 Westside Dr
LaGrange, GA 30240
Contact: Tim Donahue
Tel: 706-883-7741
Email: tdonahue@nimlok-westgeorgia.com
Website: www.nimlok-westgeorgia.com
Trade Show booths, Exhibits, Graphic Design, Display Advertising, Commercial Photography, Advertising Services, Design Services (Woman, estab 1996, empl 8, sales $2,180,000, cert: WBENC)

7661   VYD and Associates, LLC
3306 Blanton Dr
Scottdale, GA 30079
Contact: Vonetta Daniels CEO
Tel: 404-966-8411
Email: vonetta.daniels@gmail.com
Website: www.vydandassociates.com
Management consulting: business strategy, business process engineering, supply chain management, revenue cycle & cost optimization; program performance measurement & evaluation, strategic planning, budget & performance. (Woman/AA, estab 2010, empl 1, sales , cert: NMSDC, WBENC, 8a)

Illinois

7662   B2B Strategic Solutions, Inc.
150 N Michigan Ave Ste 2800
Chicago, IL 60601
Contact: Donna Bryant President
Tel: 312-368-1700
Email: info@b2bssi.com
Website: www.b2bssi.com
Management consulting, information technology, technical training, strategic planning, professional development, leadership, customer service, training, business writing. (Woman/AA, estab 2003, empl 20, sales $1,254,000, cert: State, NMSDC)

7663   CGN & Associates, Inc.
415 SW Washingotn
Peoria, IL 61602
Contact: Patrick Dierker Associate Partner
Tel: 309-495-2100
Email: patrick.dierker@cgnglobal.com
Website: www.cgnglobal.com
Business consulting: operations, execution & technology mgmt, analysis, design & implementation of complex operational transformations, strategy development, solution design, implementation & optimization techniques. (As-Pac, estab 1995, empl 125, sales $ 0, cert: State, NMSDC)

7664   Comprehensive Consulting Group LLC
15443 Sunset Dr
Dolton, IL 60419
Contact: Stetson Marshall CEO
Tel: 708-369-3361
Email: smarshall@compconsulting.net
Website: www.compconsulting.net
Management consulting, accounting, risk advisory/ management and program management services. (AA, estab 2018, empl 6, sales , cert: State)

7665   EMS Consulting
477 W Happfield Dr
Arl, IL 60004
Contact: Liz Kistner President
Tel: 224-465-1115
Email: lkistner@enrollmentmarketingsolutions.com
Website: www.emsconsultgroup.com
Project & program management consulting. (Woman, estab 2006, empl 1, sales $ 0, cert: WBENC)

7666   Executive Consultants United, LLC
180 N Stetson Ave, Ste 3500
Chicago, IL 60601
Contact: Wheeler Coleman CEO
Tel: 312-268-5829
Email: wcoleman@ec-united.com
Website: www.ec-united.com
Data Strategy / Roadmap, Advanced Analytics, Reporting, Dashboards & Scorecards, Data Strategies, Data Lakes, Data Platforms & Data Management, Data Scientists & DBAs Specialists, Analytics (Consumer, Provider, etc.) (AA, estab 2016, empl 5, sales $164,000, cert: NMSDC)

7667   Kairos Consulting Worldwide
935 West Chestnut Ste 455
Chicago, IL 60642
Contact: Managing Principal
Tel: 312-757-5197
Email:
Website: www.kairosworldwide.com
Technology consulting: change management & process reengineering, process management, strategic planning & project management. (Woman/AA, estab 2004, empl 1, sales , cert: State, WBENC)

7668 MarketZing Inc.
875 N Michigan Ave Ste 3100
Chicago, IL 60611
Contact: Aleen Bayard Principal
Tel: 312-794-7880
Email: aleen@aleenbayard.com
Website: www.marketzing.org
Change management project design & execution, culture & values alignment work, strategic planning facilitation & implementation support, employee engagement and team effectiveness, organizational & leadership development. (Woman, estab 1999, empl 1, sales $350,000, cert: WBENC)

7669 Mary O'Connor & Company
220 W River Dr
St. Charles, IL 60174
Contact: Mary O'Connor President
Tel: 630-443-4300
Email: moconnor@mocandco.com
Website: www.mocandco.com
Meeting & event mgmt, online event registration, program dev, employee training & dev, speaker svcs, hotel mgmt, transportation, food & beverage mgmt. (Woman, estab 1995, empl 17, sales $3,400,000, cert: WBENC)

7670 MJ Learning Inc.
605 S Maple Ave
Oak Park, IL 60304
Contact: Sarah Gee CEO
Tel: 708-613-5401
Email: sarah@mjlearning.com
Website: www.mjlearning.com
Professional & management development training. (Woman, estab 2010, empl 5, sales $500,000, cert: WBENC)

7671 Multilingual Connections, LLC
847 Chicago Ave, Ste 250
Evanston, IL 60202
Contact: Jill Bishop CEO
Tel: 773-292-5500
Email: jill@mlconnections.com
Website: http://multilingualconnections.com
Translation/interpretation services (all languages), workplace language training (Spanish and ESL - English as a Second Language), diversity training and workplace harassment prevention training and leadership development. (Woman, estab 2005, empl 25, sales $3,122,086, cert: WBENC)

7672 Nancy Conner Consulting, LLC
1235 Berry Lane
Flossmoor, IL 60422
Contact: Nancy Conner CEO
Tel: 847-456-5601
Email: nancy@nancyconner.com
Website: http://nancyconner.com
Supply chain, supplier development, small business partnerships, negotiation, community outreach & advocacy. (Woman, estab 2016, empl 1, sales , cert: WBENC)

7673 Professional Dynamic Network, Inc.
20280 Governors Hwy Ste 106
Olympia Fields, IL 60461
Contact: CEO
Tel: 708-747-4361
Email:
Website: www.pndseek.com
Temporary & permanent staffing, recruitment, management consulting, education & training. (Woman/AA, estab 1995, empl 167, sales $3,415,745, cert: City, NMSDC)

7674 PTS Consulting Services LLC
1700 Park St, Ste 212
Naperville, IL 60563
Contact: Reshma Multani Client Servicing Mgr
Tel: 630-635-8328
Email: reshma.multani@ptscservices.com
Website: www.ptscservices.com
IT consulting and Business Consulting Services. (As-Pac, estab 2012, empl 50, sales $7,000,000, cert: State)

7675 Renee Francque Consulting
505 N Lake Shore Dr Ste 613
Chicago, IL 60611
Contact: Renee Francque Owner
Tel: 312-953-9121
Email: reneefrancqueconsulting@gmail.com
Website:
Program, Project, Product & Process Management, Organizational Change Management, Communication Strategy, Advisory Consulting for Senior Leadership, Corporate Strategy, Business Plan Development. (Woman, estab 2010, empl 1, sales $212,750, cert: City, WBENC)

7676 RGMA
980 N Michigan Ave Ste 1230
Chicago, IL 60611
Contact: Ralph Moore President
Tel: 312-419-7250
Email: ralphmoore@rgma.com
Website: www.rgma.com
Provides supplier diversity services to drive shareholder value in an increasingly diverse, global economy. (AA, estab 1979, empl 6, sales , cert: City, NMSDC)

7677 Sandstorm Design, Inc.
4619 N Ravenswood Ste 300
Chicago, IL 60640
Contact: Lisa Holmes Dir Business Dev
Tel: 773-348-4200
Email: info@sandstormdesign.com
Website: www.sandstormdesign.com
Internal Communications, Annual Reports. (Woman, estab 1998, empl 14, sales $2,000,000, cert: WBENC)

7678 The Grossman Group
312 N May St Ste 101
Chicago, IL 60607
Contact: David Grossman CEO
Tel: 312-829-3252
Email: bcorson@yourthoughtpartner.com
Website: www.yourthoughtpartner.com
Internal communications and leadership communications consulting services and training. (Minority, estab 2000, empl 8, sales $4,000,000, cert: State)

7679 Tooty Inc.
P.O. Box 696
Orland Park, IL 60462
Contact: President
Tel: 708-478-5772
Email:
Website: www.tootyinc.com
Evaluation Services, Customized Training Programs, Customer Service Recognition Program, Employee Performance Scoring Systems, Secret Shopper phone calls, Call center training, Problem Solving, Workplace Culture, Listening Skills. (Woman, estab 1988, empl 10, sales $650,000, cert: WBENC)

7680 TrainSmart, Inc.
1600 Golf Rd, Ste 1200
Rolling Meadows, IL 60008
Contact: President
Tel: 847-991-8181
Email:
Website: www.trainsmartinc.com
Computer training, performance solutions, team building, customer service, leadership skills, manufacturing quality training, needs analysis, instructural design, assessments, programming. (Woman, estab 1994, empl 6, sales $1,500,000, cert: WBENC)

7681 Trilogy Consulting Group, Inc.
2021 Midwest Rd, Ste 200
Oak Brook, IL 60523
Contact: Kathy Martin-Smith VP
Tel: 630-953-6278
Email: kmartin-smith@trilogy-consulting.com
Website: www.trilogy-consulting.com
Health plan administration reviews & audits. (Woman, estab 1995, empl 3, sales $679,217, cert: State, WBENC)

7682 Trinal, Inc.
329 W 18th St, Ste 401
Chicago, IL 60616
Contact: Gladys Rodriguez GM
Tel: 312-738-0500
Email: info@trinalinc.com
Website: www.trinalinc.com
Strategic business management consulting, procurement policy development & economic development program monitoring. (Woman/AA, Hisp, estab 1997, empl 14, sales , cert: State)

7683 Tristana R Harvey Career Planning & Consulting Series LLC
5135 S Kenwood Ave, Box 504
Chicago, IL 60615
Contact: Tristana Harvey Owner
Tel: 312-351-0272
Email: tristana_harvey@harveycareerplanning.com
Website: www.harveycareerplanning.com
Counseling, coaching & consulting, training programs that create awareness, increase education & produce behavior change. (Woman/AA, estab 2010, empl 2, sales $125,000, cert: State, City, 8a)

7684 Universal. Innovative. Intelligent, Inc.
P.O. Box 1711
Bolingbrook, IL 60440
Contact: Kimberly Johnson President
Tel: 630-981-1931
Email: kjohnson@universal3i.com
Website: www.myfavoritethings-u3i.com
Management & marketing consulting. (Woman/AA, estab 2003, empl 1, sales , cert: State)

7685 ZOI Incorporated
2114 Rugen Rd, Unit A
Glenview, IL 60026
Contact: Susanna Alvarado CEO
Tel: 847-834-4787
Email: info@zoiinc.com
Website: www.zoiinc.com
Project, Product and Logistics Management, Change Management, and Training Development, e-Commerce, Cloud, Cognitive & Data Analysis. (Woman/Hisp, estab 2011, empl 5, sales $115,000, cert: NMSDC, WBENC)

Indiana

7686 Advanced Systems
508 Sunshine Dr
Valparaiso, IN 46385
Contact: Christy Poturkovic Reg Sales Mgr
Tel: 317-845-5017
Email: christyp@successstrategiesllc.com
Website: www.processspecialist.com
Business consulting services, education & training: process improvement, strategic planning, leadership development, management & supervision training, sales training, customer service training, quality improvement. (Woman, estab 1997, empl 1, sales , cert: City)

7687 Bulldog Consulting Services
P.O. Box 65
Leo, IN 46765
Contact: Sharon Miller President
Tel: 517-455-7016
Email: smiller@bulldogmeansbusiness.com
Website: www.BulldogMeansBusiness.com
Process Assessment, Process Improvements, Program/Project Management, Process Documentation, and Training. (Woman, estab 2007, empl 3, sales $200,000, cert: State)

7688 Growing Kids Pediatrics, LLC
3707 Charlestown Rd, Ste C1
New Albany, IN 47150
Contact: Rosie Nolot Office Mgr
Tel: 812-944-4575
Email: contact@growingkidspediatrics.com
Website: http://growingkidspediatrics.com/
Pediatric Office-we see children from 0 - 21 years of age. (Woman, estab 2010, empl 4, sales , cert: State)

7689 Intrinz Inc.
12175 Visionary Way, Ste 430
Fishers, IN 46037
Contact: Patricia Musariri Gurnell President
Tel: 317-288-2267
Email: patricia.musariri@intrinzincorp.com
Website: www.intrinzincorp.com
Project Management, Corporate Treasury, Corporate Tax, International Business, Global Sourcing, Language Translation, Business Strategy & Business Consulting Services. (Woman/AA, estab 2011, empl 5, sales $1,250,000, cert: NMSDC)

7690 KPG Global Enterprises, LLC
P.O. Box 857
Fishers, IN 46038
Contact: Kevin Grimes Managing Partner
Tel: 317-915-0671
Email: kgrimes@kpgglobal.com
Website: www.kpgglobal.com
Data integration & warehousing, management consulting, mergers & acquisitions, strategy, business valuation & planning, corporate finance & planning, e-marketing, intl mgmt, business process reengineering, auditing & assessments. (AA, estab 2000, empl 100, sales $3,000,000, cert: State)

7691 Prairie Quest Consulting
4211 Hobson Court Ste A
Fort Wayne, IN 46815
Contact: Martha Martin Program Mgr
Tel: 260-420-7374
Email: mmartin@pqcworks.com
Website: www.pqcworks.com
Project mgmt: application development, business case analysis, conceptual & functional process design, project plans, budgets, tracking assessment & metrics. (Woman, estab 2004, empl 150, sales $12,340,945, cert: WBENC)

7692 Raymond Young & Associates, LLC
10705 Club Chase
Fishers, IN 46037
Contact: Raymond Young President
Tel: 317-459-0797
Email: rayyoungjr@msn.com
Website: http://raymondyoungassociates.com
Business consulting, planning, business preformance, competitive analysis, service quality & retention, project management & six sigma principals. (AA, estab 2007, empl 1, sales , cert: State)

Kentucky

7693 Catalyst Learning Co.
310 W Liberty St, Ste 403
Louisville, KY 40202
Contact: Elizabeth LaRue Accountant
Tel: 502-584-7737
Email: elarue@catalystlearning.com
Website: http://catalystlearning.com
Provides proven learning & development tools. (Woman, estab 1994, empl 14, sales , cert: NWBOC)

Louisiana

7694 Henry Consulting LLC
1010 Common St Ste 2500
New Orleans, LA 70112
Contact: Allen Square Dir
Tel: 504-529-9890
Email: allen.square@henryconsulting.net
Website: www.henryconsulting.net
Management consulting services. (AA, estab 2001, empl 15, sales $1,941,921, cert: NMSDC)

7695 Scroggins Consulting, LLC
P.O. Box 6258
Shreveport, LA 71136
Contact: Tiya Scroggins CEO
Tel: 800-539-5831
Email: ty@scrogginsconsulting.com
Website: www.scrogginsconsulting.com
Management services: process assessment, conflict resolution, diversity, leadership development & motivation. (Woman/AA, estab 2002, empl 4, sales , cert: State)

7696 WCJ Consultants, LLC
16415 Crepemyrtle Dr
Baton Rouge, LA 70817
Contact: Kimberly Bardell Co-Owner
Tel: 225-921-6314
Email: kbardell@wcjconsultants.com
Website: www.wcjconsultants.com
Management consulting & professional services. (Woman/AA, estab 2008, empl 3, sales , cert: 8a)

Massachusetts

7697 3D Leadership Group LLC
396 Washington St, Ste 207
Wellesley, MA 02481
Contact: Sue Williamson Co-Founder
Tel: 781-453-9800
Email: sue.williamson@3dleadershipgroup.com
Website: http://3dleadershipgroup.com
Executive Coaching, Team Coaching, Transition Coaching, Leadership Workshops, Assessments. (Woman, estab 2008, empl 2, sales $1,528,044, cert: WBENC)

7698 Chrysalis Coaching & Consulting
595 E Fourth St Ste 1
Boston, MA 02127
Contact: Karen Carmody President
Tel: 617-283-8705
Email:
kcarmody@chrysaliscoachingconsulting.com
Website: www.chrysaliscoachingconsulting.com/
Corporate coaching, organizational effectiveness, & corporate wellness services. (Woman, estab 2012, empl 1, sales , cert: WBENC)

7699 Communication Management, Inc.
5 Perkins Glen
Eastham, MA 02642
Contact: Joseph Perkins President
Tel: 508-255-3789
Email: jperkins@cmiglobal.com
Website: www.cmiglobal.com
Communications skills, training, onsite & online business writing & presentation skills training programs. (AA, estab 1991, empl 1, sales , cert: State, NMSDC)

7700 EnVision Performance Solutions
9 Pond View Cir
Sharon, MA 02067
Contact: Irene Stern Frielich President
Tel: 617-877-2719
Email: irene.frielich@envision-performance.com
Website: https://envision-performance.com/
Custom instructional design & training development services; needs assessment, curriculum development, instructor-led classes, virtual classes, elearning, on-the-job training, performance support. (Woman, estab 1998, empl 1, sales $343,000, cert: State, WBENC)

7701 Imbue Partners, LLC
      36 N Liberty St
      Middleton, MA 01949
      Contact:
      Tel: 978-887-9215
      Email:
      Website: www.imbuepartners.com
Strategic planning, organizational capability building &
process improvement. (Woman, estab , empl , sales
$505,000, cert: WBENC)

7702 Incite, Inc.
      14 St. Charles St
      Boston, MA 02116
      Contact: Beth Rogers President
      Tel: 617-521-9050
      Email: brogers@pointtaken.net
      Website: www.pointtaken.net
Custom communication skills training workshops; Presentation Skills, Facilitation Skills, Negotiation Skills. (Woman,
estab 1997, empl 4, sales $1,800,000, cert: WBENC)

7703 Inspiration Zone, LLC
      Two Heritage Dr, Ste 302
      Quincy, MA 02171
      Contact: Juliette Mayers CEO
      Tel: 617-328-0953
      Email: info@inspirationzonellc.com
      Website: www.inspirationzonellc.com
Strategic advisory services: HR/Talent, Diversity, and
Inclusion, Multicultural Marketing & Leadership Develop-
ment. (AA, estab 2011, empl 1, sales $130,000, cert: State,
NMSDC)

7704 She Geeks Out, LLC
      50 Milk St, 15th Fl
      Boston, MA 02109
      Contact: Co-CEO
      Tel: 617-388-3463
      Email:
      Website: www.shegeeksout.com
Empower women in the workplace and educate, promote,
and support diverse and inclusive companies and organizations. (Woman, estab 2015, empl 5, sales $366,325,
cert: WBENC)

7705 The Asaba Group
      220 N Main St, Ste 102
      Natick, MA 01760
      Contact: Katrice Rivers Business Mgr
      Tel: 508-655-8100
      Email: krivers@asabagroup.com
      Website: www.asabagroup.com
Strategic assessments, strategic support services, organizational improvement. (AA, estab 1999, empl 10, sales
$1,000,000, cert: NMSDC)

Maryland

7706 Andean Consulting Solutions International, LLC
      11140 Rockville Pike Ste 100-155
      Rockville, MD 20852
      Contact: Andres Echeverri President
      Tel: 202-618-1455
      Email: andres@acsitranslations.com
      Website: http://acsitranslations.com
Language translation & interpretation services in over 60
languages. (Hisp, estab 2011, empl 2, sales $585,000, cert:
State, 8a)

7707 Applied Development LLC
      7 S Front St Ste 200
      Baltimore, MD 21202
      Contact: Kimberly Citizen
      Tel: 410-571-4016
      Email: kcitizen@applied-dev.com
      Website: www.applied-dev.com
Process improvement, automation, analytics & cyber
security, project management, business process improvement, strategic communications, cybersecurity &
administrative support. (Woman/AA, estab 2011, empl
12, sales $687,000, cert: State, City, NMSDC, WBENC, 8a)

7708 Cheseldine Management Consulting, LLC
      P.O. Box 1307
      Leonardtown, MD 20650
      Contact: Margaret Cheseldine CEO
      Tel: 301-475-2272
      Email: margiec@md.metrocast.net
      Website: www.cheseldine.org
Management consulting, asset, property & construction
management. (Woman, estab 2008, empl 11, sales
$512,000, cert: State)

7709 Contracting Resources Group, Inc.
      1133 Light St
      Baltimore, MD 21230
      Contact: Moira Rivera Sr Evaluation Assoc
      Tel: 443-708-0908
      Email: mrivera@contractingrg.com
      Website: www.contractingrg.com/
Management consulting, federal government contracting solutions, program & project management, training,
acquisition support, financial management support,
marketing & communications, IT professional services.
(Woman, estab 2002, empl 51, sales $2,500,000, cert:
8a)

7710 Destiny Management Services, LLC
      8737 Colesville Rd Ste 710
      Silver Spring, MD 20910
      Contact: Donna Mitchell President
      Tel: 301-650-0047
      Email: donnam@destinymgmtsvcs.com
      Website: www.destinymgmtsvcs.com
Management Consulting, Business Solutions, Information Technology, Staff Augmentation, Compliance
Reviews, Contacts Management, Human Capitol Development. (Woman/AA, estab 1996, empl 10, sales
$1,300,000, cert: State, WBENC)

7711 DPN Group, LLC
      516 N Charles St Ste 303
      Baltimore, MD 21201
      Contact: Andrea Jackson Principal
      Tel: 410-905-4036
      Email: ajackson@dpngroup.net
      Website: www.dpngroup.net
Management consulting: public outreach, supplier
diversity & inclusion consulting, strategic planning,
workforce development, performance evaluation, policy
development, & compliance monitoring. (Woman/AA,
estab 2008, empl 4, sales $204,000, cert: State)

7712 Ivy Planning Group, LLC
15204 Omega Dr, Ste 110
Rockville, MD 20850
Contact: Cynthia Featherson President
Tel: 301-963-1669
Email: cfeatherson@ivygroupllc.com
Website: www.ivygroupllc.com
Diversity consulting & training, strategic planning, change mgmt, customer service, executive coaching, assessments & surveys, knowledge mgmt, performance measurement & mgmt, training & development. (Woman/AA, estab 1990, empl 30, sales $ 0, cert: WBENC)

7713 Lord and Tucker Management Consultants, LLC
4140 Holbrook Ln
Huntingtown, MD 20639
Contact: Dawn Tucker President
Tel: 866-517-0477
Email: info@ltmctraining.com
Website: www.ltmctraining.com
Staff development & training: life skills, career development & entrepreneurship, customer service, time mgmt, organizational dev, financial mgmt, budgeting, resume writing & interview skills. (Woman/AA, estab 2004, empl 1, sales , cert: State)

7714 Mitaja Corporation
8115 Maple Lawn Blvd, Ste 350
Fulton, MD 20759
Contact: Dir of Sales
Tel: 301-332-0649
Email:
Website: www.mitajacorp.com
Staff Augmentation, RPO, Managed Services, Managed Projects, and Consulting Services. (As-Pac, estab 2014, empl 50, sales $3,000,000, cert: 8a)

7715 Muse GME Enterprises LLC
2 Wisconsin Circle, Ste 700
Chevy Chase, MD 20815
Contact: CEO
Tel: 301-244-4947
Email:
Website: http://gmeenterprises.net
Organizational governance, program review and development, professional and management development, quality management, strategic planning, committee establishment, regulatory compliance, risk governance. (Woman/AA, estab 2014, empl 3, sales $154,300, cert: State, WBENC, SDB)

7716 NAID (Native American Industrial Distributors,Inc)
9706 Pennsylvania Ave
Upper Marlboro, MD 20772
Contact: Ann Marie Gardner Marketing Media Specialist
Tel: 912-925-8674
Email: agardner@naid.com
Website: www.naid.com
Information & telecommunications systems life cycle support; security & anti-terrorism products & svcs, mgmt svcs, training svcs. (Nat Ame, estab 1983, empl 31, sales $8,800,000, cert: State)

7717 Performance Development Corporation
17308 Twin Ridge Court
Silver Spring, MD 20905
Contact: Sharon Fountain President
Tel: 301-421-0118
Email: sharon@sharonfountain.com
Website: www.SharonFountain.com
Training: interpersonal competence, communication, feedback, assertiveness, conflict management, self-esteem/self confidence, leadership/management/supervisory skills, team building, organizational skills, time management/managing multiple priorities. (Woman, estab 1980, empl 1, sales , cert: NWBOC)

7718 Pivotal Practices Consulting
6301 Ivy Lane, Ste 800
Greenbelt, MD 20770
Contact: Business Development Assoc
Tel: 301-220-3179
Email:
Website: www.pivotalpractices.com
Organizational climate assessments & engagements: surveys & diagnostic tools, improve individual, team & organizational performance. (Woman/AA, estab 2011, empl 10, sales $2,307,552, cert: NMSDC, WBENC, 8a)

7719 PositivePsyche.Biz Corp.
401 E Pratt St, Ste 2432
Baltimore, MD 21202
Contact: Enrique Ruiz President
Tel: 410-844-5060
Email: enrique@positivepsyche.biz
Website: www.positivepsyche.biz
Program Management, design, planning, staffing, measurement, execution, management, QA and QC of large-scale operations. (Hisp, estab 2008, empl 150, sales $5,400,000, cert: 8a)

7720 Sheila Lee & Associates, LLC - Learning Everywhere
1518 W Pratt St
Baltimore, MD 21223
Contact: Sheila S. Lee CEO
Tel: 410-233-6922
Email: sheilalee@learningeverywhere.com
Website: www.learningeverywhere.com
Organizational development, curriculum design & training. (Woman/AA, estab 2005, empl 8, sales $ 0, cert: State, NMSDC, WBENC)

7721 TrailBlazer Consulting, LLC
199 E Montgomery Ave, Ste 100
Rockville, MD 20850
Contact: President
Tel: 240-599-7983
Email:
Website: www.trailblazer.us.com
Program design & development, Management & organizational support for enterprise-wide operations, Electronic content management (ECM) solution selection, design, development, & implementation, Records & Information Management. (Woman, estab 2013, empl 7, sales $2,000,000, cert: WBENC)

Michigan

7722 ASG Renaissance
27655 Middlebelt Rd Ste 140
Farmington Hills, MI 48334
Contact: Maureen Michaels Acct Mgr
Tel: 248-477-5432
Email: mmichaels@asgren.com
Website: www.asgren.com
Consulting svcs: information technology, public relations, engineering, mktg, minority technical assistance programs, etc. (Woman/Hisp, estab 1987, empl 200, sales $206,586,000, cert: NMSDC, WBENC)

7723 Bigelow Family Holdings LLC
3223 15 Mile Rd
Sterling Heights, MI 48310
Contact: President
Tel: 586-306-8962
Email:
Website: www.mettleops.com
Program management, engineering, and business development. (Woman, estab 2013, empl 10, sales , cert: WBENC, 8a)

7724 BTS Consulting & Training LLC
211 N. First St #200
Brighton, MI 48116
Contact: Mary Temple Managing Partner
Tel: 586-322-3065
Email: mary.temple@btsmichigan.com
Website: www.btsmichigan.com/
Designs, develops & delivers customized training solutions, instructional design, course development, training delivery, project and curriculum management, conference and event coordination, travel administration. (Woman, estab 1991, empl 10, sales $2,600,000, cert: WBENC)

7725 Coach for Higher
2015 Geddes Ave
Ann Arbor, MI 48104
Contact: Owner
Tel: 734-255-7833
Email:
Website: www.CoachForHigher.com
Executive & Leadership Coaching Services for Individuals, Teams & Organizations. (Woman, estab 2010, empl 1, sales , cert: WBENC)

7726 Contract Source & Assembly Inc.
5230 33rd St SE
Grand Rapids, MI 49512
Contact: Bryce Cooper
Tel: 616-897-2185
Email: bryce@contractmi.com
Website: www.contractmi.com
Light Manufacturing & Contract Assembly, Contract Packaging & Inventory Management, Supply Chain Management, Inspection & Re-work. (As-Pac, estab 2001, empl 13, sales $18,000,000, cert: NMSDC)

7727 DSSI LLC
40 Oak Hollow St Ste 225
Southfield, MI 48033
Contact: Kathy Young
Tel: 248-208-8340
Email: kyoung@directsourcing.com
Website: www.directsourcing.com
Purchasing services. (As-Ind, estab 2000, empl 100, sales $110,000,000, cert: NMSDC)

7728 Focused Coaching LLC
2022 Liberty HTS
Ann Arbor, MI 48103
Contact: Lisa Pasbjerg CEO
Tel: 734-663-0420
Email: lpasbjerg@focusedcoaching.net
Website: www.focusedcoaching.net
Leadership development, executive coaching, assessment & facilitation services. (Woman, estab 2006, empl 1, sales $104,000, cert: WBENC)

7729 Global LT, Inc.
1871 Woodslee Dr
Troy, MI 48083
Contact: Chris Brotherson VP of Sales
Tel: 248-786-0999
Email: CBrotherson@global-lt.com
Website: www.Global-LT.com
English, foreign language, cross-cultural, diversity training; relocation translation, interpreting svcs; video/film narration. (AA, estab 1979, empl 75, sales $25,000,000, cert: NMSDC)

7730 GSHA Quality Services
P.O. Box 1452
Ann Arbor, MI 48103
Contact: CEO
Tel: 734-263-7399
Email:
Website: www.gshasolutions.org
Quality management services, stabilize processes, reduce cost, reduce waste, improve effectiveness, and efficiency to achieve sustainable, transformational performance improvements. (Woman/AA, estab 2009, empl 8, sales $400,000, cert: NMSDC, WBENC)

7731 Hays Innovations
10550 Killarney Hwy
Onsted, MI 49264
Contact: Gregory Hays President
Tel: 419-214-1140
Email: teamhays@haysinc.org
Website: www.haysinnovations.com
Management consulting. (AA, estab 2015, empl 2, sales , cert: NMSDC)

7732 Innovative Learning Group, Inc.
1130 Coolidge Highway
Troy, MI 48084
Contact: Gayle Holsworth Performance Consultant
Tel: 248-544-1568
Email: gayle.holsworth@innovativelg.com
Website: www.innovativeLG.com
Human performance consulting, needs assessment, training design & development, evaluation. (Woman, estab 2004, empl 17, sales $5,000,000, cert: WBENC)

7733 Jim Roberts Enterprises LLC
515 Ship St Ste 211
Saint Joseph, MI 49085
Contact: Jim Roberts President
Tel: 269-982-4188
Email: jim@jimrobertsenterprises.com
Website: www.jimrobertsenterprises.com
Management consulting, financial, facility management, real estate & project management consulting services. (Nat Ame, Hisp, estab 2004, empl 1, sales $163,000, cert: NMSDC)

7734 Learning Designs, Inc.
6001 North Adams, Ste 100
Bloomfield Hills, MI 48304
Contact: Julie Gieraltowski Operations Mgr
Tel: 248-269-0808
Email: jgieral@learningdesigns.com
Website: www.learningdesigns.com
Training & consulting: performance consulting, instructional design, training delivery, technology solutions & evaluation. (Woman, estab 1984, empl 18, sales $2,029,000, cert: WBENC)

7735 LWH Enterprises
1515 W. Wackerly St.
Midland, MI 48640
Contact: Anne Herron VP
Tel: 989-835-5811
Email: aherron@allisinfo.com
Website: www.allisinfo.com
Business research, market research, business intelligence, marketing services, IT support. (Woman/As-Pac, estab 1979, empl 17, sales $1,884,979, cert: WBENC)

7736 OMNEX
315 E Eisenhower Pkwy Ste 110
Ann Arbor, MI 48108
Contact: Jason Hicks Pulishing Coord
Tel: 734-761-4940
Email: jhicks@omnex.com
Website: www.omnex.com
Consulting & training services in Quality, Environmental, Health & Safety standards-based management systems, ISO 9001:2000, ISO 14000, ISO/TS 16949:2002 & QOS. (As-Ind, estab 1985, empl 200, sales $2,000,001, cert: NMSDC)

7737 Pyramid Quality Solutions & Innovations, Inc.
2075 West Big Beaver Ste 415
Troy, MI 48084
Contact: Ossie Nunn CEO
Tel: 248-577-1356
Email: onunn@pqsiinc.com
Website: www.pqsiinc.com
Quality & industrial engineering consulting: sequencing (JIT), rework & repair svcs, manuals & procedures, kitting & assembly, supplier representation, logistics, quality standards implementation, error & mistake proofing, etc. (AA, estab 2002, empl 150, sales $3,450,000, cert: NMSDC)

7738 Richalin Digue, LLC
46036 Michigan Ave Ste 201
Canton, MI 48188
Contact: Richalin Digue Mgr
Tel: 313-213-3103
Email: rich.digue@rnd-engineering.com
Website: www.rnd-engineering.com
Marketing & project management. (AA, estab 2004, empl 2, sales $800,000, cert: NMSDC)

7739 Syncreon.US Inc.
2851 High Meadow Circle Ste 250
Auburn Hills, MI 48326
Contact: Oswald Reid CEO
Tel: 248-377-4700
Email: oswald.reid@syncreon.com
Website: www.syncreon-us.com
Supply chain management, material follow-up & transportation management and cross-dock. Complex material handling and material integration. (AA, estab 2000, empl 1100, sales $671,200,000, cert: NMSDC)

7740 Utility Reduction Analysts, Inc.
12935 S West Bay Shore Dr Ste 240
Traverse City, MI 49684
Contact: Jennifer Wynn Stoll President & CEO
Tel: 888-586-2121
Email: jwstoll@utilityreduction.com
Website: www.utilityreduction.com
Full service utility cost reduction company. Our thorough analysis provides information on rates/tariffs, promotions, refund processing, market opportunities, consumption patterns, & available deregulation options. (Woman, estab 1991, empl 5, sales $410,000, cert: WBENC)

7741 Vani Quality Quest, Inc.
41000 Woodward Ave Ste 350
Blomfield Hills, MI 48304
Contact: Jagdish Vani President
Tel: 248-733-0000
Email: jvani@vqqinc.com
Website: www.vqqinc.com
Containment inspection, rework svcs, SQI consulting & training, problem solving, customer liaison, QC employee staffing services. (As-Pac, estab 1992, empl 60, sales $ 0, cert: NMSDC)

7742 VAS Consulting Services
33228 W 12 Mile Rd
Farmington Hills, MI 48334
Contact: Glenn Stafford President
Tel: 248-553-6603
Email: gstafford@vas4.com
Website: www.vas4.com
Consulting services: develop minority supplier programs, strategic alliances & joint ventures. (AA, estab 2001, empl 1, sales $250,000, cert: NMSDC)

Minnesota

7743 Alliant Consulting, Inc.
555 7th St W, Ste 101
Saint Paul, MN 55102
Contact: CFO
Tel: 651-291-0607
Email:
Website: www.alliantconsulting.com
Management consulting: operational assessment, redesign & implementation to improve service, quality & productivity (Woman, estab 1997, empl 4, sales $505,200, cert: WBENC)

7744 Beehive Strategic Communication GBC
P.O. Box 11373
St Paul, MN 55111
Contact: Rebecca Martin SVP, Culture & Talent
Tel: 651-789-2236
Email: rmartin@beehivepr.biz
Website: www.beehivepr.biz
Strategic planning, competitive intelligence, brand positioning, crisis management, media coaching, communications. (Woman, estab 1998, empl 13, sales $2,298,348, cert: WBENC)

7745 CultureBrokers, LLC
      1610 5th St NE
      Minneapolis, MN 55413
      Contact: Lisa Tabor President
      Tel: 651-321-2167
      Email: lisa@culturebrokers.com
      Website: www.culturebrokers.com
Diversity & inclusion services, diversity recruitment,
cultural competence training, strategic planning, inclusion
initiatives, employee engagement and retention, community relations, community engagement, equity initiatives.
(Woman/AA, estab 2005, empl 1, sales , cert: City)

7746 ECM Instructional Systems
      5816 11th Ave S
      Minneapolis, MN 55417
      Contact: Michael Mazyck President
      Tel: 888-685-0877
      Email: mazyck@ecminstructionalsystems.com
      Website: http://ecminstructionalsystems.com
Instructional design, training, professional development &
evaluation services, Learning & Development. (AA, estab
2004, empl 4, sales , cert: State, City)

7747 Hollstadt & Associates, Inc.
      1333 Northland Dr, Ste 220
      Mendota Heights, MN 55120
      Contact: Molly Jungbauer CEO
      Tel: 952-898-6813
      Email: mjungbauer@hollstadt.com
      Website: www.hollstadt.com/
Management & technology consulting: portfolio, program
& project management, business analysis, training programs. (Woman, estab 1990, empl 200, sales $26,053,034,
cert: WBENC)

7748 JIT Energy Services
      23505 Smithtown Rd Ste 280
      Excelsior, MN 55331
      Contact: Jamie Aragon CEO
      Tel: 952-474-3410
      Email: jamie.a@jitservicesinc.com
      Website: www.jitservicesinc.com
Energy efficiency consulting & energy mgmt services.
(Woman/Hisp, estab 1991, empl 12, sales $173,840,860,
cert: NMSDC, WBENC)

7749 MDA Leadership Consulting
      150 S 5th St, Ste 3300
      Minneapolis, MN 55402
      Contact: Linda Barrett Dir Business Dev
      Tel: 612-332-8182
      Email: info@mdaleadership.com
      Website: www.mdaleadership.com
Talent management, leadership development, organizational performance (Woman, estab 1981, empl 31, sales
$4,422,000, cert: State)

7750 Nelson Consulting LLC
      1330 Lagoon Ave 4th Fl
      Minneapolis, MN 55408
      Contact: Owner
      Tel: 612-460-5250
      Email:
      Website: www.pivotstrategiesconsulting.com
Communications strategy, organizational change management, reputation management, sustainability, corporate
social responsibility, (Woman, estab 2015, empl 12, sales
$1,500,000, cert: WBENC)

7751 Risk Management Consulting Services, LLC.
      35 Pineview Lane N
      Plymouth, MN 55441
      Contact: Gwen McFadden Managing Partner
      Tel: 952-544-0354
      Email: gwen@rmcsllc.com
      Website: www.riskconsultingservices.net
Insurance placement, insurance & risk management
consulting services, RFP/RFQ consulting, insurance
placement, risk management consulting, due diligence
projects, claims consulting & management. (Woman/AA,
estab 1997, empl 2, sales $150,000, cert: NMSDC, 8a)

7752 Talencio, LLC
      708 N 1st St Ste 341
      Minneapolis, MN 55401
      Contact: Paula Norbom President
      Tel: 612-703-4236
      Email: pnorbom@talencio.com
      Website: www.talencio.com
Accounting & Finance, Clinical Research, Data Analysis &
Statistics, Engineering, Health Care Policy & Reform,
Human Resource Management, Informatics, Information
Technology, Interim Leadership, Lean & Six Sigma,
Marketing, Operations. (Woman, estab 2008, empl 6,
sales $1,037,000, cert: WBENC)

7753 Vuelta Management Group, LLC
      1507 Chelmsford St
      Saint Paul, MN 55108
      Contact: Scott Hamilton President
      Tel: 651-329-8609
      Email: shamilton@vueltamanagement.com
      Website: http://vueltamanagement.com
Project Management; Process Improvement; Lean Six
Sigma; Supply Chain Management; Inventory Management; Purchasing; Production Management. (Hisp, estab
2009, empl 1, sales $162,117, cert: State, NMSDC)

7754 Women On Point, LLC
      5775 Wayzata Blvd, Ste 700
      Minneapolis, MN 55416
      Contact: Partner
      Tel: 612-418-7776
      Email:
      Website: www.womenonpointleadership.com/
Leadership development, strategic succession planning
and innovative training. (Woman, estab 2015, empl 3,
sales $136,440, cert: WBENC)

Missouri

7755 Kwame Building Group, Inc.
      1204 Washington Ave, Ste 200
      Saint Louis, MO 63103
      Contact: Joshua Randall VP
      Tel: 314-862-5344
      Email: jrandall@kwamebuildinggroup.com
      Website: www.kwamebuildinggroup.com
Program & construction mgmt services: project scheduling, estimating, cost controls, document controls, value
engineering, quality assurance & project inspection.
(Hisp, estab 1991, empl 75, sales $6,100,000, cert: City)

7756 Mustardseed Cultural & Environmental Services, LLC
      222 W Gregory Blvd, Ste 211
      Kansas City, MO 64114
      Contact: Timberlyn Smith, CHMM President
      Tel: 816-333-2424
      Email: tsmith@m-c-e-services.net
      Website: www.m-c-e-services.net
Environmental, safety & cultural resource management
consulting. (Woman/AA, estab 2003, empl 5, sales
$227,305, cert: State, City)

7757 P/Strada, LLC
      406 W 34th st.
      Kansas City, MO 64111
      Contact: Patrice Manuel CEO
      Tel: 816-256-4577
      Email: pat@pstrada.com
      Website: www.pstrada.com
Organizational development & homeland security consulting. (Woman/AA, estab 2001, empl 42, sales $3,370,000,
cert: State, City, NMSDC)

7758 Project Controls Group, Inc.
      2 Campbell Plaza, Bldg C
      St. Louis, MO 63139
      Contact: Viola Pancratz Principal
      Tel: 314-647-0707
      Email: vpancratz@projectcontrolsgroup.com
      Website: www.projectcontrolsgroup.com
Cost engineering & estimating, CPM scheduling, claims
analysis, document control, claims analysis, construction
management, program management. (AA, estab 2003,
empl 22, sales $1,430,353, cert: State, NMSDC)

7759 PryCor Technologies, LLC
      20 S Sarah St
      St Louis, MO 63108
      Contact: Seqwana Pryor CEO
      Tel: 302-528-0965
      Email: ceo.prycortechnologies@gmail.com
      Website: www.prycortechnologies.com
Management consulting & training: Lean Six Sigma &
operational excellence. (Woman/AA, estab 2016, empl 1,
sales , cert: WBENC)

7760 Standing Partnership
      1610 Des Peres Rd Ste 200
      St. Louis, MO 63131
      Contact: Melissa Lackey CEO
      Tel: 314-469-3500
      Email: mlackey@standingpartnership.com
      Website: www.standingpartnership.com
Strategy, corporate social responsibility (CSR), public
affairs, internal communications and issues and crisis
management. (Woman, estab 1991, empl 26, sales
$3,824,984, cert: WBENC)

Mississippi

7761 AGF Enterprise LLC
      1060 E Countyline Rd Ste 3A-104
      Ridgeland, MS 39157
      Contact: Anthony Fairley Managing Partner
      Tel: 601-500-2325
      Email: anthonygf@agfenterprise.com
      Website: www.agfenterprise.com
Learning Mgmt System (LMS), Tracking & Reporting Easily
track goal progress, knowledge gains, ROI, Regulatory
Compliance Train. (AA, estab 2013, empl 1, sales $376,000,
cert: NMSDC)

North Carolina

7762 Aseptic Haven LLC
      3330 Black Jack Simpson Rd
      Greenville, NC 27858
      Contact: Felicia Richardson Owner
      Tel: 252-258-5935
      Email: feliciarichardson@aseptichaven.com
      Website: www.aseptichaven.com
Consulting & training services, Life Sciences, Workforce
Development, Inclusion & Diversity. (Woman/AA, estab
2014, empl 1, sales , cert: State)

7763 Dynamic Consulting Solutions
      163 Stratford Ct, Ste 165
      Winston-Salem, NC 27103
      Contact: Kale Evans
      Tel: 336-724-0501
      Email: kale_dcs@northstate.net
      Website: www.dcs-corp.net
Motivational speaking, leadership training & development, change mgmt process consulting, strategic
planning, business process consulting, call center
operations & sales analysis. (AA, estab 2001, empl 2,
sales $125,000, cert: State)

7764 Flash Domain
      56 Contesky Dr
      Cherokee, NC 28719
      Contact: Kimberly Peone CEO
      Tel: 828-736-0234
      Email: kapeone67@gmail.com
      Website:
Strategic consulting technology services & managed
services. (Woman/Nat Ame, estab 2010, empl 2, sales ,
cert: State)

7765 Flynn Heath Holt Leadership, LLC
      309 E Morehead St, Ste 230
      Charlotte, NC 28202
      Contact: Maggie Norris COO
      Tel: 704-632-6712
      Email: mnorris@flynnheath.com
      Website: www.flynnheath.com/
Development programs and workshops, executive
coaching and speaking. (Woman, estab , empl , sales
$4,415,000, cert: WBENC)

7766 LMK Clinical Research Consulting, LLC
      9815 J Sam Furr Rd
      Huntersville, NC 28078
      Contact: Isaiah Howard Dir of Marketing
      Tel: 704-464-3291
      Email: isaiah.howard@lmkclinicalresearch.com
      Website: www.lmkclinicalresearch.com
Strategic development, project management & quality
control of documents & content that support clinical
development. (Woman/AA, estab 2013, empl 10, sales
$285,000, cert: WBENC)

7767 Proficient Learning LLC
      1508 Military Cutoff Rd Ste 304
      Wilmington, NC 28403
      Contact: Pamela Marinko CEO
      Tel: 910-795-1376
      Email: pam.marinko@proficientlearning.com
      Website: www.proficientlearning.com
Instructor-led, virtual, eLearning & mobile learning
solutions. (Woman, estab 2005, empl 23, sales
$3,200,000, cert: WBENC)

7768   Tactegra
        18 Cabarrus Ave W
        Concord, NC 20825
        Contact: Leanne Kinsella Dir Business Devel
        Tel: 704-793-0800
        Email: info@tactegra.com
        Website: www.tactegra.com
Management consulting, program/project management, IT project support services, staff augmentation & process management. (AA, Hisp, estab 2007, empl 50, sales $3,700,000, cert: NMSDC)

7769   The Future Procurement Group, LLC
        3513 McPherson St
        Waxhaw, NC 28173
        Contact: Silas Carter
        Tel: 203-913-9598
        Email: scarter@thefutureprocurementgroup.com
        Website: www.thefutureprocurementgroup.com
Consulting Services, Strategic Sourcing, Procurement Management, Supplier Diversity, Program Devel, Training, Vendor Management, - Supplier Evaluation, Process Review & Analysis, Cost Management, Management Consulting. (AA, estab 2011, empl 1, sales , cert: NMSDC)

7770   The Thrower Group, LLC.
        11204 Waightstill Way
        Charlotte, NC 28277
        Contact: Baron Thrower CEO
        Tel: 704-215-4946
        Email: baron.thrower@thethrowergroupllc.com
        Website: www.thethrowergroupllc.com
Management consulting firm. (AA, estab 2010, empl 35, sales , cert: NMSDC)

Nebraska

7771   Inspection Experts, Inc.
        808 P St Ste 318
        Lincoln, NE 68508
        Contact: Maureen Faulconer VP
        Tel: 410-715-3939
        Email: mfaulconer@ieinc.net
        Website: www.ieinc.net
Environmental services, health & safety consulting, industrial hygiene, facilities & asset management & development. (Woman/As-Ind, estab 2004, empl 16, sales $3,365,268, cert: State)

New Jersey

7772   Candid Services
        80 Pine St
        Bridgewater, NJ 08807
        Contact: Meghana Patel CEO
        Tel: 732-874-1345
        Email: contact@candidcorp.com
        Website: http://candidcorp.com
Pharmaceutical & medical device consulting services, computer system validation, non compartmental analysis (NCA), Clinical data analysis & handling, SAS programming & Regulatory Affairs consulting. (Woman/As-Pac, estab 2015, empl 2, sales , cert: WBENC)

7773   Davis & Company, Inc.
        11 Harristown Rd
        Glen Rock, NJ 07452
        Contact: David Pitre VP consulting svcs
        Tel: 201-445-5100
        Email: david.pitre@davisandco.com
        Website: www.davisandco.com
Communication consulting & implementation, strategic planning & research, implementation, writing & design. (Woman, estab 1984, empl 17, sales $3,350,000, cert: State, WBENC)

7774   Microexcel Inc.
        One Harmon Plaza, 10th Fl
        Secaucus, NJ 07094
        Contact: Ayub Qhadri President
        Tel: 201-787-4562
        Email: ayub.qhadri@microexcel.com
        Website: http://microexcel.com
Global management consulting, technology services & outsourcing. (As-Ind, estab 2001, empl 75, sales $28,000,000, cert: State)

7775   QualComp Consulting Services LLC
        675 US Highway One Ste B203
        North Brunswick, NJ 08902
        Contact: Victor Arriaran Principal Owner
        Tel: 800-511-8758
        Email: victor.arriaran@qualcomp.com
        Website: www.qualcomp.com
Quality systems design & implementation, audit & inspection readiness, complaint remediation, process control & process improvement, risk management , design control, root cause analysis, Corrective & Preventive Action. (Hisp, estab 2010, empl 4, sales $1,521,586, cert: NMSDC)

7776   The Forefront Group
        26 Sunflower Circle
        Lumberton, NJ 08048
        Contact: Bonnie Keith Owner
        Tel: 609-265-1825
        Email: bkeith@theforefrontgroup.com
        Website: www.theforefrontgroup.com
Admin management consulting, education support svcs, professional & management development training. (Woman, estab 2002, empl 10, sales , cert: WBENC)

7777   Vitiello Communications Group
        825 Georges Rd Ste 6
        North Brunswick, NJ 08902
        Contact: Nadine Green COO
        Tel: 732-238-6622
        Email: nadine.green@vtlo.com
        Website: www.vtlo.com
Communications, employee engagement, strategic change & leadership communications. (Woman, estab 1990, empl 20, sales $3,600,000, cert: WBENC)

7778   Wet Cement, Inc.
        18 Yardley Manor Dr
        Matawan, NJ 07747
        Contact: CEO
        Tel: 917-334-3653
        Email:
        Website: www.wet-cement.com/
Coach and train on powerful presenting, public speaking and pitching skills to drive sales and develop talent. (Woman, estab 2017, empl 3, sales $120,000, cert: WBENC)

Nevada

7779 American Project Management LLC
11700 W Charleston Blvd, Ste 170-315
Las Vegas, NV 89135
Contact: Jane Lee Managing Partner
Tel: 702-220-4562
Email: jlee@apmlasvegas.com
Website: www.apmlasvegas.com
Project Scheduling & Cost Control, Earned Value Management System (EVMS) Implementation, Computer Programming & Embedded Software Development Services & Staff Augmentation. (Woman/As-Pac, estab 2003, empl 2, sales , cert: NMSDC, NWBOC)

7780 Operations Service Systems
9716 Terrace Green Ave
Las Vegas, NV 89117
Contact: Susan Beyer President
Tel: 800-878-6906
Email: sue@suebeyer.com
Website: www.suebeyer.com
Training & development: operations, dev, customer service & results oriented training systems. (Woman, estab 2000, empl 2, sales $255,000, cert: WBENC)

7781 Purpose & Action, LLC
3225 McLeod Dr, Ste 100
Las Vegas, NV 89121
Contact: Miguel de Jesus President
Tel: 760-438-9907
Email: miguel@coachmiguel.com
Website: www.coachmiguel.com
Business management, global sales/marketing. (Hisp, estab 2011, empl 1, sales , cert: NMSDC)

7782 Quality Support Services
726 S Casino Ctr, Ste 206
Las Vegas, NV 89101
Contact: Terry McCall President
Tel: 702-699-5379
Email: tmccall@qualitysupportservices.com
Website: www.qualitysupportservices.com
Support svcs: food operation, building maintainence, warehouse operations, temporary staffing. (AA, estab 1995, empl 30, sales $ 0, cert: State)

New York

7783 AIOPX Management Consulting
1007 La Quinta Dr
Webster, NY 14580
Contact: David Powe Partner & Lead Consultant
Tel: 585-627-1716
Email: dpowe@aiopx.com
Website: http://AIOPX.com
Operation Excellence (OpEx): lean, six sigma, total quality, practical process improvement & the Toyota production system. (AA, estab 2012, empl 1, sales $125,000, cert: NMSDC)

7784 Axiom Consulting LLC
126 W Main St
Endicott, NY 13760
Contact: Wayne McCray CEO
Tel: 800-563-2758
Email: info@4axiomcorp.com
Website: www.4axiomcorp.com
MRO sales, business process outsourcing, staffing, training. (AA, estab 2001, empl 150, sales $6,000,000, cert: NMSDC)

7785 Carlin Solutions, LLC
237 Flatbush Ave Ste 128
Brooklyn, NY 11217
Contact: Carla Franklin Managing Dir
Tel: 917-463-3592
Email: carla@carlinsolutions.com
Website: www.carlinsolutions.com
Requirements analysis, staff augmentation, program management, project management, operational improvement, management consulting, Strategic Planning, Business Development, Strategic Market Analysis. (Woman/AA, estab 2003, empl 3, sales $414,000, cert: City, NMSDC, WBENC)

7786 Chapman Lean Enterprise
81 Rock Hill Rd
Rochester, NY 14618
Contact: Christopher Chapman President
Tel: 585-406-7804
Email: cdchapman1@chapmanlean.com
Website: www.chapmanlean.com
Lean process improvement training & consultation services. (AA, estab 2010, empl 1, sales , cert: NMSDC)

7787 Gillespie Associates, Ltd.
1501 East Ave Ste 200
Rochester, NY 14610
Contact: Patricia Barry Business Dev Mgr
Tel: 585-244-1331
Email: pbarry@gillespieassociates.com
Website: www.gillespieassociates.com
Performance consulting, customized training & development, sales performance institute, e-learning solutions, web-based learning, technical documentation, business process documentation.
 (Woman, estab 1989, empl 9, sales $1,292,286, cert: State, WBENC)

7788 Green Silk Associates, LLC
10440 Queens Blvd., Ste 5J
Forest Hills, NY 11375
Contact: Deb Seidman President
Tel: 917-445-2443
Email: dseidman@greensilkassociates.com
Website: http://greensilkassociates.com
Organizational effectiveness & leadership development services, innovation, planning, problem-solving meeting/offsite facilitation; team development; organization design; executive coaching; & talent management consulting. (Woman, estab 2009, empl 1, sales , cert: State, City)

7789 Hyun & Associates, Inc.
222 Riverside Dr, #3B
New York, NY 10025
Contact: Jane Hyun President
Tel: 917-327-0992
Email: jhyun@hyunassociates.com
Website: www.hyunassociates.com
Leadership, diversity training & coaching services. (Woman/As-Pac, estab 1997, empl 3, sales $275,000, cert: NMSDC)

7790 Impact Consulting, LLC
1177 Ave of the Americas, 5th Floor
New York, NY 10036
Contact: CEO
Tel: 973-727-1574
Email:
Website: www.impactconsultingus.com
Leadership & organizational development, consulting, coaching & training services. (Woman/Hisp, estab 2015, empl 3, sales $428,000, cert: State, City, WBENC)

7791 International Institute for Learning, Inc. (IIL)
110 E 59th St, 31st Fl
New York, NY 10022
Contact: Amy Gershen cert Mgr
Tel: 212-758-0177
Email: amy.gershen@iil.com
Website: www.iil.com
Project management, six sigma & MSP training & consulting services. (Woman, estab 1991, empl 87, sales $1,300,000,000, cert: WBENC)

7792 JDR Consulting, LLC
4305 Broadway Ste 41
New York, NY 10033
Contact: John Rivers CEO
Tel: 917-324-2443
Email: jrivers@jdrconsulting.net
Website: www.jdrconsulting.net
Management consulting, program & project management, systems & and accounting services. (AA, estab 2004, empl 9, sales $6,000,000, cert: State, NMSDC)

7793 Jennifer Brown LLC
20 E 9th St, Ste 4U
New York, NY 10003
Contact: Jennifer Brown CEO
Tel: 917-769-1599
Email: info@jenniferbrownconsulting.com
Website: www.jenniferbrownconsulting.com
Leadership consulting, HR training, coaching, speaker, communications, diversity, global, teams, facilitator, facilitation, career planning, leaders, inclusive, inclusion, innovative, innovation, empowered, empowerment. (Woman, estab 2004, empl 15, sales $1,400,000, cert: City, WBENC)

7794 JR Language Translation Services, Inc.
2112 Empire Blvd, Ste 1C
Rochester, NY 14580
Contact: Language Solutions Specialist
Tel: 877-771-0145
Email:
Website: www.jrlanguage.com
Document Translation - Web site and software localization - Scripts - Manuals - Brochures - Contracts. (Woman/Hisp, estab 2006, empl 8, sales $1,680,371, cert: State, WBENC)

7795 KGM Consulting Inc.
30 Wall St
New York, NY 10005
Contact: Admin& finance
Tel: 212-791-1555
Email:
Website: www.kgmcon.com
Technology management solutions: echnology project mgmt, circuit provisioning mgmt & voice systems admin, carrier & telecom expense mgmt svcs, staff augmentation. (Woman, estab 1996, empl 30, sales $3,952,677, cert: City, WBENC)

7796 KnowledgeSources Consulting Inc.
23 W 73rd St Ste 1103
New York, NY 10023
Contact: Peggy Decker Principal
Tel: 212-362-1606
Email: peggy@knowledgesources.com
Website: www.knowledgesources.com
Employee/Financial Advisor Learning & Development; Customer Events.
Specifically: employee engagement, organizational development, professional development, training, coaching, facilitating. (Woman, estab 2009, empl 1, sales $400,000, cert: WBENC)

7797 Shaheen & Associates, Inc.
37 Maple Ave
Armonk, NY 10504
Contact: William Shaheen COO
Tel: 914-273-9000
Email: w.shaheen@shaheeninc.com
Website: www.shaheeninc.com
Telecom auditing & cost-containment services. (Woman, estab 1988, empl 8, sales $2,400,000, cert: WBENC)

7798 The Caswood Group, Inc.
811 Ayrault Rd, Ste 2
Fairport, NY 14450
Contact: Isabel Casamayor President
Tel: 585-425-0332
Email: icasamayor@caswood.com
Website: www.caswood.com
Specialty sales teams, analytics, data collection & management, sample management. (Woman, estab 1996, empl 38, sales $5,054,073, cert: WBENC)

7799 The Madison Consulting Group, Inc.
41 Madison Ave 31st Fl
New York, NY 10010
Contact: Consultant & Marketing Mgr
Tel: 212-532-0703
Email:
Website: www.themadisonconsultinggroup.com
Training & consulting: executive coaching, organizational consulting & strategic resourcing. (Woman, estab 1993, empl 11, sales $1,103,130, cert: City, WBENC)

7800 The Real Advice Plus LLC
108 5th Ave, Ste 20-B
New York, NY 10011
Contact: Tony Brown President
Tel: 718-812-8856
Email: tbrown@t-rap.com
Website: www.t-rap.com
Management consulting, executive search consulting, diversity consulting & career development coaching services. (AA, estab 2006, empl 1, sales , cert: State, City)

7801 Tribal Capital Markets, LLC
405 Lexington Ave 54th Fl
New York, NY 10174
Contact: Sean Harte CEO
Tel: 212-850-2295
Email: sharte@tribalcap.com
Website: www.tribalcap.com
With a strong capital structure, TCM offers client focused services in both Fixed Income trading and origination as well as Equity trading. Our Equity staff provides proficient execution capabilities (Nat Ame, estab 1995, empl 14, sales $4,000,000, cert: NMSDC)

Ohio

7802 Alegre, Inc.
3101 W Tech Rd
Miamisburg, OH 45342
Contact: Don Phillips Business Dev Mgr
Tel: 937-885-6786
Email: dphillips@alegreinc.com
Website: www.alegreinc.com
Supply chain mgmt, program mgmt, customer engineering & quality interface, warehousing & distribution processes, sorting & containment, rework processes, light assembly processes. (Woman/As-Pac, estab 1992, empl 30, sales $20,000,000, cert: NMSDC)

7803 APB & Associates, Inc.
55 Erieview Plaza Ste 328
Cleveland, OH 44114
Contact: Andre Bryan President
Tel: 216-541-2900
Email: abryan@apbandassociates.com
Website: www.apbandassociates.com
Document management services, office technology, organizational design, business process improvement, telecommunications & office automation consulting. (AA, estab 2004, empl 12, sales $2,200,000, cert: State, NMSDC, SDB)

7804 Arnold Solutions, LLC
4228 E 178th St
Cleveland, OH 44128
Contact: Reginald E. Arnold CEO
Tel: 216-533-2837
Email: arnoldsolutionsllc@gmail.com
Website: www.arnoldsolutionsllc.com
Consulting, administrative & innovative leadership, Federal Law, HR, PMP, Fleet Management, IT, BPM, Supply Chain Management, Strategic Analysis, Construction Management, Contract Procurement. (Woman/AA, estab 2014, empl 2, sales , cert: State, City)

7805 ATS Training and Consulting Co
1991 Crocker Rd Ste 340
Westlake, OH 44145
Contact: P. Rani Maddali President
Tel: 440-249-0095
Email: pm@ats-tc.com
Website: www.ats-tc.com
Training & consulting services: lean, Six Sigma, supply chain, organizational devel, change mgmt, team building & executive coaching. (Woman/As-Ind, estab 2001, empl 20, sales $1,060,000, cert: NMSDC, WBENC, 8a)

7806 Berkshire Group Inc.
2711 W Market St, Ste 5310
Akron, OH 44334
Contact: Janet Kendall White CEO
Tel: 800-556-5549
Email: janet@berkshire-leadership.com
Website: http://berkshire-leadership.com
Consulting & leadership development, strategic planning, process & profit improvement; training & development; executive coaching & facilitation. (Woman, estab 1993, empl 4, sales $309,000, cert: WBENC)

7807 C H Smith & Associates dba Scale Strategic Solution
1329 E Kemper Rd, Ste 4218E
Cincinnati, OH 45246
Contact: President
Tel: 513-252-8129
Email:
Website: www.scalestrategicsolutions.com
Management consulting and evaluation services for the public and non-profit sectors. (Woman/AA, estab 2011, empl 3, sales $290,354, cert: WBENC)

7808 Compass Consulting Services, LLC
P.O. Box 221347
Beachwood, OH 44122
Contact: Tameka Taylor President
Tel: 216-299-7335
Email: tameka@compassconsultingservices.com
Website: www.compassconsultingservices.com
Organizational development, diversity & inclusion management, conflict management, communication, leadership development, team building. (Woman/AA, estab 2008, empl 2, sales $170,000, cert: State, NMSDC, WBENC)

7809 Diverse Supply Chain Partner, LLC
4132 E Village Dr
Mason, OH 45040
Contact: Cheryl El-Alfi President
Tel: 513-274-8035
Email: cheryl@diversepartner.com
Website: http://diversepartner.com
Strategic business development consulting services to help diverse business enter & grow within the corporate supply chain. (Woman, estab 2014, empl 1, sales , cert: WBENC)

7810 Equilibrium Perceptum LLC
11839 Pearl Rd, Ste 101
Strongsville, OH 44136
Contact: Ramana Gaddamanugu
Tel: 216-278-1866
Email: ramana@epfocus.com
Website: www.epfocus.com
Management consulting services: systems & process reviews, strategy documentation, risk management / risk assessments / risk analysis assistance, data analysis, data review, data preparation. (As-Pac, estab 2014, empl 1, sales , cert: State, City)

7811 GPI Enterprises Inc.
3637 Medina Rd, Ste 60
Medina, OH 44256
Contact: Christopher Murillo President
Tel: 330-321-2461
Email: chris.murillo@e-gpi.com
Website: www.e-gpi.com
Management consulting services, process analysis/ development, data analysis, project management & IT support. (Hisp, estab 2001, empl 16, sales $1,050,000, cert: State, 8a)

7812   Howse Solutions LLC
       17325 Euclid Ste 2030
       Cleveland, OH 44112
       Contact: Christopher Howse President
       Tel: 440-318-4720
       Email: chowse@howsesolutions.com
       Website: www.howsesolutions.com
experience leading analysts, developers, and project
teams; and defining, creating, and delivering business
solutions.
Company Data DUNS number: 027010665 EIN number: 26-
3326464 (AA, estab , empl 1, sales $255,000, cert: State,
City, SDB)

7813   Impact Instruction Group, LLC
       P.O. Box 632
       Hilliard, OH 43026
       Contact: CEO
       Tel: 614-286-8265
       Email:
       Website: www.impactinstruction.com
Corporate training & development, leadership training
programs & professional development strategies for
emerging women leaders. (Woman, estab 2007, empl 8,
sales $ 0, cert: WBENC)

7814   Improve Consulting & Training Group LLC
       4600 Euclid Ave Ste 320
       Cleveland, OH 44103
       Contact: Ellen Burts-Cooper Sr Managing Partner
       Tel: 216-539-8737
       Email: ellen@improveconsulting.biz
       Website: www.improveconsulting.biz
Leadership development & continuous improvement.
(Woman/AA, estab 2005, empl 10, sales $700,000, cert:
State)

7815   Monterey Consultants, Inc.
       5335 Far Hills Ave, Ste 311
       Dayton, OH 45429
       Contact: Gary Munoz President
       Tel: 937-436-4536
       Email: gary.munoz@mcix.com
       Website: www.mcix.com
Management consulting, organizational development &
business process improvement, strategic planning, change
management, process improvement, outreach & marketing & customer service. (Hisp, estab , empl , sales
$2,704,856, cert: NMSDC)

7816   Pep Promotions
       151 W Fourth St Ste 700
       Cincinnati, OH 45202
       Contact: Dave Kroeger President
       Tel: 513-826-3871
       Email: kroegerd@peppromotions.com
       Website: www.peppromotions.com
Project management, promotional programs. (AA, estab
2004, empl 125, sales $11,000,000, cert: NMSDC)

7817   SimpleQuE, Inc.
       249 S Garber Dr
       Tipp City, OH 45371
       Contact: Jim Lee President
       Tel: 740-305-0868
       Email: jlee@simpleque.com
       Website: www.simpleque.com
Management consulting services. (As-Pac, estab 2005,
empl 26, sales $2,100,000, cert: NMSDC)

7818   Sritech Global Inc.
       341 S 3rd St, Ste 100
       Columbus, OH 43215
       Contact: Sheela Kunduru President
       Tel: 614-477-2944
       Email: ksheela@sritechglobal.com
       Website: www.sritechglobal.com
Business process consulting, Business process improve-
ment, Enterprise process & product quality assurance,
Independent verification & validation. (Woman/As-Ind,
As-Pac, estab 2013, empl 1, sales $339,640, cert: State,
WBENC)

7819   SRM & Associates, LLC
       1123 Firth Ave
       Worthington, OH 43085
       Contact: Victoria Schneider President
       Tel: 614-505-1209
       Email: vschneider@srm-consulting.net
       Website: http://srm-consulting.net
Risk Management Consulting services, Safety & Envi-
ronmental Consulting, Process Safety Management,
Risk Management Planning, Safety & Environmental
Program Development, Auditing & Training. (Woman,
estab 2011, empl 4, sales $370,000, cert: WBENC)

7820   The CADD Department, Inc.
       13916 Euclid Ave Ste 5
       East Cleveland, OH 44112
       Contact: Wayne Grant CEO
       Tel: 216-269-5901
       Email: wgrant@thecaddept.net
       Website: www.thecaddept.net
Progressive civil / structural engineering, construction
supervision & surveying, design, surveying & construction phase services. (AA, estab 2007, empl 4, sales ,
cert: State, City)

Oklahoma

7821   Gina Sofola & Associates, Inc.
       5801 Broadway Extension Ste 310
       Oklahoma City, OK 73118
       Contact: Gina Sofola President
       Tel: 203-613-9471
       Email: gsofola@sofolaassociates.com
       Website: www.sofolaassociates.com
Project mgmt: facility mgmt, transportation, strategic
planning, engineering & feasibility studies, cost control,
scheduling, building assessment, document mgmt,
contract admin, interior design, transportation analysis,
environmental assessment. (Woman/AA, estab 1999,
empl 20, sales $ 0, cert: State)

Oregon

7822   Robinson Client Services Group, Inc.
       125 S 1st Ave, Unit 3189
       Hillsboro, OR 97123
       Contact: Jamie Robinson CEO
       Tel: 888-408-7274
       Email: bdo@teamcorvus.com
       Website: www.rcsgsolutions.com
We provide management consulting services, to include
portfolio, program, and project management (Agile and
traditional/waterfall). Additionally, we provide change
management and process improvement/design
services. (AA, estab 2019, empl 6, sales $606,000, cert:
State)

Pennsylvania

7823 Clarity Concepts Inc.
      240 Dechert Dr
      Gulph Mills, PA 19406
      Contact: Jane Downey President
      Tel: 610-825-3705
      Email: janedowney@clarityconceptsinc.com
      Website: www.clarityconceptsinc.com
Customized training programs.Leadship training.
Personal branding.Team development.Risk management
services. (Woman, estab 1996, empl 2, sales $220,000,
cert: WBENC)

7824 Deidre Anderson Enterprises
      3959 Welsh Rd Ste 170
      Willow Grove, PA 19090
      Contact: Valerie Brown-Baul COO
      Tel: 215-618-2435
      Email: info@trailblazers-inc.com
      Website: www.trailblazers-inc.com
Management solutions, leadership, continuous improvement, productivity, profit & performance, training &
coaching programs, goal attainment, leadership development & mental performance. (Woman/AA, estab 2005,
empl , sales $125,000, cert: State)

7825 Elevate USA Inc
      1606 Jackson St
      Philadelphia, PA 19145
      Contact: Michael Shalek Consultant
      Tel: 561-445-3845
      Email: michael@elevate4success.com
      Website: www.elevate4success.com
Training services: custom, interactive & practical workforce
education, on-site training, e-learning, & coaching solutions. (Woman, estab 2007, empl 5, sales $600,500, cert:
State, WBENC)

7826 Evolve Advisors I, LLC
      85 Overhill Rd
      Bala Cynwyd, PA 19004
      Contact: Peri Higgins President
      Tel: 610-420-5535
      Email: phiggins@evolveadvisors.com
      Website: www.evolveadvisors.com
Management consulting, assess, baseline, restructure &
redesign business processes. (Woman/AA, estab 2012,
empl 3, sales $108,000, cert: NMSDC, WBENC)

7827 Innovative Business Products & Services, LLC
      514 Firethorne Dr
      Monroeville, PA 15146
      Contact: Harvey Smith, Sr. CEO
      Tel: 412-894-3132
      Email: ibpshssr@outlook.com
      Website: www.artistecard.com/ibps
Diversity, inclusion & sensitivity training, recruiting
diversity talent services; diversity website review; diversity
mission/vision statement development; & re-entry of ex-
offenders into job market services. (Woman/AA, estab
2015, empl 7, sales , cert: NMSDC)

7828 KnowledgeStart, Inc.
      300 King St
      Pottstown, PA 19464
      Contact: Bryan Yingst Internet Dir
      Tel: 610-650-0448
      Email: byingst@knowledgestart.com
      Website: www.knowledgestart.com
Diversity & Inclusion training. (Minority, estab 2001, empl
12, sales $850,000, cert: NMSDC)

7829 Lapine Group, Inc.
      8200 Greensboro Dr Ste 900
      McLean, PA 22102
      Contact: Judy Honig Managing Partner
      Tel: 703-940-6005
      Email: lapineinfor@lapinegroup.com
      Website: www.lapinegroup.com
Management consulting. (Woman, estab 2006, empl 10,
sales $3,770,000, cert: WBENC)

7830 Lima Consulting Group, LLC
      40 Lloyd Ave Ste 108B
      Malvern, PA 19335
      Contact: Paul Lima Managing Partner
      Tel: 212-671-0309
      Email: plima@limaconsulting.com
      Website: www.LimaConsulting.com
Administrative Management & General Management
Consulting, Marketing Consulting, Process, Physical
Distribution & Logistics Consulting. (Hisp, estab 2004,
empl 26, sales $739,087, cert: NMSDC)

7831 Nexlevel Consulting Services, LLC
      1122 Parkview Dr
      New Kensington, PA 15068
      Contact: Tammy Davis CEO
      Tel: 412-436-9098
      Email: tldavis@nexlevelconsultingllc.com
      Website: www.nexlevelconsultingllc.com
Training, Organizational Change Management, Communications (Woman/AA, estab 2006, empl 4, sales
$235,000, cert: State, WBENC)

7832 Quacoapit LLC
      7121 Lynford St
      Philadelphia, PA 19149
      Contact: Chea Kunwon CEO
      Tel: 267-315-5147
      Email: ckunwon@quacoapit.com
      Website: www.quacoapit.com
Quality & Compliance Consulting Services. (AA, estab
2017, empl 3, sales , cert: NMSDC)

7833 Quality Solutions Now, Inc.
      3251 Olympic Dr
      Emmaus, PA 18049
      Contact: Brette Travaglio President
      Tel: 610-462-4090
      Email: brette@qualitysolutionsnow.com
      Website: www.qualitysolutionsnow.com
Strategic, on-demand support & tactical project
management svcs, product launch, regulatory compli-
ance, large-scale change, process improvement.
(Woman, estab 2004, empl , sales $2,064,000, cert:
NWBOC)

7834 Sustainable Solutions Corporation
      155 Railroad Plaza Ste 203
      Royersford, PA 19468
      Contact: Tara Radzinski CEO
      Tel: 610-569-1047
      Email: tara@sustainablesolutionscorporation.com
      Website:
      www.sustainablesolutionscorporation.com
Sustainable Buildings & Operations, Corporate
Sustainability, Training & Education, Seminars. (Woman,
estab 2001, empl 16, sales $882,045, cert: WBENC)

7835   TayganPoint Consulting Group
       1118 General Washington Memorial Blvd. Ste 210
       Washington Crossing, PA 08977
       Contact: CEO
       Tel: 215-302-2500
       Email: info@tayganpoint.com
       Website: www.tayganpoint.com
Consulting services: business process improvement,
strategy development & execution, change management &
communications, program management. (Woman, estab
2009, empl 69, sales $18,700,000, cert: WBENC)

7836   Taylor Consulting & Contracting LLC
       625 Main St
       Avoca, PA 18641
       Contact: CEO
       Tel: 570-414-0880
       Email:
       Website: www.taylorcc.com
Management & consulting services. (Woman, estab 2001,
empl 15, sales $564,000, cert: State)

7837   The Claiborne Consulting Group, Inc.
       1800 JFK Blvd, Ste 300
       Philadelphia, PA 19103
       Contact: Julian Gray VP HR, Staffing GM
       Tel: 914-388-4165
       Email: julian.gray@claibornecg.com
       Website: www.claibornecg.com
Business Process Re-engineering, Business Case Development, Software Selection, Organization Change Management, Technical Content Writing, Startup Consultation,
Digital Brand Management. (AA, As-Pac, estab 2015, empl
10, sales , cert: NMSDC)

7838   Veris Associates, Inc. dba VerisVisalign
       P.O. Box 245
       West Point, PA 19486
       Contact: Trisha Daly Office Mgr
       Tel:
       Email: trishadaly@verisvisalign.com
       Website: www.verisvisalign.com
Consulting & training: process engineering, compliance
consulting & corporate learning. (Woman, estab 2003,
empl 38, sales $3,500,000, cert: State, WBENC)

7839   XCELLAS, LLC
       275 Dilworth Ln
       Langhorne, PA 19047
       Contact: Maria T. Alvarez CEO
       Tel: 215-287-9488
       Email: maria.alvarez@xcellas.com
       Website: www.xcellas.com
Consulting assessment & requirements, project management solution strategies, implementation & optimization.
(Woman/Hisp, estab 2013, empl 10, sales $1,308,715,
cert: State, NMSDC, WBENC)

Puerto Rico

7840   Development Management & Consulting Group
       P.O. Box 142343
       Arecibo, PR 00614
       Contact: Eduardo Hernandez Principal Engineer
       Tel: 787-897-0830
       Email: eduardo.hernandez@dmcginc.com
       Website: www.dmcginc.com
Validation Master Planning/Management, Commissioning
& Qualification (C&Q), Decommissioning & Records
Management, GMP Documentation Review / Generation,
Cleaning & Process/Packaging Validation. (Hisp, estab
2000, empl 44, sales $4,089,547, cert: NMSDC)

7841   Impactivo LLC
       1357 Ashford Ave
       San Juan, PR 00907
       Contact: Maria Fernanda Levis-Peralta CEO
       Tel: 787-993-1508
       Email: maria.levis@gmail.com
       Website: www.impactivo.com
Systems Research, Policy Analysis, Strategic Planning &
Financial Sustainability, Community Health Needs
Assessment, Strategic Planning, Data Driven Decision
Making, Project Planning, Technical Assistance, Perfor-
mance Improvement. (Woman/Hisp, estab 2010, empl 5,
sales $ 0, cert: NMSDC)

7842   Integrated Management & Controls, Inc.
       P.O. Box 229
       Manati, PR 00674
       Contact: Ismael Jaime President
       Tel: 787-462-4739
       Email: ismael.jaime@imanagementcontrols.com
       Website: www.imanagementcontrols.com
Program Management, Portfolio Management, Project
Management, Construction Management, Project
Controls, Cost Control, Planning, Scheduling, Document
& Contract Management, Engineering, Design, Qualifica-
tion Schedule, Design Schedules. (Hisp, estab 2014, empl
3, sales $390,000, cert: NMSDC)

Rhode Island

7843   Granger Warburton Consulting, LLC
       79 West St
       East Greenwich, RI 02818
       Contact: Bethany Warburton Principal Consultant
       Tel: 401-965-1288
       Email: bethany@grangerwarburton.com
       Website: www.grangerwarburton.com
Learning management system design & deployment,
elearning creation, software application development,
project management, business analysis, change management, documentation & process design. (Woman, estab
2013, empl 2, sales $127,000, cert: State)

South Carolina

7844   DESA, Inc
       400 Percival Rd
       Columbia, SC 29206
       Contact: Diane Sumpter CEO
       Tel: 803-256-3212
       Email: dianes@desainc.com
       Website: www.desainc.com
Conference management, construction management,
facilities management, business services. (Woman/AA,
estab 1986, empl 75, sales $1,811,901, cert: State)

7845   GIME LLC
       1544 Remount Rd Ste B
       North Charleston, SC 29405
       Contact: Angela Gailliard President
       Tel: 843-277-7552
       Email: gime.llc@gmail.com
       Website: www.bbizsolutions.com
Workforce Solutions, Consulting Services, Administrative
& Management Support, Professional Business Services.
(Woman/AA, estab 2009, empl 1, sales , cert: State)

7846 Sharp Business Consulting Services LLC
1320 Main St Ste 300
Columbia, SC 29210
Contact: Mitchell Wyatt CEO
Tel: 803-600-7941
Email: mitchell.wyatt@gmail.com
Website: www.sharpbusinessconsulting.com
Growth & market penetration, profitability, repeat clients, customer service & strong community presence. (AA, estab 2006, empl 23, sales $1,642,774, cert: State, 8a)

Tennessee

7847 Remnant Management Group Inc.
2550 Meridian Blvd Ste 200
Franklin, TN 37067
Contact: Stephanie Beard CEO
Tel: 615-403-1567
Email: info@remnantgroup.com
Website: www.theremnantgroup.com
Employee development training & construction management services, leadership training & development, workforce development, curriculum selection & customization, construction management workforce development. (Woman/AA, estab 2006, empl 5, sales $103,774, cert: State)

Texas

7848 2M Research Services, LLC
1521 N Cooper St, Ste 600
Arlington, TX 76011
Contact: Marcus Martin CEO
Tel: 817-707-6483
Email: mmartin@2mresearch.com
Website: www.2mresearch.com
Research, program evaluation & technical assistance, substantial research, program assessment, data collection, program assessments, evaluation design efforts, program evaluations, data collection, performance measurement. (AA, estab 2011, empl 30, sales $750,000, cert: 8a)

7849 ABT International Corporation
2591 Dallas Pkwy, Ste 300
Frisco, TX 75034
Contact: Mike Buckhaulter Owner
Tel: 469-879-2642
Email: mbuckhaulter@abticorp.com
Website: http://abticorp.com/pages/3/index.htm
Project management agreements.
(AA, estab 2003, empl 5, sales , cert: State)

7850 Access Sciences Corporation
1900 West Loop South Ste 1450
Houston, TX 77027
Contact: Todd Brown
Tel: 713-664-4357
Email: tbrown@accesssciences.com
Website: www.accesssciences.com
Information & records mgmt, enterprise content mgmt & regulatory compliance, information management consulting & outsourcing. (Woman, estab 1985, empl 62, sales $ 0, cert: State, WBENC)

7851 AHRMDCO International LLC
14405 Walters RdSte 1002
Houston, TX 77014
Contact: Roderick Lemon President
Tel: 713-589-3688
Email: rlemon@ahrmdcoint.com
Website: www.ahrmdcoint.com
Organizational development: customer service, time mgmt, partenering & team building, supervisor, executive coaching, project mgmt, web & graphic design, employee assessment surveys & interviewing techniques. (AA, estab 2002, empl , sales $115,000, cert: State, NMSDC)

7852 Alfa Management Solutions LLC
1228 Grant Ave
Lantana, TX 76226
Contact: Frank Wilson Managing Dir
Tel: 214-642-5907
Email: fwilson@aflams.com
Website: www.alfams.com/
Critical Path Method Scheduling & Control, Project & Program Management Support, Develop, Implement & Monitor Schedule, Report Progression of Program/ Projects, Customize Schedule for Client Specific Needs. (AA, estab 2007, empl 2, sales $313,500, cert: 8a)

7853 Austin Texas Mediators LLC
4500 Williams Dr. Ste 212-111
Georgetown, TX 78633
Contact: Barbara Allen Owner
Tel: 512-966-9222
Email: info@motexas.com
Website: www.mediatorsoftexas.com
Train the trainer; sensitivity training; sexual harassment in the workplace training; non-confrontational communication skills training; conflict resolution in the work place. (Woman, estab 2014, empl 15, sales , cert: State, WBENC)

7854 Beacon Training Services
1229 Mohawk Trail
Richardson, TX 75080
Contact: Diana Stein Managing Principal
Tel: 972-404-0069
Email: diana@beacontraining.com
Website: www.beacontraining.com
Computer/technical, management/supervisory, professional development & project management training. (Woman, estab 1987, empl 4, sales $1,000,000, cert: State, WBENC)

7855 Brittain-Kalish Group, LLC
P.O. Box 8577
Fort Worth, TX 76124
Contact: Heather Randolph Consultant
Tel: 817-991-0705
Email: bkg@theupconsultants.com
Website: www.brittainkalishgroup.com
Management consulting firm comprised of trusted advisors, valued resources and trainers who strategically collaborate to create optimal results in a timely manner. (Woman, estab 2010, empl 3, sales , cert: WBENC)

7856   CAET Project Management Consultants
       1139 Keller Pkwy Ste B
       Keller, TX 76248
       Contact: President
       Tel: 817-741-6546
       Email:
       Website: www.caetpmc.com
Owner Representation & Financial Consulting, Development of project budget, cost estimation, Assist & develop contract strategies, Conduct requests for proposals (RFPs) & manage process for receipt & review. (Woman, estab 2016, empl 5, sales $150,000, cert: State, WBENC)

7857   Caldwell Everson PLLC
       2777 Allen Pkwy, Ste 950
       Houston, TX 77019
       Contact: Faye Caldwell Managing Partner
       Tel: 713-654-3000
       Email: fcaldwell@caldwelleverson.com
       Website: www.caldwelleverson.com
Management employment, drug-testing, commercial, product liability & general civil litigation. (Woman, estab 1997, empl 6, sales $940,180, cert: State, WBENC)

7858   Career Management International, Inc.
       4801 Woodway Dr Ste 300 East
       Houston, TX 77056
       Contact: Jim Tye CEO
       Tel: 713-623-8780
       Email: jimt@careermanagement.com
       Website: www.careermanagement.com
Career transition & outplacement; training; team building & organizational development. (Woman, estab 1975, empl 18, sales $3,000,000, cert: City, WBENC)

7859   Deirdre Sanborn & Associates
       4321 Bretton Bay Lane
       Dallas, TX 75287
       Contact: Deirdre Sanborn Owner
       Tel: 214-308-1408
       Email: deirdre@deirdresanborn.com
       Website: http://deirdresanborn.com
Executive Coaching, Leadership Coaching, Team Integration, Team Management & Strategic consulting. (Woman, estab 2014, empl 3, sales , cert: WBENC)

7860   DiversityInPromotions, Inc.
       5057 Keller Springs Rd Ste 300
       Addison, TX 75001
       Contact: Rodney Woods
       Tel: 469-718-5589
       Email: rwoods@diversityinpromotions.com
       Website: www.diversityinpromotions.com
Program Assessment, Strategic Planning, Policy Development, Metrics Development, Communication Plan (Internal & External), Mentor/Protege Development, Government Reporting (Subcontract Plan). (AA, estab 1998, empl 18, sales $1,200,000, cert: State, NMSDC)

7861   D'Onofrio Consulting Partners
       1700 Post Oak Blvd
       Houston, TX 77056
       Contact: Margaret D'Onofrio Principal & Exec Coach
       Tel: 713-963-3673
       Email: margaret@donofrioconsultingpartners.com
       Website: http://donofrioconsultingpartners.com
Coaching for individuals, teams & organizations. (Woman, estab 2007, empl , sales $1,168,885, cert: WBENC, NWBOC)

7862   Dramatic Conclusions, LLC
       3900 Vitruvian Way Ste 231
       Addison, TX 75001
       Contact: Pam Boyd Owner
       Tel: 469-855-0543
       Email: pam@dramaticconclusions.com
       Website: www.dramaticconclusions.com
Management & employee training & consulting. (Woman, estab 1999, empl 1, sales , cert: State, WBENC)

7863   FFG Strategic Consulting LLC
       363 N. Houston Pkwy E Ste 1100
       Houston, TX 77060
       Contact: Colette Lewis
       Tel: 832-412-2524
       Email: colette.lewis@ffgsconsulting.com
       Website: www.ffgsconsulting.com
Program/project management, engineering consulting, technical resources, project planning, construction management, project scheduling, project controls, system engineering, six sigma methodology analysis, mechanical engineering. (Woman/AA, estab 2011, empl 5, sales , cert: State, NMSDC, WBENC)

7864   Hybrid Teams, Inc.
       3023 Cape Buffalo Trail
       Frisco, TX 75034
       Contact: Mac Choi President
       Tel: 847-530-9034
       Email: info@hybridteams.com
       Website: www.hybridteams.com
Enterprise content management professional services, document management, consulting services. (As-Pac, estab 2006, empl 3, sales $306,000, cert: NMSDC)

7865   JFE International Consultants, Inc.
       18705 Stoneridge Dr
       Dallas, TX 75252
       Contact: J. Francisco Escobar President
       Tel: 214-728-6903
       Email: francisco@jfeintl.com
       Website: www.jfeintl.com
Management consulting, contract diagnostics, compensation principles, negotiations, performance evaluations & measurements, internal/external process audits. (Hisp, estab 2003, empl 1, sales $214,595, cert: NMSDC)

7866   Jill Hickman Companies
       1721 Palomino Ln
       Kingwood, TX 77339
       Contact: Jill Hickman President
       Tel: 281-358-8580
       Email: jill@jillhickman.com
       Website: www.jillhickman.com
Training & development services: leadership, supervision, consultative sales, customer service & team building, pre-employment assessment, executive advisement, strategic planning. (Minority/Woman, estab 1998, empl 1, sales $141,956, cert: WBENC)

7867   Languages Houston
       1001 S Dairy Ashford Ste 100
       Houston, TX 77077
       Contact: Elena Tsilina CEO
       Tel: 832-359-4226
       Email: info@languageshouston.com
       Website: www.languageshouston.com
Foreign language classes & translation services. (Woman, estab 2015, empl 20, sales , cert: State, WBENC)

7868 Lone Star Interpreters LLC
2800 Post Oak Blvd, Ste 1400 Ste 4100
Houston, TX 77056
Contact: Marie Mills CEO
Tel: 832-399-2100
Email: marie.mills@lonestarinterpreters.com
Website: www.lonestarinterpreters.com
Language services in over 200 languages: Translation &
Localization, Transcription, Interpretation: On Site,
Telephonic & Video, Voice Prompt Translating, Voice
Prompt Recording. (Woman/AA, estab 2007, empl 40, sales
$2,480,000, cert: State)

7869 Michael Resource Group LLC
1325 Daja Lane Ste 604
Grand Prairie, TX 75050
Contact: Brandon Russell Sales
Tel: 888-313-8688
Email: brussell@mrgroupllc.com
Website: www.mrgroupllc.com
Management Consulting. (AA, estab 2014, empl 4, sales
$100,000, cert: State, NMSDC)

7870 Mind The Gap, LLC
901 Parkwood Ct
McKinney, TX 75070
Contact: Beth Anagnos Principal
Tel: 314-378-6426
Email: betha@mindthegapcoaching.com
Website: http://mindthegapcoaching.com
Leadership coaching, customized coaching programs for all
levels of leadership. (Woman, estab 2007, empl 5, sales ,
cert: WBENC)

7871 Niche Assurance LLC
9894 Bissonnet St
Houston, TX 77036
Contact: Peter Kiilu
Tel: 281-636-2749
Email: peter.kiilu@nicheconsult.net
Website: www.nicheconsult.net
Financial & IT risk management, business performance
improvement, Internal control design & implementation,
Sarbanes-Oxley Act compliance, FCPA compliance, internal
audits, I.T. audits, cyber security, SAP security. (AA, estab
2007, empl 4, sales $150,000, cert: State, NMSDC)

7872 Obsidian Technical Communications, Ltd.
3522 White Oak Dr
Houston, TX 77007
Contact: Erik Pettine Dir of Sales
Tel: 281-732-5940
Email: erikp@obsidianlearning.com
Website: www.obsidianlearning.com
Consulting: job performance, end-user performance
support, custom training strategy & development, docu-
mentation, e-learning, knowledge mgmt & change mgmt.
(Woman, estab 1998, empl 26, sales $3,700,000, cert:
WBENC)

7873 PABULUM Consulting, LLC
1002 Gemini St Ste 225D
Houston, TX 77058
Contact: Ferrel Bonner CEO
Tel: 713-538-4719
Email: ferrelbonner@pabulumconsulting.com
Website: www.pabulumconsulting.com
Military Intelligence, Security & Emergency Manage-
ment, Special Operations & Tactical Communications.
(AA, estab 2007, empl 4, sales $150,000, cert: State, City,
8a)

7874 Peck Training Group LLC
907 Glen Rose Dr
Allen, TX 75013
Contact: Holly St John Peck President
Tel: 214-495-9499
Email: holly@pecktraining.com
Website: http://pecktraining.com
Professional development training & coaching. (Woman,
estab 1985, empl 2, sales $325,000, cert: WBENC)

7875 Phoenix Translations
2110 White Horse Trail
Austin, TX 78757
Contact: Deborah Wright CEO
Tel: 512-343-8389
Email: service@phoenixtranslations.com
Website: www.phoenixtranslations.com
Technical translation services. (Woman/AA, Hisp, estab
2000, empl 20, sales $2,500,000, cert: State, WBENC)

7876 Phronetik
5851 Legacy Circle 6th Fl
Plano, TX 75024
Contact: Tania Martin-Mercado President & CEO
Tel: 877-844-3575
Email: taniame@phronetik.com
Website: www.phronetik.com
Research & Development, Technical Support,
Interoperability, Patient Portal Development, Privacy &
Security, Clinical Documentation, Mobile Health,
Decision Support Systems, Telemedicine, Custom
Development. (Woman/Hisp, estab 2013, empl 11, sales
, cert: WBENC)

7877 Possible Missions, Inc.
150 W Parker Rd., Ste 602
Houston, TX 77076
Contact: Paula Mendoza CEO
Tel: 713-271-3746
Email: paula@possiblemissions.com
Website: www.possiblemissions.com
Project management solutions, plan, execute & com-
plete projects within budget and on schedule. (Woman/
Hisp, estab 2001, empl 33, sales $2,100,000, cert: State,
City, NMSDC, WBENC, 8a)

7878 Proje Inc.
6942 FM 1960 E, Ste 362
Humble, TX 77346
Contact: COO
Tel: 832-293-5633
Email:
Website: www.projeinc.com
Project Management Leadership & analytical thinking,
Crisis Management, Integration & Consolidation, Risk
Analysis & Adjustment, Medicare Advantage. (Woman,
estab 2004, empl 38, sales $8,800,119, cert: WBENC)

7879   Risk Integrity Safety Knowledge, Inc.
       2257 N Loop 336 W. Ste. 140-423
       Conroe, TX 77304
       Contact: Janet Benaquisto Marketing Dir
       Tel: 510-837-8913
       Email: janet.benaquisto@psmrisk.com
       Website: www.psmrisk.com
Process safety & risk management technical consulting,
training & staffing services. (Woman, estab 2010, empl 7,
sales $1,200,000, cert: State)

7880   Risk Mitigation Worldwide
       9800 Northwest Frwy Ste 600
       Houston, TX 77092
       Contact: Michele Ward VP Business Dev
       Tel: 713-864-9997
       Email: michele@legalwatch.com
       Website: www.legalwatch.com
Training & consulting services: communications to mini-
mize & avoid potential lawsuits, claims & internal disputes.
(Woman/AA, estab 1997, empl 6, sales $ 0, cert: State,
NMSDC, WBENC)

7881   RWG Consulting, Inc.
       2560 King Arthur Blvd. Ste 124-34
       Dallas, TX 75056
       Contact: Anton Gates Managing Partner
       Tel: 972-386-7601
       Email: agates@rwgconsulting.com
       Website: www.rwgconsulting.com
Training, Instructional Design, Project Management,
Organizational Change Management, SAP Training Devel-
opment,
Staff Augmentation, Business Process Optimization,
Contract to Hire. (AA, estab 2013, empl 15, sales $900,000,
cert: State, NMSDC)

7882   Sales Trac Coaching & Mgmt Development
       10012 SIlvertree Dr
       Dallas, TX 75243
       Contact: David Tyson CEO
       Tel: 214-215-1108
       Email: davidt@salestrac.net
       Website: www.salestrac.net
Leadership Development & Performance Management,
Management training, Sales Management training, sales
training, service focused training, customer service
training
Generational training. (AA, estab 2007, empl 1, sales , cert:
State, NMSDC)

7883   Seilevel Partners, LP
       3410 Far West Blvd Ste 265
       Austin, TX 78731
       Contact: Christine Wollmuth
       Tel: 512-527-9952
       Email: cwollmuth@seilevel.com
       Website: www.seilevel.com
Business analysis consulting, business analyst staffing,
assessment, mentoring & training. (As-Ind, estab 2000,
empl 30, sales , cert: State, NMSDC)

7884   Shea Writing and Training Solutions, Inc.
       5807 Benning Dr
       Houston, TX 77096
       Contact: Evalyn Shea President
       Tel: 713-723-9142
       Email: info@sheaws.com
       Website: www.sheaws.com
Technical writing & editing, risk assessment & meeting
scribing, web content, training materials, proposals,
presentations, reports, technical manuals, etc. (Woman,
estab 1997, empl 12, sales $861,472, cert: WBENC)

7885   Sirius Solutions, LLLP
       1233 West Loop South Ste 1800
       Houston, TX 77027
       Contact: Kathy Pattillo Dir Business Devel
       Tel: 713-888-0488
       Email: kpattillo@sirsol.com
       Website: www.sirsol.com
Management consulting: finance, internal audit,
information technology, accounting, risk, operations,
process improvement, strategy & tax. (Woman, estab
1998, empl 230, sales , cert: WBENC, NWBOC)

7886   Stalwart Consulting, LLC
       23501 Cinco Ranch Blvd Ste H120 #129
       Katy, TX 77494
       Contact: CEO
       Tel: 513-722-6852
       Email:
       Website: http://stalwartmc.com
Management consulting & advisory service, technology
development & delivery, project management &
business analysis & projections. (Hisp, estab 2016, empl
5, sales , cert: City)

7887   The Conxsis Group, Inc.
       1910 McCartney Court
       Arlington, TX 76012
       Contact: Abdul Shakir President
       Tel: 817-348-0060
       Email: ashakir@conxsis.com
       Website: www.conxsis.com
Environmental consulting, financial, economic, business
consulting, large & small business teaming, M/WBE
Programs, marketing & business development. (AA,
estab 2002, empl 16, sales $370,000, cert: State)

7888   The I4 Group Consulting, LLC
       5830 Granite Pkwy, Bldg 5, Ste 1050
       Plano, TX 75024
       Contact: Charles Maddox Sr. Business Dir
       Tel: 612-207-2751
       Email: charles.sr@thei4group.com
       Website: www.thei4group.com
Training & coaching for Scaled Agile, Agile, and IT
business process improvement, Lean Six Sigma, project
management training & certification. (AA, estab 2013,
empl 42, sales $8,250,120, cert: NMSDC, 8a)

7889   The Tagos Group, LLC
       8 E Greenway Plaza Ste 1340
       Houston, TX 77046
       Contact: Maria Traver Office Mgr
       Tel: 713-850-7031
       Email: mtraver@tagosgroup.com
       Website: www.tagosgroup.com
Business consulting, services & products: supply chain
mgmt, transportation & logistics mgmt, speciality
maintenance & call center operations. (AA, estab 2007,
empl 9, sales $500,000, cert: NMSDC)

7890 Tray-Tec, Inc.
2598 Wilson Rd
Humble, TX 77396
Contact: DARELL FOWLER VP
Tel: 281-441-7314
Email: traytec@traytec.com
Website: www.traytec.com
Installers of process equipment such as trays, packings, distributors in towers, reactors, and drums. We perform installation and repairs of nozzles, and we perform vessel shell repairs. (Hisp, estab 2005, empl 20, sales $10,000,000, cert: State)

7891 Tre Weekly Magazine
3202 N Shiloh Rd
Garland, TX 75044
Contact: Shayne Hohman Marketing Coord
Tel: 972-675-4383
Email: marketing@trenews.com
Website: http://baotreonline.com/
Tre magazine circulates nearly 125,000 publications nationwide on a weekly basis: with a readership census of 112,000 people in Dallas alone. (As-Pac, estab 1997, empl 25, sales $1,600,000, cert: NMSDC)

Virginia

7892 A. Reddix & Associates Inc.
1215 N Military Hwy, Ste 754
Norfolk, VA 23502
Contact: Contracts Dir
Tel: 757-410-7704
Email:
Website: www.ardx.net
Workforce training & technical assistance, innovative information technology & security solutions & support, collaborative conferencing & events management, quality, compliance & revenue audits, policy documentation & management. (Minority/Woman, estab 2006, empl 105, sales , cert: State)

7893 AEi International LLC
7686 Richmond Hwy, Ste 118
Alexandria, VA 22306
Contact: Jenna Reese CEO
Tel: 410-988-3966
Email: jenna.reese@aeiintl.com
Website: www.aeiintl.com
Management consulting & technology, strategic consulting, digital experience & enterprise technology related-services, staff augmentation. (Woman/AA, estab 2007, empl 12, sales $1,200,000, cert: 8a)

7894 Aerobodies Fitness Company, Inc.
950 N Washington St Ste 311
Alexandria, VA 22314
Contact: CEO
Tel: 703-402-8477
Email:
Website: www.afmsco.com
Program management services, acquisition support, organizational development, and occupational health services to federal and private sector agencies. (Woman/AA, estab 1997, empl 25, sales $750,000, cert: WBENC, 8a)

7895 Assura, Inc.
7814 Carousel Ln, Ste 202
Richmond, VA 23294
Contact: Karen Cole CEO
Tel: 804-672-8714
Email: karen.cole@assuraconsulting.com
Website: www.assurainc.com
Consulting: Governance, Risk & Compliance (GRC), Enterprise Risk Management (ERM), cyber-security, business continuity planning & Information Technology (IT) audit. (Woman, estab , empl , sales , cert: State, WBENC)

7896 Avyance
11718 Bowman Green Dr, Ste 230
Reston, VA 20190
Contact: Tatiana Jeromskaia President
Tel: 703-577-0046
Email: t.jeromskaia@avyance.com
Website: www.avyance.com
Management consulting, strategic communications and change management. (Woman, estab 2017, empl 14, sales $800,000, cert: State)

7897 Burton-Fuller Managment
4905 Radford Ave Ste 105
Richmond, VA 23230
Contact: Vicki Funk Office Mgr
Tel: 804-217-6380
Email: support@burtonfuller.com
Website: www.burtonfuller.com
Management consulting. (Woman, estab 1989, empl 5, sales $ 0, cert: State)

7898 C.W. Hines and Associates, Inc.
344 Churchill Cir, Sanctuary Bay
White Stone, VA 22578
Contact: Cheryl Hudson President
Tel: 804-435-8844
Email: turtlecwh@aol.com
Website: www.cwhinesassociates.org
Management training & consulting: performance excellence coaching, diversity, teambuilding, leadership development, communications, customer service, strategic thinking, strategic planning, supervisory effectiveness, executive coaching, mediation. (Woman/AA, estab , empl , sales $850,000, cert: State, City)

7899 Capitol Management Consulting Services, Inc.
1600 Chain Bridge Rd
McLean, VA 22101
Contact: Akshat Prasad President
Tel: 571-318-6404
Email: akshat@capitolmcs.com
Website: www.capitolmcs.com
Management consulting, organizational governance, performance optimization, strategy, technology, and training services. (As-Ind, estab 2011, empl 7, sales , cert: NMSDC, 8a)

7900 Comprehensive Professional & Proposal Services
44 Mine Rd Ste 2
Stafford, VA 22554
Contact: Linda Davies Owner
Tel: 540-318-7848
Email: wendy.theodore@cp2susa.com
Website: www.cp2susa.com
Custom support services: proposal development support; capture management; business development strategy, planning, and management; branding and publication graphics; and organizational, planning, and communication support. (Woman, estab , empl , sales $1,000,000, cert: 8a)

7901   DP Distribution & Consulting, LLC
12240 Hunting Horn Lane
Rockville, VA 23146
Contact: Darren Reeves President
Tel: 804-307-7706
Email: dreeves@dpdconline.com
Website: www.dpdconline.com
Quality Assurance & Regulatory for Manufacturing,
Auditing, 510K, FDA regulation. (Woman, estab 2000, empl
1, sales $300,000, cert: State)

7902   EMY Consulting LLC
13406 Poplar Woods
Chantilly, VA 20151
Contact: President
Tel: 703-943-8129
Email:
Website: www.emyconsulting.biz
Management consulting solutions. (Woman, estab 2013,
empl 1, sales $201,000, cert: State, WBENC)

7903   Evans Inc.
2750 Property Ave, Ste 425
Fairfax, VA 22031
Contact: Office Mgr
Tel: 703-663-2480
Email:
Website: www.evansincorporated.com
Business process consulting, change mgmt &
reengineering, enterprise IT investment analysis & integration, ethical leadership training, process & data modeling,
performance mgmt, competency framework changes &
development, user interface. (Woman, estab 1993, empl
10, sales $1,500,000, cert: WBENC)

7904   FM Solutions, PLLC
901 E Byrd St Ste 1210
Richmond, VA 23219
Contact: Wendy Henley Principal
Tel: 804-288-3173
Email: wendyh@fmsolutions-us.com
Website: www.fmsolutions-us.com
Project & program mgmt, facilities mgmt, consulting &
supplemental staffing, space allocation analyses & pro-
gramming, strategic space & facilities planning, relocation
mgmt. (Woman, estab 2003, empl 4, sales $394,143, cert:
State)

7905   ITMC Solutions
12841 Braemar Village Plaza
Bristow, VA 20136
Contact: Nicole Johnson business devel assoc
Tel: 571-239-1653
Email: njohnson@itmcsolutions.com
Website: www.itmcsolutions.com
Strategic consulting: program mgmt, capital planning,
portfolio mgmt, performance mgmt, business process re-
engineering, IT strategic planning, Cloud Ccmputing
strategic planning, enterprise architecture, risk manage-
ment, IV &V. (Woman/AA, estab 2010, empl 3, sales
$500,000, cert: State)

7906   KAPAX Solutions LLC
44308 Navajo Dr
Ashburn, VA 20147
Contact: Katrecia Nolen President
Tel: 571-239-0653
Email: katrecia.nolen@kapaxsolutions.com
Website: www.kapaxsolutions.com
Professional services & management consulting,
strategic planning, system integration & project manage-
ment support services. (Woman/AA, estab 2011, empl 1,
sales , cert: State)

7907   KickStart Specialists, LLC
11809 Crown Prince Circle
Henrico, VA 23238
Contact: Robert Riley Principal
Tel: 855-454-2578
Email: rriley@kickstartspecialists.com
Website: www.KickStartSpecialists.com
Leadership development & training; roles & responsibili-
ties, business objectives, business case evaluation, team-
building; project & program management consulting;
project board training; health checks. (Woman, estab
2011, empl 2, sales , cert: State)

7908   Mindseeker, Inc.
20130 Lakeview Center Plaza, Ste 320
Ashburn, VA 20147
Contact: Cassie Kelly VP, Client Services & Opera-
tions
Tel: 304-549-9281
Email: ckelly@mindseeker.com
Website: www.mindseeker.com
Information Technology, Financial, Clerical and Enter-
prise Performance Management services and solutions.
(Woman/AA, estab , empl 234, sales $2,000,000, cert:
State, WBENC)

7909   OmniTek Consulting, Inc.
8260 Greensboro Dr Ste 120
McLean, VA 22102
Contact: Matthew Donahue GM
Tel: 240-344-7914
Email: support@omnitekconsulting.com
Website: http://omnitekconsulting.com/
Consulting, Contingent, and Professional Service
Engagements: Program & Project Management, Business
Process Management (BPM), Change Management &
Training, Systems Implementation & Integration,
Business Analytics & Data Management. (As-Pac, estab
2005, empl 41, sales $3,736,515, cert: NMSDC)

7910   Project Management and Consulting LLC
512 Lafayette Boulevard, Ste 2
Fredericksburg, VA 22401
Contact: Bryan Rock CEO
Tel: 800-971-3194
Email: brock@pmcllcva.com
Website: www.pmcva.com
Business management & consulting, small business
consulting, minority-owned business consulting. (AA,
estab 2007, empl 1, sales $195,000, cert: State)

7911 SAK Management Consulting
2217 Princess Anne St Ste 204-1
Fredericksburg, VA 22401
Contact: Semy Kakoma Principal
Tel: 570-328-0405
Email: semyk@sak-consultingcpas.com
Website: www.sak-consultingcpas.com
DOD audit readiness, IT audits for NIST 800 compliance,
Fed accounting, Fed financial statement support, Real
Property accounting & compliance, human resources &
information technology management & advisory services.
(AA, estab 2011, empl 6, sales $950,000, cert: 8a)

7912 Savi Solutions, Inc.
8200 Greensboro Dr, Ste 900
McLean, VA 22102
Contact: CEO
Tel: 571-258-7602
Email:
Website: www.savisolutions.biz
Strategic Planning, Program/Project Management, Merger
& Acquisition Support, Systems Implementation (ERP/
CRM/SCM), Cloud Based Implementation Solutions,
Business Requirement Analysis, System Design and
Development. (Woman/As-Ind, estab 2010, empl 3, sales
$552,551, cert: WBENC)

7913 The Boulevard Consulting Group, LLC
2001 Jefferson Davis Hwy Ste 412
Arlington, VA 22202
Contact: James Bagg Managing Partner
Tel: 703-566-6895
Email: james.bagg@boulevardcg.com
Website: http://boulevardcg.com
Operations Research/Analysis, Lean Six Sigma, Systems &
Process Improvement/Analysis, Modeling & Simulation,
Optimization, Strategic Planning, Risk Analysis, Risk
Management, Financial Modeling/Forecasting & Analysis.
(Nat Ame, estab 2013, empl 4, sales $600,000, cert: 8a)

7914 The MASY Group
6214 Old Franconia Rd Ste B
Alexandria, VA 22310
Contact: Mia Elsheikh Operations Mgr
Tel: 703-888-8121
Email: mia.elsheikh@masygroup.com
Website: www.masygroup.com
Intelligence & risk management services, accountable &
innovative intelligence & security solutions. (As-Pac, estab
2006, empl 45, sales $7,000,000, cert: 8a)

7915 The Perspectives Group
7620 Little River Turnpike Ste 205
Annandale, VA 22003
Contact: Dir Business Development
Tel: 703-837-1197
Email:
Website: www.theperspectivesgroup.com
Public participation & outreach, advisory boards &
governance, collaboration, facilitation, graphic design,
mediation & dispute resolution, message development,
policy development, process design, strategic planning,
training & education. (Woman, estab 1991, empl 6, sales
$990,000, cert: State)

7916 TMS Consulting LLC
2776 S Arlington Mill Dr Ste 114
Arlington, VA 22206
Contact: Tafadzwa Matinenga President
Tel: 703-864-9965
Email: info@tmsconsultingservices.us
Website: www.tmsconsult.us
Global management consulting. (Woman/AA, estab
2015, empl 3, sales , cert: State)

7917 Visions2000 Inc.
312 Tides Run
Yorktown, VA 23692
Contact: Che Henderson VP
Tel: 757-898-5010
Email: che@visions2000inc.com
Website: www.visions2000inc.com
Consulting & training solutions: diversity, leadership,
teambuilding, change management, life work planning &
job search assistance. (Woman/AA, estab 1990, empl 2,
sales , cert: NMSDC)

Washington

7918 Brightwork Consulting, Inc.
200 W Mercer St, Ste 108
Seattle, WA 98119
Contact: Creative Director
Tel: 206-659-0643
Email:
Website: www.brightworkconsulting.net
Risk management, solution deployment, smart deci-
sions, and change management. (Woman, estab 2017,
empl 15, sales $4,000,000, cert: WBENC)

7919 Cascade Management and Consulting
26211 178th St SE
Monroe, WA 98272
Contact: Amy Hoyt Owner
Tel: 206-778-4322
Email: info@cascademgtconsulting.com
Website: http://cascademgtconsulting.com
Project & program management, IT & global rollouts,
business continuity/disaster recovery, brand integrity,
change management & collaborative communications.
(Woman, estab 2015, empl 1, sales , cert: State)

7920 Groundwork Tech, LLC
P.O. Box 489
Bellevue, WA 98004
Contact: Jeff Foster Principal
Tel: 425-209-0588
Email: jeff@groundworktech.com
Website: www.groundworktech.com
Professional Management Services, consulting services
& resources to enhance, re-engineer & develop cus-
tomer business. (AA, estab 2014, empl 3, sales
$180,000, cert: State)

7921   Rafael A Colon Voices Internacional
       5145 Illahee Ln NE
       Olympia, WA 98516
       Contact: Rafael Colon President
       Tel: 360-459-7228
       Email: rafael@voicesinternacional.com
       Website: http://voicesinternacional.com
Consulting, training, organizational operations & administration, leadership & management development, program
development & management, communication effectiveness & meeting facilitation, peak performance & team
unity practices. (Hisp, estab 1994, empl 1, sales $217,500,
cert: State, NMSDC)

7922   Rivet Consulting LLC
       2212 Queen Anne Ave N, Ste 127
       Seattle, WA 98109
       Contact: Courtney Klein Managing Partner
       Tel: 888-201-1422
       Email: courtney@rivetconsulting.com
       Website: www.rivetconsulting.com
Project Managers, Program Managers, Marketing Managers, Marketing Coordinators, Financial Analysts, Business
Analysts, Social Media Experts, Search Marketing Experts,
Data Analysts,   Market Researchers, Marketing Communications Managers. (Woman, estab 2013, empl 30, sales ,
cert: WBENC)

7923   Shee Atiká Technologies, LLC
       218 Main St Ste 425
       Kirkland, WA 98033
       Contact: Lauren Engle Operations Mgr
       Tel: 858-254-3312
       Email: lauren.engle@sheeatikatech.com
       Website: www.sheeatikatech.com
Engineering, technical support services, resource planning
& management svcs, studies & analysis, operations
analysis, strategic planning, business process improvement, system requirements, training & education requirements. (Nat Ame, estab 2005, empl 32, sales $5,371,107,
cert: 8a)

Wisconsin

7924   Urban Strategies US LLC DBA SMCG
       759 N Milwaukee St Ste 414
       Milwaukee, WI 53202
       Contact: Jim Milner CEO
       Tel: 414-221-9500
       Email: jmilner@sectormanagement.biz
       Website: www.sectormcg.com
Leadership development, assessing/shaping organizational
culture, stretching leadership capacity & accelerating the
development of those who follow through effective
coaching. (AA, estab 2002, empl 3, sales , cert: State,
NMSDC)

PROFESSIONAL SERVICES: Public Relations/ Marketing

Provide services including business research and marketing plans, data collection and analysis, meeting planning, needs assessments, corporate imaging enhancement, focus groups, fundraising, technical writing, media relations, etc. NAICS Code 54

Alabama

7925   Marketry Inc.
1630 29th Ct S
Birmingham, AL 35209
Contact: Gillian Waybright Business Mgr
Tel: 205-802-7252
Email: gwaybright@marketryinc.com
Website: www.marketryinc.com
Qualitative marketing research: focus groups, ethnography, online discussions, online video focus groups, interviews, dyads, triads, observational research, ideation, shop-a-longs, online bulletin boards, video diaries. (Woman, estab 1995, empl 5, sales , cert: WBENC)

7926   PM Group, Inc.
4324 Midmost Dr Ste 200
Mobile, AL 36609
Contact: Juan Peasant
Tel: 251-445-7804
Email: juan@pmgroupnow.com
Website:
Branding & Marketing, Social Media Marketing, creative & design development, print, web development & video production. (AA, estab 2004, empl 3, sales $226,910, cert: NMSDC)

Arizona

7927   Class Act Designs
18239 N 40th St, Ste 109
Phoenix, AZ 85032
Contact: Debbie Perkins CEO
Tel: 602-843-3109
Email: classactdesigns@peoplepc.com
Website:
Advertising, public relations, media, graphic design & strategy marketing. (Woman/AA, estab 1992, empl 6, sales , cert: City)

7928   EventPro Strategies, Inc.
7373 N. Scottsdale Road, Ste B-120
Scottsdale, AZ 85283
Contact: Kelly Springs-Kelley Dir of Marketing
Tel: 480-449-4100
Email: kkelley@eventprostrategies.com
Website: www.eventprostrategies.com
Marketing, public relations & promotional events. (Woman, estab 1999, empl 32, sales $6,700,000, cert: WBENC)

7929   JVJ Can 22 Corp
3260 N Hayden, Ste 210
Scottsdale, AZ 85251
Contact: Michelle Candelaria CEO
Tel: 480-626-7919
Email: mc@cts10.com
Website: http://CTS10.com
SEO Search Engine Optimization, Social Media Mgmt, Reputation monitoring, Video Upload to Social Media sites Social Shopping Carts. (Woman/Hisp, estab 2016, empl 7, sales , cert: NMSDC)

7930   Katherine Christensen & Associates, Inc.
107 S Southgate Dr
Chandler, AZ 85226
Contact: Katherine Christensen, CMP, DMCP President
Tel: 480-893-6110
Email: kc@kc-a.com
Website: www.kc-a.com
Meeting management, trade association management & public relations. (Woman, estab 1992, empl 12, sales $731,957, cert: WBENC)

7931   MakPro Services, LLC
2036 N Gentry
Mesa, AZ 85213
Contact: Teresa Makinen Principal
Tel: 480-890-1927
Email: teresa@makprosvc.com
Website: www.makprosvc.com
Public outreach, public involvement, meeting facilitation, construction partnering, organizational management & event planning services. (Woman, estab 1998, empl 5, sales $300,000, cert: State)

7932   Morrissey & Associates, LLC
P.O. Box 25967
Scottsdale, AZ 85255
Contact: Neysa Morrissey CEO
Tel: 480-515-2688
Email: admin@morrisseytravel.com
Website: www.MorrisseyTravel.com
Meeting, Event & Travel, Analysis & Cost Containment Solutions, Contract Negotiations & Risk Mitigation, Strategic Meetings Management (SMM); Program Itinerary & Agenda Development, Housing & Registration, Trade Show Management. (Woman/As-Pac, estab 2007, empl 1, sales $151,168, cert: State, WBENC, 8a)

7933   Phoenix Electronic Business Solutions, LLC
1001 E Warner Rd, Ste 102
Tempe, AZ 85284
Contact: President
Tel: 480-897-8479
Email:
Website: www.systrends.com
Promotion & marketing collateral, brochures, trade shows, website content, technical writing & specifications, requirements, user documentation, projects & plans, schedules, reports. (Woman, estab 1986, empl 5, sales $1,968,978, cert: CPUC)

7934   Squala LLC
2909 E Broadway
Phoenix, AZ 85040
Contact: Angela Lawrence Dir natl sales
Tel: 602-547-7020
Email: alawrence@sherrimayco.com
Website: www.sherrimayco.com
Brand development, graphic design, copy writing, direct marketing integrated campaigns, websites, mobile, data analytics & public relations, web, sheetfed, digital variable, large format, flexo, retail packaging & folding cartons. (Woman, estab 2010, empl 10, sales $3,550,646, cert: State)

7935   The Event Concierge
3218 E Bell Rd, Ste 142
Phoenix, AZ 85032
Contact: Julie Wong President
Tel: 602-569-5333
Email: julie@eventconcierge.com
Website: www.eventconcierge.com
Event Planning and Meeting Management. (Woman/ As-Pac, estab 2005, empl 2, sales $330,029, cert: State, City, WBENC)

California

7936 Acento Advertising, Inc.
11400 West Olympic Blvd
Los Angeles, CA 90064
Contact: Donnie Broxson CEO
Tel: 310-843-8300
Email: dbroxson@acento.com
Website: http://acento.com
Integrated marketing programs for the U.S. Hispanic & total market segments. (Hisp, estab 1983, empl 30, sales $32,067,933, cert: NMSDC, CPUC)

7937 Acme Arts Inc.
19709 Horseshoe Dr
Topanga, CA 90290
Contact: Scott Ferguson Partner
Tel: 310-455-1413
Email: scott@sferguson.com
Website: http://sferguson.com
Marketing communications services, copywriting, creative direction, strategic brand consulting, original music, complete production for educational & promotional corporate videos. (Woman/Hisp, estab 1990, empl 2, sales $234,000, cert: CPUC, WBENC)

7938 Afaf Translations, LLC
15655 Liberty St
San Leandro, CA 94578
Contact: Afaf Steiert President
Tel: 510-684-4586
Email: afaf@afaftranslations.com
Website: www.afaftranslations.com
Translation, interpreting, voice-over, desktop publishing, transcription, localization, language proficiency evaluations & cultural consultation. (Woman/AA, estab 2004, empl 2, sales , cert: WBENC)

7939 AfterViolet Inc.
1100 Glendon Ave Ste 1715
Los Angeles, CA 90024
Contact: Christopher Bodmer Innovation Consultant
Tel: 917-331-5637
Email: cab@afterviolet.com
Website: www.afterviolet.com
Innovation & branding, Product, service & experience design, Marketing & innovation strategy, Graphic design services, Consumer research. (Hisp, estab 2013, empl 6, sales $243,857, cert: NMSDC)

7940 Alter Agents
617 S Olive St, Ste 1010
Los Angeles, CA 90014
Contact: Angela Woo Co-Founder
Tel: 213-612-0356
Email: angela@alteragents.com
Website: www.alteragents.com
Market research & brand strategy, brand building, targeting, marketing strategy/development, product development, shopper insights & in-market performance. (Woman, estab 2010, empl 10, sales , cert: NWBOC)

7941 AP42
2303 Camino Ramon, Ste 280
San Ramon, CA 94583
Contact: CEO
Tel: 925-901-1100
Email:
Website: www.ap42.com
Create ads, direct marketing programs, website content, logo design, email blasts, collateral materials. (Woman/As-Pac, estab 2001, empl 7, sales $720,000, cert: WBENC)

7942 Artisan Creative Inc.
1830 Stoner Ave Ste 6
Los Angeles, CA 90025
Contact: Katty Douraghy President
Tel: 310-312-2062
Email: kattyd@artisancreative.com
Website: www.artisancreative.com
Design & development solutions: marketing, advertising, communications & production teams in the digital, broadcast, mobile & print space. (Woman, estab 1996, empl 15, sales $3,000,000, cert: WBENC)

7943 Avere Global Solutions Co.
1421 N Wanda, Ste 120
Orange, CA 92867
Contact: Ava Seavey SVP
Tel: 714-361-5200
Email: avas@avalanchecreative.tv
Website: www.avereglobal.com
Digital Marketing and Advertising, Social Marketing, Strategic Communications, Branding, Media Relations, Digital Engagement, Design and Editorial, Training and Technical Assistance, Analytics, Measurements and Effectiveness, Challenges and Competitions, (Woman/AA, estab 2003, empl 29, sales $400,000, cert: SDB)

7944 AW Distributing, Inc.
2024 Middlefield Rd
Redwood City, CA 94063
Contact: Joseph Lam Category Specialist
Tel: 408-835-4816
Email: josephlam@awdus.com
Website: www.awdus.com
Product development, market research, product sales & marketing, product design, promotion, manufacture, logistics, warehouse & IT management. (Woman/As-Pac, estab 2007, empl 20, sales $15,000,000, cert: State)

7945 Bleu Marketing Solutions
101 Lucas Valley Road Ste 300
San Rafael, CA 94903
Contact: Jennifer Giordano Acct Director
Tel: 415-345-3317
Email: jgiordano@bleusf.com
Website: www.bleumarketing.com
Direct marketing, strategy & consulting, media planning & procurement, design & creative implementation, marketing program systems & IT support. (Woman, estab 2001, empl 25, sales $2,500,000, cert: WBENC)

7946 BrandGov
125 Humphrey Lane
Vallejo, CA 94591
Contact: K Patrice Williams President
Tel: 800-215-0280
Email: supplier@brandgov.com
Website: www.brandgov.com
Brand Strategy & Lobbying, Integrated Branding & Marketing Solutions, Supplier Diversity Outreach, Website & Mobile Application Dev, Logo Dev, Brochures, Graphic Designs, Technical Procurement. (Woman/AA, estab 2007, empl 4, sales , cert: NMSDC, CPUC)

7947 Briabe Media, Inc.
634A Venice Blvd
Venice, CA 90291
Contact: James Briggs CEO
Tel: 310-694-3283
Email: james.briggs@briabemedia.com
Website: www.briabemedia.com
Multicultural mobile marketing solutions, SMS & MMS campaigns, mobile advertising & mobile website development. (AA, Hisp, estab 2006, empl 15, sales $3,000,000, cert: NMSDC)

7948 Captura Group
408 Nutmeg St
San Diego, CA 92103
Contact: Walter Boza GM
Tel: 619-681-1856
Email: diversity@capturagroup.com
Website: www.capturagroup.com/
Strategic, data-driven consulting with digital first in-language and in-culture marketing services. (Woman/Hisp, estab 2001, empl 16, sales $4,800,000, cert: NMSDC, WBENC)

7949 CCS/PR, Inc.
2888 Loker Ave East Ste 316
Carlsbad, CA 92010
Contact: Gayle Mestel President & CEO
Tel: 760-929-7514
Email: gaylem@ccspr.com
Website: www.ccspr.com/
Marketing communications/consulting products & services: case studies, magazine articles, press releases/kits, video scripts, website content, blogs, PPTs, newsletters, marketing collateral, testimonial quotes, brochures, pitches. (Woman, estab 1966, empl 6, sales $1,405,334, cert: WBENC)

7950 Chica Intelligente LLC
5757 Wilshire Blvd Penthouse 3
Los Angeles, CA 90036
Contact: Katrina Jefferson Owner
Tel: 323-360-4191
Email: katrina@chicaintelligente.com
Website: www.chicaintelligente.com
Digital marketing, enhance or develop digital marketing programs through integrated experiential Marketing, online branding & increase target audience. (Woman/AA, Hisp, estab 2013, empl 2, sales , cert: CPUC)

7951 CLC Publicidad
4528 Stern Ave
Sherman Oaks, CA 91423
Contact: Carlos Cordoba President
Tel: 818-635-7318
Email: ccordoba@sherpa-marketing.com
Website: www.sherpa-marketing.com
Consumer research & insights into the Hispanic population, qualitative & quantitative research services. (Hisp, estab 1996, empl 5, sales $1,500,000, cert: State)

7952 Coast to Coast Conferences & Events
100 W Broadway Ste 250
Long Beach, CA 90802
Contact: Michelle Manire President & CEO
Tel: 562-980-7566
Email: michelle@ctcconferences.com
Website: www.ctcconferences.com
Meeting & event management: site selection, contract negotiations, housing, on line registration, transportation, on site services, on site registration, exhibit management, event planning & destination management. (Woman, estab 1994, empl 4, sales $700,000, cert: State, WBENC)

7953 Cook & Schmid, LLC
740 13th St, Ste 502
San Diego, CA 92101
Contact: Jon Schmid President
Tel: 619-814-2370
Email: jschmid@cookandschmid.com
Website: www.cookandschmid.com
Public relations, advertising and marketing agency. (As-Pac, Hisp, estab 2006, empl 10, sales $1,006,305, cert: NMSDC, CPUC)

7954 Corporate Translations, Inc.
222 N. Pacific Coast Hwy., Ste 2000
El Segundo, CA 90245
Contact: Toni Andrews President
Tel: 310-376-1400
Email: projects@corporatetranslations.com
Website: http://CorporateTranslations.com
Provides native-speaking, technical language translation, multilingual document publishing, audio/video production & certified interpreting. (Woman, estab 1995, empl 10, sales $1,205,000, cert: State, CPUC)

7955 Cuadra Associates, Inc.
11835 W Olympic Blvd, Ste 855
Los Angeles, CA 90064
Contact: Carlos Cuadra President
Tel: 310-478-0066
Email: carlos@cuadra.com
Website: www.cuadra.com
Develop software, manage information collections, in both paper and electronic form, in libraries, museums, archives, and records departments. (Hisp, estab 1978, empl 22, sales , cert: State)

7956 Culturati Research & Consulting, Inc.
12625 High Bluff Dr, Ste 218
San Diego, CA 92130
Contact: Lisa Raggio Acct Exec
Tel:
Email: lisa.raggio@culturatiresearch.com
Website: www.CulturatiResearch.com
Market research, custom research solutions. (Woman/Hisp, estab 2004, empl 18, sales $1,000,000,000, cert: CPUC)

7957 DM Connect LLC
4223 Glencoe Ave, Ste A-130
Marina Del Rey, CA 90292
Contact: Dawn Perdew Managing Partner
Tel: 800-778-2990
Email: accounting@dumontproject.com
Website: www.thedumontproject.com
Marketing Consulting Services. (Woman, estab 2008, empl 23, sales $1,700,000, cert: WBENC)

7958 DoubleShot Creative, LLC
499 Seaport Court Ste 205
Redwood City, CA 94063
Contact: Kathy Hutton VP, Strategy
Tel: 415-992-7468
Email: kathy@doubleshotcreative.com
Website: www.doubleshotcreative.com
Creative & strategic marketing services, executive communications, marketing strategy and implementation, presentations, videos, messaging, campaign strategy, event creative concepts, social media, blogs, professional bios. (Woman, estab 2007, empl 2, sales $1,000,000, cert: WBENC)

7959 Elevate Planning
13575 Zivi Ave
Chino, CA 91710
Contact: Viviana Salvia Owner
Tel: 951-217-1028
Email: viviana@elevateplanning.com
Website: www.elevateplanning.com
Experiential marketing & event planning. (Woman, estab 2003, empl 1, sales , cert: WBENC)

7960   Everfield Consulting, LLC
2075 W 235th Pl
Torrance, CA 90501
Contact: Delbara Dorsey Partner
Tel: 310-251-7165
Email: deldorsey@everfieldconsulting.com
Website: www.everfieldconsulting.com
Marketing Consulting Services, Administrative & Management, Display Advertising, Advertising, Public Relations, Media Buying, Direct Mail Advertising, Advertising Material Distribution Services. (Woman/AA, As-Pac, estab 2011, empl 2, sales , cert: State, City, CPUC)

7961   ExpoMarketing Group LLC
2741 Dow Ave
Tustin, CA 92780
Contact: Laurie Pennacchi CEO
Tel: 949-777-1051
Email: laurie@expomarketing.com
Website: www.expomarketing.com
Trade show exhibits: custom rental & custom-built exhibits, portable exhibits & peripherals, large format graphics, program management & logistics, & in-house design & creative services. (Woman, estab 1991, empl 13, sales $2,596,339, cert: CPUC, WBENC)

7962   Freddie Georges Production Group
15362 Graham St.
Huntington Beach, CA 92649
Contact: Joe Kurzer Dir Acct Development
Tel: 714-367-9260
Email: joek@fgpg.com
Website: www.freddiegeorges.com
Trade show & special events: design, fabrication, project management, rental solutions & logistical support. (Woman, estab 2001, empl 24, sales $3,677,944, cert: WBENC)

7963   Hard Hat Communications
77386 Preston Trail
Palm Desert, CA 92211
Contact: Beverly Voran Owner
Tel: 760-772-6035
Email: hardhatcomm@verizon.net
Website:
Public affairs, group process facilitation, strategic planning, board development, fund development planning & implementation & translation services. (Woman, estab 1997, empl 1, sales , cert: State, CPUC)

7964   HispaniSpace LLC
2100 W Magnolia Blvd Ste A/B
Burbank, CA 91506
Contact: Mario X. Carrasco Partner
Tel: 818-843-0220
Email: mario@thinknowresearch.com
Website: www.thinknowresearch.com
Online market research solutions for the U.S. Hispanic consumer. (Hisp, estab 2010, empl 8, sales $1,583,661, cert: NMSDC, CPUC)

7965   Hunter-Blyden, Katherine
P.O. Box 94893
Pasadena, CA 91104
Contact: Katherine Hunter-Blyden Managing Dir
Tel: 626-344-8730
Email: khb@katherinehunterblyden.com
Website: www.khbmarketinggroup.com
Develop marketing strategies, evaluate marketing channels & tactics & define programs that align with growth profitable goals. (Woman/AA, estab 2012, empl 1, sales , cert: CPUC)

7966   Ilana Ashley Events
24226 Park Granada
Calabasas, CA 91302
Contact: Ilana Rosenberg CEO
Tel: 818-963-8670
Email: ilana@ilanaashleyevents.com
Website: http://IlanaAshleyEvents.com
Full-service event production, plan and design corporate events, gala affairs, holiday parties, soirées, weddings, and other social events. (Woman, estab 2013, empl 2, sales $108,476, cert: WBENC)

7967   Innovate Marketing Group
300 S Raymond Ave
Pasadena, CA 91105
Contact: Amanda Ma CEO
Tel: 626-817-9588
Email: amanda@innovatemkg.com
Website: www.innovatemkg.com
Experiential event & production agency, product launch, conferences, meetings, sponsorship activations, award & galas. (Woman/As-Pac, estab 2014, empl 3, sales , cert: NMSDC, CPUC, WBENC)

7968   JR Resources
1130 Camino Del Mar Ste H
Del Mar, CA 92014
Contact: Waren Katz Acct Exec
Tel: 858-481-1074
Email: warren@jrresources.com
Website: www.jrresources.com
Promotional products & marketing services. (Woman, estab 1991, empl 10, sales $4,151,500, cert: CPUC, WBENC)

7969   Language Select, LLC.
7590 N Glenoaks Blvd, Ste 100
Los Angeles, CA 91504
Contact: Paolo Santa
Tel: 818-394-3407
Email: psantamaria@languageselect.com
Website: www.languageselect.com
Simultaneous & consecutive interpreting services. (As-Pac, Hisp, estab , empl , sales $11,700,000, cert: NMSDC)

7970   Latin Nation Live LLC
3245 N San Fernando Rd
Los Angeles, CA 90065
Contact: Ricardo Gieseken President
Tel: 213-924-5683
Email: ricardo@lnlagency.com
Website: www.lnlagency.com
Experiential Marketing, Diversity Marketing, Tastemaker/influencer marketing, Event production, Government affairs/tradeshows, Asset design & procurement, Brand Strategy, Brand Development, Shopper Marketing. (Hisp, estab 2008, empl 10, sales $1,000,000, cert: NMSDC)

7971   Liehr Marketing & Communications, Inc.
1899 Western Way Ste 400A
Torrance, CA 90501
Contact: Elisa Liehr President
Tel: 310-781-3727
Email: eliehr@lmconline.net
Website: www.lmconline.net
Marketing & research, copywriting, design, interactive, video, web development, design & programing. (Woman, estab 1987, empl 6, sales $780,000, cert: WBENC)

7972   Lightbox Libraries
320 Hedge Rd
Menlo Park, CA 94025
Contact: Cindy Lee Founder
Tel: 650-298-4759
Email: cindy.lee@lightboxlibraries.com
Website: www.lightboxlibraries.com
Lightbox Libraries is a custom photography and video production company. We specialize in producing On-Brand image libraries for all your Marcom materials, shooting both domestic and internationally. (Woman/As-Pac, estab 2011, empl 2, sales $1,954,051, cert: NMSDC)

7973   Livings Life Science Solutions, LLC
3446 Glen Ave
Carlsbad, CA 92010
Contact: Owner
Tel: 747-777-2226
Email:
Website: http://livingslifesciencesolutions.com
Strategic marketing, strategic business consulting, scientific & commercial planning, marketing operations & tactical execution. (Woman/AA, estab 2015, empl , sales $600,000, cert: NMSDC, WBENC, NWBOC)

7974   Luth Research
1365 4th Ave
San Diego, CA 92101
Contact: Candice Hinds assoc Dir business dev
Tel: 619-234-5884
Email: chinds@luthresearch.com
Website: www.luthresearch.com
Market research, enhanced data & data collection solutions, qualitative & quantitative research methodologies. (Woman, estab 1977, empl 90, sales , cert: WBENC)

7975   Marketing Maven Public Relations, Inc.
2390 C Las Posas Rd, Ste 479
Camarillo, CA 93010
Contact: John Carnett Dir Business Devel
Tel: 310-994-7380
Email: john@marketingmavenpr.com
Website: www.marketingmavenpr.com
Public Relations, Hispanic Marketing, Social Media Management, Digital Advertising, Deep Dive Research, Brand Analysis, Graphic Design, Media Traning, Clip Tracking, Event Execution. (Woman/Nat Ame, estab 2009, empl 13, sales $1,259,534, cert: State, CPUC, WBENC, 8a)

7976   Meeting Planners Plus
3069 Taylor Way
Costa Mesa, CA 92626
Contact: Rosa McArthur President
Tel: 714-668-1126
Email: rlmcarthur@meetingplannersplus.com
Website: www.meetingplannersplus.com
Meeting & special event management; tradeshow production, seminars, conferences, retreats, board meetings. (Woman/AA, estab 1993, empl 1, sales , cert: CPUC)

7977   Meijun LLC
9888 Carroll Centre Rd Ste#210
San Diego, CA 92126
Contact: Huy Ly
Tel: 619-333-8698
Email: hly@meijun.cc
Website: http://meijun.cc
Web development & marketing agency, custom software solutions, web & mobile development, design & strategy, digital marketing services, SEO, content marketing & marketing automation integration. (As-Pac, estab 2011, empl 5, sales , cert: NMSDC, CPUC)

7978   Multi-Cultural Convention Services Network (MCCSN)
212 Sweetwood St
San Diego, CA 92114
Contact: Clara Carter CEO
Tel: 619-265-2561
Email: info@mccsn.com
Website: https://mccsn.com
Meeting & event management, hotel sourcing & contract negotiations & business consulting services. (Woman/AA, estab 2004, empl 1, sales , cert: CPUC)

7979   Netpace Inc.
5000 Executive Pkwy, Ste 530
San Ramon, CA 94583
Contact: Omar Khan President
Tel: 925-543-7760
Email: rfp@netpace.com
Website: www.netpace.com
Lead generation and brand awareness, web development and design practices. (As-Ind, estab 1996, empl 120, sales $22,771,314, cert: NMSDC)

7980   Outward Media, Inc.
9229 Sunset Blvd, Ste 410
Los Angeles, CA 90069
Contact: Paula Chiocchi President
Tel: 310-274-5312
Email: paula@outwardmedia.com
Website: www.outwardmedia.com
Email marketing; creative design, deployment, statistical reporting & campaign management. (Woman, estab 1998, empl 8, sales $5,000,000, cert: WBENC)

7981   Parle Enterprises, Inc.
800 Airport Blvd, Ste 21
Burlingame, CA 94010
Contact: Mary Shulenberger CEO
Tel: 415-467-3100
Email: mary@parle.com
Website: www.parle.com
Media, marketing sponsorships, advertising, oppportunity programs, promotional marketing. (Woman/Hisp, estab 1997, empl 8, sales $1,400,000, cert: NMSDC, CPUC)

7982   PLAN C Agency
120 E 8th St Ste 912
Los Angeles, CA 90014
Contact: Giancarlo Pacheco President
Tel: 310-492-5298
Email: giancarlo@plancagency.com
Website: www.plancagency.com
Multicultural marketing & public relations agency with expertise reaching Asian American Market. (As-Pac, estab 2003, empl 15, sales $2,000,000, cert: State)

7983   ProExhibits
48571 Milmont Dr
Fremont, CA 94538
Contact: Acct Exec
Tel: 916-364-9013
Email: msanzone@proexhibits.com
Website: www.proexhibits.com
Trade show exhibit & events. (Woman, estab 1987, empl 40, sales $1,040,000, cert: CPUC)

7984   Purpose Generation LLC
       535 Mission St 14th Fl
       San Francisco, CA 94105
       Contact: Nellie Morris Co-Founder
       Tel: 917-243-4777
       Email: nellie@purposegeneration.com
       Website: www.purposegeneration.com/
Millennial marketing, market research, millennials, gen Y,
project management, consulting, strategy, consumer
insights, quantitative research, product sampling, product
co-creation, quantitative research, influencer strategy.
(Woman, estab 2013, empl 4, sales $758,280, cert:
WBENC, NWBOC)

7985   RED Company
       10323 Los Alamitos Blvd
       Long Beach, CA 90720
       Contact: President
       Tel: 562-498-1270
       Email:
       Website: www.redcompany.com
Meeting & event planning: site review, contract negotiation, vendor relations, sponsorship cultivation to onsite
management, ground transportation, registration services,
staffing, hotel block/rooming lists, hospitality, activities.
(Woman, estab 2007, empl 22, sales $11,600,000, cert:
WBENC)

7986   Red Kite Business Advisors LLC
       3525 Del Mar Heights Rd, Ste 202
       San Diego, CA 92130
       Contact: Principal
       Tel: 858-232-4555
       Email:
       Website: www.redkitesite.com
Marketing, advertising, public speaking, seminars, workshops, strategic planning, brand assessment & development, integrated campaign strategies, media plan development, online & traditional marketing. (Woman/As-Pac,
estab 2007, empl 1, sales , cert: CPUC, WBENC)

7987   RevOne Design, Inc.
       1649B Adrian Rd
       Burlingame, CA 94010
       Contact: Sean Carlin Dir Business Dev
       Tel: 650-468-2996
       Email: sean@revonedesign.com
       Website: http://revonedesign.com
Graphic & Production Design, Photography & Photo
Retouching, Digital/Web & Print Communications, Creative
Concepting & Campaign Design & Copywriting. (Woman/
Hisp, estab 2011, empl 7, sales $300,000, cert: NMSDC,
WBENC)

7988   RMD Group Inc.
       2311 E South St
       Long Beach, CA 90805
       Contact: Laura Milanes COO
       Tel: 562-866-9288
       Email: laura@rmdgroupinc.com
       Website: www.rmdgroupinc.com
Experiential Marketing, Digital & Social Media, Large
Format Graphic Printing, Vehicle Fabrication, Trade Show
Design, Trade Show Booth Builder, Millwork, Data Collec-
tion. (Hisp, estab 1993, empl 25, sales $6,000,000, cert:
NMSDC)

7989   Ruiz Strategies
       1900 Ave of the Stars Ste 1800
       Los Angeles, CA 90067
       Contact: Michele Ruiz President & CEO
       Tel: 310-853-3605
       Email: inquiries@ruizstrategies.com
       Website: www.RuizStrategies.com
Develop & execute transformational content messaging
strategies, social media, new media, traditional media &
virtual technologies. (Woman/Hisp, estab 2011, empl
12, sales $1,036,000, cert: NMSDC, CPUC, WBENC)

7990   Samantha Smith Productions LLC
       2325 Third St Ste 407
       San Francisco, CA 94107
       Contact: Samantha Smith Owner
       Tel: 415-626-7925
       Email:
       samantha@samanthasmithproductions.com
       Website: www.samanthasmithproductions.com
Meeting & event planning. (Woman, estab 2003, empl 5,
sales $1,500,000, cert: WBENC)

7991   Sax Productions Inc.
       1055 W 7th St 33rd Fl PH
       Los Angeles, CA 90017
       Contact: Tamara Keller COO
       Tel: 213-232-1682
       Email: tamara@saxproductions.com
       Website: www.saxproductions.com
Brand marketing & storytelling, digital strategy, innovation & public relation. (Woman/AA, estab 2012, empl 6,
sales , cert: NMSDC, WBENC)

7992   Shiloh Event Management
       P.O. Box 2772
       Santa Clara, CA 95050
       Contact: Huong Burrow Dir of Events
       Tel: 408-899-5464
       Email: huong@shiloh-events.com
       Website: www.shiloh-events.com
Event strategies, event production, event marketing
solutions & event management services. (As-Pac, estab
2013, empl 3, sales , cert: NMSDC)

7993   Specialized Marketing Services, Inc.
       3421 W Segerstrom Ave
       Santa Ana, CA 92704
       Contact: John Snook Exec VP
       Tel: 714-955-5450
       Email: jsnook@teamsms.com
       Website: www.teamsms.com
Strategic marketing devel, copywriting, print mgmt,
database mgmt/processing, mailing svcs, warehousing,
fulfillment/hand assembly, internet application,
telemarketing.
 (Woman/Hisp, estab 1988, empl 23, sales $8,161,000,
cert: WBENC)

7994   Strategic Business Communications
       12175 Dearborn Pl
       Poway, CA 92064
       Contact: Jim Hernandez President
       Tel: 858-679-1805
       Email: jhernandez@sbcinc.com
       Website: www.sbcinc.info
Sales & Marketing Training & Consulting, Meeting &
Event Planning. (As-Pac, estab 1987, empl 10, sales
$2,400,000, cert: NMSDC)

7995 Strive Well-Being, Inc.
5920 Friars Rd, Ste 103
San Diego, CA 92108
Contact: Amit Sangani President
Tel: 619-684-5700
Email: reg@strive2bfit.com
Website: www.strive2bfit.com
Onsite Physical Activity Classes, Onsite Stress Management Classes, Musculoskeletal Strengthening Classes, Fitness Center Staffing & Management, Fitness & Wellness Program Management, Fitness Facility Design & Development. (As-Ind, estab 2008, empl 40, sales $1,500,000, cert: City, NMSDC, 8a)

7996 Sundial Marketing Research, Inc.
30 Center St
San Rafael, CA 94901
Contact: Nancy Kelber President
Tel: 415-200-1461
Email: nancy@sundialresearch.com
Website: http://sundialresearch.com
Market research to the medical device, pharmaceutical & biotechnology industries. (Woman, estab 2010, empl 6, sales $2,500,000, cert: WBENC)

7997 Undisclosed Location, Inc
5761 Sonoma Mountain Rd
Santa Rosa, CA 95404
Contact: Barbara Gorder President
Tel: 415-295-4920
Email: barbara.gorder@unlo.com
Website: www.unlo.com
Marketing, advertising & communications solutions, strategic brand advertising, mobile marketing consulting & content development, website development, packaging design, presentation consulting & event promotions. (Woman, estab 2003, empl 10, sales $1,000,000, cert: WBENC)

7998 Valencia, Perez & Echeveste
1605 Hope St, Ste 250
South Pasadena, CA 91030
Contact: Patricia Perez President
Tel: 626-403-3200
Email: patricia@vpepr.com
Website: www.vpepr.com
Public relations & marketing communications. (Hisp, estab 1987, empl 25, sales , cert: NMSDC)

7999 Vic Salazar Enterprises, LLC
2514 Jamacha Rd, Ste 502-21
El Cajon, CA 92019
Contact: Vic Salazar President
Tel: 619-517-4744
Email: vicsalazar@cox.net
Website: www.vicsalazar.com
Public Relations, Hispanic Marketing, Video Production, Media Training, Advertising, Crisis Communications, Hard Drive Storage, Printing, Labeling, Promotional Items, Event Production. (Hisp, estab 2008, empl 1, sales , cert: CPUC)

Colorado

8000 Egg Strategy, Inc.
1360 Walnut St Ste 102
Boulder, CO 80302
Contact: Matthew Sommers Dir of Operations
Tel: 303-546-9311
Email: boulderinfo@eggstrategy.com
Website: www.eggstrategy.com
Marketing consulting, innovation, brand strategy, market research, consumer insight. (Woman, estab 2005, empl 50, sales $10,000,000, cert: WBENC)

8001 MorSports & Events, Inc.
3333 S Bannock St Ste 790
Englewood, CO 80110
Contact: Betsy Mordecai President
Tel: 720-381-5000
Email: betsy@morevents.com
Website: www.morevents.com
Event planning, meeting coordination & hospitality mgmt. (Woman, estab 1996, empl 12, sales $4,000,000, cert: WBENC)

8002 Translation Excellence
2620 S Parker Rd Ste 210
Aurora, CO 80014
Contact: Nisar Nikzad President
Tel: 720-325-0459
Email: info@translationexcellence.com
Website: http://translationexcellence.com
Translation, interpretation, interpretation equipment & language classes. (As-Ind, estab 2010, empl 5, sales $422,000, cert: City, 8a)

8003 Vladimir Jones
P.O. Box 387
Colorado Springs, CO 80901
Contact: Trudy Rowe CFO
Tel: 719-473-0704
Email: trowe@vladimirjones.com
Website: www.vladimirjones.com
Marketing services: strategic planning, research, advertising & public relations, creative development & production, television, print, radio, out of home, digital & on-line communications, media planning & buying, account planning. (Woman, estab 1970, empl 71, sales $21,863,320, cert: NWBOC)

Connecticut

8004 Adams & Knight, Inc.
80 Avon Meadow Lane
Avon, CT 06001
Contact: SVP Financial Services
Tel: 860-676-2300
Email:
Website: www.adamsknight.com
Integrated marketing: research, strategy, brand development, advertising, design, collateral development, public relations, social media, experiential, event marketing, digital experiences including websites & interactive tools, SEO/SEM. (Minority, Woman, estab 1987, empl 39, sales $8,547,385, cert: State)

8005 BCM Media
30 Old Kings Highway S
Darien, CT 06820
Contact: Managing Dir
Tel: 203-326-1477
Email:
Website: www.bcmmedia.biz/
Advertising, Media Consulting, Media Planning, Negotiations, B2B Advertising, B2C Advertising, Trade Advertising, Multimedia Planning and Buying, Global Media Planning, National Media Planning, Local Media Planning, Public Relations. (Woman, estab 2013, empl 9, sales $855,047, cert: WBENC)

8006　CYMA Systems Inc.
360 Tolland Turnpike Ste 2D
Manchester, CT 06042
Contact: Nisha Sunil HR Mgr
Tel:　860-791-6356
Email: hr@cymasys.com
Website: www.cymasys.com
CYMA Systems Inc. is a professional staffing and solutions firm headquartered in the Greater Hartford Area, CT. We provide customers with leading edge technology solutions and augment their IT staff needs. (As-Ind, estab 2006, empl 179, sales $16,800,000, cert: NMSDC)

8007　Domo Domo IMG
28 Castle Meadow Road
Newtown, CT 06470
Contact: Deb Adams CEO
Tel:　203-270-3515
Email: judy@domomarketing.com
Website: www.domomarketing.com
Brand strategy & optimization, strategic positioning, new product launches, line extensions, NPD innovation, trend & market analyses. (Woman, estab 1997, empl 10, sales $845,000, cert: WBENC)

8008　Peralta Illustration & Design LLC
431 Howe Ave
Shelton, CT 06484
Contact: Ramon Peralta
Tel:　203-513-2222
Email: ramon@peraltadesign.com
Website: www.peraltadesign.com
Digital interactive design: web development, web applications, corporate identity & marketing, branding. (Hisp, estab 2003, empl 6, sales , cert: NMSDC)

8009　Touchpoint Integrated Communications, LLC
16 Thorndal Circle
Darien, CT 06820
Contact: Karen Kluger CEO
Tel:　203-665-7705
Email: kkluger@tpointmedia.com
Website: www.tpointmedia.com
Communication: broadcast, print, digital, social, mobile, email, direct mail, out of home & alternative. (Woman, estab 2010, empl 40, sales $9,591,292, cert: WBENC)

8010　TruEvents LLC
P.O. Box 893
Madison, CT 06443
Contact: CEO
Tel:　203-980-3495
Email:
Website: www.be-tru.com
Marketing, Graphic Design, Creative Design, Web, Retail Packaging, Retail Strategy, Digital, Digital Store Displays, Retail POS, Merchandising,
Tradeshows, Meeting Production, Event Production, Ideation, Strategy. (Woman, estab 2000, empl 4, sales $2,082,729, cert: WBENC)

District of Columbia

8011　Delucchi Plus
2101 L St. NW
Washington, DC 20037
Contact: VP
Tel:　202-349-4000
Email:
Website: www.delucchiplus.com/
Global strategic communications, research & brand strategy, digital marketing & public relations. (Woman, estab 2007, empl 41, sales $11,200,000, cert: State)

8012　JPA Health Communications
1101 Connecticut Ave NW Ste 600
Washington, DC 20036
Contact: Carrie Jones Principal
Tel:　202-591-4000
Email: carrie@jpa.com
Website: www.jpa.com
Public Relations, Health Communications, Influencer Relations (Media relations, advocacy engagement, social & digital media, policy & issues advocacy, stakeholder engagement). (Woman, estab 2007, empl 21, sales $7,700,000, cert: NWBOC)

8013　OmniStudio, Inc.
1140 19th St NW, Ste 320
Washington, DC 20036
Contact: President
Tel:　202-785-9605
Email:
Website: www.omnistudio.com
Corporate & product identity, publications & periodicals, annual reports, collateral material, advertisements & direct mail, exhibits & trade show support, conference & meeting packages, directories & data publishing. (Woman, estab 1980, empl 14, sales $1,890,025, cert: WBENC)

8014　P.A.L.S. LLC
1808 I St NW
Washington, DC 20006
Contact: Richette Haywood Managing Member
Tel:　202-396-7257
Email: richettehaywood@palsllc.biz
Website: www.palsllc.biz
Marketing & public relations, event management, administration support, concierge. (Woman/AA, estab 1995, empl 3, sales $350,000, cert: State)

8015　Premier Consultants International, Inc.
1020 16th St NW Ste 201
Washington, DC 20036
Contact: Renard H. Marable
Tel:　202-319-1211
Email: rmarable@premiercon.com
Website: www.premiercon.com
Marketing & business development services. (AA, estab 2000, empl 1, sales , cert: State, City)

8016　Scott Circle Communications, Inc.
1900 L St, NW Ste 705
Washington, DC 20036
Contact: Laura Gross Principal
Tel:　202-695-8225
Email: lgross@scottcircle.com
Website: www.scottcircle.com
Public relations & event-planning. (Woman, estab 2006, empl 11, sales $974,635, cert: WBENC)

8017　SEW, Inc.
717 D St NW Ste 300
Washington, DC 20004
Contact: Thedis Miller CEO
Tel:　202-403-4739
Email: tmiller@4sew.com
Website: www.4sew.com
Human capital mgmt svcs, customer relationship mgmt (CRM) & [roject mgmt (PMP), large team operations support, business planning, executive coaching, administrative support. (Woman/AA, estab 2004, empl 1, sales $104,000, cert: NMSDC)

8018   Swanson Communications
       1025 Vermont Ave NW Ste 1005
       Washington, DC 20005
       Contact: Kelly Swanson President
       Tel: 202-783-5500
       Email: kswanson@swansonpr.com
       Website: http://swansonpr.com
Marketing & public relations, business development,
communications outreach & relationship building.
(Woman, estab 2006, empl 3, sales $372,849, cert: State)

8019   Washingtonian Custom Media
       1828 L St NW, Ste 200
       Washington, DC 20036
       Contact: James Byles President
       Tel: 202-862-3500
       Email: jbyles@washingtonian.com
       Website: www.washingtoniancustommedia.com
Communications strategy, print & digital publications,
magazines, brochures, white papers, annual reports,
content development, content strategy, audience development, writing, editing, website design, graphic design,
website development. (Woman, estab 1965, empl 80, sales
$10,000,000, cert: WBENC)

Delaware

8020   Barron Marketing Communications
       833 Washington St
       Wilmington, DE 19801
       Contact: Patricia D. Barron President
       Tel: 302-658-1627
       Email: pbarron@barronmarketing.com
       Website: www.barronmarketing.com
Mktg print communications: direct mail, catalogs, displays,
premiums, POS, broadcast, packaging, media, outdoor.
(Minority, Woman, estab 1976, empl 9, sales $1,000,000,
cert: State)

Florida

8021   A-Plus Meetings and Incentives
       901 Ponce de Leon Blvd. Ste 600
       Coral Gables, FL 33134
       Contact: Jay Klein COO
       Tel: 786-888-3203
       Email: jklein@aplusmeetings.com
       Website: www.aplusmeetings.com
Meeting planning, online registration, venue selection,
audio-visual management, production development,
airline travel, ground transportation & hospitality desk
staffing. (Woman, estab 1993, empl 21, sales $10,382,504,
cert: CPUC, WBENC)

8022   Avenue Event Group LLC
       501 N Orlando Ave Ste 313-312 Orlando, FL 32789
       Orlando, FL 32801
       Contact: Sean Hughes Marketing
       Tel: 650-784-0175
       Email: sean@avenueeventgroup.com
       Website: http://avenueeventgroup.com
National event planning & logistics services: Venue
Selection, Meeting Logistics, Hotel Coordination, Group
Transportation, Vendor Procurement, Unique Entertain-
ment. (Woman, estab 2013, empl 5, sales $1,300,000, cert:
WBENC)

8023   Chasm Communications, Inc.
       13045 W Linebaugh Ave Ste 101
       Tampa, FL 33626
       Contact: Jennifer Williams President
       Tel: 813-283-0908
       Email: jwilliams@chasmcommunications.com
       Website: www.chasmcommunications.com
Marketing & web design, app design, digital marketing &
traditional print marketing. (Woman, estab 2006, empl
7, sales $845,317, cert: WBENC)

8024   Clarocision Research & Marketing
       2818 N University Dr
       Coral Springs, FL 33065
       Contact: Karlene Facey CEO
       Tel: 954-741-2234
       Email: kfacey@crmfirm.com
       Website: www.crmmfrm.com
Focus Groups & Surveys, diverse consumer & healthcare
panels, research tools & processes, fully-equipped
facilities, Taste testing. (Woman/AA, estab 2007, empl
30, sales $1,000,000, cert: State)

8025   Cordova Marketing Group
       2702 Wright Ave
       Winter Park, FL 32789
       Contact: Tom Cordova President
       Tel: 321-972-8181
       Email: tom@covacova.com
       Website: www.covacova.com
Multi-culutral Marketing, Sponsorship, Broadcasting,
Naming Rights, Events, Ticket Sales, Community Outreach, Executive Recruitment. (Hisp, estab 1998, empl 2,
sales $375,000, cert: NMSDC)

8026   Creative Zing Promotion Group
       189 S Orange Ave Ste 1130a
       Orlando, FL 32801
       Contact: Pamela D Aniello President
       Tel: 407-514-0044
       Email: pamela@creativezing.com
       Website: www.creativezing.com
Integrated marketing & promotions, complex contest &
sweepstakes administration. (Woman, estab 2007, empl
9, sales $1,300,000, cert: WBENC)

8027   Detail Planners, LLC
       1452 Distant Oaks Dr
       Wesley Chapel, FL 33543
       Contact: President
       Tel: 813-991-1348
       Email:
       Website: www.detailplanners.com
Plan & manage corporate meetings & events. (Woman,
estab 2004, empl 5, sales $1,900,000, cert: WBENC)

8028   Diper Designers LLC
       7306 Exchange Dr
       Orlando, FL 32809
       Contact: Ricardo Contreras Business Developer
       Tel: 407-208-2226
       Email: rcontreras@diper.com
       Website: www.diper.com
Designing & build customized exhibit displays; booths,
pavilions, corporate events, retail stores, kiosks, among
others. (Hisp, estab 1999, empl 19, sales $516,352, cert:
City)

8029 EuroAmerican IP, LLC
2511 NW 16th Lane
Pompano Beach, FL 33064
Contact: Tami Dana Mgr of Operations
Tel: 866-972-6467
Email: tami@euroamericanproducts.com
Website: www.EuroAmericanProducts.com
Manufacturers Reps/Distribution based business that provides various industries and government facilities with our unique line of products within the medical, outdoor and health & beauty arenas. (Woman, estab 2007, empl 15, sales $500,000, cert: State)

8030 Executive Meeting Management, Inc.
6996 Piazza Grande Ave Ste 314
Orlando, FL 32835
Contact: Heather Wilson President
Tel: 407-399-7681
Email: hwilson@execmm.com
Website: www.execmm.com
Meeting management. (Woman, estab 2004, empl , sales $1,026,779, cert: WBENC)

8031 Fortes Laboratories
1005 W Busch Blvd Ste 101
Tampa, FL 33612
Contact: Steven Seigel CFO
Tel: 813-390-6536
Email: info@forteslabs.com
Website: www.forteslabs.com
Drug testing, national forensic, toxicology laboratory, drug & alcohol testing. (Woman, estab 1994, empl 15, sales , cert: State)

8032 Fusion Communications, Inc.
8725 NW 18 Terrace, Ste 103
Miami, FL 33172
Contact: Annabel Beyra Partner
Tel: 786-574-2330
Email: annabel@fusioncomminc.com
Website: http://fusioncomminc.com
Public relations agency. (Woman/Hisp, estab 2006, empl 5, sales $1,279,242, cert: NMSDC)

8033 HAS Art Solutions LLC
3139 Philips Hwy, Ste 100
Jacksonville, FL 32207
Contact: Heather Sams President
Tel: 904-503-9800
Email: hasams@hasartsolutions.com
Website: www.HASartsolutions.com
We are an art consulting, art design, and procurement firm with over 25 years of experience in providing clients with solutions to their aesthetic needs. We provide artwork and artwork programs to all types of businesses, from interior design (Woman, estab 2010, empl 7, sales $355,000, cert: State)

8034 HMB Enterprises LLC
5401 S Kirkman Rd, Ste 310
Orlando, FL 32819
Contact: Harry Bailey President
Tel: 678-887-7670
Email: hbailey@hmbenterprises.net
Website: www.hmbenterprises.net
Healthcare Risk Management System (HRMS) Airborne Pathogen Elimination system (KIlls MRCR, Staph and many other airborne pathogens under 3 microns) Purlalizer(KIlls MRCR, Staph (AA, estab 2005, empl 5, sales $425,000, cert: State, NMSDC)

8035 Imagine Enterprises International
8600 Commodity Circle, Ste 109
Orlando, FL 32819
Contact: Heidi Brumbach CEO
Tel: 407-409-7310
Email: heidi@technischcreative.com
Website: http://technischcreative.com
Event Planning & Production, Venue Research & Selection, Venue Negotiation & Contracting, Room Block Management, Speaker Selection, Event Marketing, Food & Beverage Management, Event Registration, Audio Visual. (Woman, estab 1999, empl 4, sales , cert: WBENC)

8036 Ingenium Research Boutique, Inc.
8057 Solitaire Ct
Orlando, FL 32836
Contact: Maria Parra President
Tel: 407-309-2742
Email: mlparra@ingeniumresearch.com
Website: www.ingeniumresearch.com
Qualitative marketing research, focus groups, ethnographic interviews, in-depth interviews, shop-alongs, qualitative techniques. (Woman/Hisp, estab 2011, empl 2, sales $500,000, cert: WBENC)

8037 Inktel Direct
13975 NW 58th Ct
Miami Lakes, FL 33014
Contact: Jason Schlenker VP Business Devel
Tel: 305-523-1129
Email: jason.schlenker@inktel.com
Website: www.inktel.com
Direct marketing: call center, fulfillment, direct mail, database marketing. (Hisp, estab 1997, empl 580, sales , cert: NMSDC)

8038 JCQ Services, Inc
7200 Lake Ellenor Dr, Ste 130
Orlando, FL 32809
Contact: Eliana Fuguet Project Coord
Tel: 407-889-4944
Email: eliana@jcqservices.com
Website: www.jcqservices.com
We are a complete renovation subcontractor, from flooring to ceiling and moving, storage and transportation and selective demolition (Hisp, estab 2000, empl 25, sales $1,550,000, cert: State)

8039 Lingua Franca Translations, LLC
1111 Brickell Ave Ste 1140
Miami, FL 33156
Contact: Marcela Arbelaez CEO
Tel: 305-913-7193
Email: marcela.arbelaez@lftranslations.com
Website: www.lftranslations.com
Translations, interpretations & transcriptions into and from over 240 languages. (Woman/Hisp, estab 2011, empl 3, sales $138,000, cert: NMSDC)

8040 M. Gill & Associates, Inc.
4770 Biscayne Blvd, Ste 1050
Miami, FL 33137
Contact: Marie Gill CEO
Tel: 305-576-7888
Email: info@mgillonline.com
Website: www.mgillonline.com
Management & public relations consulting. (Woman/AA, estab 1990, empl 10, sales , cert: State)

8041 Media Global Group, LLC
2000 Ponce de Leon Blvd
Coral Gables, FL 33134
Contact: Maria Gonzalez-Pacheco CEO
Tel: 786-431-4555
Email: mgonzalez@mggmedia.com
Website: www.mggmedia.com
Digital Media Outlets & Out-of-Home (OOH), TV, Radio &
Print Media. (Woman/Hisp, estab 2008, empl 10, sales
$3,600,000, cert: NMSDC)

8042 Nobles Research, Inc.
8321 Golden Prairie Dr
Tampa, FL 33647
Contact: Kevin Nobles President
Tel: 813-977-7700
Email: kevin@noblesresearch.com
Website: www.noblesresearch.com
Qualitative research. (AA, estab 2001, empl 1, sales
$270,000, cert: NMSDC)

8043 Orlando Conference Management Group, Inc.
13124 Sunkiss Loop
Windermere, FL 34786
Contact: Lori Lombardi Ryan President
Tel: 407-948-5706
Email: llr@ocmg.net
Website: www.ocmg.net
Meeting management, logistics & events planning.
(Woman, estab 1993, empl 2, sales , cert: State, WBENC)

8044 Paragon Events, Inc.
352 NE 3rd Ave
Delray Beach, FL 33444
Contact: Renee Radabaugh CEO
Tel: 561-243-3073
Email: info@paragon-events.com
Website: www.paragon-events.com
Meeting & special events. (Woman, estab 1989, empl 12,
sales $5,514,280, cert: WBENC)

8045 Prestige Auto Specialists
4250 St. Charles Way
Boca Raton, FL 33434
Contact: Marcello Serrato President
Tel: 954-428-6689
Email: mserrato@prestigeautous.com
Website: www.prestigeautous.com
Event production, media fleet management, marketing &
communication. (Hisp, estab 1985, empl 30, sales
$52,000,000, cert: NMSDC)

8046 Quest Corporation of America
17220 Camelot Court
Land O'Lakes, FL 34638
Contact: Sharlene Francois President
Tel: 813-926-2942
Email: corporate@usa.com.com
Website: www.QCAusa.com
Public relations, partnering, marketing, creative services,
media, publications, printing, aerial photography, advertis-
ing, technology support, web design & data storage,
transportation support svcs. (Woman, estab 1995, empl
14, sales $3,075,300, cert: State)

8047 RBB Public Relations LLC
355 Alhambra Cir Ste 800
Coral Gables, FL 33134
Contact: Marsha Rhymer Controller
Tel: 305-448-7450
Email: marsha.rhymer@rbbpr.com
Website: www.rbbpr.com
Marketing, Public Relations. (Woman, estab 2001, empl
81, sales $6,401,984, cert: WBENC)

8048 Republica, LLC
2153 Coral Way 5th Fl
Miami, FL 33145
Contact: Jorge A. Plasencia CEO
Tel: 786-347-4700
Email: jp@republica.net
Website: www.republica.net
Branding, advertising, promotions, digital and communi-
cations company. (Hisp, estab 2006, empl 100, sales
$14,500,000, cert: State, NMSDC)

8049 ROUGE 24, Inc.
5279 Grande Palm Cir
Delray Beach, FL 33484
Contact: Todd Victor Dir of Accts
Tel: 561-213-0260
Email: todd.victor@rouge24.com
Website: www.rouge24.com
Brand Strategy, Identity Design, Packaging, Style Guides,
Adaptation, Process Management, Marketing Materials,
In-Store Signage. (Woman, estab 2009, empl , sales
$2,500,000, cert: WBENC)

8050 SFM Services, Inc.
9700 NW 79th Ave
Hialeah Gardens, FL 33016
Contact: Christian Infante VP
Tel: 305-818-2424
Email: cinfante@sfmservices.com
Website: www.sfmservices.com
Complete janitorial services, landscape services, and
security guard services. (Hisp, estab 1987, empl 480,
sales $12,000,000, cert: NMSDC)

8051 Trickey Jennus, Inc.
5300 W Cypress St Ste 285
Tampa, FL 33607
Contact: Kathie Craft Comella COO
Tel: 813-831-2325
Email: kathie@trickeyjennus.com
Website: www.trickeyjennus.com
Strategy review & rational, collaborative account
planning, strategic media planning, specialized direct
marketing, campaign development, web services, social
media strategy, creative services. (Woman, estab 2005,
empl 7, sales $1,015,266, cert: State)

8052 Vistra Communications, LLC
18315 N US Highway 41
Lutz, FL 33549
Contact: BRIAN A. BUTLER President & CEO
Tel: 813-961-4700
Email: brian@consultvistra.com
Website: www.ConsultVistra.com
Public relations, strategic communications, homeland
security, information technology, management consult-
ing, training & curriculum development. (AA, estab
2007, empl 101, sales $21,863,345, cert: City, NMSDC,
8a)

8053 Wragg & Casas Public Relations, Inc.
1221 Brickell Ave Ste 730
Miami, FL 33131
Contact: Ramon Casas President
Tel: 305-372-1234
Email: rcasas@wraggcasas.com
Website: www.wraggcasas.com
Strategic counseling, media relations, reputation & crisis
management, brand visibility & public affairs. (Hisp,
estab 1991, empl 8, sales $1,200,000, cert: NMSDC)

Georgia

8054 Benchmarc360, Inc.
6340 Sugarloaf Pkwy Ste 200
Atlanta, GA 30097
Contact: CEO
Tel: 678-291-0011
Email:
Website: www.benchmarc360.com
Strategic solutions, strategic event marketing, conference, meeting & event mgmt, destination mgmt, trade shows, incentive programs, site selection & contract negotiations. (Woman, estab , empl , sales $32,800,000, cert: NWBOC)

8055 CKSports and Associates LLC
3655 Altama Ave
Brunswick, GA 31520
Contact: Charles Loving CEO
Tel: 912-547-7504
Email: charles@cksportsandassociates.com
Website: www.cksportsandassociates.com
Football Helmet Shaped Cooler-Carrier on Wheels, Baseball Cap and Player Head Cooler-Carrier on Wheels, Football Helmet Grill, Baseball Helmet Grill, Racecar Grill. (AA, estab 2016, empl 6, sales , cert: NMSDC)

8056 CMT Agency
1417 Dutch Valley Place Ste A
Atlanta, GA 30324
Contact: Shelly Justice CEO
Tel: 404-233-4644
Email: sjustice@cmtagency.com
Website: www.cmtagency.com
Spokesmodels, event staffing, brand ambassadors, product demonstrators, celebrity look-a-likes & corporate present-ers. (Woman, estab 2001, empl 11, sales $2,119,677, cert: WBENC)

8057 Colour One O One, Inc.
4995 Avalon Ridge Pkwy Ste 100
Norcross, GA 30071
Contact: Taylor Lepera Sales Assoc
Tel: 404-350-1700
Email: tlepera@studio101.com
Website: http://colour101.com
Strategic marketing programs for the retail, food, bever-age, sports & entertainment industries. (Woman, estab 1983, empl 9, sales $697,000, cert: WBENC)

8058 Creative Juice LLC
75 Marietta St, Ste 503
Atlanta, GA 30303
Contact: Octavia Gilmore Owner
Tel: 404-947-8599
Email: octavia@itscreativejuice.com
Website: www.itscreativejuice.com
Graphic design & web design services, logo, branding, print design, infographics, brochures, tradeshow graphics, marketing, web design & development, Wordpress, email marketing, copy writing, blogging, local SEO & motion graphics. (Woman/AA, Hisp, estab 2013, empl 4, sales $315,000, cert: City)

8059 e-Transform
10945 State Bridge Rd, Ste 401-234
Alpharetta, GA 30022
Contact: Kimberly Graver CEO
Tel: 888-290-9556
Email: kimberly.graver@e-transform.com
Website: www.e-transform.com
Customer engagement call center solutions, help desk services, IT managed services, and lead generation. (Woman, estab 2011, empl 4, sales $1,017,435, cert: WBENC)

8060 EventEssentials, LLC
1227 Rockbridge Rd Ste 208-238
Stone Mountain, GA 30087
Contact: Qualena Odom-Royes President
Tel: 404-642-6064
Email: qualena@eventsessential.com
Website: www.eventsessential.com
Marketing, branding & messaging, special events, meetings, corporate sponsorships, event promotion & production, best practices, public relations. (Woman/AA, estab 2002, empl 2, sales $125,055, cert: NMSDC)

8061 Folio, Inc. Design & Illustration
1145 Zonolite Rd NE, Ste 2
Atlanta, GA 30306
Contact: Margaret Lisi
Tel: 404-888-6599
Email: margaret@stir-marketing.com
Website: www.stir-marketing.com
Marketing & communications services, create content & media, employee engagement/change management & event marketing. (Woman, estab 1993, empl 10, sales $1,200,000, cert: WBENC)

8062 Freeman Resources Group LLC.
730 Shorter Terr
Atlanta, GA 30318
Contact: David Freeman COO
Tel: 404-696-7224
Email: dafreeman4@gmail.com
Website:
Medical Supplies/Equipment -Bandadges ,First Aid Kits,Gloves,Mask Wheel Chairs,Defribillattors Industrial Safety Supplies-Work Clothing ,Boots ,Ear ,Head and Eye Protection (AA, estab 2007, empl 15, sales $205,000, cert: State)

8063 Global Organization and Planning Services, LLC
2727 Skyview Dr. Unit #76
Lithia Springs, GA 30122
Contact: Vanessa Whitehead Managing Dir
Tel: 770-574-4415
Email: vanessa@globalorganizationplanning.com
Website: www.globalorganizationplanning.com
Event planning & management services: business meetings, conferences, tours, trips, receptions, cruises, accommodations & travel, program & agenda develop-ment, logistics management, etc. (Woman/AA, Nat Ame, estab 2002, empl 20, sales , cert: State, City)

8064 Grow Now, LLC
1320 Ellsworth Industrial Blvd NW
Atlanta, GA 30318
Contact: Bob McNeil CEO
Tel: 404-254-3281
Email: b.mcneil@grownowllc.com
Website: www.grownowllc.com
Marketing communications, advertising, promotional marketing, public relations & activations. (AA, estab 2013, empl 24, sales $8,600,000, cert: State, NMSDC)

8065 Harris HR Services, Inc.
3340 Peachtree Rd, Ste 1800 Tower Place 100
Atlanta, GA 30326
Contact: Derrick Harris President
Tel: 678-264-8679
Email: dbharris@standbytalent.com
Website: www.standbytalent.com
Public Relations. (Minority, estab 0, empl , sales , cert: NMSDC)

8066   Insights Marketing
3131 Piedmont Rd. Ste 205
Atlanta, GA 30305
Contact: Keshia Walker President
Tel: 404-872-9899
Email: kw@insights-mpc.com
Website: www.insights-mpc.com
Multi-cultural research development & analysis, marketing, promotion, special event program development & execution. (Woman/AA, estab 1998, empl 10, sales $390,000, cert: NMSDC, WBENC)

8067   LightPath OM LLC dba strut AGENCY
1235 Oriole Dr, SW
Atlanta, GA 30311
Contact: Tashion Macon, PhD, MBA President
Tel: 404-855-4568
Email: tashion@strutagency.com
Website: www.strutagency.online
Creative design, cross-cultural communications, and consumer marketing strategy. (Woman/AA, estab 2008, empl 15, sales $325,000, cert: NMSDC, WBENC)

8068   Maveryck Marketing Group, LLC
3726 Upton Ct
Ellenwood, GA 30294
Contact: Keith Philpot Managing Member
Tel: 770-681-0731
Email: kphilpot@maveryckmarketing.com
Website: www.maveryckmarketing.com
Strategic market planning & implementation. (AA, estab 2005, empl 1, sales , cert: NMSDC)

8069   McDowell Information Group Public Relations LLC.
233 Mitchell St, Ste 500
Atlanta, GA 30303
Contact: Anita Carlyle Sr Managing Partner
Tel: 844-462-3693
Email: acarlyle@mccevents.ca
Website: http://mcdowellpr.com
Public relations, Web Development, Voice Overs, Military/Corporate engagement, Minority Community Relations, Stage Productions, lighting & Event Planning. (AA, estab 2014, empl 10, sales , cert: NMSDC)

8070   Modo Modo Agency LLC
3175 Northside Parkway NW Bldg 300, Ste 700
Atlanta, GA 30327
Contact: Moira Vetter CEO
Tel: 770-436-3100
Email: moira@modomodoagency.com
Website: www.modomodoagency.com
Marketing, brand development, thought leadership, lead generation, internal communications, publications, web sites, integrated marketing campaigns, direct response. (Woman, estab 2007, empl 15, sales $1,535,000, cert: WBENC)

8071   National Business Advisory Group, Inc.
540 Powder Springs St, Ste C16
Marietta, GA 30064
Contact: Silah Williams CEO
Tel: 770-974-8100
Email: swilliams@mynbag.com
Website: www.mynbag.com
Market research & strategy consulting services. (AA, estab 2011, empl 5, sales $150,000, cert: NMSDC)

8072   Printing Systems, LLC
2759 Delk Rd, Ste 2300
Marietta, GA 30067
Contact: Sherrica Davis New Business Devel
Tel: 404-855-3021
Email: sdavis@printingsys.com
Website: www.printingsys.com
At Printing Systems we utilize innovation to maximize target marketing success, increase return on investments and impact CRM through increasing consumer databases and identifying consumer purchasing habits. (AA, estab 2002, empl 7, sales $2,300,000, cert: NMSDC)

8073   Q&A Entertainment Inc.
1514 E Cleveland Ave Ste 116
East Point, GA 30344
Contact: Sheila Merritt Dir New Business Devel
Tel: 404-762-5665
Email: smerritt@qandaentertainment.com
Website: www.QandAEntertainment.com
Event production & marketing services: production & management, marketing & promotion, ideation & creation & sponsorships. (Woman, estab 1999, empl 3, sales $830,788, cert: WBENC)

8074   Sensis Inc.
1040 W Marietta St
Atlanta, GA 30318
Contact: Marli Crowe Business Dev Mgr
Tel: 404-963-1325
Email: mcrowe@sensisagency.com
Website: www.sensisagency.com
Online marketing, display advertising, email marketing, media planning & buying, contextual targeting, web site design. (Hisp, estab 1998, empl 90, sales $24,000,000, cert: NMSDC)

8075   Sojo, Inc.
4400 N Point Pkwy Ste 153
Alpharetta, GA 30022
Contact: Sophie Gibson President
Tel: 770-360-6330
Email: sophie.gibson@sojoinc.com
Website: www.sojoinc.com
Technology marketing, marketing communications. (Woman/AA, estab 2001, empl 11, sales $2,300,000, cert: NMSDC)

8076   Southeast Exhibits and Events
1000 Marietta St Ste 124
Atlanta, GA 30318
Contact: Jamal Lewis President
Tel: 470-865-2007
Email: info@southeastexhibit.com
Website: http://Southeastexhibit.com
Trade show exhibits & design. (Woman/AA, estab 2014, empl 5, sales , cert: NMSDC)

8077   SPAR Solutions, LLC
360 Interstate North Pkwy SE Ste 220
Atlanta, GA 30339
Contact: Swami Ganapathy Dir Solutions Consulting
Tel: 855-772-7765
Email: sganapathy@sparsolutions.com
Website: http://sparsolutions.com
CRM Solutions for Sales, Marketing, Customer Service, Field Service, Contract Management
Contact Centers - Omni-channel customer interactions - Telephony, Email, Chat, Social Media
Complex business process automation and management, Systems Integratio (As-Ind, estab 2003, empl 60, sales $3,670,000, cert: NMSDC)

8078 TDEFERIAMEDIA, Inc.
9795 Talisman Dr
Johns Creek, GA 30022
Contact: Antenor Tony President
Tel: 404-630-0639
Email: contact@tdeferiamedia.com
Website: http://tdeferiamedia.com
Marketing, branding consulting & creative production, ethnic market study & plans, media buying, translation & interpretation in Spanish, digital & social media expertise. (Hisp, estab 2007, empl 1, sales $140,000, cert: NMSDC)

8079 The Capre Group
115 Perimeter Center Place Ste 1120
Atlanta, GA 30346
Contact: Kim Gavlak Controller
Tel: 678-443-2280
Email: kgavlak@capregroup.com
Website: www.capregroup.com
Strategic marketing consulting. (Woman, estab 2001, empl 14, sales $4,750,000, cert: WBENC)

8080 The Crafton Group, Inc.
1107 Lanier Blvd
Georgia, GA 30306
Contact: Crafton Langley President
Tel: 404-873-3019
Email: crafton.langley@thecraftongroup.com
Website: www.thecraftongroup.com
Marketing & communications: research, strategy, branding, design, advertising, promotion, product development, media. (Woman, estab 1996, empl 15, sales , cert: City, WBENC)

8081 VonCreations, Inc.
2886 Branchwood Dr
East Point, GA 30344
Contact: Yvonne J. Wiltz CEO
Tel: 404-347-1054
Email: vonco3@bellsouth.net
Website: www.voncreations.com
Meeting planning & management, conferences, special events & marketing campaigns. (Woman/AA, estab 1989, empl 2, sales $145,279, cert: NMSDC, WBENC, 8a)

Idaho

8082 Milligan Events
1116 S Vista Ave #189
Boise, ID 83705
Contact: Milligan Events Owner
Tel: 208-387-0770
Email: diversitymatters@milliganevents.com
Website: www.milliganevents.com
Event & meeting planning & logistics. (Woman, estab 1994, empl 8, sales $756,972, cert: WBENC)

Illinois

8083 Bamboo Worldwide Inc.
30 N Racine Ave, Ste 300
Chicago, IL 60607
Contact: Tracy Thirion President
Tel: 773-227-4848
Email: tracyt@bambooinc.com
Website: www.bambooworldwide.com
Consulting services specializing in branding, innovation & market research. (Woman, estab , empl , sales $1,700,545, cert: WBENC)

8084 Beaman Public Relations, Inc.
401 N Michigan Ave, Ste 1300
Chicago, IL 60611
Contact: Robin Beaman President
Tel: 312-751-9689
Email: rbeaman@beamaninc.com
Website: www.beamaninc.com
Public relations, marketing & advertising services. (Woman/AA, estab 1996, empl 7, sales $1,084,431, cert: State, City, NMSDC, WBENC)

8085 Belle Communications
1390 Jaycox Rd
Chicago, IL 60673
Contact: Kate Finley CEO
Tel: 614-304-1463
Email: kate@bellecommunication.com
Website: http://bellecommunication.com/
Digital public relations and social media agency. (Woman, estab 2013, empl 16, sales $1,112,921, cert: WBENC)

8086 Classical Marketing LLC
2300 Cabot Dr, Ste 390
Lisle, IL 60532
Contact: Managing Partner
Tel: 847-969-1696
Email:
Website: www.classicalmarketing.com
Marketing programs in Business to Business and Business to Consumer categories for clients in retail, financial services, automotive, health care. (Woman, estab 1999, empl 8, sales $3,057,182, cert: WBENC)

8087 Creative & Response Research Services, Inc.
500 N Michigan Ave, 12th Fl
Chicago, IL 60611
Contact: Robbin Jaklin CFO
Tel: 312-828-9200
Email: robbinj@crresearch.com
Website: www.crresearch.com
Custom market research, internet surveys, phone surveys, focus groups, qualitative & quantitative research. (Woman, estab 1960, empl 120, sales $23,268,888, cert: State, WBENC)

8088 Customer Lifecycle, LLC
1112 W Boughton Rd, Ste 365
Bolingbrook, IL 60440
Contact: Principal
Tel: 630-412-8989
Email:
Website: www.customerlifecycle.us
Full-service qualitative and quantitative market research, plan, support and deploy customer satisfaction and loyalty research and align the stages of the customer lifecycle to improve customer loyalty. (Woman, estab 2008, empl 16, sales $200,000, cert: WBENC)

8089 Data Research Inc.
2525 Cabot Dr Ste 107
Lisle, IL 60532
Contact: Leslie Gunner Losh President
Tel: 630-281-8307
Email: lgunnerlosh@mindseyeresearch.com
Website: www.mindseyeresearch.com
Market research services. (Woman, estab 1982, empl 46, sales $3,600,000, cert: WBENC)

8090 DCC Marketing, LLC
2130 N 22nd St
Decatur, IL 62526
Contact: Kara Demirjian Huss President
Tel: 217-421-7580
Email: ksd@dccmarketing.com
Website: www.dccmarketing.com
Integrated marketing, communications and digital services.
(Woman, estab 2000, empl 10, sales $1,200,000, cert:
State, WBENC)

8091 Elemento L2, LLC
401 S LaSalle St, Ste 1501
Chicago, IL 60605
Contact: Ivan Lopez Managing Dir
Tel: 312-465-2355
Email: chemistry@elementol2.com
Website: www.elementol2.com
Multicultural marketing, experiential, PR, shopper & digital
marketing. (Hisp, estab 2011, empl 15, sales $1,048,333,
cert: NMSDC)

8092 Eved Services, Inc.
4811 Oakton St, Ste 250
Skokie, IL 60077
Contact: Alexis Feczko Dir of Sales Operations
Tel: 773-764-7000
Email: sales@eved.com
Website: www.eved.com/
Event services, destination management, technology
services. (Woman, estab 2004, empl 25, sales $8,100,000,
cert: WBENC)

8093 Fridkin Valo, Inc. dba TPG Live Events
210 N Cass Ave, Ste A
Westmont, IL 60559
Contact: Christina Piedlow CEO
Tel: 630-353-1308
Email: cpiedlow@tpgliveevents.com
Website: www.tpgliveevents.com
Event management and marketing expertise, creativity.
(Woman, estab 1994, empl 13, sales $7,310,726, cert:
WBENC)

8094 Frontline Public Strategies, Inc.
100 E. Washington St
Springfield, IL 62701
Contact: Kim Robinson President
Tel: 217-528-3434
Email: kimrobinson@frontline-online.net
Website: www.frontline-online.net
Public relations, marketing, event planning & public affairs.
(Woman, estab 2001, empl 12, sales $1,200,000, cert:
State, WBENC)

8095 Gerard Design, Inc.
28371 Davis Pkwy
Warrenville, IL 60555
Contact: Carolyn Gerard President
Tel: 630-355-0775
Email: carolyn@gerarddesign.com
Website: www.gerarddesign.com
Strategic Branding and Design, Communications, Graphic
Design. (Woman, estab 0, empl , sales , cert: WBENC)

8096 Gladstone Painting Company
P.O. Box 871
Elmhurst, IL 60126
Contact: Mary Hinchley President
Tel: 630-782-0973
Email: gladstoneptg@aol.com
Website:
commercial painting contractor (Woman, estab 1975, empl
10, sales , cert: City, WBENC)

8097 Group O, Inc.
4905 77th Ave
Milan, IL 61264
Contact: Mike De La Cruz Sr. VP, Business Develop-
ment & Diversity
Tel: 210-213-2258
Email: supplierdiversity@groupo.com
Website: www.groupo.com
Single source integrated marketing solutions, customer
loyalty, rebate administration & fulfillment, gift cards,
inbound & outbound call center services, 4-color
printing, print personalization, direct mail & fulfillment.
(Hisp, estab 1974, empl 1200, sales $900,424,000, cert:
NMSDC)

8098 Ivan Carlson & Associates
2224 W Fulton
Chicago, IL 60612
Contact: Tina Carlson President
Tel: 312-829-4616
Email: tina@ivancarlson.com
Website: www.ivancarlson.com
Event production & management, logistics, staging,
sound & lighting. (Woman, estab 1974, empl 25, sales
$3,370,000, cert: WBENC)

8099 JAK Graphic Design, LLC/DBA: JAK Creative Design
1450 S. Plainfield Rd. Ste 4
Darien, IL 60561
Contact: Jill Kerrigan CEO
Tel: 630-512-0500
Email: jill@jakcd.com
Website: www.jakcd.com
Creative concepting, design and final art production in
both print and digital channels including, direct mail,
internal corporate employee communications, POP,
emails, landing pages, animated and static banner ads,
wireframes and web. (Woman, estab 1995, empl 6, sales
$1,500,000, cert: WBENC)

8100 JRS Consulting, Inc.
1316 Gregory Ave
Wilmette, IL 60091
Contact: President
Tel: 847-920-1701
Email:
Website: www.JRSconsulting.net
Market research, management consulting, marketing &
internal & external communications initiatives. (Woman,
estab 2002, empl 1, sales , cert: WBENC)

8101 JumpGarden Consulting, LLC
1534 Washington Ave
Wilmette, IL 60091
Contact: Sheila Cahnman President
Tel: 312-286-0119
Email: sheila@jumpgardenllc.com
Website: www.jumpgardenllc.com
Healthcare design, planning & marketing solutions.
(Woman, estab 2014, empl 1, sales , cert: State, City,
WBENC)

8102 K.O. Strategies
2903 N Wolcott Ave, Ste B
Chicago, IL 60657
Contact: CEO
Tel: 312-307-4206
Email:
Website: www.kostrategies.com
Strategic communications, public affairs, stakeholder
relations, crisis leadership & strategic planning/presen-
tations. (Woman, estab 2006, empl 1, sales , cert:
WBENC)

8103 Kathy Schaeffer and Associates, Inc.
      17 N State St, Ste 1690
      Chicago, IL 60602
      Contact: Kathy Schaeffer President
      Tel: 312-251-5100
      Email: kschaeffer@ksapr.com
      Website: www.ksapr.com
Public relations. (Woman, estab 1994, empl 5, sales , cert:
City)

8104 L3 Agency
      1452 E 53rd
      Chicago, IL 60615
      Contact: Larvetta Loftin CEO
      Tel: 312-268-5207
      Email: larvetta.loftin@l3eventeurs.com
      Website: http://thel3agency.com
Marketing and communications, digital content creation,
PR, advertising, brand experiences, corporate sponsorship,
community outreach, and social philanthropy. (Woman/
AA, estab 2000, empl 4, sales , cert: NMSDC)

8105 Liberty Lithographers, Inc.
      18625 W Creek Dr
      Tinley Park, IL 60477
      Contact: Angela Hipelius CEO
      Tel: 708-633-7450
      Email: ahipelius@libertycreativesolutions.com
      Website: www.libertycreativesolutions.com
Marketing services: graphic design, direct mail campaigns,
research, promotions & loyalty campaigns, marketing
collateral, advertising, web design, brand development,
corporate identity. (Woman, estab 1964, empl 65, sales
$12,000,001, cert: WBENC)

8106 Live Marketing
      1201 N Clark St
      Chicago, IL 60610
      Contact: Alyssa Lavik Relationship Mgr
      Tel: 312-787-4800
      Email: alavik@livemarketing.com
      Website: www.livemarketing.com
Trade show engagement strategies. (Woman, estab 1978,
empl 175, sales $7,100,000, cert: WBENC)

8107 Magnolia Insights
      350 N Orleans St, Ste 9000N
      Chicago, IL 60654
      Contact: CEO
      Tel: 646-768-4279
      Email:
      Website: www.magnoliainsights.com
Integrated marketing communications agency. (Hisp, estab
2014, empl 5, sales , cert: NMSDC)

8108 Marketing Innovators International Inc.
      9701 W Higgins Rd Ste 400
      Rosemont, IL 60018
      Contact: Merrie Marinovich Acct Exec
      Tel: 847-696-1111
      Email: mmarinovich@marketinginnovators.com
      Website: www.marketinginnovators.com
Employee recognition award programs. (Woman, estab
1978, empl 70, sales , cert: WBENC)

8109 Matrex Exhibits
      301 S Church St
      Addison, IL 60101
      Contact: VP Business Dev
      Tel: 630-628-2233
      Email:
      Website: www.matrexhibits.com
Tradeshow exhibits, design, construction & mgmt, graphic
design & production, tradeshow svcs. (Woman, estab
1987, empl 66, sales $27,000,000, cert: WBENC)

8110 Media Link, Inc.
      1902 17th St
      Rock Island, IL 61201
      Contact: Marketing Consultant
      Tel: 309-786-5142
      Email:
      Website: http://medialinkinc.com
Media Buying, Advertising, Marketing, PR, Public
Relations, Media Campaign, Marketing Research.
(Woman, estab 2001, empl 4, sales $1,046,821, cert:
State, WBENC)

8111 Mekky Media Relations
      913 S. I-Oka Ave
      Mount Prospect, IL 60056
      Contact: Bill Rossi COO
      Tel: 312-315-0181
      Email: supplierdiversity@mekkymedia.com
      Website: www.mekkymedia.com
Public relations firm. (Woman, estab 2016, empl 5, sales
$598,928, cert: WBENC)

8112 Metaphrasis Language and Cultural Solutions, LLC
      1147 W Ohio, Ste 306
      Chicago, IL 60714
      Contact: Elizabeth Colon President
      Tel: 815-464-1423
      Email: ecolon@metaphrasislcs.com
      Website: www.metaphrasislcs.com
Language services, interpretation, translation & corporate trainings. (Woman/Hisp, estab 2007, empl 6, sales
$100,001, cert: State, WBENC)

8113 MHJohnson & Associates, Inc.
      1918 S Michigan Ave Ste 302
      Chicago, IL 60616
      Contact: Marilyn Johnson Principal
      Tel: 312-949-9164
      Email: marilyn@mhjohnson.com
      Website: www.mhjohnson.com
Marketing management, program, product development
& mgmt, organizational development. (Woman/AA, estab
2001, empl 2, sales $225,000, cert: WBENC)

8114 PACO Communications, Inc. d/b/a PACO Collective
      400 S. Green St Unit H
      Chicago, IL 60607
      Contact: Ozzie Godinez CEO
      Tel: 312-281-2040
      Email: marketing@pacocollective.com
      Website: www.pacocollective.com
Hispanic marketing, advertising, public relations &
community outreach, web design & development. (Hisp,
estab 2006, empl 40, sales $19,900,000, cert: NMSDC)

8115 PCH Communications
      600 W Fluton Fl 4
      Chicago, IL 60661
      Contact: Alice Pollard SVP Operations
      Tel: 312-384-1906
      Email: alice@discovercg.com
      Website: http://commongroundmgs.com
Advertising/Marketing, Strategic Planning/Development,
Creative, Public Relations, Event Marketing, Multicultural
Marketing, Digital Marketing , Shopper/Retail Marketing,
Content Development, Research Promotions/
Sponsorship's. (AA, Hisp, estab 2014, empl 256, sales
$35,276,000, cert: NMSDC)

8116 Production Partners Company LLC
911 Rock Spring Rd
Naperville, IL 60565
Contact: Haves McNeal CEO
Tel: 312-735-1486
Email: haves@pp-co.biz
Website: www.pp-co.biz
Marketing Communications. (AA, estab 2017, empl 5, sales
, cert: NMSDC)

8117 Public Communications Inc.
1 E Wacker Dr Ste 2450
Chicago, IL 60601
Contact: Pamela Oettel CFO/COO
Tel: 312-558-1770
Email: poettel@pcipr.com
Website: http://pcipr.com
Develop integrated communications strategies: Advocacy
Programs, Board Counsel, Branding & Positioning, Com-
petitive Analysis, Consumer Marketing, Conservation &
Wildlife Issues, Crisis/Issues Management & Monitoring.
(Woman, estab 1962, empl 50, sales $6,111,500, cert:
State, WBENC)

8118 Quicksilver Associates, Inc.
18 W Ontario St
Chicago, IL 60654
Contact: Diane MacWilliams President & CEO
Tel: 312-943-7622
Email: dianem@quicksilvernow.com
Website: www.quicksilvernow.com
Print, video, meeting planning, production, web & interac-
tive media. (Woman, estab 1976, empl 22, sales
$4,600,000, cert: WBENC)

8119 Reilly Connect
625 N Michigan Ave Ste 1705
Chicago, IL 60611
Contact: President
Tel: 312-600-6780
Email:
Website: www.reillyconnect.com/
Social media marketing, brand activation & events, video
production, public relations. (Woman, estab 1996, empl 5,
sales , cert: WBENC)

8120 Research Explorers, Inc
1111 New Trier Ct
Wilmette, IL 60091
Contact: Lisa Gaines McDonald President
Tel: 847-853-0237
Email: lisa@researchexplorers.com
Website: www.reserachexplorers.com
Market research & consulting services: qualitative re-
search, focus groups, in-depth interviews, ethnographies,
brain storming & idea generation sessions. (Woman/AA,
estab 1994, empl 1, sales $305,087, cert: City)

8121 Signature Media Group Talk
1327 W Washington Blvd
Chicago, IL 60607
Contact: Pam Redwood President
Tel: 312-226-5552
Email: pam@smgspeakers.com
Website: www.smgspeakers.com
Public communications, speakers bureau,
brand creation awareness, client advertising, ad manage-
ment, creative services, custom publishing, event plan-
ning, media planning, media relations, corporate commu-
nications. (Woman/AA, estab 2009, empl 2, sales
$400,000, cert: State, City)

8122 Simple Truth Communication Partners Inc
314 W Superior St Ste 300
Chicago, IL 60654
Contact: Rhonda Kokot Managing Partner
Tel: 312-376-0360
Email: m.person@yoursimpletruth.com
Website: www.yoursimpletruth.com
Brand strategy & positioning, B2B, sales force & corpo-
rate/internal communications. (Woman, estab 1988,
empl 20, sales $9,803,864, cert: WBENC)

8123 Strategic Marketing, Inc.
350 S Northwest Hwy Ste 304
Park Ridge, IL 60068
Contact: Leslie Reinhardt Controller
Tel: 847-720-7500
Email: lreinhardt@smialcott.com
Website: www.smialcott.com
Marketing research services. (Woman, estab 1980, empl
23, sales $7,636,812, cert: WBENC)

8124 Total Event Resources
1920 N Thoreau Dr Ste 105
Schaumburg, IL 60173
Contact: Lynnea Walsh Dir of Operations
Tel: 847-397-2200
Email: lwalsh@total-event.com
Website: www.total-event.com
Corporate communications, event production, entertain-
ment [roduction, meeting management, experiential
learning & destination management. (Woman, estab
1995, empl 15, sales $3,320,000, cert: WBENC)

8125 Wedgeworth Business Communications
2215 Enterprise Dr, Ste 1506
Westchester, IL 60154
Contact: Pamela G. Wedgeworth President
Tel: 708-223-0019
Email: pamela@wedgeworthbiz.com
Website: www.wedgeworthbiz.com
Visual communications: video production, multimedia
creation, print & electronic collateral, event coordina-
tion. (Woman/AA, estab 1999, empl 2, sales $320,000,
cert: City, WBENC)

Indiana

8126 Coles Marketing Communications
3950 Priority Way Ste 106
Indianapolis, IN 46240
Contact: Barbara Coles President
Tel: 317-571-0051
Email: bcoles@colesmarketing.com
Website: www.colesmarketing.com
Marketing communications services: graphic design,
web design, e-communications, public relations, media
relations, word of mouth marketing, videography,
photography. (Woman, estab 1985, empl 10, sales
$1,250,000, cert: State, City)

8127 TalentCode Management Group
1801 S Liberty Dr, Ste 300
Bloomington, IN 47403
Contact: Melanie Hoffman Business Development
Tel:
Email: melanie.hoffman@employbridge.com
Website: www.employbridge.com
Staffing services. (Minority, estab 1997, empl 3000, sales
$3,000,000,000, cert: NMSDC)

Kansas

8128　A.S.K. Associates, Inc.
1505 Kasold Dr
Lawrence, KS 66047
Contact: Kenneth Martinez President
Tel:　800-315-4333
Email: kenm@askusa.com
Website: www.askusa.com
Conference, convention, trade show, meeting, seminar support services. (Woman/Hisp, estab 1979, empl 15, sales $6,600,000, cert: WBENC)

8129　Exhibit Arts, LLC
326 N Athenian
Wichita, KS 67203
Contact: Beth Harshfield Managing Member
Tel:　316-264-2915
Email: beth@exhibitarts.net
Website: www.exhibitarts.net
Exhibit design, fabrication & management, project management, conference support services, warehousing & fulfillment center services. (Woman/Nat Ame, estab 2000, empl 160, sales $18,843,000, cert: NMSDC, NWBOC)

8130　Meeting Excellence, Inc.
7300 West 110th St Ste 700
Overland Park, KS 66210
Contact: Kory Oplinger Dir of Sales
Tel:　913-693-4675
Email: koplinger@meeting-excellence.com
Website: www.meeting-excellence.com
Corporate meetings, events & incentive travel services. (AA, estab 2003, empl 4, sales $1,113,929, cert: NMSDC)

8131　The Lexinet Corporation
701 N Union
Council Grove, KS 66846
Contact: Lindsey Boyer President
Tel:　620-767-7000
Email: indseyb@lexinetcorporation.com
Website: http://lexinetcorporation.com
Marketing campaigns & programs, custom personalized variable data printed direct mail, fully-integrated marketing centers, complete multi-channel solutions. (Woman, estab 1991, empl 18, sales $3,100,000, cert: WBENC)

Kentucky

8132　ConvenePro
1792 Alysheba Way Ste 160
Lexington, KY 40509
Contact: Delphine Hepp Acct Director
Tel:　859-276-0065
Email: dhepp@convenepro.com
Website: www.convenepro.com
Event management, marketing & communications, live speaker programs, conferences & trade shows, promotional presentations, satellite broadcasts/webcasts, live & virtual training workshops, product training. (Woman, estab 1995, empl 50, sales , cert: NWBOC)

8133　Corporate World Public Relations
4017 Whiteblossom Estates Ct
Louisville, KY 40241
Contact: Ray Callender, Jr. VP
Tel:　678-592-8516
Email: ray.callender@corpworldpr.com
Website: www.corpworldpr.com
Exhibits design & management services. (AA, estab , empl , sales $262,000, cert: NMSDC)

8134　Digital Business Solutions, Inc.
517 S Fourth St
Louisville, KY 40202
Contact: Cynthia Masters CEO
Tel:　502-562-7895
Email: rfp@dbswebsite.com
Website: www.dbswebsite.com
Web & digital development, design, strategy & marketing, websites, apps, mobile, hosting, interactive infographics, SEO, digital business strategy, lead generation online marketing. (Woman, estab 2000, empl 20, sales $1,700,000, cert: WBENC)

8135　Intrinzic Marketing & Design
One Levee Way, Ste 3121
Newport, KY 41071
Contact: Tami Beattie Office Mgr
Tel:　859-292-5061
Email: tami@intrinzicinc.com
Website: www.intrinzicinc.com
Marketing & design: marketing, design & interactive svcs, creative concepting, campaign dev, graphic design, copywriting, public relations, website design, email marketing & media planning. (Woman, estab 1989, empl 12, sales , cert: WBENC)

8136　Mackey Group LLC
2250 Mackey Pike
Nicholasville, KY 40356
Contact: Nancy Wiser President
Tel:　859-887-0866
Email: nancy@wiserstrategies.com
Website: http://wiserstrategies.com
Public relations, marketing, market research, corporate relations, crisis planning & response, media relations, branding, writing, graphic design, photography, video production & editing, print production mgmt. (Woman, estab 2011, empl 1, sales $300,000, cert: WBENC)

8137　New West LLC
9630 Ormsby Station Rd
Louisville, KY 40223
Contact: Melvin Graham Managing Dir
Tel:　888-867-7811
Email: mgraham@newwestagency.com
Website: www.newwestagency.com
Advertising, Public Relations, Brand Strategy, Website & Mobile App Dev, Social Media, Multicultural Marketing, SEO/SEM/PPC, Event Planning & Video Production. (AA, estab 2002, empl 28, sales $5,500,000, cert: NMSDC)

Massachusetts

8138　Causemedia, Inc.
50 Hunt St Ste 140
Watertown, MA 02472
Contact: Donna Latson Gittens Principal
Tel:　617-558-6850
Email: info@causemedia.com
Website: www.moreadvertising.com
Communications, advertising & marketing agency. (Woman/AA, estab 1997, empl 8, sales $4,636,330, cert: State, NMSDC, WBENC)

8139　Color Media Group, LLC
4 Copley Pl, Ste 120
Boston, MA 02116
Contact: Josefina Bonilla President
Tel:　617-266-6961
Email: josefina@colorboston.com
Website: www.colormagazineusa.com
Web advertising, signature events, event management, strategic marketing initiatives, new markets, media buying services, public relations. (Woman/Hisp, estab 2007, empl 3, sales $289,000, cert: State)

8140 Conover + Gould Strategic Communications, Inc.
69 Milk St #101
Westborough, MA 01581
Contact: Heather Conover CEO
Tel: 508-789-9273
Email: hconover@conovergould.com
Website: www.conovergould.com
Public relations & marketing communications, environmental communications & event management. (Woman, estab 1984, empl 9, sales $1,528,016, cert: State)

8141 Consolidated Marketing Services, Inc.
841 Woburn St
Wilmington, MA 01887
Contact: Andrew Bausman key acct Mgr
Tel: 800-474-5756
Email: abausman@cmsassociates.com
Website: www.cmsassociates.com
Marketing svcs: fulfillment, printing, mailing, promotional products, graphics & catalogs. (Woman, estab , empl , sales $4,000,000, cert: WBENC)

8142 Early Bird Power LLC
1 Adams St
Milton, MA 02186
Contact: Shaun Pandit CEO
Tel: 888-763-2759
Email: shaunpandit@earlybirdpower.com
Website: http://earlybirdpower.com
Facilitator of procurement services for electricity, natural gas, and renewable energy credits. Energy Consulting and risk management. (As-Ind, estab 2009, empl , sales $500,000, cert: State)

8143 EMI Strategic Marketing Inc.
15 Broad St
Boston, MA 02109
Contact: Paul OBrien VP Finance
Tel: 617-224-1101
Email: pobrien@emiboston.com
Website: www.emiboston.com
Marketing services. (Woman, estab 1989, empl 45, sales $7,000,000, cert: State, WBENC)

8144 Full Circle Design
380 Main St Unit 301
Stoneham, MA 02180
Contact: President
Tel: 781-333-8878
Email:
Website: http://fullcircledesign.co
Branding, print and graphic design, web design and development, and varios digital marketing services. (Woman, estab 2011, empl 4, sales , cert: WBENC)

8145 Global Link Language Services, Inc.
71 Commercial St Ste 218
Boston, MA 02109
Contact: Carol Ann Managing Dir
Tel: 617-451-6655
Email: cmichel@gleneagleadv.com
Website: www.languagetranslate.com
Intl communication svcs: translation, interpretation, localization, multilingual typesetting & desktop publishing. (Woman, estab 1996, empl 4, sales $650,000, cert: State)

8146 Grand Design, Inc.
42 Chestnut St Ste 2
Salem, MA 01970
Contact: Debra Glabeau Principal
Tel: 978-741-0112
Email: dglabeau@greatisland.com
Website: www.greatisland.com
Graphic design & marketing communications solutions, brand development, logos & corporate identity systems, naming & taglines, collateral & brochures, websites, email & direct mail programs, print advertising, sales kits. (Woman, estab 1982, empl 4, sales $223,742, cert: State)

8147 Inspired Marketing
20 Maple St 4th Fl, Ste 1
Springfield, MA 01103
Contact: Lauren Mendoza Office Mgr
Tel: 413-303-0101
Email: lauren@inspiredmarketing.biz
Website: www.inspiredmarketing.biz
Marketing, Event Planning, Social Media, Media Buying, Advertising, Graphic Design (Woman, estab 2009, empl 6, sales $632,920, cert: WBENC)

8148 Kelley Chunn & Associates
184 Dudley St, Ste 106
Boston, MA 02119
Contact: Kelley Chunn Principal
Tel: 617-427-0997
Email: kc4info@aol.com
Website: www.kelleychunn.com
Multicultural marketing & public relations services. (Woman/AA, estab 1991, empl 1, sales $160,000, cert: State)

8149 NXTevent, Inc.
60K St, 4th Fl
Boston, MA 02127
Contact: Joanne O'Connell GM
Tel: 617-904-9053
Email: connect@nxtevent.com
Website: www.nxtevent.com
Event & destination management. (Woman, estab 2001, empl 8, sales $2,447,766, cert: State, WBENC)

8150 The Castle Group, Inc.
38 Third Ave Ste 200
Charlestown, MA 02129
Contact: Wendy Spivak Treasurer
Tel: 617-337-9535
Email: wspivak@thecastlegrp.com
Website: www.thecastlegrp.com/
Public relations & events management. (Woman, estab 1996, empl 23, sales $5,300,000, cert: WBENC)

8151 Twirling Tiger Press Inc.
7 Jeffrey Road
Franklin, MA 02038
Contact: Maureen Joyce President
Tel: 508-520-3258
Email: mjoyce@twirlingtigermedia.com
Website: www.twirlingtigermedia.com
Writing & graphic design, creation of design & imagery, development, scheduling & trafficking, & content generation, advertising, printing, promotions, publications, RFPs & proposals, social media, websites, white papers. (Woman, estab 2013, empl 2, sales $270,000, cert: WBENC)

Maryland

8152 Bates Creative Group, LLC
1119 East West Hwy
Silver Spring, MD 20910
Contact: Debra Bates Schrott President
Tel: 301-495-8844
Email: debbie@batescreative.com
Website: www.batescreative.com
Branding & Identity, Magazine Design & Redesign, Event Marketing, Marketing Collateral, Web Design & Development, iPad UI Design, Annual Reports, Media Kits. (Woman, estab 2003, empl 11, sales , cert: WBENC)

8153 BrightKey, Inc.
60 West St Ste 300
Annapolis, MD 21401
Contact: Krystal Dyer Business Solutions
Tel: 301-604-3305
Email: businessdevelopment@brightkey.net
Website: www.brightkey.net/
Marketing research, strategy & creative services. (Woman, estab 1988, empl 600, sales $34,212,531, cert: WBENC)

8154 DESTIN Enterprises, LLC
8630 Guilford Rd, Ste 114
Columbia, MD 21046
Contact: Edward Crenshaw President
Tel: 443-538-1351
Email: ej_crenshaw@destinenterprises.com
Website: http://destinenterprises.com
DESTIN Enterprise, LLC is a diversity consulting, training and solutions fir that specializes in raising awareness toward disabilities and veterans transition issues. Our signature diversity training program is "Preparing Employers to Reintegrate (AA, estab 2008, empl 8, sales , cert: State)

8155 Hargrove Inc.
One Hargrove Dr
Lanham, MD 20706
Contact: Meghan Muniz Natl Sales Exec
Tel: 301-306-3000
Email: meghanmuniz@hargroveinc.com
Website: www.hargroveinc.com
Events, exhibits & trade shows: venue selection, staffing, design, menu development, security, building of stages, set design, AV & lighting services. (Woman, estab 1946, empl 225, sales $73,000,000, cert: WBENC)

8156 Humdinger Enterprises LLC
P.O. Box 4542
Crofton, MD 21114
Contact: Alexis Jenkins Managing Member
Tel: 410-279-0205
Email: alexis@humdingerenterprise.com
Website: http://humdingerenterprises.com
Event planning: festivals, concerts, meetings, award shows & broadcast events. (Woman, estab 2008, empl 5, sales $230,681, cert: State)

8157 JDC Events, LLC
8720 Georgia Ave Ste 801
Silver Spring, MD 20910
Contact: Jennifer Collins President & CEO
Tel: 240-512-4219
Email: jennifer@jdc-events.com
Website: www.jdc-events.com
Meeting & event management: custom-designed logistical solutions, guidance & communications, meetings, conferences & special events. (Woman/AA, estab 1997, empl 4, sales $2,040,000, cert: NMSDC, WBENC, 8a)

8158 McMillon Communications, Inc.
12902 Argyle Circle
Fort Washington, MD 20744
Contact: CEO
Tel: 301-292-9141
Email:
Website: www.mcmilloncommunications.com
Marketing support solutions, public relations & strategic partnership development. (Woman/AA, estab 1986, empl , sales $4,528,979, cert: State, WBENC)

8159 Mjach Designs
5100 Buckeystown Pike Ste 250
Frederick, MD 21704
Contact: Admin
Tel: 410-366-0505
Email: rose@mjachdesigns.com
Website: www.mjachdesigns.com
Graphic design, marketing & communications, web design & implementation, print production, marketing & advertising, public relations, media planning & buying, research & copywriting. (Woman, estab 2003, empl 5, sales $336,640, cert: State, City)

8160 MultiLingual Solutions, Inc.
11 N Washington St Ste 300
Rockville, MD 20850
Contact: Paul Keys VP Business Devel
Tel: 301-424-7444
Email: pkeys@mlsolutions.com
Website: http://mlsolutions.com
Document Translation, On-site and Remote Interpretation, Website & Software Localization, Multicultural Marketing & Advertising, Language, Cultural and Executive Training & Curriculum Development, Desktop Publishing. (Woman/Hisp, estab 2002, empl 162, sales $9,729,040, cert: NMSDC, WBENC)

8161 Pensari, LLC
107 Theodora Court
Forest Hill, MD 21050
Contact: Hans Plate
Tel: 410-588-5465
Email: hans.plate@pensari.com
Website: www.pensari.com
Market research specializing in healthcare research, qualitative & quantitative research. (Hisp, estab 2013, empl 1, sales , cert: NMSDC)

8162 Program Management of America
1153 N Bentalou St
Baltimore, MD 21216
Contact: Walter G Brooks Sr
Tel: 410-945-7489
Email: wbrooks@pmamerica.com
Website: www.pmamerica.com
Conferences, & exhibits (show site arr. & logistical support); warehousing/distribution (order fulfillment, mass mail, courier svcs); database design/maintain(materials request process, mailing list mgmt, etc.). (AA, estab 1996, empl 2, sales , cert: State)

8163 Slice, Inc dba SliceWorks
20301 Highland Hall Dr
Montgomery Village, MD 20886
Contact: Kathleen Rabil CEO
Tel: 301-519-8101
Email: kathi@slice-works.com
Website: www.slice-works.com
Graphic design, marketing strategy consulting, marketing communications & campaign development, social media strategy consulting & execution, website design & development, brand consulting, publication layout & design. (Woman, estab 1997, empl 4, sales $445,690, cert: WBENC)

8164   Sutter Design, Inc. dba The Sutter Group
       4640 Forbes Blvd. Ste 160A
       Lanham, MD 20706
       Contact: Karen Sutter President
       Tel: 301-459-5445
       Email: karen@sutter-group.com
       Website: www.sutter-group.com
Marketing, advertising & public relations: brand, creating
logos, corporate collateral, websites, direct mail & e-
marketing campaigns, advertising & public relations.
(Minority, Woman, estab 1987, empl 8, sales $1,000,000,
cert: State)

8165   TMNcorp
       8720 Georgia Ave, Ste 206
       Silver Spring, MD 20910
       Contact: Nhora Barrera Murphy President & CEO
       Tel: 301-565-0770
       Email: nbarrera@tmncorp.com
       Website: http://tmncorp.com
Communication & social marketing, advertising, media
relations, research & evaluation & cultural adaptation
services. (Woman/Hisp, estab 1999, empl 20, sales
$4,850,000, cert: State)

8166   Transient Identiti, Inc.
       11 Webster Hill Ct
       Clarksburg, MD 20871
       Contact: Albert Thompson Dir Brand Strategy
       Tel: 301-792-8535
       Email: albert@transientidentiti.com
       Website: www.transientidentiti.com
Digital Marketing: mobile, social, display, search, apps,
email, advanced targeting. (AA, estab 2002, empl 7, sales
$424,000, cert: NMSDC)

Michigan

8167   Airfoil Public Relations, Inc.
       336 N Main St
       Royal Oak, MI 48067
       Contact: Sharon Neumann SVP, Finance & Admin
       Tel: 248-304-1400
       Email: neumann@airfoilgroup.com
       Website: www.airfoilgroup.com
Marketing communications. (Woman, estab 2000, empl
37, sales $7,200,000, cert: WBENC)

8168   Archer Corporate Services
       6703 Haggerty Ste B
       Belleville, MI 48111
       Contact: Dennis Archer Dir of Operations
       Tel: 734-713-3100
       Email: diversity@theacsadvantage.com
       Website: www.theacsadvantage.com
Marketing support svcs: B2B fulfillment, rebates, direct
response, sweepstakes, customer service, merchandising.
(AA, estab 2004, empl 25, sales $15,400,000, cert: NMSDC)

8169   BPI Communications, LLC
       13700 Oakland Ave
       Highland Park, MI 48203
       Contact: Jim Suddendorf EVP sales/mlktg
       Tel: 313-957-5459
       Email: j.suddendorf@bpicommunications.com
       Website: www.bpicommunications.com
Fulfillment & direct marketing solutions. (AA, estab 2005,
empl 10, sales $107,000,000, cert: NMSDC)

8170   Bromberg & Associates, LLC
       3141 Caniff St.
       Hamtramck, MI 48212
       Contact: Carly Priehs Business Develop Mgr
       Tel: 313-871-0080
       Email: carly@brombergtranslations.com
       Website: www.brombergtranslations.com
Translations & interpretations: over 60 languages.
(Woman, estab 1999, empl 20, sales , cert: WBENC)

8171   Collaborative Advantage Marketing
       2987 Franklin St
       Detroit, MI 48207
       Contact: Sales Rep
       Tel: 248-723-0793
       Email:
       Website: http://camtrade.com
Category Management Quality Assurance Programs
Total Product Design Business Analysis Brand Manage-
ment Full Service Marketing Headquarter Selling.
(Woman, estab 1999, empl 18, sales , cert: WBENC)

8172   Essential Events & Travel Planners
       20001 Greenfield
       Detroit, MI 48235
       Contact: Marion Allbritton Owner
       Tel: 313-891-4612
       Email: essparty1@yahoo.com
       Website: www.essentialpartyplanners.com
Event coordinating svcs, corporate events, charter bus
svcs, catering & decorating, rental svcs. (Woman/AA,
estab 1993, empl 6, sales , cert: State)

8173   Harris Marketing Group, Inc.
       102 Pierce St
       Birmingham, MI 48009
       Contact: Wendy Vadnais Finance Director
       Tel: 248-723-6300
       Email: wvadnais@harris-hmg.com
       Website: www.harris-hmg.com/
Integrated marketing campaigns, loyalty programs,
brand advertising, targeted direct mail, fulfillment,
media, public relations, training materials, website
development, event marketing & viral marketing.
(Woman, estab 1976, empl 10, sales $4,425,995, cert:
WBENC)

8174   M3D Experiences, Inc.
       16753 Black River Dr
       Northville, MI 48168
       Contact: Matthew Binkowski Principal, Chief
       Creative Officer
       Tel:
       Email: mattb@m3de.com
       Website: www.m3dexperiences.com
Brand identities & multi-sensory experiences, successful
marketing campaigns & develop memorable logos,
marketing collateral & content. (Woman, estab 2011,
empl 4, sales , cert: WBENC)

8175   Maestro LLC
       7107 ELM VALLEY DR
       Kalamazoo, MI 49009
       Contact: Tagg Petersen Dir Business Dev
       Tel: 800-319-2122
       Email: tagg@meetmaestro.com
       Website: www.meetmaestro.com
Training, brand consulting, management consulting
services, solution based contractors. (Woman, estab
2007, empl 31, sales $7,612,178, cert: WBENC)

8176 RSVP Premier Group, LLC
900 Wilshire Dr Ste 202
Troy, MI 48084
Contact: Tamika Brown CEO
Tel: 248-663-4107
Email: tbrown@rsvppremier.com
Website: www.rsvppremier.com
Event planning & management, meeting planning, conference planning, incentive trips, trade shows/expos, event design & décor, event production, celebrity entertainment, talent & speaker booking. (Woman/AA, estab 2002, empl 4, sales $109,450, cert: WBENC)

8177 Skyline Exhibits West Michigan
4768 Danvers Dr. SE
Kentwood, MI 49512
Contact: Eloy Cantu President
Tel: 616-301-8708
Email: cantul@skylinewm.com
Website: www.skyline.com
Trade show marketing, seminars, workshops. (Hisp, estab 2004, empl 5, sales $900,000, cert: NMSDC)

8178 Smith-Dahmer Associates, LLC
116 State St
Saint Joseph, MI 49085
Contact: Lori Stanwood Dir Key Accts
Tel: 269-983-4748
Email: loristanwood@smithdahmer.com
Website: http://smithdahmer.com
Marketing research & consulting, custom qualitative & quantitative methodologies, innovation & design research processes. (Woman, estab 1995, empl 30, sales $9,000,000, cert: WBENC)

8179 Special D Events, Inc.
535 Woodward Heights
Ferndale, MI 48220
Contact: Carol Galle CEO
Tel: 248-336-8600
Email: administrator@specialdevents.com
Website: www.specialdevents.com
Corporate event planning. (Woman, estab 1992, empl 17, sales $2,200,000, cert: WBENC)

8180 Strategic Market Research Group, Inc.
37129 Saint Martins St
Livonia, MI 48152
Contact: Ami Nienus President
Tel: 734-452-9104
Email: ami@smrginc.com
Website: www.smrginc.com
Market research. (Woman/As-Ind, estab 2007, empl 1, sales , cert: WBENC)

8181 Uproar Communications Ltd.
3772 PLAZA DRIVE Ste 5
Ann Arbor, MI 48108
Contact: President
Tel: 734-975-8888
Email:
Website: www.uproarcom.com
Communications & marketing services. (Woman, estab 1998, empl 20, sales , cert: WBENC)

8182 Wilson-Taylor Associates, Inc.
242 Lighthouse Circle
Manistee, MI 49660
Contact: Joanne Cleaver President
Tel: 231-291-1275
Email: jycleaver@wilson-taylorassoc.com
Website: www.wilson-taylorassoc.com
Content strategy & execution, writing, editing, research, website content, digital publishing, strategic communication consulting, communication training, career training, media training, communication coaching. (Woman, estab 1998, empl 2, sales $110,000, cert: WBENC)

Minnesota

8183 AllOut Marketing, Inc.
5775 Wayzata Blvd Ste 700
St. Louis Park, MN 55416
Contact: Ruth Lane CEO
Tel: 952-404-0800
Email: ruthlane@alloutsuccess.com
Website: www.alloutsuccess.com
Medical marketing consulting, market research, web development, graphic design, event management & public relations. (Woman/Hisp, estab 1995, empl 8, sales $722,000, cert: State)

8184 Azul 7, Inc.
800 Hennepin Ave Ste 700
Minneapolis, MN 55403
Contact: Sara O'Brien business devel lead
Tel: 612-767-4335
Email: hello@azul7.com
Website: www.azul7.com
Build better brands, products & services, strategy & innovation consulting, research, digital product & service design along with innovation process training. (Woman, estab 2007, empl 16, sales $1,868,437, cert: WBENC)

8185 Creative Connections
4049 Blackhawk Rd
Eagan, MN 55122
Contact: Marianne Badar Ohman Owner
Tel: 651-261-7886
Email: marianne@creativeconnections.net
Website: www.creativeconnections.net
Communications consulting, marketing communications project management, conference, meeting, tradeshow & event planning & production, team leadership, teambuilding training & services. (Woman, estab 1998, empl 1, sales , cert: City)

8186 D.Trio Marketing Group
401 N Third St, Ste 480
Minneapolis, MN 55401
Contact: Fred Driver Business Develop Dir
Tel: 612-436-0401
Email: fdriver@dtrio.com
Website: www.dtrio.com
Direct marketing, strategy, creative, list, DP, print and lettershop production, fulfillment & graphic design services. (Woman, estab 2000, empl 12, sales $3,500,000, cert: WBENC)

8187 deZinnia, Inc.
      1032 W 7th St
      St. Paul, MN 55102
      Contact: Michele Boone CEO
      Tel: 651-695-1041
      Email: sbboone@dezinnia.com
      Website: www.dezinnia.com
Program management, graphic design, marketing, marketing communications, digital architecture. (Woman, estab 1993, empl 14, sales $1,322,045, cert: State, City, WBENC)

8188 Dyvig Driver Devine Inc.
      401 N 3rd St, Ste 480
      Minneapolis, MN 55401
      Contact: Megan Devine Owner
      Tel: 612-787-3333
      Email: cwahl@dtrio.com
      Website: www.dtrio.com
Marketing, graphic design, branding, digital, strategy, copywriting, email coding, content, SEO, SEM, video creating, animation, multi-channel marketing, production management. (Woman, estab 2000, empl 9, sales , cert: WBENC)

8189 Five Star Productions
      7400 Metro Blvd
      Minneapolis, MN 55439
      Contact: Cindy Black President
      Tel: 952-831-7309
      Email: cjblack@fivestarproductions.net
      Website: http://fivestarproductions.net
Full-service production and event management, national sales meetings and conventions; recognition, incentive, and awards programs; entertainment and keynote speakers; product launches; philanthropic and special events. (Woman, estab 1989, empl 3, sales $1,300,000, cert: WBENC)

8190 Futura Marketing, Inc.
      9531 W 78th St Ste 250
      Eden Prairie, MN 55344
      Contact: Kelly Wold Smith President
      Tel: 952-843-5400
      Email: kelly@futuramarketing.com
      Website: www.futuramarketing.com
Marketing svcs: strategic planning, project management & creative design. (Woman, estab 1999, empl 13, sales $1,146,520, cert: WBENC)

8191 Group Ventures Inc.
      1770 James Ave S, Ste 2
      Minneapolis, MN 55403
      Contact: Ann Wellmuth President
      Tel: 612-821-0511
      Email: ann@groupventuresinc.com
      Website: www.groupventuresinc.com
Event & meeting planning, coordination & execution of incentive trips, sales & organizational meetings, board of directors meetings, conventions & tradeshows. (Woman, estab 1997, empl , sales $14,000,000, cert: WBENC)

8192 KDG InterActive, Inc.
      8010 Demontreville Trail
      Lake Elmo, MN 55042
      Contact: Lynette Kramer President
      Tel: 651-748-8480
      Email: lynette@kdg.com
      Website: www.kdg.com
Design & develop interactive marketing, education & training solutions. (Woman, estab 1991, empl 11, sales $1,200,000, cert: WBENC)

8193 LEE Branding
      945 Broadway St NE Ste 280
      Minneapolis, MN 55413
      Contact: Terri Lee CEO
      Tel: 612-843-8477
      Email: terri@leebranding.com
      Website: www.leebranding.com
Consumer-minded, strategic brand dev. (Woman, estab 2011, empl 15, sales $4,100,000, cert: WBENC)

8194 Neka Creative LLC
      P.O. Box 211481
      Saint Paul, MN 55121
      Contact: Rosemary Ugboajah President
      Tel: 651-207-9656
      Email: rosemaryu@nekacreative.com
      Website:
Brand development, Competitive Analysis, Brand Audits, Qualitative & Quantitative Research, Strategic Positioning, Brand Development, Culture Plans, Brand Workshops Brand Blueprints, Marketing/Communication. (Woman/AA, estab 2009, empl 1, sales , cert: NMSDC)

8195 Nina Hale Inc.
      100 S 5th St, Ste 2000
      Minneapolis, MN 55402
      Contact: Sarah Petit Sales/Mktg Mgr
      Tel: 612-392-2427
      Email: businessinquiry@ninahale.com
      Website: www.ninahale.com
Digital direct marketing; search engine optimization (SEO), paid placement, social media consulting, analytics & reporting, local search. (Woman/Nat Ame, As-Ind, As-Pac, Hisp, estab , empl , sales $14,000,000, cert: WBENC)

8196 One 2 One Marketing Inc.
      12101 12th Ave South
      Burnsville, MN 55337
      Contact: Elaine Grundhauser CEO
      Tel: 952-567-2730
      Email: elaine.g@one2onemktg.com
      Website: www.one2onemktg.com
Strategic promotional programs. (Woman, estab 1995, empl 9, sales $1,606,966, cert: WBENC)

8197 Perkins & Associates, LLC
      400 Grovaland Ave, Ste 2309
      Minneapolis, MN 55403
      Contact: Frank Perkins Owner
      Tel: 612-810-8361
      Email: frank@perkinsbridge.com
      Website: www.perkinsbridge.com
Marketing & business development. (AA, estab 2000, empl 1, sales $125,000, cert: City, NMSDC)

8198 Showcraft, Inc.
      1357 Larc Industrial Blvd
      Burnsville, MN 55337
      Contact: Jeryl Beaulieu President
      Tel: 952-890-4200
      Email: jeryl@showcraft.com
      Website: www.showcraft.com
Trade show exhibits, events & environments. (Woman, estab 1996, empl 14, sales $500,000, cert: WBENC)

8199 SmartBase Solutions LLC
      411 Washington Ave N
      Minneapolis, MN 55401
      Contact: Kris Lynch CEO
      Tel: 612-767-9940
      Email: klynch@smartbasesolutions.com
      Website: www.smartbasesolutions.com
Database marketing solutions, measure, analyze, & improve marketing & sales activities. (Woman, estab 2005, empl 20, sales , cert: WBENC)

8200   The Research Edge LLC
        1821 University Ave W, Ste N177
        St. Paul, MN 55104
        Contact: Cheryl Powers President
        Tel: 651-644-6006
        Email: cheryl@theresearchedge.com
        Website: http://theresearchedge.com
Marketing research services, focus groups, in-depth
interviews, qualitative research, quantitative research,
phone surveys, online surveys, online focus groups,
customized market research services full-service market
research services. (Woman, estab 1995, empl 5, sales
$303,360, cert: WBENC)

8201   Touch Of Magic Inc.
        P.O. Box 9311
        St. Paul, MN 55109
        Contact: Lori Hurley Chief Entertainment Officer
        Tel: 651-748-9442
        Email: lori@atouchofmagicentertainment.com
        Website: https://atouchofmagicentertainment.com
Event planning, Company Picnics, Corporate Events,
Holiday Parties, Banquets, Trade Shows, Sales Meetings,
Festivals, Fairs, Mitzvahs, Birthday Parties, Team Building,
Schools, Churches, etc. (Woman, estab 1986, empl 2, sales
$250,000, cert: WBENC)

8202   Tunheim
        8009 34th Ave South
        Minneapolis, MN 55425
        Contact: Ginny Melvie Sr. Exec Asst/Consultant
        Tel: 952-851-1600
        Email: gmelvie@tunheim.com
        Website: www.tunheim.com
Public Relations, Public Affairs, Strategic Communications,
Crisis Communications, Branding - Marketing, Research &
Opinion Polling. (Woman, estab 1990, empl 25, sales
$5,000,000, cert: WBENC)

8203   Type A Events, LLC
        10701 Red Circle Dr
        Minnetonka, MN 55343
        Contact: CEO
        Tel: 763-682-4846
        Email:
        Website: www.typeaevents.com
Strategic event management. (Woman, estab 2009, empl
40, sales $9,000,000, cert: WBENC)

8204   Visions, Inc.
        8801 Wyoming Ave N
        Brooklyn Park, MN 55445
        Contact: Jon Otto President & CEO
        Tel: 763-425-4251
        Email: jon.otto@visionsfirst.com
        Website: www.visionsfirst.com
Web design, print design, advertising & promotion,
corporate identification, logo branding, packaging,
interactive media, flash animation, video & special effects,
3D animation, web-based applications. (Nat Ame, estab
1985, empl 109, sales $14,207,330, cert: NMSDC)

Missouri

8205   Brighton Agency, Inc.
        7711 Bonhomme Ave Ste 100
        Saint Louis, MO 63105
        Contact: Tina VonderHaar CEO
        Tel: 314-726-0700
        Email: accounting@brightonagency.com
        Website: www.brightonagency.com
Strategic planning, brand development, digital marketing & production, marketing consulting, public relations,
advertising, promotions, media planning, audio & video
production, event marketing, online, mobile & app
development. (Woman, estab 1989, empl 71, sales
$9,030,143, cert: State, WBENC)

8206   Credit Financial Group Inc.
        141 Chesterfield Business Pkwy
        Chesterfield, MO 63005
        Contact: Vincent Andaloro President & CEO
        Tel: 636-536-5344
        Email: vince@latinpak.com
        Website: www.latinpak.com
Direct marketing services. (Hisp, estab 1996, empl 11,
sales $1,600,000, cert: State, NMSDC)

8207   Decision Insight Inc.
        2940 Main St
        Kansas City, MO 64108
        Contact: Tami Kaegi Office Mgr
        Tel: 816-221-0445
        Email: info@decisioninsight.com
        Website: www.decisioninsight.com
Market research services. (Woman, estab 1983, empl 22,
sales $3,440,000, cert: WBENC)

8208   Moxi Events, LLC
        1904 Grassy Ridge Rd
        Saint Louis, MO 63122
        Contact: Jaime Ratino Acct Mgr
        Tel: 615-454-2008
        Email: jratino@moxievents.com
        Website: www.moxievents.com
Corporate event planning, meetings, conferences,
incentive programs & special events. (Woman, estab
2008, empl 7, sales $267,125, cert: WBENC)

8209   Mozaic Management, Inc.
        5257 Shaw Ave Ste 204
        St. Louis, MO 63110
        Contact: Mary Ann Gibson CEO
        Tel: 314-446-6400
        Email: mgibson@mozaicltd.com
        Website: www.mozaicltd.com
Marketing communications: strategic brand consulting,
concept & design, creative execution, digital photography, illustration, photo retouching, interactive web
services, art production, prepress, large format digital
printing, sales promotion, etc. (Woman, estab 2003,
empl 130, sales $30,000,000, cert: WBENC)

8210   MT & Associates, LLC
        222 S. Meramec Ave., Ste 202
        St. Louis, MO 63105
        Contact: Shelly Tisius President
        Tel: 314-896-0275
        Email: mt@mtapractice.com
        Website: www.MTAPractice.com
Sign language interpreting services. (Woman, estab
2013, empl 5, sales , cert: State, City, WBENC)

8211 Ole Tyme Produce Inc.
3840 Millstone Pkwy
Saint Charles, MO 63301
Contact: Jim Adams President
Tel: 314-436-5010
Email: jadams@oletyme.com
Website: http://oletyme.com
Monday-Saturday fresh produce deliveries to Saint Louis and the surrounding area. (Woman, estab 1973, empl 48, sales , cert: State, City, WBENC)

8212 Pixie Stuff LLC
18 Brighton Way
Clayton, MO 63105
Contact: Jennifer Hein Chief Business Officer
Tel: 314-368-4730
Email: jennifer@hiredink.com
Website: http://hiredink.com
Develop outreach programs that engage, educate and empower your target audience. (Woman, estab 2003, empl 10, sales $800,000, cert: State, WBENC)

8213 Stakeholder Insights, LLC
319 N 4th St Ste 820
St. Louis, MO 63102
Contact: Lisa Richter Managing Principal
Tel: 314-454-1923
Email: lisa@stakeholderinsights.com
Website: www.stakeholderinsights.com
Market & employee research services, supports branding, change management, competitive intelligence, customer experience, employee engagement and retention, message testing, public opinion & website usability. (Woman, estab 2006, empl 3, sales $408,312, cert: WBENC)

8214 The Vandiver Group, Inc.
16052 Swingley Ridge Rd Ste 210
St. Louis, MO 63017
Contact: Donna Vandiver CEO
Tel: 314-991-4641
Email: tvg@vandivergroup.com
Website: www.vandivergroup.com
Strategic communications & public relations, corporate image & reputation management, branding, market research & training. (Woman, estab 1993, empl 10, sales $1,432,900, cert: State, WBENC)

North Carolina

8215 3 Birds Marketing, LLC
505-B W Franklin St
Chapel Hill, NC 27516
Contact: Layton Judd President
Tel: 919-913-2750
Email: layton@3birdsmarketing.com
Website: www.3birdsmarketing.com
Technology, software, integrated marketing platform, marketing, digital marketing, multichannel marketing, email marketing, email newsletters, digital newsletters, social media management, social media marketing. (Woman, estab 2009, empl 60, sales $3,769,500, cert: WBENC, NWBOC)

8216 ABZ Design Group, Inc.
1300 S Mint St, Ste 100
Charlotte, NC 28203
Contact: President
Tel: 704-374-1072
Email:
Website: www.abzdesign.com
Marketing communications & graphic design. (Woman, estab 1982, empl 11, sales , cert: State)

8217 Avantgarde Translations
5960 Fairview Rd Ste 400
Charlotte, NC 28210
Contact: Jael Williams Admin Asst
Tel: 704-496-2735
Email: submissions@avantgardetranslations.com
Website: www.avantgardetranslations.com
Translating written material, interpretation services, revising, editing, proofreading & laying out translated documents, cultural consulting. (Woman/AA, estab 2004, empl 3, sales $200,789, cert: NMSDC, WBENC)

8218 Bellomy Research, Inc.
175 Sunnynoll Ct
Winston-Salem, NC 27106
Contact: Glen Kelley Sr Dir of Admin
Tel: 336-721-1140
Email: glen.kelley@bellomy.com
Website: www.bellomyresearch.com
Marketing research services: design, data collection, analysis, interpretation, reporting & delivering point-of-view. (Woman, estab 1977, empl 100, sales $14,600,000, cert: State)

8219 Confero, Inc.
535 Keisler Dr Ste 204
Cary, NC 27518
Contact: Elaine Buxton President
Tel: 919-469-5200
Email: ebuxton@conferoinc.com
Website: www.conferoinc.com
Mystery shopping & customer satisfaction studies, training, brand management. (Woman, estab 1987, empl 23, sales $2,670,000, cert: WBENC)

8220 Content Spectrum
1832 Folly Gate Ct
Charlotte, NC 28262
Contact: David Springston Owner
Tel: 980-309-1465
Email: contentspectrum@gmail.com
Website: www.contentspectrum.net
Copywriting, Editing, Graphic design (banners, fliers, magazines, newsletters, posters, etc.), Translation services, Website development & maintenance. (Woman/AA, estab 2015, empl 1, sales , cert: NMSDC)

8221 GNB Ventures, LLC DBA Sisco Safety
1800F Associates Lane Ste F
Charlotte, NC 28217
Contact: Naomi Reale CEO
Tel: 704-488-4468
Email: Naomi@siscosafety.com
Website: www.SiscoSafety.com
Event planning services. (Woman, estab 2011, empl 24, sales $2,000,000, cert: State)

8222 It's My Affair, LLC
8711 Walden Ridge Drive
Charlotte, NC 28216
Contact: Kenneth Fields President
Tel: 704-394-4928
Email: kffields@it-henhouse.com
Website: www.itsmyaffair.com
Special events & meeting management: meetings, conferences, tradeshow management, grand openings, corporate recognition, launch parties, incentives. (Woman/AA, estab 2002, empl 2, sales , cert: WBENC, 8a)

8223 Lockman-Brooks Marketing Services, LLC
      6135 Park Dr S Ste 510
      Charlotte, NC 28210
      Contact: Linda Lockman-Brooks President
      Tel: 704-293-5666
      Email: linda@lockmanbrooks.com
      Website: www.lockmanbrooks.com
Strategic marketing consulting: commununity relations &
outreach, leadership consulting, communications planning
& project management. (Woman/AA, estab 1998, empl 1,
sales , cert: NMSDC)

8224 TCG Events
      2923 S. Tryon St Ste 230
      Charlotte, NC 28203
      Contact: Travis Holmes President
      Tel: 704-376-1943
      Email: info@tbsfreightmanagement.com
      Website: www.tcgevents.com
Event planning & production, video production, graphic
design and art direction, conference management,
entertainment production, incentive programs, corporate
awards programs, destination management. (Woman,
estab 1985, empl 5, sales $2,400,000, cert: WBENC)

8225 The Media Pro
      4613 Hunters Creek Lane
      Raleigh, NC 27606
      Contact: Jill Hammergren Owner
      Tel: 919-805-1061
      Email: jill@themediapro.biz
      Website: www.themediapro.biz
Media, marketing & communications, visual storytelling,
creative writing, videos, animations & graphic, live TV,
network programming, PSAs, video, film, e-learning,
government, training & & multimedia purposes. (Woman,
estab 1987, empl 0, sales , cert: WBENC)

8226 The Special Event Company
      6112 Saint Giles St
      Raleigh, NC 27612
      Contact: Ly Nguyen Dir Business Devel
      Tel: 919-459-8785
      Email: bp@recredit.co
      Website: www.specialeventco.com/
Event & meeting management. (Woman, estab 2001, empl
15, sales $5,000,000, cert: WBENC)

8227 Wray Ward, LLC
      900 Baxter St
      Charlotte, NC 28204
      Contact: Kent Panther VP, strategic planning
      Tel: 704-332-9071
      Email: kpanther@wrayward.com
      Website: www.wrayward.com
Marketing communications, strategic planning, brand
development, account leadership, advertising, media
planning and buying, interactive & web marketing, direct
marketing, public relations & social media. (Woman, estab
1977, empl 65, sales $23,345,000, cert: State)

North Dakota

8228 Global Sales Advisors
      523 Belmont Rd
      Grand Forks, ND 58201
      Contact: Andra Hargrave Owner
      Tel: 701-792-3394
      Email: andralazar@earthlink.net
      Website:
Marketing, direct marketing, diversity outreach, sales
training. (AA, estab 2002, empl 2, sales , cert: State)

Nebraska

8229 Bozell and Jacobs LLC
      1022 Leavenworth St
      Omaha, NE 68102
      Contact: Robin Donovan President
      Tel: 402-965-4300
      Email: rdonovan@bozell.com
      Website: www.bozell.com
Marketing Communications, Branding, Digital Marketing,
Interactive Design & Dev, Social Media, Media, Public
Relations, Market Research, Data Analytics. (Woman,
estab 1921, empl 38, sales $3,200,000, cert: WBENC)

New Jersey

8230 AG Marketing & Consulting Group
      554 W Broad St 1st Fl Rear
      Westfield, NJ 07090
      Contact: April Gregory President
      Tel: 908-456-5700
      Email: april@aprilgregoryinc.com
      Website: www.agmarketingconsulting.com
Brand development, event marketing & marketing
planning, social media & web implementation services.
(Woman/AA, estab 2000, empl 3, sales $250,000, cert:
State)

8231 Baldwin & Obenauf, Inc.
      50 Division St Ste 401
      Somerville, NJ 08876
      Contact: Joanne Obenauf CEO
      Tel: 908-685-1510
      Email: jmobenauf@baldwinandobenauf.com
      Website: http://bnoinc.com
Marketing & communications, strategic, creative &
production, brand strategy, identity packages, advertising, print & digital collateral, web & mobile sites,
corporate intranets, mobile apps, social media campaigns, videos. (Woman, estab 1981, empl 46, sales
$7,824,663, cert: State, WBENC)

8232 Breakthrough Marketing Technology
      110 E. Shearwater Court Ste 11
      Jersey City, NJ 07305
      Contact: Elaine Harris President
      Tel: 201-604-3600
      Email: elaine@breakthroughgroup.com
      Website: www.breakthroughgroup.com
Marketing, strategic planning, market research, learning,
coaching, implementation planning. (Woman/AA, estab
2002, empl 13, sales $432,000, cert: State, WBENC)

8233 Briechle-Fernandez Marketing Services
      625 Industrial Way West, Ste 7
      Eatontown, NJ 07724
      Contact: Lorenzo Fernandez President
      Tel: 732-982-8222
      Email: lorenzo.fernandez@bfmarketing.com
      Website: www.bfmarketing.com
Advertising, public relations, promotional items,
graphics design. (Hisp, estab 1984, empl 24, sales
$5,063,096, cert: State)

8234 BUZZRegistration
      3525 Quakerbridge Rd Ste 908
      Hamilton, NJ 08619
      Contact: Michael Rayner CEO
      Tel: 888-202-2262
      Email: michaelr@buysmart-gsa.com
      Website: www.buzzregistration.com
Registration management services for meeting planners.
(Woman, estab 2011, empl 25, sales $4,647,794, cert:
WBENC)

8235 Cajam Marketing, Inc.
8 Haviland Dr
Millstone Twp, NJ 08535
Contact: Kathy Gould President
Tel: 609-371-1325
Email: kgould@cajammarketing.com
Website: www.cajammarketing.com
Offline & online marketing initiatives through analytics.
(Woman, estab 2001, empl 5, sales $400,000, cert: State)

8236 Digital Brand Expressions
100 Overlook Center 2nd Fl
Princeton, NJ 08540
Contact: Veronica Fielding President
Tel: 609-688-8558
Email: vfielding@digitalbrandexpressions.com
Website: www.digitalbrandexpressions.com
Search engine marketing consultancy & services firm.
Focus: search engine marketing/optimization/advertising
and/or search engine image protection. (Woman, estab
2002, empl 10, sales $860,000, cert: WBENC)

8237 Distinctive Marketing, Inc.
516 Bloomfield Ave
Montclair, NJ 07042
Contact: Diane Spencer
Tel: 973-746-9114
Email: dmiassociates@verizon.net
Website: www.distinctivemktg.com
Marketing research, focus groups, telephone surveys,
event planning & mgmt, consulting, etc. (Woman/AA,
estab 1990, empl 12, sales , cert: State)

8238 Executive Meetings & Incentives, Inc.
685 US Hwy 202/206 N 2nd Fl
Bridgewater, NJ 08876
Contact: Larry Hambro Business Dev Mgr
Tel: 908-864-5800
Email: rgiaimo@eminj.com
Website: www.eminj.com
Meeting planning, global, full service meeting, event &
incentive planning, logistic services. (Woman, estab 1982,
empl 18, sales $2,746,000, cert: State)

8239 FirstEye Media Works
59 Lincoln Park Ste 375
Newark, NJ 07102
Contact: Kimberlee Williams CEO
Tel: 973-494-9705
Email: kwilliams@femworksllc.com
Website: www.femworksllc.com
Integrated campaigns, events & custom campaign photog-
raphy. (Woman/AA, estab 2004, empl 5, sales $503,611,
cert: NMSDC, WBENC)

8240 Focus USA, Inc
95 North State Route 17 Ste 109
Paramus, NJ 07652
Contact: Meg Ugenti Corporate Dir of Sales &
Marketing
Tel: 201-489-2525
Email: megu@focus-usa.com
Website: www.focus-usa.com
Direct & data marketing services, consumer & business
database aggregator, buyer behavior profiling, data &
email appending, email marketing, digital solutions,
mobile marketing, social media marketing. (Woman, estab
1994, empl 14, sales $3,840,000, cert: WBENC)

8241 GenZ Publishing LLC
57 Reids Hill Rd
Morganville, NJ 07751
Contact: Madalyn Rupprecht Corporate Liason
Tel: 732-306-7559
Email: team@drrissy.com
Website:
We offer 360* writing and marketing services. (Woman,
estab 2015, empl , sales $300,000, cert: WBENC)

8242 Global Planners, Inc.
3525 Quakerbridge Rd Ste 909
Hamilton, NJ 08619
Contact: Megan Buzzetta CEO
Tel: 609-689-0001
Email: wbereg@globalplanners.com
Website: www.globalplanners.com
Meeting & event coordination, contract negotiation, on
line attendee registration, on site staff support, site
selection, travel agency. (Woman, estab 2000, empl 14,
sales $3,368,000, cert: WBENC)

8243 Impact Consulting Enterprises LLC
172 S Clinton St
East Orange, NJ 07018
Contact: Cheryl McCants Principal
Tel: 973-337-2028
Email: cmccants@eimpactconsulting.com
Website: www.eimpactconsulting.com
Marketing, Communication, Special Campaigns & Media
Relations. (Woman/AA, estab 1989, empl 12, sales
$175,000, cert: State, NMSDC, WBENC, 8a)

8244 InGroup, Inc.
P.O. Box 206
Midland Park, NJ 07432
Contact: Marlene Bauer President
Tel: 201-612-1230
Email: mbaur@ingroupinc.com
Website: www.ingroupinc.com
Strategy & customized support services for marketing
programs, outreach communications & public relations.
(Woman, estab 1995, empl 5, sales $461,884, cert:
State, City, SDB)

8245 Iris Communications LLC
11 Belaire Dr
Roseland, NJ 07068
Contact: Barbara Bochese Managing Dir
Tel: 973-902-7027
Email: bbochese@iriscommunications.org
Website: www.iriscommunications.org
Marketing services, corporate communications &
branding, presentations-internal/corporate, brand
deliverables, educational/training, video production &
animation, website design & development, media
planning & buying. (Woman, estab 2011, empl 12, sales ,
cert: State, NWBOC)

8246 Magee Enterprises, LLC dba Event1Source
68 Abbond Court
Plainfield, NJ 07063
Contact: Dion Magee Co-Owner
Tel: 888-299-2250
Email: dion@event1source.com
Website: www.event1source.com
Event management & meeting sourcing. (Woman/AA,
estab 1994, empl 2, sales $195,000, cert: State)

8247 Marketsmith Inc.
2 Wing Dr
Cedar Knolls, NJ 07927
Contact: President
Tel: 973-889-0006
Email:
Website: www.marketsmithinc.com
Media: strategic consulting; media planning, buying &
optimization; traditional; programmatic display; mobile;
paid social; social CRM. (Woman, estab 1999, empl 72,
sales $9,417,082, cert: WBENC)

8248 MarketView Research Group, Inc.
115 River Rd, Ste 105
Edgewater, NJ 07020
Contact: VP
Tel: 201-840-5300
Email:
Website: www.marketviewresearch.com
Quantitative marketing research. (Woman, estab 1989,
empl 35, sales $8,021,000, cert: State, WBENC)

8249 Meadowlands Consumer Center Global Marketing
Resea
301 Rt. 17N Ste 503
Rutherford, NJ 07070
Contact: Andrea C. Schrager CEO
Tel: 201-865-4900
Email: info@consumercenters.com
Website: www.consumercenters.com
Qualitative market research & strategic consulting: study
design, strategy development, branding & new product R
& D. (Woman, estab 1984, empl 50, sales $5,200,000, cert:
State, WBENC)

8250 Meeting Logistics, LLC
890 Mountain Ave
New Providence, NJ 07974
Contact: President
Tel: 908-771-0804
Email:
Website: www.mtglogistics.com
Meeting, event, convention management, trade show
support, incentive programs, special events, advisory
boards, awards, educational programs, training programs.
(Woman, estab 2000, empl 5, sales $1,933,790, cert:
WBENC)

8251 MMI Inc.
350 W Passaic St
Rochelle Park, NJ 07662
Contact: President
Tel: 201-556-1188
Email:
Website: www.marketanalytics.com
International research: customer, competitive & market
intelligence solutions, qualitative & quantitative solutions.
(Woman, estab 2002, empl 10, sales $1,200,000, cert:
State, WBENC)

8252 Mona Terrell & Associates LLC
1610 Division Ave
Piscataway, NJ 08854
Contact: Mona Terrell President & CEO
Tel: 732-752-4690
Email: mona@monaterrell.com
Website: www.monaterrell.com
Corporate communications, public relations, public affairs,
social responsibility & sustainability programs. (Woman/
AA, estab 2009, empl 1, sales $150,000, cert: State,
WBENC)

8253 Paragon Productions Inc.
1900 Shadow Brook Dr
Wall Township, NJ 07719
Contact: Susanne Ardolino President
Tel: 732-282-9088
Email: susanne@paragonproductionsinc.com
Website: www.paragonproductionsinc.com
Marketing & communications, Design, Scheduling,
Staging, Audio Visual, Guest Speaker & Entertainment
requirements. (Woman, estab 1995, empl 4, sales
$895,000, cert: State)

8254 Raare Solutions LLC
4 Lorettacong Dr
Lake Hopatcong, NJ 07849
Contact: Business Develop Dir
Tel: 800-693-2994
Email:
Website: www.raaresolutions.com
CRM & customer data analysis, marketing campaign
design & management services, focusing on luxury
brands. (Woman, estab 2004, empl 17, sales $2,100,000,
cert: WBENC)

8255 Smith Design Associates Inc.
8 Budd St
Morristown, NJ 07960
Contact: Jenna Smith CEO
Tel: 973-429-2177
Email: jenna@smithdesign.com
Website: www.smithdesign.com
Brand Identity & Package Design, Seamless Account +
Project Management, Visual Strategy + Positioning,
Verbal Expression + Brand Package Design, Design
Production + Realization.
Visual (Woman, estab 1978, empl 25, sales $7,100,000,
cert: State, WBENC)

8256 Snap Creative Marketing
354 Route 46 West, Ste 2A
Hackettstown, NJ 07840
Contact: Roberta Rivinius Managing Partner
Tel: 908-441-6220
Email: Roberta@snapcreativemarketing.com
Website: www.snapcreativemarketing.com
Campaign Development & Strategy, Brand Management,
Direct Mail & Fulfillment, Lettershop/Mailhouse, Print
Production, Multicultural Marketing, Graphic Design,
Web Development & Interactive Design, Social Media &
TV & Radio Production, Promotions. (Woman, estab
2013, empl 21, sales $13,800,000, cert: WBENC)

8257 Stokes Creative Group, LLC
1666 Route 206
Southampton, NJ 08088
Contact: Adrienne Kanter Business Dev Mgr
Tel: 609-859-8400
Email: akanter@stokescg.com
Website: http://stokescg.com
Website design & branding; safety & training videos;
construction photography; public relations; advertising.
(Woman, estab 1989, empl 25, sales $1,700,000, cert:
WBENC)

8258 Strategic Research I
101 Morgan Lane
Plainsboro, NJ 08536
Contact: Venky Jagannathan Principal
Tel: 609-751-5231
Email: venky.jagan@srinsights.com
Website: www.srinsights.com
Pharmaceutical Marketing Research, Marketing Consult-
ing, Big Data Analysis. (As-Ind, estab 2006, empl 20,
sales , cert: State)

8259 Taurus Market Research
1810 Englishtown Rd
Old Bridge, NJ 08857
Contact: Beth Kamenitz Dir Client Relations
Tel: 732-251-7772
Email: beth@taurusresearch.com
Website: www.taurusresearch.com
Qualitative & quantitative market research: concept, product, packaging & advertising testing, one-on-one in-depth interviewing, intercept/exit interviewing, ethnographies & consumer panels, in-house recruiting. (Woman, estab 1992, empl 53, sales $1,000,000, cert: City)

8260 The Lane Group LLC
14-25 Plaza Rd North Ste 3N
Fair Lawn, NJ 07410
Contact: Tracey Lane President
Tel: 201-398-9230
Email: tlane@tlgmeetings.com
Website: www.tlgmeetings.com
Event & meeting planning, production & management (Woman, estab 2000, empl 15, sales $2,226,800, cert: State, WBENC)

8261 TMW Enterprises, Inc.
76 Park Ave
Flemington, NJ 08822
Contact: President, Exec Producer
Tel: 908-638-6070
Email:
Website: www.tmwenterprises.com
Audio visual equipment & staging services: sales meetings, product launches & award ceremonies. (Woman, estab 1992, empl 6, sales $2,650,000, cert: WBENC)

8262 Vanadams Sports Group LLC
623 Eagle Rock Ave Ste 317
West Orange, NJ 07052
Contact: Van Adams Principal
Tel: 888-435-8006
Email: vadams@vanadamssports.com
Website: www.VanAdamsSports.com
Marketing Athletes & Events, Consulting, Event Development, national events and promotions, contract negotiations, budget creation. (Woman/AA, estab 2004, empl 1, sales $225,000, cert: State)

8263 Websignia
60 Park Place Ste 404
Newark, NJ 07102
Contact: Steve Jones CEO
Tel: 973-732-4750
Email: diversity@websignia.net
Website: www.websignia.net
Digital marketing, visual design for web & print, digital marketing & custom web & mobile applications. (AA, estab 2003, empl 13, sales $670,000, cert: NMSDC)

New Mexico

8264 Slow Life Games, LLC
9 Piedras Negras
Santa Fe, NM 87505
Contact: Jason Zeaman President
Tel: 505-603-8930
Email: jason@handcraftedlearning.com
Website: www.HandcraftedLearning.com
We design and develop custom training for our clients in multiple formats: virtual webinars, in-person classroom, and stand alone eLearning. We specialize in highly interactive training that simulates what people do on the job and allows them to practice (Woman/As-Pac, estab 2011, empl 2, sales $716,617, cert: NMSDC, WBENC)

Nevada

8265 Ad Hoc Communication Resources, LLC
6 Benevolo Dr
Henderson, NV 89011
Contact: Shelli Ryan President
Tel: 702-567-1115
Email: shelli@adhoccr.com
Website: www.adhocCR.com
Business & corporate management consulting svcs: editing, technical writing, public realtions, news & publicity, product launches, media outreach, industry analyst outreach, whitepapers, press releases. (Woman, estab 1996, empl 2, sales $304,129, cert: WBENC)

8266 Fresh Wata, LLC
3905 W Diablo Dr, Ste 100
Las Vegas, NV 89118
Contact: Tricia Costello President
Tel: 913-269-3849
Email: tricia@freshwata.com
Website: www.freshwata.com
Create extraordinarily meaningful brand moments that drive connection, engagement and dialogue. (Woman/AA, estab , empl , sales $10,400,000, cert: WBENC)

8267 INTU Corporation
7065 W Ann Rd, Ste 130-332
Las Vegas, NV 89130
Contact: Joanna Lai Project Coord
Tel: 702-656-4503
Email: events@intucorporation.com
Website: www.intucorporation.com
Chair massage therapy, corporate wellness, spa oasis, casino gaming, luxury poolside services, sporting sky boxes, golf tournaments, themed parks, special events. (Woman, estab 2005, empl 150, sales , cert: WBENC)

New York

8268 aLanguageBank
159 W 25th St, 6th Fl
New York, NY 10001
Contact: Maxwell Davidson Mgr of New Business
Tel: 212-213-3336
Email: maxwelld@alanguagebank.com
Website: www.alanguagebank.com
Translation & localization services. (As-Pac, estab 1999, empl 10, sales $950,000, cert: NMSDC)

8269 BuzzBack Market Research dba Buzzback LLC
989 Sixth Ave
New York, NY 10036
Contact: Andrea Levene SVP Finance & Admin
Tel: 646-315-7575
Email: info@buzzback.com
Website: www.buzzback.com
Full service market research. (Woman, estab 2000, empl 37, sales , cert: WBENC)

8270 CBA Research Corp.
59 Clubhouse Ln
Scarsdale, NY 10583
Contact: Judy Bernstein VP, Qualitative Insights
Tel: 914-478-9355
Email: judy_bernstein@cba-link.com
Website: www.cba-link.com
Qualitative marketing research, focus groups, insights, moderating, analysis, ethnographies, depth interviews, shop-alongs, brand imagery, new product development, concept/messaging. (Woman, estab 1967, empl 3, sales $1,063,279, cert: WBENC)

8271   Company 20, Inc.
         555 Eighth Ave Ste 2201
         New York, NY 10018
         Contact: Michele Lasky VP
         Tel: 212-784-6453
         Email: michelelasky@company20.com
         Website: www.company20.com
Event marketing; planning; management; consulting;
production; charity fundraisers; celebrity; athlete foundations; cause-related; sports; special events; corporate
meetings; consumer promotions; incentives; hospitality.
(Woman, estab 2005, empl 5, sales $2,085,000, cert:
WBENC)

8272   Complemar Partners
         500 Lee Rd Ste 200
         Rochester, NY 14606
         Contact: President
         Tel: 585-647-5890
         Email:
         Website: www.complemar.com
Marketing & sales communication programs. (Woman,
estab 2004, empl 65, sales $5,195,389, cert: WBENC)

8273   Converge Marketing Services, LLC
         33 E 33rd St 3rd Fl
         New York, NY 10016
         Contact: Maarten Terry President
         Tel: 203-536-9414
         Email: maarten@convergedirect.com
         Website: www.convergemarketingservices.com
Media buying, planning & strategy, print production
services & paper procurement. (AA, estab 2017, empl 17,
sales , cert: NMSDC)

8274   D Exposito & Partners, LLC
         875 6th Ave, 25th Fl
         New York, NY 10001
         Contact: Louis Maldonado Managing Dir
         Tel: 646-747-8814
         Email: lmaldonado@dex-p.com
         Website: www.newamericanagency.com
Hispanic Marketing Solutions, Spanish language, In-Culture
and English language communications programs to reach
America's Hispanics no matter where they live, work or
play. (Woman/Hisp, estab 2005, empl 28, sales $5,077,000,
cert: State, NMSDC, WBENC)

8275   Design & Source Productions, Inc.
         143 W 29th St 3rd Fl
         New York, NY 10001
         Contact: Laura Tufariello President
         Tel: 212-265-8632
         Email: laura@dsnyc.com
         Website: www.design-and-source.com
Design & develop branded & private label products, custom
creative packaging solutions. (Woman, estab 1996, empl 7,
sales $8,400,000, cert: City, WBENC)

8276   DEVLINHAIR Production Inc.
         120 Wooster St 3rd Fl
         New York, NY 10012
         Contact: Dorothy Devlin Co-Founder
         Tel: 212-941-9009
         Email: supplier-diversity@devlinhair.com
         Website: www.devlinhair.com
Corporate event planning: meetings, conferences, internal
sales/mktg campaigns, film, video training programs,
interactive media. (Woman, estab 1991, empl 13, sales
$14,938,324, cert: WBENC)

8277   Ebony Marketing Systems, Inc.
         79 Alexander Ave, Ste 31-A
         Bronx, NY 10454
         Contact: Operations Dir
         Tel: 718-742-0006
         Email: kfuentes@ebonysystems.com
         Website: www.ebonysystems.com
Market research studies & services. (Woman/AA, estab
2011, empl , sales $650,000, cert: City, NMSDC)

8278   Eclipse Direct Marketing LLC
         173 Mineola Blvd Ste 402
         Mineola, NY 11501
         Contact: Kris Thelen CEO
         Tel: 212-931-8344
         Email: kthelen@eclipsedm.com
         Website: www.eclipsedm.com
Tracking & analytics, strategy planning with marketing
departments. (Woman, estab 2003, empl 7, sales
$1,600,000, cert: WBENC)

8279   Extrovertic Communications, LLC
         30 W 21st St 3rd Fl
         New York, NY 10010
         Contact: Dorothy Wetzel Chief Extrovert
         Tel: 646-312-6001
         Email: dorothy@extrovertic.com
         Website: www.extrovertic.com
Creative (print, video and digital), relationship marketing, patient education, social media, & marketing
consulting. (Woman, estab 2009, empl 27, sales
$7,933,003, cert: WBENC)

8280   Foglamp Research Corp.
         100 Greenwich Rd
         Bedford, NY 10506
         Contact: Kate Horn CEO
         Tel: 914-682-4127
         Email: kate.horn@foglampresearch.com
         Website: www.foglampresearch.com
Due diligence, reputational risk inquiries, surveys,
interviews & local market intelligence research in
emerging & frontier markets. (Woman, estab 2013, empl
3, sales $237,811, cert: WBENC)

8281   Greater Than One Inc.
         395 Hudson St
         New York, NY 10014
         Contact: Elizabeth Izard Apelles CEO
         Tel: 917-549-4202
         Email: eapelles@gthegtogroup.com
         Website: www.thegtogroup.com
marketing services: strategies, assessments, metrics
analytics, consumer research, behavior analytics,
communications planning, engagement. (Woman, estab
2000, empl 120, sales $28,000,000, cert: WBENC)

8282   Human Touch Translations Ltd.
         1010 Northern Boulevard Ste 208
         Great Neck, NY 11021
         Contact: President
         Tel: 646-358-4972
         Email: enagy@humantouchtranslations.com
         Website: www.humantouchtranslations.com
Translation servivces, 120 languages, interpreting
documents, technical documents, legal documents,
scientific papers, journal and magazine articles, educational materials, medical documents, market research
surveys. (Woman, estab 2010, empl 5, sales , cert: State,
WBENC)

8283 Imagine 360 Marketing
340 E 64th St Ste 17N
New York, NY 10065
Contact: President
Tel: 212-313-9616
Email:
Website: http://i360m.com
Strategic marketing and innovative design to increase brand awareness, acquire new business and retain existing customers. (Woman, estab 2005, empl 7, sales , cert: WBENC)

8284 Intstrux LLC
15 W 39th St, 13th Fl
New York, NY 10018
Contact: Sanjiv Mody CEO
Tel: 646-688-2782
Email: sanjiv.mody@pixacore.com
Website: www.pixacore.com
Digital communication, strategy & implementation services, marketing, training, corporate communication, live events initiatives. (As-Ind, estab 2007, empl 30, sales $7,577,436, cert: NMSDC)

8285 Ivy Cohen Corporate Communications, Inc.
2098 Frederick Douglass Blvd. Ste 10M
New York, NY 10026
Contact: Ivy Cohen CEO
Tel: 212-399-0026
Email: ivy@ivycohen.com
Website: www.ivycohen.com
Branding, promotions, corporate communications & organizational issues. (Woman, estab 2001, empl 1, sales $326,063, cert: City, WBENC)

8286 Keeper of the Brand
894 Otsego Rd
West Hempstead, NY 11552
Contact: Donyshia Boston-Hill CEO
Tel: 917-697-1699
Email: db@keeperofthebrand.com
Website: www.keeperofthebrand.com/
Marketing Plans & Strategies, Media Buying, TV, Radio, Print & Digital Solutions, Broadcast Media Distribution, Brand Development, Consumer Insight, Copyright, Transactional Engagement, Programming & Campaign Mgmt, Graphic Design, Creative Services. (Woman/AA, estab 2013, empl 6, sales $125,000, cert: State, NMSDC, WBENC)

8287 Kipany Productions, Ltd.
32 E 39 St
New York, NY 10016
Contact: Salman Ali President
Tel: 212-883-8300
Email: rfp@kipany.com
Website: www.kipany.com
Marketing communication svcs: direct response TV sales & outbound telemarketing; video, print, Internet direct mktg/web design & placement. (Woman, estab 1979, empl 30, sales , cert: WBENC)

8288 Kupcha Marketing Services
2 Hayes Rd
Amity Harbor, NY 11701
Contact: Elizabeth Kupcha President
Tel: 917-432-9481
Email: liz@kupchamkt.com
Website: www.kupchamkt.com
Marketing consulting: proposal management, presentation preparation/coaching, publicity & event planning. (Woman/AA, estab 2010, empl 1, sales , cert: State, City)

8289 Lightbeam Communications Corp
1787 Madison Ave, Ste 710
New York, NY 10035
Contact: Roben Allong CEO
Tel: 917-498-1738
Email: robena@lightbeamnyc.com
Website: www.lightbeamnyc.com
Qualitative research. (Woman/AA, estab 2009, empl 1, sales $284,000, cert: City)

8290 LilyGild Ltd.
199 Carlton Ave
Brooklyn, NY 11205
Contact: Co-President
Tel: 718-797-4656
Email:
Website: www.lilygild.com
Communications svcs: event, meeting & media production. (Woman, estab 1991, empl 3, sales $890,323, cert: WBENC)

8291 Mico Promotions, Inc.
1350 6th Ave, 4th Fl
New York, NY 10019
Contact: Maia Michaelson President
Tel: 212-255-5785
Email: maia@micopromotions.com
Website: www.micopromotions.com
Creative and art studio services. (Woman, estab 1992, empl 5, sales $1,295,287, cert: WBENC)

8292 Mirror Show Management
855 Hard Rd
Webster, NY 14580
Contact: Kelsey Calaci Dir of Sales & Marketing
Tel: 585-232-4020
Email: supplierdiversity@msmxp.com
Website: www.msmxp.com
Exhibit design & management firm. (Woman, estab 1993, empl 40, sales $20,000,000, cert: WBENC)

8293 Novatek Communications, Inc.
500 Helendale RdSte 280
Rochester, NY 14609
Contact: Amy Castronova CEO
Tel: 585-482-4070
Email: patty.setchell@novatekcom.com
Website: www.novatekcom.com
User & service writing, computer-based training, e-learning & multimedia. (Woman, estab 1989, empl 29, sales $1,504,910, cert: State, WBENC)

8294 Percepture
104 W 40th St.
New York, NY 10018
Contact: Thor Harris CEO
Tel: 800-707-9190
Email: supplierdiversity@percepture.com
Website: http://percepture.com
Public relations & marketing. (AA, estab 2004, empl 4, sales $3,389,825, cert: State)

8295 Sage Advertising LLC
71 Atkinson Rd
Rockville Centre, NY 11570
Contact: Jodi O'Sullivan Owner
Tel: 516-320-9225
Email: jodi@sage-agency.com
Website: www.sage-agency.com
Marketing strategies & materials, print, collateral, digital, trade show & video production. (Woman, estab 2008, empl 5, sales $720,258, cert: WBENC)

8296   Site Solutions Worldwide
       1023 Route 146
       Clifton Park, NY 12065
       Contact: Business Relations Specialist
       Tel: 518-399-7181
       Email:
       Website: www.sitesolutionsworldwide.com
Meeting svcs: site selection, meeting management,
contract negotiations, online registration, speaker coordination, exhibitor coordination & on-site meeting management. (Woman, estab 2001, empl 14, sales $8,764,783,
cert: State, WBENC)

8297   Spiral Design Studio, LLC
       135 Mohawk St
       Cohoes, NY 12047
       Contact: Lauren Payne Managing Partner
       Tel: 518-326-1135
       Email: lauren@spiraldesign.com
       Website: www.spiraldesign.com
Graphic design, advertising, marketing, website design, web
page design, responsive design, mobile website design,
internet marketing, digital marketing, email marketing,
branding, logo design, corporate identity, print design, print
marketing. (Woman, estab 1989, empl 10, sales $948,500,
cert: State, WBENC)

8298   Strategic Marketing & Promotions, Inc.
       10 N Main St
       Pearl River, NY 10965
       Contact: Greg Caglione President
       Tel: 845-623-7777
       Email: gcaglione@smpglobal.com
       Website: www.smpglobal.com
Mfr, design & produce point of purchase display fixtures,
signage, retail consumer packaging. Assembly, fulfillment,
inventory management, distribution center. (Minority,
Woman, estab 2001, empl 85, sales $5,000,000, cert: State)

8299   StudioLabs LLC.
       247 W 30th St Ste 12A
       New York, NY 10001
       Contact: Liz Young CEO
       Tel: 646-880-6892
       Email: liz@studiolabs.com
       Website: www.studiolabs.com
Websites, online software, mobile applications, digital ads,
online tools & digital marketing products. (Woman, estab
2003, empl 27, sales $3,999,300, cert: WBENC)

8300   The CementBloc
       32 Old Slip 15th Fl
       New York, NY 10005
       Contact: Art Chavez Partner
       Tel: 646-829-2002
       Email: achavez@thebloc.com
       Website: www.thebloc.com
Global branding, full-service professional promotion,
medical strategy, patient education, payer strategy, digital
strategy & communications planning/execution. (Woman,
estab 2000, empl 175, sales $41,900,000, cert: WBENC)

8301   The Mixx
       350 7th Ave Ste 1403
       New York, NY 10001
       Contact: Olympia Lambert Client Services Director
       Tel: 212-695-6663
       Email: hi@themixxnyc.com
       Website: www.themixxnyc.com
Strategic branding, messaging & marketing firm: corp
identity & brand platforms, brand collateral, annual reports
& Bbochures, advertising campaigns, direct mail campaigns,
web design & dev, multi-media marketing plans. (Woman,
estab 1996, empl 18, sales $900,000, cert: WBENC)

8302   The Mundial Group, Inc.
       28 E 28th St
       New York, NY 10016
       Contact: Felix Sencion
       Tel: 212-213-1400
       Email: billing@mundialgroup.net
       Website: www.mundialsportsnetwork.com
Marketing; Print Sport Publication; Print Advertising;
Digital Advertidsing: display, flash, mobile, pre-roll,
branded content production (Hisp, estab 1999, empl 11,
sales , cert: NMSDC)

8303   The Thomas Collective LLC
       37 w 28th st 12th floor
       New York, NY 10001
       Contact: Erin Donley Special Projects Coordinator
       Tel: 212-229-2294
       Email: edonley@thethomascollective.com
       Website: www.thethomascollective.com
Marketing communications, Brand Development, Public
Relations & Digital/Social Media. (Woman, estab 2004,
empl 20, sales $700,000, cert: WBENC)

8304   TITANIUM Worldwide LLC
       350 7th Ave Ste 1403
       New York, NY 10001
       Contact: Chief Financial Operations Officer
       Tel: 646-952-8440
       Email:
       Website: www.titaniumww.com
Media, marketing, communications & consulting:
Branding/Creative/Strategy, Content/Messaging, Digital/
Social/Mobile, Film/Video Production, Event Marketing,
Business Intelligence, Data Warehousing, Development/
Deployment. (Woman, estab 2014, empl 4, sales , cert:
State, WBENC)

8305   UX Design Collective LLC
       672 Carroll St, Unit 3
       Brooklyn, NY 11215
       Contact: Ariel Rey Head of Product and Projects
       Tel: 929-352-4489
       Email: services@uxdesigncollective.com
       Website: www.uxdesigncollective.com
Design websites, mobile apps, strategize, design, and
build thoughtful, transformative digital products.
(Woman/As-Pac, estab 2017, empl 4, sales , cert: State,
City, WBENC)

8306   View Finders Market Research
       11 Sandra Ln
       Pearl River, NY 10965
       Contact: Janet Gaines Owner
       Tel: 845-735-7022
       Email: jgaines@view-finders.com
       Website: www.view-finders.com
Focus group management, consumer & business
research, advertising testing, product definition, concept
development, attitudinal research, usage testing,
customer satisfaction & new product development.
(Woman, estab 1983, empl 25, sales $700,000, cert:
WBENC)

8307   Weinman Schnee Morais, Inc.
       250 W 57th St Ste 2212
       New York, NY 10107
       Contact: Cynthia Weinman Principal
       Tel: 212-906-1900
       Email: cweinman@wsm-inc.com
       Website: www.wsm-inc.com
Marketing research, 50% qualitative & 50% quantitative.
(Woman, estab 1993, empl 12, sales , cert: WBENC)

8308 Yorkville Marketing Consulting LLC
425 E 79 St Ste 11M
New York, NY 10075
Contact: Dina Shapiro CEO
Tel: 646-284-2481
Email: dina.shapiro@yorkvilleconsulting.com
Website: www.YorkvilleConsulting.com
Corporate Brand Strategy, Marketing, Organization
Planning, Marketing Capabilities, Training. (Woman, estab
2013, empl 1, sales , cert: WBENC)

8309 Zebra Strategies
421 7th Ave Ste 1100
New York, NY 10001
Contact: Denene Jonielle Rodney CEO
Tel: 212-244-3960
Email: denene@zstrategies.net
Website: www.zstrategies.net
Qualitative market research services. (Woman/AA, estab
2001, empl 10, sales $1,541,000, cert: WBENC)

Ohio

8310 Acadia Lead Management Services Inc.
4738 Gateway Circle Ste A100
Kettering, OH 45440
Contact: Tami Randall Mgr
Tel: 888-605-3194
Email: tlr@acadialms.com
Website: www.acadialms.com
Customized industry data, marketing information & sales
leads, lead qualification, lead nurturing, marketing
dashboard & lead management. (Woman, estab 1999,
empl 21, sales $958,835, cert: WBENC)

8311 Affordable Language Services
8944 Blue Ash Road
Cincinnati, OH 45242
Contact: Kristi Reynek CEO
Tel: 513-745-0888
Email: kreynek@affordablelanguages.com
Website: www.affordablelanguages.com
Translation & interpreting services, voice-over & transcrip-
tion. (Woman, estab 2000, empl 14, sales $2,209,000, cert:
WBENC)

8312 B63 Line
31 S Second St, Ste 201
Miamisburg, OH 45342
Contact: President
Tel: 937-490-4000
Email:
Website: www.b63line.com
Produce technical reviews, research reports, brochures,
infographics, videos, websites, and electronic communica-
tions. (Woman, estab 2009, empl 5, sales $351,000, cert:
WBENC)

8313 Baker Creative Ltd.
386 Main St
Groveport, OH 43125
Contact: Michele Cuthbert Principal
Tel: 614-836-3845
Email: mbaker@baker-creative.com
Website: www.baker-creative.com
Graphic Design, Marketing Consulting, Advertising, Public
Relations, Display Advertising. (Woman/Hisp, estab 2003,
empl 10, sales $150,000, cert: State, WBENC, SDB)

8314 Bascom & Adams Business Solutions, LLC
1209 Hill St North Ste 227
Pickerington, OH 43147
Contact: Christine Adams President
Tel: 614-252-7880
Email: chrisadams@bascomadams.com
Website: www.bascomadams.com
Marketing communications, public relations, special
events, outreach & engagement. (Woman/AA, estab
2002, empl 1, sales , cert: State, City)

8315 Charm Consulting
2957 Cranbrook Dr
Cincinnati, OH 45251
Contact: Toyia Montgomery CEO
Tel: 513-290-6357
Email: charmconsulting3@gmail.com
Website: www.charmconsulting3.com
Branding, public relations & event services. (Woman/
AA, estab 2014, empl 3, sales , cert: State)

8316 EVOLUTION Creative Solutions
7107 Shona Dr Ste 110
Cincinnati, OH 45237
Contact: Robert Miller Sales Rep
Tel: 513-864-3761
Email: bob.miller@evo-creative.com
Website: www.evo-creative.com
Marketing plans, graphic design & production, website
creation & maintenance, and social media. (Woman,
estab 2011, empl 6, sales , cert: WBENC)

8317 Gong Gong Communications
746 Green Crest Dr
Westerville, OH 43081
Contact: Amanda Sage CEO
Tel: 614-388-8918
Email: amanda@gonggongcommunications.com
Website: http://gonggongcommunications.com
Corporate, non-profit event planning & marketing,
Offline & online experiential marketing campaigns,
Target social media & e-mail marketing campaigns,
Podcast production & promotion. (Woman, estab 2009,
empl 3, sales , cert: WBENC)

8318 Illumination Research, Inc.
5947 Deerfield Blvd Ste 203
Mason, OH 45040
Contact: Karri Bass President
Tel: 513-774-9588
Email: kbass@illumination-research.com
Website: www.illumination-research.com
Qualitative market research. (Woman, estab 0, empl 29,
sales $6,593,000, cert: WBENC)

8319 Incite Visual Communications
P.O. Box 1017
Milford, OH 45150
Contact: Michael Perry Business Develop Dir
Tel: 513-575-5100
Email: mike@incitevisual.com
Website: http://incitevisual.com
Branding/marketing design, Branding, Package Design,
Print & Digital Sales/Marketing Assets, Point of Sale
materials, Product Sell Sheets, FSI, Event Promotional
assets. (Woman, estab 2001, empl 2, sales $186,000,
cert: WBENC)

8320 Market Inquiry, Inc.
5825 Creek Rd
Cincinnati, OH 45242
Contact: Cathy Noyes Owner
Tel: 513-794-1088
Email: cathy@marketinquiry.com
Website: www.marketinquiry.com
Qualitative & quantitative research. (Woman, estab 1995, empl 20, sales $1,164,000, cert: WBENC)

8321 MMP LLC
7588 Central Parke Blvd, Ste 321
Mason, OH 45040
Contact: Linda Dektas Owner
Tel: 513-234-0560
Email: linda@creativestorm.com
Website: www.creativestorm.com
Websites, ads-print & broadcast, brochures, logo design, digital marketing, direct mail, social media, promotions, displays, promotional items & apparel. (Woman, estab 1999, empl 5, sales $1,000,000, cert: WBENC)

8322 Partners In Planning One Inc.
7061 Larkspur Lane
Liberty Township, OH 45044
Contact: Nancy Caine President
Tel: 513-755-1091
Email: ncainepip@aol.com
Website: http://partnersinplanning.org
Meeting planning & event svcs: food & beverage negotiation, budget control, meeting set up & contract negotiations. (Woman, estab 1997, empl 1, sales , cert: WBENC)

8323 Penn and Associates, Inc.
3547 Fenley Rd
Cleveland Heights, OH 44121
Contact: Catherine Penn President
Tel: 216-932-4368
Email: catherine@pennandassociates.com
Website: www.pennandassociates.com
Marketing research & evaluation consulting. Quantitative research (primary research), Secondary research, Economic Analysis, Program evaluation, Online surveys, Data analysis, Report writing. (Woman, estab 1987, empl 1, sales , cert: State, City)

8324 Power Presentations, Inc.
8225 Brecksville Rd, Ste 100
Brecksville, OH 44141
Contact: Cate Huff Finance/Admin Mgr
Tel: 440-526-4400
Email: ch@power-presentations.com
Website: www.power-presentations.com
Communication and presentations skills training for all types of communication, standing, seated and virtual. (Woman, estab 1993, empl 7, sales , cert: WBENC)

8325 Quez Media Marketing
1138 Prospect Ave E
Cleveland, OH 44115
Contact: Jose Vasquez CEO
Tel: 216-910-0202
Email: info@quezmedia.com
Website: www.quezmedia.com
Marketing communications, online storefronts, data services, creative services, print. (Hisp, estab 2009, empl 17, sales $1,646,098, cert: State, City, NMSDC)

8326 R/P Marketing Public Relations
1500 Timberwolf Dr
Holland, OH 43528
Contact: Robin Walters VP Business Dev
Tel: 614-428-6056
Email: rwalters@r-p.com
Website: www.r-p.com
Marketing, advertising & public relations services. (Woman, estab 1993, empl 25, sales $5,559,217, cert: WBENC)

8327 Rhonda Crowder & Associates LLC
1465 E 112th St
Cleveland, OH 44106
Contact: Wayne Dailey Creative Dir
Tel: 216-352-3330
Email: wayne@rhondacrowderllc.com
Website: www.rhondacrowderllc.com
Communications, content creation, graphic design, fundraising & media relations services. (Woman/AA, estab 2011, empl 5, sales , cert: State)

8328 SCANVenger Hunt LLC
1275 Kinnear Rd
Columbus, OH 43212
Contact: Sean Fields Dir Business Dev
Tel: 800-975-5161
Email: sean@scanvengerhunt.biz
Website: www.scanvengerhunt.biz
Event services, event applications, registration badges for attendees. (AA, estab 2012, empl 3, sales $155,000, cert: NMSDC)

8329 Various Views Research, Inc.
11353 Reed Hartman Hwy, Ste 200
Cincinnati, OH 45241
Contact: Doug van der Zee Dir Business Dev
Tel: 513-387-2208
Email: dvanderzee@variousviews.com
Website: www.variousviews.com
Market research, qualitative research methodologies, focus groups, in-depth interviews & product tests. (Woman, estab 2007, empl 75, sales $3,500,000, cert: WBENC)

8330 Visibility Marketing, Inc.
24700 Chagrin Blvd Ste 306
Beachwood, OH 44122
Contact: Montrie Rucker Adams Chief Visibility Officer
Tel: 440-684-9920
Email: mra@visibilitymarketing.com
Website: www.visibilitymarketing.com
Marketing communications & public relations, public & media relations services & strategic marketing campaigns. (Woman/AA, estab 2000, empl 2, sales , cert: State, City, WBENC, 8a)

Oklahoma

8331 Bullseye Database Marketing, LLC
5546 S 104th East Ave
Tulsa, OK 74146
Contact: Deborah Kobe Norris CEO
Tel: 918-587-1731
Email: dnorris@bullseyedm.com
Website: www.bullseyedm.com
Direct marketing, direct mail, email, mobile & social media, strategic campaign direction, creative services, on-time, on-budget, error-free production, response tracking & analysis. (Woman, estab 1988, empl 8, sales $1,638,390, cert: WBENC)

Oregon

8332 Paulette Carter Design, Inc. (PCD Group)
5257 NE MLK Jr Blvd, Ste 301
Portland, OR 97211
Contact: Danielle Bastron Controller
Tel: 503-525-2989
Email: danielle@pcdgroup.com
Website: www.pcdgroup.com
Marketing svcs: custom websites, intranets & online applications, content mgmt, customer relationship mgmt tools, custom work flow & productivity applications, e-commerce, systems & data integration. (Woman, estab 1996, empl 12, sales , cert: WBENC)

8333 Stewart Marketing Group, LLC
905 N Harbour Dr, Unit 3
Portland, OR 97217
Contact: Michael Stewart President
Tel: 503-270-7857
Email: michael@stewartmarketinggroup.com
Website: www.stewartmarketinggroup.com
Conference & event planning, training & seminar materials, travel & hospitality, point of purchase displays, media & CD/DVD disc storage, office supplies. (AA, estab 2006, empl 1, sales $130,000, cert: State)

8334 The Kingfisher Group, LLC
10260 SW Greenburg Rd Ste 400
Portland, OR 97223
Contact: Mary Lou Kayser CEO
Tel: 503-567-8730
Email: mlk@maryloukayser.com
Website: http://maryloukayser.com
Content Marketing Strategies, Visual Strategic Planning, Creativity & Innovation, Training & Development, Presentation Skills Development. (Woman, estab 2012, empl 1, sales , cert: State)

Pennsylvania

8335 2nd Spark Consulting LLC
31 E Butler Ave 1st Fl
Ambler, PA 19002
Contact: Stefanie Freeling Finance Mgr
Tel: 215-948-3055
Email: sfreeling@2ndspark.com
Website: www.2ndspark.com
Marketing consulting & creative advertising, customer insights, situation analysis, war games, portfolio architecture strategy, buying process, positioning, messaging, branding, campaign development, media planning, tactical planning. (Woman/As-Pac, estab 2009, empl 20, sales $1,726,022, cert: WBENC)

8336 aiaTranslations LLC
4387 W. Swamp Rd#556
Doylestown, PA 18902
Contact: Molly Naughton President
Tel: 908-955-5201
Email: molly.naughton@aiatranslations.com
Website: www.aiaTranslations.com
aiaTranslations is the only full-service US-based agency specializing in healthcare and life science translation. (Woman, estab 2010, empl 4, sales $1,500,000, cert: WBENC)

8337 Apex Impact Marketing LLC
1720 Kendarloren Dr Ste 714
Jamison, PA 18929
Contact: Howard Wilensky Partner
Tel: 215-489-5460
Email: howard@focusmx.com
Website: www.focusmx.com
Marketing Strategy, Digital Strategy & Planning Websites, Microsites, Landing Pages, Creative & Design (Wordpress,Kentico, Sitecore, .NET), eCRM Programs, Social Media Campaigns, Mobile & Tablet Applications, Online Advertising. (Woman, estab 2009, empl 14, sales , cert: WBENC)

8338 Bosha Design Inc.
921 Childs Ave
Drexel Hill, PA 19026
Contact: President
Tel: 610-622-4422
Email:
Website: www.boshadesign.com
Print & web graphic design: corporate communications, business collateral, annual reports, web design & dev, identity systems, brochures, newsletters, advertising, exhibits & signage. (Woman, estab 1986, empl , sales $85,019,107, cert: WBENC)

8339 Brandwidth Solutions, LLC
108 Samantha Lane
Lansdale, PA 19446
Contact: Debra Harrsch CEO
Tel: 215-997-8575
Email: dharrsch@brandwidthsolutions.com
Website: www.brandwidthsolutions.com
Marketing communications, digital, 3D interactive, video & social media. (Woman, estab 2005, empl 7, sales $718,392, cert: WBENC)

8340 Chelsea Partners Inc.
108 Arch St Ste 1202
Philadelphia, PA 19106
Contact: Tempa Berish President
Tel: 215-603-7300
Email: tempa@chelseapartners.com
Website: www.chelseapartners.com
Graphic design, printing (digital, flat sheet and web), presort mailing services & fulfillment. (Woman, estab 1998, empl 13, sales $2,120,795, cert: State, City, WBENC)

8341 Community Marketing Concepts, Inc.
7300 City Ave Ste 330
Philadelphia, PA 19151
Contact: Daud Hadi Public Relations
Tel: 215-871-0900
johnpaul@communitymarketingconcepts.com
www.communitymarketingconcepts.com
Public relations & marketing, research, strategic development, social & issue management programs, brand messaging, publicity & media placement, event planning, corporate & community relations, sponsorships, graphic & web design. (Woman/AA, estab 1998, empl 10, sales $2,400,000, cert: State, City, NMSDC)

8342 DaBrian Marketing Group
500 Penn St, Ste 201
Reading, PA 19602
Contact: Owner
Tel: 610-743-5602
Email:
Website: http://dabrianmarketing.com
Digital marketing agency, original and strategic digital marketing solutions. (AA, estab 2008, empl 9, sales $949,000, cert: State, NMSDC)

8343 Eitzen Creative LLC
202 Dudley Ave
Narberth, PA 19072
Contact: Pamela Eitzen President
Tel: 610-660-0220
Email: pam@eobcreative.com
Website: http://eobcreative.com
Graphic design, strategic communications, branding, advertising, video, animation, corporate & employee communications, corporate identity, investor relations materials, websites, exhibit design & meeting support. (Woman, estab 2012, empl 3, sales $268,944, cert: WBENC)

8344 Fox Specialties, Inc. dba Encompass Elements
2750 Morris Rd Ste C
Lansdale, PA 19446
Contact: Nadine Hodges New Business Devel
Tel: 267-209-4133
Email: nhodges@encompasselements.com
Website: www.encompasselements.com
Marketing communications. (Woman, estab 1995, empl 65, sales $25,000,000, cert: WBENC)

8345 GLOBO
145 Greenwood Ave
Wyncote, PA 19095
Contact: Alec Kissell Sales Operations Mgr
Tel: 800-555-3010
Email: alec@helloglobo.com
Website: http://helloglobo.com
Translation, telephone interpreting & video remote interpreting services. (Hisp, estab 2010, empl 43, sales , cert: NMSDC)

8346 Gray Consulting, Inc.
190 N Independence Mall West Ste 201
Philadelphia, PA 19107
Contact: Scott Gray CEO
Tel: 215-413-7880
Email: scott.gray@clincierge.com
Website: www.clincierge.com
Meeting & event planning, logistical services, travel, attendee mgmt, web conferencing, audio/visual production, food & beverage coordination, on-site mgmt, incentive trips, sales meetings. (Woman, estab 1994, empl 35, sales $3,413,602, cert: State)

8347 Linguis-Techs, Inc.
408 Executive Dr
Langhorne, PA 19047
Contact: Lisa O'Rourke Dir of Finance
Tel: 215-860-8152
Email: lisa@sommerconsulting.com
Website: www.sommerconsulting.com
Qualitative marketing research, strategy & motivational profile of target audiences on conscious, unconscious & emotional levels. (Woman/Hisp, estab 1991, empl 11, sales $3,855,315, cert: NMSDC, WBENC)

8348 Markitects, Inc.
107 W Lancaster Ave, Ste 203
Wayne, PA 19087
Contact: Francine Carb CEO
Tel: 610-687-2200
Email: fcarb@markitects.com
Website: www.markitects.com
Strategic marketing, branding, public relations & communications. (Woman, estab 1994, empl 12, sales $2,000,000, cert: WBENC)

8349 mdgroup
575 East Swedesford Road Ste 101
Wayne, PA 19087
Contact: LaQuinta Jernigan Sr Dir Business Dev
Tel: 610-825-2660
Email: laquinta.jernigan@mdgroup.com
Website: www.mdgroup.com
Global strategic meeting management, incentive travel, sales meetings, corporate events, product launches, training, road shows, corporate retreats, and board of director meetings. (Woman, estab 2002, empl 61, sales $17,713,000, cert: State)

8350 MFR Consultants, Inc.
128 Chestnut St
Philadelphia, PA 19106
Contact: Maria Roberts CEO
Tel: 215-238-9270
Email: mfrizelle@mfrconsultants.com
Website: www.mfrconsultants.com
Strategic marketing, multimedia, graphic design, web & application development, management consulting. (Woman/AA, estab 1989, empl 15, sales $4,114,966, cert: State, WBENC)

8351 MOD Worldwide
1429 Walnut St Fl 2
Philadelphia, PA 19102
Contact: Nina Stanley President
Tel: 215-732-7666
Email: nina@modworldwide.com
Website: www.modworldwide.com
Brand, marketing, digital, 3D visualization, graphic design, digital media, internet marketing, film, website development, production, visual effects, and print production. (Woman, estab 2002, empl 20, sales $3,000,000, cert: City, WBENC)

8352   Modern Graphics
       118 Dickerson Rd Ste B
       North Wales, PA 19454
       Contact: President
       Tel: 215-619-4700
       Email:
       Website: www.modernsbc.com
Branding, web design, collateral & digital literature, logo
design, graphic design, internal & external corporate
communications. (Woman, estab 1999, empl 8, sales
$2,100,000, cert: WBENC)

8353   Naxion, Inc.
       1835 Market St
       Philadelphia, PA 19103
       Contact: Patricia Green special projects
       Tel: 215-496-6870
       Email: pgreen@naxionthinking.com
       Website: www.naxionthinking.com
Provide trusted decision support in innovation, opportunity assessment & pricing, launch strategy, brand health &
lifecycle management. (Woman, estab , empl , sales
$22,000,000, cert: WBENC)

8354   Rector Communications, Inc.
       2300 Chestnut St, Ste. 360
       Philadelphia, PA 19103
       Contact: Marion Rector President
       Tel: 215-963-9661
       Email: marion@rector.com
       Website: www.rector.com
Corporate Communications, Employee Communications,
Branding, Business Development, Marketing Services,
Management Consulting, Graphic Design & Annual
Reports. (Woman, estab 1983, empl 5, sales $654,514,
cert: City, WBENC)

8355   Slice Communications, LLC
       234 Market St, Fl 4
       Philadelphia, PA 19106
       Contact: Brian McDonnell Business Development
       Tel: 215-600-0050
       Email: bmcdonnell@slicecommunications.com
       Website: http://slicecommunications.com/
Public relations & social media, stories, editorials, re-
search, data, trends, case studies, events & digital assets.
(Woman, estab 2008, empl 15, sales , cert: City, WBENC)

8356   SPRYTE Communications
       200 S Broad St, Ste 1160
       Philadelphia, PA 19102
       Contact: Lisa Simon CEO
       Tel: 215-545-4715
       Email: lsimon@sprytecom.com
       Website: www.sprytecom.com
Public relations & marketing consulting. (Woman, estab
1990, empl 6, sales $1,527,267, cert: State, WBENC)

8357   The Melior Group, Inc.
       1528 Walnut St, Ste 1414
       Philadelphia, PA 19102
       Contact: Linda McAleer President
       Tel: 215-545-0054
       Email: lmcaleer@meliorgroup.com
       Website: www.meliorgroup.com
Marketing research & consulting, analysis, implications &
recommendations. (Woman, estab 1982, empl 10, sales
$1,500,000, cert: State)

Puerto Rico

8358   DC Engineering Group, PSC
       FIrst Federal Savings Bldg, Ste 820 Ponce de Leon
       Ave 1519
       San Juan, PR 00693
       Contact: Daianyk Cordova CEO
       Tel:
       Email: dcordova@dc-eng.com
       Website: www.dc-eng.com
DC Engineering is a Professional Services Corporation
that offer Project Management and Inspection Services
During Construction. We also provide permit procure-
ment services and environmental services. (Woman/
Hisp, estab 2011, empl 8, sales , cert: NMSDC)

8359   Desde Mi Huerto, Inc.
       P.O. Box 61
       Patillas, PR 00723
       Contact: Raul Rosado Administrator
       Tel: 787-202-0392
       Email: desdemihuerto@gmail.com
       Website: www.caribbeanecoseeds.com
We can deliver and merchandize in the island of Puerto
Rico and ship to the southern USA (Woman/Hisp, estab
2012, empl 6, sales , cert: NMSDC)

8360   Maremar Design, Inc.
       Urb Casa Linda Court 20 B St
       Bayamon, PR 00959
       Contact: Marina Rivon President
       Tel: 787-731-8795
       Email: marina@maremar.com
       Website: www.maremar.com
Graphic design, corporate identity, logos, stationary,
graphic standards manual, design consultancy, sales
literature, collateral, point of purchase, annual peports,
corporate profiles, brochures, newsletters. (Woman/
Hisp, estab 1997, empl 2, sales , cert: NMSDC)

Rhode Island

8361   Advertising Ventures, Inc. dba (add)ventures
       20 Risho Ave
       East Providence, RI 02914
       Contact: Joseph R Miech COO
       Tel: 401-453-4748
       Email: jmiech@addventures.com
       Website: www.addventures.com
Marketing, branding, public relations, advertising,
graphic & interactive design. (Hisp, estab 1989, empl 42,
sales $9,891,991, cert: State)

8362   FAVOR Design + Communications
       582 Great Rd Ste 201
       North Smithfield, RI 02896
       Contact: Rene Payne Principal
       Tel: 508-272-0522
       Email: rene@favordesignco.com
       Website: www.favordesignco.com
Graphic & web design svcs, branding, creative direction,
brand identity, content creation, copywriting, positioning, book design, packaging, interactive design, product
design, editorial, environmental retail. (Woman/AA,
estab 2004, empl 1, sales $335,817, cert: WBENC)

8363 Katie Schibler & Associates LLC
      5875 Post Rd, Unit 1
      East Greenwich, RI 02818
      Contact: Katie Schibler Founder
      Tel: 401-398-0830
      Email: partnerships@schiblerandassociates.com
      Website: www.katieschibler.com
Project Management, Event Planning, Marketing Consult-
ing, Social Media Planning, Social Media Strategy,
Copywriting, Sales Strategy, Strategic Planning, Partnership
Consulting, PR/Media Relations. (Woman, estab 2011, empl
4, sales , cert: WBENC)

8364 North Star Marketing, Inc.
      1130 Ten Rod Rd Ste D-208
      North Kingstown, RI 02852
      Contact: April Williams President
      Tel: 401-294-0133
      Email: april@fortheloveofmarketing.com
      Website: www.fortheloveofmarketing.com
Marketing & PR: direct mail, advertising, strategy, email
marketing & public relations. (Woman, estab 1997, empl
10, sales $708,613, cert: State, WBENC)

Tennessee

8365 Behind the Scenes
      7850 Stage Hills Blvd Ste 103
      Bartlett, TN 38133
      Contact: Project Mgr
      Tel: 901-937-3926
      Email:
      Website: www.btsmemphis.com
Procurement, warehousing, mail merge & related activities,
event & production management. (Woman, estab 2000,
empl 17, sales $2,000,000, cert: WBENC)

8366 Bytes of Knowledge, Inc.
      1212 6th Ave N
      Nashville, TN 37208
      Contact: Nancy Bass Lead Visual Artist, eLearning
      Tel: 615-383-9005
      Email: sales@bytesofknowledge.com
      Website: www.bytesofknowledge.com
Website design, mobile & software dev, brand support,
social marketing, digital elearning, business strategy,
network design, entrepreneur consulting. (Woman, estab
1995, empl 22, sales $2,964,288, cert: WBENC)

8367 Genome Explorations
      711 Jefferson Ave, Ste 415
      Memphis, TN 38163
      Contact: Ed Henderson Dir sales/mktg
      Tel: 800-344-5708
      Email: ehenderson@genome-explorations.com
      Website: www.genome-explorations.com
Genome Explorations provides researchers with a (As-Pac,
estab 2002, empl 7, sales $1,000,000, cert: State)

8368 Miller Tanner Associates, LLC
      2070 Lebanon Rd
      Lebanon, TN 37087
      Contact: Dawn Barnes Dir Global Sales
      Tel: 615-466-2600
      Email: dawn@millertanner.com
      Website: www.millertanner.com
Global meeting & event planning. (Woman, estab 1997,
empl 50, sales $26,000,000, cert: WBENC)

8369 Shelton Communications Group, Inc.
      111 E Jackson Ave, Ste 201
      Knoxville, TN 37915
      Contact: Gwen Meadows Accountant Asst
      Tel: 865-524-8385
      Email: gmeadows@sheltongrp.com
      Website: www.sheltongrp.com
Green advertising; green marketing; consumer research;
enviironmental research. (Woman, estab 0, empl , sales ,
cert: WBENC)

8370 Superior DataWorks, LLC
      340 Poplar View Ln E Ste 1
      Collierville, TN 38017
      Contact: President
      Tel: 901-861-6301
      Email:
      Website: www.superiordataworks.com
Market research: ad testing, A&U studies, customer/
employee satisfaction measurement, new product
testing, web-based survey research, database management & fulfillment services. (Woman, estab 1992, empl
4, sales $167,400, cert: WBENC)

Texas

8371 70kft, LLC
      325 N. St. Paul St Ste 3000
      Dallas, TX 75201
      Contact: Tiffany Bryant
      Tel: 214-653-1600
      Email: tiffany@70kft.com
      Website: www.70kft.com
Design, public relations & digital marketing disciplines.
(AA, estab 2003, empl 25, sales $3,251,230, cert: State,
NMSDC)

8372 All About Events
      7810 Chinon Circle
      Houston, TX 77071
      Contact: Elmer Rogers Owner
      Tel: 713-723-1618
      Email: elmer@allaevents.com
      Website: www.allaevents.com
Event planning, ceremonies, conferences, conventions,
exhibitions, fundraisers, meetings, receptions, seminars
& trade shows. (Woman/AA, estab 2005, empl 2, sales ,
cert: State, City, NMSDC)

8373 Boone DeLeon Communications, Inc.
      3100 S Gessner, Ste 110
      Houston, TX 77063
      Contact: Leo De Leon Jr President
      Tel: 713-952-9600
      Email: leo@boonedeleon.com
      Website: www.boonedeleon.com
Marketing, advertising, public relations, promotions,
retail overlays, couponing & sampling, Spanish translations. (Hisp, estab 1979, empl 7, sales $1,656,911, cert:
State, City)

8374 BrandEra, Inc.
219 S Main St Ste 301
Fort Worth, TX 76104
Contact: Elizabeth Owens Principal
Tel: 817-927-7750
Email: bo@branderamarketing.com
Website: www.branderamarketing.com
Strategic planning, sales/promotional initiatives, advertising, press materials, designing/maintaining websites, marketing materials, planning special events. (Woman, estab 2004, empl 4, sales $935,118, cert: State, WBENC)

8375 Consumer and Market Insights, LLC (CMI)
3010 Lyndon B Johnson Fwy Ste 1200
Dallas, TX 75234
Contact: President & CEO
Tel: 972-939-9500
Email:
Website: www.thecmiteam.com
Market research, training & strategic event planning. (Woman/AA, estab 1998, empl 16, sales , cert: State, NMSDC, WBENC, SDB)

8376 CS Creative
9108 Chancellor Row
Dallas, TX 75247
Contact: Cindy Slayton President
Tel: 214-905-8008
Email: cindy@cs-creative.com
Website: www.cs-creative.com
Graphic design svcs: corporate communications, identity devel & mgmt. (Woman, estab 1989, empl 20, sales , cert: WBENC)

8377 Cybersoft Technologies Inc.
4422 FM 1960 W, Ste 300
Houston, TX 77068
Contact: Milind Sethi
Tel: 281-453-8504
Email: milind.sethi@cybersoft.net
Website: www.cybersoft.net
Cybersoft Technologies was founded in Houston, Texas in 1996, providing "superior" IT Business solutions an services to clients nation-wide.
Solutions include ERP, WEB Technologies, EAI, Microsoft Technologies, Data Management, (As-Ind, estab 1996, empl 50, sales $7,000,000, cert: State, NMSDC)

8378 Dallas Fan Fares, Inc.
14900 Landmark Blvd. Ste 300
Dallas, TX 75254
Contact: Christine Spradling
Tel: 972-239-9969
Email: cspradling@fanfares.com
Website: www.fanfares.com
Corporate meeting, incentive trips & sporting event planning. (Woman, estab 1980, empl 35, sales $14,412,000, cert: WBENC)

8379 DirecToHispanic, LLC
4909 N McColl Rd
McAllen, TX 78504
Contact: Lauren Boyle
Tel: 562-624-4680
Email: lauren.boyle@directohispanic.com
Website: www.directohispanic.com
Marketing promotions agency. (Hisp, estab 2004, empl 12, sales $2,700,000, cert: NMSDC)

8380 Elias Events, LLC
6214 Beverly Hill, Ste 24
Houston, TX 77057
Contact: Deborah Elias President
Tel: 713-334-1800
Email: deborah@eliasevents.com
Website: www.eliasevents.com
Meeting planning, production schedules, resource & staff management, marketing & communications strategy & delivery, graphic design, public relations, marketing/press collateral, website development & social media support. (Woman, estab 1998, empl , sales $10,111,567, cert: City)

8381 ETC Group, Inc.
1112 Copeland Rd Ste 400
Arlington, TX 76011
Contact: Bill Nichols VP
Tel: 817-462-0103
Email: bnichols@etconline.net
Website: www.etconline.net
Corporate travel management, groups, meeting & incentive, promotional marketing. (Woman, estab 1989, empl 25, sales $40,000,000, cert: State, WBENC)

8382 Event Source Professionals, inc.
4109 Gateway Court
Colleyville, TX 76034
Contact: Dara Hall EVP
Tel: 817-267-6698
Email: dara@espinc-usa.com
Website: www.espinc-usa.com
Executive meeting, corporate conference & event planning services, travel, site selection, trade shows, exhibits, security, destination management, online and/ or onsite registration. (Woman, estab 1988, empl 4, sales $2,489,000, cert: WBENC)

8383 Farrow-Gillespie & Heath LLP
1700 Pacific Ave Ste 3700
Dallas, TX 75201
Contact: Liza Farrow-Gillespie Managing Partner
Tel: 214-361-5600
Email: liza@fghlaw.net
Website: www.fghlaw.com
Employment law; employment litigation and arbitration defense; internal employment investigations; internal audits; employee handbooks; contract preparation and review; personal injury defense; advertising (Woman, estab 2007, empl 22, sales $1,761,000, cert: CPUC, WBENC)

8384 Focus Latino
720 Barton Creek Blvd
Austin, TX 78746
Contact: Guy Antonioli President
Tel: 512-306-7393
Email: gcafocuslatino@austin.rr.com
Website: www.focuslatino.com
Qualitative Research & Strategic Planning, Focus Groups, Triads, Dyads, IDIs, Ethnographies (In-Homes & Shop-Alongs) & Quanti-Qualis. (Woman/Hisp, estab 1996, empl 5, sales $814,366, cert: State)

8385   Galloway Research Services
4751 Hamilton Wolfe, Ste 100
San Antonio, TX 78229
Contact: Linda Brazel GM
Tel: 210-734-4346
Email: lbrazel@gallowayresearch.com
Website: www.gallowayresearch.com
Design, conduct & analyze marketing research surveys.
(Woman, estab 1965, empl 150, sales , cert: State)

8386   Garcia Baldwin Inc.
8647 Wurzbach Rd Ste J100
San Antonio, TX 78240
Contact: Yvonne Garcia CEO
Tel: 210-222-1933
Email: ygarcia@mvculture.com
Website: www.mvculture.com
Market & advertising, promotions/merchandising, event marketing, market research creative services, media strategies. (Woman/Hisp, estab 1998, empl 42, sales $12,791,077, cert: State, NMSDC, WBENC, NWBOC)

8387   Global Exhibit Management
P.O. Box 331641
Fort Worth, TX 76163
Contact: President
Tel: 817-370-1400
Email:
Website: www.globalexhibitmanagement.com
Exhibit & event svcs: rental or purchase options, design & project management. (Woman, estab 2002, empl 10, sales $737,681, cert: State, WBENC)

8388   Integrated Focus
6523 Embers Rd
Dallas, TX 75248
Contact: Valerie Pelan, MBA, PCC President
Tel: 214-454-5376
Email: vpelan@integratedfocus.com
Website: www.integratedfocus.com
Leadership management, sales training, branding, sales marketing integration. (Woman, estab 2004, empl 1, sales , cert: WBENC)

8389   Integrity International, Inc.
11767 Katy Frwy, Ste 750
Houston, TX 77079
Contact: Susan Lake Project Mgr
Tel: 877-955-0707
Email: info@tarrenpoint.com
Website: www.tarrenpoint.com
Documentation consulting services, project management, content development (technical documentation), graphic design, technical illustration, desktop publishing, editing & quality assurance, indexing, localization & translation. (Woman, estab 1994, empl 63, sales $6,000,000, cert: State, WBENC)

8390   Ivie & Associates, Inc.
601 Silveron Blvd
Flower Mound, TX 75028
Contact: Jodi Marsh SVP Communications & Business Development
Tel: 972-899-4723
Email: jodi.marsh@ivieinc.com
Website: www.ivieinc.com
Advertising & marketing support services: print procurement, print management, media, creative, digital, development, communication/PR services, shopper marketing, kitting & fulfillment, staffing, publishing, CRM. (Woman, estab 1993, empl 650, sales $1,065,000,000, cert: WBENC)

8391   JODesign
440 S Main St
Fort Worth, TX 76104
Contact: Business Dev Mgr
Tel: 817-335-0100
Email:
Website: www.jodesign.com
Full service marketing, public relations and advertising: branding, public relations, graphic design, market research, marketing campaigns, digital marketing, etc. (Woman, estab 1998, empl 10, sales $950,825, cert: WBENC)

8392   K. Fernandez and Associates LLC
10601 RR 2222 Ste R13
Austin, TX 78730
Contact: Karla Fernandez Parker CEO
Tel: 210-614-1052
Email: karla@kfernandez.com
Website: www.kfernandez.com
Marketing services. (Woman/Hisp, estab 1996, empl 11, sales $2,640,615, cert: State)

8393   Listo Translating Services & More LLC
830 S Mason Rd, Ste B2-A
Katy, TX 77450
Contact: Roxana Heredia CEO
Tel: 832-592-9264
Email: roxana@listotranslating.com
Website: http://houston-translation.com/
Translation & interpretation services. (Woman/Hisp, estab 2012, empl 2, sales $150,000, cert: State, City, NMSDC)

8394   LNT 3 Group
545 E John Carpenter Frwy Ste 300
Irving, TX 75062
Contact: Marqueax Price President
Tel: 214-650-9966
Email: marqueax.price@lnt3group.com
Website: www.lnt3group.com
Marketing, e-communications, business development & new media services & support. (Woman/AA, estab 2010, empl 1, sales , cert: State)

8395   Magic Moments Parties and Events
4760 Preston Rd Ste 244-257
Frisco, TX 75034
Contact: Courtney Rai VP Sales/Mktg
Tel: 214-688-9900
Email: courtney@magicmomentsevents.com
Website: www.magicmomentsevents.com
Event planning, custom design & décor, floral design, event lighing, drapery, theme decor, props, interactive LED dance floor, custom artwork. (Woman, estab 2004, empl 12, sales $550,000, cert: WBENC)

8396   Malkoff Promotions
4904 Stony Ford Dr
Dallas, TX 75287
Contact: Lynne Malkoff President
Tel: 972-248-4354
Email: lynne@lmpspecialties.com
Website: www.lmpspecialties.com
Marketing & promotional solutions. (Woman, estab 1989, empl 5, sales , cert: State, WBENC)

8397 Mobius Partners Enterprise Solutions
1711 Citadel Plaza
San Antonio, TX 78209
Contact: Arlene Watson Principal
Tel: 216-621-9653
Email: arlene@mobiusgrey.com
Website: www.mobiusgrey.com
Design & visual communications, marketing development & branding. (Woman/AA, Hisp, estab 2002, empl , sales $33,600,000, cert: State, NMSDC)

8398 MSR Group, Inc.
3060 Communications Pkwy, Ste 200
Plano, TX 75093
Contact: Lauren Dunnaway Dir Sales & Marketing
Tel: 214-291-2920
Email: lauren.dunnaway@infinxglobal.com
Website: www.infinixglobal.com
Meeting management, Site selection, negotiation & venue contracting. (Woman, estab 1994, empl 25, sales $14,787,000, cert: State, WBENC)

8399 OMS Strategic Advisors, LLC
2591 Dallas Pkwy, Ste 300
Frisco, TX 75034
Contact: Lawrence Gardner President
Tel: 214-207-7720
Email: lawrence.gardner@omsstrategicadvisors.com
Website: www.omsstrategicadvisors.com
Strategic marketing and related consulting. (Woman/AA, estab 2009, empl 2, sales $560,000, cert: State, NMSDC)

8400 Onyx Power and Gas LLC
13155 Noel Rd Ste 900
Dallas, TX 75240
Contact: Loraine Sutton Mgr
Tel: 214-871-5574
Email: vinnies@onyxpg.com
Website: www.onyxpg.com
Energy management and procurement; power sales; consultation concerning strategies to control and reduce energy costs; consultation concerning market and bid analysis and contract evaluation. (AA, estab 2009, empl 14, sales $250,000, cert: State, NMSDC)

8401 Open Channels Group, LLC
1320 S. University Dr Ste 220
Fort Worth, TX 76107
Contact: Tonya Veasey CEO
Tel: 817-332-0404
Email: info@ocgpr.com
Website: www.ocgpr.com
Public Relations, Multicultural Strategy Development, Integrated Communications, Digital Strategies, Public Involvement, Advertising & Marketing. (Woman/AA, estab 2005, empl 20, sales $1,794,160, cert: NMSDC)

8402 Outreach Strategists LLC
2727 Allen Pkwy., Ste 1300
Houston, TX 77019
Contact: Mustafa Tameez Managing Dir
Tel: 713-247-9600
Email: marketing@outreachstrategists.com
Website: www.outreachstrategists.com
Corporate & strategic communications, messaging, government affairs, public relations & marketing, ethnic & media relations, advocacy, constituent engagement, community outreach, graphic design, crisis management. (As-Ind, estab 2003, empl 5, sales $500,000, cert: State)

8403 Planning Professionals, Ltd.
1210 W McDermott Ste 111
Allen, TX 75013
Contact: Mollie Wallace CEO
Tel: 469-854-6991
Email: mwallace@planningprofessionals.com
Website: www.planningprofessionals.com
Web dev, logistical support, hotel site selection, electronic mktg, on-site staffing, food & beverage selection, contract negotiation, transportation, airfare, event marketing, signs, graphics, premiums & giveaways, mail fulfillment. (Woman, estab 1994, empl 12, sales $6,265,000, cert: WBENC)

8404 Production & Event Services, Inc.
9425 Sandy Ln
Manvel, TX 77578
Contact: Cindy Kutch President
Tel: 281-585-0569
Email: cindy@eventsplanning.com
Website: www.EventsPlanning.com
Special event services: sound, lighting, staging, theme decor, drapery, entertainment, catering, event planning, production & show management. (Woman, estab 2003, empl 10, sales $240,000, cert: WBENC)

8405 Regali Inc.
518 N Interurban St
Richardson, TX 75081
Contact: Renee Dutia President
Tel: 972-726-8830
Email: renee@regaliinc.com
Website: http://regaliinc.com
Diversified global marketing & technology services, integrating promotional programs, creative development & technology. (Woman/As-Ind, estab 1989, empl 7, sales , cert: State, NMSDC)

8406 Rutherford Enterprises, Inc.
17304 Preston Rd Ste 1020
Dallas, TX 75252
Contact: Al Rutherford President
Tel: 214-438-1185
Email: alrutherford@teamrutherford.net
Website: www.teamrutherford.net
Convention, meeting & event planning, event management, communications, sourcing & site selection, housing management, attrition mitigation exhibit & logistics management, senior executive travel support. (AA, estab 1998, empl 10, sales $1,032,594, cert: NMSDC)

8407 Sanders Wingo Advertising, Inc.
303 N Oregon Ste 1200
El Paso,, TX 79901
Contact: Leslie Wingo President & CEO
Tel: 915-533-9583
Email: lwingo@sanderswingo.com
Website: www.sanderswingo.com
Strategic planning, account planning, public relations, research, brand creation, account services, media planning, buying & creative services. (AA, Hisp, estab 1958, empl 76, sales $27,800,000, cert: NMSDC)

8408   Steel Digital Studios, Inc.
     6414 Bee Cave Rd, Ste B
     Austin, TX 78746
     Contact: Andrea Wallace Business Develop Dir
     Tel: 800-681-8809
     Email: andrea.wallace@steelbranding.com
     Website: www.steelbranding.com
Family targeted marketing. (Woman, estab 2000, empl 25, sales $4,321,750, cert: State, WBENC)

8409   Strategar LLC
     3100 Independence Pkwy, Ste 311-204
     Plano, TX 75075
     Contact: Yareli Esteban CEO
     Tel: 972-948-3781
     Email: yareli@strategar.com
     Website: www.strategar.com
Marketing services: marketing, advertising, translations, web development, creative services, SEM, traditional media, content production & support of promotional events. (Woman/Hisp, estab 2013, empl 3, sales , cert: State)

8410   Studio B Dallas, LLC
     2719 Randal Lake lane
     Spring, TX 77388
     Contact: MJ Moreau President
     Tel: 281-528-7000
     Email: mj@studiobdallas.com
     Website: http://studiobdallas.com
Strategic design, brand identity, packaging, retail store design & restaurant store design & merchandising. (Woman, estab 2009, empl 1, sales $165,000, cert: City)

8411   Studio J Designworks LLC
     7750 N. Macarthur Blvd Ste 120-356
     Irving, TX 75063
     Contact: Gina Jacobson Owner
     Tel: 972-556-0511
     Email: gina.jacobson@studiojdesignworks.com
     Website: www.studiojdesignworks.com
Visual communication solutions, branding, tag line development, trade show & event marketing, copywriting & copy editing, flash animation & development. (Woman, estab 2008, empl 2, sales , cert: State, WBENC)

8412   T3
     1801 N Lamar Blvd
     Austin, TX 78701
     Contact: Gay Gaddis CEO
     Tel: 512-499-8811
     Email: austin.hegarty@t-3.com
     Website: www.t-3.com
Integrated marketing solutions. (Woman, estab 1989, empl 150, sales , cert: WBENC)

8413   Tandem Axle Inc. dba Mixed Media Creations
     2300 Rockbrook Dr Ste D
     Lewisville, TX 75067
     Contact: Whitney Stockstill Business Operations Mgr
     Tel: 972-221-1600
     Email: whitney@mailmmc.com
     Website: www.mixedmediacreations.com
Graphic Design, Large-Scale Design, Web Development, Digital Media, Photography / Videography, Printing Services, Creative Consultation, Copywriting / Editing, Marketing Campaigns, Branded Merchandise. (Woman, estab 2007, empl 27, sales $2,800,000, cert: State, WBENC)

8414   Teneo Linguistics Company, LLC
     4700 Bryant Irvin Ct. Ste 301
     Fort Worth, TX 76107
     Contact: Hana Laurenzo CEO
     Tel: 817-441-9974
     Email: hana@tlctranslation.com
     Website: www.tlctranslation.com
Foreign language translation & interpreting services. (Woman, estab , empl , sales $1,400,000, cert: State, WBENC)

8415   The Backshop, Inc. DBA Mercury Mambo
     1107 S 8th St
     Austin, TX 78704
     Contact: Liz Arreaga Partner
     Tel: 512-447-4440
     Email: liz@mercurymambo.com
     Website: http://mercurymambo.com
Research & strategic planning, sales promotions, shopper marketing, retail merchandising, online/social media, field management, brand advertising experiential marketing, bilingual local market staffing. (Woman/Hisp, estab 1999, empl 3, sales $1,062,732, cert: NMSDC, WBENC)

8416   The ID Development Group
     8811 Teel Pkwy, Ste 100 - 5233
     Frisco, TX 75035
     Contact: Julian Dorise President
     Tel: 214-295-5414
     Email: jdorise@iddevelop.com
     Website: www.iddevelop.com
Project designs, creative interior environments, tradeshow events & marketing campaigns. (AA, estab 2010, empl 5, sales , cert: NMSDC)

8417   The Maxcel Company
     6600 LBJ Freeway Ste 109
     Dallas, TX 75240
     Contact: Gwenna Brush President
     Tel: 972-644-0880
     Email: gwenna.brush@maxcel.net
     Website: www.maxcel.net
Plan & manage meetings, conventions & incentive travel programs. (Woman, estab 1995, empl 6, sales , cert: State, WBENC)

8418   Trilogy LLC
     5601 Democracy Dr Ste 105
     Plano, TX 75024
     Contact: Jeff Hoedebeck VP Business Dev
     Tel: 972-473-8911
     Email: jeffh@trilogymktg.com
     Website: www.trilogymktg.com
Experiential marketing: product sampling, product demonstrations, product merchandising & sponsorship activations. (AA, Hisp, estab 2002, empl 10, sales $3,500,000, cert: State, NMSDC)

8419   Ultimate Ventures
     4400 Beltway Dr
     Addison, TX 75001
     Contact: Val Lenington VP
     Tel: 972-732-8433
     Email: val@ultimateventures.com
     Website: www.ultimateventures.com
Special events, transportation, conference & convention services, corporate meeting & team building, inbound incentive programs & customized sightseeing tours. (Woman, estab 1993, empl 12, sales , cert: WBENC)

8420   Ward Creative Communications, Inc.
       P.O. Box 701219
       Houston, TX 77270
       Contact: Deborah Buks President
       Tel: 713-869-0707
       Email: dbuks@wardcc.com
       Website: www.wardcc.com
Media, community & employee relations; public affairs;
marketing communications, graphic design; special events;
crisis management. (Woman, estab 1990, empl , sales
$1,200,000,000, cert: State)

Utah

8421   Andavo Meetings & Incentives
       5588 S Green St Ste 300
       Salt Lake City, UT 84123
       Contact: Jessica Perez
       Tel: 720-398-5504
       Email: jessica.perez@andavomeetings.com
       Website: www.andavomeetings.com
Meetings, incentives & event planning & management.
(Woman, estab 1982, empl 162, sales $36,989,079, cert:
WBENC)

8422   Andinas dba/ Inlingua Utah
       602 E 300 S
       Salt Lake City, UT 84102
       Contact: Don Durham Business Development
       Tel: 801-355-3775
       Email: don@inlinguautah.com
       Website: www.inlinguautah.com
Language classes, interpretation & translation services,
translate websites, technical & legal documents. (Woman/
Hisp, estab 1996, empl 15, sales $1,013,000, cert: NMSDC)

Virginia

8423   360 Virtual Assistance, LLC
       905 22nd St
       Newport News, VA 23607
       Contact: Natalie Robertson CEO
       Tel: 757-244-1045
       Email: sales@360virtualassistance.com
       Website: www.360virtualassistance.com
Integrated document preparation, multimedia creation,
content design, layout, printing, optical scanning, research,
technical writing. (AA, estab 2013, empl 1, sales , cert:
State, NMSDC)

8424   AetherQuest Solutions, Inc.
       6400 Arlington Blvd Ste 850
       Falls Church, VA 22042
       Contact: Andrea Bauerfeind Dir Event Svcs
       Tel: 571-297-4000
       Email: abauerfeind@aetherquest.com
       Website: www.aetherquest.com
Event management, conference planning, site selection
venue contract negotiation; comprehensive registration
services; exhibit hall management; sponsorship programs;
speaker management; housing and travel. (As-Pac, estab
2002, empl 23, sales $3,124,665, cert: State)

8425   All About Presentation, LLC
       707 E Main St Ste 1615
       Richmond, VA 23219
       Contact: CEO
       Tel: 804-381-4002
       Email:
       Website: http://allaboutpresentation.com
Event management: plan, design, manage and produce
corporate events. (Woman/AA, estab 2007, empl 5, sales
, cert: State)

8426   Bare International Inc.
       3702 Pender Dr, Ste 305
       Fairfax, VA 22030
       Contact: Lynne Brighton Sr VP
       Tel: 703-995-3132
       Email: lbrighton@bareinternational.com
       Website: www.bareinternational.com
Mystery shopping, employee surveys, video mystery
shopping. (Woman, estab 1987, empl 300, sales
$16,000,000, cert: WBENC)

8427   Candice Bennett & Associates, Inc.
       9621 Masey McQuire Ct
       Lorton, VA 22079
       Contact: Candice Bennett President
       Tel: 703-919-6231
       Email: clb@candicebennett.com
       Website: www.candicebennett.com
Market research, communications, organizational
assessment & development. (Woman, estab 2003, empl
7, sales $619,866, cert: State, WBENC)

8428   Customer Relationship Metrics
       100 Glenn Dr, Ste A-11
       Sterling, VA 20164
       Contact: Dr. Jodie Monger President
       Tel: 410-643-1136
       Email: jmonger@metrics.net
       Website: www.metrics.net
Automated, email & website customer surveys, metrics
designs, customer satisfaction & loyalty programs, data
collection, analysis, reporting & consulting. (Woman,
estab 1993, empl 14, sales $3,500,000, cert: WBENC)

8429   DGS Create, Inc.
       6400 Arligton Blvd
       Falls Church, VA 22042
       Contact: Christine Francis Owner
       Tel: 703-776-1919
       Email: christine@printdgs.com
       Website: www.dgscreate.com
Graphic design, digital printing, mailing & e-mailing
services & online communication channels. (As-Ind,
Hisp, estab 2012, empl 21, sales $1,854,501, cert:
NMSDC)

8430   Elizabeth Coffey Design
       1616 Claremont Ave
       Richmond, VA 23227
       Contact: Elizabeth Coffey Principal
       Tel: 804-266-2193
       Email: ecoffey@elizabethcoffeydesign.com
       Website: www.elizabethcoffeydesign.com
Graphic design solutions, brochures, publications,
catalogs, advertisements, direct mail, websites, displays
and banners, invitations, logos & identity packages.
(Woman, estab 2000, empl 1, sales , cert: State)

8431　Exhibit Edge Inc.
　　　4315-A Walney Road
　　　Chantilly, VA 20151
　　　Contact: Bev Gray President
　　　Tel:　703-230-0000
　　　Email: bev.gray@exhibitedge.com
　　　Website: www.exhibitedge.com
Trade show exhibit services: design & fabricate custom exhibits, rent trade show displays & exhibits, large format graphics & banners. (Woman, estab 1992, empl 20, sales $3,450,000, cert: WBENC)

8432　Frontline Marketing LLC
　　　2248 Dabney Rd, Ste J
　　　Richmond, VA 23230
　　　Contact: Henry Howells President
　　　Tel:　804-359-2422
　　　Email: h.howells@frontline-exhibits.com
　　　Website: www.frontline-exhibits.com
Mfr, design & dist trade show & outdoor event exhibits & office environments. (Woman, estab 1992, empl 5, sales $635,000, cert: State)

8433　Johnson, Inc.
　　　201 W Broad St Ste 600
　　　Richmond, VA 23220
　　　Contact: Andre Dean Corp VP
　　　Tel:　804-644-8515
　　　Email: adean@johnsonmarketing.com
　　　Website: www.johnsonmarketing.com
Marketing & communications. (AA, estab 1993, empl 15, sales $2,750,000, cert: State)

8434　KTL Communications LLC
　　　5055 Seminary Rd, 1220 Unit
　　　Alexandria, VA 22311
　　　Contact: Amir Khan Owner
　　　Tel:　703-662-0465
　　　Email: amir@ktl-communications.com
　　　Website: www.ktl-communications.com
Language Service Provider (LSP), translation, in person interpretation, DTP, localization, language tutoring & language authentication services. (Woman/As-Ind, estab 2013, empl 2, sales , cert: State)

8435　LeapFrog Solutions, Inc.
　　　3201 Jermantown Rd Ste 350
　　　Fairfax, VA 22030
　　　Contact: Kathleen Jerabek Contracts and Pricing Mgr
　　　Tel:　703-273-7900
　　　Email: kjerabek@leapfrogit.com
　　　Website: www.leapfrogit.com
Strategic marketing communications: web site design, graphic design, branding/marketing campaigns, multimedia, corporate collateral materials. (Woman, estab 1996, empl 11, sales $893,494, cert: State, WBENC)

8436　Montage Marketing Group, LLC
　　　8000 Westpark Dr Ste 480
　　　McLean, VA 22102
　　　Contact: Mercedita Roxas-Murray CEO
　　　Tel:　703-215-4201
　　　Email:
　　　mroxasmurray@montagemarketinggroup.com
　　　Website: http://montagemarketinggroup.com
Full cycle integrated experiential marketing: Audience intelligence/data & market analysis, Strategy development, campaign conceptualization, creative development, experiential design. (Woman/As-Pac, estab 2015, empl 3, sales $1,900,000, cert: State, NMSDC, WBENC, 8a)

8437　National Events LLC
　　　4003 Westfax Dr, Ste L
　　　Chantilly, VA 20151
　　　Contact: Ruth Crout CEO
　　　Tel:　703-961-1105
　　　Email: RCrout@nationaleventsllc.com
　　　Website: http://nationaleventsllc.com
Strategic event planning, comprehensive event management, and all-inclusive event production services for private, corporate, government, and not-for-profit organizations. (Woman, estab 2003, empl 8, sales $2,154,730, cert: WBENC)

8438　Nexus Direct, LLC
　　　101 W Main St Ste 400
　　　Norfolk, VA 23510
　　　Contact: Suzanne Nowers CEO
　　　Tel:　757-340-5960
　　　Email: suzanne@nexusdirect.com
　　　Website: http://nexusdirect.com
Direct marketing, marketing spend, strategy, creative, messaging, production, media buying, data analytics, processing, modeling & overall analysis & attribution of the direct marketing program results. (Woman, estab 2004, empl 30, sales $6,243,833, cert: WBENC)

8439　ORI
　　　171 Elden St Ste 160
　　　Herndon, VA 20170
　　　Contact: Kathleen Benson CEO
　　　Tel:　571-257-3205
　　　Email: kathyb@oriresults.com
　　　Website: www.ORIresults.com
Strategic research planning, sample & questionnaire design, qualitative & quantitative research, data collection, technology-based online research, data coding & entry, database mgmt & integration, statistical analysis & interpretation. (Woman, estab 1988, empl 75, sales $22,971,050, cert: WBENC)

8440　Rhudy & Co. Communications and Marketing, Inc.
　　　14342 Lander Rd
　　　Midlothian, VA 23113
　　　Contact: Michele Rhudy President
　　　Tel:　804-897-0762
　　　Email: michele@rhudy.biz
　　　Website: www.rhudy.biz
Public relations, communications & marketing consulting: strategic communications planning, media relations, writing services. (Woman, estab 2003, empl 16, sales $2,200,000, cert: State, WBENC)

8441 The Dominion Group Marketing Research & Consulting
1800 Alexander Bell Dr Ste 515
Reston, VA 20191
Contact: Susan Wyant President
Tel: 703-234-2360
Email: swyant@thedominiongrp.com
Website: www.thedominiongrp.com
Marketing research, competitive intelligence, & consulting, qualitiative methodologies. (Woman, estab 1993, empl 7, sales $2,934,757, cert: WBENC)

8442 The InnovateHers
713 Huntsman Rd
Sandston, VA 23150
Contact: Tasha Chambers Principal
Tel: 804-263-0491
Email: info@theinnovatehers.com
Website: http://theinnovatehers.com
PR Communications Plans News Releases Crisis Communications Executive Speeches Media Monitoring Community Engagement Events Theme Conceptualization Venue Selection Celebrity/Talent Contract Negotiation Event Styling Volunteer Management Guest Management. (Woman/AA, estab 2017, empl 1, sales , cert: State)

Washington

8443 Blue Crest Creative, LLC
5108 S Myrtle St
Seattle, WA 98118
Contact: Troy Shelby Creative Director
Tel: 800-476-0128
Email: shelbyt@bluecrestcreative.com
Website: www.bluecrestcreative.com
Corporate Identity Design, Branding, Logo, Letterhead, Business Cards, Print Design, Brochures, Invitations, Direct Mail, Newsletters, Internet Design, Architecture planning, Web Design, eNewsletters, Maintenance, SharePoint. (AA, estab 2011, empl 1, sales $105,600, cert: City, NMSDC)

8444 Green Cat Dzine, Inc.
5412 101st St SW
Mukilteo, WA 98275
Contact: Elisabeth Rumpelsberger President
Tel: 206-406-8329
Email: liz@greencatdzine.com
Website: www.greencatdzine.com
Graphic design: print, online (web), environmental graphics, strategic branding, promotions, online development, logo work, posters, brochures, invitations, tradeshow exhibit designs. (Woman, estab 2001, empl 1, sales $148,000, cert: State)

8445 Northwest Interpreters, Inc.
7700 NE Parkway Dr, Ste 205
Vancouver, WA 98662
Contact: Vic Marcus COO
Tel: 360-566-0492
Email: vmarcus@nwiglobal.com
Website: www.nwiglobal.com
Multicultural communication services: on-site interpretation, over-the-phone interpretation, translation & localization, multilingual desktop publishing, sign language services. (Woman, estab 1992, empl 12, sales $1,270,000, cert: State)

8446 PRR, Inc.
1501 4th Ave, Ste 550
Seattle, WA 98101
Contact: Business Development Asst
Tel: 206-623-0735
Email:
Website: www.prrbiz.com
Public relations, marketing, market research, social & digital media, graphic design, facilitation, public involvement & advertising services. (Woman, estab 1981, empl 86, sales , cert: State)

Wisconsin

8447 Market Probe, Inc.
2655 N Mayfair Rd
Milwaukee, WI 53226
Contact: Bonnie Lockwood Sr VP
Tel: 414-778-6000
Email: info@marketprobe.com
Website: www.marketprobe.com
Market research & cstmr satisfaction research svcs. (As-Ind, estab 1976, empl 125, sales $40,000,000, cert: State, NMSDC)

8448 Mazur/Zachow, Inc.
1025 S Moorland Rd Ste 300
Brookfield, WI 53005
Contact: Michele Conway President
Tel: 262-938-9244
Email: michelec@mazurzachow.com
Website: www.mazurzachow.com
data collection services, marketing research studies, focus groups, IDI's, ethnographic studies, in-home product placements & music tests. (Woman, estab 1983, empl 16, sales $315,000, cert: WBENC)

8449 Meetings & Incentives Worldwide, Inc.
10520 7 Mile Road
Caledonia, WI 53108
Contact: Dan Tarpey VP, Sales & Marketing
Tel: 773-851-0908
Email: dtarpey@meetings-incentives.com
Website: www.meetings-incentives.com
Global strategic meeting & event management, strategic meeting management implementation, global strategic sourcing & contracting, attendee management. (Woman, estab 1967, empl 310, sales $115,000,000, cert: WBENC)

8450 Revelation, LLC
222 N Midvale Blvd Ste 18
Madison, WI 53705
Contact: Brian Lee President
Tel: 608-622-7767
Email: brian@experiencerevelation.com
Website: www.experiencerevelation.com
Public relations, media buying, ad buying, advertising, social media consulting, internet marketing, web marketing & speaking engagements. (As-Pac, estab 2010, empl 3, sales $170,000, cert: NMSDC)

8451 Rivera & Associates, Inc.
1543 S 14th St
Milwaukee, WI 53204
Contact: Michael Rivera CEO
Tel: 414-736-1255
Email: michael.rivera@riveraprfirm.com
Website: www.riveraprfirm.com
Public Relations, Marketing, Strategic Communication, Multicultural Marketing, Public Information & Outreach, Media Relations, Language Translations, Management Consulting, Brand Awareness, Environmental Marketing. (Hisp, estab , empl , sales , cert: State)

8452 The Dieringer Research Group, Inc.
200 Bishops Way
Brookfield, WI 53005
Contact: Nicola Riggleman Sr Dir Business Devel
Tel: 262-432-5222
Email: supplierdiversity@thedrg.com
Website: www.thedrg.com
Customer Experience, Brand Awareness, Product Development, and Market Opportunity. (Woman, estab 1974, empl 74, sales $6,720,000, cert: WBENC)

West Virginia

8453 CRA Communications LLC dba Charles Ryan Associates
601 Morris St, Ste 301
Charleston, WV 25301
Contact: Susan Lavenski CEO
Tel: 304-342-0161
Email: slavenski@charlesryan.com
Website: www.charlesryan.com
Account Management, Planning, Advertising, Branding, Communications, Crisis Communications, Graphic Design, Media Buying, Media Relations, Media Training, Message Development, Public Relations, Social Media, Strategy. (Woman, estab 2015, empl 25, sales $6,941,054, cert: WBENC)

PROFESSIONAL SERVICES: Staffing Services

Firms provide temporary and permanent personnel placement, contract and direct hire, personnel consulting, training and employment services. NAICS Code 54

Alabama

8454 CD Covenant Distributors International LLC
1400 Commerce Blvd Ste 12
Anniston, AL 36207
Contact: Rod Lemon CEO
Tel: 256-832-4385
Email: rlemon@cdcovenant.com
Website: http://cdcovenant.com
CD Covenant Distributors International (CD) is a Minority Owned, Small/ Disadvantage, Service Disable Veteran Owned Small Business Business (MBE, SBE, DBE). CD was incorporated in 2001 in the State of Alabama. We are a reputable provider of MRO Products a (AA, estab 2001, empl 6, sales $254,000, cert: City, NMSDC, 8a)

8455 EALI Logistics Solutions LLC
123 N 7th St
Gadsden, AL 35901
Contact: JT Johnson President
Tel: 785-213-5493
Email: jt@ealilogistics.com
Website: www.EaliLogistics.com
EcoChemPro product is 100% biodegradable cleaner/ degreaser, contains no VOC's, no acids, no alkalis, no butyl, and has a neutral pH, and it is safe for people to use and it is environmental friendly. This product can replace multiple (AA, estab 2014, empl 6, sales , cert: NMSDC)

8456 Providence Staffing LLC
15 Windsweep Ct, Ste 114
Phenix City, AL 36870
Contact: Albert Williams President
Tel: 706-358-8926
Email: albertwilliams@get2worknow.com
Website: www.get2worknow.com
Broad-based staffing and recruiting solutions, temporary, temp-to-hire, and permanent employees. (AA, estab 2018, empl 1, sales , cert: State)

8457 RecruitSource, Inc.
3532 Seventh Ct S
Birmingham, AL 35222
Contact: Jane Smith CEO
Tel: 205-322-6822
Email: jsmith@recruitsource.org
Website: www.rsi-services.com
Contract management services: staff augmentation, advertising & marketing. (Woman/As-Pac, estab 2001, empl 4, sales , cert: WBENC)

8458 Sirius Technical Services, Inc.
6215 Rangeline Rd, Ste102
Theodore, AL 36582
Contact: COO
Tel: 251-443-1166
Email:
Website: www.siriustechnical.com
Temporary & permanent personnel. (Woman, estab 2005, empl 400, sales $28,000,000, cert: State, WBENC, NWBOC)

8459 SK Services, LLC
45281 US Hwy 78
Lincoln, AL 35096
Contact: S. K. SERVICES, LLC President
Tel: 205-763-1818
Email:
Website: www.skstaffing.com
Staffing, temp to hire & contingent staffing. (Woman, estab 2010, empl 9, sales , cert: WBENC)

8460 Tech Providers, Inc.
2117 Magnolia Ave S
Birmingham, AL 35205
Contact: Eleanor Estes CEO
Tel: 205-930-9664
Email: eleanorestes@techproviders.com
Website: www.techproviders.com
Permanent IT staffing needs, IT software developers, IT systems or database administrators, financial staffing & engineering staffing. (Woman, estab 1998, empl 135, sales $10,701,387, cert: WBENC)

Arkansas

8461 Temporaries Plus, Inc.
601 E Eighth Ave
Pine Bluff, AR 71601
Contact: Kayla Cheatwood Sales
Tel: 870-535-5507
Email: kcheatwood@ateamtemp.com
Website: www.ateamtemp.com
Temporary staffing services. (Woman/AA, estab 1995, empl 7, sales $5,300,000, cert: WBENC)

Arizona

8462 All About People, Inc.
4422 East Indian School Road
Phoenix, AZ 85018
Contact: Charles Mitchell CEO
Tel: 602-955-1212
Email: charles@allaboutpeople.net
Website: https://allaboutpeople.net/
Temporary & executive level staffing. (AA, estab 2002, empl 87, sales , cert: NMSDC)

8463 Axis Employment Services
7000 N 16th St, Ste 120-501
Phoenix, AZ 85020
Contact: Tran Tran CEO
Tel: 602-301-8115
Email: tran@axisemployment.com
Website: www.axisemployment.com
Temporaries, temp-to-hire & direct hire searches, drug testing, Criminal/County searches, software testing, education & employment verification. (Woman/As-Pac, estab 2002, empl 6, sales $2,130,000, cert: State, City)

8464 AZ Construction Resources, Inc., dba AZCR Staffing
2601 W Dunlap Ave Ste #4
Phoenix, AZ 85021
Contact: Kim Jones Dir of Sourcing
Tel: 602-870-3515
Email: kjones@azcrstaffing.com
Website: www.azcrstaffing.com
Temporary and Temp to Perm Employees to the Industrial, Oil & Construction Industries (Woman/Hisp, estab 2006, empl 100, sales $11,093,000, cert: NMSDC, WBENC)

8465 Bridgeport Resources, LLC
930 W Watson Dr
Tempe, AZ 85283
Contact: Diana Lemos-Marquez
Tel: 480-456-6031
Email: diana@bridgeportresources.com
Website: www.bridgeportresources.com
Direct placement staffing service, Finance, Accounting, Administration, Customer Service, Education, Engineering, IT, Healthcare, Management, Manufacturing, Sales/Marketing, Human Resources. (Woman/Hisp, estab 2013, empl 2, sales , cert: NMSDC)

8466 Creative Human Resources Concepts LLC
4710 E Falcon Dr, Ste 125
Mesa, AZ 85215
Contact: Rosa Roy President & CEO
Tel: 480-654-4606
Email: rosa@chrc4work.com
Website: www.chrc4work.com
Staffing: contract, full-time, part-time, temporary, long & short-term. (Woman/Hisp, estab 1997, empl 205, sales $1,723,389, cert: NMSDC, CPUC, WBENC)

8467 DuffyGroup, Inc.
4727 E Union Hills Dr, Ste 200
Phoenix, AZ 85050
Contact: Kathleen Duffy Ybarra President
Tel: 602-942-7112
Email: kduffy@duffygroupinc.com
Website: www.duffygroupinc.com
Executive search, sourcing, HR contracting & direct hire, short-term, extended assignments. (Woman, estab 1991, empl 25, sales $2,600,000, cert: WBENC)

8468 Egnite LLC
4747 E Elliot Rd Bldg 29, Ste 600
Phoenix, AZ 85044
Contact: Alex Luevano VP
Tel: 602-931-5000
Email: alex.luevano@egniteinc.com
Website: http://egniteinc.com
Direct placement, contract, contract to hire & project solutions. (Woman/Hisp, estab 2007, empl 5, sales $325,000, cert: State)

8469 Elsner Human Resources
7409 E Chaparral Rd Ste A110 - PMB106
Scottsdale, AZ 85250
Contact: Krisanne Elsner CEO
Tel: 480-657-8638
Email: ke@southwestrecruiting.com
Website: www.elsnerhr.com
Recruiting, talent acquisition, executive search. (Woman, estab 2003, empl 1, sales $115,000, cert: WBENC)

8470 JBN & Associates, LLC.
4040 E Camelback Rd Ste 280
Phoenix, AZ 85018
Contact: Dainiz Alvarez Exec Search Mgr
Tel: 480-344-2822
Email: info@jbnassociates.com
Website: www.jbnassociates.com
Recruiting firm, direct/perm placements, executive search & C-level positions. (Woman, estab 1999, empl 12, sales , cert: WBENC)

8471 Safe T Professionals LLC
241 S Washington St
Chandler, AZ 85249
Contact: Anna Martinez CEO
Tel: 800-502-9481
Email: info@safetpros.com
Website: www.safetpros.com
Safety staff augmentation and consulting services. (As-Pac, Hisp, estab 2011, empl 57, sales $8,700,000, cert: NMSDC)

8472 Scott Business Group, LLC
668 N 44th St Ste 300
Phoenix, AZ 85008
Contact: Milagros Gonzalez-Scott
Tel: 480-694-2619
Email: millie@scottbiz.net
Website: www.scottbiz.net
Contract & temporary staffing. (AA, estab 2003, empl 105, sales $3,451,356, cert: State, City, NMSDC)

8473 Source Group Professionals
4729 E Sunrise Dr Ste 244
Tucson, AZ 85718
Contact: GM
Tel: 520-870-5114
Email:
Website: www.sourcegrouppros.com
Staffing services. (Woman, estab 2003, empl 35, sales $1,273,000, cert: WBENC)

8474 Triumphant Staffing LLC
3255 S Dorsey Ln Ste 1081
Tempe, AZ 85282
Contact: John Galloway CEO
Tel: 480-306-9653
Email: john.galloway@triumphantstaffing.com
Website: www.triumphantstaffingllc.com
Provide Temp to Perm Services, Permanent Hire, Temp Hire. (AA, estab 2016, empl 5, sales $150,000, cert: State)

California

8475 3 Bridge Networks LLC
601 Montgomery St Ste 715
San Francisco, CA 94111
Contact: Caleb Hill Managing Partner
Tel: 415-692-6944
Email: caleb.hill@3bridgenetworks.com
Website: www.3bridgenetworks.com
Recruiting services, direct hire & temporary consults ranging from staff to VP levels within Accounting & Finance. (As-Pac, estab 2011, empl 7, sales , cert: NMSDC, CPUC)

8476 A.P.R., Inc. (Alpha Professional Resources)
100 E Thousand Oaks Blvd Ste 240
Thousand Oaks, CA 91360
Contact: Rick C. Ramirez VP Operations
Tel: 805-371-5644
Email: rick@alphaprotemps.com
Website: www.alphaprotemps.com
Technical IT personnel on contract or contract to hire or permanent. (AA, Hisp, estab 1993, empl 155, sales $15,605,246, cert: NMSDC, CPUC)

8477   Absolute Employment Solutions, Inc.
       P.O. Box 2446
       Culver City, CA 90231
       Contact: Penelope Sherman- Hunt President
       Tel: 323-931-6262
       Email: phunt@absoluteemploymentsolutions.com
       Website: www.absoluteemploymentsolutions.com
Staffing services: direct-hire, temporary-to-hire & temporary. (Woman/AA, estab 2001, empl 3, sales $350,000,
cert: State, CPUC, SDB)

8478   AgileTalent, Inc.
       1900 S Norfolk Ave.
       San Mateo, CA 94403
       Contact: Jay Singh
       Tel: 650-931-2572
       Email: jay.singh@agiletalentinc.com
       Website: www.agiletalentinc.com
IT contract staffing & recruiting. (As-Ind, estab 2011, empl
48, sales $4,600,000, cert: NMSDC, CPUC)

8479   Allstem Connections, Inc.
       327 W Broadway
       Glendale, CA 91204
       Contact: Penni Rich VP
       Tel: 505-417-5718
       Email: prich@ain1.com
       Website: www.allstemconnections.com
Specialty recruiting and staffing firm for the temporary,
temp-to-permanent and direct hire placement of talent in
STEM (Science, Technology, Engineering and Mathematics)
positions. Unique talent development programs include
apprenticeships, internships, (Woman/AA, estab 2018,
empl 2800, sales $965,741,349, cert: NMSDC, WBENC)

8480   APR Consulting, Inc.
       1370 Valley Vista Dr Ste 280
       Diamond Bar, CA 91765
       Contact: Daniel Benninghoff VP
       Tel: 909-396-5375
       Email: dbenninghoff@aprconsulting.com
       Website: www.aprconsulting.com
Supporting Managed Staffing (MSP)/Vendor Management,
System (VMS) Programs, Direct Hire Search, Contract
Labor, Administrative & Clerical, Accounting & Finance,
Human Resources, Call Center & Customer Care, Informa-
tion Technology. (Woman/As-Pac, estab 1980, empl 1382,
sales $75,000,000, cert: NMSDC, CPUC, WBENC)

8481   ATR International, Inc.
       1230 Oakmead Pkwy Ste 110
       Sunnyvale, CA 94085
       Contact: Angelique Alvarez Chief Diversity Relations
       Officer
       Tel: 408-328-8085
       Email: angeliques@atr1.com
       Website: www.atrinternational.com
Temporary employment svcs. (Woman/Hisp, estab 1988,
empl 100, sales $96,000,000, cert: NMSDC)

8482   Berkhemer Clayton
       241 S Figueroa St Ste 300
       Los Angeles, CA 90012
       Contact: Exec Admin
       Tel: 213-621-2300
       Email:
       Website: www.berkhemerclayton.com
Executive search firm. (Woman, estab 1994, empl 8, sales
$140,000, cert: CPUC, WBENC)

8483   Bratton & Co., Inc. DBA Hyperdrive Agile
       1547 Palos Verdes Mall, Ste 198
       Walnut Creek, CA 94597
       Contact: Mary Louie Owner
       Tel: 925-330-6970
       Email: mary@brattoninc.com
       Website: www.hyperdriveagile.com
Temporary staffing: administration, project management, technology, marketing & public relations.
(Woman/As-Pac, estab 2009, empl 2, sales $3,000,000,
cert: WBENC)

8484   Canon Recruiting Group LLC
       26531 Summit Circle
       Santa Clarita, CA 91351
       Contact: Recruiting Mgr
       Tel: 661-252-7400
       Email:
       Website: www.canonrecruiting.com/index.htm
Identification, evaluation & recruit Executives, Professionals, IT Technical, Accounting, Environmental &
Industrial staffing. (Woman, estab 1980, empl 300,
sales $15,000,000, cert: WBENC)

8485   Crowdstaffing, a Zenith Talent Company
       6030 Hellyer Ave Ste 100
       San Jose, CA 95138
       Contact: Bret Bass Dir Content Strategy
       Tel: 844-467-2300
       Email: bret@crowdstaffing.com
       Website: www.crowdstaffing.com
Staffing & recruiting: software and OS, hardware, QA &
automation, IT, mobile applications & platforms &
professional. (As-Ind, estab 2000, empl 25, sales
$14,000,000, cert: NMSDC)

8486   Dawson & Dawson Staffing Inc.
       26522 La Alameda Ste 110
       Mission Viejo, CA 92691
       Contact: Kathy Dawson President
       Tel: 949-421-3966
       Email: kathy.dawson@dawsondawsoninc.com
       Website: www.dawsondawsoninc.com
National search & staffing employment services.
(Woman, estab 2008, empl 14, sales $3,544,239, cert:
WBENC)

8487   Delta Computer Consulting, Inc.
       25550 Hawthorne Blvd Ste 106-108
       Torrance, CA 90505
       Contact: Acct Exec
       Tel: 310-541-9440
       Email:
       Website: www.deltacci.com
Human Capital Recruiting & Deployment, IT Staff
Recruiting & Augmentation. (Woman, estab 1987, empl
165, sales $28,000,000, cert: WBENC, NWBOC)

8488   Domar Companies, LLC
       14742 Beach Blvd, Ste 256
       La Mirada, CA 90638
       Contact: Don Martinez CEO
       Tel: 714-674-0391
       Email: martinezd@domarcompanies.com
       Website: www.domarcompanies.com
Executive search recruiting Hispanic & Multicultural
Diversity Executives & Professionals. (Woman/Hisp,
estab 2011, empl 8, sales $27,500,000, cert: CPUC)

8489 Enterprise Resource Services, Inc.
400 Continental Blvd Ste 6170
El Segundo, CA 90245
Contact: Ladie Ella Daya Natl Sales Mgr
Tel: 424-888-3771
Email: ella@ersstaffing.com
Website: www.ersstaffing.com
Staffing, payroll & IT consulting services: temp, temp-to-hire & direct hire. (As-Pac, estab 2001, empl 25, sales $3,851,150, cert: CPUC)

8490 Genesis Professional Staffing, Inc.
2600 West Olive Ave 5th Fl
Burbank, CA 91505
Contact: Marcus T. Moore CEO
Tel: 818-333-5153
Email: marcus.moore@gpstaffing.com
Website: www.gpstaffing.com
Staffing: permanent hires, temp-to-hire, temporary placement, payrolling & consulting. (AA, estab 2003, empl 25, sales , cert: NMSDC)

8491 Government Staffing Associates
101 Howard St, Ste 490
San Francisco, CA 94105
Contact: Steven Strawser Owner
Tel: 415-692-6905
Email: sf@govstaff.org
Website: http://govstaff.org
Temporary, contract & permanent staffing solutions. (As-Pac, estab 2009, empl 11, sales $833,429, cert: City, NMSDC, CPUC)

8492 Grove Technical Resources
9035 Rosewood Ave
West Hollywood, CA 90048
Contact: President
Tel: 786-390-7119
Email:
Website: www.grovetechnicalresources.com
Technical staffing & consulting services. (Woman, estab 2005, empl 2, sales , cert: CPUC, WBENC)

8493 Hart Employment Services
220 S Kenwood St #320
Glendale, CA 91205
Contact: Rhonda Minarcin President
Tel: 626-405-0778
Email: gsa@hartjobs.com
Website: www.hartjobs.com
Staffing services. (Woman, estab 1988, empl 6, sales $1,833,485, cert: WBENC)

8494 Harvest Technical Services
1839 Ygnacio Valley Rd, Ste 390
Walnut Creek, CA 94598
Contact: Renee Bush Sales
Tel: 925-937-4874
Email: renee@harvtech.com
Website: www.harvtech.com
Temporary technical staffing personnel. (Woman, estab 1997, empl 85, sales $12,018,213, cert: WBENC)

8495 HBL Search
118 Prospect Ave Ste 4
Long Beach, CA 90803
Contact: Halvern Logan President
Tel: 562-754-6925
Email: halvern@hblsearch.com
Website: www.hblsearch.com
Staffing: accountants, finance, banking, IT, engineering, sales & HR. (AA, estab 2013, empl 1, sales , cert: NMSDC)

8496 Human Potential Consultants, LLC
454 E Carson Plaza Dr, Ste 102
Carson, CA 90746
Contact: Garnett Newcombe CEO
Tel: 310-756-1560
Email: drnewcombe@aol.com
Website: www.hpcemployment.org
Staffing services: administrative, janitorial, warehouse & production service workers. (Woman/AA, estab 1997, empl 7, sales $580,000, cert: City, NMSDC, WBENC)

8497 IMS
7755 Center Ave Ste 1100
Huntington Beach, CA 92647
Contact: Kristi Newman Dir Client Services
Tel: 714-840-3775
Email: knewman@imssvs.com
Website: www.imssvs.com
IT Contract, Consulting, Contract-to-Hire & Full Time placement services. (Woman, estab 1973, empl 35, sales $7,600,293, cert: State)

8498 Inconen Corporation
6133 Bristol Pkwy Ste 232
Culver City, CA 90230
Contact: Gordon Ross CEO
Tel: 310-410-1931
Email: register@inconen.com
Website: www.inconen.com
Temporary employees & pay-rolled employees. (As-Ind, estab 1978, empl 120, sales $13,351,317, cert: NMSDC, CPUC)

8499 Integrated Talent Solutions, Inc. dba Vivo
7901 Stoneridge Dr Ste 440
Pleasanton, CA 94588
Contact: Marilyn Weinstein CEO
Tel: 925-271-6800
Email: info@vivoinc.com
Website: www.vivoinc.com
Staffing services: contract, contract-to-hire & full-time/direct positions. (Woman, estab 2006, empl 15, sales $5,100,000, cert: WBENC)

8500 Integritas Resources, Inc.
12304 Santa Monica Blvd. Ste 300
Los Angeles, CA 90025
Contact: Lindy Huang Werges CEO
Tel: 310-584-7295
Email: lhwerges@integritasresources.com
Website: http://integritasresources.com
Executive search, recruitment & staffing, direct hire, contract, contract-to-hire, temporary, or project basis. (Woman/As-Pac, estab 2014, empl 3, sales $646,557, cert: City, NMSDC, CPUC, WBENC)

8501 Invero Group
8560 Vineyard Ave Ste 504
Rancho Cucamonga, CA 91730
Contact: Daniel Phillips President
Tel: 909-373-8120
Email: daniel@inverogroup.com
Website: www.inverogroup.com
Staffing & recruiting: temporary, direct hire & contingent staffing solutions. (Woman, estab 2001, empl 75, sales $1,988,644, cert: WBENC)

8502   Josephine's Professional Staffing, Inc.
2158 Ringwood Ave
San Jose, CA 95131
Contact: Josephine Hughes CEO
Tel: 408-943-0111
Email: josephine@jps-inc.com
Website: www.jps-inc.com
Staffing svcs: temp, contract, yemporary-to-hire, full-time
placement, payroll svcs, vendor-on-site. (Woman/As-Pac,
estab 1988, empl 10, sales $3,248,000, cert: State,
NMSDC, WBENC)

8503   Kavaliro
5401 Old Redwood Hwy Ste 104
Petaluma, CA 94954
Contact: Timothy M. Harrington Managing Dir
Tel: 704-525-3457
Email: tharrington@kavaliro.com
Website: www.kavaliro.com
Staffing services: Information Technology (IT); Engineering;
Finance & Accounting; Administrative & Professional; &
Project Solutions & Delivery. (Woman/As-Pac, estab 2003,
empl 200, sales $41,700,000, cert: NMSDC, CPUC)

8504   Lighthouse Management Group Inc.
1650 The Alameda
San Jose, CA 95126
Contact: Nirav Shah Managing Dir
Tel: 408-579-6200
Email: nirav.shah@lighthousemg.com
Website: www.lighthousemg.com
Staffing, temporary & temp-to-hire, senior-level consulting
& management professionals. (As-Ind, estab 2006, empl
20, sales $8,500,000, cert: NMSDC)

8505   Loan Administration Network Inc.
18952 MacArthur Blvd Ste 315
Irvine, CA 92612
Contact: Charlene Nichols President
Tel: 949-752-5246
Email: charlene_nichols@lani.com
Website: www.lani.com
Temporary, Temp-to-Hire, Direct Hire staffing services:
Accounting, Finance, Healthcare, Banking, Credit Unions,
Title, Escrow, Mortgage industries. Clerical, mid-level,
Management, Executive positions. (Minority, estab 1992,
empl 12, sales $5,600,000, cert: CPUC)

8506   MIDCOM
1275 N Manassero St
Anaheim, CA 92807
Contact: Anastacia Warunek VP
Tel: 714-507-3723
Email: stacy@midcom.com
Website: www.midcom.com
Recruit & place technical & professional personnel.
(Woman, estab 1979, empl 635, sales $120,000,000, cert:
CPUC, WBENC)

8507   Mynela Staffing LLC
17777 Center Court Dr N Ste 600
Cerritos, CA 90703
Contact: CEO
Tel: 562-246-5317
Email:
Website: www.mynela.com
Healthcare staffing services, per diem, temp & direct hire
services of physicians, nurses, clinical, allied & administra-
tive staff. (As-Pac, Hisp, estab 2015, empl 75, sales
$2,000,000, cert: NMSDC)

8508   netPolarity, Inc.
900 E Campbell Ave
Campbell, CA 95008
Contact: Sweta Sanyal Business Develop Mgr
Tel: 408-971-1100
Email: swetas@netpolarity.com
Website: www.netpolarity.com
Temporary staffing, staff augmentation, contingent
workforce staffing for information technology, project
management, application development, professional
services, marketing, finance and accounting. (As-Pac,
estab 2000, empl 36, sales $14,500,000, cert: NMSDC)

8509   NetSource, Inc.
P.O. Box 590665
San Francisco, CA 94159
Contact: VP, Sales
Tel: 415-831-3681
Email:
Website: www.netsourceweb.com
pPacement, contracting & consulting services. (Woman,
estab 1997, empl 50, sales $800,000, cert: State, CPUC,
WBENC)

8510   Partners In Diversity, Inc.
690 E Green St Ste 101
Pasadena, CA 91101
Contact: Arlene Apodaca President
Tel: 626-793-0020
Email: arlene.apodaca@p-i-d.biz
Website: www.partnersindiversity.com
Staffing support: clerical & non-clerical. (Woman/Hisp,
estab 2002, empl 100, sales $3,584,272, cert: State,
CPUC, WBENC)

8511   Peoples Choice Staffing, Inc.
1269 W Pomona Rd, Ste 107
Corona, CA 92882
Contact: Denise Peoples CEO
Tel: 951-735-0550
Email: dapeoples@peopleschoicestaffing.com
Website: www.peopleschoicestaffing.com
Staffing: temporary, temporary-Hire or full-time
placement services. (Woman/AA, estab 2003, empl 200,
sales $19,037,280, cert: NMSDC, CPUC)

8512   PFITECH
17011 Beach Blvd, Ste 9
Huntington Beach, CA 92647
Contact: Sean Scully Reg Sales Mgr
Tel: 310-824-1800
Email: sean.scully@PFITECH.COM
Website: www.PFITECH.com
Staffing and desktop solutions. (Hisp, estab 2001, empl
200, sales $16,318,677, cert: NMSDC, CPUC)

8513   Pivotal Search Partners
2531 Greenwich St
San Francisco, CA 94123
Contact: President
Tel: 415-323-6339
Email:
Website: www.pivotalsearchpartners.com
Staffing Solutions: IT, Engineering & Accounting &
Finance, Direct Hire, Contract & Contract to Hire & VSP /
MSP Contingent Workforce staffing solutions. (As-Ind,
estab 2012, empl 6, sales $538,000, cert: NMSDC, CPUC)

8514 Plan b Solutions, Inc.
      29222 Rancho Viejo Rd
      San Juan Capistrano, CA 92675
      Contact: CEO
      Tel: 949-221-9301
      Email:
      Website: www.planbsolutions.com
IT staffing & professional services, contract, contract-to-
hire & permanent placement staffing, process consulting.
(Woman, estab 2000, empl 20, sales $4,800,000, cert:
WBENC)

8515 PM Business Holdings LLC
      733 Hindry Ave, Ste C205
      Inglewood, CA 90301
      Contact: Derrick Ferguson CEO
      Tel: 310-242-3171
      Email: pmbh14@gmail.com
      Website: www.brilliantmindssolutions.com
Computer Systems Design Services, employment placement & executive search services (AA, estab 2012, empl 1,
sales , cert: NMSDC)

8516 POGO Inc.
      6265 Greenwich Dr Ste 103
      San Diego, CA 92122
      Contact: Regional Director
      Tel: 858-587-4970
      Email:
      Website: http://getpogo.com
Temporary staffing services. (Woman, estab 2011, empl 7,
sales $2,500,000, cert: CPUC, WBENC)

8517 Proven Solutions Inc
      9444 Waples St Ste 440
      San Diego, CA 92121
      Contact: Louis Song Sr Partner
      Tel: 858-412-1122
      Email: lsong@provenrecruiting.com
      Website: www.provenrecruiting.com
Consulting, staffing & solutions. (As-Pac, estab 2007, empl
49, sales $16,800,000, cert: NMSDC, CPUC)

8518 PTS Advance Life Sciences
      2860 Michelle Dr, Ste 150
      Irvine, CA 92606
      Contact: Jayne Gill Managing Dir
      Tel: 949-268-4021
      Email: jayne.gill@ptsadvance.com
      Website: www.ptsadvance.com
Engineering & professional staffing: petrochemical, power,
transportation & infrastructure. (Woman, estab 1995,
empl 200, sales $28,000,000, cert: WBENC)

8519 Quality Driver Solutions, Inc.
      320 S Milliken Ave, Ste A
      Ontario, CA 91761
      Contact: Angelica Dazhan Regional Mgr
      Tel: 510-453-4655
      Email: angelica@qualitydriversolutions.com
      Website: www.qualitydriversolutions.com
Offices located in Northern California and Pacific Northwest. In addition, we have offices in Southern California,
Houston and Dallas, TX, with plans for Full service staff:
temps, temp to hire, long term dedicated & direct hire
placements. (Hisp, estab 2004, empl 23, sales , cert:
NMSDC)

8520 RennickBarrett Recruiting, Inc.
      82-408 Brewster Dr
      Indio, CA 92203
      Contact: Vinette Morris President
      Tel: 760-863-0076
      Email: vinette@rennickbarrett.com
      Website:
Direct & temporary/contract labor, high level, hard to fill
positions at the senior and executive management
levels. (Woman/AA, estab 2008, empl 4, sales
$1,246,000, cert: City)

8521 SearchPros
      6363 Auburn Blvd
      Citrus Heights, CA 95621
      Contact: Myla Ramos CEO
      Tel: 916-721-6000
      Email: myla@spstaffing.com
      Website: www.spstaffing.com
Human capital staffing & solutions: temporary staffing,
contract to hire, long-term contract, project staffing,
direct hire, payrolling services, retained searches,
outplacement services. (Woman/AA, As-Pac, estab 2005,
empl 100, sales $20,000,000, cert: NMSDC)

8522 SuperbTech, Inc.
      5800 Hannm Ave Ste 150
      Culver City, CA 90230
      Contact: Jan Davis President
      Tel: 310-645-1199
      Email: jdavis@superbtechinc.com
      Website: www.superbtechinc.com
Staffing:contract, temporary & permanent placement.
(Woman/AA, estab 1998, empl 7, sales , cert: CPUC,
WBENC)

8523 The ACT 1 Group, Inc.
      1999 W 190th St
      Torrance, CA 90504
      Contact: Gary Randazzo Dir of natl communica-
      tions
      Tel: 800-383-1965
      Email: hrcg-rfxmanager@act-1.com
      Website: www.act1group.com
Staffing, payrolling & workforce mgmt svcs: financial,
energy, healthcare & high technology industries.
(Woman/AA, estab 1978, empl 1535, sales
$476,000,000, cert: NMSDC, CPUC)

8524 The Mice Groups, Inc.
      1730 S Amphlett Blvd Ste 100
      San Mateo, CA 94402
      Contact: Sofia Gomez VP Recruiting + Strategy
      Tel: 650-655-7655
      Email: sofia@micegroups.com
      Website: www.micegroups.com
IT contract, contract-to-hire & full-time employment
positions. (Hisp, estab 2000, empl 100, sales
$100,000,000, cert: NMSDC, CPUC)

8525 TheraEx Rehab Services, Inc.
      1191 Central Blvd Ste E
      Brentwood, CA 94513
      Contact: Rey Rivera President
      Tel: 707-342-5200
      Email: info@theraexstaffing.com
      Website: www.theraexstaffing.com
Healthcare staffing: Registered Nurses (RN), Licensed
Vocational Nurses (LVN), Certified Nurse Assistants
(CNA), Physical therapist (PT), Occupational Therapist
(OT). (As-Pac, estab 2009, empl 64, sales $3,545,324,
cert: NMSDC)

8526   Tiffany Stuart Solutions, Inc.
       390 Diablo Rd. Ste 220
       Danville, CA 94526
       Contact: President
       Tel: 925-855-3600
       Email:
       Website: www.go2dynamic.com
Temporary contractors, temp to hire & direct hire.
(Woman, estab 1997, empl 100, sales $5,200,000, cert:
CPUC, WBENC)

8527   Two Roads Professional Resources, Inc.
       5122 Bolsa Ave, Ste 112
       Huntington Beach, CA 92649
       Contact: Tammy Gottschalk President
       Tel: 714-901-3804
       Email: tgotts@2roads.com
       Website: www.2roads.com
Provide temporary staffing in the technical, engineering,
and information technology services. (Woman, estab 1996,
empl 125, sales $12,168,000, cert: CPUC)

8528   Vertisystem Inc.
       39300 Civic Center Dr, Ste 230
       Fremont, CA 94538
       Contact: Shaloo Jeswani Sr. BDM
       Tel: 702-241-5131
       Email: shaloo@vertisystem.com
       Website: www.vertisystem.com
Staff Augmentation, Full-Time Placements, contract to
Hire, IT Projects & Consulting. (Woman/As-Pac, estab
2008, empl 120, sales $20,000,000, cert: City, CPUC)

8529   Vitesse Recruiting & Staffing, Inc.
       1432 Edinger Ave, Ste 100
       Tustin, CA 92780
       Contact: Kim N. Zastrow President & CEO
       Tel: 714-210-5959
       Email: knzastrow@vitesserecruiting.com
       Website: www.VitesseRecruiting.com
Temporary or permanent human resources employment
services. (Woman/As-Pac, estab 2000, empl 3, sales , cert:
State, CPUC)

8530   Voigt & Associates, Inc.
       22981 Sonriente Trail
       Coto de Caza, CA 92679
       Contact: Barbara Voigt President
       Tel: 949-766-1100
       Email: bvoigt@voigtinc.com
       Website: www.voigtinc.com
Executive search services. (Woman, estab 2005, empl ,
sales $1,200,000, cert: CPUC)

8531   Whitham Group Executive Search
       8130 Luisa Way
       Windsor, CA 95492
       Contact: President
       Tel: 888-238-1273
       Email:
       Website: www.WhithamGroup.com
Executive search & recruiting specializing in Utilities,
Renewable Energy & Environmental Services. (Woman,
estab 2010, empl 2, sales $1,174,000, cert: CPUC, WBENC)

8532   Workforce Solutions Group
       26090 Towne Centre Dr
       Foothill Ranch, CA 92679
       Contact: Colleen Jones COO
       Tel: 949-588-5812
       Email: cjones@wsgcorp.com
       Website: www.workforcesolutionsgroup.com
Staffing & direct hire: contract, temporary & direct hire
placement. (Woman/Hisp, estab 2002, empl 11, sales ,
cert: City, NWBOC)

8533   WorkSquare West
       4401 Crenshaw Blvd, Ste 220
       Los Angeles, CA 90043
       Contact: Natasha White President
       Tel: 323-294-9675
       Email: natasha@worksquare.com
       Website: http://www.worksquare.com
Recruiting,Temporary to Permanente Staffing Firm
(Woman/AA, estab 2008, empl 4, sales , cert: NMSDC)

8534   Xtra Pair of Hands
       4307 San Joaquin Plz
       Newport Beach, CA 92660
       Contact: Kym Smith Managing Partner
       Tel: 404-825-4398
       Email: info@xtrapairofhands.com
       Website: www.xtrapairofhands.com
Staffing & recruiting: temp, temp-to-hire & direct hire
placements. (Woman/AA, estab 2007, empl 4, sales
$250,000, cert: State, CPUC)

8535   Zempleo, Inc.
       4000 Executive Parkway Ste 240
       San Ramon, CA 94583
       Contact: Sabrina Chisholm VP
       Tel: 925-284-0377
       Email: schisholm@zempleo.com
       Website: www.zempleo.com
Temporary staffing, payrolling & direct hire services.
(Hisp, estab 2005, empl 1000, sales $62,860,000, cert:
NMSDC, CPUC)

Colorado

8536   Action Staffing Solutions
       1409 W 29th St
       Loveland, CO 80538
       Contact: Robin Fischer CEO
       Tel: 970-667-4202
       Email: robin@myactionstaffing.com
       Website:
Temporary to permanent employee placement, contract
personnel, long-term, executive placement, direct hire,
on-site management. (Woman/AA, estab 2008, empl 7,
sales $1,500,000, cert: State, City, 8a)

8537   Colorado Network Staffing, Inc.
       8787 Turnpike Dr, Ste 220
       Westminster, CO 80031
       Contact: President
       Tel: 303-430-1441
       Email:
       Website: www.conetstaff.com
Non-technical & technical staff augmentation. (Woman,
estab 1996, empl 12, sales , cert: WBENC)

8538   Equity Staffing Group, Inc.
        8310 S. Valley highway Ste 135
        Englewood, CO 80112
        Contact: Stacey L Moore Operations Mgr
        Tel: 720-897-8714
        Email: stacey.moore@equitystaffing.com
        Website: www.equitystaffing.com
Staffing, consulting, contingent, or direct-hire workforce
solutions. (Nat Ame, estab 2009, empl 60, sales
$85,617,000, cert: NMSDC)

8539   IntelliSource
        1899 Wynkoop St Ste 900
        Denver, CO 80202
        Contact: Matt Pollard SVP
        Tel: 303-692-1100
        Email: mpollard@intellisource.com
        Website: www.intellisource.com
Staffing solutions, temporary, temp to perm, project
management, outsourcing, contract & direct hire. (Woman,
estab 1999, empl 300, sales , cert: WBENC)

8540   Job Store, Inc.
        7100 E Hampden Ave Ste A
        Denver, CO 80224
        Contact: Julie DeGolier President
        Tel: 303-757-7686
        Email: julie@jobstorestaffing.com
        Website: www.jobstorestaffing.com
Tempoary office, clerical admin support, accounting &
technical & light industrial personnel. (Woman, estab 1974,
empl 14, sales $8,400,419, cert: WBENC)

8541   Lakeshore Talent, LLC
        5251 DTC Parkway, Ste 400
        Denver, CO 80111
        Contact: Mary Clark President
        Tel:
        Email: mclark@lakeshoretalent.com
        Website: www.lakeshoretalent.com
Staffing and recruiting, contract, contract to hire, direct hire
and payroll services. (Woman, estab 2017, empl 15, sales
$10,529,849, cert: WBENC)

8542   MHa Technical Staffing, Inc.
        7475 Dakin St, Ste 350
        Denver, CO 80221
        Contact: Thomas R. Leyba VP Operations
        Tel: 303-428-1728
        Email: t.leyba@martinez-hromada.com
        Website: http://mhatech.com/
Temporary eng support personnel: civil, electrical, structural, mechanical, HVAC, programmers, subcontract,
construction mgmt, designers & drafters. (Hisp, estab 1992,
empl 65, sales , cert: City, NMSDC)

8543   Nexus Staffing Solutions Corp.
        4701 Marion St, Ste 307
        Denver, CO 80216
        Contact: Barbara Butler Business Develop Mgr
        Tel: 303-736-2008
        Email: bonnie@nexusstaffingllc.com
        Website: www.nexusstaffingllc.com/
Staffing: Engineering, Construction & Call Centers. (Woman,
estab 2010, empl 12, sales , cert: WBENC)

8544   Prestige Staffing, Inc.
        1873 S Bellaire St, Ste 320
        Denver, CO 80222
        Contact: President
        Tel: 303-691-0111
        Email:
        Website: www.prestigecareer.com
Permanent, contract & temp positions. (Woman, estab
2003, empl 2, sales $350,000, cert: WBENC)

8545   Primesource Staffing
        400 S. Colorado Blvd, Ste 400
        Denver, CO 80246
        Contact: Dennis Hatcher controller
        Tel: 303-869-2990
        Email: dhatcher@primesourcestaffing.com
        Website: www.primesourcestaffing.com
Staffing services. (Woman, estab 1996, empl 27, sales
$20,600,000, cert: WBENC)

Connecticut

8546   JOBPRO Temporary Services, Inc.
        36 Main St
        East Hartford, CT 06118
        Contact: Catherine Beck President
        Tel: 800-404-7795
        Email: cbeck@job-pro.com
        Website: www.jobproworks.com
Staffing: temporary, temp-to-hire & direct placements:
office, accounting, light industrial & technical niches.
(Woman, estab 1981, empl 10, sales , cert: State)

8547   Key Alliance Staffing, LLC
        406 Farmington Ave
        Farmington, CT 06032
        Contact: Sandra Hathaway
        Tel: 860-676-7733
        Email: shathaway@keyalliancestaff.com
        Website: www.keyalliancestaffing.com
Staffing: contract, contract to hire, or direct hire personnel. (Woman, estab 2008, empl 32, sales $2,586,000,
cert: State)

8548   MY HR Supplier
        1266 E Main St Ste 700R
        Stamford, CT 06902
        Contact: Omer Mutaqi COO
        Tel: 203-274-8595
        Email: omutaqi@myhrsupplier.cm
        Website: www.myhrsupplier.com
Human capital talent: IT, administrative & office support,
clerical & accounting. (Woman/As-Ind, estab 2011, empl
53, sales , cert: State, NMSDC)

8549   Skylightsys, LLC
        175 Capital Blvd Ste 402
        Rocky Hill, CT 06067
        Contact: Shalu Arora President
        Tel: 860-289-9096
        Email: arora@skylightsys.com
        Website: www.skylightsys.com
Staffing services. (Woman/As-Ind, estab 2005, empl 9,
sales , cert: State)

8550   Stratoserve LLC
        18 Colonial Ct
        Cheshire, CT 06410
        Contact: Subroto Roy President
        Tel: 203-768-5690
        Email: subroto.roy@stratoserve.com
        Website: www.stratoserve.com
consulting, research and training for the following
NAICS codes:541720,541613,611430 and is committed
to provide quick and measurable value to its clients.
(As-Pac, estab 2005, empl 1, sales , cert: NMSDC)

8551 Talus Partners, LLC
      321 Main St
      Farmington, CT 06032
      Contact: Steve Massucci Mgr
      Tel: 860-678-4410
      Email: accounting@taluspartners.com
      Website: www.taluspartners.com
IT, Engineering & Accounting contract & direct hire
staffing. Certified Project Managers, Web Developers,
Analysts. (Woman, estab 2011, empl 35, sales $5,500,000,
cert: NWBOC)

8552 Technical Staffing Solutions Corp.
      P.O. Box 102
      Southport, CT 06890
      Contact: Robert Martinez President
      Tel: 203-259-7200
      Email: tecstasol@aol.com
      Website: www.technicalstaffingsolutions.com
Technical search & placement: permanent & contract.
(Hisp, estab 1990, empl 50, sales , cert: State)

8553 The Good Search, LLC
      4 Valley Rd
      Westport, CT 06880
      Contact: CEO
      Tel: 203-227-8615
      Email:
      Website: www.thegoodsearchllc.com
Retained search & recruitment research, strategic recruitment initiatives of internal search teams. (Woman, estab
1999, empl , sales $662,398, cert: State, WBENC)

8554 Walt Medina & Associates, LLC
      1224 Mill St Bldg D, Ste 200
      East Berlin, CT 06023
      Contact: Walt Medina CEO
      Tel: 860-357-5002
      Email: wm@waltmedina.com
      Website: www.waltmedina.com
Healthcare recruiting, recruit military personnel (veter-
ans). (Hisp, estab 2003, empl 2, sales $400,000, cert:
NMSDC)

District of Columbia

8555 Adept Professional Staffing Inc.
      1629 K St, NW Ste 300
      Washington, DC 20006
      Contact: Elizabeth Joseph CEO
      Tel: 301-883-4308
      Email: tavares@adeptprostaffing.com
      Website: www.adeptprostaffing.com
Recruitment service for Accounting, Legal & Administrative
Assistants, Permanent & Temporary placements. (Woman/
AA, estab 2010, empl , sales $795,000, cert: State, WBENC,
8a)

8556 JustinBradley, Inc.
      1725 I St, NW Ste 300
      Washington, DC 20006
      Contact: Andrew Chase EVP
      Tel: 202-457-8400
      Email: asc@justinbradley.com
      Website: www.JustinBradley.com
Recruiting & staff augmentation. (Woman, estab 2002,
empl 65, sales $5,566,000, cert: WBENC)

8557 Midtown Personnel, Inc.
      1130 Connecticut Ave. NW Ste 1101
      Washington, DC 20036
      Contact: Proposal Mgr
      Tel: 202-887-4747
      Email: Accounting@themidtowngroup.com
      Website: www.themidtowngroup.com
Staffing services: direct hire, temp to hire, temporary,
executive search. (Woman, estab 1989, empl 35, sales
$15,400,000, cert: WBENC)

8558 National Associates, Inc.
      1130 Connecticut Ave, NW Ste 530
      Washington, DC 20036
      Contact: Oscar Hannaway President
      Tel: 202-223-7606
      Email: ohannaway@naipersonnel.com
      Website: www.naipersonnel.com
Permanent & temporary staffing: administrative, clerical,
professional, technical & light industrial. (AA, estab
1987, empl 18, sales $9,600,000, cert: NMSDC)

8559 Proxy Personnel, LLC
      1100 H St, NW Ste 260
      Washington, DC 20005
      Contact: Kim Siew
      Tel: 202-639-9300
      Email: kim.siew@proxypersonnel.com
      Website: www.proxypersonnel.com
Temporary staffing, recruiting & administrative services.
(AA, estab 2004, empl 100, sales $5,000,000, cert: State)

Florida

8560 ABSP Staffing, LLC
      2339 Vintage St
      Sarasota, FL 34240
      Contact: Ashley Black COO
      Tel: 941-587-4974
      Email: amyersblack@abspstaffing.com
      Website: www.abspstaffing.com
Staffing, contract, contract-to-perm & permanent hiring.
(Minority, Woman, estab 2015, empl 2, sales , cert:
State)

8561 Airetel Staffing, Inc.
      P.O. Box 915864
      Longwood, FL 32791
      Contact: Mike Tomaso Natl Aquisitions Mgr
      Tel: 407-788-2015
      Email: mt@airetel.com
      Website: www.airetel.com
Full-time, contract & contract-to-hire staffing solutions.
(Woman, estab 2000, empl 10, sales $3,570,000, cert:
WBENC)

8562 Albion Healthcare Staffing
      10162 W Sample Rd
      Coral Springs, FL 33065
      Contact: Francisco Arteaga Division Dir
      Tel: 954-796-3336
      Email: francisco@albionbiomed.com
      Website: www.albionstaffing.com
Staffing services for Pharmaceutical & Medical Device
companies. (Woman, estab 2005, empl 5, sales , cert:
State)

8563   Alpha1 Staffing/Search Firm, LLC.
3350 SW 148th Ave, Ste 220
Miramar, FL 33027
Contact: Garrie Harris President
Tel: 954-734-2744
Email: gharris@alpha1staffing.com
Website: www.alpha1staffing.com
Staffing solutions, recruitment, assessment, training,
development, and career management, to outsourcing
and workforce consulting. (Woman/AA, estab 2007, empl
500, sales $13,000,000, cert: NMSDC)

8564   Ascendo Resources, LLC
500 West Cypress Creek Road Ste 230
Fort Lauderdale, FL 33309
Contact: Melissa Mitchell Partner
Tel: 321-251-3762
Email: mmitchell@ascendo.com
Website: www.ascendo.com
Executive recruiting & temporary staffing, temporary &
project opportunities. (Hisp, estab 2009, empl 100, sales
$39,000,000, cert: NMSDC)

8565   BioStaff Solutions Inc.
4007 Blushing Rose Court
Oviedo, FL 32766
Contact: Jim Owens
Tel: 407-542-6006
Email: jowens@biostaffsolutions.com
Website: www.biostaffsolutions.com
Provide clinical staffing services: contract, contract to hire
& direct placements in SAS Programming, Clinical Program-
ming, Biostatistics, Clinical Data Management,
Pharmacovigilance, Clinical Monitoring. (Woman/Hisp,
estab 2014, empl 3, sales , cert: NMSDC)

8566   Blue Palm Recruitment Group
20568 Long Pond Rd
N Fort Myers, FL 33917
Contact: J. Connor Galloway Chief Business Officer
Tel: 239-284-9206
Email: jconnor.galloway@gmail.com
Website: www.bluepalmrecruitmentgroup.com/
Executive search, staffing, and recruitment partner.
(Woman, estab 2019, empl 3, sales , cert: State)

8567   Career Center, Inc.
1236 NW 18th Ave
Gainesville, FL 32609
Contact: Carolynn Buchanan Owner
Tel: 352-378-2300
Email: cbuchanan@tempforce.net
Website: www.tempforcegainesville.com
Staffing: temporary, temp to perm & direct hire. (Woman,
estab , empl , sales $934,261, cert: State, City)

8568   Career Solutions International Inc.
400 Lexington Green Lane
Sanford, FL 32771
Contact: Suzette DiMascio CEO
Tel: 866-484-4752
Email: suzette@csigroup.net
Website: www.csigroup.net
Executive search & recruiting services. (Woman, estab
2002, empl 8, sales $3,400,000, cert: WBENC)

8569   CareersUSA, Inc.
6501 Congress Ave Ste 200
Boca Raton, FL 33487
Contact: Jennifer Johnson Exec VP & General
Counsel
Tel: 561-995-7000
Email: jjohnson@careersusa.com
Website: www.careersusa.com
Temporary, temp-to-hire, direct hire placements &
payrolling services. (Woman, estab 1981, empl 10000,
sales $32,000,000, cert: State, WBENC)

8570   CAREERXCHANGE®, Inc.
10689 N Kendall Dr Ste 209
Miami, FL 33176
Contact: Nick Alonso President & COO
Tel: 305-595-3800
Email: nick@cxcinc.com
Website: www.careerxchange.com
Staffing solutions, full-time direct hire placement,
executive search, temporary & temp to hire placement.
(Woman/Hisp, estab 1988, empl 25, sales $10,930,000,
cert: State)

8571   Future Force Personnel
15800 NW 57th Ave
Miami Lakes, FL 33014
Contact: Adela Gonzalez CEO
Tel: 407-851-0039
Email: adela@futureforcepersonnel.com
Website: www.futureforcepersonnel.com
Temporary, temp to hire & direct hire placements.
(Woman/Hisp, estab 1992, empl 15, sales $17,500,000,
cert: NMSDC)

8572   Garcia & Ortiz Staffing, LLC
888 Executive Center Dr W, Ste 101
St. Petersburg, FL 33702
Contact: Jeremy Lavin Operations Mgr
Tel: 727-342-1007
Email: jlavin@garciaortiz.com
Website:
Staffing: accounting, finance & banking professionals on
a temporary, project & permanent basis. (Hisp, estab
2005, empl 5, sales $900,000, cert: State)

8573   GDKN Corporation
9700 Stirling Road Ste 110
Cooper City, FL 33024
Contact: Gary Dhir VP
Tel: 954-985-6650
Email: gdhir@gdkn.com
Website: www.gdkn.com
Staffing: information technology, engineering, profes-
sional, administrative & clerical, IT consulting, custom
application development. (As-Ind, estab 1993, empl 400,
sales $18,000,000, cert: NMSDC)

8574   Genesis Global Recruiting
3000 SW 148 Ave, Ste 116
Miramar, FL 33027
Contact: Jim Cochran Dir of Recruiting
Tel: 800-780-2232
Email: jcochran@genesis-global.com
Website: www.genesis-global.com
Staffing & workforce solutions: direct hire, temporary
workforce & contract consulting. (Woman/Hisp, estab
1999, empl 167, sales $16,500,000, cert: WBENC)

8575   Genoa Employment Solutions, Inc.
1560 Sawgrass Corporate Pkwy FL 4
Sunrise, FL 33323
Contact: Walter Ruf CEO
Tel: 954-604-6056
Email: wruf@genoausa.com
Website: www.genoausa.com
Staffing services: engineering, IT, office support, human resources & purchasing. (Hisp, estab 2009, empl 162, sales $19,878,000, cert: NMSDC)

8576   GlobalVise Inc.
10335 Cross Creek Blvd Ste 8
Tampa, FL 33647
Contact: Sanjay Mehta President
Tel: 813-333-0400
Email: sanjay@globalvise.com
Website: www.globalvise.com
Permanent, temporary & contract staffing solutions. (As-Ind, estab 2008, empl 8, sales $2,758,764, cert: State, NMSDC, 8a)

8577   Hamilton-Malone Corp
31958 US 19 N
Palm Harbor, FL 34684
Contact: Eileen McQuown President
Tel: 727-781-7747
Email: eileen@accordstaff.com
Website:
Temporary & temp to hire staffing, executive search. (Woman, estab 1993, empl , sales $80,000,000, cert: State)

8578   Innovative Systems Group of Florida, Inc. dba ISGF
100 E Pine St Ste 605
Orlando, FL 32801
Contact: Thomas Bryan Managing Partner
Tel: 407-481-9580
Email: tbryan@isgf.com
Website: www.isgf.com
Temporary, contract, contract to hire, direct hire staffing & recruitment in information technology, accounting & finance, sales & marketing. (As-Pac, estab 1996, empl 30, sales $3,210,000, cert: State, City, NMSDC, CPUC)

8579   I-Tech Personnel Services, Inc.
5627 Atlantic Blvd, Ste 1
Jacksonville, FL 32207
Contact: Marco Tran President
Tel: 904-381-1911
Email: mtran@itechpersonnel.com
Website: www.itechpersonnel.net
Staffing svcs: clerical, technical professionals & light industrial, temporary to permanent, direct hire placement & on-site management. (As-Pac, estab 1998, empl 125, sales $3,580,000, cert: State, NMSDC)

8580   Key Technical Resources, Inc.
5763 N Andrews Way
Fort Lauderdale, FL 33309
Contact: President
Tel: 954-771-1554
Email:
Website: www.keytechnical.com
Full time, contract & temporary placement: information technology, accounting & finance. (Woman, estab 1999, empl 15, sales $1,828,000, cert: WBENC)

8581   KeyStaff, Inc.
3540 Forest Hill Blvd #203
West Palm Beach, FL 33406
Contact: Jessica Irons Business Dev Mgr
Tel: 561-688-9184
Email: jirons@mykeystaff.com
Website: www.mykeystaff.com/
IT/technical staffing solutions. (Woman, estab 1990, empl 60, sales $50,000,000, cert: State, WBENC)

8582   Premier Advisors Staffing and Sales, LLC
7138 Spikerush Ct
Lakewood Ranch, FL 34202
Contact: Richard Burns President
Tel: 313-869-8868
Email: rburns@premierhealthcareadvisors.com
Website: http://premierhealthcareadvisors.com
Staffing and Recruiting. (AA, estab 2015, empl , sales $1,000,000, cert: State, NMSDC)

8583   Pro-Staffing Agency
981 W Commercial Blvd
Fort Lauderdale, FL 33309
Contact: Marie Morency Owner
Tel: 954-530-2894
Email: marie@pro-staffinggroup.com
Website: www.pro-staffinggroup.com
Recruiting, staffing & business management. (Woman/AA, estab 2016, empl 2, sales , cert: NMSDC)

8584   Qualese, LLC
3035 Honeysuckle Rd
Largo, FL 33770
Contact: Roberto Filippelli President
Tel: 727-488-6373
Email: roberto.filippelli@qualese.com
Website: www.qualese.com
Recruiting & staffing agency. (Hisp, estab 2015, empl 1, sales , cert: NMSDC)

8585   Rapid Staffing, Inc.
P.O. Box 602
Valrico, FL 33595
Contact: Lani Harless President
Tel: 813-651-1242
Email: lani@rapidstaffing.com
Website: www.rapidstaffing.com
Staffing services: temporary & temporary to permanent employees. (Woman/Hisp, estab 2002, empl 5, sales $2,227,174, cert: State, NMSDC)

8586   Resource Employment Solutions
5900 Lake Ellenor Dr, Ste 100
Orlando, FL 32809
Contact: Eddy Dominguez VP Business Dev
Tel: 321-234-9363
Email: eddy_d@resourceemployment.com
Website: http://resourceemployment.com
Employment agency, staffing services & recruitment company. (Hisp, estab 1995, empl 35000, sales $111,000,000, cert: NMSDC)

8587   Spherion Corporation
8130 Baymeadows Way W Ste 103
Jacksonville, FL 32256
Contact: Shelley Sherman Sr. Mgr, Qualification
Tel: 904-448-9102
Email: info@spherion.com
Website: www.spherion.com
National staffing: temp, temp to perm & direct placement staffing. (Woman, estab 1946, empl 1500, sales $14,089,000, cert: WBENC)

8588   Staffing By Choice LLC
7975 NW 154th St, Ste 380
Miami Lakes, FL 33016
Contact: Matthew Marsh VP of Business Acq
Tel: 954-417-5627
Email: mmarsh@cpabychoice.com
Website: www.staffingbychoice.com
Staffing, recruiting & executive search services: account-
ing, finance, sales & operations professionals, permanent,
temp to perm & contract roles. (As-Pac, estab 2002, empl
7, sales $360,000, cert: NMSDC)

8589   StaffWorks, Inc.
11880 28th St N Ste 101
Saint Petersburg, FL 33716
Contact: Toni Baroncelli President
Tel: 727-322-1320
Email: toni@staffworks.net
Website: www.staffworks.net
Staffing: permanent or temporary placement of executive
level, consulting, support & clerical positions. (Woman,
estab 1998, empl 9, sales $550,000, cert: State)

8590   Techno-Transfers of Florida, Inc.
4609 NW 26th Ave
Boca Raton, FL 33434
Contact: Virginia Mendiola Director
Tel: 561-212-2383
Email: vmendiola@techno-transfers.com
Website: http://techno-transfers.com
IT personnel for temporary contract, temp-to-perm roles &
full-time positions. (Woman/Hisp, estab 1992, empl 6,
sales $350,000, cert: State)

8591   The CALER Group, Inc.
23337 Lago Mar Cir
Boca Raton, FL 33433
Contact: Colleen Perrone President
Tel: 561-394-8045
Email: cperrone@calergroup.com
Website: www.calergroup.com
Executive recruiting. (Woman, estab 1995, empl 6, sales
$1,200,000, cert: WBENC)

8592   TransHire
3601 W Commercial Blvd Ste 12
Fort Lauderdale, FL 33309
Contact: Yvonne Rasbach President
Tel: 954-484-5401
Email: yvonne@transhiregroup.com
Website: www.TransHiregroup.com
Staffing svcs: office, clerical, admin support, word process-
ing, light industrial, on-site mgmt programs & payrolling
svcs, temp, contract & permanent placement. (Woman/
Hisp, estab 1984, empl 9, sales $21,575,122, cert: State,
NMSDC)

8593   Vinali LLC
2860 Delaney Ave
Orlando, FL 32806
Contact: Acct Mgr
Tel: 407-574-2000
Email:
Website: http://vinalistaffing.com/
Permanent and temporary staffing services across technol-
ogy, accounting, logistics and healthcare. (Woman/Hisp,
estab 2016, empl 15, sales $5,000,000, cert: State,
WBENC)

Georgia

8594   Apollos Partners LLC
P.O. Box 49755
Atlanta, GA 30359
Contact: Bryan Payne Managing Partner
Tel: 404-437-7500
Email: bryan@apollospartners.com
Website: www.apollospartners.com
Direct-hire placements, accounting & finance positions.
(AA, estab 2009, empl 1, sales $225,000, cert: NMSDC)

8595   Ashton Staffing, Inc
3590 Cherokee St
Kennesaw, GA 30144
Contact: Jennifer Coon-Leeper Major Accts Mgr
Tel: 770-419-1776
Email: jleeper@ashtonstaffing.com
Website: www.ashtonstaffing.com
Direct hire & contract recruiting: technology, financial,
management. (Woman, estab 1995, empl 35, sales
$16,100,000, cert: WBENC)

8596   ASK Staffing, Inc.
3805 Crestwood Parkway Ste 260
Duluth, GA 30096
Contact: Manish Karani President
Tel: 770-813-8947
Email: mkarani@askstaffing.com
Website: www.askstaffing.com
Permanent placement & information technology staff
augmentation. (Woman/As-Pac, estab 1995, empl 300,
sales $22,000,000, cert: NMSDC, WBENC)

8597   Bison Data Systems, Inc.
5425 Peachtree Pkwy
Peachtree Corners, GA 30092
Contact: Wesley Owens CEO
Tel: 888-242-5737
Email: sscott@bisonstaffing.com
Website: www.bisonstaffing.com
Staffing, Technology, Light, Industrial & Health Care
industries. (AA, estab 2014, empl 37, sales $12,000,000,
cert: NMSDC)

8598   Blue Ocean Ventures LLC
2814 Spring Rd Ste 116
Atlanta, GA 30339
Contact: Robert Jordan
Tel: 404-279-2777
Email: robert.jordan@blue-oceanventures.com
Website: www.blue-oceanventures.com
Recruting, permanent hire & staffing. (AA, As-Ind, estab
2012, empl , sales $109,690, cert: NMSDC)

8599   Boomers Consulting, LLC
P.O. Box 246
Lithonia, GA 30058
Contact: Managing Dir
Tel: 678-476-8243
Email:
Website: www.boomersconsultingllc.com
Talent acquisition & consulting, staffing/recruiting
services. (Woman/AA, estab 2011, empl 1, sales , cert:
State, City)

8600 COMFORCE
2400 Meadowbrook Pkwy
Duluth, GA 30096
Contact: Shivani Sardana Recruiter
Tel: 678-648-7422
Email: shivani.sardana@comforce.com
Website: www.comforce.com
Contingent staffing, information technology consulting & human resource outsourcing solutions. (As-Ind, estab 1962, empl 500, sales $438,000,000, cert: NMSDC)

8601 Corporate Temps, Inc.
5950 Live Oak Parkway Ste 230
Norcross, GA 30093
Contact: Shawn Menefee President & CEO
Tel: 770-934-1710
Email: shawn@corporatetemps.com
Website: www.corporatetemps.com
Temporary & permanent staffing. (AA, estab 1991, empl 250, sales $11,670,618, cert: State, City, NMSDC)

8602 CorTech
710 Morgan Falls Road
Atlanta, GA 30350
Contact: JP Rogers Sr VP Sales
Tel: 770-628-0268
Email: jrogers@cor-tech.net
Website: www.cor-tech.net
Recruiting svcs: technical, professional services, vendor mgmt (VMS). (Hisp, estab 1999, empl 7500, sales $260,543,521, cert: NMSDC)

8603 DoverStaffing
2451 Cumberland Pkwy Ste 3418
Atlanta, GA 30339
Contact: Sanquinetta Dover CEO
Tel: 770-434-3040
Email: sdover@doverstaffing.com
Website: www.doverstaffing.com
Staffing, training, call center svcs. (Woman/AA, estab 1996, empl 200, sales , cert: NMSDC)

8604 EC London & Associates
101 Marietta St NW, Ste 3310
Atlanta, GA 30303
Contact: Edward C. London CEO
Tel: 404-688-6607
Email: elondon@bellsouth.net
Website: www.eclondon.com
Facilities support & staffing services. (AA, estab 1981, empl 50, sales $1,821,984, cert: City)

8605 Enterprise Project Solutions Group Corporation
204 Kobuk Court
Canton, GA 30114
Contact: Dir of Sales
Tel: 678-592-2256
Email:
Website: www.epsgcorp.com
Staff Augmentation (Woman, estab 2005, empl 5, sales $1,500,000, cert: WBENC)

8606 Excel Staffing Inc.
1174 Grimes Bridge Rd Ste 100
Roswell, GA 30075
Contact: Khushnood Elahi Sales/ Marketing Mgr
Tel: 678-461-8701
Email: k.elahi@4esi.com
Website: www.4esi.com
Staffing svcs: sales & marketing, executive, accounting & finance, engineering & manufacturing, industrial, office professionals, IT managed svcs & e-business svcs. (As-Ind, estab 2001, empl 10, sales $9,000,000, cert: NMSDC)

8607 FirstPro Inc.
P.O. Box 420559
Atlanta, GA 30342
Contact: Michelle Kennedy Dir of Mktg
Tel: 404-250-7179
Email: m.kennedy@firstproinc.com
Website: www.firstproinc.com
Executive search, professional placement & staffing: accounting, administrative, call center, clerical, collections, finance, healthcare, human resources, information technology, legal, light industrial, life sciences, management consulting. (Woman, estab 1986, empl 125, sales $31,900,000, cert: WBENC)

8608 Forar Tech, LLC.
902 Lenox Blvd NE
Atlanta, GA 30324
Contact: Unmesh Mishra VP Sales
Tel: 404-379-3900
Email: unmesh.mishra@forartech.com
Website: www.forartech.com
Executive Staffing services, technical % administration. (Woman/As-Ind, estab 2006, empl 2, sales $788,000, cert: 8a)

8609 Futurewave Systems Inc.
5 Concourse Pkwy Ste 3000
Roswell, GA 30075
Contact: Raj Prabhu CEO
Tel: 678-640-1167
Email: raj.prabhu@futurewavesystems.com
Website: www.futurewavesystems.com
Staffing services. (As-Ind, estab 2006, empl 267, sales $3,292,000, cert: NMSDC)

8610 Global Personnel Solutions, Inc.
1143 Laney Walker Blvd
Augusta, GA 30901
Contact: Giselle Brown Acct Mgr
Tel: 706-722-4222
Email: gbrown@gapersonnel.com
Website: www.globalpersonnelsol.com
Full service staffing services. (Woman/AA, estab 1987, empl 10, sales $4,475,681, cert: NMSDC)

8611 Heagney Logan Group, LLC
2002 Summit Blvd Ste 300
Atlanta, GA 30319
Contact: Jeannette Weigelt Principal
Tel: 404-267-1351
Email: info@heagneylogan.com
Website: www.heagneylogangroup.com
Management Consulting, IT Consultant Staffing, Project Management, ERP Consulting, Remote Development, Contract Technical Staffing. (AA, estab 2009, empl 3, sales $924,954, cert: State, NMSDC)

8612 Healthcare Resources Staffing Agency
2107 N Decatur Rd, Ste 256
Decatur, GA 30033
Contact: Terrilyn Ferguson Director
Tel: 770-820-7874
Email: terri@hrsagency.com
Website: www.hrsagency.com
Healthcare Resources Staffing (HRS) Agency is a medical staffing company providing Nurses, Therapists, Nursing Assistants and other Healthcare medical and non-medical professionals.
We provide medical staffing services and related products to Medical (AA, estab 2016, empl 2, sales $1,100,000, cert: NMSDC)

8613 Infinite Resouce Solutions
2400 Herodian Way SE Ste 205
Smyrna, GA 30080
Contact: Leigh Sicina COO
Tel: 404-645-7065
Email: lsicina@infiniters.com
Website: www.infiniters.com
Resource management & professional staffing. (Woman, estab 2013, empl 50, sales $2,464,410, cert: WBENC)

8614 Kinetix LLC
50 Glenlake Parkway Ste 625
Atlanta, GA 30328
Contact: CEO
Tel: 770-390-8360
Email:
Website: www.kinetixhr.com
Recruiting & placement services. (Woman, estab 1990, empl , sales $100,000, cert: WBENC)

8615 Lorentine Green & Associates, Inc.
12104 Jefferson Creek Dr
Alpharetta, GA 30005
Contact: Lorentine F. Green President
Tel: 770-616-6326
Email: lorentine@lorentinegreen.com
Website: www.lorentinegreen.com
Recruiting & project management, Permanent Placement, Contract & Contract to Permanent. (AA, estab 2013, empl 7, sales $300,000, cert: NMSDC)

8616 MarketPro Inc.
53 Perimeter Center E Ste 200
Atlanta, GA 30346
Contact: Cindy Underwood VP
Tel: 404-978-1005
Email: cindy@marketproinc.com
Website: www.marketproinc.com
Contract, contract to hire or direct hire: marketing, advertising & communications. (Woman, estab 1996, empl 20, sales $15,650,000, cert: WBENC)

8617 Olivine LLC
970 Peachtree Industrial Blvd. Ste 100
Suwanee, GA 30024
Contact: Rajeev Maddur Sr Acct Mgr
Tel: 770-596-5155
Email: rajeevm@olivinellc.com
Website: www.olivinellc.com
IT Consulting Services, Contract, Contract to Hire and Direct hire placements. (As-Ind, estab 2006, empl 20, sales $235,000, cert: NMSDC)

8618 Pareto Solutions Group, Inc.
8 Piedmont Center Ste 210
Atlanta, GA 30305
Contact: Shaun Harvill CEO
Tel: 770-804-8020
Email: sharvill@paretosg.com
Website: www.paretosg.com
Staffing: temporary, temp-to-hire & direct hire placement of accounting, finance & IT professionals. (Woman/Hisp, estab 2006, empl 55, sales $570,000, cert: WBENC)

8619 Perimeter Entertainment, Inc.
P.O. Box 464003
Lawrenceville, GA 30042
Contact: CEO
Tel: 678-866-4066
Email:
Website: www.perimeterent.com
Content Creation & Professional Recruiting Services for Entertainment, Media, Government and Big Brand Companies. (Woman/AA, estab 2010, empl 4, sales , cert: NMSDC, WBENC)

8620 PharmaCare Solutions, Inc.
5555 Glenridge Connector Ste 200
Atlanta, GA 30342
Contact: Cassandra Tancil CEO
Tel: 404-459-2847
Email: ctancil@pharmacaresolutions.com
Website: www.pharmacaresolutions.com
Contract & temporary health professional staffing, analytical data reporting, health management initiatives & clinical support services. (Woman/AA, estab 2003, empl 1, sales , cert: NMSDC)

8621 Preferred Personnel Solutions, Inc.
425 Barrett Pkwy Ste 4045
Kennesaw, GA 30144
Contact: Business Develop Mgr
Tel: 678-662-6471
Email:
Website: www.preferredpersonnel.com
Staffing svcs: light industrial, manufacturing, logistics & distribution, office & admin, call center, accounting & finance, executive search. (Woman, estab 2002, empl 500, sales $11,900,000, cert: WBENC)

8622 ProKatchers LLC
1766 Baxley Pine Trace
Suwanee, GA 30024
Contact: Samay Shah CEO
Tel: 706-254-7008
Email: samay@prokatchers.com
Website: www.prokatchers.com/
Traditional staffing & recruiting, direct placement & payroll services, workforce solution programs. (As-Pac, estab 2015, empl 200, sales $12,000,000, cert: NMSDC, CPUC)

8623 Quality Staffing of America, Inc.
3525 Piedmont Rd NE
Atlanta, GA 30305
Contact: Ken Richards President
Tel: 404-477-0020
Email: ken@qualitystaffingamerica.com
Website: www.QualityStaffingAmerica.com
Temporary/contingent staffing services. (Woman, estab 2013, empl 200, sales $7,400,000, cert: WBENC)

8624 R. Beverly Consulting, LLC dba Silver Fox Staffing
1140 Newpark View Place
Mableton, GA 30126
Contact: Jeannine Lewis Managing Dir
Tel: 404-512-6441
Email: info@silverfoxstaffs.com
Website: www.silverfoxstaffs.com
Staffing, temporary, part-time and seasonal employees for sporting and special events, conferences, corporate and organizational meetings, trade shows. (AA, estab 2011, empl 1, sales $167,000, cert: NMSDC)

8625 Search Wizards, Inc.
1427 Cartecay Dr NE
Atlanta, GA 30319
Contact: Leslie O'Connor President & CEO
Tel: 404-846-9500
Email: leslie@searchwizards.com
Website: www.searchwizards.net
Staffing: IT, finance & human resources, contract, contract-to-hire & full time. (Woman, estab 2000, empl 71, sales $10,840,732, cert: WBENC)

8626 Soft Source, Inc.
      3883 Rogers Bridge Rd Ste 404B
      Duluth, GA 30097
      Contact: Mohammad Malik
      Tel: 678-957-1049
      Email: malik@softsourceinc.com
      Website: www.softsourceinc.com
Staffing, recruiting, staff augmentation, placement,
engineering, environmental remediation, design build. (As-
Ind, estab 1999, empl 10, sales $4,200,000, cert: State)

8627 Southern Crescent Personnel, Inc.
      7179 Jonesboro Rd Ste 101
      Morrow, GA 30260
      Contact: President
      Tel: 770-968-4602
      Email:
      Website: www.scp-jobs.com
Temporary, temp-to-hire & perm placement: administrative, medical & dental positions. (Woman, estab 1993,
empl 4, sales , cert: WBENC)

8628 The Experts Bench, Inc.
      1325 Satellite Blvd
      Suwanee, GA 30024
      Contact: Ramsey A'Ve Market Practice Lead
      Tel: 770-757-5831
      Email: ramseya@tebww.com
      Website: www.tebww.com/
Professional services. staff marketing & accounting
contractors. (Woman, estab 2002, empl 20, sales
$1,819,000, cert: WBENC)

8629 The Mom Corps, Inc.
      1205 Johnson Ferry Rd Ste 136-507
      Marietta, GA 30068
      Contact: Allison OKelly CEO
      Tel: 888-438-8122
      Email: allison@momcorps.com
      Website: www.momcorps.com
Temporary staffing. (Woman, estab 2005, empl 15, sales
$11,240,405, cert: WBENC)

8630 The Royster Group, Inc.
      934 Glenwood Ave SE Ste 280
      Atlanta, GA 30316
      Contact: Taunton Ken President & CEO
      Tel: 770-507-3353
      Email: krtaunton@roystergroup.com
      Website: www.roystergroup.com
Diversity search: healthcare, financial services, consumer
products & industrial. (AA, estab 2001, empl 80, sales
$18,000,000, cert: NMSDC)

8631 VersoGenics Inc, dba Comforce
      990 Hammond Dr Ste 700
      Atlanta, GA 30328
      Contact: Julie Weissman Sr. Business Dev. Mgr
      Tel: 813-349-1779
      Email: julie.weissman@comforce.com
      Website: http://comforce.com
Temporary staffing services, permanent placement
services & Statement of Work projects. (As-Ind, estab
1974, empl 12000, sales , cert: NMSDC)

Iowa

8632 CareerPros, LLC dba Sedona Staffing Services
      2065 Holliday Dr
      Dubuque, IA 52002
      Contact: Nikki Kiefer President
      Tel: 563-556-3040
      Email: nikki@careerpros.com
      Website: www.careerpros.com
Staffing services: temporary, temp-to-hire, smart-hire,
contract & staff leasing. (Woman, estab 1993, empl 18,
sales $11,700,000, cert: WBENC)

8633 Chenhall's Staffing, Inc
      2119 E 12th St
      Davenport, IA 52803
      Contact: Bob Hickman President
      Tel: 563-386-3800
      Email: bhickman@chenhallstaffing.com
      Website: www.chenhallstaffing.com
Staffing augmentation, recruiting & HR, temp to perm &
transitional probationary staffing recruitment, screening, testing & placement; corporate recruitment, career
counseling & outplacement. (Nat Ame, estab 1955, empl
7, sales , cert: NMSDC, 8a)

8634 SelectOne Staffing Services LLC
      222 Third Ave SE Ste 240-B
      Cedar Rapids, IA 52401
      Contact: Vincent Clayton President
      Tel: 319-373-2325
      Email: vclayton@genatek.net
      Website: www.genatek.net
Recruiting & staffing: engineering, IT development,
telecommunications, technical support. (AA, estab 2003,
empl 10, sales , cert: NMSDC)

Illinois

8635 AltaStaff LLC
      19 S La Salle Ste 800
      Chicago, IL 60603
      Contact: Taz Wilson President
      Tel: 312-269-9990
      Email: kkossack@altastaff.com
      Website: www.altastaff.com
Staffing services: temporary, temp-to-hire & direct-hire
placements for administrative, creative, financial & sales
support. (Woman, estab 2007, empl 5, sales , cert: State)

8636 Amazing Edibles Gourmet Catering, Inc.
      2419 W 14th St Unit C
      Chicago, IL 60608
      Contact: Andrea Herrera President
      Tel: 312-563-1600
      Email: amazingedibles@aol.com
      Website: www.amazingediblescatering.com
Amazing Edibles is a custom, full service caterer. We
provide breakfast, brunch, lunch, dinner, snacks, and
party options. We deliver to the Chicago Metropolitan
Area. We specialize in Professional Development and
Training Catering. (Woman/Hisp, estab 1994, empl 10,
sales $963,488, cert: State)

8637 Anchor Staffing Inc.
      9901 S Western Ave, Ste 206
      Chicago, IL 60643
      Contact: Joyce Johnson CEO
      Tel: 773-881-0530
      Email: jjohnson@anchorstaffing.com
      Website: www.anchorstaffing.com
Temporary & direct hire staffing & employment services.
(Nat Ame, As-Ind, estab 2002, empl 350, sales
$2,600,000,000, cert: State, City, NMSDC)

8638   A-PRO EXECS, LLC
       208 S Lasalle St Ste 1450
       Chicago, IL 60604
       Contact: Gladys Jossell Owner
       Tel: 312-855-1515
       Email: gjossell@aol.com
       Website: www.aprotemps.com
Temporary & permanent placement
services:administrative/legal office support, accounting,
customer service & information technology. (Woman/AA,
estab 2004, empl 4, sales $2,700,000, cert: WBENC)

8639   Arlington Resources, Inc.
       4902 Tollview Dr
       Rolling Meadows, IL 60008
       Contact: Patricia Casey President
       Tel: 224-232-5900
       Email: pcasey@arlingtonresources.com
       Website: www.arlingtonresources.com
Temporary staffing services, temp to hire & direct hire
placement of Human Resources Professionals. (Woman,
estab 1997, empl 25, sales $6,000,000, cert: City)

8640   Arrow Strategies
       233 N. Michigan Ave Ste 1960
       Chicago, IL 60601
       Contact: Mike Colles Division Director
       Tel: 312-561-9202
       Email: mikec@arrowstrategies.com
       Website: www.arrowstrategies.com
Recruiting: source, profile & present high-end talent. (Nat
Ame, estab 2002, empl 300, sales $48,000,000, cert:
NMSDC)

8641   Assured Healthcare Staffing LLC - Gurnee, IL
       495 N Riverside Dr Ste 203
       Gurnee, IL 60031
       Contact: Leslie Kischer President
       Tel: 847-775-7445
       Email: leslie.kischer@assuredhealthcare.com
       Website: www.assuredhealthcare.com
Healthcare staffing: Registered Nurses, Licensed Practical
Nurses, Certified Nurses Aids, Pharmacists, Pharmacy
Techs, Medical Assistants, Medical Billers. (Woman, estab
2007, empl 70, sales $2,751,000, cert: WBENC)

8642   Carrington & Carrington
       230 W Monroe St Ste 2250
       Chicago, IL 60606
       Contact: Marian H Carrington Principal
       Tel: 312-606-0503
       Email: mcarrington@carringtonandcarrington.com
       Website: www.carringtonandcarrington.com
Executive search, recruitment & placement of diverse
professionals for senior management & executive level
positions. (Woman/AA, estab 1979, empl 6, sales , cert:
City, WBENC)

8643   Cube Hub Inc.
       600 N Commons Dr Ste 109
       Aurora, IL 60504
       Contact: Sunil Bakhshi Business Develop Mgr
       Tel: 630-746-1239
       Email: sunil@cube-hub.com
       Website: www.cube-hub.com
Technology, Training, Staffing & Professional Services,
Staffing/Recruiting services, Software Development, IT,
Engineering, Professional, Marketing, Healthcare, Clinical,
Scientific, Finance/Audit, Telecommunication, etc.
(Woman/AA, As-Ind, estab 2014, empl 28, sales
$3,580,640, cert: NMSDC)

8644   DC McIssac Corp. dba FPC Arlington, Inc.
       1400 Renaissance Dr Ste 100
       Park Ridge, IL 60068
       Contact: Cathy McIsaac President
       Tel: 847-228-7205
       Email: cathy@fpcarlington.com
       Website: www.fpcarlington.com
Executive search & recruiting services. (Woman, estab
1959, empl 7, sales $800,000, cert: WBENC, NWBOC)

8645   Deegit, Inc.
       1900 E Golf Rd. Ste 925
       Schaumburg, IL 60173
       Contact: Jim Dimitriou CEO
       Tel: 847-330-1985
       Email: jdimitriou@deegit.com
       Website: www.deegit.com
Temp and Perm, project-based services(SOW) & Recruitment process outsourcing(RPO). (As-Ind, estab 1993,
empl 150, sales $30,000,000, cert: State, NMSDC)

8646   DMD Consulting, LLC
       230 S Clark St Ste 113
       Chicago, IL 60604
       Contact: Darlene Drab CEO
       Tel: 312-809-6987
       Email: darlene@dmdconsulting.net
       Website: www.dmdconsulting.net
Permanent placement, interim resourcing, and co-
sourcing, Audit & Compliance, Accounting and Finance,
Tax and Information Technology. (Woman/AA, estab
2008, empl 20, sales $408,865, cert: State, City, WBENC)

8647   Elsko, Inc.
       3601 Algonquin Rd, Ste 130
       Rolling Meadows, IL 60008
       Contact: Christina LaSalvia President
       Tel: 847-691-2869
       Email: clasalvia@elskoinc.com
       Website: www.elskoinc.com/home
Executive staffing. (Woman/Nat Ame, estab 1976, empl
8, sales $550,000, cert: WBENC)

8648   Furst Services
       2580 Charles St
       Rockford, IL 61125
       Contact: Darlene Furst President
       Tel: 815-997-1426
       Email: darlene.furst@furststaff.com
       Website: www.furststaff.com
Recruiting services. (Woman, estab 1971, empl 55, sales
$25,000,000, cert: WBENC)

8649   Global Staffing Services, Inc.
       925 S Main St
       Rockford, IL 61101
       Contact: Michele Caldwell CEO
       Tel: 815-968-5797
       Email: mec611@earthlink.net
       Website: www.global-staffing.com
Staffing: flexible, contract & permanent placement,
employment & background assessment. (Woman/AA,
estab 2000, empl 4, sales , cert: NMSDC)

8650   Ignition Network dba Fieldday
       400 W Erie
       Chicago, IL 60654
       Contact: Josh Miller Partner
       Tel: 708-223-1191
       Email: diversesupplier@fieldaymarketing.com
       Website: www.fieldaymarketing.com
Recruit human resources professionals. (Woman, estab ,
empl 5, sales $753,000, cert: WBENC)

8651 IlinkResources Staffing
      24402 W Lockport Rd Ste 226
      Plainfield, IL 60544
      Contact: VP Sales
      Tel: 815-230-5256
      Email:
      Website: www.ilinkresources.com
Recruiting & staffing. (Woman, estab 2011, empl 6, sales ,
cert: WBENC)

8652 JRA Consulting Services, Inc.
      10225 W Higgins Rd
      Rosemont, IL 60018
      Contact: Ross Wolfson Talent Acquisition Mgr
      Tel: 847-430-3682
      Email: rwolfson@hrcontracting.com
      Website: www.hrcontracting.com
Human resources staffing, permanent & contract posi-
tions. (Woman, estab 1997, empl 4, sales $2,000,000, cert:
NWBOC)

8653 LBF Recruitment Strategies, LLC
      330 N Clinton St Ste 606
      Chicago, IL 60661
      Contact: Lisa Frank CEO
      Tel: 312-725-8544
      Email: lisa@lbfstrategies.com
      Website: www.LBFStrategies.com
Executive Search & Career Coaching. (Woman, estab 2012,
empl 1, sales $112,000, cert: WBENC)

8654 Loftus & O'Meara Staffing Inc.
      211 E Ontario Ste 1050
      Chicago, IL 60611
      Contact: Cindy Loftus Co-Owner
      Tel: 312-944-2102
      Email: cloftus@loftusomeara.com
      Website: www.loftusomeara.com
Staffing: temporary, temp-to-hire & direct hire. (Woman,
estab 1978, empl 7, sales $1,804,597, cert: WBENC)

8655 Mullins & Associates, Inc.
      522 S Northwest Hwy
      Barrington, IL 60010
      Contact: Terri Mullins
      Tel: 847-382-1800
      Email: tmullins@thebigcom.com
      Website:
Contract, contract for hire & permanent placement
services: engineering & IT fields. (Woman, estab 1964,
empl 41, sales $5,000,000, cert: WBENC)

8656 Mutual Target Associates, Inc.
      7002 Hamilton Dr
      Gurnee, IL 60031
      Contact: Chandra Govind CEO
      Tel: 847-855-0059
      Email: cgovind@mtaincorporated.com
      Website: www.mtaincorporated.com
Permanent placements, contract & contract to hire
services. (As-Pac, estab 2005, empl 6, sales $750,000, cert:
NMSDC)

8657 My Future Consulting, Inc.
      15255 S 94th Ave Ste 500
      Orland Park, IL 60462
      Contact: Anthony Fletcher CEO
      Tel: 708-428-6462
      Email: anthony.fletcher@myfutureconsulting.com
      Website: www.myfutureconsulting.com
Executive search & recruitment. (AA, estab 2012, empl 17,
sales $420,000, cert: NMSDC)

8658 Myerson & Associates, Inc.
      2 W Delaware Pl, Ste 3005
      Chicago, IL 60610
      Contact: Pamela Myerson CEO
      Tel: 312-943-7722
      Email: pam@myersonassociates.com
      Website: www.myersonassociates.com
Executive recruiting services within Global Financial
Markets. (Woman, estab 0, empl , sales , cert: WBENC)

8659 Myriad Technical Services
      40 Shuman Blvd Ste 210
      Naperville, IL 60563
      Contact: Mihir Dash President
      Tel: 630-369-6369
      Email: jobs@myriadcorp.com
      Website: www.myriadcorp.com
Staffing recruiting. (As-Pac, estab 1997, empl 40, sales
$4,000,000, cert: State)

8660 Premier Systems, Inc
      14489 John Humphrey Ste 202 Ste 202
      Orland Park, IL 60462
      Contact: Tariq Khan Acct Mgr
      Tel: 708-349-9200
      Email: tkhan@premiersystemsinc.com
      Website: www.premiersystemsinc.com
IT consulting & staffing, project mgmt, systems programming & admin: IBM mainframe midrange, client server,
PeopleSoft, SAP & Microsoft based systems; e-commerce devel. (As-Pac, estab 1993, empl 30, sales
$2,713,000, cert: City, NMSDC)

8661 Professional Dynamic Network, Inc.
      20280 Governors Hwy Ste 106
      Olympia Fields, IL 60461
      Contact: CEO
      Tel: 708-747-4361
      Email:
      Website: www.pndseek.com
Temporary & permanent staffing, recruitment, management consulting, education & training. (Woman/AA,
estab 1995, empl 167, sales $3,415,745, cert: City,
NMSDC)

8662 PSI Resources, LLC
      2001 Butterfield Rd, Ste 1040
      Downers Grove, IL 60515
      Contact: Scott Fleckenstein SVP, Strategic Partner-
      ships
      Tel: 602-696-5727
      Email: sfleckenstein@psiresources.com
      Website: www.psiresources.com
Staffing & recruiting services. (Woman, estab 1993, empl
45, sales $1,411,062, cert: State, City, WBENC)

8663 Redline Resources, Inc.
      100 S State St, 4th Fl
      Chicago, IL 60603
      Contact: President
      Tel: 312-508-4970
      Email:
      Website: http://redlineresources.com
Recruiting/Staffing, accounting, finance, and office
professionals for their team. (Woman, estab 2012, empl
20, sales $3,200,000, cert: WBENC)

8664　Remedy Intelligent Staffing
211 53RD STREET
MOLINE, IL 61265
Contact: Dir of Sales
Tel: 309-762-7716
Email: kathys@remedystaff.com
Website: www.remedystaff.com
Staffing services: administrative, finance, accounting, customer service, IT, logistics & light industrial. (Woman, estab 1963, empl , sales $6,000,000,000, cert: State)

8665　Resource Technology Associates, LLC
10225 W Higgins Rd
Rosemont, IL 60018
Contact: Andrew Konik VP
Tel: 847-430-3667
Email: akonik@rta-inc.com
Website: www.rta-inc.com
Staffing support, outbound recruitment. (Woman, estab 1984, empl 22, sales $2,000,000, cert: NWBOC)

8666　RJSL Group
1956 W Erie St Unit 1E
Chicago, IL 60622
Contact: Richard Lee CEO
Tel: 312-282-4654
Email: richard@rjslgroup.com
Website: www.rjslgroup.com
Staffing and recruiting agency, IT & business resources. (As-Pac, estab 2006, empl 10, sales $201,804, cert: State, City, NMSDC)

8667　Seville Staffing LLC
180 N Michigan Ave Ste 1510
Chicago, IL 60601
Contact: Janet Sloan President
Tel: 312-368-1144
Email: jsloan@sevillestaffing.com
Website: www.sevillestaffing.com
Temporary staffing: clerical, office, administrative, light industrial. (Woman, estab 1979, empl 7, sales $5,000,000, cert: State)

8668　Shar Enterprises Inc dba HKA Staffing Services
800 Waukegan Rd Ste 200
Glenview, IL 60025
Contact: Kristin Haffner President
Tel: 847-998-9300
Email: khaffner@hkastaffing.com
Website: www.hkastaffing.com
Staffing services. (Woman, estab 1989, empl 45, sales $1,200,000, cert: WBENC)

8669　Sterling Engineering, Inc.
Two Westbrook Corporate Center Ste 300
Westchester, IL 60154
Contact: Rama Kavaliauskas President
Tel: 630-993-3433
Email: rama@sterling-engineering.com
Website: www.sterling-engineering.com
Engineering & technical staff augmentation solutions. (Woman, estab 1969, empl 75, sales $2,691,294, cert: WBENC)

8670　Superior Staffing
P.O. Box 1551
Melrose Park, IL 60161
Contact: Heriberto Vale CEO
Tel: 630-516-3505
Email: hvale@superior-staffing.com
Website:
Staffing: temp light industrial & clerical. (Hisp, estab 2001, empl 600, sales $15,000,000, cert: NMSDC)

8671　Synergy Global Systems Inc
1580 S Milwaukee Ave, Ste # 425 Ste 425
Libertyville, IL 60048
Contact: Renu Suri Director
Tel: 630-768-2975
Email: renusuri@synergygbl.com
Website: http://synergygbl.com/
Staffing solutions & services, temporary staffing, permanent placement, career transition, talent development, outsourcing. (Woman/As-Ind, estab 2006, empl 1113, sales $434,765,600, cert: NMSDC, WBENC)

8672　US Surgitech Inc.
470 Mission St, Unit 6
Carol Stream, IL 60188
Contact: President
Tel: 630-456-4114
Email:
Website: www.ussurgitech.com
Temporary & permanent staffing solutions. (As-Ind, estab 2003, empl 7, sales $1,206,246, cert: NMSDC)

8673　Workforce Management Inc.
525 W Wise Rd, Ste C
Schaumburg, IL 60193
Contact: President
Tel: 847-466-5335
Email:
Website: http://workforcemgmtinc.com
Staffing solutions, recruitment, placement & management. (Woman, estab 2014, empl 3, sales , cert: WBENC)

Indiana

8674　Alpha Rae Personnel, Inc.
347 W Berry St, Ste 700
Fort Wayne, IN 46802
Contact: Rae Pearson President & CEO
Tel: 260-426-8227
Email: businessoffice@alpha-rae.com
Website: www.alpha-rae.com
Contract & temporary staffing, executive search, HR management & HR department outsourcing, employee training, electronics & embedded software contract engineering & manufacturing development. (Woman/AA, estab 1980, empl 400, sales , cert: State, WBENC)

8675　DaMar Staffing Solutions
8900 Keystone Crossing, Ste 1060
Indianapolis, IN 46240
Contact: Tiffany Thompson President
Tel: 317-566-8320
Email: tthompson@damarstaff.com
Website: www.damarstaffing.com
Staffing: direct hire, temp-to-hire, temporary. (Woman/AA, estab 2003, empl 7, sales $622,423, cert: State, City, 8a)

8676　Diverse Staffing Services
6325 Digital Way, Ste #100
Indianapolis, IN 46278
Contact: Amber Slaughter Business Develop Mgr
Tel: 317-813-8000
Email: aslaughter@diversestaffing.com
Website: www.diversestaffing.com
Recruiting & staffing solutions: information technology, engineering, life sciences, sales & business operations. (AA, estab 1999, empl 3000, sales , cert: State, NMSDC)

8677   First Call Temporary Services Inc.
6960 Hillsdale Ct
Indianapolis, IN 46250
Contact: John Kulish Sales Mgr
Tel: 317-596-3280
Email: jkulish@fcqs.com
Website: www.firstcallinc.com
Staffing services: temp and temp-hire. (Woman, estab 1991, empl 31, sales $18,000,000, cert: WBENC)

8678   Smart IT Staffing, Inc.
6500 Technology Center Dr Ste 300
Indianapolis, IN 46278
Contact: Bill Ryle Dir of Sales
Tel: 513-530-0600
Email: bryle@getsmarterit.com
Website: www.getsmarterit.com
Information Technology Workforce Solutions. (Woman/AA, estab 2005, empl 480, sales $47,900,000, cert: NMSDC, WBENC)

8679   Specialized Staffing Solutions, LLC
1001 E Jefferson
South Bend, IN 46617
Contact: Jacqueline Barton President
Tel: 574-234-9944
Email: jbarton@specializedstaffing.biz
Website: http://specializedstaffing.biz
Temporary, permanant, technical & professional staffing, employment services, human resource mgmt, managed services. (Woman/As-Pac, estab 2002, empl 27, sales $17,000,000, cert: State, WBENC)

Kansas

8680   Choson Resource LLC
1999 N Amidon, Ste 100B
Wichita, KS 67203
Contact: Kim Silcott President
Tel: 316-729-0312
Email: kim@chosonresource.com
Website: www.Chosonresource.com
Aerospace engineering & staffing services for the air, defense & space industries. (Woman/As-Pac, estab 2010, empl 4, sales $4,254,100, cert: NMSDC)

8681   Kansas Personnel Services, Inc
2815 SW Wanamaker Rd
Topeka, KS 66614
Contact: Patricia Bossert President
Tel: 785-272-9999
Email: patti@keystaffing.com
Website: www.keystaffing.com
Temporary staffing services, long-term & short-term: clerical, office, light industrial, warehouse, & environmental personnel. (Woman, estab 1989, empl 126, sales $3,000,000, cert: State)

8682   Staffing Kansas City Inc.
9930 College Blvd
Overland Park, KS 66210
Contact: Michelle Hays Sales Exec
Tel: 913-663-5627
Email: michelle@staffingkc.com
Website: www.staffingkc.com
Temporary & permanent employment placement. (Woman, estab 1998, empl 5, sales $2,283,865, cert: State)

Kentucky

8683   Anew Technology Solutions, Inc.
3310-C Gilmore Industrial Blvd
Louisville, KY 40213
Contact: Nina Carter President
Tel: 502-472-7461
Email: anewtechnology@aol.com
Website:
products and services that help to increase the safety, health and sustainability of our environment. Our services range from environmental cleanup, testing and an innovative focus on sustainability. (Woman/AA, estab 2009, empl 1, sales , cert: State)

8684   Astute Sourcing, LLC
10200 Forest Green Blvd. Ste 112
Louisville, KY 40223
Contact: Dorothy Abernathy Exec Asst/Office Administrator
Tel: 502-499-9440
Email: info@tktandassociates.com
Website: www.astute-sourcing.com
Staffing services: telecommunications, healthcare, government, financial services, utilities, manufacturing and supply/chain logistics, contingent staffing, direct hire, permanent staffing, rapid deployment. (Woman/AA, estab 2012, empl 14, sales $2,692,927, cert: NMSDC, WBENC)

8685   J.Y. Legner Associates, Inc.
800 W Market St, Ste 102
Louisville, KY 40202
Contact: Josephine Legner CEO
Tel: 502-585-9000
Email: jlegner@jyla.com
Website: www.jyla.com
Staffing & HR mgmt, temporary staffing, long-term employee leasing. (Woman/AA, estab 1999, empl 70, sales $1,000,000, cert: NMSDC)

8686   QP1, Inc. dba Luttrell Staffing Group
1435 Campbell Lane
Bowling Green, KY 42104
Contact: Monica Shuffett VP
Tel: 270-250-3446
Email: mshuffett@lstaff.com
Website: www.lstaff.com
Manufacturing and industrial employment agency, exceptional administrative, call center, technical and professional placement services. (Woman, estab 1977, empl 150, sales $24,251,513, cert: WBENC)

Louisiana

8687   Delta Personnel, Inc.
2709 L & A Rd
Metairie, LA 70001
Contact: Ingrid Delahoussaye Owner
Tel: 504-833-5200
Email: tlawrence@deltapersonnel.com
Website: www.deltapersonnel.com
Staffing & payroll payroll services. (Woman/Hisp, estab 1968, empl 6, sales $3,000,000, cert: State, NMSDC, WBENC)

8688 Frazee Recruiting Consultants, Inc.
      2351 Energy Dr, Ste 1100
      Baton Rouge, LA 70808
      Contact: Chris Bien Business Dev Mgr
      Tel: 225-231-7880
      Email: sales@frazeerecruit.com
      Website: www.frazeerecruit.com
Professional staffing, direct hire search, contract/tempo-
rary. (Woman, estab 1998, empl 150, sales $6,000,000,
cert: WBENC)

8689 Infinitive Solutions
      1615 Poydras St Ste 900
      New Orleans, LA 70112
      Contact: President
      Tel: 504-648-6810
      Email:
      Website: http://infinitive-solutions.com
Staffing services including temporary and contract.
Professional, Healthcare, Educational support personnel.
(Woman/AA, estab 2013, empl 125, sales $1,185,950, cert:
WBENC)

8690 Jean Simpson Personnel Services, Inc.
      1318 Shreveport-Barksdale Hwy
      Shreveport, LA 71105
      Contact: Angel Scott Admin Asst
      Tel: 318-869-3494
      Email: ascott@jeansimpson.com
      Website: www.jeansimpson.com
Temporary & full-time staffing: clerical, industrial &
professional. (Woman, estab 1974, empl 33, sales , cert:
WBENC)

8691 Preferred Standards, LLC
      654 Lobdell Ave
      Baton Rouge, LA 70806
      Contact: Derrick Toussaint CEO
      Tel: 225-924-9552
      Email: dtoussaint@pstandards.net
      Website: www.pstandards.org
Professional staffing, recruiting & payroll services. (AA,
estab 2013, empl 5, sales $1,312,529, cert: NMSDC)

8692 SureTemps LLC
      1631 Elysian Fields Ave
      New Orleans, LA 70117
      Contact: Maxine A. President
      Tel: 504-947-3353
      Email: sunsoundconcerts@yahoo.com
      Website: www.suretemps.biz
Personnel staffing: labors, data entry clerks, custodial
services, full food services & supervisors/managers for
long or short term basis. (AA, estab 2011, empl 500, sales
$1,550,000, cert: City)

8693 Topp Knotch Personnel, Inc.
      401 Whitney Ave Ste 312
      Gretna, LA 70056
      Contact: Diedria Joseph CEO
      Tel: 866-744-2974
      Email: diedria@tkpsi.com
      Website: www.tkpsi.com
Staffing svcs: admin, clerical, customer service, accounting,
marketing, computer technology. (Woman/AA, estab ,
empl , sales $4,055,182, cert: City, WBENC)

8694 Universal Personnel, LLC
      1100 Poydras St Ste 1300
      New Orleans, LA 70163
      Contact: Michele Vignes President
      Tel: 504-561-5627
      Email: michelev@universal-personnel.com
      Website: www.universal-personnel.com
Technical staffing, career & contract job placement:
engineering, drafting, architecture & information
technology, professional, administrative & clerical.
(Woman, estab 1980, empl 650, sales $57,118,011, cert:
WBENC)

Massachusetts

8695 East Coast Staffing Solutions
      651 Orchard St Ste 307
      New Bedford, MA 02744
      Contact: Randy Silva Business Dev Mgr
      Tel: 508-990-7670
      Email: randy@eastcoaststaffingsolutions.com
      Website:
Staffing, direct hires, temporary placements & contractual assignments. (AA, estab 2009, empl , sales
$105,650,836, cert: State)

8696 Griffin Staffing Network, LLC
      1145 Main St Ste 508
      Springfield, MA 01103
      Contact: Michelle O'Meara
      Tel: 413-788-0751
      Email: momeara@griffinstaffingnetwork.com
      Website: www.griffinstaffingnetwork.com
Staffing services. (Woman/AA, estab 2013, empl 2, sales
, cert: State)

8697 Hollister Staffing, Inc.
      75 State St, 9th Fl
      Boston, MA 02109
      Contact: Kip Hollister CEO
      Tel: 617-654-0200
      Email: kip@hollisterstaff.com
      Website: www.hollisterstaff.com
Recruiting services: direct hire, contract & contract-to-
hire. (Woman, estab 1988, empl 70, sales $31,100,000,
cert: WBENC)

8698 John Leonard Employment Services, Inc.
      75 Federal St, Ste 1120
      Boston, MA 02110
      Contact: President
      Tel: 617-348-2607
      Email:
      Website: www.johnleonard.com
Temporary employment: office support personnel.
(Woman, estab 1969, empl 18, sales $7,009,497, cert:
State, City, WBENC)

8699 KNF&T Staffing Resources
      3 Post Office Square
      Boston, MA 02109
      Contact: Joanna DiTrapano Dir of Marketing
      Tel: 617-574-8200
      Email: jditrapano@knft.com
      Website: www.knft.com
Staffing services: administrative, accounting, finance &
healthcare personnel. (Woman, estab 1983, empl 35,
sales $14,000,000, cert: State, WBENC)

8700 S & S Staffing, LLC
50 Lake Ave
Worcester, MA 01604
Contact: Karen DeMichele President
Tel: 508-799-7171
Email: karen@savvystaffing.com
Website: www.savvystaffing.com
Staffing solutions: long or short term, temporary & permanent. (Woman, estab 2006, empl 15, sales $12,000,000, cert: State)

8701 Scout Exchange LLC
501 Boylston St, Ste 3101
Boston, MA 02116
Contact: Farla Russo Dir of Admin
Tel: 617-535-4561
Email: frusso@goscoutgo.com
Website: www.goscoutgo.com
Hosted software to find specialty recruiters to fill their positions. integrated with Applicant Tracking System (ATS). (As-Pac, estab 2013, empl 58, sales , cert: NMSDC)

8702 Snelling Staffing Services
3 Courthouse Lane Ste 2
Chelmsford, MA 01824
Contact: Bernice Kaiser Owner
Tel: 978-970-3434
Email: bernice@snelling-ma.com
Website: www.snelling.com/chelmsford
Staffing: engineering, administrative, finance & accounting, sales & marketing, manufacturing direct hire/temp-to-hire/contract labor. (Woman, estab 1988, empl 6, sales $2,000,000, cert: WBENC)

8703 The Panther Group Inc.
5 Mill & Main Place Ste 430
Maynard, MA 01754
Contact: VP Business Devel
Tel: 617-248-0780
Email:
Website: http://thepanthergrp.com
Temporary, Temp to Hire & Direct Hire staffing solutions & Managed Service Programs (MSP) for contingent labor. (AA, estab 1992, empl 65, sales , cert: NMSDC)

8704 The Resource Connection, Inc.
161 S Main St Ste 300
Middleton, MA 01949
Contact: President
Tel: 978-777-9333
Email:
Website: www.resource-connection.com
Staffing services: temporary, temp-to-hire, & direct placement of administrative, clerical & light industrial personnel. (Woman, estab 1987, empl 9, sales $8,300,000, cert: State, City, WBENC)

8705 The Vesume Group, LLC
21 High St Ste 210A
North Andover, MA 01845
Contact: Jori Blumsack COO
Tel: 978-687-6000
Email: jori@thevesumegroup.com
Website: http://thevesumegroup.com
Staffing, contract, contract-to-hire & permanent placement of IT, Engineering, Manufacturing, Accounting/Finance & Call Center professionals. (Woman, estab 2009, empl 9, sales $3,663,666, cert: WBENC)

8706 Total Technical Services, Inc.
225 Wyman St
Waltham, MA 02451
Contact: Tim Hovey VP
Tel: 800-776-0562
Email: thovey@total-tech.com
Website: www.total-tech.com
Temporary, contract & permanent staffing svcs, on-site managed vendor program & payroll svcs. (AA, Hisp, estab 1992, empl 300, sales , cert: NMSDC)

8707 United Personnel Services
289 Bridge St
Springfield, MA 01103
Contact: Jennifer Brown VP Business Devel
Tel: 413-314-6073
Email: jbrown@unitedpersonnel.com
Website: www.unitedpersonnel.com
Staffing: temporary, temp-to-hire & full-time placements. (Woman, estab 1984, empl 39, sales $27,000,000, cert: State, WBENC)

Maryland

8708 All-Pro Placement Service, Inc.
116 Old Padonia Rd, Ste D
Cockeysville, MD 21030
Contact: Jennifer Quinn VP
Tel: 410-308-9050
Email: jennifer@allproplacement.com
Website: www.allproplacement.com
Staffing: temp, temp-to-perm & direct hire permanent placements, clerical, executive level, warehousing. (Minority, Woman, estab 2002, empl 8, sales $4,364,791, cert: State, City)

8709 Beacon Staffing Alternatives
16-2 S Philadelphia Blvd
Aberdeen, MD 21001
Contact: Sheryl Kohl President
Tel: 410-297-6600
Email: sheryl@beaconstaffing.com
Website: www.Beaconstaffing.com
Staffing services. (Woman, estab 1999, empl 300, sales $4,441,779, cert: State, WBENC)

8710 BizyBee Professional Staffing & Biz'Ness Solutions
8181 Professional Place ste 205
Hyattsville, MD 20785
Contact: Danae Hubbard President
Tel: 301-459-1233
Email: bzbpro@yahoo.com
Website: www.bzbpro.com
Temporary staffing, employment, recruitment, staff augmentation & HR that services. (Woman/AA, estab 2011, empl 5, sales $500,000, cert: State, 8a)

8711 Contemporaries, Inc.
1010 Wayne Ave, Ste 400
Silver Spring, MD 20910
Contact: VP Business Dev
Tel: 301-775-4392
Email:
Website: www.contemps.com
Administrative temporary & permanent placement services. (Woman, estab 1991, empl 6, sales $1,021,514, cert: WBENC)

8712   Crews Control Inc
       11820 West Market Place Ste L
       Fulton, MD 20759
       Contact: Laura A. Monaco VP of Operations
       Tel: 301-604-1200
       Email: Laura@crewscontrol.com
       Website: https://crewscontrol.com
Recruitment, staffing & payroll services. (Woman, estab
1988, empl 12, sales , cert: WBENC)

8713   Crosby Corporation
       14405 Laurel Place, Ste 201
       Laurel, MD 20707
       Contact: Howard Petty President
       Tel: 301-585-3105
       Email: hpetty@crosbycorp.com
       Website: www.crosbycorp.com
Human capital solutions: technical staff augmentation,
direct placement services, outsourced projects, educational services & comprehensive workforce management
solutions. (AA, estab 2001, empl 100, sales $4,000,000,
cert: City, 8a)

8714   Federal Staffing Resources LLC
       2200 Somerville Rd Ste 300
       Annapolis, MD 21401
       Contact: Tracy Balazs CEO
       Tel: 410-990-0795
       Email: tbalazs@fsrpeople.com
       Website: www.fsrpeople.com
Workforce solutions & integrative business solutions,
recruitment & staffing. (Woman/As-Pac, estab 2004, empl
266, sales $31,325,000, cert: State, NMSDC, WBENC)

8715   Infojini Inc.
       10015, Old Columbia Road, Ste B 215
       Columbia, MD 21046
       Contact: Sandeep Harjani Director
       Tel: 443-257-0086
       Email: commercialrfi@infojiniconsulting.com
       Website: www.infojiniconsulting.com
Recruitment, training, assessment, outsourcing & consult-
ing services, temporary & permanent positions. (As-Ind,
As-Pac, estab 2006, empl 130, sales $183,611,191, cert:
NMSDC)

8716   PMC Group Inc dba Piper Staffing
       8117 Harford Rd, Ste D
       Baltimore, MD 21234
       Contact: Kimberley West President
       Tel: 410-286-1874
       Email: kimberley@pmcgrpinc.com
       Website: www.piperstaffing.com
Multiple & diverse staffing solutions. (Woman/AA, estab
2010, empl 104, sales $1,669,345, cert: State)

8717   The All-Star Group Companies, Inc.
       3710 Commerce Dr, Bldg 1005
       Baltimore, MD 21227
       Contact: Tyrone Cypress VP Sales/Mktg
       Tel: 443-543-7801
       Email: sales@allstarcompanies.net
       Website: www.allstarcompanies.net
Human capital assets; recruiting & staffing. (AA, estab
1995, empl 800, sales $19,200,000, cert: State)

8718   The BOSS Group
       4350 East West Hwy, Ste 307
       Bethesda, MD 20814
       Contact: Truelove, Charisse Owner
       Tel: 301-802-3672
       Email: linda@thebossgroup.com
       Website: www.thebossgroup.com
Human capital solutions, source, evaluate & place
exclusive creative, marketing, communications &
interactive talent. (Woman, estab 0, empl , sales , cert:
WBENC)

8719   The HR Source
       8181 Professional Place Ste 120
       Landover, MD 20785
       Contact: Patricia Hall Jaynes CEO
       Tel: 301-459-3133
       Email: pathj@thehrsource.com
       Website: www.thehrsource.com
Human resources staffing & consulting services, interim/
temporary & permanent staffing services, outplacement
& payroll services, administrative interim/temporary &
permanent staffing services. (Woman/AA, estab 1994,
empl 5, sales $2,894,265, cert: State, NMSDC, WBENC)

Michigan

8720   Abacus Service Corporation
       35055 W Twelve Mile, Ste 215
       Farmington Hills, MI 48331
       Contact: Chris Mills Business Dev Mgr
       Tel: 503-542-7409
       Email: chris@abacusservice.com
       Website: www.abacusservice.com
Staff augmentation, contract, temporary & permanent
placement services. (Woman/As-Ind, As-Pac, estab 2004,
empl 325, sales $22,200,000, cert: NMSDC, WBENC, 8a)

8721   Accura Services, LLC
       51470 Oro Dr
       Shelby Township, MI 48315
       Contact: Jenifer Cugliari Member
       Tel: 586-884-4417
       Email: jen@accuraservicesllc.com
       Website: www.accuraservicesllc.com
Direct & contract staffing services specializing in Engineering, Technical & Professional areas. (Woman, estab
2015, empl 3, sales , cert: WBENC)

8722   Aegis Group Search Consultants, LLC
       1358 Village Dr
       Detroit, MI 48207
       Contact: John Green President
       Tel: 248-344-1450
       Email: jgreen@aegis-group.com
       Website: www.aegis-group.com
Executive search services. (AA, estab 1991, empl 4, sales
$700,000, cert: NMSDC)

8723   Arps International LLC
       3003 Silver Spring Dr
       Ann Arbor, MI 48103
       Contact: Arun Nikore VP
       Tel: 734-945-3000
       Email: sales@arpsint.com
       Website: www.arpsint.com
Executive recruiting services: engineering, information
technology, manufacturing & operations, supply chain.
(Woman/As-Ind, estab 2002, empl 2, sales $106,127,
cert: NMSDC)

8724   Blake Group LLC
30986 Stone Ridge Dr Ste 14205
Wixom, MI 48393
Contact: THE BLAKE GROUP Sr Exec VP
Tel: 248-238-5776
Email:
Website: www.blakegroupllc.com
Information Technology professional executive staffing. (Woman/AA, estab 2010, empl 7, sales , cert: NMSDC)

8725   CIMA Consulting Group
901 Tower Dr, Ste 420
Troy, MI 48098
Contact: Scott Foreman CFO
Tel: 586-226-2000
Email: sforeman@cimacg.com
Website: www.cimacg.com
Talent Management Solutions. (Woman/Hisp, estab 2016, empl 6, sales $260,000, cert: NMSDC, WBENC)

8726   Community Based Staffing
4369 Seebaldt
Detroit, MI 48204
Contact: David Cross President
Tel: 313-744-5771
Email: david.cross@cb-staffing.com
Website: https://cb-staffing.com
Direct hire & staffing: machine operators, production associates, welders, quality inspectors, press operators. (AA, estab 2016, empl , sales $150,000, cert: NMSDC)

8727   CrossFire Group LLC
691 N Squirrel Rd Ste 118
Auburn Hills, MI 48326
Contact: Deborah Schneider CEO
Tel: 866-839-2600
Email: dschneider@xfiregroup.com
Website: www.xfiregroup.com
Recruiting, Staffing, Business Process Outsourcnig, professional temporary & contract staffing, permanent placement, vendor management &payroll services to large and medium size firms. (Woman, estab 2002, empl 1500, sales $10,000,000, cert: WBENC)

8728   Crystal Employment Services, LLC
32355 Howard St
Madison Heights, MI 48071
Contact: Michael Stanley Partner
Tel: 248-588-9540
Email: mstanley@crystaleng.com
Website: http://crystaleng.com
Staffing services. (Hisp, estab 2004, empl 300, sales , cert: NMSDC)

8729   Entech Staffing Solutions
1800 Crooks Road
Troy, MI 48084
Contact: Colleen Myers Dir of Sales and Recruiting
Tel: 248-528-1444
Email: cmyers@teamentech.com
Website: www.teamentech.com
Temporary staffing: administrative, technical, medical & light industrial positions, short term, long term & permanent employment. (Woman, estab , empl , sales $11,500,000, cert: WBENC)

8730   Galaxy Software Solutions, Inc.
5820 N Lilley Rd, Ste 8
Canton, MI 48187
Contact: Dileep Tiwari VP
Tel: 734-717-7969
Email: dileep@galaxy-soft.com
Website: www.galaxy-soft.com
Staffing, contract and on a full-time basis. (Woman/As-Pac, estab 2004, empl 251, sales $24,000,000, cert: WBENC)

8731   Gonzalez Production Systems
1670 Highwood East
Pontiac, MI 48340
Contact: Bill Kelly New Business Devel
Tel: 248-884-0315
Email: bkelly@gonzales-group.com
Website: www.gonzalez-group.com
Contract Placement, Contract to Direct, Direct Placement, Managed Services. (Hisp, estab 1975, empl 800, sales $50,000,000, cert: NMSDC)

8732   G-TECH Services, Inc.
17101 Michigan Ave
Dearborn, MI 48126
Contact: Shelby Medina Dir of Business Devel
Tel: 313-425-3666
Email: smedina@gogtech.com
Website: www.gogtech.com
Contract & direct hire staffing solutions, engineering/technical support; information technology; finance/accounting; scientific; administration/clerical; co-employment training & payroll services. (Woman, estab 1986, empl 650, sales $56,000,000, cert: WBENC)

8733   Harvard Resource Group
210 W Big Beaver Rd Ste 310
Troy, MI 48084
Contact: Mark Hicks VP
Tel: 248-528-1110
Email: mhicks@hrgus.com
Website: www.harvardresourcegroup.com
Staffing: permanent, contract, temp to perm, professional & organizational dev, mgmt & leadership dev, wireless dev & deployment svcs. (Nat Ame, estab 2001, empl 6, sales $3,000,000, cert: NMSDC)

8734   Hattrick Professional Staffing
3228 Norton Lawn
Rochester Hills, MI 48307
Contact: Julie Campbell Owner
Tel: 248-289-6241
Email: julie.campbell@hattrick-staffing.com
Website: www.hattrick-staffing.com
Staffing, Direct Hire, Contract or Temp to hire placements within areas of Engineering, Design, Finance/Accounting, IT, Professional, Technical placements & Executive positions. (Woman, estab 2015, empl 1, sales , cert: WBENC)

8735   Human Capital Staffing LLC
6001 N Adams Rd, Ste 208
Bloomfield Hills, MI 48304
Contact: Mary Adams President
Tel: 248-593-1950
Email: madams@hcsteam.com
Website: www.hcsteam.com
Staffing services. (Woman/Nat Ame, estab 0, empl 10, sales , cert: NMSDC, WBENC)

8736   Inteligente Solutions, Inc.
17199 N Laurel Park Dr Ste 321
Livonia, MI 48152
Contact: Kathy DeCaires VP
Tel: 734-338-8970
Email: kdecaires@igsstaff.com
Website: www.igsstaff.com
Staffing svcs; general labor & light industrial; long term to permanent, clerical & admin support staffing. (Hisp, estab 1993, empl 500, sales , cert: NMSDC)

8737   K&A Staffing, LLC
38700 Van Dyke Rd. Ste 150
Sterling Heights, MI 48312
Contact: Justin Tappero COO
Tel: 586-806-6614
Email: jtappero@knaresourcegroup.com
Website: http://knaresourcegroup.com
Staffing services. (As-Ind, estab 2011, empl 16, sales , cert: NMSDC)

8738   Linked, LLC
6633 18 Mile Rd
Sterling Heights, MI 48314
Contact: Marie Khoury President
Tel: 586-231-1234
Email: marie.khoury@linkedps.com
Website: www.linkedps.com
Staffing, candidate search, recruitment, contract & direct placement services. (Woman, estab 2012, empl 4, sales , cert: WBENC)

8739   MCM Staffing, LLC
415 W 11 Mile Rd
Madison Heights, MI 48076
Contact: Courtney Morales Hofmann President
Tel: 248-436-2616
Email: courtney@mcmstaffing.com
Website: www.mcmstaffing.com
Staffing services. (Woman/Hisp, estab 2011, empl 950, sales $19,500,000, cert: NMSDC, WBENC)

8740   Michigan Staffing
29400 Van Dyke Ste 308
Warren, MI 48093
Contact: Frances Lucido VP
Tel: 586-506-7524
Email: francy@michiganstaffing.com
Website: www.michiganstaffing.com
Temp, contract & direct staffing: administrative, customer service, light industrial, technical, professional & skilled trades. (Woman, estab 2002, empl 75, sales , cert: WBENC)

8741   Moreno Services LLC
5140 State St #103
Saginaw, MI 48603
Contact: Yvette Serrato CEO
Tel: 989-401-3996
Email: yvette@morenoservices.com
Website: www.morenoservices.com
Professional recruiting, on site services, and indirect and direct placements, temporary staffing. (Hisp, estab 2010, empl 4, sales $12,564,679, cert: NMSDC)

8742   National Career Group
1745 Hamilton Rd
Okemos, MI 48864
Contact: Nadia Sellers CEO
Tel: 517-706-0111
Email: barbara@nationalcareergroup.com
Website: www.nationalcareergroup.com
Permanent staffing & Human Relations Training. (Woman/AA, estab 1997, empl 10, sales $700,000, cert: WBENC)

8743   National Career Group Training & Development
1745 Hamilton Road Ste 340
Okemos, MI 48864
Contact: Joni Fixel VP of HR & Recruiting
Tel: 517-225-6680
Email: joni@nationalcareergroup.com
Website: www.nationalcareergroup.com
Executive staffing & training svcs, permanent & contract staffing; diversity, team building, workplace violence & leadership training. (Woman/AA, estab 1997, empl 3, sales $350,000, cert: WBENC)

8744   NexTech Professional Services
25200 Telegraph Rd. Ste 110
Southfield, MI 48033
Contact: Rosanne Davis President
Tel: 248-416-1718
Email: rosanne.davis@nextechps.com
Website: www.nextechps.com
Contract & permanent placement: engineering, technology, finance & executive recruiting. (As-Pac, estab 1994, empl 10, sales $2,600,000, cert: NMSDC)

8745   PDS Services, LLC
37633 Pembroke
Livonia, MI 48152
Contact: Derek Dyer President
Tel: 734-953-3300
Email: derek@pdsstaffing.com
Website: www.pdsstaffing.com
Staffing services: contract, contract to hire & permanent placements. (AA, estab 2005, empl 260, sales $9,000,000, cert: NMSDC)

8746   Personnel Unlimited Inc.
29400 Van Dyke Ave
Warren, MI 48093
Contact: Frances Lucido President
Tel: 586-751-5608
Email: fllucido@personnel-unlimited.com
Website: www.personnel-unlimited.com
Temporary & Contract Staffing for Admin, Clerical, Tech/Professional. (Woman, estab 2008, empl 7, sales $2,462,679, cert: WBENC)

8747   Populus Group, LLC
3001 W Big Beaver Rd Ste 400
Troy, MI 48084
Contact: Danielle Hein Sr Proposal Mgr
Tel: 248-712-7900
Email: dhein@populusgroup.com
Website: PopulusGroup.com
Temporary staffing services. Professional Payrolling Services, Independent Contractor Engagement Services/1099 Compliance, Immigration Employment Solutions, Managed Services, Strategic Partnerships, Diverse Talent Management Solutions. (Hisp, estab 2002, empl 270, sales $577,322,374, cert: NMSDC)

8748   Premier Automation Contractors
9015 Davison Rd
Davison, MI 48423
Contact: Lisa VanWyk Engineering Mgr
Tel: 248-421-7360
Email: lisa@premierac.com
Website: www.premierac.com
Direct & contract hire staffing for skilled trades. (Woman, estab 2008, empl 200, sales $12,000,000, cert: WBENC)

8749   Premier Staff Services
16250 Northland Dr Ste 224
Southfield, MI 48075
Contact: Michael Garcia Acct Mgr
Tel: 248-809-9675
Email: michael.garcia.rep@gmail.com
Website: www.premierstaffservices.net
Contract staffing, temporary help & direct placement of clerical, administrative, financial, janitorial, maintenance, engineering & IT human resources. (AA, estab 2011, empl 24, sales $11,000,000, cert: NMSDC, 8a)

8750   Reliance One, Inc.
       1700 Harmon Rd Ste One
       Auburn Hills, MI 48326
       Contact: Chad Toms VP Sales
       Tel: 248-922-4500
       Email: ctoms@reliance-one.com
       Website: www.reliance-one.com
Staffing, direct & contract, employment, payroll. (Hisp, estab 1998, empl 700, sales , cert: NMSDC)

8751   Scope Services, Inc.
       2095 Niles Rd
       St. Joseph, MI 49085
       Contact: TRISH MELCHER President
       Tel: 269-982-2888
       Email: tmmelcher@scope-services.com
       Website: www.scope-services.com
Human capital management, contract &project staffing & managed staffing/consulting, executive search, contingency direct hire placement, career consulting & outplacement services. (Woman, estab 1965, empl 569, sales $58,000,000, cert: WBENC)

8752   Snelling Personnel Services
       2265 Livernois
       Troy, MI 48083
       Contact: Larry Wright CEO
       Tel: 248-362-5090
       Email: ldwright@snellingmetrodetroit.com
       Website: www.snellingmetrodetroit.com
Temporary, temporary-to-hire & permanent placement: clerical, medical, technical, professional, engineering & information technology. (Woman/AA, estab 1987, empl 25, sales , cert: WBENC)

8753   Staffing Source Personnel dba DriverSource
       15340 Michigan Ave
       Dearborn, MI 48126
       Contact: David J. Olshansky Co-Founder
       Tel: 313-624-9500
       Email: dolshansky@driversource.net
       Website: www.driversource.net
Commercial driver leasing & recruiting services. (Woman/Hisp, estab 1998, empl 350, sales , cert: WBENC)

8754   The Targa Group
       33228 W 12 Mile Rd #108
       Farmington Hills, MI 48334
       Contact: Rob Ganesan President
       Tel: 248-514-2295
       Email: rganesan@thetargagroup.com
       Website: www.thetargagroup.clom
Staffing, Process Improvement & Information Technology. (As-Pac, estab 2009, empl 6, sales $250,000, cert: NMSDC)

8755   Therapy Staff, LLC
       801 W Ann Arbor Trail, Ste 200
       Plymouth, MI 48170
       Contact: William Klabo RVP
       Tel: 877-366-2580
       Email: wklabo@therapystaff.com
       Website: www.Therapystaff.com
Therapist recruiting and staffing. (As-Ind, estab 2000, empl 53, sales $15,400,000, cert: NMSDC)

8756   Trialon Corporation
       1477 Walli Strasse Blvd
       Burton, MI 48509
       Contact: Robert Feys Sales Engineer
       Tel: 810-742-8500
       Email: rfeys@trialon.com
       Website: www.trialon.com
Technical Staffing and Engineering & Test Services to the Automotive, Aerospace, Military, Consumer Electronics, Medical, and Telecommunications Industries. (Woman, estab 1982, empl 750, sales $25,050,000, cert: WBENC)

8757   Venator Staffing
       888 W Big Beaver Rd, Ste 450
       Troy, MI 48084
       Contact: Michael Teats Sales Mgr
       Tel: 248-269-0000
       Email: michael@venatornet.com
       Website: www.venatornet.com
Accounting, finance & administrative staffing: temp & permanent placement. (As-Pac, estab 2001, empl 25, sales $2,500,000, cert: NMSDC)

8758   VETBUILT Services, Inc.
       1927 Rosa Parks Blvd Ste 125
       Detroit, MI 48216
       Contact: Hector Malacara CEO
       Tel: 989-493-1240
       Email: hmalacara@vetbuilt.com
       Website: http://vetbuiltservices.com
Staffing services. (Hisp, estab 2013, empl 300, sales $6,853,851, cert: NMSDC)

8759   Wrightway Enterprises, Inc.
       744 Lothrop
       Detroit, MI 48202
       Contact: Larry Wright President
       Tel: 248-362-5090
       Email: ldwright@snellingmetrodetroit.com
       Website: www.snellingmetrodetroit.com
Staffing services: permanent & temporary. (AA, estab 1987, empl 13, sales $2,550,000, cert: NMSDC)

Minnesota

8760   Advent Creative Group
       7101 York Ave S, Ste 240
       Edina, MN 55435
       Contact: Mary Younggren Owner
       Tel: 952-746-5668
       Email: mary@adventgroupco.com
       Website: www.adventcreativegroup.com
Advertising, communications, creative, marketing & interactive hiring resources, contract & full-time basis. (Woman, estab 2007, empl 4, sales $606,822, cert: WBENC)

8761   Avenue Staffing Inc.
       7000-57th Ave N Ste 120
       Minneapolis, MN 55428
       Contact: Chuck Okitikpi President
       Tel: 763-537-6104
       Email: chuck@avenuestaffing.com
       Website: www.Avenuestaffing.com
Temporary & permanent employment. (AA, estab 2006, empl 48, sales $1,200,000, cert: NMSDC)

8762   Billinda Group LLC
       4651 Nicols Rd, Ste 106-108
       Eagan, MN 55122
       Contact: Bill Fitch CEO
       Tel: 651-379-5082
       Email: bill@techpoweres.com
       Website: http://Techpoweres.com
Contract, contract to permanent & direct placement.
(Woman, estab 2005, empl 28, sales $3,700,000, cert:
WBENC)

8763   Celarity
       8120 Penn Ave Ste 220
       Minneapolis, MN 55431
       Contact: Marlene Phipps President & CEO
       Tel: 952-941-0022
       Email: marlene@celarity.com
       Website: www.celarity.com
Contract, temporary recruiting, staffing, full-time direct
hires. (Woman, estab 1992, empl 110, sales $7,092,546,
cert: WBENC)

8764   Dahl Consulting, Inc.
       418 County Rd D East
       St. Paul, MN 55117
       Contact: Corey Johnson CEO
       Tel: 651-772-9225
       Email: corey@dahlconsulting.com
       Website: www.dahlconsulting.com
Vendor management services, staff augmentation,
permanent search. (Woman, estab 1993, empl 808, sales
$87,902,216, cert: WBENC)

8765   Doherty Staffing Solutions, Inc.
       7645 Metro Blvd
       Edina, MN 55439
       Contact: David Tuenge Program Mgr
       Tel: 952-818-3251
       Email: dtuenge@dohertystaffing.com
       Website: www.dohertystaffing.com
Contract & temporary staffing. (Woman, estab 1980, empl
151, sales $400,337,900, cert: WBENC)

8766   Finnesse Partners LLC
       5000 W 36th St Ste 220
       St. Louis Park, MN 55416
       Contact: Janie Finn President
       Tel: 952-232-6170
       Email: janie@finnessepartners.com
       Website: www.finnessepartners.com
Recruit for the medical device industry. (Woman, estab
2012, empl 5, sales $804,442, cert: WBENC)

8767   HighCloud Solutions Inc
       445 Minnesota St Ste 1552
       Saint Paul, MN 55101
       Contact: Raghu Chejarla President
       Tel: 612-479-3333
       Email: raghu@highcloudsolutions.com
       Website: www.highcloudsolutions.com/
Staffing, contracting/temp job positions. (Woman/As-Ind,
estab 2015, empl 9, sales $774,113, cert: State, City,
NMSDC, 8a)

8768   IG, Inc. dba Indrotec
       17 Washington Ave N
       Minneapolis, MN 55401
       Contact: Kathleen Dolphin CEO
       Tel: 612-371-7402
       Email: kathydolphin@mydolphingroup.com
       Website: www.myindrotec.com
We supply companies with light industrial and assembly
staff. (Woman, estab 1968, empl 16, sales $20,000,100,
cert: WBENC)

8769   Just In Case, Inc.
       6900 Shady Oak Rd, Ste 250
       Eden Prairie, MN 55344
       Contact: Diane Blomberg CEO
       Tel: 952-925-3789
       Email: diane.blomberg@justincasestaffing.com
       Website: www.casestaffingsolutions.com/
Staffing, consulting & integration: packaging, shipping &
receiving, taping & assembly, clerical positions, administrative jobs, inbound call center positions, customer
support. (Woman, estab 1981, empl 9, sales $5,900,000,
cert: WBENC)

8770   Latitude Technology Group, Inc.
       6800 France Ave South Ste 500
       Edina, MN 55435
       Contact: Dorreen Schmidt CEO
       Tel: 952-767-6802
       Email: dschmidt@latitude-group.com
       Website: www.latitude-group.com
Staffing svcs: contract, contract to hire & permanent
placement services. (Woman, estab 2002, empl 45, sales
$6,000,000, cert: WBENC)

8771   Nexpro Personnel Services, Inc.
       5353 Gamble Dr, Ste 112
       Minneapolis, MN 55416
       Contact: Julia Zimmer Owner
       Tel: 952-224-9855
       Email: jzimmer@nexprojobs.com
       Website: www.nexprojobs.com
Staffing services: administrative, clerical, temporary,
contract, word processors, data entry, customer service
reps, accounting & payroll, light industrial, receptionist,
executive assistants (Woman, estab 2000, empl 40, sales
$5,000,000, cert: WBENC)

8772   Pelican Staffing Solutions
       401 N 3rd St Ste 425
       Minneapolis, MN 55401
       Contact: Ebi Itie President
       Tel: 612-545-5330
       Email: ebi@pelicanstaffing.com
       Website: www.pelicanstaffing.com
Contract & temporary staffing, staff & vendor manage-
ment. (Woman/AA, estab 2011, empl 11, sales , cert:
City, NMSDC)

8773   Select Source International
       13911 Ridgedale Dr, Ste 230
       Minnetonka, MN 55305
       Contact: Mandeep Sodhi CEO
       Tel: 952-546-3300
       Email: sales@selectsourceintl.com
       Website: www.SelectSourceIntl.com
Temporary Staffing, Information Technology Staffing,
Information Technology Services, Engineering Services,
Financial Services, Government Services, Retail Services,
Energy & Utility Services, Application Development,
Mobile Development. (Nat Ame, estab 2000, empl 771,
sales , cert: NMSDC)

8774   Serenity Staffing LLC
       6180 W 143rd St
       Savage, MN 55378
       Contact: Jennifer Sabby President
       Tel: 612-834-6444
       Email: jsabby@serenity-staffing.com
       Website: www.serenity-staffing.com
Place Human Resource professionals. (Woman, estab
2005, empl 5, sales $281,316, cert: WBENC)

8775 Synico Staffing
3033 Excelsior Blvd Ste 495
Minneapolis, MN 55416
Contact: Jerry Marsh VP
Tel: 612-926-6000
Email: jmarsh@synico.com
Website: www.synico.com
Staffing services. (AA, estab 1996, empl 450, sales $13,000,000, cert: NMSDC)

8776 The Mazzitelli Placement Group
500 Lake St, Ste 212
Excelsior, MN 55331
Contact: Teresa Mazzitelli President
Tel: 952-476-5449
Email: tm@mazzsearch.com
Website: www.mazzsearch.com
Executive search, recruitment & placement services. (Woman, estab 1988, empl 1, sales $110,000, cert: WBENC)

Missouri

8777 Above All Personnel dba S.M. Huber Ent., Inc.
2228 S Big Bend Blvd
St. Louis, MO 63117
Contact: Susan Huber President
Tel: 314-781-6008
Email: team@aboveallpersonnel.com
Website: www.aboveallpersonnel.com
Temporary, temp-to-hire, direct hire employment svcs: clerical, accounting, customer service, data processing. (Woman, estab 1995, empl 750, sales $3,400,000, cert: State)

8778 American Staffing LLC
11424A Dorsett Rd
Maryland Heights, MO 63043
Contact: Diane Fennel President
Tel: 314-872-7070
Email: dfennel@americanstaffingstl.com
Website: www.americanstaffingstl.com
Staffing: temp, temp to hire & permanent. (Woman, estab 2002, empl 12000, sales $6,777,000, cert: State)

8779 Applications Engineering Group
12300 Old Tesson Rd, Ste 100-G
St. Louis, MO 63128
Contact: Chris Rakel VP Operations
Tel: 314-842-9110
Email: chris.rakel@aeg-inc.com
Website: www.aeg-inc.com
Provide contract, contract to hire & direct hire IT employment services. (Hisp, estab 1992, empl 35, sales , cert: State)

8780 C & S Business Services, Inc.
1731 Southridge Dr
Jefferson City, MO 65109
Contact: Paula Benne President
Tel: 573-635-9295
Email: paula@cs-business.com
Website: www.cs-business.com
Staffing, temporary, direct hire, contract, employment verification, criminal background checks. (Woman, estab 1977, empl 12, sales $4,000,000, cert: State)

8781 Chief of Staff LLC
601 E 63rd St
Kansas City, MO 64110
Contact: Marny Burke Govt Accts Mgr
Tel: 816-581-2776
Email: government@chiefofstaffkc.com
Website: www.chiefofstaffkc.com
Temporary administrative staffing services, office management, receptionist, accounting & finance, HR, customer service/call room & data entry/records management positions. (Woman, estab 2011, empl 8, sales $1,190,023, cert: State)

8782 Creatives On Call Inc.
101 S Hanley Road Ste 710
St. Louis, MO 63105
Contact: Corey Zinser Acct Exec
Tel: 513-218-5596
Email: corey.zinser@creativesoncall.com
Website: www.creativesoncall.com
Placement agency, recruit professionals with creative, marketing, communications and/or interactive expertise for permanent, contract & freelance positions. (Woman, estab 1995, empl 12, sales $4,500,000, cert: State, WBENC)

8783 Critique Personnel Service, Inc.
1100 S Jefferson Ave
St. Louis, MO 63104
Contact: Monique Jeans Dir Client Services
Tel: 314-772-5445
Email: mjeans@critiquepersonnel.com
Website: www.critiquepersonnel.com
Temporary & permanent staffing services. (AA, estab 1997, empl 50, sales , cert: State)

8784 EH, Inc. dba HireLevel
415 S 18th St. Ste 205
St. Louis, MO 63103
Contact: Nicole Kline Sr. Natl Business Development
Tel: 314-550-8626
Email: nkline@hirelevel.com
Website: www.hirelevel.com
Staffing services, temporary employment, temporary-to-hire & direct hire. (Woman, estab 1995, empl 60, sales $37,813,000, cert: WBENC)

8785 NextGen Information Services Inc.
906 Olive St Ste 600
Saint Louis, MO 63101
Contact: Christy Herschbach Admin Asst
Tel: 314-588-1212
Email: supplierdiversity@nextgen-is.com
Website: www.nextgen-is.com
IT consulting services: project mgmt, custom application dev, legacy transition svcs & staff augmentation, staff augmentaion. (Woman/Hisp, estab 1997, empl 300, sales , cert: State, City, WBENC)

8786 Pangaea, Inc.
1403 Hwy F
Defiance, MO 63341
Contact: Heather Everett President
Tel: 314-925-1783
Email: heverett@pangaea-inc.com
Website: www.Pangaea-inc.com
Supplemental staffing services, contract, direct placement, and contract to hire resources. (Woman, estab 2008, empl 10, sales $750,000, cert: State)

8787 Shelgin Partners
9211 Phoenix Village Pkwy
O'Fallon, MO 63368
Contact: Gerri Lynn Zschetzsche Partner
Tel: 636-625-2333
Email: glz@shelgin.com
Website: www.shelgin.com
Recruiting agency: direct recruitment, advertising, job boards, candidate referrals & partner referrals. (Woman, estab 2005, empl 5, sales $553,000, cert: State)

8788 Supplemental Medical Services, Inc.
10916 Schuetz Road
St. Louis, MO 63146
Contact: Gretchen Curry President
Tel: 314-997-8833
Email: gcurry@stafflinkusa.com
Website: www.stafflinkusa.com
Temporary, contract, travel & direct hire healthcare personnel. (Woman/AA, estab 1987, empl 125, sales $2,643,128, cert: State, NMSDC)

8789 The Herring IMPACT Group
12977 N Outer 40 Dr Ste 300
St. Louis, MO 63141
Contact: Kristy King Exec Asst
Tel: 314-453-9002
Email: diversity1@impactgrouphr.com
Website: www.impactgrouphr.com
Career transitions, relocation support, talent development, and outplacement services. (Woman, estab 1988, empl 121, sales $15,000,000, cert: State, WBENC)

Mississippi

8790 HRD Results, LLC
P.O. Box 13333
Jackson, MS 39236
Contact: Richard L Conerly Owner
Tel: 601-213-6358
Email: richard@hrdresults.com
Website: www.hrdresults.com
Provide excellent products and services to buyers in a timely manner. (AA, estab 2006, empl 10, sales , cert: State)

8791 RAKS Fire Sprinkler LLC
215 Mobile St
Hattiesburg, MS 39401
Contact: Romero Ali CEO
Tel: 601-261-0820
Email: rali75@yahoo.com
Website: www.raks.co/
Fire Protection Services and Products: Fire Sprinkler System, (Wet, Dry, and Special Hazards) Design, New Installation, Inspection and Maintainance. Fire Alarm system, Design New Installation (AA, estab 2010, empl 8, sales $291,046, cert: State)

Montana

8792 Brady Co., Inc
50 West 14th St Ste 300
Helena, MT 59601
Contact: Anna Kazmierowski CEO
Tel: 406-443-7664
Email: anna@a2zmontana.com
Website: www.a2zmontana.com
Workforce solutions, temporary staffing, temporary to permanent placement & direct hire services, employee payroll, scientific & technical staffing, technical & professional recruitment & construction labor. (Woman, estab 2003, empl 7, sales $4,517,215, cert: State, WBENC, SDB)

North Carolina

8793 Associate Staffing, LLC
303C Atkinson St
Laurinburg, NC 28352
Contact: Director
Tel: 980-224-8754
Email:
Website: http://associatestaffingllc.com
Recruiting & staffing, contract, contract to permanent & direct placement basis. (Woman, estab 2008, empl 450, sales $13,400,000, cert: WBENC)

8794 Aten Solutions, Inc.
5404 Hillsborough St Ste A
Raleigh, NC 27606
Contact: COO
Tel: 919-949-3503
Email:
Website: www.a10clinical.com
Staffing solutions: clinical research, clinical data management, statistical programming & biostatistics space, clinical trial svcs & staffing support. (Woman/AA, estab 2004, empl 64, sales $1,800,000, cert: NMSDC, WBENC)

8795 BPN Concepts
8305 University Executive Park Dr Ste 330
Charlotte, NC 28262
Contact: Brenda Harris Owner
Tel: 980-335-0656
Email: info@bpnconcepts.com
Website: www.bpnconcepts.com
Executive search & staffing services. (Woman/AA, estab 2011, empl 6, sales , cert: State, City)

8796 CEO Inc.
412 Louise Ave
Charlotte, NC 28204
Contact: Deborah Millhouse President
Tel: 704-372-4701
Email: debby@ceohr.com
Website: www.ceohr.com
Temporary staffing, payrolling, HR consulting, executive search & placement. (Minority, Woman, estab 1994, empl 15, sales $2,995,605, cert: State)

8797 Citywide Courier Service
1409 East Blvd Ste 1E
Charlotte, NC 28203
Contact: William Locklear Owner
Tel: 704-344-0092
Email: william@citywidecouriersvc.com
Website: www.citywidecouriersvc.com
Whether you need one quick pick-up and delivery or daily service, Citywide Courier Service is THE courier service to fill your needs. Citywide Courier Service is available 24 hours a day. (Nat Ame, estab 1998, empl 15, sales $216,889, cert: State)

8798 Concierge Staffing LLC
160 S Main St
Graham, NC 27253
Contact: Denise Brown Owner
Tel: 336-270-3035
Email: denise.brown@concierge-staffing.com
Website: www.concierge-staffing.com
Staffing services and solutions. (Woman/AA, estab 2014, empl , sales $100,000, cert: State)

8799　CrossComm, Inc.
　　　P.O. Box 673
　　　Durham, NC 27702
　　　Contact: Beverly Williams Business Operations Mgr
　　　Tel:　919-667-9432
　　　Email: beverlywilliams@crosscomm.com
　　　Website: www.crosscomm.com
Business Summary
CrossComm is a mobile and web application development studio that builds custom iOS, Android, Web and Augmented Reality/Virtual Reality apps. A minority owned small business since its founding in 1998, CrossComm has worked on over 250 (As-Pac, estab 2000, empl 8, sales $975,000, cert: NMSDC)

8800　Cyber Shield Consulting Inc.
　　　8300 Boone Blvd, Ste 500
　　　Vienna, NC 22182
　　　Contact: Doug Marland Business Dev Mgr
　　　Tel:　571-358-5602
　　　Email: operations@cybershieldincorporated.com
　　　Website: www.cybershieldincorporated.com
Human capital services, temporary & permanent on a nationwide. (AA, estab 2013, empl 25, sales , cert: NMSDC)

8801　Elite Touch Cleaning Services, Inc.
　　　4105-A Stuart Andrew Blvd
　　　Charlotte, NC 28217
　　　Contact: Mario Mendigana President
　　　Tel:　704-266-0623
　　　Email: mario@elitetouchcleaning.com
　　　Website: http://elitetouchcleaning.com
Janitorial Services, Floor Maintenance, Carpet care, Construction clean up (Hisp, estab 2007, empl 5, sales $1,668,000, cert: NMSDC)

8802　Golden Tech Systems Inc.
　　　2704 Twinberry Ln
　　　WAXHAW, NC 28173
　　　Contact: Pushpinder Garcha President
　　　Tel:　704-236-2939
　　　Email: pushpinder@golden-tech-systems.com
　　　Website: www.golden-tech-systems.com
Staff augmentation. (As-Ind, estab 2007, empl 5, sales $753,550, cert: State, City, NMSDC, 8a)

8803　Greer Group
　　　3109 Charles B. Root Wynd
　　　Raleigh, NC 27612
　　　Contact: Mark Blume client devel Mgr
　　　Tel:　919-571-0051
　　　Email: sales@thegreergroup.com
　　　Website: www.thegreergroup.com
Staffing services: temporary staffing, temporary to direct hire staffing, direct hire recruitment, payrolling services & onsite staffing management. (Woman, estab 1986, empl 16, sales $15,802,034, cert: WBENC)

8804　Gregory Art Services Inc
　　　14700 Eastfield Rd
　　　Huntersville, NC 28078
　　　Contact: Eugene Gregory President
　　　Tel:　704-947-5503
　　　Email: information@gregoryartservices.com
　　　Website: http://gregoryartservices.com
We provide artwork and custom picture framing, security mount installations, repairs, refurbish pick-up and delivery, art consulting, art placement, large art installations on time service and all work is guaranteed with competitive pricing. (AA, estab 2001, empl , sales $35,963,600, cert: NMSDC)

8805　Greytree Partners
　　　121 Greenwich Rd Ste 211
　　　Charlotte, NC 28211
　　　Contact: Clarence Fisher Chief Solutions Architect
　　　Tel:　704-899-4082
　　　Email: clarence.fisher@greytreepartners.com
　　　Website: www.GreytreePartners.com
Identification, recruitment & placement of information technology and engineering services professionals on a contract or permanent basis. (AA, estab 2004, empl 30, sales $2,400,000, cert: State, NMSDC)

8806　Jennifer Temps, Inc.
　　　1973 JN Pease Pl Ste 201
　　　Charlotte, NC 28262
　　　Contact: Jennifer Singleton President
　　　Tel:　212-964-8367
　　　Email: jsingleton@jennifertemps.com
　　　Website: www.jennifertemps.com
Temporary staffing. (Woman/AA, estab 1992, empl 8, sales $4,500,000, cert: NMSDC)

8807　nDemand Consulting LLC
　　　2923 S Tryon St, Ste 220
　　　Charlotte, NC 28203
　　　Contact: Oscar Frazier Owner
　　　Tel:　704-965-0781
　　　Email: ofrazier@ndemandconsulting.com
　　　Website: www.ndemandconsultingllc.com
Recruiting & staffing services. (Woman/AA, estab 2004, empl 10, sales , cert: State)

8808　Omni Source Solutions
　　　13016 Eastfield Rd
　　　Huntersville, NC 28078
　　　Contact: Charisma Smith Managing Member
　　　Tel:　704-412-3031
　　　Email: charisma@omnisourcesolutions.net
　　　Website: http://omnisourcesolutions.net
Offer skilled quality self-performing contractors throughout the Southeast. We provide flexible, reliable and safety-minded tradesmen for a wide range of commercial construction jobs. We understand the importance of having the right (Woman/AA, estab 2012, empl 2, sales , cert: City, NMSDC)

8809　Quality Staffing Solutions, Inc.
　　　120 Towerview Ct
　　　Cary, NC 27513
　　　Contact: CEO
　　　Tel:　919-481-4114
　　　Email:
　　　Website: www.quality-staffing.com
Staffing solutions. (Woman, estab 1995, empl 400, sales $6,526,751, cert: WBENC)

8810　Reblee, Inc. dba Allegiance Staffing
　　　7701-O Sharon Lakes Rd
　　　Charlotte, NC 28210
　　　Contact: Lisa Gaddy Acct Mgr
　　　Tel:　704-556-1770
　　　Email: lgaddy@allegiancestaffing.com
　　　Website: www.allegiancestaffing.com
Contract staffing. (Woman, estab 1993, empl 8, sales $4,500,000, cert: State)

8811 Right Choice Solutions, Inc.
316 W Millbrook Rd Ste 213
Raleigh, NC 27609
Contact: Layce Adams Operations Mgr
Tel: 919-324-3557
Email: layce@thercsolutions.com
Website: www.thercsolutions.com
Staffing: temporary staffing, temp to hire & direct hire
quality candidates. (Woman/AA, estab 2005, empl 7, sales
$101,369, cert: NMSDC)

8812 Sappenfield Staffing, Inc.
1014 S Tryon St Ste 101
Charlotte, NC 28203
Contact: VP
Tel: 704-332-4710
Email:
Website: www.sappenfieldstaffing.com
Staffing: temporary, temp/hire, direct hire & payroll
services. (Woman, estab 1995, empl 3, sales $1,800,000,
cert: State)

8813 Talented Fish, Inc.
111 W Lewis St Ste 120
Greensboro, NC 27406
Contact: Tracey Wallace COO
Tel: 336-279-7665
Email: tracey@talentedfish.com
Website: www.talentedfish.com
Executive Search & Placement. (AA, estab 2017, empl 3,
sales , cert: NMSDC)

8814 Two Hawk Employment Services, Inc.
3021 N Roberts Ave
Lumberton, NC 28360
Contact: Harvey Godwin, Jr. Owner
Tel: 910-738-3014
Email: harvey.godwin@twohawk.net
Website: www.twohawk.net
Temporary & permanent employment services: general
labor, supervisory & administration positions. (Nat Ame,
estab 1999, empl 50, sales $24,000,000, cert: NMSDC)

8815 Xcentri, Inc.
412 Louise Ave
Charlotte, NC 28204
Contact: Debby Millhouse President
Tel: 704-369-3211
Email: deborah.millhouse@xcentri.com
Website: www.xcentri.com
Staffing & recruiting (temp, contract to hire and direct
hire); HR Consulting; Background Checks; Drug Screening
(Woman, estab 2014, empl 200, sales $9,586,491, cert:
WBENC)

New Hampshire

8816 CCSI Inc.
62 Portsmouth Ave
Stratham, NH 03885
Contact: Sarah Latiolais Acct Mgr
Tel: 800-598-0255
Email: sarah@ccsiinc.com
Website: www.ccsiinc.com
Temporary & permanent staffing: IT, accounting, finance,
HR, sales, administration, marketing & clinical staff.
(Woman, estab 1998, empl 256, sales $16,000,000, cert:
WBENC)

8817 The Spencer Thomas Group LLC
One Falkland Place
Portsmouth, NH 03801
Contact: Lori Perkins Acct Mgr
Tel: 603-835-3707
Email: lori.perkins@spencer-thomas.com
Website: www.spencer-thomas.com
Recruiting, staffing, consulting, PeopleSoft, SAP, Oracle,
web deveoplers, project management, program manag-
ers, outsourced payroll services, employee leasing.
(Woman, estab 1998, empl , sales $20,000,000, cert:
WBENC)

New Jersey

8818 22nd Century Staffing, Inc.
1 Executive Dr Ste 285
Somerset, NJ 08873
Contact: Eva Gaddis-McKnight Contracts Admin
Tel: 732-537-9191
Email: com@tscti.com
Website: www.tscti.com
Staffing services, IT staffing & workforce management
services, contract or permanent positions. (Woman/As-
Pac, estab 2013, empl 191, sales $2,907,117,800, cert:
State, NMSDC)

8819 Accountants For You Inc.
1175 Marlkress Road, Ste 1040
Cherry Hill, NJ 08034
Contact: Marcia Libes President
Tel: 215-988-7200
Email: marcia.libes@accountantsforyou.com
Website: www.accountantsforyou.com
Staffing & recruiting: temporary, temporary to perma-
nent & permanent placement of accounting, finance,
human resource & office professionals. (Woman, estab
2006, empl 10, sales $1,376,195, cert: WBENC)

8820 ACCU Staffing Services
911 Kings Hwy N
Cherry Hill, NJ 08034
Contact: Debra Fordyce Operations Mgr
Tel: 856-482-2222
Email: cherryhill@accustaffing.com
Website: www.accustaffing.com
Staffing svcs: human resources, planned staffing, direct
placement, corporate outplacement svcs & on-site
consulting/mgmt funcations. (Woman, estab 1979, empl
100, sales , cert: WBENC)

8821 APN Consulting Inc.
1100 Cornwall Rd
Monmouth Junction, NJ 08852
Contact: Francis Moser Business Develop Mgr
Tel: 609-924-3400
Email: francis@apnconsultinginc.com
Website: www.apnconsultinginc.com
Contract, contract-to-hire & full time staffing services.
(As-Ind, estab 2002, empl 250, sales $20,300,000, cert:
NMSDC)

8822 CNC Consulting
50 E Palisades Ave Ste 422
Englewood, NJ 07631
Contact: Business Develop Mgr
Tel: 201-541-9122
Email:
Website: www.cncconsulting.com
IT professionals for consulting contracts. (AA, estab
1996, empl 25, sales $3,000,000, cert: State)

8823   Datanomics, Inc.
       991 US Hwy 22 West Ste 201
       Bridgewater, NJ 08807
       Contact: Lori Vail CEO
       Tel: 908-707-8200
       Email: vail@datanomics.com
       Website: www.datanomics.com
IT staffing, helpdesk, desktop support,
administration, technical writers, validation specialists,
business/systems
analysts, programmers, mainframe, client/server, & web.
(Woman, estab 1982, empl 100, sales , cert: State)

8824   Elite Personnel Group, LLC
       220 Davidson Ave. Ste 102
       Somerset, NJ 08873
       Contact: Junior Recruiter
       Tel: 908-722-1111
       Email:
       Website: www.eliteitpersonnel.com
National recruiting and talent acquisition. (As-Pac, estab
2007, empl 40, sales $45,000,000, cert: State)

8825   Fabergent, Inc.
       63 Ramapo Valley Rd, Ste 214
       Mahwah, NJ 07430
       Contact: Ratna Silpa Gorantla President
       Tel: 201-378-0036
       Email: ratna@fabergent.com
       Website: www.fabergent.com
Contract & full-time positions IT staffing in Java, .Net,
SharePoint, SAP, Oracle, BI, Analytics, networking & IT
security. (Woman/As-Pac, estab 2005, empl 125, sales ,
cert: State)

8826   Frink-Hamlett Legal Solutions
       P.O. Box 2022
       Teaneck, NJ 07666
       Contact: Katherine Frink-Hamlett President
       Tel: 201-357-8975
       Email: katherine@frinkhamlett.com
       Website: www.frinkhamlett.com
Provide legal professionals: attorneys, compliance &
paralegals on a temporary and permanent basis. (Woman/
AA, estab 2004, empl 3, sales $1,383,371, cert: City,
NMSDC, WBENC)

8827   Glenmont Group Inc.
       39 S Fullerton Ave Ste 9
       Montclair, NJ 07042
       Contact: President
       Tel: 973-746-0600
       Email:
       Website: www.glenmontgroup.com
Recruiting & staffing. (Woman, estab 2001, empl 22, sales
$2,404,882, cert: State, WBENC)

8828   Harita Infotech
       601 Crest Stone Circle
       Princeton, NJ 08540
       Contact: Kaushal Sampat President
       Tel: 609-216-1844
       Email: kaushalsampat@haritainfotechinc.com
       Website: www.haritainfotechinc.com
Consulting & Permanent resources in the Business, IT &
general fields. (As-Pac, estab 2014, empl , sales $130,000,
cert: State)

8829   Industrial Staffing Services inc.
       25 Kennedy Blvd Ste 200
       East Brunswick, NJ 08816
       Contact: Steve Dern VP
       Tel: 303-323-5179
       Email: SDern@evaluentsolutions.com
       Website: www.industrial-staffing.com
Contract & permanent staffing: staff augmentation,
payroll-servicing, &project staffing with qualified &
certified pre-screened personnel. (Woman, estab 2003,
empl 25, sales , cert: State, City, WBENC)

8830   Integrated Resources, Inc.
       4 Ethel Rd, Ste 403B
       Edison, NJ 08817
       Contact: Chris Byram VP
       Tel: 732-549-2030
       Email: chris@irionline.com
       Website: www.irionline.com
Staffing services, Direct Hire, Temporary/Contract and
Contract-to-Hire. (As-Pac, estab 1996, empl 750, sales
$53,000,000, cert: State, NMSDC)

8831   IT Staffing, Inc.
       5 Bliss Court Ste 200
       Woodcliff Lake, NJ 07677
       Contact: Jerry G. Myers Dir Business Devel
       Tel: 201-505-0493
       Email: jerry.myers@itstaffinc.com
       Website: www.itstaffinc.com
Strategic contract sourcing, consulting, staff augmentation, managed teams & outsourcing. (Minority/Woman,
estab 1998, empl 78, sales $11,500,000, cert: State)

8832   JBK Associates International, Inc.
       607 E Palisade Ave
       Englewood Cliffs, NJ 07632
       Contact: Shari Caloz Exec Admin
       Tel: 201-567-9070
       Email: scaloz@jbkassociates.net
       Website: www.jbkassociates.net
Executive recruitment. (Woman, estab 2003, empl 17,
sales $4,642,327, cert: WBENC)

8833   Jersey Staffing Solutions, LLC
       400 Valley Rd Ste 106
       Mt. Arlington, NJ 07856
       Contact: Kristi Telschow CEO
       Tel: 973-810-4495
       Email: ktelschow@jerseystaffing.com
       Website: www.jerseystaffing.com
Staffing, temporary, temp-to-perm & permanent
staffing. (Woman, estab 2010, empl 35, sales
$2,160,000, cert: WBENC)

8834   Jomsom Staffing Services
       4390 US Highway One, Ste 203
       Princeton, NJ 08540
       Contact: Ross Lazio Business Develop Exec
       Tel: 973-446-5627
       Email: rlazio@jomsomjobs.com
       Website: www.jomsomstaffing.com
Staffing solutions, full-time & part-time resources,
temporary, temporary to permanent & permanent
placement basis. (Woman/As-Ind, estab 2008, empl 55,
sales $3,500,000, cert: NMSDC)

8835 Knoodae Staffing, LLC
525 Rt 73N, Ste 104
Marlton, NJ 08053
Contact: Anitra Green Owner
Tel: 856-804-0321
Email: anitra@knoodaestaffing.com
Website: www.knoodaestaffing.com
Professional recruiting and staffing. (AA, estab 2021, empl 70, sales , cert: State)

8836 L & L Associates Global Search, Inc.
770 E Main St
Moorestown, NJ 08057
Contact: LaCarole Faulkner President
Tel: 856-778-7488
Email: lllacarole@erols.com
Website: www.llassociatessearch.com
Executive search services. (Woman/AA, estab 1993, empl 5, sales , cert: State)

8837 MetaSense Inc.
100 Technology Way, Ste 320
Mt. Laurel, NJ 08054
Contact: Jatin V Mehta CEO
Tel: 856-873-9950
Email: jmehta@metasenseusa.com
Website: www.metasenseusa.com
Information system staffing, software development, web design, outsourcing, business process outsourcing, knowledge pocess outsourcing. (Woman/As-Pac, estab 1999, empl 5, sales $767,000, cert: State)

8838 Net2Source Inc
270 Davidson Ave, Ste 704 Ste 704
Somerset, NJ 08873
Contact: Ashish Garg CEO
Tel: 201-340-8700
Email: supplier_registrations@net2source.com
Website: www.net2source.com
Staffing & recruitment services. (As-Ind, As-Pac, estab 2007, empl 5000, sales $128,000,000, cert: NMSDC)

8839 Next Step Staffing
725 River Road
Edgewater, NJ 07020
Contact: CEO
Tel: 646-829-1800
Email:
Website: www.nsstaff.com
IT solutions, full-time, permanent placement or temporary contract basis. (Woman/AA, Hisp, estab 2012, empl 5, sales $1,804,633, cert: NMSDC, WBENC)

8840 Perry Temps, Inc.
525 Route 73, South Ste 201
Marlton, NJ 08053
Contact: Wendy Brooks Dir Business Dev
Tel: 856-596-9400
Email: wbrooks@perryresources.com
Website: http://perryresources.com
Temporary staffing: administrative, accounting, clerical, customer service call center personnel. (Woman, estab 1986, empl 8, sales $2,174,927, cert: WBENC)

8841 Professional Resource Partners
14 Rickland Dr
Randolph, NJ 07869
Contact: Stefanie Wichansky CEO
Tel: 201-259-4739
Email: swichansky@prp-us.com
Website: www.professionalresourcepartners.com
Life Science Consulting & Staffing: contract, contract-to-perm, permanent basis across functional areas. (Woman, estab 2012, empl 20, sales $454,478, cert: WBENC)

8842 RHO, Inc.
507 Omni Dr
Hillsborough, NJ 08844
Contact: Deborah Johnson President
Tel: 908-359-0808
Email: deborah.johnson@rho-inc.com
Website: www.rho-inc.com
Staffing, consulting & training services. (Woman/Hisp, estab 1981, empl 120, sales , cert: WBENC)

8843 Sage Group Technologies Inc
3400 Highway 35 S Ste 9A
Hazlet, NJ 07730
Contact: Shruthi Reddy Exec VP
Tel: 732-994-6792
Email: sreddy@sagegroupinc.com
Website: www.sagegroupinc.com
Contingent Workforce Services • Contract Staffing, Contract to Hire Staffing • IT & Non-IT Staffing • Clinical & Scientific Staffing • Permanent Staffing • Professional Staffing • Payroll Services. (Nat Ame, As-Pac, estab 2004, empl 120, sales $63,200,000, cert: State, NMSDC)

8844 Sharpened Image, Inc.
2004 Morris Ave. Ste 1
Union, NJ 07083
Contact: Tamara Mangum President
Tel: 908-349-8403
Email: tthomas@sharpenedimage.com
Website: www.sharpenedimage.com
Staffing & employment services: temporary, temp-to-perm, permanent employee searches. (Woman/AA, estab 2004, empl 35, sales $1,540,000, cert: State)

8845 Software Folks, Inc. dba Saviance Technologies
16 Bridge St
Metuchen, NJ 08840
Contact: Anuj Sakhuja Client Relationsip Mgr
Tel: 732-593-8015
Email: anuj.sakhuja@saviance.com
Website: www.saviance.com
Information technology staffing: contract, contract-to-hire & permanent. (As-Pac, estab 1999, empl 60, sales $7,725,180, cert: NMSDC)

8846 TNT Staffing
70 Kinderkamack Rd, Ste 202
Emerson, NJ 07630
Contact: Jacqueline Tarnowski Dir of Recruiting
Tel: 201-497-6305
Email: jackie@tntstaffing.com
Website: www.tntstaffing.com
Staff Augmentation & Direct Full Time Placement Services. (Woman/AA, estab 2005, empl 25, sales $4,328,500, cert: State, WBENC)

8847 TSK Products, Inc.
12 Windsor Dr
Eatontown, NJ 07724
Contact: Eric Klein VP
Tel: 732-982-1090
Email: esklein@tskproducts.com
Website: www.tskproducts.com
TSK Products manufacturers or represents companies who manufacture products that improve safety, for both patients and staff, plus improves comfort for patients receiving treatment during the delivery of healthcare services. (Woman/As-Pac, estab 2000, empl 3, sales $989,849, cert: State, City)

8848   UserEdge Technical Personnel
       1812 Front St.
       Scotch Plains, NJ 07076
       Contact: Jay Madlangbayan President
       Tel: 908-387-7601
       Email: jay@useredge.com
       Website: www.useredge.com
Direct hire recruitment, short & long-term contract
assignments, outsourced staffing. (As-Pac, estab 1995,
empl 30, sales $1,750,000, cert: State, NMSDC)

New Mexico

8849   Sabio Systems, LLC
       4520 Montgomery NE Ste 2
       Albuquerque, NM 87109
       Contact: Nick Truyol President
       Tel: 505-792-8604
       Email: nick@sabiosystems.com
       Website: www.sabiosystems.com
Staffing services: information technology, MIS, accounting
& finance. (Hisp, estab 2006, empl 10, sales $1,480,000,
cert: 8a)

Nevada

8850   My Next Career Path Staffing, LLC
       400 S. Fourth St, Ste 500
       Las Vegas, NV 89101
       Contact: Renee Boyce President & CEO
       Tel: 844-579-6627
       Email: rboyce@mncpstaffing.com
       Website: www.mncpstaffing.com
Consulting & staffing: analysts, system/network administrators, project managers, developers, bookkeepers,
designers, customer service experts & marketing specialists. (AA, estab 2014, empl 40, sales $1,000,000, cert:
State, NMSDC, CPUC, 8a)

New York

8851   Admiral Staffing Inc.
       18 W 30th St
       New York, NY 10001
       Contact: Ray Rafeek
       Tel: 212-714-3543
       Email: irshaad@admiralstaffinginc.com
       Website: www.admiralstaffinginc.com/index.html
Temporary to permanent staffing services. (As-Pac, estab
2010, empl 25, sales $492,000, cert: City, NMSDC)

8852   ANR Staffing Solutions, LLC
       21702 Jamaica Ave, Ste 2
       Queens Village, NY 11428
       Contact: Alecia C. Grant CEO
       Tel: 516-881-7658
       Email: agrant@anrstaffingsolutions.com
       Website: http://anrstaffingsolutions.com
ANR Staffing Solutions, LLC provides supplemental staffing
of clinical and non-clinical personnel to hospitals,
homecare agencies, government agencies and individuals.
(AA, estab 2013, empl 40, sales , cert: City)

8853   Associate Resource Management, Inc.
       2527 Merrick Rd
       Bellmore, NY 11710
       Contact: Kim Robertson Exec Director
       Tel: 516-785-6211
       Email: kim@armi.bz
       Website: http://armi.bz
Staffing solutions. (Woman, estab 2006, empl 6, sales
$1,700,000, cert: WBENC)

8854   Atrium Staffing LLC
       387 Park Ave S, 3rd Fl
       New York, NY 10016
       Contact: Kelly Couto VP
       Tel: 732-902-5917
       Email: supplierdiversity@atriumstaff.com
       Website: www.atriumworks.com
Temporary & direct-hire staffing: administration,
finance, professional services & science. (Woman, estab
1995, empl 240, sales $293,646,368, cert: WBENC)

8855   CompliStaff, Inc.
       381 Lewis St
       West Hempstead, NY 11552
       Contact: April Bernstein VP
       Tel: 646-595-0040
       Email: april.bernstein@complistaff.com
       Website: www.complistaff.com
Staffing & recruitment solutions in legal, compliance,
accounting, audit & risk management. (Woman, estab
2010, empl 8, sales $1,270,000, cert: City, WBENC)

8856   Custom Staffing, Inc.
       420 Lexington Ave Ste 550
       New York, NY 10017
       Contact: Managing Dir
       Tel: 212-818-0300
       Email: mrodriguez@customstaffing.com
       Website: www.customgroupofcompanies.com
Staffing, temporary and permanent positions, contract
and permanent attorneys and paralegals. (Woman/AA,
estab , empl , sales $17,240,885, cert: State)

8857   Dale Workforce Solutions, LLC
       1751 2nd Ave, Ste 103
       New York, NY 10128
       Contact: Lois Dale Holtzman President
       Tel: 212-860-2000
       Email: ldale@daleworkforce.com
       Website: http://daleworkforce.com/
Staff Augmentation, Independent Contractor Compliance, Payroll Services. (Woman, estab 2012, empl 10,
sales $1,200,000, cert: WBENC)

8858   Distinctive Personnel
       424 W 33rd St
       New York, NY 10001
       Contact: Gonzalo Vergara Founder/Chairman
       Tel: 917-952-2766
       Email: gus@distinctivepersonnel.com
       Website: www.distinctivepersonnel.com
Staffing services: temporary, permenant, executive
search, managed service providers, vendor managed
services/, payroll outsourcing. (Hisp, estab , empl , sales
$710,000,000, cert: City)

8859   Elmark Group, Inc.
       499 7th Ave 22 N Tower
       New York, NY 10018
       Contact: President
       Tel: 212-856-9888
       Email:
       Website: www.marcusjobs.com
Contingency & retained accounting & finance search
services in the areas of financial reporting, general
accounting, accounting policy, internal audit, SOX
compliance, risk management, financial & strategic
analysis. (Woman, estab 1991, empl 5, sales $1,243,000,
cert: WBENC)

8860   ER Select LLC (dba TalentBridge Network)
       7 Linden Park
       Rochester, NY 14625
       Contact: Susan Johnson Business Dev Mgr
       Tel: 515-224-2696
       Email: sjohnson@talentbridgenetwork.com
       Website: http://talentbridge.com
Recruiting and staffing, short-term, permanent and
contract solutions. (Woman, estab 2011, empl 100, sales
$83,000,000, cert: WBENC)

8861   Geneva Consulting Group, Inc.
       14 Vanderventer Ave Ste 250
       Port Washington, NY 11050
       Contact: Gina Santorio Dir Business Dev
       Tel: 516-767-6695
       Email: gsantorio@genevaconsulting.com
       Website: www.genevaconsulting.com
IT consulting & full-time placement services, payrolling
services. (Woman, estab 1997, empl 50, sales $8,021,175,
cert: WBENC)

8862   HireTalent
       135 W 26th St, Ste 7B
       New York, NY 10001
       Contact: Ashish Kaushal President
       Tel: 646-495-1558
       Email: vms@hiretalent.com
       Website: www.hiretalent.com
Staffing services. (As-Ind, estab 1996, empl 250, sales
$29,105,000, cert: NMSDC)

8863   iT Resource Solutions.net, Inc.
       10 Technology Dr, Ste 1
       East Setauket, NY 11733
       Contact: Andrea Dunkle Dir of Diversity Management
       Tel: 631-941-2622
       Email: adunkle@it-rs.net
       Website: www.it-rs.net
Staffing: information technology consultants. (Woman,
estab 1995, empl 45, sales , cert: City, WBENC)

8864   Journee Technology Staffing Inc..
       2117Buffalo Rd Ste 275
       Rochester, NY 14624
       Contact: President
       Tel: 585-210-5314
       Email:
       Website: www.journeetechnologystaffing.com
Staffing solutions. (Woman/AA, estab 2007, empl 2, sales
$310,000, cert: State)

8865   NetPro Resources, Inc.
       444 E 75th St, Ste 16e
       New York, NY 10021
       Contact: Pam Lindheim VP Client Relations
       Tel: 212-650-1665
       Email: pam@netproresources.com
       Website: www.netproresources.com
Accounting, finance, Human Resources, Administrative,
Legal and Treasury recruitment and placement of temporary, permanent and consultative professionals (Woman,
estab 1999, empl 1, sales $175,000, cert: WBENC)

8866   Noor Associates, Inc.
       622 Third Ave, 7th Floor
       New York, NY 10017
       Contact: Jake Eletto Chief of Staff
       Tel: 212-812-3390
       Email: jake@noorinc.com
       Website: www.noorinc.com
Professional services: staffing, consulting & project based
solutions. (As-Ind, estab 2005, empl 100, sales $10,000,000,
cert: City, NMSDC)

8867   Noor Staffing Group, LLC
       295 Madison Ave 14th Fl
       New York, NY 10017
       Contact: Frank Cumbo Sr VP
       Tel: 212-878-2000
       Email: contracts@noorgov.us
       Website: www.promptpersonnel.com
Staffing, skills evaluation, reference, background checks
& market intelligence. (As-Ind, estab 2005, empl 200,
sales $55,000,000, cert: City, NMSDC)

8868   Nueva Solutions Inc
       1410 Broadway Ste 1904
       New York, NY 10018
       Contact: Punit Shetty Business Dev Mgr
       Tel: 212-937-0056
       Email: punit@nuevainc.com
       Website: www.nuevainc.com
IT Staffing - contingent & permanent. (Woman/As-Ind,
estab 2008, empl 17, sales $3,200,000, cert: State)

8869   Penda Aiken, Inc.
       330 Livingston St, 2 Fl
       Brooklyn, NY 11217
       Contact: Susie Fryer Business Develop Mgr
       Tel: 718-643-4880
       Email: sfryer@pendaaiken.com
       Website: www.pendaaiken.com
Staffing & HR solutions: testing & evaluating, recruiting
& retention, quality control, insurance protection,
prompt service & guarantee. (Woman/AA, estab 1990,
empl 225, sales $6,815,855, cert: State, City, NMSDC)

8870   Pride Healthcare, LLC
       420 Lexington Ave 30th Fl
       New York, NY 10170
       Contact: Bhavin Shah Director
       Tel: 212-235-5309
       Email: bhavin.shah@pride-health.com
       Website: www.pride-health.com
Staff Augmentation, Vendor Management, IT Hardware
Procurement Services and Business Processing
Outsourcing. (Hisp, estab 2003, empl 350, sales
$358,000,000, cert: NMSDC)

8871   Pride Healthcare, LLC
       222 S 9th St
       New York, NY 10170
       Contact: Jenny Davis Dir of Strategic Accts
       Tel: 612-806-0971
       Email: jennifer.davis@russelltobin.com
       Website: http://pridehealthcare.com
Direct Hire, Temporary, and Temp to Hire staffing
services for Administrative, Allied Health, Healthcare IT,
Clinical Research, Pharmacy, and Travel/Local Nursing.
(Hisp, estab 2010, empl 35, sales $40,000,000, cert:
NMSDC)

8872   Pride Technologies LLC
       420 Lexington Ave Ste 2220
       New York, NY 10170
       Contact: David Hellard Major Accts Mgr
       Tel: 614-991-5895
       Email: joshua.kaplan@pridetech.com
       Website: www.pridetech.com
Project management & staffing services. (Hisp, estab
1983, empl 800, sales $97,000,000, cert: NMSDC)

8873 Procare USA, LLC
      845 3rd Ave, Fl 6
      New York, NY 10022
      Contact: Dominic Sequeira President
      Tel: 631-880-6917
      Email: dominic@procareus.com
      Website: www.procareus.com
Short-term and long-term healthcare staffing solutions.
(As-Ind, estab 2011, empl 80, sales $6,200,000, cert: City)

8874 QED National
      350 Seventh Ave, 10 Fl
      New York, NY 10001
      Contact: Colleen Molter President
      Tel: 212-481-6868
      Email: cmolter@qednational.com
      Website: www.qednational.com
IT temporary & permanent staffing. (Woman, estab 1993,
empl 40, sales $14,281,567, cert: State)

8875 Russell Tobin & Associates, LLC
      420 Lexington Ave, 29th Floor
      New York, NY 10170
      Contact: Jenny Davis Sr Director
      Tel: 212-235-5300
      Email: jennifer.davis@russelltobin.com
      Website: www.russelltobin.com
Recruitment and staffing, labor staffing, direct hire
recruitment and payroll services. (Hisp, estab , empl 500,
sales $80,000,000, cert: NMSDC)

8876 Temporary Staffing by Suzanne, Ltd.
      370 Lexington Ave, Ste 902
      New York, NY 10017
      Contact: Suzanne G. Davis President
      Tel: 212-856-9500
      Email: sdavis@suzannenyc.com
      Website: www.suzannenyc.com
Temporary staffing: administrative, secretarial, computer,
reception, research, clerical, editorial, project coordinator,
events registration & data entry positions. (Woman, estab
1999, empl 6, sales $3,085,963, cert: State, City)

8877 The Burgess Group - Corporate Recruiters Intl
      10 Barclay St Ste 16-C
      New York, NY 10007
      Contact: William H. Burgess, III CEO
      Tel: 212-406-2400
      Email: billburgess@theburgessgroup.com
      Website: www.theburgessgroup.com
Mid to senior level executive search, diversity recruiting,
training & management development consulting. (AA,
estab 1997, empl 5, sales , cert: NMSDC)

8878 The May Consulting Group Inc.
      174 County Hwy 67
      Amsterdam, NY 12010
      Contact: Sheila Greco CEO
      Tel: 518-843-4611
      Email: sgreco@sgatalent.com
      Website: www.sgatalent.com
Recruitment research & strategic recruiting solutions.
(Woman, estab 1989, empl 20, sales , cert: WBENC)

8879 Tower Legal Solutions
      65 Broadway 17th Fl.
      New York, NY 10006
      Contact: CEO
      Tel: 212-430-6300
      Email:
      Website: www.towerls.com
Staffing: temporary attorneys, paralegals & project space.
(Woman, estab 2007, empl 74, sales $51,956,340, cert:
WBENC)

Ohio

8880 Acloche Staffing
      1800 Watermark Dr Ste 430
      Columbus, OH 43215
      Contact: Kimberly Shoemaker CEO
      Tel: 614-824-3700
      Email: kshoemaker@acloche.com
      Website: www.acloche.com
Human capital strategies & workforce resources,
recruiting, customized search program. (Woman, estab
1968, empl 100, sales $36,494,135, cert: WBENC,
NWBOC)

8881 Career Connections Staffing Services Inc.
      26260 Center Ridge Road
      Westlake, OH 44145
      Contact: Brian DeChant President
      Tel: 866-424-1233
      Email: bdechant@go2itgroup.com
      Website: www.go2itgroup.com
Temporary & permanent information technology &
medical support staffing. (Woman, estab 1996, empl 45,
sales $3,776,350, cert: WBENC)

8882 Crown Services, Inc.
      2800 Corporate Exchange Dr Ste 120
      Columbus, OH 43231
      Contact: Stacey Diana VP of Business Develop-
      ment
      Tel: 614-844-5429
      Email: sdiana@crownservices.com
      Website: www.crownservices.com
Staffing services. (Woman, estab 1968, empl 245, sales
$123,000,000, cert: WBENC)

8883 Dash Technologies Inc.
      565 Metro Pl S,
      Dublin, OH 43017
      Contact: Vikas Tiwari Business Develop Exec
      Tel: 614-812-0348
      Email: vikas.t@rekrooting.com
      Website: http://dashtechinc.com/
Contingency recruitment, Executive recruitment,
Retained recruitment, Staffing contracts in IT and non IT
labor categories. (Nat Ame, As-Pac, estab 2010, empl
145, sales $5,600,071, cert: State)

8884 Diversity Search Group LLC
      2600 Corporate Exchange Dr Ste 110
      Columbus, OH 43231
      Contact: Shelby Craft Business Develop Mgr
      Tel: 614-352-2988
      Email: info@diversitysearchgroup.com
      Website: www.diversitysearchgroup.com
Executive search. (Woman/AA, estab 2002, empl 3, sales
, cert: State)

8885 Eastern Personnel Services, Inc.
      619 Central Ave.
      Cincinnati, OH 45202
      Contact: Angelita Jones VP employment svcs
      Tel: 513-421-4666
      Email: ajones@easternpersonnelservices.com
      Website: www.easternpersonnelservices.com
Staffing: professional, contract, temporary, temp to hire,
contract management & on-site supervision. (Woman/
AA, estab 1987, empl 7, sales $3,625,356, cert: State,
NMSDC, WBENC)

8886　Great Work Employment Services, Inc.
2034 E Market St
Akron, OH 44312
Contact: Bob Frankish Dir Business Dev
Tel:　330-535-3800
Email: bfrankish@greatwork.jobs
Website: www.greatwork.cc
Temporary staffing services. (Woman, estab 1992, empl 16, sales $7,600,000, cert: WBENC)

8887　Howard & O
29525 Chagrin Blvd Ste 100
Cleveland, OH 44122
Contact: Lee Ann Howard
Tel:　216-514-8980
Email: lah@howardobrien.com
Website: www.howardobrien.com
Executive search consulting services. (Woman, estab 2001, empl 4, sales $1,900,000, cert: WBENC)

8888　Hunter International, Inc.
38100 Colorado Ave
Avon, OH 44011
Contact: Gabrielle Christman President
Tel:　440-389-0023
Email: gchristman@hirecruiting.com
Website: www.hirecruiting.com
Project based staffing solutions, contract or temporary, contract to permanent. (Woman, estab 2006, empl 100, sales $15,700,000, cert: WBENC)

8889　IM Creative
1020 Dennison Ave, Ste 304
Columbus, OH 43201
Contact: Phil Fregeau VP Business Dev
Tel:　614-300-3736
Email: philfregeau@i-m-creative.com
Website: www.i-m-creative.com
Included in List Services. (Minority, estab 1999, empl 15, sales $5,600,000, cert: State)

8890　JLS Staffing & Management dba Total Staffing
Solutions
11562 Chester Rd
Cincinnati, OH 45246
Contact:　Owner
Tel:　513-771-9675
Email:
Website: www.totalstaffsolutions.com
Staffing Solutions: temporary positions, temp to hire, as well as direct hire placements. (Woman, estab 2012, empl 10, sales $10,200,000, cert: WBENC)

8891　KNK Recruiting, LLC
6562 Pleasant Valley Court
Loveland, OH 45140
Contact: Matt Baker CEO
Tel:　513-265-5741
Email: mbaker@knkrecruiting.com
Website: www.knkrecruiting.com
Recruitment Process Outsourcing (RPO), recruiting & placement solutions. (AA, estab 2009, empl 1, sales $230,871, cert: State)

8892　Laura Licursi, LLC
P.O. Box 360843
Strongsville, OH 44149
Contact: Laura Licursi Owner
Tel:　440-973-7005
Email: laura@elitevirtualassist.com
Website: http://elitevirtualassist.com
Staffing, document preparation, digital document filing & organization, research & digital marketing support, social media and email marketing. (Woman, estab 2015, empl 35, sales $268,516, cert: State, City)

8893　Maverick Direct, Inc.
P.O. Box 1247
Bath, OH 44210
Contact: Cindy Janos President
Tel:　330-668-1800
Email: cjanos@callmaverick.com
Website: www.callmaverick.com
Staffing & search firm capabilities in the IT and IS arena. (Woman, estab 1999, empl 43, sales $5,200,000, cert: NWBOC)

8894　Minority Executive Search
3060 Monticello Blvd.
Cleveland, OH 44118
Contact: Eral Burks CEO
Tel:　216-932-2022
Email: eral@minorityexecsearch.com
Website: www.minorityexecsearch.com
Women & Minority job placements. (AA, estab 1985, empl 10, sales , cert: NMSDC)

8895　OneSource Services
6700 Beta Dr Ste 110
Mayfield Village, OH 44143
Contact: Tom Puletti Operations
Tel:　440-565-4434
Email: tpuletti@1-sourceservices.com
Website: www.1-sourceservices.com
Temporary, temporary to hire, direct hire & payroll services for technical, professional, and light industrial skill sets. (Woman, estab 2014, empl 25, sales $500,000, cert: NWBOC)

8896　Portfolio Creative, LLC
777 Goodale Blvd Ste 300
Columbus, OH 43212
Contact: Shelli Welch Dir Operations
Tel:　614-839-4897
Email: shelli@portfoliocreative.com
Website: www.portfoliocreative.com
Staffing services: marketing, advertising, design, project management. (Woman, estab 2005, empl 60, sales $6,500,000, cert: WBENC)

8897　Proteam Solutions, Inc.
2750 Airport, Ste 120
Columbus, OH 43219
Contact: Tracy Stearns Dir Client Relations
Tel:　614-454-6488
Email: tstearns@psi92.com
Website: www.psi92.com
Supplemental staffing, direct hire, temp-to-hire, light industrial, administrative & career placement. (AA, estab 1992, empl 16, sales $10,482,357, cert: NMSDC)

8898　Quick Employment LLC
2800 Euclid Ave, Ste 310
Cleveland, OH 44101
Contact: Sherall Hardy President
Tel:　216-361-3030
Email: quickemp@cs.com
Website: www.quickemp.com
Employment services: office services, data entry, receptionist, accounting clerks, file clerks, office administrative, IT, General Labor, shipping & receiving, porters, maintenance, drivers, CDL A, CDL B, dental assistants & medical assistants. (Woman/AA, estab 2001, empl 30, sales $537,946, cert: State, City)

8899 Reesential Inc.
15804 Terrace Dr
Cleveland, OH 44112
Contact: Charee Fountain President
Tel: 216-451-1820
Email: cfountain@reesential.com
Website: www.reesential.com
Information Technology Staffing: contract, contract to hire & direct hire placement services. (Woman/AA, estab 2014, empl 2, sales , cert: WBENC)

8900 Spherion of Lima Inc.
216 N Elizabeth St
Lima, OH 45801
Contact: Judith Cowan VP
Tel: 419-224-8367
Email: judithc@spherion-schulte.com
Website: www.spherion.com/nwohio
Recruiting and staffing. (Woman, estab 1982, empl 38, sales $26,000,000, cert: WBENC)

8901 Staffing Solutions Enterprises
5915 Landerbrook Dr Ste 100
Cleveland, OH 44124
Contact: Amy Elder Sales Team Mgr
Tel: 440-684-7218
Email: aelder@staffsol.com
Website: www.staffsol.com
Staffing & workforce management: temporary, temp-to-hire, direct placement, recruiting, managed staffing services, payrolling. (Woman, estab 1974, empl 20, sales $10,434,625, cert: City, WBENC)

8902 Supplemental Staffing
5333 Southwyck Blvd.
Toledo, OH 43614
Contact: Mary Stoneking President
Tel: 419-866-8367
Email: mstoneking@supplemental.com
Website: www.supplemental.com
Employment services. (Woman, estab 1978, empl 3000, sales , cert: WBENC)

Oregon

8903 BeginRight Employment Services
3708 NE 122nd Ave.
Portland, OR 97220
Contact: Cindy Wilkerson VP Sales and Service
Tel: 503-254-5959
Email: cwilkerson@beginright.com
Website: www.beginright.com/
Temporary, seasonal, contract to hire & direct hire staffing services: clerical, administrative, accounting, technical, engineering & professional placements, payrolling services. (Woman, estab 1985, empl 15, sales $7,200,000, cert: State)

8904 Collaborative Vision LLC
7883 SW Barnard Dr
Beaverton, OR 97007
Contact: Lisa Matar Founder
Tel: 503-941-9444
Email: lisa@cvhires.com
Website: http://cvhires.com
Staffing, Direct Hire, Permanent, Contract, Temp, Contingent Staffing Support. (Woman/As-Ind, estab 2008, empl 19, sales $579,845, cert: State)

8905 OLSA Resources, Inc
3485 NE John Olsen Ave
Hillsboro, OR 97124
Contact: Olsa Martini
Tel: 503-608-7895
Email: olsamartini@olsaresources.com
Website: www.olsaresources.com
Staffing & recruiting svcs: IT & engineering. (Woman, estab 1996, empl 75, sales $12,000,000, cert: WBENC, SDB)

8906 S. Brooks and Associates Inc.
1130 NE Alberta St
Portland, OR 97211
Contact: Lynn Sanders
Tel: 503-284-7930
Email: lsanders@sbrooks.com
Website: www.sbrooks.com
Staffing: permanent & temporary. (Woman/AA, estab 1981, empl 5, sales $3,000,000, cert: State)

Pennsylvania

8907 Advantage Resource Group
1600 Valley View Blvd
Altoona, PA 16602
Contact: Bonnie Williams VP Admin
Tel: 814-944-3571
Email: bonnie.williams@theadvantages.com
Website: www.theadvantages.com
Temporary Staffing, Temporary to hire/contract staffing, Direct Hire, Executive Placement, HR audits, Employee handbooks & Job Descriptions, HR Consulting & training, Resume writing & exit interviews. (Woman, estab 1953, empl 12, sales $3,000,000, cert: State, WBENC)

8908 American Personnel Managers and Consultants, Inc.
3607 Rosemont Ave, Ste 101
Camp Hill, PA 17011
Contact: Pat Gingrich CEO
Tel: 717-465-5637
Email: patg@apmci.com
Website: www.amerijob.com
Staffing, Human Resource Management, Consulting, Testing & Training, Procurement, Information Technology Staffing, Project Management. (Woman, estab 1998, empl 45, sales $3,000,000, cert: State)

8909 America's Staffing Partner, Inc.
35 E Elizabeth Ave, Ste 41
Bethlehem, PA 18018
Contact: Jorge Cruz CEO
Tel: 610-625-2511
Email: jcruz@americasstaffingpartner.com
Website: www.americasstaffingpartner.com
Contracted support personnel: administrative, logistics, healthcare, technical & trades. (Hisp, estab 2006, empl 250, sales $7,040,000, cert: 8a)

8910 Assurance Staffing, Inc.
4660 Trindle Rd Ste 100
Camp Hill, PA 17011
Contact: Cinde Holste Mgr
Tel: 717-920-9190
Email: jobs@assurancestaf.com
Website: www.assurancestaf.com
Professional Staffing Services, Temporary, Temp to Hire & Direct Hire placements. (Woman, estab 2003, empl 35, sales $879,179, cert: State, WBENC)

8911　Becker Technical Staffing, Inc.
312 Old Lancaster Rd
Merion Station, PA 19066
Contact: Renee Becker CEO
Tel:　610-667-9155
Email: renee@beckertek.com
Website: www.beckertek.com
Staffing: technical, pharmaceutical/healthcare, marketing sciences & financial/accounting talent acquisition. (Woman, estab 2008, empl 30, sales $2,000,000, cert: State, WBENC)

8912　Blue Plate Minds, Inc.
P.O. Box 1428
Paoli, PA 19301
Contact: Owner
Tel:　610-240-9001
Email:
Website: www.blueplateminds.com
Full time & freelance staffing: advertising & marketing, graphic & web designers/directors, editors, writers & proofreaders. (Woman, estab 1999, empl 25, sales $1,893,000, cert: WBENC)

8913　Bradley Temporaries, Inc. dba Bradley Staffing Gro
1400 Liberty Ridge Dr Ste 103
Wayne, PA 19087
Contact: Brad Burns VP
Tel:　610-254-9999
Email: brad@bradleystaffinggroup.com
Website: www.BradleyStaffingGroup.com
Temporary & direct hire placement services. (Woman, estab 1984, empl 6, sales $2,030,000, cert: WBENC)

8914　Choice Counsel, Inc.
535 Smithfield St, Ste 614
Pittsburgh, PA 15222
Contact: Cynthia Scott President
Tel:　412-355-0900
Email: cynthiascott@choicecounsel.com
Website: www.choicecounsel.com
Legal staffing, attorneys & paralegals in temporary and temporary-to-hire positions. (Woman, estab 1998, empl 50, sales $2,400,000, cert: WBENC)

8915　Choice One Staffing Group, Inc.
2009 MacKenzie Way Ste 250
Cranberry Township, PA 16066
Contact: Julie Sacriponte President
Tel:　724-452-5800
Email: julie@choice1staffing.com
Website: www.choice1staffing.com
Temporary, temp to hire & direct hire capacities, custom employee testing, background screens, drug screens, payroll services & skill marketing. (Woman, estab 2003, empl 525, sales $3,300,000, cert: WBENC)

8916　Clutch Group LLC DBA-Clutch
417 South St, Ste 3-4
Philadelphia, PA 19147
Contact:　CEO
Tel:　215-240-6672
Email:
Website: https://clutchnow.com
Flexible staffing solutions: Advertising, Digital, Creative, and Marketing, Freelance/Contract, Temp to Hire, Direct Hire, and Retained Search. (Woman, estab 2018, empl 7, sales $2,000,000, cert: WBENC)

8917　HTSS, Inc.
860 Broad St Ste 111
Emmaus, PA 18049
Contact: Pat Howells President
Tel:　610-432-4161
Email: phowells@htss-inc.com
Website: www.htss-inc.com
Staffing & recruiting services. (Woman, estab 1993, empl 7, sales $4,900,000, cert: State, WBENC)

8918　JH Technical Services, Inc.
3935 Washington RdUnit 1405
Canonsburg, PA 15317
Contact: Cynthia Harrison Henry President
Tel:　412-788-1174
Email: charrison@jhtechnical.com
Website: www.jhtechnical.com
Staffing services. (Woman, estab 1996, empl 20, sales $3,443,126, cert: State, WBENC)

8919　JURISolutions dba JuriStaff, CYLA, JXP Search
1500 JFK Boulevard Ste 1850
Philadelphia, PA 19102
Contact: John O'Donnell Operations Mgr
Tel:　215-383-3547
Email: jodonnell@jsl-hq.com
Website: www.jurisolutions.com
Temporary & permanent legal staffing. (Woman, estab 1997, empl 125, sales $11,049,778, cert: CPUC, WBENC)

8920　Krown Employment Services, LLC
801 Vinial St, Ste 102
Pittsburgh, PA 15212
Contact:　President
Tel:　412-567-7136
Email:
Website: www.krownempsvc.com
Staffing: Admin, Accounts Payable/Receivable Call Center, Clerical, General Labor, Hospitality, Light Indus-trial, Janitorial, Maintenance & Warehouse. (Woman, estab 2013, empl 250, sales $1,250,000, cert: WBENC)

8921　McCallion Temps, Inc.
601 N Bethlehem Pike
Montgomeryville, PA 18936
Contact: Lisa McCallion President
Tel:　215-855-8000
Email: lmccallion@mccalliongroup.com
Website: www.mccallionstaffing.com
Staffing, temporary, temp to hire & direct hire person-nel. (Woman, estab 1979, empl 12, sales $7,001,821, cert: NWBOC)

8922　Partner's Consulting, Inc.
2004 Sproul Road, Ste 206
Broomall, PA 19008
Contact:　Delivery & Engagement Mgr
Tel:　215-939-6294
Email:
Website: http://partners-consulting.com
Information technology recruiting for full-time, temp-to-perm & contract positions. (Woman, estab 2006, empl 40, sales $6,000,000, cert: State, WBENC)

8923　RomAnalytics
1117 Bridge Road
Creamery, PA 19430
Contact: Kathy Roman President
Tel:　484-961-8213
Email: kathy.roman@romanalytics.com
Website: http://romanalytics.com/
Recruiting & staffing, contract staffing or permanent staff recruiting. (Woman, estab 2013, empl 15, sales $1,900,000, cert: State, WBENC)

8924   Solomon International, LLC
       635 Coles Ct
       Harleysville, PA 19438
       Contact: Paul Solomon President
       Tel: 609-510-9705
       Email: paul.solomon@solomonsint.com
       Website: www.solomonsint.com
Employment services, temporary & direct hire employment & IT consulting services. (Woman/As-Pac, estab
2004, empl 20, sales $1,018,354, cert: State)

8925   Staffing Pharm, LLC
       P.O. Box 23
       Cresco, PA 18326
       Contact: Dora Pereda President
       Tel: 610-272-4993
       Email: dora.pereda@staffingpharm.com
       Website: www.staffingpharm.com/
Professional staffing services: pharmaceutical, healthcare,
biotechnology & research industries. (Woman/Hisp, estab
2012, empl 1, sales , cert: NMSDC)

8926   STAFFusion
       210 W. Pike St Ste 3
       Canonsburg, PA 15317
       Contact: Paula Davey President
       Tel: 724-916-4772
       Email: paula@staffusion.us
       Website: www.staffusion.com
Staffing, recruiting professionals, personnel, office,
administrative, (Woman, estab 2003, empl 5, sales
$2,800,000, cert: WBENC)

8927   StarsHR, Inc.
       1700 N Highland Rd Ste 200
       Pittsburgh, PA 15241
       Contact: Dir Placement Svcs
       Tel: 412-927-0369
       Email:
       Website: www.StarsHR.com
Executive placement services. (As-Ind, estab 2007, empl 5,
sales $2,700,000, cert: State)

8928   The Carney Group
       1777 Sentry Parkway West VEVA 14, Ste 301
       Blue Bell, PA 19422
       Contact: Jacquelyn Fowler Client Relationship Mgr
       Tel: 215-646-6200
       Email: jfowler@carneyjobs.com
       Website: www.carneyjobs.com
Staff augmentation or permanent hire. (Woman, estab
1992, empl 20, sales $10,000,000, cert: State, WBENC)

8929   The Drexel Group, Inc
       1832 Market St
       Camp Hill, PA 17011
       Contact: Romayne Johnson President
       Tel: 717-730-9841
       Email: romayne@thedrexelgroup.com
       Website: www.thedrexelgroup.com
Staffing: temporary, permanent, temp to hire, direct hire &
contingency. (Woman, estab 1994, empl 200, sales
$3,430,086, cert: State, WBENC)

Puerto Rico

8930   Careers Inc.
       208 Ave Ponce De Leon, Ste 1100 Banco Popular
       Ctr
       San Juan, PR 00918
       Contact: Blankie Hernandez Curt VP Admin
       Tel: 787-764-2298
       Email: blankieh@careersincpr.com
       Website: www.careersincpr.com
Executive Search & Management Recruiting. (Woman/
Hisp, estab 1970, empl 21, sales $2,179,173, cert:
NMSDC)

8931   Caribbean Temprorary Services, LLC
       P.O. Box 11873
       San Juan, PR 00910
       Contact: Xiomara Villamil VP Corporate Affairs
       Tel: 787-620-5500
       Email: xiomara.villamil@ctspr.com
       Website: www.ctspr.com
Staffing services. (Woman/Hisp, estab 1983, empl 5000,
sales , cert: NMSDC)

8932   Job Hunters LLC
       P.O. Box 56012
       Bayamon, PR 00960
       Contact: JOHN BRUNO
       Tel: 787-998-7210
       Email: bruno@jobhunters-pr.com
       Website: www.clasificadosonline.com/
       PartnersListingJ
Temporary & permanent staffing. (Woman/Hisp, estab
2013, empl 50, sales $1,200,000, cert: NMSDC)

8933   PSS Pathfinders Inc.
       CIM II 90 carr 165 Ste 310
       Guaynabo, PR 00958
       Contact: Georyanne Rios Alvarez President
       Tel: 787-622-6868
       Email: grios@psspathfinders.com
       Website: www.psspathfinders.com
Staffing solutions: temporary, temporary to hire &
executive search. (Woman/Hisp, estab 1985, empl 425,
sales $8,448,618, cert: WBENC, SDB)

8934   The Cervantes Group
       P.O. Box 16409
       San Juan, PR 00908
       Contact: Joanna Bauza President
       Tel: 787-729-7597
       Email: joanna@thecervantesgroup.com
       Website: www.thecervantesgroup.com
Staffing solutions, short or long-term requirements.
(Woman/Hisp, estab 2004, empl 22, sales $2,800,000,
cert: WBENC)

8935   Weil Group, Inc.
       Urb. Villa Blanca Calle Aquamarina #78 Ste 1
       Caguas, PR 00725
       Contact: Milagros del R Gonzalez GM
       Tel: 787-633-0025
       Email: clopez@weilgroup.com
       Website: www.weilgroup.com
Temporary employment agency, outsourcing IT &
automation services: management and/or admin, help
desk, servers, WAN, email system, desktop, maintenance, backup & restore. (Hisp, estab 1994, empl 215,
sales $12,000,000, cert: NMSDC)

8936 Wisdom Resources, Inc.
350 Chardon Ave. Ste 119
San Juan, PR 00918
Contact: Aissa Betancourt President
Tel: 787-963-1048
Email: aissa@snellingpr.com
Website: www.snellingpr.com
Staffing services: executive, career, temporary, temp-to-hire & contractors, background check & drug testing services. (Woman/Hisp, estab 2008, empl 137, sales $5,200,000, cert: NMSDC, WBENC)

Rhode Island

8937 Silverman McGovern Staffing
284 W Exchange St
Providence, RI 02903
Contact: Managing Partner
Tel: 401-632-0580
Email:
Website: www.silvermanmcgovern.com
Staffing: Legal, Marketing/Creative, Accounting/Finance, Administrative, Technical. (Woman, estab 2003, empl 7, sales , cert: WBENC)

South Carolina

8938 Augusta Temporaries, Inc. dba Manpower
101 Broadus Ave
Greenville, SC 29601
Contact: Pamelia Davis COO
Tel: 864-233-4162
Email: pamelia.davis@manpowersc.com
Website: http://manpowersc.com
Temporary staffing & customer service. (Woman, estab 1978, empl 300, sales $16,711,520, cert: WBENC)

8939 Benchmark Contracting, Inc.
215 E Bay St
Charleston, SC 29401
Contact: Jennifer Courville Dir of Business Devel
Tel: 843-628-5999
Email: courvillej@benchmarkcontracting.org
Website: https://BenchmarkContractingSC.com
Staff augmentation. (AA, estab 1998, empl 20, sales $10,267,000, cert: State, City)

8940 DP Professionals, Inc.
3741 Landmark Dr Ste 200
Columbia, SC 29204
Contact: President
Tel: 803-738-0066
Email:
Website: www.dppit.com
Staffing & recruiting: information technology professionals for contract employment & direct placement. (Woman, estab 1996, empl 100, sales , cert: NWBOC)

8941 Eastern Design Services
25 Woods Lake Rd, Ste 301
Greenville, SC 29607
Contact: John Crain Office Mgr
Tel: 864-271-1228
Email: jcrain@easterndesign.com
Website: www.easterndesign.com
Technical & professonal staffing: engineers, designers, drafters, office professionals, information technology & administrative personnel. (Woman, estab 1979, empl 5, sales $2,714,000, cert: State)

8942 Express Employment Professionals
9557 Two Notch Rd Ste N
Columbia, SC 29223
Contact: Northan Golden CEO
Tel: 803-788-8721
Email: northan.golden@expresspros.com
Website: www.expresspros.com
Temporary & permanent staffing. (AA, estab 2007, empl 4, sales $450,000, cert: NMSDC)

8943 G&S Janitorial Services, Inc.
1008 Fontaine Rd
Columbia, SC 29223
Contact: Leroy Green CEO
Tel: 803-786-9710
Email: tgnsservicesinc@aol.com
Website: www.gandscarpetservices.com
G&S Janitorial Services entails carpet and upholstery cleaning services as well as building and dwellings. G&S has over 22 years of janitorial experience. (AA, estab 1988, empl 30, sales $1,600,000, cert: State)

8944 Marketplace Staffing Services Inc.
200 Adley Way
Greenville, SC 29606
Contact: Jason Mitchell Dir of Sales
Tel: 864-286-3900
Email: jmitchell@marketplacestaffing.com
Website: http://marketplacestaffing.com
Comprehensive staffing & onsite managed contract labor services: manufacturing, warehouse & light industrial staffing solutions. (AA, estab 1996, empl 25, sales $9,000,000, cert: NMSDC)

8945 Onin Staffing
950 Sunset Blvd. Ste E
Columbia, SC 29169
Contact: Lynn Bradley Area Mgr
Tel: 803-667-4676
Email: lbradley@excelsiorstaffing.com
Website: www.excelsiorstaffing.com
Staffing services: temporary, temporary to permanent, direct placement & VNP. (AA, estab 2007, empl 4, sales , cert: NMSDC)

8946 Perceptive Recruiting, LLC
221 Meadow Rose Dr
Travelers Rest, SC 29690
Contact: Jill Rose President
Tel: 864-908-0105
Email: info@perceptiverecruiting.com
Website: www.perceptiverecruiting.com
Recruiting and staffing services. (Woman, estab 2014, empl 5, sales $3,311,462, cert: WBENC)

Tennessee

8947 A-One, LLC
3639 New Getwell Rd., Ste 1 & 2
Memphis, TN 38118
Contact: Sterlyn Howell Owner
Tel: 901-367-5757
Email: astaffing2@yahoo.com
Website: www.aonestaffing.com
Temp, temp-to-perm & permanent placement. (Woman/ AA, estab 2001, empl 32, sales $2,200,000, cert: City, WBENC)

8948 Atlas Management Corporation
750 Old Hickory Blvd Bldg Two, Ste 265
Brentwood, TN 37027
Contact: Warren Sawyers President
Tel: 615-620-0977
Email: wsawyers@atlasmanagement.us
Website: www.atlasmanagement.us
Recruiting, staffing, call center services, business unit outsourcing. (AA, estab 2003, empl 10, sales $2,600,000, cert: State, SDB)

8949 Comprehensive Medical Staffing, Inc.
1540 Castalia St
Memphis, TN 38114
Contact: COO
Tel: 901-779-4168
Email:
Website: www.compmedstaffing.com
Contingent staffing, temporary medical employees (RN, Registered Nurse, LPN, Licensed Practical Nurse, CNA Certified Nursing Assistants). (AA, estab 2015, empl 75, sales $225,000, cert: State, City)

8950 Gem Quality
2033 Castaic Lane
Knoxville, TN 37932
Contact: Jason Campbell President
Tel: 865-560-9891
Email: jcampbell@gem-quality.com
Website: www.gemcareinc.com
HR services, temporary to hire, direct placement, commercial & professional staffing. (Woman/AA, estab 2005, empl 200, sales $6,428,737, cert: NMSDC, WBENC)

8951 MasterStaff, Inc.
611 Potomac Pl, Ste 103
Smyrna, TN 37167
Contact: Jennifer Sheets CEO
Tel: 615-223-5627
Email: jennifer@masterstaffemployment.com
Website: www.masterstaffemployment.com
Professional recruitment & placement, temporary & temp to hire employees, human resource consulting & contract staffing. (Woman, estab 1999, empl 450, sales $12,789,203, cert: WBENC)

8952 neMarc Professional Services, Inc.
2500 Mt. Moriah Rd, Ste H231
Memphis, TN 38115
Contact: Carmen Bassett President
Tel: 901-360-1804
Email: carmenbassett@bellsouth.net
Website: www.nemarcstaffing.com
Temporary, permanent placement, temp-to-perm staffing svcs: clerical, administrative, distribution, warehouse, IT, accounting & professional placement. (Woman/AA, estab 2002, empl 5, sales $742,000, cert: State, NMSDC)

8953 Omni Staffing Plus, Inc.
80 N Tillman, Ste 201
Memphis, TN 38111
Contact: Dinah Terry
Tel: 901-843-8433
Email: dterry@omnistaffingplus.com
Website: www.omnistaffingplus.com
Temporary/permanent staffing. (Woman/AA, estab 1999, empl 6, sales $1,874,214, cert: NMSDC)

8954 Presidio Service Solutions, Inc.
701 Scarboro Rd Ste 222
Oak Ridge, TN 37830
Contact: Alfredo F. Rodriguez President
Tel: 865-481-8007
Email: alrod@presidio-ssi.com
Website: www.presidio-ssi.com
Technology and Engineering Staffing and Services Firm that provides innovative project related staffing solutions and professional services. (Hisp, estab 2007, empl 14, sales $900,000, cert: State)

8955 Provide Staffing Services LLC
6765 E Shelby Dr
Memphis, TN 38141
Contact: Pat Morris Mgr
Tel: 901-505-0005
Email: pat@provide-staffing.com
Website: www.pscstaffing.net
Temporary Employees, Clerical positions. (Woman, estab 2013, empl 170, sales , cert: City)

8956 Reliable Building Solutions, Inc.
6232 Airpark Dr
Chattanooga, TN 37421
Contact: Kathy Sok President
Tel: 423-954-9834
Email: ksok6322@aol.com
Website: www.rbsi-online.com
We provide Complete facility management service to include: Janitorial, Floor maintenance, Emergency services, and provide wholesale of Janitorial supplies, equipment and chemicals. (Woman/As-Pac, estab 1992, empl 45, sales $2,800,000, cert: State)

Texas

8957 ADASTAFF, Inc.
702 Hunters Row Court
Mansfield, TX 76063
Contact: Aaron Flaherty Call Ctr Solutions Expert
Tel: 817-469-6234
Email: aflaherty@adastaff.com
Website: www.adastaff.com
Temporary, Temporary-to-Hire Staffing, Payroll Administration, Executive Placement, Safety Consulting and Training, Direct Hire and Special Project Outsourcing. Our specialty is in Administrative, Clerical. (Woman, estab 1993, empl 225, sales $7,187,978, cert: WBENC)

8958 Adventus Technologies, Inc.
6001 Savoy Ste 511
Houston, TX 77036
Contact: Vicki Semander
Tel: 713-995-4446
Email: vsemander@adventus-tech.com
Website: http://adventus-tech.com
Professional, para professional & admin personnel: Project Mgt, Finance & Accounting, General Consulting Services, Acquisition and Procurement Mgt, Publication, & Logistic Support Services. (Woman/AA, estab 2005, empl 8, sales $376,000, cert: State, City, NMSDC, 8a)

8959 Akorbi (Elahi Enterprises dba Akorbi)
6010 W Spring Creek Pkwy Ste 238
Plano, TX 75024
Contact: President
Tel: 214-256-9222
Email:
Website: www.akorbi.com
IT consulting & recruitment, telecommunications, professional services & language solutions, custom application development & business communications. (Woman/AA, estab 2003, empl 964, sales $34,000,000, cert: State, NMSDC, WBENC)

8960   All Temps 1 Personnel
2606 MLK Jr. Blvd
Dallas, TX 75215
Contact: Stacie McGill Sales & Marketing Mgr
Tel: 214-426-2700
Email: jjeffrey@alltemps1.com
Website: www.alltemps1.com
Staffing services. (AA, estab 1994, empl 15, sales
$11,800,000, cert: NMSDC)

8961   Alleare Consulting, LLC
3625 N. Hall St Ste 685
Dallas, TX 75219
Contact: Lana Arnold CFO
Tel: 214-559-9878
Email: larnold@alleareconsulting.com
Website: www.alleareconsulting.com
Recruiting, staffing & consulting services: permanent
placement, contract & contract-to-hire. (Woman, estab ,
empl , sales $816,030, cert: State, WBENC)

8962   AllTex Staffing & Consulting LLC dba Abba Staffing
2350 Airport Fwy Ste 130
Bedford, TX 76022
Contact: Darla Beggs CEO
Tel: 817-354-2800
Email: darla@abbastaffing.com
Website: www.abbastaffing.com
Direct Placement, Contingent-to-hire-Personnel, Contract
personnel, Temporary personnel. (Woman, estab 2001,
empl , sales $390,000,000, cert: State, WBENC)

8963   AMP Personnel Services, LLC
3700 N 10th St, Ste 302
McAllen, TX 78501
Contact: Marisa Sonnier Admin
Tel: 956-627-0477
Email: amppersonnelservices@gmail.com
Website: www.amppersonnel.com
Staffing services: professional, administrative & commercial
job placement. (Woman/Hisp, estab 2012, empl 2, sales
$100,000, cert: State, 8a)

8964   Applicantz, Inc.
10235 W Little York Road, Ste 235
Houston, TX 77040
Contact: Nikhil Jain Director
Tel: 713-834-4909
Email: nikhilj@applicantz.com
Website: www.applicantz.com
IT Contingent Staffing: Contract, Contract-to-hire, and
Permanent and Remote Technology Staffing. (Woman/Nat
Ame, As-Pac, estab 2001, empl 125, sales $14,800,000,
cert: NMSDC)

8965   ASAP Personnel Inc.
17311 Dallas Pkwy
Dallas, TX 75248
Contact: Evelyn Touchette President
Tel: 972-432-6667
Email: evelyn@asapdo.com
Website: www.asapdo.net
Staffing & Personnel Services. (Woman, estab 2010, empl
22, sales $500,000, cert: State, City)

8966   AXIS Staffing
1111 W Mockingbird Ln
Dallas, TX 75247
Contact: Jacob Joseph President
Tel: 214-638-4000
Email: jacob_joseph@axisstaff.com
Website: www.axisstaff.com
Staffing services. (As-Pac, estab 1993, empl 10, sales
$4,500,000, cert: State)

8967   Barbara J. Charles dba Perfection Staffing
16502 Brightling Ln
Houston, TX 77090
Contact: Barbara Charles Owner
Tel: 281-781-7587
Email: bcharles@perfectionstaffing.agency
Website: www.perfectionstaffing.agency
Staffing and Recruitment Agency, Direct Hire, Contract/
Contract-to-Hire, and Temporary talent for Exempt and
Non-Exempt positions.
Our staffing efforts are (AA, estab 2018, empl 2, sales ,
cert: City, NMSDC)

8968   BBM Staffing
4242 Medical Dr, Bldg 2200
San Antonio, TX 78229
Contact: Liz Moreno Operations Mgr
Tel: 210-822-0717
Email: lmoreno@bbmstaffing.com
Website: www.bbmstaffing.com
Recruiting, temporary, temp to hire & direct hire
solutions. (Woman/Hisp, estab 2009, empl 300, sales
$11,000,000, cert: State, NMSDC)

8969   Bestica, Inc.
3463 Magic Dr Ste 303
San Antonio, TX 78229
Contact: Harvinder Singh CEO
Tel: 210-614-4198
Email: harvinder@bestica.com
Website: www.bestica.com
IT consulting & staffing firm. (As-Ind, estab 2005, empl
198, sales $7,500,000, cert: NMSDC, 8a)

8970   Brooke Staffing Companies, Inc.
3900 Essex, Ste 555
Houston, TX 77027
Contact: Joe Stephens Treasurer
Tel: 713-337-2222
Email: joes@brookecompanies.com
Website: www.brookecompanies.com
Temporary & full-time placement services. (Woman,
estab 1989, empl 213, sales $8,718,523, cert: City,
WBENC)

8971   Burnett Specialists
9800 Richmond Ave Ste 800
Houston, TX 77042
Contact: Rick Burnett VP, Regional Mgr
Tel: 713-358-1437
Email: rick@burnettspecialists.com
Website: www.burnettspecialists.com
Temporary, contract & direct-hire placement: clerical &
administrative, accounting & financial, legal, human
resources, information technology, sales, medical,
customer service, light industrial & electronics personnel. (Woman, estab 1974, empl 115, sales $66,200,000,
cert: WBENC)

8972   Burns Search LLC
1415 Legacy Dr, Ste 310
Frisco, TX 75034
Contact: CEO
Tel: 214-213-4053
Email:
Website: www.burnssearch.com
Staffing, recruiting, consulting: technical, accounting,
finance, executive search. (Woman, estab 1999, empl 8,
sales $1,394,555, cert: WBENC)

8973 C&T Information Technology Consulting, Inc.
201 S Lakeline Ste 803
Cedar Park, TX 78613
Contact: Jennifer Conway Dir Sales/Marketing
Tel: 512-610-0040
Email: sales@candttech.com
Website: www.candttech.com
Entry level, High End & Mid-Level Technical Staffing &
Consulting. Project Management, Enterprise Architecture
& Technical Solutions Provider Perm Placement, Technical
Recruiting. (Woman, estab 2003, empl 34, sales
$5,115,202, cert: State)

8974 Cambay Consulting LLC
1838 Snake River Road, Ste A
Katy, TX 77449
Contact: Faaiz Rangrej Business Develop Mgr
Tel: 469-393-9501
Email: Faaiz.r@cambaycs.com
Website: www.cambaycs.com
Temporary & permanent staffing solutions. (As-Ind, As-Pac,
estab 2012, empl 137, sales $19,200,000, cert: NMSDC)

8975 Choice Hire Staffing LLC
3106 Highway 377 S
Brownwood, TX 76801
Contact: Melissa Mauricio Owner
Tel: 325-643-1416
Email: melissa@choicehirestaffing.com
Website: www.choicehirestaffing.com
Temporary, seasonal, temp to hire & direct placement.
(Woman, estab 2013, empl 3, sales , cert: State)

8976 Confidential Search Solutions, LLC.
7330 San Pedro Ave, Ste 610
San Antonio, TX 78216
Contact: CEO
Tel: 210-802-4771
Email:
Website: www.confidentialsearchsolutions.com
Staffing/recruiting: direct hire, temp-to-hire, temporary,
contract & payroll recruiting services in accounting &
finance, human resources, sales & marketing, supply chain
management, project management, IT helpdesk. (Woman/
AA, estab 2009, empl 3, sales , cert: State, City, NMSDC,
WBENC)

8977 Employee Risk Management Co. Inc.
4639 Corona, Ste 99
Corpus Christi, TX 78411
Contact: Laura Escobar President
Tel: 361-808-8367
Email: laura@atrecruiters.com
Website: www.atpersonnelservices.com
Recruiting, direct hire & temporary placement, Back-
ground checks, Drug screens, Safety Assured. (Woman/
Hisp, estab 1994, empl 10, sales $6,000,000, cert: State)

8978 Evins Personnel Consltants
6430 Richmond Ave Ste 415
Houston, TX 77057
Contact: Helen Royston Acct Rep
Tel: 713-977-8555
Email: staffing@hrnetconnection.com
Website: www.HRnetConnection.com
Temporary staffing, direct hire, temp to hire staffing.
(Woman, estab 1967, empl 5000, sales $15,000,000, cert:
State)

8979 Execusane Inc
2306 Stillwater Dr
Mesquite, TX 75181
Contact: Shiree Alexander President
Tel: 972-277-1176
Email: shayes@execusane.com
Website: http://execusane.com
Direct Placement, Executive Recruiting, HR Consulting,
Staffing/Contract Recruiting. (Woman/AA, estab 2012,
empl 1, sales , cert: State)

8980 Foremost Staffing, Inc.
3991 West Vickery
Fort Worth, TX 76107
Contact: Vicki Jordan President
Tel: 817-346-4738
Email: vjordan@foremoststaffing.com
Website: www.foremoststaffing.com
Staffing: temporary, temp to hire, direct placements &
payroll services. (Woman, estab 2007, empl 100, sales
$2,261,595, cert: State, WBENC)

8981 Fulgent Solutions Inc.
5700 Granite Pkwy Ste 200
Plano, TX 75024
Contact: Shan Adaikalam President
Tel: 972-506-7335
Email: shan.adaikalam@fulgentsol.com
Website: www.fulgentsol.com
Enterprise business consulting & staffing, technology,
temporary, temporary-to-hire & permanent placement
services. (As-Ind, estab 2013, empl 15, sales $1,500,000,
cert: State)

8982 GS Infovision LLC dba Global Systems LLC
1200 Walnut Hill Lane, Ste 2220
Irving, TX 75038
Contact: Shekhar Gupta VP
Tel: 214-717-4344
Email: account@globalsyst.com
Website: www.globalsyst.com
IT Consulting, Staffing, BPO, IT Consulting, temporary,
contract, temp to perm & permanent staffing solutions.
(Woman/As-Pac, estab 2005, empl 110, sales
$11,000,000, cert: NMSDC)

8983 Hawkins, Associates, Inc.
909 NE Loop 410, Ste 104
San Antonio, TX 78209
Contact: Elizabeth Hawkins VP
Tel: 210-349-9911
Email: liz@hawkinspersonnel.com
Website: www.hawkinspersonnel.com
Temporary, temp-to-hire, direct hire professional
services, payrolling services & on-site management
services. (Woman, estab 1977, empl 35, sales
$18,000,000, cert: State, City)

8984 HirePower Personnel, Inc.
14100 Southwest Freeway Ste 320
Sugar Land, TX 77478
Contact: Travis Hamblet Global Operations Mgr
Tel: 281-455-6802
Email: travis.hamblet@hppstaffing.com
Website: www.hppstaffing.com
Temp, Temp to Hire & Direct Hire Placements. (Woman,
estab 0, empl , sales $4,000,000, cert: State, WBENC)

8985 ICON Information Consultants, LP
100 Waugh Dr Ste 300
Houston, TX 77007
Contact: Pamela O'Rourke CEO
Tel: 713-438-0919
Email: porourke@iconconsultants.com
Website: www.iconconsultants.com
Recruit information technology, accounting & finance professionals. (Woman, estab 1998, empl 6000, sales $233,000,000, cert: WBENC)

8986 Imprimis Group
4835 LBJ Frwy, Ste 1000
Dallas, TX 75244
Contact: Valerie Freeman CEO
Tel: 972-419-1635
Email: vfreeman@imprimis.com
Website: www.imprimis.com
Staffing; temp, temp to hire, direct hire: admin/office, accounting, bilingual, cstnmr svc, legal, mktg, medical, mortgage, etc. (Woman, estab 1982, empl 60, sales $21,000,000, cert: State, WBENC)

8987 InGenesis, Inc.
10231 Kotzebue St
San Antonio, TX 78217
Contact: Dr. Veronica Edwards CEO
Tel: 210-366-0033
Email: commercial@ingenesis.com
Website: www.ingenesis.com
Workforce solutions: direct placement, direct hire, executive search, temporary staffing, contingent staffing, managed vendor, recruitment process outsourcing, managed services programs & locum tenens. (Woman/Hisp, estab , empl , sales $174,785,000, cert: NMSDC, WBENC)

8988 Inreach IT Solutions, LLC
P.O. Box 1311
Wylie, TX 75098
Contact: CEO
Tel: 972-442-5332
Email:
Website: www.InreachITSolutions.com
Staffing, payroll services & project management, direct hire, contract-to-hire, temporary. (Woman/AA, estab 2012, empl 1, sales , cert: State, WBENC)

8989 International Genesis Professional Solutions, Inc.
P.O. Box 692205
San Antonio, TX 78269
Contact: Shelah Simmons CEO
Tel: 210-867-4182
Email: simmons@genesisprofsol.com
Website: www.genesisprofsol.com
Human Capital, Business Process Optimization & Project Management, Strategic Executive
Recruitment, Human Resources Staffing (Temporary Help Service). (Woman/AA, estab 2006, empl 5, sales $149,100, cert: State)

8990 JK Flenory & Company, LLC
P.O. Box 5069
Frisco, TX 75035
Contact: Marcellas Flenory Sr. CEO
Tel: 972-480-2667
Email: recruiter@jkfcompany.com
Website: www.JKFCompany.com
Staffing, recruiting, retention & outplacement services. (AA, estab 2012, empl 1, sales , cert: City)

8991 KeyStaff Inc.
2909 Hillcroft St, Ste 620 Ste 620
Houston (HARRIS), TX 77057
Contact: Tammie Jeffers Branch Mgr
Tel: 713-422-2710
Email: tammie.jeffers@keystaffinc.com
Website: www.keystaffinc.com
Staffing: temporary, temp-to-perm & direct-hire placements. (Woman, estab 2004, empl 20, sales $18,989,644, cert: State, City)

8992 King Finders, LLC
6575 West Loop South, Ste 500
Bellaire, TX 77401
Contact: Manny Coronado President
Tel: 713-936-2695
Email: mcoronado@kingfinders.com
Website: www.kingfinders.com
Temp-to-Hire, Contingent & Direct Hire placements for Business & Admin, Oil & Gas, Energy, Finance & Accounting, Information Technology and Manufacturing. (Hisp, estab 2018, empl 25, sales , cert: State)

8993 Labor On Demand Inc., Dba, LOD Resource Group
851 Culebra Road
San Antonio, TX 78201
Contact: Richard Tovar Business Development
Tel: 210-865-0445
Email: rtovar@lodresourcegroup.com
Website: http://lodresourcegroup.com/
Temporary & permanent employment services. (Woman/Hisp, estab 2003, empl 31, sales $13,475,568, cert: State, 8a, SDB)

8994 LiveWell Insurance Products, Inc.
2425 Holly Hall, Ste H 106
Houston, TX 77054
Contact: Glen Reaux President
Tel: 281-827-7909
Email: g.reaux@thenewfaceofhealthcare.com
Website: www.thenewfaceofhealthcare.com
Marketing & advertising services. (AA, estab 2013, empl 4, sales , cert: State, NMSDC)

8995 LK Jordan & Associates
7550 IH 10 West Ste 105
San Antonio, TX 78229
Contact: Stefanie Chavez Business Development
Tel: 210-488-9360
Email: stefanie.chavez@lkjordan.com
Website: www.lkjordan.com
Staffing services: temporary, temporary to hire & direct hire employees. (Woman, estab 1990, empl 52, sales $25,000,000, cert: State)

8996 Lotus Staffing Group, LLC
1925 E Beltline Rd Ste 419
Carrollton, TX 75006
Contact: Tyra Roberts Managing Dir
Tel: 972-410-3685
Email: tyra@lotusstaffingagency.com
Website: http://lotusstaffingagency.com
Contingent staffing solutions. (Woman/AA, Hisp, estab 2008, empl 23, sales $3,450,000, cert: State, City)

8997 Magnum Staffing Services, Inc.
2900 Smith St, Ste 250
Houston, TX 77006
Contact: Caroline Brown President
Tel: 713-658-0068
Email: caroline.brown@magnumstaffing.com
Website: www.magnumstaffing.com
Background, drug-screening, SS verification, temporary placement, temp-to-hire, direct hire, industrial, clerical & managerial arenas. (Woman, estab 1996, empl 43, sales $38,000,000, cert: WBENC)

8998 MIT Professionals, Inc.
22611 Duncan Brush Trace
Richmond, TX 77469
Contact: Rebecca Morgan President
Tel: 713-934-9700
Email: rebecca@mitprof.com
Website: www.mitprof.com
Staffing services: information technology, supply chain resources, engineering & professional services. (Woman, estab 1995, empl 50, sales , cert: State)

8999 Mobile Temporary Services
9110 Jones Rd Ste 131
Houston, TX 77065
Contact: Allison Holmes President
Tel: 713-344-4148
Email: allison@mobiletempstaff.com
Website: www.mobiletempstaff.com
Temporary employees, direct hire, temp-to-perm & contract employees, on-site applications, backgrounds checks, drug-screen & on-boarding. (Woman/AA, estab 2016, empl 4, sales , cert: WBENC, SDB)

9000 Nelson Search Group
3001 Lake Oak Dr
Arlington, TX 76017
Contact: D. Gayle Barton Principal
Tel: 817-466-7117
Email: gayle@nelsonsearchgroup.com
Website: www.nelsonsearchgroup.com
Ethical, consultative, confidential, quality-driven direct recruiting & on-boarding (full life-cycle). (Woman, estab 2009, empl 1, sales $150,000, cert: State, WBENC)

9001 Primary Services LP
520 Post Oak Blvd Ste 550
Houston, TX 77027
Contact: MaryKay Foy-Hinton Strategic Accts Mgr
Tel: 713-850-7010
Email: marykay@primaryservices.com
Website: http://primaryservices.com
Staffing solutions, contract, contract-to-hire & direct hire placement. (Woman, estab 1988, empl 39, sales $44,928,501, cert: WBENC)

9002 QSTAFF Incorporated
P.O. Box 580622
Houston, TX 77258
Contact: Richard Green
Tel: 281-218-6574
Email: r.green@qualified-staff.com
Website: www.qualified-staff.com
Staffing svcs: accounting, admin, clerical, chemical plant operators, data entry, engineering, IT, light industrial. (Woman/Hisp, estab 1999, empl 75, sales $3,000,000, cert: State, WBENC)

9003 RD Data Solutions
2340 E Trinity Mills Ste 349
Carrollton, TX 75006
Contact: Reuben D'Souza CEO
Tel: 972-899-2334
Email: reuben.dsouza@rddatasolutions.com
Website: www.rddatasolutions.com
Technology staffing: SAP & ERP. (Woman/As-Pac, estab 2002, empl 26, sales $25,000,000, cert: State, NMSDC)

9004 Recruiting Force, LLC
1464 E. Whitestone Blvd. Ste 1903
Cedar Park, TX 78613
Contact: Rudy Uribe President
Tel: 512-996-0999
Email: rudy.uribe@recruitveterans.com
Website: www.recruitveterans.com
Direct hire professional executive search, permanent placement, information technology, engineering, project management, logisitics, finance, accounting. (Hisp, estab 2003, empl 60, sales $4,437,363, cert: NMSDC, 8a)

9005 Recruiting Source International
21414 Julie Marie Ln, Ste 2301
Katy, TX 77449
Contact: Bianca Jackson COO
Tel: 281-277-1411
Email: bjackson@recruiting-source.com
Website: www.recruiting-source.com
Executive Search, Staffing & 1099 Management Services. (Woman/AA, estab , empl , sales $1,410,000, cert: State, City, NMSDC, WBENC, SDB)

9006 Resource Personnel Consultants, LLC
14070 Proton Rd
Farmers Branch, TX 75244
Contact: Acct Mgr
Tel: 972-371-2934
Email:
Website:
Staffing: clerical, administrative & customer service employees, temporary, temporary to permanent or direct hire. (Woman/Hisp, estab 2001, empl 8, sales $1,827,499, cert: State)

9007 RG Talent Solutions, LLC
445 E FM 1382 Ste 3-254
Cedar Hill, TX 75104
Contact: Reginald W Calhoun, Sr. CEO
Tel: 817-405-2838
Email: rcalhoun@rgtalentsolutions.com
Website: www.rgtalentsolutions.com
Business process outsourcing (BPO), talent management, talent acquisition, agency and marketing firm. (AA, estab 2009, empl 14, sales $4,000,000, cert: State)

9008 RightStaff, Inc
4919 MCKINNEY AVENUE
Dallas, TX 75205
Contact: CEO
Tel: 214-615-6015
Email:
Website: www.rightstaffinc.com
Staffing services: permanent, temporary, project staff augmentation, computer software & hardware, computer programing, systems design, technology infrastructure. (Woman, estab 1998, empl 7, sales $2,862,677, cert: State, WBENC)

9009 Riverway Business Services
5213 Spruce St Ste 100
Bellaire, TX 77401
Contact: Margo Costello President
Tel: 713-664-5900
Email: margo.costello@riverway.jobs
Website: www.riverway.jobs
Staffing services: administrative/clerical, accounting, human resource, professional & information technology. (Woman, estab 1990, empl 22, sales $2,000,000, cert: WBENC)

9010   RMPersonnel, Inc.
       4707 Montana Ave
       El Paso, TX 79903
       Contact: Debra Underwood Branch Mgr-San Antonio
       Tel: 915-565-7674
       Email: debras@rmpersonnel.com
       Website: www.rmpersonnel.com
Staffing services: employee leasing, temporaries, temp to
hire, executive recruiting & HR consulting services.
(Woman/Hisp, estab 1990, empl 33, sales $34,000,000,
cert: WBENC)

9011   Saba Quaility System
       1456 FM 1960 W
       Houston, TX 77090
       Contact: Patricia Carter Mgr/HR Business Devel
       Tel: 281-537-7676
       Email: qualitysystem.qs@gmail.com
       Website: http://qualitysystemssite.com
IT staffing, sourcing, prescreening, interviewing & placement. (Woman/As-Ind, estab 2010, empl 14, sales
$1,700,000, cert: State)

9012   Search Plus International
       5900 Balcones Dr Ste 242
       Austin, TX 78731
       Contact: Bruce Bagwell Managing Dir
       Tel: 512-459-8200
       Email: bbagwell@searchplustexas.com
       Website: http://searchplustexas.com
Executive mid-management & highly-technical searches.
(Woman, estab 1988, empl 9, sales $500,000, cert:
WBENC)

9013   Smith & Dean, Inc.
       11511 Katy Freeway Ste 430
       Houston, TX 77079
       Contact: Jennifer Dean President
       Tel: 713-785-7483
       Email: jdean@dpsinc-texas.com
       Website: www.deansprofessionalservices.com
Staffing solutions, recruiting, workshops & seminars, IT
consulting. (Woman/AA, estab 1993, empl 2180, sales
$10,681,149, cert: State, City, NMSDC, WBENC)

9014   SNS Global Corporation
       1000 Heritage Center Circle
       Round Rock, TX 78664
       Contact: Misty Carr HR
       Tel: 512-250-2959
       Email: m.carr@snsglobalstaffing.com
       Website: www.snsglobalstaffing.com
Staffing services. (As-Ind, estab 2003, empl 20, sales , cert:
State, NMSDC)

9015   Softel Techsource LLC
       2100 Alamo Rd., Ste T,
       Richardson, TX 75080
       Contact: Mohammed Al-Baki Managing Partner
       Tel: 469-475-2297
       Email: malbaki@softeltechsource.com
       Website: www.softeltechsource.com
Recruiting practices & continuous training. (Woman/As-
Ind, estab 2010, empl 10, sales $348,603, cert: State)

9016   SOLRAC Corporation
       6 Founders Blvd Ste A
       El Paso, TX 79906
       Contact: Masazumi Aso Exec VP & COO
       Tel: 915-772-3073
       Email: maso@solraccorp.com
       Website: http://solraccorp.com
Assembly, sorting & rework operation, staffing services,
warehouse & logistic operation. (Hisp, estab 1989, empl
300, sales $1,000,000, cert: State, NMSDC)

9017   Solution Tech Staffing Inc.
       2825 Wilcrest, Ste 678
       Houston, TX 77042
       Contact: Emon Carroll President
       Tel: 713-988-5325
       Email: emon@ststaff.com
       Website: www.ststaff.com
Staffing: short term temporary, long term temporary,
temp-to-hire & direct hire. (Woman/AA, estab 2001,
empl 7, sales , cert: State, City)

9018   Southwest Staffing
       12025 Rojas, Ste L
       El Paso, TX 79936
       Contact: James Tidwell Director
       Tel: 915-857-9719
       Email: info@southweststaffing.com
       Website: www.southweststaffing.com
Temporary employee placement & management,
staffing & recruiting solutions in technical & professional
placement. (Woman/Hisp, estab 1994, empl 23, sales
$15,298,011, cert: State)

9019   SV Meditrans, Inc.
       100 S 8th St
       Richmond, TX 77469
       Contact: Rohini Dinesh CEO
       Tel: 832-520-8742
       Email: rohinid@svmtinc.com
       Website: www.svmtinc.com
Staffing services, interviews, screening & training.
(Woman/As-Pac, estab 2002, empl 20, sales $1,650,000,
cert: WBENC)

9020   The Burchell Group
       11200 W Broadway, Ste 2348
       Pearland, TX 77584
       Contact: Jamie Burchell President
       Tel: 281-607-5990
       Email: jamie@theburchellgroup.com
       Website: www.theburchellgroup.com
Staffing solutions: engineering, information technology
& GIS. (Hisp, estab 2001, empl 45, sales , cert: NMSDC)

9021   The Omega Staff, LLC
       14756 Dallas Pkwy, Ste 805
       Dallas, TX 75254
       Contact: Michelle Deriggs Owner
       Tel: 972-948-7754
       Email: mderiggs@omegastaff.com
       Website: www.omegastaff.com
Professional recruiting & staffing services to automotive,
engineering, defense, and manufacturing companies.
(Woman/AA, estab 2007, empl 6, sales $130,000, cert:
State, City)

9022 The Unbeatable Connection LLC
111 Brand Lane, Ste 3
Stafford, TX 77477
Contact: La Teasha Smith Owner
Tel: 832-363-2566
Email: tuctruckingsales@gmail.com
Website: www.tuctrucking.com/
Staffing services: temp, temp to perm & direct hire positions. (Woman/AA, estab 2010, empl 5, sales $308,826, cert: City, NMSDC)

9023 TMC Workforce Solutions
2313 W Sam Houston Pkwy N Ste 155
Houston, TX 77043
Contact: James Morris President
Tel: 832-473-3993
Email: james.morris@tmcworkforce.com
Website: www.tmcworkforce.com
Staffing, Recruiting and Procurement Services. (AA, estab 2016, empl 342, sales $12,000,000, cert: NMSDC)

9024 TriQuest Business Services, LLC
13526 George Rd, Ste 201
San Antonio, TX 78230
Contact: Stephanie Balditt President
Tel: 210-598-1539
Email: stephanie@triquestbusiness.com
Website: http://triquestbusiness.com
Temporary & permanent placement services: IT, Accounting, Finance, Administrative & Human Resource placement. (Woman/Hisp, estab 2010, empl 6, sales $931,239, cert: State)

9025 Walker Elliott, LP
11200 Westheimer
Houston, TX 77042
Contact: Victor M. Taveras Contract Mgr
Tel: 713-482-3750
Email: belliott@walker-elliott.com
Website: www.walker-elliott.com
Information technology & healthcare direct hire, contract & contract to hire placement firm. (Woman, estab 2006, empl 17, sales , cert: WBENC)

Utah

9026 Premier Employee Solutions LLC
3596 Mountain Vista Parkway, #2
Provo, UT 84606
Contact: Dan Riley Dir of Natl Sales
Tel: 800-385-0855
Email: driley@thepremierpride.com
Website: www.thepremierpride.com
Staffing & payroll services. (Woman, estab 2005, empl 500, sales $391,331,571, cert: WBENC)

Virginia

9027 ABBTECH Professional Resources
45625 Willowpond Plaza
Sterling, VA 20164
Contact: Lawrence Brady COO
Tel: 703-450-5252
Email: larry.brady@abbtech.com
Website: www.abbtech.com
Staffing: temporary/contract, temporary/contract to direct hire or direct placement services. (Woman, estab 1992, empl 500, sales , cert: State)

9028 Action Technology, Inc.
3121 E Boundary Ct
Midlothian, VA 23112
Contact: Thomas Hammerstone Reg Mgr
Tel: 804-464-1271
Email: thammerstone@action-tech.com
Website: www.action-tech.com
Staff augmentation: direct hire, contract & temporary. (Woman, estab 1982, empl 200, sales $8,000,000, cert: State, CPUC, WBENC)

9029 Alcove Resources
1900 Campus Commons Dr, Ste 100
Reston, VA 20191
Contact: Quan Woodard CEO
Tel: 703-652-4732
Email: info@alcoveresources.com
Website: www.alcoveresources.com
Recruiting & executive search services, information management consulting. (Woman/AA, estab 2005, empl 5, sales $100,000, cert: State)

9030 ARK Solutions Inc.
1939 Roland Clarke Pll Ste 300
Reston, VA 20191
Contact: Anuj Khurana Managing Dir
Tel: 703-502-6999
Email: anuj@arksolutionsinc.com
Website: www.arksolutionsinc.com
Staffing & consulting, staffing support, Enterprise IT Solutions, Information Assurance Solutions, Business Process Management & Integration Competency. (Woman/As-Ind, estab 2003, empl 43, sales , cert: State)

9031 BEST Employment SoluTions, LLC
110 Coliseum Crossing
Hampton, VA 23666
Contact: Kipland Albright Owner
Tel: 757-589-2675
Email: kalbright@thebestllc.com
Website: www.thebestllc.com
Staffing: Light Industrial, Warehousing, Manufacturing, Admin Clerical, Customer Support, & Transportation positions. (AA, estab 2016, empl 20, sales , cert: State, NMSDC)

9032 Cammas & Associates
5870 Trinity Pkwy Ste 170
Centreville, VA 20120
Contact: Diane Cammas Owner
Tel: 703-579-1100
Email: diane.cammas@snelling.com
Website: www.Snelling.com/NoVa
Staffing & recruiting services: Administrative & Support, Information Technology, Accounting & Finance, Human Resources, Engineering, Manufacturing & Production, Construction, Pharmaceutical, Sales & Marketing. (Woman, estab 2008, empl 3, sales , cert: WBENC)

9033 Cynet Systems Inc.
21000 Atlantic Blvd #700
Sterling, VA 20166
Contact: Arpit Paul AVP - Strategy & Partnerships
Tel: 571-645-5910
Email: arpitp@cynetsystems.com
Website: www.cynetsystems.com
IT & engineering staffing consulting, direct/full time hiring, contract (temp hiring) or contract to hire services. (As-Ind, As-Pac, estab 2010, empl 1012, sales $56,000,000, cert: NMSDC)

9034   Gillman Services, Inc.
3300 Tyre Neck Rd Ste E
Portsmouth, VA 23703
Contact: Jeremy Andrews Exec acct Mgr
Tel: 757-439-0800
Email: jandrews@gillmannservices.com
Website: www.gillmanservices.com
Staffing services. (Woman, estab 2008, empl 300, sales $8,850,000, cert: State)

9035   Hire 1 Staffing
P.O. Box 34337
Richmond, VA 23234
Contact: Sandra Smith Owner
Tel: 804-223-2110
Email: ssmith@hire1staffing.net
Website: www.hire1staffing.net
Temporary staffing: administrative, clerical, call center/customer service representatives & light industrial positions. (Woman/AA, estab 2005, empl 1, sales , cert: State)

9036   Key Personnel, Inc.
5540 Falmouth St, Ste 100
Richmond, VA 23230
Contact: Thomas Bowles President & CEO
Tel: 804-716-9450
Email: thomasbowles@keypersonnel.net
Website: www.keypersonnel.net
Staffing: temporary, temporary to hire & direct hire employment services. (AA, estab 1998, empl 40, sales $2,000,000, cert: State)

9037   Leading Edge Systems Richmond
3711-A Westerre Pkwy
Richmond, VA 23233
Contact: Adish Jain Mgr
Tel: 804-673-5100
Email: adishj@leadingedgesys.com
Website: www.leadingedgesys.com
Staffing svcs; information tech, clerical support & professional svcs. (As-Ind, estab 1997, empl 42, sales $4,500,000, cert: State)

9038   McKinley Marketing Partners, Inc.
201 N. Union St Ste 110
Alexandria, VA 22314
Contact: Susie President & CEO
Tel: 703-836-4445
Email: clientservices@mckinleyinc.com
Website: www.mckinleymarketingpartners.com/
Staffing: short-term marketing mgrs. (Woman, estab 1995, empl 15, sales $9,395,256, cert: WBENC)

9039   MillenniumSoft, Inc
8301 Arlington Blvd, Ste 504,
Fairfax, VA 22031
Contact: Swathi Billa
Tel: 703-698-9232
Email: time@millenniumsoft.com
Website: www.millenniumsoft.com
Permanent, long term or short term staffing. (Woman/As-Ind, As-Pac, estab 2000, empl 45, sales $293,466,000, cert: State, NMSDC)

9040   Outcomes Inc.
4215 Lafayette center Dr Ste 6
Chantilly, VA 20151
Contact: Sonali Kakatkar CEO
Tel: 703-996-8833
Email: sonali@out-comes.com
Website: www.out-comes.com
Staffing, recruiting, payroll services & vendor managed services. (Woman/As-Ind, estab 2002, empl 8, sales $3,000,000, cert: State, WBENC, SDB)

9041   Preferred Staffing Group/Preferred Temporary Services, Inc.
2001 Jefferson Davis Hwy Ste 303
Arlington, VA 22202
Contact: Barbara Posner President
Tel: 703-415-0182
Email: ejackson@ourpsg.com
Website: www.ourpsg.com
Staffing svcs: administrative, telecommunications fiber optic, IT, legal, light construction, housekeeping. (Woman, estab 1987, empl 150, sales $1,500,000, cert: WBENC)

9042   ProTask Inc.
542 Springvale Road
Great Falls, VA 22066
Contact: Jessie Covington Sr Acct Mgr
Tel: 703-231-4275
Email: jcovington@protaskinc.com
Website: www.protaskinc.com/
Staffing solutions, IT contractors, IT consultants, IT Staff Augmentation, Traditional direct hire talent search (full life cycle), Executive recruitment. (Woman, estab 2010, empl 22, sales $3,300,000, cert: State, WBENC)

9043   Seaborn Health Care Inc.
16600 Jefferson St
Amelia Court House, VA 23002
Contact: Jacqueline Amadio President
Tel: 727-398-1710
Email: jacky@seabornhc.com
Website: www.seabornhc.com
Staffing svcs: medical, clerks & administration, IT Tech, legal & accounting. (Woman, estab 1995, empl 50, sales $1,000,000, cert: 8a)

9044   Skill Path Talent, Inc.
8300 Boone Blvd, Ste 500
Vienna, VA 22182
Contact: Sharon Campbell Business Dev Mgr
Tel: 571-358-5602
Email: operatons@skillstalent.com
Website: www.skillstalent.com
Human capital services, temporary & permanent placement. (AA, estab 2013, empl 25, sales , cert: NMSDC)

9045   TeamPeople LLC
180 S Washington St Ste 200
Falls Church, VA 22046
Contact: Kathy Roma Development Consultant
Tel: 917-751-6088
Email: kroma@teampeople.tv
Website: www.teampeople.tv
Media Staffing & Support Services. (Woman, estab 2004, empl 600, sales $51,714,354, cert: WBENC)

9046   Temporary Solutions, Inc.
10550 Linden Lake Plaza, Ste 200
Manassas, VA 20109
Contact: VP of Marketing and Contract Services
Tel: 703-361-2220
Email:
Website: www.eeihr.com
Staffing services: temporary staffing, temp-to-hire staffing, direct placement, on-site services & single source mgmt solutions. (Woman, estab 1980, empl 921, sales $7,245,894, cert: State, WBENC)

Washington

9047 2rbConsulting, Inc.
19515 North Creek Parkway Ste 310
Bothell, WA 98011
Contact: Betta Beasley CEO
Tel: 425-406-7644
Email: betta@2rbconsulting.com
Website: www.2rbconsulting.com
Provide contract consultants, permanent staff & managed services at all levels of expertise. (Woman, estab 2007, empl 25, sales $3,200,000, cert: WBENC)

9048 All StarZ Staffing & Consulting, Inc.
24437 Russell Rd, Ste 200
Kent, WA 98032
Contact: Tyler Crass COO
Tel: 253-277-4000
Email: inquiries@allstarzstaffing.com
Website: www.allstarzstaffing.com
Staffing consulting services. (Woman, estab 2011, empl 10, sales $4,000,000, cert: WBENC)

9049 All StarZ Staffing and Consulting LLC
841 Central Ave N Ste C-208
Kent, WA 98032
Contact: Debra Kerner Mgr
Tel: 253-277-4000
Email: debra@allstarzstaffing.com
Website: www.allstarzstaffing.com
Staffing solutions: candidate sourcing, screening, selection, retention & labor cost management. (Woman, estab 2005, empl 150, sales $3,043,715, cert: WBENC)

9050 Allegiance Staffing
400 Industry Dr, Ste 180
Tukwila, WA 98188
Contact: Luis Perez Acct Mgr
Tel: 253-854-7000
Email: lperez@allegiancestaffing.com
Website: www.allegiancestaffing.com
Staffing solutions: temporary, contract employees, executive search & permanent placement. (Woman, estab 1994, empl 10, sales $6,500,000, cert: State)

9051 Allovus Design, Inc.
15822 Peacock Hill Ave NW
Gig Harbor, WA 98332
Contact: Hayley Nichols Client Services Director
Tel: 253-222-0274
Email: hayley@allovus.com
Website: www.allovus.com
Staffing services, direct hire, staff augmentation & studios project teams. (Woman, estab 2009, empl 75, sales $9,000,000, cert: WBENC)

9052 Archer & Associates I, Inc.
16625 Redmond Way, Ste M8
Redmond, WA 98052
Contact: Ann-Marie Archer CEO
Tel: 425-869-6350
Email: aarcher@archer-associates.com
Website: www.archer-associates.com
Executive search & consulting. (Woman, estab 2000, empl 2, sales $852,500, cert: State)

9053 Ci2i Services, Inc.
410 Bellevue Way SE Ste 205
Bellevue, WA 98004
Contact: Raul Ramos CEO
Tel: 425-279-7992
Email: raul@ci2iservices.com
Website: www.Ci2iServices.com
IT Consulting & Staffing services: Program & Project Management, Software development, Business strategy & Marketing resource needs. (As-Ind, estab 1998, empl 40, sales $3,600,000, cert: State, NMSDC)

9054 MB Diversity
6523 California Ave SW, Ste B-255
Seattle, WA 98136
Contact: Anthony Burnett Owner
Tel: 206-941-2834
Email: anthony@mbdiversity.com
Website: www.MBDiversity.com
Staffing recruiting & managed resources. (AA, estab 2014, empl 10, sales $573,315, cert: State, City, NMSDC)

9055 VanderHouwen & Associates, Inc.
2018 156th Ave NE Ste 220
Bellevue, WA 98007
Contact: Jennifer Boyle Client Specialist
Tel: 425-453-7300
Email: jennifer@vanderhouwen.com
Website: www.vanderhouwen.com
Professional Staffing Services: IT, Engineering, Accounting, and Administrative talent. (Woman, estab 1987, empl 410, sales , cert: WBENC)

Wisconsin

9056 Division 10 Personnel Services of Milwaukee, Inc.
4425 N Port Washington Rd, Ste 401
Milwaukee, WI 53212
Contact: Wendy Koppel, CPC President
Tel: 414-963-8700
Email: wendy@division10personnel.com
Website: www.division10personnel.com
Recruiting & staffing: Administrative & Professional level candidates. (Woman, estab 1980, empl 30, sales $1,563,690, cert: State, WBENC)

9057 Elite Human Capital Group
155 S Executive Dr Ste 200
Brookfield, WI 53005
Contact: Aaron Sramek Mgr of Professional Services
Tel: 262-785-0900
Email: aarons@elitehumancapital.com
Website: www.elitehumancapital.com
Human resource outsourcing, temporary & permanant placement. (Woman, estab 2003, empl 35, sales $6,953,826, cert: State)

9058 Hatch Staffing Services
700 W Virginia St, Ste 400
Milwaukee, WI 53204
Contact: Lucas Harvey Branch Mgr
Tel: 414-272-4544
Email: lucas@hatch.com
Website: http://hatch.com
Staffing services: temp, temp to hire & direct hire candidates. (Woman, estab 1983, empl 23, sales $12,269,000, cert: WBENC)

9059 SEEK Careers/Staffing, Inc.
      P.O. Box 148
      Grafton, WI 53024
      Contact: Debbie Fedel VP Business Dev
      Tel: 262-377-8888
      Email: dfedel@seekcareers.com
      Website: www.seekcareers.com
Staffing services, office/accounting, light industrial &
skilled manufacturing positions. (Minority, Woman, estab
1971, empl 96, sales $53,824,639, cert: State)

9060 Victory Personnel Services, Inc.
      735 N Water St Ste 1411
      Milwaukee, WI 53202
      Contact: Mike Farrell VP
      Tel: 414-271-0749
      Email: mfarrell@victoryprofessional.com
      Website: www.victorypersonnel.com
Staffing: temporary, permanent & payroll services. (AA,
estab 1991, empl 400, sales $18,510,506, cert: NMSDC)

RECORDING & VIDEO PRODUCTION
Produce videos (in studio or remote), TV shows, records, sound recordings, pre and post production services, talent arrangers, video distribution. NAICS Code 51

Arizona

9061   Blade Inc
3033 N Central Ave Ste 440
Phoenix, AZ 85012
Contact: Louise Parker President
Tel: 602-307-5577
Email: louise@bladeinc.com
Website: www.bladeinc.com
Production, Editing, Video Production, Video Editing, Post Production, 3D Animation, Animation, Motion Graphics, VFX, Visual Effects, Visual Design, Motion Design, Illustration. TV Commercials, Web, Training, Corporate. (Woman, estab 2002, empl 65, sales $704,000, cert: WBENC)

California

9062   Aahs Entertainment, Inc.
10707 Camarillo St, Ste 312
Toluca Lake, CA 91602
Contact: Gwenn Smith President
Tel: 818-279-2416
Email: gwenn@aahsentertainment.com
Website: http://aahsentertainment.com
Video Production Services, Media Production, Media Services, Advertising, Marketing, Content Creation, Branded Content, Brand Marketing, DVD Extras, DVD Special Features, Marketing, Advertising, EPKs. (Woman/AA, estab 2011, empl 1, sales , cert: WBENC)

9063   Agnew Multilingual
2625 Townsgate Road Ste 330
Westlake Village, CA 91361
Contact: Irene Agnew President
Tel: 805-494-3999
Email: i.agnew@agnew.com
Website: www.agnew.com
Translation, interpretation & audiovisual production. (Woman, estab 1986, empl 9, sales $800,000, cert: CPUC, WBENC, SDB)

9064   Fire Starter Studios, LLC
1023 N Hollywood Way, Ste 202
Burbank, CA 91505
Contact: Rachel Klein CEO
Tel: 747-201-7400
Email: bids@firestarterstudios.com
Website: http://firestarterstudios.com
Media, animation, live-action and VR/AR. (Woman, estab 2012, empl 5, sales $600,000, cert: WBENC)

9065   Hybrid Edit, LLC
5782 W. Jefferson blvd.
Los Angeles, CA 90016
Contact: Susan Munro President
Tel: 310-586-9799
Email: diversity@hybridcollective.tv
Website: www.hybridcollective.tv
Commercial, television & motion picture post production & production services: creative editorial offline, online/compositing, color correction, graphic design, motion graphic design, sound design & mixing. (Woman, estab 2009, empl 8, sales $1,400,000, cert: WBENC)

9066   International Communication Network
901 Lane Ave, Ste 200
Chula Vista, CA 91914
Contact: Michelle Diaz COO
Tel: 619-421-0426
Email: mdiaz@inctv50.com
Website: www.Inctv50.com
Television broadcasting, video production, marketing, Hispanic market. (AA, estab 1997, empl 5, sales , cert: NMSDC)

9067   Little Minx
1758 Berkeley St
Santa Monica, CA 90404
Contact: Controller
Tel: 310-566-0536
Email:
Website: www.littleminx.tv
Commercials, independent films, branded content & high-profile music videos. (Minority, estab 2001, empl 4, sales $2,440,338, cert: CPUC)

9068   Panaloma Productions, LLC
2015 Half South Sherbourne Dr
Los Angeles, CA 90034
Contact: Rashaan Dozier-Escalante President
Tel: 424-298-0966
Email: rashaan@panalomaproductions.com
Website: www.PanalomaProductions.com
Develop & produce media, event production, films (training, PSA's, security, informational for employees & the public, documentaries) & written (training classes, SOPs, curriculums). (Woman/AA, estab 2012, empl 1, sales $150,000, cert: 8a)

9069   Pellinore Productions, Inc.
5215 Sepulveda Blvd, Unit 11D
Culver City, CA 90230
Contact: Exec Producer
Tel: 310-391-9021
Email:
Website: http://pellinore.net
Digital/video/film production & post-production, commercials, promos, videos for corporate communications, integrated marketing & branded marketing for broadcast, internet & social media. (Woman/As-Pac, estab 2009, empl , sales $823,637, cert: CPUC, WBENC)

9070 Showreel International Inc.
639 S. Glenwood Place, Ste. 200
Burbank, CA 90038
Contact: Jessica Ristic CEO
Tel: 323-464-5111
Email: jessica@weareshotglass.com
Website: www.weareshotglass.com
Film & video production. (Woman, estab 1985, empl 7, sales $ 0, cert: State)

9071 The Traveling Picture Show Company
1531 N. Cahuenga Blvd
Los Angeles, CA 90028
Contact: Partner
Tel: 323-769-1115
Email:
Website: www.thetpsc.com
Commercial video production services, television commercials, online branded content &visual media. (Minority, Woman, estab 2011, empl 9, sales $5,500,000, cert: WBENC)

9072 Total Media Group
432 N Canal St
South San Francisco, CA 94080
Contact: Megan McKenna Acct Exec
Tel: 650-583-8236
Email: megan@totalmediagroup.com
Website: www.totalmediagroup.com
Video production, motion graphics, 3D animation, editorial, event production, web design & mobile apps. (Woman, estab 1971, empl 10, sales $4,900,000, cert: WBENC)

Connecticut

9073 Anderson Productions Inc.
71 Dolphin Rd
Bristol, CT 06010
Contact: Tom Stanwicks Sales/Marketing Mgr
Tel: 503-287-3004
Email: tstanwicks@anderson3.com
Website: http://andersonprod.com
Video production, post production, graphics, animations, sound design, audio editing, product models, digital signage. (Woman, estab 1994, empl 24, sales $4,500,000, cert: WBENC)

9074 Creative Video Corporation
9 Mott Ave, Ste 108
Norwalk, CT 06850
Contact: Francisca Bogdan Production Specialist
Tel: 203-866-8700
Email: francisca.bogdan@creativevideocorp.com
Website: www.creativevideocorp.com
Corporate communication videos & multi-media products, internal communications, sales & markeitng, event opening video, promotional video, event coverage. (Woman/Hisp, estab 1997, empl 4, sales $380,000, cert: NMSDC)

Delaware

9075 DelVideo Productions
583 Barley Court
Smyrna, DE 19977
Contact: Milton Melendez VP
Tel: 302-223-4049
Email: info@delvideo.com
Website: www.delvideo.com
Bilingual video production, Pre-Production, Pre-Planning & vision writing, Location & set assessment, Research, Script writing, Talent arrangement, Recording Services, Video recording, Audio capture & recording, Project management, Directing. (Woman/AA, Hisp, estab 2013, empl 2, sales , cert: State, 8a)

Florida

9076 Campbell Advertising and Design, LLC
103 NE 4th St
Delray Beach, FL 33444
Contact: Principal
Tel: 561-562-6119
Email:
Website: www.campbellcreative.com
Photography, art direction, web videos, social content, broadcast commercials, testimonial videos, training videos, animated videos. (Woman, estab 2010, empl 6, sales $1,600,000, cert: WBENC)

9077 Coda Sound Inc.
4819 N Hale Ave
Tampa, FL 33614
Contact: Maritza Astorquiza Owner
Tel: 813-353-8151
Email: maritza@codasoundusa.com
Website: http://codasoundusa.com
Event production: sound, lights, stages & audio visual. (Woman/Hisp, estab 1998, empl 2, sales $471,000, cert: State, City, NMSDC)

9078 Graphix 360, LLC
7777 N Wickham Rd Ste 12710
Melbourne, FL 32940
Contact: Bobbi Gerardot CEO
Tel: 321-693-9293
Email: bobbi@graphix360.com
Website: www.Graphix360.com
Multimedia design, photo, video, graphic/web design & printing services, multimedia equipment. (Woman, estab 2013, empl 4, sales , cert: City)

9079 Kreative Kontent Co.
3019 Ravenswood Road Ste 110
Fort Lauderdale, FL 33312
Contact: President
Tel: 954-312-3660
Email:
Website: www.kreativekontent.com
Production specializing in content creation, broadcast, web based, theatrical & marketing fulfillment programs, broadcast commercials, corporate video communications, product placement, branded content, promotional products. (Woman, estab 2010, empl 4, sales $2,000,000, cert: State, WBENC)

Georgia

9080 A-1 Audio Visual, LLC
863 Flat Shoals Rd SE Ste C359
Conyers, GA 30094
Contact: Keith McNeil CEO
Tel: 800-805-7210
Email: kmcneil@a1audiovisual.com
Website: www.a1audiovisual.com
Audio visual, video & lighting. (AA, estab 2003, empl 6, sales $190,000, cert: State, NMSDC)

9081 Onyx Media Services, Inc.
57 Forsyth St NW Ste 250-G
Atlanta, GA 30303
Contact: Jennifer Rocke VP of Finance
Tel: 404-420-0030
Email: info@onyxmsgroup.com
Website: www.onyxmsgroup.com
Production services: audio visual, facility, technical production design, presentation video, graphic design, sound reinforcement, theatrical lighting. (AA, estab 2006, empl 15, sales $300,000, cert: NMSDC)

9082 Popoff Enterprises Inc.
3035 Wallace Circle SE
Atlanta, GA 30339
Contact: Dana Popoff President
Tel: 404-307-1979
Email: popoffdana@gmail.com
Website: http://popoffenterprises.com
Video production & still photography services, commercial distribution, web sites, point of purchase, social media, internal corporate communications - training, company meetings & conferences, President's address, legacy knowledge, etc. (Woman, estab 1997, empl 1, sales $138,750, cert: WBENC)

9083 Positive Promotions Ltd. TV
2118 Sableshire Way SE
Conyers, GA 30013
Contact: Josetta Shropshire President & CEO
Tel: 404-644-9245
Email: service@positivepromotionsltd.com
Website: www.positivepromotionsltd.com
Televison & video production services. (Woman/AA, estab , empl , sales $166,000, cert: SDB)

9084 Works of Bawbee Films
704 Brambling Way
Stockbridge, GA 30281
Contact: Brian Ezeike Video Producer
Tel: 478-390-7375
Email: info@wobfilms.com
Website: www.wobfilms.com
Video production/digital content creation, write, shoot & edit a wide variety of video content. (AA, estab 2010, empl 1, sales , cert: NMSDC)

Illinois

9085 Hootenanny LLC
230 E Ohio St Ste 700
Chicago, IL 60611
Contact: Elizabeth Tate President
Tel: 312-266-0777
Email: liz@hootenanny.tv
Website: www.hootenanny.tv
Post-production, creative editorial, finishing, graphic design & visual effects, television, print, web, corporate video & interactive media. (Woman, estab 2008, empl 11, sales $2,100,000, cert: State, WBENC)

9086 Rocket Productions Inc.
1100 W Cermak Rd Ste 301-B
Chicago, IL 60607
Contact: Hector Perez
Tel: 312-431-1040
Email: hector@rocketchicago.com
Website: www.rocketchicago.com
Video production, TV commercials, infomercials & training videos, media buying, documentaries, public service announcements (PSAs) & educational videos. (Hisp, estab 2002, empl 6, sales $258,419, cert: State)

Indiana

9087 Holloway House Productions
501 San Ricardo Court
Greenwood, IN 46142
Contact: Lisa Holloway creative visionary
Tel: 310-963-0409
Email: lisa-holloway@att.net
Website:
Full service video production. (Woman, estab 2010, empl 1, sales , cert: State)

9088 Multitek Corporate Communications
6531 Greencove Ave
Evansville, IN 47715
Contact: Earl Milligan President
Tel: 812-760-7488
Email: earl.milligan@gmail.com
Website: http://multitekcorporate.com
Corporate safety & training video production services, construction archival videos, 3 d survey mapping, drone aerial photography & videography. (AA, estab 1984, empl 1, sales , cert: State)

Massachusetts

9089 Real Cool Productions, Inc. dba RCP Learning
800 S Main St, Ste 203
Mansfield, MA 02048
Contact: President
Tel: 508-878-8907
Email:
Website: www.rcplearning.com
Integrated communications, technology & production services, internal & external facing content (mixed media, animations and videos), corporate overviews, business documentaries, executive interviews & announcements, testimonials, product videos, training (Woman, estab 2010, empl 10, sales $1,100,000, cert: WBENC)

Michigan

9090 Freshwater Film, Inc.
3061 Myddleton Court
Troy, MI 48084
Contact: CEO
Tel: 248-840-5400
Email:
Website: www.mediumfilm.com
Film & digital production, influential storytelling, relevant creative content & serious production expertise. (Woman, estab 1991, empl , sales $656,756, cert: WBENC)

9091 Seventy 7 Productions
620 Cherry Ave
Royal Oak, MI 48073
Contact: Nora Urbanski Producer
Tel: 313-610-0109
Email: nora@seventy7productions.com
Website: http://seventy7productions.com
Full service video production, post production & creative services for broadcast commercials, social media videos, 360 and VR videos, etc. (Hisp, estab 2011, empl 5, sales , cert: NMSDC)

9092 ShawneTV Inc
29558 English Way
Novi, MI 48377
Contact: CEO
Tel: 248-444-7573
Email:
Website: www.shawnetv.com
Promotional & sponsorships, media & networking training, TV production. (Woman, estab 1999, empl 2, sales $150,000, cert: WBENC)

9093 VideoWorks Production Services, Inc.
4851 Fernlee Ste 100
Royal Oak, MI 48073
Contact: Ruben Rodriguez President
Tel: 248-563-0371
Email: ruben@videoworksonline.com
Website: www.videoworksonline.com
Video production: instructional & training videos, corporate, communications, news-style event coverage, multi-camera events & live media tours. (Hisp, estab 1995, empl 2, sales $150,000, cert: NMSDC)

Minnesota

9094 Orange Filmworks Inc.
3912 Harriet Ave
Minneapolis, MN 55409
Contact: Marco Baca Owner
Tel: 612-868-7875
Email: marco@orangefilmworks.com
Website: http://orangefilmworks.com
Broadcast television commercials, videos or commercials for web, long format instructional video, internal & in-store content. (Hisp, estab 2005, empl , sales $674,623, cert: NMSDC)

9095 Peterson Productions LLC
1501 Spring Valley Rd
Golden Valley, MN 55422
Contact: Janie Peterson President
Tel: 763-521-4746
Email: janie@petersonproductionslive.com
Website: www.PetersonProductionsLive.com
Video production house for corporate communications. (Woman, estab 2007, empl 2, sales $195,000, cert: State)

9096 Slang Productions, LLC
3207 E 51st St
Minneapolis, MN 55417
Contact: Sue Lang Principal
Tel: 612-310-4622
Email: sue@slangproductions.net
Website: www.slangproductions.net
Production: live events, video, audio & interactive media. (Woman, estab 2003, empl 2, sales $200,560, cert: WBENC)

Missouri

9097 CAC REPS, LLC
5965 jamieson ave
St. Louis, MO 63109
Contact: Charlene Colombini Owner
Tel: 314-752-0994
Email: charlenecolo@hotmail.com
Website: www.cacreps.com
Design, illustration, photography, computer imaging, computer 3D Rendering, video production & post, videography & on set styling. (Minority, Woman, estab 2008, empl 1, sales , cert: State, CPUC)

9098 Haller Concepts, Inc.
4501 Mattis Rd
St Louis, MO 63128
Contact: Mike Haller President
Tel: 314-913-5626
Email: mikeh@hallerconcepts.com
Website: http://hallerconcepts.com
Corporate, event, training, web & TV video production filming. (Woman, estab 1982, empl 2, sales $174,400, cert: State)

New Jersey

9099 Harlan Media LLC
494 Broad St, Ste 104
Newark, NJ 07102
Contact: Harlan Brandon CEO
Tel: 973-623-6200
Email: hb@harlanmedia.com
Website: http://harlanmedia.com
Film & Video Production, Marketing, Advertising, Public Relations, Graphic Design, Independent Artist and Writers, Direct Mail Advertising, Commercial Photography (AA, estab 2008, empl 8, sales , cert: NMSDC)

9100 KVibe Productions, LLC
591 Summit Ave Ste 101
Jersey City, NJ 07306
Contact: Khoa Le CEO
Tel: 201-936-8033
Email: khoa.le@kvibe.com
Website: www.kvibe.com
Video production, product video, corporate video, commercial production, feature films. (As-Pac, estab 2005, empl 2, sales $ 0, cert: State)

9101 Modat Productions
29 Windermere Rd
Montclair, NJ 07043
Contact: Amy Scott Founder
Tel: 201-763-6666
Email: shana@modat.tv
Website: www.mOdat.tv
Full service video production, digital and broadcast content for television, businesses, social media and the government with end to end production. (Woman, estab 2010, empl 5, sales $300,000, cert: State, WBENC)

New York

9102 Adrienne Nicole Productions, LLC
14 Dekalb Ave 3rd Fl
Brooklyn, NY 11201
Contact: Adrienne Nicole Exec Producer
Tel: 646-599-4911
Email: info@producedbyanp.com
Website: www.producedbyanp.com
Videography, aerial video, drone video photography, drone photography, progress photos, story development, pre-production, post-production, motion graphics and animation, casting, photography, progress photos. (Woman/AA, estab 2011, empl , sales $986,000, cert: State, City, NMSDC)

9103 Amber Heavenly USA, Ltd.
250 Lafayette St 4th Fl
New York, NY 10012
Contact: Michelle Curran President
Tel: 212-352-1888
Email: michelle@ambermusic.com
Website: www.ambermusic.com
Commercial music production, composition, music licensing & publishing. (Woman, estab 1997, empl 7, sales $1,400,000, cert: State, WBENC)

9104 Bardin Palomo Ltd.
432 W 19th St Ste 3
New York, NY 10011
Contact: Robert Palomo President
Tel: 212-989-6113
Email: rrpalomo@bardinpalomo.com
Website: www.bardinpalomo.com
Special Events design and production company specializing in floral design, lighting design, stage design, prop and furniture rental. We sdesign and supply all visuals for any type of event. (Hisp, estab 1992, empl 5, sales $3,200,000, cert: NMSDC)

9105 Be Real Company
114 W 26th St, Fl 8
New York, NY 10001
Contact: CEO
Tel: 551-574-7006
Email:
Website: http://berealcompany.com
Integrated creative & production services: Live Action Shoots: commercials, documentaries, social videos, branded content Post-Production: editing, CGI, color correction, animation, music composing and mix, websites. (Woman, estab 2017, empl 5, sales $100,000, cert: WBENC)

9106 Cutter Productions
236 W 27th St Ste 1001
New York, NY 10001
Contact: Hillary Cutter Exec Producer
Tel: 646-588-1133
Email: hillary@cutterproductions.com
Website: www.cutterproductions.com
Full-service production. (Woman, estab 2005, empl 4, sales , cert: WBENC)

9107 Loftin Productions
104 Belmont Pkwy
Hempstead, NY 11550
Contact: Dushka Petkovich Co-Owner
Tel: 917-825-5412
Email: vze26rdi@verizon.net
Website: www.loftinpro.com/
Produce product demonstration & employee training videos. (Woman/AA, estab 1991, empl 2, sales , cert: State)

9108 MaRY NITTOLO, INC., DBA the STUDIO
80- 8th Ave Ste 307
New York, NY 10011
Contact: Mary Nittolo CEO
Tel: 212-661-1363
Email: mary@studionyc.com
Website: www.studionyc.com
Art & animation studio, 3d/2d animation, motion capture, animatics, pre-vis, storyboards, presentation art, digital art, comps & character design. (Woman/AA, As-Pac, Hisp, estab 1988, empl 30, sales $3,500,000, cert: WBENC)

9109 Media2, Inc. dba M2
72 Madison Ave, Fl 2
New York, NY 10016
Contact: Cathy Humphrey Producer
Tel: 212-213-4004
Email: cathy@m2nyc.tv
Website: www.m2nyc.tv
Creative offline editorial, 2D/3D design & animation, television & live event production, install digital & high definition production studios, monitors, cameras & lighting. (AA, Hisp, estab 1997, empl 10, sales $25,000,000, cert: NMSDC)

9110 Resilient Media
      10 E 39th St, 4th Fl
      New York, NY 10016
      Contact: Emilio Mahomar CEO
      Tel: 646-580-9391
      Email: emilio@resilient.tv
      Website: www.resilient.tv
Production, post production, duplication & language
localization (translation, closed captions, subtitles, language dubbing). (Hisp, estab 2010, empl 2, sales $200,000,
cert: NMSDC)

9111 TimeLine Video
      One Bridge St
      Irvington, NY 10533
      Contact: Timothy Englert VP Development
      Tel: 914-591-7360
      Email: tim@timelinevideo.com
      Website: www.timelinevideo.com
Video, production & post-production, graphic design.
(Woman, estab 1994, empl 7, sales $1,700,000, cert:
WBENC)

9112 Transcendent Enterprise
      37 W 26th St, Ste 408
      New York, NY 10010
      Contact: Chris Alvarez CEO
      Tel: 718-304-6384
      Email: chris@t-enter.com
      Website: http://transcendententerprise.com
Video production, live stream services, post production,
editing & filming, photography. (Woman/AA, As-Pac, Hisp,
estab 2004, empl 4, sales $230,000, cert: City, NMSDC)

9113 VMIX, LLC.
      163 William St, 3 Fl
      New York, NY 10038
      Contact: Wening Cintron relationship Mgr
      Tel: 800-436-8618
      Email: wening@vmix.tv
      Website: www.vmix.tv
Digital media, audio/visual (A/V) content, music, television
& urban entertainment. (AA, estab 2004, empl 2, sales ,
cert: State)

9114 Wild Child Editorial, Inc.
      44 West 28th St
      New York, NY 10001
      Contact: Scott Spanjich Managing Dir
      Tel: 212-725-5333
      Email: scott@wildchildpost.com
      Website: www.wildchildpost.com
TV commercials, music videos, feature films & emerging
media. (Woman/Hisp, estab , empl , sales $4,500,000, cert:
WBENC)

Ohio

9115 New Vision Media Inc.
      6804 Caine Rd
      Columbus, OH 43235
      Contact: Jerrud Smith Co-Owner
      Tel: 614-222-0966
      Email: jsmith@newvisionmediainc.com
      Website: http://newvisionmediainc.com
Video production services including aerial drone cinema-
tography. (AA, estab 2000, empl 3, sales $350,000, cert:
NMSDC)

Pennsylvania

9116 Crossover Ent. LLC
      728 Copeland St
      Pittsburgh, PA 15232
      Contact: Freya Saxon Producer
      Tel: 651-347-3831
      Email: fs@deepcea.com
      Website: www.deepcea.com
Script to screen production, Corporate Videos, Training
Videos, Commercials, Film & Documentaries. (AA, estab
2014, empl 14, sales , cert: State)

9117 Karasch & Associates
      1646 W Chester Pike Ste 4
      West Chester, PA 19382
      Contact: Edward Sarkissian Sales Mgr
      Tel: 800-621-5689
      Email: esarkissian@karasch.com
      Website: www.karasch.com
Video production, duplications & captioning services.
(Woman, estab 1980, empl 25, sales $4,000,000, cert:
State, WBENC)

9118 Panta Rhei Media, Inc.
      565 Beulah Rd
      Turtle Creek, PA 15145
      Contact: Martha O'Grady President
      Tel: 412-824-8858
      Email: info@panta-rhei.com
      Website: www.panta-rhei.com
Video production with a specialty in health care,
product demonstration and promotion, web testimonials, employee communications and streaming live
events, consultation, concepts, script writing, location
and studio video. (Woman, estab 1984, empl , sales $
0, cert: WBENC)

South Carolina

9119 Mad Monkey, Inc.
      1631 Main St
      Columbia, SC 29201
      Contact: Lorie Gardner CEO
      Tel: 803-252-2211
      Email: lorie@gomadmonkey.com
      Website: www.gomadmonkey.com
Creates video stories for television, laptops, mobile
devices & social platforms. (Woman, estab 2000, empl
15, sales $1,650,351, cert: State, WBENC)

9120 Red Heritage Media, LLC
      1974 Carolina Place, Ste 200C
      Fort Mill, SC 29708
      Contact: Gerry Martin Exec Producer
      Tel: 803-792-7331
      Email: gerry@redheritagemedia.com
      Website: www.redheritagemedia.com
Content creation, film, documentary, commercial &
episodic television production industry. (Nat Ame, estab
2015, empl 3, sales , cert: 8a)

Texas

9121 1820 Productions, LLC
6301 N Riverside Dr Bldg One, Ste 2C
Irving, TX 75039
Contact: Sara Madsen Miller COO
Tel: 972-869-7777
Email: sara@1820productions.com
Website: www.1820productions.com
Television & film production, creative concept development, producing, directing, editing, graphics and animation, marketing, script writing, industrial or marketing videos from script to screen. (AA, estab 2001, empl 5, sales $1,012,000, cert: State, NMSDC)

9122 Abernethy Media Professionals, Inc.
10763 Sanden Dr
DALLAS, TX 75355
Contact: SANDY MASON ABERNETHY President
Tel: 214-632-4518
Email: mason@ampcreative.com
Website: www.ampcreative.com
Video production services. (Woman, estab 2002, empl 25, sales $4,021,000, cert: State, WBENC)

9123 Cactex Media
2231 Valdina St, Unit 100
Dallas, TX 75207
Contact: Head of Business Devel
Tel: 214-346-3456
Email:
Website: www.cactexmedia.com
Video & Interactive production, video production, B2B videos, Web video, Webcast/live stream, Sales tools, Explainer videos, Training videos, Executive interviews, Customer testimonials, Case studies. (Woman, estab 2006, empl 14, sales $4,000,000, cert: State, WBENC)

9124 CM Productions, Inc.
4228 North Central Expressway Ste 340
Dallas, TX 75206
Contact: Carrie Martinez President & CEO
Tel: 214-528-2700
Email: carrie@cmproductions.tv
Website: www.cmproductions.tv
Video production, employee & marketing communications, documentaries, commercials, scriptwriting, stunning photography & sharp editing, still photography. (Woman, estab , empl , sales $194,628, cert: WBENC)

9125 IS Productions, Inc.
1957 E Irving Blvd
Irving, TX 75060
Contact: President
Tel: 214-924-6481
Email:
Website: www.i-s-p.net
Teleproduction, graphic design services, motion picture & video production. (Woman/Hisp, estab 1998, empl 3, sales $700,000, cert: State, WBENC)

9126 Julye Newlin Productions, Inc.
129 E 13th St
Houston, TX 77008
Contact: Owner
Tel: 713-869-3609
Email:
Website: www.julyenewlin.com
Video, film & photography services: digital video, digital editing, web, broadcast, print advertising, CD business cards, DVD presentations, etc. (Woman, estab 1993, empl 3, sales $ 0, cert: City, WBENC)

9127 Small Pond Video Productions, Inc.
2217 Clarebrooke Dr.
Grand Prairie, TX 75050
Contact: Silvana Rosero President & CEO
Tel: 214-686-1092
Email: silvana@lagunamg.com
Website: www.lagunamg.com
Video production & meeting support, marketing, motivational, product introductions, testimonials, training videos & broadcast commercials. (Woman/Hisp, estab , empl , sales $178,412, cert: State, NMSDC, WBENC)

9128 Sue Abrams Productions, LLC
2709 Prestonwood Dr
Plano, TX 75093
Contact: Sue Abrams Owner
Tel: 972-418-2034
Email: sue@saproductions.net
Website: www.saproductions.net
Video production: sales pieces, public education videos, corporate overviews, recruiting videos, commercials, training pieces, product launches, event videos & video news releases. (Woman, estab 1999, empl 1, sales $152,620, cert: WBENC)

9129 ZapBoomBang Studios, LLC
3336 Richmond Ave
Houston, TX 77098
Contact: Catherine Lopez Negrete
Tel: 713-877-8777
Email: cathy@zapboombang.com
Website: www.zapboombang.com
Audio, Video Post Production Services (Woman, estab 0, empl , sales $ 0, cert: WBENC)

Virginia

9130 Chitra Productions, LLC
4873 S Oliver Dr Ste 100
Virginia Beach, VA 23455
Contact: Vibhaa Vermani CEO
Tel: 757-495-0234
Email: vibhaa@chitraproductions.com
Website: www.chitraproductions.com
Education & training support, research & development, administration & management support, logistics & scheduling, information technology, professional support services, engineering support services, graphics & multimedia support. (Woman/As-Ind, estab 2008, empl 80, sales $8,921,613, cert: 8a)

Washington

9131 Native Ways LLC - Apachewolf Productions
15313 NE 13th Place
Bellevue, WA 98008
Contact: Freddie Begay CEO
Tel: 360-930-9615
Email: chipbegay@gmail.com
Website: www.apachewolf.com
Video productions, video shooting & editing services,
develop & create television & radio commercials, video
streaming, DVD & CD duplication, Radio/TV broadcast
development & marketing. (Minority, estab 2015, empl 1,
sales , cert: State, SDB)

TELECOMMUNICATIONS

Manufacture and distribute telecommunications systems and products: CATV, telephones, intercoms, test and control equipment, etc. Includes firms which provide cellular and internet services, phone line installation, service and consulting. NAICS Code 51

Alabama

9132 Palco Telecom Service Inc.
2914 Green Cove Rd
Huntsville, AL 35803
Contact: President
Tel: 256-527-0213
Email:
Website: www.gotopalco.com
Telecommunications: logistics, forward & reverse, technical product repair upgrade & remanufacture, warranty fulfillment. (Woman, estab 1986, empl 250, sales $17,193,208, cert: WBENC)

Arizona

9133 Denali Telecom Solutions, Inc.
6524 S McAllister Ave
Tempe, AZ 85283
Contact: Karen Tynan CEO
Tel: 855-239-7776
Email: karen.tynan@denalicorp.com
Website: www.denalicorp.com
Mfr telecommunications products & value added service solutions for Broadband & Network Projects. (Woman/As-Pac, estab 2013, empl 4, sales $1,000,000, cert: WBENC)

9134 Native Technology Solutions Inc.
7065 W Allison Rd
Chandler, AZ 85226
Contact: Mabel Tsosie
Tel: 480-639-1234
Email: mtsosie@gilarivertel.com
Website: http://native-tech.net
Cabling & computing services, structured cabling, phone, security systems, video conferencing, & technology solutions. (Nat Ame, estab 2007, empl 14, sales $4,000,000, cert: State)

9135 Tower Safety and Instruction
3620 S 40th St
Phoenix, AZ 85040
Contact: Kathy Brand CEO
Tel: 480-313-0678
Email: kathy@towersafety.com
Website: www.towersafety.com
Safety School for the Wireless/Crane Industry, Wireless & Microwave, Construction & Telecommunications-Fiber Optics/Copper Installation & Testing, Project Management, Installation, Telecommunications Maintenance & Testing. (Woman, estab 2013, empl 8, sales , cert: WBENC)

California

9136 Aponi Products and Services
3805 Florin Rd Ste 1228
Sacramento, CA 95823
Contact: Lisa M Davis Iacy Owner
Tel: 916-392-6571
Email: lisad@aponitelecommunication.com
Website: http://aponitelecom.com
Telecommunication Equipment, Installation, Voice, Data, Cabling, Maintenance, Repair, Security System, DVR, Security Cameras. (Nat Ame, estab 2007, empl 7, sales $360,000, cert: State, 8a)

9137 Business Communications Solutions
9910 Irvine Center Dr
Irvine, CA 92618
Contact: Afsaneh Rajab CEO
Tel: 949-333-1000
Email: srajab@bcsconsultants.com
Website: www.bcsconsultants.com
Telecommunication & networking: phone systems, internet & telephone services, cabling, networking, & server room design & installation. (Minority, Woman, estab 2001, empl 15, sales $3,700,000, cert: State)

9138 Cico Electrical Contractors Inc.
365 Whipporwill Dr
Riverside, CA 92507
Contact: Ron Veloz Office Mgr
Tel: 951-213-2229
Email: ron.veloz@cicoele.com
Website: www.cicoele.com
Electrical, Electrical Subcontractor, New Construction, Remodeling, Renovations, Improvements-Relocations, Maintenance, Switchgear Change out, Critical Power-UPS, Generators, Predictive Maintenance (circuit (Hisp, estab 2004, empl 25, sales $4,464,384, cert: NMSDC)

9139 Clean Sweep Group Inc
8306 Wilshire Blvd Ste 7009
Beverly Hills, CA 90211
Contact: Leo Williams, II CEO
Tel: 310-985-0504
Email: leo.williams@csgiusa.com
Website: http://csgiusa.com
We are a veteran minority business enterprise. We provide an ultraviolet light disinfection and education service which greatly reduces the threat of hospital acquired infections and their increased costs and safety risks. (AA, estab 2011, empl 16, sales , cert: NMSDC)

9140 Coast to Coast Communications
34145 Pacific Coast Hwy 635
Dana Point, CA 92629
Contact: Nikki Clark Natl Sales Mgr
Tel: 949-481-6550
Email: nikki@c2ccomm.com
Website: www.c2ccomm.com
Voice, data cabling & phone systems. (Woman, estab 2000, empl 10, sales $5,040,175, cert: WBENC)

9141 DataOptek Corp.
573 E Fairview Blvd, Ste 2
Inglewood, CA 90302
Contact: Roderick Byrd Business Dev Mgr
Tel: 310-367-2826
Email: rbyrd@dataoptek.com
Website: www.dataoptek.com
Structured cabling, LAN, WAN, VoIP, wireline, wireless network infrastructure installations & maintenance. (AA, estab 1999, empl 10, sales $300,000, cert: NMSDC)

9142   E-3 Systems
       1220 Whipple Rd
       Union City, CA 94587
       Contact: Kofi Tawiah President
       Tel: 510-487-7393
       Email: kofi@e3systems.com
       Website: www.e3systems.com
Low voltage voice & data structured cabling, electronic
security systems & telecom. (AA, estab 1989, empl 58,
sales $3,900,000, cert: NMSDC, CPUC)

9143   GovMobile, LLC
       120 Vantis, Ste 300
       Aliso Viejo, CA 92656
       Contact: Lambert Matias President
       Tel: 949-505-9600
       Email: lmatias@govmobile.com
       Website: www.govmobile.com
Mobility, Wireless & Internet of Things (IoT)solutions. (As-
Pac, estab 2013, empl 2, sales $1,200,000, cert: 8a)

9144   Herca Telecomm Services Inc
       18610 Beck St
       Perris, CA 92570
       Contact: Hector Castellon CEO
       Tel: 951-940-5941
       Email: hector.castellon@hercatelecomm.com
       Website: www.hercatelecomm.com
Tower erection, lines & antennas, microwave, general
construction, excavation, trenching, electrical, concrete,
demolition. (Hisp, estab 2005, empl 29, sales $4,035,556,
cert: State)

9145   JM Fiber Optics, Inc.
       13941 Ramona Ave Ste A
       Chino, CA 91710
       Contact: Marlene Vidana Business Develop Mgr
       Tel: 909-628-3445
       Email: mvidana@jmfiberoptics.com
       Website: http://jmfiberoptics.com
Fiber optic & copper voice, video & data communication
systems, transit system passenger information systems &
intrusion dectection systems. (Hisp, estab 1992, empl 8,
sales $5,701,490, cert: State, City, NMSDC, CPUC, SDB)

9146   Pinnacle Telecommunications, Inc. (PTI Solutions)
       4242 Forcum Ave, Ste 200
       McClellan, CA 95652
       Contact: Accounts Payable Marketing Program Mgr
       Tel: 916-426-1046
       Email: ap@pti-s.com
       Website: www.pti-s.com
Install communications cabling & equipment, cell tower
upgrades, structured wire, WiFi & laser communications.
(Woman, estab 1984, empl 140, sales $17,000,000, cert:
CPUC, WBENC)

9147   Rincon Technology
       810 East Montecito St
       Santa Barbara, CA 93103
       Contact: Mike Bartling Founder EVP Sales
       Tel: 805-319-7830
       Email: mbartling@rincontechnology.com
       Website: www.rincontechnology.com
Wireless transmission gear T1 to 3DS3 capacity, native
Ethernet/IP backhaul, up to 800mbps transmission,
wireless SONET backhaul. (Hisp, estab 2003, empl 45, sales
$55,000,000, cert: State, NMSDC)

9148   Serene Innovations
       14731 Carmenita Rd
       Norwalk, CA 90650
       Contact: James McGehee Sales Coord
       Tel: 562-407-5400
       Email: j.mcgehee@sereneinnovations.com
       Website: www.sereneinnovations.com/
Amplified Phones, TV Listening Devices, Ringer/Flasher,
Alerting Notification System, Telephone Amplifier. (As-
Pac, estab 2004, empl 15, sales $3,000,000, cert:
NMSDC)

9149   Tempest Telecom Solutions, LLC
       136 W Canon Perdido Ste 100
       Santa Barbara, CA 93101
       Contact: Elda Rudd VP Marketing
       Tel: 805-879-4800
       Email: tempestsupplier@tempesttelecom.com
       Website: www.tempesttelecom.com
New & refurbished networking equipment. (Woman,
estab 2005, empl 160, sales , cert: CPUC, WBENC)

9150   Unified TelData Inc.
       425 2nd St
       San Francisco, CA 94107
       Contact: Eric Clauss GSS
       Tel: 415-977-7031
       Email: eclauss@utdi.com
       Website: www.utdi.com
Communications solutionsL Avaya, Cisco & Nortel
hardware & services. (Woman, estab 1981, empl 50,
sales $10,000,000, cert: CPUC, 8a)

9151   Universal Network Development Corp.
       2555 Third St Ste 112
       Sacramento, CA 95818
       Contact: Cinthia Larkin Kazee President
       Tel: 916-475-1200
       Email: undc@undc.com
       Website: www.undc.com
Telecommunication eng, fiber optic & copper splicing,
installation & repair, project mgmt, CAD drafting.
(Woman/As-Pac, estab 1980, empl 75, sales $4,234,625,
cert: CPUC, WBENC)

9152   WP Electric & Communications, Inc.
       14198 Albers Way
       Chino, CA 91710
       Contact: President
       Tel: 909-606-3510
       Email:
       Website: www.wpelectric.com
Electrical & network cabling services. (Woman, estab
1975, empl 45, sales $7,800,000, cert: CPUC, WBENC)

Colorado

9153   M.R. Research
       8003 S Corona Way
       Centennial, CO 80122
       Contact: Madeline K. Reilly President
       Tel: 303-795-4353
       Email: rkreilly@aol.com
       Website: www.m-r-research.com
Applied research, electronic design & telecommunications components for satellites, base stations & mobile
wireless systems. (Woman/Hisp, estab 2010, empl 4,
sales $334,900, cert: NMSDC)

9154 Sage Telecommunications Corp.
6700 Race St
Denver, CO 80229
Contact: President
Tel: 303-227-0986
Email:
Website: www.sagecom.net
Engineers, build & maintain fiber optic, cable & other networks. (Woman, estab 1992, empl 90, sales $10,000,000, cert: State)

9155 Tripwireless, Inc.
4941 Allison St Ste 7 & 8
Arvada, CO 80022
Contact: CEO
Tel: 720-361-4998
Email:
Website: www.tripwireless.com
Network infrastructure equipment & services, cell sites, microwave, outside power plant, transmission, routers, data centers, de-commissioning, trenching, fiber, installation & preventative maintenance. (Woman, estab 2005, empl 6, sales , cert: WBENC)

Connecticut

9156 IQ Telcom, LLC dba IQ Telecom
78 Beaver Road
Wethersfield, CT 06109
Contact: Carol Guerra Dir Business Devel
Tel: 860-882-0500
Email: carol.guerra@iqt360.com
Website: https://iqt360.com
Telecommunications expense: voice, data & wireless, audit, optimization, spend base lining, invoice processing, monthly reporting for cost allocation, vendor/carrier mgmt; contract negotiation, network design & optimization. (Woman, estab 2001, empl 35, sales $3,000,000, cert: State, WBENC)

9157 VisionPoint LLC
152 Rockwell Rd
Newington, CT 06111
Contact: Louise Mastroianni Acct Mgr, Diversity Champion
Tel: 860-436-9673
Email: visionpointct@gmail.com
Website: www.visionpointllc.com
Technology acquisition, integration, design, installation, technical meeting support & service. (Woman, estab 2003, empl 24, sales $7,002,015, cert: WBENC)

District of Columbia

9158 MJS Communications LLC
1343 First St NW
Washington, DC 20001
Contact: Marlon Boykin President
Tel: 888-829-1658
Email: mboykin@mjscommunications.biz
Website: www.mjscommunications.biz
Information technology, telecommunications services, structure cabling system, voice/data cabling, CCTV cabling, POS & wireless, CCTV, digital video recorders, Interior/exterior cameras, monitors, perimeter security. (AA, estab 2009, empl 2, sales $110,000, cert: State, City)

9159 National Fiber and Copper, Inc.
1701 Pennsylvania Ave NW Ste 300
Washington, DC 20006
Contact: Kimberly Valentine President
Tel: 202-729-6339
Email: kimvalentine@nationalfiberandcopper.com
Website: www.nationalfiberandcopper.com
Low-voltage communication installation & services, communications, structured cabling, fiber optics, network installation & management, VOIP, phone systems, security solutions, on-site & support services. (Woman, estab 1999, empl 10, sales $1,350,000, cert: City, WBENC, SDB)

9160 Tecknomic LLC
2322 First St NW
Washington, DC 20001
Contact: Dexter Spencer President
Tel: 202-829-2953
Email: dspencer@tecknomic.com
Website: www.tecknomic.com
Emergency management & services training, information technology, wireless/wireline communications. (AA, estab 2003, empl 12, sales $391,000, cert: State, 8a)

Florida

9161 Advanced IT Concepts, Inc.
1351 Sundial Point
Winter Springs, FL 32708
Contact: Gabriel Ruiz President
Tel: 407-914-2484
Email: eve.maldonado@aitcinc.com
Website: www.aitcinc.com
Telecommunications & Information Technology services. (Hisp, estab 2006, empl 51, sales $24,860,693, cert: City, 8a)

9162 Call One Inc
400 Imperial Blvd
Cape Canaveral, FL 32920
Contact: Kris Torres Acct Mgr
Tel: 800-749-3160
Email: ktorres@calloneonline.com
Website: www.calloneonline.com
Dist telecommunications equipment: audio video teleconferencing & headsets. (Woman, estab 1987, empl 65, sales , cert: WBENC)

9163 Cell Antenna
12453 NW 44th St
Coral Springs, FL 33065
Contact: Barbara Melamed Owner
Tel: 954-340-7053
Email: barbara@cellantenna.com
Website: www.cellantenna.com
Signal enhancement using Distributed Antenna Systems for cell phone carriers (AT&T, Verizon, T-Mobile and Sprint) (Woman, estab 2002, empl 21, sales $8,000,000, cert: State)

9164 ClearTone Communications Inc.
840 Edgewood Ave S, Ste 209
Jacksonville, FL 32205
Contact: Jerry Irizarry President
Tel: 904-240-0490
Email: jerry@cleartonejax.com
Website: www.cleartonejax.com
Telecommunications, voice, data & structured cabling. (Hisp, estab 2007, empl 1, sales , cert: State)

9165 Data Stream Mobile Technologies Inc.
11521 Interchange Circle S
Miramar, FL 33025
Contact: New Business Devel
Tel: 954-271-1240
Email:
Website: www.dswltech.net/
Wireless communications, cable, twisted pair, & fiber optics. (AA, estab 1998, empl 42, sales , cert: State, NMSDC)

9166 Data Voice, Inc.
1900 S Harbor City Blvd, Ste 124
Melbourne, FL 32901
Contact: Amanda Mktg Coord
Tel: 321-724-1231
Email: amanda@data-voice.net
Website: www.data-voice.net
Telecommunications, electronic communications system, structured cabling, hardware, software, peripherals, electronic mfg. (AA, estab 1989, empl 40, sales $4,290,000, cert: State)

9167 FermiTron, Inc.
440 Plumosa Ave Ste 1020
Casselberry, FL 32707
Contact: Guilford Cantave President & CEO
Tel: 407-513-2716
Email: gcantave@fermitron.com
Website: https://fermitron.com
Commercial, industrial, medical & military/aerospace development; R&D, Analog & Digital Circuit Design, Firmware Development & Implementation, Schematic Capture, PCB Layout, RF, Wireless, Circuit Prototyping & Assembly. (AA, estab 2012, empl 6, sales $310,000, cert: State)

9168 Satya Acquisition Management, Inc. dba SAM, Inc.
3300 South OBT Ste 106
Orlando, FL 32839
Contact: Bob Chopra President
Tel: 267-973-4228
Email: bchopra@sam-inc.com
Website: www.sam-inc.com
Telecommunications, new site builds, antenna modifications, generator installations, microwave installations, temporary cell site installations, small cells & Distributed Antenna Systems. (As-Pac, estab 2006, empl 2, sales $350,000, cert: NMSDC)

9169 SENCOMMUNICATIONS, INC.
9208 FLORIDA PALM DRIVE
Tampa, FL 33619
Contact: STACIE MILLER CEO
Tel: 813-626-4404
Email: rgeneral@sencomm.com
Website: www.sencomm.com
Provides telephone headsets, desksets, teleconferencing units, and other products. (Woman, estab 1989, empl 16, sales $14,528,491, cert: WBENC)

9170 Smith Corona/Comfort Telecommunications
1407 SE 47th Terr
Cape Coral, FL 33904
Contact: Louise Bergen Sales
Tel: 800-399-3224
Email: louise@comfortel.com
Website: www.comfortel.com
Mfr & dist telephone headsets & accessories. (Woman, estab 1985, empl 15, sales $5,000,000, cert: State)

9171 TSG Enterprises, LLC dba RadiusPoint
1211 State Rd436, Ste 295
Casselberry, FL 32707
Contact: CEO
Tel: 407-661-6840
Email:
Website: www.radiuspoint.com
Telecommunications & utility invoices auditing, expense management & bill processing. (Woman, estab 1992, empl 42, sales , cert: WBENC)

9172 USA Telecom Solutions
2700 W Cypress Creek Rd Ste D100
Fort Lauderdale, FL 33309
Contact: President
Tel: 954-970-0098
Email:
Website: www.usatelecomsolutions.com
Telecommunications services & business technology solutions. (AA, estab 2003, empl 5, sales , cert: NMSDC)

Georgia

9173 Agile Perspective
27 Edwin Pl
Atlanta, GA 30318
Contact: Rae-Anne Alves
Tel: 917-648-7544
Email: rae-anne.alves@anagileperspective.com
Website: www.anagileperspective.com
Telecommunication sourcing, cost reduction initiatives, strategic management, best practice benchmarking, technology integration. (Woman/AA, Hisp, estab 2012, empl 1, sales , cert: NMSDC, WBENC)

9174 Atlanta Communications Co.
1510 Huber St
Atlanta, GA 30318
Contact: Carrie Davis Exec Asst
Tel: 404-875-9316
Email: cdavis@atlantacomm.com
Website: www.atlantacomm.com
Dist, service, install, rent, site preparation & project management of two-way communications equipment. (Woman/AA, estab 1947, empl 43, sales , cert: WBENC)

9175 Concise, Inc.
191 Peachtree St, Ste 3300
Atlanta, GA 30303
Contact: David Johnson CEO
Tel: 404-736-3669
Email: info@conciseinc.com
Website: www.conciseinc.com
Telecommunications svcs: network & telephone cabling, wireless networks, surveillance & security systems. (AA, estab 2003, empl 2, sales $560,000, cert: NMSDC, 8a)

9176 Digicomm Systems, Inc.
3221 Hill St, Ste 103-B
Duluth, GA 30096
Contact: Undra Patrick VP Operations
Tel: 770-497-8080
Email: management@digicommsystems.com
Website: www.digicommsystems.com
Telecommunication services: data center design & consulting, data network design & consulting, systems integration & installation, internal communications, low-voltage cabling, equipment relocation. (Woman/AA, estab 1988, empl 7, sales , cert: City, NMSDC)

9177 FamTeck, LLC
4484 Covington Hwy, Ste 105
Decatur, GA 30038
Contact: Conrad Meertins CEO
Tel: 404-822-1117
Email: cmeertins@famteck.com
Website: www.famteck.com
FamTeck leverages new technologies and mobility to
provide next generation applications to meet today's
challenges. We develop solutions that provide optimal
performance allowing you to do more with less.Core
Competencies•Streamline IT Operations with Pre (AA,
estab 2006, empl 7, sales , cert: NMSDC)

9178 HYPEFAN
3560 Morning Ivy Way
Suwanee, GA 30024
Contact: Derrick Brown CEO
Tel: 404-217-7933
Email: ds@hypefan.com
Website: www.hypefan.com
No Cheerstix! No Thunderstix! No foam hands! Bring the
HYPE with HypeSticks . There is nothing quite like the
HypeStick, with 6 distinct areas of real estate for cross-
marketing opportunities, two faces on the main, two on
the handle, a lanyard can be at (AA, estab 2004, empl 3,
sales , cert: NMSDC)

9179 Litra Manufacturing Inc.
6733-A Jones Mill Ct
Norcross, GA 30092
Contact: Skip York Sales Mgr
Tel: 800-445-4617
Email: skipyork@litramfg.com
Website: www.litramfg.com
Mfr copper & pre-terminated fiber optic cable assemblies:
coax, multipair copper cable assemblies, high strand fiber
assemblies, single-mode, multi-mode, fiber jumpers,
components & accessories. (Woman, estab 1986, empl 25,
sales , cert: CPUC)

9180 Norris Sapp, Inc.
2469 Winshire Dr
Decatur, GA 30035
Contact: Norris Sapp President
Tel: 770-593-3762
Email: norrissapp@hotmail.com
Website: www.norrissappinc.com
Freight transportation : general supplies, construction,
heavy equipment, building materials, hazardous materials,
less than truckload, and courrier services. (AA, estab 1996,
empl 3, sales $5,005,000, cert: State)

9181 North Georgia Telecom, Inc.
1755 Enterprise Dr Ste D
Buford, GA 30518
Contact:
Tel: 678-482-0015
Email:
Website: www.ngtinc.com
Install, deinstall, switching sales, asset mgmt. (Woman,
estab 1994, empl 20, sales , cert: WBENC)

9182 ProComm Telecommunications, Inc.
1377 Business Center Dr
Conyers, GA 30094
Contact: VP Operations
Tel: 770-760-8660
Email:
Website: www.procommtelecom.com
Installation, engineering & design telecommunications
networks: wireless, fiber optics, digital cross connects,
switch, multiplexer & channel bank, calibrate & repair
test equipment. (Woman, estab 1989, empl 55, sales
$7,000,000, cert: WBENC)

9183 Washington Communications Group LLC
6465 Hwy 85
Riverdale, GA 30274
Contact: Stacy Washington President
Tel: 770-991-3000
Email: washingtoncommunication@yahoo.com
Website: http://washingtoncommunication.com
Structured Network Cabling, Fiber Optic Installation,
Single mode, Multimode, Fiber Optic Testing & Termina-
tions, Voice/Data Network Installation, Business & VoIP
Phone Systems, Patch panel installation & termination.
(AA, estab 2013, empl 10, sales $190,000, cert: State)

Illinois

9184 Chicago Communications, LLC
200 W Spangler Ave
Elmhurst, IL 60126
Contact: Lisa MacGillivray Mktg Dir
Tel: 630-832-3311
Email: sales@chicomm.com
Website: www.chicomm.com
Dist, install & maintain communication equipment.
(Woman, estab 2004, empl 68, sales $10,000,000, cert:
State, WBENC)

9185 ClearSounds Communication
1743 Quincy Ave, Ste 155
Naperville, IL 60540
Contact: Michelle Maher Dir of sales/ops
Tel: 866-657-2855
Email: michelle.maher@clearsounds.com
Website: www.clearsounds.com
Amplified phones, Bluetooth headsets, amplified
neckloops, mobile accessories & listening systems for
people with hearing loss and those looking for a remark-
able listening experience. (Woman, estab 2004, empl 15,
sales , cert: WBENC)

9186 Integrated Installations, inc.
514 Pratt Ave N
Schaumburg, IL 60193
Contact: Kate Novelle Contracts/Sales Dir
Tel: 847-985-1170
Email: kate@i3install.com
Website: www.i3install.com
Telecom installation services, Wireless & Wireline
Industries. (Woman, estab 2000, empl 25, sales
$2,330,161, cert: State, City, WBENC, SDB)

9187   Level-(1) Global Solutions, LLC
233 S. Wacker Dr 84th Fl
Chicago, IL 60606
Contact: CEO
Tel: 312-202-3300
Email:
Website: www.level-1.com
Infrastructure solutions: office technology & data ctr facilities, IDF/telecom infrastructure, UPS power protection, emergency generator power, HVAC enviromental systems, fire protection, security & access control, CATV & LAN/WAN video surveillance. (AA, estab 2001, empl 25, sales $1,800,000, cert: City)

9188   Phoenix Business Solutions LLC
12543 S Laramie Ave
Alsip, IL 60803
Contact: Peggy Hrindak CEO
Tel: 708-388-1330
Email: phrindak@getpbsnow.com
Website: www.getpbsnow.com
Design, install & maintain telecom & data systems. (Woman, estab 2000, empl 35, sales $5,853,538, cert: WBENC)

9189   Raptor Industries, Inc.
1602 N Park Dr
Mount Prospect, IL 60056
Contact: Anthony Kalama
Tel: 708-417-9190
Email: gkalama@raptorindustriesinc.com
Website: http://raptorindustriesinc.com
Voice, Data, Fiber Optic & CATV Cable Installation and Certification, Copper and Fiber Optic Splicing, Audio/Visual, CCTV, Riser Management, Intercom. (As-Pac, estab 2013, empl 5, sales $162,554, cert: State, City, NMSDC)

9190   SI Tech Inc.
1101 N Raddant Rd
Batavia, IL 60510
Contact: Ramesh Sheth (ramesh@sitech-bitdriver.com) President
Tel: 630-761-3640
Email: admin@sitech-bitdriver.com
Website: www.sitech-bitdriver.com
Mfr & develop fiber optic communications products. (As-Ind, estab 1984, empl 20, sales , cert: NMSDC)

9191   TelePlus, Inc.
724 Racquet Club Dr
Addison, IL 60101
Contact: Mike Warda Sales Mgr
Tel: 630-543-3066
Email: mwarda@telepluscom.com
Website: www.telepluscom.com
Voice/data low voltage cabling systems, electrical, paging systems, CCTV, Nortel BCM and Norstar telephone systems. (Woman, estab 1986, empl 56, sales $6,250,000, cert: City, WBENC)

9192   The Northridge Group, Inc.
9700 W Higgins Rd Ste 600
Rosemont, IL 60018
Contact: Katherine Francis Dir of Marketing
Tel: 847-692-7022
Email: registrations@northridgegroup.com
Website: www.northridgegroup.com
Telecommunications. (Woman/AA, Hisp, estab 1999, empl 82, sales $10,000,000, cert: City, WBENC)

9193   Viadata1 Communications Inc.
3118 Elder Ln
Franklin Park, IL 60131
Contact: Eddie Villariny President
Tel: 773-593-1346
Email: edvilla@viadata1.net
Website: http://viadata1.net
Low Voltage Cabling, Fiber Optic, CCTV, Card Access, Wireless Access Points, Network Data Center design & Installation, Data & Voice Cabling. Computer equipment installation. (Hisp, estab 2008, empl 4, sales $800,000, cert: NMSDC)

Indiana

9194   C-CAT, Inc.
1726 W. 15th St
Indianapolis, IN 46202
Contact: Kristi Johnson President
Tel: 317-568-2899
Email: kjohnson@c-cat.com
Website: www.c-cat.com
Infrastructure & low-voltage cabling services: video, voice & data, security/safety cabling & Cat 5E, Cat-6 & fiber-optic wiring systems. (Woman, estab 2001, empl 30, sales $5,200,000, cert: WBENC)

9195   Communications Products, Inc.
7301 E. 90th St Ste 111
Indianapolis, IN 46256
Contact: Nancy Doucette
Tel: 317-576-0332
Email: ndoucett@commprod.com
Website: www.commprod.com
Nortel voice maintenance programs, voice & data cabling, overhead paging systems, fiber terminations, patch panels, data switches, VPN's, IP network security, T1 routers, wireless LANS, WIFI telephones. (Hisp, estab 1982, empl 60, sales $11,000,000, cert: State)

9196   Dixon Phone Place, Inc.
5335 N Tacoma Ave, Ste 3
Indianapolis, IN 46220
Contact: Juli Fritsch
Tel: 317-251-3504
Email: dixonphoneplace1@att.net
Website: http://dixonphone.com
Telephone equipment, plantronics telephone & computer headsets, cell phone corded & bluetooth headsets, corded & wireless headsets, telephone parts, line & handset cords, polycom conference equipment, cordless phones, business phones. (Woman, estab 1983, empl 2, sales , cert: State, City)

9197   Summitline Industries, Inc.
7822 Opportunity Dr
Fort Wayne, IN 46825
Contact: Stan Richard President & CEO
Tel: 260-490-2213
Email: stan.richard@summitline.com
Website: www.Summitline.com
Telecommunications, supply chain solutions, material mgmt, warehousing & kit fulfillment. (AA, estab 1983, empl 20, sales $15,000,000, cert: NMSDC, CPUC)

9198 Telamon Corporation
      1000 E 116th St
      Carmel, IN 46032
      Contact: John L. Weeks Dir of Sales
      Tel: 317-818-6757
      Email: john.weeks@telamon.com
      Website: www.telamon.com
Mfr & dist voice & data communications products: cables
& connectors to cstmrs specs, modular voice & data
accessories; engineering & install telecommunication
equip. (As-Pac, estab 1984, empl 1100, sales , cert:
NMSDC)

Louisiana

9199 New Orleans Teleport, Inc.
      201 B Travis St
      Lafayette, LA 70503
      Contact: Barbara Lamont President
      Tel: 337-704-0550
      Email: customercare@callsplus.net
      Website:
Telecommunications, audio & video productions, SAT
trucks, call center, satellite transmission, voice, video,
data, internet, broadcast services. (Woman/AA, estab
1987, empl 33, sales , cert: State)

9200 TCN
      1016 Harimaw Court E
      Metairie, LA 70001
      Contact: Victor Hess Sales Mgr
      Tel: 504-838-9600
      Email: vhess@executonesystems.com
      Website: www.executonesystems.com
Furnish & install wiring, digital & Voice over IP telephone
systems, Overhead Paging, Music, Sound, Masking, School
Intercom & Mass Notification Systems. (Woman, estab
1947, empl 28, sales $357,531,124, cert: WBENC)

Massachusetts

9201 C.E. Communication Services, Inc.
      25 Grove St
      Franklin, MA 02038
      Contact: Bruce Baltz
      Tel: 866-966-1555
      Email: bruceb@cecommunication.com
      Website: www.cecommunication.com/
Dist telecommuncations & networking products. (Minority,
Woman, estab 1998, empl 10, sales , cert: State)

9202 C4Cable, LLC
      257 Scadding St
      Taunton, MA 02780
      Contact: Carole Derringer Principal
      Tel: 508-944-5573
      Email: caroled@c4cable.com
      Website: www.c4cable.com
Dist Telecommunications & Data Networking Products:
Bulk Copper & Fiber Optic Cables, Patch Panels, Enclo-
sures, Copper & Fiber Patch Cords, Pre-Terminated MTP/
MPO Backplane Fiber Cables & Cassettes, Free Standing
Racks. (Woman, estab 2014, empl 2, sales , cert: State,
WBENC)

9203 Coastal Telecommunications Inc.
      35 Main St Ste 116C
      Topsfield, MA 01983
      Contact: Angela Gill President
      Tel: 978-744-4900
      Email: angela@gocti.us
      Website: http://gocti.us
Low Voltage Cabling, Voice & Data Structured Cabling,
Communication System Design, Installation & Mainte-
nance, Voice & Network Equipment & Service Solutions.
(Woman/AA, estab 1990, empl 5, sales $250,000, cert:
State, WBENC)

Maryland

9204 Crest Telecom, Inc.
      P.O. Box 410
      Bel Air, MD 21014
      Contact: Tammy Halley Principal
      Tel: 410-420-1044
      Email: tammy.halley@cresttelecom.com
      Website: www.cresttelecom.com
Wireless & wireline telecommunication products:
routers, microwave radios, central service units, cross
connect panels, fuse alarm panels, racks, fiber management systems, filters, duplexers, cable, channel element
cards, etc. (Woman, estab 2007, empl 10, sales , cert:
WBENC)

9205 G TECH Contracting, LLC
      8008 Dorado Terr
      Brandywine, MD 20613
      Contact: CEO
      Tel: 240-793-8908
      Email:
      Website: www.gtechcontracting.com
Integrated security, voice/data communications,
residential & small commercial A/V systems. (Hisp, estab
2013, empl 5, sales $1,200,000, cert: 8a)

9206 KSC Consultant Services LLC
      18216 Darnell Dr
      Olney, MD 20832
      Contact: Kimberlie Manns Owner
      Tel: 240-389-1882
      Email: kmanns@kscconsultants.net
      Website: www.kscconsultants.net
Telecommunication consulting & infrastructure wiring,
designing & installing voice & data infrastructure/
cabling, troubleshoot, repair, testing & installing voice &
data lines, rewiring, installing & replacing jacks.
(Woman/AA, estab 2004, empl 2, sales , cert: State, SDB)

9207 SRL TotalSource LLC
      83 High St Ste B
      Waldorf, MD 20602
      Contact: John Johnson COO
      Tel: 301-885-0097
      Email: jjohnson@srltotalsource.com
      Website: www.srltotalsource.com/
Wireless Telecommunications Carriers, Data Processing,
Hosting, and Related Services. (AA, estab 2011, empl 6,
sales $589,253, cert: State, 8a)

Michigan

9208   Cellular Solutions Signal Enhancing Specialists
       2737 N Meridian Rd
       Sanford, MI 48657
       Contact: Devin O'Neil Acct Exec
       Tel: 989-687-4023
       Email: aimeek@cellularsolutions.com
       Website: www.cellularsolutions.com
Cellular signal enhancement throughout homes, vehicles,
small commercial buildings & large facilities. (Woman,
estab 2004, empl 13, sales $8,000,000, cert: WBENC)

9209   Communication Brokers, Inc.
       437 44th St SW
       Grand Rapid, MI 49548
       Contact: Mimi Micu CEO
       Tel: 616-301-3733
       Email: mmicu@cbitelecom.com
       Website: www.cbitelecom.com
Telecommunications consulting services, data, local &
wireless communications analysis. (Woman, estab 1991,
empl 30, sales $5,000,000, cert: WBENC)

9210   Federated Service Solutions, Inc.
       30955 Northwestern Highway
       Farmington Hills, MI 48334
       Contact: Susan Troyer Sales Admin
       Tel: 248-539-9000
       Email: stroyer@federatedservice.com
       Website: https://federatedservice.com
POS, server, kiosks/self-service, low voltage cabling (voice/
data/video/audio), security/LP, network devices, and
wireless (Woman, estab 2004, empl 70, sales $13,300,000,
cert: WBENC)

9211   Prima Communications, Inc.
       P.O. Box 338
       Schoolcraft, MI 49087
       Contact: Charlotte Hubbard Owner
       Tel: 269-679-3800
       Email: primaadmin@voyager.net
       Website: www.primacommunications.com
Technical communications. (Woman, estab 1991, empl 25,
sales , cert: WBENC)

Minnesota

9212   Building Systems Solutions, Inc.
       1250 E Moore Lake Dr Ste 230
       Fridley, MN 55432
       Contact: Megan Beaver CEO
       Tel: 763-502-1515
       Email: meganb@bssmn.com
       Website: www.buildingsystemssolutions.com
Design commercial audio & communications systems:
paging, sound masking, music & emergency notification
systems. (Woman, estab 2003, empl 2, sales $200,145,
cert: State)

9213   Seacom
       2150 Third St Ste 6&14
       White Bear Lake, MN 55110
       Contact: President
       Tel: 651-653-3200
       Email:
       Website: www.seacomllc.com
Telecommunication solutions: legacy equipment, VoIP,
video conferencing, voice & data cabling, electrical cabling,
data networking & security systems. (Woman, estab 2010,
empl 7, sales $1,600,000, cert: WBENC)

9214   Technology Management Corporation
       4790 Lakeway Terr
       Shorewood, MN 55331
       Contact: Brendon O'Brien Dir Business Devel
       Tel: 952-470-0217
       Email: bobrien@tmc-1.com
       Website: www.tmc-1.com
Telecommunications consulting: cable design; phone
system design; phone, data, & internet network design,
data/server room design. telecommunications audit &
contract negotiation. (Woman, estab 1988, empl 12,
sales $788,715, cert: State, City, WBENC, SDB)

9215   TRiCOM Communications
       1301 Corporate Center Dr, Ste 160
       Eagan, MN 55121
       Contact: Diane Evans President
       Tel: 651-686-9000
       Email: diane.evans@tricom1.com
       Website: www.tricom1.com
Design & install structured cabling: copper & fiber
optics, Data Centers, Telecom Rooms, Equipment
Rooms, Outside Plant Construction, Security Cameras,
Card Access Systems, In-Building Wireless Distributed
Antenna Systems (DAS). (Woman, estab 1989, empl 20,
sales $2,250,000, cert: State, City, WBENC)

Missouri

9216   American Cable Products LLC
       4 Forest Park Circle Dr
       Lake St. Louis, MO 63367
       Contact: Richard Politte Managing Partner
       Tel: 636-265-6602
       Email: rmpolitte@amercp.net
       Website: www.americancableproducts.com
Install voice & data cable, routers, switches, modems,
racks, wireless equipment, fiber optic cable & hardware,
PA & video systems, arial cable & single mode fiber &
buried drop service, trenching, boring, etc. (As-Pac,
estab 2002, empl 25, sales $12,000,000, cert: State, City,
CPUC, SDB)

9217   Capital International Communications, LLC
       8762 St. Charles Rock Rd Ste 101
       St. Louis, MO 63021
       Contact: Dr. Don Cook, Sr. CEO
       Tel: 314-707-7717
       Email: dr_doncook@capintlcomm.com
       Website: www.capintlcomm.com
Dist telecommunications, electrical & industrial supplies,
public payphone services provider. (AA, estab 2002,
empl 3, sales $2,700,000, cert: State)

9218   eTech Solutons, LLC
       1813 Zumbehl Rd
       Saint Charles, MO 63303
       Contact: Sara Hagemeyer Owner
       Tel: 314-282-8318
       Email: brad@etechstl.com
       Website: www.etechstl.com
Cellphone supplier, Cellphone repair, Tablet repair,
Tablet supplier, small electronic repair - ie micro soldering, laptop repair, Cellphone & tablet data recovery,
Chipoff data recovery, jtag data recovery, cellphone
forensics. (Woman, estab 2012, empl 2, sales $530,000,
cert: WBENC)

North Carolina

9219 Atlantic Communication Products, Inc.
4324 Barringer Dr Ste 112
Charlotte, NC 28217
Contact: Winn Pray President
Tel: 704-676-5880
Email: w.pray@goacp.com
Website: www.goacp.com
Resell voice & data products, installation & maintenance services of wire & cabling. (Hisp, estab 1997, empl 10, sales $900,000, cert: NMSDC)

9220 Lexair Electronics Sales Corp.
4807-B Koger Blvd
Greensboro, NC 27407
Contact: Paula Edwards Contract Mgr
Tel: 336-294-5300
Email: alisawatts@lexairsales.com
Website: www.lexair.com
Dist communications equipment: headsets, telephones, audio conferencing equipment & peripherals. (Woman, estab 1998, empl 15, sales $6,550,000, cert: WBENC)

9221 Quantum Technology Group, LLC
P.O. Box 762
Cornelius, NC 28031
Contact: Adam Jones President
Tel: 800-918-3510
Email: amjones@qtg-llc.com
Website: www.qtg-llc.com
Information technology, cabling infrastructure, IP converged telephony systems, voice mail solutions, access control, paging systems, mass notification systems, video teleconferencing, CATV. (AA, estab 2007, empl 16, sales $338,454, cert: 8a)

9222 Team Telecom, LLC
220 N. Main St
Lexington, NC 27292
Contact: Jennifer Sturgell
Tel: 888-305-4772
Email: jsturgell@teamtelecom.net
Website: www.teamtelecom.net
Dist new, surplus & refurbished telecommunications equipment. (Woman/AA, estab 2005, empl 8, sales $3,050,000, cert: State, NMSDC, WBENC)

9223 TelExpress
406 Interstate Dr
Archdale, NC 27263
Contact: Tabitha Brock Sr scct Mgr
Tel: 434-990-2644
Email: tabitha@telexpressinc.com
Website: www.telexpressinc.com
Mfr central office, wireless, cable, fiber & DC power equipment. (Woman, estab 1992, empl 35, sales $5,785,800, cert: WBENC)

9224 Walker and Associates, Inc.
7129 Old Hwy 52
Welcome, NC 27374
Contact: Jane Brightwell VP Business Dev
Tel: 336-731-5236
Email: governcon@walkerfirst.com
Website: www.walkerfirst.com
Dist data & telecommunication equip, material mgmt & installation. (Woman, estab 1970, empl 120, sales , cert: CPUC)

Nebrasks

9225 Mills Marketing & TeleServices, LLC
P.O. Box 8500
Omaha, NE 68108
Contact: Lee Mills CEO
Tel: 402-707-5654
Email: teleservices.leemills@usa.net
Website:
Outsourcing, local & long distance telephone service, bilingual VoIP customer contact center, 50 seats. (AA, estab 1990, empl 57, sales , cert: State)

New Jersey

9226 D.M. Radio Service Corp.
45 Perry St
Chester, NJ 07930
Contact: Sandy Drysdale President
Tel: 908-879-2525
Email: sdrysdale@csiradio.com
Website: www.csiradio.com
Dist two-way radio communications equipment, design/build service, supply & support for radio systems, Emergency Call Boxes, BDA & DAS systems. (Woman, estab 1968, empl 6, sales $700,000, cert: State, WBENC)

9227 e.comm Technologies
11 Melanie Ln
East Hanover, NJ 07936
Contact: Chuck Tarantino global acct Mgr
Tel: 973-503-5814
Email: ctarantino@ecommt.com
Website: www.ecommtechnologies.com
Avaya's Radvision video conferencing, contact center, call recording, speech access, predictive dialers, wireless solutions, video conferencing both room to room & desktop to desktop. (Woman, estab 1999, empl 20, sales $6,622,113, cert: State)

9228 Kane Communications LLC
572 Whitehead Rd Ste 201
Trenton, NJ 08619
Contact: Dir Business Dev
Tel: 609-586-8800
Email:
Website: www.kanecomm.com
Voice & data, sound & secuirty, audio & video, building automation, inside & outside plant copper & fiber systems. (Woman, estab 2003, empl 46, sales $4,600,000, cert: State, WBENC)

9229 Spectrotel, Inc.
3535 Route 66, Building 7
Neptune, NJ 07753
Contact: Premier Acct Specialist
Tel: 732-345-7936
Email:
Website: www.spectrotel.com
Dedicated Voice Services, Business Calling Services (POTs), VoIP Services, Conferencing Services, Managed Services, Network Monitoring, Managed Security, Cyber Security, SD-WAN, Dedicated Network Services, Dedicated Internet Access, Virtual Network Svcs. (Hisp, estab 1997, empl 130, sales $78,000,000, cert: NMSDC)

9230　The Seideman Company
　　　4 Canterbury Ct
　　　Marlton, NJ 08053
　　　Contact: Patricia Seideman Owner
　　　Tel:　856-988-0117
　　　Email: pseideman@aol.com
　　　Website: www.seidemancompany.com
Telecommunications & data networking services. (Woman, estab 1991, empl 2, sales $156,382, cert: WBENC)

9231　TRAK Communications, Inc.
　　　710 Tennant Rd Ste 101
　　　Manalapan, NJ 07726
　　　Contact:　President
　　　Tel:　732-786-1355
　　　Email:
　　　Website: www.trakcommunications.com
Telecommunications Billing Audit & Consulting Services, Contract Negotiations, contract compliance audits, wireless audits & optimizations, Bid Management Services, Vendor Management, Telecom Expense Management. (Woman, estab 1999, empl 2, sales $338,371, cert: WBENC)

New York

9232　Annese & Associates, Inc.
　　　4781 Route 5 W
　　　Herkimer, NY 13350
　　　Contact: Yvonne Annese LoRe VP Corp projects
　　　Tel:　315-849-9194
　　　Email: yannese@annese.com
　　　Website: www.annese.com
Design, install & maintain IP telephony, wireless, voice & data networks, remote monitoring, 24 x 7 maintenance, security. (Woman, estab 1970, empl 94, sales $53,000,010, cert: State)

9233　Coranet Corp
　　　277 Fairfield Road Ste 320A
　　　Fairfield, NY 07004
　　　Contact: Kevin O'Brien Acct Exec
　　　Tel:　212-635-2770
　　　Email: kobrien@coranet.com
　　　Website: www.coranet.com
VoIP convergence solutions, data networking, project mgmt, video networking, structured cabling systems, mobility & wireless solutions, installation & maintenance, IP audits, call center applications, billing audits, e-collaboration. (Woman, estab 1987, empl 85, sales $63,000,000, cert: State, WBENC)

9234　HAVE, Inc.
　　　309 Power Ave
　　　Hudson, NY 12534
　　　Contact: Lowell Stringer Sales
　　　Tel:　518-828-2000
　　　Email: lstringer@haveinc.com
　　　Website: www.haveinc.com
Custom audio/video/data cable assemblies, dist bulk cable, connectors, tools & accessories. (Woman, estab 1977, empl 18, sales $3,120,541, cert: City)

9235　Information Transport Solutions Inc.
　　　3204 Route 22
　　　Patterson, NY 12563
　　　Contact:　President
　　　Tel:　855-472-7701
　　　Email:
　　　Website: www.4yourITS.com
Wireless & structured cabling: wifi, DAS, AV, Access Control & Sound Masking. (Woman, estab 2001, empl 5, sales $2,000,000, cert: WBENC)

9236　Pivotel LLC
　　　6066 State Hwy 12
　　　Norwich, NY 13815
　　　Contact: Ronald Martin Jr tech sales eng
　　　Tel:　607-334-7400
　　　Email: ron.martin@pivotelonline.com
　　　Website: www.pivotelonline.com
Communications & network wiring: AC/DC & fiber optic cabling & terminations. (Woman, estab 2001, empl 30, sales $200,000, cert: WBENC)

9237　Reliance Communications, LLC
　　　555 Wireless Blvd
　　　Hauppauge, NY 11788
　　　Contact: Jeanne Healey VP Marketing
　　　Tel:　631-952-4800
　　　Email: jeanne.healey@reliance.us
　　　Website: www.reliance.us
Dist wireless communications handsets & accessories. (As-Ind, estab 2005, empl 290, sales $715,079,538, cert: NMSDC)

9238　Saia Communications, Inc.
　　　100 Stradtman St
　　　Buffalo, NY 14206
　　　Contact: Cheryl Kirchmeyer Sales
　　　Tel:　716-892-2900
　　　Email: cheryl.kirchmeyer@saiacomm.com
　　　Website: www.saiacomm.com
Motorola two-way radio products. (Woman, estab 1980, empl 25, sales $5,000,000, cert: State)

9239　Sintel Satellite Services
　　　373 Nesconset Hwy #133
　　　Hauppauge, NY 11788
　　　Contact: Sanjay Singhal COO
　　　Tel:　212-202-0678
　　　Email: sanjay@sintelsat.com
　　　Website: www.sintelsat.com
Satellite communication & terrestrial telecom solutions, infrastructure rebuilding, IP connectivity, fiber, microwave & satellite, Vsat, broadcasting & IT solutions. (Woman/As-Ind, estab 1997, empl 30, sales $1,132,000, cert: State, City)

Ohio

9240　Ameridial, Inc.
　　　4877 Higbee Ave NW, 2nd Fl
　　　Canton, OH 44718
　　　Contact: Ganesh Marve SVP
　　　Tel:　234-401-8104
　　　Email: ganesh.marve@fusionbposervices.com
　　　Website: www.ameridial.com
Customer service,Tele-sales,Telephone Answering Services, Debt recovery,Technical support services, Order Taking, Online Order Processing, Collection Services. (As-Pac, estab 1987, empl 663, sales $42,391,472, cert: CPUC)

9241　Cincinnati Cable Technology
　　　1177 W 8th St, Ste A
　　　Cincinnati, OH 45203
　　　Contact: Sheryl Yeager President
　　　Tel:　513-579-1888
　　　Email: sherylyeager@ccablet.com
　　　Website: www.ccablet.com
Structured cabling, fiber optics, coax network infrastructure, wireless networks, security solutions, IP based door entrance, IP security cameras, audio/visual system design. (Woman, estab 2010, empl 7, sales $1,500,000, cert: WBENC)

9242 ClarkTel Communications Corp.
1661 Copley Rd
Akron, OH 44320
Contact: Terence N Clark President & CEO
Tel: 330-869-8657
Email: tclark@clarktel.net
Website: www.clarktel.net
Design, installation, warranty & service business tele-
phone systems: NEC, Nortel, Mitel, Toshiba, Panasonic,
Comdial, Vodavi Sprint, voice/data cable. (AA, estab 1996,
empl 10, sales $216,939, cert: NMSDC)

9243 DTE Inc.
110 Baird Pkwy, P.O. Box 1727
Mansfield, OH 44901
Contact: Bridget Hatcher Consultant
Tel: 419-544-1232
Email: bhatcher@dteinc.com
Website: www.dteinc.com/
Low voltage Cabling, VoIP Systems, Hosted VoIP Systems,
Integrated Voice Mail Systems, Paging Systems, Business
Phone & Internet Access, SIP Trunking, Repairs on all
Telephone and Paging Equipment, Wi-Fi/ Wireless
Networking. (Woman, estab 1991, empl 14, sales , cert:
State)

9244 Fine Line Communications Inc.
P.O. Box 91
Aurora, OH 44202
Contact: Barbara Hoover President
Tel: 330-562-0731
Email: bhoover@finelinecomm.com
Website: www.finelinecomm.com
Design, intall & maintain voice & data network systems.
(Woman, estab 1981, empl 25, sales $2,480,000, cert:
State, WBENC)

9245 Net Activity
9535 Midwest Ave, Ste 114
Garfield Heights, OH 44125
Contact: John Marion CFO
Tel: 216-503-5150
Email: info@netactivity.us
Website: www.netactivity.us
Hardware & Software reseller, VoIP Phone Systems; hosted
& on-site, Connectivity; dedicated data & voice communi-
cation, Cloud Back-up; proprietary infrastructure &
Microsoft Azure, Remote network & hardware managed
services. (As-Ind, estab 2002, empl 11, sales $1,377,695,
cert: 8a, SDB)

9246 Ohio Cables, LLC
5288 Dietrich Ave
Orient, OH 43146
Contact: Owner
Tel: 614-991-0404
Email:
Website: www.ohiocables.com
Mfr & dist cables. (Woman, estab 2008, empl 2, sales
$950,000, cert: City)

9247 One Source Mobile
1066 Reading Rd
Mason, OH 45040
Contact: Amy Baumhower President
Tel: 513-870-9300
Email: abaumhower@onesourcemobile.com
Website: www.onesourcemobile.com
Telecommunication services: wireless cell phone accesso-
ries, bluetooth items, car chargers & holsters etc.
(Woman, estab 2005, empl 10, sales $925,000, cert:
WBENC)

9248 SpeakSpace, LLC
600 Superior Ave, Ste 1300
Cleveland, OH 44114
Contact: Behan Rebecca Managing Partner
Tel: 440-263-1919
Email: beckybehan@speakspace.com
Website: www.speakspace.com
Teleconferencing services/conference calling, audio, web
& video conferencing services. (Woman, estab 1999,
empl 5, sales $800,000, cert: WBENC)

9249 US Communications and Electric
4933 Neo Pkwy
Garfield Heights, OH 44128
Contact: Jim Connole COO
Tel: 216-478-0810
Email: jconnole@uscande.com
Website: www.uscande.com
Technology-based communications cabling systems,
design & install outdoor copper systems, horizontal
copper cabling solutions. (Woman, estab , empl , sales
$17,000,000, cert: State, City, WBENC)

Oklahoma

9250 Leader Communications Inc.
4600 S.E. 29th St. Ste 300
Del City, OK 73115
Contact: Thomas L. Long Operations Mgr
Tel: 405-670-9000
Email: tom.long@lcibest.com
Website: www.lcibest.com
System engineering, program mgmt, telecommunica-
tions & logistics mgmt, antenna installs, telephone
installations, coummincations facilities operations &
maintenance. (AA, estab 1999, empl 259, sales , cert:
State)

Oregon

9251 Tribal One Broadband Technologies, LLC
3201 Tremont
North Bend, OR 97459
Contact: Karl Kennedy Mgr
Tel: 541-756-3899
Email: kkennedy@orcacomm.com
Website:
Metro ethernet & TDM transport, internet access, LAN
support, colocation. (Nat Ame, estab 2002, empl 5, sales
, cert: State)

Pennsylvania

9252 Clark Resources, Inc.
321 N Front St
Harrisburg, PA 17101
Contact: Christa Anderson
Tel: 717-230-8861
Email: christaanderson@fclarkresources.com
Website: www.fclarkresources.com
Inbound and outbound telephone services. Call Center/
Customer Support Center. (AA, estab 2002, empl 180,
sales $6,000,000, cert: State, NMSDC)

9253 Enterprise Cable Group, Inc.
     805 W Fifth St
     Lansdale, PA 19446
     Contact: WBE dir
     Tel: 215-361-4114
     Email:
     Website: www.enterprisecablegroup.com
Communication & computer cable systems design & installation. (Woman, estab 2001, empl 20, sales $2,420,839, cert: WBENC)

9254 Fiber Business Solutions Inc.
     P.O. Box 103
     Fairview Village, PA 19409
     Contact: President
     Tel: 484-576-0876
     Email:
     Website:
Fiber Optic Cable Placement & Splicing, Copper Cable Placement & Splicing, Right of Way & Permit Acquisition Services, Engineering & Design Services, CAD & As-Built Services, Project Management Services. (Woman, estab 2004, empl 8, sales $1,300,000, cert: WBENC, 8a)

9255 MobileStrat, Inc.
     642 Cowpath Rd, Ste 390
     Lansdale, PA 19446
     Contact: Larry Blackshear CEO
     Tel: 215-237-3874
     Email: lb@mobilestrat.com
     Website: www.mobilestrat.com
Wireless, cellular, voice & data, gap analysis, billing management, WiFi site surveys
wire line, WAN design, WiFi security. (AA, estab 2004, empl 18, sales , cert: NMSDC)

Puerto Rico

9256 B&B Communications Group
     220 Plaza Western Auto PMB-370 Ste 101
     Trujillo Alto, PR 00976
     Contact: Benjamin Bravo Sales
     Tel: 787-760-2698
     Email: bbravo@bbcorp.net
     Website: www.bbcorp.net
Communications, Fiber Optics, UPS, Cabling, Network, Cat-5e, cat-6, cat-6a, telecomm, telecommunications, voice, data, IP phones, power supply, design, site survey, training, service (Woman/Hisp, estab 2014, empl 5, sales , cert: State, NMSDC)

South Carolina

9257 Globenet Telecommunications, LLC
     210 Titus Ln
     Pineville, SC 29468
     Contact: Cavid Middleton President
     Tel: 828-320-3291
     Email: dlmiddleton@charter.net
     Website: www.globenetusa.net
Low voltage system integration, install security devices & fiber optic cable. (AA, estab 2007, empl 32, sales $14,500,000, cert: CPUC)

Tennessee

9258 Ashaun
     5100 Poplar Ave Ste 726
     Memphis, TN 38137
     Contact: Anthony Tate CEO
     Tel: 901-312-7025
     Email: atate@ashaun.com
     Website: www.ashaun.com
Call center services. (AA, estab 2000, empl 35, sales , cert: State, NMSDC)

9259 Madison Group Inc.
     6551 Stage Oaks Dr. Ste 1
     Bartlett, TN 38134
     Contact: VP
     Tel: 901-791-4116
     Email:
     Website: www.madisong.com
Dist telecommunication products; central office integration, switching, transport, carrier, access, data, power; kitting, cable assemblies, material mgmt. (Woman, estab 1991, empl 9, sales $3,500,000, cert: State, CPUC, WBENC)

9260 Power & Telephone Supply Co,
     2673 Yale Ave
     Memphis, TN 38112
     Contact: Annmarie Templeton Natl Sales Mgr
     Tel: 800-238-7514
     Email: annmarie.templeton@ptsupply.com
     Website: www.ptsupply.com
Communications products. (Woman, estab 1963, empl 350, sales , cert: State, City, CPUC, WBENC)

9261 Tel-XL
     5462 McGill
     Memphis, TN 38120
     Contact: Linda Hawkins President
     Tel: 866-848-3595
     Email: lhawkins@tel-xl.com
     Website: www.tel-xl.com
Dist new & refurb telecom equip, systems, accessories. (Woman, estab , empl , sales , cert: WBENC)

9262 Walker Warren Communications
     155 S Mendenhall Rd
     Memphis, TN 38117
     Contact: Principal
     Tel: 901-337-6326
     Email:
     Website: www.ww911.net
Radio Systems /Infrastructure, 2-way radios, mobile (vehicles), Telephone Systems, GPS, Logger Recorders, Computer Aided Dispatch Systems, Redundancy analysis for critical applications. (Woman/AA, estab 2016, empl 2, sales , cert: City, WBENC)

Texas

9263 Austin Tele-Services Partners, LP dba Genesis ATS
     4209 S Industrial Dr Ste 300
     Austin, TX 78744
     Contact: Patrick Manning VP Business Devel
     Tel: 512-437-3041
     Email: pmanning@genesis-ats.com
     Website: www.genesis-ats.com
IT, Networking, Telecommunications & Computer related equipment & services. (Hisp, estab 2003, empl 45, sales $25,000,000, cert: State, NMSDC)

9264   Can-Am Wireless LLC dba Can-Am IT Solutions
1333 Corporate Dr, Ste 110
Irving, TX 75038
Contact: Johan Rahardjo Dir of Engineering
Tel: 866-976-4177
Email: johan.rahardjo@canamitsolutions.com
Website: www.canamitsolutions.com
Telecommunications and Information Technology Hard-
ware & Software. (As-Pac, estab 2001, empl 7, sales
$1,020,000, cert: NMSDC)

9265   Clayborn Inc.
P.O. Box 703212
Dallas, TX 75370
Contact: Jacquelyn Clayborn CEO
Tel: 469-751-8494
Email: onc@oncnational.com
Website: www.oncnational.com
Installation (Cat5 Cat6) Voice, Data, Fiber Optic, Coax (tv),
Wireless access point installation, splicing of building
entrance and riser cable, cable abatement, abandoned
cable removal, sound masking systems, extensions
services. (Woman/AA, estab 2016, empl 5, sales $569,399,
cert: NMSDC, WBENC)

9266   Clearvue Networks, LLC
100 E Main St Ste 201
Round Rock, TX 78664
Contact: Shanna Schmidt Admin Asst
Tel: 512-861-5319
Email: shanna.schmidt@clearvuenetworks.com
Website: www.clearvuenetworks.com
Business networking solutions, work station installs/
configs, server installs/configs, network assessments,
wireless installs, telecom services, voice/data/fiber
cabling, alarm/surveillance systems, card access security
systems. (Hisp, estab 2011, empl 9, sales , cert: State)

9267   Continental Wireless
10455 VISTA PARK RD
Dallas, TX 75238
Contact: RITA WEBER President
Tel: 972-926-7443
Email: RITA.WEBER@CNTLWIRE.COM
Website: www.cntlwire.com
Wireless communication, dist & rent two way radios.
(Woman, estab 2000, empl 25, sales $15,263,348, cert:
State, WBENC)

9268   Crystal Application Software Services, LLC
3201 Cherry Ridge Dr Ste B-218
San Antonio, TX 78230
Contact: Veronica Vela Acct Mgr
Tel: 210-698-2410
Email: veronica.vela@cnetcable.com
Website: www.cnetcable.com
Design-build telecommunications, low voltage cabling,
wireless & access points, voice & data networks, security
cameras, audio & visual, fiber optics, phone systems &
microwave. (Hisp, estab 2014, empl 10, sales , cert: State)

9269   Diamond P Enterprises, Inc.
P.O. Box 483
Brownwood, TX 76804
Contact: Erin Toft Operations Mgr
Tel: 325-643-5629
Email: admin.assist@diamondpenterprises.com
Website: www.diamondpenterprises.com
Cable Placing Materials, Closures/Splicing Materials,
Copper Cable, Cutting & Distribution, Corrugated
Products, Fiber Optic Cable, Cutting & Distribution.
(Hisp, estab , empl , sales $60,309,360, cert: NMSDC,
CPUC)

9270   Dynamic Voice Data
4403 Greenbriar Dr
Stafford, TX 77477
Contact: Tina Greenfield Business Develop Mgr
Tel: 800-838-5070
Email: tgreenfield@dvd-inc.com
Website: www.dvd-inc.com
Mfr custom OEM products using injection mould
technology, interconnect products & telephone parts,
harnesses & power supplies. (Woman/As-Pac, estab
1993, empl 15, sales $11,300,000, cert: State, NMSDC)

9271   Genesis Networks Integration Services, LLC
600 N. Loop 1604 East
San Antonio, TX 78232
Contact: Nicole Nash supplier diversity Asst
Tel: 210-489-6600
Email: nicole.nash@genesisnet.com
Website: www.genesisnet.com
Provides engineering, furnish & installation services for
data & phone networks, network management architecture, implementation & support, information systems
security management, server & virtualization management. (Hisp, estab 2010, empl 77, sales $16,526,811,
cert: State, NMSDC)

9272   JG Haney & Associates LLC
9711 Haven Crossing Court
Houston, TX 77065
Contact: Joyce Haney CEO
Tel: 281-653-2441
Email: haney@jghaneyassociates.com
Website: www.jghaneyassociates.com
Telecommunications Services, IT products & services,
data acquisition systems, telemetry products, circuit
card assemblies, shipping containers, test set cases,
special nonmetallic, preformed packing material &
acquisition program management. (Woman/AA, estab
2011, empl 2, sales $300,000, cert: 8a)

9273   KMM Telecommunications
4051 N Hwy 121 Ste 400
Grapevine, TX 76051
Contact: Sarah McNab Dir HR & Marketing
Tel: 844-566-8488
Email: s.mcnab@kmmcorp.net
Website: www.kmmcorp.net
Sourcing products & services; contract management;
inventory planning & procurement; material manage-
ment & deployment; material warehousing; material
fulfillment, 3PL services; last-mile staging services;
reverse logistics. (Woman, estab 1991, empl 130, sales
$892,823,959, cert: CPUC, WBENC)

9274 Matrix Telecommunication Services, Inc.
11127 Shady Trail, Ste 103 Ste 515
Dallas, TX 75229
Contact: President
Tel: 972-438-7161
Email:
Website: www.Cableinstalling.com
Install & maintain voice, data & fiber structured cabling systems. (Woman/AA, estab 1984, empl 13, sales $1,000,000, cert: State)

9275 Micro-Design, Inc.
10210 Monroe Dr
Dallas, TX 75229
Contact: Douglas Ramsey VP Operations
Tel: 972-488-8725
Email: dramsey@levelcon.com
Website: www.micro-design.com
Remote telemetry solutions: wireless, WiFi, cellular & satellite, engineering & solutions for CNG pump stations & infrastructure. (Woman, estab 1984, empl 15, sales $2,000,000, cert: State)

9276 On Air Solutions, Inc.
5415 Chevy Chase
Houston, TX 77056
Contact: Dir
Tel: 713-961-3990
Email:
Website: www.onairsol.com
Wireless infrastructure projects & telecommunications svcs: in-building wireless system engineering & installation, tower erection/construction; site maintenance, site acquisition, project management. (Woman, estab 2003, empl 6, sales , cert: State)

9277 Operational Technologies Corporation
4100 NW Loop 410, Ste 23
San Antonio, TX 78229
Contact: Louisa Alaniz Sr. Mgr. Client Services
Tel: 210-731-0000
Email: louisa.alaniz@otcorp.com
Website: www.otcorp.com
Fulfillment center kitting, warehousing & distribution, telecommunications & communications engineering & installation, environmental svcs. (Hisp, estab 1986, empl 70, sales $15,192,216, cert: State, NMSDC)

9278 Premier Paging, Inc.
12220 Murphy Rd Ste F
Stafford, TX 77477
Contact: Lea Bogle President
Tel: 281-575-8500
Email: lea.bogle@premierwirelesstx.com
Website: www.premierwirelesstx.com
Wireless equipment, accessories & service, GPS tracking for fleets & assets, electronic forms. (Woman, estab 1993, empl 17, sales $2,500,000, cert: State, WBENC)

9279 Ransor, Inc.
7055 Pipestone
Schertz, TX 78154
Contact: Randy Sorrell VP
Tel: 210-651-6451
Email: randy@ransor.com
Website: www.ransor.com
Install communication equipment & maintains monopoles, guyed & self supporting towers, tower construction, tower modifications & tower maintenance. (Woman, estab 1987, empl 7, sales $984,000, cert: State)

9280 Sky Communications, Inc.
6101 Long Prairie Rd, Ste 744-162
Flower Mound, TX 75028
Contact: Exec VP
Tel: 214-789-5090
Email:
Website: www.skycomglobal.com
Telecommunications services, engineering, design, implementation & managed services, unified communications, VOIP, call center & project management. (AA, estab 1995, empl 13, sales $1,735,567, cert: State, NMSDC)

9281 Telecom Electric Supply Company
1304 Capital Ave
Plano, TX 75074
Contact: Christy Moses Sales Exec
Tel: 972-422-0012
Email: cmoses@tes85.com
Website: www.tes85.com
Dist electric, utility, construction & telecommunication supplies. (AA, estab , empl , sales $33,858,031, cert: State, NMSDC)

9282 Teltech Communications LLC
3211 Internet Blvd Ste 300
Frisco, TX 75034
Contact: Lisa Hanlon CEO
Tel: 469-713-3801
Email: lhanlon@teltech.com
Website: www.teltech.com
Network infrastructure equipment, wireless, wireline, asset & inventory management services. (Woman/Nat Ame, estab 1999, empl 106, sales $34,827,298, cert: State, NMSDC, CPUC, WBENC)

9283 The Wilkins Group, Inc.
1710 Firman Dr, Ste 200
Richardson, TX 75081
Contact: ConTrenia McKinzie Cameron VP, Admin
Tel: 972-479-1090
Email: trenia@wilkins.com
Website: www.wilkins.com
Telecommunications services, equipment installation, voice, video & data systems. (Woman/AA, estab 1986, empl 30, sales $7,400,000, cert: State, NMSDC)

Virginia

9284 Opterna-AM Inc.
44901 Falcon Pl Ste 116
Sterling, VA 20166
Contact: Matt Onojafe Dir Govt Contracting
Tel: 571-294-7652
Email: matt.onojafe@opterna.com
Website: www.opterna.com
Fiber optic products & solutions, fiber optic communication solutions. (As-Ind, estab 1994, empl 17, sales $10,000,000, cert: NMSDC)

9285   Secured Network Solutions, Inc.
        929 Ventures Way Ste 113
        Chesapeake, VA 23320
        Contact: President
        Tel: 757-819-7647
        Email:
        Website: www.eamsns.com
Telecommunications & information technology: cabling,
design, install, fiber optics single/multi-strand, fiber fusion
& splicing, LAN/WAN/wireless network engineering,
drafting & information systems security. (AA, estab 2006,
empl 11, sales , cert: State)

9286   Shore Communications, Inc.
        600 N Witchduck Rd, Ste 106
        Virginia Beach, VA 23462
        Contact: Laura Castner President
        Tel: 757-468-0855
        Email: lcastner@shorecomusa.com
        Website: www.shorecomusa.com
Engineering, design, installation & testing structured
cabling systems, telephone & paging systems, including
adds, moves or changes to existing systems. (Woman,
estab 1995, empl 28, sales , cert: State)

9287   Simba Enterprises LLC
        21 Fort Evans Rd, Ste F
        Leesburg, VA 20176
        Contact: Ali Sajjad CEO
        Tel: 703-782-4042
        Email: asajjad@simbacom.net
        Website: www.simbacom.net
Satellite-based telecommunications & information technology solutions worldwide. (As-Ind, estab 2005, empl 10,
sales $3,500,000, cert: State)

9288   TEKCONNX
        608 Westwood Office Park
        Fredericksburg, VA 22401
        Contact: Kevin Wlliams CEO
        Tel: 703-635-4439
        Email: kevinw@tekconnx.com
        Website: www.tekconnx.com
Interactive Audio Visual (IAVT) Solutions & Integration, A/V
Telepresence Conferencing (HW & SW), Design/Build
Interactive Audio Visual Solutions, Command & Control
Centers, Wireless Video/Audio Solutions. (AA, estab 2013,
empl 3, sales $850,000, cert: State, NMSDC)

Washington

9289   Roadswest Construction Inc.
        307 N Olympic Ave, Ste 209
        Arlington, WA 98223
        Contact: Kirby Lundberg VP
        Tel: 360-403-8782
        Email: roadswestinc@verizon.net
        Website: www.RoadsWestInc.com
Dist, service & install voice & data wiring & audio/vidio
systems. (Nat Ame, estab 1987, empl 30, sales $873,949,
cert: State)

9290   SurgiMark, Inc.
        1703 Creekside Loop Ste 110
        Yakima, WA 98902
        Contact: Barbara Yarger President
        Tel: 509-965-1911
        Email: custserv@surgimark.com
        Website: www.surgimark.com
SurgiMark's VIA-GUARD® line of disposable surgical
suction tips features a unique blend of industry-leading
performance, inventory consolidation, and infection
control for every hospital operating room and outpa-
tient surgery center, land or sea. With qua (Woman,
estab 1987, empl 5, sales , cert: State)

Wisconsin

9291   1Prospect Technologies, LLC
        P.O. Box 1045
        Rhinelander, WI 54501
        Contact: Brad Kowieski Dir of Business Develop
        Tel: 715-369-1119
        Email: info@1prospect.com
        Website: www.oneprospect.com
Design & build flexible cabling infrastructure supporting
multiple voice, data, video & multimedia systems. (Nat
Ame, estab 2000, empl 33, sales $10,400,000, cert:
State)

9292   Onyx Communication
        11016 N Mequon Square Dr
        Milwaukee, WI 53092
        Contact: Jess Ferguson Owner
        Tel: 262-236-0648
        Email: regferg@aol.com
        Website:
Voice & data cable installation, ethernet hubs switches
& routers, phone systems, wireless bridges & service
furniture. (AA, estab 1999, empl 5, sales , cert: State)

TEXTILES
Includes thread, trimmings, woven and nonwoven material manfucaturers. NAICS Code 31

California

9293 A & R Tarpaulins Inc.
16246 Valley Blvd
Fontana, CA 92335
Contact: Didi Truong aerospace project Mgr
Tel: 909-829-4444
Email: didi@artech2000.com
Website: www.artech2000.com
Multilayer insulation, Acoustic blankets, payload fairing, sound barriers, high temperture insulation & protection, thermal radiational heat control, EMI & RFI shielding, antistatic & security enclosures. (Woman/As-Pac, estab 1976, empl 49, sales $4,500,000, cert: CPUC)

9294 H & A Enterprise
530 N Baldwin Park Blvd
City Of Industry, CA 91746
Contact: Huma Latif Owner
Tel: 909-714-3960
Email: ahuma@hotmail.com
Website: www.hnaenterprise.com
Dist textile goods, socks, towels, bar mops . (Woman/As-Ind, estab 2012, empl 1, sales , cert: NMSDC)

9295 International Textile and Apparel, Inc.
1875 Century Park E Ste 1040
Los Angeles, CA 90067
Contact: Shoaib Kothawala CEO
Tel: 310-556-8088
Email: nbaresabidia@intlinen.com
Website: www.donothaveone.com
Mfr towels, bar mop towels & shop towels, weaving dye & finish, cut & sew. (As-Pac, estab 1983, empl 15, sales , cert: NMSDC)

9296 Venus Group, Inc.
25861 Wright St
Foothill Ranch, CA 92610
Contact: Ryen Masters Sales Mgr
Tel: 800-421-4595
Email: rmasters@venusgroup.com
Website: www.venusgroup.com
Mfr, cut and sew textiles, towels, sheets and napery. (As-Ind, estab 1972, empl 130, sales $75,000,000, cert: NMSDC)

Georgia

9297 PBR Inc.
335 Athena Dr
Athens, GA 30601
Contact: Palak Patel Exec Business Devel
Tel: 706-354-3700
Email: palak@skaps.com
Website: www.skaps.com
Fabricate Geosynthetic & nonwoven drainage products, produce polypropylene & polyester needle-punched nonwoven geotextiles from 2 to 32 ounces per square yard. (As-Pac, estab 1995, empl 250, sales $390,000,000, cert: NMSDC)

9298 Unitex International Inc.
2222 Northmont Parkway Ste 100
Duluth, GA 30096
Contact: Anwer Shakoor Director
Tel: 770-232-0060
Email: a.shakoor@unitexonline.com
Website: www.unitexonline.com
Textile & fabric finishing. (As-Ind, As-Pac, estab 1990, empl 29, sales $50,680,000, cert: NMSDC)

Illinois

9299 R&R Textile Mills Inc.
1101 N Lombard Rd
Lombard, IL 60148
Contact: Rajan Barad COO
Tel: 630-424-8000
Email: rbarad@rrtextilemills.com
Website: www.rrtextilemills.com
Mfr & dist textile products. (Minority, estab 1988, empl 40, sales $9,800,000, cert: NMSDC)

Maine

9300 Auburn Manufacturing, Inc.
P.O. Box 220
Mechanic Falls, ME 04256
Contact: Kathie M Leonard CEO
Tel: 207-345-8771
Email: kleonard@auburnmfg.com
Website: www.auburnmfg.com
Design & mfr heat-resistant textiles for MRO applications. (Woman/Hisp, estab 1979, empl 49, sales $10,300,000, cert: WBENC)

Michigan

9301 National Manufacturing, Inc.
25426 Ryan Rd
Warren, MI 48091
Contact: Paul Cano Sales
Tel: 586-755-8983
Email: paul.cano@nationalmanufacturinginc.com
Website: www.nationalmanufacturinginc.com
Leather & vinyl wrapping of steering wheels, pull handles, shift knobs, arm rests, bolsters. We as well can sew by hand or machine. Which we have done emergency kits, jack bags, utility bags, tools bags for the automotive industry. (Woman/Hisp, estab 1964, empl 32, sales , cert: NMSDC, WBENC)

Missouri

9302 Phoenix Textile Corporation
21 Commerce Dr
O'Fallon, MO 63366
Contact: Laura Mahnken Sales Admin
Tel: 314-291-2151
Email: lmahnken@phoenixtextile.com
Website: www.phoenixtextile.com
Reusable institutional textiles & interior products. (Woman, estab , empl , sales , cert: WBENC)

North Carolina

9303   Kilop USA, Inc.
       4100 Mendenhall Oaks Pkwy
       High Point, NC 27265
       Contact: Christine Chen President
       Tel: 336-402-5979
       Email: cchen@kilopusa.com
       Website: www.kilopusa.com
Global nonwoven and textile raw material supply chain
services. (Woman/As-Pac, estab 0, empl , sales $ 0, cert:
NMSDC, WBENC)

New Jersey

9304   Centryco Inc.
       300 W Broad St
       Burlington, NJ 08016
       Contact: Mary Gordon President
       Tel: 609-386-6448
       Email: mtg@centryco.com
       Website: www.centryco.com
Mfr point of operation barriers for machinery & equipment: bellows, way covers, telescoping covers, flat bellows
& screens, spring guards/covers. (Woman, estab 1949,
empl 35, sales $3,910,958, cert: WBENC)

9305   Offray Specialty Narrow Fabrics, Inc.
       4 Essex Ave Ste 403
       Bernardsville, NJ 07924
       Contact: Denise A. Offray CEO
       Tel: 908-879-3636
       Email: doffray@osnf.com
       Website: www.osnf.com
Engineer & mfr quality, high performance, innovative
narrow fabric textiles, weave specialty branded yarns.
(Woman, estab 1921, empl 45, sales $8,674,420, cert:
State)

New York

9306   Sigmatex, Inc
       551 Fifth Ave, Ste 1110
       New York, NY 10176
       Contact: Marcia Rodriguez GM
       Tel: 212-593-0934
       Email: mrodriguez@sigmatexlanier.com
       Website: www.sigmatexlanier.com
Mfr institutional textile products: terry towels, sheets &
pillowcases, table linens, kitchen linen, aprons, blankets.
(Woman/As-Ind, estab 1976, empl 25, sales $18,155,425,
cert: State)

Ohio

9307   Casco Manufacturing Solutions, Inc.
       3107 Spring Grove Ave
       Cincinnati, OH 11111
       Contact: Melissa Mangold President
       Tel: 800-843-1339
       Email: mmangold@cascosolutions.com
       Website: www.cascosolutions.com
Design & mfr fabric or textiles products. (Woman, estab ,
empl , sales $5,300,000, cert: WBENC)

South Carolina

9308   Calitex International
       106 Thousand Oaks Ct
       Summerville, SC 29485
       Contact: John Sylvester President
       Tel: 864-278-2621
       Email: john@calitexintl.com
       Website: www.calitex.us
Dist Industrial Fabrics 26" to 144", Cotton Canvas, Single
fill duck, Numbered Ducks, Army Duck, Twill, 100%
cotton and Polycotton Blends,
Treated fabric for Tarps, Tents, Tipis, Boat covers.
(Woman/As-Ind, estab 2005, empl 2, sales $1,500,000,
cert: NMSDC)

9309   MVP Textiles and Apparel, Inc.
       1031 Le Grand Blvd
       Charleston, SC 29492
       Contact: Mary Propes CEO
       Tel: 843-216-8380
       Email: marypropes@mvpgroupint.com
       Website: www.mvptextiles.com
Mfr textiles. (Woman, estab 2005, empl 15, sales
$16,800,000, cert: WBENC)

Texas

9310   Orr Textile Co., Inc.
       4777 Blalock
       Houston, TX 77041
       Contact: Hilary Orr VP Sales
       Tel: 713-939-7788
       Email: hilary@orrtextile.com
       Website: www.orrtextile.com
Dist sheets, towels, blankets, pillows, bath mats, robes,
slippers, kitchen towels, bar mops, table linen, napkins,
janitorial supplies, mops, buckets and wringers, mattress
pads, pillow slips, pool towels, spa linen, chef wear, etc.
(Woman, estab 1967, empl 11, sales , cert: WBENC)

Washington

9311   Lancs Industries Holdings, LLC
       12704 NE 124th St, Bldg 36
       Kirkland, WA 98034
       Contact: Raymond Suarez
       Tel: 425-823-6634
       Email: rsuarez@lancsindustries.com
       Website: www.lancsindustries.com
Mfr custom lead wool blankets, glovebags, tents,
protective clothing, related shielding & containment
products & supplies for nuclear naval shipyards &
maintenance facilities; nuclear remediation, decontamination, decommissioning & laboratory sites. (AA, estab
2010, empl 65, sales $6,000,000, cert: State)

Alabama

9312　ARD Logistics, LLC
　　　10098 Brose Dr
　　　Vance, AL 35490
　　　Contact: Courtney Waters Sales & Marketing Rep
　　　Tel:　205-393-5207
　　　Email: cwaters@ardlogistics.com
　　　Website: www.ardlogistics.com
Distribution operations: sequencing, sub-assembly, warehousing, inventory mgmt, shipping & receiving materials handling maintenance, packaging & repackaging, transportation mgmt, transportation svcs. (AA, estab 1998, empl 900, sales $68,717,549, cert: NMSDC)

9313　ARI Logistics LLC
　　　204 20th St North Ste 200
　　　Birmingham, AL 35203
　　　Contact: Brennan Waters Sales
　　　Tel:　205-271-4434
　　　Email: brennan.waters@actn.com
　　　Website: www.actn.com
Hazardous waste transport, in-plant, remediation, & logistics services. (AA, estab 2008, empl 55, sales $202,000,000, cert: NMSDC)

Arkansas

9314　Heartland Supply Company
　　　1248 Pump Station Rd
　　　Fayetteville, AR 72702
　　　Contact: Timothy J McNicholas Key Acct Mgr
　　　Tel:　773-617-6214
　　　Email: tmcnicholas@heartlandsupply.com
　　　Website: www.heartlandsupply.com
Logistic, distribution, supply chain optimization & warehousing services. (Nat Ame, estab 1987, empl 15, sales $100,000,000, cert: NMSDC)

9315　WMJ Enterprises, LLC.
　　　P.O. Box 979
　　　Lowell, AR 72745
　　　Contact: Justin Winberry VP
　　　Tel:　888-782-5828
　　　Email: jwinberry@leon-cannon.com
　　　Website: www.leon-cannon.com
Asset based transportation & logsitics. (Hisp, estab 1994, empl 38, sales $27,200,000, cert: State)

Arizona

9316　Aerocean Freight Solutions, Inc.
　　　9414 E. San Salvador Dr Ste 242
　　　Scottsdale, AZ 85258
　　　Contact: Yeon-Hee (Jennifer) Hwang President
　　　Tel:　480-515-1912
　　　Email: jennifer@aeroceanfreight.com
　　　Website: www.aeroceanfreight.com
Third party logistical services, road transportation, rail, ocean freight transportation. (Woman/As-Pac, estab 2006, empl 4, sales $5,314,734, cert: WBENC)

9317　Mach 1 Global Services, Inc.
　　　1530 W Broadway Rd
　　　Tempe, AZ 85282
　　　Contact: Jamie Fletcher CEO
　　　Tel:　480-921-3900
　　　Email: jfletcher@mach1global.com
　　　Website: www.mach1global.com
Transportation & logistics, domestic heavy weight expedited freight forwarding, international freight forwarding, ocean & air import & export, distribution, warehousing & supply chain management. (Woman/As-Pac, estab 1988, empl 290, sales $165,000,000, cert: WBENC)

9318　Patriot Movers, LLC
　　　3060 N Ridgecrest, Unit 128
　　　Mesa, AZ 85207
　　　Contact: Christopher Palos COO
　　　Tel:　877-793-7775
　　　Email: patriotmovers57@yahoo.com
　　　Website: http://Patriotmover.us
Moving & Transportation, Local a& nd Long Distance Moving, (intrastate and interstate), Packing, Unpacking, Crating, Specialized Freight,　Residential, Commercial, Office, Relocation services. (Woman/Hisp, estab 2012, empl 5, sales $103,573, cert: City)

9319　QBP Logistics, Inc.
　　　6006 N 83rd Ave Ste 201
　　　Glendale, AZ 85303
　　　Contact: Marlin Banks Operations Mgr
　　　Tel:　602-314-5099
　　　Email: marlin@landstarmail.com
　　　Website: www.qbpfreight.com
Transportation. Truckload transportation, Rail Intermodal service, Heavy Haul Specialized transport, Ocean freight forwarding, Expedited ground transport & Air freight forwarding. (AA, estab 2007, empl 6, sales $560,000, cert: CPUC)

9320　Reflex Logistics, LLC
　　　7114 E Stetson Dr Ste 400
　　　Scottsdale, AZ 85251
　　　Contact: Cory Clapper VP Sales
　　　Tel:　602-859-5969
　　　Email: coryclapper@reflexlogistics.com
　　　Website: www.reflexlogistics.com
Domestic full truckload van, refrigerated & flatbed transportation services. (Woman, estab 2013, empl 8, sales $750,000, cert: WBENC)

9321   Team Worldwide
       3837 E Wier Ave Ste 8
       Phoenix, AZ 85040
       Contact: Susanne Ingram Owner
       Tel: 602-305-7488
       Email: susanne.ingram@teamww.com
       Website: www.teamww.com
Logistics, air, land & sea. (Woman, estab 2001, empl 5,
sales $1,624,039, cert: State, City, WBENC)

9322   The ILS Company
       8350 E Old Vail Rd
       Tucson, AZ 85747
       Contact: Roy Austin Business Develop Dir
       Tel: 520-618-4309
       Email: roy.austin@ilscompany.com
       Website: www.ilscompany.com
International Freight Forwarding & Logistics Services, Door
to Door Transportation Management (Air, Ground, Ocean
and Rail), Project Cargo Management, Vendor Managed
Inventory, Hot Shot, Remote & White Glove. (Hisp, estab
2002, empl 54, sales $24,320,000, cert: NMSDC)

California

9323   Aeronet Logistics Inc.
       42 Corporate Park
       Irvine, CA 92606
       Contact: Andres Aceves President
       Tel: 949-474-9292
       Email: diversity@aeronet.com
       Website: www.aeronet.com
Global integrated logistics svcs: freight & cargo transportation, distribution & supply chain mgmt, air freight, expedited ground freight & urgent shipments, ocean cargo,
import & export. (Hisp, estab 1982, empl 125, sales
$70,858,000, cert: NMSDC, CPUC)

9324   Aeronet, Inc.
       P.O. Box 17239
       Irvine, CA 02397
       Contact: Benita Rosendal Business Dev Mgr
       Tel: 949-474-3000
       Email: diversityl@aeronet.com
       Website: www.aeronet.com
Integrated logistics solutions, global supply chain management, domestic & international shipping & handling. (Hisp,
estab 1982, empl 140, sales $48,700,000, cert: NMSDC,
CPUC)

9325   Bulk or Liquid Transport, LLC
       576 Camino Mercado
       Arroyo Grande, CA 93420
       Contact: Tracy Thomas CEO
       Tel: 800-975-2658
       Email: tthomas@bolt-transport.com
       Website: www.BOLT-Transport.com
Interstate transportation: liquid food-grade products.
(Woman, estab 2006, empl 12, sales $2,666,567, cert:
WBENC)

9326   Casas International Brokerage, Inc.
       9355 Airway Rd, Ste 4
       San Diego, CA 92154
       Contact: Syliva Casas President
       Tel: 619-710-4619
       Email: s.casas@casasinternational.com
       Website: www.casasinternational.com
US Customs broker & freight forwarder, warehouse &
distribution. (Woman/Hisp, estab 1984, empl 85, sales
$6,055,615, cert: NMSDC)

9327   Contractors Cargo Companies
       500 S Alameda St
       Compton, CA 90221
       Contact: Steve Cummins Natl Sales Mgr
       Tel: 310-609-1957
       Email: scummins@contractorscargo.com
       Website: www.contractorscargo.com
Heavy haul transportation company, oversized, over-
weight or overdimensional cargo, rail logistics, heavy
haul transport & shipping, nationally & internationally.
(Woman, estab 1929, empl 85, sales $24,000,000, cert:
CPUC)

9328   CurDor Group Inc.
       2321 Del Amo Blvd
       Rancho Dominguez, CA 90220
       Contact: Curlee Dorn President
       Tel: 310-885-5200
       Email: curlee.dorn@360globaltransportation.com
       Website: www.360globaltransportation.com
Intermodal, Import / Export, Haz-mat, Over-Weight
Containers, Warehousing, Less Than truck Load,
Transloading, Dedicated Services, Flatbed, Reefer, Rail
Services, Cross-Drocking, Truckload (TL), Outsourcing,
Dryvan. (AA, estab 2012, empl 7, sales $400,000, cert:
NMSDC)

9329   D.W. Morgan Company, Inc.
       4185 Blackhawk Plaza Circle Ste 260
       Danville, CA 94506
       Contact: Dawn Kim Dir of Business Development
       Tel: 310-938-9091
       Email: dawn.kim@dwmorgan.com
       Website: www.dwmorgan.com
Supply chain consulting, transportation management,
and thrid-party logistics. (As-Pac, estab 1990, empl 750,
sales $98,310,000, cert: NMSDC)

9330   EXCEL Moving Services
       30047 Ahern Ave
       Union City, CA 94587
       Contact: Bruce Owashi President
       Tel: 800-392-3596
       Email: bruce@excelmoving.com
       Website: www.excelmoving.com
Moving & storage, employee relocations, storage &
distribution, air-ride inside PU/Del transportation, intl
shipping/receiving, household goods specialist. (AA, As-
Pac, estab 1994, empl 55, sales $4,000,000, cert: State,
NMSDC, CPUC)

9331   FNS, Inc.
        18301 S Broadwick St
        Rancho Dominguez, CA 90220
        Contact: Josh Taxon Sales/Marketing Mgr
        Tel: 310-747-8530
        Email: joshua.taxon@pantos.com
        Website: www.fnsusa.com
Global third party logistics: ocean transport, air transport, trucking, warehousing & custom house brokerage. (As-Pac, estab 1995, empl 250, sales $12,881,358, cert: NMSDC)

9332   Freight Express Shipping Corp (FESCO)
        15330 Fairfield Ranch Rd., Unit G
        Chino Hills, CA 91709
        Contact: Michael Yu GM
        Tel: 909-586-3000
        Email: service@fescous.com
        Website: www.fescous.com
Import & export freight forwarding services. (Woman/As-Pac, estab 2012, empl 6, sales $900,000, cert: State)

9333   Global Freight Experts, Inc.
        1950 E Miner Ave
        Stockton, CA 95205
        Contact: Rajinder Singh President
        Tel: 209-547-9210
        Email: raj@gfbontime.com
        Website: www.gfbontime.com
Asset based trucking. (As-Pac, estab 2010, empl 25, sales $3,100,000, cert: NMSDC)

9334   Golden Gate Air Freight Inc.
        1809 Sabre St
        Hayward, CA 94545
        Contact: John Cardenas President
        Tel: 510-785-5720
        Email: jcardenas@ggaf.com
        Website:
Domestic & international freight forwarding. (Hisp, estab 1982, empl 22, sales $8,055,928, cert: NMSDC)

9335   Intrade Industries, Inc.
        2559 S East Ave
        Fresno, CA 93706
        Contact: Tracy Farrell logistics/mktg Mgr
        Tel: 559-256-3291
        Email: tracy.intradeindustries@gmail.com
        Website: http://intradeindustries.com
Transportation services for refrigerated cargo & freight from coast to coast. (Woman/As-Ind, estab 1997, empl 14, sales $23,000,000, cert: NMSDC)

9336   KLS Air Express, Inc. dba Freight Solution Provide
        2870 Gold Tailings Ct.
        Rancho Cordova, CA 95670
        Contact: Chrissie Cruz Natl Exec Accts Mgr
        Tel: 513-532-1297
        Email: chrissie_cruz@shipfsp.com
        Website: www.shipfsp.com/about/index.html
Customized frieght transportation, logistics, warehousing & supply chain management solutions. (Woman/As-Pac, estab 1989, empl 110, sales $42,000,000, cert: NMSDC, WBENC)

9337   KW International, Inc.
        18655 Bishop Ave
        Carson, CA 90746
        Contact: Steve Cho Sr Mgr
        Tel: 310-354-6944
        Email: steve@kwinternational.com
        Website: www.kwinternational.com/default.aspx
Total logistics, transportation, freight forwarding, in-house customs brokerage, warehousing & distribution, reverse logistics, customer call center, field service, drayage, information & technology. (As-Pac, estab 1996, empl 1000, sales , cert: NMSDC)

9338   Music Express Limousine Service
        2601 Empire Ave
        Burbank, CA 91504
        Contact: Gary Dye GM
        Tel: 818-260-6630
        Email: gdye@musiclimo.com
        Website: www.musiclimo.com
National & international limousine svcs. (Woman, estab , empl , sales , cert: WBENC)

9339   Northwest Freightway Inc.
        3421 Industrial Dr
        Yuba City, CA 95991
        Contact: Nicholas Schlaff Dir of Sales
        Tel: 539-788-2742
        Email: nick@nwfreightway.com
        Website: www.nwfreightway.com
Freight transportation services. (AA, estab 2007, empl 26, sales $28,000,000, cert: NMSDC)

9340   Oakley Relocation LLC
        13026 Stowe Dr
        Poway, CA 92064
        Contact: Dir of Business Development
        Tel: 858-602-1010
        Email:
        Website: www.oakleyrelocation.com
Full-service moving & storage company. (Woman, estab 2008, empl 15, sales $4,250,000, cert: WBENC)

9341   Postal Delivery Systems, LLC
        27240 Turnberry Lane, Ste 200
        Valencia, CA 91355
        Contact: Mike Singh Member
        Tel: 818-792-8397
        Email: postaldeliverysystems@gmail.com
        Website:
Transportation & logistics services. (As-Pac, estab 2013, empl 40, sales $3,500,000, cert: NMSDC)

9342   Public Special
        3147 Progress Circle
        Mira Loma, CA 91752
        Contact: Anna Aguiar President
        Tel: 951-360-4466
        Email: aaguiar@publicspecial.net
        Website: www.publicspecial.net
Transportation, US and Canada. (Woman/Hisp, estab 1980, empl , sales $22,048,000, cert: NMSDC)

9343 Red Rose Transportation, Inc
5705 N West Ave
Fresno, CA 93711
Contact: Mark Rose Operations Mgr
Tel: 559-277-1060
Email: mark@redrosetrans.net
Website: www.redrosetransportation.com
Logistic services, dedicated truckloads, Heavy haul, 53' dry van & reefers, flatbeds & LTL. (Woman/As-Pac, estab 2007, empl 7, sales $8,300,000, cert: CPUC, WBENC)

9344 Roland International Freight Services, Inc.
5710 W Manchester Ave Ste 104
Los Angeles, CA 90045
Contact: Roland Furtado President & CEO
Tel: 310-337-1775
Email: roland@rolandfreight.com
Website: www.rolandfreight.com
International freight forwarder handling shipments by air & ocean. (As-Ind, estab 1991, empl 4, sales $1,310,617, cert: State, CPUC, 8a)

9345 Say Cargo Express, Inc.
700 E Debra Lane
Anaheim, CA 92805
Contact: Doug Childers President
Tel: 714-772-7735
Email: dchilders@saycargo.com
Website: www.saycargo.com
Freight; Shipping; Expedited; Cargo; Oversized; Tradeshows; Logistics; LTL; Air Freight; Truckload, domestic freight forwarder that specializes in expedited freight. (Woman/Hisp, estab 2000, empl 13, sales $2,200,000, cert: State, WBENC)

9346 Trans Global Shipping Alliance, LLC
25255 Cabot Rd, Ste 212
Laguna Hills, CA 92653
Contact: William Cordova President
Tel: 949-699-1491
Email: bill@trustglobal.com
Website: www.trustglobal.com
Global shipping, trucking, ocean, air & special air couriers - standard & charter, full truckloads, flatbeds to LTL. (Woman, estab 2000, empl 5, sales $338,896, cert: State, CPUC)

9347 Transit Air Cargo Inc.
2204 East 4th St
Santa Ana, CA 92705
Contact: Gulnawaz Khodayar President
Tel: 714-915-0657
Email: gkhodayar@transitair.com
Website: www.transitair.com
Global tradeshow logistics: air, ocean & ground. Product freight services international & domestic. (Woman/As-Ind, estab 1989, empl 55, sales $23,933,988, cert: NMSDC, WBENC)

9348 Tricor America, Inc.
P.O. Box 8100 - SFIA
San Francisco, CA 94128
Contact: Scott Tanaka Major Acct Exec
Tel: 650-877-3650
Email: scott.tanaka@mail.tricor.com
Website: www.tricor.com
National & intl courier services. (As-Pac, estab 1957, empl 500, sales , cert: NMSDC)

Colorado

9349 Craters and Freighters
331 Corporate Circle, Ste J
Golden, CO 80401
Contact: Chad Brockmeyer Natl Sales Mgr
Tel: 720-287-7805
Email: chad@cratersandfreighters.com
Website: www.cratersandfreighters.com
Custom wood crating, plastic hard cases and freight services. (Woman, estab 1990, empl 12, sales $55,000,000, cert: WBENC)

9350 FAK, Inc.
10885 E 51st Ave
Denver, CO 80239
Contact: Ron Harms GM
Tel: 303-289-5433
Email: rharms@fakinc.com
Website: www.fakinc.com
Transportation: refrigerated, dry van, flatbed, specialized & intermodal. US & Canada. (Woman, estab 1983, empl 62, sales $69,359,561, cert: WBENC)

9351 Innovative Solutions Development
13404 Locust St
Thornton, CO 80602
Contact: Darryl Johnson Owner
Tel: 303-428-6034
Email: darrylj@landstarmail.com
Website:
Transportation, distribution, logistics, warehousing, & information management domestically & globally. (AA, estab 2000, empl 3, sales $1,500,000, cert: State)

9352 Logistics Innovators Inc. dba Adcom Worldwide
16600 E 33rd Dr, Unit 26
Aurora, CO 80011
Contact: Toni Brock President
Tel: 303-329-0702
Email: tbrock@adcomworldwide.com
Website: www.adcomworldwide.com
Worldwide logistics, customs brokerage, ocean, air ground, warehouse. (Woman, estab 1997, empl 10, sales $2,167,000, cert: WBENC)

Florida

9353 Air Marine Forwarding Co., Inc.
3409-B NW 72 Ave
Miami, FL 33122
Contact: Roger Madan President
Tel: 305-477-3496
Email: r.madan@airmarine.com
Website: www.airmarine.com
Global logistics, intl air & ocean freight forwarding, customs brokerage, NVOCC, warehousing & distribution, bonded facilities & trucks, packing & crating. (Hisp, estab 1968, empl 28, sales $3,108,366, cert: NMSDC)

9354 Avanti Limousine Service, LLC.
      5425 N Dixie Hwy
      Boca Raton, FL 33487
      Contact: Serena Leverrier Affiliate Relations Dir
      Tel: 561-241-9955
      Email: res@avanticar.com
      Website: www.avanticar.com
Global ground transportation to and from anywhere in the
world. (Woman, estab 1985, empl 12, sales $1,000,000,
cert: WBENC)

9355 Clover Systems Inc.
      1910 NW 97th Ave
      Miami, FL 33172
      Contact: Dir Business Dev
      Tel: 305-499-7056
      Email:
      Website: www.clovergroup.com
Integrated logistics, air & ocean shipping, domestic & intl
distribution svcs, warehouse, export packing & trucking.
(Hisp, estab 1985, empl 70, sales , cert: NMSDC)

9356 Edward Estevez CHB, Inc.
      6910 Main St, Ste 150
      Miami Lakes, FL 33014
      Contact: Edward Estevez President
      Tel: 786-247-1961
      Email: admin@eechb.com
      Website: www.eechb.com
U.S. Customs brokerage & logistics services. (Hisp, estab
2004, empl 1, sales , cert: State)

9357 Faith Transport & Logistics, Inc.
      190 SE 3rd Ave
      Deerfield Beach, FL 33441
      Contact: Aldo Goncalves Jr. President
      Tel: 954-274-0357
      Email: transportwithfaith@faithtlinc.com
      Website: http://transportwithfaith.com
Transportation & logistics, United States & Canada as an
Interstate Motor Carrier. (Hisp, estab 2012, empl 3, sales
$244,948, cert: NMSDC)

9358 Florida Freight Lines Inc.
      451 Harbor Dr N
      Indian Rocks Beach, FL 33785
      Contact: Marie Mazzara President
      Tel: 727-800-9870
      Email: mmazzara@floridafreightlines.com
      Website: www.FloridaFreightLines.com
LTL (Less Than Truckload), Full Truckload, Dry, Fresh,
Frozen. (Woman, estab 2013, empl 2, sales $245,570, cert:
WBENC)

9359 GlobalTransService Corp.
      10200 W State Rd84 Ste 205
      Davie, FL 33324
      Contact: President
      Tel: 954-414-0561
      Email:
      Website: www.globaltransservicecorp.com/
Dry Van, Reefer, Flat Bed, Tracking Shipment, Logistics.
(Woman, estab 2014, empl 5, sales $1,777,675, cert:
WBENC)

9360 Harbor Transport, Inc.
      7320 NW 70th St
      Miami, FL 33166
      Contact: Roberto Victorero President
      Tel: 305-592-5357
      Email: roberto@harbor.com
      Website: www.harbor.com
Transportation services. (Woman/Hisp, estab 1987, empl
7, sales , cert: NMSDC)

9361 Hermes Global Logistic Services, LLC
      5323 Millenia Lakes Blvd Ste 300
      Orlando, FL 32839
      Contact: Dena Kirschbaum
      Tel: 407-734-4046
      Email: dena.kirschbaum@hglservices.com
      Website: http://hglservices.com
3PL supply chain management solutions, integrating
operations, warehousing & transportation services.
(Woman/AA, estab 2015, empl 4, sales $500,000, cert:
NMSDC)

9362 Interstate Transport, Inc.
      324 1st Ave North
      St. Petersburg, FL 33701
      Contact: Zach Aufmann COO
      Tel: 727-822-9999
      Email: WBENC@interstatetransport.com
      Website: www.InterstateTransport.com
TL (truckload) & LTL (less than truckload) freight in US &
Canada. Specialized freight capabilities (live goods,
plants, perishables, lumber) dry, flatbed & refrigerated
(reefer/refer) trailers, utilizing single or team drivers.
(Woman, estab 2002, empl 50, sales $30,745,013, cert:
WBENC)

9363 Newco Services, Inc.
      1831 16th St
      Boynton Beach, FL 33435
      Contact: Sales
      Tel: 561-375-9930
      Email:
      Website: www.newcoservices.com
Transportation, warehousing, repair, refurbishment,
prevenative maintenance, data reporting & consolidated
billing svcs. (Woman, estab 1994, empl 20, sales
$4,200,000, cert: WBENC)

9364 Ocean Cargo Logistics Group, LLC
      12161 SW 132 Ct
      Miami, FL 33186
      Contact: Lorenzo Macias Sales
      Tel: 305-471-8442
      Email: lorenzo@oceancargologistics.com
      Website: www.oceancargologistics.com
Freight Forwarding, Air transportation, Domestic
Trucking Transportation, Deep Ocean Transportation,
Packing & Crating, LCL, FCL, LTL. (Hisp, estab 2008, empl
4, sales $1,200,000, cert: 8a)

9365   One Horn Transportation Inc.
8374 Market St #470
Lakewood Ranch, FL 34202
Contact: Mary Morra Operations Mgr
Tel: 973-595-7700
Email: help@onehorn.com
Website: www.OneHorn.com
Freight brokerage, flatbed & dry van tractor-trailer services, 48 contiguous states & Canada. (Woman/AA, estab 2005, empl 40, sales $20,000,000, cert: NMSDC, WBENC)

9366   Prime Air Cargo Inc.
1316 NW 78th Ave
Doral, FL 33126
Contact: Omar Zambrano GM
Tel: 305-592-2044
Email: ozambrano@primeaircargo.com
Website: http://primeaircargo.com
Air, land & ocean transport services. (Hisp, estab 2004, empl 15, sales , cert: NMSDC)

9367   Robertson Forwarding Company Inc.
1951 NW 7th Ave Ste 600
Miami, FL 33136
Contact: Stefan Ahrens GM
Tel: 305-477-5548
Email: sahrens@rfclogistics.com
Website: www.rfclogistics.com
Logistics, warehousing, import & export documentation, air charter brokerage, in house customs broker, trucking, hazardous documentation, out of gage cargo, NVOCC, ocean shipments. (Woman/AA, estab 1968, empl 10, sales $2,500,000, cert: State)

9368   Time Definite Services Transportation, LLC
1935 CR525E
Sumterville, FL 33521
Contact: Michael Suarez President
Tel: 800-466-8040
Email: sales@timedefinite.com
Website: www.timedefinite.com
Freigth transportation: truckload LTL air freight, hot shots, warehousing, domestic & international. (Hisp, estab 1990, empl 60, sales $45,700,000, cert: NMSDC)

9369   Timus, Inc
8131 Baymeadows Cir W Ste 202
Jacksonville, FL 32256
Contact: Mr. Adam P. Kulig VP Business Dev
Tel: 904-641-6206
Email: adam.kulig@timusinc.com
Website: www.timus.com
Full truckload, intermodal (rail). (Nat Ame, estab 1999, empl 5, sales $5,040,000, cert: State)

Georgia

9370   AFCLS Logistics Services LLC
975 Cobb Place Blvd Ste 101
Kennesaw, GA 30144
Contact: Brenda Collins Brown VP
Tel: 770-514-1456
Email: brenda.collinsbrown@afcls.com
Website: www.afcls.com
Global freight logistics svcs: motor freight forwarding, freight brokerage, ocean transportation intermediary & non-vessel operating common carrier services & indirect air carriage. (AA, estab 2008, empl 10, sales $1,300,000, cert: NMSDC)

9371   Axiom Logistics LLC
5000 Austell-Powder Springs Rd Ste 189
Austell, GA 30106
Contact: Morgan Perry CEO
Tel: 770-694-6248
Email: morgan@axiomtrans.com
Website: www.axiomtrans.com
Logistics, Dry, frozen & refrigerated truckload, Flatbed, drop deck & double drop, Over-Dimensional, heavy haul & expedited, Power Only, Team & expedited truckload and (LTL) less than truckload services. (Woman/AA, estab 2012, empl 6, sales $1,099,963, cert: NMSDC, WBENC)

9372   Bennett International Group LLC
1001 Industrial Pkwy
McDonough, GA 30253
Contact: VP of Diversity
Tel: 770-957-1866
Email:
Website: www.bennettig.com
Transportation: NVOCC, customs brokerage, freight forwarding air & ocean, project cargo, domestic trucking, oversized & over weight cargo, warehousing, third party logistics. (Woman, estab 1973, empl 650, sales , cert: WBENC)

9373   CorTrans Logistics, LLC
6465 E Johns Crossing Ste 300
Johns Creek, GA 30097
Contact: Gloria Cortez CEO
Tel: 678-969-9529
Email: bcortez@cortrans.com
Website: www.cortrans.com
Transportation svcs: air freight, charters, next day, second day, and deferred delivery, logistics svcs & supply chain mgmt. (Woman/Hisp, estab 1999, empl 20, sales $18,500,000, cert: WBENC)

9374   Eagle Transportation Services, Inc.
731 Queen City Pkwy Ste 101
Gainesville, GA 30501
Contact: Lynn Mull President
Tel: 770-965-1242
Email: lynn@eagletransportation.com
Website: www.eagletransportation.com
Third party logistics. (Woman, estab 1988, empl 6, sales , cert: WBENC)

9375 Efficient Courier & Logistics Services LLC
      5475 Tulane Dr
      Atlanta, GA 30336
      Contact: Patrick Chukwudolue Exec Director
      Tel: 800-590-2155
      Email: partners@ecourierlogistics.com
      Website: www.ecourierlogistics.com
Integrated end to logistics & freight services, customized
supply chain, warehousing, logistics & delivery. (AA, estab
2013, empl 5, sales , cert: NMSDC)

9376 Expedited Transportation Services, Inc
      505 Plantation Park Dr
      Atlanta, GA 30052
      Contact: President
      Tel: 770-413-1700
      Email:
      Website: www.ets-atlanta.com
Mail & cargo transport, air cargo, local area trucking,
marine cargo, rail cargo, regional or natl trucking, vehicle
carrier services, air charter transport. (Woman, estab
1982, empl 11, sales , cert: WBENC)

9377 KCH Trucking, LLC
      6695 Peachtree Industrial Blvd Ste 250
      Atlanta, GA 30360
      Contact: Alan Whitten VP Sales
      Tel: 770-962-6829
      Email: awhitten@kchtrans.com
      Website: www.kchtrans.com
National truckload transportation services. (Woman, estab
2006, empl 5, sales $8,000,001, cert: WBENC)

9378 MIMCH, Inc. dba GOEH Distribution
      200 Piedmont Crt, Ste-B
      Doraville, GA 30340
      Contact: Stanley Michel GM
      Tel: 770-849-0086
      Email: stmichel@bellsouth.net
      Website: www.goehmoving.com
Warehousing, moving & distribution. (Woman/AA, estab
1994, empl 25, sales $485,900, cert: State)

9379 PEI Logistics, Inc.
      598 Red Oak Rd
      Stockbridge, GA 30281
      Contact: President
      Tel: 404-361-0073
      Email:
      Website: www.shippei.com
Transportation & logistic services. (Woman, estab 1993,
empl 35, sales $11,000,000, cert: WBENC)

9380 Premier Expediters, Inc.
      598 Red Oak Rd
      Stockbridge, GA 30281
      Contact: Jeff George Business Dev Mgr
      Tel: 859-331-7447
      Email: cvg@shippei.com
      Website: www.shippei.com
Transportation, Carrier Authority, Freight Forwarding
Authority & Brokerage, FTL, LTL, Expedited, Specialized, Air
& Ocean Freight services. (Woman, estab 1992, empl 32,
sales $13,000,000, cert: WBENC)

9381 R2 Trucking Solutions
      1882 Princeton Ave, Ste 1
      College Park, GA 30337
      Contact: Amari Ruff CEO
      Tel: 770-892-3699
      Email: aruff@r2truckingsolutions.com
      Website: www.r2truckingsolutions.com
Global logistics, air, ocean & ground carriers. (AA, estab
2014, empl 22, sales $1,867,989, cert: NMSDC)

9382 S-2international LLC
      395 McDonough Pkwy
      McDonough, GA 30253
      Contact: Jennifer Mead CEO
      Tel: 678-432-9502
      Email: jennifer.mead@s-2international.com
      Website: www.s-2international.com
Transportation services, expedited/JIT movement, LTL,
Airfreight, Charter & Ocean shipments. (Woman, estab
2005, empl 30, sales $17,200,000, cert: WBENC)

9383 Southeastern Transfer & Storage Co., Inc.
      2561 Plant Atkinson Rd
      Smyrna, GA 30080
      Contact: Debra Wallace Co-Owner
      Tel: 404-794-2401
      Email: dwallace@setransfer.com
      Website: www.setransfer.com
Transportation services: heavy-haul trucking & storage,
48 states authority. (Woman, estab 1929, empl 30, sales
$3,000,000, cert: WBENC)

9384 Transgroup World Wide Logistics
      650 Atlanta S Pkwy, Ste 109
      Atlanta, GA 30349
      Contact: Tamara Barnes President
      Tel: 404-725-3660
      Email: tamib.atl@transgroup.com
      Website: www.transgroup.cam
Domestic Air: Next flight out, Next Day AM, Second day,
3-5 day service, Air Charters, Express LTL & Full Truckload, Flatbed/Oversize loads, Trade Show Services,
Canada/Mexico TransBoarder. (Woman, estab 1986,
empl 37, sales $291,000,000, cert: NWBOC)

9385 Tribe Express
      2251 Jesse Jewell Pkwy NE
      Gainesville, GA 30507
      Contact: Fred Schloth Dir New Business Dev
      Tel: 904-222-0445
      Email: fschloth@tribetrans.com
      Website: www.tribeexpress.com
Asset based transportation, Expedited Services, Power
Only, Dedicated Services, Logistics Services for Temp
Controlled, Deep Frozen & all Dry modes. (Woman/Nat
Ame, estab 2005, empl 118, sales $39,000,000, cert:
NMSDC)

9386 Upward Global Logistics & Distribution
5421 Legacy Trail
Douglasville, GA 30135
Contact: Nick Byers President
Tel: 949-484-5231
Email: nrbyers@uglad.us
Website: www.uglad.us
Freight Brokerage, transportation solutions to
air, ground, rail, expedited, drayage or port
logistics; coordinating the movement of freight between
plants, ports, warehouses, job sites, or any destination.
(As-Pac, estab 2010, empl 6, sales $315,000, cert: 8a)

9387 Vector Global Logistics LLC
887 W Marietta St NW, Ste M201
Atlanta, GA 30318
Contact: Enrique Alvarez Managing Dir
Tel: 404-554-1150
Email: enrique.alvarez@vectorgl.com
Website: www.VectorGL.com
Sea freight, air freight, truck, rail & general logistics. (As-Pac, Hisp, estab 2012, empl 19, sales $9,100,000, cert:
NMSDC)

Iowa

9388 JMS Transportation Inc.
5650 6th St SW
Cedar Rapids, IA 52404
Contact: Riley Larson GM
Tel: 800-877-1529
Email: rileylarson@jmstransport.com
Website: www.jmstransport.com
Trucking & logistics, asset-based transportation, Midwest
regional LTL & FTL dry van freight hauling. (Woman, estab
1990, empl 39, sales $19,048,850, cert: NWBOC)

9389 Weinrich Truck Line, Inc.
27932 C 60
Hinton, IA 51024
Contact: Ranae Allen Operations Mgr
Tel: 800-831-0814
Email: ranaewtl@hotmail.com
Website: www.weinrichtruckline.com
Liquid bulk food grade transportation. (Woman, estab
1960, empl 75, sales $9,284,328, cert: WBENC)

Illinois

9390 A & T Trucking Co.
2920 S 19th Ave
Broadview, IL 60155
Contact: Marlon K. Hooper VP-Sales
Tel: 708-344-3770
Email: mkhoopship@yahoo.com
Website:
Local & out of state trucking & warehousing. (AA, estab
1983, empl 45, sales , cert: State, City)

9391 AGT Global Logistics
800 Roosevelt Rd, Building C, Ste 300
Glen Ellyn, IL 60137
Contact: Jeff Mock MR
Tel: 630-953-4366
Email: jeffm@agt3pl.com
Website: www.agt3pl.com
Certified 3rd Party Logistics, air freight carrier, asset
based. (Woman, estab 2005, empl 21, sales
$1,141,103,297, cert: WBENC, NWBOC)

9392 All Girl Transportation & Logistics, Inc
216 S Prater
Northlake, IL 60164
Contact: Angela Mock President
Tel: 877-816-5477
Email: amock@allgirlstrucking.com
Website: www.allgirlstrucking.com
Transportation: ground & ground expedited, air &
airfreight, small package, auditing, transportation
management services. (Woman, estab 2005, empl 30,
sales $12,000,000, cert: WBENC)

9393 Box Truck Logistics, LLC
1517 Golfview Court
Glendale Heights, IL 60139
Contact: Hayden Lynch President
Tel: 312-602-2639
Email: hlynch@boxtrucklogistics.com
Website: www.boxtrucklogistics.com
Freight brokerage - FTL, LTL shipments, project freight &
out of gauge shipments. (AA, estab 2014, empl 2, sales ,
cert: NMSDC)

9394 Chela Logistics Inc.
1521 Brummel Ave
Elk Grove Village, IL 60007
Contact: President
Tel: 847-290-9040
Email:
Website: www.chelalogistics.com
Local & nationwide transportation. (Woman, estab 2001,
empl 11, sales $2,500,000, cert: WBENC)

9395 CTL Global, Inc.
11697 W Grand Ave
Northlake, IL 60164
Contact: VP Strategic Initiatives
Tel: 708-223-1196
Email:
Website: http://ctlglobalsolutions.com
Fulfillment & logistics, transportation & technology
services. (Woman, estab 1978, empl 250, sales
$53,723,000, cert: WBENC)

9396 DSC Logistics, Inc.
1750 S Wolf Rd
Des Plaines, IL 60018
Contact: Tracy Drake Dir Diversity
Tel: 847-390-6800
Email: tracy.drake@dsc-logistics.com
Website: www.dsclogistics.com
Supply chain mgmt, strategic solutions-based consulting,
business process integration, process improvement &
management, logistics operations, warehousing,
transportation, packaging & fulfillment. (Woman, estab
1960, empl 2200, sales $330,000,000, cert: WBENC)

9397 GTS Express, Inc.
13851 S Janas Pkwy
Homer Glen, IL 60491
Contact: Olivia Metelanski President
Tel: 844-487-9777
Email: olivia@gtsexpressinc.com
Website: www.gtsexpressinc.com
Asset based transportation logistics & 3PL. (Woman, estab 2013, empl 12, sales $550,000, cert: NWBOC)

9398 Mid-West Moving & Storage, Inc.
1255 Tonne Rd
Elk Grove Village, IL 60007
Contact: Luis Toledo President
Tel: 847-593-7201
Email: diversity@midwestmoving.com
Website: www.midwestmoving.com
Office & residential moving, record storage & destruction, ware housing, distribution & local hauling. (Hisp, estab 1983, empl 100, sales $7,306,878, cert: NMSDC, 8a)

9399 Milano Railcar Services
P.O. Box 1357
Mount Vernon, IL 62864
Contact: Mary Burgan President
Tel: 618-242-4004
Email: mary@milanorail.com
Website: www.milanorail.com
Logistics, Storage, Pipe Laydown Yard, Trucking, Logistics, Inventory Control, Warehousing, Materials Handling, Transloading, Consulting. (Woman, estab 2009, empl 3, sales $264,085, cert: WBENC)

9400 New Age Transportation, Distribution & Warehousing
1881 Rose Rd
Lake Zurich, IL 60047
Contact: Pam Troy VP of Admin
Tel: 847-545-9200
Email: pamt@newagetransportation.com
Website: www.newagetransportation.com
National & international transportation & logistics: dist, warehousing, fulfillment & e-commerce, expedition & rail shipments, freight bill auditing. (Woman, estab 1989, empl 45, sales $28,000,000, cert: WBENC)

9401 Pactrans Air & Sea, Inc.
951-961 W Thorndale Ave
Bensenville, IL 60106
Contact: Kitty Pon President
Tel: 847-766-9988
Email: kittyp@pactrans.com
Website: www.pactrans.com
International freight forwarding: air & sea freight consolidation logistics, world wide charter, warehousing, distribution, trucking & Customs brokerage services. (Woman/As-Pac, estab 1991, empl 50, sales $30,000,000, cert: City, NMSDC)

9402 Passion Transportation Inc.
145 Sayton Road Ste C
Fox Lake, IL 60020
Contact: Suzanne Thompson WBE Liasion/ Customer Relations
Tel: 847-587-2700
Email: quotes@passiontrans.com
Website: www.passiontrans.com
Truckload, less than truckload & partial truckloads, air, ocean, expidited, temperature controlled & flatbed freight. (Woman, estab 2007, empl 6, sales $4,134,507, cert: WBENC)

9403 Pelican Logistics Inc.
101 Frontier way
Bensenville, IL 60106
Contact: Keith Kim Sales Mgr
Tel: 847-337-5255
Email: keith.kim@pelicanloginc.com
Website: http://pelicanti.com
Air freight transportation. (Woman/As-Pac, estab 1995, empl 8, sales $10,000,000, cert: WBENC)

9404 Reilly International Ltd.
1555 N Michael Dr
Wood Dale, IL 60191
Contact: Vickie Reilly President
Tel: 630-238-4900
Email: vickie@reillyinternational.com
Website: www.reillyinternational.com
International freight forwarding, consolidation & brokerage. (Woman, estab 1984, empl 20, sales $8,417,000, cert: WBENC)

9405 Riverbend Logistics Solutions, Inc.
65 E Ferguson Ave
Wood River, IL 62095
Contact: MURDOCK MOSS
Tel: 618-254-2687
Email: mmoss@rls-global.com
Website: www.rls-global.com
Third-party logistics, freight management & shipping. (Woman, estab 1992, empl 8, sales $2,680,000, cert: State, NWBOC)

9406 Servex, Inc.
1567 Frontenac Rd
Naperville, IL 60563
Contact: John Rizek Dir mktg/sales
Tel: 630-369-9500
Email: j.rizek@servex.com
Website: www.servex.com
Third party warehousing & warehousing services (Woman, estab 1981, empl 35, sales , cert: CPUC)

9407 Towers Alliance Inc.
4901 W. Quincy
Chicago, IL 60644
Contact: John Chambers President
Tel: 708-268-1094
Email: jchambers@towersalliance.com
Website: www.towersalliance.com
A dynamic minority owned company providing quality, sustainable goods to our customers. We are committed to delivering innovative products and services as your supply chain partner. (AA, estab 2013, empl 5, sales $150,000, cert: NMSDC)

9408 Williams NationaLease, Ltd.
404 W Northtown Road Ste B
Normal, IL 61761
Contact: Sandy Hotlen President
Tel: 800-779-8785
Email: shotlen@wnlgroup.com
Website: www.wnlgroup.com
Truck leasing & rental: 130 power units & 180 trailers.
(Woman, estab 1984, empl 210, sales $36,000,000, cert:
State, WBENC)

Indiana

9409 Butler Tillman Express Trucking, Inc.
P.O. Box 1017
Beverly Shores, IN 46301
Contact: Sue Lundberg Office Mgr
Tel: 219-764-2100
Email: info@btexpresstrucking.com
Website: www.btexpresstrucking.com
Tanker trucking, bulk liquid and dry materials. (Woman/
AA, estab 2003, empl 6, sales $388,518, cert: NMSDC)

9410 Chaser, LLC
415 E 31st St
Anderson, IN 46016
Contact: Nammy Eskar CEO
Tel: 765-640-8620
Email: neskar@chaserllc.com
Website: www.chaserllc.com
Transportation & logistics, hauling truckload shipments of
general commodities in both interstate & intrastate
commerce. (As-Ind, As-Pac, estab 2011, empl 50, sales ,
cert: NMSDC)

9411 HeLP Logistics, Inc.
13578 East 131st St Ste #260
Fishers, IN 46037
Contact: Lorri Lord CEO
Tel: 866-504-9620
Email: lorri.lord@helplogistics.com
Website: www.helplogistics.com
Transportation & logistics. (Woman, estab 2007, empl 12,
sales $3,768,517, cert: State, WBENC)

9412 Langham Logistics Inc.
5335 W 74th St
Indianapolis, IN 46268
Contact: Cathy Langham President
Tel: 317-471-5120
Email: cathylangham@elangham.com
Website: www.elangham.com
Global freight management: FF, expedite, warehousing,
distribution, fulfillment. (Woman, estab 1988, empl 150,
sales , cert: State, WBENC)

9413 Mid-American Specialized Transport, Inc.
2827 W State Rd 66
Rockport, IN 47635
Contact: Paula Joyner President
Tel: 812-649-2599
Email: paula.joyner@mastusa.com
Website: www.mastusa.com
General freight & hazardous materials, transportation
logistics, brokerage, third party logistics & transportation
consuting services. (Woman, estab 2008, empl 19, sales
$8,000,000, cert: WBENC)

9414 MyWay Logistics LLC
1300 E 86th St, Ste 14 # 128
Indianapolis, IN 46240
Contact: Owner
Tel: 888-557-4213
Email:
Website: www.myway-logistics.com
Non-asset based logistics. Licensed & bonded to service
all 48 states & Canada. (Woman, estab 2014, empl 3,
sales $913,754, cert: WBENC)

Kansas

9415 Gold Star Transportation, Inc.
9424 Reeds Rd
Overland Park, KS 66207
Contact: Anthony Janiak
Tel: 913-433-4133
Email: tonyj@goldstartrans.com
Website: www.goldstartransportation.com
Third party transportation logistics. (Woman, estab
1982, empl 29, sales $24,781,811, cert: NWBOC)

9416 Nationwide Transportation & Logistics Services
Inc.
P.O. Box 3190
Shawnee, KS 66203
Contact: Kim Isenhower President
Tel: 913-888-1685
Email: kim@nationwidetransportation.com
Website: www.nationwidetransportation.com
Transportation freight brokerage services. (Woman,
estab 1998, empl 18, sales $20,000,000, cert: WBENC)

Kentucky

9417 HJI -Vascor Logistics LLC
13200 Complete Court
Louisville, KY 40223
Contact: Brian Palmer Sr Mgr inbound logistics
Tel: 502-638-8021
Email: bpalmer@vascorltd.com
Website: www.vascorlogistics.com
Transportation services. (Woman/AA, estab 2012, empl
500, sales $20,000,000, cert: WBENC)

9418 Liberty Transportation, Inc. dba Team Worldwide
1348 Jamike Dr
Erlanger, KY 41018
Contact: Bobbie Mattis President
Tel: 859-282-0505
Email: bobbie.mattis@teamww.com
Website: www.teamww.com
Freight forwarding & logistics services. (Woman, estab
1989, empl 15, sales $6,000,000, cert: WBENC)

9419 Stett Transportation Inc.
224 Grandview Dr
Ft. Mitchell, KY 41017
Contact: Chris Jolevski Sales Team Lead
Tel: 859-384-2400
Email: chris@stett.net
Website: www.stett.net
Non-asset based 3PL transporting liquid bulk, both
Hazmat & non hazardous products. (Woman, estab
1995, empl 24, sales $11,500,000, cert: WBENC)

Massachusetts

9420 Advantage Global Logistics
41 Highland Ave
Randolph, MA 02368
Contact: Maureen Powers VP, Sales
Tel: 781-986-3832
Email: maureen.powers@landstarmail.com
Website: www.landstar.com
Domestic & international, white glove inside delivery, debris removal & scheduled appointment deliveries, exporting & importing, air or ocean, door to door or door to airport/port, clear customs. (Woman, estab 1960, empl 5000, sales $2,200,000,000,000, cert: State)

9421 Normandin Transportation Services Inc.
10 Tandem Way, Ste B
Hopedale, MA 01747
Contact: Stephen Normandin VP, Strategy
Tel: 508-278-6579
Email: steve@normandintrans.com
Website: normandintrans.com
Transportation & logistics, LTL & truckload service. (Woman, estab 2008, empl 56, sales , cert: WBENC)

9422 One World Logistics dba Mainfreight
14 Jewel Dr Ste 8
Wilmington, MA 01887
Contact: MAINFREIGHT INC President
Tel: 617-567-6800
Email:
Website: www.Mainfreightusa.com
Freight transportation shipping services for domestic, international, air, road & ocean. Local, Nationwide & worldwide services. (Woman, estab 2006, empl 16, sales $1,750,000, cert: State, WBENC)

9423 Performance Trans. Inc.
70 Benson St
Fitchburg, MA 01420
Contact: Julie Taylor President
Tel: 978-345-5300
Email: julie@performancetransinc.com
Website: http://performancetransinc.com
Transportation: haul petroleum products (gas,diesel, heating oil, bio diesel, etc), building materials. (Woman, estab 1985, empl 45, sales $8,000,000, cert: State)

Maryland

9424 C J International Inc.
519 S Ellwood Ave
Baltimore, MD 21224
Contact: Samya Murray Compliance Officer
Tel: 410-563-6020
Email: sdmurray@cjinternational.com
Website: www.cjinternational.com
Global Logistics: air/ocean/ground freight transportation, warehousing & Customs brokerage services. (Woman, estab 1987, empl 50, sales $3,600,000, cert: WBENC)

9425 Dream Management Inc.
210 W 28th St
Baltimore, MD 21211
Contact: Joseph DeCarlo President
Tel: 443-552-5512
Email: jdecarlo@dream-mgmt.com
Website: http://dream-mgmt.com
Transportation services, including but not limited to, shuttle services, wheelchair equipped vehicle services, passenger vans, passenger buses, passenger motor coach buses, sedan vehicles, and limousine (Hisp, estab 1999, empl 63, sales $2,500,000, cert: State)

9426 Patriot Air Freight, Inc.
806 Cromwell Park Dr
Glen Burnie, MD 21061
Contact: Heidi Gordon Acct Exec
Tel: 410-766-2422
Email: hgordon@aitworldwide.com
Website: www.aitworldwide.com
Domestic Air Freight, Ground Transportation, International Air & Ocean, Custom House Brokerage, Transborder Services. (Woman, estab 1980, empl 16, sales $4,790,000, cert: WBENC)

9427 Samuel Shapiro & Company, Inc.
1215 E Fort Ave Ste 201
Baltimore, MD 21230
Contact: Olga Lyakhovetskaya Mktg & Business Dev
Tel: 410-539-0540
Email: web@shapiro.com
Website: www.shapiro.com
Transport management/freight forwarding, ocean, air, surface, documentation & letters of credit, Automated Export System (AES), classification & binding rulings, export compliance & consulting, public & private export seminars. (Woman, estab 1915, empl 120, sales $12,284,800, cert: WBENC)

9428 Velocity Global Logistics, Inc.
6805 Douglas Legum Dr Ste 201
Elkridge, MD 21075
Contact: Joseph Armstead President
Tel: 888-845-9855
Email: joe.armstead@velocitygloballogistics.com
Website: www.velocitygloballogistics.com
Global transportation. (Woman/AA, estab 2005, empl 2, sales $158,000, cert: NMSDC)

Michigan

9429 Acme Global Logistics, Inc.
31500 W 13 Mile Rd, Ste 219
Farmington Hills, MI 48334
Contact: Corey Dickerson Freight Broker
Tel: 844-260-0463
Email: cdickerson@aglogistics.us
Website: www.aglogistics.us
Freight Brokerage, Logistics Consulting, Specialized Pick-Up & Delivery, Intermodal. (AA, estab 2015, empl 6, sales , cert: NMSDC)

9430   Aero Expediting Inc.
       37529 Huron Pointe Dr
       Harrison Township, MI 48045
       Contact: Colleen Taylor President
       Tel: 586-260-2456
       Email: colleenliz@comcast.net
       Website: www.aeroexp.com
Air freight forwarding services. (Woman, estab 1988, empl
3, sales $750,000, cert: WBENC)

9431   BLT Logistics LLC
       34450 Goddard Rd
       Romulus, MI 48174
       Contact: Joe Goryl VP Supply Chain
       Tel: 586-467-1437
       Email: jgoryl@bltship.com
       Website: www.bltship.com
Transportation & logistics services in the U.S., Canada, and
Mexico, domestic intermodal, drayage, air & ocean
forwarding services. (Woman, estab 2014, empl 22, sales
$1,500,000, cert: WBENC)

9432   BNM Transportation Services, LLC
       91 N Saginaw, Ste 100
       Pontiac, MI 48342
       Contact: Marsha Rutherford Owner
       Tel: 866-832-7114
       Email: m.rutherford@bnmtrans.com
       Website: www.bnmtransportation.com
Transportation & logistics. (Woman/AA, estab 2008, empl
45, sales $12,000,000, cert: NMSDC, WBENC)

9433   Camryn Logistics LLC
       36500 Ford Rd
       Westland, MI 48185
       Contact: JIMMIE COMER Business Dev Mgr
       Tel: 866-670-8680
       Email: jcomer@camrynlogistics.com
       Website: www.camrynlogistics.com
Freight management, warehousing, sequencing, parts
assembly, custom packing & transportation. (AA, estab
2008, empl 15, sales $600,000, cert: NMSDC)

9434   Chat of Michigan Inc.
       35790 Northline Rd
       Romulus, MI 48174
       Contact: Greg Katcher President
       Tel: 734-941-5004
       Email: chatgk@aol.com
       Website: www.chatofmichigan.com
Transportation, crating, rigging, plant relocation, freight
forwarding. (AA, estab 1995, empl 40, sales $5,758,000,
cert: NMSDC)

9435   E.L. Hollingsworth & Co.
       3039 Airpark Dr N
       Flint, MI 48507
       Contact: Steven Barr President
       Tel: 810-233-7331
       Email: sbarr@hollingsworthgroup.com
       Website: www.elhc.net
Transportation services: truckload & expedite delivery,
warehouse & packaging svcs. (Nat Ame, estab 1927, empl
501, sales $45,000,000, cert: NMSDC)

9436   El Camino Transport Logistics & Management, LLC
       P.O. Box 28
       Union Lake, MI 48387
       Contact: Mary Kilgore President
       Tel: 248-242-0047
       Email: mkilgore@elcaminotransport.com
       Website:
Warehousing specializing in pick & pack, kitting, sequencing & building batches. (Woman/Hisp, estab 2007,
empl 4, sales , cert: NMSDC)

9437   EPJ Logistics Inc.
       50270 E Russell Schmidt
       Chesterfield Township, MI 48051
       Contact: Pamela Flynn CEO
       Tel: 586-421-1375
       Email: pflynn@epjlogistics.com
       Website: www.epjlogistics.com
Domestic & international transportation svcs, warehouse storage, fulfillment, inventory control, design &
layout. (Woman, estab 1998, empl 9, sales $2,200,000,
cert: WBENC)

9438   Expedite Express Transportation Inc.
       20411 W 12 Mile Rd Ste 200
       Southfield, MI 48076
       Contact: William Hamblin VP
       Tel: 248-443-1970
       Email: dispatch@expeditexp.com
       Website: www.expeditexp.com
Local & long distance TL & FTL, dedicated, same day &
next day services to small & large businesses within the
auto industry. (Woman/AA, estab 2005, empl 7, sales
$622,635, cert: WBENC)

9439   February 14 Inc.
       4525 - 50th St SE
       Grand Rapids, MI 49512
       Contact: Bridget Carey President
       Tel: 616-656-0267
       Email: bridgetcarey@ffitransportation.com
       Website: www.FFItransportation.com
Transportation logistics. (Woman, estab 1984, empl 75,
sales $18,875,000, cert: WBENC)

9440   First Choice of Elkhart
       10888 US Highway 12
       White Pigeon, MI 49099
       Contact: Misty Campagna President
       Tel: 269-483-2010
       Email: mfirstchoice@gmail.com
       Website: www.firstchoiceautotransport.com
Automotive transportation & logistics. (Woman, estab
1992, empl 2, sales $3,407,867, cert: WBENC)

9441   Global TEAM Associates, LLC
       11301 Metro Airport Center Dr Ste 170
       Romulus, MI 48174
       Contact: Petra Clark CEO
       Tel: 734-992-3208
       Email: petra.clark@globalteamusa.com
       Website: http://globalteamusa.com
Freight Forwarding & Customs House Brokerage ser-
vices. (Woman, estab 2013, empl 21, sales , cert:
WBENC)

9442   Grupo Logico, LLC
     42400 Grand River Ave, Ste 103
     Novi, MI 48375
     Contact: Darin Dittenber Dir Sales/Marketing
     Tel: 248-613-1699
     Email: ddittenber@grupologico.com
     Website: www.grupologico.com
Full service logistics solutions. (Hisp, estab 2004, empl 25, sales , cert: NMSDC)

9443   Gumro and Associates
     69 N Squirrel Ct
     Auburn Hills, MI 48326
     Contact: Ryan Gumro CEO
     Tel: 248-652-6200
     Email: rgumro@gumroandassociates.com
     Website: http://gumroandassociates.com
3PL trucking logistics, heavy haul, curtain sides, double drop, Lift-gate Straight truck & Vans. (Woman, estab 1974, empl 15, sales $20,000,000, cert: WBENC)

9444   HNT Logistics LLC
     P.O. Box 603
     New Boston, MI 48164
     Contact: Mark Bowers VP Operations
     Tel: 866-984-8840
     Email: sales@hntlogistics.net
     Website: http://hntlogistics.com
3PL logistics, truck freight, bulk freight, ocean freight, air freight, expedited freight & rail freight. (Woman, estab 2005, empl 34, sales $23,000,000, cert: WBENC)

9445   Hollingsworth Logistics Group, L.L.C.
     14225 W Warren Ave
     Dearborn, MI 48126
     Contact: Greg Martinez Jr Dir of Govt Sales
     Tel: 313-768-1306
     Email: gmartinez@hlgllc.com
     Website: www.hlgllc.com
Warehousing, container management, packaging services, kit packaing, fullfillment services, direct ship,d istribution, transportation OTR/LTL. (Nat Ame, estab 1991, empl 1900, sales , cert: NMSDC)

9446   KACE Logistics, LLC
     862 Will Carleton Rd
     Carleton, MI 48117
     Contact: Paul Pavelich VP Business Dev
     Tel: 734-946-8600
     Email: pavelichp@kcintegrated.com
     Website: www.kcintegrated.com
Logistics management, freight brokerage & management, parts sequencing, parts sub assembly, quality containment & rework warehousing. (Hisp, estab 2014, empl 125, sales $27,200,000, cert: NMSDC)

9447   LB Transportation Group & Omni Warehouse
     966 Bridgeview S
     Saginaw, MI 48604
     Contact: Tony Lander CEO
     Tel: 989-759-5544
     Email: tlander@lb-omni.com
     Website: www.lb-omni.com
Transportation: expediting & dedicated svcs, warehousing, inspection, kitting, assembly, repacking. (Hisp, estab 1976, empl 70, sales $9,859,567, cert: NMSDC)

9448   MBA Logistics, LLC
     11455 Narin Dr
     Brighton, MI 48114
     Contact: Martin Stapleton Operations
     Tel: 810-225-0295
     Email: mbalogistics@comcast.net
     Website:
International ocean freight forwarding, freight management, U.S. Customs compliance & general logistics services. (Woman/As-Pac, estab 2004, empl 1, sales , cert: NMSDC)

9449   Mexus Transport, Inc.
     18600 Northville Rd, Ste 900
     Northville, MI 48167
     Contact: Alba R. McConell President
     Tel: 248-344-8060
     Email: alba@mexustransport.com
     Website: www.mexustransport.com
Transportation: general freight, machinery & heavy haul, Canada, United States & Mexico. (Woman/Hisp, estab 2003, empl 5, sales $300,000, cert: State)

9450   New Dimension Logistics, LLC
     12256 Universal Dr
     Taylor, MI 48180
     Contact: Kurmmell Knox CEO
     Tel: 734-865-9960
     Email: kwknox@ndlx.us
     Website: www.ndlx.us
Integrated supply chain solutions delivering safe, specialized transportation, warehousing and logistics services. (AA, estab 2007, empl 14, sales $3,588,000, cert: NMSDC)

9451   Northfield Trucking Company, Inc.
     28800 NORTHLINE RD
     ROMULUS, MI 48174
     Contact: Leigh Ann Frederick President
     Tel: 313-624-4900
     Email: leighannl@northfieldtruck.com
     Website: www.northfieldtruck.com
Transportation, regional, long haul & dry freight long distances operation. (Woman, estab 2002, empl 100, sales $12,000,000, cert: WBENC)

9452   O & I Transport Inc.
     P.O. Box 807
     Dearborn, MI 48121
     Contact: Mike Schofiled Sales Mgr
     Tel: 800-270-0020
     Email: mschofield@oitransport.com
     Website:
Flatbed trucking. (AA, estab 1981, empl 21, sales $25,000,000, cert: NMSDC)

9453   Oneida Solutions Group
     10049 Harrison, Ste 500A
     Romulus, MI 48174
     Contact: Fred Rogers Exec. Dir.
     Tel: 248-252-2260
     Email: frogers@oneidasolutions.com
     Website: www.oneidasolutions.com
Transportation svcs: intl household & office moving, project mgmt. (Woman/Nat Ame, estab 2001, empl 200, sales $1,722,279, cert: WBENC)

9454 Palmer Logistic Services
24660 Dequindre Rd.
Warren, MI 48091
Contact: Terri Palmer Burton President
Tel: 313-220-5433
Email: terripb@palmerlogisticsservices.com
Website: http://palmerls.com
Global household relocation, commercial relocation, regional distribution, trade show transportation & store fixture distribution. (Woman, estab 2007, empl 9, sales $42,000,000, cert: WBENC)

9455 Prime Time Delivery
9354 Harrison Rd
Romulus, MI 48174
Contact: Paul Davis CEO
Tel: 800-336-3678
Email: pdavis@ptlogistics.com
Website: www.ptlogistics.com
Nationwide airfreight & ground transportation. (AA, estab 1997, empl 11, sales $3,000,000, cert: NMSDC)

9456 Promesa Logistics, LLC
3068 Highland Dr
Hudsonville, MI 49426
Contact: Lon Agular President
Tel: 800-646-1016
Email: lonagu@chartermi.net
Website:
Dedicated route transportation, Local Transportation, Brokerage, Warehouse, Distribution, Consolidation, Expediting, Cargo Van, Straight Truck, Semis. (Hisp, estab 1997, empl 10, sales $2,400,000, cert: NMSDC)

9457 Promesa Transportation
3068 Highland Dr
Hudsonville, MI 49426
Contact: Lon Aguilar President
Tel: 616-748-2340
Email: lonagu@chartermi.net
Website: www.chartermi.net
Transportation services. (Hisp, estab 0, empl , sales , cert: NMSDC)

9458 Renaissance City Transportation
1457 Bewick
Detroit, MI 48214
Contact: Charlie Hall VP
Tel: 313-550-8045
Email: hall4384@sbcglobal.net
Website:
Trucking & general warehousing. (AA, estab 1984, empl 4, sales , cert: NMSDC)

9459 Rich Davis Enterprises, Inc.
4831 Wyoming Ave
Dearborn, MI 48126
Contact: Melissa Matsos Acct Exec
Tel: 313-584-3334
Email: melmatsos@richdavistrucking.com
Website: www.richdavistrucking.com
Transport auto parts, steel, machinery & general commodity freight. (Woman, estab 1987, empl 17, sales $1,995,074, cert: WBENC)

9460 RSP Express Inc.
28169 Van Born Road
Romulus, MI 48174
Contact: Maria Pop President
Tel: 734-578-0799
Email: rspexpress1@yahoo.com
Website: www.rspexpress.com
Brokerage and Transportation Services. (Woman, estab 2006, empl 140, sales $19,896,325, cert: WBENC)

9461 Rush Trucking Corporation
35160 E Michigan Ave
Wayne, MI 48184
Contact: Rob Allgary Dir of Sales
Tel: 800-526-7874
Email: rallgary@rushtrucking.com
Website: www.rushtrucking.com
Truckload transportation, expedited transportation. (Woman/Nat Ame, estab 1984, empl 950, sales $125,000,000, cert: NMSDC, WBENC)

9462 Sterling Services Ltd.
1530 Commor
Hamtramck, MI 48212
Contact: Jason Eddleston VP
Tel: 248-298-2973
Email: jason@sterlingoilchem.com
Website: www.sterlingoilchem.com
Provides high-quality bulk liquid storage, custom blending, warehousing & bulk liquid transport services. (Woman, estab 1985, empl 9, sales $2,036,474, cert: WBENC)

9463 T & M Incorporated
930 Interchange Dr
Holland, MI 49423
Contact: Helen Zeerip President
Tel: 269-751-8050
Email: helen@teddystransport.com
Website: www.teddystransport.com
Transportation svcs, expediting to all 48 states & Ontario/Quebec, Canada, dedicated fleet services, full-truck load services. (Woman, estab 1982, empl 75, sales $7,276,168, cert: WBENC)

9464 The Outbound Group
9900 Harrison
Romulus, MI 48174
Contact: Karl Randolph President
Tel: 734-947-1333
Email: karlr@outboundgroup.com
Website: www.outboundgroup.com
Interstate & intrastate motor truck transportation service, fright brokerage, air freight forwarding services & warehouseing. (Woman/AA, estab 1982, empl 100, sales $7,200,000, cert: NMSDC)

9465 Three Star Trucking Co.
36860 Van Born Rd
Wayne, MI 48184
Contact: Tedd Rowe Logistics Mgr
Tel: 734-728-5500
Email: operations@threestartrucking.com
Website: www.threestartrucking.com
Transportation svcs; automotive. (Woman/Hisp, estab 1979, empl 60, sales , cert: NMSDC, WBENC)

9466 Trans Overseas Corporation
28000 Goddard Road
Romulus, MI 48174
Contact: Brett Ouellette VP - Sales & Logistics
Tel: 734-946-8750
Email: bouellette@trans-overseas.com
Website: www.trans-overseas.com
US Customs Broker, International Air/Ocean Freight Forwarder, Bonded Warehouse, Foreign Trade Zone, Container Freight Station, Barcode Labeling, Inspections, Repackaging & Distribution. (Woman, estab 1978, empl 56, sales $6,200,000, cert: WBENC)

9467 Transphere Inc.
5800 Commerce Dr
Westland, MI 48185
Contact: Smita Koradia CEO
Tel: 734-727-1307
Email: skoradia@transphereinc.net
Website: www.transphereinc.com
International logistics/transportation, warehousing, cargo by sea, air & land. (Woman/As-Ind, estab 1987, empl 3, sales $980,000, cert: NMSDC)

9468 University Moving & Storage
23305 Commerce Dr
Farmington Hills, MI 48335
Contact: Ben Cross VP
Tel: 248-949-5755
Email: bcross@universitymoving.com
Website: www.universitymoving.com
Transportation, moving & storage. (Woman, estab 1969, empl 150, sales $14,490,725, cert: WBENC)

9469 Warehouse Properties, Inc.
16000 W. Nine Mile Rd. Ste 302
Southfield, MI 48075
Contact: Kathleen Eberle President
Tel: 248-569-6106
Email: keberle@npotransportation.com
Website: www.npotransportation.com
Truckload transportation services: seating companies, kitting & JIT components. (Woman, estab 1984, empl 4, sales $1,641,592, cert: WBENC)

Minnesota

9470 Jade Logistics, Inc.
1590 Thomas Center Dr Ste 100
Eagan, MN 55122
Contact: Ni Corbin Owner
Tel: 651-405-3141
Email: ni@shipjade.com
Website: www.shipjade.com
Domestic & international freight transportation services. (Woman/As-Pac, estab 2007, empl 15, sales , cert: State, NMSDC, WBENC)

9471 Malark Logistics
P.O. Box 438
Maple Grove, MN 55369
Contact: Sr Sales Exec
Tel: 763-428-3564
Email:
Website: www.malark.com
Logistics, transportation, warehousing, trucking, airfreight, expedited, freight auditing, crating, claims filing, distribution, pick and pack, LTL, tradeshow services, 3PL & 4PL. (Woman, estab 1994, empl 60, sales $35,000,000, cert: WBENC)

Missouri

9472 All America Transportation, Inc.
910 S Kirkwood Rd Ste 120
St Louis, MO 63122
Contact: Lianne Reizer President
Tel: 314-835-9499
Email: lianne@allamericatrans.com
Website: www.allamericatrans.com
Licensed freight broker, truckload shipments throughout US & Canada. (Woman, estab 1996, empl 7, sales $2,579,000, cert: State, CPUC, WBENC)

9473 Crossland Carriers Inc.
421 Cedar Hills Rd
Ozark, MO 65721
Contact: Patricia Schmig President
Tel: 800-217-0898
Email: tschmig@crosslandcarriers.us
Website: www.crosslandcarriers.com
Trucking long haul, short haul, partial truckload, logistics, mobile home, mobile office moves, heavy haul, specialized logistics. (Woman, estab 1999, empl 3, sales $1,750,000, cert: State)

9474 Marleon International, LLC
5630 NE Lake Dr
Kansas City, MO 64118
Contact: Marquez Cesar CEO
Tel: 816-249-2319
Email: camarquez@mar-leon.com
Website: www.marleoninternational.com
Freight transportation: less than container load, less than truckload, full truckload, flatbed freight, air transportation services, distribution & warehousing services. (Hisp, estab 2005, empl 4, sales $560,000, cert: State, NMSDC)

9475 The Thomas Family Business, Inc.
8194 Lackland Rd
Saint Louis, MO 63114
Contact: Rolondo Thomas CEO
Tel: 314-423-6111
Email: rolondo.thomas@ttfbcompanies.com
Website: www.ttfbcompanies.com
Transportation services, local & regional, warehousing, supply chain management & logistics. (AA, estab 2009, empl 7, sales $750,000, cert: City)

9476 ValDivia Enterprises, Inc.
       #5C The Pines Court
       St. Louis, MO 63141
       Contact: steve ellis VP Sales
       Tel: 314-275-7941
       Email: steve@valdiviaenterprises.net
       Website: http://valdiviaenterprises.net
Transportation services serving North America & Mexico.
(Woman/Hisp, estab 2006, empl 1450, sales , cert: State)

Montana

9477 Bridger Trnasportation LLC
       186 Garden Dr, Ste 103
       Bozeman, MT 59718
       Contact: Kyle Pena Broker
       Tel: 888-586-0648
       Email: orders@bridgertrans.com
       Website: www.bridgertrans.com
Full service logistics, supply chain management, OTR, LTL,
FTL & rail in the U.S. & Canada. (Woman, estab 2007, empl
11, sales $10,000,000, cert: WBENC)

9478 Meadow Lark Companies
       935 Lake Elmo Dr
       Billings, MT 59105
       Contact: Chris Verlanic Dir of Freight Management
       Tel: 406-657-8645
       Email: cverlanic@meadowlarkco.com
       Website: www.meadowlarkco.com
Transportation, Freight Management & Logistics: TL, LTL,
Vans/Reefers, Flatbed & Heavy Haul. (Woman, estab 1983,
empl 160, sales $65,000,000, cert: WBENC)

North Carolina

9479 All-State Express, Inc.
       121-I Shields Park Dr
       Kernersville, NC 27284
       Contact: Sherri Squier President
       Tel: 336-992-6880
       Email: sherri@all-stateexpress.com
       Website: www.all-stateexpress.com
Transportation Services, Expedited Trucking, Air Charter,
TruckLoad, Expedite Trucking, Truck Load (TL), Milk Runs,
Dedicated Truck Load, Air Freight, Air Charter, Hazmat
Carrier 48 States, Canada and Mexico. (Woman, estab
1996, empl 28, sales $23,755,580, cert: WBENC)

9480 Graebel Vanlines Holdings, LLC
       2901 Stewart Creek Blvd
       Charlotte, NC 28216
       Contact: Colin Holden VP of Corporate Sales
       Tel: 704-281-7129
       Email: colin.holden@graebelmoving.com
       Website: www.graebelmoving.com
Facility management services, commercial moving services, warehousing services. (Woman, estab 1960, empl
1360, sales $266,000,000, cert: WBENC)

9481 Intermodal Logistics Consulting, Inc.
       301 N Main St, Ste 2409B
       Winston-Salem, NC 27101
       Contact: President
       Tel: 540-257-3830
       Email:
       Website: www.imlconsulting.com
Transportation Planning, Travel Demand Modeling and
Forecasting, Data Management and Analytics, Aviation
Systems Modeling, Simulation, and Analysis, and
Technical Research Studies. (AA, estab 2013, empl 10,
sales $200,000, cert: 8a)

9482 Logical Logistics Solutions
       7508 E Independence Blvd Ste 112
       Charlotte, NC 28227
       Contact: Noel Sanchez President
       Tel: 704-566-4770
       Email: nsanchez@llsolutions.com
       Website: www.llsolutions.com
Logistics services: freight cost reduction & administration, warehousing, consolidation & distribution &
inventory management. (AA, estab 1996, empl 5, sales
$3,128,798, cert: City)

9483 Synchrogistics, LLC
       900 Ridgefield Dr Ste 350
       Raleigh, NC 27609
       Contact: Mary MacIsaac Mgr Admin
       Tel: 877-879-0668
       Email: mary@synchrogistics.com
       Website: www.synchrogistics.com
National transportation, domestic truckload and LTL
transportation, intermodal, international shipping,
warehousing. (Woman, estab 2010, empl 24, sales
$18,803,598, cert: WBENC)

Nebraska

9484 Kirsch Transportation Services Inc.
       1102 Douglas
       Omaha, NE 68102
       Contact: Lucas Bird Govt Operations
       Tel: 531-213-2153
       Email: lucasb@kirschtrans.com
       Website: http://kirschtrans.com
Dry Van, Open Deck and Temp Control Over-Dimensional
and Heavy Haul Intermodal - Domestic and Cross Border
Freight Management. (Woman, estab 2001, empl 60,
sales $128,033,344, cert: NWBOC)

9485 Kirsch Transportation Services, Inc.
       1102 Douglas St
       Omaha, NE 68102
       Contact: Joe Casper Sr Project Mgr
       Tel: 531-213-2130
       Email: cam@kirschtrans.com
       Website: www.kirschtrans.com
Transportation services, flatbed, dry van & specialized
hauling including super loads. (Woman, estab 2001,
empl 55, sales $79,210,000, cert: NWBOC)

9486   Nationwide Auto Transport, Inc.
       730 Pier 3
       Lincoln, NE 68528
       Contact: Julie Delp President
       Tel: 402-742-4000
       Email: nwat90@tahoo.com
       Website: www.nwat.com
Automobile transport services. (Woman, estab 2001, empl
35, sales $3,900,000, cert: WBENC, SDB)

New Jersey

9487   Andrew Vazquez Inc.
       24 Tuttle Ave
       Bedminster, NJ 07921
       Contact: Andrew Vazquez President
       Tel: 908-719-2444
       Email: avaquez@dlgroup.com
       Website: www.aviquality.com
Vehicle Logistics Services (Hisp, estab 1979, empl 30, sales
$4,500,000, cert: NMSDC)

9488   Bett-A-Way Traffic Systems Inc.
       110 Sylvania Pl
       South Plainfield, NJ 07080
       Contact: Betty Vaccaro VP
       Tel: 908-222-2500
       Email: laura.vaccaro@bettaway.com
       Website: www.bett-a-way.com
Logistics management, freight nationwide, truck load &
LTL, dry & refrigerated. (Woman, estab 1982, empl 107,
sales , cert: WBENC)

9489   Blisset Transportation
       50 Triangle Blvd.
       Carlstadt, NJ 07072
       Contact: Roseanne Magliato President & CEO
       Tel: 201-549-0672
       Email: rmagliato@blissetllc.com
       Website: www.blissetllc.com
Transportation & logistics services, warehousing, fulfillment & technology solutions. (Woman/Hisp, estab 1991,
empl 35, sales $10,000,001, cert: NMSDC, WBENC)

9490   Bohren's Moving & Storage/United Van Lines
       3 Applegate Dr
       Robbinsville, NJ 08691
       Contact: Charlene Heath Sales/Marketing Mgr
       Tel: 800-326-4736
       Email: cheath@bohrensmoving.com
       Website: www.bohrensmoving.com
Transportation & storage svcs; brokerage & international
divisions. (Woman, estab 1924, empl 90, sales
$28,798,613, cert: WBENC)

9491   Global Transit Solutions
       110 Chestnut Ridge Rd, Ste 188
       Montvale, NJ 07645
       Contact: Fernando Mateo Co-Owner
       Tel: 201-949-8755
       Email: FM@gowithgts.com
       Website: www.gowithgts.com
Third Party Logistics throughout the nation, transportation services, trucks, and intermodal, full truck loads (FTL),
and less than a trailer. (Hisp, estab 2018, empl 2, sales ,
cert: State)

9492   Royal Coachman Worldwide
       88 Ford Rd, Unit 26
       Denville, NJ 07834
       Contact: Amy Birnbaum CEO
       Tel: 973-400-3200
       Email: amy.birnbaum@royalcoachman.com
       Website: www.royalcoachman.com
Corporate limousine & transportation svcs: luxury
sedans, stretch limousines, 14 passenger motor coaches.
(Woman, estab 1969, empl 150, sales $13,034,000, cert:
WBENC)

New Mexico

9493   Loadstone Transportation, LLC
       1811 Copper Loop, Ste K
       Las Cruces, NM 88007
       Contact: Bridgette Snow Marketing Coord
       Tel: 575-523-7000
       Email: bridgette@loadstonetransportation.com
       Website: www.loadstonetransportation.com
Transportation services, multitude of local, state, &
federal government contracts. (Woman, estab 2011,
empl 6, sales $5,823,500, cert: State, WBENC)

Nevada

9494   Full Tilt Logistics LLC
       150 Isidor Court
       Sparks, NV 89441
       Contact: Customer Management Team
       Tel: 702-852-2228
       Email: remit@fulltiltlogistics.com
       Website: http://fulltiltlogistics.com
LTL, Partial loads, Full truck load, Rail, Heavy haul.
(Woman, estab 2014, empl 11, sales $16,403,958, cert:
WBENC)

9495   Railroad Industries Inc.
       1575 Delucchi Ln, Ste 210
       Reno, NV 89502
       Contact: Anastacia Sullivan Dir of Operations
       Tel: 775-329-4855
       Email: reg@railroadindustries.com
       Website: www.railroadindustries.com
Transportation consulting. (Woman/AA, As-Pac, estab
1983, empl 9, sales $775,382, cert: State)

New York

9496   A & Z Trucking, Inc.
       115 Corporate Dr
       New Windsor, NY 12550
       Contact: Broker
       Tel: 845-569-7299
       Email:
       Website: http://AandZtrucking.com
Transportation solutions, temperature-controlled reefer
trucks, dry vans, flatbeds, full truckload (TL), less-than-
truckload (LTL), refrigerated freight. (Woman/As-Pac,
estab 2003, empl 15, sales , cert: NMSDC)

9497 AWLI Group, Inc.
147-60 175 St
Jamaica, NY 11434
Contact: Keith Milliner VP
Tel: 718-244-8923
Email: keith@amberworldwide.com
Website: www.amberworldwide.com
International freight forwarding. (Woman, estab 1990, empl 20, sales $12,594,223, cert: State)

9498 MSL Express, Inc.
160-19 Rockaway Blvd
Jamaica, NY 11434
Contact: Chester Tong President & CEO
Tel: 718-528-1833
Email: chester.tong@mslexpress-us.com
Website: www.mslexpress.com
International freight transportation: ocean & air, imports/exports, air charters. (As-Pac, estab 1988, empl 9, sales $7,000,000, cert: State)

9499 Native Trax Logistics LLC
767 Warren Rd
Ithaca, NY 14850
Contact: Ryan Van Alstine GM
Tel: 607-319-5122
Email: ryan@nativetraxlogistics.com
Website: www.nativetraxlogistics.com
Transportation Management, Nationwide service, Asset tracking & reporting, Driver safety screenings, Driver credential checks, Timely proof of delivery, On call 24 hours. (Nat Ame, estab 2014, empl 5, sales $3,500,000, cert: NMSDC)

9500 Spearhead Transportation Services, Inc.
P.O. Box 1984
Blasdell, NY 14219
Contact: Joe Dotterweich CFO
Tel: 716-823-4942
Email: joed@spearheadlogistics.com
Website: www.spearheadlogistics.com
Transportation & logistics services. (Nat Ame, estab 0, empl , sales $14,000,000, cert: NMSDC)

9501 V G Francis Logistics Inc.
800 Et 180th St
Bronx, NY 10460
Contact: Victor Francis President
Tel: 866-970-8866
Email: vgfrancislogistics@gmail.com
Website: www.vgfrancislogistics.com
Transportation, logistics & related information services: air, rail & sea transportation. (AA, estab 2006, empl 1, sales , cert: City, NMSDC)

9502 Walker SCM, LLC
70 E Sunrise Hwy Ste 611
Valley Stream, NY 11581
Contact: Emmett F. Walker CEO
Tel: 516-568-2080
Email: sales@walkerscm.com
Website: www.walkerscm.com
International transportation, logistics, sub- assembly, sequencing, kitting, warehousing, distribution & customs brokarage. (AA, estab 1989, empl 750, sales $112,000,000, cert: NMSDC, SDB)

Ohio

9503 ASW Global, LLC
3375 Gilchrist Rd
Mogadore, OH 44260
Contact: Pam Harris Dir Marketing & Supplier Diversity
Tel: 330-733-8176
Email: pharris@aswglobal.com
Website: www.aswglobal.com
Third-party logistics, warehousing, order fulfillment, pick pack & ship, pkging/re-packaging, contract logistics retail supply chain support, real estate devel proj mgmt, bulk resin transloading, records retention, file storage, & retrieval services. (AA, estab 1983, empl 120, sales $27,000,000, cert: NMSDC)

9504 BD Transportation, Inc.
9590 Looney Rd
Piqua, OH 45356
Contact: Tom Stirnaman Sales
Tel: 309-531-1370
Email: toms@ptc-inc.net
Website: www.ptc-inc.net
Dry van freight, 62 tractors & 125 dry van trailers. (Woman, estab 2000, empl 95, sales $14,600,000, cert: WBENC)

9505 Cam Logistics, LLC
7800 Robinett Way
Canal Winchester, OH 43110
Contact: Patrick Shea VP
Tel: 614-409-1776
Email: patrick@camlogisticsllc.com
Website: www.camlogisticsllc.com
Third party logistics, transportation, truckload & intermodal arrangements. (Woman, estab 2006, empl 9, sales $5,400,000, cert: WBENC)

9506 Cimarron Express Inc.
21611 State Rt 51
Genoa, OH 43430
Contact: Jim Shepperd/Gloria Snow VP /Admin Asst
Tel: 419-855-7713
Email: jshepperd@cimarronexpress.com
Website: www.cimarronexpress.com
Motor carrier svcs, truckload. (AA, estab 1984, empl 325, sales , cert: NMSDC)

9507 Cincinnati's Best Brokerage LLC
4005 Borman Dr
Batavia, OH 45429
Contact: Brad Judy Mktg Dir
Tel: 513-478-4559
Email: info@burdbrothers.com
Website:
Third party logistics, truckload-shipping services. (Woman, estab 2003, empl 10, sales $500,000, cert: WBENC)

9508 Cordell Transporation Company LLC
2942 Boulder Ave
Dayton, OH 45414
Contact: Lori Van Opstal President
Tel: 937-277-7271
Email: lvanopstal@cordelltransportation.com
Website: www.cordelltransportation.com
Provides dedicated Truckload Transportation services throughout the US and Canada. (Woman/Nat Ame, As-Pac, estab 1999, empl 225, sales $20,947,709, cert: NMSDC, WBENC)

9509 Debo Enterprises Incorporated
16021 Dunbury Dr Ste 103
Maple Heights, OH 44137
Contact: Tommie Rodgers Operations Dir
Tel: 404-333-5008
Email: deboenterprise@gmail.com
Website: www.deboenterprises.com
Logistics & transportation services, Short term & long term line haul services, railroad/shipyards, Hauling services for construction worksites. (AA, estab 2001, empl 3, sales $137,000, cert: State)

9510 Grand Aire, Inc.
11777 W. Airport Service Road
Swanton, OH 43558
Contact: Katrina Cheema Business Dev Mgr
Tel: 419-861-6700
Email: diversity@grandaire.com
Website: www.grandaire.com
Air charter transportation: passengers & cargo. (As-Ind, estab 1997, empl 29, sales $18,894,688, cert: NMSDC, SDB)

9511 H & W Trucking
15 W Locust St
Newark, OH 43055
Contact: Barcy Vidt President
Tel: 800-572-2120
Email: barcy@handwtrucking.com
Website: www.handwtrucking.com
Third party logistics & freight, LTL & rail, US & Canada. (Woman, estab 1979, empl 3, sales $5,300,000, cert: WBENC)

9512 InterChez Global Services, Inc.
600 Alpha Pkwy
Stow, OH 44224
Contact: Ivette Tam Exec VP
Tel: 330-923-5080
Email: itam@interchez.com
Website: www.interchezglobal.com
Logistics engineering, network modeling, logistics execution, freight bill payment, premium freight management, logistics consulting, translation, interpretation. (Woman/Hisp, estab 2001, empl 12, sales $18,000,000, cert: State, NMSDC, WBENC)

9513 Kingsgate Transportation Services LLC
9100 West Chester Towne Centre
West Chester, OH 45069
Contact: Amy Barnett Managing Partner
Tel: 513-874-7447
Email: abarnett@kingsgatetrans.com
Website: www.kingsgatetrans.com
Freight services: truck, rail, air or ocean. (Woman, estab 1986, empl 21, sales $19,500,000, cert: WBENC)

9514 KLN Logistics dba AIT Worldwide Logistics
6749 Eastland Rd, Ste C
Middleburg Heights, OH 44130
Contact: Kimberly Martinez-Giering Owner
Tel: 440-816-1505
Email: info@klnlogistics.com
Website: www.klnlogistics.com
Air freight, expedited trucking, import, export, logistics. (Woman/Hisp, estab 2005, empl 28, sales $427,000,000, cert: State, NMSDC, WBENC)

9515 Marine Services International, Inc.
14508 S Industrial Ave
Cleveland, OH 44137
Contact: Kenton Woodhead President
Tel: 216-587-3500
Email: kenton@marineservicesintl.com
Website: www.marineservicesintl.com
Air, Sea, Land International Freight Transportation (freight forwarder), warehousing, labeling, repackaging, packaging & re-palletizing capabilities. (Woman/As-Ind, As-Pac, estab 2006, empl 18, sales $5,000,000, cert: State)

9516 Priority Logistics Group
4667 Malsbary Rd
Cincinnati, OH 45242
Contact: VP
Tel: 513-794-3160
Email:
Website: www.shipplg.com
Third party logistics services, Expedited Same Day, On demand expedited service, Next Day Distribution. (Woman, estab 1973, empl 80, sales $6,500,000, cert: WBENC)

9517 Rush Expediting, Inc.
P.O. Box 2810
Dayton, OH 45401
Contact: Steve Parker President
Tel: 800-989-7874
Email: parkersl@rush-delivery.com
Website: www.rush-delivery.com
Freight transportation services. (Woman, estab 2004, empl 200, sales $1,000,000, cert: WBENC)

9518 T.V. Minority Company, Inc.
30 Lau Parkway
Clayton, OH 45315
Contact: Mgr
Tel: 313-299-2177
Email: info@tvmtrucking.com
Website: www.tvmtrucking.com
Freight distribution and transportation. (AA, estab 1990, empl 2, sales , cert: NMSDC)

9519   Western Reserve Technology
       34194 Aurora Rd, Ste 200
       Solon, OH 44139
       Contact: Kim Cahuas Owner
       Tel: 440-498-9500
       Email: kim@gowrt.com
       Website: www.gowrt.com
Western Reserve Technology Oracle Resources:
Oracle Business Intelligence Enterprise Edition (OBIEE)
Consultants, ORACLE CORE DBAs, ORACLE APPLICATIONS
DBAs, ORACLE APPLICATIONS FUNCTIONAL ANALYSTS
(Woman/Hisp, estab 2005, empl , sales $1,100,000, cert:
State, NMSDC)

Oklahoma

9520   STI Trucking LLC
       P.O. Box 700
       Kiefer, OK 74041
       Contact: Sam Mookerjee Accountant
       Tel: 918-446-6181
       Email: twyla.johnson@stonetrucking.com
       Website: http://stonetrucking.com
Premier legal flatbed, oversize & heavy haul carrier
servicing the US, Canada & Mexico. Hot shot trucks,
tankers, pole trucks, slick backs, RGN's. (AA, estab 1945,
empl 200, sales , cert: NMSDC)

Oregon

9521   Alliance Trucking Inc.
       1209 Stowe Ave
       Medford, OR 97501
       Contact: Jordan Kell Acct Exec
       Tel:
       Email: jkell@alliancetrucking.com
       Website: www.alliancetrucking.com
Asset-based trucking, haul truckload & LTL shipments via
vans, flatbeds, step decks & multi-axle heavy haul trailers,
48 states, Canada & Mexico. (Woman, estab 1996, empl
20, sales $9,726,975, cert: State)

9522   Lile International Companies
       8060 SW Pfaffle St, Ste 200
       Tigard, OR 97223
       Contact: Diane DeAutremont President
       Tel: 503-726-4800
       Email: diane.deautremont@lile.com
       Website: www.lile.com
National & international transportation svcs, warehousing,
distribution & logistics. (Woman, estab 1959, empl 275,
sales , cert: WBENC)

9523   Mulino Trading, LLC
       16570 SE McLoughlin Blvd
       Oak Grove, OR 97267
       Contact: Mike Theis agent
       Tel: 503-786-8000
       Email: info@mulinotrading.com
       Website: www.mulinotrading.com
Freight truck transportation, broker forwarding. (Hisp,
estab 2012, empl 6, sales , cert: State)

Pennsylvania

9524   Advanced Shipping Technologies
       526 W Ogle St
       Ebensburg, PA 15931
       Contact: Jane Sandifeer VP Business Solutions
       Tel: 877-692-0570
       Email: diversity@astship.com
       Website: www.astship.com
Third party logistics: on-line transportation management
system. (Woman, estab 2002, empl 18, sales , cert:
WBENC)

9525   Allegheny Valley Transfer Co., Inc.
       1512 Lebanon Church Rd
       Pittsburgh, PA 15236
       Contact: Mary Jessup Owner
       Tel: 412-653-1200
       Email: alleghenyallied@aol.com
       Website: www.pghmover.com
Moving, storage & packing of household & office goods.
(Woman, estab 1925, empl 45, sales $1,561,882, cert:
State, WBENC)

9526   Horwith Trucks, Inc.
       P.O. Box 7 Rt329, 1449 Nor-Bath Blvd.
       Northampton, PA 18067
       Contact: Regina Grim President
       Tel: 610-261-2220
       Email: info@horwithfreightliner.com
       Website: http://horwithfreightliner.com
Transportation of hazardous and non hazardous waste,
deicing salt, wall panels, general freight. (Woman, estab
1968, empl 84, sales , cert: WBENC)

9527   Knichel Logistics
       5347 William Flynn Hwy
       Gibsonia, PA 15044
       Contact: Ashley Caloia Marketing Coord
       Tel: 724-449-3300
       Email: acaloia@knichellogistics.com
       Website: www.knichellogistics.com
Intermodal, drayage & truckload services. (Woman,
estab 2003, empl 42, sales $73,000,000, cert: WBENC)

9528   Maroadi Transfer & Storage
       1801 Lincoln Hwy
       North Versailles, PA 15137
       Contact: Mary V. Maroadi President
       Tel: 412-824-4420
       Email: mary@maroadi.com
       Website: www.maroadi.com
Local, interstate & international moving services, office
& electronics moving, household goods moving, displays
& exhibits. (Woman, estab 1967, empl 45, sales
$3,800,000, cert: WBENC)

9529   Parks Moving Systems
       1234 Wrights Ln
       West Chester, PA 19380
       Contact: Relocation Consultant
       Tel: 610-429-4125
       Email:
       Website: www.parksmoving.com
Transportation: local, long distance, storage, record storage, trade show moves, etc. (Woman, estab 1992, empl 20, sales $1,300,000, cert: WBENC)

Puerto Rico

9530   Nestor Reyes, Inc.
       P.O. Box 9023474
       San Juan, PR 00902
       Contact: Edmundo Rodriguez President
       Tel: 787-289-6465
       Email: e.rodriguez@nreyes.com
       Website: www.nreyes.com
Foreign freight forwarding. (Hisp, estab 1973, empl 35, sales $7,753,580, cert: NMSDC)

9531   PR Global Logistics JP Corporation
       200 Rafael Cordero Ave, Ste 140 PMB 223
       Caguas, PR 00726
       Contact: Ivelisse Baba-Portalatin VP
       Tel: 787-653-5070
       Email: ivelisse@prgloballogistics.com
       Website: www.prgloballogistics.com
Logistics & distribution operations, packaging, quality control, supply chain technology, and organizational excellence. (Woman/Hisp, estab 2007, empl 2, sales , cert: NMSDC)

Rhode Island

9532   Trans-Link LLC
       1249 Oaklawn Ave
       Cranston, RI 02920
       Contact: President
       Tel: 401-463-3862
       Email:
       Website: http://translinkllc.com
Transportation & trucking: LTL, truckload, rail & flatbeds, refrigerated & dry freight, 48 states & Canada. (Woman, estab 2000, empl 5, sales $5,600,000, cert: State)

South Carolina

9533   Alpha Logistics Solutions, LLC
       8201 Arrowridge Blvd ste 123
       Charlotte, SC 28273
       Contact: Arthur Cottingham COO
       Tel: 877-356-6102
       Email: arthur@alphals-biz.com
       Website: www.alphals-biz.com/
Less Than Truckload (LTL), Truckload (TL), Domestic Air & Ground Expedited Shipping, International, Intermodal. (Woman/AA, estab 2014, empl 5, sales $350,000, cert: NMSDC)

9534   Atlantic-Pacific Express, Inc.
       1350 Browning Rd, Ste B
       Columbia, SC 29210
       Contact: Irene Brotherton President
       Tel: 877-739-1116
       Email: irene@apexpedite.com
       Website: www.apexpedite.com
Asset based & non-asset based ground & air freight. (Woman, estab , empl 13, sales $28,000,000, cert: WBENC)

9535   Holy City Solutions, LLC
       904 Commerce Cir
       Charleston, SC 29410
       Contact: President
       Tel: 843-202-2149
       Email:
       Website: www.holycitysolutions.com
Transportation logistics, warehousing, transportation & consulting. (Woman, estab 2006, empl 1, sales $146,610, cert: WBENC)

9536   Kontane Inc.
       1000 Charleston Regional Pkwy
       Charleston, SC 29492
       Contact: Rusty Byrd President
       Tel: 843-352-0011
       Email: rusty@kontanelogistics.com
       Website: http://kontanelogistics.com
Logistics, warehousing & distribution, cross-docking, freight consolidation, import material receipt, line sequencing, parts distribution, development of logistics information systems, sub-assembly & foreign trade zones services. (Woman, estab 1975, empl 100, sales $40,000,000, cert: WBENC)

9537   Warehouse Services, Inc.
       58 S Burty Rd
       Piedmont, SC 29673
       Contact: Michelle Dender Mktg Coord
       Tel: 864-422-6079
       Email: michelledender@wsi-ismi.com
       Website: www.wsionline.com
Warehousing, transportation svcs: distribution, client system integration, domestic & international supply chain (SC) enhancement. (Woman, estab 1985, empl 2000, sales $220,000,000, cert: WBENC)

Tennessee

9538   Ewing Moving Services
       4006 Air Park St
       Memphis, TN 38118
       Contact: Ashleigh Hayes Natl Acct Coordinator
       Tel: 901-774-2197
       Email: admin@ewingmovingservice.com
       Website: www.ewingmovingservice.com
Moving & storage services. (AA, estab 1980, empl 57, sales $3,047,104, cert: NMSDC)

9539 Total Control Logistics
1519 Union Ave, Ste 177
Memphis, TN 38104
Contact: Terica Lamb President
Tel: 901-830-1864
Email: tlamb@tclogistix.com
Website: www.tclogistix.com
Third party logistics provider (3PL), Warehousing & Distribution. (Woman/AA, estab 2009, empl 1, sales , cert: NMSDC)

Texas

9540 A-1 Freeman Relocation
4727 Macro
San Antonio, TX 78218
Contact: Jonathan Hightower Corporate Relocation & Logistics Consultant
Tel: 210-661-1404
Email: jhightower@a-1freeman.com
Website: www.a-1freemanrelo.com
Domestic & international household goods moving & transportation services. (Woman, estab 1994, empl 450, sales $10,000,000, cert: WBENC)

9541 Action Transportation Services, Inc.
P.O. Box 15711
Houston, TX 77220
Contact: Lucy Bowerman Sales
Tel: 713-673-4817
Email: actiontransport@sbcglobal.net
Website: http://actionfrtservices.com
Transportation services: flatbeds, van, stepdecks, hotshots, power only, local & specialized equipment for partial & full loads, US & Canada, 24 hrs a day 7 days a week. (Woman, estab 1998, empl 3, sales $245,878, cert: State, WBENC)

9542 Americorp Xpress Carriers
5201 N Veterans Blvd
Pharr, TX 78577
Contact: Frank Flores President
Tel: 956-283-0052
Email: fflores@axcarriers.com
Website: www.axcarriers.com
Transportation services. (Hisp, estab 2010, empl 250, sales , cert: NMSDC)

9543 A-Rocket Moving & Storage, Inc.
3401 Corder St
Houston, TX 77021
Contact: Lewis Grisby VP Operations
Tel: 713-748-6024
Email: rocketsales@arocket.com
Website: www.arocket.com
Relocation services: material handling & warehousing, local, long-distance & international. (AA, estab 1959, empl 60, sales $3,700,000, cert: State, City, NMSDC)

9544 Candor Expedite
1404 Gables Court, Ste 202
Plano, TX 75075
Contact: John Kennedy Sr Business Development
Tel: 469-661-3360
Email: jkennedy@candorexp.com
Website: http://candorexp.com
Expedite transportation and nationwide hotshot services. (Woman, estab 2017, empl 21, sales $6,000,000, cert: WBENC)

9545 Cargo One Logistics, LLC
5802 Val Verde, Ste 165
Houston, TX 77057
Contact: Diego Alexander President
Tel: 713-290-9922
Email: dalexander@cargo1logistics.com
Website: www.cargo1logistics.com
Transportation services, over the road, full truck load, Mexico, US & Canada. (Hisp, estab 2000, empl 7, sales $4,000,000, cert: NMSDC)

9546 EP Logistics LLC
9601 Pan American Dr
El Paso, TX 79927
Contact: Ingrid Hurtado Marketing Business Development Mgr
Tel: 915-881-9100
Email: ingridh@eplogistics.com
Website: www.eplogistics.com
Warehousing, customs brokerage, sorting/rework services, transportation. (Hisp, estab 2005, empl 50, sales $1,200,000, cert: State, NMSDC)

9547 Epsilon Brokerage Corporation
12110 Sara Rd
Laredo, TX 78045
Contact: Rick Laurel President
Tel: 956-728-8713
Email: rick.laurel@epsilonbrokerage.com
Website: www.epsilonbrokerage.com
Logistics, customs broker, freight forwarding, warehousing. (Hisp, estab 2011, empl 50, sales $4,000,000, cert: State, NMSDC)

9548 Expedited Specialized Logistics LLC
801 Pellegrino Court
Laredo, TX 78045
Contact: Armando Correa Commercial Dir
Tel: 956-712-8350
Email: acorrea@es-logistics.net
Website: www.es-logistics.net
USA and International Truck Load Transportation Services. Dryvan Trailers Flatbeds Stepdecks double drop open or curtain trailers. RGN Lowboys. (Hisp, estab 2011, empl 30, sales $7,661,250, cert: NMSDC)

9549   Group of Global Suppliers, LLC
279 Shadow Mountain, Ste 200
El Paso, TX 79912
Contact: Roberto Gonzalez President
Tel: 915-727-2811
Email: sales@ggscorporation.com
Website: www.ggscorporation.com
Logistics, warehousing, inspection, sorting, etc. (Minority, estab 2013, empl 5, sales $1,620,000, cert: State, NMSDC)

9550   InstiCo Freight Management, Inc.
3011 Gateway Dr. Ste 340
Irving, TX 75063
Contact: Cory Allen Business Develop Exec
Tel: 469-293-9549
Email: callen@insticologistics.com
Website: www.insticologistics.com
International Services- Ocean cargo, Air cargo, and Non-Vessel Operating Common Carrier. (Hisp, estab 2011, empl 25, sales , cert: NMSDC)

9551   Intercon Carriers
19810 FM 1472
Laredo, TX 78045
Contact: Enrique Serna Managing Partner
Tel: 956-725-7275
Email: enrique.serna@intercomlogistics.com
Website: www.interconcarriers.com
Transportation & logistics services in the United States, Canada & Mexico. (Hisp, estab 1996, empl 175, sales , cert: State, NMSDC)

9552   Kaliber Choice, LLC
12705 S Kirkwood Rd, Ste 213
Stafford, TX 77477
Contact: Valesco Raymond President
Tel: 512-774-5838
Email: vraymond@nxglogistics.com
Website: www.nxglogistics.com
Freight brokerage: LTL (Less-Than-Truckload), Full Truckload (FTL), Airfreight, Ocean Container (20/40ft) Drayage, Small package ecommerce shipping (Fedex, UPS, DHL). (AA, estab 2016, empl 9, sales $997,898, cert: NMSDC)

9553   Logisti-K USA, LLC
13151 S Unitec
Laredo, TX 78045
Contact: Cesar Roberto Flores Dir of Inland Forwarding
Tel: 956-723-7606
Email: cflores@logisti-k.com.mx
Website: http://logisti-k.com.mx
Truckload, Flatbed, Refrigerated & Intermodal services. (Hisp, estab 2005, empl 30, sales $1,225,062, cert: State, NMSDC)

9554   MagRabbit.com
1464 E. Whitestone Blvd Ste 1001
Cedar Park, TX 78613
Contact: Tommy Hodinh President & CEO
Tel: 512-993-5730
Email: tommy.hodinh@magrabbit.com
Website: www.magrabbit.com
Global supply chain solutions, air, surface & ocean tranportation. (As-Pac, estab 1991, empl 200, sales $15,000,000, cert: State, NMSDC)

9555   MagRabbit-Alamo Iron Works, LLC
P.O. Box 2341
San Antonio, TX 78298
Contact: Wayne Dennis Diversity Coord
Tel: 210-704-8520
Email: wdennis@aiwnet.com
Website: www.magrabbit-aiw.com
Dist industrial supplies, steel service & fabrication, hand & power tools, equipment repair & installation, logistics, transportation & freight forwarding. (As-Pac, estab 2004, empl 150, sales $1,573,543, cert: NMSDC)

9556   Moore Transport of Tulsa LLC
661 N Plano Rd Ste 319
Richardson, TX 75081
Contact: Gary Moore Owner
Tel: 972-578-0606
Email: danchase@mooretransport.com
Website: www.mooretransport.com
Freight transportation. (AA, estab 2005, empl 300, sales $63,000,000, cert: NMSDC)

9557   Multi-Trans, Inc.
606 Grand Central Blvd.
Laredo, TX 78045
Contact: Emilio Villarreal New Projects
Tel: 210-418-4889
Email: evillarreal@multitransinc.com
Website: www.multitransinc.com
Air, Sea & Land Transportation service, LTL, TL & Sea Containers, Flat Beds, Lowboys, Drop Decks & Heavy Equipment Hauling, Air Charters. (Woman/Nat Ame, estab 2000, empl 8, sales $10,000,000, cert: State)

9558   MW Logistics, LLC
12770 Coit Road, Ste 1040
Dallas, TX 75251
Contact: Brian Thompson Sr Director
Tel: 214-393-8211
Email: bthompson@mwlogistics.com
Website: www.mwlogistics.com
Transportation & logistics: over the road, intermodal & bulk. (AA, estab 2001, empl 17, sales $16,800,000, cert: NMSDC)

9559   Navigator Express
14587 Kelmscot Dr
Frisco, TX 75035
Contact: Furqan Khan VP Operations
Tel: 972-330-2340
Email: ops@navex.us
Website: www.navex.us
Authorized motor carrier, interstate transportation of commodities to all 48 contiguous states. (As-Ind, estab 2009, empl 15, sales $250,000, cert: State)

9560   Purpose Transportation, LLC
701 Hanover Dr
GRAND PRAIRIE, TX 75053
Contact: Greg Crawford VP of Sales
Tel: 972-746-4585
Email: chuck@purposetransportation.com
Website: www.purposetransportation.com
Domestic transportation, freight & logistics services. (Woman, estab 2011, empl 10, sales $4,874,185, cert: State, WBENC)

9561   Royal Freight, LP
       407 W Sioux Rd
       Pharr, TX 78577
       Contact: Mike Kelley Sales Mgr
       Tel: 956-283-2200
       Email: mikek@royalfreight.net
       Website: www.royalfreight.net
Direct, Truckload, Asset Based Carrier, serving U.S.(48),
Canada, and Mexico, Satelitte equipped (tractors and
trailers). (Woman, estab 2001, empl 350, sales , cert:
State)

9562   Russell Transport Inc.
       12365 Pine Springs
       El Paso, TX 79928
       Contact: Rosa Marin President
       Tel: 915-542-1495
       Email: rmarin@russelltransport.com
       Website: www.russelltransport.com
Full TL & logistics. (Woman/Hisp, estab 1992, empl 300,
sales $27,000,000, cert: State, NMSDC)

9563   Shire Express Transportation
       6651 Watauga Rd, Ste 48803
       Fort Worth, TX 76148
       Contact: Brenda Jackson Logistics Coord
       Tel: 214-243-5872
       Email: brenda.jackson@landstarmail.com
       Website: http://shireexpressgov.com/
Transportation & logistic services across the United States
and Canada. (AA, estab 2015, empl 7, sales , cert: State)

9564   Siam Logistics
       2320 Dean Way Ste 160
       Southlake, TX 76092
       Contact: Sarah Baldwin Acct Mgr
       Tel: 734-619-8576
       Email: sarah.baldwin@siam-logistics.com
       Website: www.siam-logistics.com
Transportation, oversized loads, specialized equipment &
special weight requirements, US, Mexico & Canada.
(Woman/As-Pac, estab 2009, empl 13, sales $1,920,000,
cert: NMSDC, WBENC)

9565   Southwest Freight Lines
       P.O. Box 371736
       El Paso, TX 79936
       Contact: Jesus Lares Operations Mgr
       Tel: 915-860-8592
       Email: jesus.lares@swflines.com
       Website: www.swflines.com
Truckload services, 48 states & Mexico. (Hisp, estab 1988,
empl 300, sales $50,000,000, cert: State)

9566   Sunrise Delivery Inc.
       2020 Lawrence St
       Houston, TX 77008
       Contact: Lanette Martinez President
       Tel: 713-864-2020
       Email: lm@sditex.com
       Website: www.sunrisedeliveryinc.com
LTL freight, warehousing & logistics. (Woman/Hisp, estab
1981, empl 15, sales $799,616, cert: City, NMSDC, CPUC,
WBENC)

9567   Swift Logistics, Inc.
       1809 Stoney Brook Dr Ste 204
       Houston, TX 77063
       Contact: Rosemarie Patterson Logistics Consultant
       Tel: 713-425-4175
       Email: rpatterson@swiftlogisticsinc.com
       Website: www.swiftlogisticsinc.com
Freight brokerage. (Woman, estab 2014, empl 4, sales ,
cert: WBENC)

9568   Texas Freight
       1207 NE Big Bend Trail, Ste L
       Glen Rose, TX 76043
       Contact: Preston Shuffield Broker
       Tel: 254-898-1117
       Email: preston@texasfreight.net
       Website: www.texasfreight.net
Commercial motor carrier, brokerage authority serving
48 states, flatbeds, drop decks, RGN's, lowboys, and dry
vans. (Woman, estab 2002, empl 8, sales , cert: NWBOC)

9569   The First Name in Freight, Inc.
       P.O. Box 4906
       McAllen, TX 78502
       Contact: Edward Pequeno President
       Tel: 956-682-0188
       Email: firstinfreight@yahoo.com
       Website: www.firstinfreight.com
Truckload & LTL transportation, 48 states. (Woman/Hisp,
estab 1992, empl 20, sales $2,490,301, cert: State)

9570   Trans-Expedite Inc
       7 Founders Blvd Ste 100
       El Paso, TX 79906
       Contact: Claudia Fuentes CEO
       Tel: 915-205-5500
       Email: diversity@trans-expedite.com
       Website: www.trans-expedite.com
Transportation & logistics: air charters, warehousing,
customs brokerage. (Woman, estab 2001, empl 12, sales
$30,000,000, cert: CPUC, WBENC)

9571   Tri Star Freight System Inc.
       5407 Mesa Dr
       Houston, TX 77028
       Contact: Shana Whittington Admin Asst
       Tel: 713-631-1095
       Email: shanaw@tristarfreightsys.com
       Website: www.tristarfreightsys.com
Linehaul, FTL & LTL, airport pick up & delivery, drayage,
local & OTR container drayage, warehousing. (Woman,
estab 1987, empl 89, sales $32,634,980, cert: NWBOC)

9572   Twenty-Two Global Transport, LP
       P.O. Box 62588
       Houston, TX 77205
       Contact: Kevin Smoot Reg Mgr
       Tel: 901-362-3707
       Email: ksmoot@22global.com
       Website: www.xxiiglobal.com
International ocean freight forwarding, customs brokerage, hot shot/expedited services, logistics services,
global information services. (AA, estab 2007, empl 4,
sales $200,000, cert: NMSDC)

9573 Verde Logistics, LLC
9525 Escobar Dr
El Paso, TX 79907
Contact: Holly Webb Business Dev Mgr
Tel: 915-791-4034
Email: holly.jones@verdelogistics.com
Website: www.verdelogisticsllc.com/home
Third party transportation, full truck load van, reefer, flat bed & heavy haul. (Woman/Hisp, estab 2010, empl 6, sales $20,000,000, cert: NMSDC, WBENC)

9574 Whitaker Logistics, LLC
P.O. Box 1283
Stafford, TX 77497
Contact: Rosalyn Whitaker Owner
Tel: 832-646-0240
Email: whitakerlogistics@yahoo.com
Website:
Freight transportation services. (Woman/AA, estab 2008, empl 2, sales $100,000, cert: State)

Virginia

9575 High Plains Logistics Consulting, LLC
P.O. Box 8
Highland Springs, VA 23057
Contact: Burt Epps VP
Tel: 804-437-0066
Email: burt_epps@msn.com
Website:
Transprotation brokerage & third party logistics. (Nat Ame, estab 2002, empl 3, sales $8,200,000, cert: NMSDC)

9576 LAS Logistical Services LLC
3031 N Lakebridge Dr
Norfolk, VA 23324
Contact: Sam Kearson CEO
Tel: 855-232-5866
Email: samkearson@laslogistical.com
Website: www.laslogistical.com
Logistic services: land, air & sea. (AA, estab 2012, empl 10, sales , cert: State)

9577 TH Logistics,LLC
2150 Magnolia St
Richmond, VA 23223
Contact: Devon Henry President
Tel: 888-929-7323
Email: dhenry@thlogistics.net
Website: www.thlogistics.net
Third party logistics & supply chain services, value added warehousing distribution, contract packaging, product acquisition, transload & transportation. (AA, estab 2016, empl 200, sales $50,000,000, cert: NMSDC)

Washington

9578 Radiant Logistics Partners, LLC
405 114th Ave SE, 3rd Fl
Bellevue, WA 98004
Contact: Bohn Crain Managing Member
Tel: 425-462-1094
Email: mbe@radiantdelivers.com
Website: www.radiantdelivers.com
Domestic and international transportation and logistics services. (Nat Ame, estab 2006, empl 20, sales $102,000,000, cert: NMSDC)

9579 Red Arrow Logistics
150 120th Ave NE, Ste F110
Bellevue, WA 98005
Contact: Liz Lasater CEO
Tel: 425-747-7914
Email: ashley.moise@redarrowlogistics.com
Website: www.redarrowlogistics.com
Warehousing & distribution services, vendor compliance programs, ground, sea & air transportation. (Woman, estab 2003, empl 8, sales $6,747,398, cert: NWBOC)

9580 VETRANS LLC
1420 Meridian E Ste 2
Milton, WA 98354
Contact: Vincent W. Santiago Owner
Tel: 253-833-4688
Email: vince@go-vetrans.com
Website: http://go-VETrans.com
Transportation, railroad transloading, other transporation brokerage services. (Woman/Hisp, estab 2006, empl 3, sales $3,967,124, cert: NMSDC)

Wisconsin

9581 Black River Truck Brokers, LLC
N613 Colonial Ave
Pittsville, WI 54466
Contact: Heather Jacobson Owner
Tel: 800-241-2785
Email: heather.brtb@yahoo.com
Website: http://blackrivertruckbroker.com
Transportation & Logistics Services. (Woman, estab 2007, empl 2, sales $4,800,000, cert: State, WBENC)

9582 Merchants Delivery Moving & Storage Co.
1215 State St
Racine, WI 53404
Contact: Jennifer Eastman President
Tel: 262-631-5680
Email: jeastman@merchants-moving.com
Website: www.merchants-moving.com
Moving services. (Woman, estab 1921, empl 84, sales , cert: WBENC)

9583 Trans International, LLC
N93 W16288 Megal Dr
Menomonee Falls, WI 53051
Contact: Denise Lawien CSMO
Tel: 262-253-3500
Email: sales@ticominc.com
Website: www.ticominc.com
Transportation consulting & logistics services: freight pre-audit & payment, post audit, transportation reporting software & tools, freight rating & routing, carrier contract negotiations & general logistics consulting. (Woman, estab 1975, empl 115, sales $5,790,000, cert: State, WBENC)

9584 Veriha Trucking, Inc.
2830 Cleveland Ave
Marinette, WI 54143
Contact: Kyle Cheney Sales Mgr
Tel: 715-330-5921
Email: kcheney@veriha.com
Website: www.veriha.com
Transportation services. (Woman, estab 1978, empl 300, sales $45,000,000, cert: WBENC)

9585 Wisconsin International Services Inc.
5600 S Westridge Dr
New Berlin, WI 53151
Contact: Michael Pflugheoft Dir of Sales
Tel: 262-501-0098
Email: mpflughoeft@wislogistics.com
Website: www.wislogistics.com
Full service logistics solutions. (As-Pac, estab 1996, empl 9,
sales $10,000,000, cert: NMSDC)

TRAVEL ARRANGEMENTS
Full service travel agencies with domestic and international capabilities. NAICS Code 48

Arizona

9586 El Sol Travel, Inc.
4500 S. Lakeshore Dr Ste 450
Tempe, AZ 85282
Contact: Christine Davidson VP Business Travel
Solutions Strategist
Tel: 480-693-0218
Email: cdavidson@elsoltravel.net
Website: www.elsoltravel.net
Full service travel agency. (Woman, estab 1986, empl 27, sales $213,395,700, cert: WBENC)

California

9587 Azzurro Travel, Inc.
4712 Admiralty Way, Ste 138
Marina Del Rey, CA 90292
Contact: Dir of Business Development
Tel: 800-835-8234
Email:
Website: www.azzurrotravel.com
Full service travel agency. (Woman, estab 2008, empl 10, sales $1,476,418, cert: WBENC)

9588 Incentive Travel Inc.
311 Fourth Ave, Ste 617
San Diego, CA 92101
Contact: Penny Wing President
Tel: 619-515-0880
Email: penny@incentiveinc.com
Website: www.incentiveinc.com
Incentive & meeting planning, consulting, creating, promoting. (Woman, estab 1988, empl 14, sales $5,000,000, cert: WBENC)

9589 Pinnacle Travel Services, LLC
390 N Sepulveda Blvd Ste 3100
El Segundo, CA 90245
Contact: Bob Singh President & CEO
Tel: 310-343-4284
Email: ptsbsingh@earthlink.net
Website: http://pinnaclecallsolutions.com
Full service travel agency. (Hisp, estab 1999, empl 150, sales $10,600,000, cert: NMSDC)

Florida

9590 Cruise.Com
255 E Dania Beach Blvd
Dania Be3ach, FL 33004
Contact: Jessica Speirs Reg Sales Dir
Tel: 954-805-7810
Email: jspeirs@cruise.com
Website: www.cruise.com
Leisure products: cruise, affinity revenue share program. (Woman, estab 2002, empl 200, sales, cert: WBENC)

9591 Landry & Kling, Inc.
1390 S Dixie Hwy
Coral Gables, FL 33146
Contact: Cyndi Murphy VP Corporate Planning
Tel: 305-661-1880
Email: cmurphy@landrykling.com
Website: www.landrykling.com
Full service travel agency. (Woman, estab 1982, empl 24, sales $11,739,216, cert: WBENC)

Georgia

9592 Four Seasons Travel
4060 Johns Creek Pkwy Bldg. D
Suwanee, GA 30024
Contact: Michael Morrison Business Dev Mgr
Tel: 770-441-2170
Email: mmorrison@travelleaders.com
Website: http://fscorporatetravel.com
Travel Fulfillment, Consulting & Analytics, and Meetings Management. (Woman, estab 1979, empl 30, sales $35,000,000, cert: WBENC)

9593 Georgia International Travel, Inc.
6285 Barfield Rd Ste 150
Atlanta, GA 30328
Contact: Vela McClam Mitchell CEO
Tel: 404-851-9166
Email: corporatetravel@dt.com
Website: www.gitravel.com
Corporate travel management. (Woman/AA, estab 1984, empl 24, sales $21,000,000, cert: NMSDC)

Illinois

9594 Corporate Travel Consultants dba CorpTrav
450 E. 22nd St #100
Lombard, IL 60148
Contact:
Tel: 630-691-9100
Email:
Website: www.corptrav.com
Full service travel agency. (Woman/AA, As-Pac, Hisp, estab 1976, empl 100, sales $ 0, cert: WBENC)

9595 Travelex International, Inc.
2500 W. Higgins Road
Hoffman Estates, IL 60169
Contact: Ursula Pearson President
Tel: 847-882-0400
Email: ursulap@travelexonline.com
Website: www.travelexonline.com
Full service travel agency, travel management. (Woman, estab 1992, empl 12, sales $725,435, cert: State, WBENC)

Kansas

9596   WingGate Travel, Inc.
       8645 College Blvd, Ste 100
       Overland Park, KS 66210
       Contact: Young Sexton CEO
       Tel: 913-451-9200
       Email: young.sexton@winggatetravel.com
       Website: http://winggatetravel.com
Full service travel management, online fulfillment, VIP executive travel & leisure travel services. (Woman/As-Pac, estab 1991, empl 38, sales $4,000,000, cert: NMSDC)

Massachusetts

9597   Atlas Travel & Technology Group, Inc.
       One Maple St
       Milford, MA 01757
       Contact: Kerin McKinnon SVP global
       Tel: 508-488-1160
       Email: kerin.mckinnon@atlastravel.com
       Website: www.atlastravel.com
Full service travel agency. (Woman, estab 1986, empl 138, sales $179,000,000, cert: WBENC)

Michigan

9598   American Center Travel
       2451 W Stadium Blvd
       Ann Arbor, MI 48103
       Contact: Sue Konarska Owner
       Tel: 734-827-1030
       Email: sue.act@travelleaders.com
       Website: www.travelleaders.com
Full service travel agency. (Woman/As-Ind, estab 1986, empl 4, sales, cert: NMSDC)

9599   Arcade Travel, Inc.
       7879 Jackson Rd, Ste A
       Ann Arbor, MI 48103
       Contact: Jim Kimble President
       Tel: 734-424-3996
       Email: jkimble@boersmatravel.com
       Website: www.boersmatravel.com
Full service travel agency. (AA, estab 1945, empl 23, sales $24,000,000, cert: NMSDC)

9600   Boersma Travel Services
       3368 Washtenaw Ave
       Ann Arbor, MI 48104
       Contact: James Kimble President
       Tel: 734-971-3148
       Email: jkimble@boersmatravel.com
       Website: www.boersmatravel.com
Full svc travel agency. (AA, estab 1945, empl 17, sales, cert: NMSDC)

9601   Departure Travel Management
       344 N Old Woodward, Ste 100
       Birmingham, MI 48011
       Contact: Maria Garcia Reg Acct Mgr
       Tel: 210-913-8016
       Email: maria@dtmdeparture.com
       Website: www.dtmdeparture.com
Full service travel agency. (Woman/AA, estab 1999, empl 21, sales $29,000,000, cert: NMSDC, WBENC)

9602   Global Business Travel, LLC
       2100 Coe Court Ste A
       Auburn Hills, MI 48326
       Contact: Nick Ladney Sales Mgr
       Tel: 877-227-8770
       Email: globaltravel@myway.com
       Website: www.gbtah.com
Full service travel agency. (AA, estab 0, empl , sales $4,600,000, cert: NMSDC)

9603   Michigan East West Travel
       400 Galleria Officentre, Ste 124
       Southfield, MI 48034
       Contact: Joanne Rhee Owner
       Tel: 248-352-2525
       Email: lime1225@gmail.com
       Website:
Travel services. (Woman/As-Pac, estab 1999, empl 4, sales , cert: NMSDC)

9604   Motor City Travel
       29566 Northwestern Hwy Ste 400
       Southfield, MI 48034
       Contact: Tracey Campbell VP Business Dev
       Tel: 248-799-0752
       Email: tcampbell@motorcitytravel.com
       Website: www.MOTORCITYTRAVEL.COM
Full service travel agency. (Woman/AA, estab 0, empl , sales $12,095,618, cert: NMSDC)

9605   Sky Bird Travel & Tours Inc.
       26500 Northwestern Hwy Ste 260
       Southfield, MI 48076
       Contact: Arvin Shah President
       Tel: 248-727-1697
       Email: info@skybirdtravel.com
       Website: www.skybirdtravel.com
Full svc travel agency. (As-Ind, estab 1976, empl 52, sales, cert: NMSDC)

9606   The Travel Exchange
       755 W Big Beaver Ste 100
       Troy, MI 48084
       Contact: Pamela Edwartoski President
       Tel: 248-269-9721
       Email: pam@travelexchangemi.com
       Website: www.travelexchangemi.com
Full service travel agency. (Woman, estab 1976, empl 15, sales $ 0, cert: WBENC)

Minnesota

9607   Metro Travel
       9298 Central Ave NE, Ste 222
       Minneapolis, MN 55434
       Contact: Diane Cyrus CEO
       Tel: 763-784-0560
       Email: dianecyrus@metrotravel.biz
       Website: www.metrotravel.biz
Full service travel management. (As-Ind, estab 1982, empl 14, sales $890,000, cert: NMSDC)

North Carolina

9608   Aquila Travel & Events
2 Mill Creek Ct
Greensboro, NC 27407
Contact: Yolande Wainwright President
Tel: 336-580-9796
Email: aquila@triad.rr.com
Website: http://eventsbyaquila.com
Corporate event & travel services. (Woman/AA, estab 2008, empl 1, sales , cert: State)

New York

9609   Van Zile Travel
3540 Winton Place
Rochester, NY 14623
Contact: Rebecca Mineo VP
Tel: 585-244-1100
Email: katie@vanzile.com
Website: www.vanzile.com
Full service travel agency. (Woman, estab 1911, empl 45, sales $35,000,000, cert: WBENC)

Ohio

9610   ATG
7775 Walton Pkwy Ste 100
New Albany, OH 43054
Contact: Paula Aquizap Sr Proposal Admin
Tel: 614-901-4100
Email: paquizap@atg.travel
Website: www.atgtravel.com
Full service travel agency. (Woman, estab 1995, empl 3000, sales $593,580,200, cert: WBENC)

9611   Uniglobe Travel Designers
480 S Third St
Columbus, OH 43215
Contact: Elizabeth Blount McCormick President
Tel: 614-237-4488
Email: elizabethb@uniglobetd.com
Website: www.uniglobetraveldesigners.com
Full service travel agency. (Woman/AA, estab , empl , sales $22,500,000, cert: NMSDC, WBENC)

Texas

9612   The Alamo Travel Group LP
8930 Wurzbach Rd   Ste 100
San Antonio, TX 78240
Contact: Patricia Pliego Stout President & CEO
Tel: 210-593-0084
Email: pstout@alamotravel.com
Website: www.alamotravel.com
Full service travel agency. (Woman/Hisp, estab 1990, empl 11, sales $111,000,000, cert: State, NMSDC, WBENC)

9613   The Travel Group LLC
5930 Royal Lane Ste E277
Dallas, TX 75230
Contact: Greg Corley COO/CFO
Tel: 800-514-9132
Email: info@thetravelgroup.travel
Website: http://thetravelgroup.travel
Full service travel agency. (Woman/As-Pac, estab 1986, empl 55, sales $15,000,000, cert: WBENC)

9614   Travel Acquisition Group, Ltd.
5700 W Plano Pkwy Ste 1400
Plano, TX 75093
Contact: Exec VP
Tel: 972-422-4000
Email:
Website: www.artatravel.com
Corporate travel, management & consulting. (Woman, estab 1980, empl 21, sales $30,500,000, cert: State, WBENC)

Virginia

9615   Omega World Travel
3102 Omega Office Park
Fairfax, VA 22031
Contact: Jackie Olt Marketing and PR Specialist
Tel: 703-359-0200
Email: jolt@owt.net
Website: www.OmegaTravel.com
Full service travel agency. (Woman, estab 1972, empl 475, sales $1,400,000,000, cert: WBENC)

Wisconsin

9616   JCCOB Smith Gardner Smith/Keystone AMEX Tvl Svs
16735 W Greenfield Ave
New Berlin, WI 53151
Contact: Art Smith President & CEO
Tel: 262-782-8750
Email: artkeystone@yahoo.com
Website: www.travelbykeystone.com
Full service travel agency. (AA, estab 1990, empl 12, sales $705,000, cert: NMSDC)

Alabama

9617 Containers Plus, Inc.
3068 Alabama Hwy 53
Huntsville, AL 35806
Contact: Ajesh Khanijow Business Dev Mgr
Tel: 256-746-8002
Email: akhanijow@containersplususa.com
Website: www.containersplususa.com
Wooden crates, pallets, cardboard boxes, heat shrink, milspec packaging, packaging, RFID, UID, Mil-std-129, mil-std-2073, warehousing, logistics, hazmat packaging. (As-Pac, estab 2014, empl 5, sales $180,000, cert: NMSDC)

California

9618 Commercial Lumber & Pallet Company, Inc.
135 Long Ln
City of Industry, CA 91746
Contact: Kathleen Dietrich VP
Tel: 626-968-0631
Email: kathy@clcpallets.com
Website:
Mfr & dist wooden pallets, skids & boxes. (Hisp, estab 1941, empl 100, sales $35,000,000, cert: CPUC)

9619 Cutter Lumber Products
10 Rickenbacker Cir
Livermore, CA 94550
Contact: Todd Samuels GM
Tel: 925-443-5959
Email: todd@cutterlumber.com
Website: www.cutterlumber.com/
Mfr wooden pallets, wooden boxes. (As-Pac, estab 1965, empl 85, sales , cert: NMSDC, CPUC)

9620 Winship Stake and Lath
P.O. Box 909
Riverside, CA 92502
Contact: Lisa Winship Hankin President
Tel: 951-682-8761
Email: lisa@winshipstakeandlath.com
Website: www.winshipstakeandlath.com
Mfr & dist wood stakes & lath used in building, surveying & landscaping. (Woman, estab 1972, empl 8, sales $400,000, cert: CPUC)

Colorado

9621 Pro Pallet, Inc.
920 E Collins
Eaton, CO 80615
Contact: Jean Kyne President
Tel: 970-353-5311
Email: propallet@qwestoffice.net
Website: www.propallet.net
New, recycled & new/recycled pallets, crates & boxes. (Woman, estab 1988, empl 45, sales $8,258,291, cert: WBENC)

Florida

9622 Pallet Consultants Corporation
951 SW 12th Ave
Pompano Beach, FL 33069
Contact: Brian Groene President
Tel: 954-946-2212
Email: brian.groene@palletconsultants.com
Website: www.palletconsultants.com
Recycle wood pallets, mfr new & used pallets. (Hisp, estab 1996, empl 178, sales $45,000,000, cert: NMSDC)

Georgia

9623 A & B Pallets, Inc.
6323 Riverview Rd
Mableton, GA 30126
Contact: Alberto Dominguez President
Tel: 404-691-0567
Email: aandbpalletsinc@yahoo.com
Website: www.aandbpalletsinc.com
Recycled, new & remanufactured pallets. (Hisp, estab 1997, empl 15, sales , cert: NMSDC)

9624 Pallet Central Enterprises, Inc.
2B Lenox Pointe
Atlanta, GA 30324
Contact: Jameson Humber Asst Sales Mgr
Tel: 404-671-3494
Email: jhumber@palletcentralent.com
Website: www.palletcentralent.com
Pallets. (Woman/As-Pac, estab 2005, empl 25, sales $26,000,000, cert: WBENC)

Illinois

9625 Harvey Pallets Inc.
2200 W 139th St
Blue Island, IL 60406
Contact: Manuel Tavarez President
Tel: 708-293-1831
Email: manuel@harveypallets.com
Website: www.harveypallet.com
Mfr wood pallets, skids, crates & lumber. (Hisp, estab 1997, empl 50, sales $24,000,000, cert: NMSDC)

9626   Perma Treat of Illinois
P.O. Box 99
Marion, IL 62959
Contact: Sara Bond CEO
Tel: 618-694-2898
Email: sara@permatreatlumber.com
Website: http://permatreatlumber.com
Wood Treated products: Utility Poles, Railroad Ties, Pallets, Wood Quality Control Inspection, Rail Spur on site can ship via rail or truck. (Woman, estab 1982, empl 7, sales $330,866, cert: State, WBENC)

9627   Phoenix Woodworking Corporation
P.O. Box 459
Woodstock, IL 60098
Contact: President
Tel: 815-338-9338
Email:
Website: http://phoenixwoodworking.com
Custom & commercial cabinetry & casework, reception centers, filing cabinets, wooden lockers & millwork, custom desks & wooden store fixtures. (Woman, estab 1996, empl 10, sales , cert: State, WBENC)

Maryland

9628   Timber Industries, LLC
P.O. Box 6879
Towson, MD 21285
Contact: Danielle Sutphen Sales & Marketing Coord
Tel: 410-823-8300
Email: danielle.sutphen@timberindustries.com
Website: www.timberindustries.com
Custom & standard pallets, skids & crates. (Woman, estab 2013, empl 6, sales $2,500,000, cert: State, WBENC)

Michigan

9629   J&G Pallets and Trucking, Inc.
2971 Bellevue
Detroit, MI 48207
Contact: Les Lance Business Mgr
Tel: 313-921-0222
Email: llance@jgpalletsandtrucking.com
Website: www.jgpalletsandtrucking.com
Wood pallets, design custom pallets, recycle/reuse wood pallets & wood pallet materials. (Woman/AA, estab 1992, empl 22, sales $1,625,000, cert: NMSDC)

Minnesota

9630   R and L Woodcraft, Inc
823 Industrial Park Dr SE
Lonsdale, MN 55046
Contact: Randall Rivers Business Dev Mgr
Tel: 507-744-2318
Email: randall@randlwoodcraft.com
Website: www.randlwoodcraft.com
Mfr commercial millwork & casework: cabinets, countertops, workstations, service counters, point of service counters, tables, booths, upholstered seating, running trim, trash recepticles, lockers & toilet partitions. (Woman, estab 1986, empl 22, sales $3,600,000, cert: WBENC)

New Jersey

9631   Bett-A-Way Pallet Systems
110 Sylvania Pl
South Plainfield, NJ 07080
Contact: Laura Vaccaro VP Business Dev
Tel: 800-795-7255
Email: laura.vaccaro@bettaway.com
Website: www.bettaway.com
Pallet management: sales, repairs, retrievals & inventory management. (Woman, estab 1996, empl 15, sales $20,986,000, cert: WBENC)

9632   US Lumber Inc.
668 S Evergreen Ave
Woodbury Heights, NJ 08097
Contact: Lita Abele CEO
Tel: 856-853-1770
Email: lita@uslumberinc.com
Website: www.uslumberinc.com
Mill & cut lumber & plywood. (Woman/As-Pac, estab 1974, empl 10, sales $5,093,000, cert: 8a)

New York

9633   Ongweoweh Corp
5 Barr Road
Ithaca, NY 14850
Contact: Brett Bucktooth Supplier Diversity Mgr
Tel: 607-266-7070
Email: supplierdiversity@ongweoweh.com
Website: www.ongweoweh.com
Mfr & dist wooden pallets & specialty containers. (Nat Ame, estab 1978, empl 96, sales $252,000,000, cert: NMSDC)

Ohio

9634 LEFCO Worthington, LLC
18451 Euclid Ave
Cleveland, OH 44112
Contact: Larry Fulton President
Tel: 216-432-4422
Email: larry.fulton@lefcoworthington.com
Website: www.LEFCOWorthington.com
Dist wooden crates, OSB Boxes, custom pallets, sub-assembly & packaging services. (AA, estab 2003, empl 30, sales $3,600,000, cert: State, NMSDC)

9635 Prime WoodCraft
5755 Granger Rd Ste 900
Independence, OH 44131
Contact: Michelle Morere Admin
Tel: 216-588-9053
Email: michelle@primewoodcraft.com
Website: www.primewoodcraft.com
Warehousing, pallets, third party logistics. (As-Ind, estab 1997, empl 300, sales , cert: NMSDC)

9636 The Lima Pallet Company, Inc.
1470 Neubrecht Rd
Lima, OH 45801
Contact: Tracie Sanchez President
Tel: 419-229-5736
Email: tsanchez@limapallet.com
Website: www.limapallet.com
Mfr wood pallets & crates. ISP certified. (Woman, estab 1977, empl 49, sales $3,000,000, cert: WBENC)

9637 Wood Concepts
2401 Train Ave
Cleveland, OH 44113
Contact: Jacquline Even President
Tel: 216-579-0500
Email: jackieeven@att.net
Website: http://woodconceptsinc.com
Mfr & fabricate casework, millwork & cabinetry. (Woman, estab 1983, empl 8, sales $1,025,215, cert: City)

Puerto Rico

9638 Caribe Pallets and Packaging Corp.
P.O. Box 1886
Trujillo Alto, PR 00977
Contact: Jose Bolivar VP
Tel: 787-755-3622
Email: caribepallets@gmail.com
Website:
Mfr wood pallets. (Hisp, estab 1988, empl 18, sales , cert: NMSDC)

9639 Paleteras Unidas, Inc.
PMB 461 HC01 Box 29030 HC 1
Caguas, PR 00725
Contact: Jorgelina González VP
Tel: 787-789-0110
Email: jgonzalez@paleteras.net
Website:
Wooden pallets, skids & crates; pre-cut lumber, pallet Heat Treatment for ISPM15 Compliance, transportation, pallet recycling. (Hisp, estab 1967, empl 40, sales , cert: NMSDC)

Texas

9640 Austin Lumber Company, Inc.
630 S Washington St
La Grange, TX 78945
Contact: Laura Culin President
Tel: 512-476-5534
Email: info@austinlumbercompany.com
Website: www.austinlumbercompany.com
Construction mill. (Woman, estab 1929, empl 5, sales , cert: State, City)

Virginia

9641 Scott Pallets Inc.
8660 Crowder St
Amelia Courthouse, VA 23002
Contact: Jo Anne Webb President
Tel: 804-561-2514
Email: joannew@tds.net
Website:
Mfr wooden pallets: standard warehouse & custom designed, cut stock, dunnage & double shredded bark mulch. (Woman, estab 1966, empl 16, sales $986,868, cert: WBENC)

DIR
DIVERSITYINFORMATIONRESOURCES

25th Annual
Supplier Diversity Seminar
"Best Practices in Supplier Diversity Strategies and Initiatives"

2022 Date and Location TBD

AGENDA

Day 1
8:00 am - 4:00 pm
Seminar General Session
5:00 - 7:00 pm
Networking Reception

Day 2
8:00 am - 4:00 pm
Seminar General Session

SEMINAR LOCATION
TBD

ACCOMMODATIONS
Hotel information will be sent with registration confirmation.

FEE
TBD/person
Fee includes all sessions. seminar materials, continental breakfast, lunch and networking reception

SEMINAR REGISTRATION
www.diversityinforesources.com
or contact DIR directly at:
612-781-6819
info@diversityinforesources.com
NOTE: There is NO on-site registration

SPONSORED BY
Diversity Information Resources
2300 Kennedy Street NE, Suite 230
Minneapolis, MN 55413
www.diversityinforesources.com

Join experienced Supplier Diversity Professionals and subject matter experts for a series of presentations and networking events

"One of the best all-around events that I have attended ... this is an event that I definitely want to have in my yearly budget!"

"Great! I'm glad I attended."

2019 TOPICS

- Professional Development
- Chief Procurement Officer (CPO) Panel: Supplier Diversity Impact
- Employee Resource Groups (ERG) & Business Resource Groups (BRG): Engaging your Organization to Promote Supplier Diversity
- How to Measure Economic Impact and ROI of Supplier Diversity
- What is Diversity Spend? Looking Beyond the Numbers
- How Innovation, Artificial Intelligence and Analytics is Impacting the Role of the Supplier Diversity Professional
- Government Contractng, Compliance, Reporting, Rules and Regulations
- Non-Governmental Organizations (NGOs): Value of Partnerships; How to Measure ROI

WHO ATTENDS?

- Supplier Diversity Professionals
- Purchasing Managers/Buyers

- VP's of Materials and Purchasing Procurement Managers
- Small Business Liaison Officers (SBLO's)
- Lead staff with responsibility for implementing supplier diversity programs
- Graduates of DIR's "Building Strategic Phases of a Supplier Diversity Process" Seminar

Since 1968, DIR has been a leader in providing information resources that support and enhance diversity initiatives.

A INDEX#

J INDEX#

J INDEX#

K

M   INDEX#

N

N   INDEX#